Cambridge University Press is part of the University of Cambridge. It is a charitable enterprise dedicated to printing and publishing for the advancement of knowledge throughout the world. In recognition of the fact that there are many parts of the world where students have difficulty in purchasing their own copies of the best international textbooks, Cambridge University Press is now publishing a series of Low Price Editions. These are reprints of internationally respected books from Cambridge University Press, specially printed and priced for the benefit of students and teachers in selected countries.

Advanced Chemistry is an accessible, up-to-date textbook which has been written to appeal directly to A-level chemistry students. It covers the syllabuses of all the main examining boards offering A-level chemistry, and contains material suitable for students beginning undergraduate study. The author places the subject in context by discussing the nature and, where relevant, the economics of the chemical industry and the wider implications and applications of chemistry.

The material is divided into four parts: physical, industrial, inorganic and organic chemistry. Each part is divided into short self-contained units each of which develops a set of well-defined themes or concepts. Students may work through the units in order, or individual units may be used separately. Each unit is divided into sections, with short questions at the end of each section, which may be used by students as a means of self-assessment. More extensive questions on the physical and industrial chemistry sections are given at the end of the book. These may be used to provide material for student assignments, and to provide students with practice in answering examination questions.

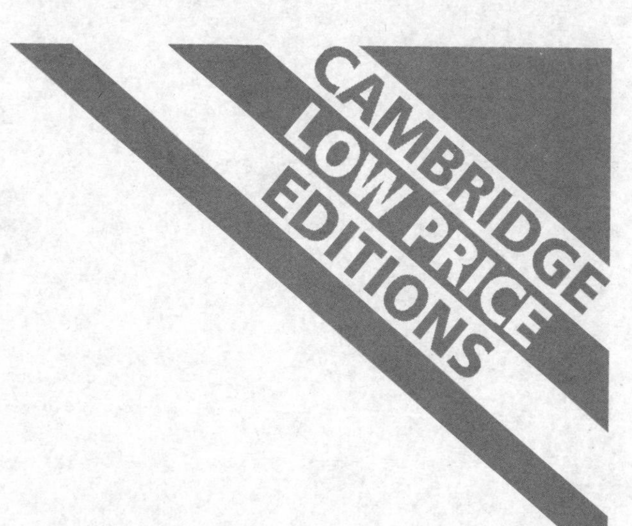

Advanced chemistry

Philip Matthews

CAMBRIDGE UNIVERSITY PRESS
Cambridge, New York, Melbourne, Madrid, Cape Town, Singapore, São Paulo, Delhi

Cambridge University Press
The Water Club, Beach Road, Granger Bay, Cape Town 8005, South Africa

www.cambridge.org
Information on this title: www.cambridge.org/9780521566988

First published as Books 1 & 2 1978
Reprinted 1995
Low price edition 1996
6th printing 2008

Printed in Hong Kong by Sheck Wah Tong Printing Press Ltd

ISBN 978-0-521-56698-8 low price paperback

Contents

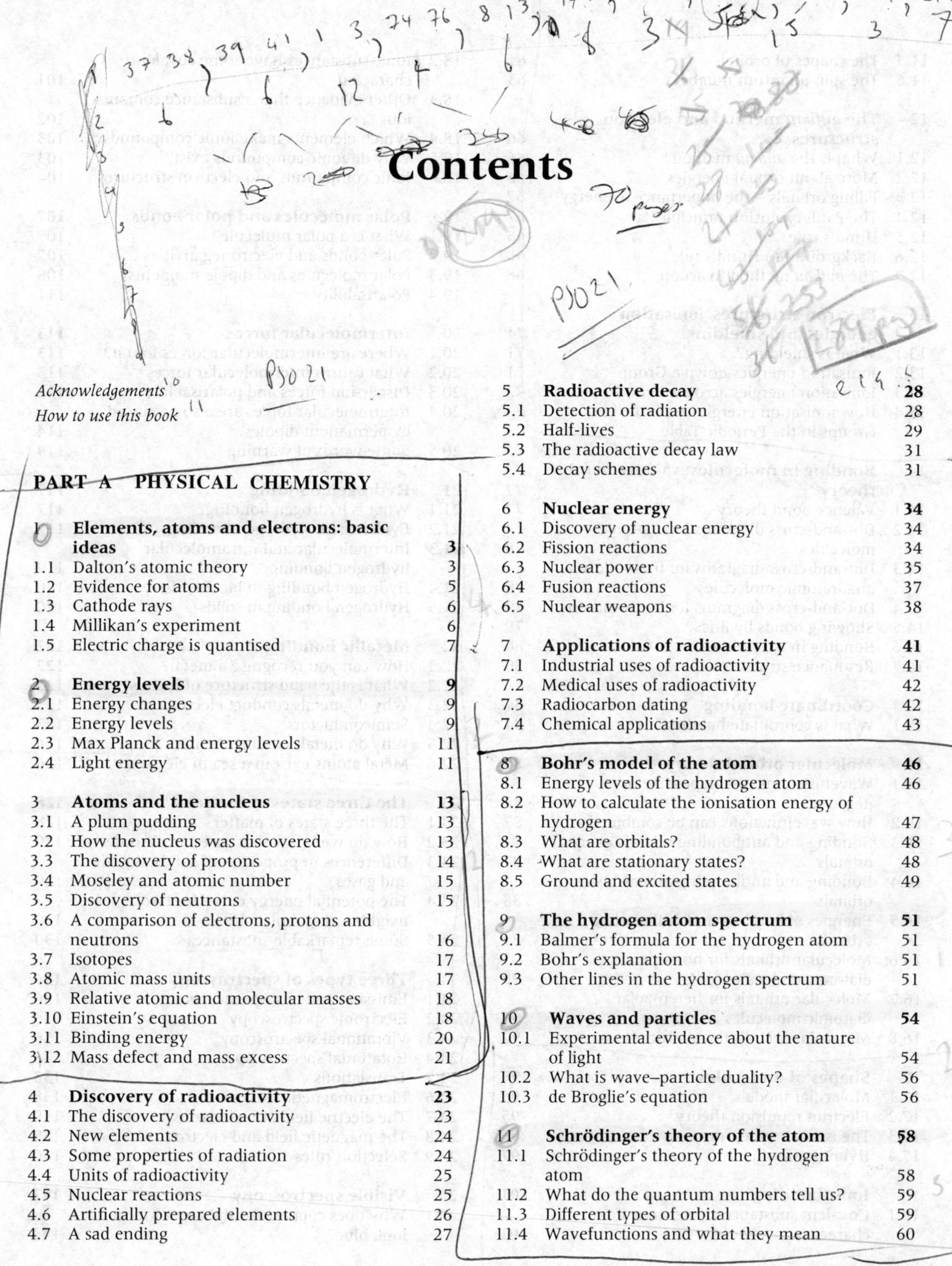

PART B INDUSTRIAL CHEMISTRY

PART C INORGANIC CHEMISTRY

INORGANIC CHEMISTRY

PART D ORGANIC CHEMISTRY

Acknowledgements

I would like to thank colleagues in Trinity College, Dublin for their advice in the preparation of this book. Dr G. R. Brown undertook the task of reading the entire typescript. His comprehensive knowledge of chemistry, and timely advice saved me from many errors. Dr D. A. Morton-Blake read the draft of the unit on entropy and his advice resulted in at least a local diminution of chaos. Dr A. P. Davis gave invaluable help with photographs of molecular graphics as did Mr B. Dempsey with other photographs.

Of the many texts and articles I have consulted in the process of writing this book, I particularly acknowledge my debt to the following: (i) the Nuffield *Advanced Chemistry* books whose enquiry-based approaches used in the Nuffield courses have greatly influenced the approach I have adopted, and (ii) the text *Chemistry: An Integrated Approach* by R. S. Lowrie and H. J. C. Ferguson (Pergamon Press, 1975), now sadly out of print, which was the origin of my treatment of the shapes of molecules in section 17.3 and of the 'CORN' rule in 123.6.

The consistency of style and presentation of the text of both volumes is almost entirely due to the timely advice and clinical eye for editorial detail of Geoff Amor. At the Cambridge University Press, Lucy Purkis has been consistently supportive, even when faced with a sometimes tardy author. Similarly, Callie Kendall has been invariably helpful in researching the photographs.

My thanks go to all these people, but especially to my wife Margaret and two boys, Alastair and Euan, who have all too often taken second place to a computer and printer.

Figures

3.8, G. Friedlauder *et al. Nuclear and Radiochemistry*, © 1964, John Wiley & Sons Inc, reprinted by permission of John Wiley & Sons Inc; 6.3 reproduced with permission from *Nuclear Physics for Engineers and Scientists* by S. E. Hunt, published in 1987 by Ellis Horwood Ltd, Chichester; 18.2 by permission of the American Physical Society; 32.8, 32.10, 32.11, 32.12, B. E. Douglas, D. H. McDaniel & J. J. Alexander *Concepts and Models of Inorganic Chemistry*, © 1983 John Wiley & Sons Inc., reprinted by permission of John Wiley and Sons Inc.; 48.2, 65.8 by permission of Oxford University Press; 83.1, 83.2, 83.4, 83.5, reproduced by permission of the McGraw Hill Book Company, 85.5, R. E. Kirk & D. F. Othmer *Concise Encyclopaedia of Chemical Technology* © 1985 John Wiley & Sons Inc., reprinted by permission of John Wiley & Sons Inc.

91.3, by permission of Paul Hamlyn Publishing, part of Reed International Ltd; 91.7, by permission of Oxford University Press; 94.5, by permission of John Wiley & Sons Inc., New York; 97.1, by permission of Professors Gordon and Zoller; 99.5, by permission of Chapman & Hall; 123.7, reprinted with permission of Macmillan Publishing Company from *Central Concepts of Biology* by Adela S. Baer, William E. Hazen, David L. Jameson and William L. Sloan. Copyright © 1971 by Macmillan Publishing Company; 123.8, 123.9, reprinted with the permission of Macmillan Publishing Company from *Biochemistry*, 2nd ed. by Geoffrey Zubay. Copyright © 1988 by Macmillan Publishing Company; 128.4, 128.6, 128.7, Harry R. Allcock/Frederick W. Lampe, *Contemporary Polymer Chemistry*, 2nd ed. © 1990, pp. 9, 505, 515, 516. Reprinted by permission of Prentice Hall, Englewood Cliffs, New Jersey.

Text

36, Topham Picture Source; 37; by courtesy of British Nuclear Fuels plc (BNFL); 38, from *The Times*, 23 March 1989, © Times Newspapers Ltd. 1989; 39, 173, Hulton-Deutsch Collection; 41, 42*l*, courtesy of British Aerospace; 42*r*, Science Photo Library; 58; Lotte Meitner-Graf/The Royal Society; 143, 161, 327, courtesy of Perkin-Elmer; 336*l*, 337, 396*l*, Andrew Lambert; 336*r*, courtesy of the Natural History Museum; 369, 497*l*, 526, 527*b*, a Shell photograph; 396*r*, Ian Hepburn; 497*r*, courtesy of Glaxo Group Research Ltd; 498, Biophoto Associates; 499, courtesy of Kemira Fertilisers, Ince, Chester CH2 4LB; 501, 527*t*, Popperfoto; 508, 535, Reproduced by permission of the Trustees of the Science Museum; 523, courtesy of British Alcan Aluminium plc.

535, 609, Science Museum Library; 558 Popperfoto; 562*t*, Jeremy Hartley/Oxfam; 562*b*, Kemira Fertilizers, Ince, Chester CH2 4LB; 563*l*, Wildlife Matters; 563*r*, Ecoscene/Ian Harwood; 571, © MacQuitty International Collection; 577, 583, 586, 590, 658*b*, Andrew Lambert; 578*t*, Courtesy of British Cement Association; 578*b*, Reproduced with the kind permission of Blue Circle Cement; 579, Courtesy of Smith and Nephew Medical Limited; 592, Redferns/photo by Andrew Putler; 593, Photo: Building Research Establishment/Crown copyright reproduced by permission of the Controller of Her Majesty's Stationery Office; 602, Courtesy of Pilkington plc; 628*tl*, by courtesy of Ohmeda, a BOC healthcare company; 628*tr*, NASA/Science Photo Library, 628*b*, Courtesy of British Oxygen Co Ltd; 649, 800, 853, Biophoto Associates; 658*t*, Nigel Luckhurst; 667, Alex Bartel/Science Photo Library; 784, Courtesy of The Scotch Whisky Association; 888, Courtesy of British Plastics Federation; 890, Sally & Richard Greenhill.

Colour section

Gold, silver, platinum: Courtesy of the Natural History Museum; **Gold mine**: Peter Ryan/Science Photo Library; **LCD display**; Malcolm Fielding/Science Photo Library; **Stained glass**: A. F. Kersting; **Diffraction pattern**; Bill Reber/Science Photo Library; **Brain scan**: Hank Morgan/Science Photo Library; **Catalysts**: A Shell photograph; **Foundry**: Photo Library International; tropical rainforest: Ecoscene/Sally Morgan; crystals/minerals: Courtesy of the Natural History Museum; smog: Wildlife Matters; fire: Courtesy of Chubb Fire Ltd; algae: Ecoscene/Sally Morgan; Piccadilly Circus: Philip Craven/Robert Harding Picture Library; cyclist, climbers, mayonnaise, paints: Andrew Lambert; detergent in river: Ecoscene/Gryniewicz.

How to use this book

About units

Advanced Chemistry is divided into four parts: physical chemistry, and industrial chemistry; inorganic and organic chemistry. In turn, these four parts are split into 130 fairly short units, rather than into a smaller number of long chapters. Each unit is designed to cover a compact area of chemistry, which you should be able to study over a period of an hour or so. Take some comfort from the fact that you are unlikely to have to know the content of every unit. All A level and AS level syllabuses cover a basic core, and then they emphasise different aspects of chemistry. If you pay attention to the syllabus that you are using, you should be able to avoid unnecessary work. Some units contain features that may not be compulsory on any of the syllabuses; mainly this is because I find those parts of chemistry especially interesting. In particular, you will find extracts from the history of chemistry, which I hope you will find intriguing.

I have written the units with the aim of helping you understand the work, rather than presenting you with a large number of isolated facts. Of course, like any subject, chemistry contains a great deal of information that you will have to learn; but you will find learning much easier if you can understand how the information fits together.

Each unit is split into sections, and near the end of almost every section is a set of study questions. No doubt you will be tempted to pass these by; but avoid temptation! The questions will allow you to test your understanding of the work as you go along. They are designed to make you think, and to discover if you have understood what you have read. It would be best to regard them as puzzles, rather than as 'trick' questions designed to catch you out. Answers to all of these questions are given near the end of each unit so you can check your progress. (There really is little point in cheating by looking up the answers until *you* have tried to work out the answers.)

As well as the shorter end-of-section questions there are questions from past AS, A and S level examinations. These are arranged at the end of the four parts. Only answers to numerical parts are provided. For help you will have to consult another book, or seek the advice of your teacher or lecturer.

Another feature is that each unit ends with a summary. This will provide you with a guide to what the unit covers, and it should serve as a useful aid to revision. However, do not expect to find explanations in the summaries.

How to find information

One of the key things that determines how well you learn chemistry is your motivation: do you really want to find things out and understand the work you are doing? If you are not in the right frame of mind, it would be better to leave study to another occasion. However, when you decide to study, study hard and for short periods.

A second point to bear in mind is that you will only make best use of your time if you know what you are trying to achieve in your study sessions. For example, if you decide that you need to 'learn about molecules' you are likely to waste a lot of time. This objective is too vague. It would be far better to aim at a clearer target. For example, you might wish to learn about 'covalent bonding in molecules' or 'the reactions of alcohol molecules'. One of the best places to find the right targets is the syllabus for your chemistry course. This will give you a detailed list of the things that you need to know about.

Once you have identified your target you should move to the index at the back of the book, or the table of contents near the front. The table of contents will, for instance, lead you to units on covalent bonding and the reactions of alcohols. If, as will often be the case, you need to look up specific pieces of information, the place to look is the chemicals and reactions index.

Part A

PHYSICAL CHEMISTRY

1

Elements, atoms and electrons: basic ideas

1.1 Dalton's atomic theory

Assuming that you have studied chemistry before, you will have met the idea that matter is made up of combinations of about 110 elements. You will also have learnt that each element has its own type of atom.

Perhaps the first passable definition of an element was given by Robert Boyle (1627–1691). In his book 'The Sceptical Chemist', published in 1661, he proposed that elements are

> . . . certain Primitive and Simple, or perfectly unmingled bodies; which not being made of any other bodies, or of one another, are the ingredients of which all those perfectly mixt Bodies are immediately compounded, and into which they are ultimately resolved.

Boyle's 'mixt Bodies' are what we call compounds. It is tempting to think that Boyle had struck upon the very essence of our modern idea of an element; but there was one most important difference. He thought that the elements themselves were made from a single basic substance. We now know that this is wrong, although all atoms have some things in common; for example, they have electrons, which travel round the nucleus.

The idea that all matter is made up of tiny particles called atoms has been in existence at least since the time of the Greek philosopher Democritus (460–370 BC). However, little was done to use ideas about atoms to explain the behaviour of chemicals until John Dalton (1766–1844) developed his *atomic theory*. In 1803 Dalton proposed that

> Each element has its own unique type of atom; that all atoms of an element are identical.
>
> The atoms of each individual element have the same size, and the same weight (the atomic weight).
>
> When elements combine together, the atoms of one element are not changed into those of another element.
>
> When elements combine together, their atoms join together in fixed proportions.

One other outcome of Dalton's work was that he invented a way of representing chemicals on paper. He produced a set of symbols for the atoms of the elements, and drew diagrams to show how the atoms might be arranged in compounds. You can see in Figure 1.1 that his symbols and formulae were not like those we use.

It is probable that you have met Dalton's atomic theory before. Often it seems quite obvious that it is correct; but that is only with the benefit of hindsight. At the time, his theory caused quite a commotion in the scientific world. Not everyone was convinced that the atomic weights of the elements were important. For example, Humphry Davy (who among other things invented the safety lamp for miners) said that Dalton was too much involved in 'vain speculation' when he drew pictures like those in Figure 1.1.

Much of the success of Dalton's theory in overcoming such criticisms lay in the way it encouraged the trend in chemistry to become *quantitative*. That is, many more chemists began measuring accurately, particularly by weighing. It also allowed people to gain a picture of how the elements in compounds might be arranged. He developed the notion that each compound had its own particular, fixed, formula. It may appear strange to us now but in Dalton's time there was considerable controversy about this – it was not at all obvious that, say, salt was always made up of the same proportions of sodium and chlorine. Likewise, it was thought by many that the weight of an element could easily be changed during the course of a reaction.

The Swedish chemist Jons Berzelius (1779–1848) was one of the first to determine the atomic weights of elements. A number of his values are surprisingly close to the modern ones. Berzelius also invented the system of giving elements a symbol by using one or two letters of the alphabet.

1.1 William Prout (1785–1850) believed that every element was made from one basic material. He thought this material to be hydrogen. As a consequence, he also held that the atomic weights of the elements were multiples of that of hydrogen. In his book 'A Short History of Chemistry' J. R. Partington points out that a contemporary of Prout, Thomas Thomson was impressed by Prout's ideas. Thomson rounded down an experimental result for an atomic

ELEMENTS

Simple

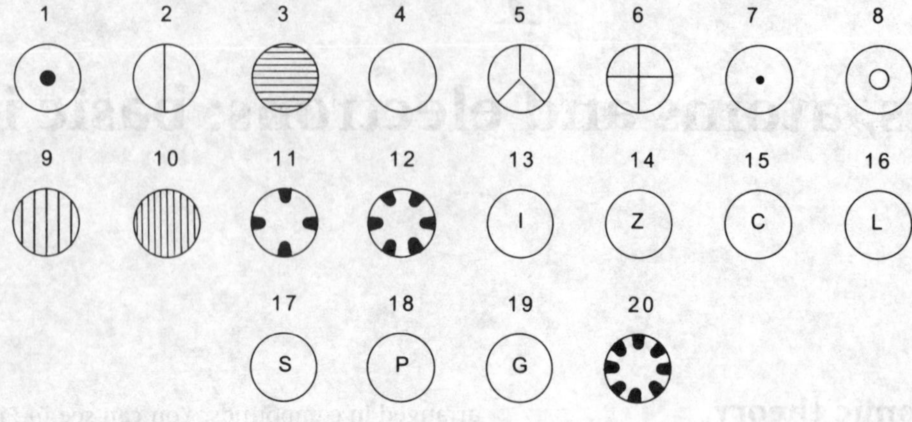

Binary

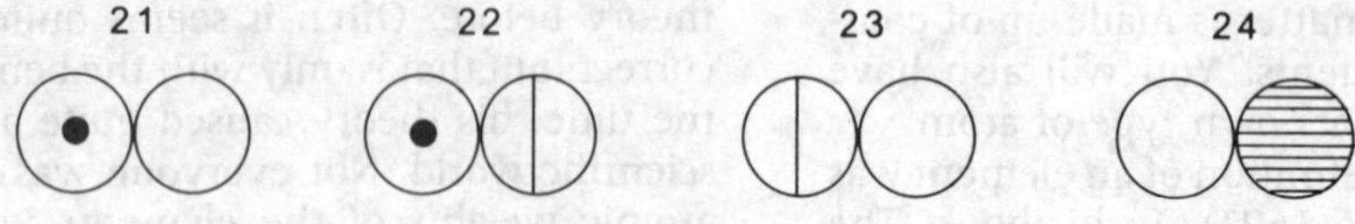

Ternary

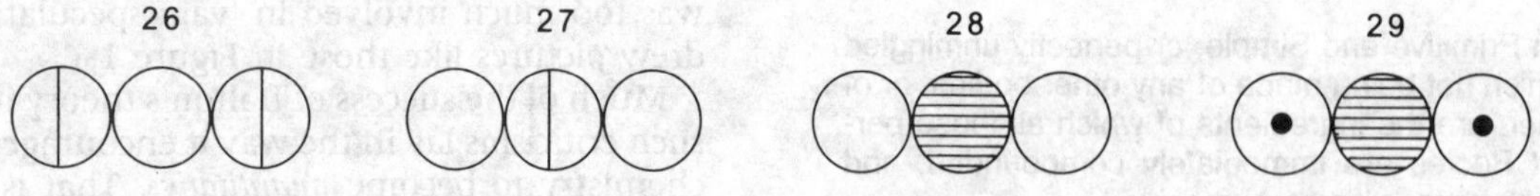

Quaternary

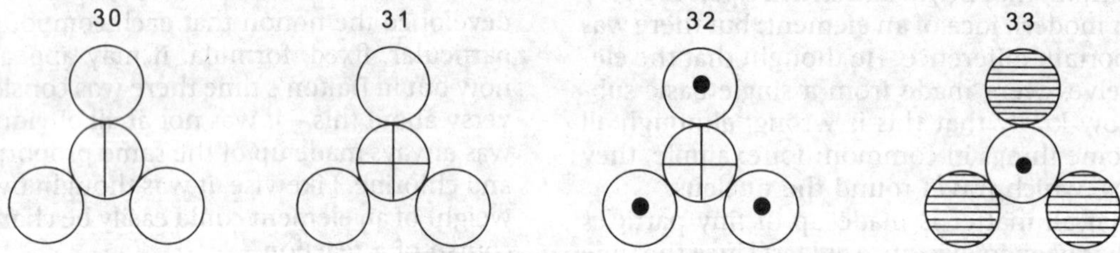

***Figure 1.1** Examples of Dalton's 'elements' as he published them in* A New System of Chemical Philosophy, *Manchester, 1808:*

Fig.			Fig.		
1.	Hydrog. its rel. weight	1	11.	Strontites,	46
2.	Azote,	5	12.	Barytes,	68
3.	Carbone, or charcoal	5	13.	Iron,	38
4.	Oxygen,	7	14.	Zinc,	56
5.	Phosphorus,	9	15.	Copper,	56
6.	Sulphur,	13	16.	Lead,	95
7.	Magnesia,	20	17.	Silver,	100
8.	Lime,	23	18.	Platina,	100
9.	Soda,	28	19.	Gold,	140
10.	Potash,	42	20.	Mercury,	167

21. An atom of water or steam, composed of 1 of oxygen and 1 of hydrogen, retained in physical contact by a strong affinity, and supposed to be surrounded by a common atmosphere of heat; its relative weight = 8
22. An atom of ammonia, composed of 1 of azote and 1 of hydrogen 6

Fig.

23. An atom of nitrous gas, composed of 1 of azote and 1 of oxygen 12
24. An atom of olefiant gas, composed of 1 of carbone and 1 of hydrogen 6
25. An atom of carbonic oxide composed of carbone and 1 of oxygen 12
26. An atom of nitrous oxide, 2 azote + 1 oxygen 17
27. An atom of nitric acid, 1 azote + 2 oxygen 19
28. An atom of carbonic acid, 1 carbone + 2 oxygen 19
29. An atom of carburetted hydrogen, 1 carbone + 2 hydrogen 7
30. An atom of oxynitric acid, 1 azote + 3 oxygen 26
31. An atom of sulphuric acid, 1 sulphur + 3 oxygen 34
32. An atom of sulphuretted hydrogen, 1 sulphur + 3 hydrogen 16
33. An atom of alcohol, 3 carbone + hydrogen 16

weight of an element from 3.2522 to 3.25 because: 'I leave out the last two decimal places because they would destroy the law pointed out by Dr. Prout.'

What do you think of Thomson's approach to chemistry?

1.2 Look at some of Dalton's work in Figure 1.1.

(i) In modern notation, what was his formula for water? Is this formula consistent with the atomic weights of hydrogen and oxygen that he used?

(ii) Try to work out (or guess) the modern names of azote, olefiant gas, carbonic oxide and carburetted hydrogen.

1.3 Why do you think that Dalton's notation (and others like it) was replaced by the notation we now use based upon Berzelius' alphabet symbols for the elements?

1.4 Why was it that gold and silver were discovered and used long before sodium and potassium?

1.2 Evidence for atoms

The main reason why people believe that, by and large, Dalton's theory is correct is that it has been used to explain successfully a vast number of observations and results of experiments. Indeed, it is (almost) impossible to think of doing chemistry now without talking about atoms and the ways they join to make compounds. Possibly the nearest we can get to direct evidence that atoms exist lies in using a *field ionisation microscope*. In this type of experiment, the surface of a metal sample in a vacuum is bombarded with helium atoms. At the same time the surface is subjected to a huge electric field. The helium atoms are converted into positive ions when they hit the sample and are attracted to a fluorescent screen by the electric field. The type of image that can be obtained is shown in the photo.

The picture is just about as near as we can get to 'seeing' atoms. But be careful; we are *not* seeing atoms. Rather, the image is one of spots of light on a screen, which has been hit by tiny charged particles of helium (Figure 1.2). We *explain* the picture by saying that the dots of light show where the helium ions came from, and that they do in fact come from atoms on the surface of the metal sample.

Another way of persuading someone who is reluctant to believe in the existence of atoms is to show him or her an *X-ray diffraction pattern*. Such a pattern is obtained by passing X-rays through a crystal and then analysing the pattern produced on photographic film placed on the other side of the crystal. In the case of the pattern of Figure 1.3, the sample was a compound that contained benzene rings. Benzene rings consist of six carbon atoms joined in the shape of a hexagon, together with a hydrogen atom bonded to each carbon atom. The pattern

This is a field ionisation image of the surface of a nickel-molybdenum alloy, Ni_4Mo. Taken from Figure 9.5 of K. M. Bowkett & D. A. Smith, Field-Ion Microscopy, North-Holland Publishing Co., Amsterdam, 1970.

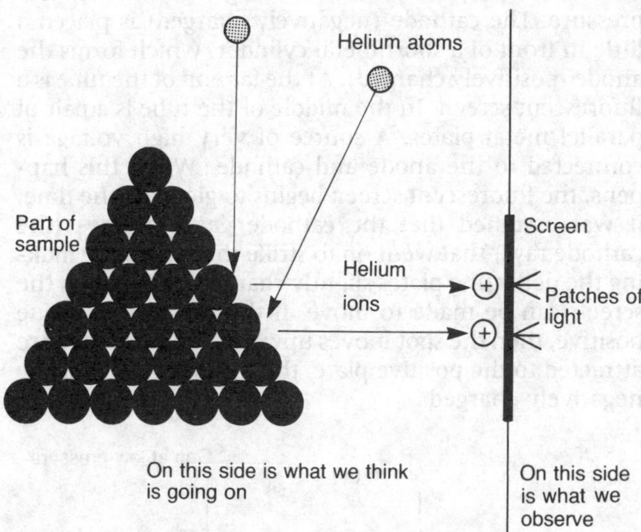

Figure 1.2 *Explanation of the image in a field ionisation microscope experiment*

shows where the electrons in a compound are most likely to be found. This particular pattern provides evidence for the hexagonal structure of benzene.

In the past, chemists have held completely different views on the nature of matter than those which we tend to take for granted now. We like to think that we are on the right track, but the history of science shows that it would be unwise to believe we are ever 100% correct.

Figure 1.3 *Part of the X-ray diffraction pattern of $C_6H_5CH_2CH_2C_6H_5$ showing a benzene ring. (Diagram taken from: Jeffrey, G. A. (1946).* Proc. R. Soc. **188,** *222)*

1.5 The X-ray pattern of the benzene ring does not show the hydrogen atoms. Why might this be?

1.3 Cathode rays

Towards the end of the last century there was a lot of interest in investigating cathode rays. These rays were produced in an apparatus like that shown in Figure 1.4. It consists of a glass tube containing a gas at very low pressure. The cathode (negatively charged) is placed a little in front of a short metal cylinder, which forms the anode (positively charged). At the far end of the tube is a fluorescent screen. In the middle of the tube is a pair of parallel metal plates. A source of very high voltage is connected to the anode and cathode. When this happens, the fluorescent screen begins to glow. At the time, it was assumed that the cathode gave off rays (the cathode rays) that went on to strike the screen. By making the deflecting plates slightly charged, the spot on the screen can be made to move. If the top plate is made positive, then the spot moves upwards. Because they are attracted to the positive plate, the cathode rays must be negatively charged.

It was Sir J. J. Thomson who, in 1897, is credited with identifying cathode rays as the things we call *electrons*. Thomson used a rather more complicated cathode ray apparatus to help him calculate a value for the ratio of the charge to mass, e/m_e, of an electron. The name 'electron' was, however, first used by the Irish physicist Johnston Stoney some years before Thomson. Stoney had also estimated the charge on the electron before Thomson. The modern value for e/m_e is nearly 1.759×10^{11} C kg^{-1}.

1.6 Use the modern value of e/m_e for an electron together with the value of e to calculate the mass of an electron ($e = 1.602 \times 10^{-19}$ C).

1.7 Values of e/m for other charged particles had been calculated by chemists who were working on the way in which electricity was conducted through solutions. Michael Faraday had discovered his laws of electrolysis around 1833, and there was a great deal of interest in trying to work out the connections between electricity (or electric charges) and the properties of chemicals. It was possible to calculate the charge to mass ratios for the ions discharged during electrolysis. One of the odd things about Thomson's result for e/m_e was that it was about 2000 times larger than the largest value found from electrolysis. Which ion might have had the highest charge to mass ratio in electrolysis? (Hint: you are looking for an ion that has either a very high charge or a very small mass.)

1.4 Millikan's experiment

The magnitude of the charge on an electron was found by a variety of methods. The one used by R. A. Millikan around 1913 is now known as Millikan's oil drop experiment (Figure 1.5). The idea was to allow tiny droplets of oil to fall through the air between two metal plates. X-rays passed into the apparatus caused molecules in the air to ionise. (That is, they would lose one

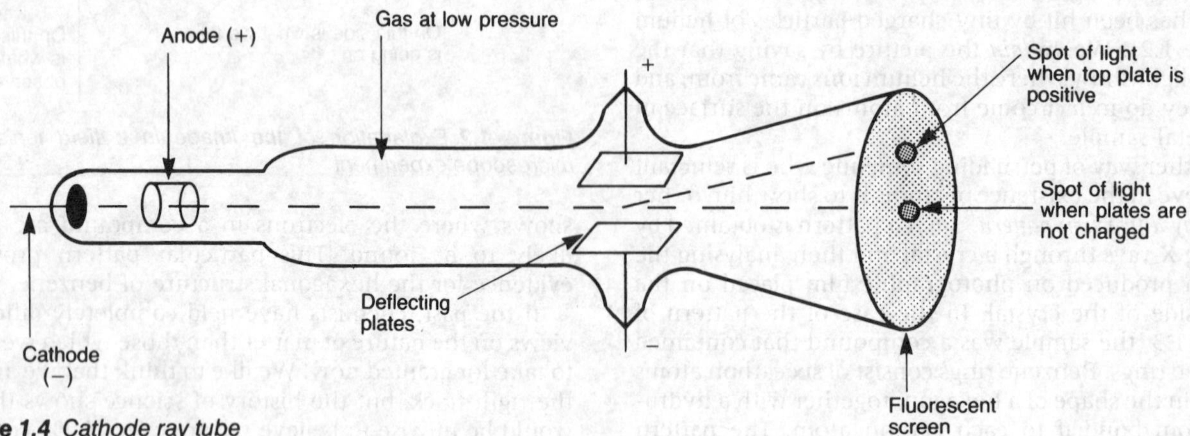

Figure 1.4 *Cathode ray tube*

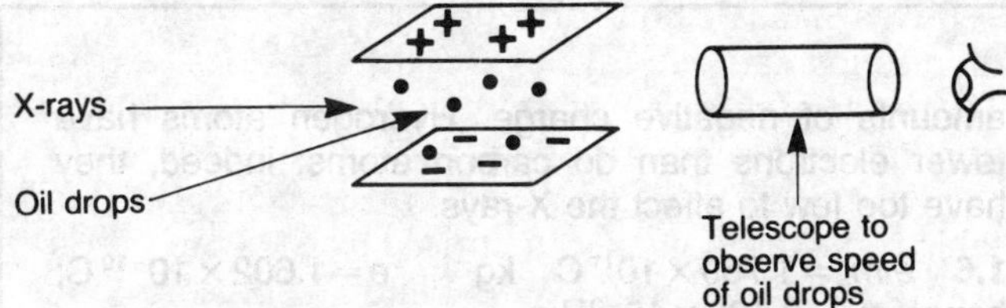

Figure 1.5 Outline of Millikan's oil drop experiment

of their electrons and become positively charged.) From time to time the ions would stick to the oil drops. The metal plates were given an electric charge, and, as the electric field between the plates was increased, it was possible to make some of the drops travel upwards at the same speed as they were previously falling. By measuring the speed, and knowing things like the strength of the field and the density of the oil, Millikan was able to calculate the magnitude of the charge on the oil drops. He found that the smallest charge to be found on them was approximately 1.59×10^{-19} C. This was recognised as the charge on an electron. The modern value is 1.602×10^{-19} C.

Here we have ignored the negative sign of the electron's charge. We shall use the symbol *e* to stand for 1.602×10^{-19} C. We shall write the actual charge on an electron, taking its negative sign into account, as $-e$.

1.8 An electric current of 1 A through a wire means that 1 C of charge is passing through a cross-section of the wire in 1 s. How many electrons are involved in producing a current of 1 A?

1.5 Electric charge is quantised

Millikan found a second result: the charges on the drops were always a whole number of times larger than the electronic charge, never less. This showed that there was a limit to how small an electric charge could get. The charge on an electron was the basic stuff of electricity. A large electric charge had to be built from a combination of, perhaps, thousands of millions of these basic charges. It is impossible to get, say, 0.8×10^{-19} C or 0.4×10^{-19} C. Fractions of the basic electronic charge do not exist. There is a way of summarising this property of electric charge; we say that electric charge is *quantised* (Figure 1.6).

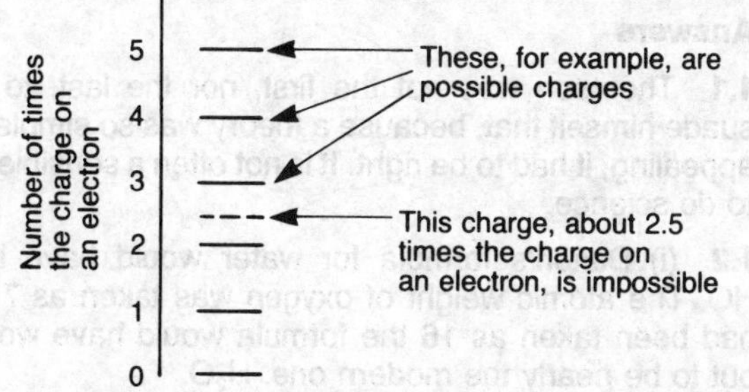

***Figure 1.6** Electric charge has to be a whole number of times the charge on an electron. That is, electric charge is quantised*

To say that something is quantised means that it comes in particular, well-defined quantities that do not change smoothly from one value to another. Rather, the change is sudden, or abrupt. We shall see that quantisation does not happen only with electric charge; energy is quantised as well.

1.9 Say which of the following things could be described as being quantised: goals scored in a hockey match; the height of waves on the sea; the lengths of hairs on your head; the number of peas in a pod.

1.10 Someone claimed to have invented a machine that can show the presence of very small numbers of electrons. The machine consists of a detector and a pointer that moves over a scale. The person who invented the machine labelled the scale as shown in Figure 1.7. Did the person really know what he or she was doing?

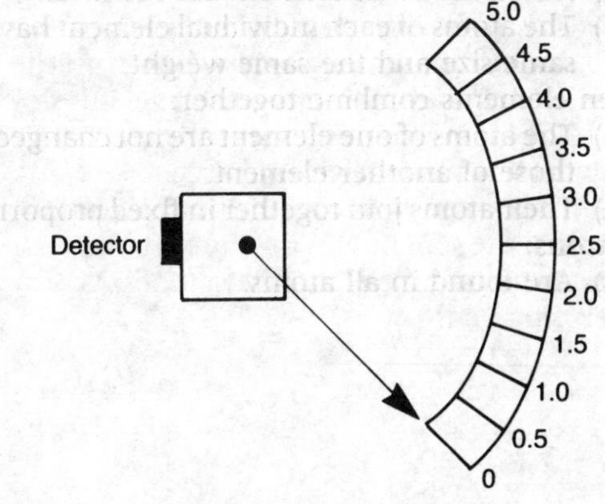

***Figure 1.7** An imaginary detector of electrons*

Answers

1.1 Thomson was not the first, nor the last, to persuade himself that, because a theory was so simple and appealing, it had to be right. It is not often a sensible way to do science.

1.2 (i) Dalton's formula for water would have been HO. The atomic weight of oxygen was taken as 7. If it had been taken as 16 the formula would have worked out to be nearly the modern one, H_2O.

(ii) Azote = nitrogen, N_2; olefiant gas = ethene, C_2H_4; carbonic oxide = carbon monoxide, CO; carburetted hydrogen = methane, CH_4. You can see how these arise by noticing that (like oxygen) the atomic weight of carbon is about half what it should be; e.g. carburetted hydrogen should have twice as many hydrogen atoms as Dalton gives it, thus giving CH_4.

1.3 The systems built on pictures were too clumsy for easy use. (Try writing equations with them!)

1.4 Gold and silver are much less reactive than sodium or potassium. They can be dug out of the ground in the pure state. Sodium and potassium are always found combined with other elements and are very hard to obtain pure.

1.5 X-rays are sensitive to the negative charge of electrons. However, they are not able to detect small amounts of negative charge. Hydrogen atoms have fewer electrons than do carbon atoms; indeed, they have too few to affect the X-rays.

1.6 $e/m_e = 1.759 \times 10^{11}$ C kg^{-1}, $e = 1.602 \times 10^{-19}$ C; hence $m_e = 9.109 \times 10^{-31}$ kg.

1.7 The ion is the hydrogen ion, H^+. This is a bare proton having the same size charge as an electron, but opposite in sign. You may have come across the fact that a proton is about 2000 times heavier than an electron.

1.8 The number of electrons will be 1 C/ $(1.602 \times 10^{-19}$ C), i.e. 6.42×10^{18}. The result shows that, even in a tiny current such as a microamp (10^{-6} A), huge numbers of electrons are involved.

1.9 Hockey goals and peas in a pod are quantised. You can only get them in whole numbers. The other two can have a continuous range of values.

1.10 Unfortunately the person appears to know nothing about quantisation of charge. It would be impossible to measure, say, 1.5 times the charge on an electron. If the machine was working properly it should only show whole number (integer) results, e.g. 0, 1, 2, . . .

UNIT 1 SUMMARY

- Dalton's atomic theory says that:
  - (i) All atoms of an element are identical.
  - (ii) The atoms of each individual element have the same size and the same weight.
- When elements combine together:
  - (i) The atoms of one element are not changed into those of another element.
  - (ii) Their atoms join together in fixed proportions.
- Electrons:
  - (i) Are found in all atoms.
  - (ii) Carry the smallest unit of negative charge, -1.602×10^{-19} C.
- Quantisation:

  To say that something is quantised means that it comes in particular, well defined quantities that do not change smoothly from one value to another. Rather, the change is sudden, or abrupt.
- Electric charge is quantised.

2

Energy levels

2.1 Energy changes

If a ball on the end of a string is given enough energy it is possible to make it move in a circle. It has gained kinetic energy. If the ball is given more energy it will move faster; given even more energy it will move faster still. In theory (if not in practice) we could continue giving the ball energy, or allowing it to lose energy, by any amount we wish. We would see the ball move round with a corresponding increase or decrease in speed. We can show on a diagram how the energy of the ball changes *continuously* from one value to another (Figure 2.1). Energy diagrams like this occur in a very large number of cases, e.g. cars, aircraft, or trains moving. At one time it was thought that only this sort of diagram could occur. The idea that it might be possible for something to change its energy by sudden jumps from one value to another was considered impossible; but this is exactly what does seem to happen with electrons in atoms and molecules.

Figure 2.1 *An energy diagram for continuous energy changes*

2.2 Energy levels

There is much evidence to show that electrons in atoms cannot gain or lose just any amount of energy. One experiment that illustrates this is done by bombarding molecules with X-rays. Some of the X-rays give energy to the electrons. Indeed, if the X-rays have sufficient energy, it is possible to knock the electrons right out of the molecule. If we were to measure the energies of the X-rays that cause electrons to be lost, we could show the results on an energy diagram. In Figure 2.2 this has been done for X-rays colliding with molecules of propanone.

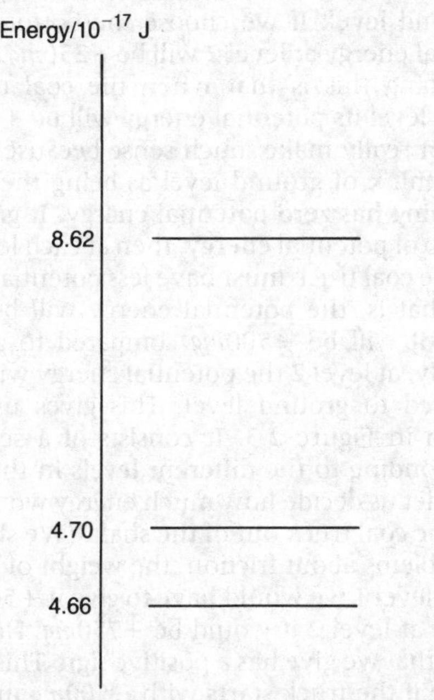

Figure 2.2 *Energy level diagram showing the energies of X-rays needed to remove electrons from propanone*

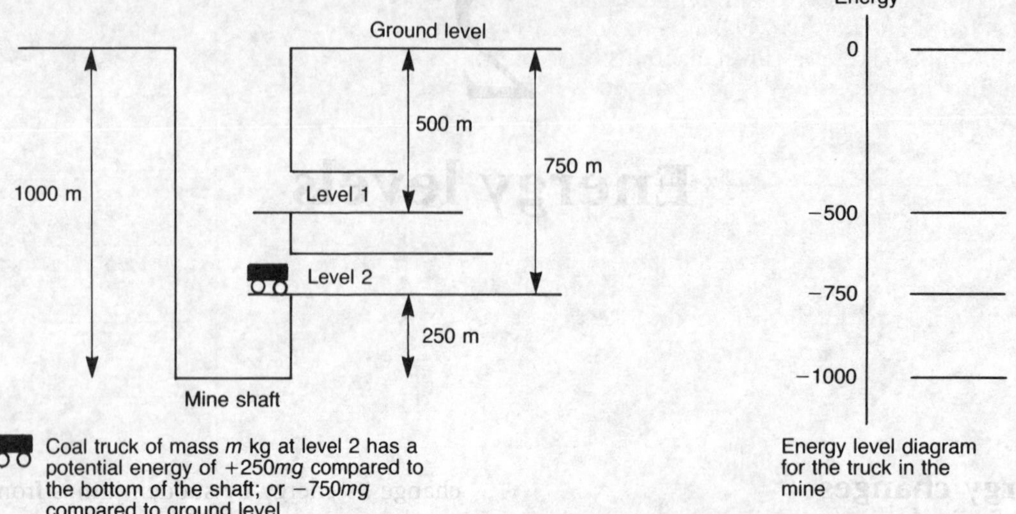

***Figure 2.3** The potential energy of a coal truck down a mine is given by multiplying its mass* m*, the acceleration due to gravity* g*, and the distance* d *from some zero level. Then, potential energy is* mgd *(or* dmg*). Compared to ground level, the potential energy values are negative. (The energy level scale has units* mg *joules)*

The diagram shows us that X-rays must have particular energies before electrons are removed. For example, X-rays with energy 4.68×10^{-17} J or 6×10^{-17} J have no effect; however, if they have energy 4.66×10^{-17} J, 4.70×10^{-17} J, or 8.62×10^{-17} J then electrons *are* knocked out of propanone.

If we are to understand this, let us first think about a more straightforward case. Imagine a mine shaft sunk deep into the ground (Figure 2.3). At various depths there are roadways running off to the coal faces. A coal truck standing at level 2 will have some potential energy. We have a choice; we can calculate its potential energy either compared to the bottom of the shaft, or compared to ground level. If we choose the bottom, the truck's potential energy at level 2 will be $+250mg$. The problem with doing this is that when the coal truck reaches ground level its potential energy will be $+1000mg$. This does not really make much sense because we normally like to think of ground level as being the place where everything has zero potential energy. If ground level *is* our zero of potential energy, then at each level down the shaft the coal truck must have less potential energy than zero. That is, the potential energy will be *negative*. At level 1 it will be $-500mg$ compared to ground level. Similarly, at level 2 the potential energy will be $-750mg$ compared to ground level. This gives us the energy diagram in Figure 2.3. It consists of a series of levels corresponding to the different levels in the mine.

Now let us decide how much energy would be needed to lift the coal truck out of the shaft. (We shall ignore all the problems about friction, the weight of cables and so on.) At level 1 we would have to give it $+500mg$ units of energy; at level 2 it would be $+750mg$. Notice that the energy that we give has a positive sign. This is important because if the truck starts with $-500mg$ units and then comes to ground level, where its potential energy is zero, we have to *add* $500mg$ to bring the total to zero.

If you have understood this, you should be able to understand why the experiment with X-rays and propanone shows that there are levels in propanone that have the energies shown in Figure 2.4. Our zero of potential energy has been taken as the world outside the molecule. That is, far enough away from the molecule that the electrons knocked out cannot feel any further attraction pulling them back into the molecule. With the world outside the molecule as our zero of energy, we have to put energy *in* to remove electrons; then (like the case of the truck down the coal mine) when electrons are in an atom or molecule we say that they have *negative* energies.

The three energy levels shown in Figure 2.4 are some

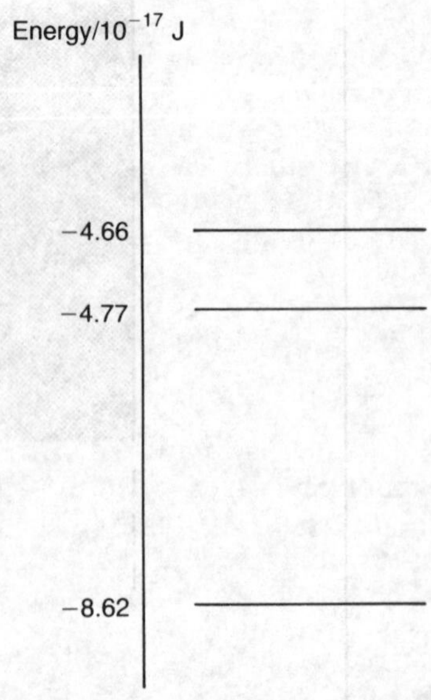

***Figure 2.4** Energy level diagram for some of the electrons in propanone*

of the energy levels for the electrons in propanone. The diagram itself is called an energy level diagram. You will discover in later units that energy level diagrams can be extremely useful in explaining the properties of electrons, atoms and molecules.

2.1 It has been discovered that the electron in a hydrogen atom can have one of a rather large number of possible energies. The values of the energy levels, E_n, depend on an integer, n, in the following way:

$$E_n = \frac{-k}{n^2}$$

where k is a constant of value nearly 2.18×10^{-18} J.

(i) Explain why the energy levels have negative signs.

(ii) Draw an energy level diagram for $n = 1, 2, 3, 4$ and 5.

(iii) Calculate the difference in energy, $E_2 - E_1$, between the first two levels.

(iv) Calculate the difference in energy between levels with $n = 100$ and $n = 101$, i.e. $E_{101} - E_{100}$.

(v) What happens to the gaps between the energy levels as n increases?

(vi) Sketch (i.e. do not try to be too accurate) the whole energy level diagram for the hydrogen atom with n starting at 1 and increasing to infinity. Don't worry about showing all the energy levels; it is the pattern that is important.

2.3 Max Planck and energy levels

We have seen that the electrons in propanone have a particular set of values. The idea that the energy of electrons might be restricted in this way was first developed by the German physicist Max Planck in 1900. He claimed that if electrons in an atom were thought to be oscillating with a frequency f, then they would have an energy given by

$E = hf$ Planck's equation

the letter h stands for a number, 6.626×10^{-34} J s, known as the Planck constant. At a frequency f an electron could not have an energy less than hf. Also, the minimum amount of energy that could be lost or gained by the electrons would be equal to hf. An electron obeying Planck's equation would have an energy level diagram like the one in Figure 2.5. Here there is a set of energy levels all equally spaced by hf. In general, the energy of each level is given by

$$E_n = nhf$$

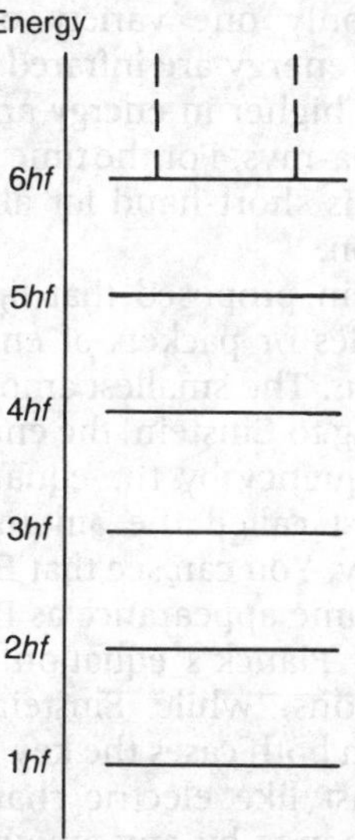

***Figure 2.5** An energy level diagram for an electron obeying Planck's equation*

where n is an integer (1, 2, 3, ...). This is a second version of Planck's equation.

2.2 The answers to these two short calculations should give you a 'feel' for the difference in scale between the behaviour of large-scale pieces of matter, and the world of electrons in atoms.

(i) A rough estimate of the frequency with which electrons oscillate in atoms is 10^{15} Hz. If an electron has an energy of 2×10^{-17} J, what value does this give for n in Planck's equation? Remember that n must be an integer, and that you will only obtain an estimate, not a precise value.

(ii) Now imagine a 1 kg mass moving at 6 m s^{-1} in a circular path with a frequency of 1 Hz. What is its kinetic energy? What value for n would be needed if Planck's equation were used for this mass?

(iii) Suppose that in the case of the 1 kg mass the value of n were to increase by 1. What would be the new value of the energy of the mass? What would be the chances of observing the difference between the new and old values?

2.4 Light energy

It has long been known that light represents one very important type of energy. The energy of light changes when the wavelength, λ, or frequency, f, changes. These two quantities are related through the equation

$$c = f\lambda$$

where c is the speed of light (about 3×10^8 m s^{-1}).

The higher the frequency, the higher the energy.

Visible light is only one variety of electromagnetic energy. Lower in energy are infrared light, radio waves and microwaves; higher in energy are ultraviolet light, X-rays and gamma-rays. For the time being we shall use the word 'light' as short-hand for all types of electromagnetic radiation.

In 1905 Einstein proposed that light consisted of a number of bundles or packets of energy, which were later called *photons*. The smallest amount of light is one photon. According to Einstein, the energy of a photon is related to its frequency by the equation $E=hf$. It was Einstein who first called the amount of energy hf a *quantum* of energy. You can see that Einstein's equation has exactly the same appearance as Planck's. The main difference is that Planck's equation was used for the energy of electrons, while Einstein's equation was applied to light. In both cases the key idea is that energy is quantised. (Just like electric charge is quantised.) Energy cannot change by any amount smoothly from one value to another. It must change by whole numbers of times the basic unit of energy, hf. It so happens that in the large-scale world of people, cars, golf balls, and the like, changes in energy appear to be smooth because the amount of energy tied up in a unit of energy such as hf is amazingly small – too small for us to observe. (Your answer to question 2.2 should have shown this to be true.)

2.3 A typical radio wave has a wavelength of 1500 m.

(i) What is its frequency?

(ii) What would be the energy of one photon having this frequency?

(iii) Repeat the calculation for red (visible) light, which has a wavelength of around 700 nm. (1 nm $=10^{-9}$ m.)

2.4 Copper(II) sulphate solution looks blue in colour. This is because it absorbs photons of red light. The photons are absorbed because their energy is used to make electrons belonging to the copper(II) ions move from a lower to a higher energy level. What is the difference between the two levels?

Answers

2.1 (i) Because the zero of potential energy is the world beyond the atom, electrons inside atoms are lower in potential energy, so they have negative values. We have to put energy *in* to get the electrons out.

(ii) See Figure 2.6.

(iii) $E_2-E_1=3k/4=1.635\times10^{-18}$ J.

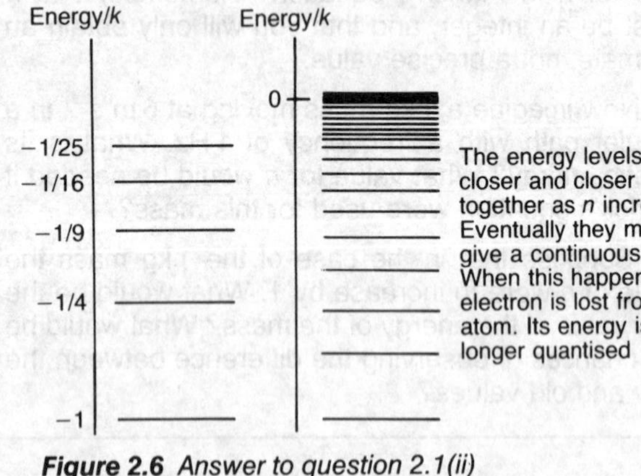

Energy/k
Energy/k
0
−1/25
−1/16
−1/9
−1/4
−1
The energy levels get closer and closer together as n increases. Eventually they merge to give a continuous band. When this happens the electron is lost from the atom. Its energy is no longer quantised

***Figure 2.6** Answer to question 2.1(ii)*

(iv) $E_{101}-E_{100}=k/(10\,100)=1.618\times10^{-22}$ J.

(v) The gap becomes increasingly small; eventually zero.

(vi) See Figure 2.6.

2.2 (i) $E_n=nhf$ gives
$n=(2\times10^{-17}\text{ J})/(6.626\times10^{-34}\text{ J s}\times10^{15}\text{ Hz})$
so $n=30$.

(ii) The energy is $mv^2/2=18$ J. With $f=1$ Hz, $n=3\times10^{34}$.

(iii) An increase of 1 in n increases the energy by around $1\times h$. The increase, which is of the order of 10^{-34} J, is completely impossible to observe.

2.3 (i) $f=c/\lambda=(3\times10^8\text{ m s}^{-1})/(1500\text{ m})=2\times10^5$ Hz.
(ii) $E=hf=6.626\times10^{-34}\text{ J s}\times2\times10^{15}\text{ Hz}=1.325\times10^{-18}$ J.
(iii) $f=c/\lambda=(3\times10^8\text{ m s}^{-1})/(700\times10^{-9}\text{ m})=4.286\times10^{14}$ Hz. This leads to $E=2.84\times10^{-19}$ J.

2.4 Using your answer to the last question, the difference between the energy levels is 2.84×10^{-19} J.

UNIT 2 SUMMARY

- Energy changes in atoms and molecules are quantised.
- Electrons, atoms and molecules have their own sets of energy levels.
- Light of frequency f has energy $E=hf$, where h is the Planck constant, 6.626×10^{-34} J s.
- The quantity hf is a quantum of energy.
- The energy levels of electrons in atoms are given by $E_n=nhf$, where n is a whole number: a quantum number.
- The equation $E=hf$, or $E_n=nhf$, is Planck's equation.

3

Atoms and the nucleus

3.1 A plum pudding

The discovery that atoms contained electrons caused some consternation. Left to themselves, atoms were known to be electrically neutral; so the negative charge of the electrons had to be balanced by an equal amount of positive charge. The puzzle was to work out how the two types of charge were arranged. An initial guess made by Sir J. J. Thomson was that the electrons were embedded in a ball of positive charge (Figure 3.1). This model of the atom was given the rather unlikely name of the 'plum pudding' model. If you were to put an imaginary hand into an atom you might be lucky enough to pull out an electron; just like the nursery rhyme character Little Jack Horner, who was fortunate enough to put his hand into a pie and pull out a plum.

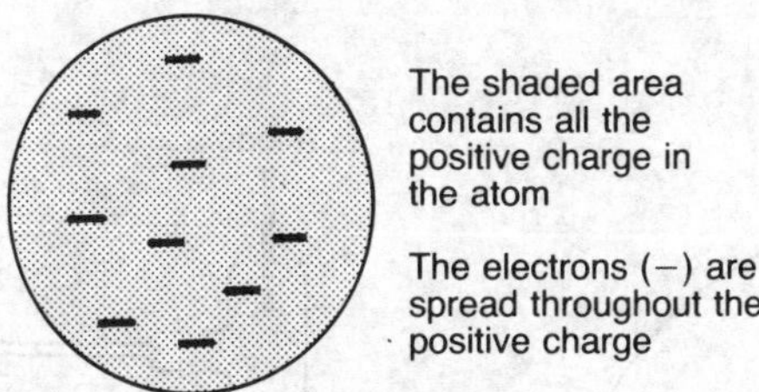
The shaded area contains all the positive charge in the atom
The electrons (−) are spread throughout the positive charge

Figure 3.1 *Thomson's model of the atom. The shaded region shows the positive charge, equal but opposite to the total charge of the electrons*

3.2 How the nucleus was discovered

You may have noticed that Thomson's model has no nucleus for the atom. In 1909 H. Geiger and E. Marsden published the results of a series of experiments that they had carried out at the University of Manchester under the direction of Ernest (later Lord) Rutherford. Rutherford had a keen interest in the new science of radioactivity that had developed following the pioneering work of Becquerel and the Curies (which we shall look at later). One of the early discoveries was that some elements gave off alpha-particles (α-particles). Alpha-particles were found to have two units of positive charge,

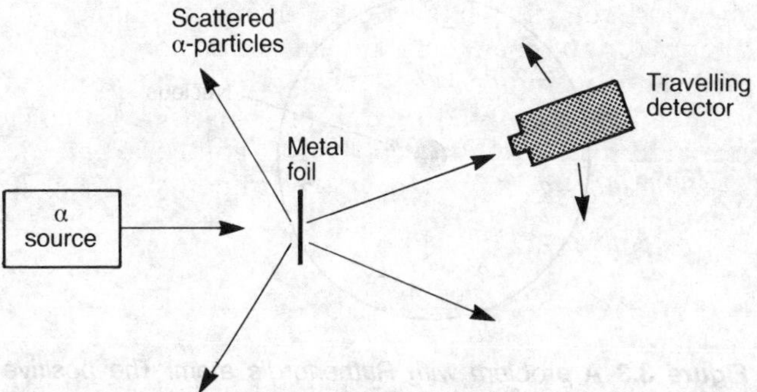
Scattered α-particles
Travelling detector
Metal foil
α source

Figure 3.2 *Geiger and Marsden's experiment on the scattering of α-particles*

and to be identical to helium atoms that had lost two electrons. That is, α-particles were helium ions, He^{2+}. Geiger and Marsden directed a stream of α-particles at thin metal foils. They discovered that the particles were deflected through a wide variety of angles (Figure 3.2). The fact that they were deflected was not a surprise because the positive charge in the atom should repel them. It was the size of the angles of deflection that was the surprise. Some of them were deflected through as much as 150°.

From the results in Table 3.1 you can see that only a tiny fraction of the particles were deflected through large angles; but the fact was that *some* were. In 1911 Rutherford showed that an atom with its positive charge spread around, like the atoms that Thomson had imagined,

Table 3.1. The numbers of α-particles scattered by a gold foil in Geiger and Marsden's experiments

Angle of deflection/degrees	*Percentage of α-particles deflected*
15	93
30	5
45	1
60	0.34
120	0.037
150	0.023

could only deflect the particles through small angles. Large deflections could only occur if the positive charge were concentrated in a tiny volume of space. Rutherford showed that for gold the charge had to be within a sphere whose radius was no more than 3.2×10^{-14} m. For other atoms much lighter than gold, this radius went down to as low as 3×10^{-15} m. At the time, the radius of an atom had been estimated to be around 2×10^{-10} m, so it does not take long to see that the positive charge in an atom must be collected in a sphere whose radius is some 10 000 to 100 000 times smaller than the radius of the atom as a whole. In other words, between them, Rutherford, Geiger and Marsden had established that atoms contained a *nucleus* (Figure 3.3).

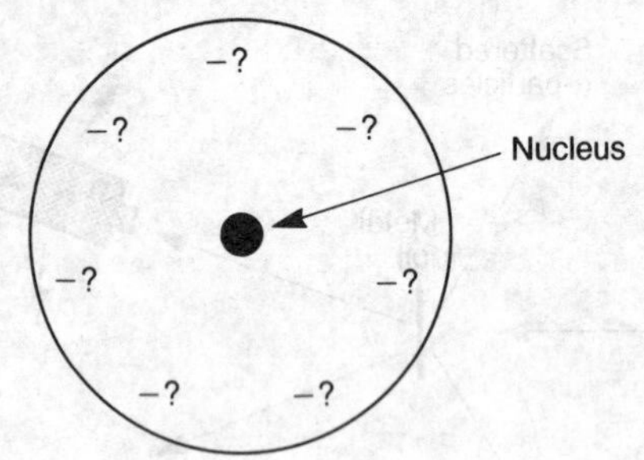

***Figure 3.3** A problem with Rutherford's atom. The positive nucleus is at the centre of the atom, but where are the electrons?*

3.1 Rutherford did not discount the idea that the nucleus could contain electrons. For example, in 1914 he said: 'Since the experimental evidence indicates that the nucleus has very small dimensions, the constituent positive and negative electrons must be very closely packed together.'

Why do you think Rutherford thought electrons might be found in the nucleus? You will find it helpful to think about the case of oxygen. This element was known to have a relative mass of 16, but it had eight positive charges on the nucleus, and only eight electrons could take part in chemical reactions.

3.3 The discovery of protons

It is now well known that the positive charge in the nucleus of an atom is due to the presence of *protons*; that is, absolutely tiny quantities of positive electric charge. The charge of a proton is exactly the same size as, but opposite in sign to, the charge of an electron. The method used to establish the existence of protons made much use of an instrument called a mass spectrograph. The inventor of the mass spectrograph was F. W. Aston. In his apparatus (Figure 3.4), atoms with a positive charge, i.e. positive ions, were passed through a magnetic field. The field was designed to bring atoms with

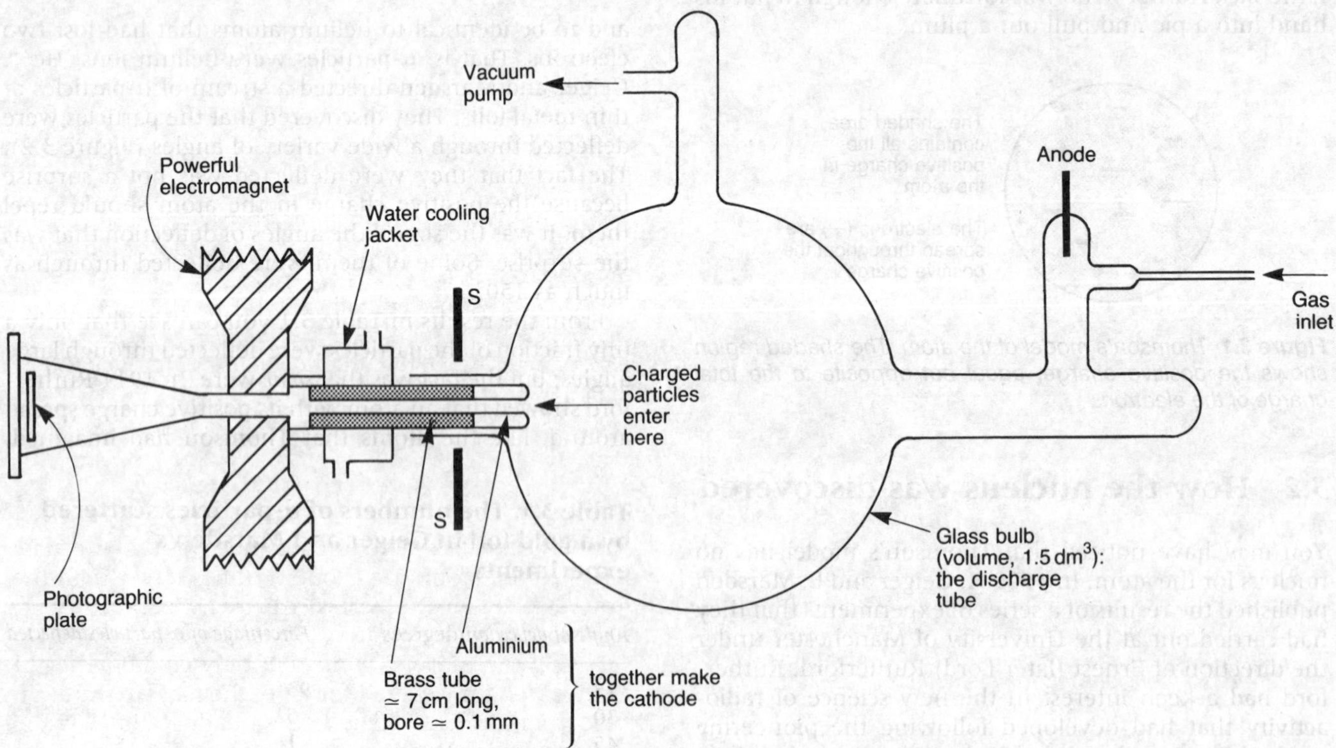

***Figure 3.4** Aston's positive ray apparatus, also known as a mass spectrograph. The voltage applied to the anode and cathode was between 30 and 50 kV. Note the relatively small scale of the apparatus. S = soft iron plates to protect discharge tube from magnetic field. (Diagram adapted from: Aston, F. W. (1924).* Isotopes, *Edward Arnold, London)*

different masses to a focus at different places on a photographic plate. When the plate was developed, lines could be seen where ions had arrived at the plate. The way that Aston had designed his apparatus meant that these lines were shaped like parabolas.

The key point about a mass spectrograph apparatus is that the path of an ion is curved when it travels through the magnetic field. The curvature depends on two things: the charge on the ion, q, and its mass, m. Ions with the same charge to mass ratio, q/m, will arrive at the same point on the detector. By doing some careful experimental work and mathematics, Aston was able to measure the charge to mass ratio of a large number of ions. From his results developed the 'whole number rule'. In effect, this rule was that the charge to mass ratio of each ion was (very nearly) a whole number of times that for the hydrogen ion. It appeared that the hydrogen ion was the simplest ion, and that it formed the basic building block of all other ions (and atoms). The name proton, taken from the Greek word *'protos'* meaning 'first', was given to the hydrogen ion.

The original mass spectrograph used by Aston. This was set up in the Cavendish Laboratory in 1919, but is now in the Science Museum, London.
A: anode connected to high potential terminal by induction coil below table; B: discharge tube; C: reservoir containing gas to be analysed; I_1, I_2: charcoal–liquid air tubes; S: soft iron plates to shield discharge from stray magnetic fields; L: leads from high tension battery to electric plates; M: magnet; T: small lamp to help with photography; V: vacuum-tight and light-tight control for moving photographic plate; W: camera showing light-tight cap on left; H: magnet-circuit ammeter; O: magnet-circuit control resistances; G: mercury pump for evacuating apparatus. Source: F. W. Aston, Mass Spectra and Isotopes, *London, Edward Arnold, 1924.*

3.4 Moseley and atomic number

The evidence that the positive charge in the nucleus was of fundamental importance was provided by H. G. J. Moseley. In experiments he performed in 1913 at the University of Manchester, Moseley bombarded a number of elements with cathode rays (electrons). The energy provided by the cathode rays caused the elements to give off X-rays. Moseley investigated the connection between the frequency of the X-rays and the nature of the element giving them off. He found that the square root of the frequency:

> . . . increases by a constant amount as we pass from one element to the next, using the chemical order of the elements in the periodic system. Except in the case of nickel and cobalt . . .. We have here a proof that there is in the atom a fundamental quantity, which increases by regular steps as we pass from one element to the next. This quantity can only be the charge on the central positive nucleus, of the existence of which we already have definite proof . . .. We are therefore led by experiment to the view that *N* (the atomic number) is the same as the number of the place occupied by the element in the periodic system.
>
> We can confidently predict that in the few cases in which the order of the atomic weights . . . clashes with the chemical order of the periodic system, the chemical properties are governed by *N* . . ..

In the following year (1914), working in Oxford, he published a chart of his results, which showed a graph of atomic number plotted against the square root of the frequency of the X-rays. You can see part of the graph in Figure 3.5.

In this way Moseley had shown that the *atomic number*, which we recognise as *the number of protons in the nucleus*, determined the order of elements in the Periodic Table.

3.5 Discovery of neutrons

One of the results that Aston obtained was that the mass of an oxygen atom was about 16 times larger than the proton. Following Rutherford's discovery of the nucleus, and Moseley's investigation of atomic number, it was clear that the nucleus of oxygen only contained eight positive charges. Where the rest of the mass of the atom came from was resolved by James Chadwick in 1932: he discovered the *neutron*.

The reason why it took so long to show the presence of neutrons was their lack of charge. This meant, for example, that neutrons would not show up in Aston's mass

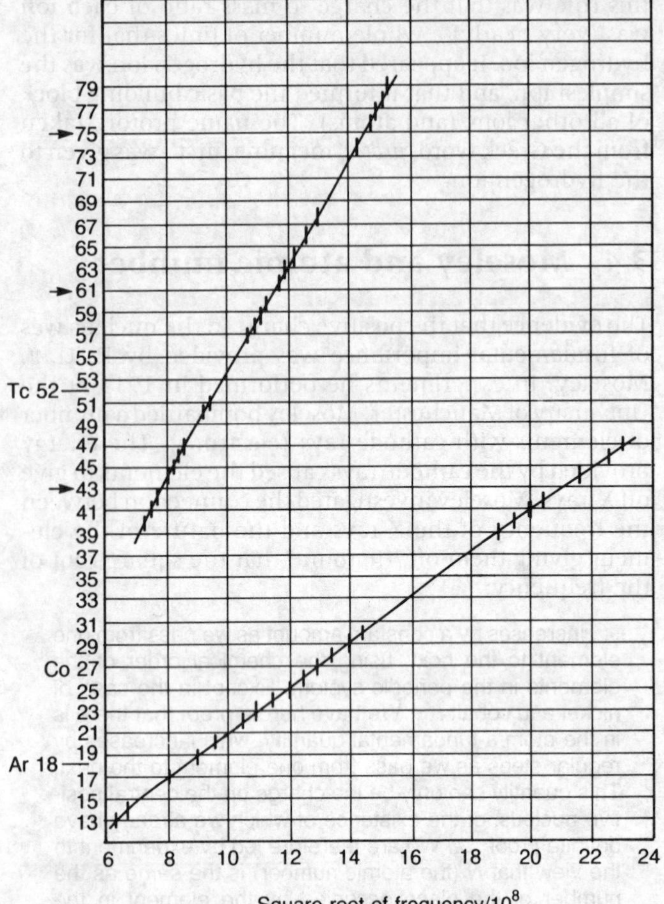

***Figure 3.5** Part of Moseley's graph of integers he assigned to the elements plotted against square root of frequency of X-rays they emit. We now recognise the integers as the atomic numbers. (i) He did not investigate all the elements. (ii) The graphs are not exactly straight lines. (iii) The arrows mark spaces for elements that Moseley predicted were yet to be discovered. (iv) He said 'The order chosen for the elements is the order of the atomic weights, except in the case of Ar, Co and Te, where this clashes with the order of the chemical properties'*

spectrograph. The basis of Chadwick's method was as follows. He placed a source of alpha-particles on one side of a sheet of beryllium. On the other side of the beryllium was a detector that would show the presence of any ions (Figure 3.6).

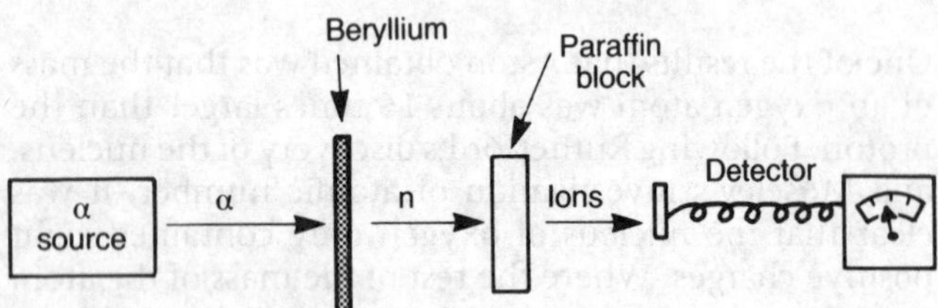

***Figure 3.6** Chadwick's discovery of neutrons. No paraffin block: no ions detected. Block present: ions detected. Therefore particles must have come from the beryllium and caused a reaction in the paraffin. The particles were neutrons*

Without anything between the beryllium and the detector, very few ions were detected. However, when a block of paraffin was placed between the beryllium and the detector, the number of ions detected increased dramatically. These ions were shown to be protons. Particles must have been emitted from the beryllium. These hit the paraffin and caused protons to be emitted. However, because they had little or no effect on the detector themselves, they had no charge of their own. The uncharged particles were neutrons.

3.2 Why could the mass of a neutron not be determined in a mass spectrograph (or spectrometer)?

3.6 A comparison of electrons, protons and neutrons

The mass of a proton was fairly easy to measure using Aston's mass spectrograph. However, as we have seen, this method could not be used for measuring the mass of a neutron. Instead, neutrons were allowed to collide with other atoms. The velocities and masses of the particles emitted were measured. Then using the law of conservation of momentum, it was possible to calculate the mass of the neutrons. The mass of a neutron was found to be almost the same as that of a proton. You will find the values of the charge and mass of a neutron, proton and electron gathered together in Table 3.2. Owing to the very small mass of electrons, nearly all of the mass of an atom is due to the neutrons and protons.

It is as well to remember that usually atoms are electrically neutral. This is because they have equal numbers of protons and electrons. The electrons travel around the nucleus in a way that we shall discuss in later units. If an atom is charged, it is because it gains or loses electrons; not because it changes its number of protons.

Table 3.2. Values of the charge and mass of protons, neutrons and electrons*

	Charge/C	*Mass*/kg	*Ratio of masses*
Proton	1.602×10^{-19}	1.673×10^{-27}	1
Neutron	0.0	1.675×10^{-27}	1
Electron	-1.602×10^{-19}	9.109×10^{-31}	1/1838

*The values in the table are only approximate. Also, the ratio of the masses ignores the difference between the masses of the proton and neutron

3.3 Let us use some 'round numbers' to estimate the sizes of atoms and their nuclei. Assume an atom to have a radius of 10^{-10} m, and a nucleus a radius of 10^{-16} m. The formula for the volume of a sphere is $4\pi r^3/3$.

(i) What is the volume of the atom?

(ii) What is the volume of the nucleus?

(iii) What percentage of the volume of the atom is the nucleus?

3.4 The mass of a hydrogen atom is about 1.7×10^{-27} kg. Use this value together with your results from the previous question to answer the next three questions.

(i) What is the density of a hydrogen atom? (Density = mass/volume.)

(ii) What is the density of the hydrogen nucleus? (Ignore the mass of the electron.)

(iii) The Earth has a mass of about 6×10^{24} kg. If the Earth had the same density as a hydrogen nucleus, what would its radius be? Compare your answer with the real radius of the Earth, which is about 6.4×10^6 m.

3.7 Isotopes

Virtually all of the mass of an atom is due to the neutrons and protons. As Moseley showed, every element has its own characteristic atomic number, and the elements in the Periodic Table are listed in the order of their atomic numbers. Together with protons, atoms also have neutrons in the nucleus. Sometimes neutrons and protons are called *nucleons*. The number of protons and neutrons added together (or, the number of nucleons) gives us the *mass number* of an atom. In future we shall use the symbol Z for the atomic number and A for the mass number. If we also use N to stand for the number of neutrons, we have

$$A = Z + N$$

One of the results of mass spectrometry was that some elements consist of atoms with several different masses. For example, a sample of bromine was always found to have atoms with mass numbers 79 and 81 (see photo in Unit 29). Now, bromine has an atomic number of 35, so to give mass numbers of 79 and 81 we must have $N = 44$ and $N = 46$. That is, the two kinds of atom are different because they have *different numbers of neutrons*. These are two *isotopes* of bromine. We can define isotopes in this way:

Isotopes are atoms that have the same atomic number but different mass numbers.

It is useful to use a special labelling system for isotopes, or indeed any atom. The system is to write down the symbol of the element and then put the mass number as a superscript, and the atomic number as a subscript:

$$\text{mass number} \rightarrow A \quad \text{atomic number} \rightarrow Z \qquad {}^{A}_{Z}\text{E}$$

For example, we would show the two isotopes of bromine as ${}^{79}_{35}\text{Br}$ and ${}^{81}_{35}\text{Br}$. We can call an atom represented in this way a *nuclide*.

We can use a similar notation to represent neutrons, protons and electrons. The scheme is shown in Table 3.3.

Table 3.3. Standard notation for neutrons, protons and electrons*

	Symbol
Neutron	${}^{1}_{0}\text{n}$
Proton	${}^{1}_{1}\text{p}$
Electron	${}^{0}_{-1}\text{e}$
Positron	${}^{0}_{+1}\text{e}$

*Here we have included the positron. A positron can be thought of as a positively charged electron. Positrons show up in the course of some nuclear reactions

It is important that you realise that the chemical properties of an element mainly depend on the numbers of protons and electrons, not the number of neutrons. This means that, as a rule:

The chemical properties of isotopes of the same element are identical.

However, physical properties of elements often depend on the mass of the atoms. Therefore, isotopes of the same element can have different physical properties, e.g. melting and boiling points. Also, the rates of some reactions can depend on the isotopes present (especially those of hydrogen).

3.5 How many neutrons and protons have the following nuclides: (i) ${}^{1}_{1}\text{H}$; (ii) ${}^{16}_{8}\text{O}$; (iii) ${}^{14}_{6}\text{C}$; (iv) ${}^{37}_{17}\text{Cl}$; (v) ${}^{127}_{53}\text{I}$?

3.8 Atomic mass units

The actual values of the masses of protons, neutrons and the atoms they make up are so small that they are not very convenient to use. Rather than use their true, or absolute, masses we can use a scale of relative values. At present the scale defines the mass of a ${}^{12}_{6}\text{C}$ atom as *exactly* 12 units. This is the *carbon-12 atomic mass scale*. Table 3.4 shows the values of the atomic masses of neutrons, protons and electrons on this scale. Notice that the atomic masses have no units.

In the past, different atomic mass scales have been

Table 3.4. Atomic masses of neutrons, protons and electrons on the carbon-12 scale

	*Atomic mass**
Neutron	1.008 665
Proton	1.007 265
Electron	0.000 549

*1 atomic mass unit (amu) = $1.660\,566 \times 10^{-27}$ kg

used. For example, the mass of an oxygen atom was once chosen to be exactly 16 units. On this scale the atomic masses differ by about 0.03%. For much of chemistry this difference is so small that it can be ignored; but for accurate work the difference must be taken into account. In this and any other modern chemistry or physics textbook, you should find that the carbon-12 scale is used.

3.9 Relative atomic and molecular masses

The majority of elements are found in nature as a mixture of isotopes. For example, a sample of bromine that you might make in the laboratory contains two isotopes: bromine-79, $^{79}_{35}Br$, and bromine-81, $^{81}_{35}Br$. A mass spectrometer can be used to find out the masses of these isotopes. Using the carbon-12 scale, their relative isotopic masses are 78.919 and 80.917, respectively. (Notice that we have used the word 'relative' here; this emphasises that we are taking their masses relative to an atom of carbon-12.) These values can be determined by using a mass spectrometer. The spectrometer will also show us the proportions of each isotope. Any naturally occurring sample of bromine contains approximately 50.52% of $^{79}_{35}Br$ and 49.48% of $^{81}_{35}Br$. Thus the *average* mass of a bromine atom will be

$$78.919 \times \frac{50.52}{100} + 80.917 \times \frac{49.48}{100} = 79.908$$

We call this figure the *relative atomic mass* of bromine. Relative atomic masses are given the symbol A_r, and we show the element to which they refer in brackets. For example,

$$A_r(\mathrm{Br}) = 79.908$$

You will probably find the value given as 79.91, 79.9, or even 80 in some tables of relative atomic masses; it depends on the accuracy of the figures in the tables. Relative atomic masses of some of the more common elements are shown in Table 3.5. The figures have been given to the accuracy normally expected of work at this level of chemistry.

In a similar way we calculate values of *relative molecular mass, M_r*. For example, the relative molecular mass of a bromine molecule, Br_2, is $2 \times A_r(\mathrm{Br})$, i.e. $M_r(\mathrm{Br_2}) = 159.816$, or, less accurately, $M_r(\mathrm{Br_2}) = 160$.

There is one small point you should know about. It is

Table 3.5. Relative atomic masses of some elements

Element	A_r	*Element*	A_r
Hydrogen	1.0	Sodium	23.0
Carbon	12.0	Magnesium	24.3
Nitrogen	14.0	Potassium	39.1
Oxygen	16.0	Iron	55.8
Sulphur	32.0	Copper	63.5
Chlorine	35.5	Silver	108.0
Bromine	79.9	Gold	197.0
Iodine	127.0	Lead	207.0

that we use relative molecular masses even for substances that are not made of molecules. An example is sodium chloride, Na^+Cl^-, which contains sodium ions and chloride ions. Even though there are no sodium chloride molecules, we use the values $A_r(\mathrm{Na}) = 23$ and $A_r(\mathrm{Cl}) = 35.5$ to give us $M_r(\mathrm{NaCl}) = 58.5$.

In Unit 29 you will discover how mass spectrometer readings can be used to determine relative molecular masses.

3.6 Why do values of relative atomic and relative molecular mass have no units?

3.7 The relative atomic mass of chlorine is quoted as 35.5. A sample of chlorine made in the laboratory is a mixture of $^{35}_{17}Cl$ and $^{37}_{17}Cl$. What are the percentages of the two isotopes in chlorine? Use the mass numbers in the calculation, as these will provide reasonable estimates of the percentages. (Hint: call X the percentage of $^{37}_{17}Cl$ and $(100 - X)$ the percentage of $^{35}_{17}Cl$.)

3.8 Calculate the relative molecular masses of the following substances: (i) H_2O; (ii) H_2SO_4; (iii) $MgSO_4$; (iv) $AgNO_3$; (v) $FeCl_3$.

3.10 Einstein's equation

Thorium-228 is an isotope that is radioactive. It gives off α-particles. Let us look at some results of measurements of the masses of the nuclides in the radioactive decay of thorium-228, $^{228}_{90}Th$:

$$^{228}_{90}\mathrm{Th} \rightarrow {}^{224}_{88}\mathrm{Ra} + {}^{4}_{2}\mathrm{He}$$

The masses of these nuclides are shown in Table 3.6.

If you add up the mass of the radium-224 and α-particle, you will find that it comes to 228.022 800 amu. This is *less* than the mass of the thorium-228 by 0.005 926 amu. This may strike you as a rather small amount; but the idea that any mass at all has 'disappeared' is a strange one. The problem is, where has the 'missing' mass gone? It is, or was, one of the basic ideas

Table 3.6. The masses of nuclides in the decay of $^{228}_{90}$Th

Nuclide	*Mass*/amu
$^{228}_{90}$Th	228.028 726
$^{224}_{88}$Ra	224.020 196
$^{4}_{2}$He	4.002 604

of science that mass cannot be created or destroyed; that is, it should be conserved. Nuclear reactions like this show that the law of conservation of mass is not strictly correct. It was Albert Einstein who provided the explanation. He showed that mass and energy were related to one another. Every mass, *m*, has an energy content, *E*, which is given by Einstein's famous equation

$E = mc^2$ Einstein's equation

where *c* is the speed of light (2.998×10^8 m s^{-1}). The *total energy* (including the energy content of the masses) must be conserved. The difference in mass that we have discovered in the case of the alpha decay of thorium-228 is due to the fact that energy is released in the decay. We can use Einstein's equation to calculate this energy.

First we must convert from atomic mass units to the normal units of mass, kilograms. We know that 1 amu = 1.661×10^{-27} kg. Therefore the 'missing' mass is $0.005\,926 \times 1.661 \times 10^{-27}$ kg, i.e. $m = 9.841 \times 10^{-30}$ kg. This gives

$$E = 9.841 \times 10^{-30}\ \text{kg} \times (2.998 \times 10^8\ \text{m s}^{-1})^2 = 8.845 \times 10^{-13}\ \text{J}$$

While this is not a great deal of energy in itself, if we had one mole of thorium-228 (about 228 g) with each of the 6.02×10^{23} atoms giving off alpha-particles, there would be $6.02 \times 10^{23} \times 8.845 \times 10^{-13}$ J, or 5.325×10^{11} J, i.e. about five hundred thousand million joules. We would need to burn at least 20 tonnes of coal to produce the

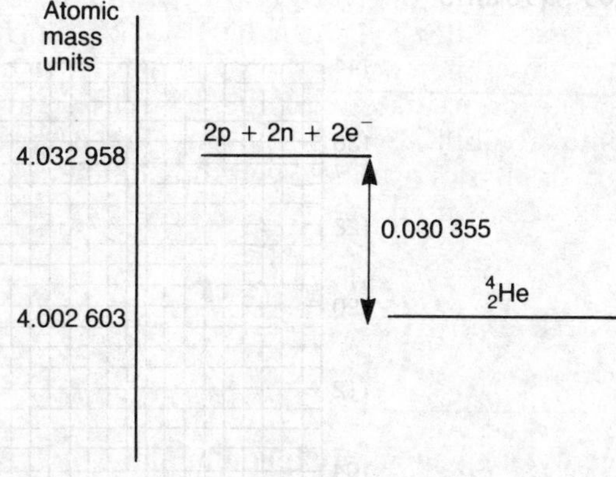

Figure 3.7 An α-particle ($^4_2$He) is energetically more stable than its component particles. (Atomic mass units are also a measure of energy)

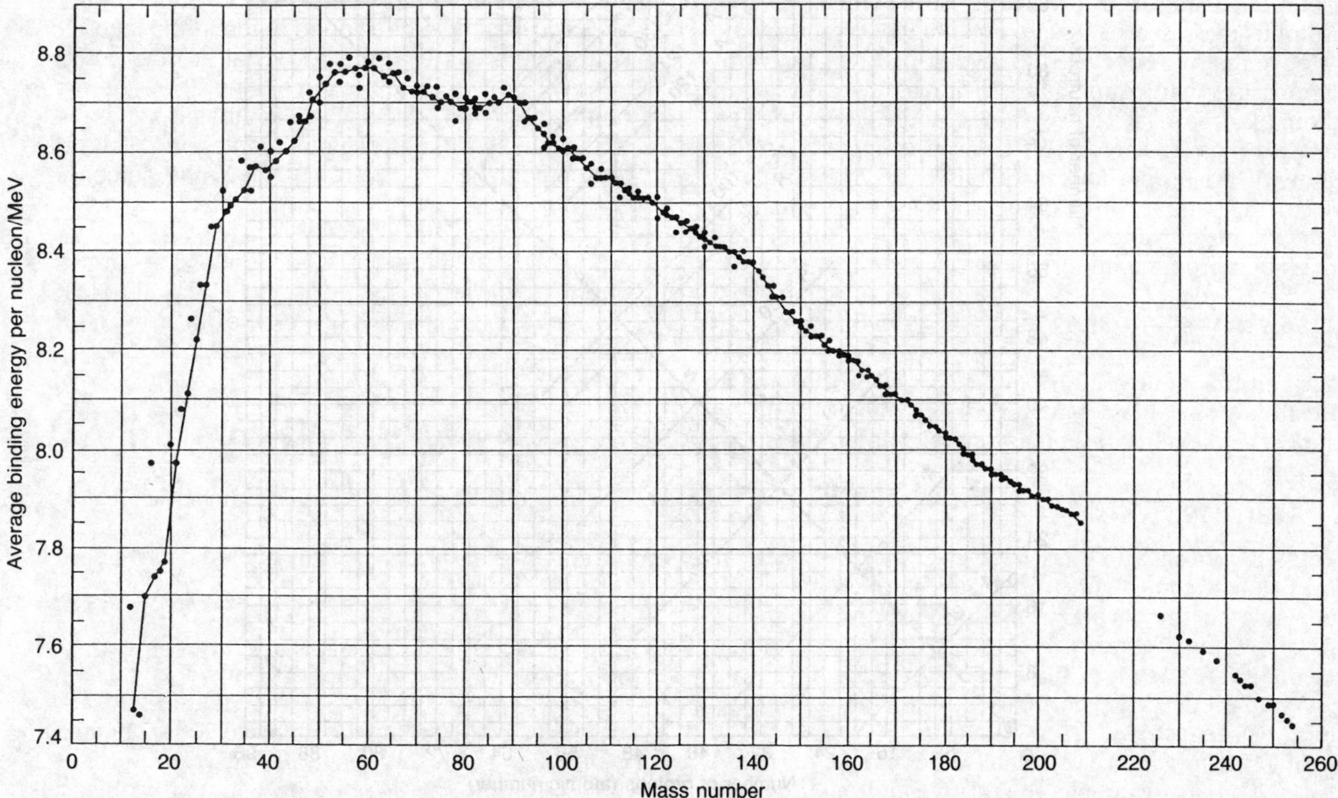

Figure 3.8 This diagram shows that the elements with greatest binding energy per nucleon have mass numbers in the range 50 to 90. This represents elements with atomic numbers between 24 and 40 approximately. (Graph adapted from: Friedlander, G., et al. (1964). Nuclear and Radiochemistry, *2nd edn, Wiley, Chichester, figure 2.1(a))*

same amount of energy! (If you do not know about the mole in chemistry, read Unit 37.)

3.11 Binding energy

We can use the figures in Table 3.4 to calculate the mass of a helium atom, ^4_2He. This atom contains two protons, two neutrons and two electrons. Adding up the masses we find that

mass of ^4_2He
$= 2 \times (1.007\,265 + 1.008\,665 + 0.000\,549)$
$= 4.032\,958$ amu

The actual mass of ^4_2He determined from experiment is 4.002 603 amu. This is 0.030 355 amu *less* than the sum of the masses of the separate particles. In terms of energy, this means that ^4_2He is *lower* in energy than the separate particles from which it is made (Figure 3.7). In the previous unit we found that a lowering in energy implies an increase in energetic stability. The energy difference is called the *binding energy* (Figure 3.8). The larger the binding energy for an atom, the more energetically stable it is compared to the separate particles from which it is made (Figure 3.9).

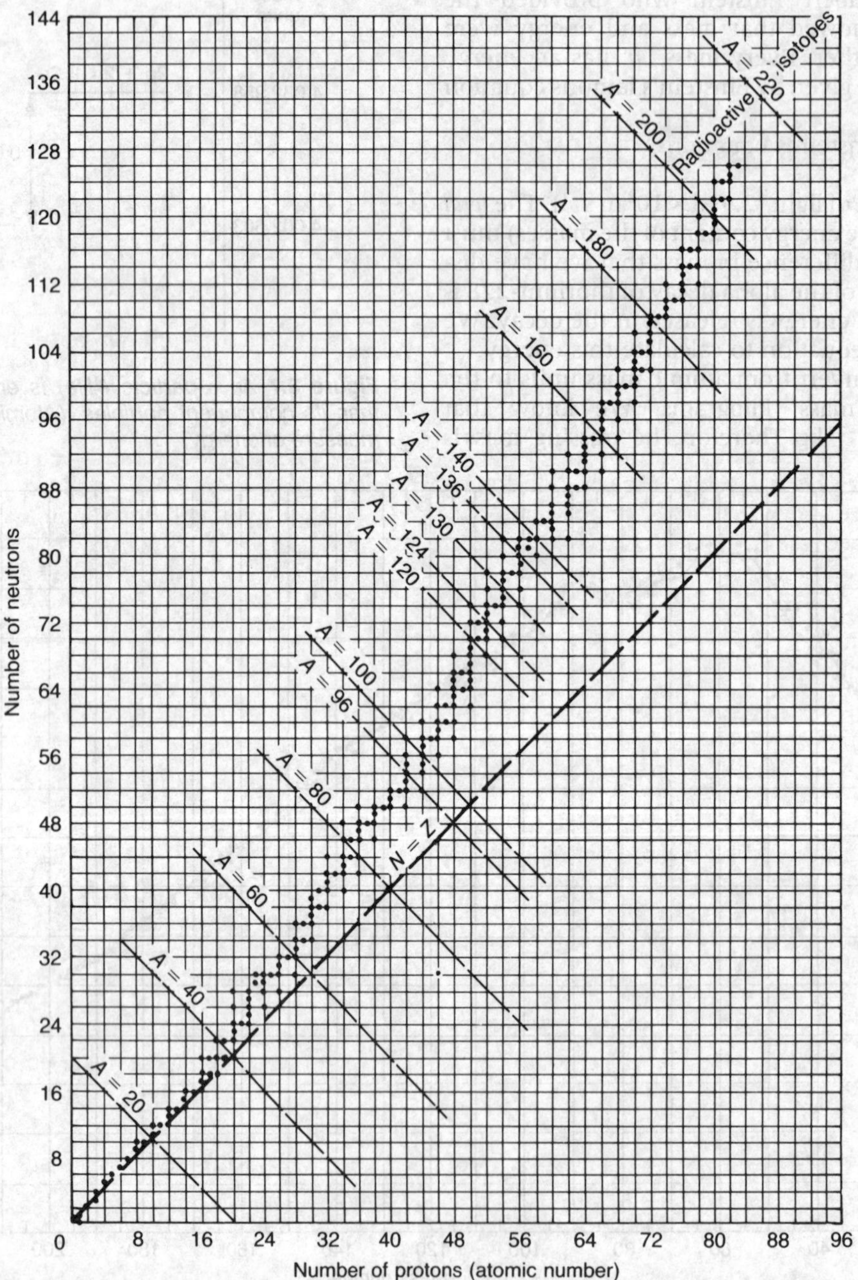

***Figure 3.9** This chart shows that elements towards the beginning of the Periodic Table tend to have equal numbers of neutrons and protons. The further down the Periodic Table, the greater the proportion of neutrons. (Adapted from: Semat, H. (1962).* Introduction to Atomic and Nuclear Physics, *4th edn, Chapman & Hall, London, figure 14.1)*

3.12 Mass defect and mass excess

Except for carbon-12 the atomic mass of an isotope is never a whole number. On the other hand, because the mass number, *A*, is the total number of protons and neutrons, it is always a whole number. The difference between them is sometimes called the *mass defect*, i.e.

mass defect = atomic mass − mass number

Carbon-12 is an exception because its atomic mass is defined to be exactly 12. The atomic number of this isotope is exactly 12 as well. Therefore, as a result of our definition of atomic mass scale, the mass defect of $^{12}_{6}C$ is exactly zero. Owing to the equivalence of mass and energy, this isotope represents a zero on an energy scale. Experiments that are used to study nuclear reactions are often designed to measure the energies of the particles rather than their masses. As a result, mass defects are usually quoted in units of energy, especially millions of electron volts, MeV. (If an electron is accelerated through a potential difference of 1 V, then it gains an energy of one electron volt, 1 eV.) Table 3.7 gives some values of mass defects. When the atomic mass is greater than the mass number, we have a positive mass defect. A positive mass defect is often called a *mass excess*. Table 3.8 shows how to convert energy and mass units.

Generally, nuclides with large mass excesses are found towards the end of the Periodic Table and they tend to be radioactive. That is, their nuclei tend to break up spontaneously and change into other particles of lower energy. However, we cannot be sure that a nuclide will be radioactive just because it has a mass excess. On the other hand, nuclides with large negative values tend not to be radioactive (but again this is not always the case). The elements in the Periodic Table beyond uranium – the transuranium elements – are all liable to be radioactive. A great deal of research has been done to try to make new transuranium elements, but with little success.

In Unit 6 you will find that mass defects can be used in calculations to discover how much energy is expected to be released in a nuclear reaction.

Table 3.7. Some mass defects and excesses

Nuclide	*Mass defect or excess*/MeV	*Nuclide*	*Mass defect or excess*/MeV
$^{1}_{1}H$	7.289	$^{56}_{26}Fe$	−60.604
$^{4}_{2}He$	2.425	$^{127}_{53}I$	−88.980
$^{9}_{4}Be$	11.348	$^{208}_{82}Pb$	−21.759
$^{12}_{6}C$	0.000	$^{232}_{90}Th$	35.447
$^{14}_{6}C$	3.020	$^{235}_{92}U$	40.916
$^{16}_{8}O$	−4.737	$^{238}_{92}U$	47.307
$^{18}_{8}O$	−0.783	$^{242}_{94}Pu$	54.715
$^{35}_{17}Cl$	−29.014	$^{251}_{98}Cf$	74.127
$^{40}_{19}K$	−33.535	$^{262}_{105}Ha$	106.04

Table 3.8. Conversion between energy and mass units

1 electron volt,	1 eV = 1.602×10^{-19} J
	1 MeV = 1.602×10^{-13} J
1 atomic mass unit,	1 amu = 1.661×10^{-27} kg
	= 935.502 MeV

Answers

3.1 The point is that neutrons were unknown, so all the mass of the nucleus was thought to be due to the positive charges in the nucleus. Hence the idea was that oxygen must have 16 positive charges in its nucleus. However, this would give it a charge of +16, which would need 16 electrons to keep the atom neutral. As only eight electrons were outside the nucleus, the assumption was that there were another eight strongly joined to eight of the positive charges in the nucleus.

3.2 The neutron has no charge, and only charged particles can be deflected in a mass spectrometer.

3.3 (i) $\text{Volume} = \dfrac{4\times\pi\times(10^{-10}\,\text{m})^3}{3} = 4.2\times10^{-30}\,\text{m}^3$.

(ii) $\text{Volume} = \dfrac{4\times\pi\times(10^{-16}\,\text{m})^3}{3} = 4.2\times10^{-48}\,\text{m}^3$.

(iii) By dividing the answer to (ii) by (i) and multiplying by 100, we have 10^{-16}%, i.e. exceedingly small.

3.4 (i) Density of the atom
$=(1.7\times10^{-27}\,\text{kg})/(4.2\times10^{-30}\,\text{m}^3) = 400\,\text{kg m}^{-3}$.

(ii) Density of the nucleus
$=(1.7\times10^{-27}\,\text{kg})/(4.2\times10^{-48}\,\text{m}^3) = 4\times10^{20}\,\text{kg m}^{-3}$.

(iii) The volume of the Earth would be

$$\frac{6\times10^{24}\,\text{kg}}{4\times10^{20}\,\text{kg m}^{-3}}$$

i.e. about $1.5\times10^4\,\text{m}^3$. This gives a radius of around 15 m. Notice that even a material like mercury (which we would consider to be very dense) pales into insignificance compared to the nuclei of atoms. Although it is unlikely that the Earth is going to collapse into a ball of 15 m radius, it is believed that this type of collapse does happen to some stars, which go on to produce 'black holes'.

3.5 (i) 1 p, 0 n; (ii) 8 p, 8 n; (iii) 6 p, 8 n; (iv) 17 p, 18 n; (v) 53 p, 74 n.

3.6 The masses are compared to those of an atom of carbon-12 (taken as 12 units). For example, the relative isotopic mass of $^{79}_{35}Br$ = 78.919 means that it is 78.919/12 times heavier than an atom of $^{12}_{6}C$. The absolute masses of the isotopes are, of course, measured in kilograms and also extremely small in value.

Answers – contd.

3.7 We must have

$$\frac{X}{100} \times 37 + \frac{(100-X)}{100} \times 35 = 35.5$$

which gives $X = 25\%$. Chlorine contains 75% $^{35}_{17}Cl$ and 25% $^{37}_{17}Cl$.

3.8 (i) 18; (ii) 98; (iii) 120.3; (iv) 170; (v) 162.3.

UNIT 3 SUMMARY

- Atoms have a radius $\approx 10^{-10}$ m.
- Each atom has a nucleus of radius $\approx 10^{-16}$ m.
- The nucleus contains neutrons and protons, which make up the bulk of the mass of an atom; electrons travel around the nucleus.
- Neutrons are electrically neutral; a proton carries a positive charge equal in magnitude to the negative charge on an electron.
- Atomic number = number of protons.
- Mass number = number of protons + number of neutrons.
- Moseley showed that the position of an element in the Periodic Table depended on its atomic number.
- Isotopes are atoms with the same atomic number but different mass numbers: we write $^{A}_{Z}E$, where A is the mass number and Z is the atomic number.
- The atomic mass scale assigns the mass of an atom of carbon-12 ($^{12}_{6}C$) to be exactly 12 units.
- The relative atomic mass of an element is the average atomic mass of its naturally occurring isotopes.
- Einstein's equation, $E = mc^2$, shows that mass and energy are related. A loss in mass during a nuclear reaction will appear as energy.

4

Discovery of radioactivity

4.1 The discovery of radioactivity

In early 1896 Henri Becquerel was carrying out a series of experiments on fluorescence. He placed a piece of photographic film between two pieces of black paper. On the top of one of the sheets of black paper he put a thin layer of potassium uranium sulphate. The small parcel was left in sunlight for a few hours. When Becquerel developed the film he found that it had the same appearance as if it had been exposed to light. He set up a further set of similar experiments, but the weather was against him: it was very cloudy for several days. In the meantime he stored his photographic plates and uranium compound in a drawer. Perhaps for no reason other than boredom or impatience, Becquerel developed one of the plates. To his surprise the plate had been blackened. This was a most unexpected result. For some time Becquerel, and others, thought that he had discovered a new type of fluorescence, but we now know that the blackening of the plate was due to the radiation given off by the uranium compound. In this rather strange way Becquerel had discovered *radioactivity*.

In fact the name 'radioactivity' was invented some time later by Marie Curie. This remarkable woman won the Nobel Prize *twice*: for Physics in 1903 in conjunction with her husband, Pierre Curie, and Henri Becquerel; and for Chemistry in her own right in 1911. She was a woman of remarkable persistence and fortitude. In the winter of 1897/98, Marie Curie set about the task of establishing the nature of the radiation from pitchblende, the major ingredient of which was uranium. Secondly, she began testing all the then known elements to see if they were radioactive. She discovered that minerals that contained uranium or thorium were invariably radioactive. However, of more interest was the fact that some minerals appeared to be far more radioactive than would be expected from the amount of uranium or thorium that they contained. This was the first indication that, lurking in these minerals, there was at least one *new*, undiscovered, element; one that was highly radioactive.

Marie and Pierre Curie with their daughter Irène in 1904. Source: Eve Curie, Madame Curie *London, Heinemann, 1943.*

4.1 Eventually it proved possible to isolate about 0.25 g of radium from 1 tonne of pitchblende residue. What was the percentage of radium in the residue? Marie Curie used to work with about 20 kg of residue at a time. What mass of radium would be present in each 20 kg load? What does this say about the accuracy with which she worked?

4.2 New elements

It was clear to the Curies that if a new element did exist it must be present in the minerals in minute amounts; otherwise it would have been discovered by the usual methods of chemical analysis. They obtained several tonnes of pitchblende residue from a mine in Austria. The process of analysing and purifying the residue was mainly the responsibility of Marie Curie. It took almost four years of hard work in the poorly equipped laboratory before the isolation of the new element was complete. Marie Curie's daughter, Eve, described the conditions in which Marie worked in this way:

> The shed in the Rue Lhomond surpassed the most pessimistic expectations of discomfort. In summer, because of its skylights, it was as stifling as a hothouse; in winter one did not know whether to wish for rain or frost; if it rained, the water fell, drop by drop, with a soft, nerve-racking noise, on the ground or on the work-tables, in places which the physicists had to mark in order to avoid putting apparatus there; if it froze, one froze.

In 1902 Marie finally succeeded in isolating about 0.1 g of the new element, radium. She measured its relative atomic mass as 225. (The modern value is 226.) A second new element, polonium, was also isolated in tiny amounts. In a neighbouring laboratory, Andre Debierne removed another new radioactive element, actinium, from some rare clays.

Two views of the shed at the school of physics on the Rue Lhomond where radium was isolated. Source: Eve Curie, Madame Curie, *London, Heinemann, 1943.*

4.3 Some properties of radiation

It was possible to detect radiation in several ways. The most straightforward was that radiation would affect photographic plates or paper. Of more interest was that, where radiation passed through air, ions could be detected. At first it was not clear whether the ions were the rays themselves, or whether the rays caused molecules in the air to form ions. In fact, it was a mixture of both. Three types of ionising radiation were discovered. These were the alpha-rays (α), beta-rays (β) and gamma-rays (γ). Alpha- and beta-rays could be bent by making them travel through electric or magnetic fields. This showed that they were charged. Beta-rays could be bent more easily so they were known to be lighter than alpha-rays. By performing experiments to measure their charge to mass ratios, it was established that the beta-rays were electrons, and the alpha-rays were helium ions, He^{2+}. Gamma-rays were uncharged. They were able to pass through matter with remarkable ease and proved to be a type of high energy electromagnetic radiation.

Alpha-particles would only travel short distances through air (about 4 or 5 cm), and were easily stopped by thin sheets of paper or aluminium (Figure 4.1). Beta-rays travelled easily through air. They were, however, stopped by sheets of aluminium a few millimetres thick. Gamma-rays were stopped only by considerable thicknesses of very dense elements like lead (Table 4.1).

These properties of radiation were soon established; other properties were discovered in more accidental ways. For example, Henri Becquerel was in the habit of carrying a tube of radium in his waistcoat pocket. Given our knowledge of the harmful effects of radiation, this seems rather reckless, especially because he soon began to suffer from 'burns' caused by the radiation. The realis-

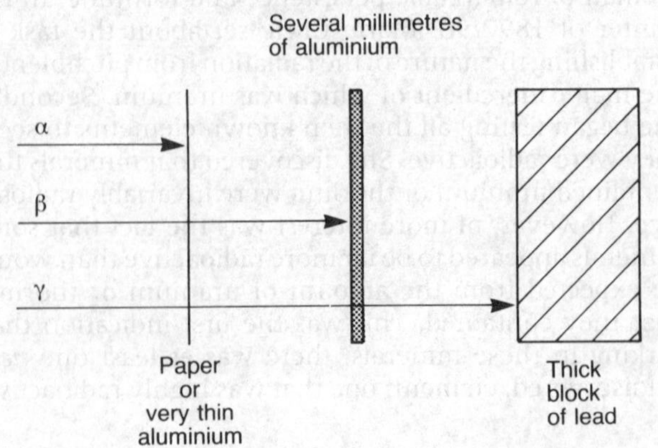

Figure 4.1 *The penetrating power of radiation follows the order: (least penetrating)* $\alpha < \beta < \gamma$ *(most penetrating)*

Table 4.1. Properties of alpha-, beta- and gamma-rays*

Type	*Alternative name*	*Charge*	*Penetrating power*	*Stopped by*
Alpha, α	Helium nucleus (2 protons + 2 neutrons)	+2	Low	Air or paper
Beta, β	Electron	−1	Medium	Thin aluminium
Gamma, γ	High energy electromagnetic radiation	0	High	Thick lead
(Positron	Positive electron	+1	Medium	Thin aluminium)

*You will see that a fourth type of radiation has been added to the list (in brackets). Positrons have the same mass as electrons, but they have positive rather than negative charge

ation that radiation could cause changes in the behaviour of the cells in living things was put to good use by treating tumours with the radiation from radium. It was found that, in many cases, tumours could be destroyed. Radium was looked upon as an almost miraculous substance. In the 1900s it became the most valuable material on Earth.

It took longer to discover that radioactivity could have fatal effects. Over a number of years, workers in laboratories where radium and other radioactive materials were used became ill, and many died. Indeed, in July 1934 at the age of 66 Marie Curie died of pernicious anaemia, almost certainly brought on by the harmful effects of radiation on her bone marrow.

> **4.2** Lord Rutherford and H. A. Geiger showed that 1 g of radium would emit about 3.6×10^{10} alpha-particles per second. The speed of the alpha-particles was nearly 10^7 m s^{-1}. Take the mass of an alpha-particle as 6.6×10^{-27} kg. Calculate the total kinetic energy of the alpha-particles emitted from 1 g of radium in 1 s.

4.4 Units of radioactivity

Radium is one of the most radioactive substances known. One gram (1 g) of pure radium emits about 3.7×10^{10} alpha-particles each second. This is also the number of disintegrations of radium atoms each second. The first unit of radioactivity, called the curie, Ci, was defined as 3.7×10^{10} disintegrations per second. However, the curie is such a large unit of radioactivity that it has fallen into disuse. The modern SI unit of activity is the *becquerel*, Bq. One becquerel is defined as one disintegration per second.

With the knowledge that radiation can be harmful, it is sensible to use a method of measuring radiation that gives us information about the effects it might have on living things. The effects of radiation depend on a number of factors. One is the length of time the radiation is present in body tissue; others are how concentrated the activity is in the tissue, and the type of radiation. For example, a quantity of radiation that is concentrated in 1 kg will be more dangerous than if it is concentrated in 100 kg. Similarly, alpha-radiation is more dangerous to health than beta-radiation. To take account of such factors, two further measures and units of radiation have come into use. These are the *gray*, Gy, and the *sievert*, Sv (Table 4.2). One gray is equivalent to 1 kg of tissue receiving a dose whose energy equivalent is one joule. (You will discover how to calculate the energy associated with radiation in Unit 6.) The sievert is related to the gray in the following way:

Table 4.2. Units of radioactivity

Name	*Symbol*	*Defined to be*
Curie	Ci	3.7×10^{10} disintegrations per second
Becquerel	Bq	One disintegration per second
Gray	Gy	1 kg of tissue receiving 1 J of energy
Sievert	Sv	gray×quality number of radiation (e.g. 20 for alpha, 1 for beta)

$$\text{sievert} = \text{gray} \times \text{quality number}$$

For example, alpha-particles have a quality number of 20, which reflects their danger compared to beta-particles, which have a quality number of 1.

There is still no agreed safe level of radiation; but no one should receive a dose of more than 0.05 Sv in a year. A concentrated dose of just 3 or 4 Sv is likely to be fatal. Around 20 to 30 workers at the Chernobyl accident received fatal doses of this size. Owing to the fairly high level of radiation represented by a sievert, a more common quantity is the millisievert, mSv. (1 mSv = 10^{-3} Sv.) You may gain an idea of how much radiation this represents if you know that the naturally occurring potassium-40 contained within your body represents a dose of about 0.2 mSv. Also, you may be receiving a dose of 1 mSv every year from cosmic rays.

4.5 Nuclear reactions

Following the discovery of radium there was a great deal of interest in finding out if any other elements were naturally radioactive. There were some successes. For example, eventually samples of potassium and rubidium were found to be very weakly radioactive. However, in early 1934 Marie Curie's daughter, Irene, and her husband F. Joliot announced that they had prepared radioactive samples of boron and aluminium in their laboratory. They had achieved this by placing the elements in a beam of alpha-particles. The radioactive samples were positron emitters. In the case of boron the following reactions took place:

first $^{10}_{5}B + ^{4}_{2}He \rightarrow ^{13}_{7}N + ^{1}_{0}n$

then $^{13}_{7}N \rightarrow ^{13}_{6}C + ^{0}_{+1}e$

The first reaction is an example of a *nuclear reaction*. The collision of an alpha-particle with a boron-10 nucleus results in the formation of another element and the emission of a neutron. We can summarise this reaction in the following way: $^{10}_{5}B(\alpha,n)^{13}_{7}N$. The starting isotope is shown at the beginning and the product isotope at the end. Between the two, in brackets, we find the particle that is used to bombard the isotope followed by the particle emitted.

In Table 4.3 are shown a number of different nuclear reactions, some of which we shall examine in more detail shortly. In each reaction, the sum of the mass numbers on the two sides of the equation must be the same. So, too, must the sums of the atomic numbers agree.

Table 4.3. Some nuclear reactions

	Reaction	*Equation*
(1)	$^{27}_{13}Al\ (\alpha,n)^{30}_{15}P$	$^{27}_{13}Al + ^{4}_{2}He \rightarrow ^{30}_{15}P + ^{1}_{0}n$
(2)	$^{14}_{7}N\ (\alpha,p)^{17}_{8}O$	$^{14}_{7}N + ^{4}_{2}He \rightarrow ^{17}_{8}O + ^{1}_{1}p$
(3)*	$^{238}_{92}U\ (n,\gamma)^{239}_{92}U$	$^{238}_{92}U + ^{1}_{0}n \rightarrow ^{239}_{92}U + \gamma$
(4)†	$^{14}_{7}N\ (n,p)^{14}_{6}C$	$^{14}_{7}N + ^{1}_{0}n \rightarrow ^{14}_{6}C + ^{1}_{1}p$

*Reaction (3) is used in nuclear power reactors to produce plutonium-239

†Reaction (4) is responsible for the production of carbon-14 in the atmosphere

4.3 Complete these nuclear equations:

(i) $^{7}_{3}Li + ^{4}_{2}He \rightarrow ^{10}_{5}B + ?$

(ii) $^{19}_{9}F + ? \rightarrow ^{22}_{11}Na + ^{1}_{0}n$

(iii) $^{240}_{96}Cm \rightarrow ^{236}_{94}Pu + ?$

(iv) $^{6}_{3}Li + ^{1}_{0}n \rightarrow ? + ^{4}_{2}He$

(v) $^{11}_{5}B + ^{4}_{2}He \rightarrow ^{1}_{1}H + ?$

(vi) $^{63}_{29}Cu + ^{1}_{1}p \rightarrow ^{24}_{11}Na + ? + ^{1}_{0}n$

4.4 Write out these changes in full:

(i) $^{27}_{13}Al(\alpha,p)^{30}_{14}Si$

(ii) $^{12}_{6}C(\gamma,\alpha)^{8}_{4}Be$

(iii) $^{7}_{3}Li(p,\alpha)^{4}_{2}He$

4.5 $^{65}_{28}Ni$ is a β-emitter.

(i) What is a β-particle?

(ii) What is made in the reaction?

4.6 $^{32}_{15}P$ is also a β-emitter. What is the product of the decay?

4.6 Artificially prepared elements

Reactions like those shown in Table 4.3 can sometimes be brought about quite simply; for example, by placing a source of alpha-particles or neutrons in front of the target element. However, this method is just not good enough for many reactions. It may be that very intense beams of particles may be needed, or that the bombarding particles have to have very high energies to penetrate the nucleus of a target atom. Different nuclei have different abilities to 'react' with an invading particle. If very high energy particles are required they can be obtained in one of the several types of accelerators that have been built. Accelerators use electric fields to accelerate particles up to very high speeds. A particle type of accelerator called a cyclotron has been used to prepare a number of completely new elements; that is, elements that do not occur naturally on Earth. For example, G. T. Seaborg used a cyclotron to accelerate the nuclei of carbon-12 atoms to high speeds and make them collide with uranium-238 atoms. The reaction that took place produced isotopes of the new element californium, Cf (element number 98 in the Periodic Table). For example,

$$^{238}_{92}U + ^{12}_{6}C \rightarrow ^{244}_{98}Cf + 6^{1}_{0}n$$

The heavy elements up to atomic number 106 have been prepared in a similar way (Table 4.4). Often they have been isolated in remarkably small amounts, perhaps as little as one or two hundred atoms. This has meant that an almost entirely new set of chemical techniques have had to be developed to deal with them.

Table 4.4. Table of artificially produced elements

Name	*Symbol*	*Atomic number*	*Discovered*
Technetium	Tc	43	1939
Astatine	At	85	1940
Neptunium	Np	93	1940
Plutonium	Pu	94	1941
Americium	Am	95	1944
Berkelium	Bk	97	1949
Californium	Cf	98	1950
Einsteinium	Es	99	1952
Fermium	Fm	100	1953
Mendelevium	Md	101	1955
Nobelium	No	102	1958
Lawrencium	Lr	103	1961
Rutherfordium (Unnilquadium)*	Rf (Unq)	104	1969
Hahnium (Unnilpentium)*	Ha (Unp)	105	1970
Unnilhexium*	Unh	106	1974

*The naming of elements after lawrencium can follow a new, systematic, pattern, which is connected with the element's atomic number. The first two letters tell us how many hundreds (e.g. Un = one), the next three how many tens (e.g. nil = 0), and the rest the units (e.g. quad = 4, pent = 5, hex = 6, hept = 7 and so on)

4.7 A sad ending

This has been a very brief account of the beginning of research into radioactivity. We have seen that the new knowledge was won at some cost. As we now know only too well this knowledge can be put to good as well as evil uses. Marie Curie realised the significance of her discoveries far better than most. One of her major achievements was the founding of the Radium Institute in Paris where much of the early work on the use of radioactivity in the treatment of disease was done. Her achievements were truly remarkable, especially so in that for the last 28 years of her life she had worked without the assistance and encouragement of her husband, Pierre. (He was a scientist of the first rank himself.) It is easy to forget that when we read about the results of achievements like those of the Curies, behind the bare information there lies the lives of human beings. By all accounts Pierre and Marie were very happily married, and in 1906 they already had two young children. Marie had to cope with running the household as well as working very long hours in her 'hut'. Not only did she cope with these two demanding aspects of her life, but also from April 1906 she coped alone. Pierre Curie was killed in a road accident. His daughter, Eve, described what happened:

> Pierre had fallen beneath the feet of the powerful horses. . .. Pierre was down, but alive and unhurt. He did not cry out and hardly moved. His body passed between the feet of the horses without even being touched, and then between the two front wheels of the wagon. A miracle was possible. But the enormous mass, dragged on by its weight of six tons, continued for several yards more. The left back wheel encountered a feeble obstacle which it crushed in passing: a forehead, a human head. The cranium was shattered and a red, viscous matter trickled in all directions in the mud: the brain of Pierre Curie.

In spite of such a personal disaster, Marie continued her work, and raised her family. Five years later she was awarded her second Nobel Prize.

Answers

4.1 0.25 g is 2.5×10^{-4} kg, and 1 tonne is 1000 kg. Thus the percentage of radium is

$$\frac{2.5 \times 10^{-4}\,\text{kg}}{1000\,\text{kg}} \times 100\% = 2.5 \times 10^{-5}\%$$

There would be $0.25\,\text{g} \times 20\,\text{kg}/1000\,\text{kg} = 0.005\,\text{g}$ of radium in each 20 kg load. She not only had to be extremely accurate but, as important, consistently this accurate over four years.

4.2 The kinetic energy ($\frac{1}{2}mv^2$) of one alpha-particle is 3.3×10^{-13} J. Thus the total energy released is $3.3 \times 10^{-13}\,\text{J} \times 3.6 \times 10^{10} = 0.0119$ J. If you think about the answer for a moment, you may realise that there is a problem: what is the origin of the energy? Put simply, where does the energy come from? The answer lies in an understanding of the structures of the nuclei of atoms. See Unit 6 about this.

4.3 The missing particles are: (i) $^1_0$n, (ii) $^4_2$He, (iii) $^4_2$He, (iv) $^3_1$H, (v) $^{14}_6$C, (vi) $^{39}_{19}$K.

4.4 (i) $^{27}_{13}\text{Al} + {}^4_2\text{He} \rightarrow {}^{30}_{14}\text{Si} + {}^1_1\text{p}$
(ii) $^{12}_6\text{C} + \gamma \rightarrow {}^8_4\text{Be} + {}^4_2\text{He}$
(iii) $^7_3\text{Li} + {}^1_1\text{p} \rightarrow {}^4_2\text{He} + {}^4_2\text{He}$

4.5 (i) An electron.
(ii) An electron is emitted when a neutron changes into a proton. This means that the atomic mass stays the same, but the atomic number increases by one. The new element made is one to the right of nickel in the Periodic Table. The nuclide made is $^{65}_{29}$Cu.

4.6 The new nuclide is sulphur-32, $^{32}_{16}$S.

UNIT 4 SUMMARY

- The three types of radiation are alpha (α), beta (β) and gamma (γ). For a review of their properties, see Table 4.1.
- In nuclear reactions, the total charge of the reactants and products must be the same. A common change that takes place in nuclear reactions is neutron $\rightarrow$ proton + electron, or $^1_0\text{n} \rightarrow {}^1_1\text{p} + {}^{\;0}_{-1}\text{e}$.

5

Radioactive decay

5.1 Detection of radiation

Becquerel's way of detecting radiation was, at first, to use photographic paper. This was of little use for accurate work. Instead, radiation was detected by measuring its charge, or the charge that it produced when it travelled through air. The main piece of equipment was called an electroscope (very much the same thing as a gold leaf electroscope that you may have come across if you have studied physics). Unfortunately, electroscopes proved very difficult to use accurately and it soon became a matter of urgency to develop better devices. In this section we shall take a brief look at some of the main methods that have been used to detect radiation.

(a) *Spinthariscopes*

A spinthariscope was essentially a tube with a zinc sulphide screen at one end (Figure 5.1). The screen was made of zinc sulphide plus a little impurity, such as copper. When alpha- or beta-rays struck the screen, a small flash of light would be given out. The experimenter would look at the screen through a microscope and count the number of flashes. Spinthariscopes could be used to measure the rate at which radioactivity was emitted, but their use could be troublesome. For the experimenter it was extremely tedious, and often errors would be made because imaginary spots of light would be seen in front of his or her eyes and counted as real spots. To get over this problem a method of automatically detecting the spots of light was needed. This was the job of scintillation counters.

(b) *Scintillation counters*

A scintillation counter is a glorified spinthariscope. Instead of using the human eye to record the small flashes of light, they are detected by a photomultiplier tube. In this type of tube the light causes electrons to be ejected, which in turn cause further electrons to be ejected, and so on. Eventually so many electrons are present that a large pulse of electricity is produced. This can be amplified and the signal sent to a meter.

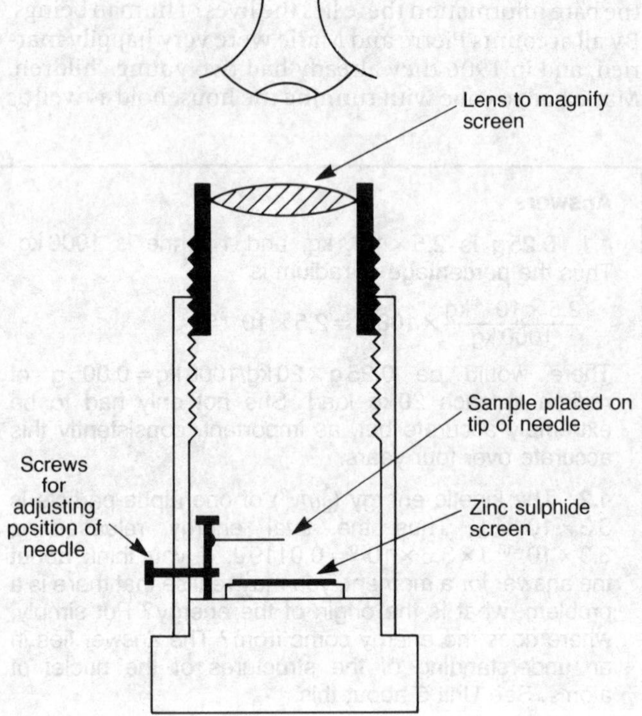

Figure 5.1 *A type of spinthariscope that was once on sale to the public*

(c) *Geiger–Muller counters*

A Geiger–Muller counter (or just Geiger counter for short) consists of a metal cylinder surrounding an inner wire (Figure 5.2). The cylinder is closed at one end, and has a window of mica or thin aluminium at the other end. The cylinder is negatively charged and the wire positively charged. Inside is trapped a small amount of argon, together with an organic vapour such as ether. When ionising radiation enters the tube, positive ions produced from collisions with argon travel towards the cylinder. These ions can, in turn, collide with more argon atoms and cause them to ionise. In this way there is an avalanche effect, where a small amount of radiation can cause a very large number of ions to be formed. Electrons, which are also produced by the collisions, go

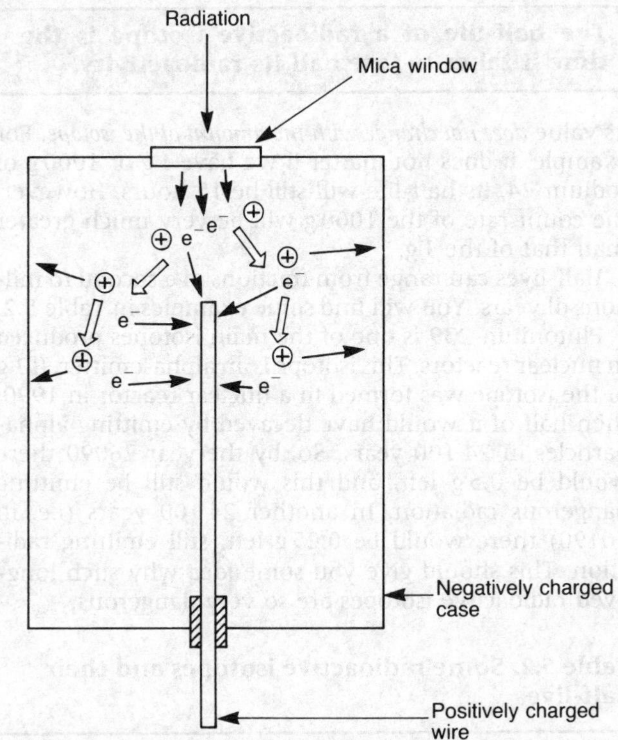

Figure 5.2 In a Geiger counter ionising radiation produces a burst of electrons and positive ions. These cause a short pulse of electricity that is amplified by the electronics connected to the tube

to the wire. The arrival of charges at the cylinder or wire produces a pulse of electricity that is amplified and fed to a meter, which records the level of radiation entering the tube. It can also be used to trigger a small loudspeaker to produce the characteristic 'click-click-click' of the counter. The organic vapour is there to 'mop up', or quench, any unwanted ions that are made when the original ions collide with the cylinder.

(d) *Cloud chambers*

The basis of the cloud chamber was invented in 1911 by C. T. R. Wilson. His apparatus made use of the ions that are produced when radiation passes through air. Water or alcohol vapour was introduced into the apparatus together with air completely cleaned of dust and other impurities. At the moment a particle of ionising radiation enters the apparatus, ions are produced. The pressure of gas inside is rapidly reduced and this causes the water or alcohol vapour to condense onto the ions. Photographs of the contents of the chamber show the white tracks of where the radiation has been.

(e) *The bubble chamber*

Cloud chambers are rarely used now. They have been replaced by bubble chambers. In a bubble chamber a liquid is momentarily raised to above its boiling point. If this is done sufficiently quickly, the liquid will not boil; it becomes superheated. However, if a particle passes through the superheated liquid, the extra energy it provides causes the liquid to boil along the path of the particle, and tiny bubbles of gas are formed. Photographs of the bubbles show up the tracks of the particles.

> **5.1** Before the dangers of radioactivity became known, the use of spinthariscopes could be rather dangerous. For instance, it was not unusual for the experimenter's eyes literally to glow in the dark owing to the radiation passing through the apparatus.
>
> (i) What type of radiation would be the most likely to enter an experimenter's eye using the arrangement shown in Figure 5.1?
>
> (ii) How would you change the apparatus to stop the radiation passing into the experimenter's eye?

5.2 Half-lives

It did not take long to discover that the amount of radioactivity given off by a substance changed in time. With modern equipment it is easy to carry out an experiment to show this. We take a radioactive sample and place it in a lead box together with a Geiger counter. The output from the counter can be fed to a computer, which can be programmed to record the number of counts in a given time interval; for example, every minute or every hour. Table 5.1 shows a typical set of results for the decay of sodium-24, ${}^{24}_{11}$Na. Ideally, the experiment would be repeated a number of times so that the average of a series of readings could be taken instead of relying on just one set of results. The figures in the table show that, even though the same mass of isotope is used in the two experiments, the count rates are different. This is to be expected because of the random nature of radioactive decay.

Before the results can be used to give us information about the radiation given off from the ${}^{24}_{11}$Na alone, we must make a correction to the figures. The correction is due to the presence of *background radiation*. This is radiation that is naturally present even in the absence of the

Table 5.1. Specimen results for the radioactive decay of ${}^{24}_{11}$Na

Experiment 1		*Experiment 2*	
Time/hours	*Number of counts*/hour^{-1}	*Time*/hours	*Number of counts*/hour^{-1}
Start	1180	Start	1201
10	735	10	755
20	460	20	481
30	282	30	303
40	178	40	190
50	128	50	129
60	83	60	75

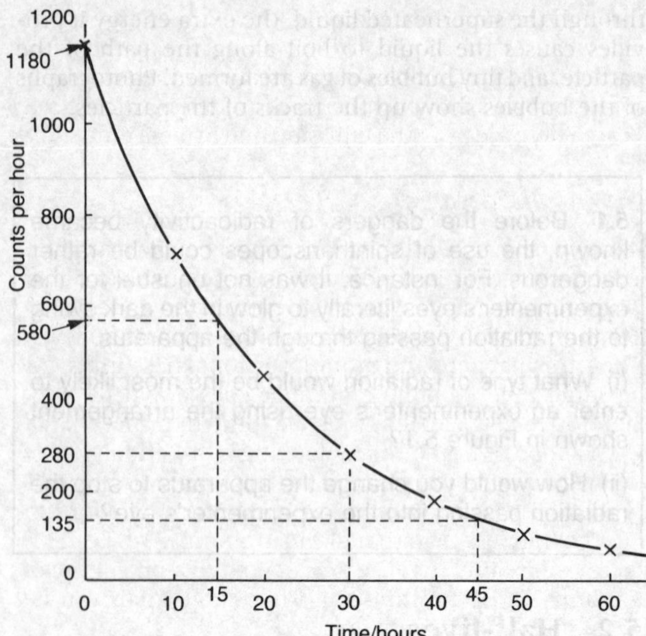

Figure 5.3 *An example of a radioactive decay curve. The count rate halves (approximately) every 15 hours*

radioactive sample. Background radiation comes from radioactive substances that may be present in the bricks or stones from which a building is made, from radioactive substances that may be present in the air, and from cosmic rays that are constantly bombarding the Earth from space. The background radiation count is not constant from one moment to the next; but over a period of some minutes the readings hover around an average value. Often the background count may be some tens of counts per minute. However, this value will change depending on where you carry out the experiment. If you were to set up your experiment over a deposit of uranium ores, you should not be surprised to get a very much higher background count. Similarly if there is a period of high sunspot activity the background count will increase because sunspots increase the number of cosmic rays. In processing the figures from Table 5.1, we shall assume that the count rates have been corrected for the background count. The results for the first experiment are shown on the graph in Figure 5.3. A graph of count rate plotted against time is called a *decay curve*.

If you look carefully at the scales used you will see that from an initial rate of 1180 counts $hour^{-1}$, after 15 hours the rate drops to 580 counts $hour^{-1}$. In another 15 hours the rate has dropped to 280 counts $hour^{-1}$; and in another 15 hours it is 135 counts $hour^{-1}$. The key thing about these figures is that the count rate goes down by (approximately) one-half every 15 hours. (You should not expect the count rate to change by exactly half because radioactive decay is a random process. However, the count rates will, on average, go down by one-half in 15 hours.) We say that sodium-24 has a *half-life* of 15 hours.

Each radioactive isotope has its own characteristic half-life. A most important thing about a half-life is that

The half-life of a radioactive isotope is the time it takes to lose half its radioactivity.

its value *does not change with the amount of the isotope*. For example, it does not matter if we have 1 g or 1000 g of sodium-24, its half-life will still be 15 hours. However, the count rate of the 1000 g will be very much greater than that of the 1 g.

Half-lives can range from fractions of a second to millions of years. You will find some examples in Table 5.2.

Plutonium-239 is one of the main isotopes produced in nuclear reactors. This isotope is an alpha-emitter. If 1 g of the isotope was formed in a nuclear reactor in 1990, then half of it would have decayed by emitting alpha-particles in 24 100 years. So, by the year 26090 there would be 0.5 g left, and this would still be emitting dangerous radiation. In another 24 100 years (i.e. in 50190) there would be 0.25 g left, still emitting radiation. This should give you some idea why such long-lived radioactive isotopes are so very dangerous.

Table 5.2. Some radioactive isotopes and their half-lives

Isotope	*Half-life*	
^{215}At	1.0×10^{-4}	seconds
^{24}Na	15.0	hours
^{131}I	8.04	days
^{59}Fe	44.6	days
^{60}Co	5.27	years
^{226}Ra	1.6×10^{3}	years
^{14}C	5.73×10^{3}	years
^{239}Pu	2.41×10^{4}	years
^{235}U	7.04×10^{8}	years
^{238}U	4.47×10^{9}	years
^{232}Th	1.4×10^{10}	years

5.2 Plot a decay curve for the second set of experimental results in Table 5.1. On the curve show how you would check that the half-life is about 15 hours.

5.3 If a proton changes into a neutron, a positron ($^{0}_{+1}e$) is also emitted.

(i) Write down a nuclear equation that shows this change.

(ii) The isotope carbon-10 ($^{10}_{6}C$) decays by positron emission with a half-life of 19.2 s. What is the product of the decay? Write down the nuclear equation.

(iii) If at time 0 the count rate was 1200 disintegrations s^{-1}, what would be the count rate after 96 s? (Hint: how many half-lives is 96 s? What is the change in count rate every half-life?)

(iv) Can you be precise about the final count rate?

5.3 The radioactive decay law

Mathematically, a radioactive decay curve is an exponential. We say that the count rate shows an exponential decrease. Every radioactive decay is governed by the equation:

$$N_t = N_0 \times \exp(-\lambda t) \qquad \text{Radioactive decay law}$$

or

$$N_t = N_0 e^{-\lambda t}$$

Here N_t is the count at time t, and N_0 is the starting count (at time 0); λ is a constant, called the *decay constant*, which is different for each radioactive nuclide.

There is a connection between the decay constant and half-life. It is that

$$t_{1/2} = \frac{0.693}{\lambda} \qquad \text{half-life}$$

(You will find this derived in panel 5.1.)

For example, for $^{24}_{11}Na$, $t_{1/2} = 0.693/(15 \text{ hour})$, i.e. $t_{1/2} = 0.046 \text{ hour}^{-1}$. Notice the units of the decay constant. They always have the dimensions of time^{-1}, e.g. s^{-1}, min^{-1}, $hour^{-1}$, $year^{-1}$.

Panel 5.1

Let us write the half-life as $t_{1/2}$. At $t_{1/2}$ we must have $N_t = N_0/2$, so

$$\tfrac{1}{2} = \exp(-\lambda t_{1/2})$$

If we take the natural logarithm (which is the inverse of taking an exponential) of each side, we have

$$\ln(\tfrac{1}{2}) = -\lambda t_{1/2} \qquad \text{or} \qquad -0.693 = -\lambda t_{1/2}$$

Hence

$$\text{half-life} = \frac{0.693}{\lambda}$$

5.4 Write a computer program that will plot a decay curve for cobalt-60 (see Table 5.2). Also, calculate the value of the decay constant.

5.5 A student showed the following set of figures to a friend.

6410	4870	3545	2492	1610	887	415
0	100	200	300	400	500	600

The student claimed that the top row was a list of counts from the radioactive decay of a single nuclide, and that the second row showed the times (in seconds) at which the counts were taken. Plot a graph of the figures and decide whether they did correspond to a radioactive decay. (Hint: look for a constant half-life.)

5.4 Decay schemes

For the most part we can concentrate on the two most important ways in which isotopes undergo radioactive decay. These are by alpha emission and by beta emission.

(a) *Alpha decay*

Uranium-238 ($^{238}_{92}U$) decays by emitting alpha-particles. You may remember that an alpha-particle is a bundle of two protons together with two neutrons, so a uranium-238 atom must lose these four particles from its nucleus. When this happens the atom loses four mass units. At the same time its atomic number goes down by two. Therefore a new element must be formed, rather than a new isotope of uranium. By looking at a Periodic Table you will find that the element with atomic number 90 is thorium. The mass number of the isotope of thorium must be four less than that of the uranium-238, i.e. 234. Therefore we find that the product of the alpha decay of uranium-238 is thorium-234. The whole affair can be summarised in an equation:

$$^{238}_{92}U \rightarrow {}^{234}_{90}Th + {}^{4}_{2}He \qquad \text{or} \qquad {}^{238}_{92}U \rightarrow {}^{234}_{90}Th + \alpha$$

This type of pattern is repeated for any isotope that decays by alpha emission. The new isotope (or daughter element) will have an atomic number two less than its parent. The daughter will therefore lie two places to the left of the parent in the Periodic Table. Also, the daughter will have a mass number four less than the parent.

(b) *Beta decay*

Some radioactive isotopes decay by emitting beta-particles (electrons). This comes about through the change of a neutron into a proton and an electron. (Such changes also occur when neutrons are knocked out of the nucleus of an atom and left to roam around freely. Some of them decay spontaneously into a proton and an electron. The half-life is about 10.6 minutes). We can represent this decay in an equation:

$$n \rightarrow p + e^-$$

However, in order to keep track of changes in mass and atomic number, it is better to write the neutron, proton and electron like this:

$$^{1}_{0}n \rightarrow {}^{1}_{1}p + {}^{0}_{-1}e$$

(The subscripts represent the atomic numbers (charges) and the superscripts the mass numbers.)

You should see that, if a beta-particle is emitted by a nucleus, there will be one more proton in the nucleus. This means that the atomic number increases by one and a new element is formed. This element will lie one place to the right of the parent element in the Periodic Table. However there is no change in the mass number because a neutron is simply replaced by a proton.

An example is lead-214 changing into bismuth-214:

$$^{214}_{82}Pb \rightarrow {}^{214}_{83}Bi + {}^{0}_{-1}e$$

(As a check on a nuclear equation like this, make sure

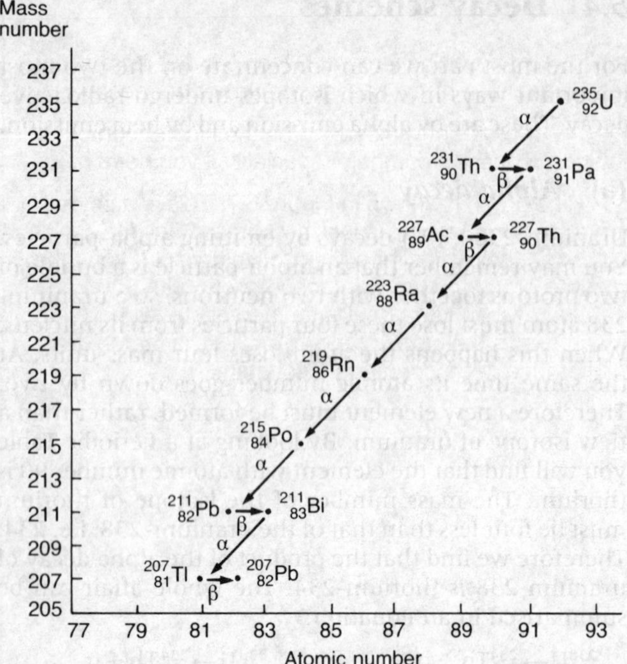

***Figure 5.4** The uranium-235 decay scheme. It ends at $^{207}_{82}Pb$, which is stable*

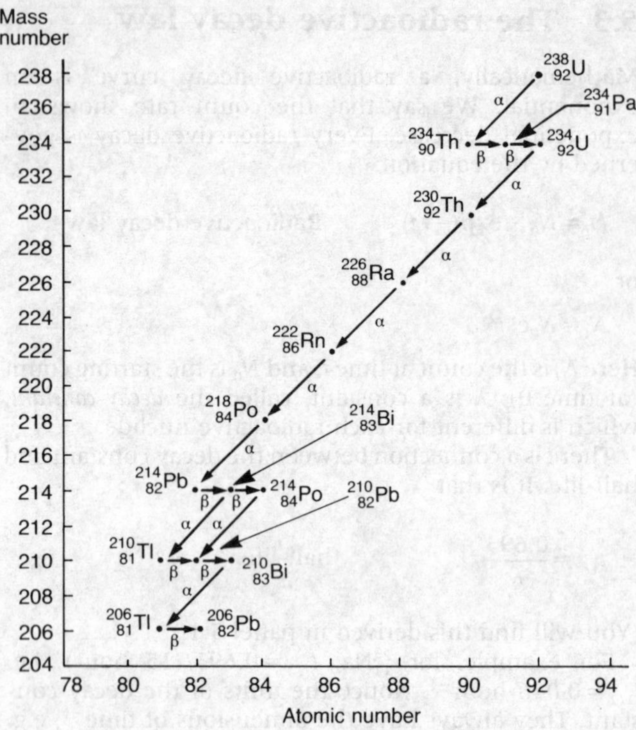

***Figure 5.5** The uranium-238 decay scheme. It ends at $^{206}_{82}Pb$, which is stable*

that the total of the atomic numbers on the left-hand side of an equation equals the total on the right-hand side. Similarly, the mass numbers must agree.)

We could go on to write down a great many such equations, but it is much easier to summarise a series of radioactive decays on a diagram. Figures 5.4 and 5.5 show the decay schemes that start with uranium-235 and uranium-238. Notice that the scales on the diagrams show atomic number horizontally and mass number vertically. You should be able to work out why an arrow pointing diagonally downwards to the left represents alpha decay, while beta decay moves horizontally by one unit to the right.

5.6 What are the products of the following changes: alpha decay of (i) $^{24}_{12}Mg$, (ii) $^{8}_{4}Be$; beta decay of (iii) $^{14}_{6}C$, (iv) $^{31}_{14}Si$?

5.7 Complete the following nuclear equations:

(i) $^{11}_{5}B + ? \rightarrow {}^{8}_{4}Be + {}^{4}_{2}He$

(ii) $^{239}_{94}Pu + {}^{4}_{2}He \rightarrow {}^{241}_{96}Cm + ?$

(iii) $^{9}_{4}Be + {}^{1}_{1}p \rightarrow ? + {}^{4}_{2}He$

(iv) $^{63}_{29}Cu + {}^{1}_{1}p \rightarrow {}^{24}_{11}Na + ? + {}^{1}_{0}n$

Answers

5.1 (i) Gamma – the most penetrating.

(ii) One way would be to place a mirror at 45 degrees to the zinc sulphide screen. Light, but not radiation, would reflect off the mirror into the observer's eye.

5.2 The graph is shown in Figure 5.6.

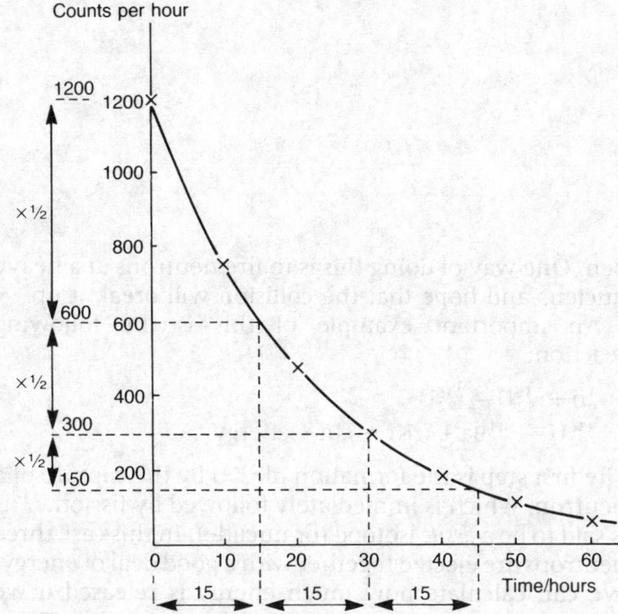

Figure 5.6 *Graph of results for question 5.2. There is a constant half-life of 15 hours*

5.3 (i) ${}^{1}_{1}p \rightarrow {}^{1}_{0}n + {}^{0}_{+1}e$

(ii) Because a proton changes into a neutron, the atomic number decreases by one although the mass number stays the same. The new element produced is one place before carbon in the Periodic Table: boron. ${}^{10}_{6}C \rightarrow {}^{10}_{5}B + {}^{0}_{+1}e$

(iii) Each half-life, the count rate decreases by one-half. 96 s is 5 × 19.2 s, i.e. five half-lives. We can draw up a table like this:

Time	0	1	2	3	4	5
Count rate /disintegrations s^{-1}	1200	600	300	150	75	37

(iv) No. It should be around 37 or 38, but this is not certain because of the random nature of the decay.

5.4 Your program will depend on the kind of computer you use. Consult a computer specialist if you need help.

5.5 The graph is shown in Figure 5.7. This is a smooth curve, but it does *not* show a constant half-life, so it *cannot* be the results for a radioactive decay. If you take from the graph the times for 'counts' of 6000, 3000 and 1500 you will find that the time intervals between them are (approximately) 220 s and 165 s. This is far too great a difference to be counted as constant.

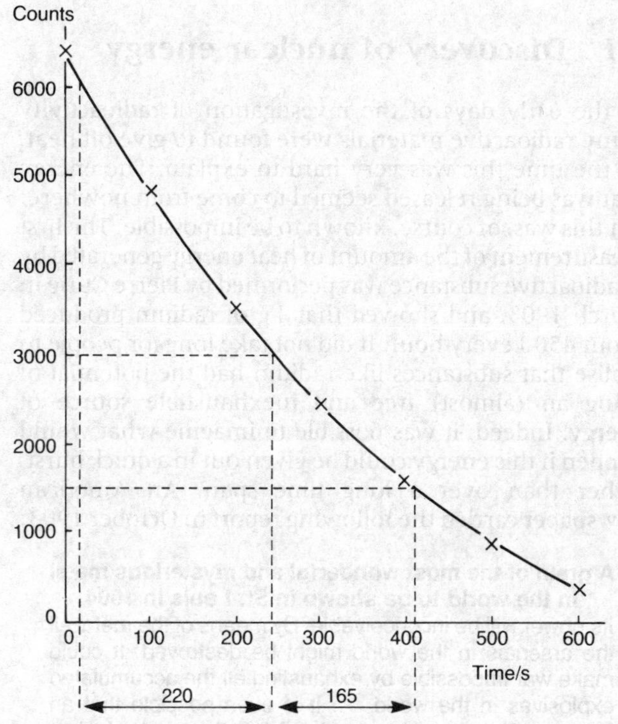

Figure 5.7 *Graph of results for question 5.5*

5.6 (i) ${}^{20}_{10}Ne$; (ii) ${}^{4}_{2}He$; (iii) ${}^{14}_{7}N$; (iv) ${}^{31}_{15}P$.

5.7 (i) ${}^{1}_{1}p$; (ii) $2 \times {}^{1}_{0}n$; (iii) ${}^{6}_{3}Li$; (iv) ${}^{39}_{19}K$.

UNIT 5 SUMMARY

- Radiation is detected by a Geiger (or Geiger–Müller) counter.
- Isotopes of some elements are radioactive.
- Radioactive decay is an exponential process with a characteristic half-life, $t_{1/2}$.
- The half-life of a radioactive isotope is the time it takes to lose half its radioactivity.
- The decay law is $N_t = N_0\exp(-\lambda t)$, where N_t is the count at time t, N_0 is the starting count and λ is the decay constant.
- Half-life, $t_{1/2} = 0.693/\lambda$.
- The half-life is independent of the amount of the isotope.
- Alpha decay of an isotope gives a product two places to the left in the Periodic Table.
- Beta decay of an isotope gives a product one place to the right in the Periodic Table.

6

Nuclear energy

6.1 Discovery of nuclear energy

In the early days of the investigation of radioactivity many radioactive materials were found to give off heat. At the time this was very hard to explain. The energy that was being released seemed to come from nowhere; but this was, of course, known to be impossible. The first measurement of the amount of heat energy generated by a radioactive substance was performed by Pierre Curie in March 1903, and showed that 1 g of radium produced about 450 J every hour. It did not take long for people to realise that substances like radium had the potential of being an (almost) free and inexhaustible source of energy. Indeed, it was possible to imagine what would happen if this energy could be given out in a quick burst, rather than over a long time span. An American newspaper carried the following report in October 1903:

> **A grain of the most wonderful and mysterious metal in the world to be shown in St. Louis in 1904**
> Its power will be inconceivable. By means of the metal all the arsenals in the world might be destroyed. It could make war impossible by exhausting all the accumulated explosives in the world.... It is even possible that an instrument might be invented which at the touch of a key would blow up the whole earth and bring about the end of the world.

6.2 Fission reactions

The nuclei of some heavy elements break up spontaneously and produce two lighter nuclei, often with the emission of protons or neutrons. This behaviour is called *spontaneous fission*. Also, a great deal of energy can be released. However, to produce enough energy to be useful (for fair means or foul) the fission reaction must not have too long a half-life. For example, a large amount of energy is produced when ^{238}U decays spontaneously to give isotopes of barium and krypton. This has a rather long half-life of around 10^{16} years, so the energy is released over too long a time span to be of any use. Faced with a problem like this, the thing to do is to try to *induce* fission, i.e. make it occur rather than wait for it to happen. One way of doing this is to fire neutrons at a heavy nucleus and hope that the collision will break it up.

An important example of this is the following reaction:

$$^{1}_{0}n + ^{235}_{92}U \rightarrow ^{236}_{92}U$$
$$^{236}_{92}U \rightarrow ^{141}_{56}Ba + ^{92}_{36}Kr + 3^{1}_{0}n + \text{energy}$$

The first step is the formation of $^{236}_{92}U$ by the capture of a neutron, which is immediately followed by fission. $^{236}_{92}U$ is said to be a *fissile* isotope (or nuclide). In this case three neutrons are ejected together with a good deal of energy. We can calculate how much energy is released if we know the mass excess (or defect) of each particle (Table 6.1).

The energy change will be the difference between the mass excesses of the products and those of the reactants. Here the reaction we are interested in is the second one, i.e. the fission of $^{236}_{92}U$. We have

mass excess of reactants
$= 44.79$ MeV
mass excess of products
$= -79.98 - 69.15 + 3 \times 8.071 = -124.917$ MeV

Figure 6.1 shows that the change in mass excess is 169.707 MeV. Because $1 \text{ MeV} = 1.602 \times 10^{-13}$ J, we find that the energy released is 2.719×10^{-11} J.

This may not seem an awful lot of energy; but remember, it is for one atom only. If we had 236 g of $^{236}_{92}U$ (1 mol) we would have 6.02×10^{23} times more energy released, i.e. about 1.6×10^{13} J, or 16 000 GJ. (One

Table 6.1. Mass defects and excesses for the induced fission of $^{235}_{92}U$

Particle	*Mass excess or mass defect*/MeV
$^{1}_{0}n$	8.071
$^{235}_{92}U$	40.916
$^{236}_{92}U$	44.79
$^{141}_{56}Ba$	−79.98
$^{92}_{36}Kr$	−69.15

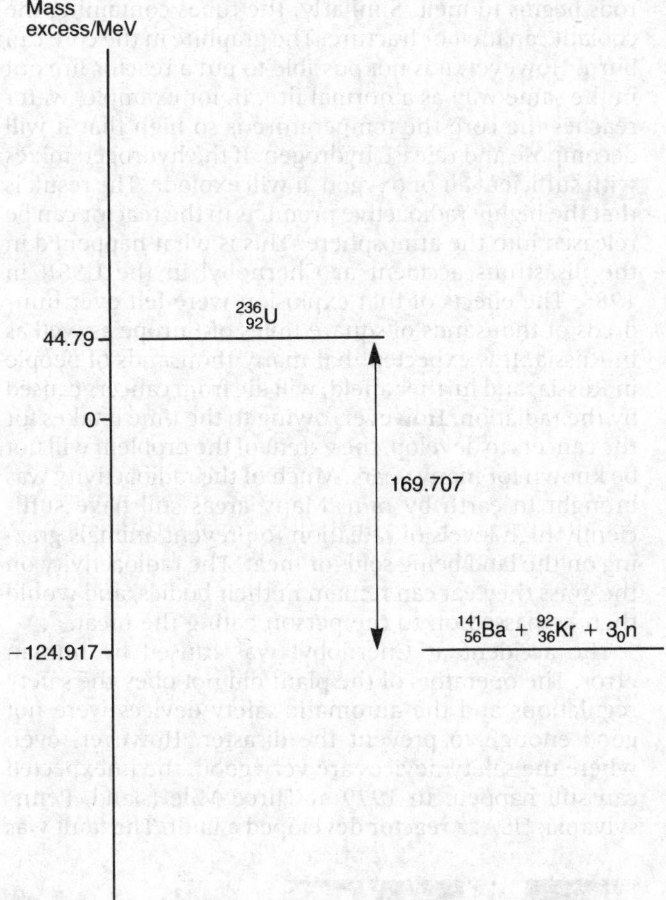

Figure 6.1 *Energy level diagram for the fission of* $^{236}_{92}U$

gigajoule, 1 GJ, is 10^9 J.) Typically, 1 tonne of coal can yield 25 GJ, and one tonne of oil 40 GJ. You can see why it has been so tempting to use fission reactions to produce energy, for example in a power station in order to generate electricity. Also, we know that the fossil fuels, coal and oil, will be used up sometime in the future; but atoms will always be with us. Harnessing the energy from nuclear reactions appears to give a way of producing energy for ever.

6.3 Nuclear power

There are huge technical problems to be overcome in order to design and make a power station that converts nuclear energy into electricity. There are so many factors that we can only consider a few of the most important ones here.

(a) *The fuel*

An essential requirement is to have a reaction that keeps itself going – a *chain reaction*. There must be a source of neutrons, which can bombard other nuclei and cause them to undergo fission. For a chain reaction to take place, the fission reaction must give out at least one new

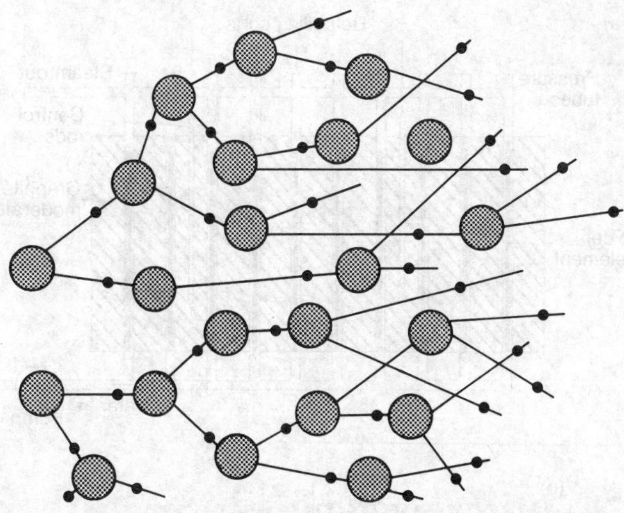

Figure 6.2 *The decay of a* $^{235}_{92}U$ *nucleus produces two neutrons. Each of these may go on to cause further nuclear reactions in neighbouring nuclides. A cascade effect is produced with a vast number of reactions taking place in a very short time. A great deal of energy is released in a short time*

neutron that, in its turn, can cause another atom to split apart. When some isotopes undergo fission they can release two (or more) neutrons. Given a suitable mix of nuclides, one of the neutrons can cause fission of another nucleus; the other can be captured to produce a new fissile nuclide (Figure 6.2). Thus the loss of one fissile nuclide breeds another. In effect the reactor makes its own fuel. Such a reactor is called a breeder. If the reactions in the breeder make use of very energetic neutrons, the reactor is called a *fast breeder*. A typical reactor may have a mix of uranium and plutonium isotopes, $^{235}_{92}U$, $^{233}_{92}U$ and $^{239}_{94}Pu$, in the form of oxides, UO_2 and PuO_2. Owing to its excellent ability to take part in nuclear reactions, plutonium makes an ideal fuel in a reactor. The uranium cannot be used directly out of the ground. It has to be put through a long process of refining, with the aim of removing impurities and increasing the proportion of uranium-235 until it reaches around 3%. (Its abundance in natural deposits of uranium ores is only about 0.7%.) This process is difficult and costly.

(b) *Reactor design*

The fuel is often in the form of small pellets, around 1 cm in diameter and a few centimetres long. They are packed into metal cylinders made of stainless steel, or an alloy that is strong and very resistant to corrosion. The fuel rods made in this way are lowered into the reactor core. Here, as well as the fuel rods, are to be found control rods containing nuclides that are able to absorb neutrons. The more control rods in the core, the more neutrons are absorbed, so there are fewer available to cause fission. In this way the amount of energy released can be controlled. The material used in the control rods is called the moderator (Figure 6.3). Boron and beryllium have often been used as moderators. The fuel rods

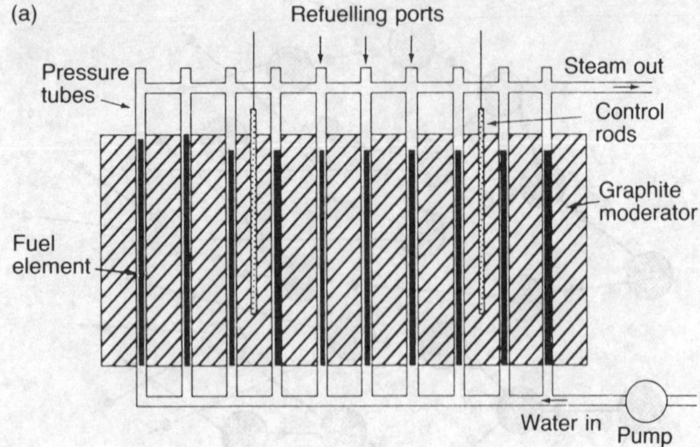

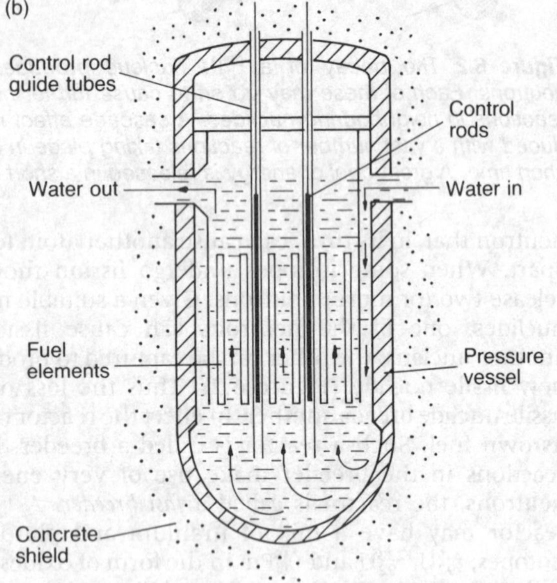

***Figure 6.3** (a) The arrangement of moderator, control rods and fuel elements in a reactor that converts water into steam. (b) A pressurised water reactor (PWR). (Taken from Hunt, S. E. (1987).* Nuclear Physics for Engineers and Scientists, *Ellis Horwood, Chichester, figures 14.8 and 14.5)*

and control rods can be lowered into the core where they are surrounded by another moderating material, often graphite.

The core must be cooled and the heat transferred to boilers, which heat water to raise steam. The steam is used to drive generators to produce electricity. The most widely used methods of cooling have used liquid sodium, carbon dioxide gas under high pressure (advanced gas cooled reactors, AGRs), or water under high pressure (pressurised water reactors, PWRs). Each design has its own problems, and advantages, over others.

(c) *Reactor safety*

If the core of a reactor is not cooled, the rate at which energy is released means that it can quickly become so hot that the metal cladding on the fuel and moderator rods begins to melt. Similarly, the tubes containing the coolant can melt or fracture. The graphite in the core can burn. However, it is not possible to put a reactor fire out in the same way as a normal fire. If, for example, water reaches the core the temperature is so high that it will decompose and release hydrogen. If the hydrogen mixes with sufficient air or oxygen, it will explode. The result is that the highly radioactive products in the reactor can be released into the atmosphere. This is what happened in the disastrous accident at Chernobyl in the USSR in 1986. The effects of that explosion were felt over hundreds of thousands of square miles of Europe as well as in Russia. It is expected that many thousands of people in Russia, and further afield, will die from cancers caused by the radiation. However, owing to the time it takes for the cancers to develop, the extent of the problem will not be known for many years. Much of the radioactivity was brought to earth by rain. Many areas still have sufficiently high levels of radiation to prevent animals grazing on the land being sold for meat. The radioactivity on the grass they eat can remain in their bodies, and would then be passed on to the person eating the meat.

The accident at Chernobyl was caused by human error. The operators of the plant did not obey the safety regulations and the automatic safety devices were not good enough to prevent the disaster. However, even where the safety devices are very good, the unexpected can still happen. In 1979 at Three Mile Island, Pennsylvania, USA, a reactor developed a fault. The fault was

In May 1986, West German cars returning from Poland were checked for radioactive contamination caused by the Chernobyl explosion.

rather unusual and the operators of the plant became confused as to its cause. The automatic safety devices began to shut down the reactor properly. However, once again human error came into play. The operators overruled the safety cut-outs. As a consequence the core came perilously close to the point known as melt-down. This is when the core becomes so hot that it is impossible to cool it down. It then reaches such a high temperature that it melts its way through the core chamber, and then goes on down through the ground. Just when and where it would stop is not entirely clear. What is certain is that the level of radioactivity released into the atmosphere would make the Chernobyl accident look insignificant by comparison.

A major nuclear accident has also occurred in Great Britain. On 8 October 1957 a fire developed in the core of the nuclear plant at Windscale (now renamed Sellafield) on the west coast of Britain. The fire was not large, but it took three or four days to bring it under control. The reactor in use at that time could release into the atmosphere gases used for cooling the core. The radioactive gases spread over large areas of Britain, Ireland and France. Especially, in Britain radioactive iodine was a great cause of concern. This could get into the food chain by being absorbed by cows eating contaminated grass. The milk they gave became rich in the iodine and could be passed on to humans, especially children. Tens of thousands of gallons of milk produced in an area of some hundreds of square miles around Windscale had to be thrown away. It is important to remember that this did not remove the radioactivity. It simply put it into the sewerage system, and eventually into rivers and the sea. The number of deaths that may have been caused by the radiation leak is not known. All we can be sure of is that there are bound to be some.

(d) *Disposal of radioactive waste*

In time, the mix of nuclides in the fuel rods changes to such an extent that the efficiency of the reactions decreases. The rods are then withdrawn from the reactor and sent for *reprocessing*. On emerging, the rods are highly radioactive. They are placed in tanks of water to allow them to lose some of the short-lived radioactivity. The rods contain much of the original radioactive nuclides and large numbers of new ones. The activity of the mixture is such that it will remain active for over ten million years. (It may, or may not, be a comfort to know that there is a large reduction after a thousand years though.) Some of the products are valuable, especially the plutonium produced.

Elaborate chemical methods have been developed to separate the wanted isotopes from the unwanted. This of course does not solve the problem over what to do with the highly active products. A variety of measures have been used and suggested. The two main options are to store them in tanks above ground or in deep mines under land or sea. No choice is perfect. There is always the danger that land masses may move and the radioactive material might be released, e.g. in an earthquake. Given the thousands of years for which storage might be

Spent Magnox Fuel is being stripped of its outer covering using a highly automated process at Sellafield.

needed, there is also the problem of material being leached out by water.

6.1 In the example of uranium-236 fission in section 6.2 we found that 236 g of the isotope could provide about 1.6×10^{13} J of heat energy. Because one joule per second (1 J s^{-1}) is the same as one watt (1 W), if the 236 g suffered fission in one second, the power output would be about 1.6×10^{13} W.

What would be the power output if 1 g of the isotope were 'used up' in one day? Give your answer to the nearest megawatt (1 MW$\equiv$10^6 W).

6.2 Power stations are about 30% efficient. That is, they only convert about 30% of heat energy to electrical energy. Suppose a nuclear power station uses fuel that generates electrical power at the rate of 1 MW g^{-1}.

(i) What would be the thermal power generated?

(ii) How many grams of fuel would have to undergo fission each day?

6.3 Assuming that one tonne of coal can release 25 GJ, how many tonnes of coal would have to be burnt every day in order to generate a constant 1000 MW of electrical power? (As before, assume the efficiency to be 30%.)

6.4 Fusion reactions

Up to now we have concentrated on the energy released when nuclei split apart. However, energy can also be released if certain nuclei join together. An important example is the following:

$${}^{2}_{1}\text{H} + {}^{3}_{1}\text{H} \rightarrow {}^{4}_{2}\text{He} + {}^{1}_{0}\text{n}$$

Scientists pursue endless power source

By Robert Matthews, Technology Correspondent

Scientists in the United States will announce today what they maintain is a breakthrough in the quest for an endless source of cheap power.

Professor Martin Fleischmann, of Southampton University, and Professor Stanley Pons, working at the University of Utah, Salt Lake City, claim to have found a radical way of achieving controllable nuclear fusion reactions.

Such reactions, which have sustained the sun for billions of years, have long been seen as a potential source of virtually limitless heat and power.

International teams of scientists in Britain, the US, Russia and Japan have so far not succeeded in achieving the right conditions to trigger the reactions on Earth.

Professor Fleischmann called his discovery "a shot in the dark". He said: "We thought it was a chance in a billion that it would work".

The professor said the research had achieved "a fairly sizeable release of energy".

The new research has concentrated on ways of starting the fusion reactions in a small reactor vessel using an isotope of hydrogen derived from seawater, known as deuterium.

A number of researchers, including a team at Imperial College, London, have investigated the possibility of **using such concentrated conditions as a way of overcoming the problems of using the giant fusion machines conventionally used for nuclear fusion experiments.**

However, the University of Utah team appears to have got closer to extracting usable energy from its machine, using electro-chemical techniques, than any other. The claims are being treated with caution in Britain.

This extract from The Times *on 23 March 1989 illustrates the wide interest in the claims for 'cold fusion'.*

This reaction is accompanied by the production of nearly 3×10^{-13} J, or about 180 GJ per mole of helium formed. The reason why fusion reactions have not been used in commercial power stations is that it is extremely difficult to control the reactions. The reacting particles (in the form of gaseous ions) have to be accelerated to high energies before the collisions are successful. Then the energy released brings with it a huge increase in temperature, perhaps as high as a hundred million degrees Celsius. The result is that the mixture of particles forms a *plasma*. The control of a plasma is no easy matter, but the main method is to trap it in a magnetic field. Making an apparatus that produces a field of sufficient strength and accuracy is difficult. As yet plasmas have only been trapped for relatively short times; certainly not for the days, weeks, or months that are necessary in a power station.

In April 1989 claims were made in America that fusion could take place on a test tube scale using an electrochemical method. At the time this caused great excitement, as it seemed to provide a basis for harnessing almost limitless amounts of energy. However, many careful experiments performed in laboratories in many countries have failed to reproduce the results. It seems that the American experiments were faulty.

Fusion reactions are the driving force behind the huge amounts of energy released by stars, such as our Sun. The Sun is a hydrogen burning star. It relies on fusion to combine two hydrogen atoms, ${}^{1}_{1}\mathrm{H}$, into a combination of one proton and one neutron, ${}^{2}_{1}\mathrm{H}$:

$${}^{1}_{1}\mathrm{H} + {}^{1}_{1}\mathrm{H} \rightarrow {}^{2}_{1}\mathrm{H} + {}^{0}_{+1}\mathrm{e}$$

Energy is also released. The interesting thing about a reaction like this is that it can be the first step on a long chain of reactions that result in the production of new elements. That is, nuclear reactions involving the simplest of particles are responsible for the genesis of the elements out of which the Universe is made.

The following are three of the reactions that take place:

$${}^{2}_{1}\mathrm{H} + {}^{1}_{1}\mathrm{H} \rightarrow {}^{3}_{2}\mathrm{He}$$
$${}^{3}_{2}\mathrm{He} + {}^{3}_{2}\mathrm{He} \rightarrow {}^{4}_{2}\mathrm{He} + 2{}^{1}_{1}\mathrm{H}$$
$${}^{3}_{2}\mathrm{He} + {}^{4}_{2}\mathrm{He} \rightarrow {}^{7}_{4}\mathrm{Be}$$

It is widely believed that the Universe began with a 'big bang' some twenty thousand million years ago. The chain of fusion reactions that started then are still going on in stars.

6.4 Suppose a carbon-12 atom is formed in a star. Which fusion reaction would convert it into an atom of nitrogen-13?

6.5 Nuclear weapons

Thus far it might seem that fission reactions were investigated because of the interest in generating electricity. However, this does not match with what actually happened. Many of the most important discoveries about the production of energy by fission reactions were made during the Second World War (1939–1945). It was realised that, as forecast in 1904 (see section 6.1), it should be possible to release the huge amounts of energy in a very short time, i.e. in an explosion. The early nuclear reactors were built with one main purpose: to discover enough about fission reactions to see if it was possible to build a nuclear bomb (Figure 6.4). As we now know the research was successful. The basic problem is to cause a fission chain reaction to take place very rapidly. This is done by bringing the bomb material together to form a critical mass. The critical mass is large enough to ensure that the majority of the neutrons being emitted do not escape but bring about further fissions. For obvious reasons the nuclear material must be kept below the critical mass until the moment when the explosion is required. A small (conventional) explosion

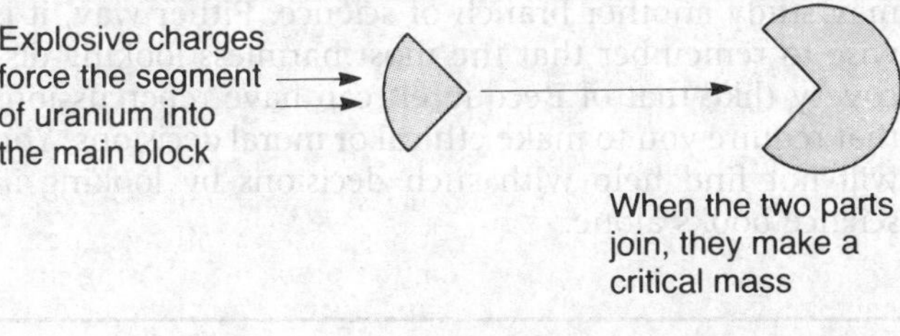
Explosive charges force the segment of uranium into the main block
When the two parts join, they make a critical mass

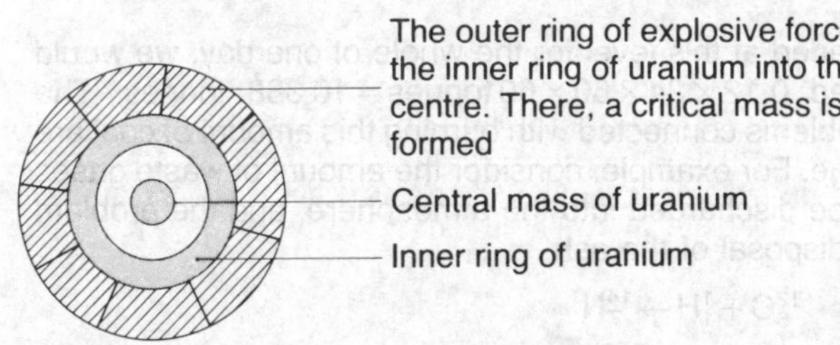
The outer ring of explosive forces the inner ring of uranium into the centre. There, a critical mass is formed
Central mass of uranium
Inner ring of uranium

Figure 6.4 *Two ways of making a nuclear bomb. In both cases the aim is to bring two pieces of uranium together to make a critical mass. In practice this is no easy matter. Also, not all nuclear weapons use uranium-235 as their active ingredient*

is used to bring the separate pieces of the nuclear material together. Fortunately this is not at all easy to do, so the chances of someone building a bomb 'in their back yard' is not very high.

Plutonium is highly regarded as a reactor fuel. It is even more highly thought of as a nuclear bomb material. Many nuclear power stations have not been built just to produce electricity. They have been used to generate plutonium (in the reactor core) for use in nuclear weapons.

Knowledge can be put to good or evil purposes. When the first atomic bomb was dropped on Japan thousands of people were killed, and many doomed to die through illnesses brought on by radiation. On the other hand, it could be that the early end to the war with Japan saved the lives of even more thousands of people. It would be a mistake to imagine that all would be well if nuclear weapons had not been invented. This would be to forget that tens of millions of people died in the Second World War; many in battle, but probably more in the concentration camps and from starvation and disease. However, the possibilities for the destruction of the Earth are infinitely greater because of the presence of nuclear weapons.

It is possible that everyone can agree that all nations should ban nuclear weapons. What is more uncertain is whether nuclear reactors should be used to generate electricity. Already there have been a number of very bad accidents in nuclear power stations, and a much larger number of smaller accidents. It remains debatable whether it really is cheaper to produce electricity by nuclear reactions. As we mentioned above, it is not unknown for 'power stations' to be in operation because of the plutonium they produce as much as for the electricity.

Critics of the nuclear industry point out that by comparison only tiny amounts of research have been done on using solar, wave and wind power to generate electricity. Similarly there is no obvious answer to the problem of nuclear waste disposal.

This bleak scene shows the absolute devastation brought about by the nuclear explosion at Hiroshima.

It is important that you consider the evidence and make up your own mind as to which direction the future should take.

Chemists have played a large part in bringing both nuclear power stations and nuclear weapons into being. You may be going on to study chemistry further, or you may study another branch of science. Either way, it is wise to remember that the most harmless looking discovery (like that of Becquerel) can have repercussions that require you to make ethical or moral decisions. You will not find help with such decisions by looking in science books alone.

Answers

6.1 The power generated is 1.6×10^{13} J/(236 g $\times 24 \times 60 \times 60$ s) $= 7.8 \times 10^5$ W, which rounds up to 1 MW.

6.2 (i) Thermal power = 3 MW. (ii) 3 g of fuel per day.

6.3 If 25 GJ (i.e. 25 000 MJ) were released in 1 s, the power would be 25 000 MW; so to produce 3 MW would need 0.12 tonnes of coal. However, if the power is needed at this level for the whole of one day, we would need $0.12 \times 24 \times 60 \times 60$ tonnes = 10 368 tonnes. The problems connected with burning this amount of coal are huge. For example, consider the amount of waste gases to be discharged into the atmosphere, and the problem of disposal of the ash.

6.4 ${}^{12}_{6}\mathrm{C} + {}^{1}_{1}\mathrm{H} \rightarrow {}^{14}_{7}\mathrm{N}$

UNIT 6 SUMMARY

- Fusion reactions:
  - (i) Take place when two or more nuclides join to make a new nuclide.
  - (ii) Take place in stars and are responsible for generating new elements from hydrogen and helium.
- Fission reactions:
  - (i) Occur when a nucleus breaks apart, producing new nuclides.
  - (ii) Are used in nuclear reactors. The release of energy from chain reactions is controlled so that it takes place gradually over a relatively long period of time. A moderator around the fuel rods, and the withdrawal of fuel rods from the reactor, are used to control the reaction.
- In nuclear weapons the chain reaction is uncontrolled, causing an explosion. Fissile material is brought together to form a critical mass, and the energy is released in a short but devastating burst.

7

Applications of radioactivity

7.1 Industrial uses of radioactivity

We have spent some time in discovering how the energy generated by nuclear reactions can be used to produce electricity. In this unit we shall take a brief look at some other uses of isotopes and the radioactivity that many of them give off.

(a) *Detection of metal fatigue*

The first passenger jet aircraft to enter service was the Comet in 1952. At the time this aircraft was very advanced; but it had the unfortunate habit of falling out of the sky for no apparent reason. After several such accidents the cause was traced to fatigue in metal surrounding the windows. Metal fatigue can be hard to spot; but checks for it are now made regularly on aircraft. One way in which this is done is to use gamma-rays from cobalt-60. Where fatigue sets in, the structure of the metal crystals changes. Gamma-rays do not pass equally well through both the good and bad areas. If the gamma-rays fall on a photographic film after passing through the metal, any differences in structure show up. A similar technique can make use of neutrons rather than gamma-rays. Tests for fatigue are essential in checking nuclear power stations.

(b) *Food preservation*

Gamma-rays are especially good at passing through matter. They are also very energetic. Recently these two properties of gamma-rays have been used in food preservation. If foodstuffs are irradiated by a beam of gamma-rays, bacteria that may be present are killed. Without the bacteria present the food will not 'go off' for a very long time, especially if it is stored in air-tight

Many think that the ill-fated Comet was the most elegant of all passenger jet airliners.

The large number of sensors on the wing of this aircraft indicate the importance now given to detecting metal fatigue.

containers. However, there has been a lot of concern about this use of gamma-rays. Many people are worried in case the food itself is changed by the gamma-rays and that it may be dangerous to eat.

7.2 Medical uses of radioactivity

The first use of radioactivity in medicine was the use of radium in the treatment of cancers. The methods used have become much more sophisticated since Marie Curie founded the Radium Institute in Paris. However, the basic idea remains the same. Radiation is focused on the growth or tumour, and the energy that the particles carry is used to disrupt the malignant cells. For example, sources of fast neutrons have been found to be very successful in treating cancers of the throat. However, it is vital that the radiation treatment is carried out with care. Healthy tissue is just as liable to damage as that of the growth.

Another technique is to use isotopes as a way of studying the chemical reactions that take place in the body. For example, iodine is an essential element for health. Normally it collects in the thyroid gland in the neck. A person suffering from a deficiency of iodine is liable to suffer from a huge growth in the neck. By feeding patients with radioactive iodine-131, it is possible to discover where the iodine collects in the body, or if it is not absorbed at all. In a direct way the presence of iodine-131 in the thyroid gland can be detected by a Geiger counter. Methods like this rely on the fact that isotopes of the same element have the same chemical properties; so iodine-131 will behave in exactly the same way as the non-radioactive iodine-127.

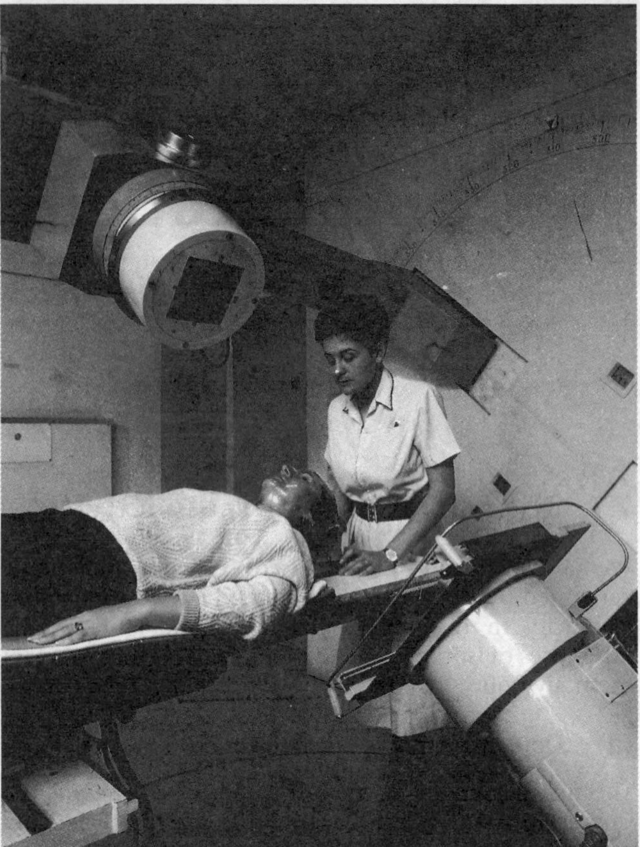

This cancer patient has had her chances of survival much increased by radio-treatment.

7.3 Radiocarbon dating

(a) *Method*

There is a great deal of carbon-12 in the world. It is to be found in all living things, tied up in organic compounds, and in the atmosphere as carbon dioxide. The energy coming to Earth as cosmic rays can cause carbon-14 atoms to be produced. The cosmic rays cause nuclear reactions to take place in the atmosphere. Some of these result in neutrons being emitted. If a neutron of the right range of energy collides with a nitrogen-14 atom, a reaction takes place:

$$^{14}_{7}N + ^{1}_{0}n \rightarrow ^{14}_{6}C + ^{1}_{1}H$$

The half-life of the carbon-14 formed is 5730 years.

Now, let us assume that the Earth is bombarded at a constant rate with cosmic rays. In this case, the rate of production of carbon-14 should be constant, and the ratio of carbon-12 to carbon-14 atoms should also be constant. The carbon-14 will wander round the atmosphere taking part in the same reactions as does carbon-12. Therefore, carbon-14 will turn up in living material such as trees, plants and humans. However, when the living material dies the reactions stop and no more carbon-12 or carbon-14 will be taken up (Figure 7.1). Now the proportion of carbon-14 in the dead material

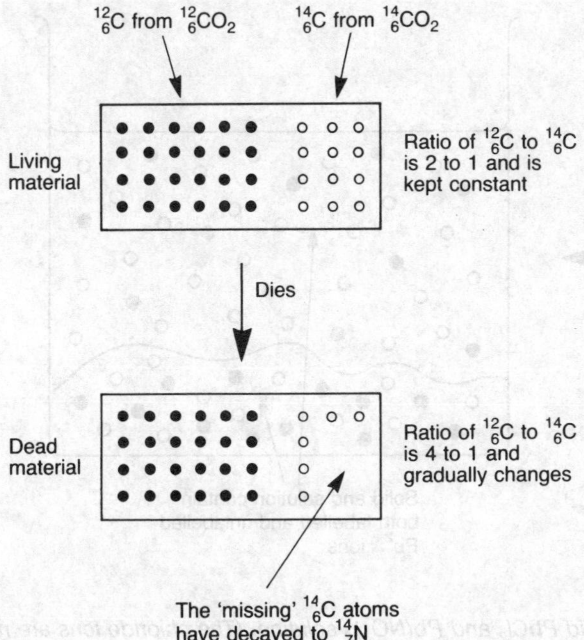
$^{12}_{6}C$ from $^{12}_{6}CO_2$
$^{14}_{6}C$ from $^{14}_{6}CO_2$
Living material
Ratio of $^{12}_{6}C$ to $^{14}_{6}C$ is 2 to 1 and is kept constant
Dies
Dead material
Ratio of $^{12}_{6}C$ to $^{14}_{6}C$ is 4 to 1 and gradually changes
The 'missing' $^{14}_{6}C$ atoms have decayed to $^{14}_{7}N$

***Figure 7.1** Illustration of the principle of radiocarbon dating. The ratios of $^{12}_{6}C$ to $^{14}_{6}C$ are only for illustration. Real values are very different*

starts to decrease. This is because of the decay of the carbon-14:

$$^{14}_{6}C \rightarrow {}^{14}_{7}N + {}^{0}_{-1}e$$

If we measure the relative proportions of $^{12}_{6}C$ and $^{14}_{6}C$, the smaller the amount of $^{14}_{6}C$, the longer ago did the uptake of the isotope stop. As a result we can use the proportion of $^{14}_{6}C$ as a measure of the age of the sample. This is the basis of radiocarbon dating.

The accuracy of carbon dating is upset by several factors. For one thing, cosmic ray activity is not constant and is known to vary considerably over periods of many thousands of years. In this century two other factors have to be taken into account as well. When fossil fuels such as coal and oil are burnt in large quantities, the carbon-14 they contain is liberated into the atmosphere. Also, the large number of nuclear bomb tests that were carried out in the 1950s and 1960s released a great deal of radiation into the atmosphere. This has also increased the amount of carbon-14 in the atmosphere.

(b) *The age of the Earth*

When uranium decays, helium gas is given off, and finally lead is formed. For every uranium-238 atom that decays, one atom of lead-206 is produced at the end of the decay chain. Along the way eight alpha-particles, i.e. helium atoms, are released. Also, we know the half-lives of all the isotopes in the decay series of uranium-238. This means that, if we are able to count the number of lead or helium atoms in a sample of uranium, we should be able to calculate how long the uranium has been decaying. Needless to say, there are many difficulties in performing the calculation. For one thing we must be sure that the lead or helium has not arrived by some other means, for example as the product of other decay schemes.

Rocks can also be dated by comparing the amounts of various other isotopes such as lead-206 and lead-204, potassium-40 and argon-40, rubidium-87 and strontium-87. Using isotope dating methods, the oldest rocks on Earth appear to be about 3.7×10^9 years old. Therefore we can say that the Earth is *at least* this old, because the isotope method can only work from the time that the rocks had solidified. For example, any helium formed while the rocks were still liquid would have boiled off. By comparison, rocks from the Moon and meteorites appear to be around 4.6×10^9 years old. The absence of ages greater than this suggests that the Universe itself was formed no more than 5×10^9 years ago.

7.1 Two other methods of isotope dating rely on the conversions of $^{40}_{19}K$ to $^{40}_{18}Ar$ and $^{87}_{37}Rb$ to $^{87}_{38}Sr$. What are the nuclear equations for the conversions?

7.2 It has been estimated that the carbon-14 in the atmosphere is responsible for producing 60 atoms of nitrogen-14 and 60 electrons every hour for each gram of carbon. We can quote this disintegration rate as 60 counts hour^{-1} g^{-1}. A sample of a sea shell found near a sea shore was found to have a count of 4 counts hour^{-1} g^{-1}. Estimate the age of the shell. (The half-life of $^{14}_{6}C$ is 5730 years.)

7.4 Chemical applications

Isotopes can be of great use in chemical research. Often they are used in *tracer* experiments; that is, where the use of an isotope can help to trace the course of a reaction. For example, lead(II) chloride, $PbCl_2$, is highly insoluble in water whereas lead(II) nitrate, $Pb(NO_3)_2$, is easily soluble in water. Naturally occurring lead is a mixture of ^{206}Pb, ^{207}Pb and ^{208}Pb, none of which are radioactive. However, ^{212}Pb is radioactive, being a beta-emitter with a half-life of around 11 hours. Suppose the $PbCl_2$ is prepared from ^{212}Pb. The $PbCl_2$ has been *labelled*, and we can show the labelled lead in a formula by using a star, like this: $*PbCl_2$. Now, imagine that $*PbCl_2$ is added to a solution of $Pb(NO_3)_2$, left for some hours, and then the solution separated from the solid (Figure 7.2). The solution can be crystallised, and the lead(II) nitrate collected. When this is done, it is found that the crystals are radioactive. That is, some of the nitrate is in the form of $*Pb(NO_3)_2$. This result is best explained by realising that an 'insoluble' substance is not 100% insoluble. Some of the labelled lead ions must have escaped from the $*PbCl_2$ crystals and dissolved in the water. There they became mixed with the ordinary isotopes of lead. When the solution was separated, some of the radioactive lead was left in the solution, and some of the non-radioactive lead found its way into the lead(II) chloride. That is, an exchange reaction had taken place.

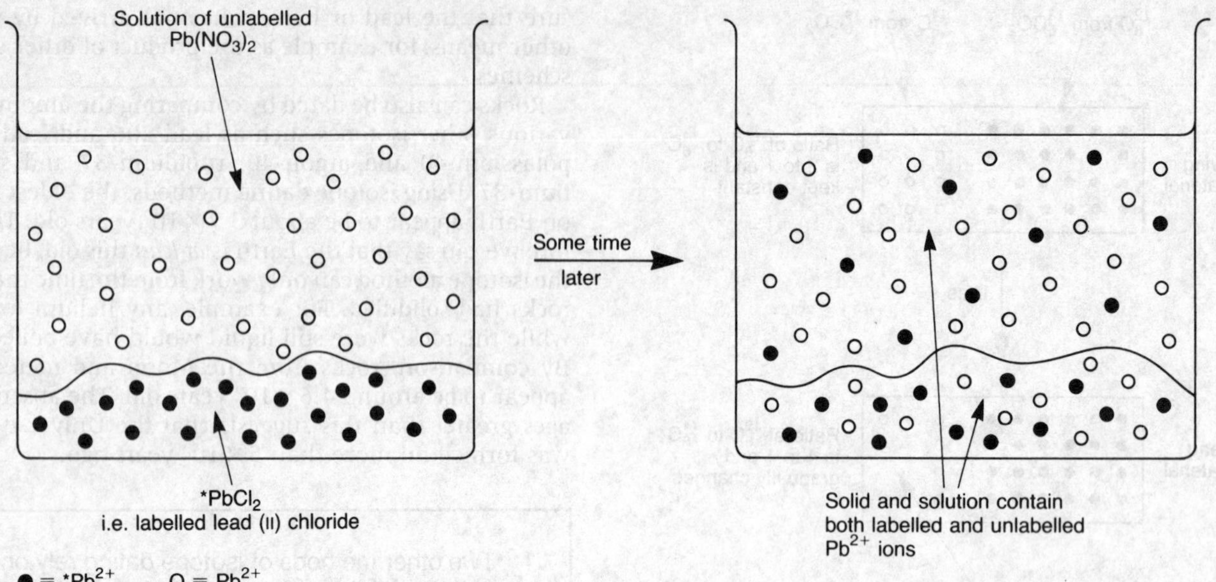

***Figure 7.2** Illustration of exchange of labelled Pb^{2+} ions between solid $PbCl_2$ and $Pb(NO_3)_2$ solution. (The chloride ions are not shown)*

7.3 Water, which normally contains oxygen-16, can be labelled with oxygen-18. We can show the labelled water as $H_2{}^*O$. Certain types of organic compounds called esters have the arrangement of atoms and bonds shown below:

$$R-\overset{\overset{\large O}{||}}{C}-O-R'$$

(A marks the C–O bond; B marks the O–R′ bond)

R and R′ are groups of atoms, the details of which are not important here.

When the ester is heated with water containing $H_2{}^*O$, two new compounds are formed:

$$R-\overset{\overset{\large O}{||}}{C}-{}^*OH + R'-OH$$

Both hydrogen atoms come from the water, as does one of the oxygen atoms.

Does the ester break apart at the point A or at the point B when it reacts with water?

Answers

7.1 ${}^{40}_{19}K + {}^{0}_{-1}e \rightarrow {}^{40}_{18}Ar$, i.e. electron capture; ${}^{87}_{37}Rb \rightarrow {}^{87}_{38}Sr + {}^{0}_{-1}e$, i.e. beta (electron) decay.

7.2 Every 5730 years the count rate would have halved.

Count rate/counts hour^{-1} g^{-1}	60	30	15	7.5	3.75
Number of half-lives	0	1	2	3	4

If the count rate had reduced to 3.75 counts hour^{-1} g^{-1}, the lapse of time would be $4 \times 5370 = 21\,480$ years. The actual count rate is a little higher than 3.75 counts hour^{-1} g^{-1}, so the shell must be somewhat less than the calculated age, say around 21 000 years old.

7.3 It breaks at the point A. The bond between the carbon and unlabelled oxygen must break if the labelled oxygen is to join to the carbon atom.

UNIT 7 SUMMARY

- Applications of radioactivity include:
  - (i) Detection of metal fatigue.
  - (ii) Food preservation.
  - (iii) Destruction of malignant tumours.
  - (iv) Tracers in medical and scientific research.
  - (v) Radiocarbon dating. This relies on measuring the amount of carbon-14 in once-living matter. The uptake of carbon from the environment stops on death. As the carbon-14 decays, the proportion of it in the sample gradually decreases. The relative amount of carbon-12 to carbon-14 is a measure of the length of time that the material has been dead.

8

Bohr's model of the atom

8.1 Energy levels of the hydrogen atom

In this unit we are going to move outwards from the nucleus to the world of electrons surrounding the nucleus. First, you should understand that it was a puzzle how electrons could remain outside the nucleus. The problem was, if the negative electrons were so very close to the nucleus, why were they not pulled into it by the attraction of its positive charge (Figure 8.1)? It was possible to give a solution to this puzzle, but at the cost of creating a new problem. The solution was to assume that the electrons were moving very speedily around the nucleus in circular or elliptical paths.

Given sufficient acceleration the electrons would not tumble into the nucleus. Unfortunately this apparently simple solution turned out to be particularly troublesome. This was because James Clerk Maxwell had shown that any electric charge that was accelerated would radiate energy. Therefore, the electrons in all atoms should be continuously radiating energy. Also, if they radiate energy then they must be losing energy continuously. Eventually they would end up by spiralling into the nucleus and the atom would collapse (Figure 8.2). It is common experience that atoms do not normally radiate energy, and that objects in the world do not collapse and disappear. In short, the discovery of the nucleus raised as many problems as it solved. As it turned out, the physics of the time could not solve the problem. Instead, *quantum theory* was invented to provide the answers. Niels Bohr was one of the people who invented the theory.

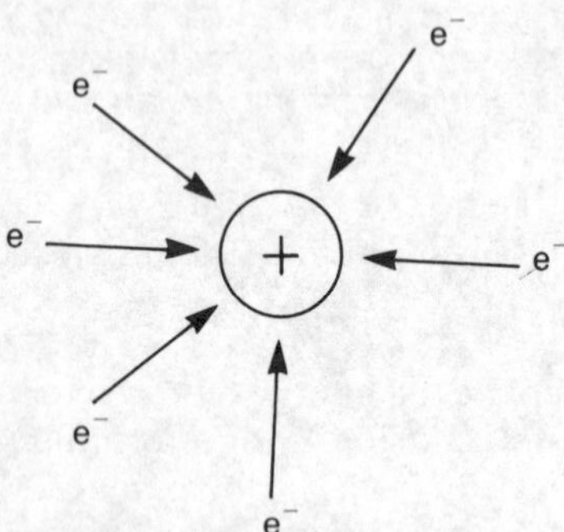

Figure 8.1 *If electrons are outside the nucleus, why are they not attracted in towards the nucleus; i.e. why do atoms not collapse?*

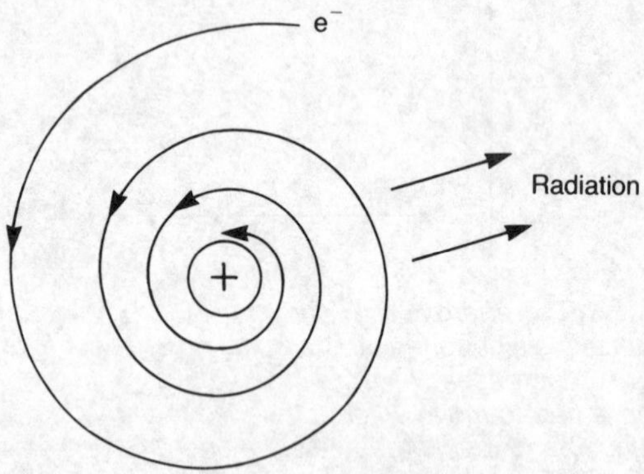

Figure 8.2 *An electron that is accelerating radiates energy. As it loses energy, it spirals in to the nucleus*

Bohr was a Danish physicist who spent some time working with Rutherford, and he also knew of Max Planck's work on energy levels. Bohr had the insight to apply some of Planck's ideas to explain the structure of atoms, in particular the hydrogen atom. The main proposal that Bohr made (in 1913) was that the electron could not have just any energy; rather it was restricted to having a particular set of energy values, which are better known as *energy levels*. That is, the energies of the electron were *quantised*. His formula for the energy levels was

$$E_n = \frac{-e^4 m_e}{8\varepsilon_0^2 h^2 n^2}$$

Notice that the energy values are negative. As we saw in Unit 2, this means that we would have to put energy into the atom in order to remove the electron.

In this formula, n is a quantum number that governs the energy. It is called the *principal quantum number*. It can take only integer (whole number) values 1, 2, 3, . . . and the energy levels have the labels E_1, E_2, E_3, ... The

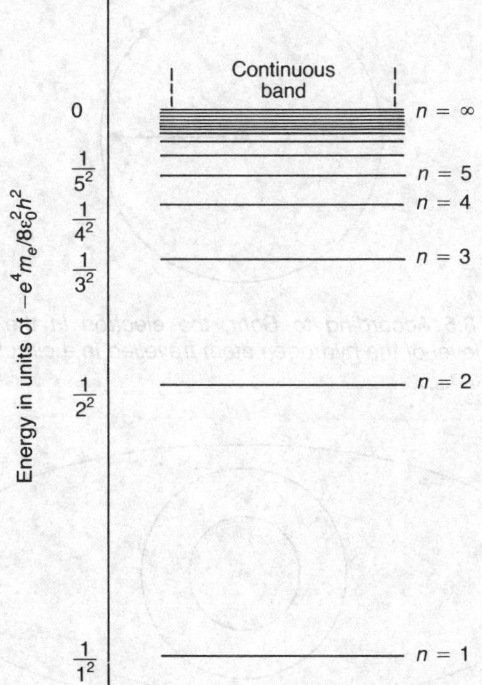

***Figure 8.3** The energy level diagram of the hydrogen atom shows the levels becoming increasingly close as the quantum number, n, increases. At n = ∞ the atom is ionised and the electron is free to move without the influence of the proton. A continuous band results because the energy of the electron is no longer quantised*

mass of the electron is shown as m_e, the magnitude of its charge is e, and h is the Planck constant. Finally, ε_0 is the permittivity of free space, and is a measure of how easy it is for electromagnetic radiation to pass through it. The values of quantities like e, h and ε_0 are listed in Appendix D, and by putting them in the formula for E_n we find

$$E_n = \frac{-k}{n^2}$$

where $k = 2.179 \times 10^{-18}$ J. If we plot these values of E_n we obtain an energy level diagram like that shown in Figure 8.3.

> **8.1** (i) How much energy would be needed to make an electron move from the ground state ($n = 1$) of the hydrogen atom to the next level, with $n = 2$?
>
> (ii) This energy could be supplied by shining 'light' on the atom. With luck, one of the photons might give up its energy to the electron to make it move between the two energy levels. Use the equation $E = hf$ to calculate the frequency needed.
>
> (iii) Convert this into a wavelength using the relation $c = f\lambda$, where c is the speed of light. In which part of the electromagnetic spectrum does this radiation appear?

> **8.2** What would be the value of the principal quantum number if an electron in a hydrogen atom was in an orbital of energy -0.242×10^{-18} J?

8.2 How to calculate the ionisation energy of hydrogen

Notice that the energy levels become closer and closer together as n increases. Eventually, as n becomes infinitely large the value of $-k/n^2$ becomes nearer and nearer to zero, and the separate energy levels merge into a continuous band. Just at the point when the continuous band begins, $n = \infty$ and $E_n = 0$. If an electron manages to reach the level with $E_n = 0$ it has gained sufficient energy just to escape from the atom. When this happens the hydrogen atom becomes simply a bare positively charged nucleus. It has been changed into a hydrogen ion, H^+. Usually we would say that the hydrogen atom has been *ionised* (Figure 8.4). The process of ionisation can be shown in an equation like this:

$$H(g) \rightarrow H^+(g) + e^-$$

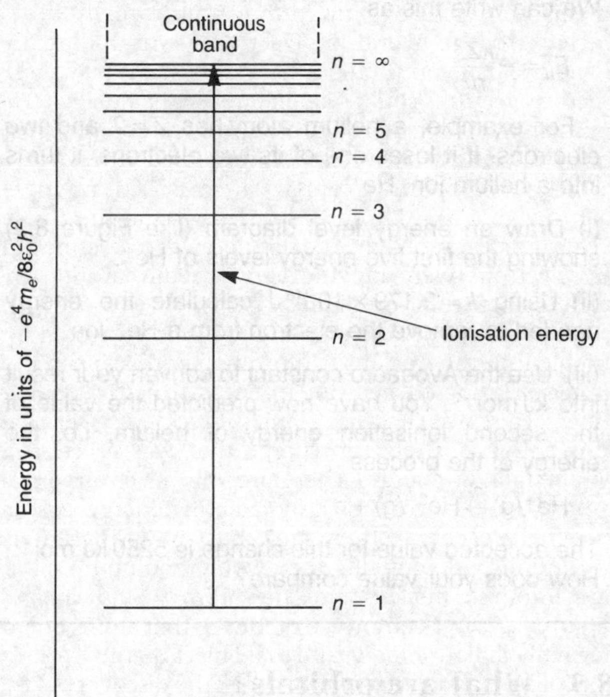

***Figure 8.4** The ionisation energy of the hydrogen atom is the energy needed to move an electron from the lowest energy level (n = 1) to the highest energy level (n = ∞)*

We can calculate the energy required to ionise a single hydrogen atom by using Bohr's formula. We need to transfer the electron from the lowest energy level ($n = 1$) to the highest possible energy level ($n = \infty$). The energy required will be the difference between the two energy level values. When $n = \infty$ we know that $E_\infty = 0$, and when $n = 1$, $E_1 = -2.179 \times 10^{-18}$ J, so we have

$$\begin{aligned}\text{ionisation energy} &= E_\infty - E_1\\ &= 0-(-2.179\times10^{-18})\text{ J}\\ &= 2.179\times10^{-18}\text{ J}\end{aligned}$$

This value is in excellent agreement with that obtained from experiment. Successes like this provided evidence that Bohr was on the right track.

8.3 Atoms more complicated than hydrogen have more than one proton in their nucleus. Let Z stand for the number of protons in a nucleus. Also, imagine that an atom loses all but one of its electrons so that it changes into a positively charged ion with just one electron. Bohr's formula for the energy levels of the hydrogen atom can easily be changed to apply to such ions. It becomes

$$E_n = \frac{-Z^2e^4m_e}{8\varepsilon_0^2h^2n^2}$$

We can write this as

$$E_n = -\frac{kZ^2}{n^2}$$

For example, a helium atom has $Z=2$ and two electrons. If it loses one of its two electrons, it turns into a helium ion, He^+.

(i) Draw an energy level diagram (like Figure 8.3) showing the first five energy levels of He^+.

(ii) Using $k=2.179\times10^{-18}$ J calculate the energy needed to remove the electron from a He^+ ion.

(iii) Use the Avogadro constant to convert your result into kJ mol^{-1}. You have now predicted the value of the second ionisation energy of helium, i.e. the energy of the process

$$He^+(g) \rightarrow He^{2+}(g) + e^-$$

The accepted value for this change is 5250 kJ mol^{-1}. How does your value compare?

8.3 What are orbitals?

One of the nice things about Bohr's theory was that it allowed scientists to conjure up imaginary pictures of how the electron in a hydrogen atom was moving around the nucleus. In the state with lowest energy, Bohr predicted that it moved in a circular path at a fixed distance from the nucleus (Figure 8.5). The radius of the circle Bohr predicted to be exactly 5.292×10^{-11} m. This distance is an important one in chemistry, and it is given a special name and symbol. It is called the *Bohr radius*, and has the symbol a_0. The path of the electron as it orbited the nucleus became known as an *orbital*. (But see Unit 11 for the modern definition of an orbital.) It was possible to predict the size and shape of the orbitals for each of the energy levels. Some of them were circles of radius larger than a_0; some were ellipses (Figure 8.6). It

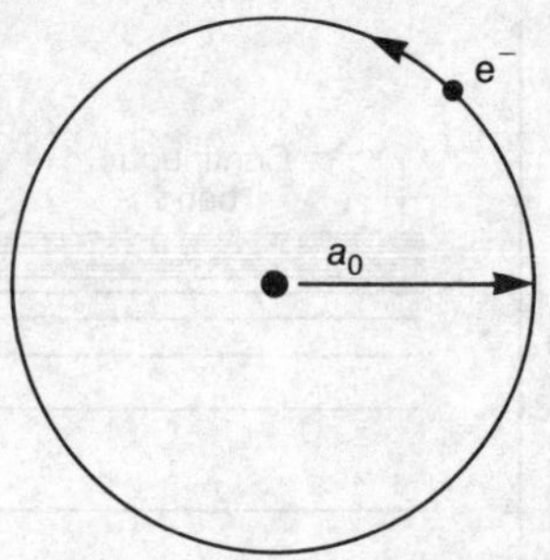

Figure 8.5 *According to Bohr, the electron in the lowest energy level of the hydrogen atom travelled in a circular path of radius* a_0

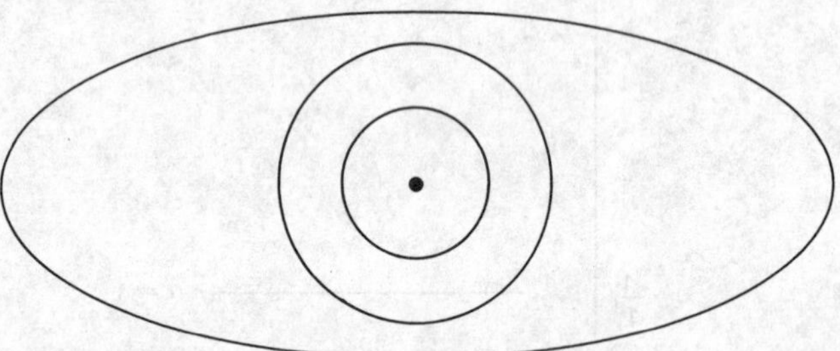

Figure 8.6 *Some of the paths of the electron in a hydrogen atom were circles and some were ellipses. These were common shapes of Bohr orbitals*

soon became common for chemists to talk about electrons being *in* a particular orbital. Really the electron is not 'in' anything; rather it is moving in a particular way around the nucleus with a particular energy. However, saying that an electron is in an orbital is a convenient shorthand.

8.4 Bohr predicted the radius of the orbit of the electron in the hydrogen atom to be

$$r_n = \frac{\varepsilon_0h^2n^2}{\pi e^2m_e}$$

(i) If an electron moves from $n=1$ to $n=2$, by how much does the radius of its orbit increase?

(ii) What is the maximum distance away from the nucleus that the electron can get? What has happened to the atom then?

8.4 What are stationary states?

In section 8.1 we said that it seemed that electrons outside the nucleus should constantly be radiating energy. The energy of the electron in a hydrogen atom should therefore be changing in time. Bohr did not give a thorough explanation of why this did not happen. It was just one of the assumptions of his theory that when an electron had one of the energies given by his formula, then the electron did not radiate energy.

The set of energy levels E_n were later given the names *stationary states*. This was not because the electrons were thought to be standing still; rather it was because the energy values did not change with time.

8.5 Ground and excited states

The electron in a hydrogen atom that has not been given any extra energy will be found in the lowest energy level, E_1. This energy level is given a special name. It is called the *ground state*. Indeed, the state of any atom or molecule in which all the electrons have their lowest energies is called the ground state. If the electrons are given extra energy and move from a lower to a higher energy, then the atom or molecule is said to be in an *excited state*. Such a change from one energy level to another is called a *transition* (Figure 8.7). Atoms or molecules that are in excited states can often lose their extra energy by giving it out as light. We shall find that our ability to make atoms or molecules change between their ground and excited states is one of the most powerful ways of discovering how atoms bond together. The general name of this method is spectroscopy. Later we shall take a long look at different types of spectroscopy.

Before leaving this unit, you might like to think about the meaning of diagrams that show circles around the nuclei of atoms. The circles are supposed to show where the electrons are to be found. You should now understand a little about how Bohr's work made such diagrams possible. Also, you should realise that Bohr made predictions about the energy of an electron in a hydrogen atom. The key idea was that the energy was quantised: only particular energy values were found to occur, and these values were related to the value of the principal quantum number, n. Although the orbitals of

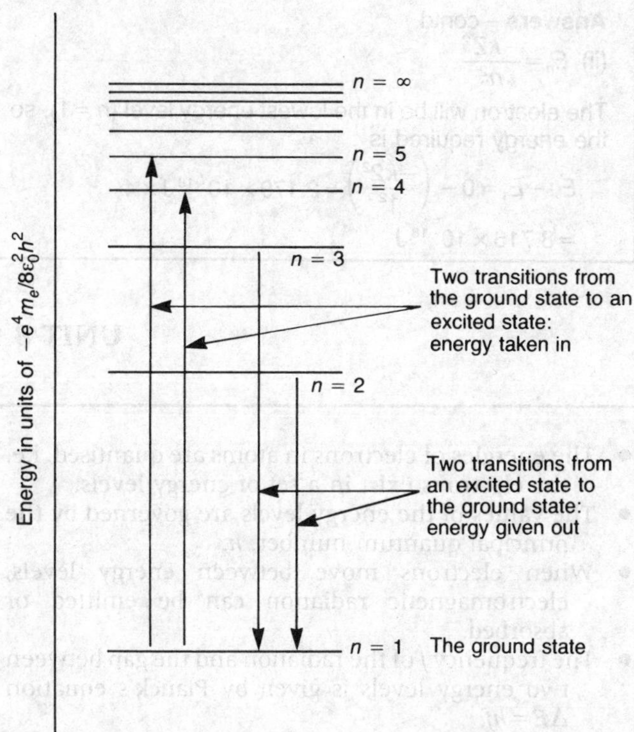

Figure 8.7 *Examples of transitions between energy levels in the hydrogen atom*

the electron are often shown as circles, you should be careful about taking Bohr's ideas to heart. In the first place, Bohr's orbits were not always circular. Secondly, and more importantly, his theory could not explain how the electrons behaved in any atom or ion that had more than one electron.

In the next unit we shall take a closer look at the successes of Bohr's theory, and its failures.

Answers

8.1 (i) Using our formula for the energy levels we have

$$E_2 - E_1 = \frac{-k}{2^2} - \frac{(-k)}{1^2} = \frac{k}{1^2} - \frac{k}{2^2} = k\left(\frac{1}{1^2} - \frac{1}{2^2}\right) = \frac{3k}{4}$$

so

$$E_2 - E_1 = \tfrac{3}{4}(2.179 \times 10^{-18}\,\text{J}) = 1.634 \times 10^{-18}\,\text{J}$$

(ii) Planck's equation rearranges to give $f = E/h$. The result is $f = 2.466 \times 10^{15}$ Hz.

(iii) The wavelength $= c/f = 1.216 \times 10^{-7}$ m. This is in the ultraviolet.

8.2 We have

$$-0.242 \times 10^{-18}\,\text{J} = \frac{-2.179 \times 10^{-18}\,\text{J}}{n^2}$$

which means that

$$n^2 = \frac{-2.179 \times 10^{-18}\,\text{J}}{-0.242 \times 10^{-18}\,\text{J}} = 9$$

Hence, $n = 3$.

8.3 (i) The energy level diagram is given in Figure 8.8.

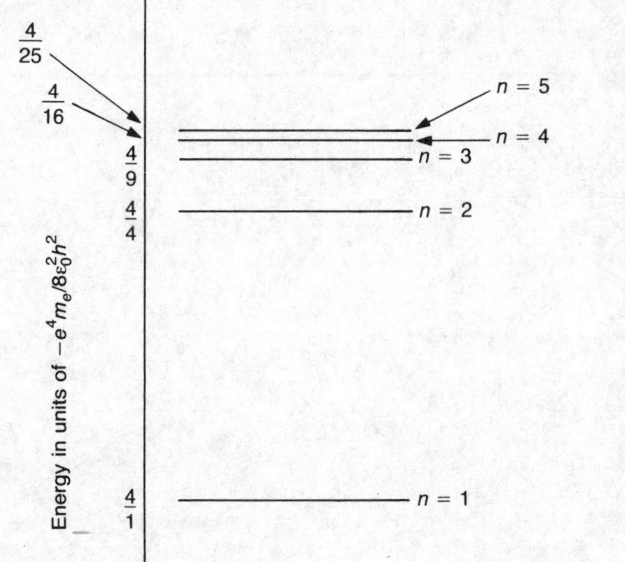

Figure 8.8 *The first five energy levels of a helium ion, He^+*

Answers – contd.

(ii) $E_n = \frac{-kZ^2}{n^2}$

The electron will be in the lowest energy level ($n=1$), so the energy required is

$$E_\infty - E_1 = 0 - \left(\frac{-k2^2}{1^2}\right) = 2.179 \times 10^{-18}\,\text{J} \times 4$$

$$= 8.716 \times 10^{-18}\,\text{J}$$

(iii) The result is 5247 kJ mol^{-1}. The agreement is very good.

8.4 (i) It increases in the ratio 2^2 to 1^2, i.e. 4 times larger.

(ii) Infinity. It has been ionised.

UNIT 8 SUMMARY

- The energies of electrons in atoms are quantised, i.e. the electrons exist in a set of energy levels.
- The values of the energy levels are governed by the principal quantum number, *n*.
- When electrons move between energy levels, electromagnetic radiation can be emitted or absorbed.
- The frequency *f* of the radiation and the gap between two energy levels is given by Planck's equation $\Delta E = hf$.
- The ionisation energy of the hydrogen atom is the energy needed to remove the electron in the ground state from the atom (i.e. it corresponds to the transition from $n=1$ to $n=\infty$).
- Stationary state:
  An electron in an atom whose energy does not change with time is in a stationary state.
- Ground state:
  This is the state of an atom or molecule in which all the electrons have their lowest energies.
- Excited state:
  If electrons are given extra energy and move from a lower to a higher state, then the atom or molecule is said to be in an excited state.

9

The hydrogen atom spectrum

9.1 Balmer's formula for the hydrogen atom

If hydrogen atoms are given energy, for example by passing electricity through them, the energy can cause the atoms to go into excited states. Instead of the electrons being found in the ground state, they are excited into the higher energy levels. On the principle that what goes up must come down, sooner or later the electrons must lose their energy and fall back down to the ground state. The most common way for this to happen is for the energy to be lost as light. Sometimes the light is visible; sometimes it is invisible, for example infrared or ultraviolet light. The light that is given out can be measured in a spectrometer and the pattern recorded on photographic paper. The pattern is called a *spectrum*. The visible part of the hydrogen spectrum looks like that in the photo on page 52.

The spectrum consists of a series of lines, and hence it is called a *line spectrum*. The appearance of a line spectrum is very different to that of a *continuous spectrum*; for example a rainbow, where one colour merges imperceptibly into another. The wavelengths of the lines were measured long before Bohr's work. It proved extremely difficult to discover any relation between the wavelengths of the lines until Johannes Balmer, a Swiss school teacher, published the formula that now carries his name. The formula was later written like this:

$$\frac{1}{\lambda}=R_{\mathrm{H}}\left(\frac{1}{2^2}-\frac{1}{m^2}\right) \qquad \text{Balmer's formula}$$

R_{H} is called the Rydberg constant. Its value is $1.0967\times10^7\ \mathrm{m}^{-1}$. Balmer's formula was successful in giving the wavelengths of the lines in the spectrum provided the number m took the series of whole number values 3, 4, 5, ...

9.2 Bohr's explanation

It was not until Bohr published his formula for the hydrogen energy levels that it became possible to explain why Balmer's formula had this rather strange appearance.

The reason was that the lines in the visible spectrum occur when the electrons fall to the level with $n=2$. To see how this gives rise to Balmer's formula, let us use the simplified equation for the hydrogen energy levels, $E_n=-k/n^2$. For the second energy level, $E_2=-k/2^2$. If we write the energy of any level above that of $n=2$ as $E_m=-k/m^2$, the energy that the electron loses in falling from E_m to E_2 is

$$\text{energy lost}=E_m-E_2=\frac{-k}{m^2}-\frac{(-k)}{2^2}=k\left(\frac{1}{2^2}-\frac{1}{m^2}\right)$$

Now we need to remember that this energy is given out as light, and that the energy of light of frequency f is just hf (h is the Planck constant – check with Unit 8 if you have forgotten about this). Then, in the present case,

$$hf=\text{energy lost}$$

so

$$f=\frac{k}{h}\left(\frac{1}{2^2}-\frac{1}{m^2}\right)$$

Finally, so that we can get the formula for the wavelength we must use the equation

$$c=f\lambda$$

which says that the speed of light, c, is given by multiplying the frequency, f, by the wavelength, λ. Rearranging this to $c/\lambda=f$, or $1/\lambda=f/c$, we find

$$\frac{1}{\lambda}=\frac{k}{hc}\left(\frac{1}{2^2}-\frac{1}{m^2}\right)$$

This is the same as Balmer's formula if we recognise that the constant k/hc is the same as the Rydberg constant R_{H}.

9.3 Other lines in the hydrogen spectrum

The Balmer series happened to be the first series of lines in the hydrogen spectrum to be investigated. This was because the lines were in the visible part of the spectrum and therefore the easiest to observe. In time, several other series of lines were discovered. These series are listed in Table 9.1.

Table 9.1. Series of lines in the hydrogen spectrum

Series	*Region of spectrum*	*Value of n*	*Values of m*
Lyman (1914)	Ultraviolet	1	2,3,4,...
Balmer (1885)	Visible	2	3,4,5,...
Paschen (1908)	Infrared	3	4,5,6,...
Brackett (1922)	Infrared	4	5,6,7,...
Pfund (1924)	Infrared	5	6,7,8,...

It is not too difficult to write down the formula that predicts the wavelengths of all the lines in the hydrogen spectrum. Every line can be thought to be produced when an electron moves from a higher energy level to a lower energy level. If we call *m* the principal quantum number of the higher level, and *n* the principal quantum number of the lower level, the energy lost by the electron is

$$\text{energy lost} = E_m - E_n = \frac{-k}{m^2} - \frac{(-k)}{n^2} = k\left(\frac{1}{n^2} - \frac{1}{m^2}\right)$$

By the same method as in Section 9.2 we find

$$\frac{1}{\lambda} = \frac{k}{hc}\left(\frac{1}{n^2} - \frac{1}{m^2}\right) \quad \text{or} \quad \frac{1}{\lambda} = R_{\mathrm{H}}\left(\frac{1}{n^2} - \frac{1}{m^2}\right)$$

Incidentally, it is common practice to state the wavelengths of spectral lines in units of nanometres, nm ($1\,\text{nm} \equiv 10^{-9}\,\text{m}$).

It is not often that line spectra are shown in colour. Usually they appear as lines on a black and white photographic plate. In a book the spectrum might look like the diagram in Figure 9.1.

Make sure that you realise that the lines become closer together at the high energy end of the scale. The high energy end is the end where *frequency is increasing,* or *wavelength decreasing.*

Given his success in accounting for the spectrum of the hydrogen atom, it might seem that all was well with Bohr's theory. Indeed, it was a great advance on any previous theory. However, it was not long before problems began to arise. Among the most important was that his method did not work properly for atoms or ions having more than one electron. The appearance of the spectra of other atoms such as oxygen or sodium had such complicated patterns of lines that a simple hydrogen-like formula for the energy levels could not be derived. Also it was noticed that the spectrum of an atom changed if it was put in a magnetic field. This was particularly difficult to explain using Bohr's method. Attempts were made to adapt his equations, sometimes with success, but a better theory was needed. We shall discover something of this improved theory in the following units.

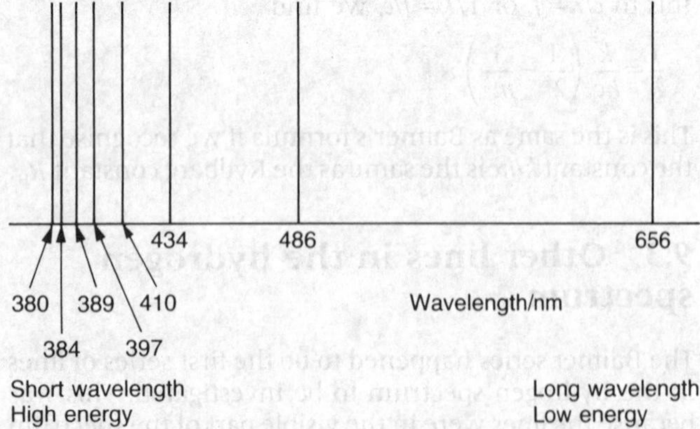

Figure 9.1 *The spectrum of hydrogen atoms shows a bewildering array of lines. Only lines in the Balmer series are shown here*

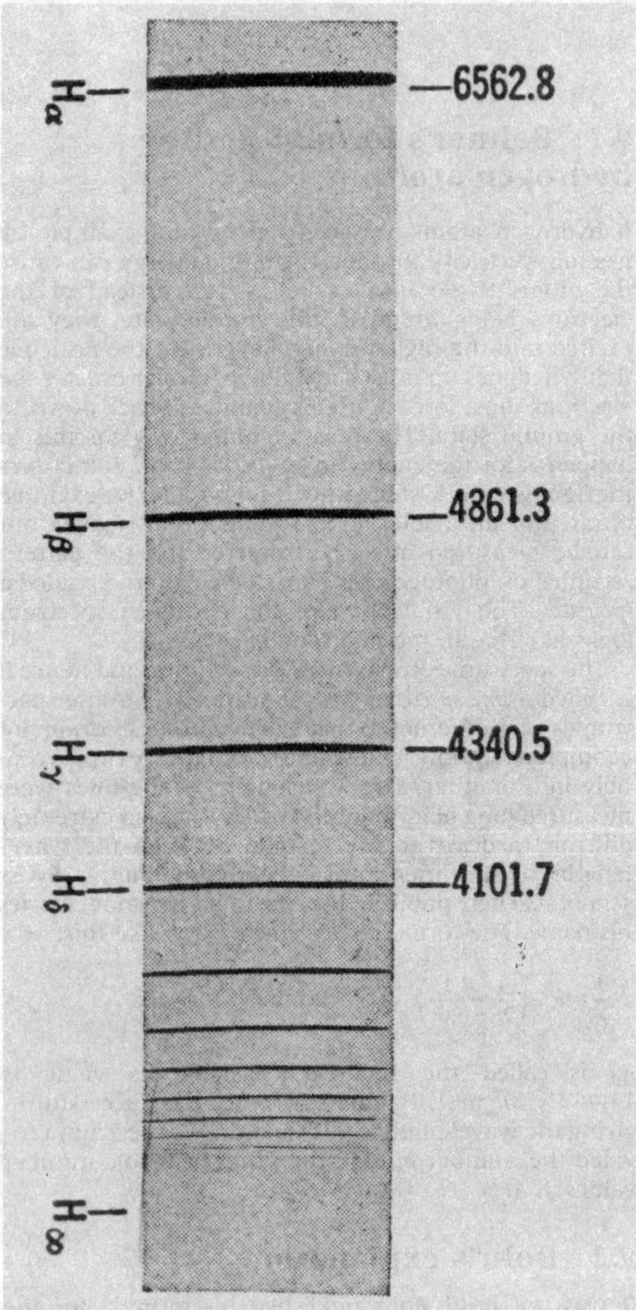

This image of the visible part of the hydrogen spectrum shows the characteristic lines which always occur in atomic spectra.

9.1 Why could you not discover the ionisation energy of the hydrogen atom by looking at the lines in the Balmer series? Which series would allow you to calculate the ionisation energy?

9.2 Which of the two diagrams in Figure 9.2 shows the axis labelled correctly?

9.3 Write a computer program that will allow you to predict the wavelength of any line in the hydrogen spectrum.

If you have the time (and the expertise) write a second program that will plot the appearance of the line spectrum for any one of the series of lines in Table 9.1.

If you would like to get an idea of how complicated the full spectrum of the hydrogen atom is, choose an appropriate scale and plot as many of the lines as possible of all the five series on the same scale.

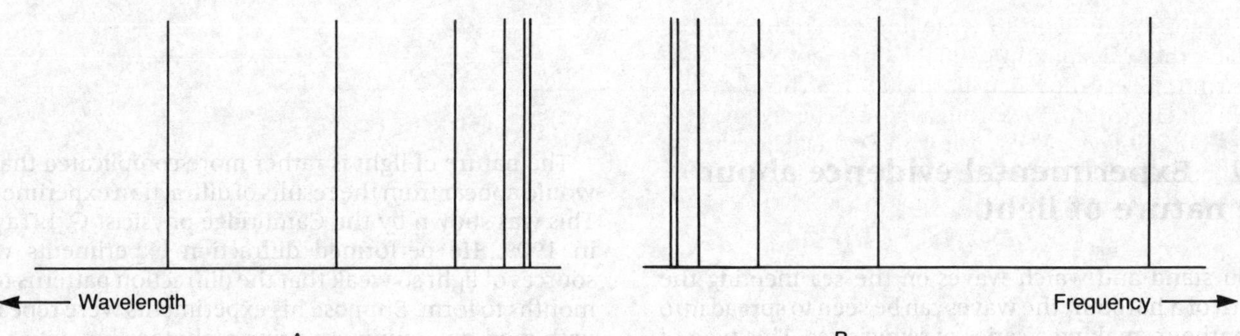

***Figure 9.2** Two diagrams showing lines in spectra. Only one of them is labelled correctly*

Answers

9.1 The ionisation energy is the energy difference between the energy levels with $n=1$ and $n=\infty$. The Balmer series only shows transitions to the level with $n=2$. The Lyman series contains the transitions to the lowest energy level, $n=1$, so this will contain the information needed to calculate the ionisation energy.

9.2 Diagram A is correct. Wavelength increasing to the left means that short wavelength is to the right. This is the high energy side, where the lines should converge. In diagram B the lines appear to converge at low frequency, i.e. low energy. This is the wrong way round.

9.3 The details of the program will depend on the computer you use.

UNIT 9 SUMMARY

- Hydrogen atom spectrum:
  - (i) The spectrum consists of a series of lines, which become closer together as wavelength decreases (or frequency increases).
  - (ii) The formula that relates the wavelength λ of lines in the hydrogen atom spectrum to the principal quantum numbers, n and m, of the energy levels involved is

$$\frac{1}{\lambda}=R_{\mathrm{H}}\left(\frac{1}{n^2}-\frac{1}{m^2}\right)$$

where R_{H} is the Rydberg constant.

  - (iii) The Balmer series involves transitions to the $n=2$ level.

10

Waves and particles

10.1 Experimental evidence about the nature of light

If you stand and watch waves on the sea meeting the mouth of a harbour, the waves can be seen to spread into the harbour, making a series of semicircles. This type of 'spreading out' behaviour is called *diffraction* and only occurs with waves (Figure 10.1). In the case of the harbour, the walls at the entrance form a *diffraction grating*. Provided a suitable grating can be found, other types of wave, and not just water waves, can be made to undergo diffraction. For example, Sir Lawrence Bragg showed that the way atoms lined up in a crystal made a diffraction grating for X-rays (see Unit 30).

Thomas Young had shown in 1807 that light could be made to show diffraction patterns. You will find details of Young's slit experiment in any book on advanced physics. Here we only need to know that in his experiment light behaves as if it were a type of wave.

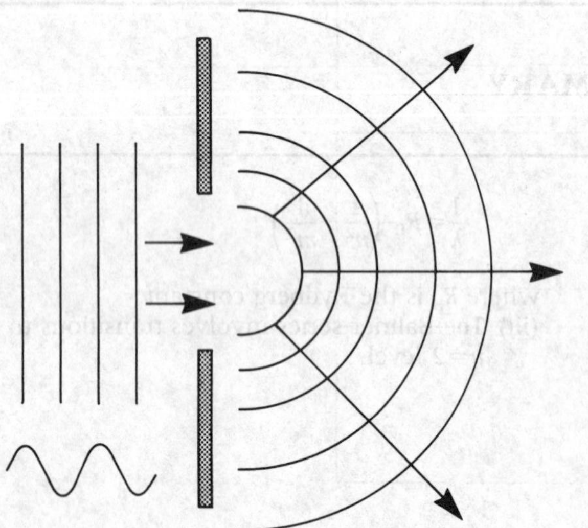

Figure 10.1 This diagram shows what happens to waves that pass through a slit. The lines show the peaks and troughs in the waves. After passing through the slit the waves spread out in semicircles. The waves have been diffracted

The nature of light is rather more complicated than it would appear from the results of diffraction experiments. This was shown by the Cambridge physicist G. I. Taylor in 1909. He performed diffraction experiments with sources of light so weak that the diffraction patterns took months to form. Suppose his experiments were repeated with modern equipment using a photocell to detect the light (Figure 10.2). Also imagine that the output of the photocell was connected to a loudspeaker. It would be found that every so often a 'click' would be heard. This means that the light energy arrives at the photocell in an all or nothing process. There is nothing gradual about this; either a click is heard or it is not. This sort of behaviour is more like that which we normally associate with particles and not with waves. It is as if the light was arriving at the photocell like a stream of bullets.

Thus although a diffraction pattern is eventually obtained (a wave-like property), the light energy appears to arrive in small packets of energy, i.e. *quanta* (which is a particle-like property). These quanta of light energy we have already called photons (Unit 2).

Gamma-rays are photons of very high energy, and should show diffraction patterns. However, in 1923 they were used by the American physicist A. H. Compton in a series of experiments where the rays were made to collide with electrons. Compton was able to prove that both the rays and the electrons behaved like particles. For example, they obeyed the law of conservation of momentum. The experiment provided further evidence for the idea that photons could display the properties of both waves and particles.

That electrons would behave like particles was not too surprising. What was astounding was that it was later shown that electrons could behave like waves. The experiment that proved that electrons could be diffracted was performed by another two Americans, C. Davisson and L. H. Germer in 1927. They did not set out to show that electrons could be diffracted; instead, they made the discovery by accident. A beam of electrons that struck a nickel crystal produced a diffraction pattern, in much the same way as Bragg's X-rays.

Here, then, was evidence that not only light but also electrons could show the properties expected of waves and particles. Indeed, it has been shown that other

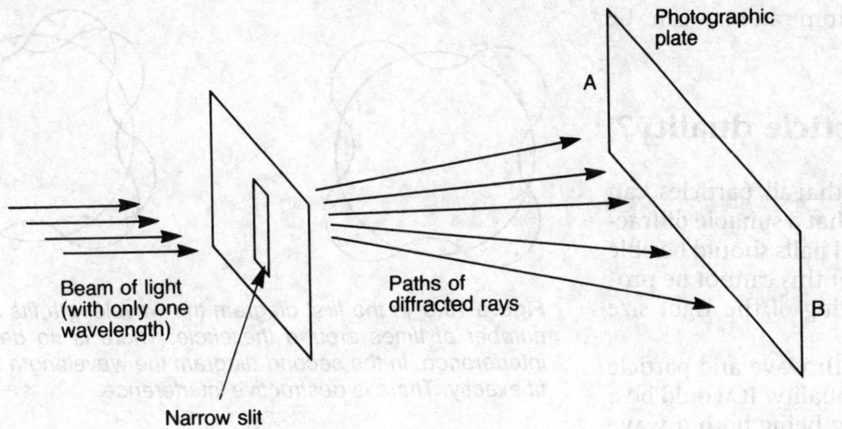

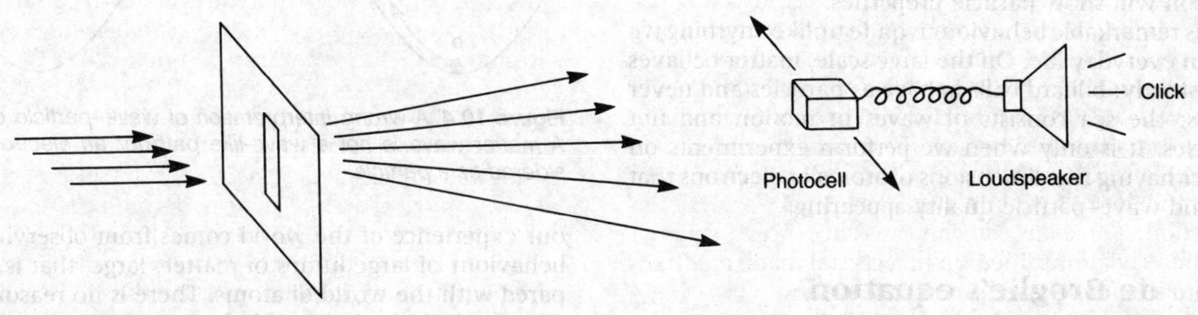

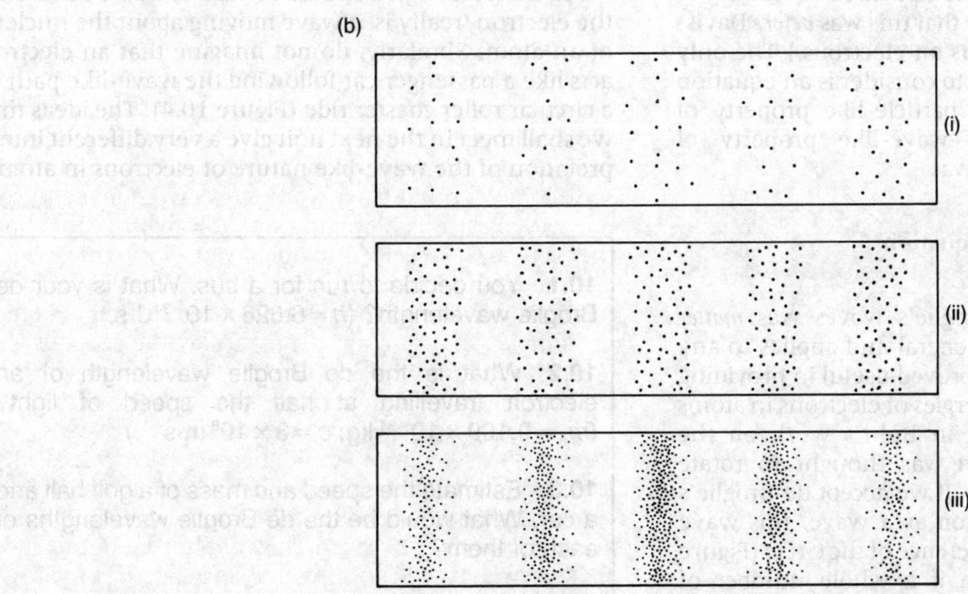

***Figure 10.2** The nature of diffraction experiments with light. (a) If the photographic plate is replaced by an electronic detector and loudspeaker, a series of individual clicks is heard. (b) These three sketches illustrate the appearance of a photographic plate in a diffraction experiment if it were developed at various times after the start of the experiment. (i) Appearance of plate soon after the start of the experiment. (ii) Appearance some time later. (iii) Appearance towards the end of the experiment. The diffraction pattern is built from a large number of individual dots*

'particles', like hydrogen or helium atoms, can be diffracted.

10.2 What is wave–particle duality?

We now have good reason to think that all 'particles' can be diffracted given one condition: that a suitable diffraction grating can be found. Even golf balls should be able to be diffracted. The problem is that this cannot be proved by experiment because a grating of the right size cannot be made.

The ability of matter to show both wave and particle behaviour is called wave–particle duality. It would be a mistake to try to imagine anything being both a wave and a particle at the same time. Rather, we need to accept that whether, for example, an electron behaves as a wave or a particle depends on the type of experiment that is being done. If we set up experiments that detect waves, then an electron will show wave properties; if we set up an experiment that detects particles, then an electron will show particle properties.

This remarkable behaviour is quite unlike anything we find in everyday life. On the large scale, matter behaves consistently: billiard balls behave as particles and never waves; the sea consists of waves in motion and not particles. It is only when we perform experiments on matter having the dimensions of atoms or electrons that we find wave–particle duality appearing.

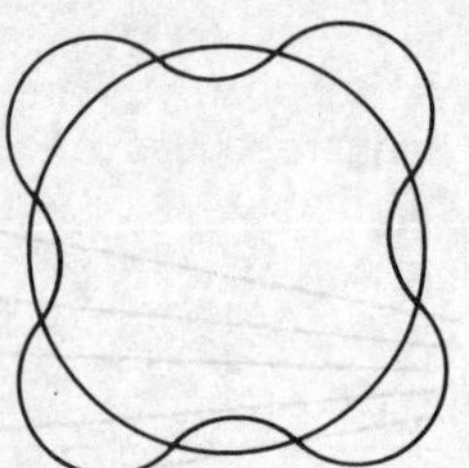

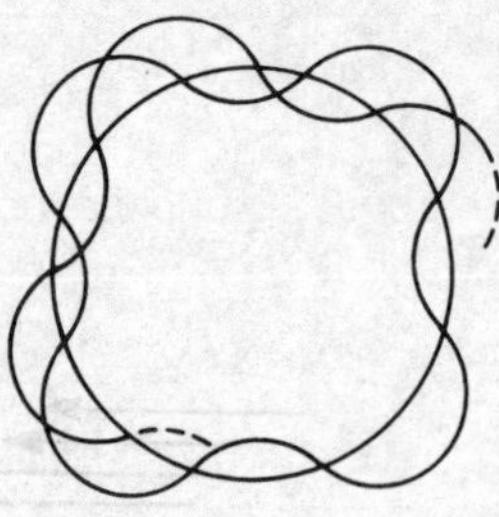

Figure 10.3 *In the first diagram the wavelength fits an exact number of times around the circle. There is no destructive interference. In the second diagram the wavelength does not fit exactly. There is destructive interference*

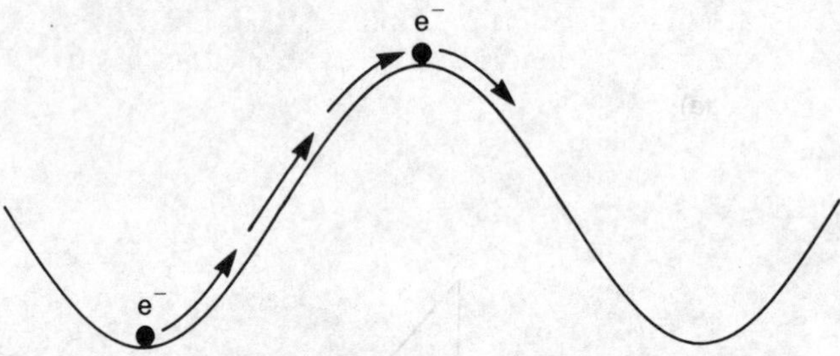

Figure 10.4 *A wrong interpretation of wave–particle duality. A matter wave is not a wave-like path for an electron considered as a particle*

10.3 de Broglie's equation

In 1924 the Frenchman Prince Louis de Broglie published an exceedingly complicated account of wave–particle duality. (Notice that this was *before* Davisson and Germer's experiments on electrons.) The only part of his work that we need to consider is an equation in which he connected the particle-like property of momentum, mv, with the wave-like property of wavelength, λ. His equation was

$$mv = \frac{h}{\lambda} \quad \text{de Broglie's equation}$$

The name given to de Broglie's waves was *matter waves.* His equation is quite general and applies to any 'particle'. de Broglie's theory proved useful in providing an explanation of why the energies of electrons in atoms are quantised. For example, in Bohr's work on the hydrogen atom, the electron was thought to rotate around the nucleus in a circle. If we accept de Broglie's idea and represent the electron as a wave, this wave must exactly fit on the circumference of the circle (Figure 10.3). This can only happen if a whole number of wavelengths will fit on the circumference. In symbols this means that $n\lambda = 2\pi r$. The whole number, n, turns out to be the principal quantum number that Bohr introduced.

This unit has introduced you to some of the strangest ideas in modern science. They appear odd partly because our experience of the world comes from observing the behaviour of large lumps of matter: large, that is, compared with the world of atoms. There is no reason why the world of atoms should behave in the same way that we expect of the large-scale world.

For this reason you should be careful not to think that the electron 'really is' a wave moving about the nucleus of an atom. Similarly, do not imagine that an electron acts like a passenger car following the wave-like path of a circular roller coaster ride (Figure 10.4). The ideas that we shall meet in the next unit give a very different interpretation of the wave-like nature of electrons in atoms.

10.1 You decide to run for a bus. What is your de Broglie wavelength? ($h = 6.626 \times 10^{-34}$ J s.)

10.2 What is the de Broglie wavelength of an electron travelling at half the speed of light? ($m_e = 9.109 \times 10^{-31}$ kg; $c = 3 \times 10^8$ m s^{-1}.)

10.3 Estimate the speed and mass of a golf ball and a car. What would be the de Broglie wavelengths of each of them?

10.4 Hydrogen molecules are among the most massive particles to produce a diffraction pattern. The mass of a hydrogen molecule is about 3.4×10^{-27} kg. If the molecule moves at a speed of 1700 m s^{-1}, what is its de Broglie wavelength?

Answers

10.1 This will depend on your mass. Suppose you are about 9 stone, i.e. about 57 kg. You might reach a speed of 8 m s^{-1} if you were in a hurry. Then, 8 m s^{-1} × 57 kg $= 6.626 \times 10^{-34}$ J s/λ, which gives $\lambda \approx 1.5 \times 10^{-36}$ m.

10.2 You should find that $\lambda = 4.85 \times 10^{-12}$ m.

10.3 For a golf ball $m \approx 0.05$ kg; for a car $m \approx 1000$ kg. Let them both have a speed of 40 m s^{-1} (about 80 mph). Then their de Broglie wavelengths should be about 3×10^{-34} m and 3×10^{-37} m respectively.

10.4 The wavelength is about 0.115×10^{-9} m, i.e. 0.115 nm.

UNIT 10 SUMMARY

- Matter can show the properties of both waves and particles, depending on the type of experiment that is performed.
- De Broglie's equation, which sums up this wave–particle duality, is $mv = h/\lambda$, where mv is momentum (a particle-like property) and λ is the wavelength.
- Only light, electrons and some atoms with very small mass will show their wave nature in experiments.

11

Schrödinger's theory of the atom

11.1 Schrödinger's theory of the hydrogen atom

During the 1920s there was a great deal of interest in wave–particle duality and de Broglie's matter waves. It was the Austrian physicist Erwin Schrödinger who invented a method of showing how the properties of waves could be used to explain the behaviour of electrons in atoms. Schrödinger published his ideas in January 1926. This date represents one of the milestones in chemistry. His work formed the basis of all our present ideas on how atoms bond together. The heart of his method was his prediction of the equation that governed the behaviour of electrons, and the method of solving it. You will find his equation in panel 11.1. Fortunately, you do not have to know anything about his equation to make use of the results of his work.

Like Bohr, Schrödinger tackled the hydrogen atom problem. Using a totally different method to Bohr's, he derived the same formula for the energy levels

Erwin Schrödinger looking more particle than wave.

Panel 11.1

Schrödinger's equation
Here is Schrödinger's equation:

$$\frac{-h^2}{8\pi^2 m}\left(\frac{\partial^2 W}{\partial x^2}+\frac{\partial^2 W}{\partial y^2}+\frac{\partial^2 W}{\partial z^2}\right)+VW=EW$$

The symbol V stands for the potential energy of an electron that can move round in the x, y and z directions in space. E is the electron's total energy, and, believe it or not, the term on the left with all the differentials tells us the kinetic energy of the electron. (Indeed, it is an unlikely looking version of the equation in elementary physics that says kinetic energy + potential energy = total energy.) W is the wavefunction of the electron. The symbols $\partial^2 W/\partial x^2$, etc., tell us to differentiate the wavefunction twice with respect to the three directions x, y and z in space if we wish to calculate the kinetic energy. To perform the differentiation is extremely difficult, and it can only be done exactly in a few cases. Fortunately the hydrogen atom is one of those cases. The wavefunction for an electron in the ground state of a hydrogen atom has the formula $W=A\exp(-r/a_0)$, where r is the distance of the electron from the nucleus, a_0 is the Bohr radius and A is a constant, equal to $(1/\pi a_0^3)^{1/2}$. This is the wavefunction of a 1s orbital. Its value decreases exponentially with distance from the nucleus. Wavefunctions for other orbitals are more complicated.

$$E_n = \frac{-e^4 m_e}{8\varepsilon_0^2 h^2 n^2}$$

The principal quantum number, n, had the same set of values as in Bohr's formula. However, this was not the only quantum number that came out of Schrödinger's calculations. In fact two more appeared. These were called the azimuthal quantum number, l, and the magnetic quantum number, m (Table 11.1). It turned out that all three quantum numbers were needed to explain many of the more peculiar properties of the hydrogen atom and other atoms.

Table 11.1. The quantum numbers *n*, *l* and *m*

Symbol	*Name*	*Information*
n	Principal	Governs the orbital energy $E_n = -e^4m_e/8\varepsilon_0^2h^2n^2$ Tells us the degeneracy, n^2
l	Azimuthal*	Governs the orbital shape
m	Magnetic	Governs the number of orbitals for each value of l Tells us what happens to the energy of orbitals in magnetic or electric fields

*In some books you may find l called the subsidiary quantum number

11.2 What do the quantum numbers tell us?

(a) *The principal quantum number, n*

We already know something about this; it governs the *energy* of the electron. Also, remember that the path of the electron around the nucleus was called an orbital. Schrödinger showed that it was possible for more than one orbital to have the same energy. Orbitals with the same energy are said to be degenerate. The value of the principal quantum number also tells us how many degenerate orbitals there are for a particular value of E_n: there are n^2 degenerate orbitals. For example, when $n=1$ the value of n^2 is 1, i.e. there is only one orbital with energy E_1. When $n=2$, we have $n^2=4$ and there are four degenerate orbitals with energy E_2.

We can show the arrangement of the degenerate orbitals for the hydrogen atom on an energy level diagram like that in Figure 11.1.

(b) *The azimuthal quantum number, l*

This quantum number is also related to the principal quantum number. When $n=1$ there is only one value for l, that is $l=0$; when $n=2$, $l=0$ or 1; when $n=3$, $l=0$, 1 or 2. You should be able to spot the pattern: l takes any positive value from 0 up to $n-1$ (Table 11.2).

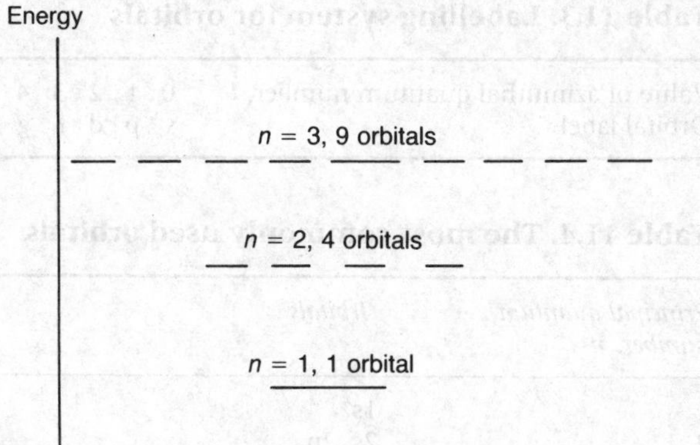

Figure 11.1 The diagram shows the degeneracy of orbitals for the hydrogen atom only. For example, for the second energy level (n=2) there are four orbitals with the same energy. Only n=1, 2 and 3 levels are shown

Table 11.2. Values of principal and azimuthal quantum numbers

Principal quantum number, n	*Azimuthal quantum number, l*
1	0
2	0, 1
3	0, 1, 2
4	0, 1, 2, 3

As you will see shortly, l gives us information about the *shapes of orbitals.*

(c) *The magnetic quantum number, m*

The magnetic quantum number tells us what happens to the energies of the different orbitals if the atom is placed in a magnetic (or electric) field. At this level of chemistry we need not worry about such complications, so for most of the time we can simply ignore the connection between m and the energy.

Of more interest is the fact that m also gives us detailed information about degenerate orbitals. In fact the value of m tells us how many orbitals there are for a particular value of the azimuthal quantum number.

11.3 Different types of orbital

The solutions of Schrödinger's equation are known as *wavefunctions*, but more often as orbitals. You can use the words 'orbital' and 'wavefunction' interchangeably. They mean very much the same thing. Schrödinger's orbitals are given names depending on the values of their quantum numbers. The names are made up of a number and a letter. The letter depends on the azimuthal quantum number as shown in Table 11.3.

The number is the value of the principal quantum number and is written in front of the letter. The letters s,

Table 11.3. Labelling system for orbitals

Value of azimuthal quantum number, l	0	1	2	3	4	...
Orbital label	s	p	d	f	g	...

Table 11.4. The most commonly used orbitals

Principal quantum number, n	*Orbitals*
1	1s
2	2s, 2p
3	3s, 3p, 3d
4	4s, 4p, 4d, (4f)

p and d come from the early days of spectroscopy. These letters are the initials of the three most common types of lines in the spectra of atoms: they were called sharp, principal and diffuse. After f, the orbital letters follow alphabetical order, g, h, ...

Examples of orbital names are 1s, 2s and 2p orbitals. The way the values of the quantum numbers n and l change (Table 11.2) means that some orbital names cannot occur. For example, when $n=1$, there is only one value for l, and that is $l=0$. Therefore only an s orbital can occur; there are no 1p or 1d orbitals. The main types of orbital that we shall meet are listed in Table 11.4.

11.4 Wavefunctions and what they mean

Just like water waves, wavefunctions can have peaks and troughs. However, the shapes of wavefunctions are often very different from the shapes of water waves. For example, a graph of a water wave might look like that in Figure 11.2a. The graph of the wavefunction for the ground state of the hydrogen atom looks rather different, as in Figure 11.2b.

Clearly the wavefunction (or orbital) that emerges from Schrödinger's method is very different from the simple circular orbit of Bohr. The problem that Schrödinger faced was to explain what his wavefunctions meant. As it happens, the explanation that he gave proved to be incorrect! It was not until later in 1926 that another German physicist, Max Born, proposed that the wavefunction *could* be used to give us information about the electron. However, this had to be obtained by using a fair amount of mathematics (which we can ignore) and the results proved to be somewhat surprising.

The wavefunction could only be used to provide information about the *probability* of finding the electron in a given region of space around the nucleus. According to Born we must give up ideas of the electron orbiting the nucleus at a precise distance. In this respect Bohr was wrong in thinking that the electron in the ground state of the hydrogen atom was always to be found at a distance a_0 from the nucleus. Rather, it was only *most probably* to be found at this distance. The electron had a smaller

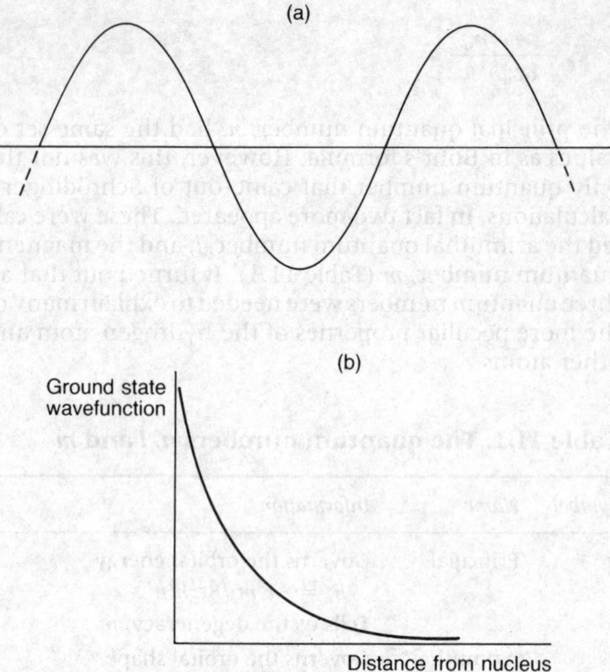

Figure 11.2 *(a) A typical wave has the shape of a sine (or cosine) wave. (b) The wavefunction for an electron in the ground state of a hydrogen atom*

probability of being found at a variety of other distances as well.

It is important to realise that we should not try to talk about finding the electron at a given *point*. The reason for this is that there is an infinite number of points around the nucleus, so the probability of finding the electron at any one of them is infinitely small, i.e. zero.

If it is impossible to predict with certainty where the electron is to be found, do we have to give up hope of visualising the orbital of an electron? The answer is no. One way out of the dilemma is to imagine carrying out an experiment in which we take a series of photographs of an atom to give us an instantaneous picture of the whereabouts of the electron. Figure 11.3a shows the type of photograph that would be obtained. If the images were combined we would end up with a picture like Figure 11.3b. The separate dots have overlapped to give regions in which the density of dots is very high, and regions where the density of dots is much lower.

In the high density regions we say that there is a high *probability density*. The maximum in the density comes at exactly the same distance, a_0, that Bohr predicted in his work. The circular symmetry of the probability density is clear. However, we should remember that atoms exist in three dimensions, so really the diagram should be shown as a sphere. It is easier to draw circles rather than spheres, so usually we draw the density diagram as a circle. Also it is common practice not to include the shading and to agree that when the circle is drawn (Figure 11.4) it provides a boundary surface within which, say, there is a 95% probability of finding the electron.

Figure 11.3 *(a) A scene where we imagine that each small dot represents the position of the electron in a hydrogen atom at different times. The important point is that the diagram illustrates that the charge of the electron is spread uniformly (spherically symmetric) over the atom. (b) Over a long period of time the electron spends most of its time a distance a_0 from the nucleus*

11.5 The shapes of orbitals

(a) s *orbitals*

All s orbitals have the same spherical symmetry. They can all be represented by circles like that of Figure 11.4. However they do vary in some ways. In particular, the higher the energy of the orbital the more it spreads out. For example, a 1s electron is most likely to be found at a distance of a_0 (i.e. 5.292×10^{-11} m) from the nucleus; a 2s electron is most likely to be found over five times further away at $5.24 \times a_0$ (i.e. 27.71×10^{-11} m).

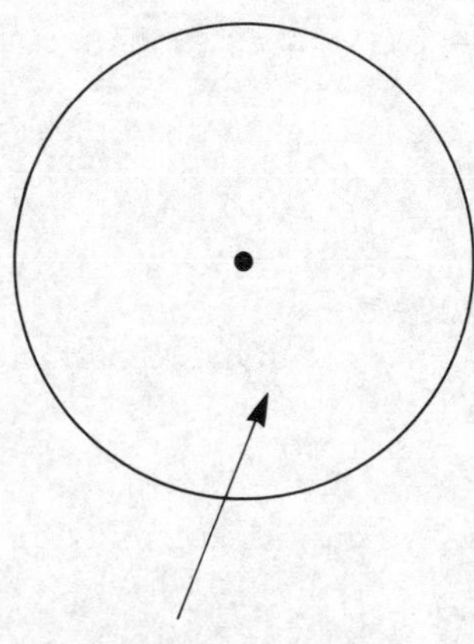

Figure 11.4 *A representation of the 1s orbital of hydrogen. On paper it looks like a circle, but it is a sphere in three dimensions*

(b) p *orbitals*

The probability density diagrams for p orbitals are very different to those of s orbitals. If you look back at section 11.2 you will find that we said that the magnetic quantum number can tell us the number of orbitals of a given type. The result is that for s orbitals, the magnetic quantum number, *m*, has only one value. This means that there is only one variety of s orbital. That is the variety we have already met: the spherically symmetric ones. For p orbitals there are three possible values of *m* (−1, 0 and +1). The three types of p orbitals are called p_x, p_y and p_z. Their shapes are shown in Figure 11.5. You will see that they are not spherically symmetric. Each one points in a particular direction along one of the three major axes.

As with s orbitals, it is tedious to try to draw three-dimensional diagrams, so usually we are content to draw a cross-section through a p orbital like that shown in Figure 11.6.

(c) d *orbitals*

There are five different types of d orbital. Their shapes are shown in Figure 11.7. You will need to know a little about d orbitals, especially when we come to discuss transition elements in Unit 105. However, for the present we shall only be concerned with elements that have electrons in s and p orbitals. There is no need for you to know anything about the shapes of f, g, . . . orbitals.

We have come a long way from the efforts of Niels Bohr to explain the structure of the hydrogen atom. His was a world of certainties. The world of Erwin Schrödinger and Max Born is one of uncertainties. Instead of simple circular orbits, the motion of an electron is admitted to

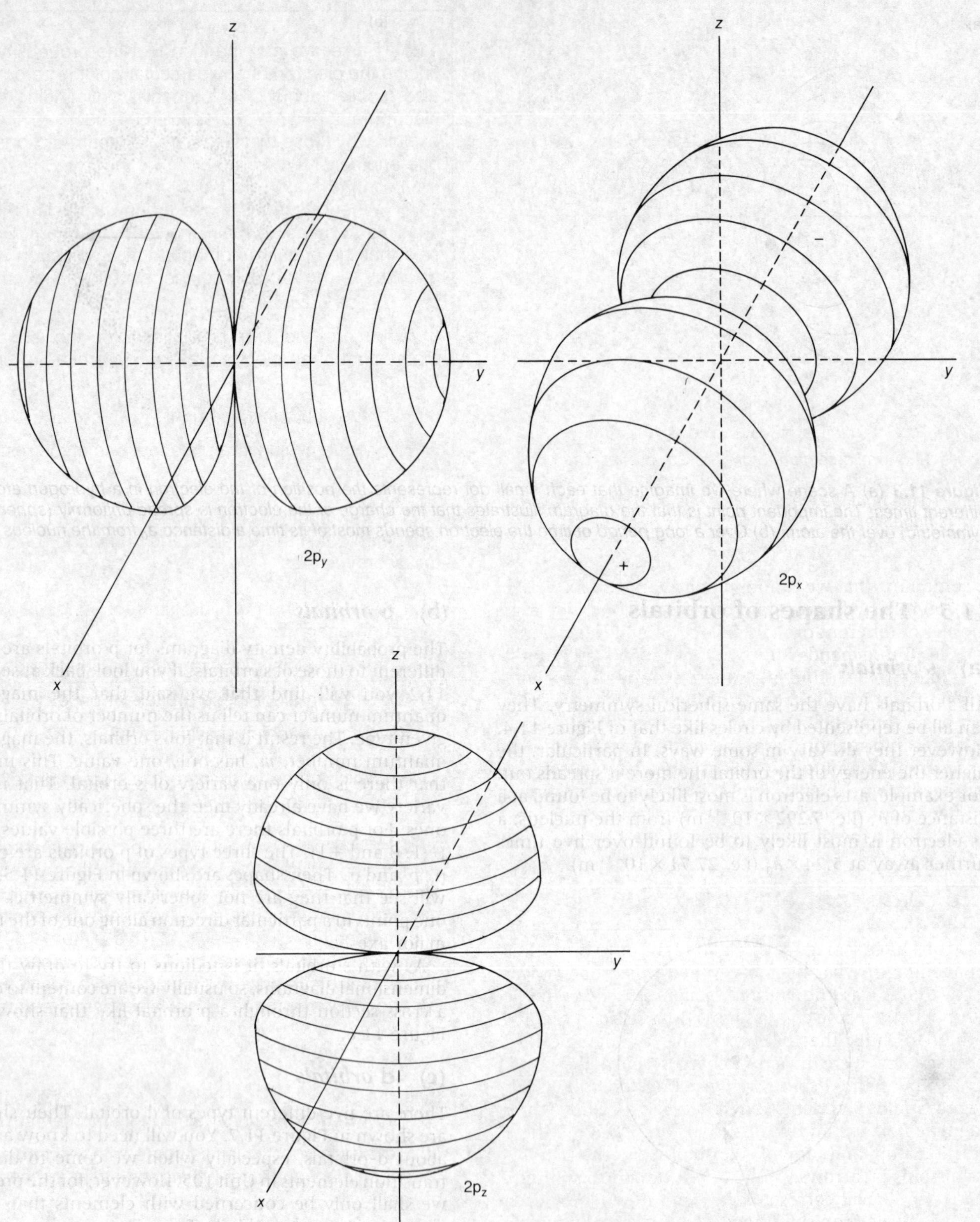

***Figure 11.5** Shapes of the three 2p orbitals. The + and − signs give the signs of the wavefunctions in the various regions of space. Within the shapes there is a high probability of finding an electron*

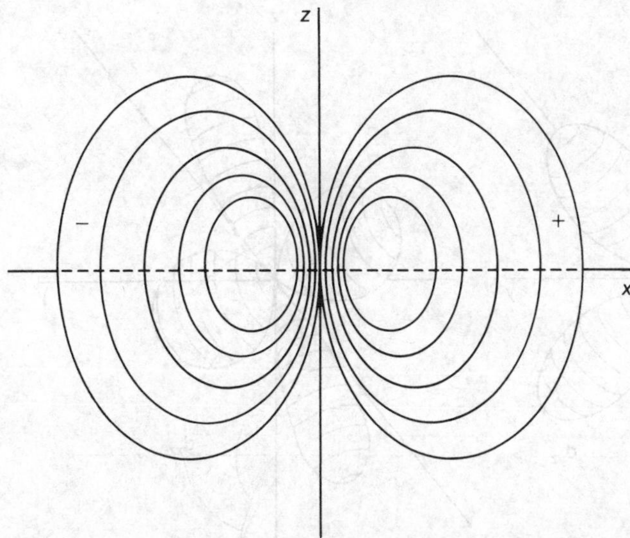

Figure 11.6 *Cross-section through a $2p_x$ orbital. The curved lines are contours where the wavefunction has a constant value. To the right the wavefunction has a positive sign; to the left it is negative*

be something that we cannot predict with certainty. The electron in a hydrogen atom can exist in one of a large number of different orbitals. Which orbital the electron finds itself in depends on its energy. In an s orbital it is most likely to be found in a sphere around the nucleus. In a p orbital it will wander through a region of space that has a dumb-bell shape.

All this information about the electron and its orbitals comes from the solutions of Schrödinger's work on the hydrogen atom. The problem still remains of explaining the behaviour of electrons in more complicated atoms. This is the theme of our next unit (Unit 12).

11.6 The spin quantum number

Electrons have a magnetic field, and in some ways they behave like tiny bar magnets. When this property was discovered it was known that a magnetic field could be set up when electric charges move in a circle. It seemed natural to think that electrons have a magnetic field because they were negative charges spinning round. Hence the name 'spin' was used to describe their magnetism. Experiments show that electrons have their magnetic fields set in two directions only. We call these directions 'up' and 'down'. We shall show the two different spins by arrows: ↿ or ↑ will stand for 'spin up', and ⇂ or ↓ will correspond to 'spin down'. For each state of the electron spin there is a corresponding value of the *spin quantum number*, m_s. We shall assign the value $m_s = +1/2$ to an electron with spin up, and $m_s = -1/2$ to an electron with spin down. Experiment shows that these are the only values that the spin quantum number can have. You will find in the next unit that spin plays a large part in determining the electron structures of atoms.

11.1 Earlier we met the idea that the probability of finding the electron at any particular *point* is zero. We also spoke about the probability of finding the electron at a given *distance* from the nucleus. Try to explain why these two ideas are not contradictions of one another.

11.2 When electrons move around a nucleus it is possible to measure their angular momentum. Bohr said that the angular momentum of an electron was given by $L = nh/2\pi$. Schrödinger said it was given by $L = \sqrt{l(l+1)}\ h/2\pi$.

(i) What are the two predictions for the angular momentum of an electron (a) in a 1s orbital, (b) in a 2p orbital?

(ii) Who do you think was right?

(iii) Is there anything strange about one of the results for the s orbital?

11.3 Draw another diagram like Figure 11.1 but this time write down the labels of the orbitals for each of the energy levels.

11.4 An electron in a hydrogen atom finds itself in the fourth energy level.

(i) Write down a list of the orbitals that it might be in.

(ii) Can it be in all of these orbitals at once?

(iii) Can you tell which orbital it is in?

11.5 Which of the following orbitals could not exist: 3s, 4s, 5s, 1p, 3p, 1d, 2d, 3d?

11.6 Werner Heisenberg derived a remarkable result using a different (but compatible) theory to that of Schrödinger. He said that it was impossible to measure with complete accuracy both the position and momentum of an electron. This statement has come to be known as Heisenberg's uncertainty principle. We can write the uncertainty in position as Δx and in momentum as Δp. Heisenberg's equation is

$$\Delta p \Delta x \geqslant h/4\pi$$

(i) If the position of an electron is known to within 10^{-12} m, what is the uncertainty in its momentum?

(ii) How does your figure compare with the momentum of an electron travelling with one-third the speed of light?

(iii) In our large-scale world, is there a limit (in principle) on the accuracy with which we can measure the momentum and position of a particle, e.g. a golf ball?

(iv) Guess the effective value of Planck's constant in the large-scale world.

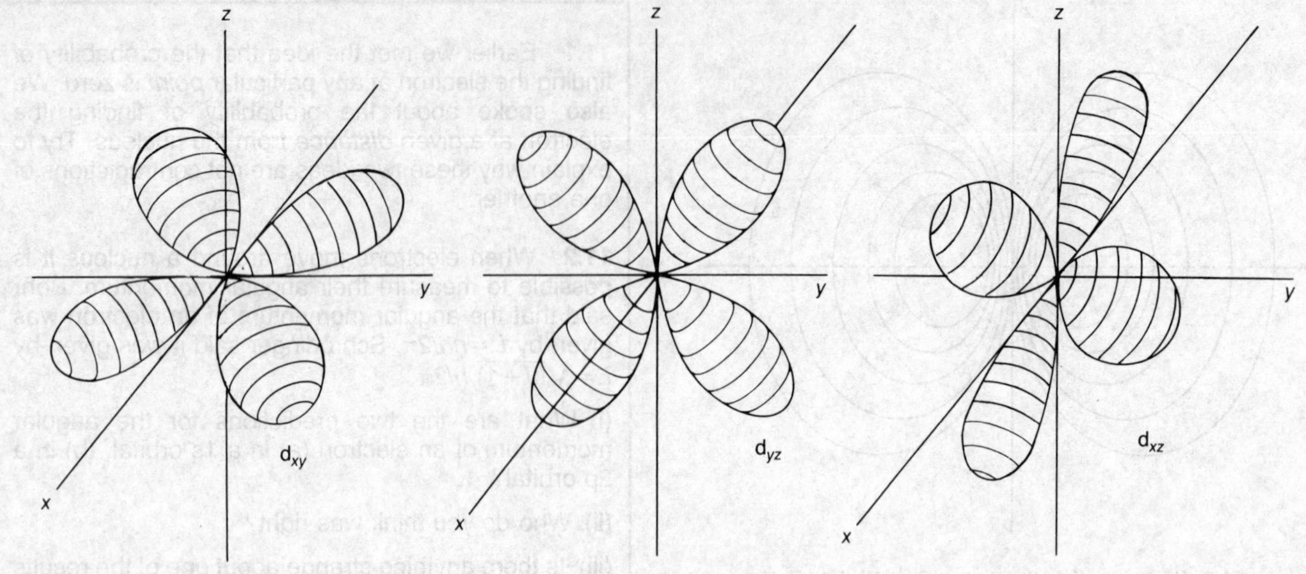

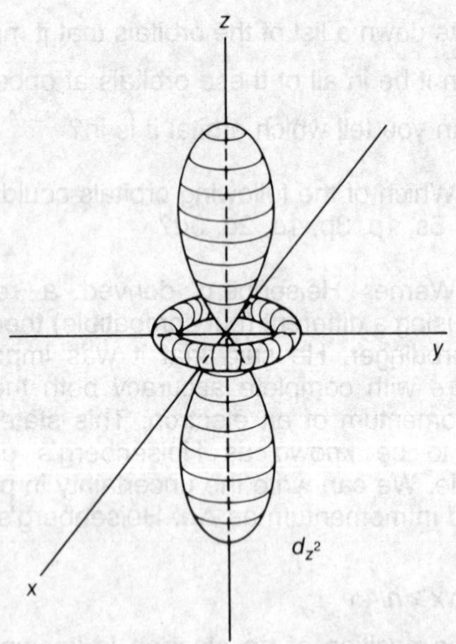

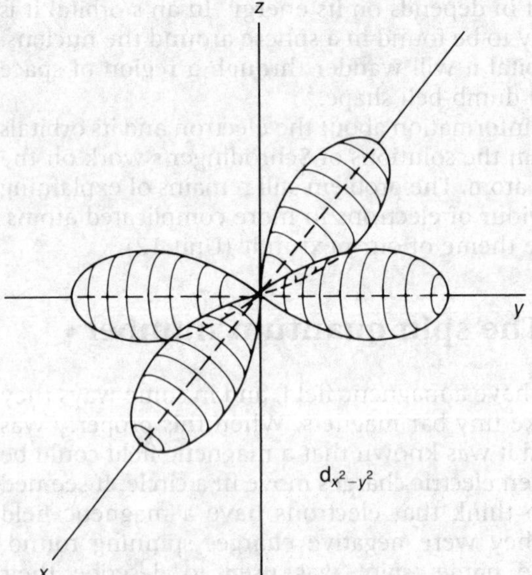

Figure 11.7 *Shapes of the five 3d orbitals*

Before we leave this section, a word of warning. You can imagine an electron as a tiny particle spinning round like a top if you want to, but if you do think like that, watch out: electrons have spin wavefunctions, as well as orbital wavefunctions. Once again, you should not expect the small-scale world of atoms and electrons to behave in the same way as large lumps of matter that we observe in the world around us.

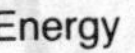

Answers

11.1 If, say, an electron in a 1s orbital is a Bohr's radius, a_0, from the centre of the atom, it could be anywhere on the *surface of a sphere* of this radius. The probability of finding the electron at a given distance is therefore proportional to the surface area of this sphere – a very different thing to an infinitely small point. This is shown in Figure 11.8.

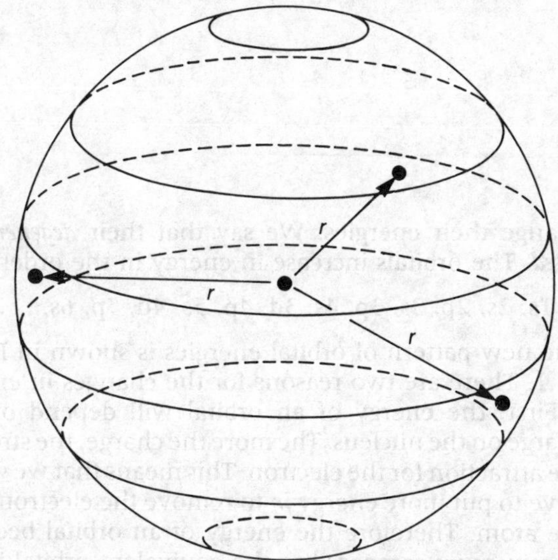

Figure 11.8 *An electron at a distance r from the nucleus can be anywhere on the surface of a sphere of radius r. The surface area of the sphere is $4\pi r^2$. The probability of finding the electron at distance r is proportional to $4\pi r^2$*

11.2 (i) (a) Bohr: $h/2\pi$ because $n=1$ for a 1s orbital; Schrödinger: 0 because $l=0$ for an s orbital. (b) Bohr: h/π because $n=2$ for a 2p orbital; Schrödinger: $\sqrt{2}h/2\pi$ because $l=1$ for a p orbital.

(ii) Schrödinger.

(iii) The result that a 1s (and any other s orbital) electron has zero angular momentum is strange from a classical point of view. However, experiment shows that *it is impossible* to measure the angular momentum of electrons in s orbitals.

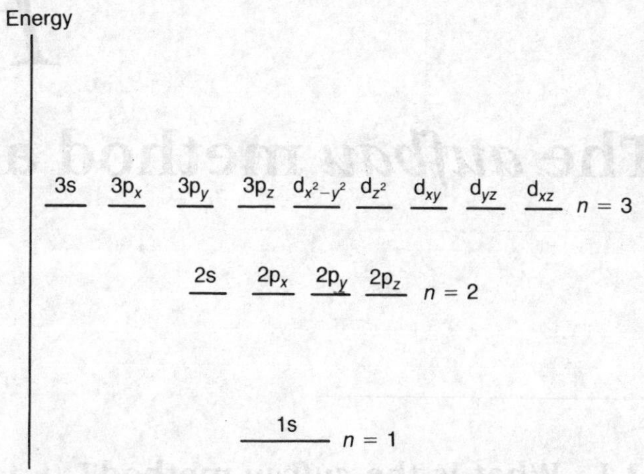

Energy

3s 3p$_x$ 3p$_y$ 3p$_z$ d$_{x^2-y^2}$ d$_{z^2}$ d$_{xy}$ d$_{yz}$ d$_{xz}$ $n = 3$

2s 2p$_x$ 2p$_y$ 2p$_z$ $n = 2$

1s $n = 1$

Figure 11.9 *Orbitals and energy levels for the hydrogen atom*

11.3 The diagram is given in Figure 11.9.

11.4 (i) 4s, 4p, 4d, 4f.

(ii) No, it will only be in one of them.

(iii) No. For the hydrogen atom, all orbitals with the same principal quantum number have the same energy (they are degenerate).

11.5 1p, 1d and 2d could not exist.

11.6 (i) $\Delta p = \dfrac{6.626 \times 10^{-34}\,\text{J s}}{4\pi \times 10^{-12}\,\text{m}} = 5.27 \times 10^{-23}\,\text{kg m s}^{-1}$

(ii) The electron's momentum will be approximately $11.1 \times 10^{-31}\,\text{kg} \times 10^{8}\,\text{m s}^{-1} = 9 \times 10^{-23}\,\text{kg m s}^{-1}$. The uncertainty is large (over 50%).

(iii) No, the limit is one of practice, not principle. In the large-scale world we often like to think that the degree of accuracy is fixed by the limits of our measuring instruments. For atoms and the like, matters are very different. There seems to be no way round the limits expressed by the uncertainty principle.

(iv) It is effectively zero.

UNIT 11 SUMMARY

- An orbital represents a region of space in which there is a high probability of finding an electron.
- A wavefunction is a solution of Schrödinger's equation and is a mathematical description of an electron.
- The three main types of orbital are s, p and d. Each type has its own characteristic shape (see Figures 11.4 to 11.7). The key orbitals at this level of chemistry are 1s, 2s, 2p, 3s, 3p, 3d and 4s.
- There are four quantum numbers that govern the behaviour of electrons in atoms:
  (i) Principal quantum number n governs the energy of an orbital.
  (ii) Azimuthal quantum number l governs the shape of an orbital.
  (iii) Magnetic quantum number m gives the number of orbitals of each type.
  (iv) Spin quantum number m_s describes the magnetic properties of an electron.

12

The *aufbau* method and electron structures

12.1 What is the *aufbau* method?

The purpose of this unit is to show you how to explain, and predict, the ways that electrons arrange themselves in the orbitals of atoms. When the arrangement has been established, we say that we know the *electron structure* or the *electron configuration* of the atom. The German word '*aufbau*' means 'building up'. We are about to discover how electron structures are built up by applying a set of three rules, which were established during the 1920s but still hold good today. These rules are listed in Table 12.1.

Table 12.1. Rules for the *aufbau* method

Rule 1	Electrons go into orbitals with the lowest energy
Rule 2	The *Pauli exclusion principle* (two versions): (a) It is impossible for two electrons with the same spin quantum number to be in the same orbital (b) An orbital can contain a maximum of two electrons
Rule 3	*Hund's rule*: Electrons will fill a set of degenerate orbitals by keeping their spins parallel

12.2 More about orbital energies

Schrödinger's theory of the hydrogen atom was very successful. You may remember that the first stage in his method was to write down the correct equation for the atom, and then solve it. For atoms with more than one electron, writing down the equation is fairly easy, but solving it is not; in fact it is impossible to solve exactly. The main reason for this is that it is very difficult to take account of the repulsions between the electrons.

The way round the difficulty is to make approximations. The most important one is to assume that the shapes of the 1s, 2s, 2p and other orbitals that we met in the last unit remain similar to those in the hydrogen atom. However, a major difference is that the energies of the orbitals change. Especially, the energies of the 2s and 2p orbitals are no longer the same. Similarly, the 3s, 3p and 3d orbitals change their energies. Indeed, all orbitals with the same value of the principal quantum number change their energies. We say that their *degeneracy is lifted*. The orbitals increase in energy in the order

1s, 2s, 2p, 3s, 3p, 4s, 3d, 4p, 5s, 4d, 5p, 6s, . . .

The new pattern of orbital energies is shown in Figure 12.1. There are two reasons for the changes in energy.

First, the energy of an orbital will depend on the charge on the nucleus. The more the charge, the stronger the attraction for the electron. This means that we would have to put more energy *in* to remove the electron from the atom. Therefore the energy of an orbital becomes *more negative* compared to the equivalent orbital in the hydrogen atom (Figure 12.2).

Secondly, when there is more than one electron, the electrons will repel one another. Owing to the different

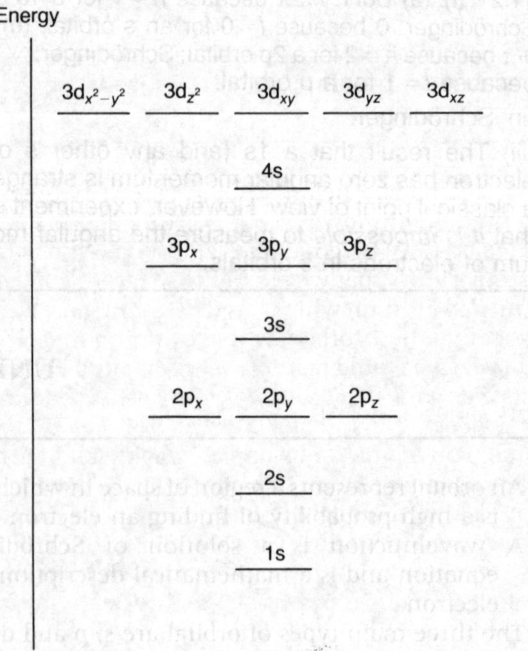

***Figure 12.1** The order of energies for the orbitals of atoms other than hydrogen. The diagram is not drawn to scale. Only orbitals up to 3d are shown*

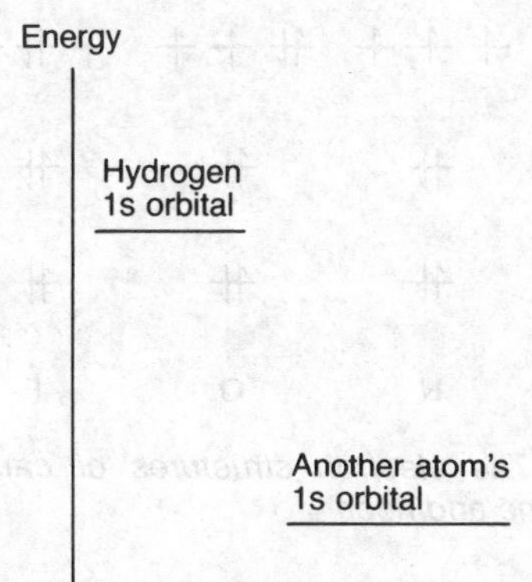

***Figure 12.2** Although they have the same label, the 1s orbital of hydrogen will not have the same energy as another atom. For example, helium with two protons in its nucleus will have a greater attraction for a 1s electron than does hydrogen. Therefore the energy of the orbital will be less than that of a hydrogen 1s*

ways that the electrons move around the nucleus (shown by the shapes of the orbitals), electrons in s, p, d, ... orbitals will repel each other by different amounts. These repulsions are responsible for the lifting of the degeneracies.

12.3 Filling orbitals – the importance of energy

We are now going to discover how to work out which orbitals are used by the electrons in an atom.

The *first rule* is that:

As far as possible, electrons will go in the orbital with the lowest energy.

For example, a helium atom has just two electrons. The orbital with lowest energy is the 1s, so we expect both electrons to go into that orbital. Indeed, spectroscopy shows that we are right. So far, so good. Now if we turn to lithium, which has three electrons, we would predict that the 1s orbital would contain three electrons. Similarly, we would predict that every atom would have all its electrons in a 1s orbital. However, evidence from spectroscopy shows that all the electrons are *not* in the 1s orbital. You might, for example, imagine taking an atom and firing photons at it. If you were to use photons of the right energy, you might be able to knock an electron out of an atom. (Usually X-rays are found to have the necessary energy.) When experiments like this are done, it is found that it is impossible to knock any more than *two* electrons out of an orbital. Given this evidence, we can tell that there must be another rule at work. This rule was first stated by Wolfgang Pauli in 1925. It refers to the property of electrons called electron spin that we met in Unit 11.

12.4 The Pauli exclusion principle

When two electrons go into the same orbital, one electron has $m_s = +1/2$ and the other has $m_s = -1/2$. We say that their spins are *paired*.

Pauli was the first person to state our *second rule*, which is known as the *Pauli exclusion principle*:

It is impossible for two electrons with the same spin quantum number to be in the same orbital.

Put in another way, it says that an orbital can contain a maximum of two electrons; and if there are two electrons in an orbital, then their spins are paired (one has spin up, the other spin down).

Figure 12.3 shows the diagrams for the elements hydrogen to boron. We create these diagrams by applying our two rules. We put the first electron into the 1s orbital with the least energy (rule 1). The second electron goes into the same orbital, but with opposite spin to the first electron (rule 2, the Pauli exclusion principle). The third electron goes into the 2p orbital because the 1s is full. By repeating this procedure, the five diagrams are obtained.

Incidentally, because each of the 2p orbitals is identical to the others, we do not know which one contains the last electron of boron. As far as drawing diagrams is concerned, the simplest thing is to put it into the $2p_x$. Also, we do not know whether this electron has spin up or spin down. It looks better if we show it with spin up.

Before we leave the exclusion principle, we should note that Pauli stated it as a result of his trying to understand the spectra of helium and more complicated atoms. The principle does not forbid electrons to do anything. Rather it is a generalisation of how electrons behave in atoms. Like the Schrödinger equation, its justification lies in its success in explaining the results of experiments.

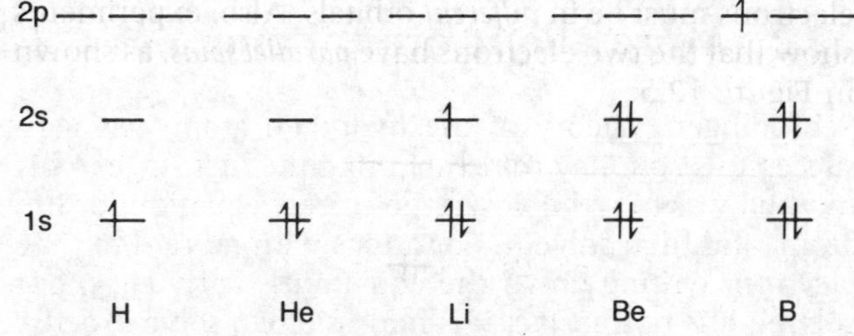

***Figure 12.3** The electron structures of hydrogen, helium, lithium, beryllium and boron. The diagram does not show the relative energies of the orbitals, only the arrangements of the electrons*

12.1 How many electrons can fit into (i) an s orbital, (ii) a set of three p orbitals, (iii) a set of five d orbitals?

12.2 There is more than one way of formulating the

Pauli exclusion principle. For example, it can be stated as: No two electrons in the same atom can have the same set of four quantum numbers n, l, m, m_s. Write down the values of these four quantum numbers for the two electrons in helium. Now pretend that another electron goes into the same 1s orbital. What could be the values of its four quantum numbers? Now explain (briefly) why this version of the exclusion principle is equivalent to the one we used earlier.

12.3 Suppose it takes 100 units of energy to make two electrons share the same s orbital. This energy we can call the *pairing energy*. Also, suppose there is a p orbital above the s orbital. If the energy gap between the s and p orbitals is 80 units, which of the diagrams in Figure 12.4 would show the correct electron structure?

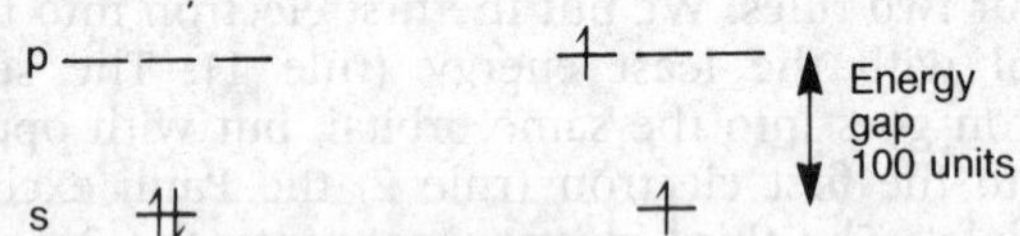

***Figure 12.4** Two possible arrangements for the electrons of question 12.3*

12.5 Hund's rule

There is just one more rule that we need to know about. To see why another rule is needed, think about building up the energy diagram for carbon. Carbon has one more electron than boron. This electron must go into one of the 2p orbitals; the problem is, which one? Because the $2p_x$, $2p_y$ and $2p_z$ orbitals all have the same energy, our first rule does not help us. Nor does the exclusion principle give us guidance. Once again we must look to the results of experiments. These show that carbon has two unpaired electrons. In turn this means that the electrons must be in *different* orbitals. Also, experiments show that the two electrons have *parallel spins*, as shown in Figure 12.5.

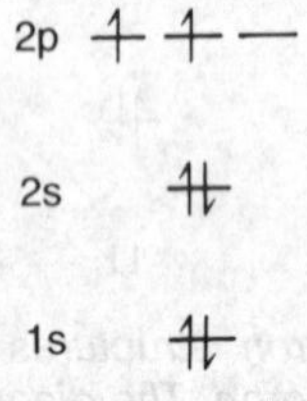

2p
2s
1s

***Figure 12.5** The electron structure of carbon. Experiment shows that the two 2p electrons have parallel spins*

This brings us to our *third rule*, which is called *Hund's rule*:

Electrons will fill a set of degenerate orbitals by keeping their spins parallel.

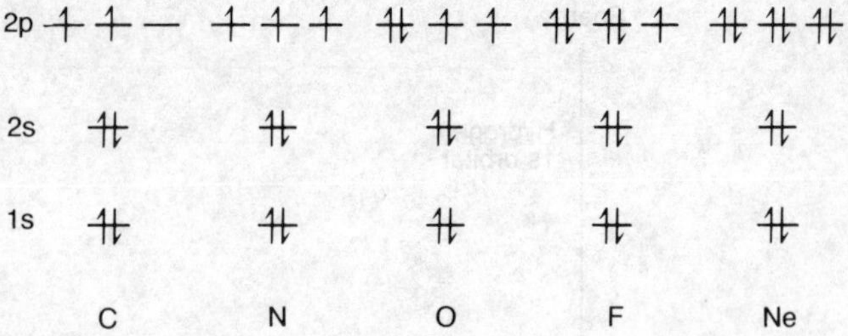

2p
2s
1s
C N O F Ne

***Figure 12.6** The electron structures of carbon, nitrogen, oxygen, fluorine and neon*

This rule does not defeat the exclusion principle. You can see this in Figure 12.6, where the energy diagrams for carbon to neon are shown. Once nitrogen is reached, where each of the 2p orbitals contains one electron, the next electron must go into one of the 2p orbitals with opposite spin to the electron already present. This is what happens for oxygen, fluorine and neon.

12.6 Background to Hund's rule

It is not too difficult to understand why, given the choice, an electron prefers to enter a different 2p orbital rather than to join another already present in the same orbital. The reason is simple. Electrons, being negatively charged, repel each other. If two electrons move in the same region of space (e.g. in a $2p_x$ orbital), then they will repel each other much more strongly than if they move in different regions of space (e.g. in $2p_x$ and $2p_y$ orbitals). Thus, it is energetically more favourable for them to go into different orbitals.

You may find that some books say that 'electrons try to keep their spins parallel'. You should be careful about reading too much into such phrases. In the first place, as we have just seen, the reason why electrons may go into different 2p orbitals is largely one of keeping electron repulsions to a minimum. Secondly, the reason why electrons in, say, nitrogen keep their spins parallel is not because of a direct interaction between the spins. Rather it is to do with how the electrons influence each other's attraction for the nucleus.

12.7 The *aufbau* method in action

You have seen how to build up the electron structures of the atoms hydrogen to neon. It would be tedious to have to draw diagrams every time that we wanted to show an electron structure. As you might expect, there is a shorter method. The idea is to write down the labels of the orbitals and to show how many electrons it contains by writing the number of electrons as a superscript. For example, helium's structure would be written $1s^2$, neon's would be $1s^22s^22p^6$. One other convention is that if an orbital contains only one electron, then we write down the orbital label without a superscript. For example, hydrogen's structure is written 1s, boron's is

Table 12.2. The ground state electron structures of the first 20 elements in the Periodic Table

Element	1s	2s	$2p_x$	$2p_y$	$2p_z$	3s	$3p_x$	$3p_y$	$3p_z$	4s	*Overall*
H	↑										$1s$
He	↑↓										$1s^2$
Li	↑↓	↑									$1s^22s$
Be	↑↓	↑↓									$1s^22s^2$
B	↑↓	↑↓	↑								$1s^22s^22p$
C	↑↓	↑↓	↑	↑							$1s^22s^22p^2$
N	↑↓	↑↓	↑	↑	↑						$1s^22s^22p^3$
O	↑↓	↑↓	↑↓	↑	↑						$1s^22s^22p^4$
F	↑↓	↑↓	↑↓	↑↓	↑						$1s^22s^22p^5$
Ne	↑↓	↑↓	↑↓	↑↓	↑↓						$1s^22s^22p^6$
Na	↑↓	↑↓	↑↓	↑↓	↑↓	↑					$1s^22s^22p^63s$
Mg	↑↓	↑↓	↑↓	↑↓	↑↓	↑↓					$1s^22s^22p^63s^2$
Al	↑↓	↑↓	↑↓	↑↓	↑↓	↑↓	↑				$1s^22s^22p^63s^23p$
Si	↑↓	↑↓	↑↓	↑↓	↑↓	↑↓	↑	↑			$1s^22s^22p^63s^23p^2$
P	↑↓	↑↓	↑↓	↑↓	↑↓	↑↓	↑	↑	↑		$1s^22s^22p^63s^23p^3$
S	↑↓	↑↓	↑↓	↑↓	↑↓	↑↓	↑↓	↑	↑		$1s^22s^22p^63s^23p^4$
Cl	↑↓	↑↓	↑↓	↑↓	↑↓	↑↓	↑↓	↑↓	↑		$1s^22s^22p^63s^23p^5$
Ar	↑↓	↑↓	↑↓	↑↓	↑↓	↑↓	↑↓	↑↓	↑↓		$1s^22s^22p^63s^23p^6$
K	↑↓	↑↓	↑↓	↑↓	↑↓	↑↓	↑↓	↑↓	↑↓	↑	$1s^22s^22p^63s^23p^64s$
Ca	↑↓	↑↓	↑↓	↑↓	↑↓	↑↓	↑↓	↑↓	↑↓	↑↓	$1s^22s^22p^63s^23p^64s^2$

$1s^22s^22p$. The electron structures of the first 20 elements in the Periodic Table are shown in Table 12.2.

There is a useful way of remembering the order of filling of orbitals. This is shown in Figure 12.7.

You should now know how to use the *aufbau* method to build up the electron structures of any atom; well, almost any atom. There are a few atoms that are a little odd, especially chromium and copper. Chromium has 24 electrons and using Figure 12.7 we would predict the electron structure to be $1s^22s^22p^63s^23p^64s^23d^4$. In fact the structure is $1s^22s^22p^63s^23p^64s3d^5$. For chromium, the

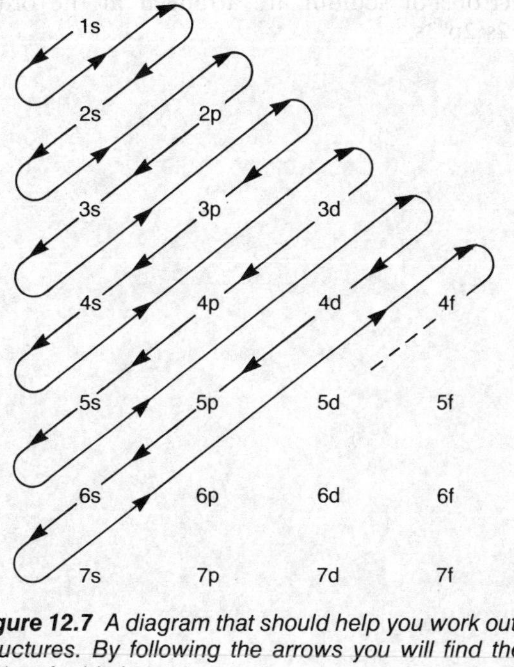

Figure 12.7 *A diagram that should help you work out electron structures. By following the arrows you will find the correct order of orbitals*

energy gap between the 4s and 3d orbitals is small. It is so small that the lowest energy overall is obtained by having six electrons each in separate orbitals rather than four in separate orbitals and two sharing the same (4s) orbital. Similarly, copper has the structure $1s^22s^22p^63s^23p^64s3d^{10}$ rather than the expected $1s^22s^22p^63s^23p^64s^23d^9$.

In this unit we have met important ideas that have been developed to explain the electron structures of atoms. Although completely accurate solutions of Schrödinger's equation are rarely available, it is possible to find very good approximate solutions. The most important solutions are orbitals that have the same names as the 1s, 2s, 2p, . . . orbitals of hydrogen. Using the Pauli exclusion principle together with Hund's rule

12.4 Write down the electron structures of (i) nickel, atomic number 28; (ii) zinc, atomic number 30; (iii) krypton, atomic number 36; (iv) rubidium, atomic number 37.

12.5 Before Schrödinger's method had allowed the electron structures of atoms to be explained in terms of orbitals, experiments had been performed that showed there were certain 'magic numbers' of electrons in atoms. Two of these numbers were 2 and 8. They are sometimes said to correspond to the filling of 'K and L shells'.

Write down the list of orbitals that are filled when the K and L shells are full.

Which atoms correspond to the filling of the shells?

Why do you think the numbers of electrons were called 'magic'?

allows us to write down the electron structure of any atom. You will find that once we know these structures it is possible to explain many of the properties of the elements; especially, how they bond together. It is to this topic of bonding that we shall turn shortly. However, before we do so, you should read the next unit, which describes how ionisation potentials vary with the electron structures of atoms.

Answers

12.1 The s orbital can contain 2, the p orbitals 6, and the five d orbitals 10 electrons.

12.2 Both electrons will be in the 1s orbital, for which $n=1$, $l=0$, $m=0$. If the first electron has $m_s=+1/2$, then the second will have $m_s=-1/2$. If a third electron is to go into the same 1s orbital, then it must have the same values for n, l and m. Also, it can only have $m_s=+1/2$ or $-1/2$. However, the electrons present already have these values; so the third electron would have to have the same set of four quantum numbers as one of the electrons already in the orbital. This is what the new statement of the exclusion principle says cannot happen. Thus it also says that an orbital can have a maximum of two electrons.

12.3 The second diagram is correct. The energy is minimised by using only 80 units to have the electrons in separate orbitals. (It would take 100 units to put them both in the same s orbital.)

12.4 (i) Nickel: $1s^22s^22p^63s^23p^64s^23d^8$.

(ii) Zinc: $1s^22s^22p^63s^23p^64s^23d^{10}$.

(iii) Krypton: $1s^22s^22p^63s^23p^64s^23d^{10}4p^6$.

(iv) Rubidium: $1s^22s^22p^63s^23p^64s^23d^{10}4p^65s$.

12.5 The K shell corresponds to $1s^2$ and the L shell to $2s^22p^6$. They correspond to the noble gases helium and neon. Helium has the K shell full, and neon both the K and L shells full. The numbers were thought to be 'magic' because at the time the noble gases were believed to be completely inert, so their electron structures were considered to be very special. (To some extent they *are* special!)

UNIT 12 SUMMARY

- Electrons fill orbitals in the order:
  1s, 2s, 2p, 3s, 3p, 4s, 3d, 4p, 5s, 4d, 5p, 6s, ...
- Rules for filling orbitals:
  (i) As far as possible, electrons will go in the orbital with the lowest energy.
  (ii) The Pauli exclusion principle says that:
  It is impossible for two electrons with the same spin quantum number to be in the same orbital.
  This rule means that an orbital can contain no more than two electrons.
  (iii) Hund's rule says that:
  Electrons will start to fill a set of degenerate orbitals keeping their spins parallel.
- Electron structures are shown by writing down the list of orbitals with the number of electrons in each orbital shown as a superscript. For example, the 11 electrons of sodium are arranged in the order $1s^22s^22p^63s$.

13

Electron structures, ionisation energies and shielding

13.1 What is shielding?

The electrons in the outer orbitals of an atom tend to spend more of their time further from the nucleus than electrons in other orbitals. If you were an electron in one of the outer orbitals you would not have a clear view of the nucleus. Rather, your view would be interrupted by a cloud of negative charge belonging to the electrons in the inner orbitals (Figure 13.1). You would be *shielded* from the nucleus by this charge cloud.

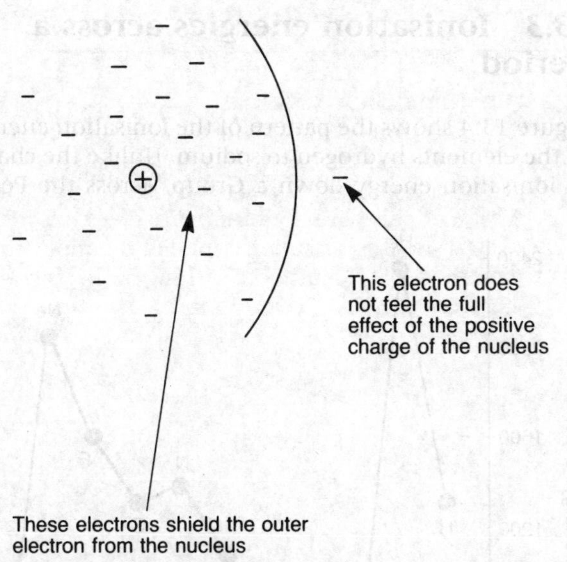

This electron does not feel the full effect of the positive charge of the nucleus
These electrons shield the outer electron from the nucleus

Figure 13.1 Electrons towards the outside of an atom are shielded from the nucleus

13.2 Ionisation energies down a Group

We know that electrons are held in an atom by the attraction they feel for the positively charged nucleus. If atoms were simple things we would expect an atom with a large number of protons to hold on to its electrons very tightly. On the other hand, an atom with a small number of protons would be expected to lose its electrons quite easily. We can check whether this actually happens by looking at a table of ionisation energies (Table 13.1).

The first ionisation energy, 1st I.E., of an element is defined as the energy change for the conversion of 1 mol of gaseous atoms into 1 mol of gaseous ions. For example,

$$Na(g) \rightarrow Na^+(g) + e^-; \qquad \text{1st I.E.} = +513\ \text{kJ mol}^{-1}$$

The second ionisation energy is the energy needed to convert the +1 charged ion into a +2 charged ion:

$$Na^+(g) \rightarrow Na^{2+}(g) + e^-; \qquad \text{2nd I.E.} = +4562\ \text{kJ mol}^{-1}$$

In similar fashion we can draw up a table of third, fourth, fifth, etc., ionisation energies. We can learn quite

Table 13.1. First, second and third ionisation energies of the elements hydrogen to calcium*

Element	*Number of electrons removed*		
	1	2	3
Hydrogen	1312		
Helium	2372	5250	
Lithium	520	7298	11815
Beryllium	899	1757	14849
Boron	801	2427	3660
Carbon	1086	2353	4620
Nitrogen	1402	2856	4578
Oxygen	1314	3388	5300
Fluorine	1681	3471	6050
Neon	2081	3952	6122
Sodium	513	4562	6912
Magnesium	738	1451	7733
Aluminium	578	1817	2745
Silicon	786	1577	3232
Phosphorus	1012	1903	2912
Sulphur	1000	2251	3361
Chlorine	1251	2297	3822
Argon	1521	2666	3931
Potassium	419	3051	4411
Calcium	590	1145	4912

*All values have units of kJ mol^{-1}. Data adapted from: *Handbook of Chemistry and Physics*, CRC Press, Boca Raton, Florida, 1989. A more complete list is given in Appendix B

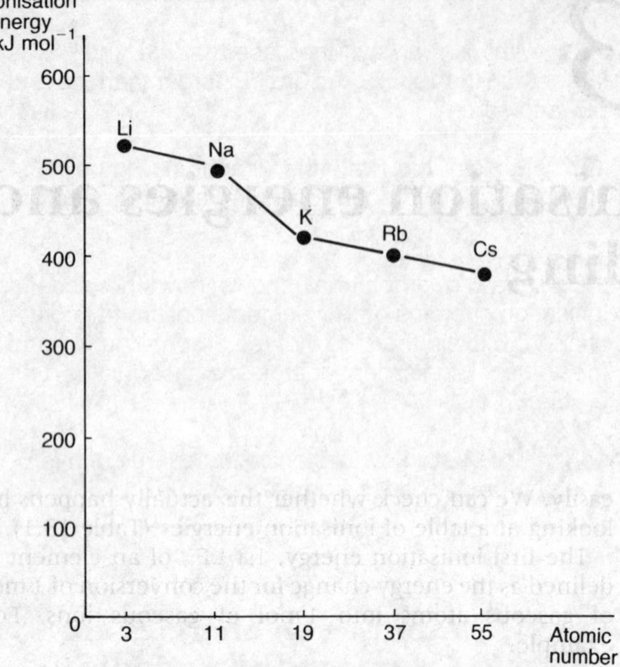

***Figure 13.2** The ionisation energies of Group I metals. (The atomic number scale is not linear)*

a lot by examining how the ionisation energies of the elements change as we go down a Group or across a Period in the Periodic Table.

We shall take the elements of Group I to illustrate the ideas. Their ionisation energies are shown in Figure 13.2.

Going down the Group the number of protons, and therefore the atomic number, increases from 3 for lithium to 55 for caesium, so we might expect caesium to be much harder to ionise than lithium. Yet caesium is *easier* to ionise than lithium. The reason why, for example, the 3s electron in sodium is easier to remove than the 2s electron in lithium is due to shielding.

The graph of Figure 13.3 shows how the electron density for a sodium atom varies with the distance from the nucleus. There are two peaks. The first applies to the two electrons in the 1s orbital (K shell) and the second to the electrons in the 2s and 2p orbitals (L shell). You can also see a curve showing the corresponding curve for a 3s orbital. The maximum in the curve comes well beyond the maxima for the K and L shells. Also, the average distance of the 3s electron from the nucleus is greater than for the K and L shell electrons. This tells us that for much of the time the 3s electron in sodium has a total of 10 electrons between it and the nucleus. This cloud of negative charge reduces the attraction of the nucleus for the 3s electron. Indeed, it is possible to estimate that, as far as the 3s electron is concerned, the effective nuclear charge is +2.2 rather than +11.

Shielding is most effective whenever there is a full shell (or shells) of electrons between the outermost electron and the nucleus. Full shells coincide with the noble gas electron structures. So there is invariably a

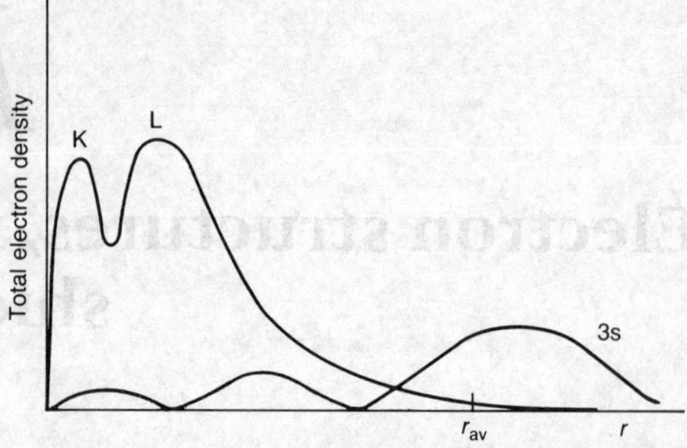

***Figure 13.3** For an atom like sodium the outer 3s electron can penetrate into the region of space occupied by the electrons in the K and L shells. However, for a sodium 3s electron $r_{av} = 1.2a_0$. This is shown on the diagram and is well beyond the bulk of K and L shell electron density*

decrease in ionisation potential going from a noble gas to the following alkali metal in Group I.

You will find that the trend down any Group in the Periodic Table is for ionisation energy to decrease. However, there are examples where the trend is not so clear. Often this happens when the atoms become large and complicated.

13.3 Ionisation energies across a Period

Figure 13.4 shows the pattern of the ionisation energies of the elements hydrogen to sodium. Unlike the change in ionisation energy down a Group, across the Period

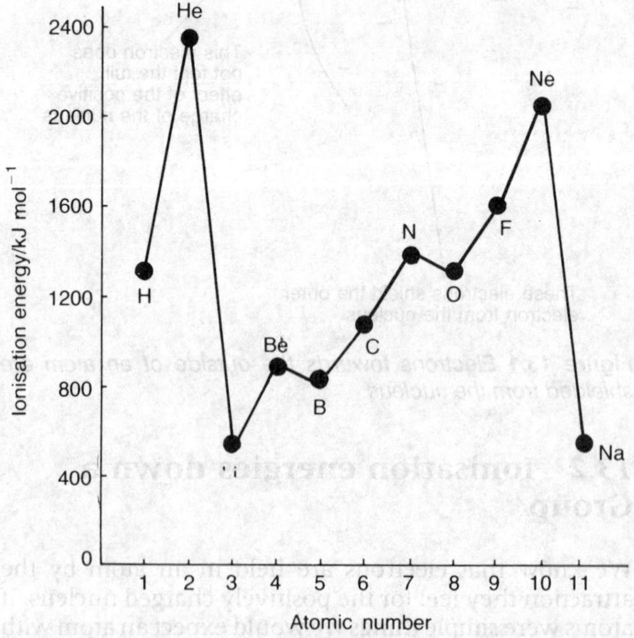

***Figure 13.4** The graph of ionisation energy against atomic number shows apparent anomalies at boron and oxygen. Their ionisation energies are lower than expected*

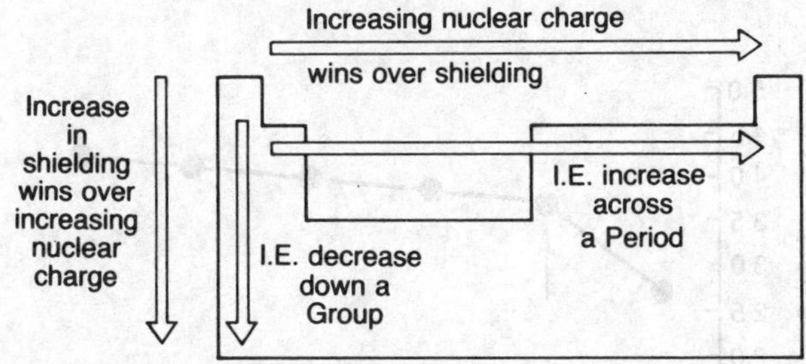

***Figure 13.5** Summary of two trends in ionisation energy in the Periodic Table*

lithium to neon the *trend* is for ionisation energy to increase as the nuclear charge increases. This is just what we would expect.

This must also mean that shielding is not so important across a Period as it is down a Group (Figure 13.5). One reason is that an electron in, say, a p_x orbital has little shielding effect on an electron in a p_y or p_z orbital. You can check this by recalling that the p orbitals are mutually at right angles to one another. Thus, to a large extent they do not shield each other from the nucleus. However, the filling of a 1s or 2s orbital will have a shielding effect because s orbitals are spherically symmetric.

Now we can look at the variation in ionisation energy in more detail. For example, we should try to explain why there are the two bumps, or dips, around beryllium/boron and nitrogen/oxygen. The dip from beryllium to boron occurs because the extra electron of boron enters a 2p orbital, and this electron will feel the effects of the shielding by the pair of electrons in the 2s orbital. The shielding has the effect of lowering the ionisation energy. The increase from boron to carbon reflects the increased nuclear charge of carbon. Also, because the two 2p electrons of carbon are in different orbitals (see section 12.5), they have little shielding effect on one another. A similar state of affairs accounts for the rise from carbon to nitrogen.

The dip from nitrogen to oxygen is a different matter. If you return to our discussion of the *aufbau* method (Unit 12), you will find that the electron structure of nitrogen is $1s^2 2s^2 2p^3$ and of oxygen is $1s^2 2s^2 2p^4$. The oxygen atom's extra electron must go into a 2p orbital that already has an electron in it. Putting two electrons into the same orbital brings about repulsion between them. For this reason it is easier to remove an electron from the 2p orbital in oxygen containing two electrons than it is from a similar orbital in nitrogen containing only one electron. This effect outweighs the effect of increasing nuclear charge from nitrogen to oxygen.

From oxygen to neon, the increase in ionisation energy reflects the increase in nuclear charge.

13.1 Why is it always the case that the 2nd I.E. is larger than the 1st I.E., the 3rd I.E. larger than the 2nd I.E. and so on?

13.2 Explain the way the graph in Figure 13.4 changes from hydrogen to lithium, and from neon to sodium.

13.3 Draw a graph that shows how the second ionisation energies of the elements helium to sodium change. Explain the shape of the graph. You will find the table of ionisation energies earlier in this unit (Table 13.1).

13.4 Briefly say how the ionisation energy of hydrogen can be calculated from its spectrum.

13.4 How ionisation energies are linked to Groups in the Periodic Table

Look at Figure 13.6, where there are graphs showing how the first six ionisation energies of sodium, magnesium and aluminium change as increasing numbers of electrons are removed. Three of the six graphs show the logarithm of the ionisation energies plotted. Logarithmic graphs can be most useful because they tend to exaggerate the degree to which the ionisation energies change at crucial points. The most important feature of the graphs is that there is a sudden increase in ionisation energy whenever a new shell of electrons is broken into. For example, the sudden rises for sodium and magnesium come when the 2p electrons are being removed:

$$Na^+(g) \rightarrow Na^{2+}(g) + e^-$$
$$1s^2 2s^2 2p^6 \quad 1s^2 2s^2 2p^5$$

$$Mg^{2+}(g) \rightarrow Mg^{3+}(g) + e^-$$
$$1s^2 2s^2 2p^6 \quad 1s^2 2s^2 2p^5$$

Aluminium atoms, which have the electron structure $1s^2 2s^2 2p^6 3s^2 3p$, have two sudden rises. The first comes when the $3s^2$ electrons are disrupted, the second when one of the $2p^6$ set is lost.

The way that the ionisation energies of an element change can tell us which group of the Periodic Table it is in. All the elements of Group I have a pattern like that of sodium (one easy to remove, then a jump), all the Group II elements are similar to magnesium (two fairly easy to remove, then a jump), and so on.

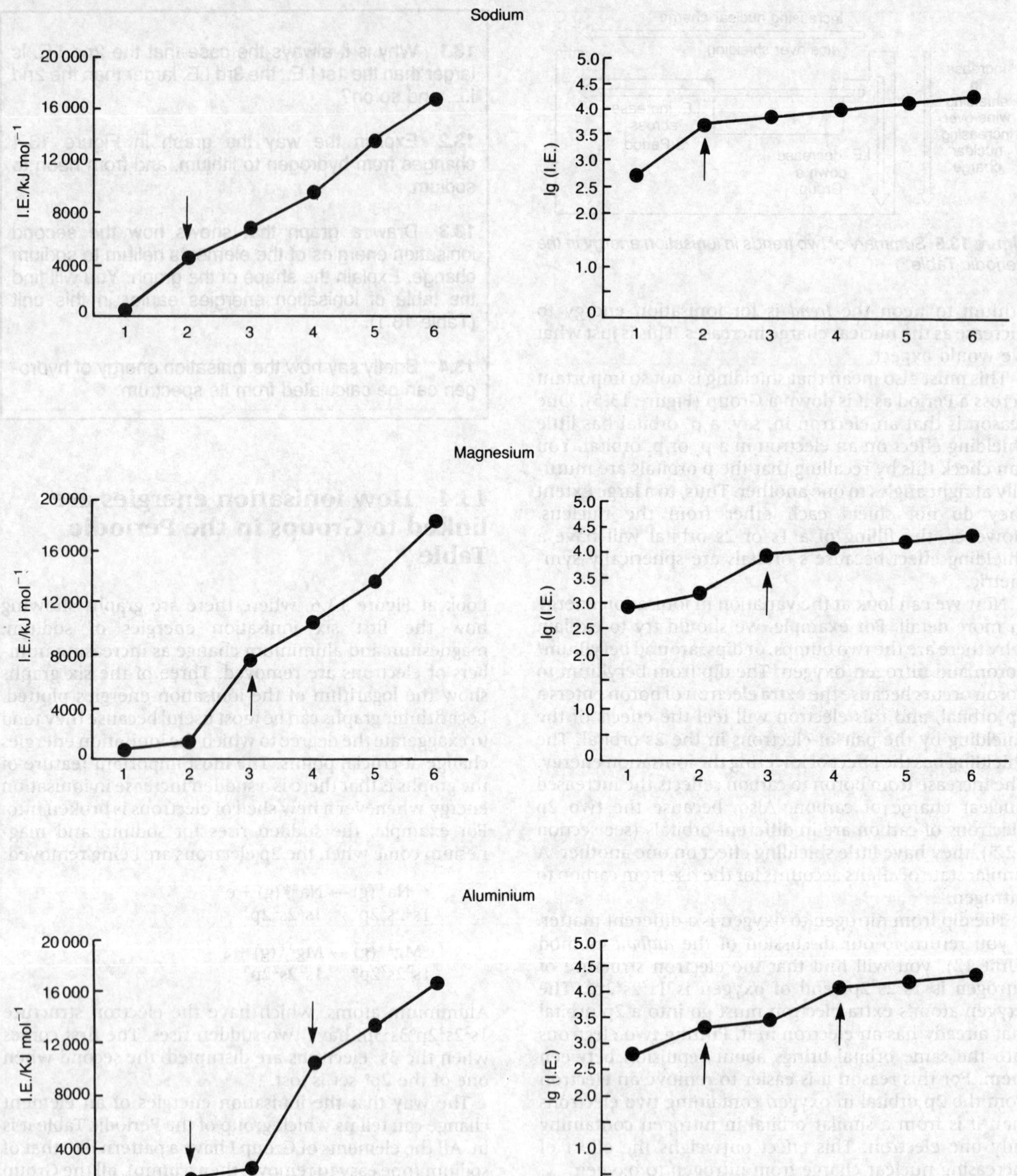

***Figure 13.6** Graphs of ionisation energy, I.E., and its logarithm, lg(I.E.), for sodium, magnesium and aluminium. The horizontal axis shows the number of electrons removed. Arrows mark where the 2s and 2p orbitals are broken into*

13.5 Plot the following (approximate) ionisation energies on suitable graphs, and say which groups of the Periodic Table the elements are in.

	Number of electrons removed					
	1	2	3	4	5	6
Element A Ionisation energy/kJ mol^{-1}	590	1100	4900	6500	8100	10 500
Element B Ionisation energy/kJ mol^{-1}	1010	1900	2900	5000	6300	21 300

13.6 The following statement was made by a student:

> The 1st I.E. of an atom takes an electron out of the orbital with highest energy, the 2nd I.E. takes an electron out of the next highest energy orbital, and so on. For example, lithium has the electron structure $1s^22s$. The 1st I.E. is 520 kJ mol^{-1}, and the 2nd I.E. is 7298 kJ mol^{-1}. Therefore the energy of the 2s orbital in the lithium atom is -520 kJ mol^{-1}, and the 1s orbital in the atom has an energy of 7298 kJ mol^{-1}.

If you were marking this passage, how many marks out of 10 would you give it? Give your reasons.

Answers

13.1 Once the atom has changed into a positive ion, there is a stronger attraction between the nucleus and the electrons that are left. (This is shown by measurements of the radii of the ions, which are always smaller than their parent atoms.) Hence it is more difficult to remove an electron, and the ionisation energy increases.

13.2 The rise from hydrogen to helium is due to the doubling of the nuclear charge. The drop from helium to lithium is because of the shielding effect of the spherically symmetric filled 1s orbital. The drop from neon to sodium is also due to the large amount of shielding as soon as a shell becomes full of electrons.

13.3 The graph is shown in Figure 13.7. The explanation of the shape follows that of the elements lithium to neon. The difference is that once lithium has lost an electron it has a noble gas electron structure, i.e. a filled set of electron shells. Like the noble gases it has a high ionisation energy. When beryllium has lost one electron it has the same structure as a lithium atom. Its single outer electron is shielded from the nucleus by a filled shell of electrons. This gives it a low second ionisation energy. In similar fashion there is a trend upwards across the Period, with dips at places where an electron is outside a filled s orbital, or where two electrons begin to fill a single p orbital.

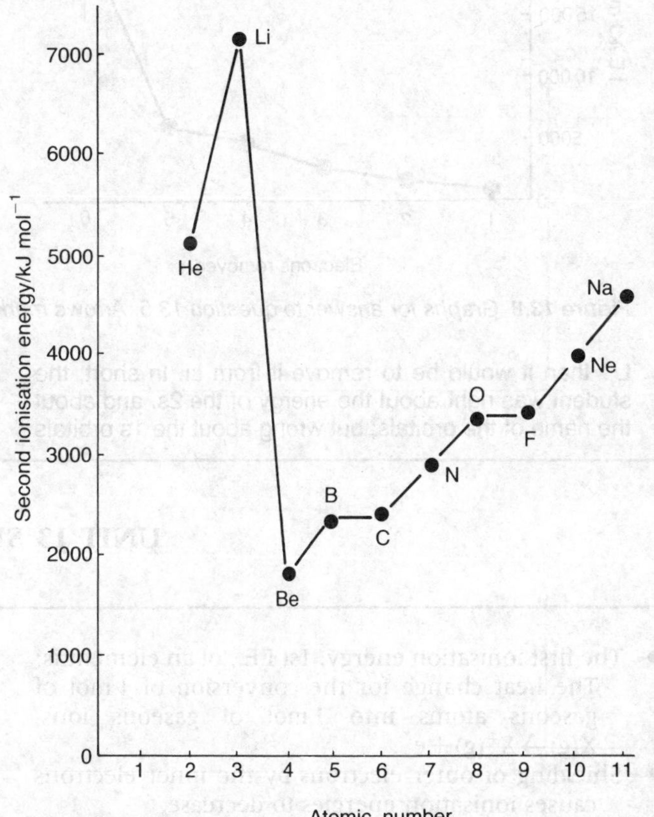

Figure 13.7 *A graph of second ionisation energy against atomic number for the elements helium to sodium*

13.4 This is described in section 8.2.

13.5 The best graphs to draw are of the logarithm of the ionisation energies. See Figure 13.8. The graph for element A shows a sudden jump after two electrons are removed. This tells us that it is in Group II (like magnesium). It is calcium, which has the structure $1s^22s^22p^63s^23p^64s^2$. For element B the jump comes after five electrons have been lost. This corresponds to an element in Group V. In fact it is phosphorus, $1s^22s^22p^63s^23p^3$.

13.6 The student is partly right, and partly wrong. The 1st I.E. does indeed tell us that the energy of the 2s orbital is -520 kJ mol^{-1}. (Just as the ionisation energy of the hydrogen atom tells us the energy of the 1s orbital in hydrogen.) However, the 2nd I.E. does not tell us the energy of the 1s orbital *in the atom*. As soon as the first electron is removed we are dealing with a lithium ion, Li^+. When the ion is made, the remaining electrons are drawn in towards the nucleus (there is less repulsion between the electrons); and the energy of the 1s orbital is decreased *below* the value it has in the atom. That is, it is harder to remove an electron from the 1s orbital in

Answers – contd.

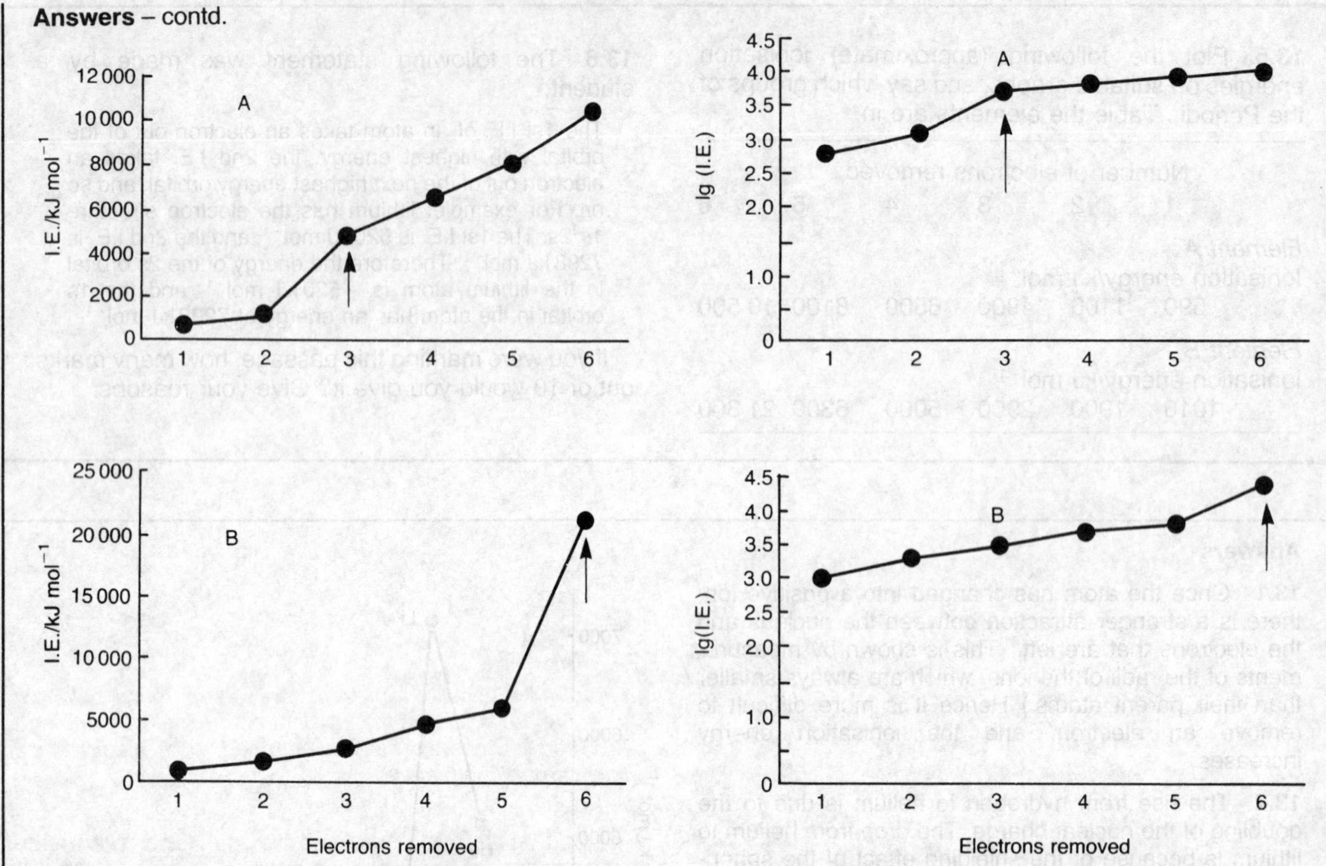

***Figure 13.8** Graphs for answer to question 13.5. Arrows mark where new shells of electrons are broken into*

Li^+ than it would be to remove it from Li. In short, the student was right about the energy of the 2s, and about the name of the orbitals; but wrong about the 1s orbitals having the same energy in the ion as in the atom. Given that this is a tricky thing to understand, 7/10 might be fair.

UNIT 13 SUMMARY

- The first ionisation energy, 1st I.E., of an element is: The heat change for the conversion of 1 mol of gaseous atoms into 1 mol of gaseous ions, $X(g) \rightarrow X^+(g) + e^-$.
- Shielding of outer electrons by the inner electrons causes ionisation energies to decrease.
- Increasing nuclear charge causes ionisation energies to increase.
- The effect of increasing nuclear charge wins across a Period; but shielding wins going down a Group.
- For these reasons, ionisation energies increase across a Period and decrease down a Group.

14

Bonding in molecules: valence bond theory

14.1 Valence bond theory

There are about 110 elements, but when the elements combine they can make a huge number of compounds. Some of these compounds were made when the world began. Some have been made by men and women, either by accident or design. Chemists have developed a wide range of skills and techniques for making new chemicals. However, rapid progress has come about in this century to the extent that hundreds or thousands of new compounds are now made each year. Some of them have no apparent use; some are beneficial to health or agriculture; others are harmful and can be put to evil uses, e.g. as nerve gas. Our ability to make so many new chemicals has largely come about because of our understanding of the bonds that hold atoms together. We are going to look at the two major theories of chemical bonding known as *valence bond theory* and *molecular orbital theory*. This unit deals with valence bond theory and Unit 16 with molecular orbital theory.

We can discover the essentials of valence bond theory by using the hydrogen molecule as an example. Let us think of two isolated hydrogen atoms, A and B, very far apart. We know that each atom will have one electron in a 1s orbital. If we now bring the atoms closer together, there will come a time when the region of space covered by one orbital will merge with that covered by the other. They will *overlap*; see Figure 14.1.

When this happens we can imagine that the electron

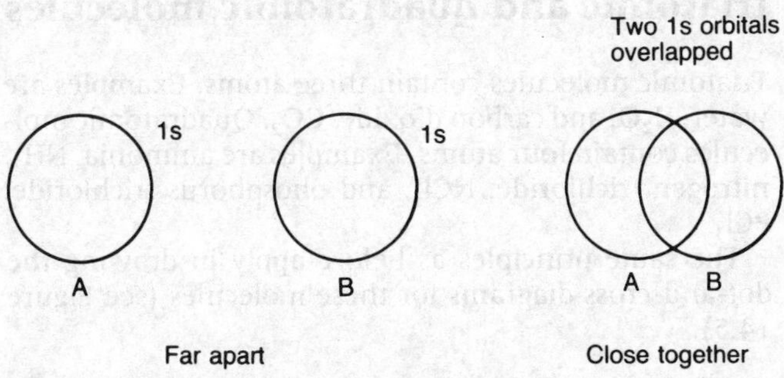

Figure 14.1 *When the atoms A and B come close, their 1s orbitals can overlap. Then A's electron can move around B and vice versa*

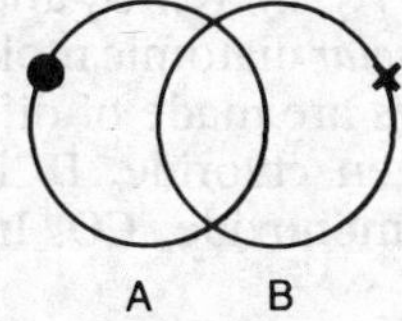

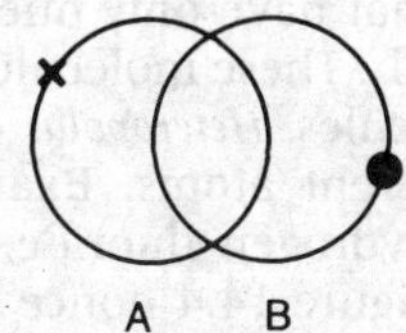

Figure 14.2 *The dot represents an electron once belonging to A; the cross represents an electron originally belonging to B. Once the orbitals have overlapped, both electrons can move around both atoms*

originally belonging to A can move around the nucleus of B, and vice versa. In valence bond theory there are two ways the electrons can be arranged in the orbitals. These are shown in Figure 14.2. The diagrams show that A's electron and B's electron can move into each other's orbital. Indeed, the electrons are *shared* between the orbitals. This perfect sharing of two electrons makes a *covalent bond*. It is possible that you may have come across diagrams like that shown in Figure 14.3 where a *dot-and-cross diagram* for the hydrogen molecule is drawn.

The dot and cross are drawn at the points where the circles join. This is meant to show the idea that the two electrons are shared between the two atoms. However, please be careful to distinguish these diagrams from the orbital probability density diagrams like those of Figure 14.1. The dot-and-cross diagrams are something of a hangover from the days of Bohr's orbits. They are not to be taken literally as showing the arrangement of the electrons, which, as we know, cannot be pinned down to such exact paths.

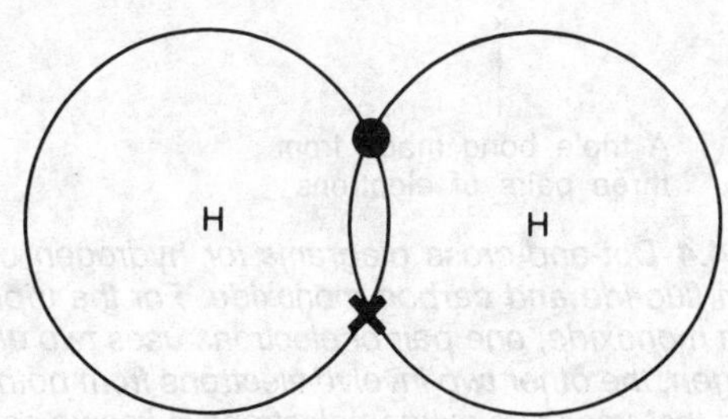

Figure 14.3 *A dot-and-cross diagram for hydrogen,* H_2

For other atoms there are more electrons to worry about. However, usually only the electrons in the outermost orbitals will be used in bonding. For example, nitrogen has the electron structure $1s^22s^22p^3$. The outermost electrons are those in the 2s and 2p orbitals. These are the *valence electrons*. When nitrogen forms a molecule (either with itself or with another atom) it is the valence electrons that are used in making the bonds. Valence bond theory takes its name because it concentrates on the valence electrons and tends to ignore the others.

14.2 Dot-and-cross diagrams for diatomic molecules

Diatomic molecules contain only two atoms. Examples that have only one type of atom are H_2, F_2, N_2, O_2 and Cl_2. These molecules are called *homopolar* diatomic molecules. *Heteropolar* diatomic molecules are made of different atoms. Examples are hydrogen chloride, HCl, hydrogen fluoride, HF, and carbon monoxide, CO. In Figure 14.4 notice that:

(i) in each case the non-valence electrons are omitted from the diagrams;
(ii) the electrons (the dots and crosses) are shown in pairs;
(iii) the circles are omitted to stop the diagrams becoming too complicated;
(iv) every pair of electrons shared between the atoms counts as a bond;
(v) every pair of electrons that is not used in bonding is called a *non-bonding* pair (often non-bonding pairs are called *lone pairs*).

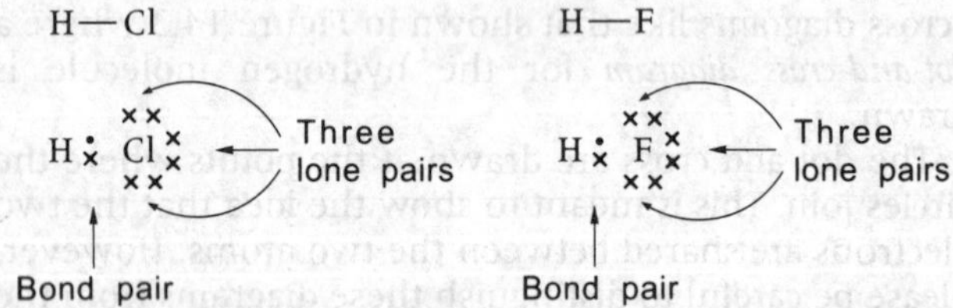

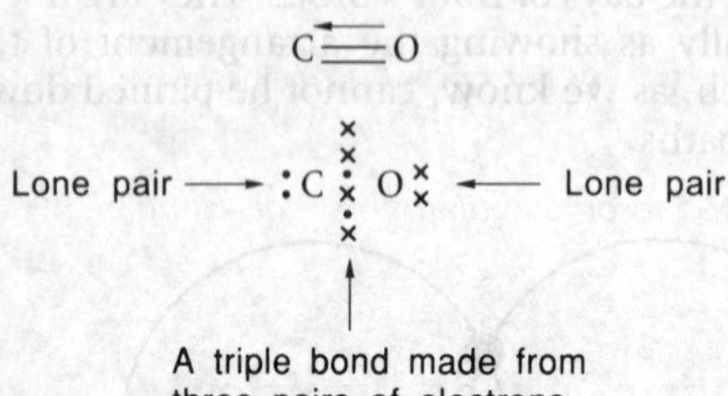

***Figure 14.4** Dot-and-cross diagrams for hydrogen chloride, hydrogen fluoride and carbon monoxide. For the triple bond in carbon monoxide, one pair of electrons uses two electrons from oxygen, the other two involve electrons from both atoms. The bond that uses two oxygen electrons is known as a coordinate bond (see Unit 15). It is often indicated by an arrow*

Table 14.1. The numbers of bonding and non-bonding pairs of electrons in some simple molecules

Molecule	*Bonding pairs*	*Non-bonding (lone) pairs*
H_2	1	0
N_2	3	2 (1 on each nitrogen)
O_2	2	? (valence bond theory gives no simple answer)
F_2	1	6 (3 on each fluorine)
Cl_2	1	6 (3 on each chlorine)
HCl	1	3 (on the chlorine)
HF	1	3 (on the fluorine)
CO	3	2 (1 on each atom)
H_2O	2	2 (on the oxygen)
CO_2	4	4 (2 on each oxygen)
NH_3	3	1 (on the nitrogen)
NCl_3	3	10 (1 on the nitrogen, 3 on each chlorine)
PCl_3	3	10 (1 on the phosphorus, 3 on each chlorine)

In Table 14.1 and Figure 14.5 are shown the bonding and non-bonding pairs for some simple molecules. Keeping the electrons in pairs helps us to keep count of them and to make sure that we have the correct number in the diagrams. Also, you will see that there is a total of two or eight electrons in the 'orbit' of each atom. Especially, when an atom fills its outer shell by having eight electrons in it, this is known as 'completing the octet'. The diagrams illustrate the idea that the atoms fill their shells when they form molecules. (See the previous unit for information about shells.) Be careful though. It is totally wrong to say that 'atoms make molecules so that they fill their shells' or that 'atoms make molecules to complete the octet'. As an explanation of bonding this is far too simple. For example, it is energetically *very* unfavourable for an isolated oxygen atom to gain two electrons to complete its octet. There are many more factors than filling shells to be taken into account if we are to explain why molecules exist. You will find more detail about such matters in Unit 46.

14.3 Dot-and-cross diagrams for triatomic and quadratomic molecules

Triatomic molecules contain three atoms. Examples are water, H_2O, and carbon dioxide, CO_2. Quadratomic molecules contain four atoms. Examples are ammonia, NH_3, nitrogen trichloride, NCl_3, and phosphorus trichloride, PCl_3.

The same principles as before apply in drawing the dot-and-cross diagrams for these molecules (see Figure 14.5).

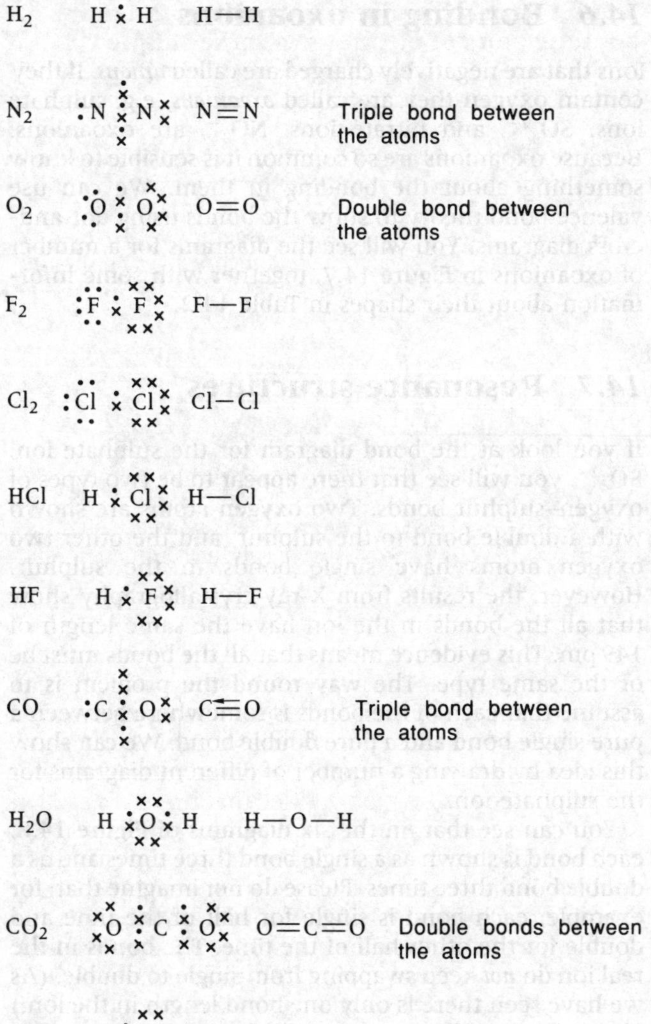

H_2	H × H	H—H	
N_2	:N ⁝ N ⁝	N≡N	Triple bond between the atoms
O_2	:O ⁝ O :	O=O	Double bond between the atoms
F_2	:F : F :	F—F	
Cl_2	:Cl × Cl :	Cl—Cl	
HCl	H × Cl :	H—Cl	
HF	H : F :	H—F	
CO	:C ⁝ O :	C≡O	Triple bond between the atoms
H_2O	H :O: H	H—O—H	
CO_2	O ⁝ C ⁝ O	O=C=O	Double bonds between the atoms
NH_3	H × N × H, H	H—N—H, H	
NCl_3	:Cl × N × Cl:, :Cl:	Cl—N—Cl, Cl	
PCl_3	:Cl × P × Cl:, :Cl:	Cl—P—Cl, Cl	

Figure 14.5 Dot-and-cross diagrams for the molecules in Table 14.1

> **14.1** Draw dot-and-cross diagrams of the following molecules: silane, SiH_4; tetrachloromethane, CCl_4; hydrazine, N_2H_4; hydrogen sulphide, H_2S; tetrafluoroethene, C_2F_4; methanol, CH_3OH.
>
> **14.2** Draw simplified diagrams of the molecules of question 14.1 showing the bonds as lines, and the lone pairs.

> **14.3** The molecules boron trichloride, BCl_3, and aluminium trichloride, $AlCl_3$, and interesting for a number of reasons. They are sometimes called *electron deficient* molecules.
>
> (i) To see why they have this name, draw their dot-and-cross diagrams. (There are only three single bonds to the boron or aluminium atoms.)
>
> (ii) How many electrons are there in the shell surrounding the boron or aluminium atoms? How many electrons would you have expected to find? Why are these molecules said to be electron deficient?

14.4 Dot-and-cross diagrams for hydrocarbons

The molecules methane, CH_4, ethane, C_2H_6, ethene, C_2H_4, and ethyne, C_2H_2, are of great importance in chemistry. Their dot-and-cross diagrams are shown in Figure 14.6. The diagrams show that all the bonds in methane and ethane are single bonds, but in ethene there is a double bond between the two carbon atoms. Ethyne has a triple bond between the carbon atoms.

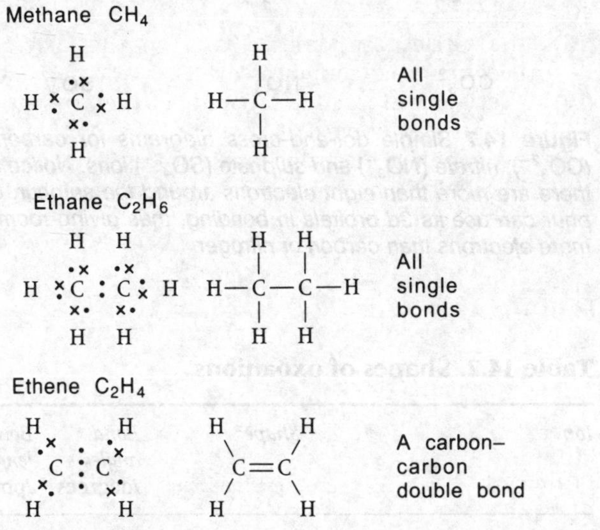

Methane CH_4 — All single bonds

Ethane C_2H_6 — All single bonds

Ethene C_2H_4 — A carbon–carbon double bond

Ethyne C_2H_2 — H × C ⁝ C × H, H—C≡C—H — A carbon–carbon triple bond

Figure 14.6 Dot-and-cross diagrams for simple hydrocarbons

14.5 Showing bonds by lines

It can be tedious to draw dot-and-cross diagrams. Once the number of pairs of bonding electrons has been discovered, it is easier to show a bond by a straight line joining the atoms. Some of the more important molecules that we have met in this unit have been shown in this way in Figures 14.4 to 14.6. If you draw such diagrams you have a choice of what to do about those molecules which have one or more lone pairs. Here the lone pairs have been indicated by a pair of dots on the atom to which they belong.

In this unit we have discussed one theory of bonding called valence bond theory. This theory claims that a bond is formed when two atoms bring their electron clouds close together. The electrons can then be shared between the atoms to make a covalent bond. This theory is useful because it concentrates on particular bonds and does not worry too much about what the non-valence electrons are doing. By focusing attention on particular bonds, the theory allows us to draw dot-and-cross diagrams. We can use these diagrams to help us visualise how the electrons in a molecule are arranged.

However, molecular orbital theory has a different way of explaining how atoms bond together. This is the theory we shall meet in Unit 16.

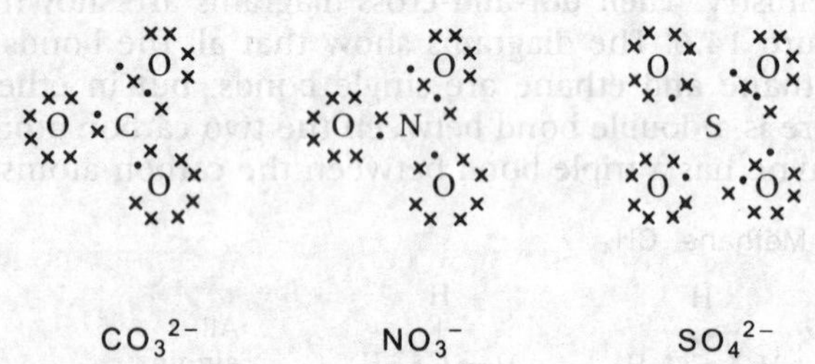

***Figure 14.7** Simple dot-and-cross diagrams for carbonate (CO_3^{2-}), nitrate (NO_3^-) and sulphate (SO_4^{2-}) ions. Notice that there are more than eight electrons around the sulphur. Sulphur can use its 3d orbitals in bonding, thus giving room for more electrons than carbon or nitrogen*

Table 14.2. Shapes of oxoanions

Ion	*Shape**	*Bond angles /degrees*	*Bond lengths /pm*
Nitrate, NO_3^-	Planar	120	122
Carbonate, CO_3^{2-}	Planar	120	130
Sulphate, SO_4^{2-}	Tetrahedral	109.5	149
Chlorate(VII), ClO_4^-	Tetrahedral	109.5	144
Phosphate(V), PO_4^{3-}	Tetrahedral	109.5	154
Manganate(VII), MnO_4^-	Tetrahedral	109.5	155

*Note that the shapes can be drawn like this:

120° 109.5°

Planar CO_3^{2-} ion
All bond angles 120°

Tetrahedral chlorate(VII) ion
All bond angles 109.5°

14.6 Bonding in oxoanions

Ions that are negatively charged are called *anions*. If they contain oxygen they are called *oxoanions*, e.g. sulphate ions, SO_4^{2-}, and nitrate ions, NO_3^-, are oxoanions. Because oxoanions are so common it is sensible to know something about the bonding in them. We can use valence bond theory to show the bonds using dot-and-cross diagrams. You will see the diagrams for a number of oxoanions in Figure 14.7, together with some information about their shapes in Table 14.2.

14.7 Resonance structures

If you look at the bond diagram for the sulphate ion, SO_4^{2-}, you will see that there appear to be two types of oxygen–sulphur bonds. Two oxygen atoms are shown with a double bond to the sulphur, and the other two oxygen atoms have single bonds to the sulphur. However, the results from X-ray crystallography show that all the bonds in the ion have the same length of 149 pm. This evidence means that all the bonds must be of the same type. The way round the problem is to assume that each of the bonds is somewhere between a pure single bond and a pure double bond. We can show this idea by drawing a number of different diagrams for the sulphate ion.

You can see that, in the six diagrams of Figure 14.8, each bond is shown as a single bond three times and as a double bond three times. Please do not imagine that, for example, each bond is single for half of the time and double for the other half of the time. The bonds in the real ion do *not* keep swapping from single to double. (As we have seen there is only one bond length in the ion.) The individual diagrams are called *resonance* structures. Sometimes resonance structures are called *resonance hybrids* (but they have nothing to do with hybridisation theory described in Unit 17).

Figure 14.9 shows one way of representing the bonding in the sulphate ion. Each of the oxygen atoms is joined by a single bond to the sulphur atom. The dotted lines also indicate that some of the electrons are delocalised over the entire ion. It is an important principle that when electrons are delocalised there is a lowering of the energy of the ion or molecule. This lowering means that the ion or molecule is harder than usual to break apart. This is true of the sulphate ion, and many of the other oxoanions in Table 14.2. Indeed, it is a general rule that the more resonance structures that we can draw for a particular ion or molecule, the more energetically stable will be the ion or molecule. We speak of them being *resonance stabilised*. However, this is not to say that such ions and molecules never break apart; it all depends on what they react with.

The fact that electrons are delocalised over the entire ion means that the negative charge is also spread over the ion. This is why the '2−' sign is shown outside the brackets in Figure 14.9 rather than on any of the oxygen atoms. If you look at Figure 14.10 you will find a similar set of diagrams for the other ions of Table 14.2.

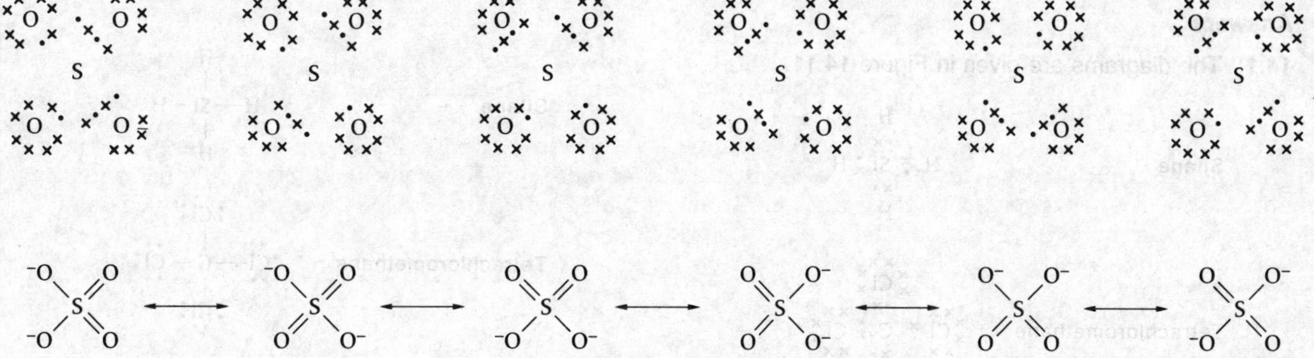

Figure 14.8 *Six resonance hybrid structures for the sulphate ion. (Note: the symbols ↔ have nothing to do with equilibrium)*

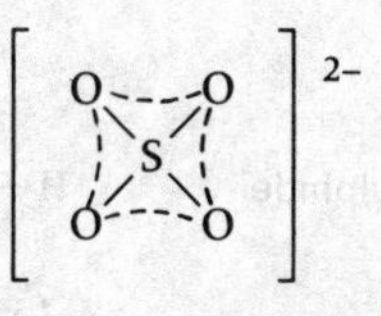

Figure 14.9 *Delocalisation of some of the electrons in the sulphate ion is shown by the dotted lines*

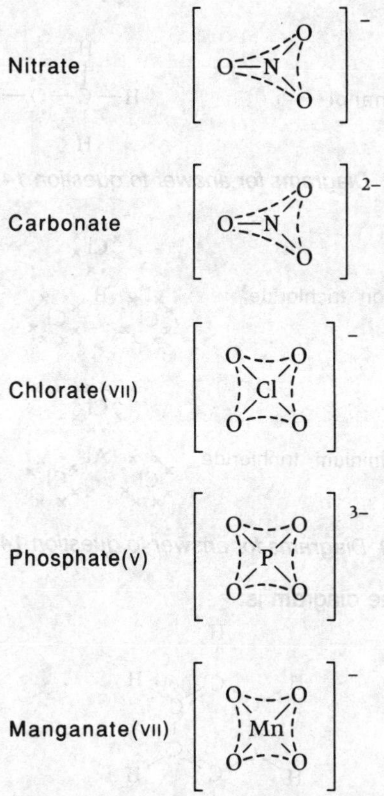

Nitrate

Carbonate

Chlorate(VII)

Phosphate(V)

Manganate(VII)

Figure 14.10 *Representations of delocalisation of electrons in oxoanions*

14.4 Methanoic acid, HCOOH, has one carbon–oxygen bond of length 123 pm, and another of 136 pm. The structure of the molecule is like this:

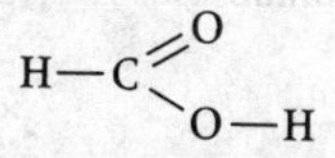

(i) Which bond has which length?

(ii) Both carbon–oxygen bonds in the methanoate ion, $HCOO^-$, have the same length (127 pm). What does this tell you about the bonding?

14.5 Benzene, C_6H_6, has a cyclic structure. One diagram of the bonding in benzene is shown below:

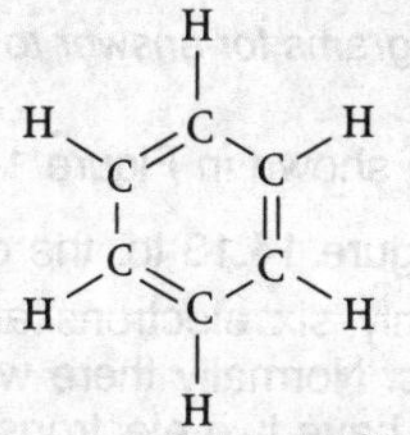

(i) There is another way of showing the arrangement of single and double bonds between the carbon atoms. What is it? Draw the diagram.

Experiment shows that there is only one carbon–carbon bond length in benzene, of value 140 pm. Normal carbon–carbon single bonds are about 154 pm long, and the length of the double bond in ethene is 135 pm.

(ii) Use the concept of resonance to explain the bonding in benzene.

Answers

14.1 The diagrams are given in Figure 14.11.

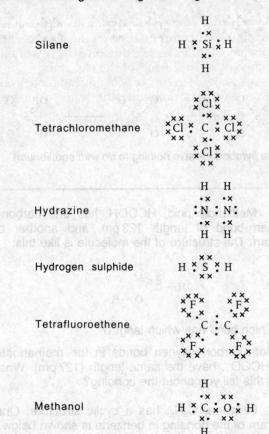

```
Silane                     H
                           •×
                         H ×• Si ו H
                           ×•
                           H

Tetrachloromethane        ××
                         ×Cl×
                          •×
                   ××Cl×•  C  ו Cl××
                          ×•
                         ×Cl×
                          ××

Hydrazine                H   H
                         •×  •×
                        :N • N:
                         •×  •×
                         H   H

Hydrogen sulphide          ××
                         H ו S ו H
                           ××

Tetrafluoroethene       ×F×     ×F×
                           C :: C
                        ×F×     ×F×

Methanol                 H
                         •×  ××
                       H ×• C ו O •× H
                         ×•  ××
                         H
```

Figure 14.11 Diagrams for answer to question 14.1

14.2 These are shown in Figure 14.12.

```
Silane                      H
                            |
                        H—Si—H
                            |
                            H

Tetrachloromethane         :Cl:
                            |
                      :Cl—C—Cl:
                            |
                           :Cl:

Hydrazine               H   H
                        |   |
                       :N—N:
                        |   |
                        H   H

Hydrogen sulphide      H—S—H
                         ••

Tetrafluoroethene    :F:     :F:
                        \   /
                         C=C
                        /   \
                     :F:     :F:

Methanol                H
                        |   ••
                     H—C—O—H
                        |   ••
                        H
```

Figure 14.12 Diagrams for answer to question 14.2

14.3 (i) See Figure 14.13 for the diagrams.

(ii) There are only six electrons around the boron or aluminium atoms. Normally there would be eight. Thus these molecules have two electrons less than we might expect: they are each deficient in two electrons.

```
Boron trichloride          ××
                          ×Cl×
                           •×
                            B
                      ××Cl       Cl××
                        ××       ××

Aluminium trichloride      ××
                          ×Cl×
                           •×
                           Al
                      ××Cl       Cl××
                        ××       ××
```

Figure 14.13 Diagrams for answer to question 14.3

14.4 (i) The double-bonded carbon–oxygen bond is shorter than the other. A double bond between two atoms is always stronger, and shorter, than a single bond between the same two atoms.

(ii) The bonding between the carbon and two oxygen atoms must be identical. Each bond has part of the character of a single bond and part of the character of a double bond. We can show this by drawing a dotted line to indicate how the electrons are delocalised over the three atoms:

```
        O
       ⁄
H—C ⁞      ⊖
       \
        O
```

Alternatively we can show the structure in terms of two resonance hybrids:

```
       O                        O⁻
      //                       /
H—C          ←————→     H—C
      \                       \\
       O⁻                      O
```

14.5 (i) The diagram is:

```
            H
            |
     H      C      H
       \  /   \\  /
        C       C
        ||      |
        C       C
       /  \\   /  \
     H      C      H
            |
            H
```

This and the other structure are two resonance hybrids for benzene.

(ii) We would expect the bonding to show characteristics of both single and double bonds, without being identical to either. In Unit 44 you will find how to calculate the extent to which benzene is more stable than either of the individual resonance structures.

UNIT 14 SUMMARY

- Valence bond theory says that covalent bonds are made between atoms that come sufficiently close together that their orbitals overlap and the electrons can move under the influence of both nuclei.
- A covalent bond is a pair of electrons shared by two atoms.
- A lone pair of electrons is not involved in bonding.
- Resonance structures exist when the bonding in an ion or molecule can be represented by two or more different arrangements of the electrons.
- Resonance leads to charge being spread more evenly over an ion or molecule, and leads to increased energetic stability.

15

Coordinate bonding

15.1 What is coordinate bonding?

Some atoms have a small number of electrons in their outer shell. Boron, for example, has the electron structure $1s^2 2s^2 2p$. The 2p orbitals contain only one electron. In the last unit we saw that boron reacts with chlorine to make BCl_3, and that this molecule is planar. If we think of the boron atom as being hybridised (see Unit 17), two of the 2p orbitals together with the 2s orbital are used in forming the three sp^2 hybrids. This leaves one of the 2p set empty.

Now consider the ammonia molecule. We know this to be a slightly distorted tetrahedron, with a lone pair of electrons on the nitrogen atom. It so happens that ammonia and boron trichloride combine with each other. The resulting molecule has a shape resembling two tetrahedra joined together. Our immediate task is to explain how these molecules react.

There is an empty 2p orbital on the boron atom, which could contain two electrons. It can gain them by this orbital overlapping with the lone pair on the nitrogen atom in ammonia. We say that the nitrogen atom donates its pair of electrons to the boron atom. The name of the bond they make is a *coordinate bond*.

You may find that the term *dative covalent bond* is used by some people instead of coordinate bond; similarly, dative bonding is an alternative name to coordinate bonding.

Often a coordinate bond is shown by an arrow with the head of the arrow pointing to the atom that accepts the pair of electrons. You can see this in Figure 15.1. However, once a coordinate bond is made, it becomes just like any other covalent bond with two electrons shared between the atoms.

The new molecule will take up the shape that minimises the repulsions between the bond pairs of electrons (see Unit 17). This is the reason why the chlorine atoms attached to the boron atom bend backwards.

The product of the reaction between the electron deficient molecule and the donating molecule is sometimes called an *adduct*. For example, boron trichloride and ammonia make the 'boron trichloride–ammonia adduct'.

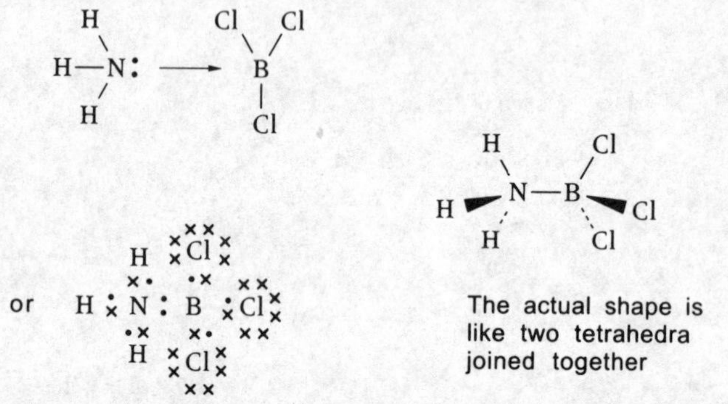

H₃N: → BCl₃

or

The actual shape is like two tetrahedra joined together

Figure 15.1 *Making a coordinate bond between ammonia and boron trichloride. The dot-and-cross diagram shows that, when the lone pair is donated to the boron, there are eight electrons around that atom, i.e. it has completed its octet. (Here ◀ shows a bond pointing towards you and --- a bond pointing away from you)*

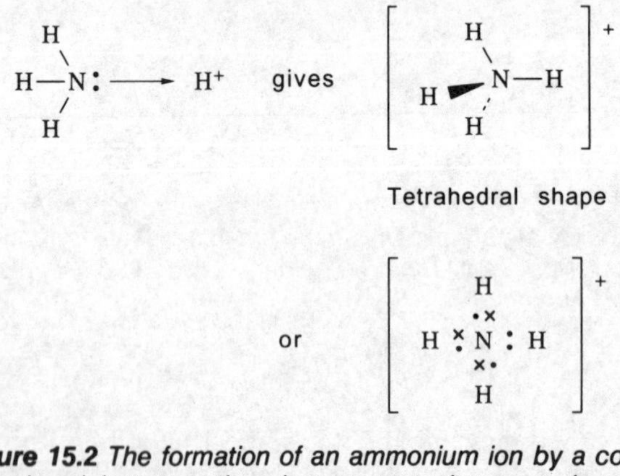

H₃N: → H^+ gives $[NH_4]^+$

Tetrahedral shape

or

Figure 15.2 *The formation of an ammonium ion by a coordinate bond between the nitrogen atom in ammonia and a hydrogen ion*

Coordinate bonds occur in a wide range of other reactions. You can see examples in Figures 15.2 to 15.6.

You might need an explanation of the reaction between copper(II) ions and ammonia molecules. Copper(II) ions, Cu^{2+}, are copper atoms that have lost two electrons. The ground state electron configuration of

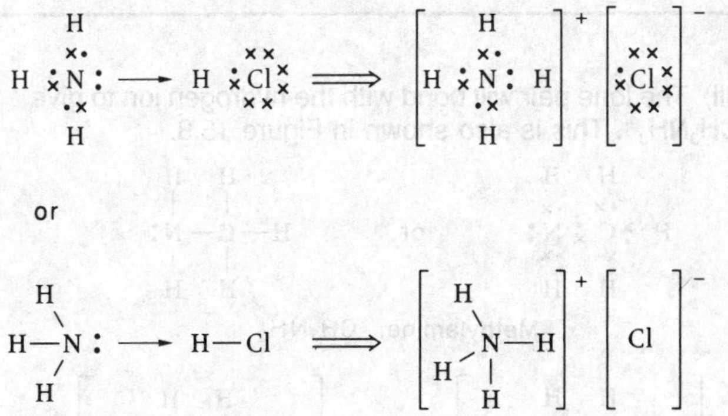

H ×N: → H ×Cl (dot-and-cross) ⟹ [H ×N: H]$^+$ [×Cl×]$^-$

or

$H_3N:$ → H—Cl ⟹ $[NH_4]^+$ [Cl]$^-$

Figure 15.3 *The ionic compound ammonium chloride ($NH_4^+Cl^-$) is made when an ammonia molecule reacts with a molecule of hydrogen chloride. We can think of one of the hydrogen atoms in NH_4^+ being held to the nitrogen atom by a coordinate bond. In fact, all four bonds in NH_4^+ are identical*

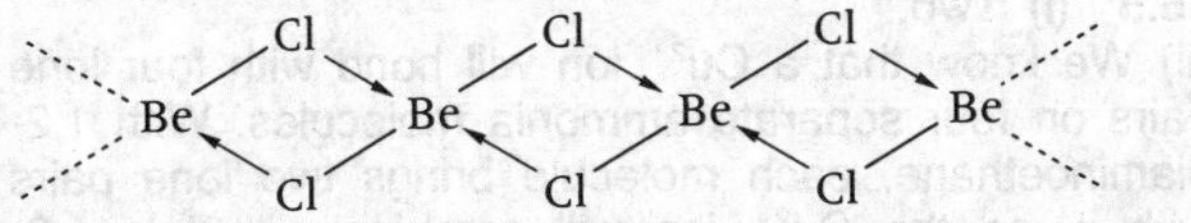

Cl Cl Cl
Be Be Be Be
Cl Cl Cl

Figure 15.4 *In the solid, beryllium chloride consists of chains of atoms arranged like those in the diagram. There are two coordinate bonds made from chlorine atoms to each beryllium atom*

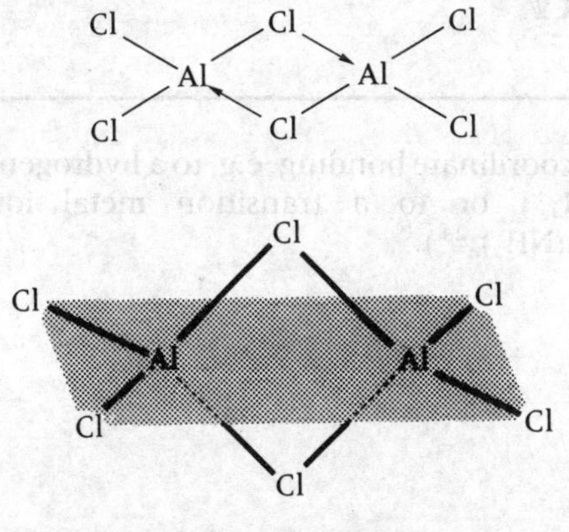

Cl Cl Cl
Al Al
Cl Cl Cl

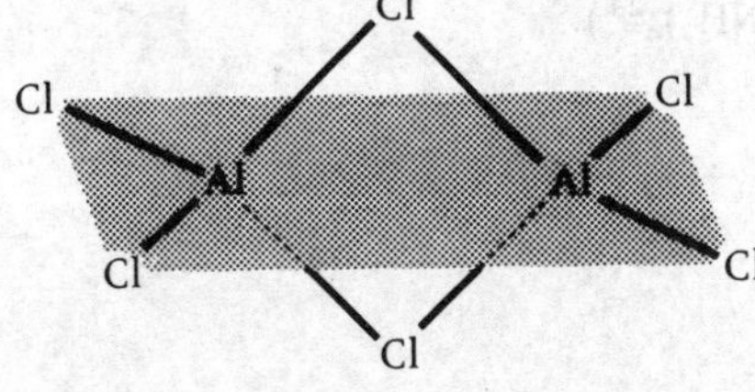

Figure 15.5 *Two of the chlorine–aluminium bonds in Al_2Cl_6 are coordinate bonds. The shape of the molecule is shown in the lower diagram. The arrangement around each aluminium atom is tetrahedral*

copper is $1s^22s^22p^63s^23p^63d^{10}4s$. When it becomes a Cu^{2+} ion, the 4s electron is lost, together with one of the 3d electrons. When copper(II) ions react with ammonia, a beautiful blue colour is produced. The ion responsible for the colour has the formula $Cu(NH_3)_4^{2+}$. It is an exam-

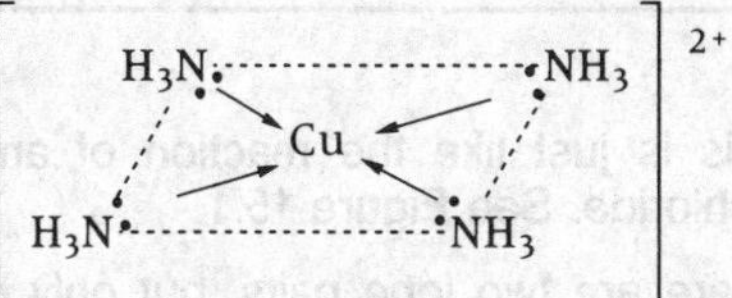

Figure 15.6 *The tetraamminecopper(II) ion, $Cu(NH_3)_4^{2+}$, has four ammonia molecules at the corners of a square. They make four coordinate bonds with a Cu^{2+} ion at the centre of the square. (There are two water molecules bonded to the Cu^{2+} ion, one above and one below the square. These are not shown in the diagram)*

ple of a complex ion; its name is the tetraammine-copper(II) ion. X-ray diffraction experiments show that the copper ion is at the centre of a square, with the four ammonia molecules at the corners forming a square planar shape.

15.1 Boron trihydride, BH_3, can react with ammonia. Predict the shape of the molecule formed and the bonding in it.

15.2 Water can react with hydrogen ions to make the oxonium ion, H_3O^+, What is present in a water molecule that allows it to react with a hydrogen ion? Describe the bonding in the oxonium ion. Draw a dot-and-cross diagram for the molecule.

15.3 Ammonia dissolves in water very easily and reacts with a large number of chemicals, e.g. copper(II) ions, Cu^{2+}. Why is it that if hydrogen ions (e.g. from sulphuric acid) are added to the water it is found that the ammonia does not react so easily with Cu^{2+} ions?

15.4 (i) Draw a dot-and-cross diagram for methylamine, CH_3NH_2.

(ii) Does the molecule have a lone pair?

(iii) Would you expect it to react with a hydrogen ion? If so, what would be the formula of the product?

15.5 (i) How many lone pairs does the molecule 1,2-diaminoethane, $NH_2CH_2CH_2NH_2$, possess?

(ii) Explain why a copper(II) ion reacts with *two* of these molecules. What would be the shape of the complex ion produced? (Hint: you will find it helpful to make molecular models.)

Answers

15.1 This is just like the reaction of ammonia with boron trichloride. See Figure 15.1.

15.2 There are two lone pairs, but only one of them makes a coordinate bond with an empty 1s orbital on a hydrogen atom. There are three bonds. In the H_3O^+ ion, all three bonds are identical; but we think of two of them as ordinary covalent bonds (originally in the water molecule), and one of them as a coordinate bond. The dot-and-cross diagram is shown in Figure 15.7.

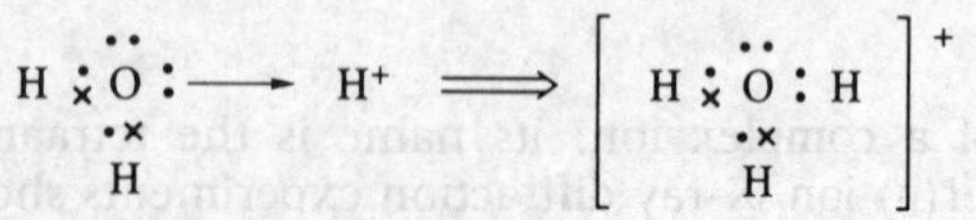

```
   ••                    ••     +
H × O :  ──► H⁺  ══►  [ H × O : H ]
   •×                    ×•
   H                     H
```

Figure 15.7 Dot-and-cross diagram for the oxonium ion, H_3O^+

15.3 The hydrogen ions bond to the lone pairs on the ammonia molecules making NH_4^+ ions. The lone pairs are no longer available for bonding, so the ammonia molecules cannot react.

15.4 (i) The diagram is given in Figure 15.8.

(ii) Yes it does, on the nitrogen atom.

(iii) The lone pair will bond with the hydrogen ion to give $CH_3NH_3^+$. This is also shown in Figure 15.8.

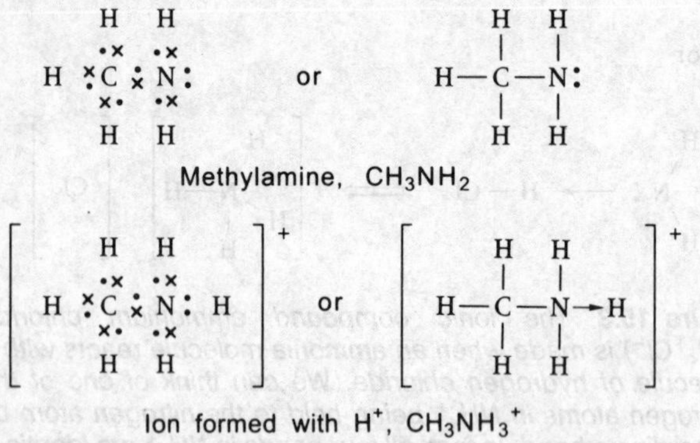

```
  H   H                H  H
  •×  •×               |  |
H ×C × N:     or     H—C—N:
  ו  •×               |  |
  H   H                H  H
```

Methylamine, CH_3NH_2

```
   H   H       +             H  H     +
   •×  •×                    |  |
[ H ×C × N: H ]     or    [ H—C—N→H ]
   ו  •×                    |  |
   H   H                     H  H
```

Ion formed with H^+, $CH_3NH_3^+$

Figure 15.8 Diagrams for answer to question 15.5

15.5 (i) Two.

(ii) We know that a Cu^{2+} ion will bond with four lone pairs on four separate ammonia molecules. With 1,2-diaminoethane, each molecule brings two lone pairs with it, so the Cu^{2+} ion will combine with two 1,2-diaminoethane molecules. The product is $Cu(NH_2CH_2CH_2NH_2)^{2+}$. The molecule is flat (planar).

UNIT 15 SUMMARY

- A coordinate bond (dative covalent bond) is a covalent bond between two atoms in which one of them provides both electrons.
- The lone pair on an ammonia molecule is often used in coordinate bonding, e.g. to a hydrogen ion (as in NH_4^+) or to a transition metal ion (as in $Cu(NH_3)_4^{2+}$).

16

Molecular orbital theory

16.1 Wavefunctions can be positive or negative

You may remember that in valence bond theory we concentrated on the individual bonds in a molecule, and tended to ignore the electrons that were not used in bonding. In molecular orbital theory there is a different emphasis. We begin by assuming that, in principle, *all* the orbitals of the atoms are able to take part in bonding. We then try to discover how the orbitals on the atoms change when they overlap in the molecule. In the next section we shall discover some of the rules and regulations that govern how molecular orbitals are made.

Every atom can have a full set of s, p, d, . . . orbitals, although not all of them will contain electrons. If we are to understand how molecular orbitals are formed, we need to know a little more about the nature of the orbitals. First, the diagrams that we use to represent orbitals show where electrons are most likely to be found. (They are probability density diagrams.) The orbitals themselves are really the solutions of Schrödinger's equation. In Unit 11 these were called wavefunctions.

Figure 16.1a shows the wavefunctions of 1s and 2p orbitals. The wavefunction of a 1s orbital is always above the *r* axis. That is, it always has a positive sign. On the other hand, the wavefunction for the 2p orbital is sometimes above the *r* axis and sometimes below it. This wavefunction can change its sign from positive to negative. In this unit we shall show the signs of the *wavefunctions* as a + or a − sign in the probability density diagrams. This has been done in Figure 16.1b. It is important that you do not think that *probabilities* can be negative; they can only be positive.

16.2 How wavefunctions can be combined

Any two waves can overlap with one another. Figure 16.2 shows two waves that overlap in different ways. In Figure 16.2a the positive parts overlap each other, and the negative parts overlap each other. Each reinforces the other. The result is a larger wave. Figure 16.2b shows the positive and negative parts overlapping. The positive part is cancelled out by the negative part, with the result that there is no wave at all. Of course, such perfect overlap rarely happens. Often waves overlap in a way somewhere between these two extremes. Then they reinforce in some places and cancel out in others.

Well, wavefunctions behave as rather special types of wave. They too can overlap in two ways: they tend either to reinforce one another, or to cancel each other out. Suppose we have two atoms, A and B, each with a 1s orbital. Let us call these orbitals $1s_A$ and $1s_B$. We can combine them in two ways.

First way: they reinforce each other. The two wavefunctions add together to give a combined wavefunction $1s_A + 1s_B$. This combination of orbitals is called a *bonding orbital*.

Second way: they cancel out. The wavefunction of one decreases the other to give a combined wavefunction $1s_A - 1s_B$. This combination of orbitals is called an *antibonding orbital*.

16.3 Bonding and antibonding orbitals using s orbitals

Figure 16.3a shows the probability density diagram of the bonding orbital $1s_A + 1s_B$. You can see that the orbital spreads around the nuclei of both atoms. This orbital really does belong to the molecule as a whole and not to the individual atoms. This contributes to holding the molecule together; hence it is called a *bonding orbital*. It is given a special name: a *sigma* (σ) orbital. To show that it is made from 1s orbitals, its full symbol is 1sσ.

Compare this with the probability density diagram of the antibonding orbital $1s_A - 1s_B$ shown in Figure 16.3b. In spite of appearances to the contrary, there really is only one orbital here; it happens to have split into two portions, sometimes called *lobes*. If electrons are in this orbital, they have a high probability of being found very near to the nucleus of each atom, but a very *low* probability of being found between the nuclei. These electrons do nothing to help the molecule keep together. Hence the orbital is called an *antibonding orbital*. It too

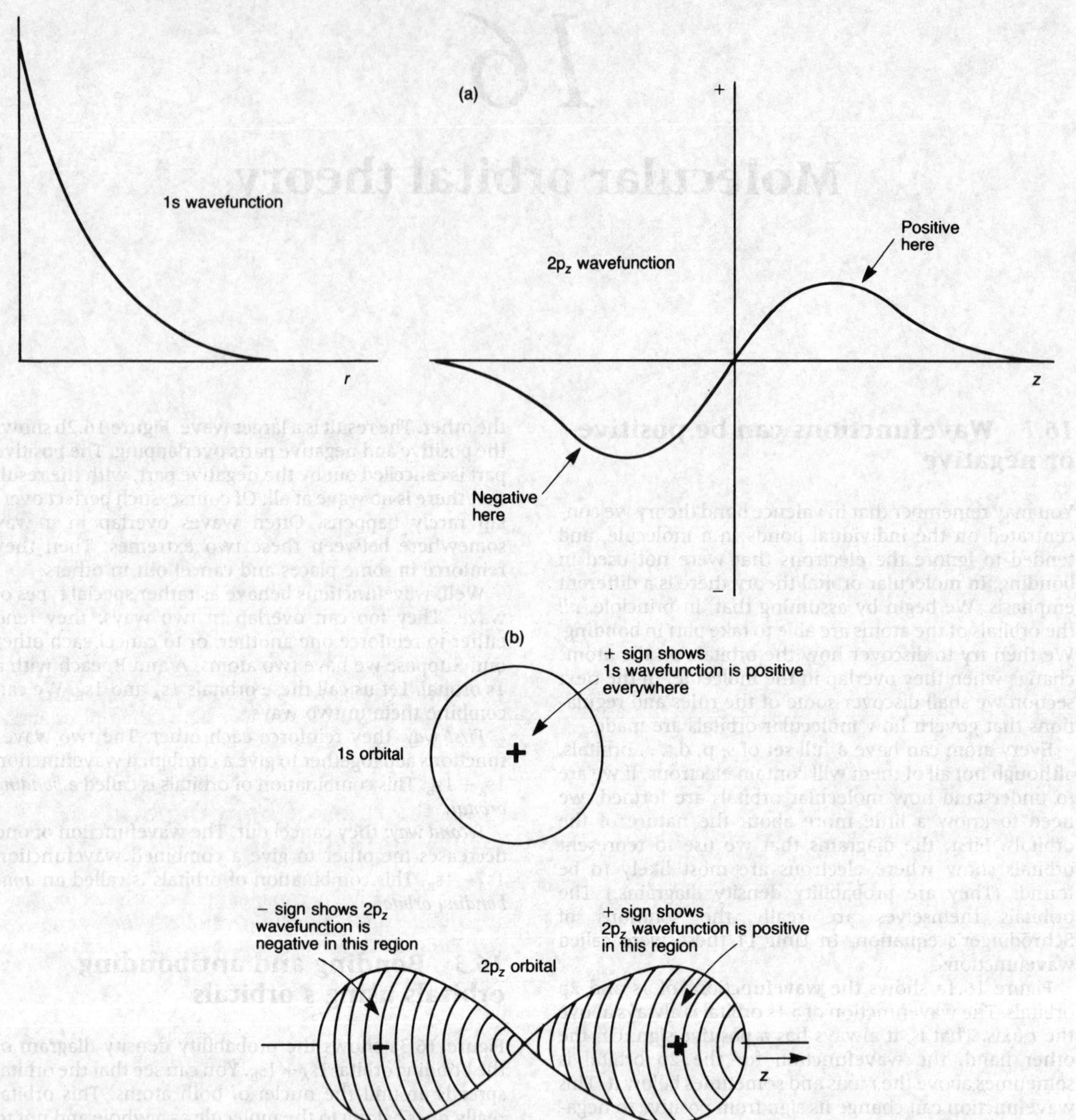

Figure 16.1 (a) The wavefunction of a 1s orbital is always positive. The wavefunction of a 2p orbital is sometimes positive and sometimes negative. (A cross-section through a $2p_z$ orbital is shown.) (b) The usual probability density diagrams for 1s and $2p_z$ orbitals showing the signs of the wavefunctions

has a special symbol: $1s\sigma^*$. The star is always used to show an antibonding orbital.

16.4 Bonding and antibonding orbitals using p orbitals

We can generalise this work on molecular orbitals to include the overlap of p orbitals as well. Figure 16.4 illustrates the formation of bonding and antibonding orbitals produced by the overlap of two $2p_y$ orbitals.

This time both the bonding and antibonding orbitals have two lobes. The bonding orbital is called a *pi* (π) orbital. A pi orbital formed from two $2p_y$ orbitals is given the symbol $2p_y\pi$. The corresponding antibonding orbital is $2p_y\pi^*$.

Two p orbitals can make sigma orbitals as well. This happens when the orbitals point along the line joining

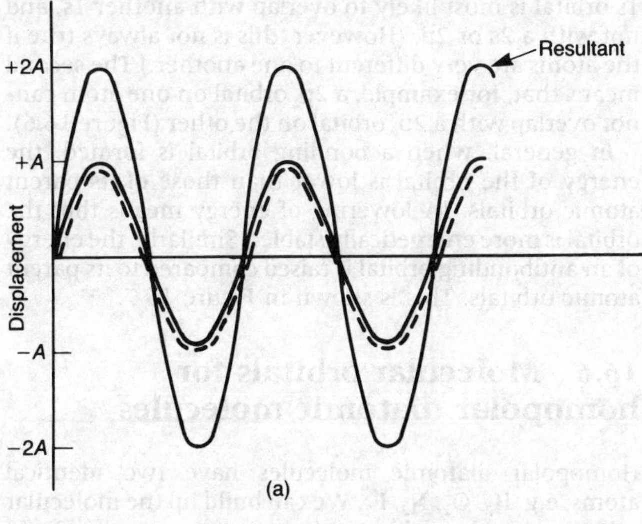

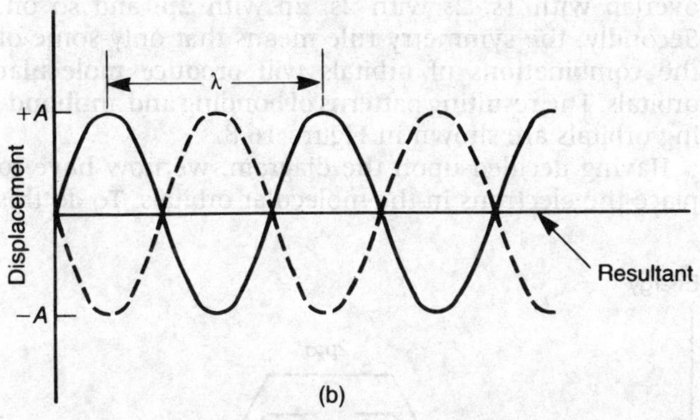

Figure 16.2 *Two ways in which waves can overlap with one another. (a) Two waves that have equal amplitude and are completely in phase interfere completely constructively. (b) Two waves that have the same amplitude and are completely out of phase give a resultant of zero amplitude. There is complete destructive interference*

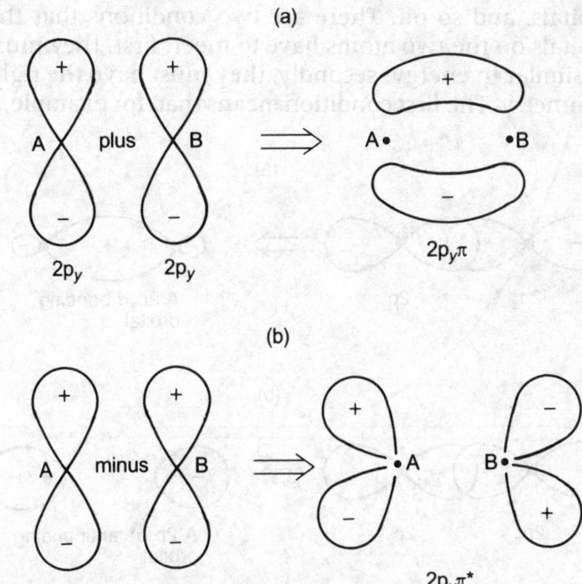

Figure 16.4 *(a) The constructive interference of two $2p_y$ orbitals gives a $2p_y\pi$ bonding orbital. Notice that the orbital has two lobes where the wavefunctions have opposite signs. (b) When destructive interference occurs, a $2p_y\pi^*$ antibonding orbital results*

the two nuclei. Figure 16.5 shows this happening. The resulting orbitals are more like sigma than pi orbitals. Hence their symbols are $2p_z\sigma$ and $2p_z\sigma^*$.

16.5 Energies of bonding and antibonding orbitals

It is possible for many combinations of orbitals to produce bonding and antibonding orbitals; for example, s orbitals may overlap with p orbitals, d orbitals with p

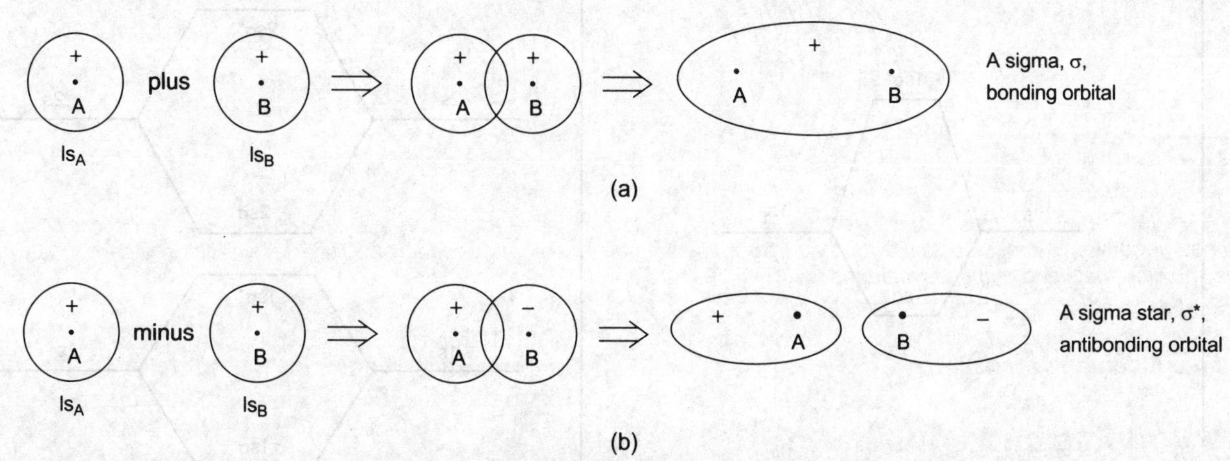

Figure 16.3 *How two s orbitals can combine (a) constructively or (b) destructively to make bonding and antibonding orbitals. (a) The orbital $1s_A + 1s_B$ is everywhere positive and encompasses regions of space around and between both atoms. The orbital is a σ orbital. (b) The orbital $1s_A - 1s_B$ consists of two lobes where the wavefunctions have opposite signs. There is a nodal surface midway between the nuclei. The two lobes form a single σ* orbital*

orbitals, and so on. There are two conditions that the orbitals on the two atoms have to meet: first, they must be similar in energy; secondly, they must have the right symmetry. The first condition means that, for example, a 1s orbital is most likely to overlap with another 1s, and not with a 2s or 2p. (However, this is not always true if the atoms are very different to one another.) The second means that, for example, a $2p_z$ orbital on one atom cannot overlap with a $2p_y$ orbital on the other (Figure 16.6).

In general, when a bonding orbital is formed, the energy of the orbital is lower than those of its parent atomic orbitals. (A lowering of energy means that the orbital is more energetically stable.) Similarly, the energy of an antibonding orbital is raised compared to its parent atomic orbitals. This is shown in Figure 16.7.

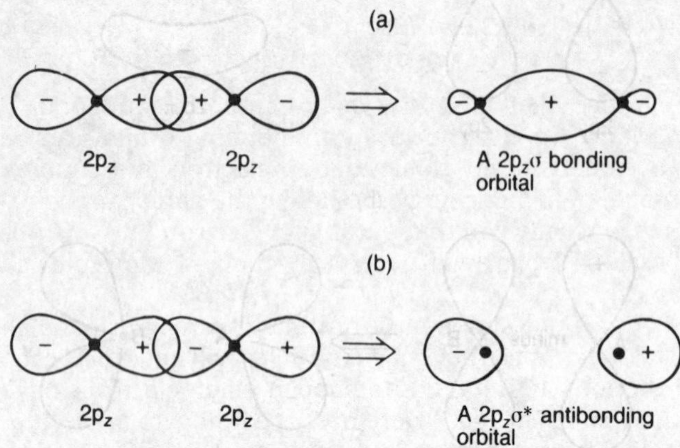

Figure 16.5 *If two $2p_z$ orbitals interfere (a) constructively, a $2p_z\sigma$ bonding orbital results; if they interfere (b) destructively, a $2p_z\sigma^*$ antibonding orbital is made*

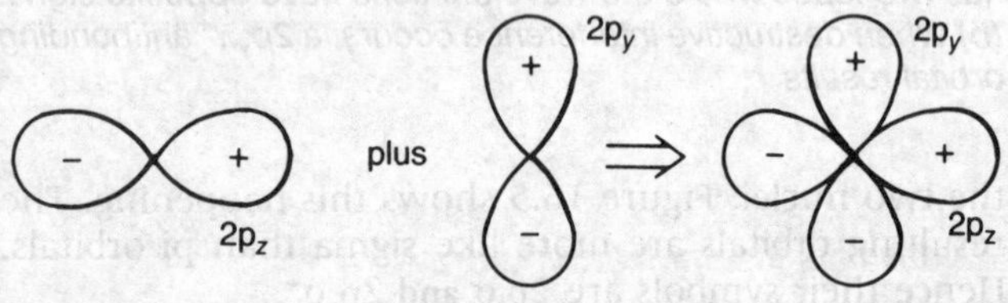

Figure 16.6 *Two p orbitals that point in different directions cannot overlap properly. They do not have the correct symmetry*

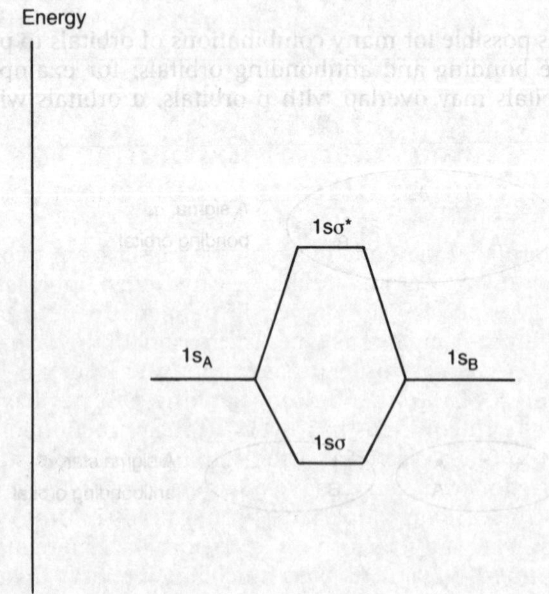

Figure 16.7 *When the 1s orbitals of identical atoms overlap, the bonding σ orbital is lower in energy than the two separate 1s orbitals. The σ* antibonding orbital, is higher in energy than the two 1s orbitals*

16.6 Molecular orbitals for homopolar diatomic molecules

Homopolar diatomic molecules have two identical atoms, e.g. H_2, O_2, N_2, F_2. We can build up the molecular orbital energy level diagram for any of these molecules in the following way. First, using our energy rule, 1s will overlap with 1s, 2s with 2s, 2p with 2p, and so on. Secondly, the symmetry rule means that only some of the combinations of orbitals will produce molecular orbitals. The resulting patterns of bonding and antibonding orbitals are shown in Figure 16.8.

Having decided upon the diagram, we now have to place the electrons in the molecular orbitals. To do this

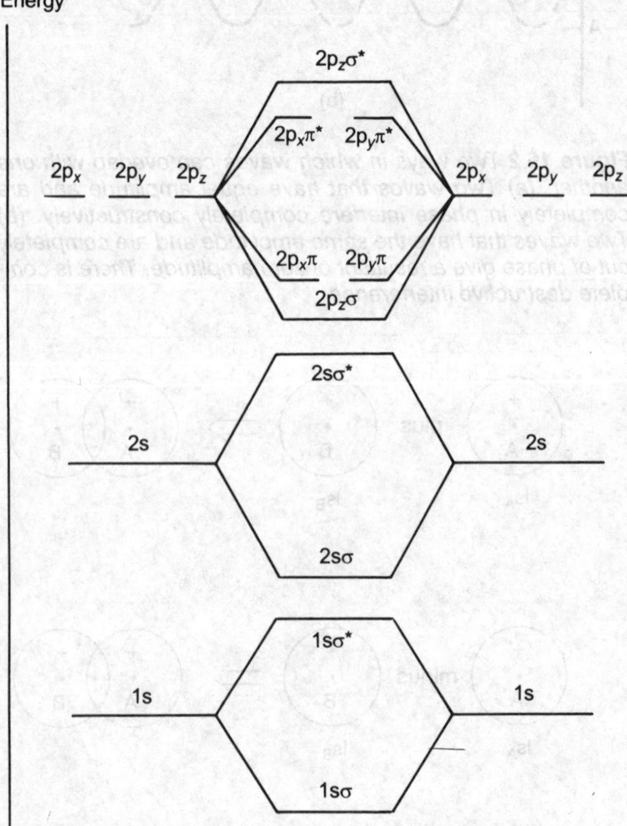

Figure 16.8 *The molecular orbital energy diagram for homopolar diatomic molecules such as H_2, N_2, O_2, F_2*

we use exactly the same rules as in the *aufbau* method for atoms. In particular, we put electrons into orbitals with the lowest available energy; but we must obey the Pauli principle and Hund's rule. You can see the method at work in the following examples.

(a) *Hydrogen molecule*, H_2

There are two electrons. They will both go into the 1sσ bonding orbital. All the other orbitals are empty. Therefore we can write the electron structure as $1s\sigma^2$.

(b) *Oxygen molecule*, O_2

With each atom bringing eight electrons, there is a total of 16 to fit into the molecular orbitals. The first two go into the 1sσ bonding orbital. The next orbital is the 1sσ* antibonding orbital. This will take the next pair of electrons. Similarly, we put two more electrons into each of the 2sσ and 2sσ* orbitals. This leaves eight more. There are three more bonding orbitals, the $2p_z\sigma$, $2p_x\pi$ and $2p_y\pi$, which will take two electrons each. This leaves two electrons. The next orbitals are $2p_x\pi^*$ and $2p_y\pi^*$ antibonding orbitals. They are degenerate (i.e. they have the same energy), so to keep the repulsions between the electrons as low as possible, one electron will go into the $2p_x\pi^*$ and one into the $2p_y\pi^*$ orbital. This gives us the molecular orbital diagram of Figure 16.9. The electron structure can be written

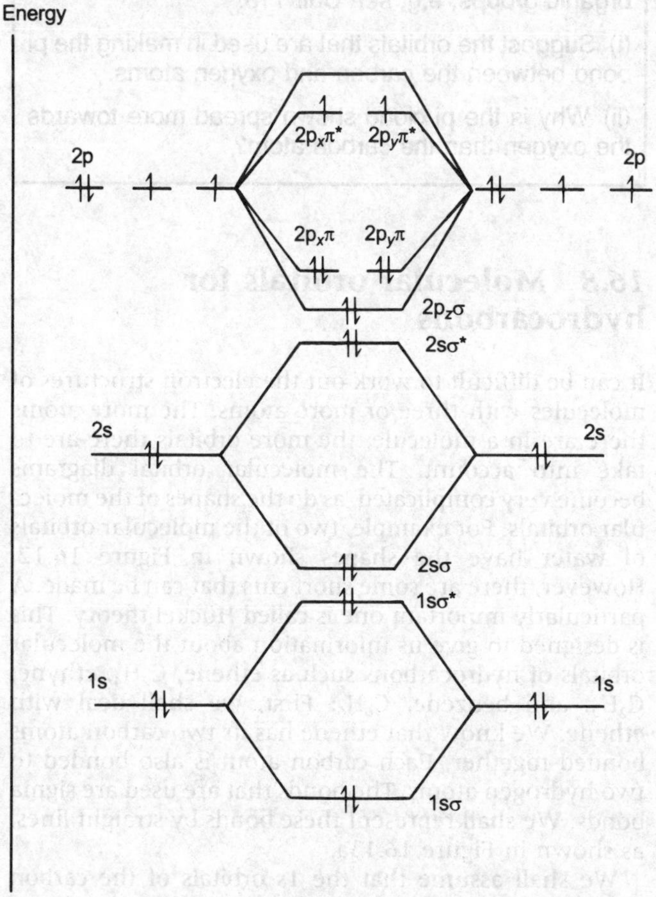

$$(1s\sigma)^2(1s\sigma^*)^2(2s\sigma)^2(2s\sigma^*)^2$$
$$(2p_z\sigma)^2(2p_x\pi)^2(2p_y\pi)^2(2p_x\pi^*)^1(2p_y\pi^*)^1$$

Figure 16.9 *The molecular orbital diagram for oxygen. Note the two unpaired electrons in the $2p_x\pi^*$ and $2p_y\pi^*$ orbitals. These electrons are responsible for the paramagnetism of oxygen*

Notice that electrons do go into the antibonding orbitals. An electron in an antibonding orbital can be *more* energetically stable that an electron in a bonding orbital of higher energy. Do not let the name 'antibonding' persuade you that putting an electron into an antibonding orbital will necessarily make a molecule fall apart.

Also, the last two electrons keep their spins parallel. This means that their magnetic fields will not cancel each other out, which tends to happen when electrons have their spins paired. Therefore, according to molecular orbital theory, oxygen should be magnetic. Indeed, experiment proves this to be the case. Thus we can have some confidence that the molecular orbital method is on the right track.

16.1 (i) Draw the dot-and-cross diagram for oxygen.

(ii) How many unpaired electrons does it show? What conclusions can you draw?

16.2 Using molecular orbital theory, work out the electron structure of the fluorine molecule, F_2.

16.3 The type of magnetism that oxygen has is called *paramagnetism*. Use your answer to question 16.2 to decide if F_2 is paramagnetic.

16.7 Molecular orbitals for heteropolar diatomic molecules

Heteropolar diatomic molecules are built from two different types of atom. We shall use hydrogen fluoride, HF, as an example. This molecule happens to be a fairly extreme example of its type. The reason for this is that on the one hand hydrogen has one proton in its nucleus, whereas on the other fluorine has nine. One result is that the fluorine nucleus has a very strong attraction for the surrounding electrons. Atoms that have such strong attractions are said to have a large *electronegativity*. (We shall take a longer look at electronegativity in Unit 19.) If you were an electron in a 1s orbital belonging to fluorine, you would have a much lower energy than the electron in the 1s orbital of hydrogen. In fact the energy of the hydrogen 1s orbital is much nearer to that of the fluorine 2p orbitals. This is shown in Figure 16.10.

The two lowest energy molecular orbitals of hydrogen fluoride are essentially the same orbitals as the 1s and 2s

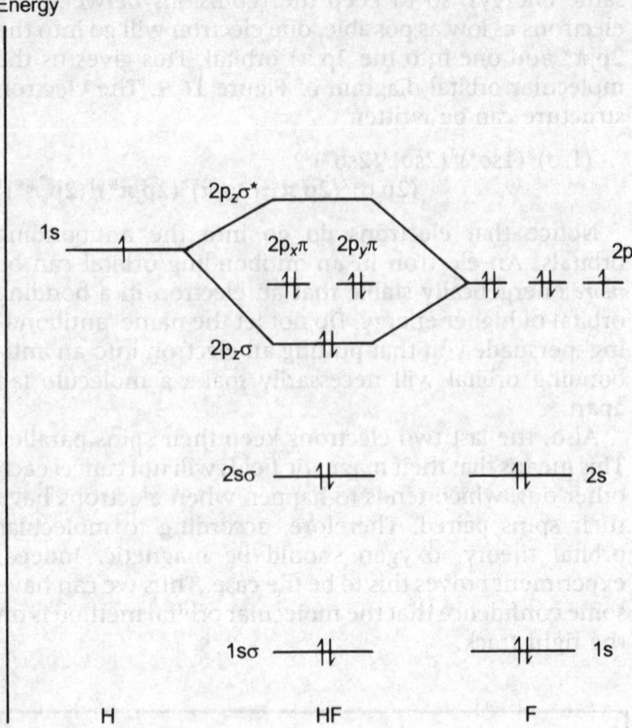

***Figure 16.10** The molecular orbital diagram for hydrogen fluoride*

orbitals of fluorine; there are no hydrogen orbitals with the right range of energy to interact with them. However, the hydrogen 1s can overlap with the $2p_z$ orbital of fluorine to form $2p_z\sigma$ and $2p_z\sigma^*$ orbitals. For reasons of symmetry the 1s orbital cannot successfully overlap with the fluorine $2p_x$ and $2p_y$ orbitals. These two orbitals form the basis of the $2p_x\pi$ and $2p_y\pi$ molecular orbitals. Now we can build up the electron structure of hydrogen fluoride:

$$(1s\sigma)^2(2s\sigma)^2(2p_z\sigma)^2(2p_x\pi)^2(2p_y\pi)^2$$

The molecular orbitals of other heteropolar molecules can be established in a similar way.

16.4 Nitrogen monoxide, NO, is a heteropolar diatomic molecule. However, nitrogen and oxygen are not so very different in their abilities to attract electrons (i.e. they have similar electronegativities). In this question, assume that their molecular orbitals are in the same order as those in Figure 16.9 for oxygen.

(i) How many electrons have to be fitted into the orbitals?

(ii) Place the electrons into the orbitals, starting with the lowest energy orbital, and write down the electron structure of nitrogen monoxide.

(iii) Are there any unpaired electrons?

(iv) Would you expect nitrogen monoxide to be paramagnetic?

16.5 In Figure 16.11 you can see a diagram representing the bonding between carbon and oxygen atoms in a carbonyl group. A carbonyl group is represented on paper as >C=O

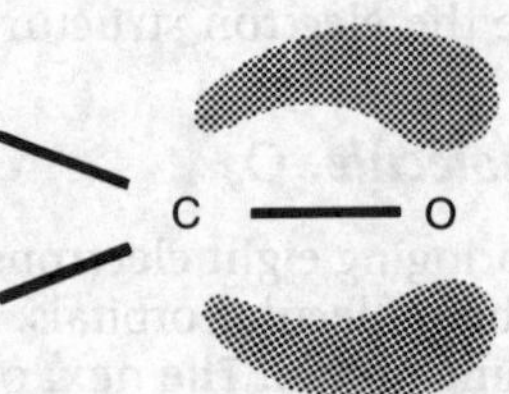

***Figure 16.11** There is a double bond in a carbonyl group, consisting of a σ and a π orbital*

indicating that there is a double bond between the carbon and oxygen atoms. The two 'spare' bonds to the carbon atom can be made to hydrogen atoms or organic groups; e.g. see Unit 118.

(i) Suggest the orbitals that are used in making the pi bond between the carbon and oxygen atoms.

(ii) Why is the pi cloud shown spread more towards the oxygen than the carbon atom?

16.8 Molecular orbitals for hydrocarbons

It can be difficult to work out the electron structures of molecules with three or more atoms. The more atoms there are in a molecule, the more orbitals there are to take into account. The molecular orbital diagrams become very complicated, as do the shapes of the molecular orbitals. For example, two of the molecular orbitals of water have the shapes shown in Figure 16.12. However, there are some short cuts that can be made. A particularly important one is called Hückel theory. This is designed to give us information about the molecular orbitals of hydrocarbons such as ethene, C_2H_4, ethyne, C_2H_2, and benzene, C_6H_6. First, we shall deal with ethene. We know that ethene has its two carbon atoms bonded together. Each carbon atom is also bonded to two hydrogen atoms. The bonds that are used are sigma bonds. We shall represent these bonds by straight lines, as shown in Figure 16.13a.

We shall assume that the 1s orbitals of the carbon atoms are not used in forming the sigma bonds. Therefore we have to keep track of 12 electrons in all. (Four electrons from each carbon plus four electrons from the four hydrogen atoms.) Ten electrons are used in the five sigma bonds. This leaves two electrons, one in a 2p

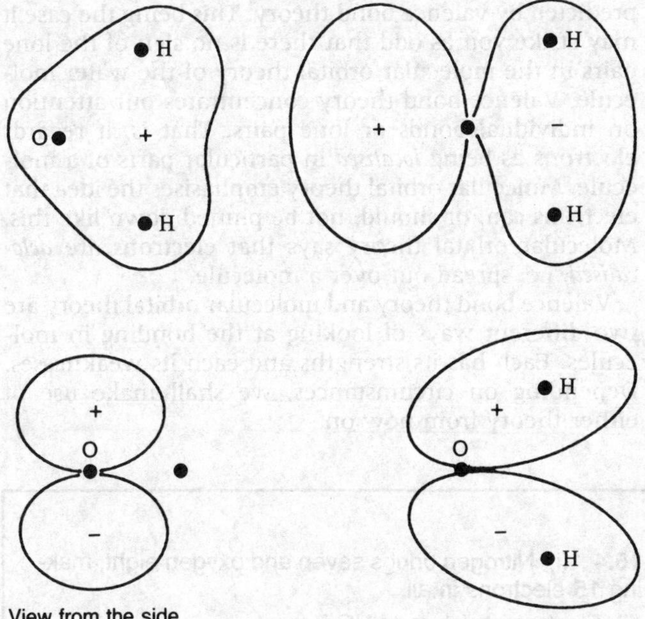

Figure 16.12 *Four molecular orbitals of water. Three of them are viewed looking down on the plane of the molecule, one from the side. Notice that a lone pair orbital is nowhere to be seen*

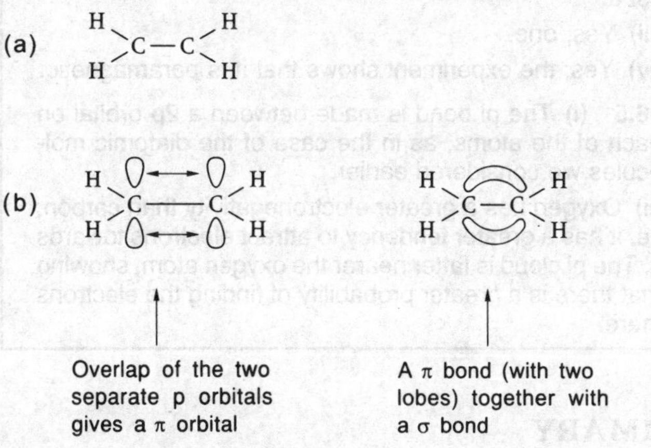

Figure 16.13 *(a) The σ framework of ethene, C_2H_4. (b) How the π orbital in ethene is made*

orbital on each carbon as shown in Figure 16.13b. Hückel theory says that these 2p orbitals form the basis of bonding pi (and antibonding pi) molecular orbitals, as shown in Figure 16.13b.

The combination of sigma and pi bonds between the carbon atoms is called a *double bond*.

The method can be extended to any hydrocarbon that has double bonds. Two examples are shown in Figure 16.14.

Benzene is a very important molecule. It has a wide range of applications in industry. For many years it provided chemists with a considerable puzzle. Its formula was known to be C_6H_6, but how were the atoms arranged in space? Much of the credit for finding the correct solution goes to August Kekulé.

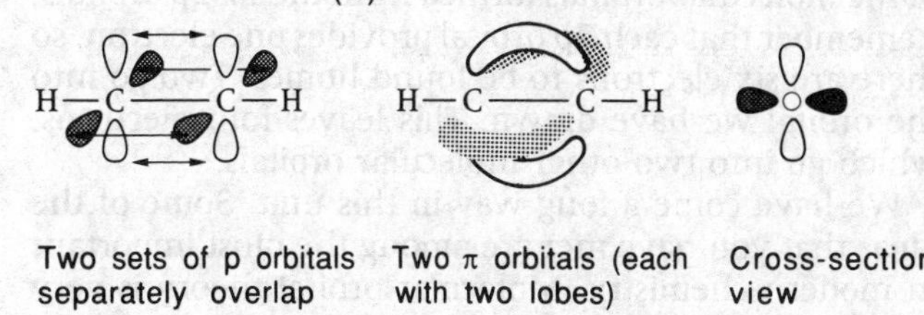

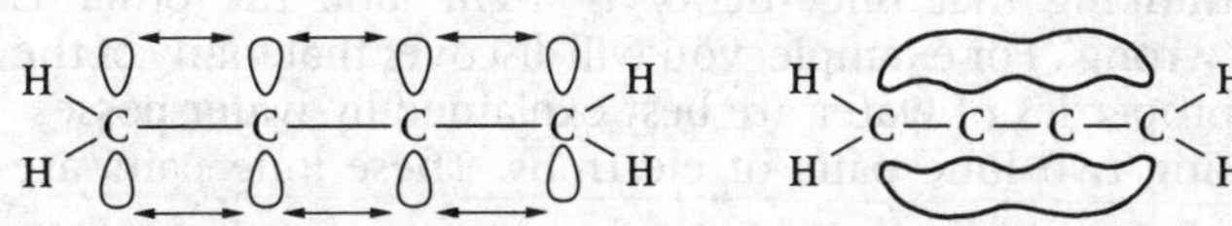

The overlap of four separate p orbitals leads to a delocalised π orbital. Each of the two central carbon atoms has a hydrogen bonded to it (not shown)

Figure 16.14 *(a) The origin of the two π orbitals in ethyne, C_2H_2. The short way of showing the bonding is H—C≡C—H. The triple bond is made from one σ and two π bonds. (b) The usual way of writing the formula of buta-1,3-diene is CH_2=CH—CH=CH_2. However, molecular orbital theory says that instead of two separate π bonds, there is a set of π bonds that can spread over the carbon atoms. The electrons in the π orbitals are delocalised over the entire molecule*

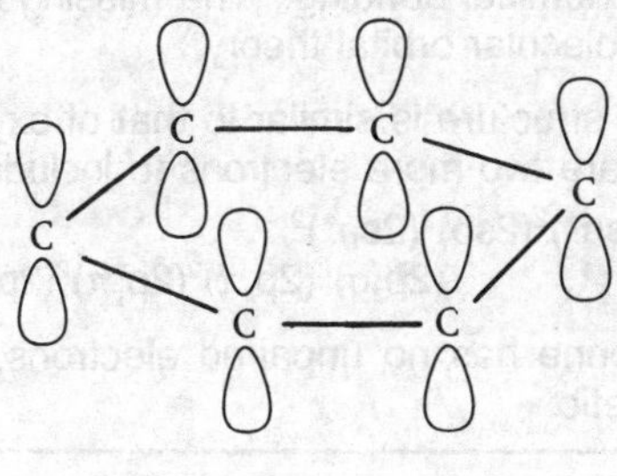

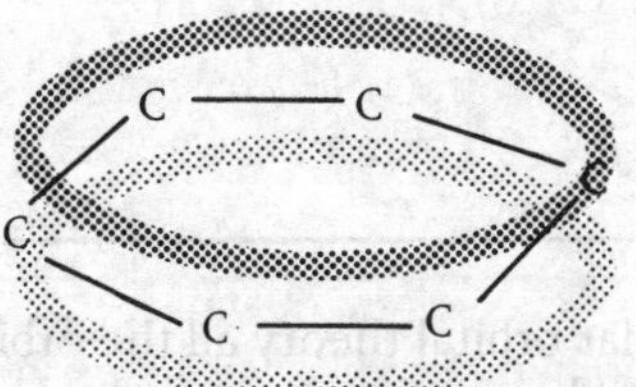

Delocalised π cloud of electrons (much simplified)

Figure 16.15 *The overlap of a p orbital on each of the six carbon atoms in benzene, C_6H_6, leads to π molecular orbitals, one of which spreads over all of the carbon atoms; i.e. the π electrons in benzene are delocalised. (Note: for convenience the hydrogen atoms have not been shown in the diagram)*

Hückel theory can be applied to benzene in much the same way as for ethene. A major difference is that the pi bond that is formed stretches in a ring around the molecule.

The pi orbital that is shown in Figure 16.15 is only one

of the molecular orbitals formed from the six 2p orbitals. Remember that each 2p orbital provides one electron, so there are six electrons to be found homes. Two go into the orbital we have drawn. This leaves four electrons, which go into two other molecular orbitals.

We have come a long way in this unit. Some of the ideas that you have met are among the most important in modern chemistry. Molecular orbital theory is very powerful. It is able to provide an explanation for many properties of molecules with which valence bond theory has difficulties. However, do not fall into the trap of thinking that one theory is 'right' and the other is 'wrong'. For example, you will discover that many of the properties of water are best explained by water possessing two lone pairs of electrons. These lone pairs are predicted by valence bond theory. This being the case it may strike you as odd that there is no sign of the lone pairs in the molecular orbital theory of the water molecule. Valence bond theory concentrates our attention on individual bonds or lone pairs. That is, it regards electrons as being *localised* in particular parts of a molecule. Molecular orbital theory emphasises the idea that electrons can, or should, not be pinned down like this. Molecular orbital theory says that electrons are *delocalised*, i.e. spread out over a molecule.

Valence bond theory and molecular orbital theory are two different ways of looking at the bonding in molecules. Each has its strengths and each its weaknesses. Depending on circumstances, we shall make use of either theory from now on.

Answers

16.1 (i) This is shown in Figure 16.16.

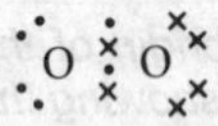

Figure 16.16 The dot-and-cross diagram for oxygen shows a double bond between the atoms, together with two lone pairs on each atom. There is no sign of unpaired electrons

(ii) There are no unpaired electrons in the diagram. Experiment shows that oxygen does have two unpaired electrons. Valence bond theory cannot be a complete theory of chemical bonding. (The missing bits are supplied by molecular orbital theory.)

16.2 The structure is similar to that of oxygen, except that there are two more electrons to include:

$$(1s\sigma)^2(1s\sigma^*)^2(2s\sigma)^2(2s\sigma^*)^2$$
$$(2p_z\sigma)^2(2p_x\pi)^2(2p_y\pi)^2(2p_x\pi^*)^2(2p_y\pi^*)^2$$

16.3 Fluorine has no unpaired electrons, so it is not paramagnetic.

16.4 (i) Nitrogen brings seven and oxygen eight, making 15 electrons in all.

(ii) Electron structure of NO is

$$(1s\sigma)^2(1s\sigma^*)^2(2s\sigma)^2(2s\sigma^*)^2(2p_z\sigma)^2(2p_x\pi)^2(2p_y\pi)^2(2p_x\pi^*)^1$$

or

$$(1s\sigma)^2(1s\sigma^*)^2(2s\sigma)^2(2s\sigma^*)^2(2p_z\sigma)^2(2p_x\pi)^2(2p_y\pi)^2(2p_y\pi^*)^1$$

We cannot tell which of the $2p_x\pi^*$ or $2p_y\pi^*$ orbitals is used.

(iii) Yes, one.

(iv) Yes; the experiment shows that it is paramagnetic.

16.5 (i) The pi bond is made between a 2p orbital on each of the atoms, as in the case of the diatomic molecules we considered earlier.

(ii) Oxygen has a greater electronegativity than carbon; i.e. it has a greater tendency to attract electrons towards it. The pi cloud is fatter nearer the oxygen atom, showing that there is a greater probability of finding the electrons there.

UNIT 16 SUMMARY

- In molecular orbital theory all the orbitals in the ion or molecule are assumed to take part in bonding. The individual orbitals are combined to give the molecular orbitals, which may stretch over the entire molecule (or ion).
- The molecular orbitals are filled with electrons using the same rules that apply to atoms (see Unit 12).

17

Shapes of molecules

17.1 Molecular models

There is now a great deal of evidence from X-ray diffraction and spectroscopy that allows us to describe the shapes of molecules ranging from the smallest, e.g. water, to the largest, e.g. a protein. In this unit we shall often show the shapes of molecules using diagrams of models. It is most important that you make molecular models yourself, or look at some that are already made.

There are a number of types of molecular model that you might use. The simplest, and cheapest, use plastic tubes to represent bonds, and small plastic rings to represent atoms. A second type has small metal springs for bonds, and plastic balls for atoms. These are easier to see, but for models of larger molecules they can lose their shape.

More expensive, but very good, are systems that use hollow plastic balls made to the same scale as the atoms that they represent. These fit together very neatly but it is quite easy to lose sight of the bonds.

Finally, a type known as PEEL models are very good for showing the volume of space taken up by the electron clouds in a molecule. The framework of the molecule may be made using the ball and spring method, and pieces of expanded polystyrene are placed around the springs to show the sigma and pi bonds.

There is a colour code used for showing atoms in models. The code is shown in Table 17.1.

Table 17.1. Model colour code

Atom	*Colour*
Carbon	Black
Chlorine	Green
Hydrogen	White
Nitrogen	Blue
Oxygen	Red
Sulphur	Yellow

17.2 Electron repulsion theory

The most straightforward way of explaining why molecules take up the shapes they do is known as electron repulsion theory. First we need to remember that electrons are negatively charged. Therefore, bonds between atoms are regions where there is a lot of negative charge. Similarly, lone pairs of electrons are regions of negative charge. There is a difference between bonding and lone pairs of electrons, though. Bonding electrons are spread out so that they spend time around both atoms in the bond. Lone pairs are attached to one atom only. The result is that lone pairs tend to congregate in a smaller volume of space than do bonding pairs. In other words, the negative charge is more concentrated in a lone pair than in a bonding pair.

Table 17.2. Order of repulsion strength

Strongest	*Medium*	*Weakest*
Lone pair–lone pair	Lone pair–bond pair	Bond pair–bond pair

One outcome is that, if you were to bring a bonding pair close to another bonding pair, they will repel each other; but if you brought a bonding pair just as close to a lone pair, these two would repel each other even more. Two lone pairs brought together would repel the most of all. You have now discovered the basic ideas of electron repulsion theory (Table 17.2). We can summarise it in this way:

> **Molecules take up the shape that minimises the repulsions between the bonding and lone pairs of electrons.**

The best way to see how the theory works is to apply it to some real cases; this is what we shall do now.

(a) *Beryllium chloride*, $BeCl_2$

An individual molecule of beryllium chloride is known to be linear (Figure 17.1). There are two bond pairs, and the only lone pairs are on the chlorine atoms. The bond pairs are arranged as far apart as possible: this minimises the repulsions between them.

Cl—Be—Cl

Figure 17.1 Beryllium chloride

A sample of solid beryllium chloride has a different arrangement of the atoms; see Figure 15.4.

(b) *Boron trichloride*, BCl_3

Here there are three bond pairs around the boron atom (Figure 17.2). The three equal bond angles of 120° mean that the chlorine atoms are all equally far apart. The only lone pairs are on the chlorine atoms.

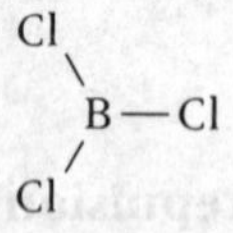

Figure 17.2 Boron trichloride

(c) *Carbon dioxide*, CO_2

Like beryllium chloride, carbon dioxide is linear (Figure 17.3). Carbon dioxide is a little more complicated, though, because it has double bonds between the carbon and oxygen atoms. There are no lone pairs on the central carbon atom, so there is no reason for the molecule to be bent.

O=C=O

Figure 17.3 Carbon dioxide

(d) *Methane*, CH_4

There are four bond pairs, but no lone pairs (Figure 17.4). At first sight the best arrangement is to make the molecule flat so that the bonds are at 90° to each other. However, it is possible to increase the angle between the bonds to over 109° if the molecule takes up a tetrahedral shape. The perfect tetrahedral angle is 109° 28′, i.e. almost 109.5°. Compounds that have only single bonds to carbon atoms have shapes that are all based on a tetrahedron.

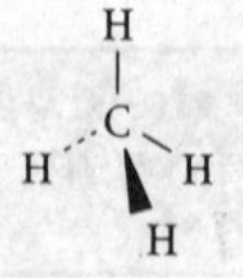

Figure 17.4 Methane

(e) *Ammonia*, NH_3

There are three bond pairs and the nitrogen has one lone pair (Figure 17.5). If there were four bond pairs we would predict the same perfectly tetrahedral shape as methane. However, the lone pair makes a difference. The greater repulsion between the lone pair and the bond pairs means that the angle between them will be greater than the angle between the bond pairs. The ammonia molecule is a slightly distorted tetrahedron with the H–N–H bond angle equal to 107°.

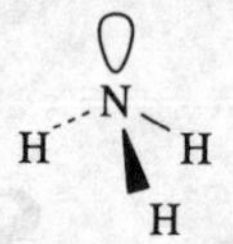

Figure 17.5 Ammonia

(f) *Water*, H_2O

Here there are two bond pairs together with two lone pairs on the oxygen atom (Figure 17.6). The effect of the two lone pairs is to squeeze the two bond pairs even further together than they are in ammonia. The H–O–H angle is 104.5°.

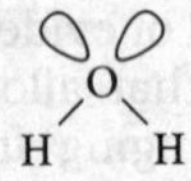

Figure 17.6 Water

17.3 The isoelectronic rule

The word 'isoelectronic' means 'having the same number of electrons'. In what follows we shall talk about molecules or ions with the same number of *valence* electrons as being isoelectronic. The isoelectronic rule says that:

> **Molecules or ions that are isoelectronic will have similar shapes.**

We can split the more common molecules into four types. They have either two, three, four, or five atoms. We can write their general formulae as AB, AB_2, AB_3 and AB_4. The simplest type, AB, are bound to be linear. Molecules of the other types can have a variety of shapes.

To begin with, let us use our previous examples of beryllium chloride and carbon dioxide. These are the AB_2 type, and both are linear. The question is, are they isoelectronic (as far as their valence electrons are concerned)? If you look at Table 17.3 you will see that they are: both have 16 valence electrons in total. AB_2 molecules like NO_2 and OCl_2 that do not have 16 valence electrons are not linear. These molecules have a lone pair, which is responsible for distorting the shape.

The triangular planar molecules BCl_3 and $AlCl_3$ both have 24 valence electrons, whereas PCl_3, which does not have 24 valence electrons, is pyramidal. Needless to say PCl_3 has a lone pair on the phosphorus atom. The lone pair pushes the phosphorus–chlorine bonds down. Molecules of the type AB_4 are not very common, but both CCl_4 and $SiCl_4$, which have 32 valence electrons, are tetrahedral. These results are summarised in Table 17.4.

Table 17.3. Numbers of valence electrons for some molecules

Molecule	*Valence electrons of atoms*		*Total valence electrons*	*Shape*
$BeCl_2$	Be: $2s^2$	Cl: $2s^22p^5$	$2+(2\times7) = 16$	Linear
CO_2	C: $2s^22p^2$	O: $2s^22p^4$	$4+(2\times6) = 16$	Linear
NO_2	N: $2s^22p^3$	O: $2s^22p^4$	$5+(2\times6) = 17$	Bent
OCl_2	O: $2s^22p^4$	Cl: $2s^22p^5$	$6+(2\times7) = 20$	Bent
BCl_3	B: $2s^22p$	Cl: $2s^22p^5$	$3+(3\times7) = 24$	Planar
$AlCl_3$	Al: $3s^23p$	Cl: $2s^22p^5$	$3+(3\times7) = 24$	Planar
PCl_3	P: $3s^23p^3$	Cl: $2s^22p^5$	$5+(3\times7) = 26$	Pyramidal
CCl_4	C: $2s^22p^2$	Cl: $2s^22p^5$	$4+(4\times7) = 32$	Tetrahedral
$SiCl_4$	Si: $3s^23p^2$	Cl: $2s^22p^5$	$4+(4\times7) = 32$	Tetrahedral

Table 17.4. The isoelectronic rule and 'magic' numbers

Molecule type	*'Magic' number**	*Shape*
AB_2	16	Linear
AB_3	24	Planar
AB_4	32	Tetrahedral

*Molecules without these numbers are often distorted. However, those with hydrogen bonded to the atom A (AH_2, AH_3, AH_4), e.g. OH_2 (water), NH_3, CH_4, do *not* fit the rule

17.4 Hybridisation

There are one or two problems lurking in the background of the work we have done on bonding and shapes of molecules. One of them is about explaining why, for example, methane has four bonds rather than two or three. Another problem is how s and p orbitals can give rise to bonding orbitals that take up such a wide range of angles to one another. We shall take these two problems in turn and use methane as our example.

(a) *Why are there four bonds in methane?*

Look again at the ground state electron structure of carbon, as shown in Figure 17.7. You can see that, although there are four valence electrons, two of them (the 2s electrons) are paired, and have different energies from the two 2p electrons. If we imagine hydrogen atoms approaching a carbon atom, we can easily see how two carbon–hydrogen bonds can form. The two unpaired hydrogen electrons could pair up with the two unpaired 2p carbon electrons. This would give us a formula of CH_2; but how do the other two bonds come about to give CH_4? One answer is that one of the 2s electrons is promoted to the empty 2p orbital. If this happens, there will be four unpaired electrons able to make four bonds (Figure 17.8).

The question is, where does the energy come from to excite the 2s electron into the empty 2p orbital? Before answering this, we should give a little more thought to the problem. At some stage during the reaction, hydrogen atoms must attach themselves to the carbon atom. Each hydrogen atom that comes near the carbon atom brings the electric charge of its proton and electron. This extra charge is bound to upset the energies of the electrons in the carbon atom. That is, we are not entitled to think that the energy level diagram of the ground state is the correct diagram for a carbon atom during a reaction. As a consequence we are unlikely to be right in thinking that the reaction happens in separate stages where *first* the 2s electron gains energy, goes into the empty 2p orbital, and *then* the reaction takes place. Things are certainly not as straightforward as this.

However, energy *is* needed at some stage to unpair the 2s electrons. We believe that the driving force for the reaction is the large amount of energy (about 1700 kJ mol^{-1}) released when four carbon–hydrogen bonds are made. Some of this energy goes into unpairing the 2s electrons.

2p

2s

1s

Figure 17.7 *The ground state electron structure of carbon*

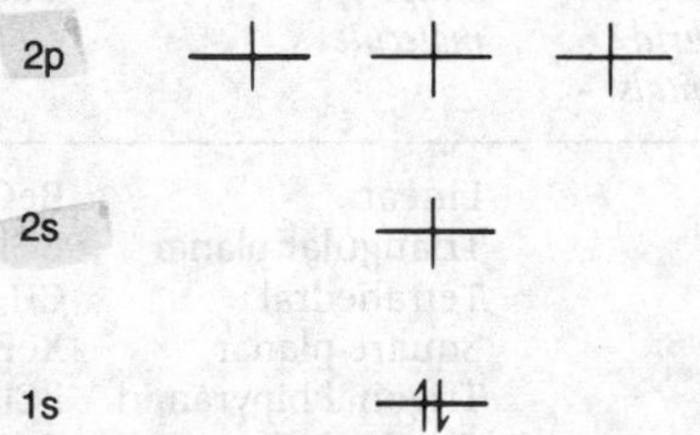

Figure 17.8 *The electron structure for a carbon atom that has gained sufficient energy for one of its 2s electrons to enter the empty 2p orbital. There are now four unpaired electrons. (Note: as this is a hypothetical state of a carbon atom we cannot say what the orientations of the spins would be. For this reason the heads are left off the arrows)*

(b) *How do* s *and* p *orbitals combine to give four bonds at 109.5° to each other?*

Let us take for granted the idea that a 2s electron of carbon is promoted to a 2p orbital. Then we have four orbitals available for bonding but, as they stand, one is spherically symmetric and the other three point at right angles to one another.

To explain how these orbitals give rise to four bonds pointing to the corners of a tetrahedron you would need to know a great deal more about Schrödinger's wave theory than is possible at this level of chemistry. For the present, you may just have to accept that one 2s and three 2p orbitals *can* overlap and interfere with one another in such a way that four new orbitals appear. The name of the theory that lies behind this method of combining orbitals is called *hybridisation*. When one s and three p orbitals combine together the orbitals they make are called sp^3 hybrid orbitals.

It is possible to produce a wide range of different hybrid orbitals. For example, this can be done by mixing one s and two p orbitals to give a set of three sp^2 hybrid orbitals. These take up the shape of the orbitals in boron trichloride. It is possible to obtain some really fancy shapes by mixing d orbitals with s and p orbitals. You will find a number of examples in Table 17.5 and Figure 17.9.

Hybridisation is a useful theory, but we should be careful not to misunderstand it. The theory does *not* predict the shapes of molecules. We have to find out the shape of a molecule from experiment *before* we can decide which orbitals to combine. Also, atoms do not know anything about hybridisation. Hybridisation is not a property of molecules like, for example, their shape or mass. The theory has been made up by chemists, and not all chemists like the theory. If you believe in valence bond theory, then you may like hybridisation theory; if you prefer molecular orbital theory, then you may prefer to do without the theory. Often electron repulsion theory gives us a believable explanation of why molecules adopt one shape rather than another.

Table 17.5. Some examples of hybrid orbitals

*Hybrid**	*Number of hybrid orbitals*	*Shape of molecule*	*Example*
sp	2	Linear	$BeCl_2$
sp^2	3	Triangular planar	BCl_3
sp^3	4	Tetrahedral	CH_4
dsp^2	4	Square planar	XeF_4
dsp^3	5	Trigonal bipyramid	PCl_5
d^2sp^3	6	Octahedral	$Co(NH_3)_6^{2+}$, SF_6
d^3s	4	Tetrahedral	MnO_4^-

*dsp^2 is the combination 4s, $3p_x$, $3p_y$, $3d_{x^2-y^2}$
dsp^3 is the combination 4s, $3p_x$, $3p_y$, $3p_z$, $3d_{z^2}$
d^2sp^3 is the combination 4s, $3p_x$, $3p_y$, $3p_z$, $3d_{z^2}$, $3d_{x^2-y^2}$
d^3s is the combination 4s, $3d_{xy}$, $3d_{xz}$, $3d_{yz}$

You should now be in a good position to use the theory and apply it to many, if not all, the molecules that you come across. Probably you will know by now that even the best of theories has the annoying habit of not working perfectly all the time; and so it is with this theory. There are a number of factors that we have not taken into account. One of these is that the shape that a molecule takes up can be different depending on whether the molecule exists as a gas or as a solid. We have applied the theory only to individual molecules, as if they were all gases. In a solid, the structure of the molecule can be disturbed by the electron clouds of neighbouring molecules. This means that bonding pairs and lone pairs are not the only repulsions to be considered. Indeed, molecules that are separate in a gas can join to form new structures when in the solid state. Sometimes this happens through the formation of the type of covalent bonding called dative covalent bonding or coordinate bonding that we considered in Unit 15.

17.1 A student wrote the following explanation of why methane is tetrahedral:

> The only correct way of describing the bonding in methane is to form sp^3 hybrid orbitals. These orbitals predict that the methane molecule should be tetrahedral. This agrees with experiment and proves the theory of hybridisation to be correct.

Write a few sentences explaining why the student has misunderstood the theory of hybridisation.

17.2 Draw dot-and-cross diagrams for the following molecules. Then use electron repulsion theory to predict or explain their shapes.

(i) Tetrachloromethane, CCl_4.

(ii) Hydrogen sulphide, H_2S.

(iii) Nitrogen trifluoride, NF_3.

(iv) Nitrogen monoxide, NO.

(v) Aluminium trichloride, $AlCl_3$.

17.3 How many valence electrons do (i) NF_3 and (ii) SO_2 have? What does the isoelectronic rule predict for their shapes?

17.4 The ethene molecule, C_2H_4, has a pi bond between the two carbons. If we ignore this bond and just draw the sigma bonds, the molecule looks like this:

```
H         H
 \       /
  C — C
 /       \
H         H
```

The angle between the bonds is approximately 120°. If you use hybridisation to explain this shape, what type of hybridisation would you need?

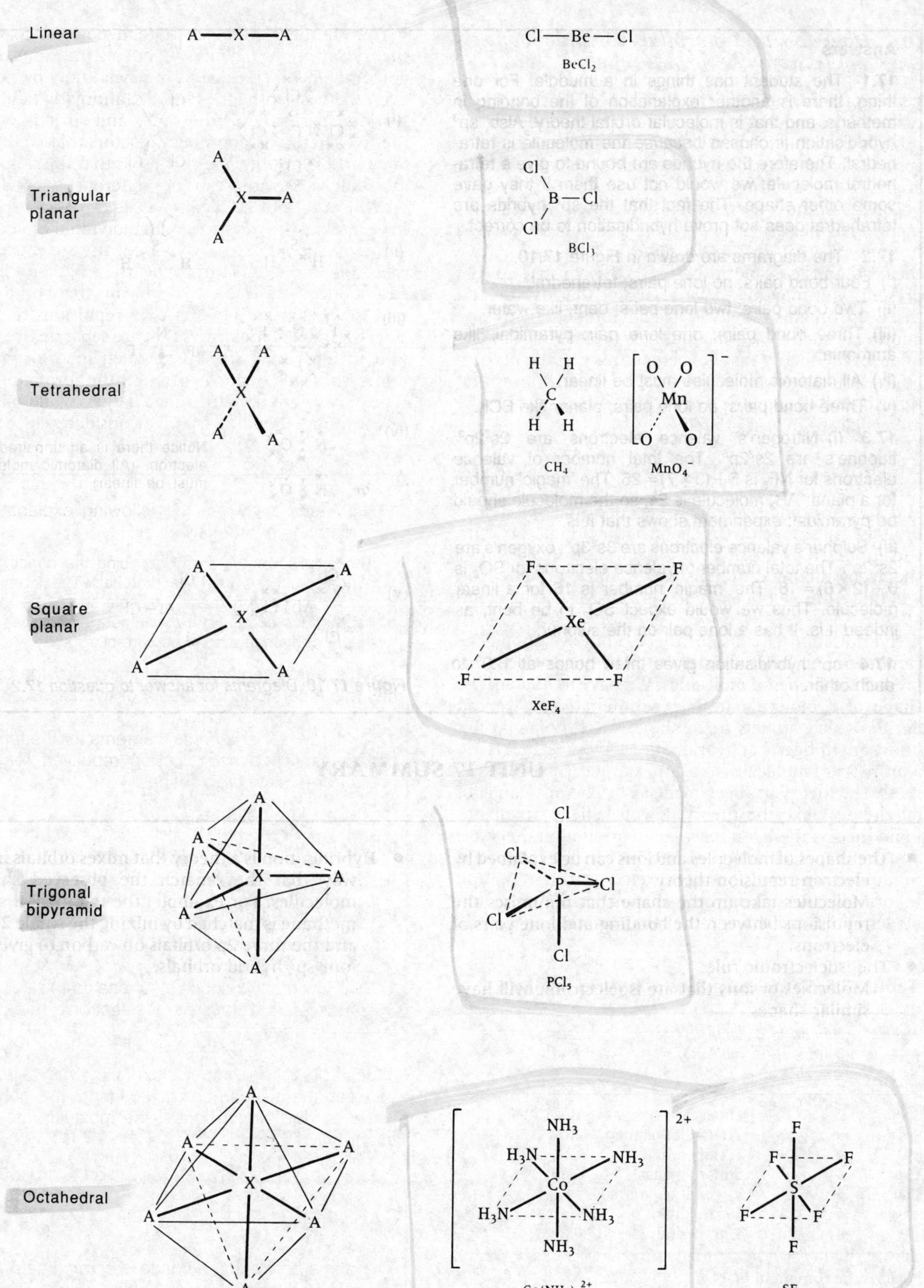

***Figure 17.9** The shapes of molecules listed in Table 17.5*

Answers

17.1 The student has things in a muddle. For one thing, there is another explanation of the bonding in methane, and that is molecular orbital theory. Also, sp^3 hybridisation is chosen *because* the molecule is tetrahedral. Therefore the hybrids are bound to give a tetrahedral molecule; we would not use them if they gave some other shape. The fact that the sp^3 hybrids are tetrahedral does not prove hybridisation to be correct.

17.2 The diagrams are drawn in Figure 17.10.

(i) Four bond pairs; no lone pairs; tetrahedral.

(ii) Two bond pairs; two lone pairs; bent, like water.

(iii) Three bond pairs; one lone pair; pyramidal, like ammonia.

(iv) All diatomic molecules must be linear.

(v) Three bond pairs; no lone pairs; planar like BCl_3.

17.3 (i) Nitrogen's valence electrons are $2s^22p^3$; fluorine's are $2s^22p^5$. The total number of valence electrons for NF_3 is $5+(3\times7)=26$. The 'magic' number for a planar AB_3 molecule is 24, so the molecule should be pyramidal; experiment shows that it is.

(ii) Sulphur's valence electrons are $3s^23p^4$; oxygen's are $2s^22p^4$. The total number of valence electrons for SO_2 is $6+(2\times6)=18$. The 'magic' number is 16 for a linear molecule. Thus we would expect SO_2 to be bent, as indeed it is. It has a lone pair on the sulphur.

17.4 sp^2 hybridisation gives three bonds at 120° to each other.

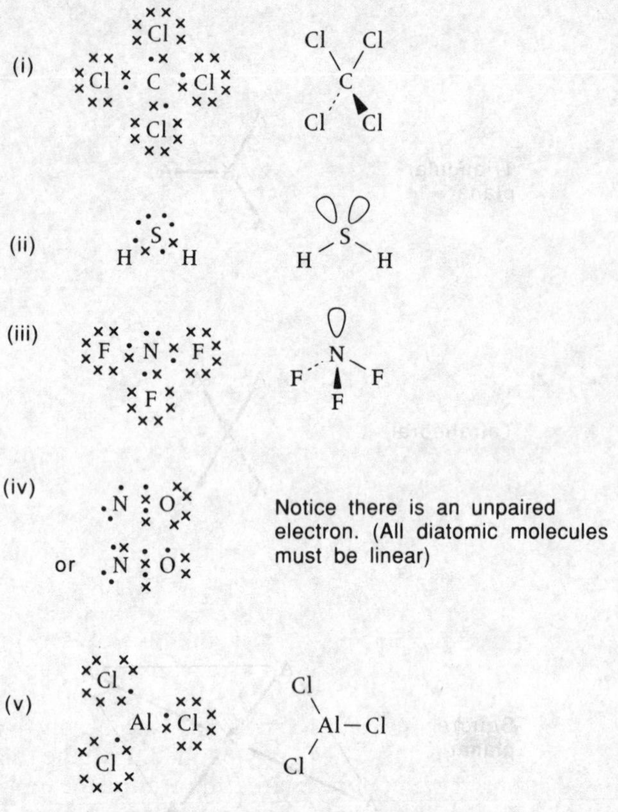

Notice there is an unpaired electron. (All diatomic molecules must be linear)

Figure 17.10 *Diagrams for answer to question 17.2*

UNIT 17 SUMMARY

- The shapes of molecules and ions can be explained by electron repulsion theory:
  Molecules take up the shape that minimises the repulsions between the bonding and lone pairs of electrons.
- The isoelectronic rule:
  Molecules or ions that are isoelectronic will have similar shapes.
- Hybridisation is a theory that mixes orbitals in such a way that they match the observed shapes of molecules. For example, the tetrahedral shape of methane is matched by mixing the single 2s orbital and the three 2p orbitals on carbon to give a set of four sp^3 hybrid orbitals.

18

Ionic bonding

18.1 Covalent substances have some ionic character

At the heart of both valence bond and molecular orbital theory is the idea that atoms join by sharing their electrons. In other words, both theories concentrate on covalent bonding. However, it would be unwise to think that there is such a thing as completely pure covalent bonding. For example, we have already said that the hydrogen molecule is covalently bonded; and so it is. But, it is *not* 100% covalently bonded. Imagine the two electrons in the molecule careering around the molecule. For some of the time there is a chance, albeit a small one, that both electrons could find themselves at the same end of the molecule. This would give that end of the molecule an overall negative charge, and leave the other end with a positive charge (Figure 18.1). The force that holds the molecule together for this fleeting moment is due to the attraction between one end that has the appearance of an H^+ ion and the other that looks like an H^- ion. Thus we can see that even in hydrogen there is at least a little *ionic bonding*. Indeed, every molecule that we would call covalent also has some ionic character.

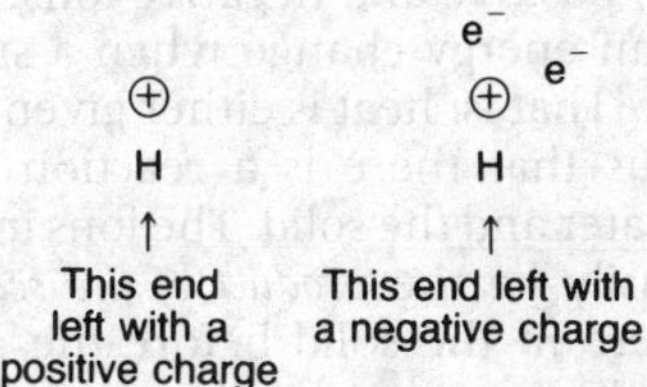

***Figure 18.1** Even in a covalent molecule like hydrogen there are brief periods of time when the charge is not spread evenly over both atoms. This leads to the molecule having some ionic character*

18.2 Ionic substances have some covalent character

Many substances are classified as *ionic compounds*. They are said to contain positive and negative ions, with the compound held together by the attractions between the oppositely charged ions. The most famous example is sodium chloride, NaCl.

If X-rays are passed through a crystal of sodium chloride, the X-rays are influenced by the electrons belonging to the sodium and the chlorine. Where there are more electrons in a given volume, the stronger is the influence. We can put this in another way by saying that the X-rays are strongly affected by regions of high electron density. The lines in Figure 18.2 are contour lines of electron density for part of a sodium chloride crystal. Where the lines are close together, the electron density is high, and vice versa. The pattern provides strong evidence that there are two centres around which the electrons congregate. It also shows that there is little electron density between the two nuclei.

This electron density diagram is often said to give clear evidence that sodium chloride contains sodium ions, Na^+, and chloride ions, Cl^-. However, the evidence is not so clear cut as we might think. In the first place, if the

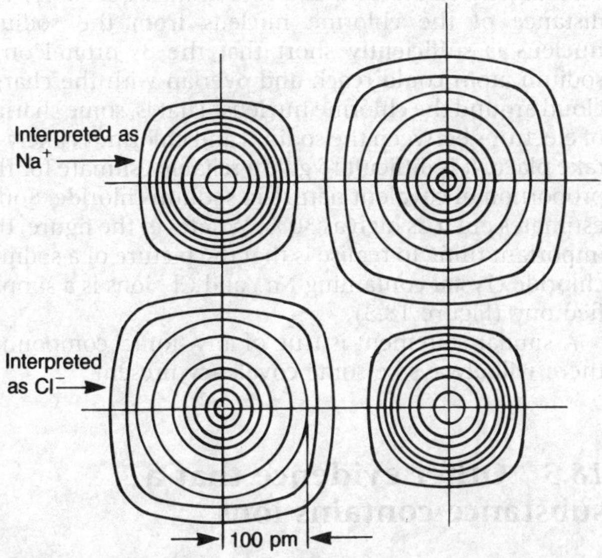

***Figure 18.2** Contours of electron density in sodium chloride obtained by interpreting X-ray diffraction patterns. (Adapted from: Witte, H. and Wolfel, E. (1958).* Rev. Mod. Phys. **30,** *51–5)*

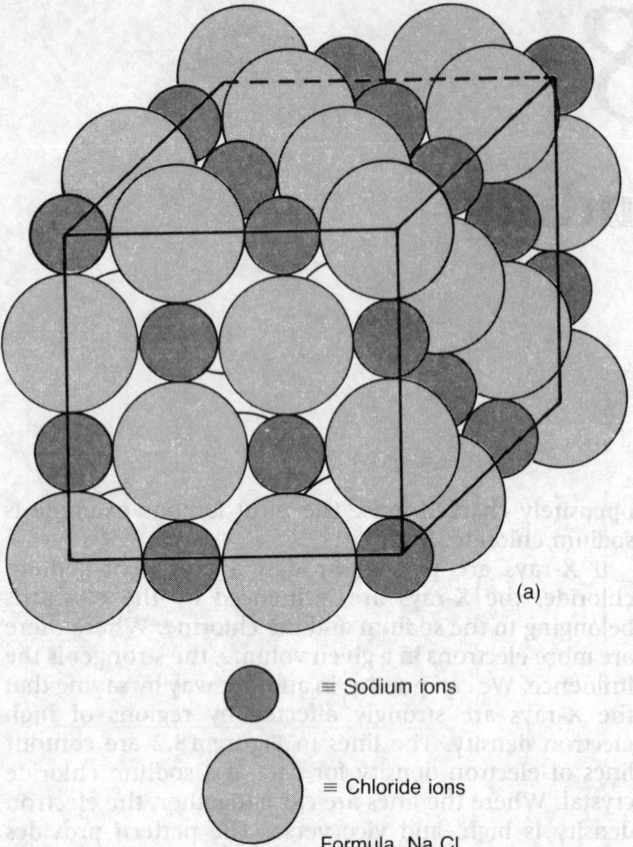

***Figure 18.3** Part of a sodium chloride lattice. The chloride ions are represented by the larger spheres, and the sodium ions by the smaller spheres. Only the outer layers of ions are shown shaded*

electron density around each of the nuclei is added up, the result is not very different from that expected for uncharged sodium and chlorine atoms. Secondly, the distance of the chlorine nucleus from the sodium nucleus is sufficiently short that the 3s orbital on a sodium atom could reach and overlap with the charge cloud around the chlorine nucleus. That is, some sharing of electrons between the sodium and chlorine is likely to take place. It is difficult to give a reliable estimate for the proportion of covalent nature in sodium chloride. Some estimates put it as high as 30%. Whatever the figure, the important thing to realise is that the picture of a sodium chloride crystal containing Na^+ and Cl^- ions is a simplified one (Figure 18.3).

A similar statement is true of any 'ionic' compound: there will always be some covalency present.

18.3 Other evidence that a substance contains ions

We have very good reason to think that true ions can exist. For example, they are formed when an atom is ionised in a gas and we measure the ionisation energy. However, this tells us nothing about the presence, or absence, of ions in a compound. You will find the type of evidence that a substance is ionic in Table 18.1.

Table 18.1. Evidence that a compound is ionic

Evidence	*Comments*
Substance exists as a solid at room temperature with a high melting point	Many substances, like diamond, silica and organic polymers, are such solids, but are covalent
Does not conduct electricity in the solid but conducts if molten or in solution*	Heating, dissolving, or passing electricity may disrupt the bonding, and help true ions to be made from partial ions in the solid
Has an electron density diagram that shows little sharing of electrons	The diagram may be hard to interpret and not give a complete answer
Lattice energy can be accurately calculated by assuming that true ions are present	This can be successful, but does not always agree with predictions made from other evidence

*Often, just below the melting point of an ionic solid the ions can move sufficiently well within the crystal lattice to allow some conduction to take place

The comments in Table 18.1 illustrate some of the difficulties with judging how good the evidence is. You will find details of the evidence from calculations of the lattice energy in Unit 46. We have already mentioned problems over evidence from X-ray diffraction.

We know that when some substances, like sodium chloride, are dissolved in water then the solution conducts electricity very efficiently. The conduction of electricity can best be explained by the presence of ions in the solution. When the ions break free from the crystal they can conduct the current through the solution: the ions become free to move (Figure 18.4). However, this does not prove that the substance itself contains complete, separate, positive and negative ions. In almost all cases there is an energy change when a substance dissolves in water. That is, heat is either given out or taken in. This tells us that there is a reaction taking place between the water and the solid. The ions in the solution could quite easily be the *product of the reaction*, rather than being there in the solid before the reaction. We shall examine this in more detail in Unit 60.

You may now realise that when we say that a compound is an 'ionic compound' we are using a type of chemical shorthand that nearly everyone uses. It means that the bonding in the substance is mainly ionic, but there is likely to be a significant amount of covalent bonding helping to hold the substance together. The key thing is that we talk, and write, about the substance as if the covalent contribution to the bonding were not there. There is nothing wrong with this provided you realise that it *is* a shorthand. The label 'ionic' is an idealisation, which may not reflect the true state of bonding. From now on we shall, like everyone else, use the shorthand.

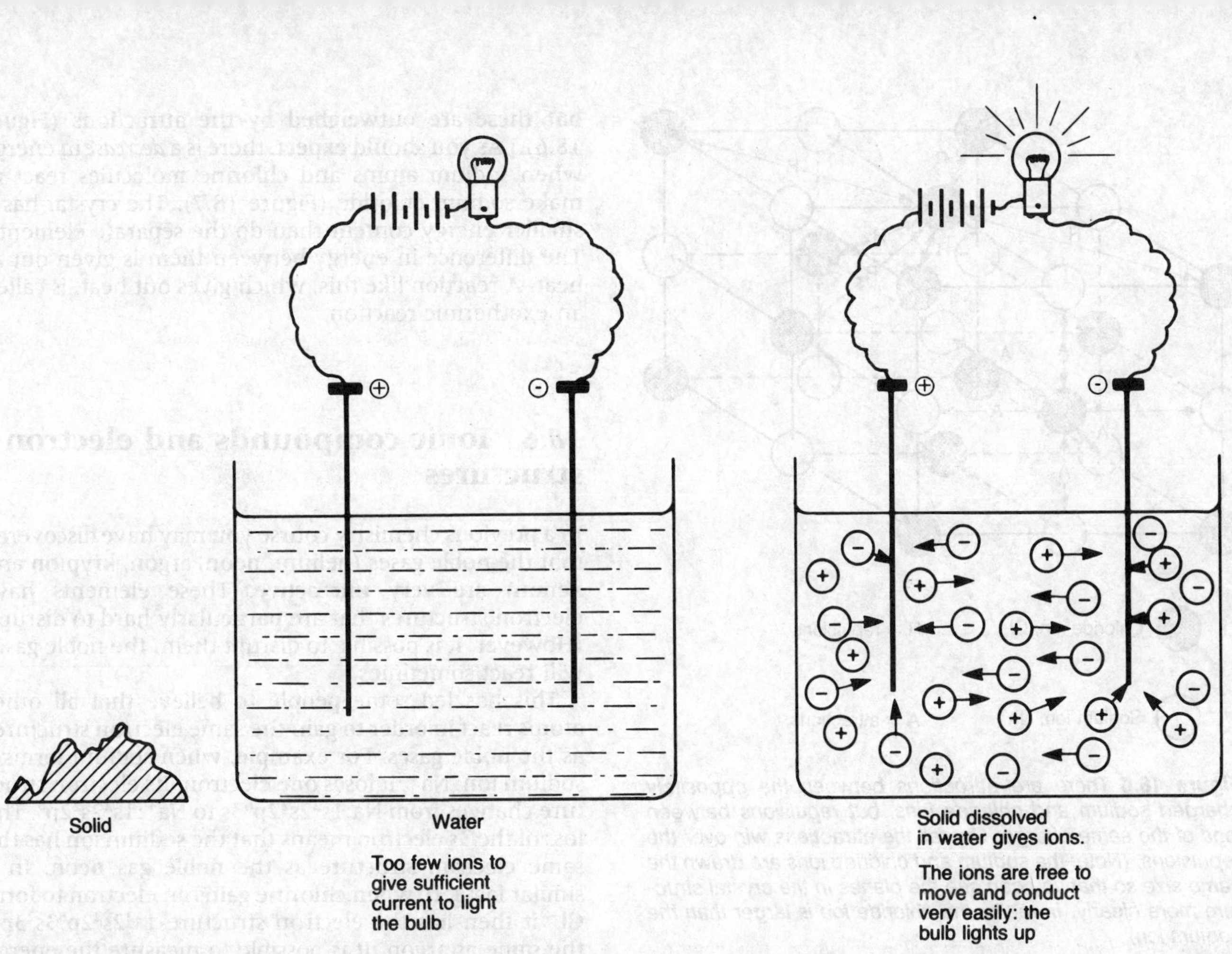

Solid

Water

Too few ions to give sufficient current to light the bulb

Solid dissolved in water gives ions.

The ions are free to move and conduct very easily: the bulb lights up

Figure 18.4 *This test should be treated carefully. If the bulb lights, there are ions present. However, the solid may not be ionic – it might react with water to make ions that were not present originally. (Aluminium trichloride does this)*

18.4 Which elements make ionic compounds?

Essentially we need an atom that easily loses one or more of its electrons, and one that can accept them. The metals in Group I and Group II of the Periodic Table have the greatest tendency to lose electrons and turn into positive ions. The non-metals of Groups VI and VII have the greatest affinity for electrons, and readily change into negative ions. The relative ease with which these elements make ions is summarised in Figure 18.5. If you want to find two elements that are bound to make an ionic compound, choose a metal towards the bottom of Group I and a non-metal towards the top of Group VII. For example, rubidium fluoride, Rb^+F^-, and potassium chloride, K^+Cl^-, are both distinctly ionic. There are many other examples, of course, often involving Groups II and VI. Magnesium oxide, $Mg^{2+}O^{2-}$, is an example.

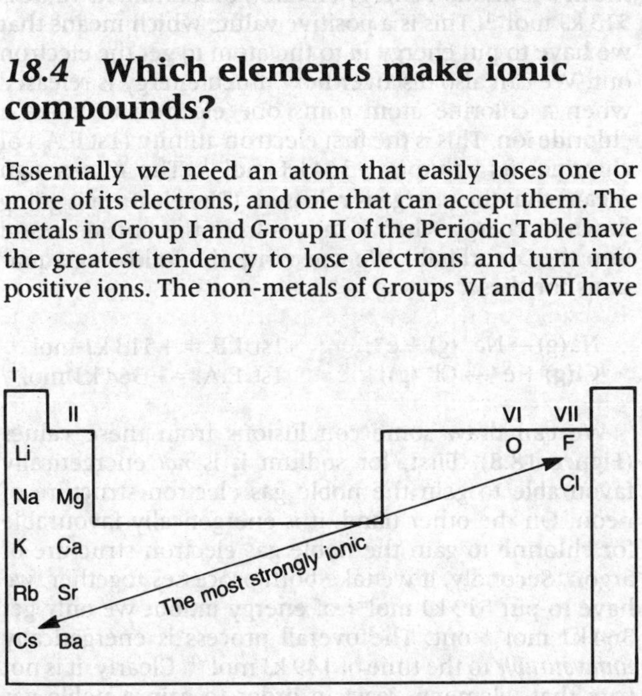

If you would like to find out the reason why elements to the left-hand side of a Period in the Periodic Table turn into positive ions, while those to the right-hand side give negative ions, read Unit 87.

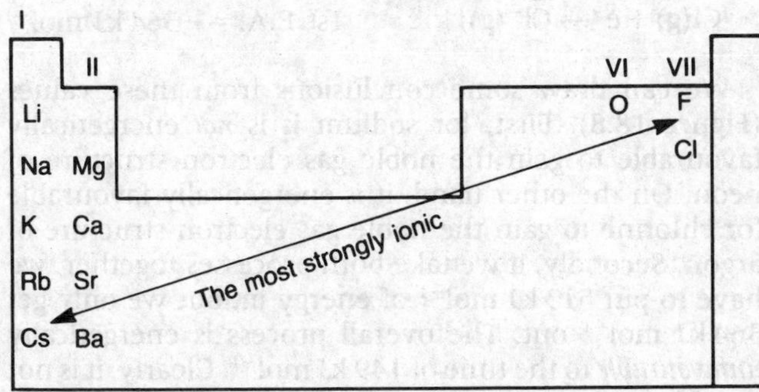

Figure 18.5 *Elements that give the most ionic compounds are to be found in Groups I and II, combining with fluorine, oxygen, or chlorine. However, many other combinations of elements lead to ionic compounds as well*

18.5 Why do ionic compounds exist?

The full answer to this question we must leave until you have worked through the units on thermodynamics (especially Unit 46). However, we can make some progress by saying that, once an ionic compound starts to be made, it is the *attractions between the oppositely charged ions that keep an ionic crystal together*. (There is a large number of repulsions between the ions having the same charge,

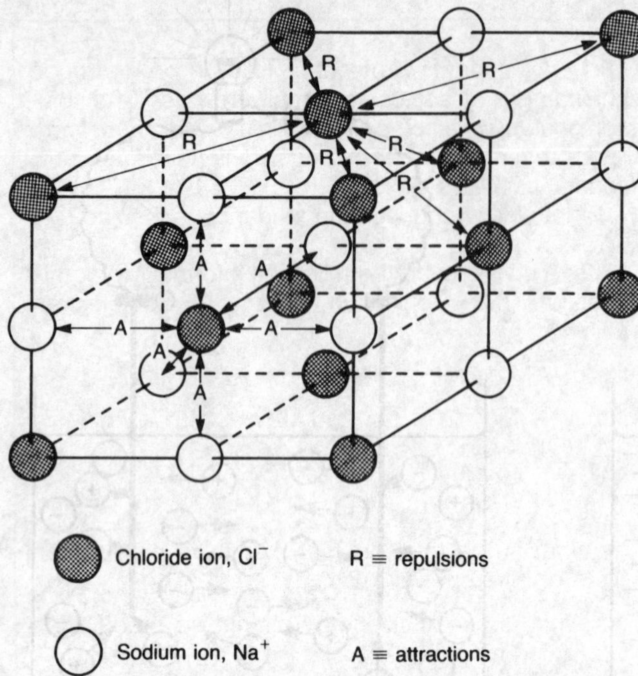

***Figure 18.6** There are attractions between the oppositely charged sodium and chloride ions, but repulsions between ions of the same charge. Overall the attractions win over the repulsions. (Note: the sodium and chloride ions are drawn the same size so that you can see the planes in the crystal structure more clearly. In reality the chloride ion is larger than the sodium ion)*

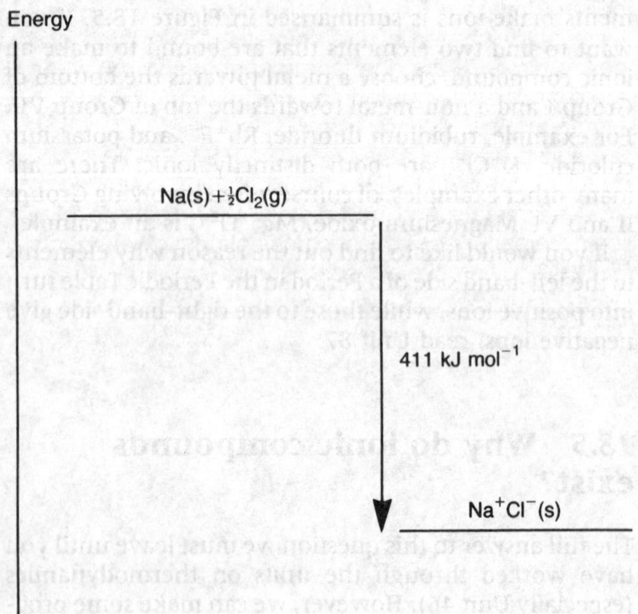

***Figure 18.7** Experiment shows that $Na^+Cl^-(s)$ is 411 kJ mol^{-1} more energetically stable than the elements from which it is made*

but these are outweighed by the attractions (Figure 18.6).) As you should expect, there is a *decrease* in energy when sodium atoms and chlorine molecules react to make sodium chloride (Figure 18.7). The crystal has a smaller energy content than do the separate elements. The difference in energy between them is given out as heat. A reaction like this, which gives out heat, is called an exothermic reaction.

18.6 Ionic compounds and electron structures

In a previous chemistry course you may have discovered that the noble gases (helium, neon, argon, krypton and xenon) are very unreactive. These elements have electron structures that are particularly hard to disrupt. (However, it is possible to disrupt them: the noble gases will react sometimes.)

This has led some people to believe that all other atoms react in order to gain the same electron structures as the noble gases. For example, when sodium forms a sodium ion, Na^+, it loses one electron. Its electron structure changes from Na:$1s^22s^22p^63s$ to Na^+:$1s^22s^22p^6$. The loss of the 3s electron means that the sodium ion has the same electron structure as the noble gas neon. In a similar fashion, when chlorine gains an electron to form Cl^- it then has the electron structure $1s^22s^22p^63s^23p^6$, the same as argon. It is possible to measure the energy needed to remove the 3s electron from sodium. This is the first ionisation energy (1st I.E.) of sodium. Its value is 513 kJ mol^{-1}. This is a positive value, which means that we have to put energy *in* to the atom to get the electron out. We can also discover how much energy is released when a chlorine atom gains one electron to make a chloride ion. This is the first electron affinity (1st E.A.) of chlorine; its value is −364 kJ mol^{-1}. The minus sign means that the energy is released. (The electron is going down in energy when it moves from the outside world into the 3p orbital.) We can write the following equations for these:

$$Na(g) \rightarrow Na^+(g) + e^-; \qquad \text{1st I.E.} = +513\ \text{kJ mol}^{-1}$$
$$Cl(g) + e^- \rightarrow Cl^-(g); \qquad \text{1st E.A.} = -364\ \text{kJ mol}^{-1}$$

We can draw some conclusions from these values (Figure 18.8). First, for sodium it is *not* energetically favourable to gain the noble gas electron structure of neon. On the other hand, it *is* energetically favourable for chlorine to gain the noble gas electron structure of argon. Secondly, if we take both processes together, we have to put 513 kJ mol^{-1} of energy in, but we only get 364 kJ mol^{-1} out. The overall process is energetically *unfavourable* to the tune of 149 kJ mol^{-1}. Clearly, it is not true that 'elements react in order to gain a noble gas electron structure'. Things are much more complicated than this. For the present we need not go into more detail except to say that it is the *attractions in the crystal* that cause atoms to make ions.

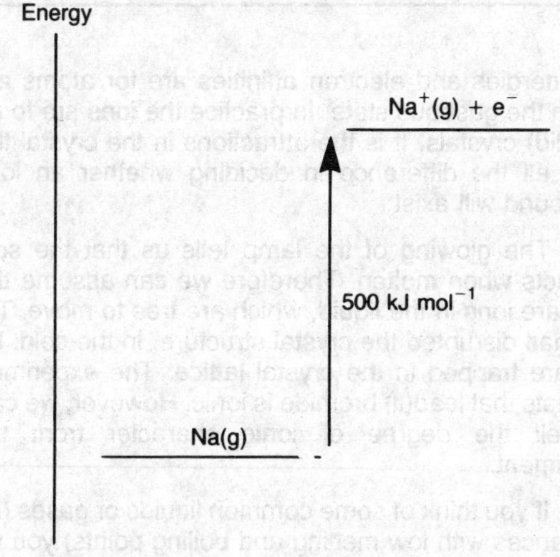

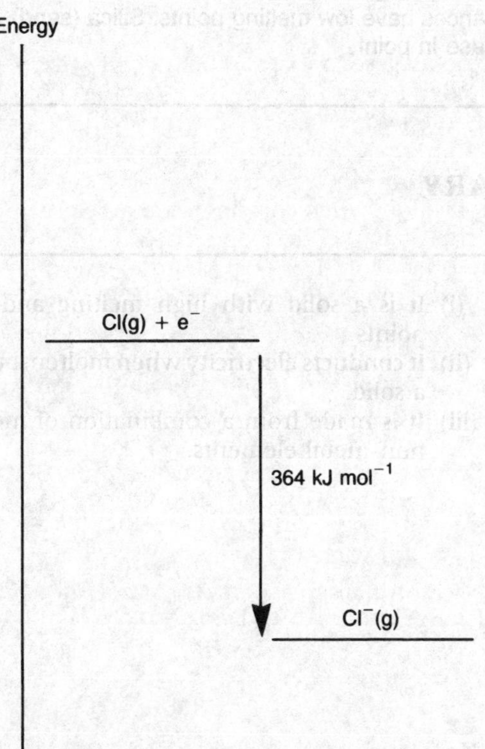

***Figure 18.8** Energy level diagrams for the processes $Na(g) \rightarrow Na^+(g) + e^-$ and $Cl(g) + e^- \rightarrow Cl^-(g)$. The first is energetically unfavourable. The second is energetically favourable. (The diagrams are not drawn to scale)*

18.1 A student wrote the following: 'Hydrogen chloride gas dissolves very easily in water. The solution conducted electricity well. This proves there were ions present and that hydrogen chloride is an ionic substance.'

What was wrong with the student's reasoning?

18.2 You will need the following information for this question (I.E. = ionisation energy; E.A. = electron affinity):

$Mg(g) \rightarrow Mg^+(g) + e^-$; 1st I.E. = +738 kJ mol^{-1}

$Mg^+(g) \rightarrow Mg^{2+}(g) + e^-$; 2nd I.E. = +1451 kJ mol^{-1}

$O(g) + e^- \rightarrow O^-(g)$; 1st E.A. = −141.4 kJ mol^{-1}

$O^-(g) + e^- \rightarrow O^{2-}(g)$; 2nd E.A. = +790.8 kJ mol^{-1}

(i) What is the total energy change to produce an $Mg^{2+}(g)$ ion from Mg(g)?

(ii) What is the total energy change to produce an $O^{2-}(g)$ ion from O(g)?

(iii) Criticise the following statement about magnesium oxide, which is an ionic compound consisting of Mg^{2+} and O^{2-} ions: 'Magnesium forms Mg^{2+} ions and oxygen forms O^{2-} ions so that both elements can reach the nearest noble gas electron structure.'

(iv) What is an important difference between the ions as they appear in the equations for ionisation energies and electron affinities, and the ions in a real ionic compound?

18.3 A sample of lead(II) bromide, $PbBr_2$, was placed in a crucible. The ends of two carbon electrodes were put in the solid and connected to a lamp and power pack. At first the lamp did not light, but when the bromide was heated and began to melt the lamp began to glow.

Explain these observations.

18.4 If metals and non-metals often react to give ionic compounds, which combinations of elements generally give covalent compounds?

Answers

18.1 The student was right about there being ions in the water (they were H_3O^+ and Cl^-). However, hydrogen chloride is a gas at room temperature, so it is most unlikely to be an ionic substance. The ions in solution are produced when the gas molecules react with the water:

$$HCl(g) + H_2O(l) \rightarrow H_3O^+(aq) + Cl^-(aq)$$

18.2 (i) $+2189\,\text{kJ mol}^{-1}$.

(ii) $+649.4\,\text{kJ mol}^{-1}$.

(iii) The two figures you have calculated are both positive, i.e. energy has to be put in to bring them about. If it were just a matter of the elements forming noble gas structures, magnesium oxide would not exist. In fact, the formation of MgO appears to be even less favourable than NaCl. It is energetically unfavourable to produce O^{2-} ions because of the large positive value for the second electron affinity of oxygen. Once the O^- ion is formed, we have to put energy *in* to overcome the repulsion between the negative charge on the ion and the second electron.

(iv) The key difference is that the equations for ionisation energies and electron affinities are for atoms and ions in the gaseous state. In practice the ions are found in (solid) crystals. It is the attractions in the crystal that make all the difference in deciding whether an ionic compound will exist.

18.3 The glowing of the lamp tells us that the solid conducts when molten. Therefore we can assume that there are ions in the liquid, which are free to move. The heat has disrupted the crystal structure. In the cold, the ions are trapped in the crystal lattice. The experiment suggests that lead(II) bromide is ionic. However, we cannot tell the degree of ionic character from this experiment.

18.4 If you think of some common liquids or gases (i.e. substances with low melting and boiling points) you will hit upon the right answer. For example, ammonia, NH_3, carbon dioxide, CO_2, and methane, CH_4, are all gases and covalent. Covalent substances are often made from *combinations of non-metals*. However, not all covalent substances have low melting points. Silica (sand), SiO_2, is a case in point.

UNIT 18 SUMMARY

- Full ionic bonding occurs when there is a complete transfer of one or more electrons from one atom to another in a compound.
- In practice, all compounds show a mix of ionic and covalent character.
- Signs that a compound may be ionic include:

(i) It is a solid with high melting and boiling points.
(ii) It conducts electricity when molten, but not as a solid.
(iii) It is made from a combination of metal and non-metal elements.

19

Polar molecules and polar bonds

19.1 What is a polar molecule?

Hydrogen chloride is a good example of a polar molecule. Imagine a hydrogen atom and a chlorine atom coming close together and forming a bond. If you were one of the two electrons in the bond you would feel two attractions; one for the 17 protons in the chlorine nucleus, and one for the single proton belonging to the hydrogen atom. In spite of the shielding of the chlorine nucleus, the chlorine tends to win the competition. You would be drawn towards the chlorine and away from the hydrogen nucleus. Remember, though, that the electrons in a molecule are far from being stationary. Each electron in the bond would still have a chance of being found near the hydrogen, but a higher probability of being nearer the chlorine. Figure 19.1 gives an impression of the spread of the electron charge cloud in hydrogen chloride.

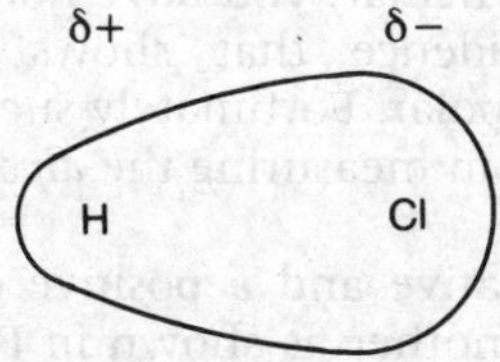

***Figure 19.1** The sigma orbital in hydrogen chloride is 'fatter' at the chlorine end; the electrons spend more of their time nearer to the chlorine than the hydrogen*

The result of this uneven distribution of charge is that one end of the molecule has a slight positive charge, and the other a slight negative charge. These slight charges are shown by the symbols δ+ and δ− respectively (δ is the Greek letter 'delta').

Hydrogen chloride is called a *polar molecule* because of its uneven distribution of charge. Notice that hydrogen chloride *is* a molecule; that is, it is predominantly covalent. Its small δ+ and δ− charges do *not* make it an ionic substance.

Many molecules are polar, some of which are shown in Figure 19.2.

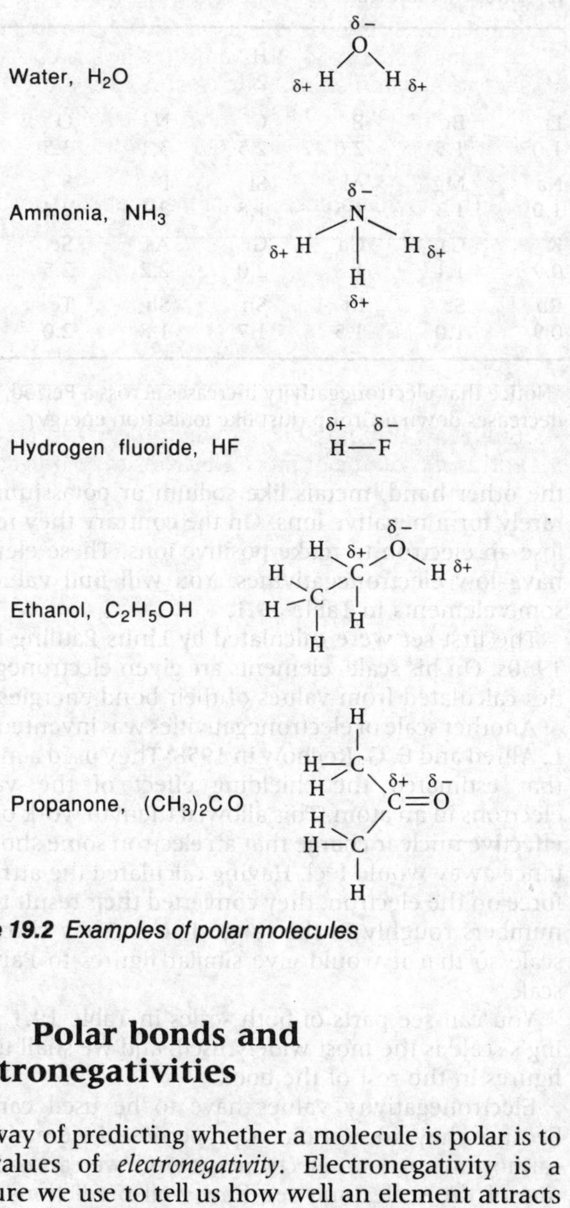

Water, H_2O

Ammonia, NH_3

Hydrogen fluoride, HF $\quad \overset{\delta+}{H}—\overset{\delta-}{F}$

Ethanol, C_2H_5OH

Propanone, $(CH_3)_2CO$

***Figure 19.2** Examples of polar molecules*

19.2 Polar bonds and electronegativities

One way of predicting whether a molecule is polar is to use values of *electronegativity*. Electronegativity is a measure we use to tell us how well an element attracts electrons in a bond. The elements fluorine and chlorine tend to attract electrons to themselves very strongly. These elements have high values of electronegativity. On

Table 19.1. Electronegativity values for some elements*

(a) Pauling scale

			H 2.1			
Li 1.0	Be 1.5	B 2.0	C 2.5	N 3.0	O 3.5	F 4.0
Na 0.9	Mg 1.2	Al 1.5	Si 1.8	P 2.1	S 2.5	Cl 3.0
K 0.8	Ca 1.0	Ga 1.6	Ge 1.8	As 2.0	Se 2.4	Br 2.8
Rb 0.8	Sr 1.0	In 1.5	Sn 1.8	Sb 1.9	Te 2.1	I 2.5

(b) Allred–Rochow scale

			H 2.1			
Li 1.0	Be 1.5	B 2.0	C 2.5	N 3.1	O 3.5	F 4.1
Na 1.0	Mg 1.3	Al 1.5	Si 1.8	P 2.1	S 2.4	Cl 2.9
K 0.9	Ca 1.1	Ga 1.8	Ge 2.0	As 2.2	Se 2.5	Br 2.8
Rb 0.9	Sr 1.0	In 1.5	Sn 1.7	Sb 1.8	Te 2.0	I 2.2

*Notice that electronegativity increases across a Period, and decreases down a Group (just like ionisation energy)

the other hand, metals like sodium or potassium very rarely form negative ions. On the contrary they tend to lose an electron to make positive ions. These elements have low electronegativities. You will find values for some elements in Table 19.1.

The first set were calculated by Linus Pauling in the 1930s. On his scale, elements are given electronegativities calculated from values of their bond energies.

Another scale of electronegativities was invented by A. L. Allred and E. G. Rochow in 1958. They used a method that estimated the shielding effect of the various electrons in an atom. This allowed them to work out the effective nuclear charge that an electron some short distance away would feel. Having calculated the attractive force on the electron, they converted their result to give numbers roughly in the range 1 to 4. They chose this scale so that it would give similar figures to Pauling's scale.

You can see parts of both scales in Table 19.1. Pauling's scale is the most widely used, and we shall use his figures in the rest of the book.

Electronegativity values have to be used carefully because they are not direct properties of elements. We cannot measure an electronegativity; we can only use one of the scales and see how well predictions made from it fit with the results of experiment (Table 19.2). In particular, the differences between values are often correlated with the degree of ionic character in a bond.

Table 19.2. Predictions from electronegativity values

Electronegativity values	*Prediction*	*Examples*
Identical	Non-polar covalent bond	H_2, Cl_2, O_2
Slightly different	Polar covalent bond*	HCl, NO, BCl_3
Very different	Ionic bond formed	RbF, NaCl, MgO

*The presence of polar *bonds* does not guarantee that a *molecule* is polar

As we have seen, the bond in hydrogen chloride has an uneven distribution of charge at each end. That is, the *bond* is polar. Because hydrogen chloride is a molecule with only one bond, the molecule must be polar as well. This fits with the difference of 0.9 in their electronegativity values, and corresponds to around 20% ionic character. The values for sodium and chlorine are 2.1 units apart, which works out at nearly 65% ionic character.

19.3 Polar molecules and dipole moments

Electronegativities are not properties of atoms like their masses or spectra: there are no machines that we can use to measure electronegativities. The different scales that have been used from time to time have proved useful in some ways; for example, in explaining why hydrogen chloride is polar. But if you think about what you have read in the previous section, one or two things might worry you. In particular, you have not been given any experimental evidence that shows that hydrogen chloride really is polar. Fortunately such evidence does exist. It comes from measuring the *dipole moment* of the molecule.

Suppose a negative and a positive charge are kept apart from one another as shown in Figure 19.3. This arrangement defines an electric dipole moment, or just dipole moment for short. The size of the dipole moment is given by multiplying the size of the charge by the distance apart, i.e.

$\mu = q \times r$ Dipole moment

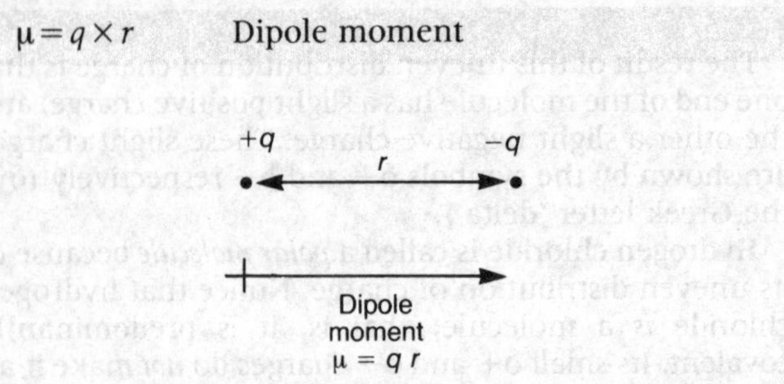

Figure 19.3 *Two charges, +q and −q, separated by a distance r possess a dipole moment. (The symbol for a dipole moment is* ⟼*)*

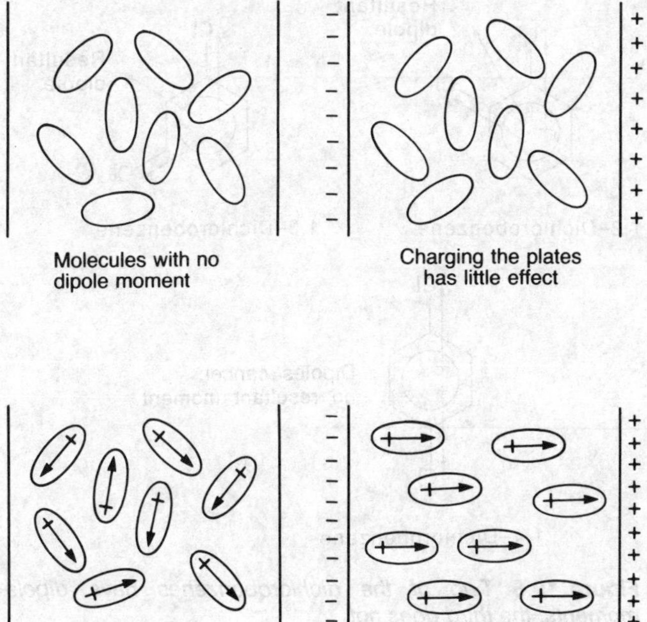

Molecules with no dipole moment
Charging the plates has little effect
Molecules with a dipole moment
Charging the plates causes the molecules to line up in the same direction

***Figure 19.4** The tendency of molecules with a dipole moment to line up in an electric field can be used to measure their dipole moments. (In practice they never line up perfectly – surrounding molecules jostle some of them out of position)*

It is possible to measure the size of a dipole moment. Suppose you were to set up two sets of metal plates as shown in Figure 19.4. Between one set of plates you place molecules with a dipole moment, and between the other pair you put molecules with no dipole moment. Now imagine charging up each pair of plates so that one became negative and the other positive. The positive end of the dipoles will be attracted to the negative plate, and the negative end towards the positive plate. These molecules tend to line up in the electric field between the plates. The field of the dipoles is in the opposite direction to the field between the plates. By using some sensitive electronics, the change in the field can be measured. On the other hand, the molecules without the dipole moment will not line up. They remain more or less randomly oriented so the electric field will change very little.

You will find that, for the simpler molecules, the sizes of the dipole moments are (approximately) proportional to the difference between the electronegativities of the atoms (see Table 19.3). For the more complicated molecules the matter is not so straightforward. The reason is that the dipole moments of the different bonds can reinforce one another, or in some cases cancel each other out. An example is tetrafluoromethane, CF_4 (Figure 19.5). The electronegativity of carbon is 2.5, while that of fluorine is 4.0. This suggests that a carbon–fluorine bond should be polar, with the carbon being positive and the fluorine negative. However, even though CF_4 has four polar bonds, the molecule as a whole is not polar.

Table 19.3. Table of dipole moments*

Molecule	*Structure*	*Dipole moment*/D
Hydrogen fluoride	δ+ H—F δ−	1.91
Hydrogen chloride	δ+ H—Cl δ−	1.08
Hydrogen bromide	δ+ H—Br δ−	0.80
Hydrogen iodide	δ+ H—I δ−	0.42
Water	δ+ H–O(δ−)–H δ+	1.85
Ammonia	δ+ H, N δ−, H δ+, H δ+	1.47
Ethanol	H₃C–C(δ+)H₂–O(δ−)–H δ+	1.68
Propanone	H₃C–C(δ+)(=O δ−)–CH₃	1.30
Chlorobenzene	δ− Cl on benzene ring, δ+	1.57
1,2-Dichlorobenzene	δ− Cl, Cl δ−, δ+	2.25
1,3-Dichlorobenzene	δ− Cl, Cl δ−, δ+	1.72
1,4-Dichlorobenzene	Cl, Cl	0.00

Table 19.3. – Cont.

Molecule	*Structure*	*Dipole moment*/D
Phenylamine	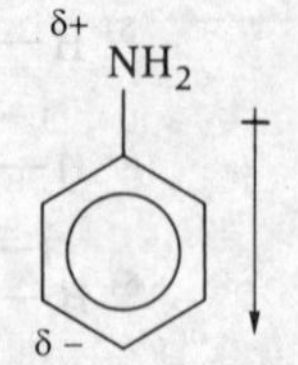 δ+ NH_2 (benzene ring) δ−	1.53
Phenol	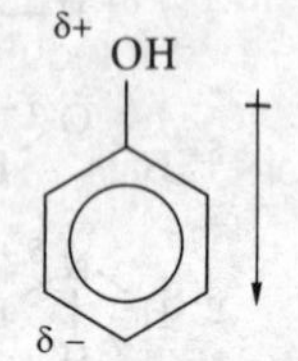 δ+ OH (benzene ring) δ−	1.45
Nitrobenzene	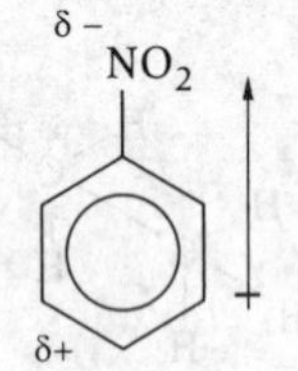 δ− NO_2 (benzene ring) δ+	4.22
Trichloromethane	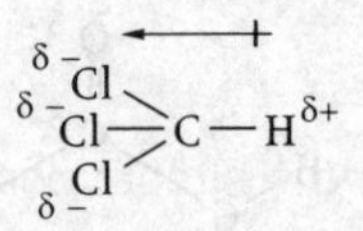 δ− Cl, δ− Cl—C—$H^{δ+}$, δ− Cl	1.02

*Dipole moments are usually stated in debyes (D). One debye equals 3.34×10^{-30} C m

δ− F, δ− F, C δ+, F δ−, F δ−

***Figure 19.5** Although tetrafluoromethane has four polar bonds, the molecule as a whole is not polar. This often happens with highly symmetric molecules*

The reason lies in the symmetrical arrangement of the bonds, and their dipole moments. The four dipole moments cancel out.

Further examples are the dichlorobenzenes listed in Table 19.3. The ways the dipoles combine are shown in Figure 19.6.

In some molecules the presence of highly electronegative atoms can affect bonds some distance away in the molecule. Trichloromethane, $CHCl_3$, is an example. Here the three highly electronegative chlorine atoms pull electrons towards them, away from the central carbon; this in turn causes electrons to be drawn towards the carbon from the hydrogen–carbon bond (Figure 19.7). In this way the hydrogen atom has a greater degree of

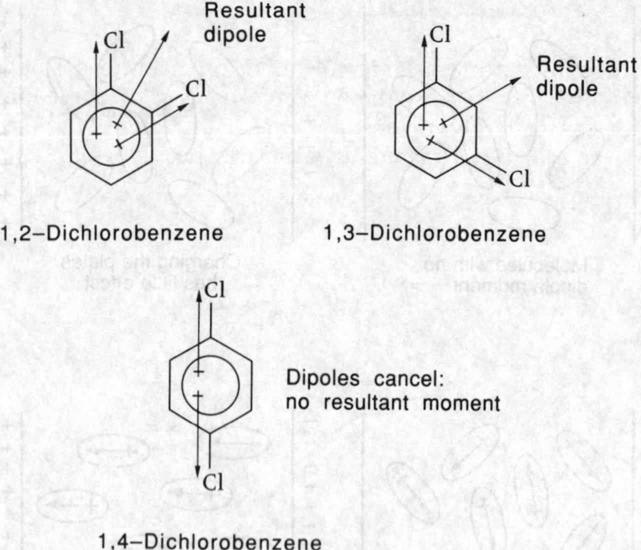

***Figure 19.6** Two of the dichlorobenzenes have dipole moments; the third does not*

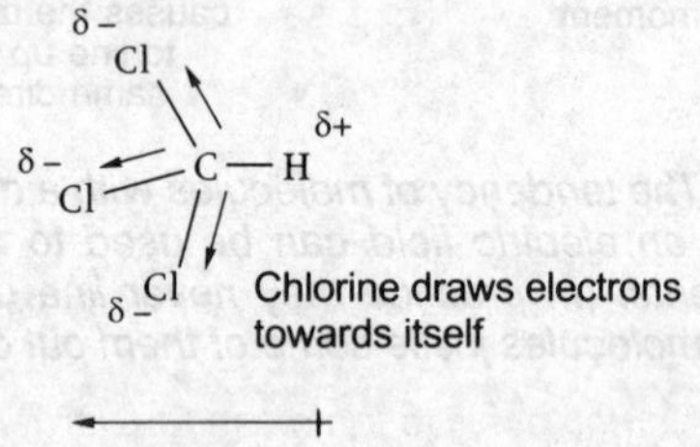

δ− Cl, δ− Cl—C—H δ+, δ− Cl

Chlorine draws electrons towards itself

***Figure 19.7** The chlorine atoms in trichloromethane draw electrons towards them. They show a negative inductive effect*

positive charge than we would expect in an 'ordinary' carbon–hydrogen bond. The electron withdrawing chlorine atoms are said to exert a *negative inductive effect*. There are groups of atoms that can exert a positive inductive effect, but we shall ignore them until later (Unit 112).

19.1 Which of the following molecules would you predict to be polar: hydrogen sulphide, H_2S; boron trichloride, BCl_3; tetrachloromethane, CCl_4; ethane, C_2H_6; carbon monoxide, CO?

19.2 Look at the diagrams of the two molecules in Figure 19.8. Would the molecules have a dipole moment?

cis-1,2-Dichloroethene *trans*-1,2-Dichloroethene

***Figure 19.8** Two forms of 1,2-dichloroethene*

19.4 Polarisability

Imagine putting a large negative ion near to a small positive ion. Because the outer electrons of the large ion are far from the nucleus, they are not held very tightly. They will be attracted towards the positive ion. The charge cloud of the negative ion will be distorted. We say that the negative ion has been *polarised* by the positive ion (Figure 19.9); or that the large negative ion is highly *polarisable*. If we were to put a much smaller negative ion close to the positive ion, it would not be polarised so much. This is because the electrons would be held tightly by the nucleus and the charge cloud could not be so easily distorted. The smaller negative ion is only slightly polarisable.

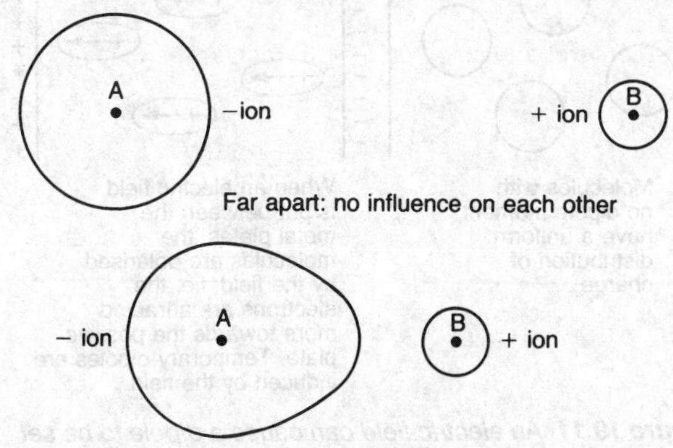
A
−ion
+ ion
B
Far apart: no influence on each other
− ion
A
B
+ ion
Closer together: the negative ion is polarised by the positive ion

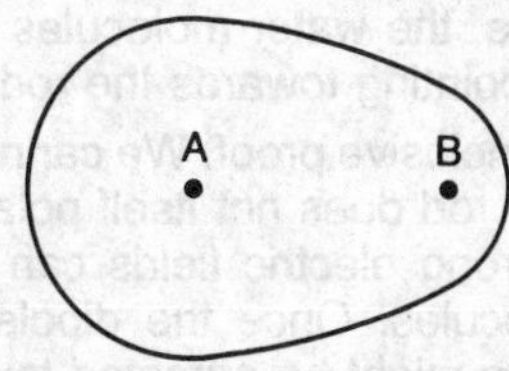
A
B
Even closer: the charge cloud of the negative ion merges with that of the positive ion; covalency results

***Figure 19.9** A small positive ion close to a larger negative ion will polarise the negative ion*

Table 19.4. Fajans' rules

An ionic compound will have a high degree of covalency if: The positive ion is small and highly charged *and* The negative ion is large (highly polarisable)
An alternative version is: Covalency is promoted by a small cation and a large anion*

*A cation is a positive ion; an anion is a negative ion

You should be able to understand that if a highly polarisable negative ion is placed near a small positive ion, then the charge cloud on the negative ion may spread over the region of influence of the positive ion. A degree of covalency results.

The ideas that we have just met lie behind a set of rules known as Fajans' rules. The rules, which are developed from a different set that Fajans published in 1924, are summarised in Table 19.4. In extreme cases, the compound may be almost entirely covalent. For example, the beryllium ion, Be^{2+}, is so small that it manages to polarise any negative ion to such a degree that its compounds are predominantly covalent.

19.3 A large negative ion is to some extent similar to a large atom or molecule. Because of their size, each of them will be highly polarisable. If you prefer, you could say that they were 'soft' or 'squashy'. The meaning is the same: both will be easily distorted by a nearby electric field. Try to give a reason why highly polarisable atoms or molecules have a tendency to line up in an electric field, even though they might have no permanent dipole moment.

19.4 Hydroxide ions react with iodomethane according to the equation

$$OH^- + CH_3I \rightarrow CH_3OH + I^-$$

In some books it is said that the iodine atom attracts electrons towards it, leaving the carbon atom slightly positively charged. The positive charge is claimed to be the reason why the hydroxide ion is attracted to the CH_3I. What do you think of this reasoning?

19.5 If a stream of water falls close to a charged rod, the stream is attracted to the rod (Figure 19.10).

(i) Explain why the stream bends.

(ii) Does this experiment prove that water molecules are polar?

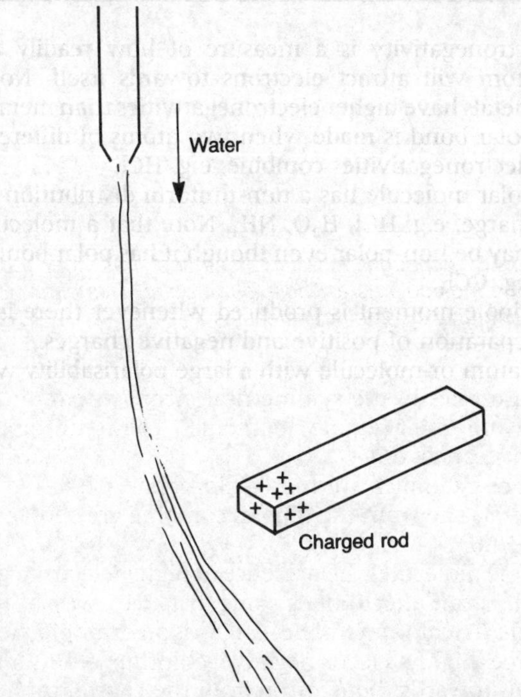
Water
Charged rod

***Figure 19.10** A stream of water will bend towards a charged rod*

Answers

19.1 All the molecules have polar bonds, but only H_2S and CO are polar molecules. The others are non-polar because of the symmetrical arrangement of the bonds.

19.2 The *cis* form has a dipole moment; the two dipoles of the *trans* form cancel out.

$$\underset{cis}{\text{Cl(H)C=C(Cl)H}} \qquad \underset{trans}{\text{H(Cl)C=C(Cl)H}}$$

19.3 If a highly polarisable molecule is placed in the apparatus sketched in Figure 19.11, it will be polarised by the field. The negative charge cloud of the electrons will be drawn towards the positive plate. That is, a dipole moment is set up, or *induced*, in the atom or molecule.

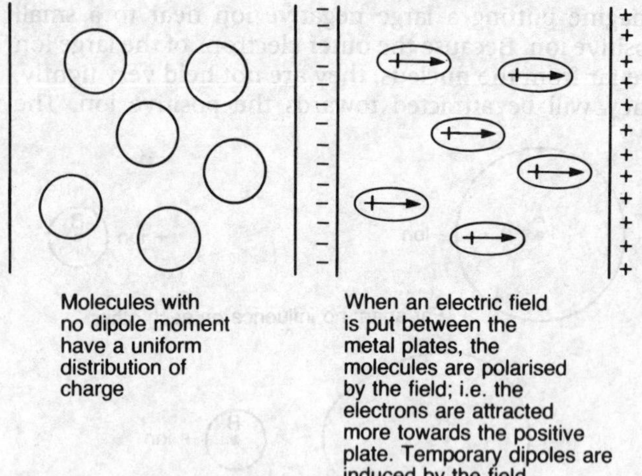

Molecules with no dipole moment have a uniform distribution of charge
When an electric field is put between the metal plates, the molecules are polarised by the field; i.e. the electrons are attracted more towards the positive plate. Temporary dipoles are induced by the field

***Figure 19.11** An electric field can cause a dipole to be set up in a molecule*

19.4 On Pauling's scale carbon and iodine have the same electronegativity. On the Allred–Rochow scale carbon is *more* electronegative than iodine. Hence we have no reason to think that the carbon is positively charged compared with the iodine. The suggested reason for the reaction cannot be completely correct.

19.5 (i) If the rod is positively charged, the oxygen atoms of the water molecules will be attracted towards it. This will swing the stream of water towards the rod. (If the rod is negative, the water molecules will have their hydrogen atoms pointing towards the rod.)

(ii) No, it is not conclusive proof. We cannot be sure that the charge on the rod does not itself polarise the water molecules; i.e. strong electric fields can induce dipole moments in molecules. Once the dipoles are set up, then the molecules might be attracted towards the rod.

UNIT 19 SUMMARY

- Electronegativity is a measure of how readily an atom will attract electrons towards itself. Non-metals have higher electronegativities than metals.
- A polar bond is made when two atoms of different electronegativities combine, e.g. HCl.
- A polar molecule has a non-uniform distribution of charge, e.g. HCl, H_2O, NH_3. Note that a molecule may be non-polar even though it has polar bonds, e.g. CCl_4.
- A dipole moment is produced whenever there is a separation of positive and negative charges.
- An atom or molecule with a large polarisability will have its electron cloud easily distorted by a neighbouring positive or negative charge.
- Fajans' rules:
  An ionic compound will have a high degree of covalency if
  (i) the positive ion is small and highly charged
  and
  (ii) the negative ion is large (highly polarisable).
  An alternative version is:
  Covalency is promoted by a small cation and a large anion.

20

Intermolecular forces

20.1 Where are intermolecular forces found?

The noble gas helium will only turn to a liquid at the very low temperature of 4 K. The question is, why does it liquefy at all? For some reason, at 4 K helium atoms stick together, while at higher temperatures they do not stick together. Helium may be an extreme case in terms of the low temperature at which it liquefies, but other elements or covalent substances follow a similar pattern. For example, iodine exists as a black solid up to 456 K (183°C). The solid contains a regular pattern of iodine molecules, I_2 (Figure 20.1). Above 456 K the crystal breaks up and the molecules escape from the crystal, giving a purple vapour.

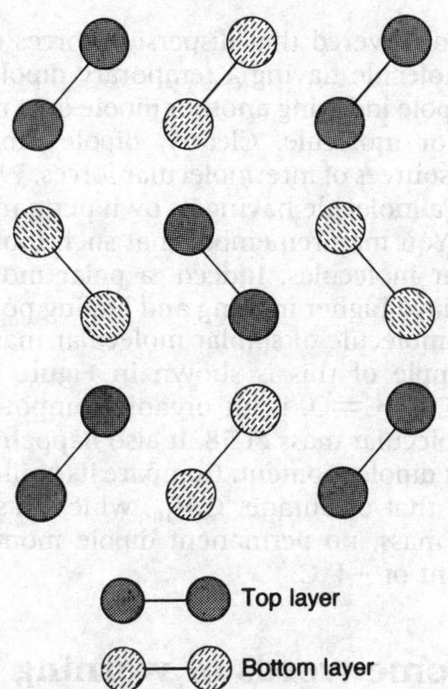
Top layer
Bottom layer

***Figure 20.1** The crystal structure of iodine. The crystal contains planes of I_2 molecules, with alternate planes staggered as shown in the diagram. One peculiarity of the crystal is that the distance between the layers is about 427 pm while the distance between molecules within the same plane is much shorter, 356 pm*

The forces that hold helium atoms, or covalent substances like iodine, together in a liquid or solid are called *intermolecular forces*. If the forces are between atoms rather than molecules, we can speak about *interatomic* forces. Another name given to the forces is *van der Waals* forces after the Dutch chemist who first investigated the origin of the forces. An important point is that intermolecular (or interatomic) forces are not meant to apply to the purely electrostatic forces that exist between oppositely charged ions. Likewise they do not include the forces that hold atoms together through covalent bonds, or hydrogen bonds (which we shall discuss in the following unit).

20.2 What causes intermolecular forces?

To find one answer to this question we shall begin with the single atom of Figure 20.2. On average the negative charge of the electrons in an atom is spread evenly around the nucleus. However, over very short periods of time (e.g. millionths of a second) the charge is not completely evenly distributed. At times more electrons will be found on one side of the atom rather than the other (see Figure 20.2). If you look back to Unit 19 on polar molecules, you should recognise that the separation of positive and negative charge produces a *dipole*. Unlike

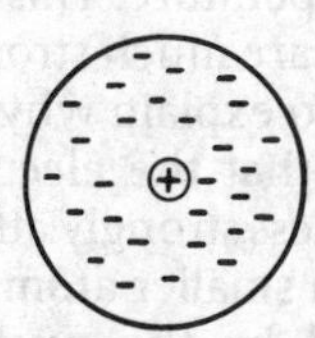
On average the negative charge of the electrons is spread evenly

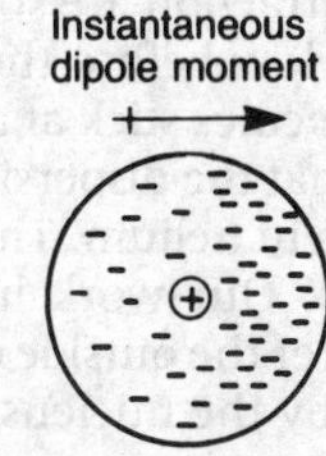
Instantaneous dipole moment
For brief periods the electrons are more on one side of an atom than another. This causes a short-lived dipole moment

***Figure 20.2** The origin of temporary dipole moments*

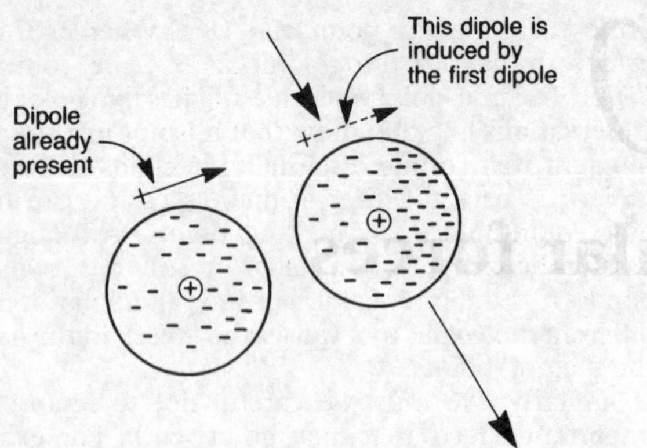

Figure 20.3 The dipole on one atom can induce a dipole on a neighbouring atom

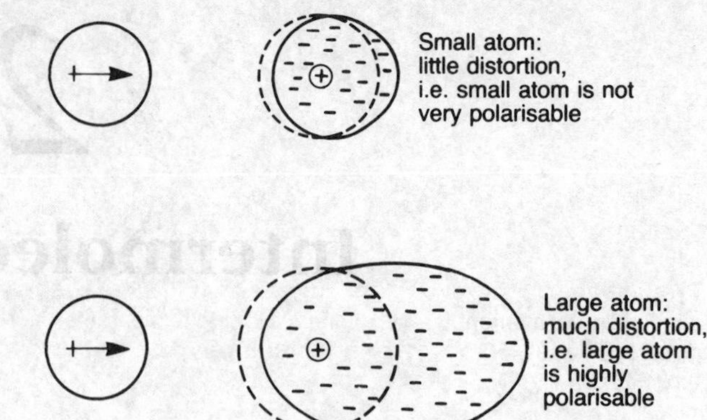

Figure 20.4 An atom with a dipole moment will polarise a large atom much more easily than a small atom

hydrogen chloride, which has a permanent dipole moment, the atom's dipole moment is only temporary.

Now, imagine that you were watching another atom passing close to the atom with the dipole. You would see the electrons in the passing atom being repelled away from the negative end of the temporary dipole. The situation is represented in Figure 20.3. For a moment the temporary dipole on the first atom has *induced* a new dipole on the second atom. These two dipoles will briefly attract one another. The force of attraction was first calculated by the German physicist Fritz London. For this reason the force of attraction between two temporary dipoles is known as a *London force*. Another name often used is to call the force a *dispersion force*. London, or dispersion, forces are just one type of intermolecular force.

20.3 Dispersion forces and polarisability

If our two atoms pass close to one another and are not travelling too quickly, the dispersion force may be strong enough to make them stick together. The way to make sure the atoms do not merely collide with one another and bounce off without sticking is to reduce their kinetic energies. The easiest way to do this is to lower the temperature. You should realise that in helium the forces of attraction are so weak that the temperature has to be *very* low before the helium will liquefy. For iodine the molecules stick at a much higher temperature. This tells us that the dispersion forces in iodine are much stronger than in helium. The next problem is to explain why this is so. Our work in Unit 13 tells us that the electrons nearer the outside of a large atom are less strongly attracted by the nucleus. The electrons in a smaller atom are, by comparison, more strongly held by the nucleus. Therefore, the outer electrons in a large atom will be attracted more easily by a neighbouring charge than the electrons in a smaller atom. Figure 20.4 shows that the electron cloud about a large atom is more easily distorted than the electron cloud around a small atom.

The shorthand way of describing the different degrees of distortion is to say that large atoms are more *polarisable* than smaller atoms. Alternatively, we say that a large atom has a larger *polarisability* than a smaller atom.

It is possible (but difficult) to calculate the polarisability of an atom. It turns out that the dispersion force between two atoms depends on the polarisability of each of them. In other words, the higher the polarisability, the stronger the dispersion force. In this case what holds true for atoms tends to hold true for molecules. The larger the atoms in a molecule, the larger is the polarisability of the molecule – hence the temperature of 456 K at which iodine vaporises.

20.4 Intermolecular forces are also produced by permanent dipoles

You have discovered that dispersion forces rely on an atom or molecule having a temporary dipole moment and this dipole inducing another dipole on a neighbouring atom or molecule. Clearly, dipole moments are important sources of intermolecular forces. What better, then, than a molecule having its own permanent dipole moment? You may remember that such molecules are called polar molecules. Indeed, a polar molecule will normally have higher melting and boiling points than a non-polar molecule of similar molecular mass.

An example of this is shown in Figure 20.5. Propanone, $(CH_3)_2C{=}O$, is an organic compound with a relative molecular mass of 58. It also happens to have a permanent dipole moment. Compare its boiling point of 57°C with that of butane, C_4H_{10}, which has the same molecular mass, no permanent dipole moment and a boiling point of −1°C.

20.5 Some words of warning

It is important not to be too dogmatic when making predictions about the relative melting or boiling points of molecules. For example, 1,2-dichlorobenzene is polar, but 1,4-dichlorobenzene is not (Figure 20.6). (They have the same molecular mass.)

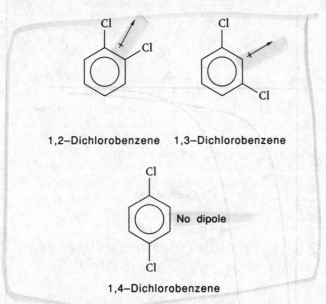

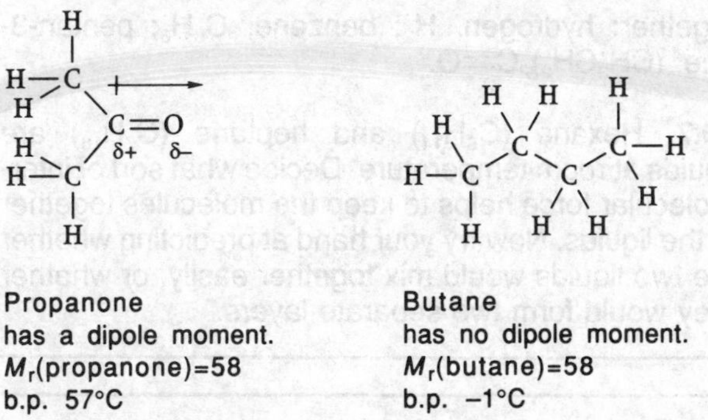

Propanone
has a dipole moment.
M_r(propanone)=58
b.p. 57°C

Butane
has no dipole moment.
M_r(butane)=58
b.p. −1°C

Figure 20.5 The difference in boiling point of propanone and butane is a result of the dipole moment in propanone

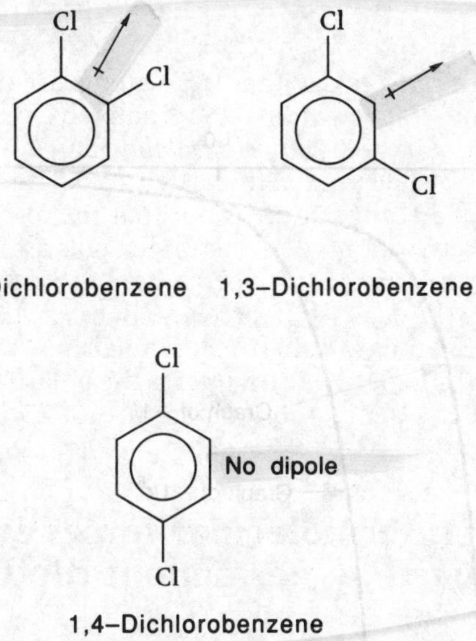

1,2–Dichlorobenzene 1,3–Dichlorobenzene

No dipole

1,4–Dichlorobenzene

Figure 20.6 All of the dichlorobenzenes have polar bonds between carbon and chlorine atoms. Only two of them have dipole moments

As expected, the boiling point of the former *is* higher than that of the latter (but only by 5° C). However, their melting points are in the reverse order. The *polar* molecule has a melting point of −18° C whereas the *non-polar* form has a melting point of 53° C, i.e. some 70° C *higher*. The non-polar molecule still has two polar bonds. Observations like this show that it is not just the dipole moment that counts. Especially, in solids the way the molecules pack together to make a crystal can have a marked influence on melting points. Although 1,4-dichlorobenzene is non-polar, it still has two polar bonds. It is the interaction between the polar bonds on different molecules that causes the 'upset' in the order of the melting points.

Similarly, we must be careful not to ignore other important effects that may be at work. For example, many polar molecules can make hydrogen bonds and the strengths of these bonds may overcome other effects solely due to induced or permanent dipole moments. Similarly, as molecules become larger and heavier, it is less likely that they will be gases, and more likely that they will be liquids or solids. Partly this is because of the influence of the large number of intermolecular forces that can arise; for example, between the long chain of atoms in a polymer. However, heavy molecules are harder to move no matter whether the intermolecular forces are weak or strong; so without a great deal of energy they will not fly around loose in a gas. A summary of the points made in this unit is given in Table 20.1.

Table 20.1. Summary of intermolecular forces

Intermolecular forces depend on dipole moments

There are three types:
- temporary dipole–induced dipole
- permanent dipole–induced dipole
- permanent dipole–permanent dipole

The larger, or heavier, the atom or molecule the greater the polarisability and the stronger the intermolecular forces

Intermolecular forces between non-polar molecules are called London or dispersion forces

Intermolecular forces are sometimes called van der Waals forces

20.1 Explain the following order of boiling points:

	Helium	Neon	Argon	Xenon
Relative atomic mass	4.0	20.2	39.9	131.3
Boiling point/K	4	27	87	165

20.2 Which of the halogens would you expect to have the highest polarisability: fluorine, chlorine, bromine, or iodine? Briefly explain your answer.

20.3 If two atoms, A and B, are a distance r apart, the dispersion energy between them varies as $-1/r^6$. For two oppositely charged ions a distance r apart, the interaction energy varies as $-1/r$. Write a computer program to plot graphs of $-1/r^6$ and $-1/r$ to the same scale. First, explain what the negative sign tells us about the energy of interaction. Secondly, when you have plotted the graphs, explain why the dispersion force is known as a short-range force, whereas the force between two ions is a longer-range force.

20.4 After looking in a data book, a student noticed that the water molecule has a permanent dipole moment. The student also remembered that, considering its fairly small molecular mass, water has an unusually high boiling point. The student wrote that the high boiling point of water was good evidence to show that the forces between polar molecules are strong. Was the student correct? Explain your answer.

20.5 Comment on the following quote: 'There are very strong intermolecular forces in sodium chloride.'

20.6 For each of the molecules in the following list, say what type of intermolecular force would hold them together: hydrogen, H_2; benzene, C_6H_6; pentan-3-one, $(CH_3CH_2)_2C{=}O$.

20.7 Hexane (C_6H_{14}) and heptane (C_7H_{16}) are liquids at room temperature. Decide what sort of intermolecular force helps to keep the molecules together in the liquids. Now try your hand at predicting whether the two liquids would mix together easily, or whether they would form two separate layers.

Answers

20.1 As the relative atomic mass increases, the number of electrons in the atom increases. This means that the outer electrons, some of which are used in bonding, are increasingly shielded by the inner electrons. The polarisability therefore increases and the dispersion force between the molecules will increase.

20.2 Iodine: this has the largest number of electrons, the most shielding and the greatest polarisability.

20.3 The negative sign tells us that the energy of interaction leads to attraction, i.e. a lowering of the energy. Notice that the $1/r^6$ graph reaches zero much more quickly than the $1/r$ graph (Figure 20.7). This tells us that the dispersion forces are effective only over very short distances. Attractions between ions are effective over much larger distances.

20.4 The student forgot that the high boiling point of water is largely due to hydrogen bonds, not directly to the dipoles of the water molecules (see Unit 21).

20.5 Sodium chloride is an ionic substance. As such it is held together by the electrostatic attractions between the ions, not by intermolecular forces. (There are no molecules in ionic substances.)

20.6 Hydrogen and benzene are non-polar. These molecules are held together in liquid or solid by dispersion forces. Pentan-3-one has a permanent dipole moment (like propanone), so here the forces are between permanent dipoles.

20.7 Each liquid has molecules held together by dispersion forces. Also, the molecules are chemically very similar. Thus, if we placed one of each type near each other we would expect them to attract by dispersion forces not greatly different to those in the separate liquids. The liquids should mix easily together. They do! You will find much more about the business of liquids mixing in Unit 61.

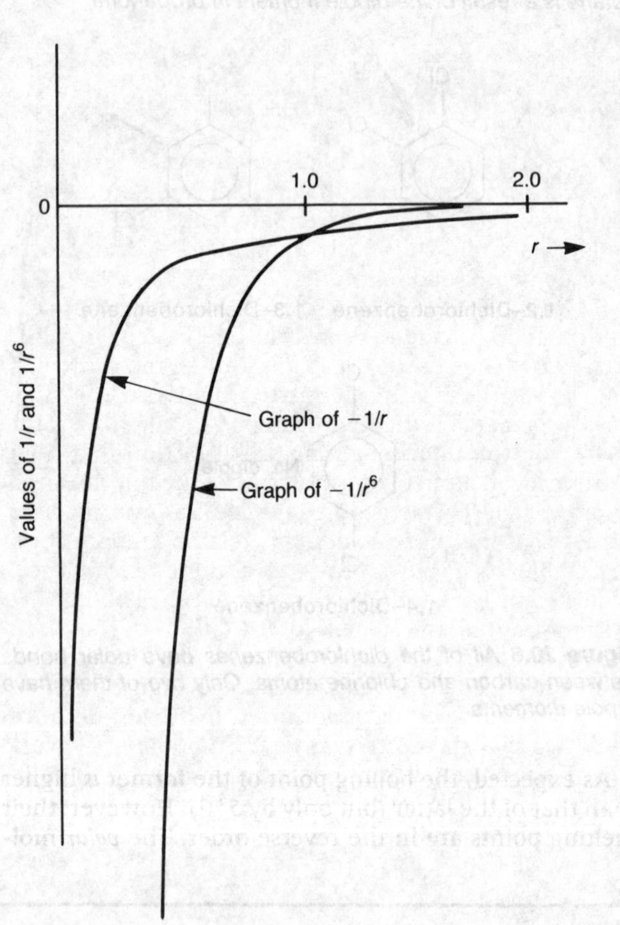

***Figure 20.7** At short distances ($r<0.5$), the magnitude of $-1/r^6$ is very much larger than $-1/r$. At longer distances ($r>1$), $-1/r^6$ becomes much smaller than $-1/r$*

UNIT 20 SUMMARY

- Intermolecular forces exist between all atoms and molecules except those of an ideal gas.
- The main types are:
  - (i) Van der Waals, which involve attractions between induced dipole moments.
  - (ii) Attractions between permanent dipole moments.
  - (iii) Hydrogen bonds.
- Molecules that show the strongest van der Waals forces are highly polarisable, i.e. their electron clouds are easily distorted. These are usually large, heavy atoms or molecules.

21

Hydrogen bonding

21.1 What is hydrogen bonding?

In Unit 19 we saw that many molecules are polar. Especially, molecules that have a highly electronegative atom connected to a hydrogen atom are often strongly polar. Examples of such molecules are hydrogen fluoride, water and ammonia (Figure 21.1).

If two molecules of hydrogen fluoride were put close to one another, the hydrogen of one molecule will be attracted to the fluorine atom of the other molecule. This happens because of the attraction between the slight positive charge on the hydrogen and the slight negative charge on the fluorine atom. The attraction that holds the hydrogen atom of one molecule to the fluorine atom of another molecule is an example of a *hydrogen bond*. Notice that hydrogen bonding is related to ionic bonding. Table 21.1 shows how the strengths of hydrogen bonds compare with the strengths of other bonds.

The structure of solid hydrogen fluoride has been shown to consist of planes of hydrogen fluoride molecules arranged in the zig-zag fashion of Figure 21.2. The fact that there are two fluorine-to-hydrogen distances indicates that there are two types of bonding at work. The shorter distance represents the covalent (but polar) bond in each molecule. The longer distance represents the hydrogen bond.

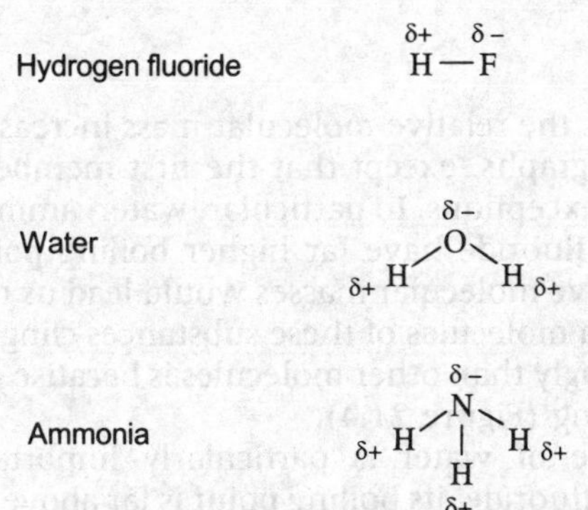

***Figure 21.1** Three molecules that have hydrogen atoms bonded to a highly electronegative atom. These molecules are often involved in hydrogen bonding*

Table 21.1. Comparison of the strengths of hydrogen, covalent and van der Waals bonds

	Typical bond energy/kJ mol^{-1}
Covalent bonds	100 to 900
Hydrogen bonds	20 to 50
Van der Waals bonds	less than 20

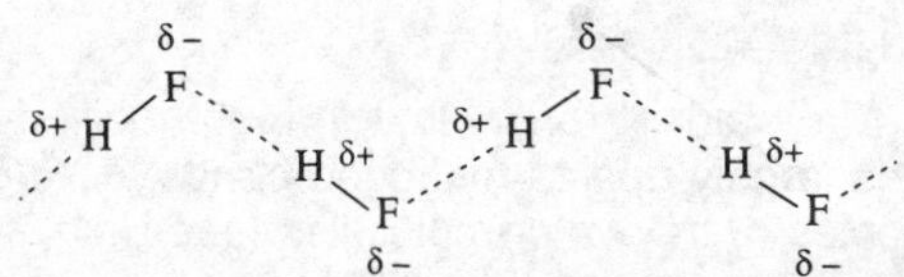

***Figure 21.2** Solid hydrogen fluoride consists of zig-zag chains of HF molecules. Neighbouring molecules are held together by hydrogen bonds. Hydrogen bonds are always shown by dotted (or dashed) lines*

> **21.1** Which is the stronger bond in hydrogen fluoride: the shorter, covalent bond, or the longer, hydrogen bond between different molecules?

21.2 Evidence for hydrogen bonding

One of the signs of hydrogen bonding between molecules comes from examining the boiling points of different compounds. We know that some substances have very high melting or boiling points. They are usually ionic compounds (like sodium chloride), or compounds with huge covalent lattices (like silica). Compounds with low melting and boiling points are usually covalent. The lower the relative molecular mass, the lower the melting and boiling points.

Figure 21.3 shows some graphs of boiling points plotted against relative molecular mass for various compounds. The graphs for the noble gases and hydrocarbons illustrate the general trend for boiling point to

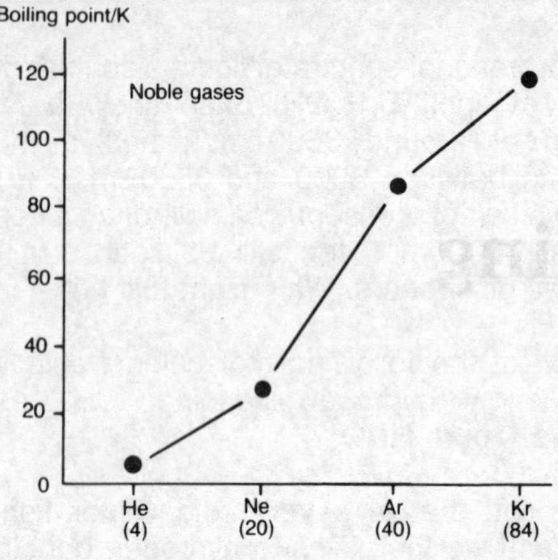

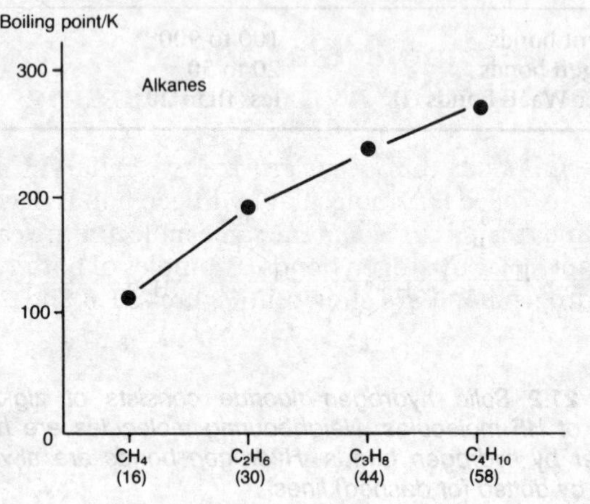

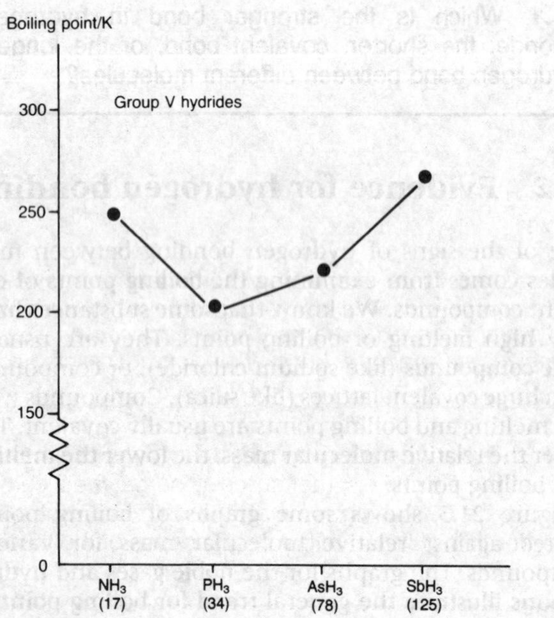

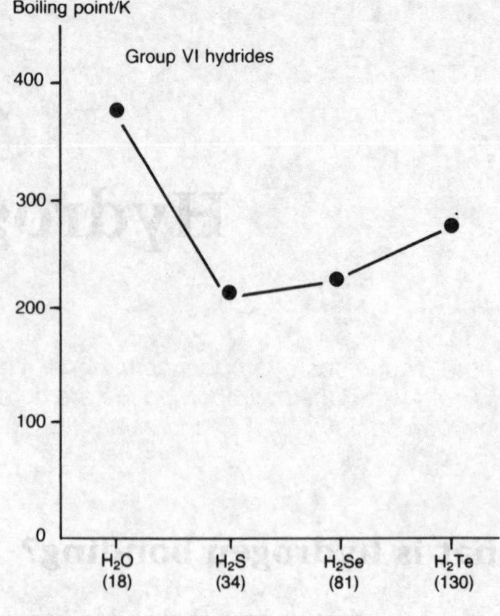

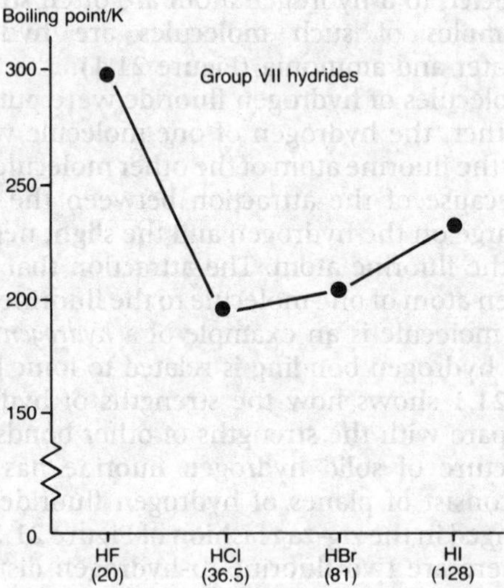

***Figure 21.3** The general trend is for boiling point to increase with increasing relative molecular mass (shown in brackets). The exceptions are when hydrogen bonding occurs, especially in HF, H_2O and NH_3. (Note: scales of relative molecular mass are not uniform)*

increase as the relative molecular mass increases. So do the other graphs, except that the first members of the series are exceptions. In particular, water, ammonia and hydrogen fluoride have far higher boiling points than their relative molecular masses would lead us to expect. The reason molecules of these substances cling together more strongly than other molecules is because of hydrogen bonding (Figure 21.4).

The case of water is particularly important. Like hydrogen fluoride, its boiling point is far above the level that we would expect. In water, the hydrogen bonding stretches from molecule to molecule right through the liquid. Hydrogen bonding is also responsible for the high value of the surface tension of water.

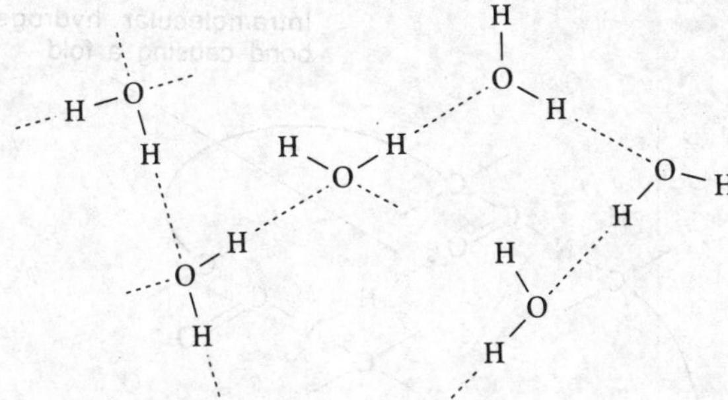

Figure 21.4 The scope for hydrogen bonding in water is enormous. In liquid water the hydrogen bonds are constantly swapping between molecules, i.e. the molecules change partners frequently

Water is one of the few substances that is less dense as a solid (ice) than it is as a liquid. If you look at Figure 21.5 you will be able to understand why this happens. The water molecules line up in such a way as to maximise the amount of hydrogen bonding between them. This leaves a tremendous amount of space in the lattice. Hence the low density of ice.

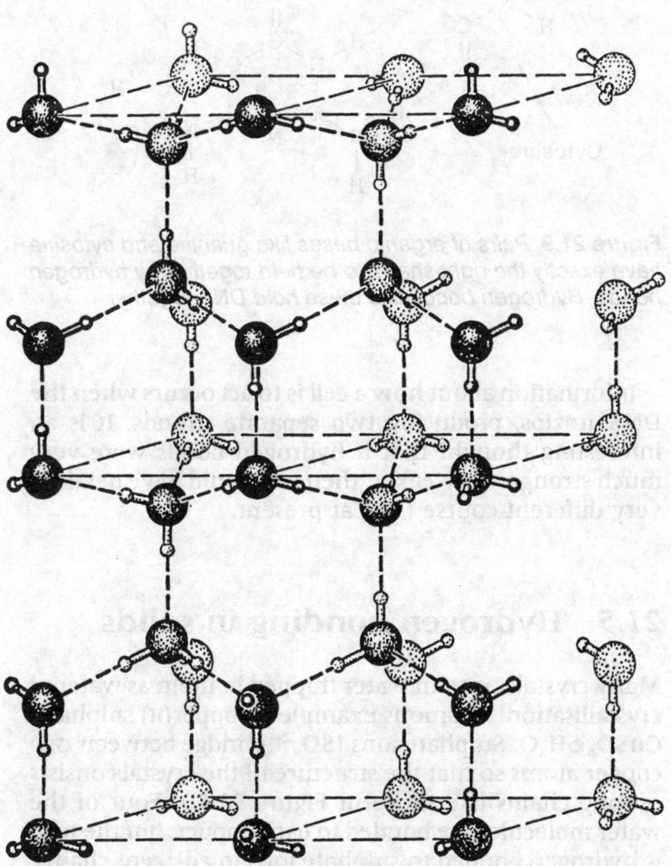

Figure 21.5 The structure of ice. (Taken from: Pauling, L. (1960). The Nature of the Chemical Bond, *3rd edn, Cornell University Press, Ithaca, NY, figure 12.6, p. 465)*

21.2 The vibrational spectra of liquid alcohols (molecules like ethanol, C_2H_5OH) often show a fairly sharp band at around 3600 cm^{-1}, and a much broader band between 3000 and 3500 cm^{-1}. If the spectrum is taken of a gaseous sample of an alcohol, the band at 3600 cm^{-1} can still be seen; but the broader band disappears. Why might this be?

21.3 Which of the following molecules would you expect to show hydrogen bonding: CH_4, HCl, HCOOH, C_6H_6, pure HNO_3?

21.4 Why is it that in a very cold winter fish in garden ponds owe their lives to hydrogen bonding? (Hint: density of ice.)

21.5 Why would you expect water and ethanol to mix easily?

21.3 Intermolecular and intramolecular hydrogen bonding

Hydrogen bonds that occur *between* two different molecules are called *inter*molecular hydrogen bonds. Hydrogen bonds that occur *within* the same molecule are called *intra*molecular hydrogen bonds. Examples of both types of hydrogen bond are shown in Figures 21.6 and 21.7.

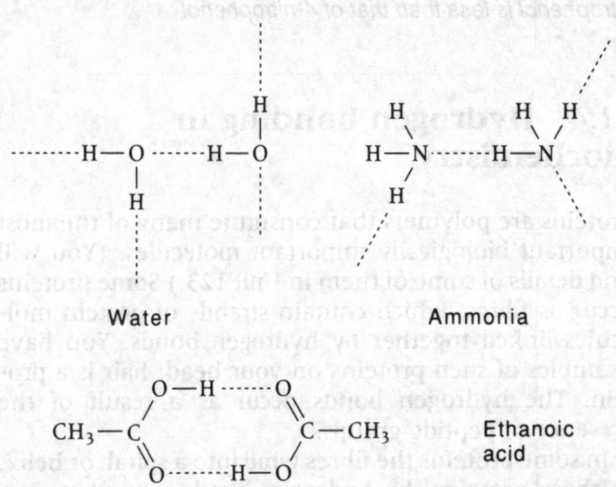

Figure 21.6 Three examples of intermolecular hydrogen bonding. The intermolecular hydrogen bonds in liquid water and liquid ammonia have no simple influence on how the molecules are arranged. But in ethanoic acid, dimers occur

21.6 When the relative molecular mass of ethanoic acid, CH_3COOH, is measured it sometimes comes out to be 60 (which is what it should be), but often nearer to 120. What might be the cause of the 'wrong' results?

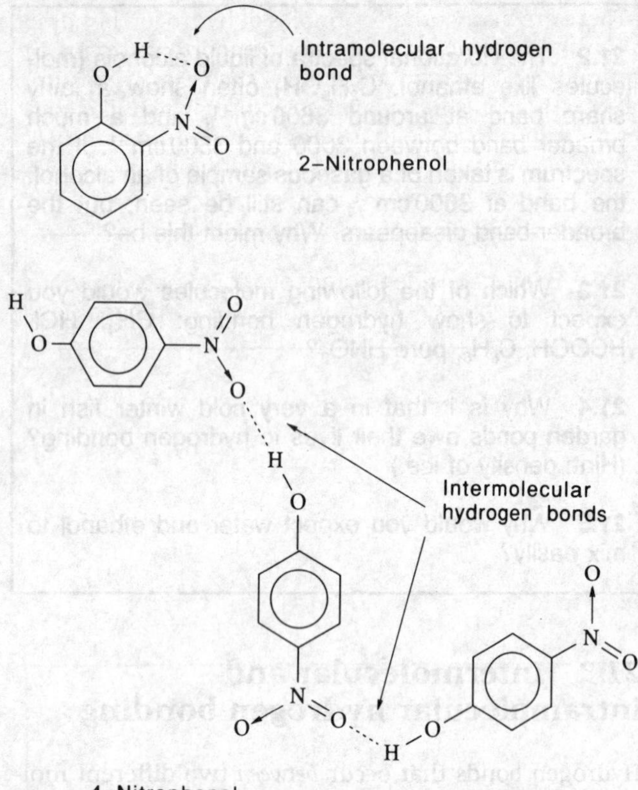

***Figure 21.7** Hydrogen bonding in 2- and 4-nitrophenol. Intramolecular hydrogen bonding in 2-nitrophenol means that there is less intermolecular hydrogen bonding than in 4-nitrophenol. As a consequence, the boiling point of 2-nitrophenol is less than that of 4-nitrophenol*

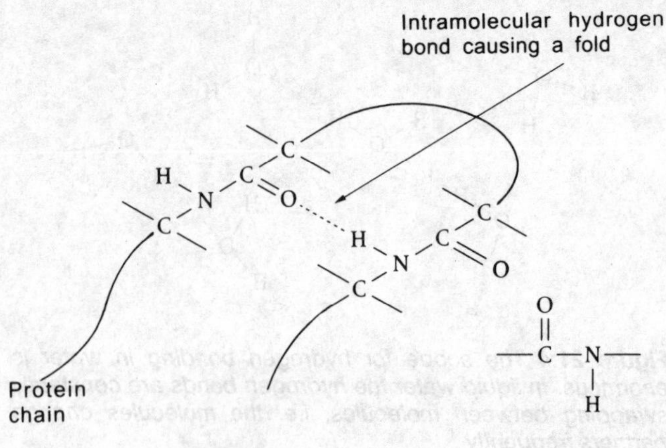

***Figure 21.8** Intramolecular hydrogen bonds can occur along a protein chain. The fold in a peptide chain can be produced by hydrogen bonds between different peptide links*

***Figure 21.9** Pairs of organic bases like guanine and cytosine have exactly the right shape to be held together by hydrogen bonds. Hydrogen bonds like these hold DNA together*

21.4 Hydrogen bonding in biochemistry

Proteins are polymers that constitute many of the most important biologically important molecules. (You will find details of some of them in Unit 123.) Some proteins occur as fibres, which contain strands of protein molecules linked together by hydrogen bonds. You have examples of such proteins on your head: hair is a protein. The hydrogen bonds occur as a result of the presence of peptide groups.

In some proteins the fibres wind into a spiral, or helix. In these proteins the hydrogen bonds occur between peptide groups at different points along the same chain (Figure 21.8). This is a form of intramolecular hydrogen bonding.

An equally important example of hydrogen bonding occurs in DNA (deoxyribonucleic acid). This remarkable material is, among other things, responsible for handing down hereditary information from one generation to another. It exists as two intertwined helices. The two strands of the double helix are held together by hydrogen bonds. These bonds occur between pairs of organic groups called 'bases'. Figure 21.9 shows how two of the bases can hydrogen bond together.

Information about how a cell is to act occurs when the DNA unzips, producing two separate strands. It is an interesting thought that if hydrogen bonds were very much stronger, or weaker, then life would have to take a very different course than at present.

21.5 Hydrogen bonding in solids

Many crystals contain water trapped in them as water of crystallisation. A famous example is copper(II) sulphate, $CuSO_4{\cdot}5H_2O$. Sulphate ions (SO_4^{2-}) bridge between two copper atoms so that the structure of the crystal consists of long chains like those in Figure 21.10. Four of the water molecules are bonded to each copper, but the fifth is hydrogen bonded to sulphate ions in adjacent chains.

If the crystals are heated, it is the hydrogen bonded water molecules that are jostled out of position first. When this happens the structure of the crystal is disrupted, and we see the crystals forming a solution.

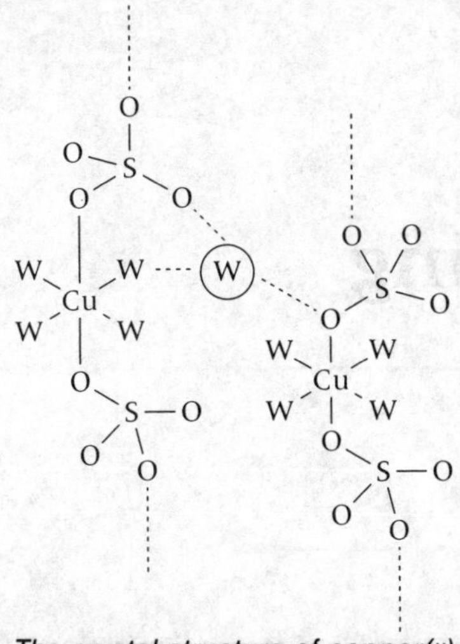

Figure 21.10 The crystal structure of copper(II) sulphate has chains of copper(II) ions bonded to four water molecules, W, and the oxygen atoms of sulphate ions. The fifth water molecule, circled, lies between the chains. It is hydrogen bonded to oxygen atoms in both chains

There are many other examples of hydrogen bonding in crystals. Some of the most important occur in naturally occurring minerals such as gypsum, $CaSO_4 \cdot 2H_2O$. This has a layer structure, which like copper(II) sulphate is held together by hydrogen bonds between water molecules and sulphate ions.

21.7 Briefly consider some of the effects on our lives if water had only a very little hydrogen bonding.

Answers

21.1 It is a general rule that, the shorter the bond, the stronger it is, and vice versa. Thus, the hydrogen bond is weaker than the covalent bond between the atoms.

21.2 In the gas, the molecules will fly apart separate from one another and they will not be hydrogen bonded. The broad band in solution that disappears in the gas is due to hydrogen bonding.

21.3 HCl, HCOOH and pure HNO_3. The others, CH_4 and C_6H_6, do not have a hydrogen atom attached to a highly electronegative atom.

21.4 In winter, any ice will float. This allows the fish to remain alive in unfrozen water below the ice. Ice is less dense than water because the hydrogen bonds hold the molecules apart in the solid, thus leaving a lot of empty space in the crystal structure.

21.5 Water and ethanol have similar structures. Both contain a hydrogen atom bonded to an oxygen atom. Both are liquids that have considerable amounts of hydrogen bonding. Each type of molecule can hydrogen bond with the other (Figure 21.11). Hence they should mix together, and hydrogen bonding is found in alcoholic drinks like wine, beer, lager, etc.

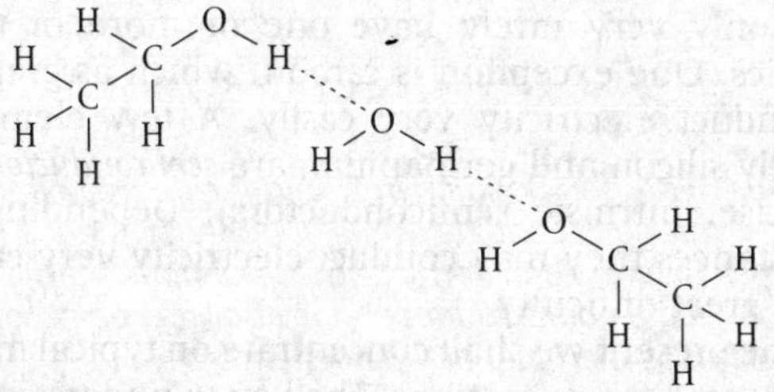

Figure 21.11 Ethanol and water molecules can hydrogen bond together

21.6 If you look back at Figure 21.6 you will see that ethanoic acid can exist as dimers. Often samples of the acid will contain a mixture of monomers and dimers. This causes the confusion over its molecular mass.

21.7 The effects would be overwhelming. For example, the cells of which we are made contain large amounts of water. This would have boiled away at room temperature! Also rain, rivers, lakes or oceans would be rather uncommon.

UNIT 21 SUMMARY

- A hydrogen bond is made between a hydrogen atom and a highly electronegative atom such as fluorine, oxygen, chlorine or nitrogen. The hydrogen atom itself must be bonded to an atom with a high electronegativity.
- Hydrogen bonds are responsible for:
  (i) The relatively high melting and boiling points of water and hydrogen fluoride.
  (ii) Holding the strands of DNA together.
- *Intermolecular* hydrogen bonds occur between *different* molecules, e.g. between water and alcohol molecules, or between ethanoic acid dimers.
- *Intramolecular* hydrogen bonds occur between groups in the *same* molecule, e.g. in 2-nitrophenol.

22

Metallic bonding

22.1 How can you recognise a metal?

Probably you will already know many of the properties of metals summarised in Table 22.1.

Of course, there are exceptions and, for example, some metals conduct heat better than others. However, non-metals only very rarely have one or more of these properties. One exception is carbon, which as graphite will conduct electricity very easily. A few elements, especially silicon and germanium, are *semiconductors* (to be precise, intrinsic semiconductors). Depending on circumstances they may conduct electricity very easily, or with great difficulty.

For the present we shall concentrate on typical metals and disregard the exceptions. The key to understanding the properties of metals lies in two areas: first, the way the *electrons* are arranged; secondly, the way the *atoms* are arranged in the crystal structure. Especially, the arrangement of the electrons is responsible for the conduction of heat and electricity, and the crystal structure relates to the malleability and ductility. We shall deal with the electron structure here, and leave the crystal structure to the unit on X-ray diffraction (Unit 30).

Table 22.1. Properties of metals

Most, but not all, metals are:
- Solids at room temperature
- Sonorous, i.e. ring when struck
- Malleable, i.e. can be beaten into various shapes
- Ductile, i.e. can be drawn out into wires
- Good conductors of electricity
- Good conductors of heat

22.2 What is the band structure of metals?

As we know that metals conduct electricity well, it follows that at least some of the electrons must be able to move easily through a metal crystal. Unless electrons completely escape from atoms (ionisation), they must be found in orbitals. Thus there must be some special orbitals in metals that are involved in conduction. Metal atoms have the ability to share their outermost orbitals with each other. Overlap of the orbitals occurs not only over two atoms (as in ethene) or six atoms (as in benzene) but over millions of atoms. With overlap of two orbitals only two energy levels result (one level for the bonding and one for the antibonding orbital). When there are so many more orbitals overlapping in a metal there are literally thousands of new energy levels. These levels are so close together in energy that they form an *energy band*.

In Figure 22.1 only s orbitals are shown overlapping, but p and d orbitals can make bands as well. Some bands are completely full; these are the bands of lowest energy. They contain the inner electrons of each atom. The atoms hold on to these electrons the most strongly. At the other extreme some bands will be so high in energy that they will be empty. Between these two extremes metals have a band that is only partly filled (Figure 22.2). On the other hand, non-metals have bands that are either completely full or completely empty. The bands that are made from the overlap of the outermost orbitals contain the valence electrons of each atom. Such a band is called a *valence band*. Depending on the metal in question, there can be several valence bands. Just as

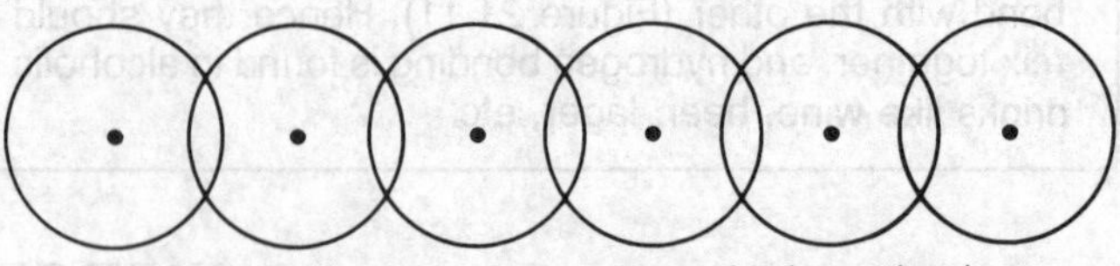

Part of a layer of atoms with outer s orbitals overlapping

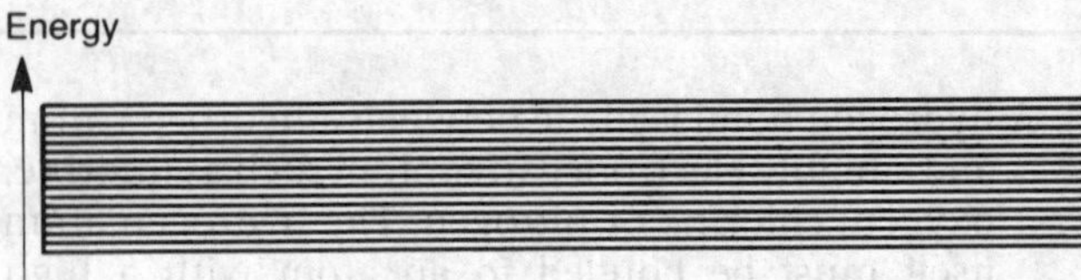

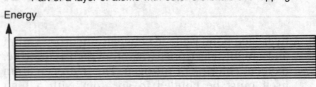

The overlap of so many orbitals gives rise to a band of energy levels

***Figure 22.1** The origin of energy bands in metals (s orbitals are not the only ones to give rise to bands)*

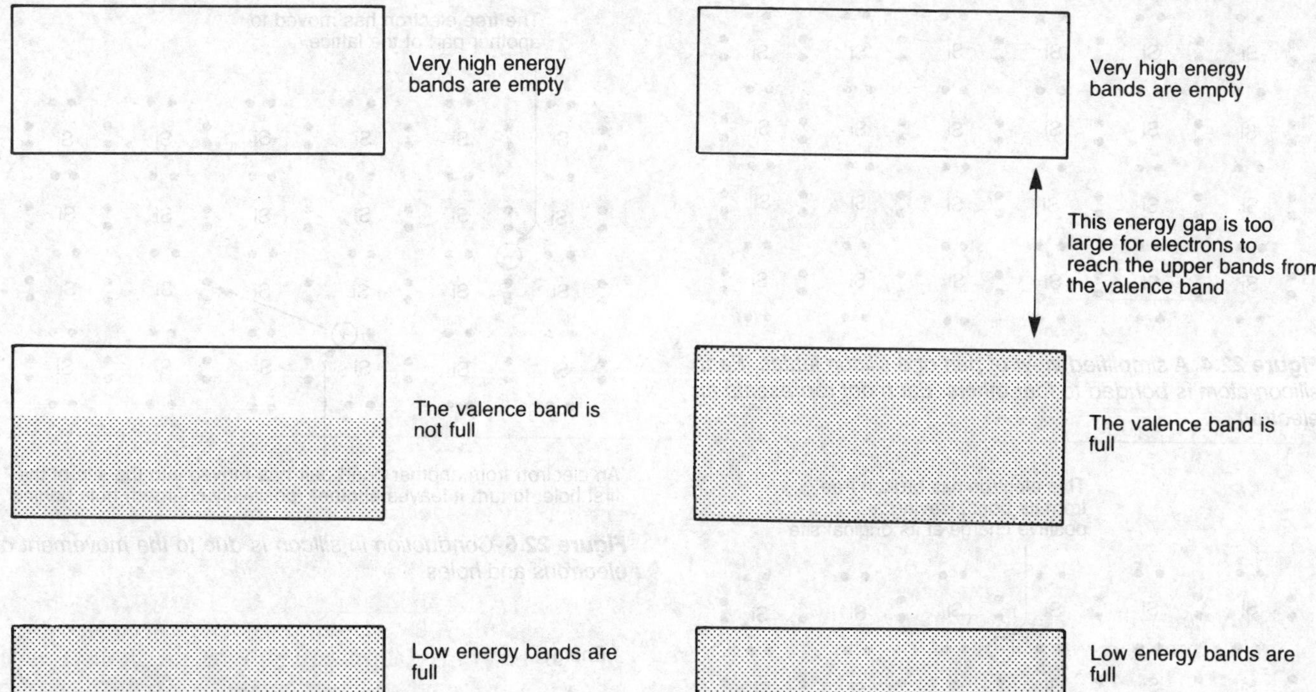
Very high energy bands are empty
The valence band is not full
Low energy bands are full
Very high energy bands are empty
This energy gap is too large for electrons to reach the upper bands from the valence band
The valence band is full
Low energy bands are full

***Figure 22.2** How band theory sees the arrangement of electrons in a good conductor of electricity. Movement of electrons can take place within the valence band*

***Figure 22.3** In an insulator, the valence band is full and electrons cannot gain energy and move within this band. If they could reach the empty bands above the valence band, then conduction could take place. However, under normal conditions the electrons cannot gain enough energy to reach the higher bands*

with atomic and molecular orbitals, the various bands are separated by an energy gap.

22.3 Why do metals conduct electricity?

First, the key thing to realise is that the electrons in a band are moving. For example, in our line of atoms of Figure 22.1, electrons would move to the left and to the right. However, on average, the same number move to the left as to the right. This means that there is no overall movement of electric charge in any one direction, so there is no electric current. If an electric current is to flow from left to right, more electrons must move to the right than move to the left. We can make this happen by giving the electrons a 'push' to the right by attaching a battery to the metal. The battery is a source of energy. If the electrons take up some of this energy, they are able to leave the particular energy level they are in and move to a higher level. In a metal there are empty levels in the main valence band. Therefore the electrons can take up the extra energy, move to a higher level, and travel through the metal. Compare this with a non-metal (Figure 22.3). Here the valence bands are completely full. An electron in the valence band cannot take up extra energy because there are no free energy levels to which it can move. It is for this reason that metals conduct electricity, but non-metals are electrical insulators.

22.1 Actually it is possible to make 'insulators' conduct electricity. Look again at Figure 22.3. There *is* a set of energy levels to which an electron in the valence band of a non-metal can move. Where is the set? Does it take a great deal of energy to make an 'insulator' conduct? How could you cause conduction to take place?

22.4 Semiconductors

In a metal the outermost electrons of each atom can move easily from one atom to another. A metal is a good conductor of electricity (and heat) because these electrons are free to move. On the other hand, in an insulator the outer (valence) electrons are held tightly to the atoms to which they belong. At room temperature the valence electrons cannot gain enough energy to break free from their bonds. Thus conduction cannot occur.

In a *semiconductor* the valence electrons are sufficiently loosely bound that some are able to break free from their bonds at room temperature. Silicon and germanium are two of the most widely used semiconductors. More properly they should be called *intrinsic semiconductors*. This is in distinction to *extrinsic semiconductors* where, for example, silicon is doped with another element.

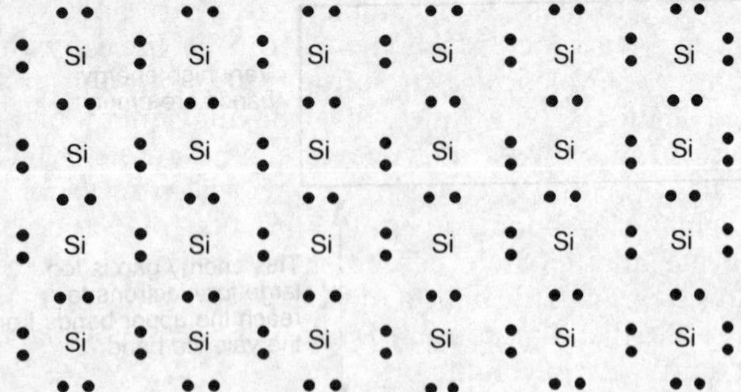

Figure 22.4 A simplified view of part of a silicon lattice. Each silicon atom is bonded to four others. Each dot represents an electron

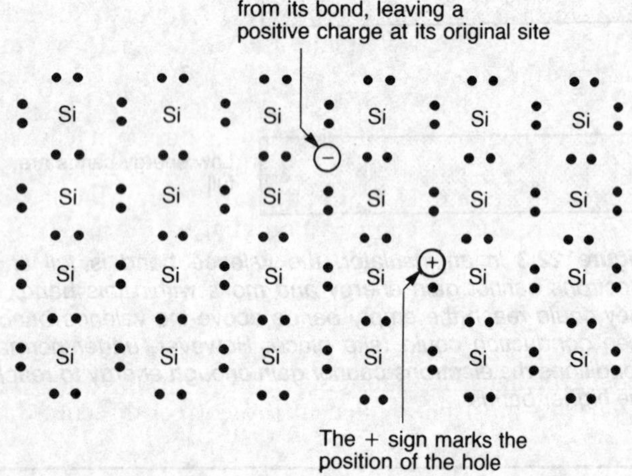
This electron has broken free from its bond, leaving a positive charge at its original site
The + sign marks the position of the hole

Figure 22.5 The creation of a free electron and hole pair

We shall take silicon as an example of an *intrinsic semiconductor*. The arrangement of atoms in a silicon crystal is shown (in a much simplified way) in Figure 22.4. By contrast, Figure 22.5 shows what happens if one of the bonding electrons gains sufficient energy to break free. The free electron can move through the lattice, thus giving rise to an electric current if a voltage is applied across the ends of the silicon. The free electron leaves behind an equal, but opposite, charge to that of the electron. The place where this positive charge is found is called a *hole*.

In fact, when a voltage is applied across a piece of silicon, conduction can arise in two ways: (i) The free electrons can move through the *conduction band*. (ii) Electrons can move into the holes. For example, an electron from an adjacent bond may swap places with the hole. In Figure 22.6 the net result is the movement of the hole from left to right. The conduction by holes occurs in the *valence band* (see Figure 22.7).

For silicon at room temperature, only 1 in 10^{12} atoms produces a free electron and hole pair.

Extrinsic semiconductors are obtained by adding an impurity to, i.e. doping, an intrinsic semiconductor.

An n-type semiconductor is obtained by doping silicon with a Group V element (P, As, Sb); a p-type semiconductor is obtained by doping silicon with a Group III element (B, Al, Ga, In).

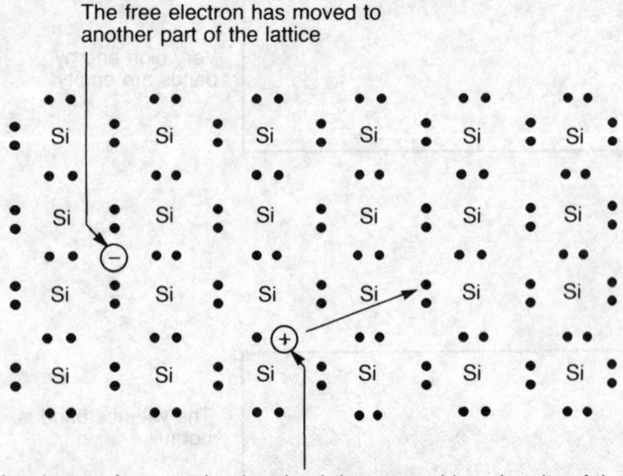
The free electron has moved to another part of the lattice
An electron from another bond pair has moved into the site of the first hole. In turn it leaves another (positively charged) hole behind

Figure 22.6 Conduction in silicon is due to the movement of electrons and holes

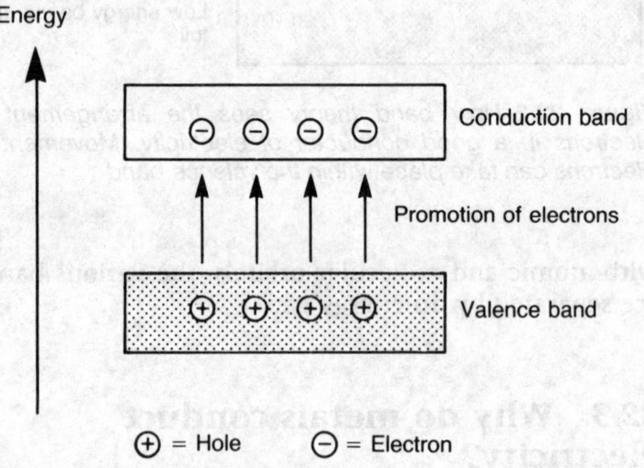
Energy
Conduction band
Promotion of electrons
Valence band
⊕ = Hole
⊖ = Electron

Figure 22.7 Conduction in silicon occurs by holes moving in the valence band, and electrons moving in the conduction band

> **In an *n-type* semiconductor the impurity provides an excess of *electrons.***
>
> **In a *p-type* semiconductor the impurity provides an excess of *holes.***

(a) *n-Type semiconductors*

Suppose silicon is doped with phosphorus. Phosphorus, in common with other Group V elements, has five valence electrons. Only four of these can be used in bonding to silicon atoms. The extra electron is not bound anywhere near as strongly as the bonded electrons, and it is easily promoted to the conduction band (Figure 22.8). Each Group V atom increases by one the number

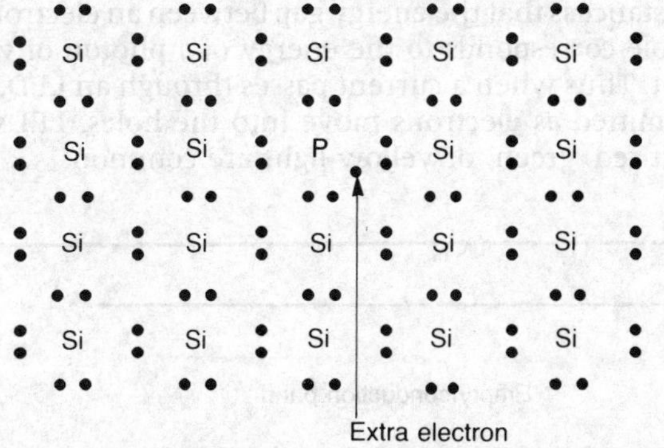

***Figure 22.8** Each phosphorus atom brings one extra electron into the lattice. The extra electrons are mainly responsible for the extra conducting ability of n-type semiconductors. (Holes and free electrons normally present in the silicon are not shown)*

of electrons available for conduction. Usually the number of Group V atoms added is far greater than the 1 in 10^{12} conduction electrons that are already present in the silicon. Therefore, the conductivity of an n-type semiconductor is mainly due to the impurity atoms.

(b) *p-Type semiconductors*

An example of a p-type semiconductor is silicon doped with a Group III element such as gallium, which has only three valence electrons. There are not enough electrons to make four complete covalent bonds with silicon. A vacancy is left, which can be filled by the transfer of a valence electron from a neighbouring atom (see Figure 22.9). Notice that the movement of an electron into the vacancy leaves behind a hole, which carries a positive charge. Another electron from a neighbouring bond can move into the hole, thereby leaving another hole behind. It is as if the hole has moved through the lattice. Indeed, it is the movement of the holes that is responsible for the conduction of charge in a p-type semiconductor.

(c) *Diodes*

A diode can be made by taking a piece of silicon and doping each half with the opposite carrier type. Where the two halves meet, there is a *p–n junction*. At the junction, electrons from the n-type side cross over to fill some of the holes on the p-type side, and vice versa. However, the transfer of an electron in this way will leave a net positive charge behind in the n-type material. Similarly, the movement of holes in the opposite direction leaves a net negative charge behind on the p-type side. Once formed, these charges hinder the further transfer of carriers across the junction. A potential barrier is set up, which can prevent the flow of charge across the junction. In order to overcome the barrier, a potential difference of around 0.6 V must act across the junction of the p- and n-type material in a silicon diode. (For a germanium diode, the figure is about 0.4 V.) However, the potential difference must be applied in the correct direction, as

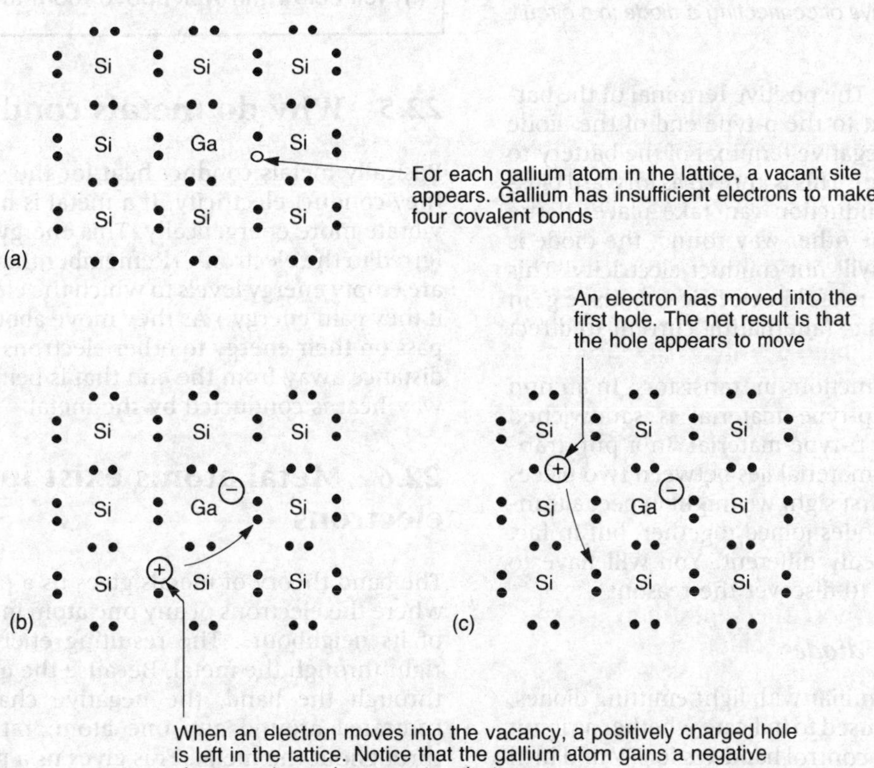

***Figure 22.9** Conduction in silicon doped by gallium, a p-type semiconductor, is mainly due to the movement of holes*

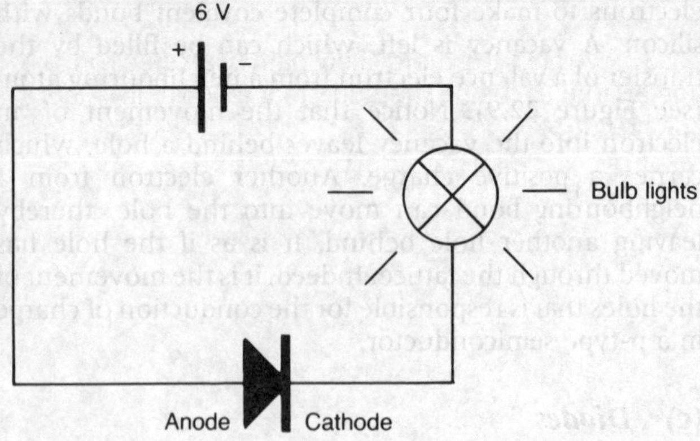

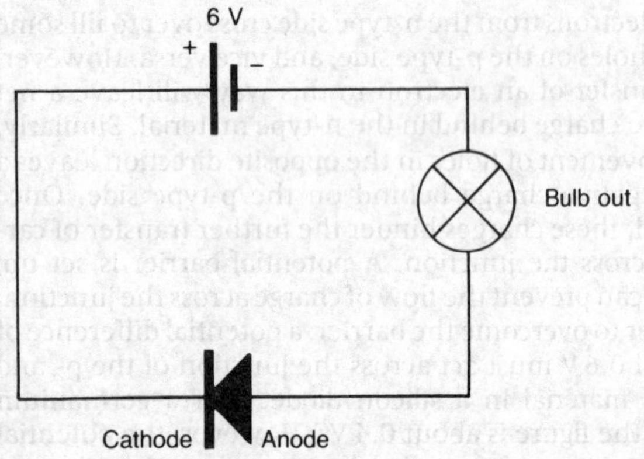

Figure 22.10 *The two ways of connecting a diode in a circuit*

shown in Figure 22.10. The positive terminal of the battery must be connected to the p-type end of the diode (the anode), and the negative terminal of the battery to the n-type end (cathode). This is known as forward biasing the diode, and conduction can take place. If the battery is connected the other way round, the diode is reverse biased, and it will not conduct electricity. This behaviour can be most useful in electric circuits, e.g. in rectification of a.c. to d.c. (alternating current to direct current).

Use is made of p–n junctions in transistors. In an npn transistor a layer of p-type material is sandwiched between two pieces of n-type material. In a pnp transistor a layer of n-type material lies between two pieces of p-type material. At first sight we might expect a transistor to act like two diodes joined together, but in fact the behaviour is markedly different. You will have to consult a physics book to discover the reason!

(d) *Light emitting diodes*

You will probably be familiar with light emitting diodes, LEDs. These are widely used to indicate whether a circuit is active, e.g. on remote control handsets for TV and hi-fi sets. LEDs are commonly made from gallium arsenide (a Group III plus a Group V compound). The beauty of this substance is that the energy gap between an electron and a hole corresponds to the energy of a photon of visible light. Thus when a current passes through an LED, light is emitted as electrons move into the holes. LEDs that emit red, green, or yellow light are common.

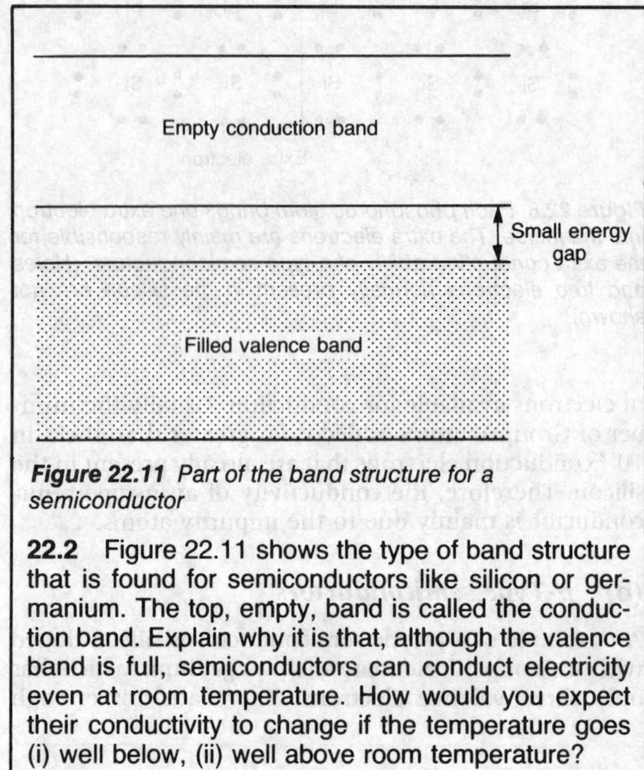

Figure 22.11 *Part of the band structure for a semiconductor*

22.2 Figure 22.11 shows the type of band structure that is found for semiconductors like silicon or germanium. The top, empty, band is called the conduction band. Explain why it is that, although the valence band is full, semiconductors can conduct electricity even at room temperature. How would you expect their conductivity to change if the temperature goes (i) well below, (ii) well above room temperature?

22.5 Why do metals conduct heat?

Basically metals conduct heat for the same reason that they conduct electricity. If a metal is heated, the atoms vibrate more energetically. This energy is mainly transferred to the electrons. (Remember that in a metal there are empty energy levels to which the electrons can move if they gain energy.) As they move about the metal they pass on their energy to other electrons and atoms some distance away from the end that is being heated. In this way heat is conducted by the metal.

22.6 Metal atoms exist in a sea of electrons

The band theory of metals gives us a picture of a metal where the electrons of any one atom interact with those of its neighbours. The resulting energy bands spread right through the metal. Because the electrons can drift through the band, the negative charge is not concentrated around any one atom; rather, it is spread throughout the metal. This gives us a picture of a metal like that of Figure 22.12. This is called the *sea of electrons* model of metallic bonding. It has been said that the

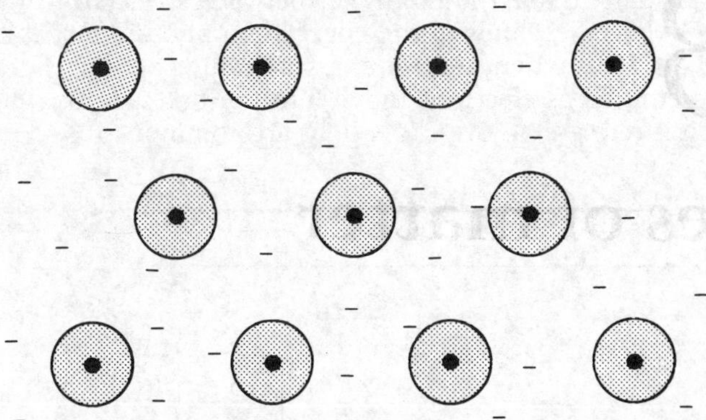

Figure 22.12 In the 'sea of electrons' model of a metal the nucleus of each atom together with its inner electrons are surrounded by the outer electrons of all the atoms. The outer electrons exist in energy bands that spread throughout the metal lattice

negatively charged sea of electrons acts like cement binding the positively charged nuclei together.

However, this model of bonding in metals cannot be the full story. We know that some metals are soft, e.g. sodium, whereas others are extremely hard, e.g. tungsten. In many metals there is a directional nature to the bonding, which holds the atoms tightly in position. Indeed, there is an entire branch of chemistry that investigates the nature of metal–metal bonds; but it is one that we shall have to ignore.

22.3 Which is the more likely path of an electron in a metal that is being heated, that shown in Figure 22.13a or b?

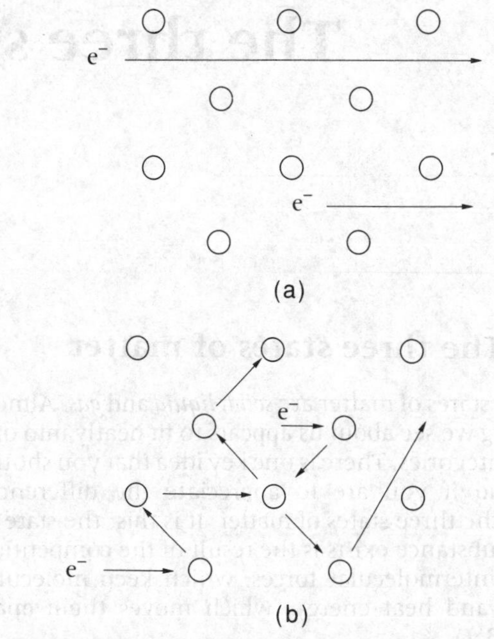

Figure 22.13 *Two possible ways for electrons to move through a metal lattice*

Answers

22.1 There is an empty band above the valence band. There is a large energy gap between the two bands. Therefore a lot of energy is needed to make electrons jump from the valence to the empty band. You could supply the energy by using a source of very high voltage, perhaps 10 000 V or more, instead of an ordinary battery.

22.2 At room temperature some, but by no means all, of the electrons have enough energy to move to the conduction band. This is unlike insulators, where the energy gap is very much larger. We would expect the conduction to decrease as the temperature decreases, and vice versa. This behaviour is also unlike metals. They conduct electricity better at low temperatures; in other words, the resistance of a metal increases with temperature. This is because the thermal energy of the electrons in the conduction band causes them to move more chaotically, so they find it harder to move in a single direction, and the current decreases.

22.3 The diagram with the more random path – Figure 22.13b.

UNIT 22 SUMMARY

- The atoms in a metal lattice are embedded in a sea of electrons. The electrons exist in energy bands that spread throughout the lattice. These electrons are free to move, and are responsible for metals being good conductors of heat and electricity.
- Conduction of electricity in non-metals takes place when electrons move between the valence band and the conduction band.
- In insulators the energy gap between the conduction and valence bands is much greater than in metals.
- Intrinsic semiconductors, e.g. silicon and germanium, have valence electrons that can be excited into the conduction band at room temperature.
- Extrinsic semiconductors:
  - (i) p-Type have been doped with a Group III element; conduction is mainly caused by the movement of positively charged holes.
  - (ii) n-Type have been doped with a Group V element; conduction is mainly caused by the movement of electrons.

23

The three states of matter

23.1 The three states of matter

The three states of matter are *solid, liquid* and *gas*. Almost everything we see about us appears to fit neatly into one of these categories. There is one key idea that you should understand if you are to appreciate the differences between the three states of matter. It is this: the state in which a substance exists is the result of the competition between intermolecular forces, which keep molecules together, and heat energy, which moves them apart (Figure 23.1).

Heat energy, which we can also call *thermal energy*, is a measure of the amount of random movement of molecules. We should not say that heat *causes* the random movement of molecules; rather thermal energy *is* the random movement of molecules. The more thermal energy a substance has, the greater is the tendency for its molecules to be jumbled up, i.e. to be more disordered. The most disorderly arrangement that molecules can achieve is in a gas. At the other extreme the most orderly arrangement is in a solid. Liquids are somewhere in between (Figure 23.2).

Intermolecular forces tend to hold molecules together. There are intermolecular forces between all molecules; but between some they are very weak and between others they are quite strong. When the forces are weak, the molecules are not likely to cling together to make a liquid or solid unless they have very little thermal energy. The noble gases are excellent examples. For instance, helium will not liquefy until the temperature is almost as low as $-269°$ C, or 4 K. On the other hand the intermolecular forces between water molecules are very strong.

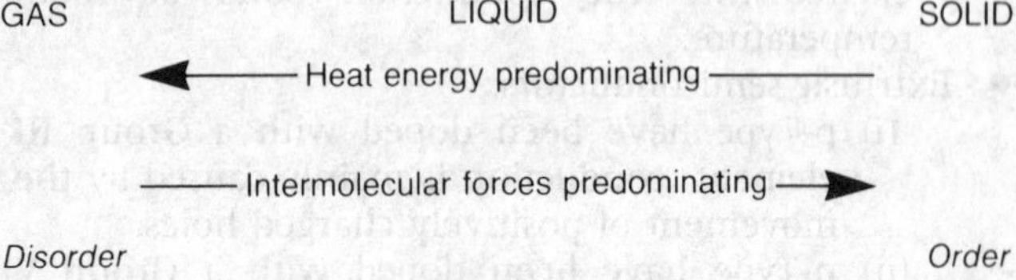

Figure 23.1 *The changes between solid, liquid and gas involve the competition between heat energy and intermolecular forces*

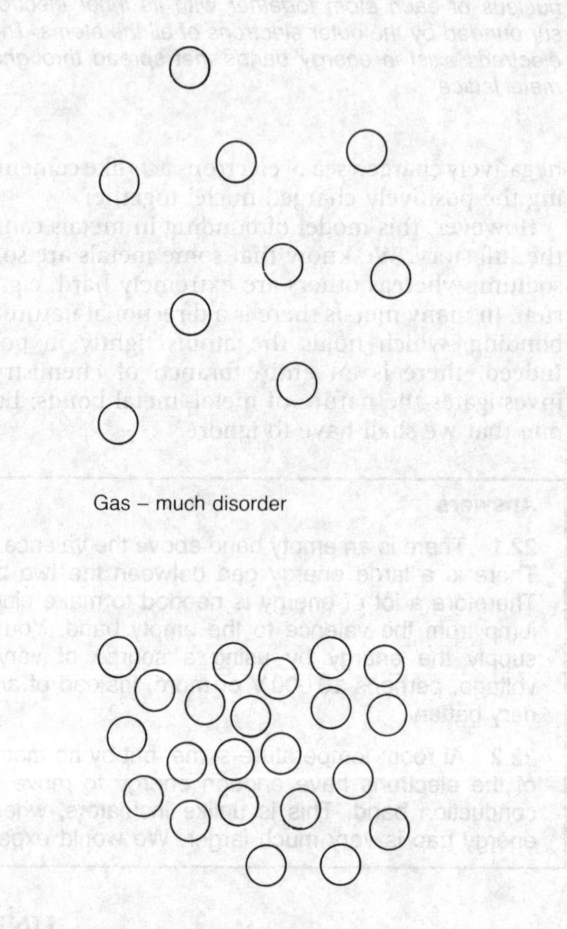

Figure 23.2 *A visual impression of the degrees of disorder in solids, liquids and gases*

To summarise, we can say that:

Intermolecular forces tend to bring order to the movements of molecules; heat energy points in the direction of randomness or chaos.

Whether a substance exists as a solid, liquid or gas depends on where the balance between these two opposing influences lies.

23.1 What is the origin of the intermolecular forces in water?

23.2 How do we know that gases are disorderly?

One piece of evidence comes indirectly from the experiments first performed by Robert Brown in 1827. He observed the movement of pollen grains on the surface of water, which he found to be completely unpredictable. The random movements of the grains, known as *Brownian motion*, were finally given a mathematical explanation by Albert Einstein (of relativity fame) in 1905. He showed that the grains went on a *random walk* (Figure 23.3). A random walk is the sort of walk that a very drunk person would go on if put out in an open space. If we assume that the drunk found it impossible to make a conscious choice, he (or she) would be as likely to walk in one direction as any other. The reason why the grains behave in this way is that they are being bombarded by molecules in the liquid, which are themselves moving in a perfectly random way.

Around 1908 Jean Perrin made observations of Brownian motion in gases. He showed that small particles, much larger than individual molecules but still very small (less than 10^{-6} m in diameter), also went on random walks. This could only be explained along the same lines as Brownian motion in liquids. The particles were being struck by the randomly moving gas molecules.

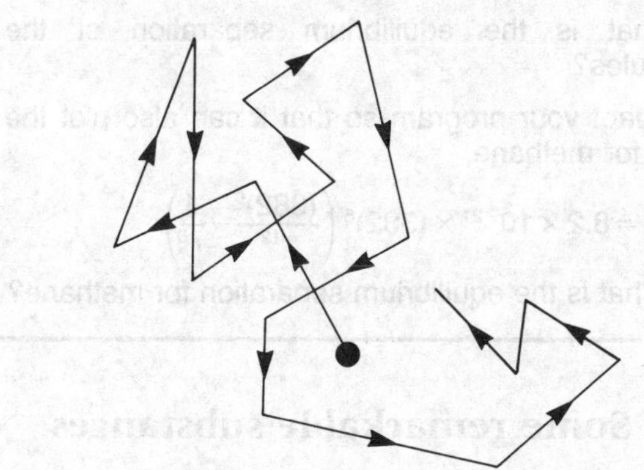

Figure 23.3 *The random walk of a pollen grain owing to the grain being biffed by water molecules*

23.2 Here are two statements about a gas:

(i) All the molecules in a gas move with the same speed.

(ii) The molecules in a gas move with different speeds, some fast, some slow, some in between.

Which of (i) or (ii) do you think is (or know to be) correct?

23.3 If you can write computer programs, use the random number generator in a computer to mimic the random walk of a gas molecule and make the computer draw the path of the particle on the screen. It is wise not to attempt to do this in three dimensions! Restrict yourself to two dimensions, moving up/down and left/right on the screen. (You are unlikely to mimic a random walk exactly. Not many computers generate true random numbers.)

23.4 A bonus from Perrin's experiments was that he was able to estimate the Avogadro constant, achieving a value of around 7×10^{23} mol^{-1}. How accurate was his value?

23.3 Differences in properties of solids, liquids and gases

The molecules in a gas are, on average, much further apart than they are in a liquid or solid. Also, the molecules in a gas travel very much faster than those in a liquid. The molecules in a solid vibrate about the same average position rather than travelling from place to place. The differences in spacing, and in speed, are the main reason for the different properties of the three states of matter. For example, gases are not very good conductors of heat. For heat to be conducted the movement energy of the molecules must be passed on from one to another. This requires the molecules to collide, which happens less easily in a gas than in a liquid.

In a solid the molecules are held in position by the overall effects of the attractions and repulsions of their neighbours. Even so, the molecules do have some movement. They *vibrate* to-and-fro, although on average they keep the same position. As the temperature gets higher they vibrate more violently, and they can pass on the energy of their vibrations to their neighbours. However, the only solids that conduct heat very well are those which have electrons that can move from place to place. Especially, metals have many *free electrons* that can carry their movement energy with them even though the atoms themselves are stuck in one place.

Owing to the large amount of empty space in a gas, it is fairly easy to squeeze the molecules into a smaller volume. That is, gases are easily *compressed*. Liquids and solids have their molecules already very close together, so they are very difficult to compress. We should think about this difference in compressibility more carefully. It seems obvious that there is a limit to how close molecules can get to one another, but *why* is there a limit? The answer lies in the structure of molecules.

> **23.5** All gases have a characteristic *critical temperature*. Above the critical temperature it is impossible to liquefy a gas. The critical temperatures of carbon dioxide and methane are 31.2°C and −81.9°C, respectively. Which gas has the stronger intermolecular forces? Briefly explain your choice.

23.4 The potential energy curve for two neighbouring molecules

When two molecules are far apart they move completely independently; neither will feel the presence of the other. However, if they come closer together then the intermolecular forces get to work. They will attract one another. The amount of the attraction depends on several factors, which are described in Unit 20. The attractions tend to bring the molecules together; but now think about them coming *very* close together. The outside of a molecule is really a layer of negatively charged electrons: the electron cloud. When molecules approach closely, the electron clouds repel one another. It is the great strength of the repulsion that puts a limit on how close the molecules can get.

Now you need to remember that attraction means a lowering of energy, repulsion means an increase in energy (Unit 2). This convention allows us to explain the energy diagram of Figure 23.4. You can see that there is a minimum in the curve. This is when the attractive and repulsive forces just balance. The molecules are then at their equilibrium distance apart. The normal equilibrium distance between molecules is of the order of 200 to 800 pm. The shape of the curve gives us an idea of why it is that gases can be difficult, and sometimes impossible, to liquefy if the temperature is too high. At high temperatures the average speed of the molecules in a gas is much higher than at a low temperature. If two molecules hit one another at great speed, their electron clouds become squashed together; this is rather like two springs being pushed together. This brings them high up the repulsion part of the curve. Then they fly apart and go off to make further collisions. At lower temperatures, when their speeds are much lower, the force of the collisions can be very much less. Now the interaction of their electron clouds may take them only part of the way up the repulsion part of the curve. If they do not go too high, they will not spring apart. Rather, they will stick together and oscillate around their equilibrium position.

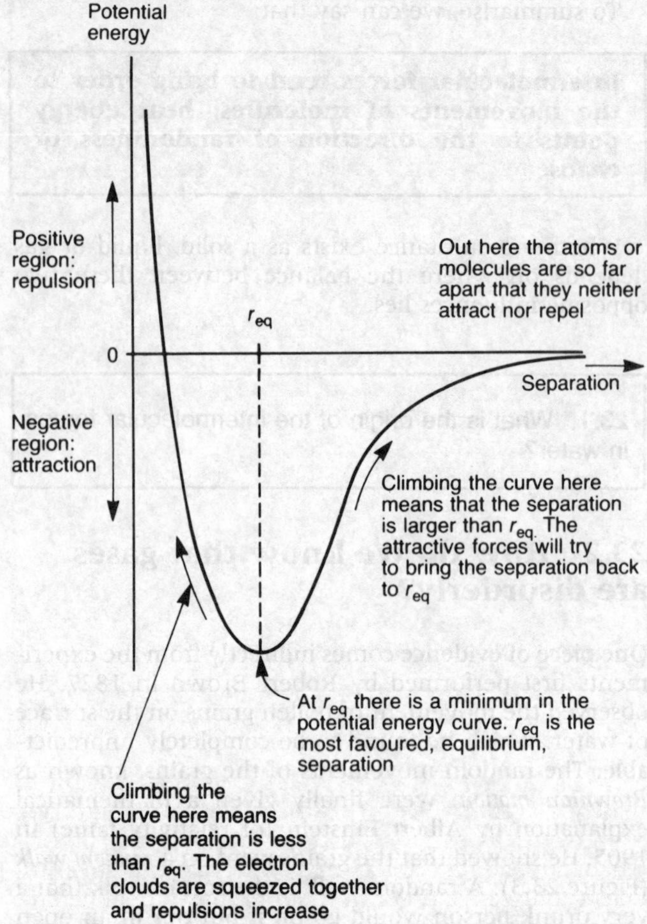

Figure 23.4 *A potential energy curve for two atoms or molecules*

> **23.6** (i) The Lennard-Jones potential (see panel 23.1) for oxygen can be written as
>
> $$V(r) = 6.5 \times 10^{-21} \times (346)^6 \left(\frac{(346)^6}{r^{12}} - \frac{1}{r^6}\right)$$
>
> where r is measured in picometres, pm (i.e. 10^{-12} m), and $V(r)$ has units of joules, J. Use a computer to plot a graph of $V(r)$ from $r=0$ to $r=500$ pm.
>
> (ii) What is the equilibrium separation of the molecules?
>
> (iii) Adapt your program so that it can also plot the graph for methane,
>
> $$V(r) = 8.2 \times 10^{-21} \times (382)^6 \left(\frac{(382)^6}{r^{12}} - \frac{1}{r^6}\right)$$
>
> (iv) What is the equilibrium separation for methane?

23.5 Some remarkable substances

In this section we shall briefly look at some substances that are hard to classify as a solid, liquid, or gas.

Panel 23.1

The Lennard-Jones potential

In 1931 J. E. Lennard-Jones fitted the shape of the curves in Figure 23.4 to a formula, called the Lennard-Jones potential, or sometimes the six–twelve (6–12) potential. His formula was

$$V(r) = \frac{A}{r^{12}} - \frac{B}{r^{6}} \qquad \text{Lennard-Jones potential}$$

Here $V(r)$ is the potential energy at a separation r. A and B are two constants, which can be calculated from theory, but are often discovered from the results of experiments. The term A/r^{12} is positive, which means that it corresponds to repulsions; being negative, the $-B/r^{6}$ term tells us about the attractions. You can prove for yourself that $1/r^{12}$ is very much larger than $1/r^{6}$ when r is very small. That is, the almost vertical part of the curve is fitted by the A/r^{12} term. However, when r is no longer very small, the $1/r^{6}$ is more important, and $-B/r^{6}$ fits the curve at larger intermolecular distances.

(a) *Liquid crystals*

It seems a contradiction to call a crystal 'liquid'. We expect crystals to be solids, and certainly not liquids. Essentially, liquid crystals are liquids that can have sufficient long range order in them to make them behave like a solid. However, they will only behave like a solid over a certain range of temperatures. Usually a liquid crystal is made from molecules that are long, thin and not very symmetrical. You will find some examples in Figure 23.5.

The intermolecular forces must be strong enough to hold the molecules together, but not so strong as to restrict their movement too much. The unsymmetrical nature of the molecules leads to an unsymmetrical packing of the molecules. When the packing is unsymmetrical we say that the arrangement is *anisotropic*. (Isotropic means the same in every direction; anisotropic is the opposite – not the same in every direction.)

$CH_3-O-C_6H_4-CH=N-C_6H_4-CH_2CH_2CH_2CH_3$

$CH_3-O-C_6H_4-CH=N-C_6H_4-CH=CH-C(=O)-O-CH_2CH(CH_3)CH_3$

$C_6H_5-C_6H_4-CH=N-C_6H_4-C(=O)-O-CH_2CH_3$

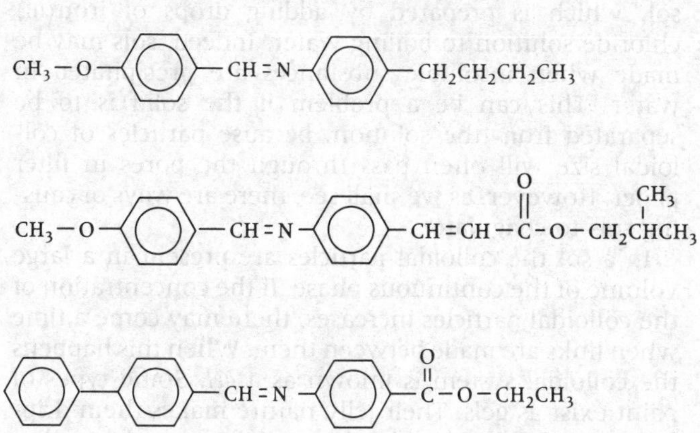

Figure 23.5 Examples of molecules that make liquid crystals

The very useful property of liquid crystals is that the arrangement of the molecules can be upset by very slight changes in their surroundings. Especially, in the liquid crystals used in calculator and computer displays, the molecules rearrange themselves when the crystal is subjected to a small electric field. The change from anisotropic to a more isotropic arrangement changes the way the crystal absorbs light.

(b) *Glass*

It may surprise you to know that glass is best considered as a liquid. It happens to be an extremely viscous liquid. Indeed, it is so viscous that many people find it very difficult to think of glass as anything but a solid. The basic building block of ordinary glass is a tetrahedron built from a silicon atom with four oxygen atoms around it (Figure 23.6). The tetrahedra join to give a three-dimensional interlocking structure that gives glass its high viscosity. However, unlike a respectable solid, glass has no long range order in its structure. Given a long enough time, glass will flow like a liquid. For example, stained glass put into cathedrals during the fifteenth century is thicker at the bottom than at the top.

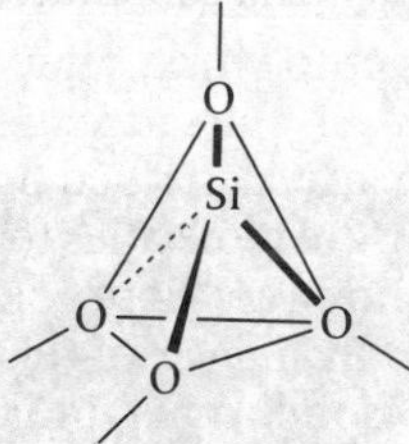

Figure 23.6 The tetrahedral group of a silicon atom and four oxygen atoms, which is the basis for the structure of glass (and many minerals, see Unit 96)

(c) *Colloids*

Colloids can take on the appearance of solids, liquids, or gases, although they are invariably mixtures of some kind. Smoke from a fire is a colloidal system. It is made of tiny particles of solid that float in air. Colloidal particles are generally between 5 and 1000 nm in diameter. This means that they are much larger than atoms or small molecules such as water, but smaller than particles that we can see clearly with the naked eye. The air in which they float is called the *continuous phase*; the particles themselves make up the *disperse phase*. (We can talk about the disperse phase existing *in* the continuous phase.)

There are eight types of colloidal system. The disperse phase and the continuous phase can be a solid, a liquid, or a gas. Table 23.1 will give you an idea of the wide variety of colloidal systems that are to be found, whether in nature or made artificially. The only combination of disperse and continuous phases that does not occur is gas in gas.

There are two approaches to making colloids; either

Table 23.1. Examples of the eight types of colloidal system*

Disperse phase	*Continuous phase*	*Name*	*Examples*
Gas	Gas	None	None
Gas	Liquid	Foam	Whipped cream, foams for hair treatment or shaving
Gas	Solid	Solid foam	Pumice stone, sponges, expanded polystyrene
Liquid	Gas	Liquid aerosol	Fog, clouds, many sprays from cans
Liquid	Liquid	Emulsion	Oil and water salad dressing, milk, paints
Liquid	Solid	Solid emulsion	Butter, pearl, opal
Solid	Gas	Solid aerosol	Smoke, atmospheric dust
Solid	Liquid	Sol, colloidal suspension	Toothpaste, gold sol, sulphur sol
Solid	Solid	Solid suspension	Coloured plastics

*Table adapted from: Shaw, D. J. (1970). *Introduction to Colloid and Surface Chemistry*, 2nd edn, Butterworths, London, Table 1.1

One of the few things that all these products have in common is that they are colloidal.

you can take large particles and make them smaller, or you can take small ones and make them larger. The first method is *dispersal*, the second is *aggregation*. An example of dispersion is making salad dressing out of oil and vinegar. Vigorous shaking of the two together breaks up the two layers of liquid into tiny droplets, many of which can be of a colloidal size. You can use an aggregation technique in some simple chemical reactions. For example, if you mix sodium thiosulphate solution with acid, the solution becomes yellow in colour. This is due to the sulphur molecules made in the reaction clinging together to make colloidal particles. The product is a sulphur sol. Sols are colloidal systems in which a solid is dispersed in a liquid (see Table 23.1).

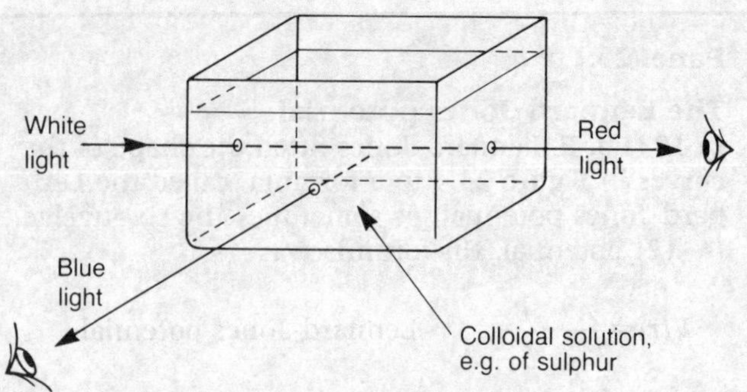

Figure 23.7 *The Tyndall effect. Colloidal particles scatter blue light, but allow red light through*

A sulphur sol is a particularly good one to show the *Tyndall effect* (Figure 23.7). In this experiment you need a strong beam of white light, which passes through a beaker or glass trough containing the sol. If you look directly at the beam through the solution you see a red colour; but if you look through one side you see a blue colour. The reason for the effect is that blue light is scattered by particles of a colloidal size much more efficiently than red light. All sols should show the effect, but it can be hard to see for lyophilic sols (see below), or if the sol is strongly coloured.

Colloidal particles sometimes will join together to make larger groupings, which we can see clearly. When this takes place we say that they have *coagulated*, or *flocculated*. Chimneys over smoke fires are full of coagulated colloidal particles of carbon, i.e. soot. However, colloidal particles can remain intact for long periods of time. The reason is that they are often electrically charged. For example, during the chemical reactions in a fire, the particles adsorb a layer of negative charge on their surfaces. Therefore, when the particles come close they repel rather than stick together.

Some sols are easily made in the laboratory, e.g. a sulphur sol as noted above, or an iron(III) oxide (Fe_2O_3) sol, which is prepared by adding drops of iron(III) chloride solution to boiling water. Indeed, sols may be made when insoluble substances are precipitated in water. This can be a problem if the solid is to be separated from the solution, because particles of colloidal size will often pass through the pores in filter paper. However, as we shall see, there are ways of causing sols to coagulate.

In a sol the colloidal particles are present in a large volume of the continuous phase. If the concentration of the colloidal particles increases, there may come a time when links are made between them. When this happens the colloidal system is known as a *gel*. Some types of paint exist as gels. Their jelly nature makes them drip-free, and therefore somewhat easier to use than other paints. They can suffer from one disadvantage. If they are brushed or stirred too vigorously, the gel can be disrupted and a sol re-formed. The viscosity of a sol is much less than that of a gel, so the paint will begin to drip. The decrease in viscosity of many colloidal systems with the increased rate at which they are agitated is also responsible for the deadly nature of quicksand. The more that a creature trapped in the sand struggles, the more the structure of the colloidal quicksand is changed, and the faster the creature will sink.

Whether a sol is negatively or positively charged depends on its nature, and the way it is made. If the charges are neutralised then there is little to stop the particles coming together and coagulating. The coagulation of some sols cannot be reversed. These are the *lyophobic* (solvent hating) sols (Figure 23.8).

We can make use of the fact that many sols contain charged particles in an electrophoresis experiment (Figure 23.9). Here, a little of the sol is placed between two electrodes. Depending on their charge, the colloidal particles travel to the positively charged or the negatively charged electrode.

Some colloids are *lyophilic* (solvent loving) sols (Figure 23.10). Normally the coagulation of a lyophilic sol can be reversed. Gelatin in water is a lyophilic sol that you may have used in cooking, and almost certainly you will have eaten. The change from the (almost) solid gel (jelly) into liquid sol can be achieved by dissolving in hot water. The process is reversed by cooling.

Biologically important colloids, often made out of proteins, are also lyophilic. The colloidal particles have a tendency to adsorb water molecules onto their surface owing to their ability to hydrogen bond with water molecules. In addition they can trap ions such as H^+ or OH^- that may be in the water.

Both lyophilic and lyophobic colloids can be coagulated by adding inorganic salts, but for different reasons. For example, proteins can be coagulated by adding large quantities of ammonium sulphate to an aqueous solution of the protein. Ammonium sulphate is very soluble in water, and when large numbers of ammonium and sulphate ions are released into water, the water molecules are pulled away from the surface of the protein to make hydration spheres around the ions. When the protecting layer of water molecules around the protein is removed, the protein molecules begin to stick together and coagulate. A positively or negatively charged hydrophobic sol can be precipitated by adding ions of the opposite charge. See questions 23.10 and 23.11 for an example.

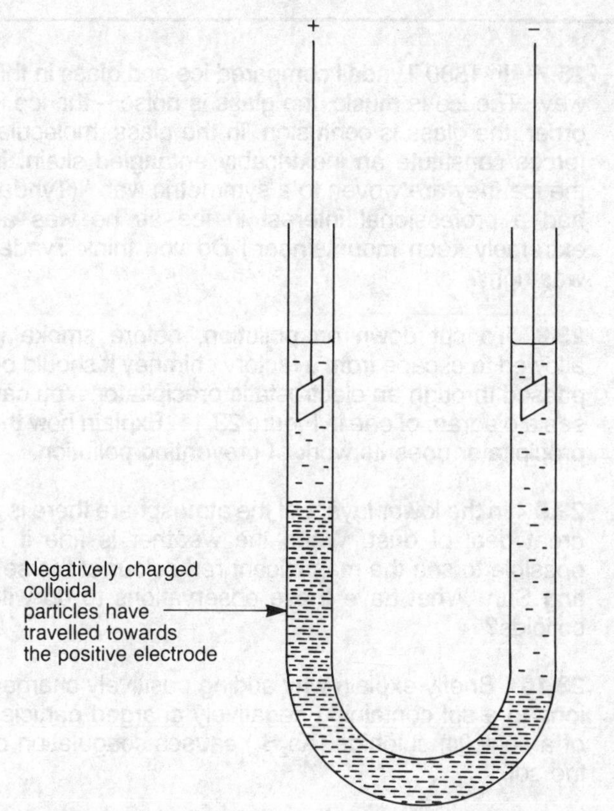
+
−
Negatively charged
colloidal
particles have
travelled towards
the positive electrode

***Figure 23.9** A simple way of demonstrating electrophoresis*

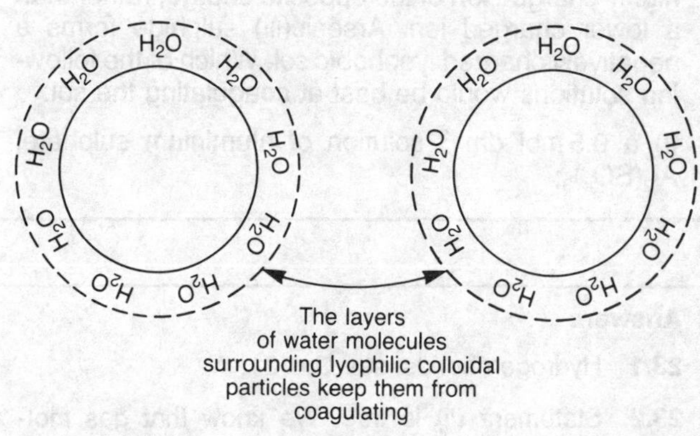
H2O
The layers
of water molecules
surrounding lyophilic colloidal
particles keep them from
coagulating

***Figure 23.10** Lyophilic colloidal particles are surrounded by water molecules*

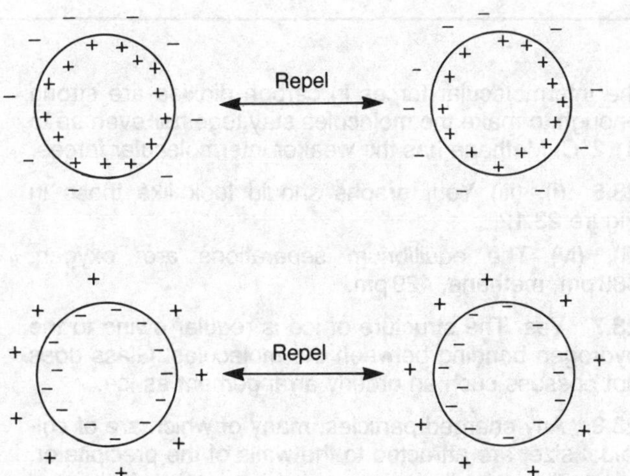
Repel
Repel

***Figure 23.8** The positive, or negative, charges on lyophobic colloidal particles keep them from coagulating. An electric double layer of charge is set up around each particle, e.g. a negatively charged particle will be surrounded by positively charged ions in the solution*

23.7 In 1880 Tyndall compared ice and glass in this way: 'The ice is music, the glass is noise – the ice is order, the glass is confusion. In the glass, molecular forces constitute an inextricably entangled skein, in the ice they are woven to a symmetric web.' (Tyndall had a professional interest in ice as he was an extremely keen mountaineer.) Do you think Tyndall was right?

23.8 To cut down on pollution, before smoke is allowed to escape from a factory chimney it should be passed through an electrostatic precipitator. You can see a diagram of one in Figure 23.11. Explain how the precipitator does its work of preventing pollution.

23.9 In the lower layers of the atmosphere there is a great deal of dust. When the weather is fine it is possible to see the magnificent red colour of the setting Sun. What have these observations to do with colloids?

23.10 Briefly explain why adding positively charged ions to a sol containing negatively charged particles of arsenic(III) sulphide (As_2S_3) causes coagulation of the sol.

23.11 There is a rule in colloid chemistry called the Hardy–Schulze rule. Essentially the rule says that, if you want to coagulate a colloid, it is best to use a highly charged ion of the opposite charge, rather than a lower charged ion. Arsenic(III) sulphide forms a negatively charged lyophobic sol. Which of the following solutions would be best at coagulating the sol:

(i) a 0.5 mol dm^{-3} solution of aluminium sulphate, $Al_2(SO_4)_3$;

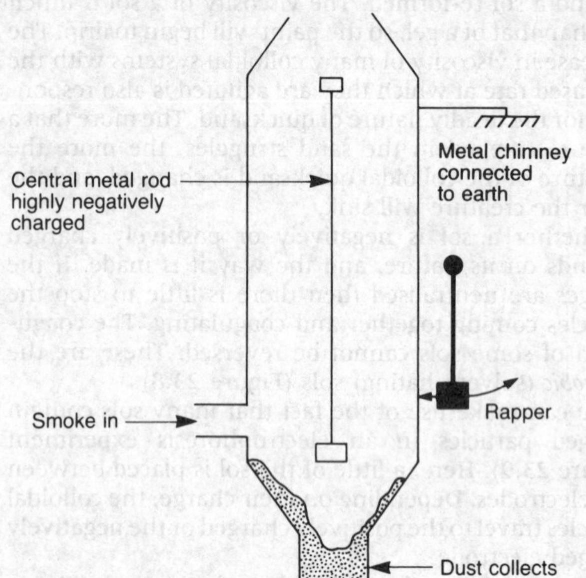

Figure 23.11 An electrostatic precipitator

(ii) a 1 mol dm^{-3} solution of magnesium chloride, $MgCl_2$;

(iii) a 1 mol dm^{-3} solution of sodium nitrate, $NaNO_3$?

Assume that you use equal volumes of each solution.

23.12 Why does smoke from a fire or a cigarette often have a blue tinge to its colour?

23.13 Look at the list of contents of a bottle of salad cream. What might be the purpose of the stabilisers?

Answers

23.1 Hydrogen bonds; see Unit 21.

23.2 Statement (ii) is true. We know that gas molecules move randomly, and that heat is connected with random motion, so it is most unlikely that they all have the same speed. However, to prove it is another matter. See Unit 35.

23.3 Your program should generate patterns like those in Figure 23.3. If you have the chance to observe Brownian motion, you will find that the paths of the particles and the graphs are very similar.

23.4 The accepted value of the Avogadro constant is 6.02×10^{23} mol^{-1}. Thus the error was 0.98×10^{23} in 6.02×10^{23}; about 16%.

23.5 The figures tell us that it is impossible to liquefy methane above −81.9°C. This means that the thermal energy available above this temperature is sufficient to stop the molecules sticking together. On the other hand, the intermolecular forces in carbon dioxide are strong enough to make the molecules stay together even up to 31.2°C. Methane has the weaker intermolecular forces.

23.6 (i), (iii) Your graphs should look like those in Figure 23.12.

(ii), (iv) The equilibrium separations are: oxygen, 388 pm; methane, 429 pm.

23.7 Yes. The structure of ice is regular owing to the hydrogen bonding between the molecules. Glass does not possess such an orderly arrangement as ice.

23.8 Any charged particles, many of which are of colloidal size, are attracted to the walls of the precipitator, where they lose their charge and coagulate. Uncharged particles that enter become charged owing to the intense electric field that is present. They too are deposited on the walls. The rapper is needed to vibrate the walls and dislodge the dust and smoke particles that stick to them.

Answers – contd.

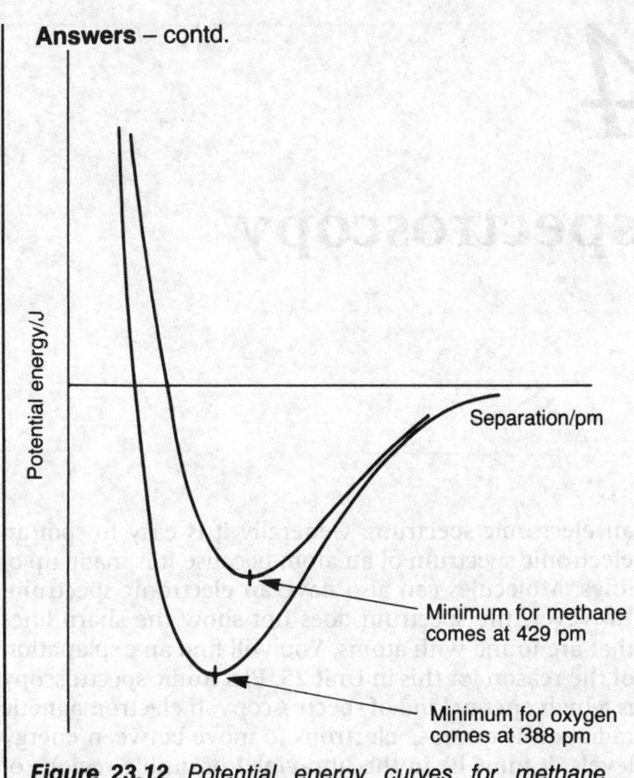
Potential energy/J
Separation/pm
Minimum for methane comes at 429 pm
Minimum for oxygen comes at 388 pm

***Figure 23.12** Potential energy curves for methane and oxygen*

23.9 Dust in the atmosphere is often colloidal. When the Sun is low down on the horizon, light from it has to pass through a great deal of dust to reach your eyes. The blue part of the light is scattered away from your eyes. You see the red part of the spectrum, which remains. Red sunsets are the Tyndall effect on a large scale.

23.10 A simple explanation is as follows. The added positive ions cling to the surface of the colloidal particles, neutralising the charge on the surface. Once this happens there is little to stop the particles clinging together and coagulating. (In practice this explanation is an oversimplification. The way the added ions affect the electric double layer around the particles is complicated; but the repulsion between them *is* reduced by the added ions.)

23.11 We are looking for positive ions to coagulate the negative sol. Solution (i) is best. With their +3 charge aluminium ions, Al^{3+}, are more efficient at causing coagulation than magnesium ions, Mg^{2+}, or sodium ions, Na^+.

23.12 The smoke is colloidal, so when it is viewed at an angle to the source of light, it appears blue; the Tyndall effect again.

23.13 The salad cream contains oily droplets dispersed in water. The stabilisers prevent the colloidal particles coagulating.

UNIT 23 SUMMARY

- The three states of matter are solid, liquid, and gas. Solids have the most order, and gases the least. In liquids there is short-range order and long-range disorder.
- When two atoms or molecules approach each other, intermolecular forces attract them together. If they come too close, their electron clouds repel and they are forced apart. The potential energy curve is given by the Lennard-Jones (6–12) potential.
- Glass is built mainly from tetrahedra of silica and oxygen atoms. There is disorder in glass very much like the disorder in liquids.
- Colloids consist of particles between 5 and 1000 nm in diameter.
- Colloidal particles exist as the disperse phase in a continuous phase.
- The Tyndall effect is shown by many colloidal systems, which scatter blue light effectively but allow red light to pass through them.
- Lyophobic sols are kept apart by layers of negative or positive charges on their surfaces. They may undergo electrophoresis.
- Lyophilic sols are surrounded by a protective layer of water molecules.

24

Three types of spectroscopy

24.1 Emission and absorption spectra

Spectroscopy is the main method we have of delving into the world of atoms and molecules. It can be used to discover the energies of electrons within atoms or molecules. It can also help us to find out how the atoms are arranged within a molecule. The outcome of an experiment in spectroscopy is a *spectrum*. There are two main ways of obtaining a spectrum. The first method is to send electromagnetic radiation into a collection of atoms or molecules, and see if any of the radiation is absorbed. The result is an *absorption spectrum*. The second method is to give the atoms or molecules energy (e.g. by heating or passing electricity through them), and measure the type of electromagnetic radiation they give out, or emit. In this case an *emission spectrum* results. Summaries of these are shown in Figure 24.1.

There is a type of spectroscopy for each of the main regions of the electromagnetic spectrum listed in Table 24.1. You will see that radio waves have the lowest energy, and gamma-rays the highest. All the different types have things in common. For example, they can all show wave-like properties, and their wavelengths and frequencies can be measured. Similarly, they can all be thought of as being made up of photons. Table 24.2 lists the key equations that allow us to calculate the energy of the photons if we know the frequency or wavelength.

In the remainder of this unit we shall take a brief look at each type. We shall start with the variety that requires the most energy, and finish with the kind that needs the least energy. If you want a more detailed explanation of how electromagnetic radiation and molecules influence one another, read sections 24.6 to 24.9.

24.2 Electronic spectroscopy

The emission spectrum of hydrogen atoms is shown in the photo in Unit 9. This type of spectrum is an atomic spectrum. It is produced by electrons moving between their various energy levels. Because the energy levels belong to the electrons, the spectrum can also be called an electronic spectrum. Generally it is easy to spot an electronic spectrum of an atom because it is made up of lines. Molecules can also have an electronic spectrum. However, the spectrum does not show the sharp lines that are found with atoms. You will find an explanation of the reason for this in Unit 25. Electronic spectroscopy is a high energy kind of spectroscopy. If electromagnetic radiation is to cause electrons to move between energy levels, it must be in the ultraviolet or visible regions of the spectrum. When electrons are held especially tightly to their parent atoms, then even X-rays may be needed to cause transitions.

24.3 Vibrational spectroscopy

Imagine you were scaled down to the size of atoms, and that you found yourself in a bottle of water vapour. If you were the oxygen atom in one of the water molecules and you looked about you, you would see the hydrogen atoms performing a rather erratic dance. The hydrogen atoms would *not* be at a constant distance from you, neither would the bond angle always be 104.5°. In short, the hydrogen atoms would be constantly *vibrating* (Figure 24.2). The oxygen–hydrogen bonds have *vibrational energy*.

If photons with the right energy strike water molecules, they can cause the molecules to vibrate more violently. As in the case of electrons, the vibrations of molecules are *quantised*. That is, molecules can vibrate with particular amounts of energy, whose values are determined by a quantum number (the vibrational quantum number). The energy needed to make molecules vibrate comes in the infrared region of the spectrum. For this reason, when chemists speak of vibrational spectra or infrared spectra they usually mean the same thing. We shall concentrate on vibrational spectroscopy in Unit 27.

24.4 Rotational spectroscopy

If we move past the infrared part of the electromagnetic spectrum we come to the microwave region. Again, if

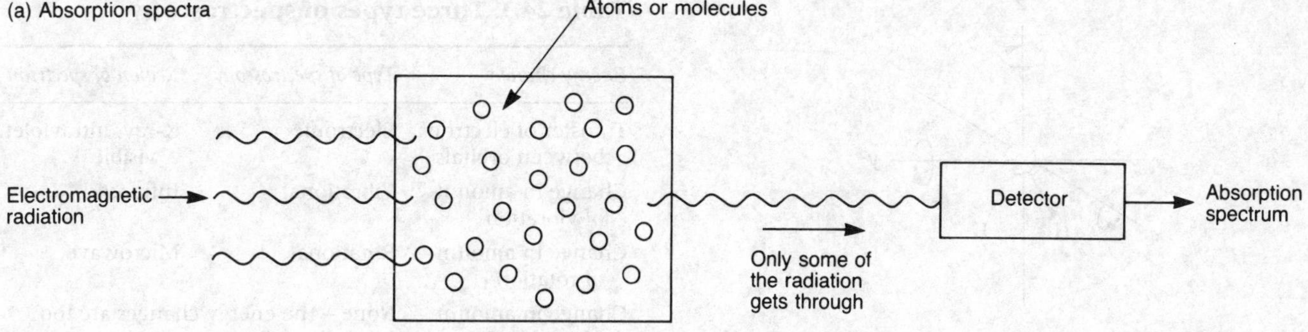

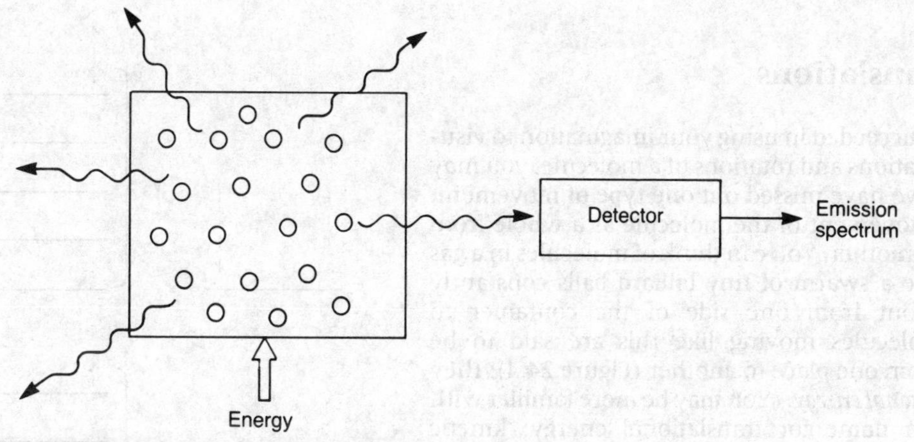

Figure 24.1 The origin of (a) absorption and (b) emission spectra

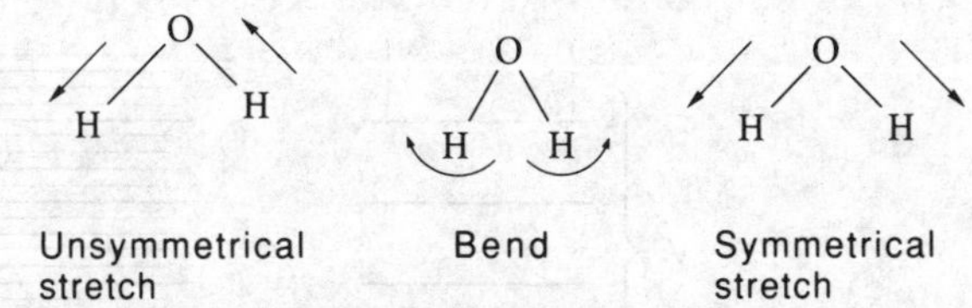

Figure 24.2 Three of the ways in which the atoms in a water molecule can vibrate

Table 24.1. Types of electromagnetic radiation

Type		*Typical frequency*/Hz	*Typical wave-length*/m^{-1}
Radio waves	(Low energy)	3×10^5	10^3
Microwaves		3×10^9	10^{-1}
Infrared		3×10^{10}	10^{-2}
Visible light		3×10^{14}	10^{-6}
Ultraviolet light		3×10^{16}	10^{-8}
X-rays		3×10^{18}	10^{-10}
Gamma-rays	(High energy)	$>3\times10^{18}$	$<10^{-10}$

Table 24.2. Key equations for electromagnetic radiation*

speed = frequency × wavelength	$c = f\lambda$
energy = Planck constant × frequency	$E = hf$
= Planck constant × speed of light / wavelength	$E = hc/\lambda$

*In a vacuum the speed of all electromagnetic radiation is $c = 2.998\times10^8$ m s^{-1}. The Planck constant is $h = 6.626\times10^{-34}$ J s

you were a molecule, not only would you be vibrating, you would also be tumbling about. That is, you would be *rotating* and you would have a corresponding amount of *rotational energy* (Figure 24.3). As you might expect, rotational energy is quantised, so photons that have the correct energy can cause molecules to change from a lower to a higher rotational energy level. The energy of the rotational level depends on the rotational quantum number. For our purposes, we can ignore rotational spectroscopy. It does provide chemists with important

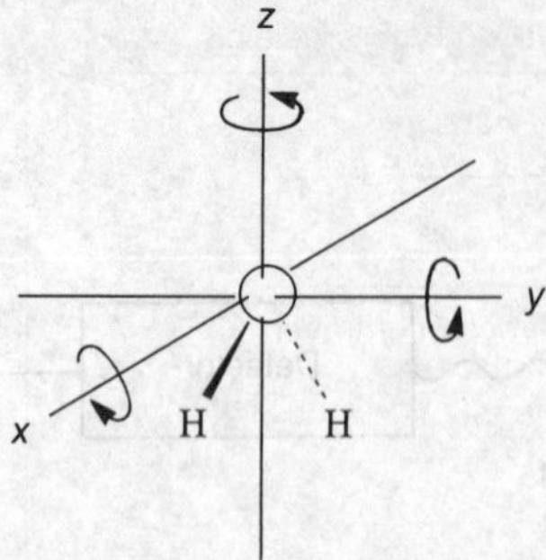

Figure 24.3 *Molecules, e.g. H_2O, can rotate about three axes*

Table 24.3. Three types of spectroscopy

Energy change	*Type of spectroscopy*	*Region of spectrum*
Transfer of electrons between orbitals	Electronic	X-ray, ultraviolet, visible
Change in amount of vibration	Vibrational	Infrared
Change in amount of rotation	Rotational	Microwave
Change in amount of translation	None – the energy changes are too small to measure	

information, but on a day-to-day basis vibrational spectroscopy is far more useful.

24.5 Translations

If you have succeeded in using your imagination to visualise the vibrations and rotations of a molecule, you may realise that we have missed out one type of movement. This is the movement of the molecule as a whole from one place to another. You can think of molecules in a gas behaving like a swarm of tiny billiard balls constantly charging about from one side of the container to another. Molecules moving like this are said to be *translating* from one place to another (Figure 24.4); they have *translational energy*. (You may be more familiar with the common name for translational energy: kinetic energy.)

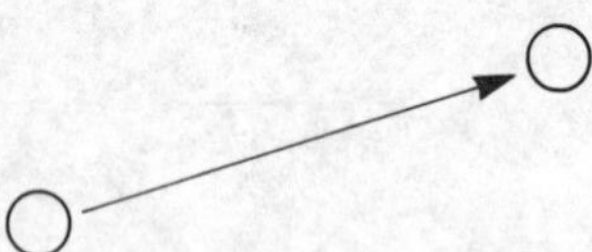

Figure 24.4 *When an atom or molecule moves from one position to a completely different position, we say that it has undergone a translation*

Strictly, translational energy is quantised; but it turns out that the energy gap between two translational energy levels is so small that we cannot measure it. Therefore you will not discover examples of 'translational spectra'. For all intents and purposes we can forget about the quantisation of translational levels and treat them as if they formed a continuous band.

These results are summarised in Table 24.3 and Figure 24.5.

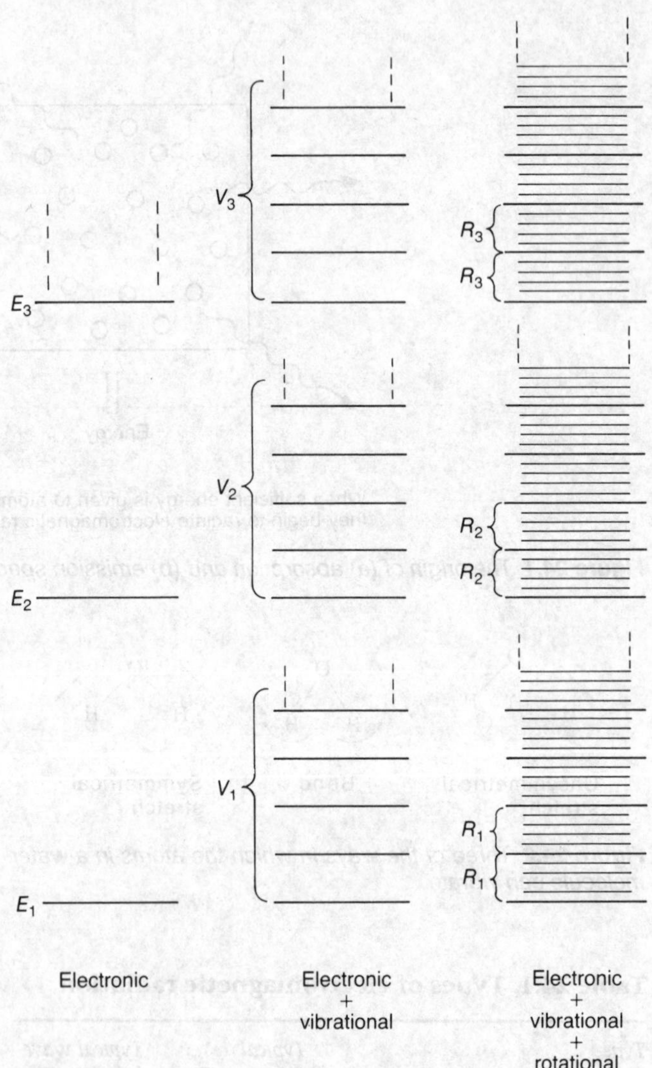

Figure 24.5 *The energy of a molecule can be split into electronic (E), vibrational (V) and rotational (R) energy levels*

24.6 Electromagnetic waves

All electromagnetic waves have an electric field and a magnetic field associated with them. The electric and magnetic fields are always at right angles to each other. The sizes of the fields change in time; so do the directions in which they point. In fact, the fields behave like vectors. The electric field vector is written ***F***, and the magnetic field vector as ***B***. The way that ***F*** and ***B*** change is shown in Figure 24.6.

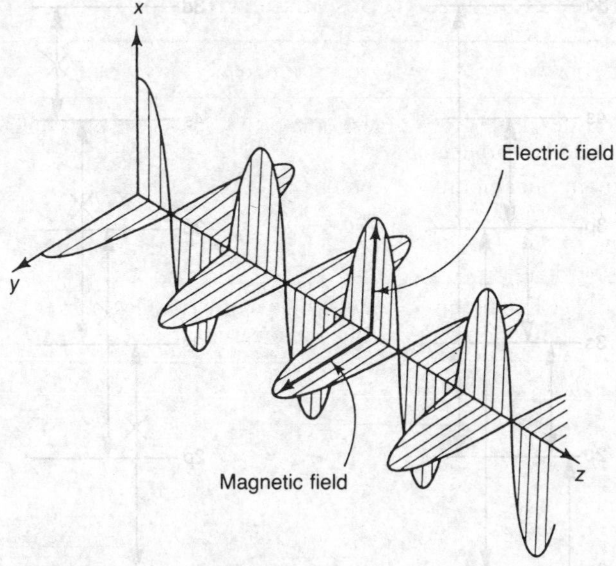

Figure 24.6 *The electric and magnetic field vectors are mutually at right angles. In the diagram, the electric field oscillates in the xz plane and the magnetic field in the yz plane*

24.7 The electric field and electrons

Electrons have a negative charge. This means that they can be attracted by positive charges, or repelled by negative charges. Suppose that two metal plates are coated with charges, positive on one and negative on the other. An electric field is set up between the plates. The direction of the field is shown in Figure 24.7 by the arrows.

Notice that the direction of the field goes from positive to negative. If electrons are placed between the plates, they will move away from the negative plate and towards the positive plate. That is, the electrons move under the influence of the electric field between the plates. Now imagine that the charges on the plates suddenly change so that the positive plate becomes negative and vice versa. Immediately, the electrons will reverse their direction of travel. If the field keeps changing its direction then the electrons would oscillate backwards and forwards. The kinetic energy they have is given to them by the field.

Now, if you concentrate on the field rather than the plates, you have a picture of what can happen when the electric field of electromagnetic radiation encounters the electrons in an atom or molecule. By virtue of the electric field $\boldsymbol{F}$, the electromagnetic radiation can give up its energy to the electrons. For this to work properly, we have to be careful to take account of the fact that the energies of the electrons in an atom or molecule are quantised. Electrons in atoms or molecules cannot gain just any amount of energy. As we have seen the energy has to be exactly equal to the difference between two energy levels (Figure 24.8). If this difference is ΔE, then using Planck's equation, the frequency of the radiation must be such that $\Delta E = hf$ (Δ is a Greek letter called 'delta').

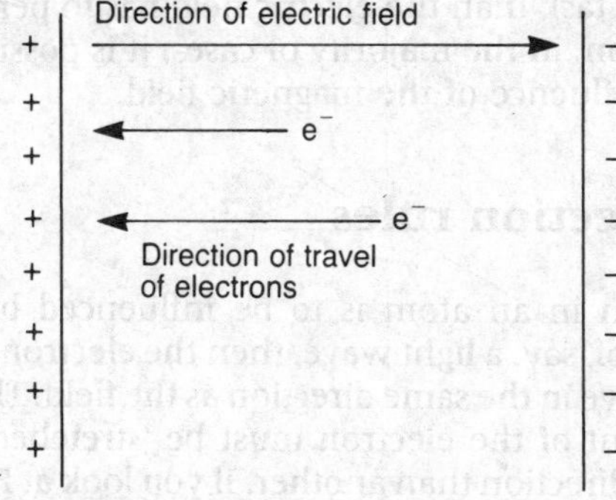

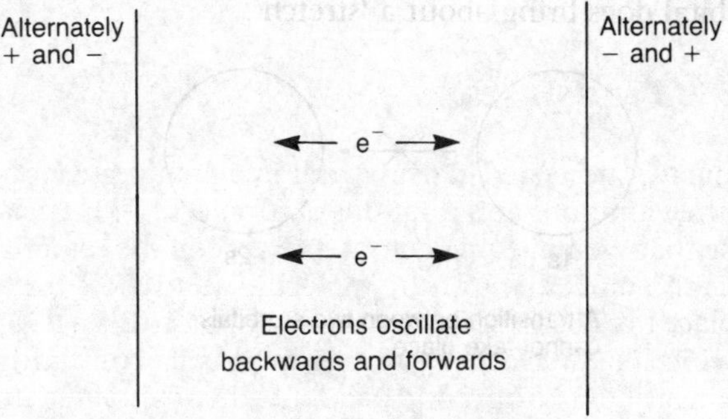

Figure 24.7 *The movement of electrons is influenced by electric fields. By causing them to move, the electric field gives energy to the electrons*

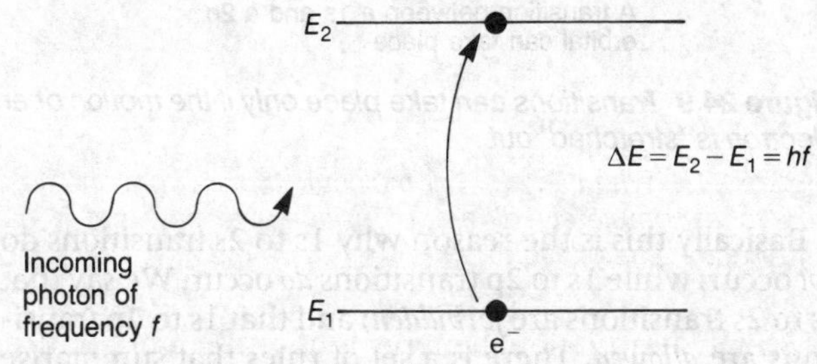

Figure 24.8 *The electric field of an incoming photon can give energy to an electron. If the photon has the right frequency, the electron can move to a higher energy level*

24.8 The magnetic field and electrons

The easiest way for electromagnetic radiation to interact with electrons is for the electric field to give them energy. However, it is possible for the magnetic field $\boldsymbol{B}$ to give energy as well. The electric field attempts to force an electron to oscillate 'up and down' in time with the oscillation of the field $\boldsymbol{F}$. The magnetic field works in a somewhat different way. This field attempts to make an electric charge move in a circular path. Usually this is a much harder task than the electric field has to perform. For this reason, in the majority of cases, it is possible to ignore the influence of the magnetic field.

24.9 Selection rules

If an electron in an atom is to be influenced by the electric field of, say, a light wave, then the electron must be able to move in the same direction as the field. That is, the movement of the electron must be 'stretched out' more in one direction than another. If you look at Figure 24.9 you should be able to see that a change from a 1s to a 2s electron does not do this. Both these orbitals are spherically symmetric – they favour no direction more than another. On the other hand, a change from a 1s to a 2p orbital does bring about a 'stretch'.

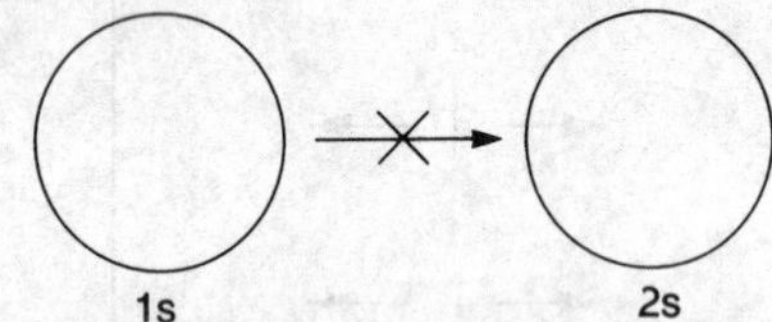

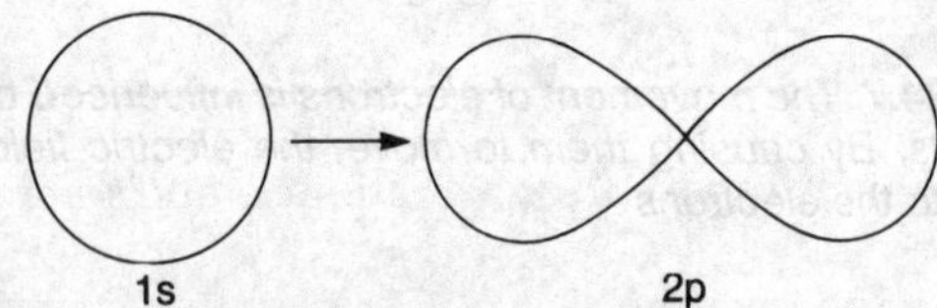

Figure 24.9 *Transitions can take place only if the motion of an electron is 'stretched' out*

Basically this is the reason why 1s to 2s transitions do *not* occur, while 1s to 2p transitions *do* occur. We say that 1s to 2s transitions are *forbidden*; and that 1s to 2p transitions are *allowed*. There is a set of rules that summarise this type of information about allowed and forbidden transitions. They are called *selection rules*. Table 24.4 lists the more important selection rules.

One result of the selection rules is that some spectral lines that might be expected from the energy level diagram of an atom do not occur. This is shown in Figure 24.10.

Table 24.4. Important selection rules

Allowed transitions	*Forbidden transitions*
s to p orbitals	s to s orbitals
p to d orbitals	s to d orbitals
	p to p orbitals
	d to d orbitals

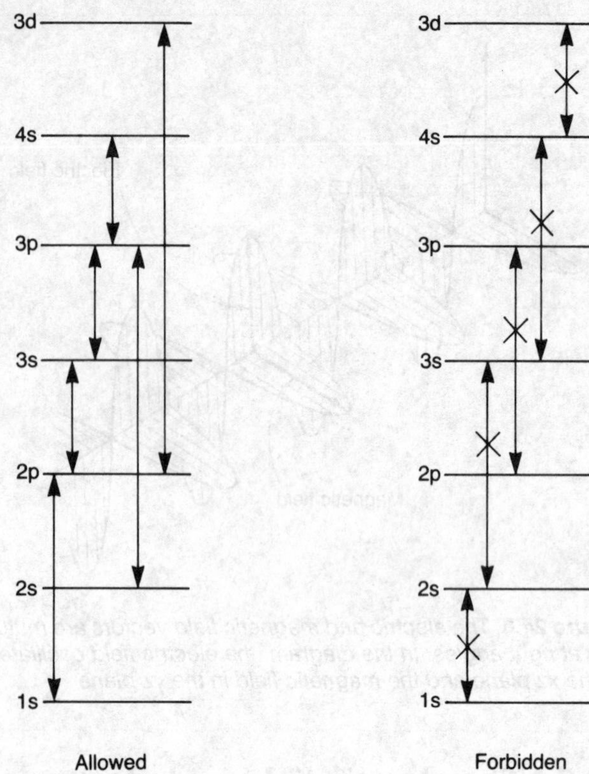

Figure 24.10 *Examples of allowed and forbidden transitions*

You should now understand a little about electromagnetic radiation and how it causes electrons to move between some energy levels but not others. In the coming five units we will make use of these ideas, and develop them further to explain other types of spectroscopy, especially those that involve molecules rather than individual atoms.

24.1 What is the energy of a microwave photon having a wavelength of 10 cm (0.1 m)?

24.2 Microwaves cause molecules to rotate more energetically. Use your answer to the last question to estimate the difference between two rotational energy levels.

24.3 It takes about 40 kJ to change 18 g of water to steam. If 18 g of water were placed in a microwave oven using 10 cm waves, how many photons would have to strike the water and give up their energy to convert 18 g of water to steam?

24.4 Suppose an electromagnetic wave causes an electron to move from a 1s to a $2p_z$ orbital. Draw a diagram showing the three *x*, *y* and *z* axes and these two orbitals. What should be the direction of the electric field of the wave? That is, should it be in the *x*, *y*, or *z* direction?

Answers

24.1 Using $E = hc/\lambda$ gives $E = 1.98 \times 10^{-24}$ J.

24.2 The difference must be of the same energy as the photons that are absorbed, i.e. the same energy as in the answer to question 24.1.

24.3 The number of photons is 40×10^3 J/ $(1.98 \times 10^{-24}$ J$) = 2.02 \times 10^{28}$.

24.4 The diagram is shown in Figure 24.11. To stretch the motion of the electron in the *z* direction, the electric field must be in the *z* direction as well.

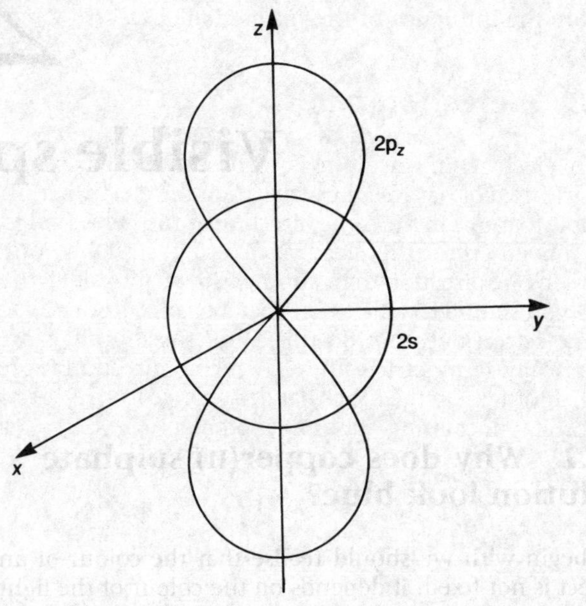

***Figure 24.11** Diagram for answer to question 24.4*

UNIT 24 SUMMARY

- Emission spectroscopy measures electromagnetic radiation given out by atoms and molecules.
- Absorption spectroscopy measures electromagnetic radiation taken in by atoms and molecules.
- Important types of spectroscopy are electronic (or atomic), infrared (or vibrational) and microwave (or rotational).
- Planck's equation $\Delta E = hf$ gives the connection between the frequency of radiation and the energy gap between the energy levels involved.

25

Visible spectroscopy

25.1 Why does copper(II) sulphate solution look blue?

To begin with we should realise that the colour of an object is not fixed: it depends on the colour of the light falling on it. For example, if copper(II) sulphate solution is placed in sunlight, i.e. white light, the solution looks a royal blue. If, however, it is placed in a photographic dark room that has a red safety light, the solution looks black. The reason for this is that copper(II) sulphate reflects blue light very efficiently; but it absorbs light of most other colours, especially light in the red area of the visible spectrum (Figure 25.1).

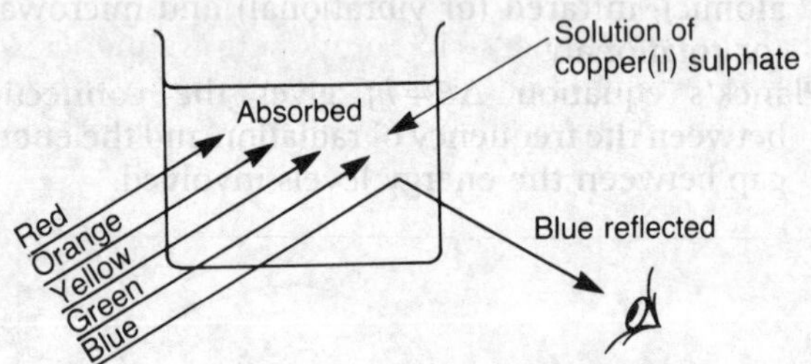

Figure 25.1 *Copper(II) sulphate solution looks blue because it absorbs most of the other colours in the spectrum*

This means that in the dark room, where there is only red light shining on the solution, the photons of red light are absorbed by the copper(II) sulphate. There are no photons of blue light to be reflected by the solution, so no light reaches our eyes and the solution looks black.

25.2 The visible spectrum of copper(II) sulphate solution

If we pass light of various frequencies through copper(II) sulphate solution, we should expect to find that very little red light would pass through the solution. On the other hand, blue light should pass through very easily. This much we can predict; but we do not know with any accuracy the exact frequencies of the light that copper(II) sulphate solution absorbs. For example, does it absorb light in the green region of the spectrum? The way to find this out is to use a *visible light spectrometer*. A diagram of this instrument is shown in Figure 25.2, and a picture of a real spectrometer is shown in the photo.

The first thing to do when using the spectrometer is to place a little of the solution, in this case copper(II) sulphate, into a sample tube (called a cuvet). An exactly similar tube is filled with water. This is the reference

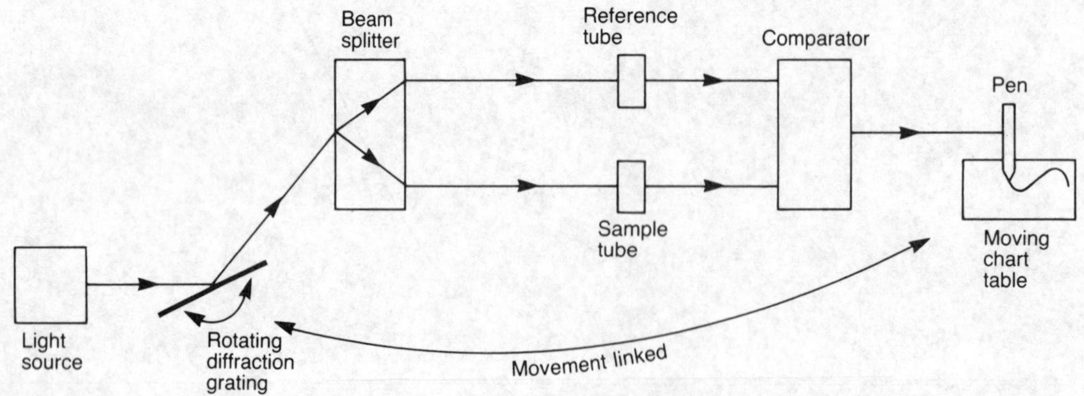

Figure 25.2 *A block diagram of a spectrometer. The wavelength of light entering the sample and reference depends on the position of the diffraction grating. The movement of the grating is linked to the movement of the chart table. The comparator compares the degree of absorption by the sample and by the reference. The output of the comparator moves the pen on the chart*

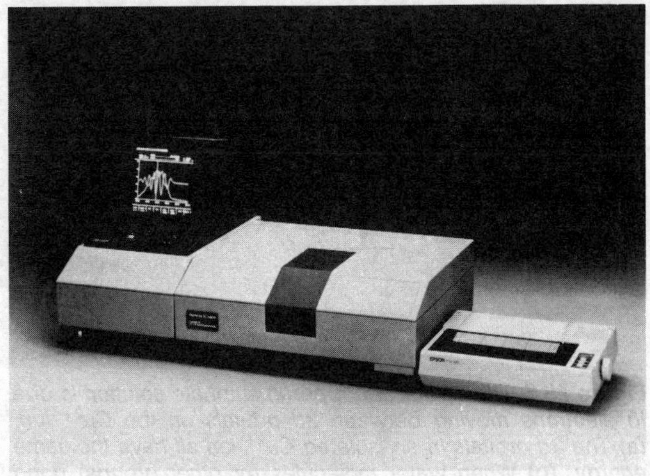

A typical modern visible/ultraviolet spectrometer which can output data to a visible display unit, and printer.

tube. A chart paper marked with a range of frequencies corresponding to visible light is placed on the recording table. When the spectrometer is switched on, the pen on the recording table moves up and down while the recording table travels from right to left under the pen. In this way a pattern is obtained on the chart paper that looks like that shown in Figure 25.3. The resulting chart is called the *visible spectrum* of copper(II) sulphate solution.

The vertical axis of the chart is marked from 0% to 100% absorption. That is, if the line reaches the 0% line, it means that light of that frequency passes right through the solution. If the line reaches the 100% line, this means that no light of this frequency gets through the solution.

Table 25.1. The wavelength of colours in the visible spectrum*

Wavelength/nm	*Colour*
(below 320	Ultraviolet)
380	Violet
420	Blue
440	Cyan
500	Green
560	Yellow
580	Orange
720	Red
(above 900	Infrared)

*These figures are only a guide. You will know from looking at a rainbow that the colours merge imperceptibly into one another

The spectrum shows that light with wavelength in the range 580 to 900 nm is heavily absorbed. This region corresponds to the yellow, orange and red regions of the spectrum. The part of the spectrum in the range 340 to 580 nm is the violet, blue and green regions of the spectrum; see Table 25.1. The low value for the absorption shows that, as we expected, blue light is only slightly absorbed.

25.3 How does a visible light spectrometer work?

White light is split up into its component frequencies by passing it through a diffraction grating. By rotating the grating, light of any particular frequency can be made to

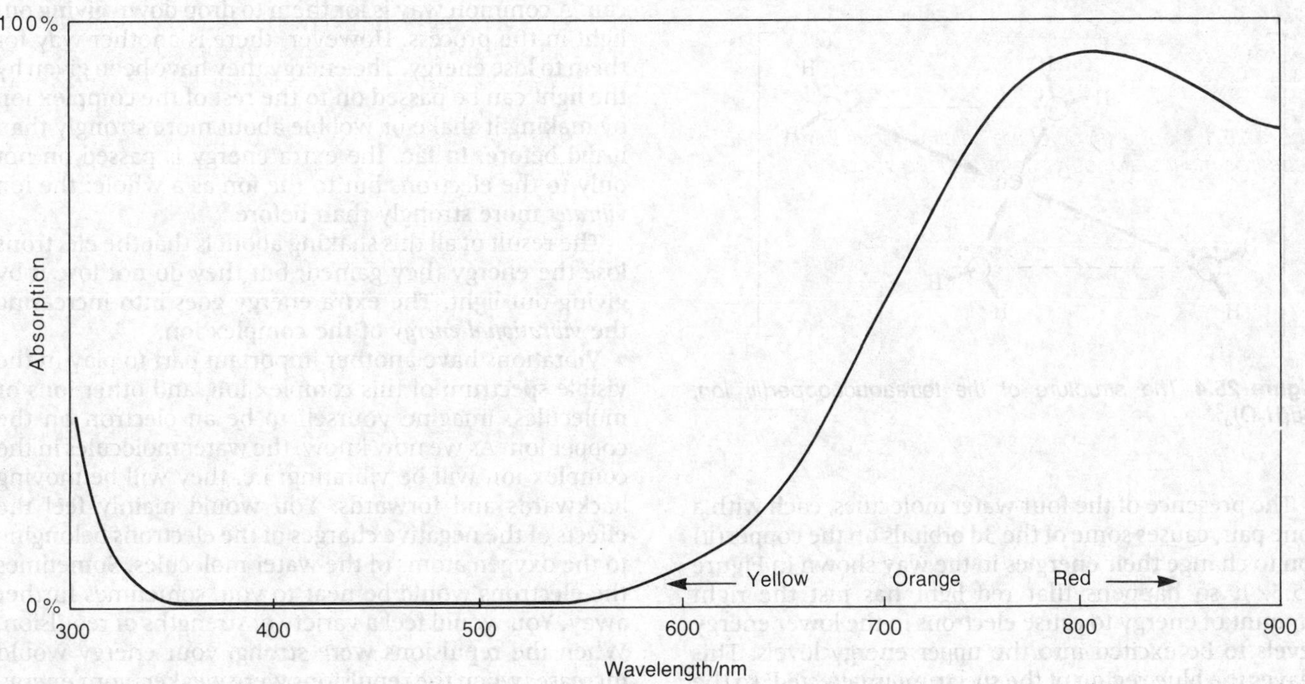

Figure 25.3 *Visible spectrum of copper(II) sulphate solution*

pass through the slit. At the same time as the grating rotates, the recording table on top of the machine is made to move. The amount of movement corresponds to the frequency of the light being passed through the slit.

After leaving the slit the beam is split into two. Both halves pass through a series of lenses and prisms to make sure they are focused properly. Then one beam passes through the sample tube, and the other beam through the reference tube. After passing through the tubes, the beams are compared by a rather complicated piece of electronics. In effect the electronics subtracts one beam from the other. The final signal that is sent to the pen is therefore due to the copper(II) sulphate rather than to the water, which is in both tubes. The higher the pen moves up the chart paper, the more light is being absorbed.

25.4 What happens to the photons absorbed by copper(II) sulphate solution?

In copper(II) sulphate solution, each copper(II) ion has four water molecules joined to it, $Cu(H_2O)_4^{2+}$ (Figure 25.4). This ion is an example of a *complex ion*, about which you will learn a great deal more in Unit 105. If you look at the colour of solutions of other copper(II) salts in water, e.g. nitrate or chloride, you will find that they too are blue or blue/green. This suggests that the colour of copper(II) salts in water is due to the same $Cu(H_2O)_4^{2+}$ complex ion rather than to the other ions in the solution.

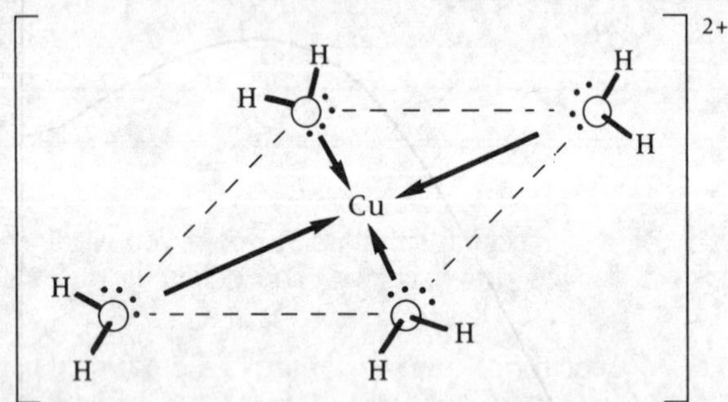

Figure 25.4 *The structure of the tetraaquocopper(II) ion, $Cu(H_2O)_4^{2+}$*

The presence of the four water molecules, each with a lone pair, causes some of the 3d orbitals on the copper(II) ion to change their energies in the way shown in Figure 25.5. It so happens that red light has just the right amount of energy to cause electrons in the lower energy levels to be excited into the upper energy levels. This leaves the blue region of the spectrum unaffected; so the solution looks blue.

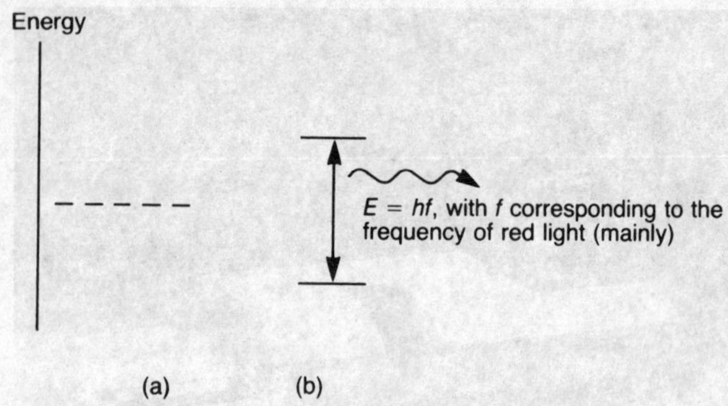

Figure 25.5 *The colour of copper(II) sulphate solution is due to electrons moving between 3d orbitals on the Cu^{2+} ion. (a) The 3d orbitals in an isolated Cu^{2+} ion all have the same energy. (b) When water molecules (or other groups) bond with the ion, the energies of the 3d orbitals change. Only two of the energy levels are shown here. For more details see Unit 105*

25.5 Why vibrations are important in visible spectra

If you have understood this explanation of why copper(II) sulphate solution looks blue, there may still be one or two problems that might worry you. For example, what happens to the electrons once they arrive in the upper energy level? If they fall down to the lower level, surely they will give out light in the red region of the spectrum? If they did this, the solution would appear colourless. Well, we know that the solution is not colourless. Also, we know that electrons in a higher energy level will find their way to a lower level if they can. A common way is for them to drop down giving out light in the process. However, there is another way for them to lose energy. The energy they have been given by the light can be passed on to the rest of the complex ion by making it shake or wobble about more strongly than it did before. In fact the extra energy is passed on not only to the electrons but to the ion as a whole: the ion *vibrates* more strongly than before.

The result of all this shaking about is that the electrons lose the energy they gained; but they do not lose it by giving out light. The extra energy goes into increasing the *vibrational energy* of the complex ion.

Vibrations have another important part to play in the visible spectrum of this complex ion, and other ions or molecules. Imagine yourself to be an electron on the copper ion. As we now know, the water molecules in the complex ion will be vibrating; i.e. they will be moving backwards and forwards. You would mainly feel the effects of the negative charges of the electrons belonging to the oxygen atoms of the water molecules. Sometimes the electrons would be near to you, sometimes further away. You would feel a variety of strengths of repulsion. When the repulsions were strong, your energy would increase; when the repulsions were weaker, your energy would decrease. With a little thought you should understand that you, as an electron, would not have a fixed energy. Your energy level would be changing from one moment to the next. Therefore the energy level diagram of Figure 25.5 is rather unrealistic. The energy gap between the top and bottom levels is not fixed, but changes. The result is that light of a *range* of frequencies can excite an electron from the lower to the upper level. This is the reason why the visible spectrum of copper(II) sulphate solution consists of a broad band, rather than the sharp lines that we find in an atomic spectrum. Incidentally, vibrations have an even more important influence than we have discovered so far. Surprisingly, if copper(II) complex ions did not vibrate at all, they would be colourless. The reason is that transitions between d orbitals are forbidden. You will find the explanation for this in Unit 105. If the orbitals of Figure 25.5 were purely 3d orbitals, light could not excite electrons from one orbital to another. The vibration of the complex ion has the result of mixing other orbitals with the 3d set. Thus, the 3d set can get mixed up with 3p orbitals. Now, a p to d transition *is* allowed. So once the orbitals get mixed up, transitions are possible. We can thank vibrations for the superb colour of copper(II) sulphate solution (and many other transition metal ion solutions).

25.1 Red light consists of photons with frequencies of the order of 4.6×10^{-18} Hz. What is the value of the energy gap between the 3d orbitals of Figure 25.5?

25.2 Figure 25.6 shows the visible spectrum of a solution containing a transition metal complex. What range of frequencies of light are absorbed the most? What colour would you expect the solution to have?

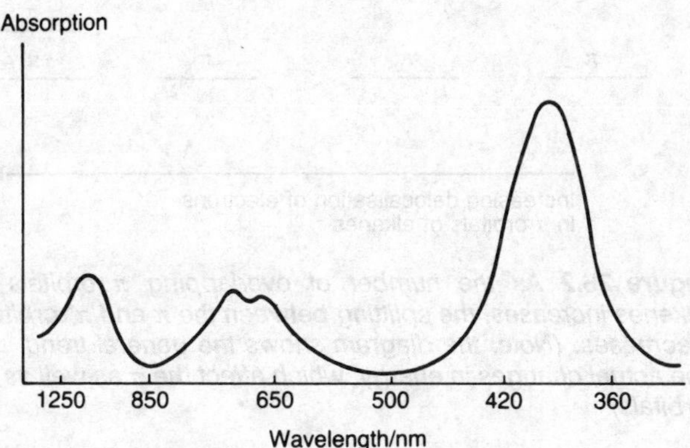

***Figure 25.6** The spectrum of $Ni(H_2O)_6^{2+}$*

25.3 If you were to take the spectrum of a solution that contained Cu^{2+} ions together with an ammonia solution, you would find it looks like Figure 25.7. What colour would the solution appear?

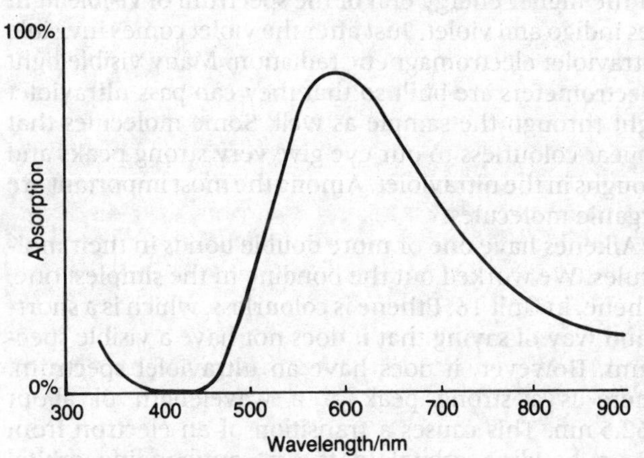

***Figure 25.7** Absorption spectrum for a solution containing copper(II) ions and ammonia*

25.1 Using Planck's equation $E=hf$ gives $E=3.05 \times 10^{-51}$ J.

25.2 There are three regions where the complex ion absorbs. The strongest is between 360 and 420 nm. This corresponds to absorption in the blue region of the visible spectrum. Another band centred around 700 nm represents the absorption of red light. This leaves the yellow and green regions unaffected. If you make up a solution of, say, nickel(II) sulphate in water, you will find it looks a definite green colour. The colour is due to $Ni(H_2O)_6^{2+}$.

25.3 The spectrum shows that there is a great deal of light absorbed in the range 450 to 800 nm. This covers all but the blue region of the spectrum. The solution does indeed look a very deep blue. The colour is due to $Cu(NH_3)_4^{2+}$ ions.

UNIT 25 SUMMARY

- The colour of a chemical corresponds to the colour of light that is *not* absorbed by the chemical; e.g. copper(II) sulphate solution appears blue because it mainly absorbs red light.
- Light is absorbed when the frequency of the light corresponds to the energy gap ΔE between two orbitals given by Planck's equation $\Delta E = hf$.

26

Ultraviolet spectroscopy

26.1 The ultraviolet spectrum of alkenes

At the higher energy end of the spectrum of visible light lies indigo and violet. Just after the violet comes invisible ultraviolet electromagnetic radiation. Many visible light spectrometers are built so that they can pass ultraviolet light through the sample as well. Some molecules that appear colourless to our eye give very strong peaks and troughs in the ultraviolet. Among the most important are organic molecules.

Alkenes have one or more double bonds in their molecules. We worked out the bonding in the simplest one, ethene, in Unit 16. Ethene is colourless, which is a shorthand way of saying that it does not have a visible spectrum. However, it does have an ultraviolet spectrum. There is a strong peak at a wavelength of about 162.5 nm. This causes a transition of an electron from the π bonding orbital to the π^* antibonding orbital (Figure 26.1). Transitions like this are to be found in any alkene. However, some alkenes have more than one double bond, and it is interesting to see what happens to the energy of the π to π^* transition as the number of double bonds increases (Figure 26.2). Some figures are given in Table 26.1. As the number of double bonds increases, the π bonds between neighbouring carbon atoms get mixed up with one another. You can see this in Figure 26.3 for buta-1,3-diene. It is difficult to isolate individual π bonds in the way that the formula $CH_2{=}CH{-}CH{=}CH_2$ suggests.

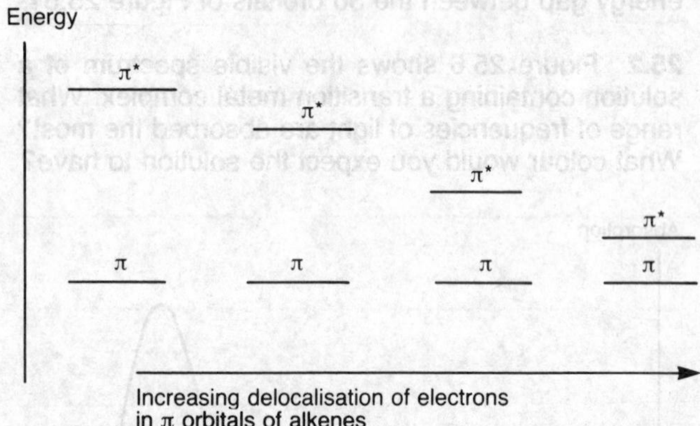

Figure 26.2 *As the number of overlapping π orbitals in alkenes increases, the splitting between the π and π^* orbitals decreases. (Note: the diagram shows the general trend, not the actual changes in energy, which affect the π as well as π^* orbitals)*

Molecules where double bonds alternate with single bonds like they do in the molecules of Table 26.1 (except for ethene, of course) are known as *conjugated* alkenes. The greater the number of alternating single and double

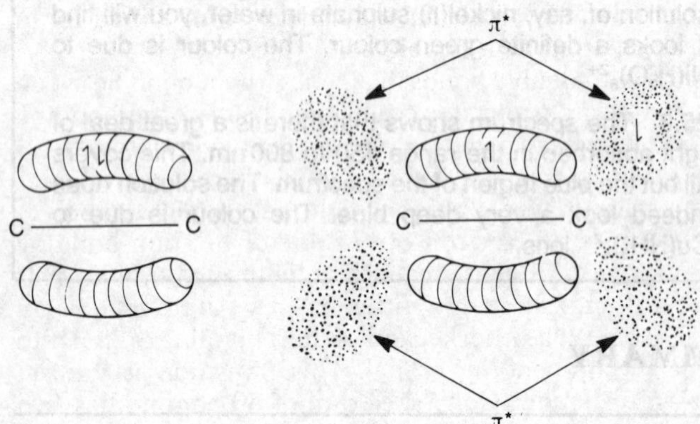

Figure 26.1 *One of the electrons in the π bond of ethene can be knocked out by a photon and go into the π^* antibonding orbital. (Note: (i) the hydrogen atoms are not shown: (ii) a π^* orbital has four lobes, which make up a single orbital)*

Table 26.1. Energies of π to π^* transitions in alkenes

Alkene	*Wavelength* /nm	*Frequency* /10^{14} Hz	*Energy* /kJ mol^{-1}
Ethene	162	18.5	740
Buta-1,3-diene	217	13.8	550
Hexa-1,3,5-triene	265	11.3	450
Vitamin A	360	8.3	330
Carotene	451	6.6	260

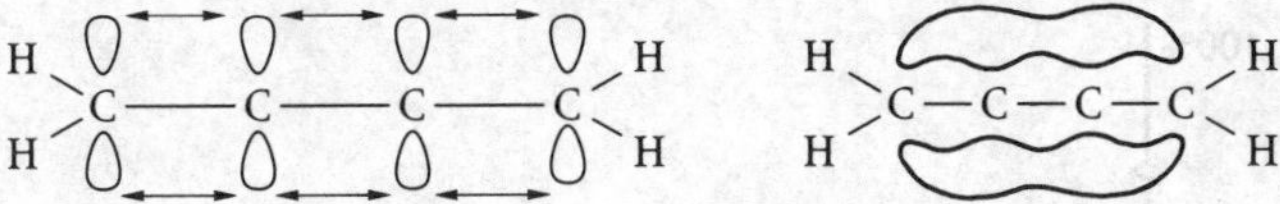

The overlap of four separate p orbitals leads to a delocalised π orbital

Figure 26.3 The usual way of writing the formula of buta-1,3-diene is CH_2=CH—CH=CH_2. However, molecular orbital theory says that instead of two separate π bonds, there is a set of π bonds that can spread over the carbon atoms. The electrons in the π orbitals are delocalised over the entire molecule

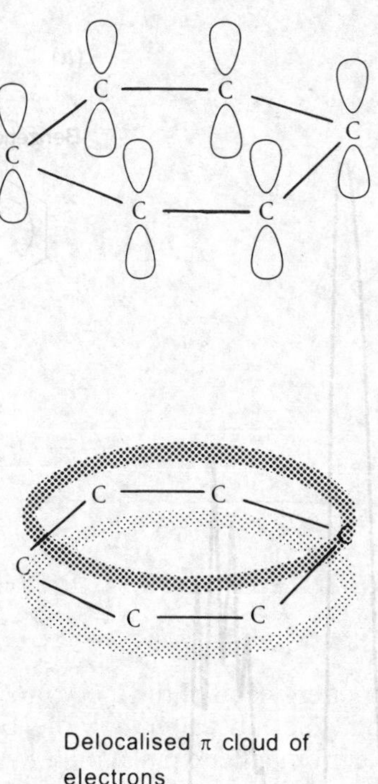

Figure 26.4 There is a π cloud of electrons that spreads all round a benzene ring

bonds, the lower is the energy needed to move an electron from a π bonding to a π* antibonding orbital. The diagrams in Figure 26.2 illustrate how electrons in the lowest energy π orbital spread over the entire molecule. The electrons are said to be *delocalised* over the molecule.

> **Whenever electrons are delocalised, the energy of the orbitals decreases.**

(However, it turns out that the energies of the π* antibonding orbitals are reduced to a greater extent than the π bonding orbitals.)

Given its name, you may not be surprised to discover that carotene is the substance responsible for the orange colour of carrots. That is, carotene's π to π* transition is reduced in energy to such an extent that it occurs in the visible part of the spectrum and not in the ultraviolet. Incidentally, carotene is also used as a food colouring, especially in 'orange' ice cream.

26.2 The ultraviolet spectrum of arenes

Arenes are organic compounds that contain one or more benzene rings. The electrons in benzene are spread around the hexagonal ring of carbon atoms (Figure 26.4).

There are many compounds that appear to be built from benzene rings. Two of them are shown in Figure 26.5. The absorptions are caused by electrons moving between π and π* orbitals. (The smaller peaks and troughs are caused by vibrations of the molecules.) The peaks occur at around 280 nm for naphthalene and 250 nm for benzene. This shows the general trend: the peaks move to higher wavelength (lower energy) as the molecule becomes more complicated. The same thing is happening here as with the conjugated alkenes. The π electrons can move from one ring to another: the π electrons are delocalised over the entire molecule. The greater the amount of delocalisation, the smaller is the energy gap between the π orbitals.

26.3 The ultraviolet spectrum of aldehydes and ketones

Aldehydes and ketones have one particular feature in common: they both have a carbon atom joined to an oxygen atom by a double bond (Figure 26.6).

As with double bonds in alkenes, the π bond between a carbon atom and an oxygen atom has a π* antibonding orbital associated with it. Also, on the oxygen atom there are two lone pairs of electrons (like there are in a water molecule). If the ultraviolet light has the right energy it can knock an electron out of one of the non-bonding (lone) pairs of electrons into an empty π* orbital. This type of transition is written n→π*. Alternatively, an electron can be knocked out of the π bonding orbital into the π* antibonding orbital. This transition is written π→π*. The ultraviolet spectrum of propanone has two peaks. The one around 190 nm corresponds to a π→π* transition; that near 280 nm is a n→π* (Table 26.2). This is a common pattern for aldehydes and ketones.

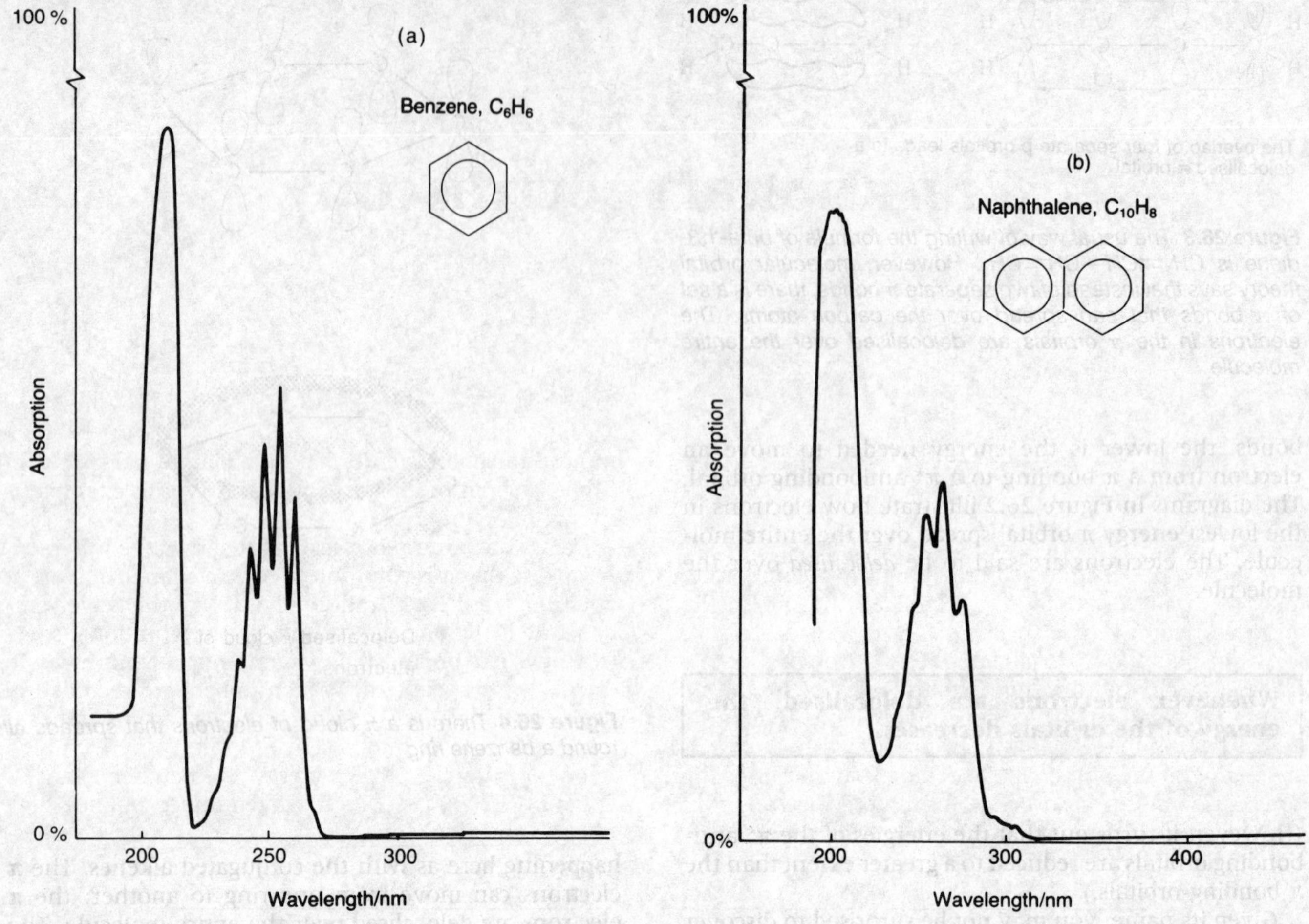

Figure 26.5 *The ultraviolet absorption spectra of (a) benzene, in ethanol as a solvent, and (b) naphthalene, in methanol as a solvent*

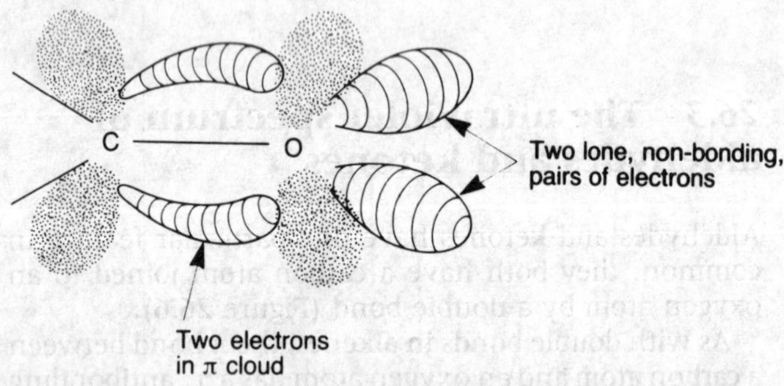

Figure 26.6 *The dotted regions indicate the four lobes of a π^* antibonding orbital. Electrons from the π or non-bonding orbitals can reach the π^* orbital if they are given the right amount of energy*

Table 26.2. Energies of ultraviolet transitions in aldehydes and ketones†

Transition	*Wavelength* /nm	*Frequency* $/10^{14}$ Hz	*Energy* /kJ mol^{-1}
$n \rightarrow \pi^*$	300	10.0	400
$\pi \rightarrow \pi^*$	200	15.0	600

†The wavelengths given are only approximate. The actual value depends on the particular molecule

UNIT 26 SUMMARY

- Many organic molecules absorb in the ultraviolet region of the spectrum.
- Absorptions by alkenes and aromatic compounds are often due to $\pi \rightarrow \pi^*$ transitions.
- Absorptions by aldehydes and ketones are due to $n \rightarrow \pi^*$ and $\pi \rightarrow \pi^*$ transitions.

27

Vibrational spectroscopy

27.1 Why is vibrational spectroscopy useful?

The energy needed to excite the bonds in a compound, making them vibrate more energetically, occurs in the infrared region of the spectrum. If we pass a beam of infrared radiation of varying frequency through a sample of a chemical, then from time to time the energy of the beam is absorbed. This happens when the energy matches the difference between vibrational energy levels belonging to the bonds. The machine that measures the amount of energy absorbed is an infrared spectrometer. The machine is designed so that the pen moves *downwards* if radiation is absorbed, so a vibrational spectrum shows a series of dips or troughs. A typical example is shown in Figure 27.1.

Across the bottom is a scale that shows the *wavenumber*. (Note that it is common to have a change of scale at 2000 cm^{-1}, as here.) Tradition has it that the wavenumber scale is the one that people use in vibrational spectroscopy. To obtain the wavenumber, you have to calculate 1/wavelength. Wavenumbers are recorded in units of cm^{-1} rather than m^{-1}. In fact, wavenumber is proportional to frequency. In the same way that high frequency implies high energy (remember Planck's equation, $E=hf$), so high wavenumber implies high energy, and vice versa.

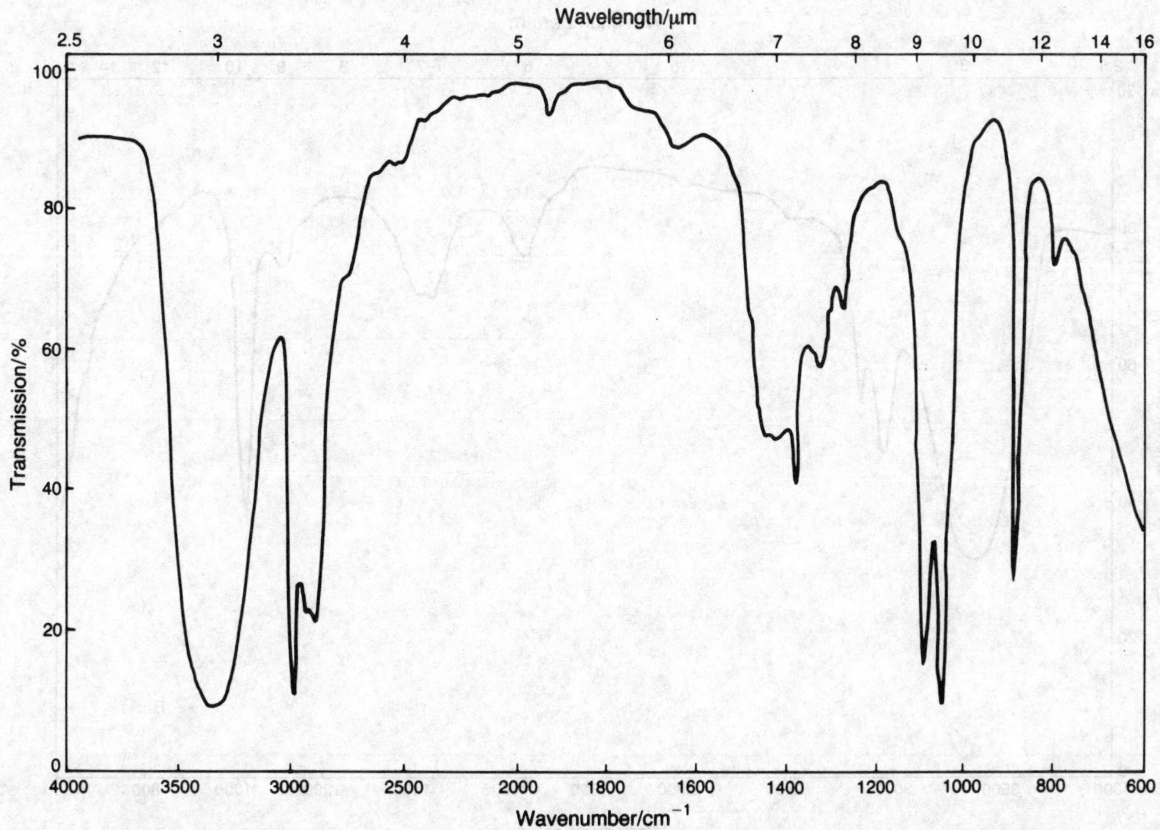

Figure 27.1 *The infrared spectrum of ethanol, CH_3CH_2OH. The band at around 3300 cm^{-1} is typical of alcohols. It is due to the stretching of the O—H bond*

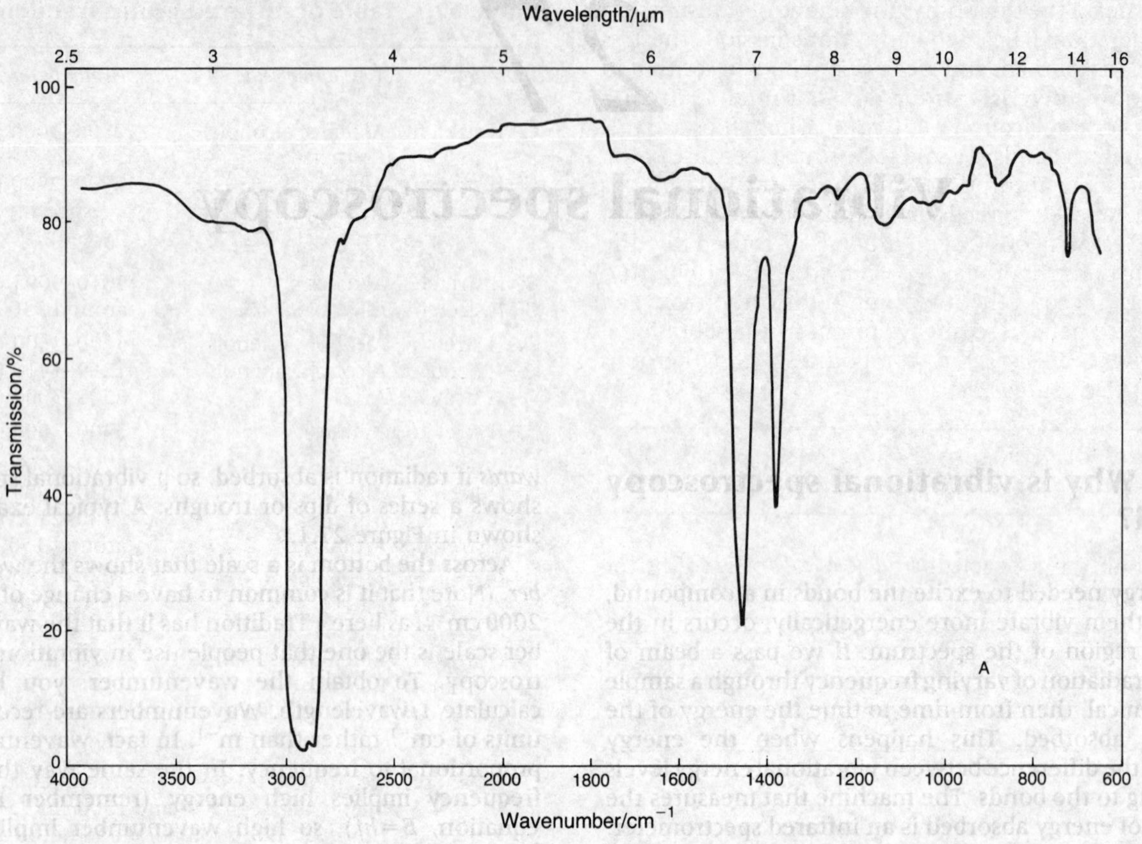

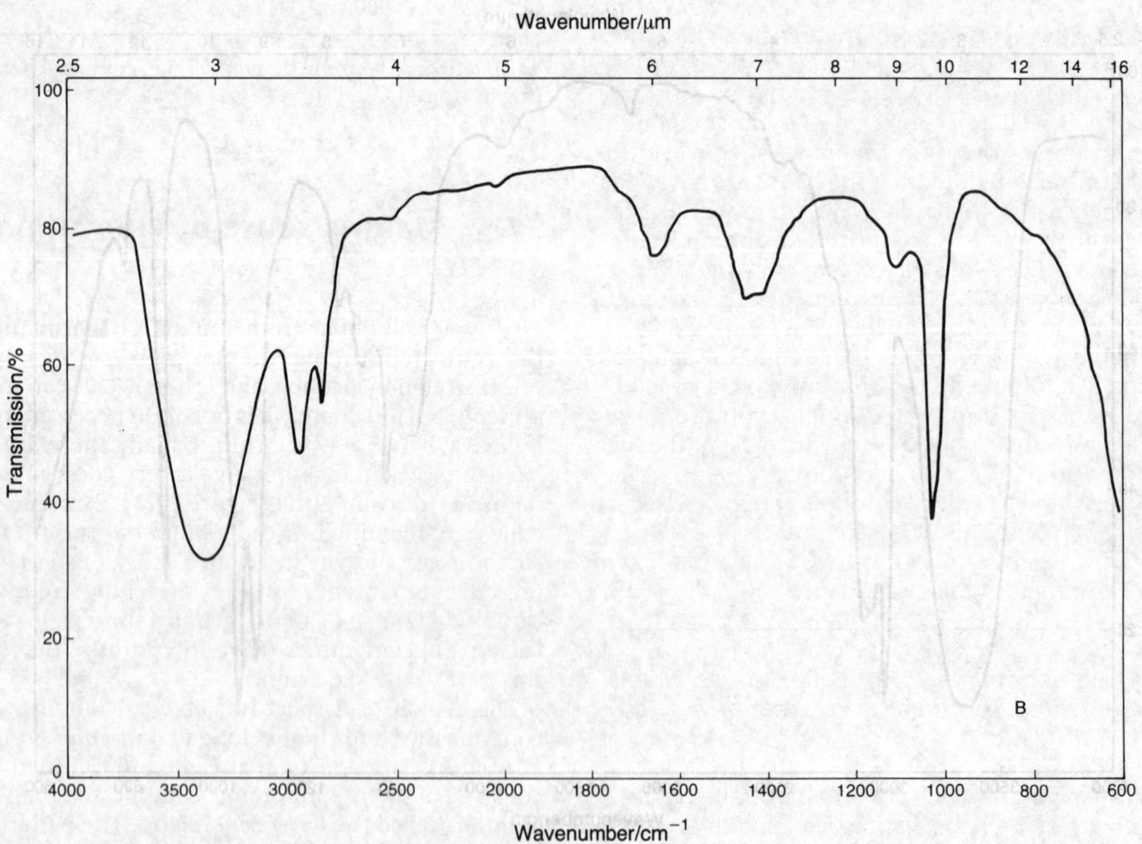

***Figure 27.2** Spectra of two organic compounds. One of them belongs to an alcohol, one does not*

The scale on the side shows the degree of transmission of the radiation. The higher the transmission, the less radiation is absorbed, and vice versa. You will see that in the spectrum there is a strong dip at around 3300 cm^{-1} and another one around 1050 cm^{-1}. These dips are called *bands*. Both bands are said to be *strong* (because of the large amount of absorption), and the one at 3300 cm^{-1} is *broad* (because it spreads over quite a wide range of frequencies). The 3300 cm^{-1} band is caused by the stretching of the hydrogen–oxygen bond; the 1050 cm^{-1} band is produced by the stretching of the carbon–oxygen bond. These bands are always found in the vibrational spectra of alcohols (organic compounds with OH groups in them). This shows us that:

One use of vibrational spectroscopy is in the identification or analysis of compounds.

From an infrared spectrum we can often identify the major types of bond in a compound.

27.1 Look at the spectra shown in Figure 27.2. Which of them belongs to an alcohol?

27.2 What are group frequencies?

You have already met two group frequencies. The bands at 3300 cm^{-1} and 1050 cm^{-1} are characteristic of the OH group in alcohols. (An alcohol always has a carbon to oxygen bond as well as the oxygen to hydrogen bond.) These are examples of group frequencies. However, it would be a mistake to think that the bands are always at these frequencies. The bands tend to move slightly depending on the nature of the rest of the molecule. Often the substance whose spectrum is being taken is dissolved in a solvent. The group frequencies can change depending on the nature of the solvent, and on factors such as the degree of hydrogen bonding in the sample.

It is usually a mistake to look for only one characteristic band in a spectrum. For example, you are more likely to identify an alcohol correctly if you spot the *two* bands at around 3300 cm^{-1} and 1050 cm^{-1}.

There are a large number of group frequencies. Some are listed in Table 27.1. The frequencies are listed together with a letter, s, m and w, which stand for strong, medium and weak respectively.

27.2 Which solvent would be better to use when taking an infrared spectrum: an alcohol or a liquid alkane?

27.3 Why might the 3300 cm^{-1} band of ethanol be much less broad if ethanol vapour is used rather than the liquid?

Table 27.1. Table of infrared group frequencies

Vibration	*Type of molecule*	*Group frequency/*cm^{-1}
C–H stretch	Alkanes, alcohols, ethers	2800–3000 (s)
C–H stretch	Aldehydes —C(=O)H	2700–2900 (w), especially 2720
C–H stretch	Alkenes	3010–3095 (m)
C–H stretch	Alkynes	around 3300 (m)
O–H stretch	Alcohols, phenols	3200–3600 (s)
O–H bend	Alcohols, phenols	1260–1410 (s)
O–H stretch	Acids	2500–3000 (s)
N–H stretch	Amines	3300–3500 (m)
C–C stretch	Alkanes	700–800 (w)
C=C stretch	Alkenes	1620–1680 (varies)
C≡C stretch	Alkynes	2100–2140 (w)
C–C stretch	Aromatics*	around 1500 (m)
C–O stretch	Alcohols	1040–1150 (s)
C–O stretch	Ethers	1070–1150 (s)
C=O stretch	Esters	1735–1750 (s)
C=O stretch	Aldehydes	1720–1740 (s)
C=O stretch	Ketones	1705–1725 (s)
C=O stretch	Carboxylic acids	1700–1725 (s)
C≡N stretch	Nitriles	2000–2500 (s)
C–H bends	Occur over a wide range of frequencies, mainly between 850 and 1500 cm^{-1}. However, non-aromatics tend not to absorb below 900 cm^{-1}; aromatics do absorb below 900 cm^{-1}	

*Aromatics are benzene derivatives, i.e. contain a benzene ring or rings

27.3 Making sense of vibrational spectra

First, you will notice from Table 27.1 that many of the different group frequencies overlap (for example, the C—H stretch in alcohols and ethers). This can make life difficult, but fortunately it is not often necessary to identify every band in a spectrum. Usually there are several bands that taken together give a very good guide to the nature of the compound (Figure 27.3). Examples of such bands are identified in the vibrational spectra of three compounds shown in Figure 27.4. Especially, the presence or absence of the stretching frequency of carbonyl groups (>C=O groups) provides a clue to the type of compound. (Few other groups overlap with this part of the spectrum.)

The region of a spectrum above 1500 cm^{-1} usually contains the bands that belong to particular groups, like OH and >C=O. The region below 1500 cm^{-1} often consists of many different, complicated bands. The region is called the *fingerprint* region. The pattern in this region is different for every molecule. For a chemist it can serve the same purpose as human fingerprints in detective work. By comparing the fingerprint regions of known and 'unknown' compounds the 'unknown' can be identified.

The vibrational spectrum is only one piece of evidence that would be used to identify a compound. For example, it would be analysed to discover which elements it contained, and its molecular mass would be determined using a mass spectrometer (see Unit 29).

You can test your skill at identifying some compounds by trying the next few questions.

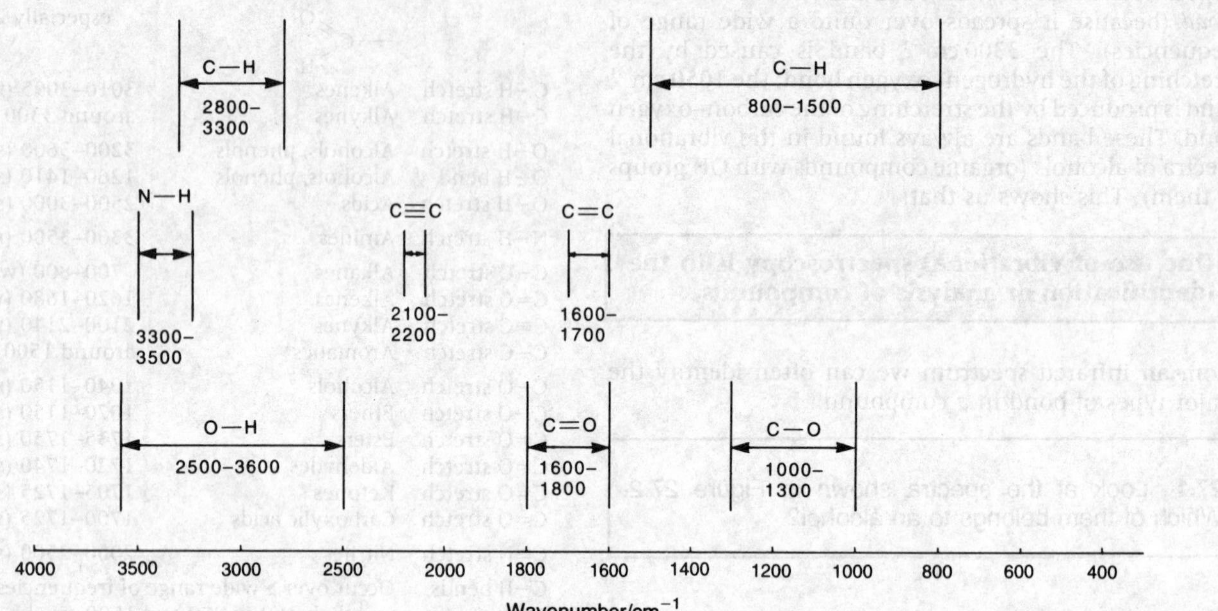

Figure 27.3 *The diagram shows where some of the most common groups appear on an infrared spectrum*

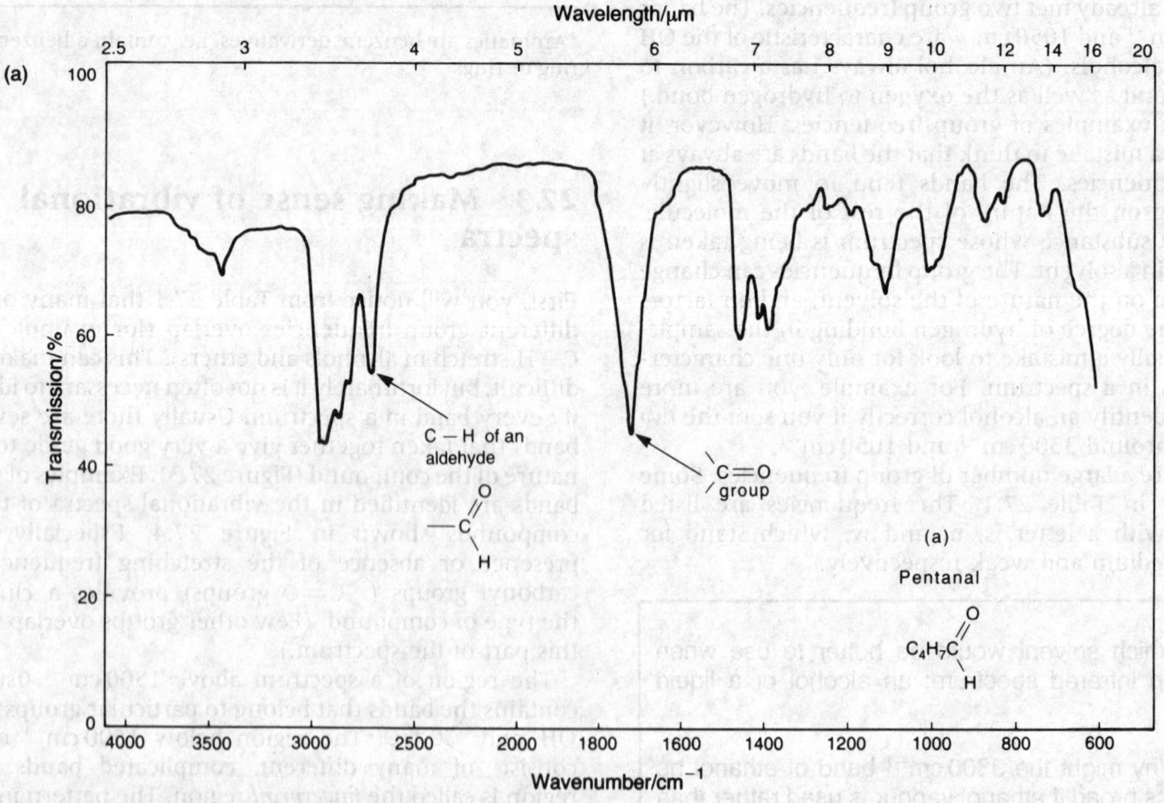

Figure 27.4 *The infrared spectra of (a) pentanal, (b) methylbenzene and (c) propanone. The key feature that distinguishes (a) and (c) from (b) is the carbonyl (C=O) stretching frequency at 1720 cm⁻¹*

Figure 27.4 cont.

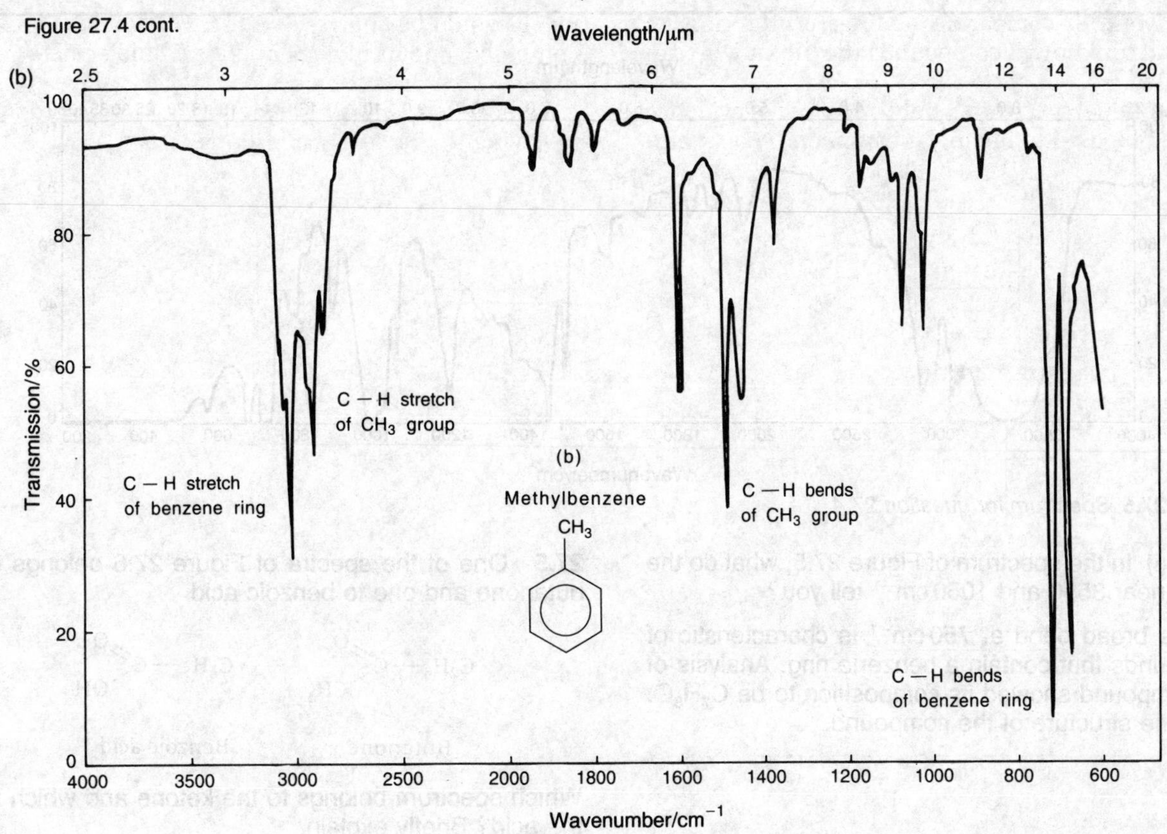

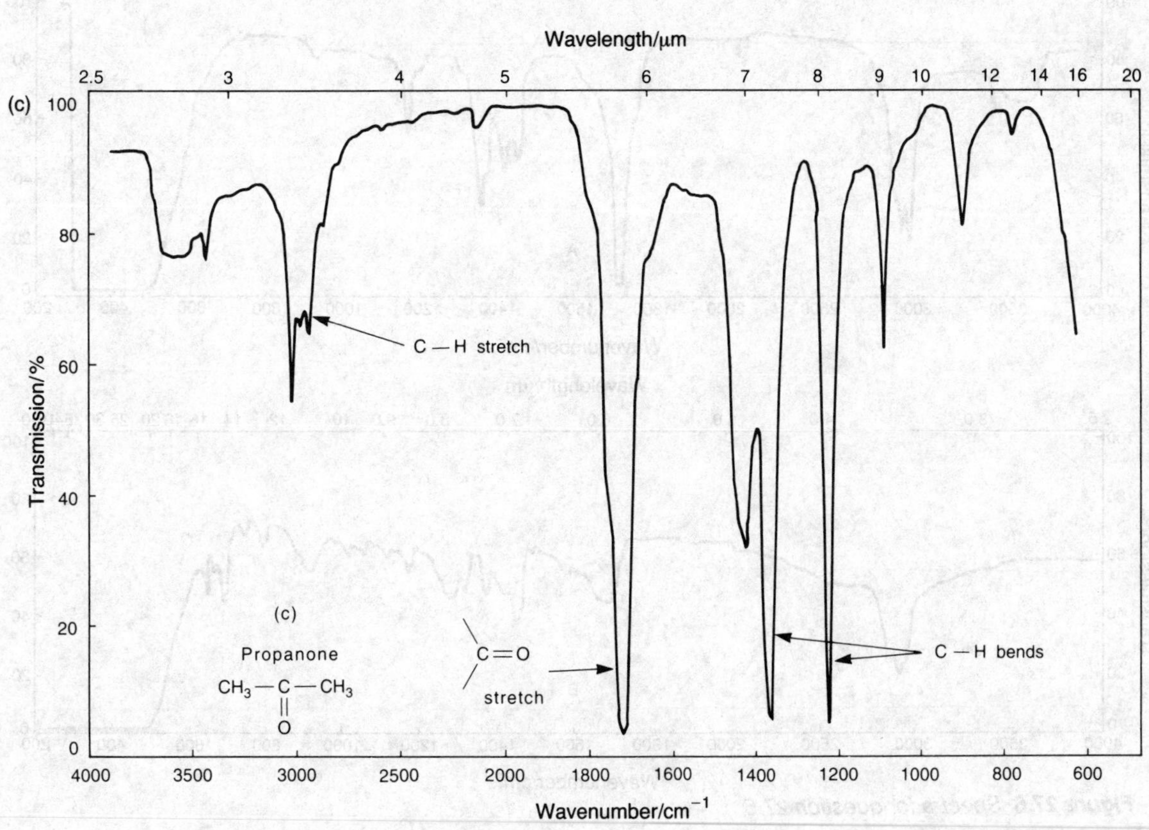

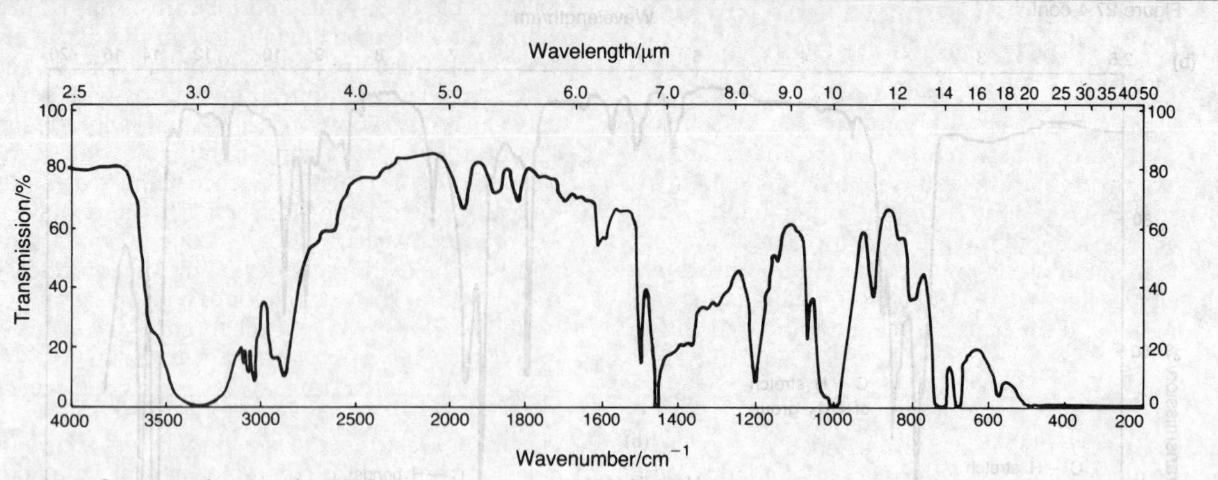

Figure 27.5 *Spectrum for question 27.4*

27.4 (i) In the spectrum of Figure 27.5, what do the bands near 3500 and 1050 cm^{-1} tell you?

(ii) The broad band at 750 cm^{-1} is characteristic of compounds that contain a benzene ring. Analysis of the compound showed its composition to be C_7H_8O. Draw the structure of the compound.

27.5 One of the spectra of Figure 27.6 belongs to butanone and one to benzoic acid.

$C_2H_5—C(=O)CH_3$ Butanone

$C_6H_5—C(=O)OH$ Benzoic acid

Which spectrum belongs to the ketone and which to the acid? Briefly explain.

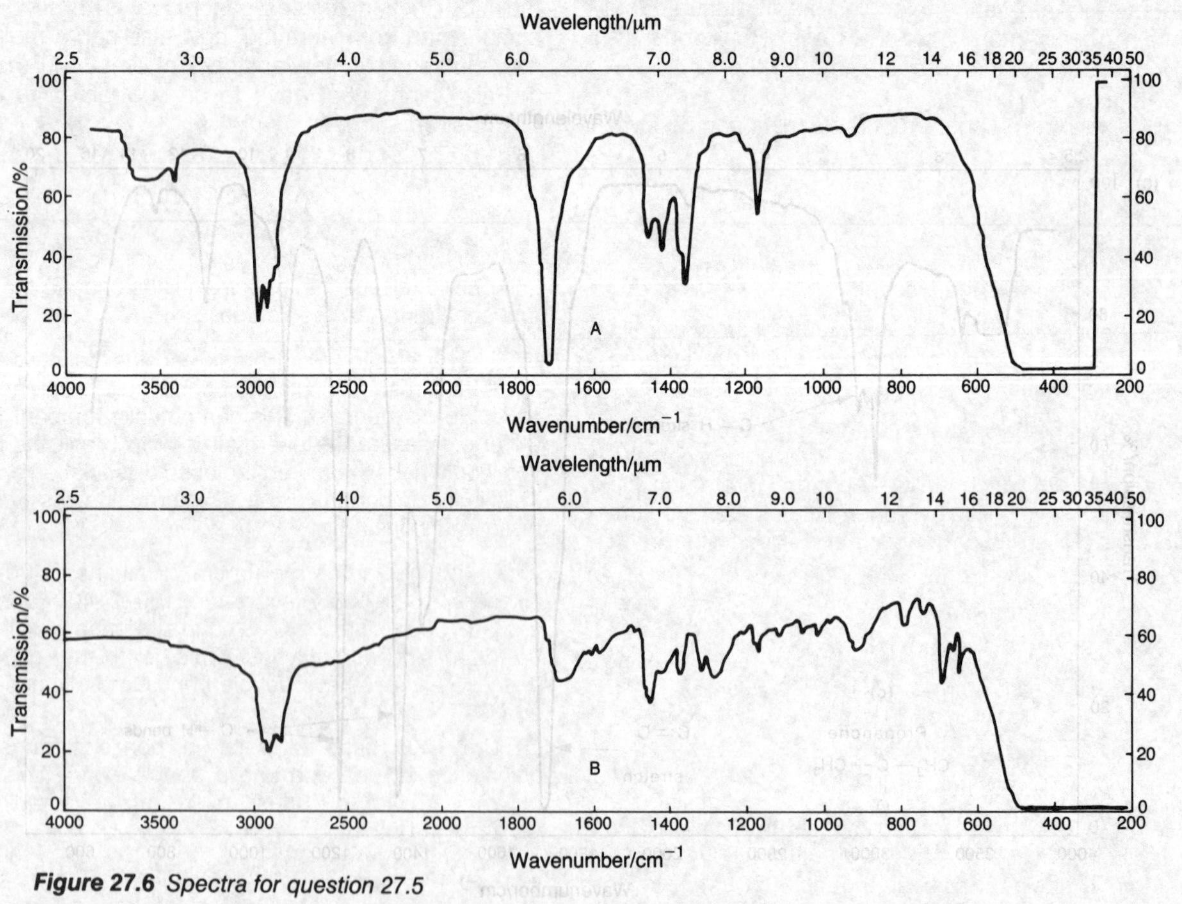

Figure 27.6 *Spectra for question 27.5*

27.4 Vibrational spectra can tell us about the strengths of bonds

Some bonds are very strong, some are very weak, and the majority are in between. If we say that a bond is strong, we mean that the atoms joined by the bond are held together very tightly. On the other hand, atoms joined by a weak bond can easily be torn apart from one another. In some ways, but on a very different scale, a bond behaves like two billiard balls joined together by a piece of elastic. If the balls are made to move then they will wobble backwards and forwards; that is, they will vibrate. It should be obvious to you that if the elastic is very thick then the balls will not vibrate so easily as when the elastic is quite thin. So it is with real bonds between atoms. Some are easy to make vibrate, some are more difficult. The stronger the bond, the higher the frequency of the radiation needed to make it vibrate with increased energy, and vice versa. Therefore, if we look at a vibrational spectrum, the stronger bonds are to be found at the high frequency, high wavenumber, end of the spectrum. The weaker bonds will appear at the lower frequency, lower wavenumber, end.

27.6 Suppose two balls on the ends of a piece of elastic were given a very great deal of energy. What might happen to the balls? What would happen if a real molecule were given a huge amount of energy?

27.7 Using Table 27.1 write down the group frequencies of carbon to carbon single, double and triple bonds. These occur in alkanes, alkenes and alkynes, respectively.

(i) Put the three bonds in order of their strength (weakest first). How does your answer match the type of bonding in these molecules?

(ii) Now compare the carbon to carbon stretching frequency in aromatic molecules, i.e. molecules that contain one or more benzene rings. How does the strength of this bond compare to the others?

27.8 The infrared spectra of molecules can become very complicated. There is a formula that allows us to calculate how many different types of vibrations a molecule might have. These different types are called *normal vibrations*. If there are n atoms in the molecule, there are $3n-6$ different normal vibrations. The exception is that if the molecule is linear, there are $3n-5$ normal vibrations.

How many normal vibrations should (i) methane, CH_4, (ii) pentane, C_5H_{12}, (iii) hydrogen chloride, HCl, have?

Should you have needed to use the formula for HCl?

27.9 The '3' in the formula $3n-6$ is connected with the idea that molecules can move in three dimensions. Apart from vibrating, how else can a molecule move in space? (Hint: look back at Unit 24.) What are the six 'things' that have to be subtracted to leave only the vibrations?

Answers

27.1 Spectrum B is the alcohol.

27.2 The alkane is better. It could not take part in hydrogen bonding. The alkane often used in infrared experiments is known as Nujol.

27.3 In liquid ethanol there is a great deal of hydrogen bonding between the OH groups. This influences the frequencies with which the O—H bond vibrates. In the vapour there is very little hydrogen bonding because the molecules are so much further apart. Hence the bond vibrates over a much smaller range of frequencies.

27.4 (i) It is an alcohol.

(ii)

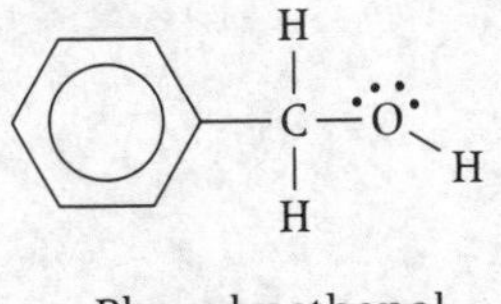

Phenylmethanol

27.5 Both spectrum A and spectrum B have the characteristic carbonyl stretch at around 1720 cm^{-1}. Spectrum B has a broad band around 3000 cm^{-1}, which is characteristic of hydrogen bonded OH groups. The latter band tells us that spectrum B belongs to the acid, and spectrum A to the ketone.

27.6 The elastic would break and the balls would fly apart. In a real molecule the bond would break and the molecule disintegrate. This can actually happen! If you were to measure the energy it took to break the bond, you would have measured the bond dissociation energy. This is an important piece of information, as you will discover in Unit 44.

27.7 (i) The figures are (in cm^{-1}): alkanes, 700–800; alkenes, 1620–1680; alkynes, 2100–2140; aromatic, around 1500. Thus, the C–C bond strengths are alkanes (lowest), alkenes, alkynes. This is to be expected because alkenes have double bonds and alkynes triple bonds.

(ii) The C–C bond strength in benzene rings lies between a single bond and a double bond. This is in agreement with our description of the bonding in benzene in Unit 14.

27.8 (i) $n=5$, number of vibrations $=3\times5-6=9$.
(ii) $n=17$, number of vibrations $=3\times17-6=45$.

Answers – contd.

(iii) $n=2$, but HCl is linear, so number of vibrations $= 3\times 2-5=1$.

For a diatomic molecule like HCl there can only be one type of vibration: that is the stretching of the bond as the atoms move closer to or further away from one another.

Note: not all the vibrations may show up in a spectrum. This is especially true of homopolar diatomic molecules like H_2, N_2 or O_2. This type of molecule does not have a vibrational spectrum at all. The reason is that there must be a dipole moment, which can interact with the electric field of the light wave. Homopolar diatomics do not have dipole moments.

27.9 A molecule can also translate and rotate. It can do these things in the three *x*, *y*, or *z* directions. That is, there can be three types of translation and three types of rotation. Hence these six types of movement have to be subtracted. In a linear molecule there is one less type of rotation: this is the rotation shown in Figure 27.7. It is a rotation about the bond.

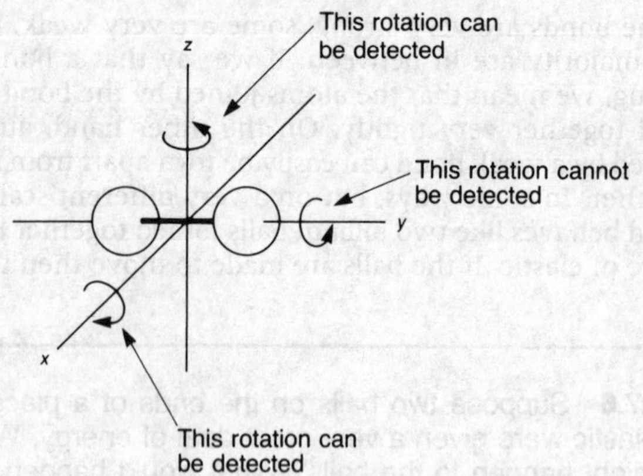

Figure 27.7 *Only two of the rotations of a linear molecule can be measured*

UNIT 27 SUMMARY

- All molecules vibrate with a range of frequencies, which depend on the groups of atoms they contain. By measuring the frequencies of vibration of an 'unknown' molecule, the groups in the molecule can be identified; e.g. carbonyl groups show up around 1725 cm^{-1}.

28

Nuclear magnetic resonance

28.1 The importance of nuclear spin

Nuclear magnetic resonance (n.m.r. for short) is a relatively new type of spectroscopy that has become increasingly important in helping chemists to understand the structures of molecules. It has also been found to be very useful in medicine. Especially, it allows surgeons to discover regions in the brain that may be the cause of illness, for example brain tumours.

In n.m.r. there are two sets of energy levels, which are rather different from the types of energy level that we met in earlier units. Here, the energy levels belong to *nuclear spins*. In the units on atomic structure you should have discovered that electrons can behave like tiny magnets: they have the property we called spin. (We have already said that the word 'spin' should not be taken too literally; it would be a mistake to imagine electrons as 'really' spinning like tops.) Well, protons and neutrons have spins as well. They, too, behave like tiny magnets. For example, if protons are placed in a magnetic field, their magnetic fields will try to line up in the applied field. We can show this on a diagram as in Figure 28.1. However, if the protons are given a little extra energy, their magnetic fields can be made to point in the opposite direction to the field. Protons with spins in these two different directions are said to be in different *spin states* (Figure 28.2). In a magnetic field of around 100 kG, the energy needed to make a proton swap between spin states is in the radio frequency region of the electromagnetic spectrum. If we use Planck's equation $E = hf$, it turns out that the frequency will be around several hundred megahertz, perhaps as much as 500 MHz.

Ordinarily, hydrogen nuclei will have no special arrangements of their spins; like electrons, some will be 'spin up' and some will be 'spin down'.

In the same way as electrons can be made to move between energy levels by visible or ultraviolet light, so nuclei can be made to change their spin energy levels. The difference is that the type of radiation needed is in the radio frequency region of the electromagnetic spectrum.

In an n.m.r. spectrometer, the sample is placed in a magnetic field. Radio waves are swept across the sample.

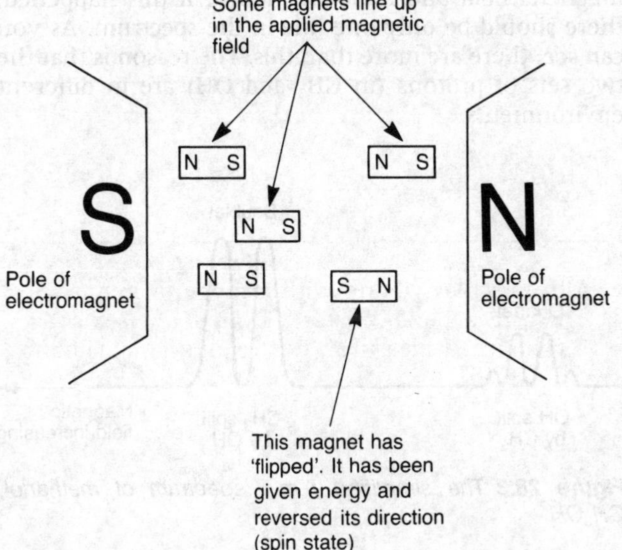

Figure 28.1 *The bar magnets represent the magnetic fields of protons. They line up in an applied magnetic field from an electromagnet. The energy needed to make a proton flip over to an opposite direction (opposite spin) is provided by a radio wave. (Note: In practice the difference in the number of protons with spins lined up and not lined up in the magnetic field is very small. The difference in populations is only about 1 in 10^5. An n.m.r. machine has to be very sensitive to detect this difference)*

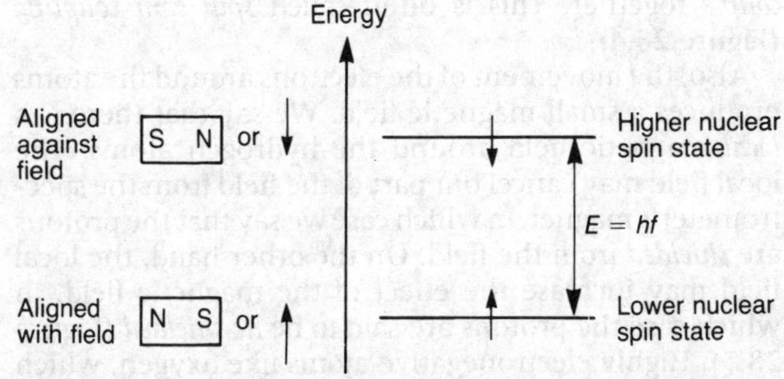

Figure 28.2 *Protons with their spins aligned with the applied field are at a lower energy than those aligned against the field. Radio waves have the right frequency to cause a transition between the two spin states*

At a particular combination of magnetic field and wavelength of the radio waves, some protons can change their spin states. This change is detected electronically and the signal fed to a recorder.

28.2 The patterns in an n.m.r. spectrum

You can see the simplified n.m.r. spectrum of methanol in Figure 28.3. In methanol there are four hydrogen atoms, but they are in two different arrangements. There is a set of three in the CH_3 group and one joined to the oxygen atom. Given that the protons in the hydrogen atoms are identical, we might expect that they would all change their spin states at the same combination of magnetic field and radio frequency. If this happened, there should be only one line in the spectrum. As you can see, there are more than this. The reason is that the two sets of protons (in CH_3 and OH) are in different environments.

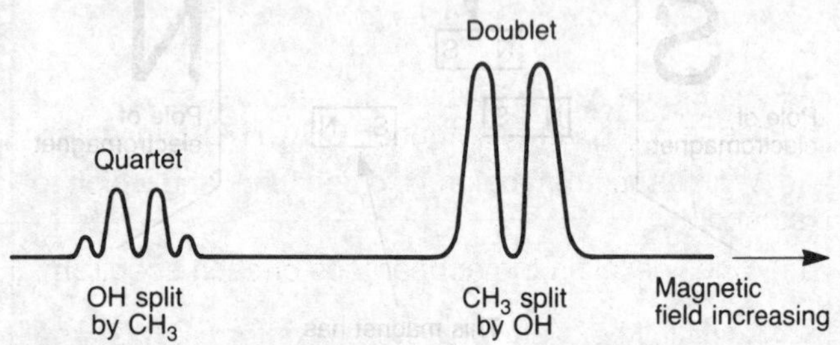

Figure 28.3 *The simplified n.m.r. spectrum of methanol, CH_3OH*

28.3 Why do protons appear in different places in the spectrum?

First, each of the protons in the CH_3 group has its own magnetic field, which can influence neighbouring protons. The spins of the protons (and their magnetic fields) can be arranged in different ways. We say that the spins *couple* together. This is often called *spin–spin coupling* (Figure 28.4).

Also, the movement of the electrons around the atoms produces a small magnetic field. We say that there is a *local* magnetic field around the hydrogen atoms. The local field may cancel out part of the field from the spectrometer's magnet, in which case we say that the protons are *shielded* from the field. On the other hand, the local field may increase the effect of the magnetic field, in which case the protons are said to be *de-shielded* (Figure 28.5). Highly electronegative atoms like oxygen, which draw electrons towards them, are very good at de-shielding protons.

The amount of spin–spin coupling depends on the number of neighbouring protons. The different patterns

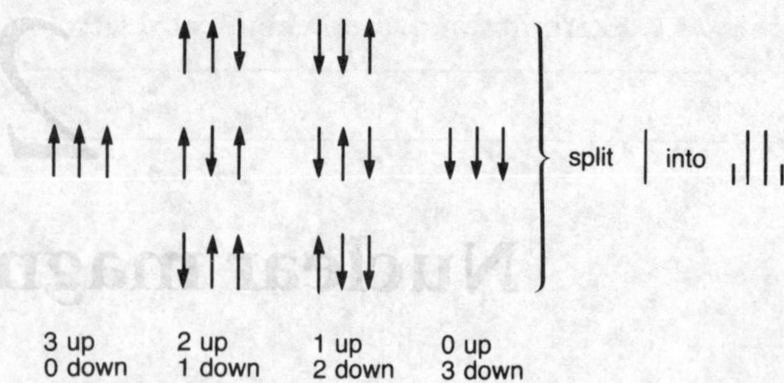

Figure 28.4 *There are eight ways that three spins can combine. There is one way only of getting 3 up, or 3 down; but three ways (each) of getting 2 up and 1 down or 1 up and 2 down. Each of the four patterns gives a different local field and will split the line of a neighbouring proton into four*

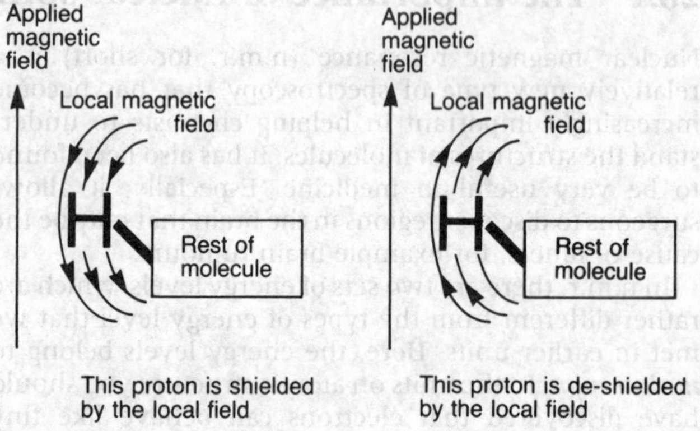

Figure 28.5 *The local field from the rest of the molecule can (i) act against the applied field or (ii) reinforce it*

of lines in the spectrum can tell us whether, for example, a CH_3 group is connected to a CH_2 group or to a benzene ring.

The effects of shielding change from one substance to another, and cause the peaks to appear at different places in the spectrum. The scale that is used to measure the position of a peak is called the *chemical shift*. The chemical shift is usually measured relative to the peaks given by a substance called tetramethylsilane, $(CH_3)_4Si$, called TMS for short. The 12 protons in TMS give a strong signal in an n.m.r. spectrum. The other peaks are measured from the TMS signal. Two scales are used: a tau, τ, scale, and more often a delta, δ, scale. Typical values are collected in Table 28.1.

28.4 N.m.r. spectra can tell us how many protons are present

One useful feature of n.m.r. spectra is that, the more protons there are of a given type, the stronger is the peak in the spectrum. In fact, the area under the peak gives us a measure of how many protons are involved. For example, in the spectrum of methanol the areas under the peaks are in the ratio 3 to 1. This confirms what we

Table 28.1. Examples of proton chemical shifts*

Substance	*Set of protons*	*δ scale*/ppm
Alkanes	$RC\mathbf{H}_3$	0.9
	$RC\mathbf{H}_2R'$	1.3
Chloroalkanes	$RC\mathbf{H}_2Cl$	3.5
Fluoroalkanes	$RC\mathbf{H}_2F$	4.0
Alcohols	$RCH_2O\mathbf{H}$	4.5
Aldehydes	$RC\mathbf{H}O$	9.7
Ketones	$C\mathbf{H}_3COR$	2.1
Carboxylic acids	$RCOO\mathbf{H}$	11.5
Aromatic compounds	$C_6\mathbf{H}_6$	7.3
	$C_6H_5C\mathbf{H}_3$	2.3

*The values given are only approximate; they vary from compound to compound. The δ scale is measured in 'parts per million' (ppm)

already know about methanol, CH_3OH; it has three protons of one type (CH_3) and one of another (OH). Imagine, though, that we did not know the formula of the compound. By using scales of chemical shifts we could begin to discover the types of groups present. Then, by measuring the areas under the peaks, we could actually count the numbers of protons. Fortunately, the measurement of the areas is done automatically by the spectrometer.

28.5 Not only hydrogen atoms can show up in n.m.r.

The protons in hydrogen atoms happen to be the easiest to detect in n.m.r., but other nuclei possessing a spin can be used. Important ones are carbon-13, fluorine-19 and phosphorus-31. (Carbon-12 has a zero nuclear spin; the spins of the six protons and six neutrons cancel out.) However, detecting these atoms requires rather more effort than detecting protons. We shall not be concerned with their n.m.r. spectra.

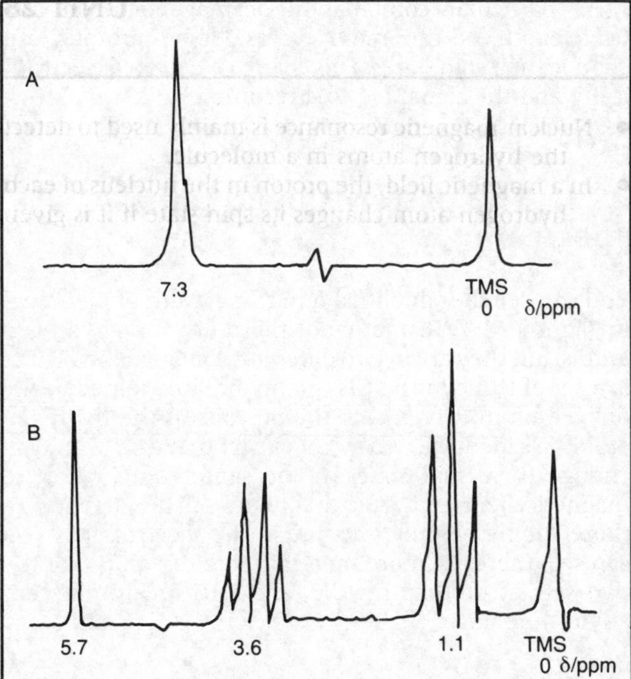

Figure 28.6 *Two n.m.r. spectra for question 28.1*

28.1 Figure 28.6 shows the n.m.r. spectra of benzene, C_6H_6, and of ethanol, CH_3CH_2OH, in water.

(i) Which spectrum belongs to benzene, and which to ethanol?

(ii) Briefly explain the appearance of each spectrum.

28.2 Briefly explain why the peaks for $RC\mathbf{H}_2Cl$ and $RC\mathbf{H}_2F$ occur at different chemical shifts (see Table 28.1).

28.3 Why might it be difficult to detect carbon-13 atoms in a naturally occurring sample of an organic compound by n.m.r.? (Hint: abundance of carbon-13 nuclei.)

Answers

28.1 (i) Spectrum A belongs to benzene. Spectrum B belongs to ethanol.

(ii) Although there are six protons in benzene, they are all in exactly the same environment. As a consequence, each proton appears at the same place in the spectrum; hence the single line.

There are three different types of proton in ethanol: three in the CH_3 group, two in the CH_2 group, and one in the OH group. This corresponds to the relative areas being in the ratio 3:2:1. The pattern is complicated because the CH_3 proton peak is split into three by the CH_2 protons. The peak corresponding to the CH_2 protons is split into four by the CH_3 protons. When ethanol is in water, the OH proton shows up as a single peak. (In pure ethanol the pattern is more complicated.)

$$\begin{array}{cccc} & CH_3- & CH_2- & OH \\ & \uparrow & \uparrow & \uparrow \\ \delta = & 1.1 & 3.6 & 5.7 \end{array}$$

28.2 Fluorine is more electronegative than chlorine. It pulls electrons away from the neighbouring hydrogen atoms more strongly than does chlorine. Therefore there is more de-shielding with fluorine, which causes the protons to show up in different parts of the spectrum. Actually there is a further complication with fluorine: ^{19}F is active in n.m.r. in much the same way as protons, so it gives rise to lines in the spectrum that are absent with chlorine.

28.3 The abundance of carbon-13 atoms is only about 1%. Therefore the spectrometer has to be extremely sensitive to detect them.

UNIT 28 SUMMARY

- Nuclear magnetic resonance is mainly used to detect the hydrogen atoms in a molecule.
- In a magnetic field, the proton in the nucleus of each hydrogen atom changes its spin state if it is given the right amount of energy. This energy is supplied by electromagnetic radiation of long wavelength. The frequency of the radiation absorbed depends on the chemical environment of the proton.

29

Mass spectrometry

29.1 What are mass spectrometers?

Mass spectrometers are used to measure the masses of atoms and molecules with great accuracy. They are also capable of detecting remarkably small amounts of an element or compound – easily less than 10^{-6} g, sometimes as little as 10^{-12} g. The first mass spectrometer was invented by Aston in 1919, although his apparatus was known as a mass spectrograph. His method, and modern mass spectrometers, makes use of the fact that, when charged particles move in a magnetic field, they travel in curved paths (Figure 29.1).

The heavier the particle, the harder it is to make it turn, and vice versa. One idea is to move a detector in the path of the particles. The position of the detector when it records the arrival of particles will be related to their mass. In real mass spectrometers, greater accuracy is obtained by keeping the detector fixed, and varying other conditions in the spectrometer.

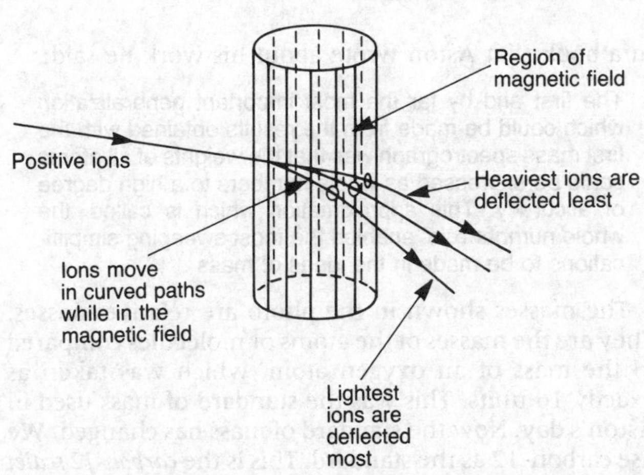

Figure 29.1 *When charged particles move through a magnetic field they travel in curved paths. Heavy ions are deflected the least, light ions the most. This is the principle of a mass spectrometer*

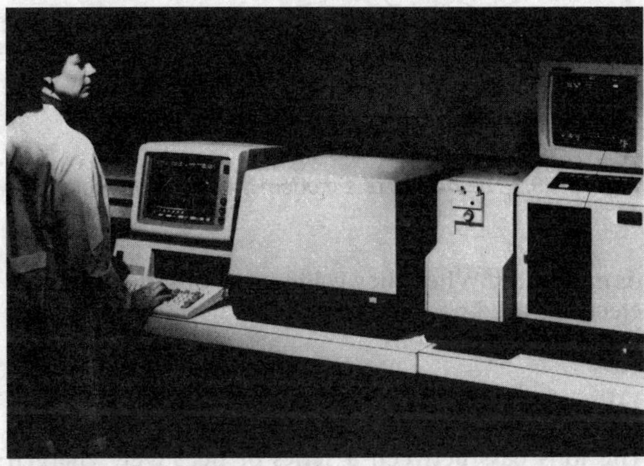

A gas chromatography apparatus (on the right) can be connected to a mass spectrometer (towards the left) with the output from each analysed by computer.

29.2 The design of a mass spectrometer

The design of a modern mass spectrometer is shown in Figure 29.2. It is vital that the whole apparatus is kept under very high vacuum. The essential parts of the spectrometer are as follows.

(a) *Entry chamber*

Gases can be directly let in to the apparatus, although precautions are necessary to prevent air getting in. Owing to the vacuum in the spectrometer, liquids will usually give off sufficient molecules from their surfaces to provide a reasonable level of vapour. Solid samples are a different matter. They may not vaporise at all easily. In this case a small amount can be placed on a wire and an electric current passed through it. The current heats the sample and vaporises it.

(b) *Electron gun*

The next task is to turn the atoms or molecules into ions. The electron gun fires high energy electrons at the atoms

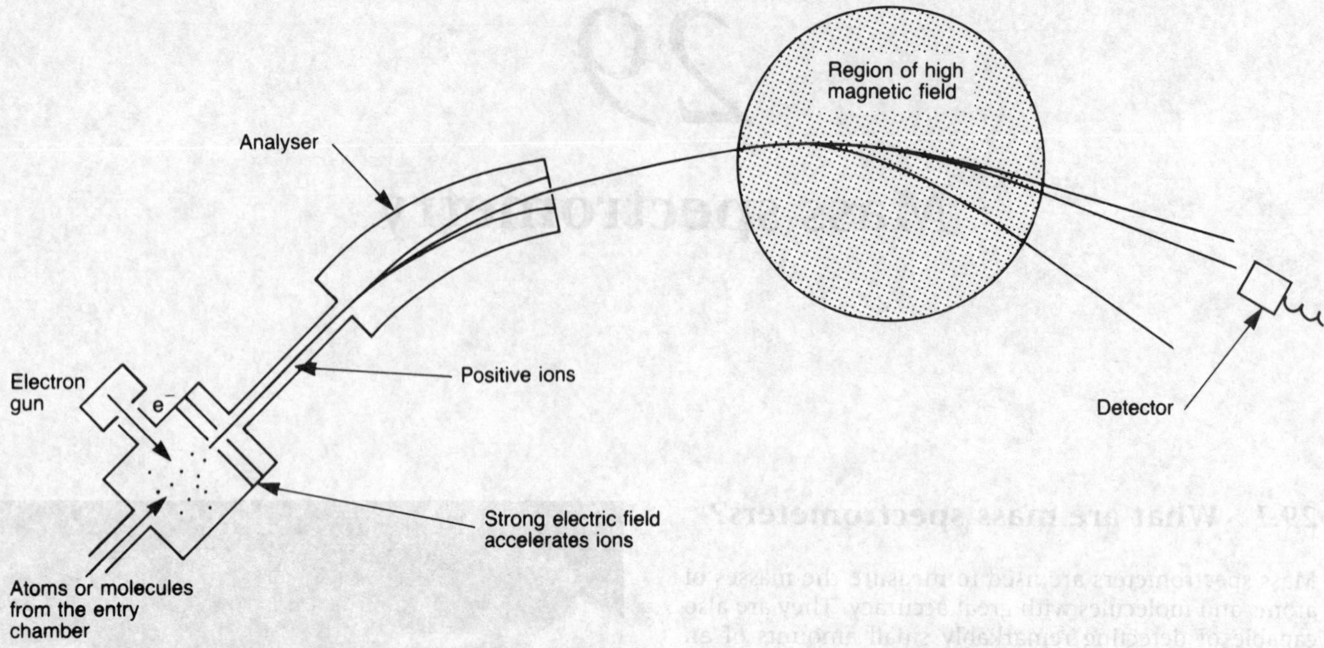

***Figure 29.2** The design of a modern mass spectrometer. The entire apparatus is kept under high vacuum*

or molecules. When they collide, one or sometimes two electrons are knocked out and the atoms or molecules turn into positive ions.

(c) *Accelerator*

The ions pass between a series of negatively charged metal plates. The plates accelerate the ions to high speeds.

(d) *Analyser*

In the analyser the positive ions pass through another electric field. However, this field makes the particles move in curved paths. Ions that emerge from the analyser all have the same kinetic energy. By changing the size of the electric field, ions with different kinetic energies can be sent into the region of the magnetic field. In other words, the analyser acts as an ion filter: only a fraction of those ions entering the analyser get through. (Notice that the analyser does *not* sort the ions according to their mass: a fast, light ion and a heavy, slow ion may have the same kinetic energy and therefore get through the analyser.)

(e) *Magnetic field*

On entering the magnetic field the ions begin to move in circular paths. The path they take depends on the ratio of their mass and charge (m/q). If the ions have a single positive charge, then q is equal in size (but opposite in sign) to the charge on an electron; in this case the mass to charge ratio is m/e. By changing the size of the magnetic field, ions with different masses can be brought to a focus on the detector.

(f) *Detector*

The detector is a very sensitive electrometer that responds to the number of ions hitting it. The signal is amplified and causes a set of mirrors to move. Ultraviolet light is reflected off the mirrors on to sensitive photographic paper. When ions arrive at the detector, a line is drawn on the paper. The height of the line is proportional to the number of ions reaching the detector.

29.3 The whole number rule and standards of mass

In a book that Aston wrote about his work he said:

> The first and by far the most important generalization which could be made from the results obtained with the first mass spectrograph was that the weights of all atoms could be expressed as whole numbers to a high degree of accuracy. This approximation which is called 'the whole number rule' enabled the most sweeping simplifications to be made in the ideas of mass . . .

The masses shown in the photo are relative masses. They are the masses of the atoms or molecules compared to the mass of an oxygen atom, which was taken as exactly 16 units. This was the standard of mass used in Aston's day. Now the standard of mass has changed. We use carbon-12 as the standard. This is the *carbon-12 scale*:

The mass of an atom of carbon-12 is defined to be exactly 12.

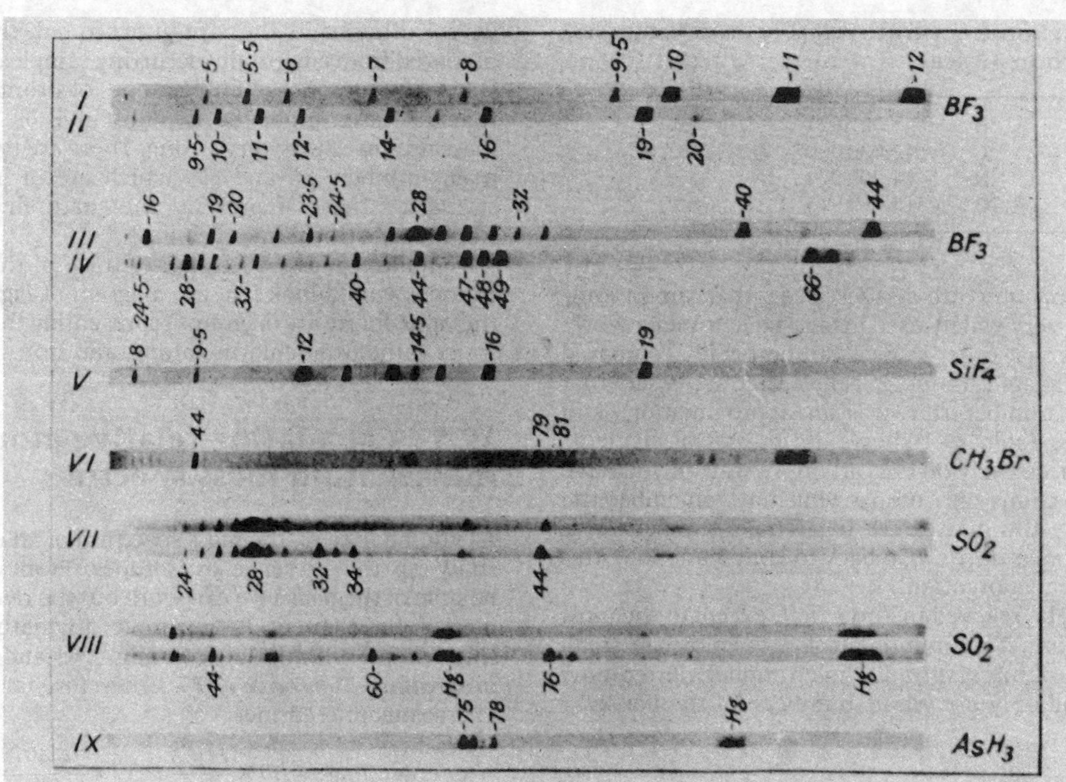

Examples of Aston's results from his mass spectrometer. Source: F. W. Aston, Mass Spectra and Isotopes, *London, Edward Arnold, 1924.*

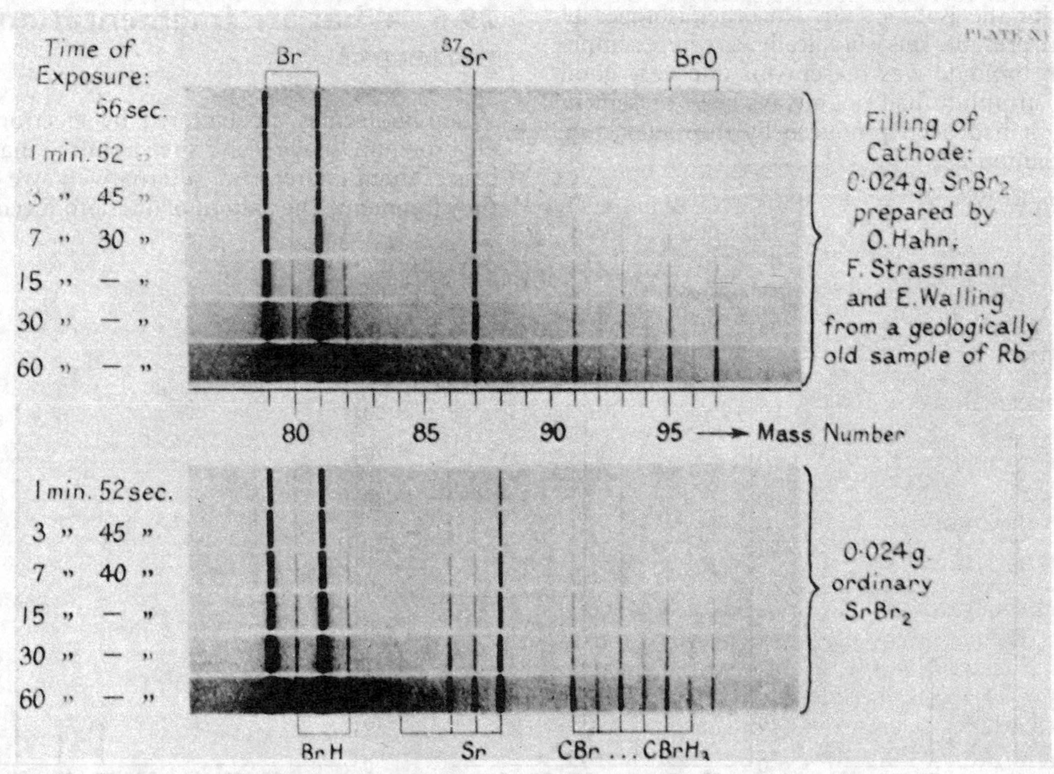

Mass spectra (taken by Aston) of two samples of strontium bromide. Source: F. W. Aston, Mass Spectra and Isotopes, *London, Edward Arnold, 1924.*

Table 29.1. Some accurate relative atomic masses on the carbon-12 scale

Hydrogen	${}^{1}_{1}H$	1.007 825
Carbon	${}^{12}_{6}C$	12.000 000
Nitrogen	${}^{14}_{7}N$	14.003 074
Oxygen	${}^{16}_{8}O$	15.994 915

One reason why carbon-12 is used is that carbon compounds are very widely used in mass spectrometer work. This means that other masses can be readily compared with the mass of carbon-12. Notice that Aston said that the whole number rule was an approximation; and indeed it is. Table 29.1 shows the masses of elements measured accurately on the carbon-12 scale. If you have read the sections on isotopes you may remember the reason why the masses are not whole numbers: it is because of *mass defects*. (Go back to Unit 3 and look this up if you have forgotten.)

You may be relieved to know that, except in the most accurate work, it is common practice to ignore the small differences of masses from whole numbers. From now on, we shall only use whole numbers for the masses.

29.4 Mass spectra and isotopes

In the photo you can see the results of two investigations of strontium bromide, $SrBr_2$. The top spectrometer trace was taken using a sample dug out of the ground, which was extremely rich in rubidium. You can see a very strong line for the isotope ^{87}Sr. No other isotopes of strontium are present. This isotopically very pure sample of strontium bromide was present for one very good reason. The strontium had not always been present in the ground, it had been produced by the radioactive decay of rubidium-87:

$${}^{87}_{37}Rb \rightarrow {}^{87}_{38}Sr + {}^{0}_{-1}e$$

On the other hand, the strontium bromide that had been prepared from a naturally occurring sample of strontium shows the presence of four isotopes of strontium. One of them, at mass number 84, is almost invisible. Another, at mass number 88, is very strong. There are two others, of mass numbers 86 and 87, which are of intermediate strength. These represent the naturally occurring isotopes of strontium.

A modern mass spectrometer trace of the strontium isotopes would look like the diagram of Figure 29.3. In the same figure are diagrams representing the mass spectra of samples of chlorine atoms and iron.

29.5 Calculating relative atomic masses from mass spectra

As you have seen, the mass spectrum of an element will show up the presence of isotopes. From the relative heights of the peaks we can work out the relative atomic mass of the element. For example, any naturally occurring sample of chlorine contains ^{35}Cl and ^{37}Cl in the proportions 75.53%:24.47%. Therefore for a sample of 100 atoms of chlorine,

$$\text{average mass} = 35 \times \frac{75.53}{100} + 37 \times \frac{24.47}{100} = 35.50$$

This is the relative atomic mass of chlorine that you will find listed in tables of atomic masses, or on a Periodic Table.

29.6 What are fragmentation patterns?

When molecules are battered by electrons from the electron gun, they receive such a thump that the energy causes them to break up. Alternatively, we can say that they fragment. The pattern of lines produced in the mass

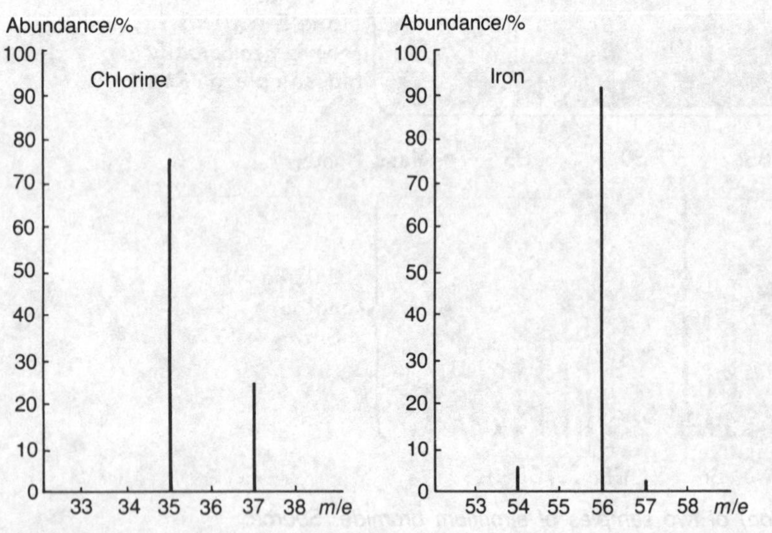

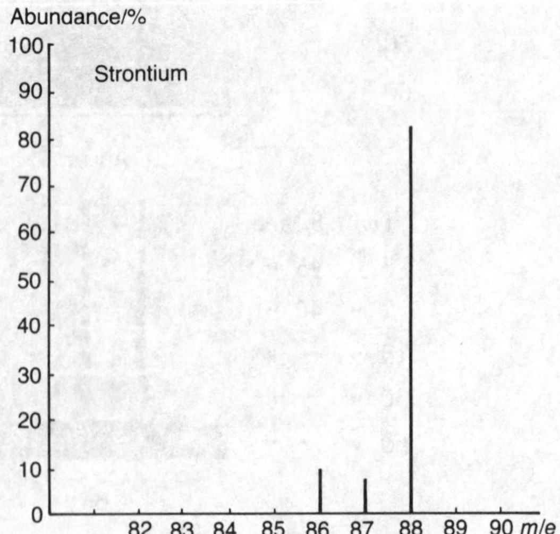

***Figure 29.3** The mass spectra of chlorine, iron and strontium atoms*

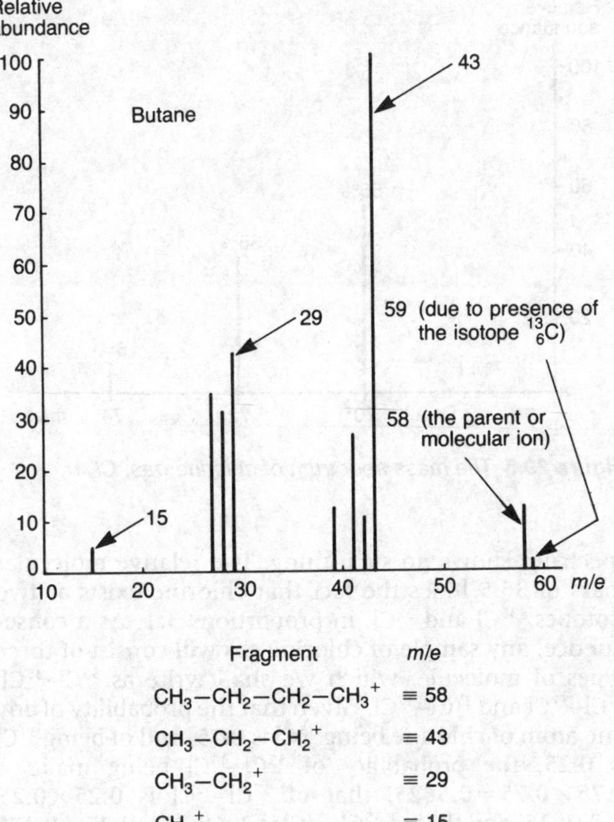

***Figure 29.4** Mass spectrum of butane. Note that the most abundant ion, at m/e = 43, is given a relative abundance of 100. The abundances of the other ions are compared with this ion*

spectrum is called a *fragmentation pattern*. Figure 29.4 shows the mass spectrum of butane, C_4H_{10}. The peak with the highest mass comes at 58. This corresponds to the *parent* or *molecular ion*, $C_4H_{10}{}^+$. You can see that this is not the most abundant ion: many of the other peaks are higher. This means that most of the $C_4H_{10}{}^+$ ions that emerge from the electron gun fall apart before they reach the detector.

If we look at the structure of butane, there are some fairly obvious places where the molecule might break apart. Especially, if an end CH_3 group is lost, this will leave $C_3H_7{}^+$ behind. This produces the peak at mass 43. Similarly, if the molecule breaks in two, we will obtain a peak at mass 29 corresponding to $C_2H_5{}^+$. The peak at mass 15 is due to $CH_3{}^+$ ions. Other peaks appear owing to the loss of hydrogen atoms, and the presence of isotopes. A further complication occurs in some spectra because the atoms change their positions during the passage of the ions through the spectrometer. This causes peaks to appear at *m/e* values that seem not to fit the original structure.

29.7 The effect of isotopes in a molecule's mass spectrum

There are always more lines in a mass spectrum of a molecule than we might expect merely by looking at places where the molecule might fall apart. One cause of this is the presence of isotopes. For example, although ^{12}C is by far the most common isotope of carbon (almost 99%), there is always 1.1% of ^{13}C. So, for every peak produced by a fragment with ^{12}C there will be another,

Panel 29.1

How the isotope ^{13}C affects the mass spectrum of a carbon compound

To understand this panel, you need to remember that experiment shows that for every 100 ^{12}C atoms, on average there are 1.1 ^{13}C atoms.

In methane, CH_4, because there is only one carbon atom, we would expect the ratio of $^{12}CH_4$ to $^{13}CH_4$ to be 100 to 1.1. For ethane, C_2H_6, there are four possibilities: $^{12}CH_3{}^{12}CH_3$, $^{13}CH_3{}^{12}CH_3$, $^{12}CH_3{}^{13}CH_3$ and $^{13}CH_3{}^{13}CH_3$. The chances of finding a molecule of ethane containing two ^{13}C atoms is so remote that we can ignore it. You can see that there are two chances of obtaining an ethane molecule with one ^{13}C in it. Thus for every 100 $^{12}CH_3{}^{12}CH_3$ molecules, there should be 2.2 molecules containing a mix of the two isotopes. We can show the pattern in this way:

			Ratio
Methane, CH_4 1 carbon atom	$^{12}CH_4$	$^{13}CH_4$	100 to 1.1
Ethane, C_2H_6 2 carbon atoms	$^{12}CH_3{}^{12}CH_3$	$^{13}CH_3{}^{12}CH_3$ $^{12}CH_3{}^{13}CH_3$	100 to 2.2
Butane, C_3H_8 3 carbon atoms	$^{12}CH_3{}^{12}CH_2{}^{12}CH_3$	$^{13}CH_3{}^{12}CH_2{}^{12}CH_3$ $^{12}CH_3{}^{13}CH_2{}^{12}CH_3$ $^{12}CH_3{}^{12}CH_2{}^{13}CH_3$	100 to 3.3
In general, *n* carbon atoms			100 to *n* × 1.1

less intense, peak due to ^{13}C. In the spectrum of butane the parent ion occurs at $m/e = 58$. The smaller peak at $m/e = 59$ is due to the presence of ^{13}C. If you study panel 29.1 you should discover the reason why, in a compound containing n carbon atoms, the ratio of the abundance of the ^{12}C parent ion compared to the abundance of an ion with a mix of ^{12}C and ^{13}C is 100 to $n \times 1.1$. If we call the parent ion peak M and the peak that follows it $M+1$, we have

$$\frac{\text{relative abundance of } M}{\text{relative abundance of } M+1} = \frac{100}{n \times 1.1}$$

For butane, the relative abundances of peaks M and $M+1$ is approximately 24 to 1. Therefore,

$$\frac{24}{1} = \frac{100}{n \times 1.1}$$

Rearranging,

$$n = \frac{100}{24 \times 1.1} = 3.8$$

Of course, n must be a whole number, so we put $n = 4$, which agrees with the formula of butane, C_4H_{10}.

This method of comparing the abundances of M and $M+1$ peaks is a relatively simple way of discovering how many carbon atoms there are in a molecule. In fact, matters are usually more complicated than this because the other atoms in a molecule may have isotopes as well.

To see this happening in a simple case, look at the mass spectrum of a sample of chlorine gas, Cl_2, shown in Figure 29.5. Given that the relative molecular mass of chlorine is listed as 35.5, we might expect a single peak corresponding to Cl_2^+ at mass 71. Of course the actual

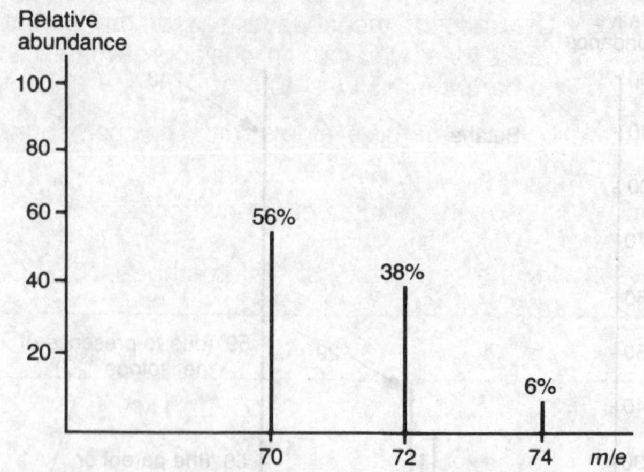

Figure 29.5 *The mass spectrum of chlorine gas, Cl_2*

spectrum shows no such thing. The relative molecular mass of 35.5 hides the fact that chlorine exists as two isotopes, ^{35}Cl and ^{37}Cl, in proportions 3:1. As a consequence, any sample of chlorine gas will consist of three types of molecule, which we shall write as $^{35}Cl{-}^{35}Cl$, $^{35}Cl{-}^{37}Cl$ and $^{37}Cl{-}^{37}Cl$. Given that the probability of any one atom of chlorine being ^{35}Cl is 0.75, and of being ^{37}Cl is 0.25, the probability of $^{35}Cl{-}^{35}Cl$ being made is $0.75 \times 0.75 = 0.5625$, that of $^{37}Cl{-}^{37}Cl$ is $0.25 \times 0.25 = 0.0625$, and that of $^{35}Cl{-}^{37}Cl$ is $2 \times 0.75 \times 0.25 = 0.375$ ($^{35}Cl{-}^{37}Cl$ is the same as $^{37}Cl{-}^{35}Cl$, hence the factor of 2). The peaks in the mass spectrum of chlorine show the expected three peaks at masses 70, 72 and 74, with relative intensities roughly in the ratio 9:6:1.

29.1 Use the mass spectra shown in Figure 29.3 to calculate the relative atomic masses of strontium and iron.

29.2 At one time it was thought that the elements in the Periodic Table were in the order of their relative atomic masses. Unfortunately for this theory, potassium, which has a relative atomic mass of 39.1, comes after argon, which has a value 39.9.

(i) The two main isotopes of potassium are ^{39}K and ^{41}K. Which isotope is the more abundant? What are the proportions of each isotope in a sample of potassium?

(ii) There are three isotopes of argon, ^{36}Ar, ^{38}Ar and ^{40}Ar. Which of these is the most abundant?

29.3 In the change $^{87}_{37}Rb \rightarrow ^{87}_{38}Sr + ^{0}_{-1}e$, what is the underlying change that takes place in the nucleus?

29.4 Cobalt comes before nickel in the Periodic Table even though their relative atomic masses are in reverse order (58.9 compared to 58.7). Briefly suggest how this comes about.

29.5 Suggest the formulae of the fragments that give rise to the marked peaks in the spectrum of ethanol, C_2H_5OH (see Figure 29.6).

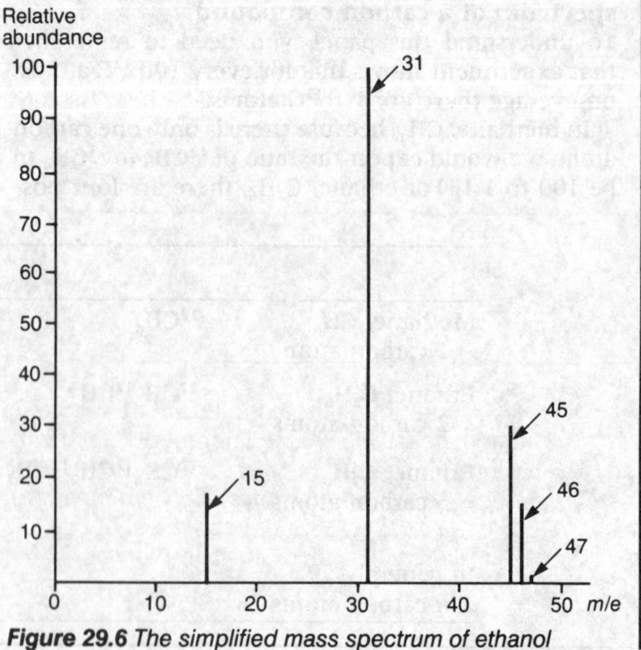

Figure 29.6 *The simplified mass spectrum of ethanol*

29.6 The ratio of the abundances of the M and $M+1$ peaks for a hydrocarbon was approximately 11 to 1. The parent mass was 106.

(i) How many carbon atoms did the compound contain?

(ii) What was the formula of the hydrocarbon?

29.7 In the spectrum of chloroethane, C_2H_5Cl, explain why there is a peak at $m/e = 64$, and a following one at $m/e = 66$ that is only about one-third as intense.

29.8 (i) Is it always true that the parent ion has the highest m/e ratio?

(ii) Does the parent ion always give the most intense peak?

Answers

29.1 For strontium, the relative atomic mass is

$$84 \times \frac{0.56}{100} + 86 \times \frac{9.86}{100} + 87 \times \frac{7.02}{100} + 88 \times \frac{82.56}{100} = 87.71$$

For iron, the relative atomic mass is

$$54 \times \frac{5.84}{100} + 56 \times \frac{91.68}{100} + 57 \times \frac{2.17}{100} + 58 \times \frac{0.31}{100} = 55.91$$

29.2 (i) If there were 50% of ^{39}K and 50% of ^{41}K, the relative atomic mass would be exactly 40. However, the average (39.1) is much less than 40, so there must be more than 50% of the ^{39}K. If we call P the percentage of ^{39}K, then in a sample of 100 atoms of potassium there will be $100 - P$ atoms of ^{41}K. Therefore we must have

$$39 \times \frac{P}{100} + 41 \times \frac{100 - P}{100} = 39.1$$

If you solve this equation you will find that $P = 95\%$. The actual values are 93.08% ^{39}K, 6.91% ^{41}K (there is also 0.012% of ^{40}K).

(ii) If the average of all the isotopes comes out to 39.9, then there must be a great deal of ^{40}Ar, and not very much of the others. (The actual figures are 0.337% ^{36}Ar, 0.063% ^{38}Ar, 99.600% ^{40}Ar.)

29.3 The mass number does not change, but the atomic number increases by one. So the change is $^{1}_{0}n \rightarrow {}^{1}_{1}p + {}^{0}_{-1}e$.

29.4 The reason is that cobalt has a fairly heavy isotope that brings its relative atomic mass up above that of nickel. Actually, cobalt has just one isotope, $^{59}_{27}Co$. Nickel has five, the most abundant (67.76%) of which is $^{58}_{28}Ni$.

29.5 The structure of ethanol is

```
   H   H
   |   |
H—C — C — O — H
   |   |
   H   H
```

The dashed lines represent the places where the molecule might split apart.

m/e	*Explanation*
15	Methyl group, CH_3^+
29	Ethyl group, $CH_3CH_2^+$
31	Fragment left after methyl group is lost, CH_2OH^+
45	$CH_3CH_2O^+$
46	The parent ion, $CH_3CH_2OH^+$
47	Ions containing ^{13}C as well as ^{12}C

29.6 (i) We have

$$\frac{11}{1} = \frac{100}{n \times 1.1} \qquad n = \frac{100}{11 \times 1.1}$$

and so $n = 8$ (to the nearest whole number).

(ii) Eight carbon atoms contribute $8 \times 12 = 96$ units of mass. This leaves 10 units for the hydrogen atoms. The formula is C_8H_{10}.

29.7 One peak at mass 64 corresponds to a parent ion containing ^{35}Cl; the other contains ^{37}Cl. The intensities are about 3:1 as we should expect because ^{35}Cl is three times more abundant than ^{37}Cl.

29.8 (i), (ii) No, in both cases.

UNIT 29 SUMMARY

- Mass spectrometers split a molecule into a large number of positively charged fragments, each with a particular charge to mass ratio (q/m). The fragments are separated by passing them through a combination of electric and magnetic fields. As the ions are detected, a fragmentation pattern is built up.
- The ion with the greatest q/m value is the parent ion. It tells us the relative molecular mass of the original molecule.
- The fragmentation pattern of an element displays the isotopes, and permits the relative atomic mass to be calculated.

30

X-ray diffraction

30.1 What causes X-ray diffraction?

X-rays are a variety of electromagnetic radiation with fairly high energies. The wavelength of X-rays is of the order 100 pm (10^{-10} m). They show the normal properties of waves; especially, they can be *diffracted*. Diffraction occurs whenever a wave meets a barrier with one or more openings that are about the same size as the wavelength. It so happens that the layers of atoms or ions in crystals are separated by distances around 100 or 200 pm. This is just the right range to cause X-rays to be diffracted. Thus, we can say that:

The layers of atoms in a crystal act as a diffraction grating for X-rays.

The reason why atoms are able to produce diffraction patterns has much to do with the number of electrons they contain. The electric field of the X-rays interacts with the cloud of electrons around an atom. The result of many thousands of the interactions produces the diffraction pattern. Large atoms have many electrons. These atoms produce the strongest patterns. Small atoms, like hydrogen, may have so few electrons that they have little effect on X-rays.

30.2 More about diffraction

Before we go into more detail about X-ray diffraction, it is important that you understand some basic ideas about diffraction in general (Figure 30.1).

If light is passed through a row of slits (known as a diffraction grating), the diffraction pattern can be captured on a photograph. By using sophisticated equipment it is possible to measure the amount of blackening of the film. This tells us the intensity of the light falling on various parts of the film. Alternatively the intensity can be measured electronically, without photographs.

As with water waves, the diffracted light waves reinforce one another provided the difference in the distances they travel is a whole number of wavelengths. If their paths are different by more or less than a wavelength, then the waves will tend to cancel out, as shown in Figure 30.2. With this background, you should be able to understand the diagram in Figure 30.3.

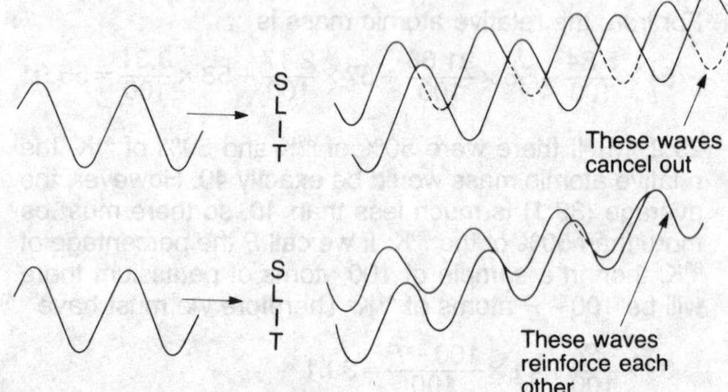

Figure 30.1 After waves pass through a narrow slit there are places where they reinforce and places where they cancel out. The overall pattern is a diffraction pattern

In the diagrams X-rays are shown encountering atoms in a layer of a crystal. The waves have their crests and troughs matching; they will reinforce constructively and give a patch of high intensity on a photographic film. We have already said that this happens if the distances that the waves travel differ by a whole number of wavelengths, λ. We shall call this whole number n. Thus, constructive interference occurs when

$$\text{path difference} = n\lambda$$

Now, if you look at Figure 30.3 you will find that

$$\text{path difference in crystal} = x \sin A$$

Thus we find

$$n\lambda = x \sin A$$

However, crystals contain many planes of atoms, which criss-cross in three dimensions, and we have only dealt with diffraction in one of these dimensions. In a real diffraction experiment not just one but three equations must be satisfied before a spot would be seen on a photographic film.

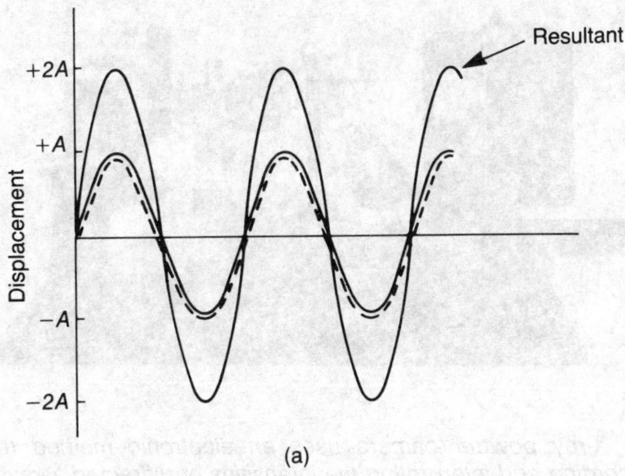

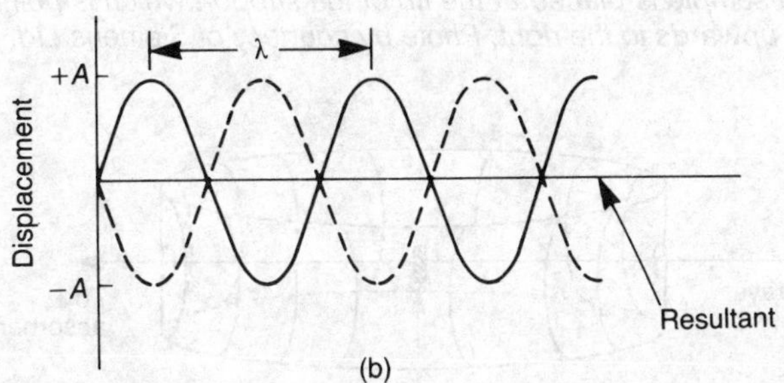

Figure 30.2 *Two ways in which waves can overlap with one another. (a) Two waves that have equal amplitude, A, and are completely in phase interfere completely constructively. (b) Two waves that have the same amplitude, A, and are completely out of phase give a resultant of zero amplitude. There is complete destructive interference*

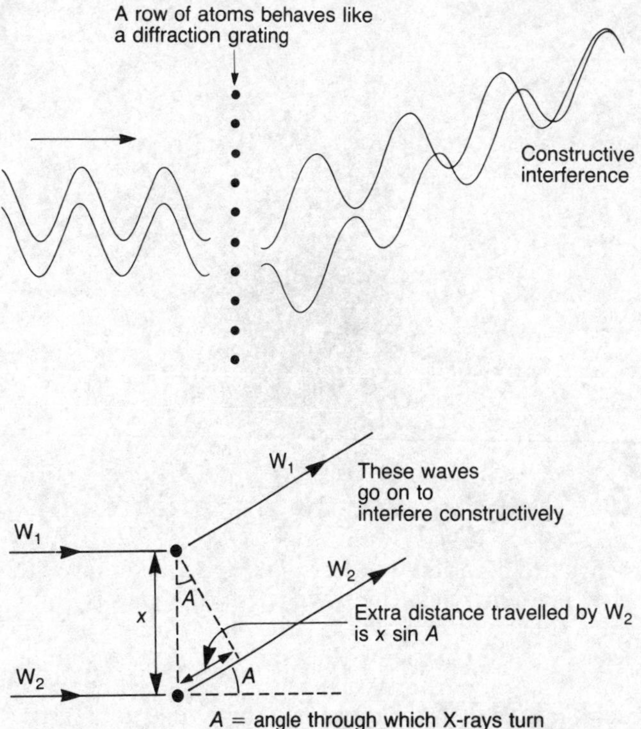

Figure 30.3 *The lower diagram is an expanded view of the upper diagram. For constructive interference, the extra distance travelled by wave W_2 must be a whole number of wavelengths, i.e. $n\lambda = x \sin A$*

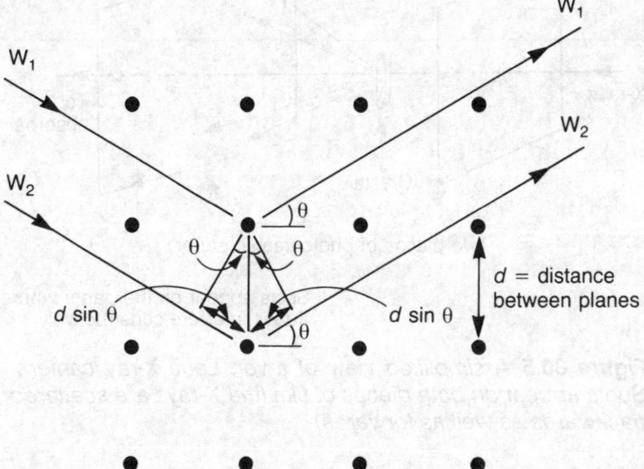

Figure 30.4 *The extra distance travelled by wave W_2 is $2 \times d \sin\theta$, i.e. $2d \sin\theta$. For constructive interference, $n\lambda = 2d \sin\theta$*

30.3 Bragg's equation

An alternative theory of X-ray diffraction was published in 1912 by Sir (William) Lawrence Bragg. He worked closely with his father, Sir William Henry Bragg, and both received the Nobel Prize for their work in using X-rays to discover the structures of crystals.

Bragg (the younger) proposed that the formation of diffraction patterns could be explained by assuming that the X-rays were *reflected* from the various planes of atoms in a crystal. (It is possible to show that the diffraction and reflection explanations are equivalent to one another. Most people find Bragg's explanation easier to work with.)

If you look at Figure 30.4 you will see that the difference in the distance travelled by rays bouncing off two different planes is $2d \sin\theta$. For constructive interference then we must have

$$n\lambda = 2d \sin\theta \qquad \text{Bragg's equation}$$

If $n = 1$ we say that a first-order reflection occurs; if $n = 2$ then we have a second-order reflection; and so on. Normally it is only necessary to bother with first-order reflections.

30.4 Different types of X-ray diffraction experiment

The first X-ray diffraction experiments were performed at the suggestion of von Laue in 1912. X-rays were produced by bombarding zinc sulphide with high energy electrons. The X-rays were passed through a single crystal (Figure 30.5).

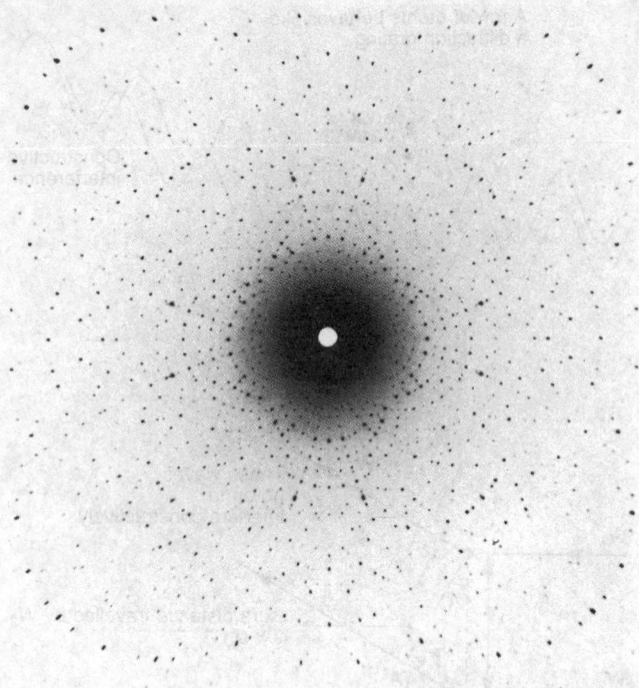

A von Laue diffraction pattern of the mineral vesuvianite. Taken from Figure 8.31 of D. McKie and C. McKie, Essentials of Crystallography, *Blackwell, Oxford, 1986.*

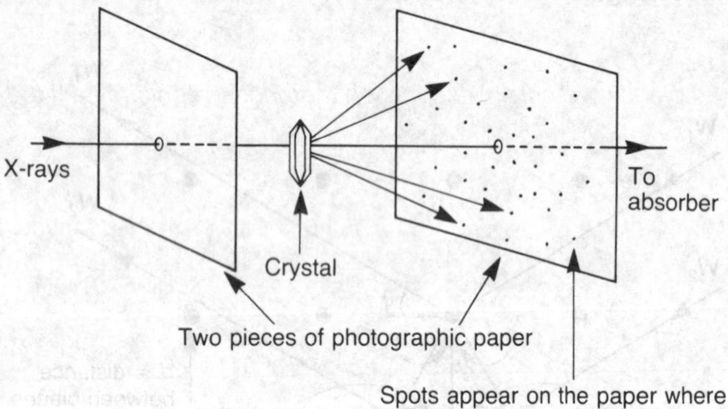

***Figure 30.5** A simplified view of a von Laue X-ray camera. Spots appear on both pieces of film (the X-rays are scattered backwards as well as forwards)*

As you may imagine, life becomes rather complicated if you attempt to work backwards from a von Laue pattern to the spacing of the atoms and planes in the crystal. In fact people soon tired of making the attempt and different methods were invented. Of these, that known as the *powder method* is widely used. It was first used by P. Debye and P. Scherrer in 1916. Crystals of the sample to be investigated are ground to a fine powder and placed in a tube made of glass, which has little effect on X-rays. The sample is surrounded by a cylindrical sheet of photographic paper (Figure 30.6). X-rays enter through a small hole in the cylinder, and pass into the sample, where diffraction occurs. Opposite to the entrance hole is

An X-ray powder camera uses an electronic method for recording and interpreting the intensities of diffracted X-rays. The X-ray source is on the right, and the analyser on the left. The sample is placed at the tip of the support which is pointing upwards to the right. Photo by courtesy of Siemens Ltd.

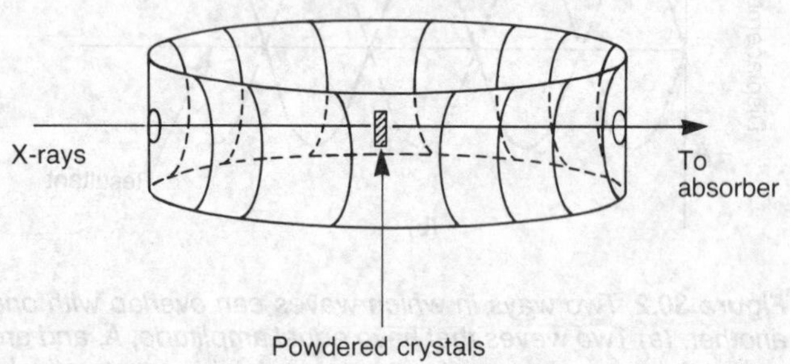

***Figure 30.6** In a powder camera the photographic plate is placed in a circular strip. The powdered crystals are at the centre. The reflections of the X-rays produce curved lines on the paper*

a piece of lead, which absorbs any X-rays that pass right through the sample.

At first sight it might seem odd to change a relatively large single crystal for a fine powder. You might expect the film to be covered in even more spots than von Laue photographs; and in a way it is, but the spots are collected in bands like those shown in the photo.

30.5 Explanation of powder photographs

Now let us think about what is happening in a powder experiment. In Figure 30.7a you can see a diagram representing one set of planes in a crystal. The separation between the planes is *d*, and the planes are shown at an angle to the incoming X-rays. In Figure 30.7b are shown the same set of planes, but they slope at a different angle. Again the planes are at the angle θ necessary to give reinforcement, and a spot on the photographic film. The key thing to understand is that if the planes are *not* at the angle θ to the incoming beam then no spot will appear on the film due to *this* set of planes (Figure 30.7c). In the

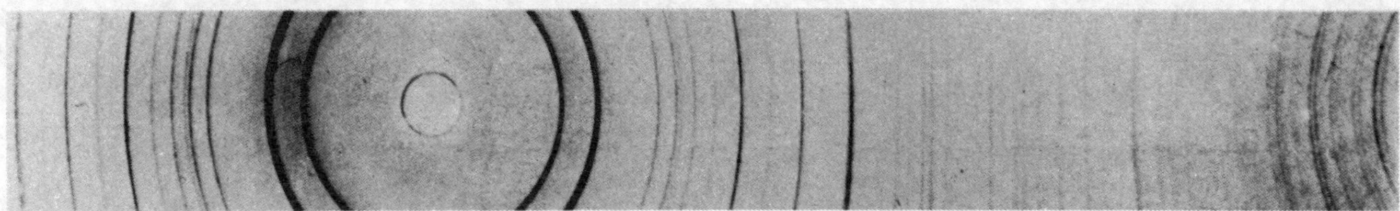

An X-ray powder photograph of quartz. Adapted from Figure 13.3 of J. P. Glusker and K. N. Trueblood, Crystal Structure Analysis, *Oxford University Press, Oxford, 1985.*

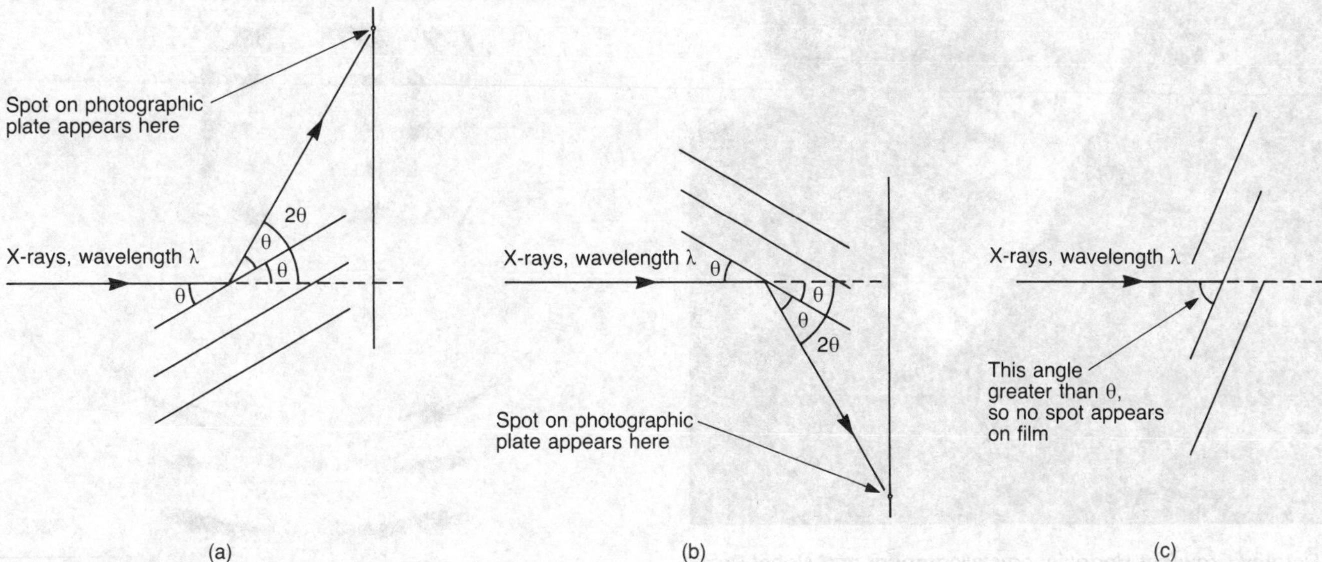

***Figure 30.7** For a given wavelength of X-rays, the same set of crystal planes will only give spots on the photographic plate if the planes make an angle θ to the X-rays*

powdered sample there are so many tens of thousands of tiny crystals that there will always be some of them with the set of planes at the angle θ to the incoming X-rays. With some thought you should be able to understand that diffractions from crystals with their sets of planes at angle θ will be arranged in a cone as shown in Figure 30.8. Because the photographic film is in the shape of a cylinder, the reflections from the crystals produce a set of curved patterns on the film.

30.6 The arrangement of planes in crystals

The first piece of information that we can gain from an X-ray powder photograph is the distance between a set of planes in a crystal. The detail of the way this is done need not concern us. However, you can get a flavour of how the distance is worked out in this way. From the powder photograph the angle θ can be measured. For sodium chloride, using X-rays of wavelength 1.54×10^{-8} cm, an intense cone is formed at $\theta = 15.87°$. Taking this as a first-order reflection we have

$$1.54 \times 10^{-8}\,\text{cm} = 2d\sin(15.87°)$$

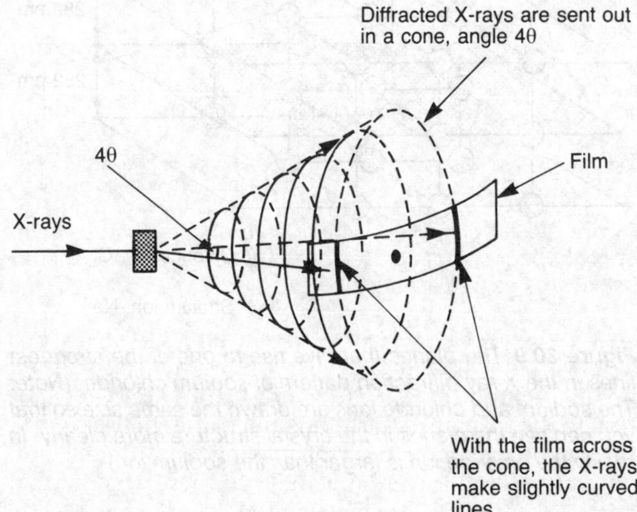

***Figure 30.8** The reason why lines on a powder photograph are curved*

so

$$d = \frac{1.54 \times 10^{-8}\,\text{cm}}{2\sin(15.87°)} = 2.82 \times 10^{-8}\,\text{cm or } 282\,\text{pm}$$

Dorothy Crowfoot Hodgkin, crystallographer and Nobel Prize winner for determining the structure of vitamin B12.

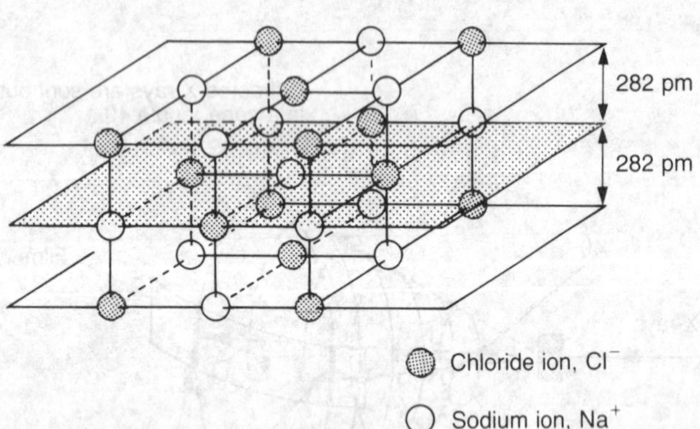

Figure 30.9 *The planes that give rise to one of the strongest lines in the X-ray diffraction pattern of sodium chloride. (Note: The sodium and chloride ions are drawn the same size so that you can see the planes in the crystal structure more clearly. In reality the chloride ion is larger than the sodium ion)*

The planes that produce the cone at 15.87° are shown in Figure 30.9.

This example is a fairly easy one. In order to interpret all the cones in the X-ray photograph we would have to take account of many other planes through the crystal. Also, the ability of sodium and chloride ions to scatter electrons is not the same. Sometimes the rays scattered by the sodium ions are cancelled out by those from the chloride ions; sometimes they reinforce.

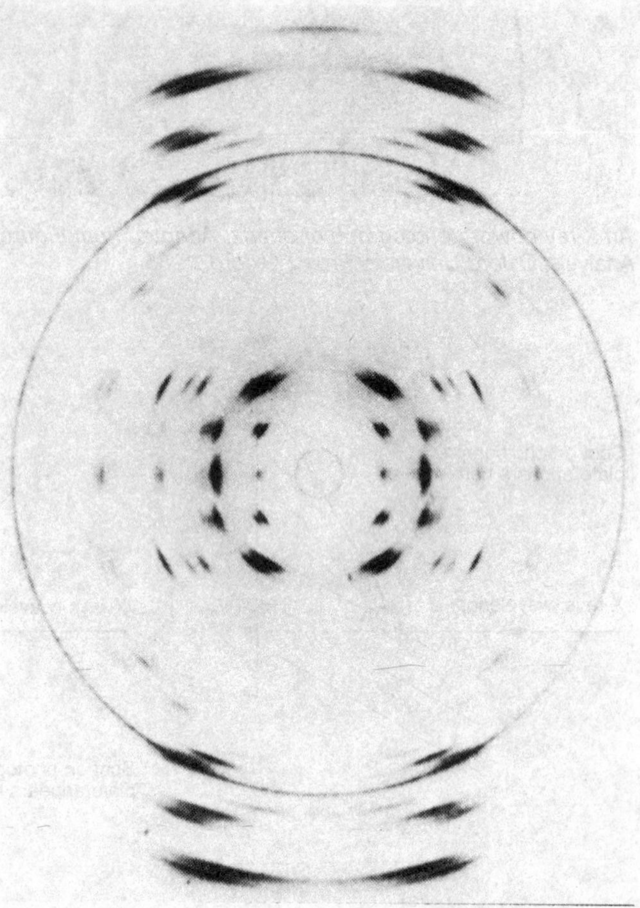

An X-ray diffraction pattern from a fibre of DNA. The pattern of spots is characteristic of helical structures. (The continuous circle is not due to DNA, but to a salt impurity.) Taken from Figure 13.2 of J. P. Glusker and K. N. Trueblood, Crystal Structure Analysis, *Oxford University Press, Oxford, 1985.*

> **30.1** The X-ray powder pattern of potassium chloride shows a cone at $\theta = 14.38°$ using X-rays of wavelength 1.54×10^{-8} cm. What is the spacing between the planes?

30.7 The arrangements of individual atoms

Hidden within the spots on an X-ray photograph is information about the intensity of the different reflections. We have already said that the greater the number of electrons in an atom, the stronger is the diffraction, or reflection. If the intensities of the individual spots can be compared accurately, then it is possible to link them to the nature of the electron cloud around the atoms. For this accurate work a machine called a *diffractometer* is used. The intensities of the various reflections are measured directly by electronic means rather than by photographs. By analysing the results using a computer, electron density maps can be produced.

The outcome of the maps is a series of contour lines, which show contours of electron density. Some examples are shown in the photo. Question 30.2 asks you to make sense of one of these maps.

We have seen that a knowledge of how X-rays interact with crystals is a powerful tool, which can be used to discover the structures of crystals. The Bragg equation plays a very important part in this process. X-ray diffraction patterns can also be used to work out the arrangements of electrons around atoms. This provides us with good evidence about the shapes of molecules. If you go on to study chemistry further you will find that several other types of diffraction experiments are used in addition to X-ray diffraction. Electrons can be used because they show wave-like properties (remember de Broglie's relation). Sometimes electron diffraction experiments are done on gases rather than solid samples. Neutrons, too, can be diffracted. However, the reason why they are diffracted is different to that of X-rays or electrons. Neutrons have a magnetic moment; that is, they behave like tiny magnets. In common with electrons they show the property we call spin. If the atoms in a crystal also have a magnetic moment then the neutrons can be scattered by the atoms, and a diffraction pattern is produced.

In the next unit we turn to a more detailed study of crystals. That is, we shall make a study of the science, and art, of crystallography.

30.2 Look at Figure 30.10. It shows the lines of electron density for part of a crystal of an organic molecule that contains carbon, hydrogen, nitrogen and oxygen atoms. (Remember that the hydrogen atoms do not show up on the pattern.) Its molecular formula is $C_6H_4N_2O_4$. Look closely at the pattern and indicate how the atoms are arranged. Draw a diagram, or make a model, of it.

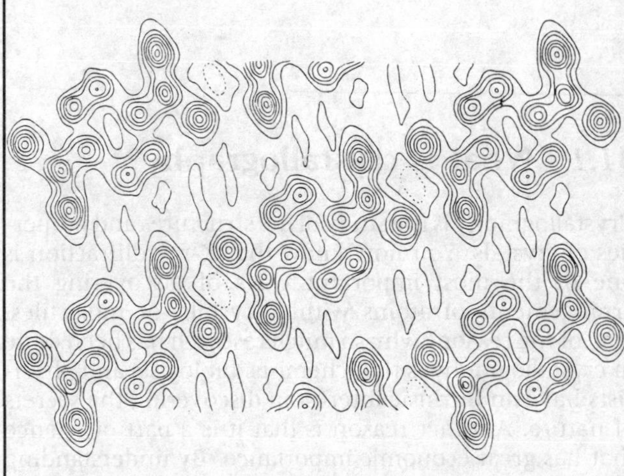

***Figure 30.10** An electron density map. (Calculated from X-ray data by: James, R. W., King, G. and Horrocks, H. (1936).* Proc. R. Soc. **153**, *225)*

Answers

30.1 Using Bragg's equation, we have

$$d = \frac{1.54 \times 10^{-8}\,\text{cm}}{2 \times \sin(14.38°)}$$

This gives $d = 3.10 \times 10^{-8}$ cm or 310 pm.

30.2 The molecule is 1,4-dinitrobenzene:

O_2N—(benzene ring)—NO_2

This structure was first established in 1935. Notice that the lines are closest at the oxygen atoms. This confirms that electron density is high at these atoms.

```
          C—C
 O       /   \       O
  \N—C         C—N/
 O/     \   /     \O
          C—C
```

Not all bonds, or hydrogen atoms, are shown.

UNIT 30 SUMMARY

- X-rays are diffracted from the layers of atoms or ions in a crystal according to Bragg's equation $n\lambda = 2d \sin \theta$.
- The diffraction pattern can be measured using single crystals or a powder.
- The intensity of the spots on an X-ray diffraction photograph depends on the electron densities of the atoms or ions. By analysing the intensities, it is possible to build up an electron density map of an entire molecule.

31 Crystallography

31.1 What is crystallography?

Crystallography is the study of the structures and properties of crystals. You now know that X-ray diffraction is one of the most important ways of discovering the arrangements of atoms within crystals, or molecules. One of the reasons why so much research has been done in crystallography is that chemists, biologists and physicists have an intrinsic interest in discovering the secrets of nature. Another reason is that it is a part of science that has great economic importance. By understanding the way atoms pack together in a crystal, we can design alloys and other materials to have specific properties.

In this unit we are going to summarise work that has been done on crystals of many types in the last 70 years. If it is at all possible, use models to help you visualise the three-dimensional structures that you see here in two dimensions on the page. There is no substitute for handling models of crystal structures if you are to gain a real understanding of them.

31.2 The closest packing of atoms

To begin with we shall think about crystals being built from one kind of atom only. We shall represent an atom by a ball. (In model making, polystyrene balls are very useful; marbles will do but they are not so good.) If you pack a number of balls closely together, you will find that they are most likely to line up as shown in Figure 31.1. Here, except at the edges, there are always six balls arranged in the shape of a hexagon around a ball in the centre of the hexagon. This type of packing is called *hexagonal close packing*. It is impossible to squeeze a greater number of balls into the same area. We can imagine a layer like this being made as the first step when real atoms come together to make a crystal.

If we imagine more atoms beginning to cling to the first layer they will drop into the small gaps where atoms in the first layer meet (Figure 31.2). Now we can place a third layer on top. However, there are two ways of doing this. Either the atoms in the third layer can fit so that they are directly above the first layer, or they can go on so that they are only partly above the first layer. In the first case the layers build up in pairs, usually known as the ABAB... structure (Figure 31.2). Here the third layer is directly above the first, the fourth directly above the second. The alternative structure is called ABCABC... (Figure 31.3). Here the pattern repeats every fourth layer; the fourth is above the first, the fifth above the second, the sixth above the third, and so on.

The three-dimensional arrangement of the atoms is called a *lattice*. In both lattices the layers are close-packed: there is the minimum amount of free space in

Figure 31.1 *Hexagonal close packing*

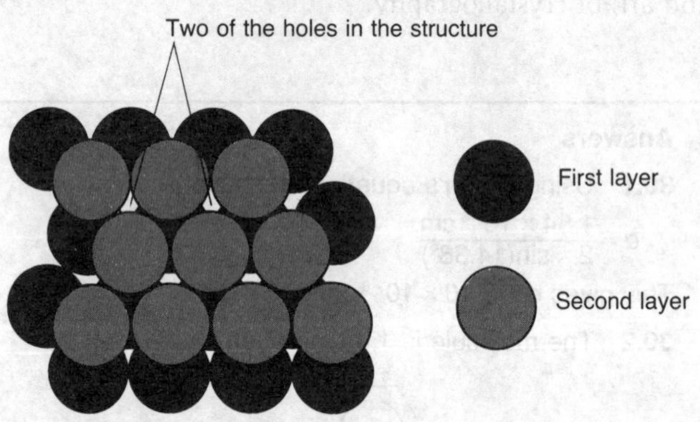

Figure 31.2 *The ABAB... pattern of packing hexagonal close-packed layers. The third layer goes directly over the first layer, the fourth over the second, and so on. The holes are never covered up*

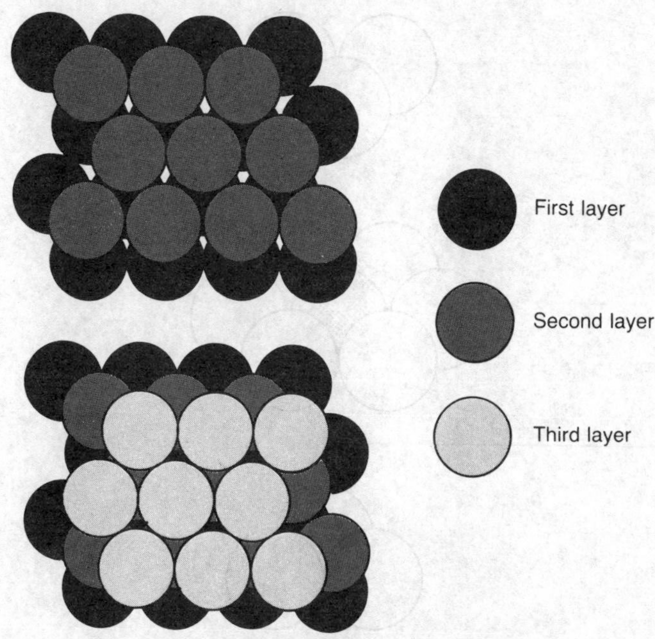

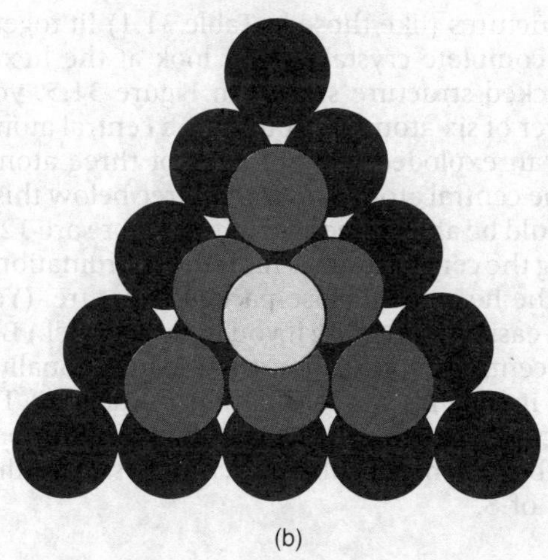
(b)

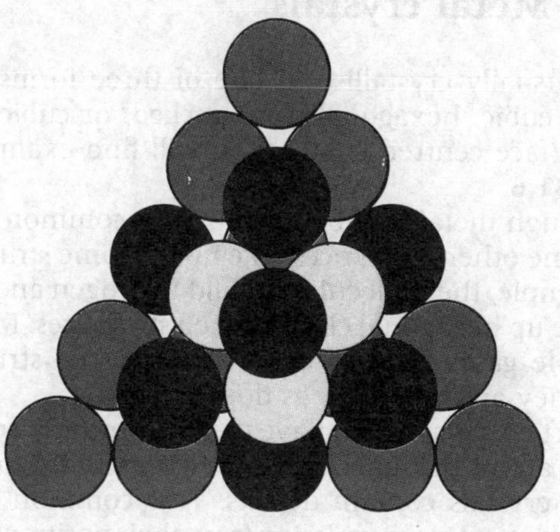
(c)

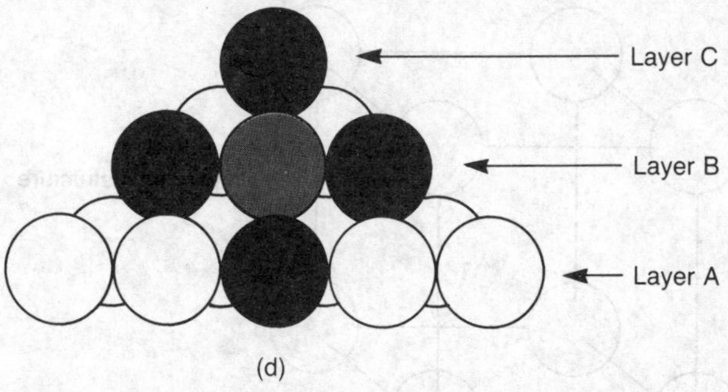

Figure 31.3 *(a) The ABCABC... pattern of packing hexagonal close-packed layers. Notice that the third layer covers up the holes left by the first two layers. (b)–(d) Three views of ABCABC... packing: (b) The ABCABC... cubic close-packed structure. It is not immediately obvious that this structure consists of interlocked face centred cubes. (c) Top view of the ABCABC... cubic close-packed structure. One of the face centred cubes is highlighted. (d) Another view of the same face centred cube. Notice that the sides of the cube are not parallel to the ABC planes*

the lattice (a little over 74% is used up by the atoms). However, as we have seen, there is a difference in the way the layers are arranged, and there are two names used to describe them.

> **The ABAB... structure is called *hexagonal close packing* (h.c.p.).**
>
> **The ABCABC... structure is called *cubic close packing* (c.c.p.).**

If you look at Figures 31.3c and d you should be able to understand the connection between the ABCABC... structure and cubic close packing. There are two views of the structure in which spheres at the corners and faces of a cube have been highlighted. One view looks from the side and one from the top. We can think of the entire structure as being built from combinations of such cubes. The presence of the spheres at the centres of the faces of each cube gives this structure the alternative name of *face centred cubic*. Unlike a body centred cube (see below), there is no room for a sphere at the centre of a face-centred cube.

You may find it useful to look at Table 31.1, which

Table 31.1. Two types of closest packing of spheres

Hexagonal close-packed layers		*Non-close-packed layers*	
ABAB... structure	ABCABC... structure	Simple cubic	Body centred cubic
Coord. no. 12	Coord. no. 12	Coord. no. 6	Coord. no. 8
Known as: hexagonal close packing, h.c.p.	Known as: cubic close packing, c.c.p., or face centred cubic, f.c.c.		

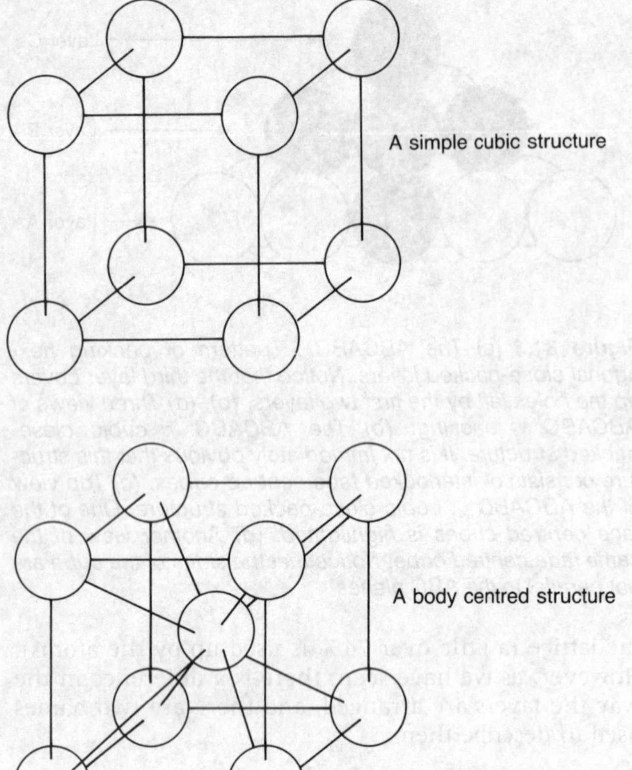

Figure 31.4 *Two structures that are not close-packed. (Note: The atoms are drawn spread apart so that you can see the structure more clearly. In practice the atoms will fit much more closely together)*

summarises the naming systems we have used so far, and those in the next section.

31.3 Structures that are not close-packed

A simple structure that is not close-packed is shown in Figure 31.4. Here atoms are placed in a square arrangement in each layer. A common way of building up a three-dimensional structure is for an atom to be at the centre of a cube. This is called *body centred cubic* packing. In this structure about 68% of the space is filled by the atoms. An even simpler form of cubic packing, called *simple cubic*, is also shown. This has atoms at the eight corners of a cube. This lattice is very far from being close-packed. Only about 52% of the space is filled by the atoms.

31.4 Coordination numbers

The *coordination number* of an atom in a lattice is the *number of its nearest neighbours*. In order to work out the coordination number you have to know the way the

Figure 31.5 *An exploded view of a hexagonal close-packed structure. Twelve atoms will touch the central atom*

basic structures (like those in Table 31.1) fit together to make a complete crystal. If you look at the hexagonal close-packed structure shown in Figure 31.5, you will see a layer of six atoms surrounding a central atom. Also there is an exploded view of a set of three atoms that touch the central atom above and three below this layer. You should be able to see that in total there are 12 atoms touching the central atom. This is the coordination number for the hexagonal close-packed structure. (You will find this easier to visualise if you build a model.) Because the face centred cubic structure is also hexagonally close-packed, it too has a coordination number of 12. The simple cubic structure has a coordination number of 6, and the body centred cubic structure has a coordination number of 8.

31.5 Metal crystals

Metals usually crystallise in one of three forms: body centred cubic, hexagonal close-packed, or cubic close-packed (face centred cubic). You will find examples in Figure 31.6.

Although metals are by far the most common examples, some other substances take up the same structures. For example, the molecules in solid hydrogen and nitrogen take up hexagonal close-packed structures. Many of the noble gases exist as cubic close-packed structures when they are solidified, as does methane.

Perfect crystals, which have the same orderly arrangement of atoms throughout the lattice, are hard to make. Usually crystals contain defects. Two common defects occur when atoms are missing from their positions in the lattice, or when extra atoms become trapped, causing the

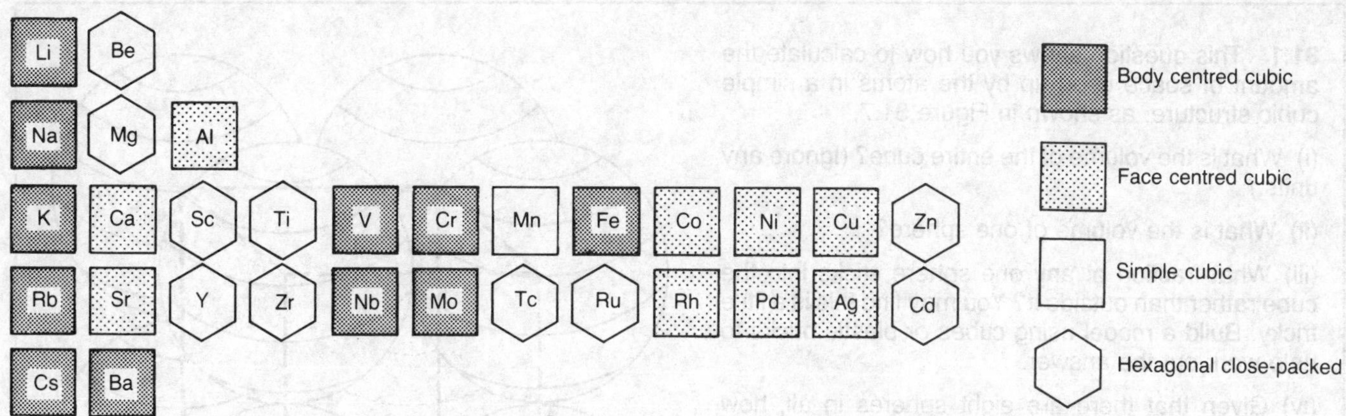

Figure 31.6 *The crystal structures of some metals at room temperature and pressure*

symmetry of the lattice to change. The photo illustrates the types of change that can happen.

A third defect that is often found is produced when atoms of an impurity are trapped in the lattice. Annoying as this might seem, it can be most useful. Indeed, in many industrial processes, impurities are added deliberately because they can radically change the properties of a metal. Perfect crystals often suffer from the layers sliding over one another. This can happen gradually, e.g. in the stretching of a metal wire, or suddenly, e.g. if cast iron is dropped and shatters. If impurity atoms find sites where they can fit into the lattice, it can become much harder for the layers to slide over one another.

Alloys are mixtures of metals that generally have properties very different to those of the pure metals. You will find details about alloys in Unit 105.

Rafts of soap bubbles produced by Sir Lawrence Bragg in 1947. The photographs give a good idea of how atoms might pack together in layers. Notice that in the second and third pictures the packing is not perfect. Defects just like these occur in real crystals. You will see the defect in the second picture more easily if you bring you eyes parallel to the plane of the paper rather than looking vertically down. Source: Sir Lawrence Bragg and J. F. Nye, Proc. Roy. Soc. *190A, 474–82, 1947.*

31.1 This question shows you how to calculate the amount of space used up by the atoms in a simple cubic structure, as shown in Figure 31.7.

(i) What is the volume of the entire cube? (Ignore any units.)

(ii) What is the volume of one sphere?

(iii) What fraction of any one sphere sticks into the cube rather than outside it? You may find this is a little tricky. Build a model using cubes or plastic bricks to help work out the answer.

(iv) Given that there are eight spheres in all, how much space do they take up *in the cube*?

(v) Combine your answers to (i) and (iv) to calculate the percentage of the space in the cube used by the spheres.

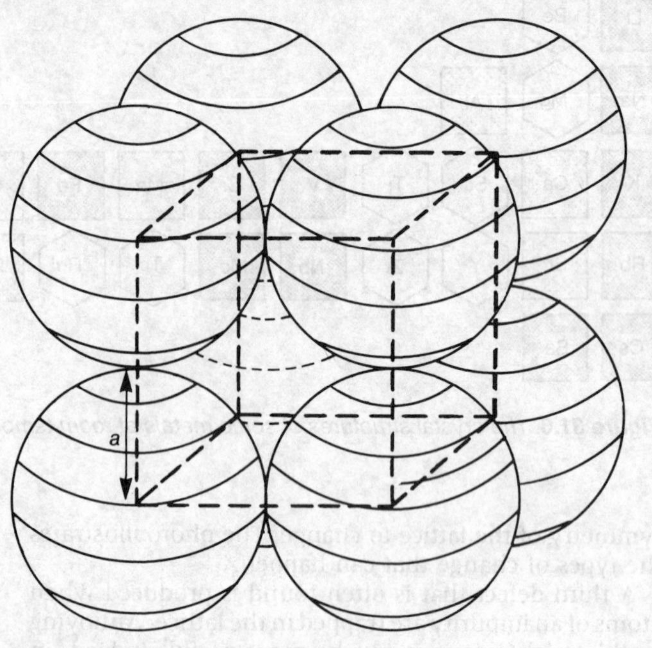

Figure 31.7 *The diagram for question 31.1*

Answer

31.1 (i) $(2a)^3 = 8a^3$.
(ii) $4\pi a^3/3$.
(iii) You should find that another seven cubes can fit round to hide any one corner. This means that a corner is shared by eight cubes in all, i.e. the answer is 1/8.
(iv) $(4\pi a^3/3) \times 8 \times 1/8 = 4\pi a^3/3$.
(v) Fraction of filled space $= (4\pi a^3/3)/8a^3 = \pi/6$
$= 0.5236$ or 52.36%.

UNIT 31 SUMMARY

- Hexagonal close packing is the most efficient way of packing atoms in a crystal lattice.
- Two versions of hexagonal close packing are the ABAB... and ABCABC... patterns.
- The coordination number of an atom is the number of its nearest neighbours. In hexagonally close-packed structures the coordination number is 12.
- Simple cubic structures have atoms at the eight corners of a cube. The coordination number is 6.
- A face centred cubic structure has an atom at the centre of the eight faces as well as at the corners of a cube. It is hexagonally close-packed, and has a coordination number of 12.
- A body centred cubic structure has an atom at the centre of a cube as well as at the eight corners. The coordination number is 8.

32

Unit cells

32.1 The seven crystal systems

The crystal shapes shown in Figure 32.1 are all different. At first sight we might expect this to mean that the way the atoms pack together within the crystals will also be different. In fact they can all be made from hexagonally close-packed layers. Different shapes are produced when parts of the layers grow at different rates.

You can see from Figure 32.1 that the *angles* between the faces remain the same although the lengths of the faces are different. The angles provide us with information about the underlying symmetry of the crystal. It turns out that all crystals have one of only seven types of symmetry. These are the *seven crystal systems*. The names of the systems are: triclinic, monoclinic, rhombic, trigonal, tetragonal, hexagonal and cubic.

32.2 The fourteen Bravais lattices

We have met the cubic system before, although in a different guise. In Unit 31 you met body centred and face centred cubic structures. In addition to these there is a simple cubic structure with atoms only at the eight corners of a cube. Thus, the cubic system consists of three separate types of structures, called *Bravais lattices*. The other six crystal systems have their own sets of Bravais lattices, shown in Figure 32.2. If you count them you will find there are fourteen in all. The basic differences between the fourteen Bravais lattices are the angles between the faces and the relative proportions of the sides. In these diagrams we have shown single atoms at the corners and faces. This is to show the shape and symmetry of each of the lattices. Real crystals often contain atoms grouped together as ions, e.g. as SO_4^{2-}, NO_3^-, CO_3^{2-} ions, or molecules. The Bravais lattices of such crystals can appear much more complicated than the diagrams in Figure 32.2.

32.3 What are unit cells?

Each of the fourteen Bravais lattices has an extremely important property. They can join together exactly with

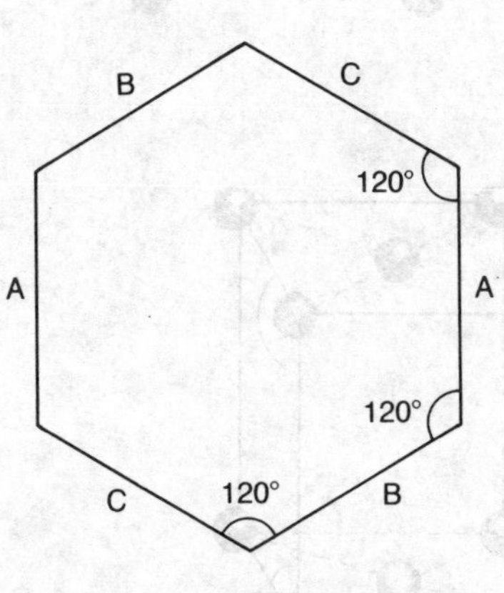

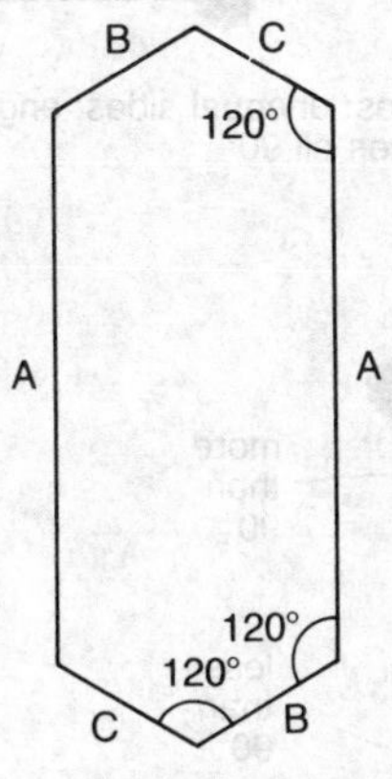

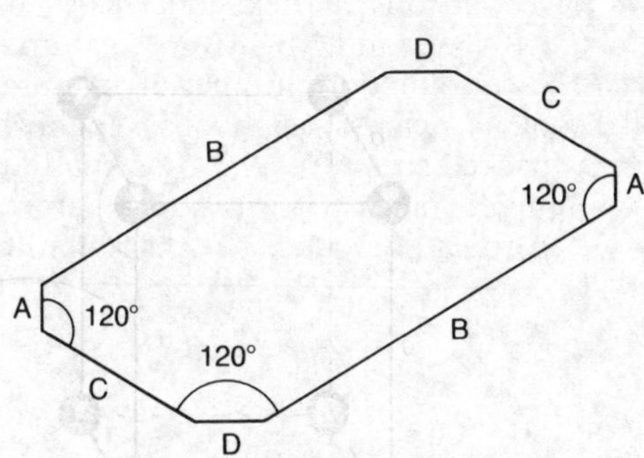

Figure 32.1 *Three different crystal shapes, but related to each other. All the angles between the faces are 120°. The main difference between them is the rate at which the faces grow*

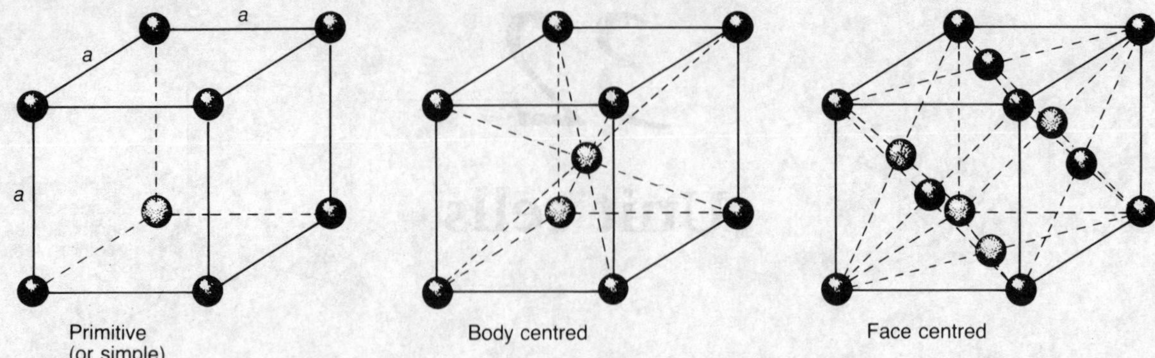

The three cubic lattices: all sides same length; angles between faces all 90°

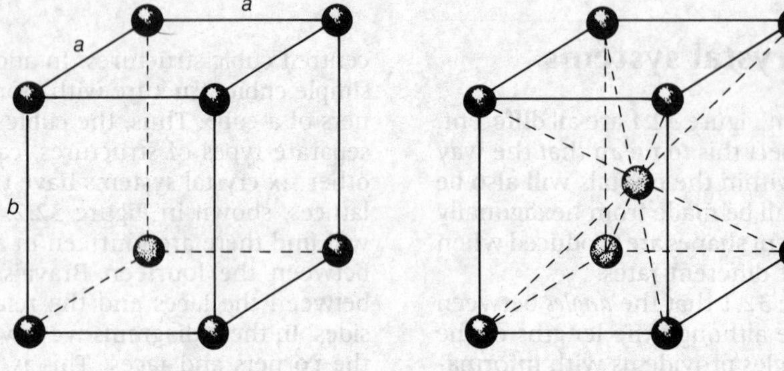

The two tetragonal lattices: one side different in length to the other two; angles between faces all 90°

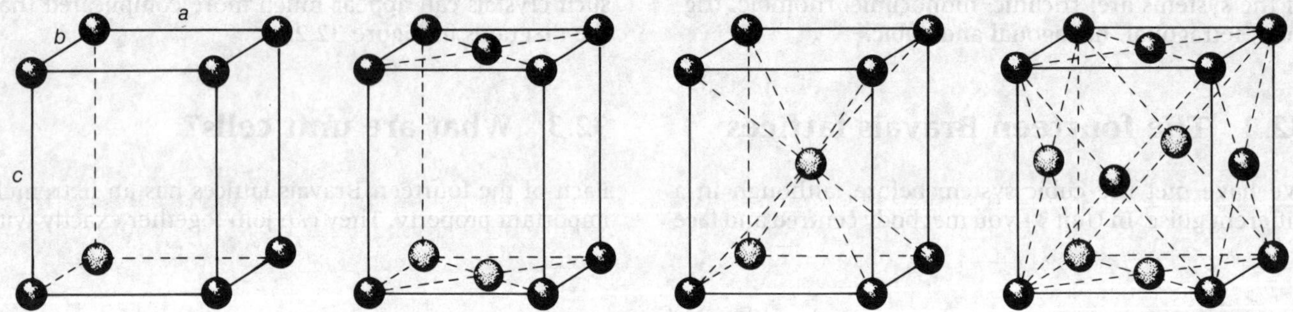

The four orthorhombic lattices: unequal sides; angles between faces all 90°

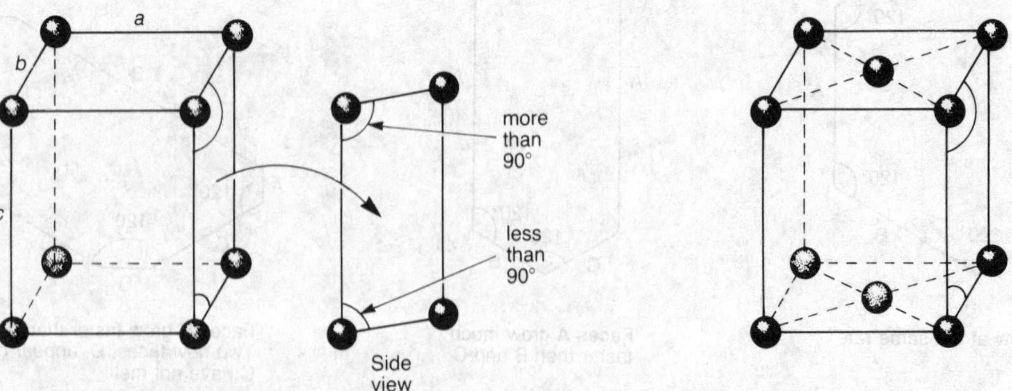

The two monoclinic lattices: unequal sides; two faces have angles different to 90°

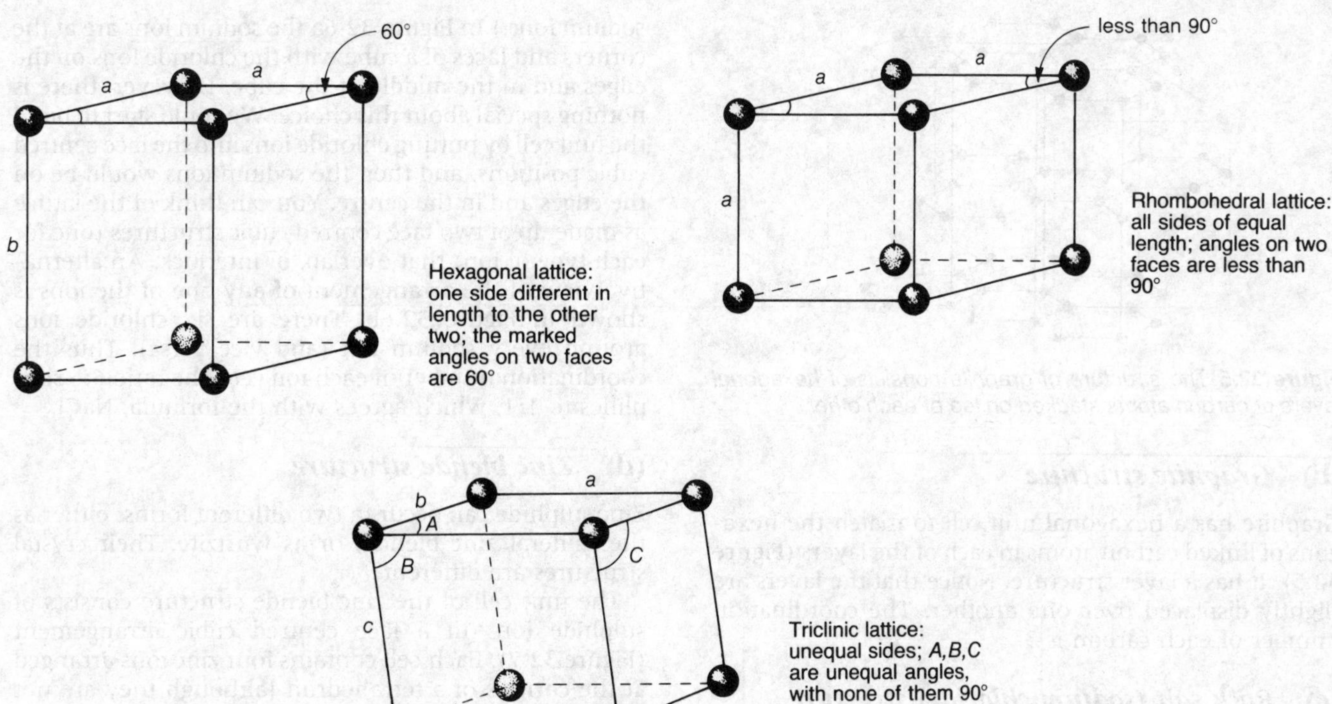
60°
a
a
b
Hexagonal lattice: one side different in length to the other two; the marked angles on two faces are 60°
less than 90°
a
a
a
Rhombohedral lattice: all sides of equal length; angles on two faces are less than 90°
b
a
A
B
C
c
Triclinic lattice: unequal sides; A,B,C are unequal angles, with none of them 90°

***Figure 32.2** The fourteen Bravais lattices*

others of the same kind to create a three-dimensional shape. (By 'exactly' we mean without leaving gaps between them.) An example is shown in Figure 32.3.

We can think of the Bravais lattices as the basic building blocks out of which crystals are made. These basic building blocks are called *unit cells*. The symmetry of the crystal must match that of the unit cell out of which it is built.

However, the structures of real crystals can be very complicated, with atoms, ions, or molecules at all sorts of different angles and distances from one another. Often crystallographers choose a unit cell that does not look like one of the Bravais lattices. They like to work with unit cells that make their calculations on X-ray diffraction patterns as simple as possible. This means that, to some extent, people are free to choose a unit cell to suit their own purposes. It does not have to be the simplest unit cell possible. Figures 32.4–32.12 show you the unit cells of some well known crystals.

(a) *Diamond structure*

This is based upon a face centred cubic structure but with extra carbon atoms inside the cube (Figure 32.4). The arrangement around each carbon is tetrahedral. The coordination number of each carbon is 4.

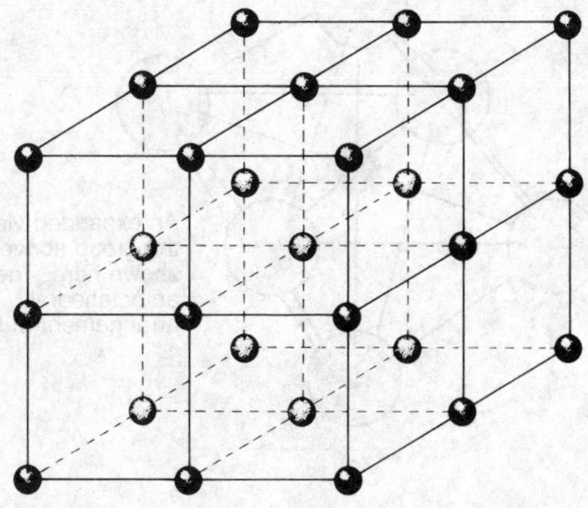

***Figure 32.3** This part of a crystal lattice is built from cubic Bravais lattices*

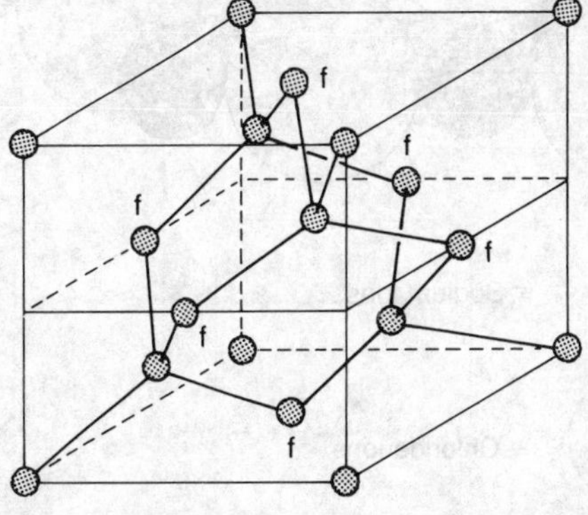
f
f
f
f
f
f

***Figure 32.4** The structure of diamond. Not all of the bonds are shown. The atoms marked 'f' are at the centres of the six faces. Bonds into neighbouring unit cells are not shown in this diagram nor the others that follow*

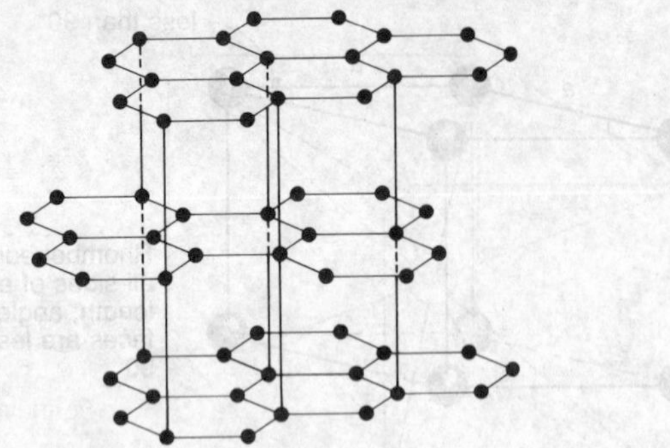

Figure 32.5 The structure of graphite consists of hexagonal layers of carbon atoms stacked on top of each other

(b) *Graphite structure*

Graphite has a hexagonal unit cell to match the hexagons of linked carbon atoms in each of the layers (Figure 32.5). It has a layer structure. Notice that the layers are slightly displaced over one another. The coordination number of each carbon is 3.

(c) *Rock salt (sodium chloride) structure*

Sodium chloride consists of sodium ions, Na^+, and chloride ions, Cl^-. (The chloride ions are larger than the sodium ions.) In Figure 32.6a the sodium ions are at the corners and faces of a cube with the chloride ions on the edges and in the middle of the cube. However, there is nothing special about this choice. We could start to build the unit cell by putting chloride ions into the face centred cubic positions, and then the sodium ions would be on the edges and in the centre. You can think of the lattice as made up of two face centred cubic structures (one for each type of ion) that overlap, or interlock. An alternative view of the arrangement of any one of the ions is shown in Figure 32.6b. There are six chloride ions around every sodium ion (and vice versa). Thus the coordination number of each ion is 6. The ratio 6:6 simplifies to 1:1, which agrees with the formula, NaCl.

(d) *Zinc blende structure*

Zinc sulphide can occur in two different forms: either as the mineral zinc blende, or as wurtzite. Their crystal structures are different.

The unit cell of the zinc blende structure consists of sulphide ions in a face centred cubic arrangement (Figure 32.7). Each cell contains four zinc ions arranged at the corners of a tetrahedron (although they are not bonded together). The tetrahedron sits completely inside the cube. The coordination number, 4, of the zinc ions is the same as the sulphide ions. You should be able to see

(a)

≡ Sodium ions

≡ Chloride ions

Formula, Na Cl

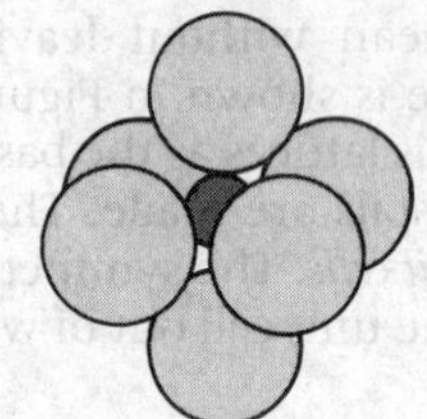

If you look at the top right-hand corner of diagram (a) you should see a group of three chloride ions close to a single sodium ion. If the lattice stretched further there would be another three chloride ions to be seen, as shown here

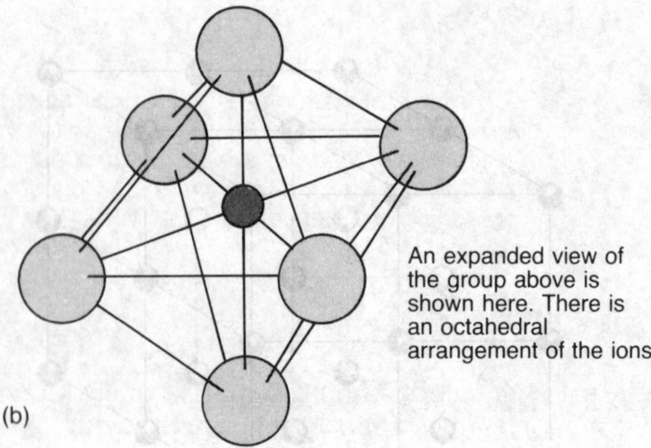

An expanded view of the group above is shown here. There is an octahedral arrangement of the ions

(b)

Figure 32.6 (a) The structure of rock salt (sodium chloride). The large spheres represent chloride ions, the smaller ones represent sodium ions. (b) Expanded views of the rock salt structure

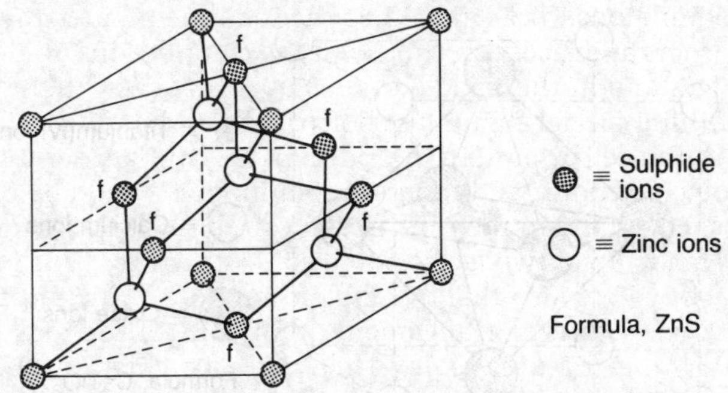

Figure 32.7 The zinc blende structure. There are fourteen sulphide ions at the corners or faces (f) of the unit cell. Within the cell, four zinc ions are bonded tetrahedrally to some of the sulphide ions

this by looking at the diagram. This agrees with the ratio of 1:1 for the formula, ZnS.

(e) *Wurtzite structure*

This is a hexagonal structure (Figure 32.8). The cell has the overall shape of a triangular prism. (Six of the prisms can join to make a hexagonal structure.) Sulphide ions are to be found at the corners of the triangular faces. Four zinc ions make up the corners of a tetrahedron centred on another sulphide ion at a central point in the cell. The coordination number of each ion is again 4.

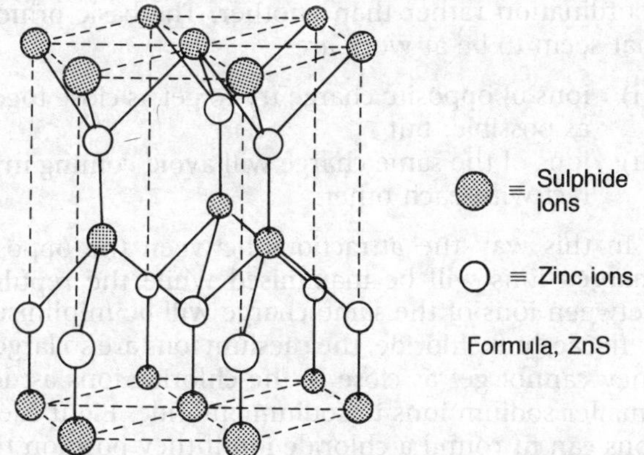

***Figure 32.8** The wurtzite structure. A second, hexagonal, structure adopted by zinc sulphide. Six of the unit cells are shown joined together. (Diagram adapted from: Douglas, B. E., McDaniel, D. H. and Alexander, J. J. (1983).* Concepts and Models of Inorganic Chemistry, *2nd edn, Wiley, New York, figure 6.9)*

(f) *Caesium chloride structure*

The caesium chloride unit cell consists of eight caesium ions in a simple cubic arrangement, with a single chloride ion at the centre of the cube (Figure 32.9). However, as with sodium chloride, this choice of cell is not the only one. We could equally have chosen to show chloride ions in a cubic arrangement, with a lone caesium ion in the centre. If you want, you can think of the structure being made of two interlocking cubic arrangements of the two ions.

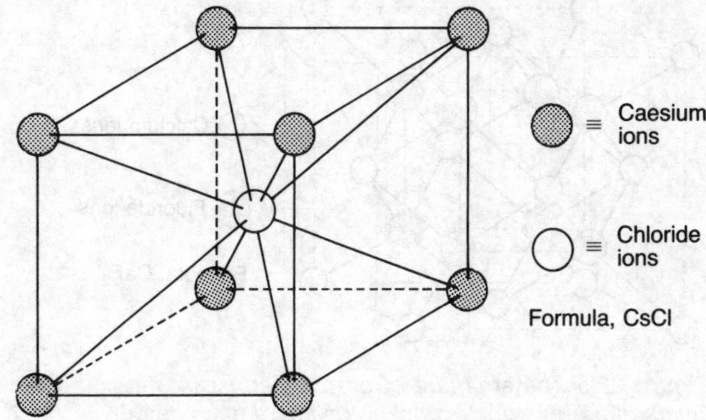

***Figure 32.9** The caesium chloride structure. There are eight caesium ions at the corners of a cube, with a chloride ion at the centre*

(g) *Rutile structure*

This is a form of titanium dioxide, TiO_2. The unit cell has a tetragonal, rather than cubic, structure (Figure 32.10). Titanium ions are at the corners and at the centre. The central one is surrounded by six oxide ions. What is harder to visualise is that when the unit cells are built up one on another, every titanium ion is surrounded by six oxide ions, and every oxide has three titanium ions as their nearest neighbours. (This gives the necessary ratio of one titanium to two oxide ions.)

(h) *Fluorite structure*

This mineral is cadmium fluoride, CdF_2. It has a remarkable structure based on two cubic arrangements (Figure 32.11a). In the diagram calcium ions are shown in a face centred cubic arrangement. Inside this cube is a second cube of fluoride ions. Another view of the arrangement is shown in Figure 32.11b. By looking carefully at the

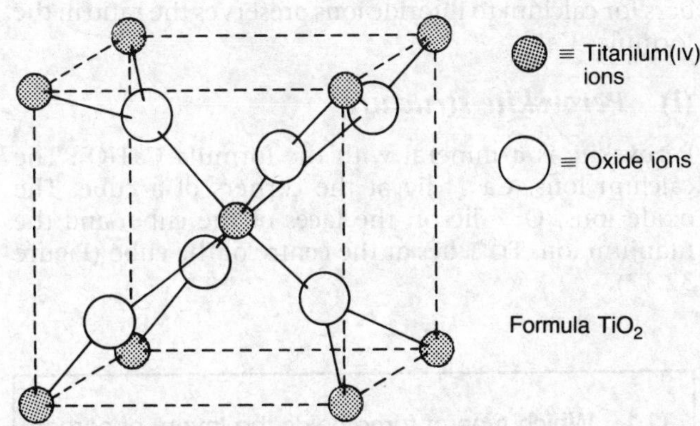

***Figure 32.10** The rutile structure. The titanium ion at the centre of the large cube is also at the centre of a set of six oxide ions. (Diagram adapted from: Douglas* et al., *op. cit., figure 6.10)*

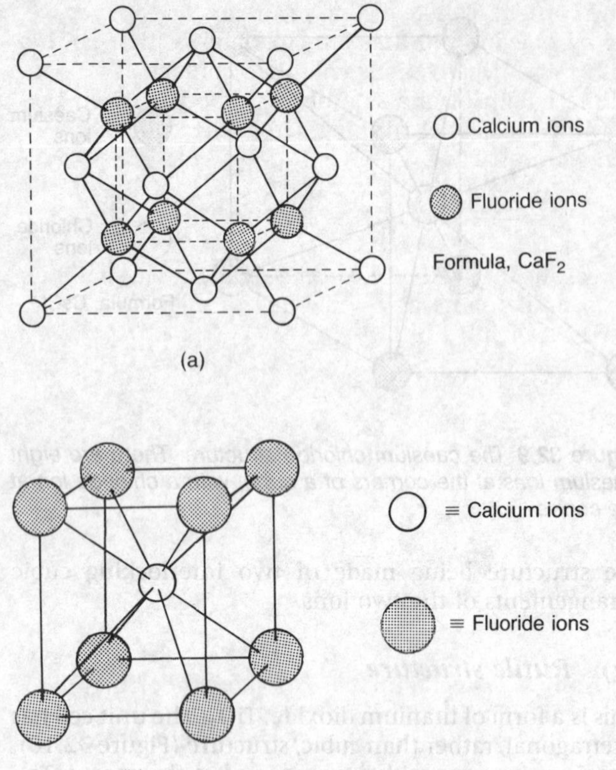

Figure 32.11 *(a) The fluorite structure. Calcium ions are at the corners and faces of the large cube. Inside there is a small cube with fluoride ions at the corners. (Diagram adapted from: Douglas* et al.*, op. cit.,* figure 6.10.*) (b) Each calcium ion has eight fluoride ions as its nearest neighbours. You can imagine that the calcium ion shown here is at the top of the large cube in diagram (a). The bottom four fluoride ions are those shown in the large cube; the top four would belong to a second large cube stacked above the first*

diagram you will see that each calcium has eight fluoride ions for its nearest neighbours. On the other hand, each fluoride ion exists within a tetrahedral arrangement of calcium ions; so the fluoride ions have four calcium ions around them. This ratio (8:4) of the coordination numbers for calcium to fluoride ions preserves the ratio in the formula, CaF_2.

(i) *Perovskite structure*

Perovskite is a mineral with the formula $CaTiO_3$. The calcium ions, Ca^{2+}, lie at the corners of a cube. The oxide ions, O^{2-}, lie on the faces of the cube, and the titanium ion, Ti^{4+}, lies at the centre of the cube (Figure 32.12).

32.1 Which type of force holds the layers of carbon atoms in graphite together? Explain why graphite is soft and can mark paper, whereas diamond is extremely hard and can cut glass.

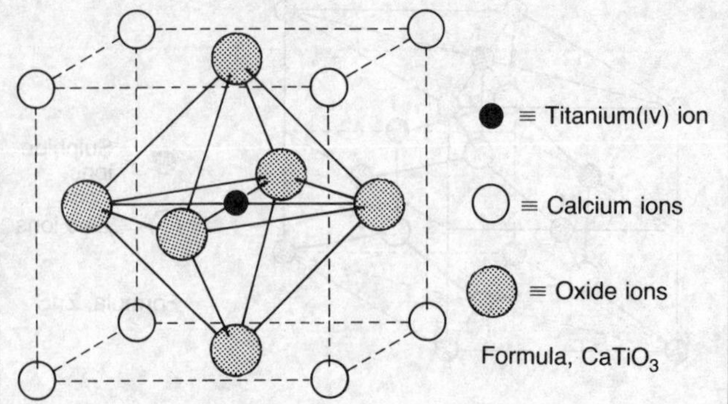

Figure 32.12 *The perovskite structure. Calcium ions lie at the corners, oxide ions at the faces, and a titanium(IV) ion at the centre. (Diagram adapted from: Douglas* et al.*, op. cit.,* figure 6.10*)*

32.2 Why is zinc sulphide not completely ionic in nature? (Hint: the radii of a sulphide ion, S^{2-}, and a zinc ion, Zn^{2+}, are 184 pm and 74 pm, respectively.)

32.4 Radius ratio rules

The structures you have seen in Figures 32.4–32.12 are examples of the most common types of coordination in crystals. Other examples are listed in Table 32.1. We shall now try to find out why ions take up one type of coordination rather than another. The basic principles that seem to be at work are:

(i) ions of opposite charge try to get as close together as possible; but
(ii) ions of the same charge will avoid coming in contact with each other.

In this way the attractions between the oppositely charged ions will be maximised while the repulsions between ions of the same charge will be minimised.

In caesium chloride, the caesium ions are so large that they cannot get as close to the chloride ions as do the smaller sodium ions in sodium chloride. Eight caesium ions can fit round a chloride ion if they position themselves at the corners of a cube. In this geometry there is no danger of the electron clouds of the caesium ions coming into contact and causing strong repulsions.

In practice the structure adopted by a crystal depends on the relative sizes of both negative and positive ions. We shall call the radius of the positive ion r^+, and that of

Table 32.1. Some examples of the most common types of coordination in crystals

Coordination	*Structure*	*Examples*
4:4	Zinc blende	AgI, HgS
	Wurtzite	CdS, ZnO
6:6	Rock salt	LiCl, KCl, MgO
8:8	Caesium chloride	CsBr, CsI, NH_4Cl

Table 32.2. Radius ratio rules

Ratio	*Structure adopted*	*Coordination number of positive ion*
$r^+/r^- = 1$	Close packing	12
$0.732 < r^+/r^- < 1$	Corners of cube	8
$0.414 < r^+/r^- < 0.732$	Octahedral (like NaCl)	6
$0.225 < r^+/r^- < 0.414$	Tetrahedral	4

the negative ion r^-. The rules that govern the ratio of the two radii (r^+/r^-) are to be found in Table 32.2.

You might like to see how these rules come about. In Figure 32.13 you will find another diagram of the caesium chloride structure. Our positive ion is at the centre of the cube and surrounded by eight negative ions

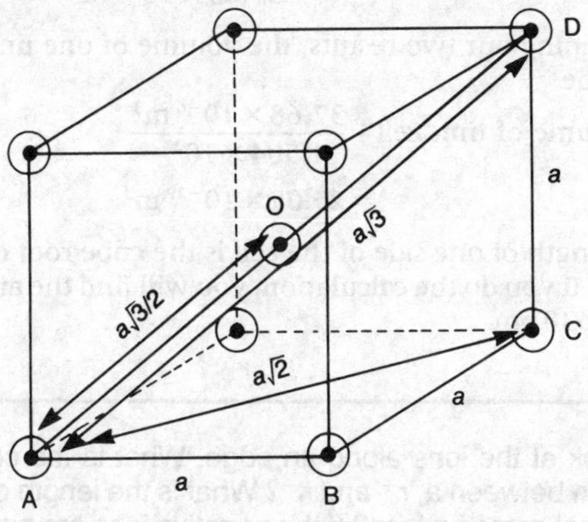

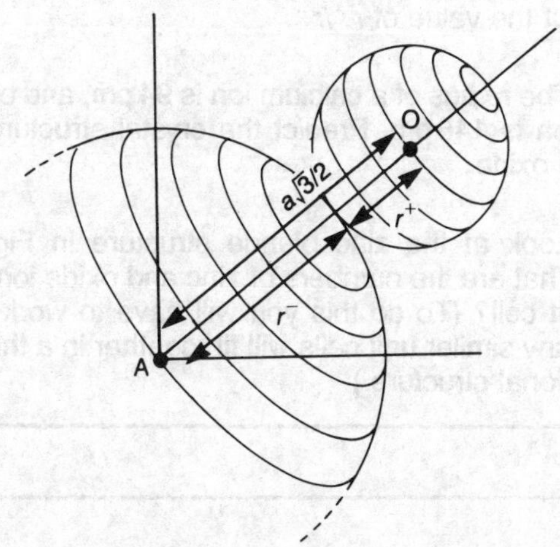

Figure 32.13 *For the caesium chloride structure,* $r^+ + r^- = a\sqrt{3}/2$. *We obtain this formula as follows. Using Pythagoras' theorem in triangle ABC,* $AC^2 = AB^2 + BC^2 = 2a^2$; *hence* $AC = a\sqrt{2}$. *Likewise, in triangle ACD,* $AD^2 = AC^2 + CD^2 = 2a^2 + a^2 = 3a^2$. *Hence* $AD = a\sqrt{3}$. *The distance AO is* $a\sqrt{3}/2$, *and this is the sum of the radii of the positive ion (at the centre, O) and the negative ion*

at the corners. The key thing to understand is that we start by obeying the first principle above; that is, the positive and negative ions will be in contact.

If the length of one side of the cube is a, then the length of a diagonal running across the cube is $a\sqrt{3}$. Then we must have

$$r^+ + r^- = \frac{a\sqrt{3}}{2}$$

For reasons that will be clear in a moment we shall put this in a different way by dividing through by r^- and then rearranging, i.e.

$$\frac{r^+}{r^-} = \frac{a\sqrt{3}}{2r^-} - 1$$

Now, the negative ions must at least be able to fit across the sides of the cube without overlapping. This means that

$$2r^- = a \quad \text{or} \quad a/r^- = 2$$

If we combine the two equations, we have

$$r^+/r^- = \sqrt{3} - 1 = 0.732$$

This is the *minimum* ratio that will allow the structure to exist without the negative ions overlapping. If they become larger than this critical size, they will overlap along the edges; strong repulsions will be set up and the crystal structure will adjust to a more favourable type. Therefore we must have $r^+/r^- > 0.732$, as shown in Table 32.2.

The derivation of the other rules is similar, but in each case you need to take care with the trigonometry.

32.5 The number of atoms or ions in a unit cell

Sometimes it is useful to be able to calculate the number of atoms or ions in a unit cell. In the simple cubic structure of Figure 32.14 we have to realise that the atoms at the corners do not belong to just one unit cell. In the

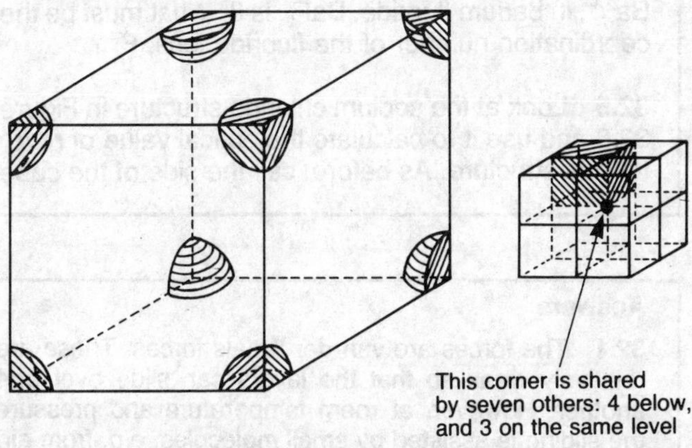

Figure 32.14 *In a simple cubic structure, only one-eighth of each corner atom belongs to the unit cell. Hence the effective number of atoms in the cell is* $8 \times 1/8 = 1$

Table 32.3. The sharing of atoms by cubic unit cells

Position of atom	*Shared by*	*Contribution to one cell*
Corner	8 cells	1/8
Edge	4 cells	1/4
Face	2 cells	1/2
Inside cell	1 cell	1

crystal itself the cells join up in three dimensions as shown. Every corner is shared by seven other cubes (making eight in all); every edge is shared by four cubes in all; every face is shared by two cubes (Table 32.3). This means, for example, that a corner atom contributes one-eighth of an atom to any one cell.

Armed with this information we can calculate the dimensions of a unit cell if we know the density of the material and the atomic (or molecular) masses of the particles in the cell. Let us use potassium chloride as an example. The essential information is:

Density of potassium chloride $= 1.98 \times 10^3$ kg m^{-3}
$M(\text{KCl}) = 74.6 \times 10^{-3}$ kg mol^{-1}
Crystal structure of potassium chloride: cubic, sodium chloride structure

Given that the structure of potassium chloride is like that of sodium chloride, we can use Figure 32.6 to help us. The ions in the unit cell are:

Potassium ions
8 at the corners, count as $8 \times 1/8 = 1$ in the cell
6 at the faces, count as $6 \times 1/2 = 3$ in the cell
total number of potassium ions present $= 4$

Chloride ions
12 at each edge, count as $12 \times 1/4 = 3$ in the cell
1 at the centre, counts as 1 in the cell
total number of chloride ions present $= 4$

Thus we have four pairs of ions in the unit cell. Now, we know that 1 mol of KCl contains 6.02×10^{23} pairs of potassium and chloride ions (see Unit 37 if you are unsure about this). So, if each unit cell contains four of these pairs there must be $1/4 \times 6.02 \times 10^{23}$ unit cells in 1 mol of KCl, i.e. number of unit cells in 1 mol $= 1.504 \times 10^{23}$. Because density = mass/volume, we also know that

$$\text{volume of 1 mol of KCl} = \frac{74.6 \times 10^{-3}\ \text{kg}}{1.98 \times 10^3\ \text{kg m}^{-3}}$$

$$= 37.68 \times 10^{-6}\ \text{m}^3$$

Combining our two results, the volume of one unit cell must be

$$\text{volume of unit cell} = \frac{37.68 \times 10^{-6}\ \text{m}^3}{1.504 \times 10^{23}}$$

$$= 25.05 \times 10^{-29}\ \text{m}^3$$

The length of one side of the cell is the cube root of this result. If you do the calculation, you will find the answer to be 630 pm.

32.3 Calculate the length of the unit cell of sodium chloride. You will need this information:

Density of sodium chloride $= 2.17 \times 10^3$ kg m^{-3}.
$M(\text{NaCl}) = 58.4 \times 10^{-3}$ kg mol^{-1}.

32.4 The unit cell of silver iodide, AgI, has four iodide atoms in it. How many silver atoms must be in the unit cell?

32.5 The coordination number of the barium ions, Ba^{2+}, in barium fluoride, BaF_2, is 8. What must be the coordination number of the fluoride ions, F^-?

32.6 Look at the sodium chloride structure in Figure 32.6 and use it to calculate the critical value of r^+/r^- for this structure. As before, call the side of the cube a. Look at the ions along an edge. What is the connection between a, r^+ and r^-? What is the length of a diagonal across a face? If the negative ions are not to overlap, what is the connection between a and r^-? Now combine the equations you have written down to work out the value of r^+/r^-.

32.7 The radius of a calcium ion is 94 pm, and of an oxide ion is 146 pm. Predict the crystal structure of calcium oxide.

32.8 Look at the zinc blende structure in Figure 32.7. What are the numbers of zinc and oxide ions in one unit cell? (To do this you will have to work out how many similar unit cells will fit together in a three-dimensional structure.)

Answers

32.1 The forces are van der Waals forces. These are relatively weak so that the layers can slide over one another. However, at room temperature and pressure the sliding is assisted by small molecules, e.g. from air, that are trapped between the layers. At high altitudes (low pressures) these small molecules are lost from the structure, and the layers slide over one another with much greater difficulty. In diamond the carbon atoms are linked by strong covalent bonds. The interconnecting tetrahedral arrangements make the diamond lattice extremely strong.

32.2 The sulphide ion is large and 'squashy'. It is easily polarised by the much smaller zinc ion, and covalency results. This is an example of Fajans' rules.

Answers – contd.

32.3 There are four ion-pairs in the unit cell of sodium chloride. Thus, the calculation follows exactly the same pattern as that for potassium chloride. So we have

$$\text{volume of one mole} = \frac{58.4\times10^{-3}\,\text{kg mol}^{-1}}{2.17\times10^{3}\,\text{kg m}^{-3}}$$
$$= 26.79\times10^{-6}\,\text{m}^3\,\text{mol}^{-1}$$

Like potassium chloride, there are four NaCl ion-pairs per unit cell so the volume of one unit cell is

$$\text{volume of unit cell} = \frac{26.79\times10^{-6}\,\text{m}^3\,\text{mol}^{-1}}{1.504\times10^{23}\,\text{mol}^{-1}}$$
$$= 17.81\times10^{-29}\,\text{m}^3$$

Taking the cube root gives the length of the cell as 562 pm.

32.4 The formula, AgI, tells us that the ratio of silver atoms to iodine atoms is 1:1. Hence, if there are four iodine atoms in the unit cell there must also be four silver atoms.

32.5 The coordination number of the barium ions tells us that it is surrounded by eight fluoride ions (charge $8\times(-1)=-8$). In order to balance out the eight negative charges, we need four barium ions (charge $4\times(+2)=+8$). Hence, the coordination number of the fluoride ions must be 4. You will find that the coordination numbers and the charges of ions always balance out to give neutrality.

32.6 Along an edge, $2r^+ + 2r^- = a$. Along a diagonal, $4r^- = a\sqrt{2}$. These give $r^+ = a/2 - r^- = (1-\sqrt{2}/2)\times a/2 = (2-\sqrt{2})\times a/4$. So $r^+/r^- = (2-\sqrt{2})/\sqrt{2} = 0.414$.

32.7 The ratio $r^+/r^- = 94\,\text{pm}/146\,\text{pm} = 0.644$. The prediction is an octahedral arrangement of the oxide ions around the calcium. Because the ions have equal but opposite charges, there must also be an octahedral arrangement of calcium ions around oxide ions. Thus we would expect a rock salt (sodium chloride) structure. This structure is confirmed by X-ray diffraction.

32.8 There are sulphide ions at each of the eight corners of the unit cell. These contribute $8\times1/8=1$ ion in all. Also, there are sulphide ions at each of the six faces. These contribute $6\times1/2=3$ ions in all. In total there are four sulphide ions to each cell. The four zinc ions are all contained within the cell, so overall there are four zinc ions and four sulphide ions in each cell.

UNIT 32 SUMMARY

- The unit cell of a crystal lattice is the basic building block of a crystal. Unit cells fit together to make up an entire lattice. They have the full symmetry of the crystal.
- All crystals belong to one of the seven crystal systems and to one of the fourteen Bravais lattices.
- The unit cell adopted by a particular crystal will depend on the radii of the atoms or ions making up the structure (see Table 32.2).
- In counting the effective number of atoms or ions in a unit cell:
  (i) Atoms at each corner count as 1/8.
  (ii) Atoms at each face count as 1/2.
  (iii) Atoms on an edge count as 1/4.
  (iv) Atoms within the cell count as 1.

33

Sizes of atoms, ions and molecules

33.1 How can we estimate the size of an atom?

We can estimate the size of an atom if we know the atomic mass of an element and its density as a solid. Taking gold as our example, a data book will provide the following information:

$M(\text{Au}) = 197\,\text{g mol}^{-1}$
density of gold $= 19\,320\,\text{kg m}^{-3}$

Therefore, the volume of 1 mol of gold (the molar volume) is

$$\text{molar volume} = \frac{197 \times 10^{-3}\,\text{kg mol}^{-1}}{19\,320\,\text{kg m}^{-3}} = 1.02 \times 10^{-5}\,\text{m}^3\,\text{mol}^{-1}$$

The number of particles in 1 mol is given by the Avogadro constant, $6.02 \times 10^{23}\,\text{mol}^{-1}$. Thus our estimate for the volume of one atom of gold is

$$\text{volume of one atom} = \frac{1.02 \times 10^{-5}\,\text{m}^3\,\text{mol}^{-1}}{6.02 \times 10^{23}\,\text{mol}^{-1}} = 1.69 \times 10^{-29}\,\text{m}^3$$

If we assume that the atoms are spherical, the radius of a gold atom is found from the formula for the volume of a sphere (volume $= 4\pi r^3/3$). So

$$(\text{radius})^3 = 3 \times 1.69 \times 10^{-29}\,\text{m}^3/4\pi$$

or

$$\text{radius} = 1.59 \times 10^{-10}\,\text{m or } 159\,\text{pm}$$

This result makes at least one big approximation. That is, we have ignored all the empty space in the crystal. However, the result is clearly of the right order of magnitude.

For an accurate measurement we can turn to X-ray diffraction. The radius found for gold is 144 pm, so our estimate above was not too bad.

33.1 The amount of empty space in a gold crystal is about 26% of the total volume. Go over the calculation of the estimate of the radius of a gold atom making allowance for the empty space.

33.2 Metallic and covalent radii

We like to think of atoms as nicely rounded things, spheres in fact. However, in any estimate or measurement of the 'radius' of an atom there is always some inaccuracy. Partly this is because of the usual errors that enter into any measurement. However, another reason is that it is impossible to define the size of an atom exactly. If you look back to our work on electron orbitals (Unit 11), you will find that we agreed to draw probability density diagrams, which show where an electron is to be found for 95% of the time (Figure 33.1). For the other 5% of the time the electrons can be anywhere outside the region that we draw.

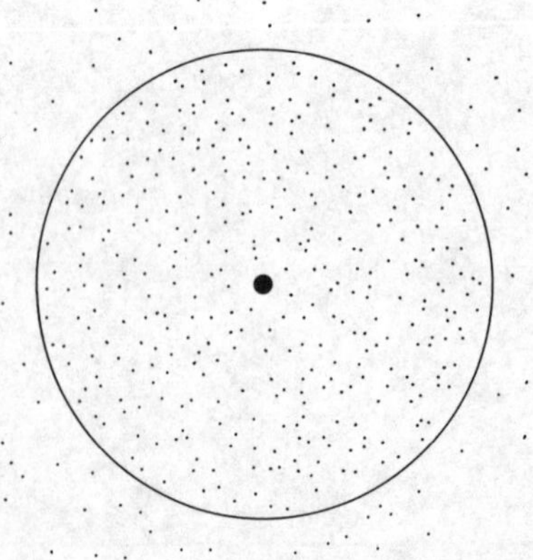

***Figure 33.1** The idea that an atom has a fixed size is not right. The circle (sphere) that we draw representing an s orbital shows only the region within which the electrons spend 95% of their time*

The point is that it is impossible to say precisely where the atom begins and ends. So the idea of an atom having a very well defined radius is mistaken. The best we can do is make our estimates as good as possible.

One sensible approach to estimating the size of an atom is to measure the distance between two atoms when they are bonded together, either in a metal (Figure 33.2) or in a covalent molecule (Figure 33.3). Then, if we halve the distance apart we can take that as the radius of the atom. Measurements on metals provide us with a table of *metallic radii* (Table 33.1). Measurements on covalent molecules lead to tables of *covalent radii* (Table 33.2).

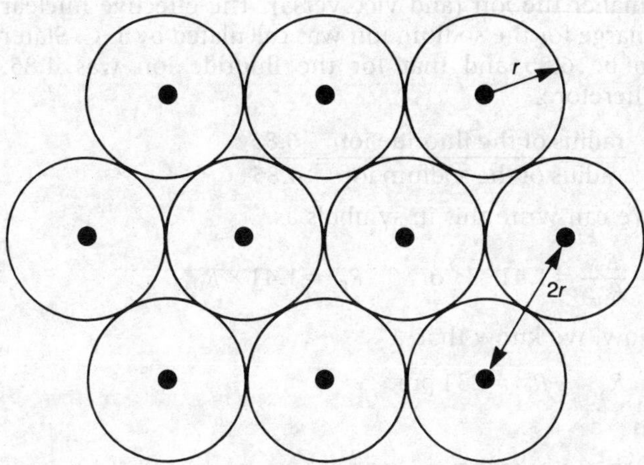

Figure 33.2 *In a metal crystal we can think of the atoms arranged as a set of touching spheres. The distance between the nuclei of adjacent atoms is twice the metallic radius, r*

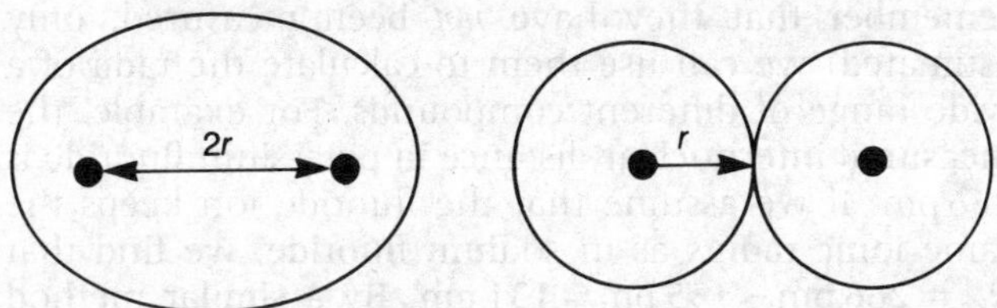

Figure 33.3 *In a covalent homonuclear diatomic molecule (e.g. hydrogen, nitrogen, chlorine) the covalent radius is also half the distance between the nuclei. Using the words 'covalent radius' suggests that the molecule is made up of two spheres. This is not true. However, the covalent radius does give us a useful idea of the size of an atom*

Table 33.1. Table of selected metallic radii

Element	Li	Be	Na	Mg	Ca	Fe	Cu	Zn	Au
Radius/pm	157	112	191	160	197	126	128	137	144

Table 33.2. Some covalent radii

Element	H	C	N	O	F	Cl	Br	I
Radius/pm	37	77	74	73	71	99	114	133

33.3 Van der Waals radii

Iodine is a solid at room temperature. The forces that hold the molecules together in the solid are the van der Waals forces that we described in Unit 20. In the crystal the molecules are arranged in layers, as shown in Figure 33.4.

The equilibrium distance between the planes is 427 pm. Half of this distance gives us the *van der Waals radius* of iodine. (In tables, the value is usually rounded up to 215 pm.) By making measurements on other

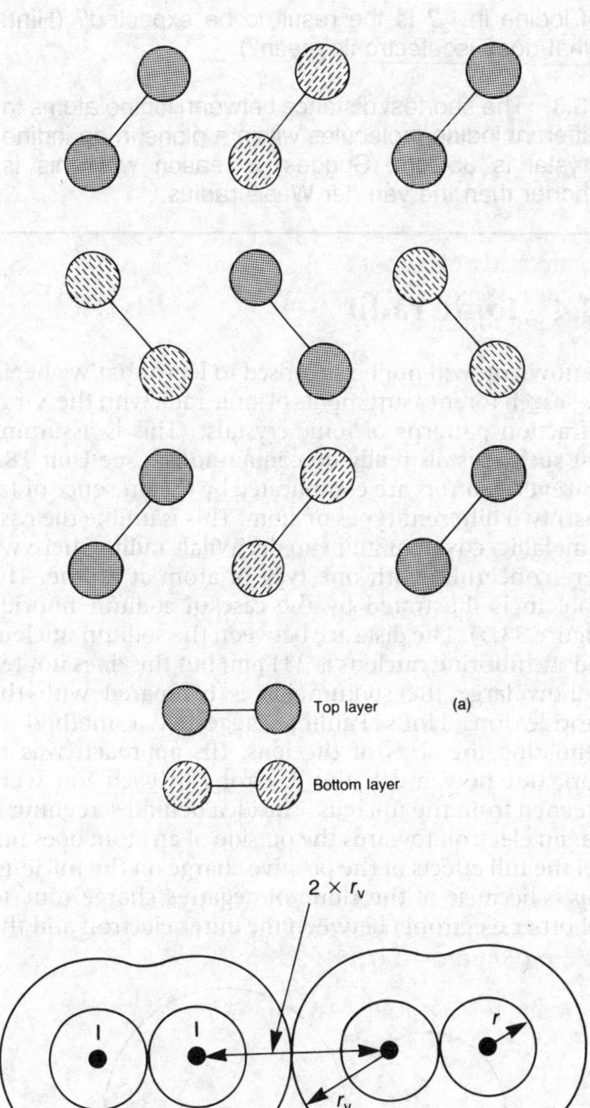

Figure 33.4 *(a) The crystal structure of iodine contains planes of I_2 molecules, with alternate layers staggered as shown. The distance between the planes is 427 pm, and the distance between molecules in the same plane is only 356 pm. (b) the van der Waals radius, r_v, of an atom is larger than the covalent radius, r. The distance between iodine atoms in neighbouring iodine molecules is twice the van der Waals radius of iodine*

Table 33.3. Some van der Waals radii

Element	H	N	O	F	Cl	Br	I
Radius/pm	120	150	140	135	180	195	215

covalent solids, the van der Waals radii can be established, some of which are listed in Table 33.3.

33.2 The van der Waals radius of xenon is 218 pm. How does this compare with the corresponding radius of iodine in I_2? Is the result to be expected? (Hint: what does isoelectronic mean?)

33.3 The shortest distance between iodine atoms in different iodine molecules within a plane in an iodine crystal is 350 pm. Suggest a reason why this is shorter than the van der Waals radius.

33.4 Ionic radii

By now you will not be surprised to learn that we begin the search for measurements of ionic radii with the X-ray diffraction patterns of ionic crystals. (This is assuming that such crystals really do contain ions – see Unit 18.) However, matters are complicated by the presence of (at least) two different types of atom. This is unlike the case of metallic, covalent and van der Waals radii, where we were concerned with one type of atom at a time. The problem is illustrated by the case of sodium fluoride (Figure 33.5). The distance between the sodium nucleus and the fluorine nucleus is 231 pm; but this does not tell us how large the sodium ion is compared with the fluoride ion. Linus Pauling suggested a method of estimating the sizes of the ions. His approach was to work out how much the electrons in each ion were screened from the nucleus. The idea behind screening is that an electron towards the outside of an atom does not feel the full effects of the positive charge on the nucleus. This is because of the cloud of negative charge (due to the other electrons) between the outer electron and the nucleus. The negative charge cuts down the attraction between the outer electron and the nucleus, i.e. it shields the outer electron from the nucleus. As far as the electron is concerned the nucleus will look like one with a smaller number of protons.

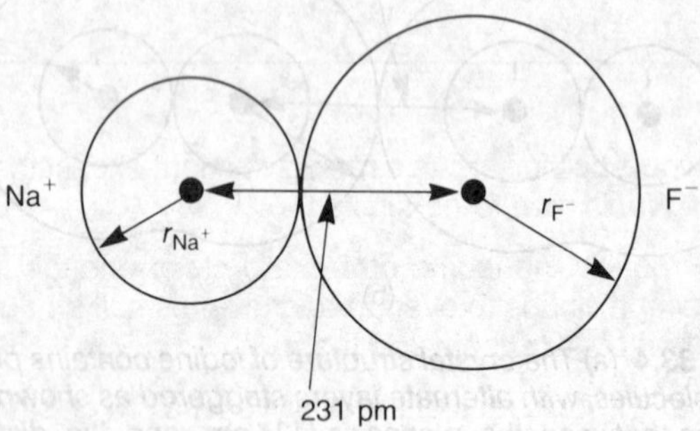

Figure 33.5 Although we can measure the distance between the nuclei of the two ions in sodium fluoride, this does not tell us the radii of the individual ions. We only know that $r_{Na^+} + r_{F^-} = 231$ *pm*

Both sodium and fluoride ions have the same number of electrons, ten. They are said to be isoelectronic. If both ions had the same effective nuclear charge we would expect them to have the same radius; but their effective nuclear charges are different. Pauling's argument was that the more the electrons were screened from the nucleus, the lower the effective nuclear charge; so the further away from the nucleus the electrons could wander. Thus the higher the effective nuclear charge, the smaller the ion (and vice versa). The effective nuclear charge for the sodium ion was calculated by J. C. Slater to be 6.85 and that for the fluoride ion was 4.85. Therefore,

$$\frac{\text{radius of the fluoride ion}}{\text{radius of the sodium ion}} = \frac{6.85}{4.85}$$

We can write this in symbols as

$$\frac{R_{F^-}}{R_{Na^+}} = 1.41 \quad \text{or} \quad R_{F^-} = 1.41 \times R_{Na^+}$$

Now, we know that

$$R_{Na^+} + R_{F^-} = 231 \text{ pm}$$

so

$$R_{Na^+} + 1.41 \times R_{Na^+} = 231 \text{ pm}$$

This gives us

$$R_{Na^+} = 95.9 \text{ pm} \quad \text{and} \quad R_{F^-} = 135.1 \text{ pm}$$

Now these two values have been established (but remember that they have *not* been measured, only estimated) we can use them to calculate the radii of a wide range of different compounds. For example, the measured internuclear distance in potassium fluoride is 266 pm. If we assume that the fluoride ion keeps the same ionic radius as in sodium fluoride, we find that $R_{K^+} = 266\text{ pm} - 135\text{ pm} = 131$ pm. By a similar method we can calculate the ionic radii of Li^+ in LiF, and Rb^+ in RbF. Then with the values of R_{Li^+}, R_{Na^+}, R_{K^+}, R_{Rb^+} established we could calculate the radii of the negative ions in ionic crystals of lithium, sodium, potassium and rubidium.

The success of this method relies on the notion that the size of an ion is independent of the compound in which it finds itself. This assumption is not a good one. The reason is clear: many 'ionic' compounds have a considerable degree of covalency. Nonetheless attempts have been made at adjusting the ionic radii to give as good a fit as possible with the wide range of compounds generally thought to be ionic. Some of these adjusted values are listed in Table 33.4.

The values give a good idea of the relative sizes of the ions; but you should not expect them to give an accurate internuclear distance in a compound. For example, the internuclear distance in lithium fluoride obtained by adding up the radii of the fluoride and lithium ions in Table 33.4 is 209 pm. From experiment the distance is 201 pm.

Table 33.4. Some ionic radii

	Charge of +1				Charge of −1			
Ion	Li	Na	K	Rb	F	Cl	Br	I
Radius/pm	76	102	138	152	133	181	196	220
	Charge of +2				Charge of −2			
Ion	Be	Mg	Ca	Sr	O	S	Se	
Radius/pm	45	72	100	118	140	184	198	
	Charge of +3				Charge of −3			
Ion	Al				N			
Radius/pm	54				146			

33.4 Compare the sizes of the atomic and ionic radii of:

(i) the Group I metals Li, Na, K, Rb;

(ii) the Group VII elements (halogens) F, Cl, Br, I.

What happens to the size of an atom when it becomes positively charged, and when it becomes negatively charged? In terms of shielding, give a short explanation for the trends you have spotted.

33.5 This question refers to the ions listed in Table 33.4.

(i) Which is the most polarisable?

(ii) Which positive ion would cause the greatest amount of polarisation in a negative ion?

(iii) Which ion is the most likely to have a large amount of covalency in its compounds?

33.5 Bond lengths

The distances between the nuclei of atoms in molecules can be measured in several ways, e.g. by X-ray diffraction. You can find a list of bond lengths in Table 33.5. In many cases the average length in different molecules is reported. For example, the C–H bond length is the average taken from a large number of organic molecules.

There are two points of which you should take special notice:

(i) The bond lengths of homopolar diatomic molecules are twice the covalent radii of Table 33.2.

(ii) The lengths of double bonds are less than the lengths of single bonds between the same two atoms, and triple bonds are even shorter than double bonds. This reflects the general rule that:

The shorter the bond length, the stronger is the bond.

You can check this rule out by comparing Table 33.5 with Table 44.3.

Table 33.5. Bond lengths

Bond	*Comment*	*Bond length*/pm
H−H	In H_2	74
H−Cl	In HCl	127
H−O	In H_2O	96
Cl−Cl	In Cl_2	199
Br−Br	In Br_2	228
I−I	In I_2	267
N−N	In N_2H_4	147
N≡N	In N_2	110
O−O	In H_2O_2	128
O=O	In O_2	121
C−H	Organics	108
C−Cl	Halogenoalkanes	177
C−O	Organic OH groups	143
C=O	Aldehydes and ketones	122
C−C	Organics	154
C=C	In C_2H_4	134
C≡C	In C_2H_2	121
C−N	Amines	147
C≡N	Nitriles	116

Answers

33.1 The actual volume occupied by the gold atoms will be 74% of $1.02 \times 10^{-5}\,m^3$, i.e. $0.755 \times 10^{-5}\,m^3$. Working with this figure eventually leads to an estimate of 143 pm for the radius.

33.2 It is almost the same. When the iodine atoms in I_2 share an extra electron with each other, they become isoelectronic with xenon. ('Isoelectronic' means having the same number of electrons.) Given that xenon has only one extra proton in its nucleus compared to iodine, we would expect that the electron clouds around the atoms would be similar. As a result we might expect their van der Waals radii to be similar.

33.3 Probably the iodine atoms are close enough for their electron clouds to overlap and give a small amount of covalent bonding between them.

33.4 (i) The ionic radii of the positive ions are all smaller than the radii of the neutral atoms.

(ii) The ionic radii of the negative ions are all greater than the radii of the neutral atoms.

Answers – contd.

When an atom loses an electron, the amount of shielding is reduced and the attraction of the nucleus for the remaining electrons increases. Therefore we would expect these electrons to be pulled a little closer to the nucleus. That is, the radius should decrease. By a similar, but opposite, argument, if an atom gains an electron, this electron will spend much of its time far from the nucleus and will be considerably shielded from the nucleus. The attraction of the nucleus for the outer electrons will be reduced, so the size increases.

33.5 (i) The iodide ion, I^-. This is the largest negative ion in the table.

(ii), (iii) The beryllium ion, Be^{2+}. This ion represents a very dense region of positive charge (it has only two electrons shielding the nucleus), so it has the greatest attraction for electrons.

UNIT 33 SUMMARY

- The volume of an atom can be estimated knowing its relative atomic mass and the density of the solid it makes.
- The metallic radius is half the distance between the nuclei of neighbouring atoms in a metal lattice.
- The covalent radius of an element E is half the distance between the nuclei of atoms within the diatomic molecule E_2.
- The van der Waals radius of an element is normally half the closest distance between the nuclei of atoms in different molecules in a lattice made up of covalent molecules.
- The ionic radius is the effective radius of an ion within a series of ionic crystals of which the ion is a part.

34

Real and ideal gases

34.1 The gas laws

The molecules in a gas are in constant random motion. In their frantic movements the molecules collide with each other, and with the walls of their container. It is the collisions with the walls that give a gas the property that we call pressure. Let us imagine a gas trapped in a container fitted with a piston and a pressure gauge (Figure 34.1). At the start the gas will be in equilibrium with its surroundings, so the pressure of the gas will be the same as the atmospheric pressure.

If we heat the gas, then the energy of the molecules increases. This means that, on average, they increase their speeds. They hit the walls of the container harder, which results in the piston moving outwards; i.e. the volume of the gas increases. However, when the gas finishes expanding, and the piston stops moving, equilibrium is established again. If we assume the outside pressure remains constant, then the pressure inside the gas at equilibrium must be the same at the end of the heating as it was at the start.

The expansion of gases was investigated by J. A. C. Charles in 1787, but it was Gay-Lussac in 1801 who first published a systematic set of results, which formed the basis of the following law:

At a constant pressure, the volume of a fixed mass of gas is proportional to its temperature.

In spite of Gay-Lussac's work, this is still known as *Charles' law*. In symbols the law says

$V \propto T$ (p constant)

or

$\frac{V}{T}$ = constant Charles' law

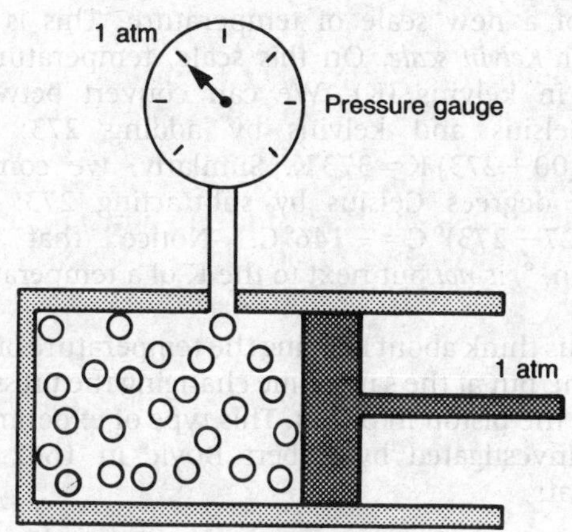

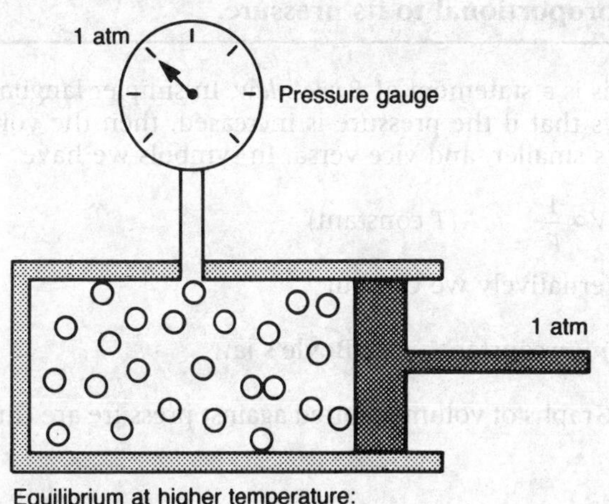

***Figure 34.1** If the pressure remains constant, equilibrium can only be achieved at two different temperatures if the volume changes*

It is most important to use the Kelvin scale of temperature here, not the Celsius scale. Graphs of volume of a gas plotted against Celsius temperature look like those of Figure 34.2. If the measurements taken around room temperature are plotted and the lines extended back, they meet at −273° C. At this temperature the volume of the gases appears to reduce to zero. Clearly this is impossible for real gases, but nonetheless the graphs show that the temperature *is* of great importance. It makes sense to avoid negative numbers where possible,

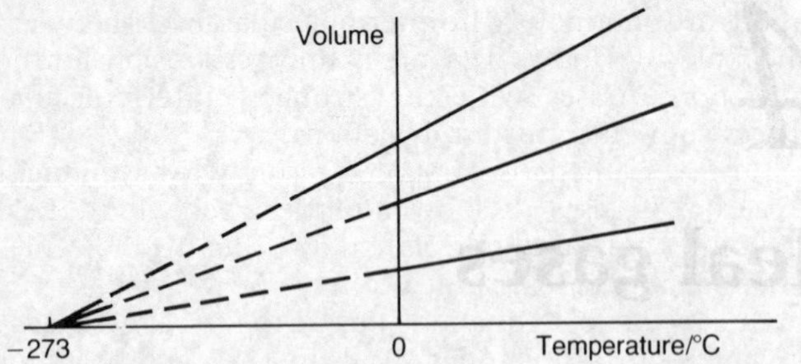

Figure 34.2 When graphs of volume against temperature are plotted for different gases the lines can be extended back to the imaginary case of zero volume. The temperature at this point is about −273° C

and we can use the −273° C point on the graph to define the zero of a new scale of temperature. This is the absolute or *Kelvin scale*. On this scale, temperature is measured in kelvins (K). We can convert between degrees Celsius and kelvins by adding 273; e.g. $100°\text{C} = (100 + 273)\text{K} = 373\text{K}$. Similarly, we convert kelvins to degrees Celsius by subtracting 273; e.g. $127\text{K} = (127 - 273)°\text{C} = -146°\text{C}$. Notice that the degrees sign, °, is *not* put next to the K of a temperature in kelvins.

Now let us think about keeping the temperature of the gas constant, but at the same time changing the pressure by moving the piston in or out. This type of experiment was first investigated by Robert Boyle in 1662. He showed that:

> **Provided the temperature is kept constant, the volume of a fixed mass of gas is inversely proportional to its pressure.**

This is a statement of *Boyle's law*. In simpler language it says that if the pressure is increased, then the volume gets smaller, and vice versa. In symbols we have

$$V \propto \frac{1}{p} \qquad (T \text{ constant})$$

Alternatively we can put

$$pV = \text{constant} \qquad \text{Boyle's law}$$

Graphs of volume plotted against pressure are curves; graphs of volume plotted against $1/p$ are straight lines (Figure 34.3).

We can combine Boyle's and Charles' laws into one grand summary of the properties of ideal gases by using the equation

$$\frac{pV}{T} = \text{constant}$$

The name given to the constant is, not too surprisingly, the gas constant, R. Its value is $8.314\,\text{J K}^{-1}\,\text{mol}^{-1}$. Then we have

$$\frac{pV}{T} = R$$

Actually, this equation is only true for 1 mol of gas. If we have n mol, we finally arrive at the *ideal gas equation*:

$$\frac{pV}{T} = nR$$

or

$$pV = nRT \qquad \text{Ideal gas equation}$$

When you use this equation, do be careful about the units: pressure p should be measured in N m^{-2} or Pa; volume V in m^3; and temperature T in K. Often pressure is also measured in atmospheres, atm. The conversion between the units can be done by noting that

$$1\,\text{atm} \equiv 1.013 \times 10^5\,\text{N m}^{-2} \quad \text{or} \quad 1\,\text{atm} \equiv 101.3\,\text{kPa}$$

However, if you use pressures in atmospheres, you will have to use the non-standard unit for the gas constant: $R = 0.082\,\text{dm}^3\,\text{atm K}^{-1}\,\text{mol}^{-1}$.

34.1 Why is it that at low pressures real gases begin to behave more like ideal gases?

34.2 The combination of temperature of 273 K and pressure of $1.013 \times 10^5\,\text{N m}^{-2}$ (0° C and 1 atm) is known as *standard temperature and pressure*, s.t.p.

Use the ideal gas equation to work out the volume that 1 mol of an ideal gas should have (i) at s.t.p., (ii) at 20° C (about room temperature) and (iii) at 100° C. Don't forget to convert to the Kelvin scale, and take the pressure as $1.013 \times 10^5\,\text{N m}^{-2}$ (1 atm if you prefer, but watch out for units!). Your answers should

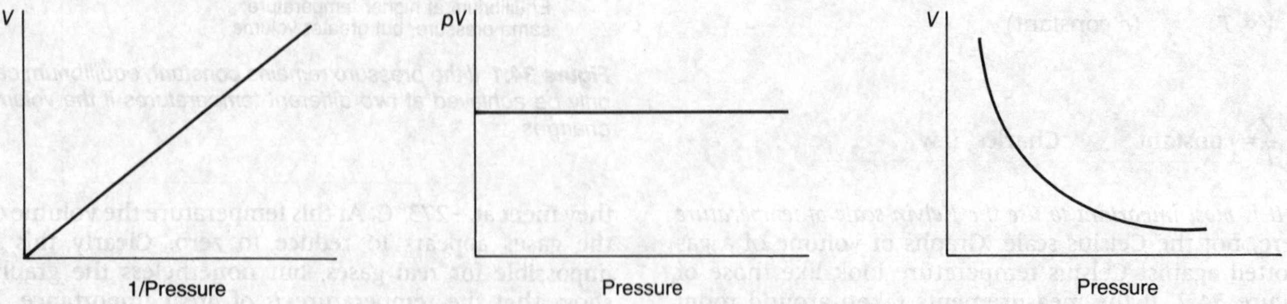

Figure 34.3 For an ideal gas, graphs of V against 1/p or pV against p are straight lines. A graph of V against p is a curve

come out as so many m^3. Convert them to dm^3 by multiplying by 10^3.

34.3 The ideal gas equation has often been used in the following way: we assume we have a gas under two different sets of conditions where the pressures, volumes and temperatures are written p_1, V_1, T_1 and p_2, V_2, T_2.

(i) Briefly explain, or show, why

$$\frac{p_1V_1}{T_1}=\frac{p_2V_2}{T_2}$$

(ii) A gas had a volume of 2 m^3 at s.t.p. Use this equation to work out the volume that the gas would occupy at 100 atm pressure ($100 \times 1.013 \times 10^5$ N m^{-2}) and 200° C.

34.2 Real gases and the van der Waals equation

It has been said that, if Boyle and Charles were doing their work with modern equipment, they would not have discovered their laws. This is not really true, but the idea behind the statement is that the sensitive apparatus that we now have available shows that no real gases obey their laws completely. Many behave in ways that would have made the laws difficult to discover. For example, if you were to use ammonia in a Boyle's law experiment performed with modern equipment, your results would fit a graph like Figure 34.4.

The graphs are definitely not straight lines. However, at low pressures the lines are very nearly straight. We call the lines that we should get from Boyle's law (or Charles' law) the *ideal gas* lines. Real gases show *deviations* from ideal gas behaviour. For some gases the deviations are very small; the noble gases helium, neon and argon are examples. For others, like ammonia, the deviations are enormous. The intermolecular forces between the molecules in a real gas are mainly responsible for the deviations. Gases with the strongest intermolecular forces show the greatest deviations.

However, there is another reason why we might expect real gases to show non-ideal behaviour. Real molecules have a volume of their own, but the molecules of an ideal gas are assumed to have no volume.

One of the first equations meant to fit real gases was invented by J. H. van der Waals in 1873 and bears his name. To see the effect of molecular size, imagine a large scale model of a gas in which tennis balls can bounce around at random in a box. If the box is a 1 m cube, its volume will be 1 m^3, or 10^6 cm^3. One tennis ball might have a volume of about 100 cm^3, so if we put one ball into the box, the next tennis ball no longer has 10^6 cm^3 to move around in. It only has $(10^6 - 100)$ cm^3. The third ball will be able to move in $(10^6 - 200)$ cm^3, and so on. (Actually the available volume is even less than these figures; to see why try question 34.4.) The key thing is that the volume of the container is not the volume in which the molecules can move. The actual volume open to them is less than that of the container. For this reason van der Waals wrote the volume of the gas as $V - nb$. Here n is the number of moles of gas, and b is the volume that is no longer available to each mole. Thus far we have

$$p(V-nb)=nRT$$

The second correction he made was to allow for intermolecular forces. If you were a molecule in the centre of a gas, or at least not close to the walls of the container, you would be surrounded by a sphere of other molecules. You would feel some attraction for them, and them for you. Because of the spherical arrangement you would experience the same strength of force in every direction (Figure 34.5). This cosy symmetrical situation does not hold near the walls of the container. Here you would have molecules on one side of you only. The

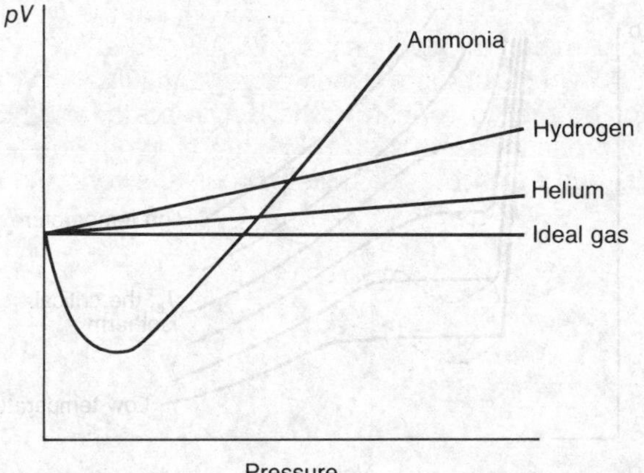

Figure 34.4 *Gases that have weak intermolecular forces give straight lines, which at low pressure are very close to the ideal gas line. Gases like ammonia, which have stronger intermolecular forces, give lines that are very different to the ideal gas line*

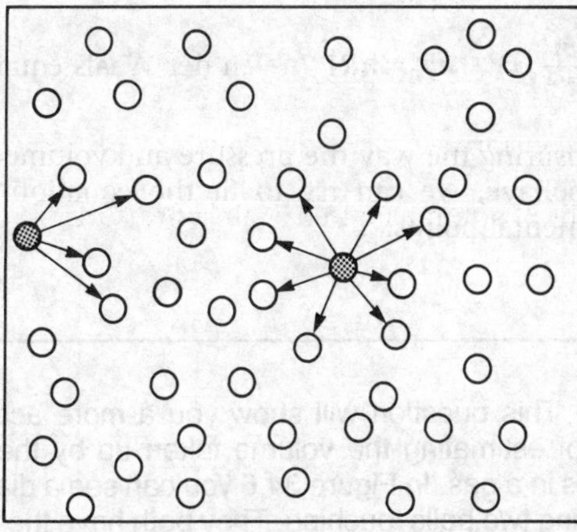

Figure 34.5 *A molecule towards the centre of a gas is surrounded by other molecules. The attractions between them tend to cancel out. A molecule near a wall of the container feels attractions that tend to pull it back into the main body of gas*

Panel 34.1

The pressure correction to the ideal gas equation

We can take n/V as a measure of the concentration (or density) of the molecules in the gas. The higher the concentration, the more molecules there will be in the body of the gas (towards the centre) and the more molecules there will be near the walls. The resulting pull will depend on both factors, so we can write:

$$\text{reduction in pressure} \propto \text{concentration of molecules near centre} \times \text{concentration of molecules near walls}$$

$$\propto \frac{n}{V} \times \frac{n}{V}$$

or,

$$\text{reduction in pressure} = \text{constant} \times \frac{n^2}{V^2} = \frac{an^2}{V^2}$$

where we have written the constant as a.

influence of their attractions would be to pull you back into the body of the gas (Figure 34.5). With this retarding force you would not collide with the walls of the container with the same speed or momentum as you would if the other molecules were absent. Given that the collisions of the molecules with the walls of the container give rise to the pressure of the gas, the effect of the intermolecular forces on the molecules near the walls is to *reduce* the pressure that the gas exerts. Therefore, if the real pressure is less than the ideal, we have to *add* a correction to the real pressure to give a value closer to the ideal figure. Van der Waals wrote the corrected pressure as $p + an^2/V^2$. You will discover the reason why in panel 34.1. Putting the volume and pressure corrections together we finally have

$$\left(p + \frac{an^2}{V^2}\right)(V - nb) = nRT \qquad \text{van der Waals equation}$$

By measuring the way the pressure and volume of real gases behave, we can try to fit the equation to the experimental points.

34.4 This question will show you a more accurate way of estimating the volume taken up by the molecules in a gas. In Figure 34.6 you can see a diagram showing two balls touching. They both have the same radius, r. Around one of the balls is a shaded circle (a sphere in three dimensions). The second ball cannot occupy the volume enclosed by the shaded sphere. (If it tried to get closer it would force the other ball out of the way.)

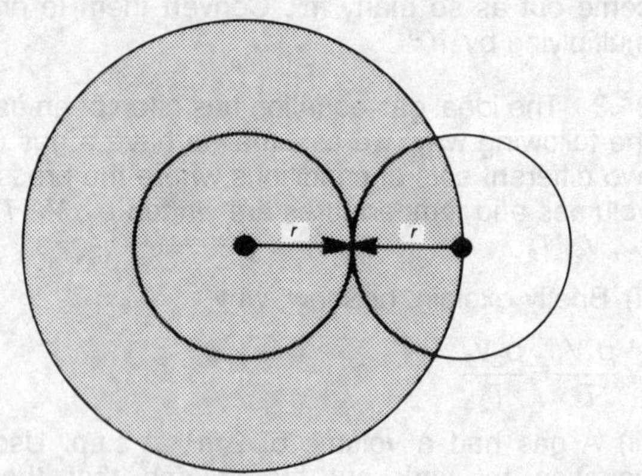

Figure 34.6 *The shaded area (volume in three dimensions) cannot contain both atoms at the same time*

(i) What is the formula for the volume around the first ball that the second ball cannot enter?

(ii) This is the volume that the *two* balls cannot both share. In a gas this would refer to two molecules rather than two balls. What is the effective volume occupied by one molecule?

(iii) How does this compare with the actual volume of one molecule?

34.3 How good is the van der Waals equation?

Figure 34.7 shows you the type of graph predicted from the van der Waals equation, and that obtained from experiment. Each of the lines on the graph shows how values of pressure and volume change at a fixed temperature. Each line is called an *isotherm*. Theory and

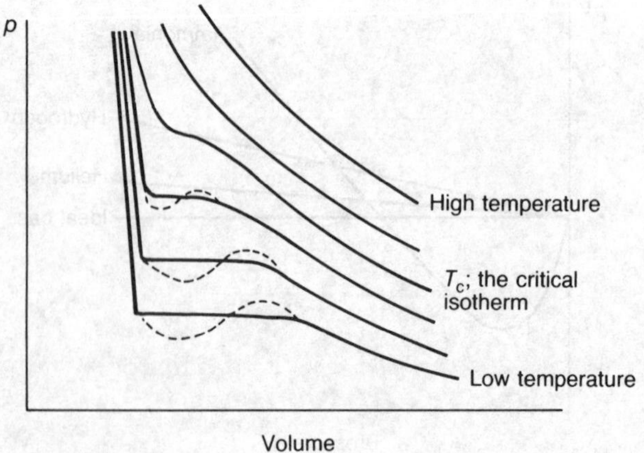

Figure 34.7 *Graphs of p against V predicted from the van der Waals equation (– – – – –) do agree with those obtained from experiment (——) at high temperature, but not at low temperature. Each curve shows the behaviour of a gas at one temperature; the curves are called isotherms*

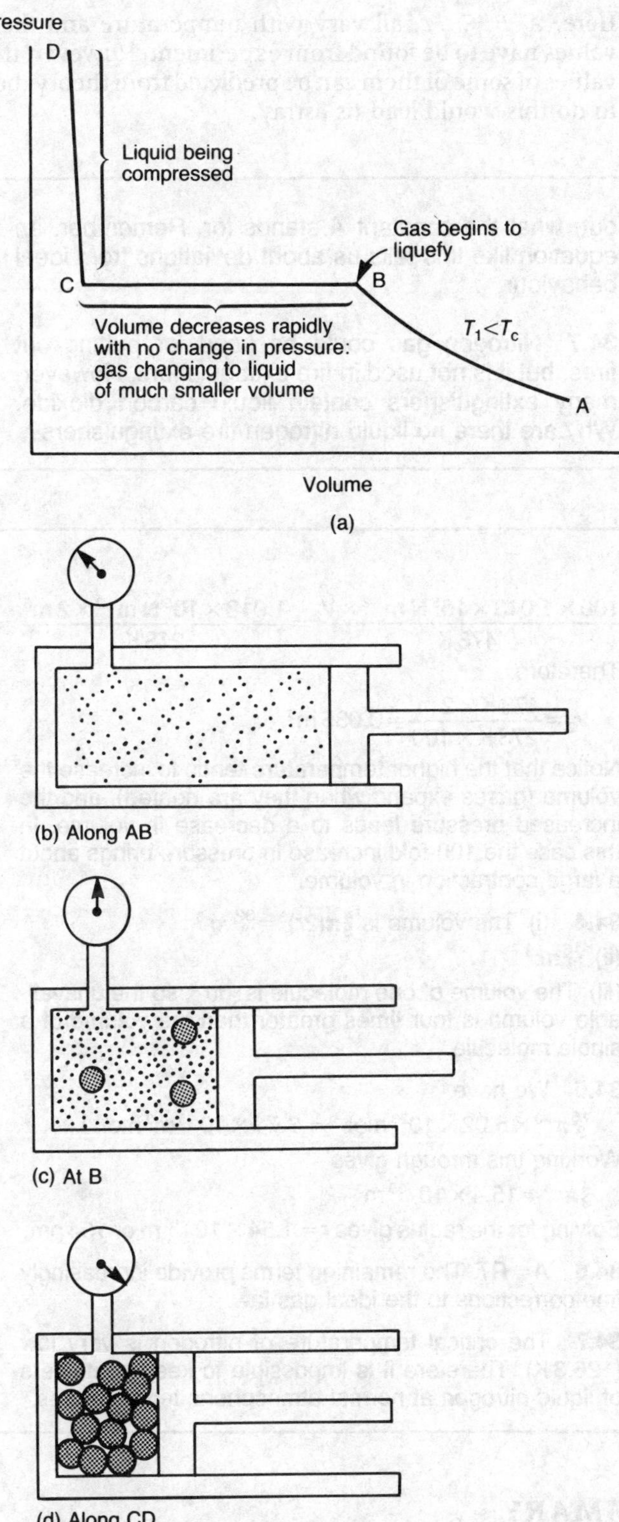

***Figure 34.8** How the volume of a real gas changes with pressure. (a) Isotherm for a gas at some temperature, T_1 (below its critical temperature). (b) At the beginning, as the piston is pushed in, the pressure increases as the molecules are confined to a smaller volume. (c) Gradually the molecules come closer and closer together. With real gases there comes a time when the molecules stick together. Liquid droplets start to appear. (d) Liquids are very hard to compress so there is little change in volume even for a large increase in pressure*

practice agree when the temperature is high. Then the isotherms look like the third graph of Figure 34.3, which fits Boyle's law. At lower temperatures, though, we run into trouble. For example, the isotherm of the real gas becomes horizontal, while the one predicted from the equation oscillates up and down. The reason for the difference is that, under particular conditions of temperature and pressure, real gases liquefy. This behaviour is not covered by the van der Waals equation.

To understand why the graph becomes horizontal, return to our example of the gas trapped in a cylinder fitted with a piston. Let us assume that we keep the gas at a low temperature, T_1 say, and that its starting volume is somewhere far to the right of the graph in Figure 34.8. As the pressure increases, the volume decreases; but at a particular pressure we know that real gases will liquefy. If you were able to look inside the cylinder you would see tiny droplets of liquid appear. The volume of the droplets will be very much smaller than the volume of the gas that it replaces, so the volume of the gas decreases rapidly. We would see the piston being pushed further into the cylinder by the outside pressure. This is what happens along the horizontal part of the graph. Eventually, when all the gas is liquefied, it takes a huge increase in pressure to change the volume. The molecules in a liquid are already very close together, so it is very hard to reduce the volume any further. This stage is shown by the lines becoming almost vertical on the graph.

One of the most interesting isotherms in Figure 34.7 is the one marked as the *critical isotherm*. This isotherm marks the border between gases and liquids. The temperature of the critical isotherm is called the *critical temperature*, T_c. Above T_c a gas will not liquefy, no matter how high the pressure. The reason for this behaviour is that the molecules have so much thermal energy that the intermolecular forces are not powerful enough to make the molecules stick together. Each gas has its own critical temperature because the strengths of the intermolecular forces in each gas are different. Below T_c a gas can be liquefied. You will find the critical temperatures of some gases in Table 34.1.

The van der Waals equation is surprisingly good when we take into account the fairly simple changes that were made to the ideal gas equation. Where it fails is in not taking intermolecular forces into account in sufficient detail to predict when a gas might liquefy. There have been other attempts to find an equation that fits real

Table 34.1. The critical temperatures of some gases

Gas	*Critical temperature/K*
Helium	5.2
Hydrogen	33.2
Nitrogen	126.3
Methane	191.1
Carbon dioxide	304.2
Ammonia	405.5

gases. One that has proved fairly successful is called the virial equation. It looks like this:

$$pV = A + \frac{B}{V} + \frac{C}{V^2} + \frac{D}{V^3} \ldots$$

Here, A, B, C, ... all vary with temperature and their values have to be found from experiment. However, the values of some of them can be predicted from theory; but to do this would lead us astray.

34.5 The value of the volume correction b in the van der Waals equation for ammonia is $3.71 \times 10^{-5}\ m^3\ mol^{-1}$. Use your answer to question 34.4 to estimate the radius of an ammonia molecule. Remember that the value of b is for 1 mol of molecules (the Avogadro constant, $L = 6.02 \times 10^{23}\ mol^{-1}$).

34.6 Look at the virial equation and guess (or work out) what the constant A stands for. Remember, an equation like this tells us about deviations from ideal behaviour.

34.7 Nitrogen gas could be used for putting out fires, but it is not used in fire extinguishers. However, many extinguishers contain liquid carbon dioxide. Why are there no liquid nitrogen fire extinguishers?

Answers

34.1 At low pressures the molecules are, on average, far apart. This means that the forces between them cannot get to work easily, so they wander around independently, like the molecules of an ideal gas.

34.2 We have $pV = RT$, or $V = RT/p$.

(i) $V = 8.314\ J\ K^{-1}\ mol^{-1} \times 273\ K / 1.013 \times 10^5\ N\ m^{-2}$
$= 22.41 \times 10^{-3}\ m^3\ mol^{-1}$

or $V = 22.41\ dm^3\ mol^{-1}$.

(ii), (iii) Similarly we find $V = 24.04\ dm^3$, and $V = 30.61\ dm^3$, respectively per mole of gas.

These results should confirm some approximations that you may have used if you have done calculations on gas volumes before. The two most important are that 1 mol of an ideal gas occupies approximately $22.4\ dm^3$ at s.t.p., and about $24\ dm^3$ at room temperature and pressure.

34.3 (i) Using $pV = nRT$ for the two conditions we have

$$p_1V_1 = nRT_1 \quad \text{or} \quad \frac{p_1V_1}{T_1} = nR$$

Similarly,

$$p_2V_2 = nRT_2 \quad \text{or} \quad \frac{p_2V_2}{T_2} = nR$$

This gives the result.

(ii) If we call p_1, etc., the final values, and p_2, etc., the starting values, we have

$$\frac{100 \times 1.013 \times 10^5\ N\ m^{-2} \times V_2}{473\ K} = \frac{1.013 \times 10^5\ N\ m^{-2} \times 2\ m^3}{273\ K}$$

Therefore,

$$V_2 = \frac{473\ K \times 2\ m^3}{273\ K \times 100} = 0.035\ m^3$$

Notice that the higher temperature tends to increase the volume (gases expand when they are heated), and the increased pressure leads to a decrease in volume. In this case the 100-fold increase in pressure brings about a large contraction in volume.

34.4 (i) The volume is $\frac{4}{3}\pi(2r)^3 = \frac{32}{3}\pi r^3$

(ii) $\frac{16}{3}\pi r^3$

(iii) The volume of one molecule is $\frac{4}{3}\pi r^3$, so the unavailable volume is four times greater than the volume of a single molecule.

34.5 We have

$$\tfrac{16}{3}\pi r^3 \times 6.02 \times 10^{23}\ mol^{-1} = 3.71 \times 10^{-5}\ m^3\ mol^{-1}$$

Working this through gives

$$\tfrac{4}{3}\pi r^3 = 15.4 \times 10^{-30}\ m^3$$

Solving for the radius gives $r = 1.54 \times 10^{-10}$ m or 154 pm.

34.6 $A = RT$. The remaining terms provide increasingly fine corrections to the ideal gas law.

34.7 The critical temperature of nitrogen is very low (126.3 K). Therefore it is impossible to keep containers of liquid nitrogen at normal atmospheric temperatures.

UNIT 34 SUMMARY

- The molecules in a gas are in a constant state of random motion.
- In an ideal gas there are no intermolecular forces and therefore no tendency for the gas to liquefy.
- An ideal gas can be thought of as a collection of tiny, hard, inelastic spheres in constant motion.
- The zero on the Kelvin scale of temperature is the temperature at which the volume of an ideal gas becomes zero.
- Charles' law says that:
  At a constant pressure the volume of a fixed mass of gas is proportional to its temperature.

- Boyle's law says that:
  Provided the temperature is kept constant, the volume of a fixed mass of gas is inversely proportional to its pressure.
- The ideal gas law is $pV/T =$ a constant or $pV = nRT$, where n is the number of moles of gas and R is the gas constant.
- Real gases do not obey the ideal gas law exactly; their behaviour is fitted better by equations that take into account intermolecular forces, e.g. the van der Waals equation.

35

Kinetic theory of gases

35.1 What is the kinetic theory of gases?

If you have read (and understood) Unit 34 you already know the basis of the theory. The main points, together with some that may be new to you, are listed in Table 35.1. Especially, pay attention to the characteristics of an ideal gas. This is a gas in which there are no intermolecular forces. No real gas is ideal, although some come close to ideal behaviour, e.g. helium. The power of the theory is that it allows us to account for the behaviour of ideal gases and, by making a few other assumptions, the properties of real gases as well. In the rest of this unit we shall see how this is done.

Table 35.1. The kinetic theory of gases

Main idea
Gases consist of molecules in a constant state of random motion
Related ideas
The pressure of a gas is due to the collisions of the molecules with the walls of the container
The molecules travel in straight lines unless they collide with one another, or with the walls of the container
In these collisions the total energy of the molecules does not change
Ideal gases
In an ideal gas the molecules have mass, but no size
In an ideal gas there are no intermolecular forces

35.2 The pressure of an ideal gas

In panel 35.1 and Figure 35.1 you will find a proof of the formula for the pressure of an ideal gas:

$$p = \tfrac{1}{3}Nm\overline{v^2}$$

This equation says that the pressure depends on N, the number of molecules per unit volume of the gas, on their mass, m, and on the mean square speed, $\overline{v^2}$.

Now, suppose the molecules were not all of the same

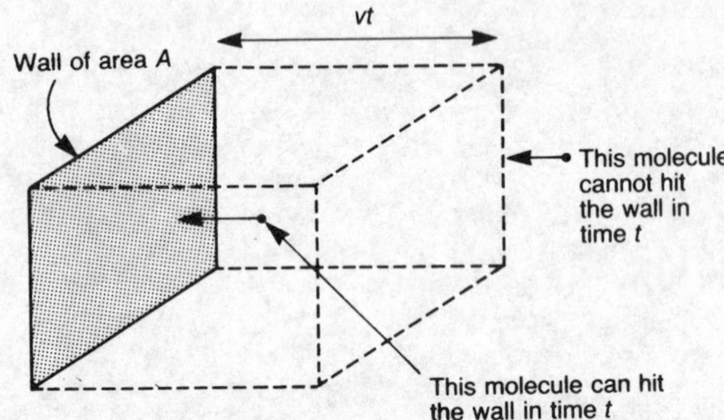

Figure 35.1 *Atoms within an imaginary box of length* vt *can hit the wall in time* t *(assuming they are travelling towards the wall)*

mass. If we had two types of molecule, say A and B, the pressure would be due to both of them bombarding the walls, and

$$\text{total pressure} = \tfrac{1}{3}N_A m_A \overline{v_A^2} + \tfrac{1}{3}N_B m_B \overline{v_B^2}$$

which is easier to write as

$$p_{total} = p_A + p_B$$

This is one way of writing *Dalton's law of partial pressures*. In words the law says that:

The total pressure of a mixture of gases is the sum of the pressures that each gas would have if it were on its own.

Strictly the law is only valid for ideal gases. Real gases do not obey the law perfectly.

35.1 (i) What happens to the average speed of the particles in a gas as the temperature increases?

(ii) Why does the pressure of a fixed volume of gas increase with temperature?

(iii) What happens to the pressure of an ideal gas if, at the same temperature, its volume is halved?

(iv) Explain your answer to (iii) in terms of the kinetic theory of gases.

35.3 The connection between energy and temperature

Another important result from kinetic theory (see panel 35.2) is that the average kinetic energy of a molecule in an ideal gas is given by

$$\tfrac{1}{2}m\overline{v^2} = \tfrac{3}{2}kT$$

where k is Boltzmann's constant, of value 1.38×10^{-23} J K^{-1}. The value of Boltzmann's constant multiplied by the Avogadro constant is the same as the gas constant, i.e. $R = Lk$, which has the value 8.314 J K^{-1} mol^{-1}.

The importance of the equation for the average kinetic energy of gas molecules is its link with the temperature of the gas. The factor 3 makes its appearance in the equation owing to the three directions in which a molecule can move. If it could only move in one direction, its average kinetic energy would only be $kT/2$. A molecule's ability to move in any one of a set number of ways is known as its *degrees of freedom*. A molecule in an ideal gas has three degrees of freedom. You may find in some more advanced books that it is said (correctly) that each degree of freedom counts an amount $kT/2$ towards the energy. Non-ideal gases may have other degrees of freedom, for example due to their vibrations and rotations. The sharing out of energy, giving $kT/2$ to each degree of freedom, is called the principle of *equipartition of energy*.

Armed with the equation and the formula for the pressure of an ideal gas, we can combine them to give

$$p = NkT$$

where N is the number of molecules per unit volume. Now let us assume that we have 1 mol of gas; then we calculate the number of particles from the Avogadro constant:

$$N = 1\text{ mol} \times 6.02 \times 10^{23}\text{ mol}^{-1} = 6.02 \times 10^{23}$$

Similarly, if we had n mol of gas,

$$N = n\text{ mol} \times 6.02 \times 10^{23}\text{ mol}^{-1}$$

In general, without writing the units,

$$N = nL$$

so

$$p = \frac{nLkT}{V}$$

or

$$pV = nRT \qquad \text{Ideal gas equation}$$

We have produced the ideal gas equation that we used in the previous unit.

Panel 35.1

The formula for the pressure of an ideal gas

To calculate the formula for the pressure of a gas, let us think about one molecule travelling towards the wall of the container, as in Figure 35.1.

To keep things simple let us assume that it is travelling at 90° to the wall. If it has a mass m and it is moving with speed v, then its momentum is mv. Now, to stop the molecule dead we would have to give it an exactly equal and opposite momentum; call this 'one lot of mv'. Now, the molecule does not stop dead; it bounces off the wall. If we assume that it loses no energy in this process, it will travel away from the wall with the same momentum, mv. To give it this momentum, an extra 'one lot of mv' is needed. Therefore the *change* in momentum during the collision with the wall is $2mv$. The force on the wall is the change in momentum divided by the time taken, so we can put

$$\text{force on wall} = \frac{2mv}{t}$$

Similarly, because pressure is force/area, for one molecule we have

$$\text{pressure on wall} = \frac{2mv}{tA}$$

We can simplify this as follows. A molecule travelling with speed v will travel a distance vt in time t. Therefore any molecule further away than this will not hit the wall in this time, and will not contribute to the pressure. However, any molecule at this distance, or nearer, *will* hit the wall. Over the area A of wall, there will be a volume $A \times vt$, or Avt, in which molecules liable to hit the wall can be found. If there are N molecules of gas per unit volume, the number of molecules hitting the wall is $NAvt$. Therefore, for the gas,

$$\text{pressure on wall} = \frac{2mv}{tA} \times NAvt = 2Nmv^2$$

Now let us look at the diagram in Figure 35.1 again. We have dealt with only one wall of the container. In fact there are six walls of area A (assuming the container is a cube), so on average only one-sixth of the molecules will hit any one wall. This means we should change our formula to

$$\text{pressure on wall} = \tfrac{1}{3}Nmv^2$$

Now for the last step. The molecules do not all travel with the same speed, so the change in momentum and the pressure they exert should be averaged. We show that we are taking an average by writing a bar above the v^2, like this: $\overline{v^2}$. This really is the final equation for the pressure in an ideal gas:

$$p = \tfrac{1}{3}Nm\overline{v^2}$$

Panel 35.2

The connection between the average kinetic energy of molecules and the temperature of a gas

Our starting point is

$$p=\tfrac{1}{3}Nm\overline{v^2}$$

We also know that $pV=RT$, so putting the two equations together,

$$\tfrac{1}{3}Nm\overline{v^2}=\frac{RT}{V}$$

N is the number of molecules per unit volume, so if we make V the volume of 1 mol of gas, then there must be 6.02×10^{23} particles present, i.e. $N=L/V$. Putting this into the left-hand side and rearranging we get

$$m\overline{v^2}=\frac{3RT}{L}$$

But $R=Lk$ where k is Boltzmann's constant, so

$$m\overline{v^2}=3kT$$

Given that the average kinetic energy is $m\overline{v^2}/2$ we find

$$\tfrac{1}{2}m\overline{v^2}=\tfrac{3}{2}kT$$

This is the equation we were looking for.

35.4 The spread of energies in a gas

One of the nice things about the kinetic theory is that we can use it to estimate the speeds of molecules in a gas. For example, let us use

$$\tfrac{1}{2}m\overline{v^2}=\tfrac{3}{2}kT$$

for helium at 25°C (298 K). In this case $m=6.64\times10^{-27}$ kg and a short calculation shows that

$$\overline{v^2}=1.86\times10^6\,\text{m}^2\,\text{s}^{-2}$$

If we take the square root of $\overline{v^2}$ we have found the value of the *root mean square* speed of the molecules. For helium it is 1.36×10^3 m s^{-1}. Alternatively, this is approaching 5000 kph (kilometres per hour). The *average* speed of the molecules is about 8% less than the root mean square speed, so the average speed of a helium atom at 25°C is approximately 1.25×10^3 m s^{-1}.

Of course, it is one thing to calculate the speeds of gas molecules from theory, quite another to measure them by experiment. One type of experiment that does just this was performed by Zartman in 1931 (although he was not the first to think of the method). A diagram of his apparatus is shown in Figure 35.2.

Zartman evaporated bismuth by placing a small amount of the element into a specially designed oven at over 800°C. Some of the bismuth atoms were able to escape through a small slit. The second slit ensured that the atoms were travelling in one direction. In front of the beam was a rotating drum, which also had a small slit in it. Once in every revolution the three slits were lined up, so bismuth atoms could enter the drum. You might like to look at Figure 35.3 to help you understand the next

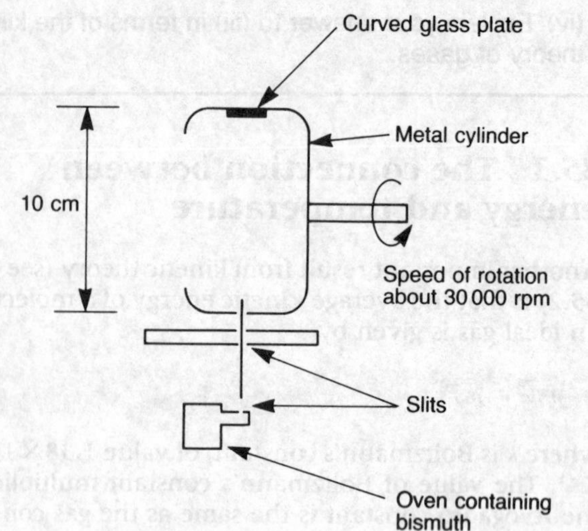

Figure 35.2 *Zartman's apparatus for determining molecular velocities. Bismuth atoms escaped from the oven through a series of narrow slits (the one in the cylinder was 0.05 mm). The atoms sped across the cylinder and were deposited on the glass plate. Afterwards the plate was removed and the darkening caused by the bismuth atoms was measured. The whole apparatus was kept in a vacuum. It took up to 22 hours for sufficient bismuth to build up on the plate*

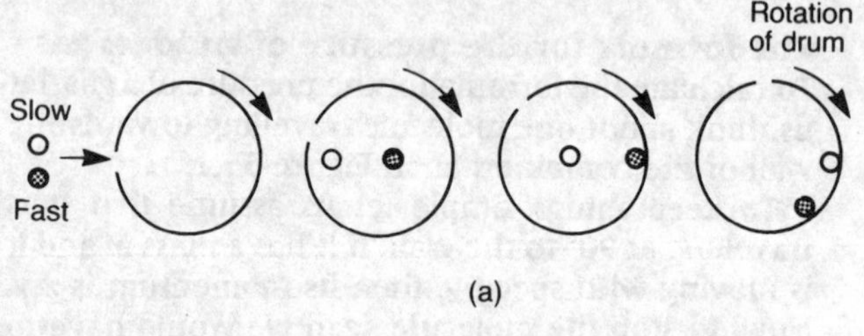

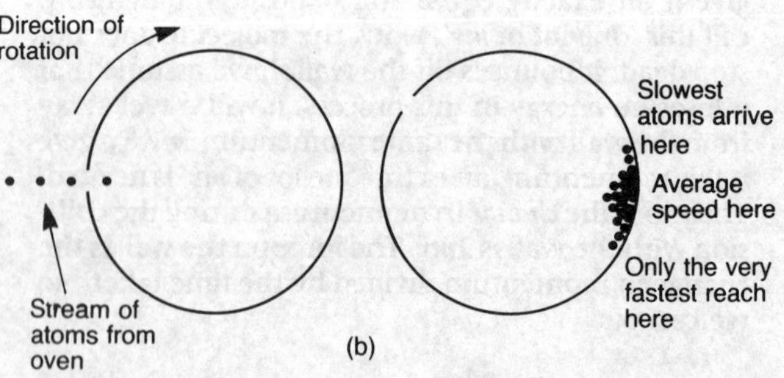

Figure 35.3 *In Zartman's experiment, atoms (or molecules) travelling with different speeds arrive at different places on the inside of the revolving drum. (a) Two atoms, one moving slowly and one moving faster, enter the rotating drum at the same time. The faster one hits the other side of the drum before the slower one. In this way the place where the atoms hit the drum is related to the speed of the atoms. (b) For a stream of atoms, a distribution is obtained on the inside of the drum*

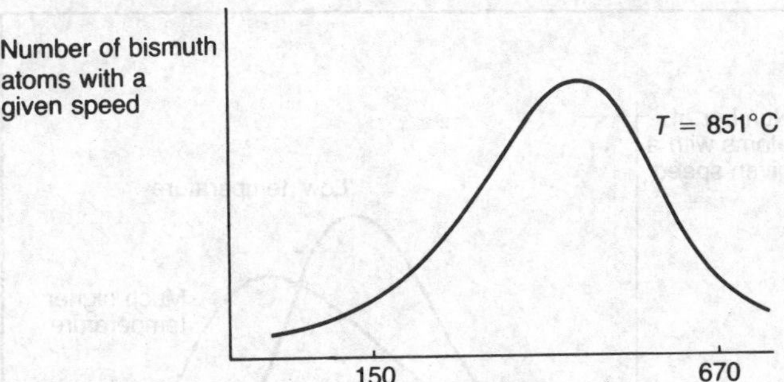

***Figure 35.4** The distribution of speeds among gaseous bismuth atoms*

stage. If you imagine yourself to be an atom moving very quickly through the slit in the drum, you would see the far surface of the drum moving clockwise (as we have drawn it). You would hit the surface at a point not quite opposite the slit. However, if you were an atom with a much slower speed, you would see the drum move a considerable distance before you collided with the far surface.

If the drum is kept rotating at a constant speed, you should realise that where an atom (or molecule) hits the inside of the drum depends on the atom's (or molecule's) speed. By measuring the degree of darkening of the surface (which was made of glass), it is possible to estimate the number of atoms (or molecules) that enter the drum with a particular speed.

A graph of the number of bismuth atoms plotted against their speed is shown in Figure 35.4. This graph shows us the *distribution* of the speeds (or velocities) of the atoms. Notice that the distribution is not symmetrical. There is a longer 'tail' at lower speeds than at higher speeds. The shape of this distribution had been worked out many years before by James Clerk Maxwell in 1860. For this reason we speak about a *Maxwellian distribution* of speeds (or velocities).

In a later unit you will find that a knowledge of the Maxwellian distribution is very helpful in explaining the rates of chemical reactions.

35.2 Write a computer program that will allow you to calculate the root mean square speed and the average speed of a molecule in any gas (assuming it is ideal). Your program should ask the user to type in the molecular mass (in grams) of the gas and the temperature. (Watch out for people who use °C, and who try to use unrealistic values.)

35.3 The formula for the Maxwellian speed distribution, $D(v)$, is

$$D(v)=\frac{4\pi M^{3/2}v^2}{2RT}\exp\left(-\frac{Mv^2}{2RT}\right)$$

Here M is the mass of 1 mol of the gas (expressed in kg). Again, use a computer to calculate values of $D(v)$ and plot them against v. Try plotting the distribution at various temperatures.

35.4 Figure 35.5 is a diagram taken from Zartman's research paper. The vertical axis gives the intensity of the deposit of atoms on the inside of the revolving drum. The horizontal axis gives the speed of the atoms hitting the drum. His scale ran from a speed of around 170 m s^{-1} to 700 m s^{-1}.

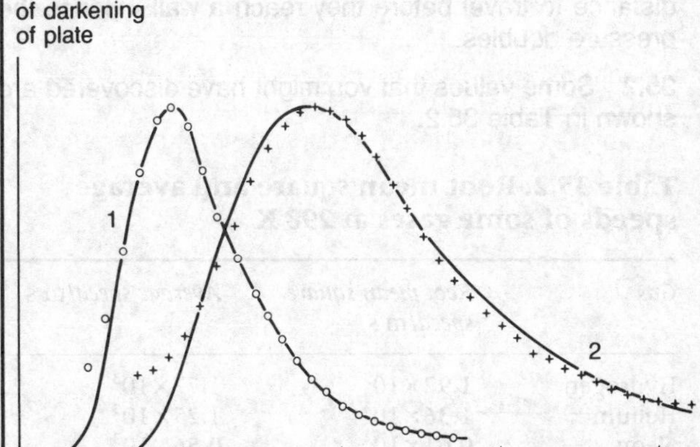

***Figure 35.5** Diagram for question 35.4. Curve 1 was found using a speed of rotation of 120.7 rps (revolutions per second) and curve 2 at 241.4 rps. (Adapted from: Zartman, I. F. (1931). Phys. Rev.* ***37**, 383–91)*

Should the high speed be on the left of the axis or the right?

35.5 Kinetic theory and Avogadro's theory

In the following unit we shall find that Avogadro's theory (equal volumes of gases contain equal numbers of molecules) was based on Gay-Lussac's experimental evidence. Here we can show that his theory is correct. If we have equal volumes of two gases, A and B, at the same temperature, they must be in equilibrium with each other. Their pressures will be the same, so we can put

$$\tfrac{1}{3}N_A m_A\overline{v_A^2}=\tfrac{1}{3}N_B m_B\overline{v_B^2}$$

But also, because they are at the same temperature, the average kinetic energies of their molecules must be the same, i.e.

$$\tfrac{1}{2}m_A\overline{v_A^2}=\tfrac{1}{2}m_B\overline{v_B^2}$$

Putting the two equations together, we must have $N_A=N_B$. That is, we have shown that, under the same conditions of temperature and pressure, equal volumes of all gases contain the same number of molecules.

Answers

35.1 (i) It increases.

(ii) As the speed increases, the momentum of the particles increases as well. Therefore the force of the collisions on any given area of the walls increases. We observe the effect as an increase in pressure.

(iii) The pressure doubles.

(iv) Halving the volume will double the number of collisions of the particles with the walls of the container. (The particles travelling across the container have a shorter distance to travel before they reach a wall.) Hence the pressure doubles.

35.2 Some values that you might have discovered are shown in Table 35.2.

Table 35.2. Root mean square and average speeds of some gases at 298 K

Gas	*Root mean square speed*/m s^{-1}	*Average speed*/m s^{-1}
Hydrogen	1.92×10^3	1.77×10^3
Helium	1.36×10^3	1.25×10^3
Neon	0.61×10^3	0.56×10^3
Nitrogen	0.51×10^3	0.47×10^3
Oxygen	0.48×10^3	0.44×10^3
Carbon dioxide	0.41×10^3	0.38×10^3

35.3 Your graphs should look like those in Figure 35.6. Notice that the curves spread out further to the right at high temperatures. As we should expect, there are more molecules with higher energies at higher temperatures. At the same time, the height of the curve decreases. This must occur because the area under the curve gives the total number of atoms, which remains constant. The more the curve stretches, the lower the height. You will find out more about this in Unit 78.

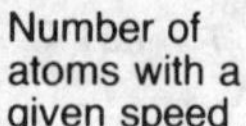

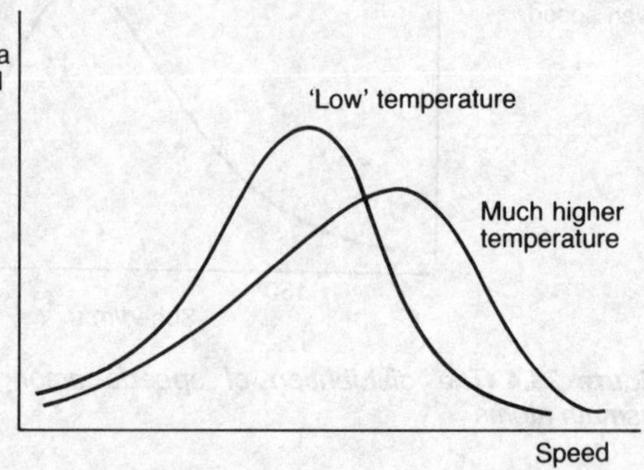

***Figure 35.6** How the distribution of molecular speeds changes with temperature*

35.4 The high speed is on the left of the scale and the low speed on the right. The distribution of molecular velocities tails off more sharply on the high speed side. Actually the distribution is not for pure bismuth atoms but a mixture containing 40% bismuth atoms, Bi, and 60% bismuth molecules, Bi_2.

UNIT 35 SUMMARY

- The kinetic theory of gases says that:
  - (i) Gas pressure reflects the collisions of molecules with the walls of the container, and the transfer of momentum to the walls.
  - (ii) The temperature of a gas is determined by the average kinetic energy of the molecules.
- The spread of energies among gas molecules can be measured by Zartman's rotating drum method.
- The distribution of molecular velocities shows that most molecules have energies near the average, with some molecules having energies considerably greater and smaller than the average.

36

Chemistry and gases

36.1 Gay-Lussac's law of combining volumes

Here is an extract from a scientific paper written by Joseph Louis Gay-Lussac in 1808:

> At least, it is my intention to make known some new properties in gases, the effects of which are regular, by showing that these substances combine amongst themselves in very simple proportions, and that the contraction of volume which they experience on combination also follows a regular law. I hope by this means to give a proof of an idea advanced by several very distinguished chemists – that we are perhaps not far removed from the time when we shall be able to submit the bulk of chemical phenomena to calculation.... Gases, ... in whatever proportions they may combine, always give rise to compounds whose elements by volume are multiples of each other.

In this passage Gay-Lussac announced the law that is now known as *Gay-Lussac's law of combining volumes*. In a more exact way the law is:

When gases combine together they do so in volumes that are in a simple whole number ratio to each other and to that of the product (if it is a gas).

It is assumed that the gas volumes are measured at the same temperature and pressure.

Gay-Lussac was also correct about the results of his experiments leading to the time when it became possible to predict not just what would be made in a chemical reaction, but *how much* would be made. However, even as great a chemist as Dalton was not entirely convinced that Gay-Lussac was correct. In 1810 Dalton wrote:

> ... The truth is, I believe, that gases do not unite in equal or exact measures in any one instance; when they appear to do so, it is owing to the inaccuracy of our experiments.

However, Dalton pointed out that:

> In fact, his [Gay-Lussac's] notion of measures is analogous to mine of atoms; and if it could be proved that all elastic fluids [gases] have the same number of atoms in the same volume, or numbers that are as 1, 2, 3, etc. the two hypotheses would be the same, except that mine is universal, and his applies only to elastic fluids.

It is clear that Dalton saw a link between Gay-Lussac's work on volumes of gases and his own idea that all chemicals were built from individual atoms. Dalton was also claiming that his ideas were the more powerful of the two. (This is not uncommon among scientists, as it is with people in general; everyone likes to think that herself or himself is right.)

36.1 Gay-Lussac reported the following results:

We may then admit the following numbers for the proportions by volume of the compounds of nitrogen with oxygen:

	Nitrogen	*Oxygen*
Nitrous oxide	100	50
Nitrous gas	100	100
Nitric acid	100	200

By looking at the proportions in which the two gases combined, see if you can work out the formulae of the gases that Gay-Lussac made. Remember that the names used when he was alive might not carry the same meaning as now.

36.2 Avogadro's theory

The idea that equal volumes of gases might contain equal numbers of atoms was given by Amadeo Avogadro in 1811. He made more exact the connection between gas volumes and atoms. The title of Avogadro's paper was 'Essay on a manner of determining the relative masses of the elementary molecules of bodies, and the proportions in which they enter into these compounds'. He said:

> It must then be admitted that very simple relations also exist between the volumes of gaseous substances and

the numbers of simple or compound molecules which form them. The first hypothesis to present itself in this connection, and apparently even the only admissible one, is the supposition that the number of integral molecules in any gases is always the same for equal volumes, or always proportional to the volumes.

The thing to notice about this passage is Avogadro's use of the term *molecule*. In his writing he tended to use this word in a variety of different senses, but he certainly used it at times in the same way that we do now. The leap in imagination that Avogadro had made was to realise that a single atom was not necessarily the basic building block of gases:

... we suppose ... that the constituent molecules of any simple gas whatever ... are not formed of a solitary elementary molecule, but are made up of a certain number of these molecules united by attraction to form a single one.

In this passage he uses the term 'elementary molecule' to mean a single atom. His 'compound molecule' is two or more atoms joined together.

Let us see how Avogadro's and Gay-Lussac's ideas work out in our modern language of chemistry. The results of Gay-Lussac's investigations had shown that hydrogen and chlorine gas reacted in the ratio of one volume of hydrogen to one volume of chlorine to give two volumes of hydrogen chloride:

$$\underset{\text{1 vol}}{\text{hydrogen}} + \underset{\text{1 vol}}{\text{chlorine}} \rightarrow \underset{\text{2 vols}}{\text{hydrogen chloride}}$$

If, as was originally thought, the smallest part of each of these gases was one atom, and if, as Dalton wondered, gases 'have the same number of atoms in the same volume', then we should have

$$\underset{\text{1 atom}}{\text{hydrogen}} + \underset{\text{1 atom}}{\text{chlorine}} \rightarrow \underset{\text{2 atoms}}{\text{hydrogen chloride}}$$

We can ask how it is possible to get only one atom of hydrogen chloride, and the answer is

$$\underset{\text{1/2 atom}}{\text{hydrogen}} + \underset{\text{1/2 atom}}{\text{chlorine}} \rightarrow \underset{\text{1 atom}}{\text{hydrogen chloride}}$$

But one of the key assumptions of the atomic theory was (and is) that fractions of atoms cannot exist. It was Avogadro who saw the way round the problem. In effect his suggestion was that the smallest part of each of the gases was a molecule; and the molecules were made out of atoms joined together. This allows us to write the reaction in a way that might be familiar to you:

$$\underset{\text{1 vol}}{\text{hydrogen}} + \underset{\text{1 vol}}{\text{chlorine}} \rightarrow \underset{\text{2 vols}}{\text{hydrogen chloride}}$$

$$H_2(g) \quad + \quad Cl_2(g) \quad \rightarrow \quad 2\,HCl(g)$$

Now we can say that one molecule of hydrogen will be made from half ***molecules***, i.e. atoms, of hydrogen and chlorine. If this seems obvious, please do appreciate that it was not always so.

In its modern version, Avogadro's theory says that:

Under the same conditions of temperature and pressure, equal volumes of all gases contain the same number of molecules.

The *Avogadro constant L* is our measure of the number of particles in each mole of a gas. Its value is approximately $6.02 \times 10^{23}\ \text{mol}^{-1}$. Notice the units of L. It is not a pure number, although you may find books call it the 'Avogadro number'. You will find the definition of the Avogadro constant in Unit 37.

36.2 Avogadro made the following observations:

100 parts of muriatic gas saturate precisely 100 parts of ammonia gas, and the salt which is formed from them is perfectly neutral, whether one or the other gases is in excess.

(i) What might be the modern name of muriatic gas?

(ii) Avogadro also mentioned that '... muriatic gas is formed by the combination of equal volumes of oxymuriatic gas and hydrogen, and that its volume is equal to their sum' and that on reacting 'muriatic gas' with oxygen, the product was 'oxygenated muriatic acid'. Can you work out what the modern name of oxymuriatic gas is, and write down the equation for the reaction?

36.3 Dalton's law of partial pressures

John Dalton was a busy man; not only did he invent the atomic theory, but he made several contributions to the understanding of the behaviour of gases. Not the least of these was his *law of partial pressures*, which he proposed in 1802. It says that:

The total pressure exerted by a mixture of gases is the sum of the pressures that the individual gases would exert if they were to occupy the same volume alone.

In symbols, for a mixture of gases A and B, the total pressure p_{total} is given by

$$p_{\text{total}} = p_A + p_B \qquad \textbf{Dalton's law of partial pressures}$$

This law is not obeyed by all mixtures of gases, but it is often a very good approximation. In the last unit we saw how this law could be explained by the kinetic theory of gases.

36.4 Graham's law of diffusion

In your laboratory you may find a small jar called a porous pot. It is made of a clay-like material, which has millions of tiny channels through it. If you were to put water in it you would see the outside become damp, but the water would not pour through in large amounts. Likewise, if you were to put oxygen in the jar (and close it with a lid) the oxygen would escape, but over a period of time. The movement of the molecules through the channels in the pot is called *diffusion*. A similar effect takes place if oxygen is trapped in a gas jar closed with a piece of card. If a pin hole were made in the card the oxygen would gradually escape. The movement of a gas through a small hole is sometimes called effusion, but we shall continue to call it diffusion. If a gas is allowed to pour out all at once from a container, mass (or bulk) flow takes place. This is quite different to diffusion.

In 1829 Thomas Graham published 'A short account of experimental researches on the diffusion of gases through each other and their separation by mechanical means'. He filled tubes like those shown in Figure 36.1

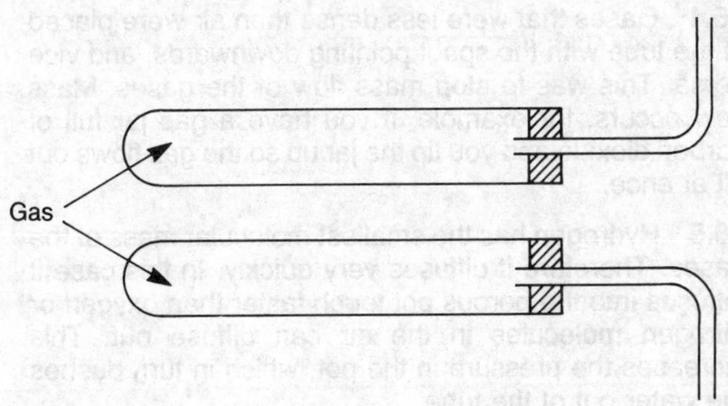

Figure 36.1 *The type of tube used by Graham to investigate diffusion*

with a measured amount of various gases. After leaving them for 10 hours he determined the amount of gas left. He said:

> It is evident that the diffusiveness of the gases is inversely as some function of their density – apparently the square root of their density.

This is *Graham's law*; in symbols it says that

$$\text{rate of diffusion of a gas} \propto \sqrt{\frac{1}{\text{density of the gas}}} \qquad \text{Graham's law}$$

If we compare two gases, A and B,

$$\frac{\text{rate for gas A}}{\text{rate for gas B}} = \sqrt{\frac{\text{density of B}}{\text{density of A}}}$$

We can put this in a different way by realising that density is proportional to relative molecular mass. This gives us

$$\frac{\text{rate for gas A}}{\text{rate for gas B}} = \sqrt{\frac{M_B}{M_A}}$$

The importance of this result was realised by Graham. In the title to his publication he referred to the separation of gases. The idea is that if a mixture of gases is allowed to diffuse through a barrier, then the lighter gases will escape from the mixture more rapidly than the heavier ones. This fact has been used in the separation of the isotopes $^{238}_{92}U$ and $^{235}_{92}U$. The isotope $^{235}_{92}U$ is the one that was the basis of the first atomic bombs. To separate this isotope from the very much more abundant $^{238}_{92}U$ (roughly 1% compared to 99%), the uranium was converted to gaseous uranium hexafluoride. The difference in rates of diffusion of $^{235}UF_6$ and $^{238}UF_6$ is small, but after many diffusion cycles, the $^{235}UF_6$ can be separated.

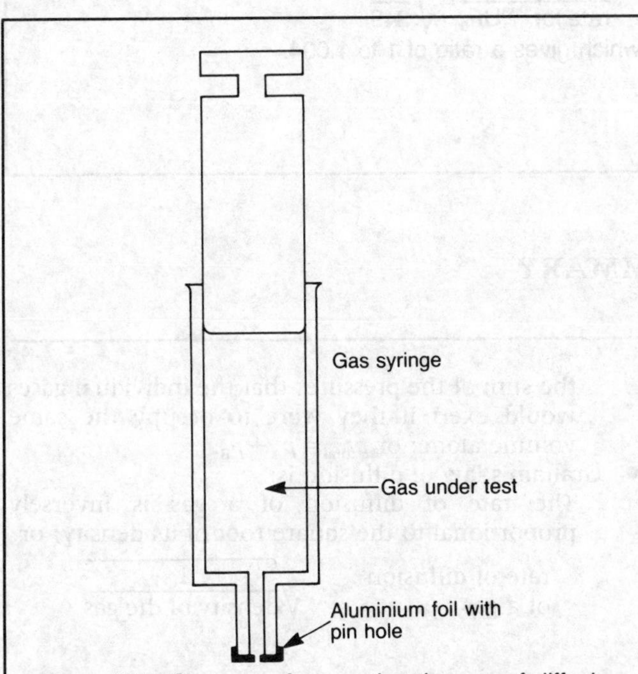

Figure 36.2 *One way of measuring the rate of diffusion of a gas*

36.3 Another way of performing Graham's experiments is shown in Figure 36.2. A gas syringe is filled with a gas. The nozzle of the syringe should be capped with a thin piece of metal foil with a tiny pin hole in it through which the gas can escape. It took 120 s for

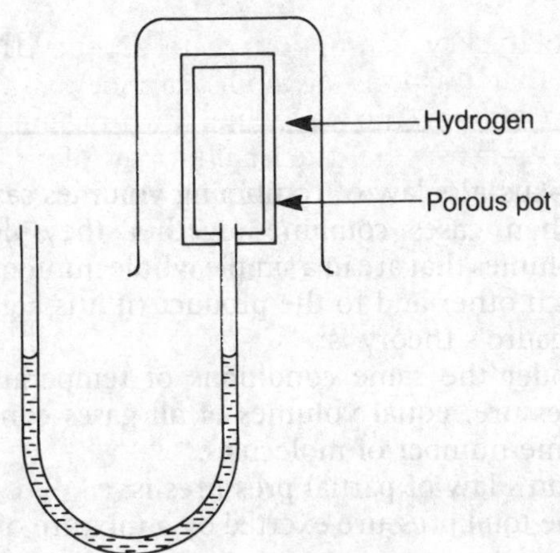

Figure 36.3 *The diagram for question 36.5*

100 cm³ of oxygen to diffuse through the hole. 100 cm³ of another gas took 170 s.

(i) What was the molecular mass of the second gas?

(ii) Can you suggest the name of the gas?

36.4 Why do you think Graham used two types of tube, one with the outlet pointing upwards, the other downwards?

36.5 Look at Figure 36.3. Why does the water rush out of the open end of the tube?

36.6 What is the relative rate of diffusion of $^{235}UF_6$ and $^{238}UF_6$? (The relative atomic masses are: $A_r(^{235}U) = 235$; $A_r(^{238}U) = 238$; $A_r(F) = 19$.)

Answers

36.1 The ratio of nitrogen molecules to oxygen molecules in the equations is the same ratio as their reacting volumes. The data he gives fit the equations

$2N_2(g) + O_2(g) \rightarrow 2N_2O(g)$ 'nitrous oxide' (dinitrogen oxide)

$N_2(g) + O_2(g) \rightarrow 2NO(g)$ 'nitrous gas' (nitrogen monoxide)

$N_2(g) + 2O_2(g) \rightarrow 2NO_2(g)$ 'nitric acid' (nitrogen dioxide)

The latter gives nitric acid when dissolved in water.

36.2 (i) *Hydrogen chloride* is the gas, and gives ammonium chloride with ammonia.

(ii) The gas is chlorine, the name first given to it by Sir Humphrey Davy. The reaction is

$$\underset{1\text{ vol}}{Cl_2(g)} + \underset{1\text{ vol}}{H_2(g)} \rightarrow \underset{2\text{ vols}}{2HCl(g)}$$

36.3 We have

$$\text{rate}_{O_2} = \frac{100\text{ cm}^3}{120\text{ s}} \qquad \text{rate}_{gas} = \frac{100\text{ cm}^3}{170\text{ s}}$$

Therefore,

$$\frac{\text{rate of diffusion of oxygen}}{\text{rate of diffusion of gas}} = \frac{170\text{ s}}{120\text{ s}} = \sqrt{\frac{\text{molecular mass of gas}}{\text{molecular mass of oxygen}}}$$

This means that

$$\frac{M_{gas}}{32} = \left(\frac{170}{120}\right)^2$$

which gives $M_{gas} = 64.2$. The likely suspect is sulphur dioxide, SO_2.

36.4 Gases that were less dense than air were placed in the tube with the spout pointing downwards, and vice versa. This was to stop mass flow of the gases. Mass flow occurs, for example, if you have a gas jar full of carbon dioxide and you tip the jar up so the gas flows out all at once.

36.5 Hydrogen has the smallest molecular mass of the gases. Therefore it diffuses very quickly. In this case it diffuses into the porous pot much faster than oxygen or nitrogen molecules in the air can diffuse out. This increases the pressure in the pot, which in turn pushes the water out of the tube.

36.6 $M_r(^{235}UF_6) = 349$; $M_r(^{238}UF_6) = 352$. Thus the relative rates are

$$\frac{\text{rate for } ^{235}UF_6}{\text{rate for } ^{238}UF_6} = \sqrt{\frac{352}{349}}$$

which gives a ratio of 1 to 1.004.

UNIT 36 SUMMARY

- Gay–Lussac's law of combining volumes says that: When gases combine together they do so in volumes that are in a simple whole number ratio to each other and to the product (if it is a gas).
- Avogadro's theory is: Under the same conditions of temperature and pressure, equal volumes of all gases contain the same number of molecules.
- Dalton's law of partial pressures is: The total pressure exerted by a mixture of gases is the sum of the pressures that the individual gases would exert if they were to occupy the same volume alone; or $p_{total} = p_A + p_B$.
- Graham's law of diffusion is: The rate of diffusion of a gas is inversely proportional to the square root of its density; or

$$\text{rate of diffusion of a gas} \propto \sqrt{\frac{1}{\text{density of the gas}}}$$

37

The mole

37.1 What is the mole?

The mole is a chemist's measure of the *amount of substance*. It is defined according to the number of particles that the substance contains. In particular, we use the definition:

One mole of a chemical species contains the same number of particles as there are atoms in 12 g of the isotope carbon-12 ($^{12}_{6}C$).

It follows that if we have 12 g of carbon-12 then we must have one mole, 1 mol, of it. Experiment shows that the number of atoms in 12 g of carbon-12 is approximately 6.022×10^{23}. This is the number of particles per mole of carbon-12, and it gives us our definition of the *Avogadro constant, L*, i.e.

$$L = 6.022 \times 10^{23}\ \text{mol}^{-1}$$

Notice that the constant has units mol^{-1}.

Using the Avogadro constant we can calculate the number of atoms in any quantity of carbon-12. For example, the number of atoms in 3 mol of carbon-12 is $6.022 \times 10^{23}\ \text{mol}^{-1} \times 3\ \text{mol} = 18.066 \times 10^{23}$. (Be sure you spot the way the units are used, and finally cancel. A pure number has no units.)

Owing to the way we have defined the mole, in 3 mol of atoms of any element there would be 18.066×10^{23} atoms. Notice that we have said 3 mol of *atoms* of any element. Some elements, such as hydrogen and chlorine, exist as diatomic molecules. If we had 3 mol of hydrogen molecules, H_2, we would have 6 mol of atoms.

Let us imagine that we had 1 mol of hydrogen atoms, and 1 mol of carbon-12 atoms. There would be an equal number (6.022×10^{23}) of each of them. However, measurements made by mass spectrometry show that an atom of hydrogen has approximately 1/12 the mass of an atom of carbon-12. It should be clear to you that this means that, for example, 100 atoms of hydrogen have 1/12 the mass of 100 atoms of carbon-12. Similarly, 6.022×10^{23} atoms of hydrogen will have 1/12 the mass of 6.022×10^{23} atoms of carbon-12. Remembering that this number of atoms represents 1 mol of substance, we can say that

1 mol of hydrogen atoms has 1/12 the mass of 1 mol of carbon-12 atoms

i.e. 1 mol of hydrogen atoms has a mass of 12 g $\times$ 1/12 = 1 g.

If necessary we could go through the same method of working to establish that 1 mol of oxygen atoms has a mass of 16 g, 1 mol of sodium atoms has a mass of 23 g, and so on.

In practice it is easier to use the information in a table of relative atomic masses (see Unit 3) to find the mass of 1 mol of atoms of an element. The relative atomic mass, A_r, tells us how the mass of one atom of an element compares with the mass of one atom of carbon-12 (taken as exactly 12 units). For example, $A_r(H) = 1$, $A_r(O) = 16$, $A_r(Na) = 23$. However, we have already said that the masses of 1 mol of atoms of each of these elements are 1 g, 16 g and 23 g, respectively. The recipe is simple: to find the mass of 1 mol of atoms of an element, express the relative atomic mass in grams. If we wish, we can draw up a table of *molar masses*. The molar mass is the mass in grams per mole of the element; its units are g mol^{-1}. (Strictly in the SI system the units should be kg mol^{-1}; however chemists often prefer to work in terms of grams.) Table 37.1 lists some of the more common molar masses you might need to use. The symbol M is used to stand for a molar mass. For example, in the case of calcium, $M(Ca) = 40\ \text{g mol}^{-1}$. (Notice that there is no subscript on the M. The *relative* molecular mass of a substance has the symbol M_r; see Unit 3.)

In some cases it may not be clear what the name of the chemical refers to. For example, suppose we were asked to find the mass of 1 mol of sulphur. As it stands we do not know if this means 1 mol of sulphur atoms, S, or 1 mol of S_8 molecules. It is always best to state the formula as well as the name of the substance if there might be any doubt.

Table 37.1. The masses of 1 mol of atoms of some elements*

Element	*Molar mass* /g mol^{-1}	*Element*	*Molar mass* /g mol^{-1}
Hydrogen	1	Sodium	23
Carbon	12	Magnesium	24
Nitrogen	14	Potassium	39
Oxygen	16	Calcium	40
Phosphorus	31	Copper	64
Sulphur	32	Zinc	65
Chlorine	35.5	Silver	108
Iodine	127	Lead	207

*Apart from chlorine, the values have been rounded to the nearest whole number

37.1 How many atoms would there be in (i) 0.5 mol of sodium, Na; (ii) 2 mol of magnesium, Mg; (iii) 5 mol of neon gas, Ne; (iv) 0.001 mol of copper, Cu?

37.2 What is the total number of moles of atoms (of all elements) in the following: (i) 1 mol of nitrogen dioxide, NO_2; (ii) 3 mol of calcium sulphate, $CaSO_4$; (iii) 1 mol of copper(II) sulphate crystals, $CuSO_4{\cdot}5H_2O$; (iv) 0.25 mol of phosphorus trichloride, PCl_3?

37.3 Why is the accurate molar mass of many elements not a whole number?

37.2 How to work with moles of compounds

The formula of water, H_2O, says that 1 mol of water contains 2 mol of hydrogen atoms and 1 mol of oxygen atoms. Similarly, to write the formula of ammonia as NH_3 tells us the molar composition of the gas: 1 mol of ammonia contains 1 mol of nitrogen atoms and 3 mol of hydrogen atoms.

Once we have established the number of moles of each element present in a covalent substance like water or ammonia, we can work out its molar mass. For water,

$$M(H_2O) = 2 \times M(H) + 1 \times M(O)$$
$$= 2 \times 1\,\text{g mol}^{-1} + 16\,\text{g mol}^{-1} = 18\,\text{g mol}^{-1}$$

Therefore,

$$\text{mass of 1 mol of water} = 18\,\text{g mol}^{-1} \times 1\,\text{mol} = 18\,\text{g}$$

This short piece of working shows how we can discover the mass of 1 mol of water while keeping track of the units of the quantities involved. However, for substances with fairly simple formulae you should be able to do the working in your head. For example, ammonia, NH_3, has $M(NH_3) = 17\,\text{g mol}^{-1}$, and the mass of 1 mol of ammonia is 17 g.

When we have an ionic compound we should be careful about the names we give to the particles present. For example, to write the formula of the ionic salt sodium chloride as NaCl means that 1 mol of the salt contains 1 mol of sodium *ions*, Na^+, and 1 mol of chloride *ions*, Cl^-. However, because the mass of an ion is not appreciably different from that of its parent atom, we have

$$M(\text{NaCl}) = M(\text{Na}) + M(\text{Cl})$$
$$= 23\,\text{g mol}^{-1} + 35.5\,\text{g mol}^{-1} = 58.5\,\text{g mol}^{-1}$$

Alternatively we can say that the mass of 1 mol of sodium chloride is 58.5 g.

If we know the mass of an element or compound and its molar mass, we can calculate the number of moles present. For example, if we have 9 g of water, and we know that $M(H_2O) = 18\,\text{g mol}^{-1}$, then we must have 0.5 mol of water.

In general,

$$\text{number of moles of a substance} = \frac{\text{mass of substance}}{\text{its molar mass}}$$

Here is another example. A bottle contains 6 g of magnesium ribbon; how many moles of magnesium are present? We have

$$\text{number of moles of magnesium} = \frac{\text{mass of magnesium}}{M(\text{Mg})}$$
$$= \frac{6\,\text{g}}{24\,\text{g mol}^{-1}} = 0.25\,\text{mol}$$

37.4 What is the mass of (i) 2 mol of calcium, Ca; (ii) 1 mol of phosphine, PH_3; (iii) 3 mol of magnesium oxide, MgO; (iv) 0.25 mol of silver nitrate, $AgNO_3$?

37.5 Work out the number of moles in each of the following: (i) 2 g of methane, CH_4; (ii) 140 g of calcium oxide, CaO; (iii) 3.31 g lead(II) nitrate, $Pb(NO_3)_2$; (iv) 25 g of copper(II) sulphate crystals, $CuSO_4{\cdot}5H_2O$.

37.3 Moles and equations

A chemical equation is an extremely useful way of summarising a lot of information. The equation should show the amount of each substance involved in the reaction, and its state. Here are some examples. In each case the equation has been written in symbols first, and then in words.

(i) $2H_2(g) + O_2(g) \rightarrow 2H_2O(g)$

2 mol of hydrogen molecules react with 1 mol of oxygen molecules to give 2 mol of water molecules, all in the gaseous state.

(ii) $H^+(aq) + OH^-(aq) \rightarrow H_2O(l)$

1 mol of hydrogen ions dissolved in water react

with 1 mol of hydroxide ions dissolved in water to give 1 mol of liquid water.

(iii) $Zn(s) + 2H^+(aq) \rightarrow Zn^{2+}(aq) + H_2(g)$

1 mol of solid zinc will react with 2 mol of hydrogen ions dissolved in water to give 1 mol of zinc ions dissolved in water and 1 mol of hydrogen gas.

37.6 Write down in words the information given by these equations:

(i) $CuO(s) + H_2(g) \rightarrow Cu(s) + H_2O(g)$

(ii) $2Cu(NO_3)_2(s) \rightarrow 2CuO(s) + 4NO_2(g) + O_2(g)$

37.4 Moles and balancing equations

One of the most important chemical laws is the law of conservation of mass. Essentially it says that:

The total mass of the products in a reaction must be the same as the total mass of the reactants.

Another way of stating the law is to say that there must be the same number of atoms at the end of the reaction as there were at the beginning. (We ignore changes in mass associated with energy changes given by Einstein's equation $E = mc^2$.) Given that the mole is also a measure of the amount of substance, we could also say that the law is satisfied if there is no change in the total number of moles of atoms of each of the elements during a reaction. Each of the equations we wrote in the last section obeys the law.

For example, in the reaction between hydrogen and oxygen,

$$2H_2(g) + O_2(g) \rightarrow 2H_2O(g)$$

On the left-hand side
2 mol of hydrogen molecules contain 4 mol of hydrogen atoms, and 1 mol of oxygen molecules contains 2 mol of oxygen atoms.
On the right-hand side
2 mol of water molecules contain 4 mol of hydrogen atoms and 2 mol of oxygen atoms.

So there is no change in the number of atoms and the law of conservation of mass (or moles of particles) is obeyed.

Be sure that you distinguish between atoms and molecules. We have just seen that the number of atoms in this reaction is conserved, but the number of *molecules* is *not* conserved. There are 3 mol of molecules at the start (2 mol of hydrogen, H_2, and 1 mol of oxygen, O_2), but only 2 mol of water molecules, H_2O, at the end. The fact that numbers of atoms do not change but the numbers of molecules can change during a reaction was a source of great confusion in the early days of chemistry.

Now look at the two examples, in which we shall use information about the number of moles of reactants and products to work out the equation of a reaction.

Example 1

4.8 g of magnesium were burnt in 3.2 g oxygen gas. The magnesium oxide, MgO, produced had a mass of 8 g. What is the equation for the reaction?

The oxygen is present as a gas, i.e. O_2 molecules, for which $M(O_2) = 32\text{ g mol}^{-1}$. Also, $M(Mg) = 24\text{ g mol}^{-1}$, and $M(MgO) = 40\text{ g mol}^{-1}$. Therefore the number of moles of each of them is:

$$\text{number of moles of oxygen molecules} = \frac{3.2\text{ g}}{32\text{ g mol}^{-1}} = 0.1\text{ mol}$$

$$\text{number of moles of magnesium} = \frac{4.8\text{ g}}{24\text{ g mol}^{-1}} = 0.2\text{ mol}$$

$$\text{number of moles of magnesium oxide} = \frac{8\text{ g}}{40\text{ g mol}^{-1}} = 0.2\text{ mol}$$

Using these figures we can write the equation as

$$0.2Mg(s) + 0.1O_2(g) \rightarrow 0.2MgO(s)$$

However, it is better to use whole numbers, so we scale the figures up by a factor of 10 (by dividing through by 0.1):

$$2Mg(s) + 1O_2(g) \rightarrow 2MgO(s)$$

We do not normally write in the number '1', so the equation becomes:

$$2Mg(s) + O_2(g) \rightarrow 2MgO(s)$$

Example 2

It is found that 1.4 g of nitrogen gas, N_2, and 0.3 g of hydrogen gas, H_2, can combine to make 1.7 g of ammonia, NH_3. What is the equation for the reaction?

First we find the number of moles of each gas:

$$\text{number of moles of nitrogen} = \frac{1.4\text{ g}}{28\text{ g mol}^{-1}} = 0.05\text{ mol}$$

$$\text{number of moles of hydrogen} = \frac{0.3\text{ g}}{2\text{ g mol}^{-1}} = 0.15\text{ mol}$$

$$\text{number of moles of ammonia} = \frac{1.7\text{ g}}{17\text{ g mol}^{-1}} = 0.1\text{ mol}$$

Now we write the equation using these numbers of moles:

$$0.05N_2(g) + 0.15H_2(g) \rightarrow 0.1NH_3(g)$$

We can scale the numbers by dividing through by the smallest number, 0.05. This gives

$$N_2(g) + 3H_2(g) \rightarrow 2NH_3(g)$$

37.7 0.3 g of nitrogen monoxide gas, NO, reacts with 0.16 g of oxygen gas, O_2, to give 0.46 g of nitrogen dioxide gas, NO_2. What is the equation for the reaction?

37.5 The empirical formula and molecular formula of a compound

We shall now look at two cases showing that, if we know the number of atoms in a compound, and its molar mass, then we can work out its *molecular formula*. This is the actual formula of the compound.

For example, the molecular formula of benzene is C_6H_6. This shows us that the molecule contains six carbon atoms and six hydrogen atoms. The molecular formula of benzene is different to its *empirical formula*, which is CH.

The empirical formula shows us the simplest whole number ratio of the atoms in a molecule.

Here we have used the word 'molecule' to refer to the simplest unit of a substance. It refers to the smallest unit of an ionic substance as much as to a covalent substance.

Now look at the molecular formula of ethyne, C_2H_2. This molecule also has the empirical formula CH. In other words, two (or more) molecules can have the same empirical formula but different molecular formulae. We can work out the molecular formula from the empirical formula if we know the relative molecular mass, or molar mass, of the substance. The two examples show you how this is done.

Example 3

A sample placed in a mass spectrometer gave a parent ion corresponding to a relative molecular mass of 44. Analysis of a sample of the oxide showed that 2.2 g of it contained 1.4 g of nitrogen atoms, and 0.8 g of oxygen atoms. The problem is to find the molecular formula of the oxide.

First we work out the number of moles of nitrogen and oxygen atoms:

$$\text{number of moles of nitrogen atoms} = \frac{1.4\,\text{g}}{14\,\text{g mol}^{-1}} = 0.1\,\text{mol}$$

$$\text{number of moles of oxygen atoms} = \frac{0.8\,\text{g}}{16\,\text{g mol}^{-1}} = 0.05\,\text{mol}$$

This shows that there is twice as much nitrogen as oxygen, i.e. the ratio is 2 mol nitrogen atoms to 1 mol oxygen atoms. This ratio gives us the empirical formula of the compound. In this case it is N_2O.

You should not think that we have proved that the molecular formula of the oxide is N_2O. We would get exactly the same empirical formula if the molecular formula was N_4O_2, N_6O_3, N_8O_4 and so on. However, the mass spectrum evidence tells us that the relative molecular mass is 44, or the molar mass is 44 g mol^{-1}. Now we can see which of the possible formulae for the oxide actually fits this molar mass. Starting with the simplest formula, N_2O, we have:

$$M(N_2O) = 2 \times M(N) + M(O) = 28\,\text{g mol}^{-1} + 16\,\text{g mol}^{-1} = 44\,\text{g mol}^{-1}$$

This fits the observed molar mass, so we have proved that the molecular formula is N_2O. (This is one compound for which the empirical and molecular formulae are the same; but for many compounds they are different.)

Example 4

A chloride of sulphur was found to have a relative molecular mass of 135. A 5.4 g sample was also found to contain 2.84 g of chlorine. What is the molecular formula of the chloride?

Before we start the calculation there are two things to notice. First, the mass of sulphur is not given directly; we are expected to work this out. Secondly, the question says it contains 2.84 g of chlorine. As this is a compound of chlorine, we should assume that the mass refers to chlorine atoms, Cl, rather than molecules, Cl_2. (If the question referred to a mass of chlorine *gas*, then this would be the mass of chlorine molecules.)

The mass of sulphur in the sample is $5.4\,\text{g} - 2.84\,\text{g} = 2.56\,\text{g}$. Then,

$$\text{number of moles of sulphur atoms} = \frac{2.56\,\text{g}}{32\,\text{g mol}^{-1}} = 0.08\,\text{mol}$$

$$\text{number of moles of chlorine atoms} = \frac{2.84\,\text{g}}{35.5\,\text{g mol}^{-1}} = 0.08\,\text{mol}$$

Here the ratio is 1 mol of sulphur atoms to 1 mol of chlorine atoms, which gives the empirical formula as SCl. The molecular formula could be SCl, S_2Cl_2, S_3Cl_3, S_4Cl_4, etc. To see which fits the molar mass, we can work out the molar masses for each of these formulae:

$$M(SCl) = M(S) + M(Cl) = 32\,\text{g mol}^{-1} + 35.5\,\text{g mol}^{-1} = 67.5\,\text{g mol}^{-1}$$

This does not match, so we try S_2Cl_2.

$$M(S_2Cl_2) = M(S) \times 2 + M(Cl) \times 2 = 64\,\text{g mol}^{-1} + 71.0\,\text{g mol}^{-1} = 135\,\text{g mol}^{-1}$$

This is consistent with the relative molecular mass we are given, so S_2Cl_2 is the correct molecular formula.

37.8 What is the molecular formula of each of the substances listed in Table 37.2?

Table 37.2. Data for question 37.8

Substance	*Molar mass /g mol^{-1}*	*Mass of sample/g*	*Element*	*Mass /g*
A	56	0.452	Calcium	0.323
			Oxygen	0.129
B	144	45.0	Copper	40.0
			Oxygen	5.0
C	120.5	2.01	Nitrogen	0.23
			Chlorine	1.78
D	101	1.35	Nitrogen	0.19
			Oxygen	0.21
			Chlorine	?

37.6 Percentage compositions

If you worked in an analytical laboratory, it is possible that part of your job would be to discover the composition of new compounds, or to check the composition of samples of old ones. Some laboratories specialise in finding the proportion of each element that a compound contains. It is standard practice to report the composition as a percentage. For example, an organic acid might have its composition recorded as C 40%, H 6.7%, O 53.3%, and its molar mass found to be 60 g mol^{-1}. From these data we can work out the empirical formula of the compound. Here is a recipe for doing the calculation.

First, draw up a table like that below with columns for each element. Then put in the information you are given. This has already been done for you in this case.

	Carbon	*Hydrogen*	*Oxygen*
100 g of compound contains	40.0 g	6.7 g	53.3 g
Number of moles present	$\frac{40.0\,\text{g}}{12\,\text{g mol}^{-1}}$	$\frac{6.7\,\text{g}}{1\,\text{g mol}^{-1}}$	$\frac{53.3\,\text{g}}{16\,\text{g mol}^{-1}}$
	=3.33 mol	=6.7 mol	=3.33 mol
Ratio of moles	$\frac{3.33\,\text{mol}}{3.33\,\text{mol}}$	$\frac{6.7\,\text{mol}}{3.33\,\text{mol}}$	$\frac{3.33\,\text{mol}}{3.33\,\text{mol}}$
		1 to 2 to 1	

Empirical formula CH_2O
Molar mass of one unit of CH_2O is

$$M(CH_2O) = 12\,\text{g mol}^{-1} + 1\,\text{g mol}^{-1} \times 2 + 16\,\text{g mol}^{-1} = 30\,\text{g mol}^{-1}$$

This does not fit the observed molar mass of 60 g mol^{-1}, so we try the formula $C_2H_4O_2$:

$$M(C_2H_4O_2) = 12\,\text{g mol}^{-1} \times 2 + 1\,\text{g mol}^{-1} \times 4 + 16\,\text{g mol}^{-1} \times 2 = 60\,\text{g mol}^{-1}$$

This equals the value we are looking for, so the molecular formula is $C_2H_4O_2$.

The first line is another way of stating the percentage composition. In the second we divide by the molar masses of the elements to find the number of moles in the 100 g. Then we find the ratio of the number of moles. The simplest way of doing this is by dividing through by the smallest number of moles. (We know we are looking for a whole number ratio, and 6.7/3.3 is near enough to 2.)

Now we have the empirical formula, and we can work out its molar mass using the same approach as in the previous section. The final step is to see if it fits with the molar mass of the substance. In this case it does not, so we try the next simplest formula: $C_2H_4O_2$. This fits, so we have determined the molecular formula.

There is nothing in the question to tell us which substance it is, but you might like to know that it was meant to be ethanoic acid, CH_3COOH. The units on organic chemistry will show you how we can deduce the structure of an organic molecule.

37.9 Work out the empirical and molecular formulae of the substances in Table 37.3.

Table 37.3. Data for question 37.9

Substance	*Molar mass /g mol^{-1}*	*Percentage composition*		
E	56	C 85.7	H 14.3	
F	180	C 40.0	H 6.7	O 53.3
G	87	Cl 81.6	O 18.4	

Answers

37.1 (i) $6.022 \times 10^{23}\ mol^{-1} \times 0.5\ mol = 3.011 \times 10^{23}$;
(ii) $6.022 \times 10^{23}\ mol^{-1} \times 2\ mol = 12.044 \times 10^{23}$;
(iii) $6.022 \times 10^{23}\ mol^{-1} \times 5\ mol = 30.110 \times 10^{23}$;
(iv) $6.022 \times 10^{23}\ mol^{-1} \times 0.001\ mol = 6.022 \times 10^{20}$.

37.2 (i) 3 mol; (ii) 18 mol; (iii) 21 mol; (iv) 1 mol.

37.3 Tables of relative atomic masses give the average relative masses of the naturally occurring isotopes of the elements. Different isotopes have different abundances, so the average rarely works out to be a whole number. See Unit 29.

37.4 (i) $40\ g\ mol^{-1} \times 2\ mol = 80\ g$;
(ii) $(31\ g\ mol^{-1} + 1\ g\ mol^{-1} \times 3) \times 1\ mol = 34\ g$;
(iii) $(24\ g\ mol^{-1} + 16\ g\ mol^{-1}) \times 3\ mol = 120\ g$;
(iv) $(108\ g\ mol^{-1} + 14\ g\ mol^{-1} + 16\ g\ mol^{-1} \times 3) \times 0.25\ mol = 42.5\ g$.

37.5 (i) $\dfrac{2\ g}{16\ g\ mol^{-1}} = 0.125\ mol$;
(ii) $\dfrac{140\ g}{56\ g\ mol^{-1}} = 2.5\ mol$;
(iii) $\dfrac{3.31\ g}{331\ g\ mol^{-1}} = 0.1\ mol$;
(iv) $\dfrac{25\ g}{250\ g\ mol^{-1}} = 0.1\ mol$.

37.6 (i) 1 mol of solid copper(II) oxide reacts with 1 mol of gaseous hydrogen to give 1 mol of solid copper and 1 mol of water as a gas (steam).
(ii) 2 mol of copper(II) nitrate crystals decompose to give 2 mol of solid copper(II) oxide, 4 mol of nitrogen dioxide gas and 1 mol of oxygen gas.

37.7

Number of moles of nitrogen monoxide $= \dfrac{0.3\ g}{30\ g\ mol^{-1}} = 0.01\ mol$

Number of moles of oxygen $= \dfrac{0.16\ g}{32\ g\ mol^{-1}} = 0.005\ mol$

Number of moles of nitrogen dioxide $= \dfrac{0.46\ g}{46\ g\ mol^{-1}} = 0.01\ mol$

Now we write the equation as

$$0.01NO(g) + 0.005O_2(g) \rightarrow 0.01NO_2(g)$$

To scale this we divide through by 0.005:

$$2NO(g) + O_2(g) \rightarrow 2NO_2(g)$$

37.8

Substance A

Number of moles of calcium $= \dfrac{0.323\ g}{40\ g\ mol^{-1}} = 0.008\ mol$

Number of moles of oxygen $= \dfrac{0.129\ g}{16\ g\ mol^{-1}} = 0.008\ mol$

The ratio is 1 mol calcium to 1 mol oxygen, hence the empirical formula is CaO; and the molecular formula will be CaO, Ca_2O_2, Ca_3O_3, etc. The correct one is CaO, as this has a molar mass of $56\ g\ mol^{-1}$.

Substance B

Number of moles of copper $= \dfrac{40.0\ g}{64\ g\ mol^{-1}} = 0.625\ mol$

Number of moles of oxygen $= \dfrac{5.0\ g}{16\ g\ mol^{-1}} = 0.313\ mol$

The ratio is almost exactly 2 mol of copper to 1 mol of oxygen, hence we have the empirical formula as Cu_2O. The molecular formula will be Cu_2O, Cu_4O_2, etc. The one which fits the molar mass is Cu_2O.

Substance C

Number of moles of nitrogen $= \dfrac{0.23\ g}{14\ g\ mol^{-1}} = 0.016\ mol$

Number of moles of chlorine $= \dfrac{1.78\ g}{35.5\ g\ mol^{-1}} = 0.05\ mol$

This ratio is very nearly 1 mol of nitrogen to 3 mol of chlorine, which gives us the empirical formula NCl_3. The possible formulae are NCl_3, N_2Cl_6, etc. The molar mass fits NCl_3.

Substance D

The first thing to do here is to calculate the mass of chlorine in the sample. This is $1.35\ g - 0.19\ g - 0.21\ g = 0.95\ g$.

Number of moles of nitrogen $= \dfrac{0.19\ g}{14\ g\ mol^{-1}} = 0.014\ mol$

Number of moles of oxygen $= \dfrac{0.21\ g}{16\ g\ mol^{-1}} = 0.013\ mol$

Number of moles of chlorine $= \dfrac{0.95\ g}{35.5\ g\ mol^{-1}} = 0.027\ mol$

These are very nearly in the ratio 1 mol nitrogen atoms to 1 mol oxygen atoms to 2 mol chlorine atoms. Thus the empirical formula is $NOCl_2$. The molecular formula will be $NOCl_2$, $N_2O_2Cl_4$, etc. $NOCl_2$ has a molar mass of $101\ g\ mol^{-1}$, so this is the correct formula.

37.9

Substance E

	Carbon	*Hydrogen*
100 g of compound contains	85.7 g	14.3 g
Number of moles present	$\dfrac{85.7\ g}{12\ g\ mol^{-1}}$	$\dfrac{14.3\ g}{1\ g\ mol^{-1}}$
	= 7.14 mol	= 14.3 mol
Ratio of moles	$\dfrac{7.14\ mol}{7.14\ mol}$	$\dfrac{14.3\ mol}{7.14\ mol}$
	1 to	2

Answers – contd.

Empirical formula CH_2
Molar mass of one unit of CH_2 is

$$M(CH_2) = 12\,\text{g mol}^{-1} + 1\,\text{g mol}^{-1} \times 2 = 14\,\text{g mol}^{-1}$$

This does not fit the observed molar mass of 56 g mol^{-1}; but you might spot that it is 1/4 of the required molar mass. This means that the molecular formula is four times the empirical formula, i.e. C_4H_8.

You should follow through the same method for the other two substances. Here are the answers:

Substance F
Empirical formula CH_2O, molecular formula $C_6H_{12}O_6$.

Substance G
Empirical formula Cl_2O, molecular formula Cl_2O.

UNIT 37 SUMMARY

- The mole is a chemist's measure of the amount of substance.
- One mole (1 mol) of a chemical species contains the same number of particles as there are atoms in 12 g of the isotope carbon-12 ($^{12}_{6}C$).
- The Avogadro constant L has the value $6.022 \times 10^{23}\,\text{mol}^{-1}$.
- The relative atomic mass of an element, A_r, gives the ratio of the mass of an atom to the mass of one atom of carbon-12 taken as exactly 12 units. A_r has no units.
- The relative molecular mass, M_r, is defined similarly.
- The symbol M is used to stand for the mass of 1 mol of any entity, i.e. the molar mass. M has units g mol^{-1}. Thus

$$\text{number of moles of a substance} = \frac{\text{mass of substance}}{\text{its molar mass}}$$

- The law of conservation of mass says that: The total mass of the products in a reaction must be the same as the total mass of the reactants.
- The empirical formula is the simplest whole number ratio of the atoms in a compound.
- The molecular formula is the actual formula of a compound.

38

Molar masses of gases and liquids

38.1 Measuring the molar mass of a gas

Following our work in Unit 36 we know that 1 mol of a gas occupies approximately 24 dm^3 at room temperature and pressure (20° C and 1 atm), or 22.4 dm^3 at standard temperature and pressure, s.t.p. (0° C and 1 atm). Looking at this in the opposite way, we can say that if we had 24 dm^3 of gas at room temperature and pressure, then we would have 1 mol of it. This is the essential idea behind the measurement of the molar masses of gases. Opposite is an example that uses simple numbers, rather than results that you might actually get in an experiment:

Now let us investigate a real experiment to determine the molar mass of a gas (Figure 38.1). There are a number of problems that we have to deal with. First, how can

> *Example*
>
> A 1 dm^3 flask was weighed empty and then filled with chlorine. The flask was found to increase in mass by 3 g. The measurements were performed at room temperature and pressure. What result does this give for the molar mass of chlorine?
>
> The figures tell us that 1 dm^3 of chlorine has a mass of 3 g at room temperature and pressure. Therefore, 24 dm^3 of chlorine would have a mass 24 times greater, i.e. 72 g. This tells us that the molar mass of chlorine is 72 g mol^{-1}. The result is not accurate (the true result is nearer to 71 g mol^{-1}), but you should be able to see the method of tackling the problem.

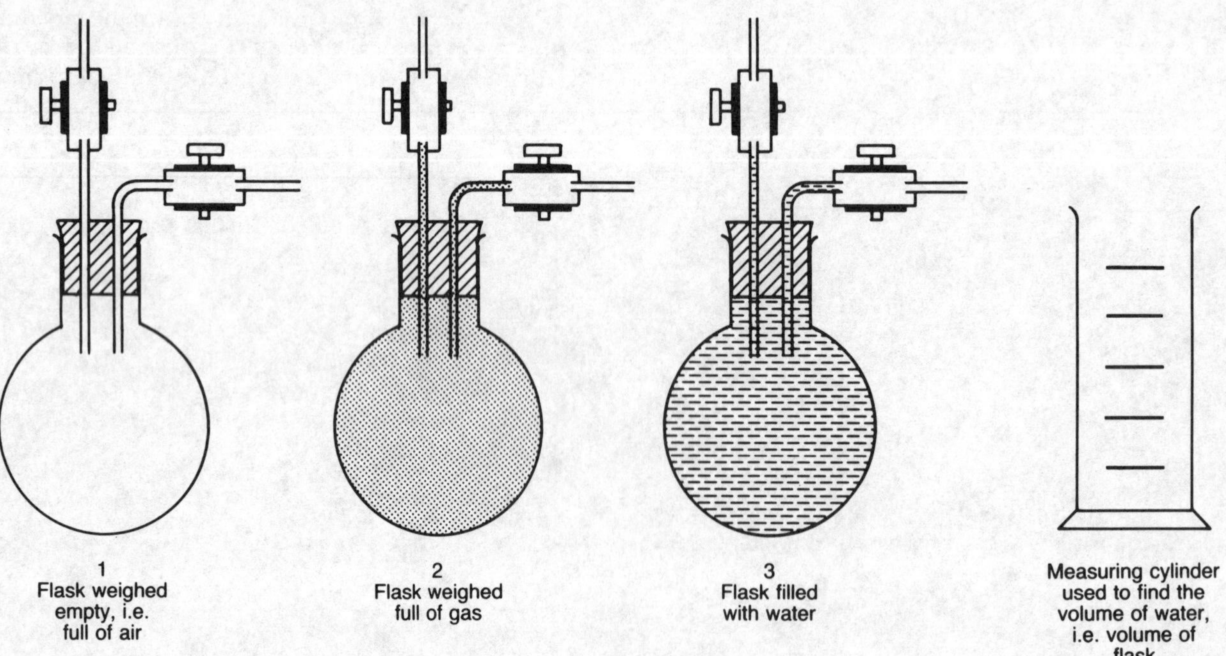
1
Flask weighed empty, i.e. full of air
2
Flask weighed full of gas
3
Flask filled with water
Measuring cylinder used to find the volume of water, i.e. volume of flask

Figure 38.1 *A simple method of determining the molar mass of a gas*

we find the volume of the flask that is to contain the gas. Secondly, we are unlikely to be able to weigh the flask empty: it will have air in it. If we are restricted to using simple apparatus, the volume of the flask can be found by filling it with water, and then finding the volume of water by pouring it into a measuring cylinder. However, this is best done as the last task in the experiment. Once we know the volume of the flask, we can use data tables to discover the density of air under the conditions of the experiment. From this we can work out the mass of air in the flask.

Here is a typical set of results using ethane as the gas. At room temperature and pressure,

density of air	$= 1.205 \times 10^{-3}$ g cm^{-3}
mass of flask + air	= 58.262 g
mass of flask + ethane	= 58.285 g
volume of flask	= 242.5 cm^3

First, we find the mass of the flask:

mass of flask = (mass of flask + air) − (mass of air)

But

mass of air = density of air × volume of air

so,

mass of flask
$= 58.262\text{ g} - (1.205 \times 10^{-3}\text{ g cm}^{-3} \times 242.5\text{ cm}^3)$
$= 58.262\text{ g} - 0.292\text{ g} = 57.97\text{ g}$

Now we use this result to give us the mass of ethane:

mass of ethane
= (mass of flask + ethane) − (mass of flask)
= 58.285 g − 57.97 g = 0.315 g

Therefore the mass of 1 mol of ethane is given by

$$0.315\text{ g} \times \frac{24\,000\text{ cm}^3}{242.5\text{ cm}^3} = 31.18\text{ g}$$

and

M(ethane) = 31.18 g mol^{-1}

In fact the molar mass of ethane is almost exactly 30 g mol^{-1}, so there is an error of nearly 4% in the result.

38.1 At s.t.p., 250 cm^3 of a gas had a mass of 0.36 g. What result does this give for the molar mass of the gas?

38.2 Why is it not a good idea to measure the volume of the flask by filling with water at the start of the experiment?

38.3 The experiment we have just described will not give a very accurate result, except by chance. This question asks you why this is so.

(i) A most important assumption has been made about putting the ethane into the flask. What is it? Why will this be a source of error in the experiment?

(ii) A student was heard to say that as the density of air is so small it is not worth taking the mass of the air in the flask into account. Was the student right? To help you decide, repeat the calculation, but this time ignore the mass of air.

(iii) Which part of the experiment is a significant source of error?

38.4 Assume that the above experiment was done at 18°C and 755 mmHg, i.e. 291 K and 100.7 kPa. Also, assume that the volume was again 242.5 cm^3.

(i) Use the ideal gas equation ($pV = nRT$) to work out how many moles of ethane were present.

(ii) If the mass of ethane in the flask was again 0.315 g, what does the experiment give for the molar mass of ethane?

38.2 Measuring the molar mass of a soluble gas

Some gases, especially hydrogen chloride, sulphur dioxide and ammonia, are very soluble in water. These gases can be used in an experiment similar to the one we have just described. A flask is weighed empty (i.e. full of air). Then the gas is passed into it for around 30 s, the tubes sealed and the flask and contents reweighed. This time one of the tubes leading into the flask is opened under water. Owing to the solubility of the gas, the pressure inside the flask is reduced and air pressure pushes water into it. Once all the gas is dissolved, no more water enters the flask. At this point the amount of water that entered is measured by pouring it into a measuring cylinder. Finally the volume of the whole flask is found by filling it completely with water. With these measurements, and knowing the density of air, the molar mass of the gas can be calculated. The method is like that for ethane earlier. You should try the next question to convince yourself that you understand the method.

38.5 Here is a set of results for sulphur dioxide, SO_2:

density of air	$= 1.205 \times 10^{-3}$ g cm^{-3}
mass of flask + air alone	= 60.325 g
mass of flask containing SO_2 and some left-over air	= 60.665 g
volume of water entering the flask	= 203.0 cm^3
total volume of flask	= 241.4 cm^3

Now answer the following questions.

(i) What was the total volume of air in the flask (i.e. with no SO_2 added)?

(ii) What is the mass of this volume of air?

(iii) What is the mass of the flask without air in it?

(iv) What is the mass of the SO_2 and left-over air when they were both together in the flask?

(v) What is the volume of SO_2 used?

(vi) What volume of air was left over in the flask?

(vii) What is the mass of this volume of air?

(viii) From your answers to (iv) and (vii), calculate the mass of SO_2 in the flask.

(ix) Now you know both the volume of SO_2 and its mass, calculate its molar mass. Assume 1 mol of gas occupies 24 dm^3 under the conditions of the experiment.

(x) The true molar mass of the gas is 64 g mol^{-1}. Why is it very common for the result of this type of experiment to give an overestimate of the molar mass?

38.6 Why does water not completely fill the flask during the experiment?

38.7 Why is it necessary to dry the flask and tubing thoroughly before they are used? What effect will the use of a damp flask have on the calculated molar mass?

38.8 Some gases do not give accurate results for their molar masses even if great care is taken over the experiment. Ammonia is an example. Why might this be so? (Hint: see Unit 20.)

38.3 Measuring the molar mass of a volatile liquid

In this case we take a known mass of the liquid, vaporise it and then measure the volume it takes up. Once we know both its mass and volume, and if we assume the vapour behaves as an ideal gas, we can work out its molar mass. The method that we shall use is one you may see for yourself in the laboratory. The major pieces of apparatus are a gas syringe and a heated container into which it fits (Figure 38.2).

The nozzle of the gas syringe is covered with a rubber cap (a septum), and the gas syringe is put in the steam jacket. Once the reading on the gas syringe shows no further change, a sample of the liquid, in this case ethoxyethane (ether), is taken up into a small syringe. The small syringe is weighed and the ethoxyethane is injected into the gas syringe. Then the small syringe is immediately reweighed. Once the ethoxyethane is in the gas syringe, the liquid quickly vaporises and the plunger is driven outwards. Eventually equilibrium is achieved and there is no further change in the volume recorded on the syringe. Provided the temperature of the steam jacket and the atmospheric pressure are known, we can calculate the molar mass.

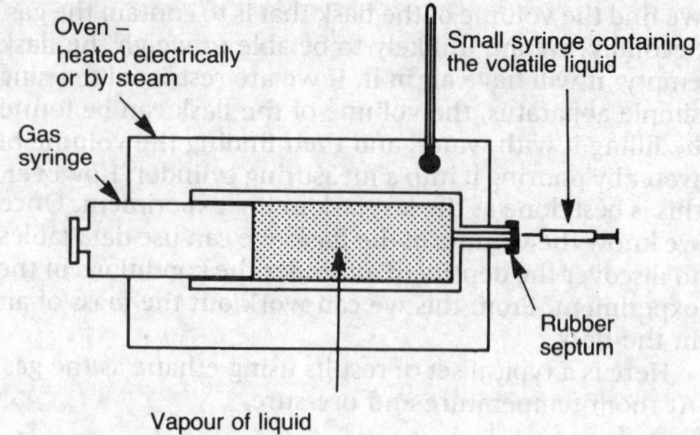

Figure 38.2 *One method of measuring the volume given by a volatile liquid using a gas syringe and oven*

Here are some sample readings:

mass of syringe and ethoxyethane before injection into gas syringe = 20.476 g
mass of syringe and ethoxyethane after injection into gas syringe = 20.252 g
initial reading on gas syringe = 1.4 cm^3
final reading on gas syringe = 96.8 cm^3
temperature of steam jacket = 99.6°C = 372.6 K
atmospheric pressure = 758 mmHg = 101.1 kPa

From these results we have

mass of ethoxyethane used = 0.224 g
volume of the vapour = 95.4 cm^3 = 95.4×10^{-6} m^3

We can use the ideal gas equation to work out the number of moles, *n*, of ethoxyethane that this volume represents. We have

$$pV = nRT$$

or

$$n = \frac{pV}{RT} = \frac{101.1 \times 10^3 \text{ Pa} \times 95.4 \times 10^{-6} \text{ m}^3}{8.314 \text{ J K}^{-1} \text{ mol}^{-1} \times 372.6 \text{ K}}$$

$$= 0.003 \text{ mol}$$

Therefore,

$$\text{molar mass} = \frac{0.224 \text{ g}}{0.003 \text{ mol}} = 74.7 \text{ g mol}^{-1}$$

The formula of ethoxyethane is $(C_2H_5)_2O$, so its true molar mass is 74 g mol^{-1}. It is quite common for results in this experiment to overestimate molar masses. To understand why, try question 38.9.

38.9 The above experiment only works with liquids that are highly volatile, i.e. those which evaporate easily.

(i) What can happen to the amount of liquid in the small syringe once it has been weighed for the first time?

(ii) How will the mass of liquid injected into the gas syringe compare with the mass put in the syringe initially?

(iii) How, and why, does this affect the calculation?

38.10 Figure 38.3 shows you a diagram of a Victor Meyer apparatus. Victor Meyer was one of the people who developed a method of measuring the molar mass of a volatile liquid.

Look carefully at the diagram and the labels. Your task is to explain how you think the apparatus was used. (Try to imagine that it was set up on the laboratory bench in front of you. Actually it is quite possible that your school or college has a Victor Meyer apparatus.) Although it looks quite different to the gas syringe arrangement, the essence of the two methods is the same.

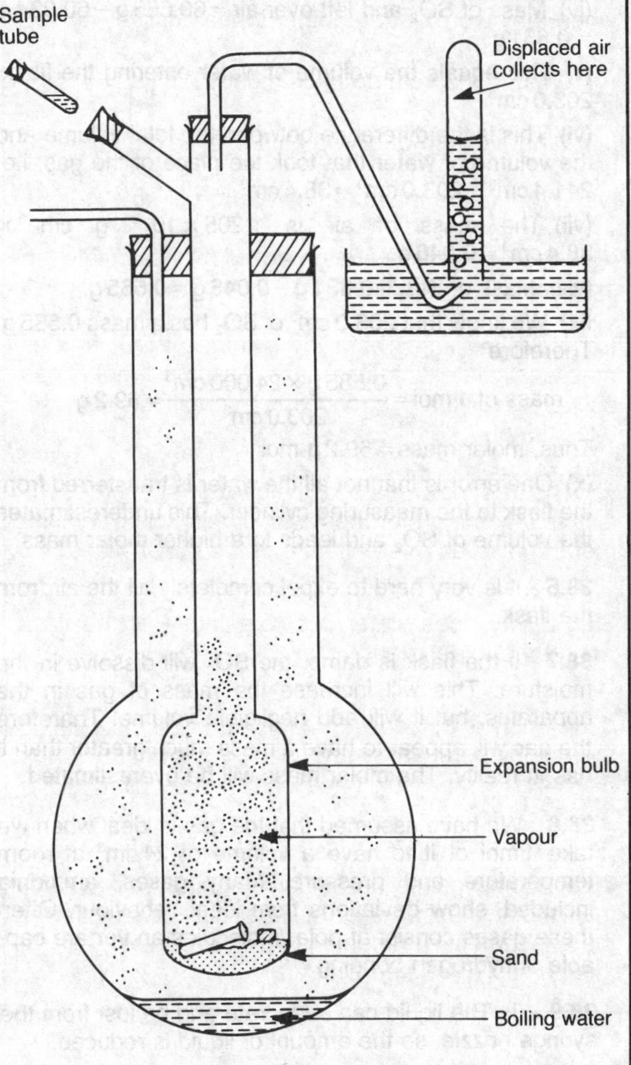

***Figure 38.3** Victor Meyer's apparatus for determining the molar mass of a volatile liquid. Here we have shown steam being used to vaporise the liquid. For liquids that boil above 100°C, the water can be replaced by, for example, an oil. (The diagram is not to scale)*

Answers

38.1 250 cm³ is 0.25 dm³. At s.t.p., 1 mol of gas occupies 22.4 dm³, so the mass of 1 mol of this gas is

$$\frac{22.4\,\text{dm}^3}{0.25\,\text{dm}^3} \times 0.36\,\text{g} = 32\,\text{g}$$

and the molar mass is 32 g mol⁻¹.

38.2 Once the flask gets wet it will be time consuming to dry it. Also, if it is damp, the gas used might dissolve in water droplets remaining. This will lead to an error in our measurement of the volume of gas in the flask.

38.3 (i) The problem is, how do we know the flask is full of ethane? The answer is, we don't. The best we can do is pass ethane into the flask for between 30 s and 1 min and hope for the best. This part of the experiment should be done in a fume cupboard, of course.

(ii) The student was wrong. The results we have used show that the masses of air and ethane are similar. If we ignore the mass of air, the flask will appear to weigh 58.262 g. Then the apparent mass of ethane is 58.285 g − 58.262 g = 0.023 g, and its molar mass becomes 2.3 g mol⁻¹. Not a good result!

(iii) Determining the volume of the flask by measuring the volume of water. It is unavoidable that water is left in the flask.

38.4 We have

$$n = \frac{pV}{RT} = \frac{100.7 \times 10^3\,\text{Pa} \times 242.5 \times 10^{-6}\,\text{m}^3}{8.314\,\text{J K}^{-1}\,\text{mol}^{-1} \times 291\,\text{K}} = 0.01\,\text{mol}$$

i.e. 0.315 g represents 0.01 mol; so the molar mass is 31.5 g mol⁻¹.

38.5 (i) 241.4 cm³.

(ii) The mass is 1.205×10^{-3} g cm⁻³ × 241.4 cm³ = 0.291 g.

(iii) Mass of empty flask = 60.325 g − 0.291 g = 60.034 g.

Answers – contd.

(iv) Mass of SO_2 and left-over air = 60.665 g − 60.034 g = 0.631 g.

(v) This equals the volume of water entering the flask, 203.0 cm^3.

(vi) This is the difference between the total volume and the volume of water that took the place of the gas, i.e. 241.4 cm^3 − 203.0 cm^3 = 38.4 cm^3.

(vii) The mass of air is 1.205×10^{-3} g $cm^{-3} \times$ 38.4 cm^3 = 0.046 g.

(viii) Mass of SO_2 = 0.631 g − 0.046 g = 0.585 g.

(ix) We know that 203.0 cm^3 of SO_2 has a mass 0.585 g. Therefore

$$\text{mass of 1 mol} = \frac{0.585\,\text{g} \times 24\,000\,\text{cm}^3}{203.0\,\text{cm}^3} = 69.2\,\text{g}$$

Thus, molar mass = 69.2 g mol^{-1}.

(x) One error is that not all the water is transferred from the flask to the measuring cylinder. This underestimates the volume of SO_2 and leads to a higher molar mass.

38.6 It is very hard to expel completely all the air from the flask.

38.7 If the flask is damp, the SO_2 will dissolve in the moisture. This will increase the mass of gas in the apparatus, but it will add negligible volume. Therefore the gas will appear to have a mass much greater than it has in reality. The molar mass will be overestimated.

38.8 We have assumed that the gas is ideal when we take 1 mol of it to have a volume of 24 dm^3 at room temperature and pressure. Many gases, ammonia included, show deviations from ideal behaviour. Often these gases consist of polar molecules and/or are capable of hydrogen bonding.

38.9 (i) The liquid can evaporate and be lost from the syringe nozzle, so the amount of liquid is reduced.

(ii) The actual mass will be smaller than you think.

(iii) It increases the value of the molar mass. To see why, let us take an impossible example, but one that illustrates the working. Suppose that the syringe and liquid start out with a mass of 3 g and that after injection their mass is 1 g. We believe that 2 g of liquid has been injected. However, let us assume that 1 g of liquid actually evaporated before the injection took place. Therefore the actual mass injected was only 1 g. If the gas occupied 100 cm^3 at room temperature and pressure, we would calculate the molar mass to be

$$2\,\text{g mol}^{-1} \times 24\,000\,\text{cm}^3/100\,\text{cm}^3 = 480\,\text{g mol}^{-1}$$

(We have already said that the numbers are not very likely!) Its true value should be

$$1\,\text{g mol}^{-1} \times 24\,000\,\text{cm}^3/100\,\text{cm}^3 = 240\,\text{g mol}^{-1}$$

half the experimental result.

38.10 The liquid in the outer jacket is boiled. This liquid could be water, but it could be one with a much higher boiling point. This causes the air inside the apparatus to expand. The bubbles of air are allowed to escape out of the delivery tube at the top. Now the small glass tube is weighed empty, and then full of the liquid under test. It is put in the top of the main tube and the stopper replaced. The apparatus is left for a few minutes until equilibrium is established. Signs that this is achieved are when the thermometer reading remains unchanged, and no more bubbles of air escape. Now the gas collection tube is placed over the delivery tube and the glass bottle allowed to drop into the bottom of the inner tube. The sand is there to break its fall. The liquid begins to vaporise, which pushes the stopper out, and vapour escapes into the inner tube. The volume of air pushed out of the tube and collected in the graduated tube equals the volume of the vapour. After a while equilibrium is re-established and no more air escapes. Before the volume of air is read from the graduated tube, the pressure inside it has to be made equal to the atmospheric pressure. This is done by lowering the tube into the water until the levels inside and outside the tube are equal. From then on the calculation of the molar mass is similar to that we have already done. However, there is one correction to be made, which we have either ignored or have not needed to make in previous examples. The air in the graduated tube will be saturated with water vapour, so the actual pressure of the air inside the tube will be lower than atmospheric pressure. It is the corrected air pressure that is used in the calculation.

UNIT 38 SUMMARY

- One mole (1 mol) of a gas occupies approximately 24 dm^3 at room temperature and pressure (20° C and 1 atm), or 22.4 dm^3 at standard temperature and pressure, s.t.p. (0° C and 1 atm).
- The molar mass of a gas can be found by weighing a known volume of the gas.
- The molar mass of a volatile liquid can be found by converting a weighed amount of it into a vapour and measuring its volume.
- Determining the mass of the parent ion in a mass spectrometer is a more reliable method of measuring molar masses.

39

Moles and titrations

39.1 Standard solutions

A major part of chemistry is being able to analyse compounds to see what and how much of a given chemical they contain. One method that is often used is volumetric analysis. This is where we use a known solution and react it with a solution of the chemical being tested. The typical method of doing this is in a titration. The method of doing a titration is described in panel 39.1.

A titration is only of use if the concentration of one of

Panel 39.1

Titrations

We shall assume that we are going to titrate an acid and an alkali. The method of doing the titration is outlined below.

Filling the burette

Close the tap of the burette and pour a little of the acid into it. By tipping the burette at an angle, allow the acid to wash the inside. Then run some of the acid out through the tap. This should push the air out of the tip of the burette and should fill it with acid.

Put the burette into a clamp, make sure the tap is closed, and slowly pour acid into the burette via a filter funnel. Be careful here, if you put too much acid into the funnel, the burette may overflow. The acid level should be above the 0 cm^3 mark near the top of the burette. Remove the funnel.

Slowly open the tap and run out acid until the bottom of the meniscus is just touching the 0 cm^3 mark. Discard the acid that you run out: it contains some of the acid used to wash the burette.

Make sure there are no air bubbles trapped in the tip of the burette. If there are, open the tap fully. The flow of acid should wash the bubbles out. Refill the burette if necessary. The burette is now ready for use.

Using the pipette

Wash two or three conical flasks with distilled water. They should be clean, but it does not matter if some of the water remains in them.

Using a safety filler, make sure the tip of the pipette is well below the surface of the alkali and suck some alkali into the pipette. (You should NOT suck liquid into a pipette by mouth.) Remove the safety filler and tip the pipette so that the alkali washes the inside. Allow the alkali to drain out of the pipette. *Note*: Be sure to consult your teacher or lecturer about the use of safety fillers. Fitting them to, or removing them from, a pipette can be dangerous if not done with care.

Again using a safety filler, fill the pipette with alkali until it is some way above the graduation mark.

With your eye on a level with the graduation mark, slowly allow alkali to escape into a beaker. If you are careful, and with some practice, you should be able to let only one or two drops of alkali escape at a time. You should allow the bottom of the meniscus just to touch the graduation mark. Drips on the end of the pipette can be removed using filter paper.

Place the end of the pipette into one of the cleaned conical flasks and allow the alkali to flow into the flask. Hold the pipette in the flask for around 30 s. At the end of this time keep the tip of the pipette in contact with the inside of the flask for about 3 s. This will allow the proper amount of alkali to be drawn out of the tip by surface tension.

Remove the pipette from the flask. You should see a little alkali left in the tip. This is meant to be there. (Do not be tempted to blow it out!) The volume of alkali (or any other liquid) that you have measured into the flask from the pipette is called an *aliquot*.

Performing the titration

A few drops of indicator should now be added to the alkali. You will discover that the indicator chosen will depend on the nature of the acid and alkali

Panel 39.1 – contd

used. We shall assume that a strong acid and a strong alkali, e.g. sulphuric acid and sodium hydroxide, are being used, in which case screened methyl orange would be a good choice. This indicator is green in alkali.

The flask should be placed with the tip of the burette well into its neck. There should be a white tile under the flask so that the colour change of the indicator shows clearly.

The initial reading on the burette should be noted down in a table of results, and then a few cm^3 of acid allowed to flow into the flask. With each addition of acid, the flask should be shaken. Eventually you will notice a change in the colour of the indicator. At this stage acid should be added more slowly until the *endpoint* is reached. The endpoint is where the indicator is just changing from its colour in alkali to its colour in acid. Screened methyl orange has a grey colour at the endpoint. If acid is added beyond the endpoint, this indicator will turn purple.

The final reading on the burette should be recorded in a table of results. The volume of acid used in the experiment is called the *titre*. A sample table is shown below. Notice that the burette reading does not have to start at exactly 0 cm^3. The important thing is that the starting reading is known, and recorded. Next, the burette is refilled, another aliquot of alkali put into a clean flask, and the titration repeated.

It is common practice to do the first titration fairly quickly, so that the volume of acid needed at the endpoint is discovered, but not with great accuracy. In the second titration acid can be run in steadily up to 2 or 3 cm^3 from the endpoint. Then acid is added much more slowly. With practice you should be able to add acid one drop at a time until the endpoint is reached. Ideally, titrations should be repeated until two consecutive titres differ by no more than 0.05 cm^3.

It is possible to read a burette to a greater accuracy than 0.05 cm^3. However, in school work it is not often worth while. One reason for this is that the burettes and pipettes that you use may not be top quality; e.g. a medium quality 25 cm^3 pipette may deliver somewhere between 24.9 cm^3 and 25.1 cm^3 of solution. (Another reason is that unless you perform titrations regularly, you are unlikely to be accurate enough in the use of the apparatus to warrant reading a burette to, say, 0.02 cm^3.)

Specimen table of results for a titration of sodium hydroxide solution with nitric acid

Liquid in burette:	nitric acid of concentration 0.1 mol dm^{-3}.
Liquid in flask:	25 cm^3 sodium hydroxide; concentration to be found.
Indicator:	screened methyl orange.
Endpoint:	change from green to clear grey.

	Titration readings		
Titration number	1	2	3
Second burette reading/cm^3	(24.20)	48.10	23.90
First burette reading/cm^3	(0.00)	24.20	0.00
Titre/cm^3	(24.20)	23.90	23.90

Average of titrations 2 and 3: 23.90 cm^3.

the solutions is known. Usually the 'known' solution is made up by taking a measured amount of a chemical and dissolving it in water to give a solution whose volume is also accurately known. The known solution is usually made up in a volumetric (or graduated) flask (Figure 39.1). Volumetric flasks have a graduation mark on their necks, which tells us the volume of the solution that they can contain. The bottom of the liquid meniscus must just touch the mark if the volume is to be accurate. There should also be a temperature quoted on the flask. The solution and flask should be at this temperature if the volume is to be accurate.

If we wish to dissolve a solid in water to give a solution of known concentration, we have to know two things: the mass of the solid we use, and the total volume of the solution. For example, we might want to make a solution of sodium chloride that has 5.85 g of the solid in 250 cm^3 of solution. It is tempting to think that all we have to do is fill the volumetric flask to the graduation mark, weigh out the sodium chloride and then put it in the flask. The problem with doing this is that the final volume of the solution would *not* be 250 cm^3. When solids dissolve in water, there is nearly always a volume change. We shall leave the explanation of why this is so until Unit 60. The way round the problem is to dissolve the solid in water (less than 250 cm^3!) first, add this to

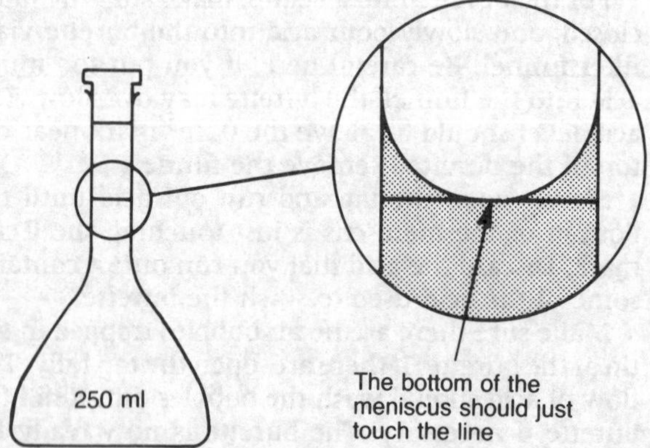
250 ml
The bottom of the meniscus should just touch the line

***Figure 39.1** A common size for a volumetric flask is 250 cm³, often written as 250 ml on the flask. It is graduated so that the flask contains exactly 250 cm³ when the bottom of the liquid meniscus touches the line on the neck of the flask*

the flask, and top up with enough water to reach the graduation mark. The way this is done partly depends on the nature of the solid being dissolved, but it always requires great care if it is to be done accurately.

Unfortunately some solutions 'go off' if left for some time. For example, a solution of an iron(II) compound will be oxidised to iron(III) by air, or through reaction with water in the flask. Such solutions are of little or no value for accurate work. To make a reliable solution we should make it from a *primary standard*. If a solid is to be a primary standard it:

(i) must be pure;
(ii) should dissolve in water easily;
(iii) should not decompose easily as a solid or in solution; and
(iv) should have a fairly high molar mass.

A solution that is made up accurately to a known concentration of a primary standard is called a *standard solution*.

39.1 The first three requirements are not surprising, but you may not immediately understand why the fourth is important. Suppose we need a solution that contains 0.01 mol of a chemical in 250 cm³ of solution. Assume that the balance that you are going to use is accurate only to 0.01 g. You have two substances, A with a molar mass of 10 g mol^{-1}, and B with a molar mass of 100 g mol^{-1}.

(i) What mass of A should you weigh out to go into a 250 cm³ flask?

(ii) What is the percentage error in your weighing?

(iii) What mass of B should you weigh out?

(iv) What is the percentage error in your weighing this time?

(v) Why is it important to use a substance of fairly high molar mass as a primary standard?

39.2 The concentration of a solution

A solution consists of at least two things:

(i) the substance dissolved, which we call the *solute*; and
(ii) the liquid in which it is dissolved, which we call the *solvent*.

There are several ways of stating the concentration of a solution. One method, which we shall rarely use, is to give the solute contained in 1 kg of solvent. If this convention is used, we use the word *molal* to describe the concentration. For example, 58.5 g of sodium chloride (1 mol) in 1 kg of water would be a 1 molal solution.

It is far more common to state the concentration of a solution by giving the number of moles of solute dissolved in 1 dm³ of solution. For example, 58.5 g of sodium chloride dissolved in 1 dm³ of solution would have a concentration of 1 mol dm^{-3}. You may know the volume 1 dm³ by the alternative name of 1 litre. (We shall use dm³ in our working because it is more directly related to the SI unit of volume, the cubic metre, m³.) You should also know that 1 dm³ = 1000 cm³.

Often 1 dm³ of a solution is far more than is needed in an experiment. For example, it is more common to make up 250 cm³ of a standard solution. However, the concentration of the 250 cm³ will still be given in mol dm^{-3}. Look at the two examples, which show you how to convert from one system to the other.

Example 1

1.06 g of anhydrous sodium carbonate, Na_2CO_3, are dissolved in 250 cm³ of solution. What is the concentration in mol dm^{-3}?

First, we need to know the molar mass of sodium carbonate. It is

$$M(Na_2CO_3) = 2M(Na) + M(C) + 3M(O) = 2\times 23\text{ g mol}^{-1} + 12\text{ g mol}^{-1} + 3\times 16\text{ g mol}^{-1} = 106\text{ g mol}^{-1}$$

This tells us that the amount of sodium carbonate is

$$n(Na_2CO_3) = \frac{1.06\text{ g}}{106\text{ g mol}^{-1}} = 0.01\text{ mol}$$

This is the number of moles in 250 cm³, but we need to know the number in 1 dm³, i.e. 1000 cm³, of solution. We will have to scale the mass upwards by a factor of 1000 cm³/250 cm³, i.e. there will be four times as many moles of sodium carbonate in 1 dm³ as in 250 cm³.

The concentration of the solution is 0.04 mol dm^{-3}.

Example 2

5 g of copper(II) sulphate crystals, $CuSO_4{\cdot}5H_2O$, were dissolved in 100 cm³ of solution. What is the concentration of the solution?

Again we start by finding out the molar mass of the solute.

$$M(CuSO_4{\cdot}5H_2O) = M(Cu) + M(S) + 4M(O) + 5M(H_2O) = (64 + 32 + 4\times 16 + 5\times 18)\text{ g mol}^{-1} = 250\text{ g mol}^{-1}$$

Thus the amount taken is

$$n(CuSO_4{\cdot}5H_2O) = \frac{5\text{ g}}{250\text{ g mol}^{-1}} = 0.02\text{ mol}$$

The number of moles in 1000 cm³ will be 1000 cm³/100 cm³, i.e. 10, times greater.

The concentration is 0.2 mol dm^{-3}.

39.2 What are the concentrations in mol dm^{-3} of the following solutions?

(i) 1.06 g anhydrous sodium carbonate in 100 cm^3;

(ii) 10.6 g anhydrous sodium carbonate in 2000 cm^3;

(iii) 25 g copper(II) sulphate crystals in 500 cm^3;

(iv) 250 g copper(II) sulphate crystals in 5 dm^3.

39.3 Concentration and molarity

A solution that has molarity of one would be given the symbol 1 M. A 1 M solution would contain 1 mol of solute in 1 dm^3 of solution. Similarly, a 2 M solution would contain 2 mol of solute in 1 dm^3 of solution, and a 0.2 M solution would contain 0.2 mol of solute in 1 dm^3 of solution. Typical concentrations of solutions you may meet are given in Table 39.1. Molarity is widely used as a shorthand way of talking about the concentration (in mol dm^{-3}) of a solution, even though the International Union of Pure and Applied Chemistry (IUPAC) has recommended that the word should no longer be used. Your teacher or lecturer will tell you if you can afford to ignore this section.

Table 39.1. Concentrations of solutions used in laboratories*

	Concentration when dilute	*Concentration when concentrated*
Acids		
Hydrochloric	2 mol dm^{-3} (2 M)	12 mol dm^{-3} (12 M)
Nitric	2 mol dm^{-3} (2 M)	16 mol dm^{-3} (16 M)
Sulphuric	1 mol dm^{-3} (1 M)	18 mol dm^{-3} (18 M)
Alkalis		
Sodium hydroxide	2 mol dm^{-3} (2 M)	10 mol dm^{-3} (10 M)
Potassium hydroxide	2 mol dm^{-3} (2 M)	10 mol dm^{-3} (10 M)
Aqueous ammonia	2 mol dm^{-3} (2 M)	15 mol dm^{-3} (15 M)

*Normally even the dilute solutions are considerably more concentrated than those used in titrations

It is useful to know how to convert from concentrations given in mol dm^{-3} to those given in terms of molarity, and vice versa. The two examples show you how to do this.

Example 3

A solution of silver nitrate, $AgNO_3$, contains 1.08 g in 250 cm^3. What is its molarity?

First we work out the concentration in mol dm^{-3}. The molar mass of silver nitrate is 108 g mol^{-1}, and so

$$n(AgNO_3) = \frac{1.08\,g}{108\,g\,mol^{-1}} = 0.01\,mol$$

This is contained in 250 cm^3, so

number of moles in 1 dm^3

$$= 0.01\,mol \times \frac{1000\,cm^3}{250\,cm^3} = 0.04\,mol$$

Thus the concentration is 0.04 mol dm^{-3}. Alternatively we say that the molarity of the solution is 0.04 M.

Example 4

A bottle of dilute hydrochloric acid is 2 M. What mass of hydrogen chloride, HCl, would be dissolved in 100 cm^3 of this acid?

Given that the molarity is 2 M, we know that its concentration is 2 mol dm^{-3}, i.e. the solution contains 2 mol of HCl in 1000 cm^3. Therefore, there will be 0.2 mol in 100 cm^3. However, $M(HCl) = 36.5$ g mol^{-1}, so there will be 36.5 g $mol^{-1} \times 0.2$ mol $= 7.3$ g in 100 cm^3.

39.3 What is the molarity of the following solutions?
(i) 100 cm^3 containing 9.8 g of sulphuric acid, H_2SO_4;

(ii) 250 cm^3 containing 1.58 g of sodium thiosulphate, $Na_2S_2O_3$.

39.4 The molarity of a solution of sodium chloride was 0.01 M. What would be the mass of sodium chloride in (i) 2 dm^3 and (ii) 10 cm^3 of the solution? $M(NaCl) = 58.5$ g mol^{-1}.

39.4 How to do calculations involving concentrations

The most important thing you should realise about calculations involving solutions is that it is the number of moles of the reactants that is important. Often we need to know the volume of the solution, but this is only because the link between concentration and volume allows us to work out the number of moles in a solution. We shall do two examples, which will show you the types of question you might have to face.

Example 5

25 cm^3 of a solution of sodium hydroxide were neutralised by 23.90 cm^3 of nitric acid of concentration 0.1 mol dm^{-3}. (These are the results from panel 39.1.) What is the concentration of the sodium hydroxide solution?

The starting point is the equation for the reaction:

$$HNO_3(aq) + NaOH(aq) \rightarrow NaNO_3(aq) + H_2O(l)$$

This tells us that the acid and alkali react together in the ratio of 1 mol HNO_3 to 1 mol NaOH. Therefore, if we know the number of moles of nitric acid used, we have immediately worked out the number of moles of sodium hydroxide present. The concentration of nitric acid is given as 0.1 mol dm^{-3}, which tells us that

1000 cm^3 of the acid contain 0.1 mol

so,

23.90 cm^3 of the acid contain

$$0.1 \text{ mol} \times \frac{23.90 \text{ cm}^3}{1000 \text{ cm}^3} = 2.39 \times 10^{-3} \text{ mol}$$

Thus, the number of moles of sodium hydroxide is also 2.39×10^{-3} mol. This number of moles is contained in 25 cm^3, so

number of moles of NaOH in 1000 cm^3

$$= 2.39 \times 10^{-3} \text{ mol} \times \frac{1000 \text{ cm}^3}{25 \text{ cm}^3} = 0.096 \text{ mol}$$

The concentration of the solution is 0.096 mol dm^{-3}.

Example 6

100 cm^3 of a solution of hydrochloric acid were exactly neutralised by 0.12 g of magnesium ribbon. What was the concentration of the acid? $M(\text{Mg}) = 24 \text{ g mol}^{-1}$; $M(\text{H}) = 1 \text{ g mol}^{-1}$; $M(\text{Cl}) = 35.5 \text{ g mol}^{-1}$.

Once again we start by writing down the equation for the reaction.

$$Mg(s) + 2HCl(aq) \rightarrow MgCl_2(aq) + H_2(g)$$

This tells us that 1 mol of magnesium will exactly react with 2 mol of HCl. Now we know that the number of moles of HCl will be double the number of moles of Mg used:

$$\text{number of moles of Mg used} = \frac{0.12 \text{ g}}{24 \text{ g mol}^{-1}} = 0.005 \text{ mol}$$

Therefore, number of moles of HCl used = 0.01 mol. This is the number of moles in 100 cm^3, so there will be 10 times as many in 1000 cm^3.

The concentration of the acid was 0.1 mol dm^{-3}.

39.5 The equation for the reaction of sodium hydroxide with sulphuric acid is

$$H_2SO_4(aq) + 2NaOH(aq) \rightarrow Na_2SO_4(aq) + 2H_2O(l)$$

In a titration, 25 cm^3 of sodium hydroxide solution were neutralised by 24 cm^3 of sulphuric acid of concentration 0.2 mol dm^{-3}. What was the concentration of the alkali?

39.6 500 cm^3 of nitric acid were neutralised by 10.6 g of anhydrous sodium carbonate. The equation for the reaction is

$$Na_2CO_3(s) + 2HNO_3(aq) \rightarrow 2NaNO_3(aq) + CO_2(g) + H_2O(l)$$

What was the concentration of the acid in terms of (i) mol dm^{-3}; (ii) molarity; (iii) g dm^{-3}?

39.7 This question is about the titration experiment described in panel 39.1.

(i) Half-way through a titration, a student noticed some drops of acid had got on to the inside of the neck of the conical flask he was using. He decided to wash the drops into the main solution using distilled water. Did he ruin his experiment? Briefly explain your answer.

(ii) Another student was worried that her pipette was dirty, so she washed it out with distilled water and then immediately filled it with 25 cm^3 of alkali. Did this student ruin her experiment?

(iii) Alkalis will absorb carbon dioxide from the atmosphere. Carbonates are made in the reaction. Why is it especially important to wash a pipette with distilled water after a titration using alkali? Why should alkali never be left in a burette?

Answers

39.1 (i) $0.01 \text{ mol} \times 10 \text{ g mol}^{-1} = 0.1 \text{ g}$.

(ii) The error is $(0.01 \text{ g}/0.1 \text{ g}) \times 100\% = 10\%$.

(iii) $0.01 \text{ mol} \times 100 \text{ g mol}^{-1} = 1 \text{ g}$.

(iv) The error is $(0.01 \text{ g}/1 \text{ g}) \times 100\% = 1\%$.

(v) By using a high molar mass we reduce the error in using a given number of moles of the solid in solution.

39.2 (i) $n(Na_2CO_3) = \dfrac{1.06 \text{ g}}{106 \text{ g mol}^{-1}} = 0.01 \text{ mol}$

This is dissolved in 100 cm^3, so 1000 cm^3 would contain $0.01 \text{ mol} \times 10 = 0.1 \text{ mol}$. The concentration is 0.1 mol dm^{-3}.

(ii) $n(Na_2CO_3) = 0.1 \text{ mol}$. Scaled down to 1000 cm^3, the concentration is 0.05 mol dm^{-3}.

(iii) $n(CuSO_4{\cdot}5H_2O) = \dfrac{25 \text{ g}}{250 \text{ g mol}^{-1}} = 0.1 \text{ mol}$

This is in 500 cm^3, so the concentration is 0.2 mol dm^{-3}.

(iv) This time, $n(CuSO_4{\cdot}5H_2O) = 1 \text{ mol}$, which is in 5 dm^3. Therefore, the concentration is 0.2 mol dm^{-3}.

39.3 (i) $n(H_2SO_4) = \dfrac{9.8 \text{ g}}{98 \text{ g mol}^{-1}} = 0.1 \text{ mol}$

This is contained in 100 cm^3, so there would be 1 mol in 1000 cm^3. The molarity is 1 M.

(ii) $n(Na_2S_2O_3) = \dfrac{1.58 \text{ g}}{158 \text{ g mol}^{-1}} = 0.01 \text{ mol}$

To scale this up to 1000 cm^3 we multiply by 4. The molarity is 0.04 M.

39.4 (i) 1000 cm^3, or 1 dm^3, contains 0.01 mol of sodium chloride, so there would be 0.02 mol in 2 dm^3. The mass of NaCl present is $0.02 \text{ mol} \times 58.5 \text{ g mol}^{-1} = 1.17 \text{ g}$.

(ii) In 10 cm^3 there will be

$$0.01 \text{ mol} \times \frac{10 \text{ cm}^3}{1000 \text{ cm}^3} = 10^{-4} \text{ mol}$$

The mass present $= 10^{-4} \text{ mol} \times 58.5 \text{ g mol}^{-1} = 5.85 \times 10^{-3} \text{ g}$.

39.5 From the equation we know that 1 mol of sulphuric acid is neutralised by 2 mol of sodium hydroxide, so once we calculate the number of moles of acid used, we know that there are twice this number of moles of sodium hydroxide. We have that

1000 cm^3 of acid contained 0.2 mol

so, 24 cm^3 of acid contained

$$0.2 \text{ mol} \times \frac{24 \text{ cm}^3}{1000 \text{ cm}^3} = 4.8 \times 10^{-3} \text{ mol}$$

The number of moles of sodium hydroxide used $= 9.6 \times 10^{-3}$ mol. This number of moles was in 25 cm^3, so in 1000 cm^3 there would be

$$9.6 \times 10^{-3} \text{ mol} \times \frac{1000 \text{ cm}^3}{25 \text{ cm}^3} = 0.38 \text{ mol}$$

The sodium hydroxide had a concentration of 0.38 mol dm^{-3}.

39.6 (i) $n(Na_2CO_3) = \dfrac{10.6 \text{ g}}{106 \text{ g mol}^{-1}} = 0.1 \text{ mol}$

and the equation tells us that there must be twice as many moles of nitric acid present as sodium carbonate. Therefore, 0.2 mol of nitric acid were present in the 500 cm^3. The concentration was 0.4 mol dm^{-3}.

(ii) 0.4 M.

(iii) $M(HNO_3) = 63 \text{ g mol}^{-1}$, so mass of HNO_3 present in $1 \text{ dm}^3 = 0.4 \text{ mol} \times 63 \text{ g mol}^{-1} = 25.2 \text{ g}$. The concentration is 25.2 g dm^{-3}.

39.7 (i) The experiment was not ruined. Adding distilled water to the conical flask does not change the number of moles of alkali in the flask, nor can it change the number of moles of acid added from the burette.

(ii) This experiment was ruined. The alkali is diluted by the water, so the concentration of the alkali run in is different to that of the alkali used as the stock solution. This means that the number of moles of alkali run into the flask is less than it should be. Another way of looking at this is to say that the water takes up room in the pipette. Therefore less than 25 cm^3 of alkali can be sucked into it, so fewer moles of alkali are run into the flask.

(iii) If alkali is left in the pipette it will become encrusted with solid carbonate and the jet may become blocked. This is not impossible to remove (using dilute nitric acid), but it is particularly annoying to have to clean someone else's dirty apparatus! Alkali in a burette may also lead to the jet being blocked. However, it can also lead to a deposit of solid carbonate in the socket of the tap. This makes the tap stick, and become extremely difficult to clean. Also, the alkali can attack the grease that may be used to lubricate the socket. This too leads to the burette being difficult, if not impossible, to use. It is best not to use an alkali in a burette.

UNIT 39 SUMMARY

- A solution of a primary standard that is made up accurately to a known concentration is called a standard solution.
- The concentration of a solution is measured in mol dm^{-3}, sometimes known as molarity, M.

40

Four types of titration

40.1 Acid–base titrations

In the last unit, panel 39.1 explained how to perform a titration between an acid and an alkali. (An alkali is a soluble base.) There are four variations of this type of titration, listed in Table 40.1.

The combination of a weak acid with a weak base is not suitable for a titration experiment. However, the other three pairings will work, but no single indicator is suitable for all of them. You will find details about the differences between strong and weak acids and bases in Unit 75. Likewise, the reasons for choosing different indicators are explained in Unit 76.

40.2 Redox titrations

(*Note*: you may prefer to read this section after you have read Unit 41.) Many titrations involve oxidation and reduction reactions, i.e. redox reactions. In particular, solutions of potassium dichromate(VI), $K_2Cr_2O_7$, and potassium manganate(VII), $KMnO_4$, are used as oxidising agents. We shall look at one example of the use of each of these solutions. You will find that when an indicator is used it has to be a special redox indicator, rather than the normal acid–base indicators of Table 40.1.

(a) *Titration of iron(II) with potassium dichromate(VI)*

Iron(II) ammonium sulphate, $Fe(NH_4)_2(SO_4)_2$, solution is a suitable source of iron(II) ions, Fe^{2+}. This substance should normally be made up by dissolving it in water mixed with dilute sulphuric acid. (The acid helps to prevent the iron(II) ions being hydrolysed.)

A 25 cm³ aliquot is placed in a conical flask in the normal way, and usually about 10 cm³ of dilute sulphuric acid added.

A few drops of diphenylamine solution are added followed by 5 cm³ of phosphoric acid. Diphenylamine is a redox indicator. It is colourless unless it is oxidised, in which case it is converted into a violet-blue dye. When dichromate(VI) ions run into the solution they oxidise iron(II) to iron(III). When all the iron(II) ions have been oxidised, the next one or two drops of the dichromate(VI) solution attack the indicator molecules. This is when the violet-blue colour appears and the end-point has been reached.

Table 40.1. Acid–base titrations

*Combination**	*Suitable indicator*	*Colour change*	
		In acid	*In alkali*
Strong acid/strong base	Methyl orange	Red	Yellow
	Bromothymol blue	Yellow	Blue
Strong acid/weak base	Methyl red	Red	Yellow
Weak acid/strong base	Phenolphthalein	Colourless	Purple
Weak acid/weak base	Not suitable for a titration		

**Typical strong acid solutions* are hydrochloric, HCl(aq), sulphuric, H_2SO_4(aq), and nitric, HNO_3(aq)
Weak acids are ethanoic, CH_3COOH(aq), and phosphoric, H_3PO_4(aq)
Typical strong bases, or alkalis, are sodium hydroxide, NaOH(aq), and potassium hydroxide, KOH(aq)
A weak alkali is aqueous ammonia, NH_3(aq), also known as ammonium hydroxide (the latter name is misleading; there is almost no NH_4OH in the solution)

The phosphoric acid combines with the iron(III) ions made during the reaction to give complex ions. This stops the iron(III) ions themselves taking part in a redox reaction with the indicator, which might mask the endpoint.

The equation for the reaction is

$$6Fe^{2+}(aq) + Cr_2O_7^{2-}(aq) + 14H^+(aq) \rightarrow 6Fe^{3+}(aq) + 2Cr^{3+}(aq) + 7H_2O(l)$$

This shows that 6 mol $Fe^{2+} \equiv$ 1 mol $Cr_2O_7^{2-}$.

> *Example 1*
>
> 25 cm³ of a solution of iron(II) ammonium sulphate needed exactly 20 cm³ of a solution of potassium dichromate(VI) of concentration 0.05 mol dm⁻³. What was the concentration of the iron(II) solution?
>
> We start by working out the number of moles of dichromate(VI) ions used in the titration.
>
> 1000 cm³ of solution contains 0.05 mol
>
> so, 20 cm³ of solution contains
>
> $$0.05\text{ mol} \times \frac{20\text{ cm}^3}{1000\text{ cm}^3} = 0.001\text{ mol}$$
>
> However, we know from the equation that 1 mol $Cr_2O_7^{2-}$ will react with 6 mol Fe^{2+}. Therefore there must have been six times the number of moles of iron(II) ions as dichromate(VI) ions, i.e. amount of iron(II) ions present in flask = 0.006 mol. This number of moles was present in 25 cm³, so
>
> 1 dm³ of solution contains
>
> $$0.006\text{ mol} \times \frac{1000\text{ cm}^3}{25\text{ cm}^3} = 0.24\text{ mol}$$
>
> Thus, we have calculated the concentration of the iron(II) solution to be 0.24 mol dm⁻³. (Alternatively, it is 0.24 M.)

(b) *Titration of ethanedioate (oxalate) ions with potassium manganate(VII)*

A solution of sodium ethanedioate, $Na_2C_2O_4$ (also known as sodium oxalate), can be used as a source of ethanedioate ions, $C_2O_4^{2-}$. A 25 cm³ aliquot should be placed in a titration flask and 10 cm³ dilute sulphuric acid added. To ensure that the reaction takes place at a suitable rate, the solution must be heated to nearly 60° C before potassium manganate(VII) solution is run in from a burette. The nice thing about manganate(VII) ions in water is that they give an intense purple colour. When they oxidise another chemical in acidic solution, the product is a solution of manganese(II) ions, which is colourless. This means that potassium manganate(VII) solution can act as its own indicator. While ethanedioate ions are still present, the manganate(VII) solution run into the flask loses its colour. Once all the ethanedioate ions have reacted, the next drop of manganate(VII) solution gives a permanent purple colour, which marks the endpoint.

The equation for the reaction is

$$5C_2O_4^{2-}(aq) + 2MnO_4^-(aq) + 8H^+(aq) \rightarrow 10CO_2(g) + 2Mn^{2+}(aq) + 4H_2O(l)$$

Therefore, 5 mol $C_2O_4^{2-} \equiv$ 2 mol MnO_4^-.

> *Example 2*
>
> 25 cm³ of a solution of sodium ethanedioate of concentration 0.1 mol dm⁻³ were placed in a titration flask. A burette was filled with potassium manganate(VII) solution of concentration 0.038 mol dm⁻³. What volume of the manganate(VII) solution would be needed to give the endpoint in the titration?
>
> Once again we work out the number of moles of the reactants:
>
> number of moles of ethanedioate ions in 25 cm³
>
> $$= 0.1\text{ mol} \times \frac{25\text{ cm}^3}{1000\text{ cm}^3} = 0.0025\text{ mol}$$
>
> From the equation we know that
>
> 5 mol $C_2O_4^{2-} \equiv$ 2 mol MnO_4^-
>
> or, 1 mol $C_2O_4^{2-} \equiv$ 0.4 mol MnO_4^-
>
> so 0.0025 mol $C_2O_4^{2-} \equiv 0.0025 \times 0.4$ mol MnO_4^-
>
> $\equiv$ 0.001 mol MnO_4^-
>
> This result means that we would have to run in 0.001 mol of MnO_4^- ions into the titration flask in order to react with all the ethanedioate ions. The final part of the problem is to decide how many cm³ of the solution in the burette would contain this number of moles of ions.
>
> Because the concentration of the manganate(VII) solution is 0.038 mol dm⁻³, we know that
>
> 0.038 mol MnO_4^- are contained in 1000 cm³ of solution,
>
> and
>
> 0.001 mol MnO_4^- are contained in
>
> $$1000\text{ cm}^3 \times \frac{0.001}{0.038} = 26.32\text{ cm}^3$$
>
> We would expect the volume of solution run in from the burette to be 26.32 cm³ (if we were to work to that degree of accuracy).

> **40.1** A sample of iron(II) sulphate crystals, $FeSO_4 \cdot 7H_2O$, had been left open to the air and some of the iron(II) ions had been converted to iron(III). 4.2 g of the impure crystals were dissolved in a total of 250 cm³ water and dilute sulphuric acid. 25 cm³ portions of this solution were titrated with a solution of potassium dichromate(VI). The concentration of

dichromate(VI) ions in this solution was 0.1 mol dm^{-3}. The average titre used was 23.5 cm^3.

Your task is to find the percentage purity of the original crystals. Here is the recipe.

(i) How many moles of dichromate(VI) ions were used in each titration?

(ii) How many moles of Fe^{2+} ions must have been present in each 25 cm^3 aliquot?

(iii) How many moles of Fe^{2+} ions would there have been in the 250 cm^3 of stock solution? This is the same number of moles as in the 4.2 g of crystals.

(iv) What is the mass of this amount of Fe^{2+} ions? M(Fe) = 56 g mol^{-1}.

(v) If you assume that the crystals were pure, how many moles of the crystals were taken? $M(FeSO_4{\cdot}7H_2O)$ = 278 g mol^{-1}.

(vi) What mass of Fe^{2+} ions should have been present in the 4.2 g of crystals?

(vii) From your answers to (iv) and (vi) calculate the percentage purity of the crystals.

40.2 An impure sample of iron of mass 2.55 g was dissolved in dilute sulphuric acid and the solution made up to 250 cm^3. The solution contained iron(II) ions together with the impurities. 25 cm^3 samples of the solution were titrated with potassium manganate(VII) solution of concentration 0.02 mol dm^{-3}. The average titre to reach the endpoint was 28.50 cm^3.

(i) How many moles of the manganate(VII) solution were used in the titration?

(ii) How many moles of iron(II) ions will react with 1 mol of manganate(VII) ions?

(iii) How many moles of iron(II) ions must have been present in 25 cm^3 of solution?

(iv) How many moles of iron(II) were there in the 250 cm^3 of stock solution?

(v) What is the mass of this number of moles of iron(II)? M(Fe) = 56 g mol^{-1}.

(vi) What was the percentage purity of the sample of iron?

40.3 Titrations involving iodine

Compounds that contain iodine are widely used in titrations. The titrations make use of one (or more) of the following changes:

(i) Iodide ions can be oxidised to iodine:

$$2I^-(aq) - 2e^- \rightarrow I_2(s)$$
colourless → black

(ii) Iodate(V) ions, IO_3^-, will oxidise iodide ions to iodine:

$$IO_3^-(aq) + 5I^-(aq) + 6H^+(aq) \rightarrow 3I_2(s) + 3H_2O(l)$$
colourless, colourless → black

(iii) Thiosulphate ions, $S_2O_3^{2-}$, can reduce iodine to iodide ions:

$$2S_2O_3^{2-}(aq) + I_2(s) \rightarrow S_4O_6^{2-}(aq) + 2I^-(aq)$$
colourless, black → colourless, colourless

Although solid iodine is black and insoluble in water, it is often the case that reactions are done in which many iodide ions are about. If iodine is produced in the presence of iodide ions, it is converted into soluble triiodide ions, I_3^-:

$$I_2(s) + I^-(aq) \rightleftharpoons I_3^-(aq)$$
black → dark brown

Small amounts of iodine molecules, I_2, can be detected by using starch as an indicator. Depending on the amount of iodine present, starch will give a blue to almost black colour.

(a) *An iodate(V)/iodide/thiosulphate titration*

Suppose we have a solution of a potassium iodate(V) whose concentration we want to determine. The method is to react the iodate(V) ions with an excess of iodide ions so that all the iodate(V) ions are converted into iodine. Having done this we can titrate the solution with thiosulphate ions in order to find the amount of iodine released. In practice we place 25 cm^3 of the iodate(V) solution in a titration flask together with at least 10 cm^3 of dilute sulphuric acid. Then an excess of potassium iodide solution is added. This liberates iodine; but because iodide ions are left over, the triiodide ions are produced rather than solid iodine. Now sodium thiosulphate of known concentration is run in from a burette. Gradually the colour of the solution fades owing to iodine being converted back into iodide ions. When the solution is a pale straw colour, starch solution is added. This gives a strong black colour. When the solution goes clear we know that all the iodine has been used up by the thiosulphate ions. This is the endpoint of the titration.

Example 3

25 cm^3 of a solution of potassium iodate(V), KIO_3, were placed in a titration flask. 20 cm^3 of a solution of potassium iodide and 10 cm^3 of dilute sulphuric acid were added to the flask. The iodine liberated was titrated using a solution of sodium thiosulphate of concentration 0.2 mol dm^{-3}, using starch as the indicator. The endpoint was reached when 24 cm^3 of the thiosulphate solution had been run in. What was the concentration of the original iodate solution?

To understand how we can do this calculation you should look carefully at the equations under (ii) and (iii) above. In words, we can summarise the first as

$$1\text{ mol } IO_3^- \equiv 3\text{ mol } I_2$$

and the second as

$$1\text{ mol } I_2 \equiv 2\text{ mol } S_2O_3^{2-}$$

Therefore,

$$3\text{ mol } I_2 \equiv 6\text{ mol } S_2O_3^{2-}$$

and overall,

$$1\text{ mol } IO_3^- \equiv 6\text{ mol } S_2O_3^{2-}$$

We have the key to the question now: if we work out the number of moles of $S_2O_3^{2-}$ ions used, we know there were 1/6 times as many moles of IO_3^- present in the flask.

Number of moles of $S_2O_3^{2-}$ ions used

$$= 0.2\text{ mol} \times \frac{24\text{ cm}^3}{1000\text{ cm}^3} = 0.0048\text{ mol}$$

Therefore,

number of moles of IO_3^- present

$$= 0.0048\text{ mol} \times 1/6 = 0.0008\text{ mol}$$

This number of moles was in 25 cm³, so in 1000 cm³ we have

$$0.0008\text{ mol} \times \frac{1000\text{ cm}^3}{25\text{ cm}^3} = 0.032\text{ mol}$$

The concentration of the potassium iodate(V) solution was 0.032 mol dm^{-3}.

40.3 Household bleach contains chlorine, mainly as chlorate(I) ions, ClO^-. These ions are oxidising agents. One way of estimating the strength of household bleach is to take a sample of the bleach and react it with a solution of an iodide. The chlorate(I) ions convert the iodide ions into iodine. The greater the concentration of chlorate(I) in the bleach, the more iodine will be produced. If we titrate the final solution containing iodine with a thiosulphate solution of known concentration, we can calculate the concentration of chlorate(I) ions in the bleach.

You will need the following equation:

$$ClO^-(aq) + 2I^-(aq) + 2H^+(aq) \rightarrow Cl^-(aq) + I_2(s) + H_2O(l)$$

Household bleach is often very concentrated and it has to be diluted before it is used in a laboratory experiment. After dilution the bleach is mixed with dilute sulphuric acid and an excess of potassium iodide solution. The resulting solution is titrated with sodium thiosulphate solution using starch as the indicator. Here are some specimen results:

Volume of bleach taken = 2.5 cm³. This was made up to 100 cm³ with distilled water. 25 cm³ portions of this solution were mixed with 10 cm³ of a solution of 0.5 mol dm^{-3} potassium iodide and 10 cm³ dilute sulphuric acid. The average titre using sodium thiosulphate of concentration 0.01 mol dm^{-3} was 24.20 cm³.

(i) How many moles of thiosulphate ions react with 1 mol of iodine?

(ii) How many moles of chlorate(I) ions give 1 mol of iodine?

(iii) What is the connection between the number of moles of thiosulphate used in the titration and the number of moles of chlorate(I) ions taken?

(iv) How many moles of sodium thiosulphate were used in the titration?

(v) How many moles of chlorate(I) ions were there in the 25 cm³ of diluted bleach solution, and in the 2.5 cm³ of the original bleach?

(vi) What is the concentration (in mol dm^{-3}) of chlorate(I) ions in the bleach?

(vii) If you were to do this experiment, how would you find out the volume of potassium iodide solution that had to be used to give an excess of iodide ions?

(viii) A student who was doing this experiment found that the bottle of dilute sulphuric acid he was using was empty. Nearby he found a bottle of dilute hydrochloric acid, so he used this to add to the bleach and iodide solution. Was this a good idea?

40.4 Silver nitrate titrations

In titrations, silver nitrate is mostly used to determine the concentrations of solutions that contain chloride ions. If you were to put a solution of sodium chloride in a flask and add silver nitrate from a burette, you would see an immediate white precipitate of silver chloride. The equation for the reaction is

$$Ag^+(aq) + Cl^-(aq) \rightarrow AgCl(s)$$

This shows that 1 mol $Ag^+ \equiv$ 1 mol Cl^-.

When all (or nearly all; see Unit 64) the chloride ions have been used up, there will be no more precipitate made. The trouble with the titration is seeing when this point is reached. In fact it is possible to use potassium chromate(VI), K_2CrO_4, solution as an indicator. Chromate(VI) ions, CrO_4^{2-}, give a red precipitate of silver chromate(VI), Ag_2CrO_4, with silver ions. However, silver chloride is more insoluble than silver chromate(VI), so if silver ions are added to a solution containing a mixture of chromate(VI) and chloride ions, it is silver chloride that is precipitated first. Silver chromate(VI) is only precipitated after the precipitation of silver chloride is completed. A difficulty with using potassium chromate(VI) as an indicator is that it will not work in an acidic solution. In acid, chromate(VI) ions are converted into dichromate(VI) ions, $Cr_2O_7^{2-}$, so the indicator is destroyed. If a chloride solution is acidic, calcium carbonate powder can be added to neutralise the acid.

Example 4

25 cm³ of a solution of potassium chloride was put in a conical flask, and a few drops of yellow potassium chromate(VI) indicator added. Silver nitrate of concentration 0.02 mol dm^{-3} was run in from a burette until the indicator gave a permanent red tinge to the solution. The titre was 22.5 cm³. What was the concentration of the chloride solution?

We start by calculating the number of moles of silver ion added:

$$\text{number of moles of Ag}^+ = 0.02\,\text{mol} \times \frac{22.5\,\text{cm}^3}{1000\,\text{cm}^3} = 0.00045\,\text{mol}$$

We know that 1 mol $Ag^+ \equiv$ 1 mol Cl^-, so the number of moles of chloride ion in the flask was also 0.00045 mol. Now we can say that

$$\text{number of moles of Cl}^- \text{ in } 1\,\text{dm}^3 = 0.00045\,\text{mol} \times \frac{1000\,\text{cm}^3}{25\,\text{cm}^3} = 0.018\,\text{mol}$$

Finally, the concentration of the potassium chloride solution was 0.018 mol dm^{-3}.

40.4 Silver nitrate titrations can be used to help us discover the formula of some chlorides. For example, if you were to pass chlorine over heated aluminium, a white solid is produced. The solid is a chloride of aluminium. For the present purposes we shall assume that we do not know its formula. You have to be careful with an experiment like this if you want to collect a pure sample of the chloride. For example, it is important to exclude moisture from the apparatus; see Figure 40.1.

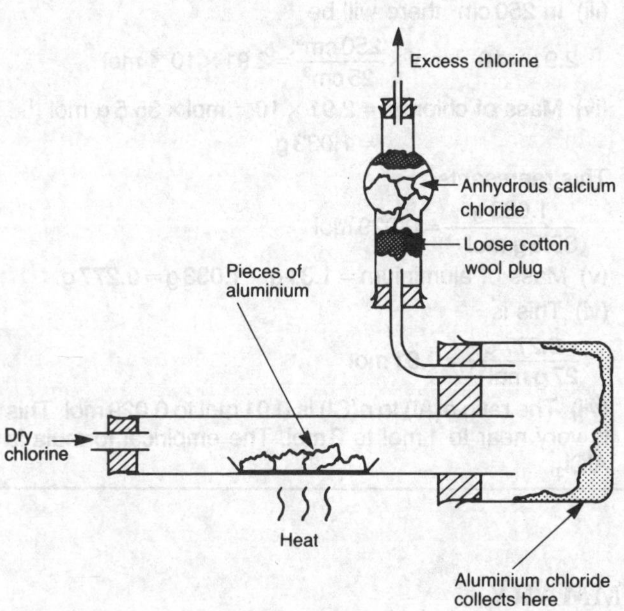

Figure 40.1 *An apparatus for preparing aluminium chloride*

A sample of the chloride is put into a pre-weighed specimen bottle, which is weighed again. Next, the bottle is opened under the surface of water in a beaker. The reaction that takes place can be quite vigorous, but the result is that the chloride is hydrolysed. The chloride originally bound up with the aluminium is released into the water as free chloride ions. This solution is then made up to 250 cm³ in a volumetric flask. 25 cm³ aliquots of this stock solution have calcium carbonate added to them and then they are titrated with silver nitrate using potassium chromate(VI) as an indicator. Here are some specimen results. By the end of the calculation we will have worked out the empirical formula of the chloride.

Mass of the aluminium chloride used = 1.31 g

Concentration of the silver nitrate solution = 0.1 mol dm^{-3}

Average titre of silver nitrate solution = 29.1 cm³

We know that $M(\text{Cl}) = 35.5\,\text{g mol}^{-1}$ and $M(\text{Al}) = 27\,\text{g mol}^{-1}$.

The plan of campaign is as follows:

(i) Find the number of moles of silver ions used in the titration.

(ii) This equals the number of moles of chloride ions in the 25 cm³ of aluminium chloride solution.

(iii) Find the number of moles of chloride ions in 250 cm³ of the stock solution.

(iv) Calculate the mass of chloride ions present. This is the mass of chlorine in the 1.31 g of aluminium chloride. How many moles of chlorine is present?

(v) Calculate the mass of aluminium in the original sample.

(vi) Calculate the number of moles of aluminium in the original sample.

(vii) Find the simplest ratio for the number of moles of aluminium, $n(\text{Al})$, to the number of moles of chlorine, $n(\text{Cl})$. Once you have done this you will have calculated the empirical formula.

Answers

40.1 (i) Number of moles used

$= 0.01\ \text{mol} \times \frac{23.5\ \text{cm}^3}{1000\ \text{cm}^3}$

$= 2.35 \times 10^{-4}$ mol

(ii) Number of moles of Fe^{2+} ions is $6 \times 2.35 \times 10^{-4}$ mol $= 1.41 \times 10^{-3}$ mol.

(iii) There would be 10 times as much, i.e. 1.41×10^{-2} mol.

(iv) Mass of Fe^{2+} ions $= 56\ \text{g mol}^{-1} \times 1.41 \times 10^{-2}\ \text{mol} = 0.79$ g.

(v) Number of moles of crystals

$= \frac{4.2\ \text{g}}{278\ \text{g mol}^{-1}} = 0.015$ mol

(vi) 1 mol of crystals contains 1 mol of Fe^{2+} ions, so 0.015 mol of crystals contains 0.015 mol of Fe^{2+} ions. Mass of Fe^{2+} ions present $= 56\ \text{g mol}^{-1} \times 0.015$ mol $= 0.84$ g.

(vii) The crystals should contain 0.84 g, but the titration shows they really contain 0.79 g. The purity is

$\frac{0.79\ \text{g}}{0.84\ \text{g}} \times 100\% = 94\%$

40.2 (i) $n(MnO_4^-)$

$= 0.02\ \text{mol} \times \frac{28.50\ \text{cm}^3}{1000\ \text{cm}^3} = 5.7 \times 10^{-4}$ mol

(ii) Manganate(VII) ions will take five electrons each, and an iron(II) ion can lose only one electron. Therefore the ratio is

1 mol $MnO_4^- \equiv 5$ mol Fe^{2+}

(iii) There were $5 \times 5.7 \times 10^{-4}$ mol $= 2.85 \times 10^{-3}$ mol.

(iv) There would be 10 times as much, i.e. 2.85×10^{-2} mol.

(v) Mass $= 56\ \text{g mol}^{-1} \times 2.85 \times 10^{-2}\ \text{mol} = 1.596$ g.

(vi) Percentage purity $= \frac{1.596\ \text{g}}{2.55\ \text{g}} \times 100\% = 62.6\%$

40.3 (i) 1 mol $I_2 \equiv 2$ mol $S_2O_3^{2-}$.

(ii) The equation shows that: 1 mol $ClO^- = 1$ mol I_2.

(iii) We have 1 mol $ClO^- \equiv 2$ mol $S_2O_3^{2-}$, i.e. number of moles of ClO^- is half the number of moles of $S_2O_3^{2-}$.

(iv) $n(S_2O_3^{2-}) = 0.01\ \text{mol dm}^{-3} \times \frac{24.20\ \text{cm}^3}{1000\ \text{cm}^3}$

$= 2.42 \times 10^{-4}$ mol

(v) There were 1.21×10^{-4} mol in 25 cm^3, and 4.84×10^{-4} mol in 100 cm^3. This is the same number as in the 2.5 cm^3 of bleach.

(vi) To get the concentration in mol dm^{-3}, we must scale up from 2.5 cm^3 to 1000 cm^3; i.e. we multiply by 400. The concentration is 0.194 mol dm^{-3}.

(vii) You would take a 25 cm^3 sample and add, say, 10 cm^3 of the potassium iodide solution. Then take a second sample and add 15 cm^3 of the iodide solution. If you titrated both solutions, and the 10 cm^3 sample gave the same result as the 15 cm^3 sample, you would know that the 10 cm^3 of iodide was enough to react with all the chlorate(I) ions. If the results were significantly different you would repeat the exercise with a third sample using 20 cm^3 of iodide solution. Eventually you would find out how much of the iodide solution was needed. In practice it is necessary to use excess iodide solution in order to keep the iodine in solution as I_3^- ions, rather than being precipitated as a solid.

(viii) No. Chlorate(I) and chloride ions react (see Unit 102):

$ClO^-(aq) + Cl^-(aq) + 2H^+(aq) \rightarrow Cl_2(g) + H_2O(l)$

Much of the chlorine bubbles out of the solution.

40.4 (i) Number of moles of silver ions

$= 0.1\ \text{mol} \times \frac{29.1\ \text{cm}^3}{1000\ \text{cm}^3} = 2.91 \times 10^{-3}$ mol

(ii) Number of moles of chloride ions $= 2.91 \times 10^{-3}$ mol.

(iii) In 250 cm^3 there will be

$2.91 \times 10^{-3}\ \text{mol} \times \frac{250\ \text{cm}^3}{25\ \text{cm}^3} = 2.91 \times 10^{-2}$ mol

(iv) Mass of chlorine $= 2.91 \times 10^{-2}\ \text{mol} \times 35.5\ \text{g mol}^{-1}$

$= 1.033$ g

This represents

$\frac{1.033\ \text{g}}{35.5\ \text{g mol}^{-1}} = 0.029$ mol

(v) Mass of aluminium $= 1.31\ \text{g} - 1.033\ \text{g} = 0.277$ g.

(vi) This is

$\frac{0.277\ \text{g}}{27\ \text{g mol}^{-1}} = 0.01$ mol

(vii) The ratio $n(Al)$ to $n(Cl)$ is 0.01 mol to 0.029 mol. This is very near to 1 mol to 3 mol. The empirical formula is $AlCl_3$.

UNIT 40 SUMMARY

- Acid–base titrations:
  A typical acid–base titration uses the neutralisation reaction between oxonium ions and hydroxide ions

  $$H_3O^+(aq) + OH^-(aq) \rightarrow 2H_2O(l)$$

- Redox titrations:
  (i) Titration of iron(II) with potassium dichromate(VI)

  $$6Fe^{2+}(aq) + Cr_2O_7^{2-}(aq) + 14H^+(aq) \rightarrow 6Fe^{3+}(aq) + 2Cr^{3+}(aq) + 7H_2O(l)$$

(ii) Titration of ethanedioate (oxalate) ions with potassium manganate(VII)

$$5C_2O_4^{2-}(aq) + 2MnO_4^-(aq) + 8H^+(aq) \rightarrow 10CO_2(g) + 2Mn^{2+}(aq) + 4H_2O(l)$$

- Titrations involving iodine:

(i) Iodide ions are easily oxidised

$$2I^-(aq) - 2e^- \rightarrow I_2(s)$$

e.g. by iodate(V) ions

$$IO_3^-(aq) + 5I^-(aq) + 6H^+(aq) \rightarrow 3I_2(s) + 3H_2O(l)$$

(ii) Iodine can be titrated with thiosulphate solution using starch as an indicator

$$2S_2O_3^{2-}(aq) + I_2(s) \rightarrow S_4O_6^{2-}(aq) + 2I^-(aq)$$

- Silver nitrate titrations:

Silver ions can be titrated with chloride ions using a solution of chromate(VI) ions, CrO_4^{2-}, as indicator

$$Ag^+(aq) + Cl^-(aq) \rightarrow AgCl(s)$$

Solid silver chromate(VI), Ag_2CrO_4, is red and is precipitated once the majority of chloride ions are removed.

41

Oxidation numbers and oxidation states

41.1 What are oxidation and reduction reactions?

We have a belief that we should be able to find patterns in the way that chemicals react. One pattern that was established in the eighteenth century was that many elements combine with oxygen to make oxides. Reactions between elements and oxygen were called *oxidation* reactions. For example, magnesium is oxidised when it burns in oxygen,

$$2Mg(s) + O_2(g) \rightarrow 2MgO(s)$$

and carbon is oxidised in the reaction

$$C(s) + O_2(g) \rightarrow CO_2(g)$$

The opposite process, taking oxygen away from an element, is known as *reduction*. The simplest method of reducing an oxide is to react it with hydrogen. For example, when hydrogen is passed over hot copper(II) oxide, the oxide is reduced:

$$CuO(s) + H_2(g) \rightarrow Cu(s) + H_2O(g)$$

If you look at this equation again you will see that the hydrogen has gained oxygen: it has been oxidised. Indeed, oxidation and reduction always take place together in a reaction.

Many reactions are more complicated than those we have considered so far. For example, ammonia will burn in oxygen:

$$4NH_3(g) + 5O_2(g) \rightarrow 4NO(g) + 6H_2O(g)$$

The nitrogen atom in ammonia loses its hydrogen, while at the same time it has gained oxygen. In fact there are many reactions that show this pattern: a loss of hydrogen is matched by a gain of oxygen. For this reason we can give two characteristics of oxidation is:

(i) the gain of oxygen, or

(ii) the loss of hydrogen.

Similarly, reduction is:

(i) the loss of oxygen,

(ii) the gain of hydrogen.

Thus far our definitions do show patterns among reactions, but they are rather restrictive. Only reactions involving oxygen or hydrogen are covered. We can broaden the definitions to include many more reactions. The method is to look at the underlying changes that take place in the bonding of the compounds during oxidation and reduction. For the oxidation of magnesium, the changes involve converting magnesium atoms into magnesium ions, Mg^{2+}, and oxygen molecules into oxygen ions, O^{2-}:

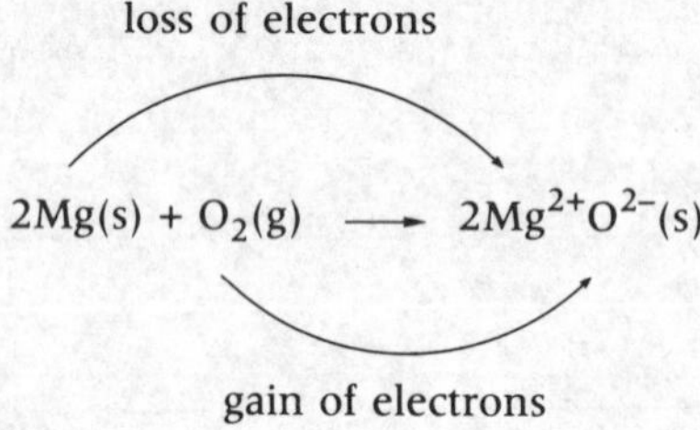

The magnesium (which is oxidised) loses electrons, while the oxygen (which is reduced) gains electrons. We shall now make the generalisation that oxidation occurs with the loss of electrons. Thus we have

Oxidation is (i) the gain of oxygen,
or (ii) the loss of hydrogen,
or (iii) the loss of electrons.

A chemical that is used to oxidise another is an oxidising agent. Table 41.1 lists some common oxidising and reducing agents.

Dichromate(VI) ions are released by potassium dichromate(VI), $K_2Cr_2O_7$, in acid solution. The solution has a vivid orange colour that turns green when it oxidises. The green colour is due to the presence of chromium(III) ions, Cr^{3+}, in water. For example,

Table 41.1. Common oxidising and reducing agents

Oxidising agents	*Reducing agents*
Oxygen, O_2	Hydrogen, H_2
Chlorine, Cl_2	Metals, e.g. Na, K, Mg
Dichromate(VI) ions, $Cr_2O_7^{2-}$	Sulphur dioxide, SO_2
Manganate(VII) ions, MnO_4^-	Hydrogen sulphide, H_2S

$$Cr_2O_7^{2-}(aq) + 3SO_2(aq) + 2H^+(aq) \rightarrow 2Cr^{3+}(aq) + 3SO_4^{2-}(aq) + H_2O(l)$$

Potassium manganate(VII), $KMnO_4$, is a convenient source of manganate(VII) ions, MnO_4^-. In solution it has a deep purple colour, and when it oxidises in the presence of acid it loses its colour. If it reacts in alkaline solution, it gives a clear solution together with a black precipitate of manganese (IV) oxide, MnO_2. For example, in acid conditions with ethanedioate ions:

$$2MnO_4^-(aq) + C_2O_4^{2-}(aq) + 16H^+(aq) \rightarrow 2Mn^{2+}(aq) + 10CO_2(g) + 8H_2O(l)$$

Both potassium dichromate(VI) and potassium manganate(VII) solutions are used to test for reducing agents. The colour changes are usually very clear.

Before we go on to the next section, you should be careful about one further point: when we call a chemical an oxidising or a reducing agent we are speaking in relative terms. A chemical we normally call an oxidising agent will itself be oxidised if it meets a more powerful oxidising agent. Chlorine is a good example. In most of its reactions it does oxidise other chemicals. But fluorine is a more powerful oxidising agent than chlorine; so if the two gases react, it is the fluorine that oxidises the chlorine. In that case, chlorine is the reducing agent.

41.1 Write down definitions of reduction.

41.2 What are oxidation numbers?

We know that a substance that loses one or more electrons has been oxidised; on the other hand, if it gains one or more electrons it has been reduced. For example, when sodium and chlorine react, the product is the ionic substance sodium chloride. This contains Na^+ and Cl^- ions:

$$2Na + Cl_2 \rightarrow 2Na^+Cl^-$$

When it is unreacted, the sodium is neither oxidised nor reduced; we shall say that its oxidation number is 0. When it is converted into a positive ion, Na^+, we shall give it an oxidation number of +1. Similarly, chlorine atoms start with an oxidation number of 0 when they are present as chlorine molecules, Cl_2. After they react, and turn into chloride ions, Cl^-, we shall give them an oxidation number of −1.

You might be able to guess the pattern that we use to assign oxidation numbers to atoms when they are present as unreacted elements and when they change into ions. The rule is:

An unreacted element has an oxidation number of 0.

An ion has an oxidation number equal to its charge.

Examples illustrating these rules are listed in Table 41.2. You can see that some elements give more than one type of ion. Usually these are the transition elements like iron, copper and manganese. However, hydrogen can also give two different ions. The most common one is the hydrogen ion, H^+, which is found in acidic solutions. The hydride ion, H^-, is found in solid hydrides like Na^+H^- and K^+H^- made when hydrogen reacts with powerful reducing metals. Likewise, oxygen almost always has a charge of −2 when it is in an ionic compound. The exception is oxygen in peroxides such as barium peroxide, BaO_2. In peroxides the O_2^{2-} ion is present. The average charge on an oxygen atom in this ion is −1, so we give the oxidation number a value of −1 as well.

Table 41.2. Oxidation numbers of elements in simple ions

Unreacted element		*Oxidation number*	*Ion*	*Oxidation number*
Hydrogen,	H_2	0	H^+ H^-	+1 −1
Oxygen,	O_2	0	O^{2-} O_2^{2-}	−2 −1
Nitrogen,	N_2	0	N^{3-}	−3
Chlorine,	Cl_2	0	Cl^-	−1
Bromine,	Br_2	0	Br^-	−1
Sodium,	Na	0	Na^+	+1
Magnesium,	Mg	0	Mg^{2+}	+2
Iron,	Fe	0	Fe^{2+} Fe^{3+}	+2 +3
Copper,	Cu	0	Cu^+ Cu^{2+}	+1 +2
Manganese,	Mn	0	Mn^{2+} Mn^{7+}	+2 +7

41.3 Oxidation numbers of elements in covalent compounds

We shall now discover how to find the oxidation number of an element when it is in a covalent compound. The way to do this is first to pretend that the substances is ionic; then ask yourself what ions would be present. Look at the first two examples.

Example 1

What are the oxidation numbers of hydrogen and oxygen in water, H_2O?

We know that hydrogen tends to make H^+ ions, and oxygen O^{2-} ions. Therefore, *if* water were ionic, it would contain H^+ and O^{2-} ions, and we say that the oxidation numbers of hydrogen and oxygen in water are +1 and −2 respectively. Notice that if we add all the oxidation numbers together we find that they cancel out:

$$\underbrace{2\times(+1)}_{\text{two hydrogens}} + \underbrace{(-2)}_{\text{one oxygen}} = 0$$

This is what should happen if we have done our working properly. (A water molecule is electrically neutral, so there should be no overall charge.)

Example 2

What are the oxidation numbers of the sulphur and oxygen atoms in sulphur dioxide, SO_2?

The key to finding the answer in a case like this is to start with an element whose oxidation number we know with some certainty. Here we shall assume that if the molecule were ionic, the oxygen atoms would be present as oxide ions, O^{2-}. Given that sulphur dioxide contains two oxygen atoms for each sulphur atom, there would be two oxide ions in the mythical ionic compound. In total the two oxide ions carry a charge of −4. Because sulphur dioxide is electrically neutral, the sulphur would have to be present as +4 ions. Therefore we say that the sulphur has an oxidation number of +4.

We can do a calculation like this in a neater way if we use a special notation. The symbol *Ox* will stand for an oxidation number. Then *Ox*(O) stands for the oxidation number of oxygen, *Ox*(Na) for the oxidation number of sodium, and so on. Because sulphur dioxide has no overall charge,

$$Ox(\mathrm{S}) + 2Ox(\mathrm{O}) = 0$$
$$Ox(\mathrm{S}) + 2(-2) = 0$$
$$Ox(\mathrm{S}) - 4 = 0$$
$$Ox(\mathrm{S}) = +4$$

41.2 What are the oxidation numbers of the elements in each of the following compounds: (i) SO_3; (ii) NH_3; (iii) N_2H_4; (iv) CO_2; (v) $MgCl_2$; (vi) Mn_2O_7?

41.4 Oxidation numbers of elements in ions

Here we shall do three examples, which will show you how to work out the oxidation numbers of elements in ions.

Example 3

What is the oxidation number of phosphorus in PO_4^{3-} ions?

We employ the same tactics as in example 2, except that we have to leave the ion with its charge of −3. Let us assume that oxygen has its normal oxidation number. Now if we balance the charges we have

$$Ox(\mathrm{P}) + 4Ox(\mathrm{O}) = -3$$
$$Ox(\mathrm{P}) + 4(-2) = -3$$
$$Ox(\mathrm{P}) - 8 = -3$$
$$Ox(\mathrm{P}) = +5$$

The oxidation numbers are +5 for the phosphorus, and −2 for each oxygen atom.

Example 4

What is the oxidation number of sulphur in the sulphate ion, SO_4^{2-}?

We set out the answer using the same method as before:

$$Ox(\mathrm{S}) + 4Ox(\mathrm{O}) = -2$$
$$Ox(\mathrm{S}) - 8 = -2$$
$$Ox(\mathrm{S}) = +6$$

Example 5

What is the oxidation number of sulphur in the tetrathionate ion $S_4O_6^{2-}$?

We have

$$4Ox(\mathrm{S}) + 6Ox(\mathrm{O}) = -2$$
$$4Ox(\mathrm{S}) - 12 = -2$$
$$4Ox(\mathrm{S}) = +10$$
$$Ox(\mathrm{S}) = +2.5$$

The oxidation number of sulphur is 2.5.

The last result may surprise you because we know that ions cannot have fractions of a positive or negative charge. However, oxidation numbers are *not* properties of atoms in the same way as their charge or mass. We cannot measure oxidation numbers. They are products of our imagination, which, as you will see, happen to be useful. Also, in the calculation we have just done, we found the average oxidation number of four sulphur atoms. If you look at the arrangement of the atoms in the ion,

```
 ┌  O             O ┐2−
 │ O═S—S—S—S═O      │
 └  O             O ┘
```

you will see that two sulphur atoms in the middle are joined only to other sulphur atoms. This is like the situation in pure sulphur, where the oxidation number of a sulphur atom would be zero. Only two sulphur atoms have oxygen atoms joined to them. If we imagine that these two atoms share the charge of +10 we would have two sulphur atoms of oxidation number 0 and two with oxidation number +5.

41.5 Rules for assigning oxidation numbers

Some atoms have only one oxidation number. For example, the Group I metals only ever give ions with a charge of +1, hydrogen almost always has the oxidation number +1, and oxygen −2. However, as we said in section 41.2 there are some exceptions: in particular, hydrogen in metal hydrides, and oxygen in peroxides. In fact the majority of elements in the Periodic Table show more than one oxidation number. It all depends with which other elements they are combined.

There are some guidelines we can use to help in deciding on an element's oxidation number. These are listed in Table 41.3.

Some of the molecules and ions made when oxygen and another non-metal combine can cause problems if you do not stick to the rules. Examples 6 and 7 show you the method to employ.

Table 41.3 Rules for assigning oxidation numbers*

Group I metals	+1
Group II metals	+2
Group III metals	+3
Hydrogen	+1 −1 in metal hydrides, e.g. NaH
Oxygen	−2 −1 in peroxides, e.g. BaO_2
Nitrogen	−3 in ammonia and in nitrides, e.g. Mg_3N_2; varies when in combination with oxygen
Halogens	−1 in direct combination with metals; varies when in combination with oxygen and in interhalogen compounds such as ICl

*Where there is doubt, the more electronegative atom usually takes the lower oxidation number

Example 6

What is the oxidation number of chlorine in Cl_2O_7?

We start by writing down the oxidation number equation and giving oxygen its normal oxidation number of −2.

$$2Ox(Cl) + 7Ox(O) = 0$$
$$2Ox(Cl) - 14 = 0$$
$$Ox(Cl) = +7$$

The oxidation number of the chlorine is +7.

Example 7

What is the oxidation number of each of the atoms in $POCl_3$?

Here it helps to know the structure of the molecule. The oxygen and chlorine atoms are combined with the phosphorus atom, but not with each other. Therefore, we assign −2 to the oxidation number of oxygen, and −1 to that of chlorine. Doing the arithmetic, we have

$$Ox(O) + 3Ox(Cl) + Ox(P) = 0$$
$$-2 \quad -3 \quad + Ox(P) = 0$$
$$Ox(P) = +5$$

41.3 What are the oxidation numbers of the elements in the following ions: (i) $S_2O_3^{2-}$; (ii) $HC_2O_4^{-}$; (iii) HPO_3^{2-}?

41.4 What is the oxidation number of oxygen in Na_2O and Na_2O_2?

41.6 Oxidation states

You will have met the names of chemicals like copper(II) sulphate, or perhaps iron(III) chloride. The number in brackets is the *oxidation state* of the element. The oxidation state is always written as a Roman numeral, but it is only another way of telling us the oxidation number. For example, copper(II) sulphate contains copper as Cu^{2+} ions, and if it were ionic there would be Fe^{3+} ions in iron(III) chloride. Transition metals in particular can exist in a variety of oxidation states. The oxidation state in the name gives us a guide to the nature of the metal ion in the compound (Table 41.4). For example, copper(I) oxide will have Cu^{+} ions present, and the formula of the oxide is Cu_2O. (We need two single positively charged ions to balance the −2 charge on the oxide ion.) On the other hand, copper(II) oxide contains Cu^{2+} ions, and its formula is CuO.

The names of transition metal compounds can be quite

Table 41.4. The names and formulae of ions and acids*

Metal ions	*Formula*	*Non-metal ions*	*Formula*
Aluminium	Al^{3+}	Bromide	Br^-
Bismuth(III)	Bi^{3+}	Chloride	Cl^-
Calcium	Ca^{2+}	Fluoride	F^-
Chromium(III)	Cr^{3+}	Hydride	H^-
Chromium(VI)	Cr^{6+}	Hydrogen	H^+
Copper(I)	Cu^+	Iodide	I^-
Copper(II)	Cu^{2+}	Oxide	O^{2-}
Iron(II)	Fe^{2+}	Peroxide	O_2^{2-}
Iron(III)	Fe^{3+}	Sulphide	S^{2-}
Lead(II)	Pb^{2+}		
Lead(IV)	Pb^{4+}		
Magnesium	Mg^{2+}		
Manganese(II)	Mn^{2+}		
Potassium	K^+		
Sodium	Na^+		
Zinc	Zn^{2+}		

Oxoanions	*Formula*	*Acids*	*Formula*
Bromate(I)	BrO^-	Bromic(I)	$HBrO$
Bromate(V)	BrO_3^-	Bromic(V)	$HBrO_3$
Carbonate	CO_3^{2-}	Carbonic	H_2CO_3
Chlorate(I)	ClO^-	Chloric(I)	$HClO$
Chlorate(V)	ClO_3^-	Chloric(V)	$HClO_3$
Chlorate(VII)	ClO_4^-	Chloric(VII)	$HClO_4$
Chromate(VI)	CrO_4^{2-}	Chromic(VI)	H_2CrO_4
Dichromate(VI)	$Cr_2O_7^{2-}$	Iodic	HIO_3
Iodate(V)	IO_3^-	Nitric	HNO_3
Nitrate	NO_3^-	Nitrous	HNO_2
Nitrite	NO_2^-	Phosphoric(V)	H_3PO_4
Phosphate(V)	PO_4^{3-}	Sulphurous	H_2SO_3
Sulphite	SO_3^{2-}	Sulphuric	H_2SO_4
Sulphate	SO_4^{2-}		
Peroxodisulphate(VI)	$S_2O_8^{2-}$		
Thiosulphate	$S_2O_3^{2-}$		

*Oxoanions are negative ions that contain oxygen
A positive ion that is often found in solution is the oxonium (or hydronium) ion, H_3O^+
Hydrochloric acid consists of hydrogen chloride, HCl, in water

confusing at first. You will find information about this in Unit 105, but here we shall look at two substances that are often used as oxidising agents. They are potassium manganate(VII), $KMnO_4$, and potassium dichromate(VI), $K_2Cr_2O_7$. To see why the oxidation state of the manganese is VII, we put

$$Ox(\mathrm{K}) + Ox(\mathrm{Mn}) + 4Ox(\mathrm{O}) = 0$$
$$1 + Ox(\mathrm{Mn}) - 8 = 0$$
$$Ox(\mathrm{Mn}) = +7$$

Similarly, for potassium dichromate(VI):

$$2Ox(\mathrm{K}) + 2Ox(\mathrm{Cr}) + 7Ox(\mathrm{O}) = 0$$
$$2 + 2Ox(\mathrm{Cr}) - 14 = 0$$
$$2Ox(\mathrm{Cr}) = +12$$
$$Ox(\mathrm{Cr}) = +6$$

which gives us the oxidation state of VI.

Oxidation states are sometimes written for ions that do not contain transition metals; for example, the bromate(V) ion, BrO_3^-. The oxidation number equation for this ion is

$$Ox(\mathrm{Br}) + 3Ox(\mathrm{O}) = -1$$
$$Ox(\mathrm{Br}) - 6 = -1$$
$$Ox(\mathrm{Br}) = +5$$

which agrees with the oxidation state of V written in the name of the ion.

When you see the ending 'ate' in a name it always means that the substance contains oxygen; e.g. bromate(V), dichromate(VI) and manganate(VII) ions. This is a clue we can use to work out the name of an ion if we are given its formula.

Example 8

What is the name of the ClO^- ion?

We have

$$Ox(\mathrm{Cl}) + Ox(\mathrm{O}) = -1$$
$$Ox(\mathrm{Cl}) - 2 = -1$$
$$Ox(\mathrm{Cl}) = +1$$

Given that the ion contains chlorine and oxygen it will be a chlorate ion, and we have shown that the oxidation state is I; hence the complete name is chlorate(I) ion. (The name 'hypochlorite ion' was once used.)

41.5 What is the formula of (i) iron(II) chloride, (ii) iron(III) chloride and (iii) copper(II) nitrate?

41.6 What is the oxidation state of

(i) the chromium atom in $Cr(H_2O)_6^{3+}$;

(ii) the copper atom in $Cu(NH_3)_4^{2+}$;

(iii) the nickel atom in $Ni(NH_3)_2Cl_2$?

(Hint: are the water and ammonia molecules in these ions charged?)

41.7 Using oxidation numbers with equations

Many, but not all, reactions are redox reactions, i.e. they involve a combination of oxidation and reduction. For example, the reaction between sodium and chlorine is a redox reaction. We have seen that the oxidation number of the sodium changes from 0 to +1. This represents the loss of one electron, from each atom. Conversely the oxidation number of the chlorine goes down, from 0 to −1. Indeed, it is a rule that:

Oxidation involves an increase in oxidation number.

Reduction involves a decrease in oxidation number.

A change in oxidation number of one unit represents the apparent transfer of one electron from one atom or group to another.

It is worth noting that atoms in a high oxidation state (i.e. with a high oxidation number) are likely to be strong oxidising agents. They are likely to take electrons and move to a lower oxidation state.

We can use the rules to help us decide whether a reaction is a redox reaction. Indeed:

The key to deciding if a reaction is a redox reaction is to look for changes in oxidation numbers.

Example 9

Which of the following are redox reactions?

(i) $H_2(g) + Cl_2(g) \rightarrow 2HCl(g)$

(ii) $NaOH(aq) + H_2SO_4(aq) \rightarrow NaHSO_4(aq) + H_2O(l)$

(iii) $KCl(aq) + AgNO_3(aq) \rightarrow AgCl(s) + KNO_3(aq)$

The first thing to do is to work out the oxidation numbers of the elements in each equation. If there is a change in oxidation number from one side of the equation to the other, then we have a redox reaction. We shall write the oxidation numbers below each element, and with the formulae stretched out:

(i) $\underset{0}{H_2}(g) + \underset{0}{Cl_2}(g) \rightarrow 2\underset{+1}{H}\,\underset{-1}{Cl}(g)$

Here there is a change in oxidation number. This is a redox reaction.

(ii) $\underset{+1}{Na}\ \underset{-2}{O}\ \underset{+1}{H}(aq) + \underset{+1}{H_2}\ \underset{+6}{S}\ \underset{-2}{O_4}(aq) \rightarrow$

$\underset{+1}{Na}\ \underset{+1}{H}\ \underset{+6}{S}\ \underset{-2}{O_4}(aq) + \underset{+1}{H_2}\underset{-2}{O}(l)$

There is no change in the oxidation numbers. This is not a redox reaction. It is best regarded as an acid–base (neutralisation) reaction.

(iii) $\underset{+1}{K}\ \underset{-1}{Cl}(aq) + \underset{+1}{Ag}\ \underset{+5}{N}\ \underset{-2}{O_3}(aq) \rightarrow$

$\underset{+1}{Ag}\ \underset{-1}{Cl}(s) + \underset{+1}{K}\ \underset{+5}{N}\ \underset{-2}{O_3}(aq)$

Again there is no change in oxidation number, so this is not a redox reaction. It is a precipitation reaction (used in the test for a chloride).

Now we come to the point where we shall use oxidation numbers to balance equations. Example 10 will show you the method.

Example 10

Manganate(VII) ions, MnO_4^-, react with iron(II) ions in acid solution to give iron(III) ions and manganese(II) ions. What is the equation for the reaction?

The two important changes, together with the oxidation numbers, are

$\underset{+7}{Mn}\ O_4^- \rightarrow \underset{+2}{Mn^{2+}}$ and $\underset{+2}{Fe^{2+}} \rightarrow \underset{+3}{Fe^{3+}}$

Decrease (−5) in ox. no. Increase (+1) in ox. no.

We can see that one manganate(VII) ion can accept (or take) five electrons. (This is why it is sometimes called a five-electron oxidising agent.) On the other hand, a single iron(II) ion can only give up one electron. Therefore, if we are to keep a balance in the changes in oxidation numbers, it must be that one manganate(VII) ion reacts with five iron(II) ions. Now we can begin to write the equation for the change:

$$MnO_4^- + 5Fe^{2+} \rightarrow Mn^{2+} + 5Fe^{3+}$$

However, this is not balanced. Two things are wrong. First, the charges do not match on each side of the equation; secondly, the oxygen atoms do not appear on both sides. The clue to putting both of these matters right is given to us in the question: the reaction takes place in acid conditions. Indeed, there is a rule of thumb in balancing this type of equation, which tells us to add sufficient hydrogen ions to convert all the oxygen to water. We can do this by adding eight hydrogen ions to the left-hand side:

$$MnO_4^- + 5Fe^{2+} + 8H^+ \rightarrow Mn^{2+} + 5Fe^{3+} + 4H_2O$$

Now the equation is balanced, in terms of both charge and number of atoms. To be really respectable we should add the state symbols to the chemicals:

$$MnO_4^-(aq) + 5Fe^{2+}(aq) + 8H^+(aq) \rightarrow Mn^{2+}(aq) + 5Fe^{3+}(aq) + 4H_2O(l)$$

Example 11

What is the equation for the reaction between acidified dichromate(VI) ions, $Cr_2O_7^{2-}$, and sulphur dioxide solution? The chief products are chromium(III) ions and sulphate ions, SO_4^{2-}.

As in the last example, we write down the two main changes.

$$\begin{array}{llll} Cr_2 & O_7^{2-} \rightarrow 2Cr^{3+} & \text{and} \quad S\ O_2 \rightarrow S\ O_4^{2-} \\ 2\times(+6) & 2\times(+3) & +4 \quad\quad +6 \\ =+12 & =+6 & \\ \text{Decrease } (-6) \text{ in ox. no.} & & \text{Increase } (+2) \text{ in ox. no.} \end{array}$$

This tells us that one $Cr_2O_7^{2-}$ ion is capable of oxidising three molecules of SO_2. (It is a six-electron oxidising agent.) Now we begin to write the equation:

$$Cr_2O_7^{2-} + 3SO_2 \rightarrow 2Cr^{3+} + 3SO_4^{2-}$$

Again the oxygen atoms and the charges are unbalanced, so we add hydrogen ions to the left-hand side. We can work out how many hydrogen ions to add by checking either the oxygen atoms or the charges. To be on the safe side we shall do both. First, the oxygen atom balance. On the left-hand side there are a total of 13 oxygen atoms, and on the right there are only 12. We can supply the missing atom by assuming that it is converted into a water molecule by hydrogen ions. Each water molecule requires two hydrogen atoms for each oxygen atom. Therefore we add two hydrogen ions to the left-hand side:

$$Cr_2O_7^{2-} + 3SO_2 + 2H^+ \rightarrow 2Cr^{3+} + 3SO_4^{2-} + H_2O$$

Now the second method, where we concentrate on the charges. In the incomplete equation there is an overall charge of -2 on the left-hand side, and a charge of zero on the right-hand side. In order to balance the charges we add two positive charges to the left-hand side. These charges come in the guise of two hydrogen ions, H^+. We have produced the same equation as in the first method,

$$Cr_2O_7^{2-}(aq) + 3SO_2(aq) + 2H^+(aq) \rightarrow 2Cr^{3+}(aq) + 3SO_4^{2-}(aq) + H_2O(l)$$

but this time we have added the state symbols.

41.7 Which of the following equations represent redox reactions?

(i) $BaCl_2(aq) + H_2SO_4(aq) \rightarrow BaSO_4(s) + 2HCl(aq)$

(ii) $ClO_3^-(aq) + 3Zn(s) + 6H^+(aq) \rightarrow Cl^-(aq) + 3Zn^{2+}(aq) + 3H_2O(l)$

(iii) $2Cu^{2+}(aq) + 4I^-(aq) \rightarrow 2CuI(s) + I_2(aq)$

If it is a redox reaction, identify the oxidising agent and the reducing agent.

41.8 Which is likely to be the stronger oxidising agent: lead(II) oxide, PbO, or lead(IV) oxide, PbO_2?

41.9 Use the following information, and your knowledge of oxidation numbers, to write balanced equations for the reactions involved.

(i) In acidic solution, manganate(VII) ions oxidise sulphite ions, SO_3^{2-}, to sulphate, SO_4^{2-}. The manganese is left as Mn^{2+} ions.

(ii) Again in acid solution, manganate(VII) ions oxidise $C_2O_4^{2-}$ ions to carbon dioxide. Mn^{2+} ions are left in solution.

(iii) In acid solution, dichromate(VI) ions oxidise tin(II) to tin(IV) ions. Chromium(III) ions are also produced.

(iv) Also in acid solution, dichromate(VI) ions oxidise iodide ions to iodine with chromium(III) ions remaining.

41.8 Half-equations

Before we leave the subject of equations, you will find it useful to know about half-equations. Two half-equations add up to give the whole equation for a redox reaction. They can be built up by using oxidation numbers. We shall build the half-equations for the reaction between manganate(VII) ions and iron(II) ions, which we discussed in example 10.

We said that the change of a MnO_4^- ion into a Mn^{2+} ion requires the gain of five electrons. (There is an oxidation number change of +7 to +2.) We also said that the oxygen in the MnO_4^- ion is converted into water, which needs the addition of $8H^+$ ions. Both pieces of information are summarised in the half-equation:

$$MnO_4^-(aq) + 5e^- + 8H^+(aq) \rightarrow Mn^{2+}(aq) + 4H_2O(l)$$

The half-equation for the conversion of Fe^{2+} into Fe^{3+} is:

$$Fe^{2+}(aq) \rightarrow Fe^{3+}(aq) + e^-$$

We obtain the full equation by scaling up the second half-equation by five, to give

$$5Fe^{2+}(aq) \rightarrow 5Fe^{3+}(aq) + 5e^-$$

and then adding the first half-equation:

$$\begin{array}{r} MnO_4^-(aq) + 5e^- + 8H^+(aq) \rightarrow Mn^{2+}(aq) + 4H_2O(l) \\ 5Fe^{2+}(aq) \rightarrow 5Fe^{3+}(aq) + 5e^- \\ \hline MnO_4^-(aq) + 5Fe^{2+}(aq) + 8H^+(aq) \rightarrow Mn^{2+}(aq) + 5Fe^{3+}(aq) + 4H_2O(l) \end{array}$$

The $5e^-$ cancels out as it appears on both sides of the final equation. If two half-equations have been drawn up properly, the number of electrons should always cancel.

You will find that half-equations are very useful in working with electrochemical cells; see Unit 66.

41.10 Work out the half-equation for each of the changes below, and give the overall equation.

(i) Titanium(III), Ti^{3+}, ions can be reduced to titanium(II), Ti^{2+}, by silver, Ag. The silver changes into Ag^+.

(ii) Acidified dichromate(VI) ions, $Cr_2O_7^{2-}$, can oxidise sulphite ions, SO_3^{2-}, to sulphate, SO_4^{2-}. The chromium is left as chromium(III) ions, Cr^{3+}. (First, decide on the oxidation number of sulphur in the sulphite and sulphate ions. Then assume that the extra oxygen in each sulphate ion is obtained from a sulphite ion and a passing water molecule.)

41.11 When manganate(VII) ions act as oxidising agents in alkaline solution they are converted into the black solid manganese(IV) oxide, MnO_2, rather than Mn^{2+} ions.

(i) Write down the half-equation for the conversion of MnO_4^- ions into MnO_2. (Be careful, you will find that 'alkaline' is best regarded as 'not very acidic'.)

(ii) Write down the half-equation for the conversion of ethanedioate (oxalate) ions, $C_2O_4^{2-}$, into carbon dioxide, CO_2.

(iii) What is the full equation for the reaction between ethanedioate ions and alkaline manganate(VII) ions.

(iv) This reaction is not normally done in the laboratory. It is much more common to use acidified manganate(VII). In acid solution the colour change is pink to clear. What would you expect to see using an alkaline solution?

Answers

41.1 Reduction is (i) the loss of oxygen, or (ii) the gain of hydrogen, or (iii) the gain of electrons.

Notice that oxidation and reduction are opposites, or inverses of each other. If you have to learn these definitions, only commit one set firmly to memory. If you need the second definition, work it out from the one you know.

41.2 In each of these examples, oxygen has the oxidation number −2 and hydrogen +1. The others are: (i) sulphur, +6; (ii) nitrogen, −3; (iii) nitrogen, −2; (iv) carbon, +4; (v) magnesium, +2; (vi) manganese, +7.

41.3 The oxidation number of hydrogen is always +1 and oxygen −2 in these ions.

(i) $2Ox(S) + 3Ox(O) = -2$

gives $Ox(S) = +2$;

(ii) $Ox(H) + 2Ox(C) + 4Ox(O) = -1$

$+1 + 2Ox(C) - 8 = -1$

gives $Ox(C) = +3$;

(iii) $Ox(H) + Ox(P) + 3Ox(O) = -2$

$+1 + Ox(P) - 6 = -2$

gives $Ox(P) = +3$.

41.4 In Na_2O we have oxide ions, O^{2-}, in which the oxidation number is −2. Na_2O_2 is a peroxide, which contains the O_2^{2-} ion; here the oxygen has oxidation number −1.

41.5 (i) $FeCl_2$; (ii) $FeCl_3$; (iii) $Cu(NO_3)_2$.

41.6 (i) The water molecules are neutral so they make no difference to our count of charges, i.e. $Ox(H_2O) = 0$. For example, $Ox(Cr) + 6Ox(H_2O) = +3$ becomes $Ox(Cr) = +3$. This is a chromium(III) ion.

(ii) Like water, $Ox(NH_3) = 0$, so $Ox(Cu) = +2$. This is a copper(II) ion.

(iii) Here, $Ox(Ni) + 2Ox(NH_3) + Ox(Cl) = 0$. But, $Ox(NH_3) = 0$ and $Ox(Cl) = -1$, which gives $Ox(Ni) = +2$. We have a nickel(II) compound.

41.7 (i) This is a precipitation reaction, not a redox reaction.

(ii) The quickest way of deciding this is to notice that the zinc atoms are converted into zinc ions. The oxidation number changes from 0 to +2; so the zinc atoms have lost electrons. They have been oxidised by the chlorate(V), ClO_3^-, ions. Notice that the chlorine in the ClO_3^- has the high oxidation number of +5; so we should not be surprised to find that it is an effective oxidising agent. As the zinc atoms have given up electrons, they are the reducing agents. Metals are almost always reducing agents.

(iii) This too is a redox reaction. The copper(II) ions are converted to copper(I) ions. They have been reduced. Some, but not all, of the iodide ions, which start with an oxidation number of −1, are converted to neutral iodine molecules, which have an oxidation number of 0. These iodide ions have been oxidised. Thus, here Cu^{2+} ions are oxidising agents, and I^- ions are reducing agents.

41.8 Lead(IV) oxide should be the better oxidising agent because the lead is in the higher oxidation state.

41.9

(i) $Mn\ O_4^- \rightarrow Mn^{2+}$ (+7 → +2; Decrease (−5) in ox. no.) and $S\ O_3^{2-} \rightarrow S\ O_4^{2-}$ (+4 → +6; Increase (+2) in ox. no.)

This shows that one MnO_4^- will oxidise two-and-a-half SO_3^{2-} ions. However, it is more sensible to say that two MnO_4^- will oxidise five SO_3^{2-} ions. This gives

$$2MnO_4^- + 5SO_3^{2-} \rightarrow 2Mn^{2+} + 5SO_4^{2-}$$

In order to balance the charges in the equation we must add six positive charges to the left-hand side. This is where we add hydrogen ions:

$$2MnO_4^-(aq) + 5SO_3^{2-}(aq) + 6H^+(aq) \rightarrow 2Mn^{2+}(aq) + 5SO_4^{2-}(aq) + 3H_2O(l)$$

(ii) $\overset{+7}{Mn}O_4^- \rightarrow \overset{+2}{Mn^{2+}}$ and $\underset{=+6}{\overset{2\times(+3)}{C_2}}O_4^{2-} \rightarrow \underset{=+8}{\overset{2\times(+4)}{2C}}O_2$

Decrease (−5) in ox. no. Increase (+2) in ox. no.

This is a similar pattern to that in part (i):

$$2MnO_4^- + 5C_2O_4^{2-} \rightarrow 2Mn^{2+} + 10CO_2$$

This time we have to add $16H^+$ to balance the equation.

$$2MnO_4^-(aq) + 5C_2O_4^{2-}(aq) + 16H^+(aq) \rightarrow 2Mn^{2+}(aq) + 10CO_2(g) + 8H_2O(l)$$

(iii) $\underset{=+12}{\overset{2\times(+6)}{Cr_2}}O_7^{2-} \rightarrow \underset{=+6}{\overset{2\times(+3)}{2Cr^{3+}}}$ and $\overset{+2}{Sn^{2+}} \rightarrow \overset{+4}{Sn^{4+}}$

Decrease (−6) in ox. no. Increase (+2) in ox. no.

We now know that one $Cr_2O_7^{2-}$ will oxidise three Sn^{2+} ions, so the equation begins with

$$Cr_2O_7^{2-} + 3Sn^{2+} \rightarrow 2Cr^{3+} + 3Sn^{4+}$$

Adding $14H^+$ balances it:

$$Cr_2O_7^{2-}(aq) + 3Sn^{2+}(aq) + 14H^+(aq) \rightarrow 2Cr^{3+}(aq) + 3Sn^{4+}(aq) + 7H_2O(l)$$

(iv) $\underset{=+12}{\overset{2\times(+6)}{Cr_2}}O_7^{2-} \rightarrow \underset{=+6}{\overset{2\times(+3)}{2Cr^{3+}}}$ and $\overset{-1}{I^-} \rightarrow \overset{0}{\tfrac{1}{2}I_2}$

Decrease (−6) in ox. no. Increase (+1) in ox. no.

The pattern is similar to the previous example. One $Cr_2O_7^{2-}$ will oxidise six I^- ions:

$$Cr_2O_7^{2-} + 6I^- \rightarrow 2Cr^{3+} + 3I_2$$

As before, we add $14H^+$:

$$Cr_2O_7^{2-}(aq) + 6I^-(aq) + 14H^+(aq) \rightarrow 2Cr^{3+}(aq) + 3I_2(s) + 7H_2O(l)$$

41.10 (i) $Ti^{3+}(aq) + e^- \rightarrow Ti^{2+}(aq)$

$$Ag(s) \rightarrow Ag^+(aq) + e^-$$

Overall,

$$Ti^{3+}(aq) + Ag(s) \rightarrow Ti^{2+}(aq) + Ag^+(aq)$$

(ii) $Cr_2O_7^{2-}(aq) + 6e^- + 14H^+(aq) \rightarrow 2Cr^{3+}(aq) + 7H_2O(l)$

The oxidation number change is from +4 in SO_3^{2-} to +6 in SO_4^{2-}. This means that we transfer two electrons. The oxygen imbalance is sorted out by adding in a water molecule:

$$SO_3^{2-}(aq) + H_2O(l) \rightarrow SO_4^{2-}(aq) + 2e^- + 2H^+(aq)$$

We find the overall equation by adding the first to three times the second.

$$Cr_2O_7^{2-}(aq) + 6e^- + 14H^+(aq) \rightarrow 2Cr^{3+}(aq) + 7H_2O(l)$$
$$3SO_3^{2-}(aq) + 3H_2O(l) \rightarrow 3SO_4^{2-}(aq) + 6e^- + 6H^+(aq)$$

$$Cr_2O_7^{2-}(aq) + 3SO_3^{2-}(aq) + 8H^+(aq) \rightarrow 2Cr^{3+}(aq) + 3SO_4^{2-}(aq) + 4H_2O(l)$$

41.11

(i) $MnO_4^-(aq) + 5e^- + 8H^+(aq) \rightarrow Mn^{2+}(aq) + 4H_2O(l)$

(ii) $C_2O_4^{2-}(aq) \rightarrow 2CO_2(g) + 2e^-$

(iii) Here we can cancel the numbers of electrons by taking twice the first half-equation and adding five times the second:

$$2MnO_4^-(aq) + 10e^- + 16H^+(aq) \rightarrow 2Mn^{2+}(aq) + 8H_2O(l)$$
$$5C_2O_4^{2-}(aq) \rightarrow 10CO_2(g) + 10e^-$$

$$2MnO_4^-(aq) + 5C_2O_4^{2-}(aq) + 16H^+(aq) \rightarrow 2Mn^{2+}(aq) + 8H_2O(l) + 10CO_2(g)$$

(iv) Black particles of manganese(IV) oxide appear.

UNIT 41 SUMMARY

- Oxidation is:
  - (i) The gain of oxygen.
  - (ii) The loss of hydrogen.
  - (iii) The loss of electrons.
  - (iv) Increase in oxidation number.
- Reduction is the converse of oxidation.
- An unreacted element has an oxidation number of 0.
- An ion of an element has an oxidation number equal to its charge.
- A change in oxidation number of one unit represents the apparent transfer of one electron from one atom or group to another.
- The oxidation state of an element is written as a Roman numeral (in brackets). It provides the value of the oxidation number.

42

Energy changes

42.1 Energy changes and chemical bonds

Coal is one of the oldest fuels known. At a high enough temperature, many of the organic chemicals in coal react with oxygen in the air. The bonds between the carbon, hydrogen and other atoms in coal break (Figure 42.1) and the atoms then join with oxygen atoms to make smaller molecules like carbon dioxide, water, sulphur dioxide and so on.

If we are to break the atoms in coal apart from one another, we have to put energy *in* to the coal. However, we know that when coal burns energy is given out. The source of this energy is the strength of the bonds made when the carbon dioxide and other molecules are formed. When bonds are made, energy is given out. For coal, more energy is produced by *making* the bonds in the products of the reaction than is needed to break the bonds in coal and oxygen molecules. The pattern is:

> **Bonds broken → energy taken in.**
>
> **Bonds made → energy given out.**

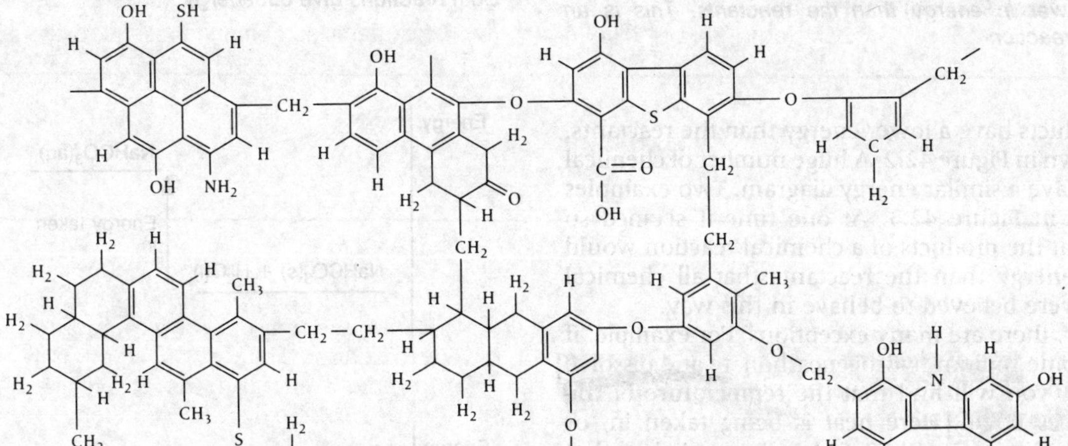

Figure 42.1 *The diagram shows a typical part of the structure of coal. Note that, to avoid cramping the diagram, —H_2 is used to indicate two —H on the same (carbon) atom. (Diagram taken from: Hall, N. F. (1984). Experimental demonstration of coal structure,* Education in Chemistry, *July)*

42.2 Energy changes and energy diagrams

You should be familiar with the idea of showing energy levels on a diagram. Here we can use similar diagrams to give us a visual impression of the energy changes that take place when chemicals react. In the case of coal, we know that energy is given out when it reacts with oxygen (Figure 42.2). We can summarise this in a word equation:

energy locked up in the bonds in coal and oxygen	→	energy in the bonds of CO_2, H_2O, etc.	+	heat energy given out

or, in general,

energy of reactants → energy of products + heat energy

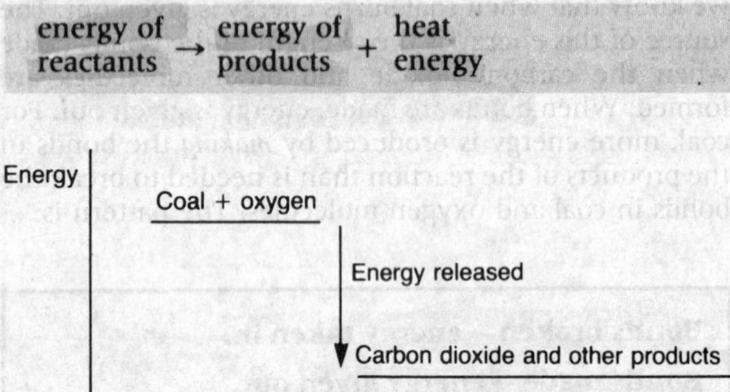

Figure 42.2 *The energy diagram for coal burning has the products lower in energy than the reactants. This is an exothermic reaction*

The products have a lower energy than the reactants. This is shown in Figure 42.2. A huge number of chemical reactions have a similar energy diagram. Two examples are shown in Figure 42.3. At one time it seemed so obvious that the products of a chemical reaction would have less energy than the reactants that all chemical reactions were believed to behave in this way.

However, there are many exceptions. For example, if you take some sodium hydrogencarbonate and dissolve it in water, you will find that the temperature of the solution goes down. Here heat is being taken in, or *absorbed*, during the reaction. Another reaction that absorbs heat is produced by mixing ammonium thiocyanate, NH_4SCN, and barium hydroxide, $Ba(OH)_2$. A suitable thermometer placed in the mixture will easily record temperatures as low as $-10°C$ (263 K). (*Warning*: You should not attempt to carry out this reaction yourself. Barium hydroxide is extremely poisonous. Great care should be taken with its use.)

The energy diagrams for these reactions all have the products at a *higher* level than the reactants (Figure 42.4).

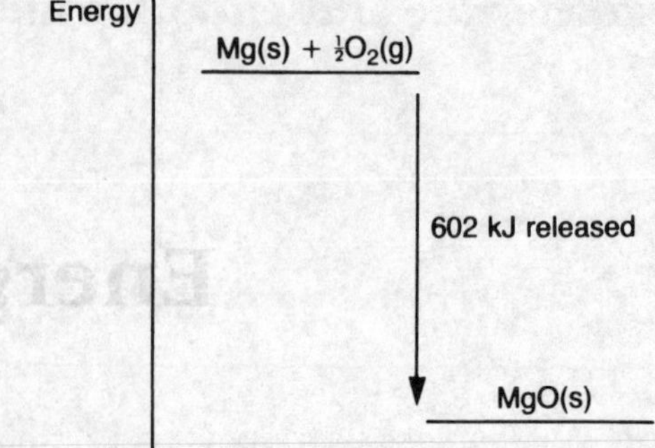

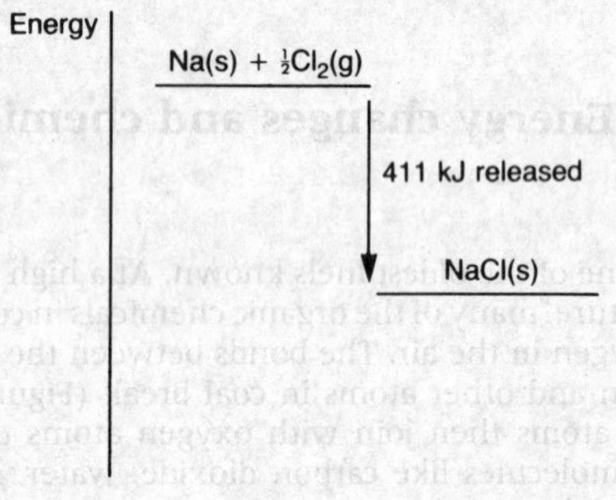

Figure 42.3 *The energy level diagrams for making magnesium oxide and sodium chloride from their elements show the products to be lower in energy than the reactants. Both reactions give out energy*

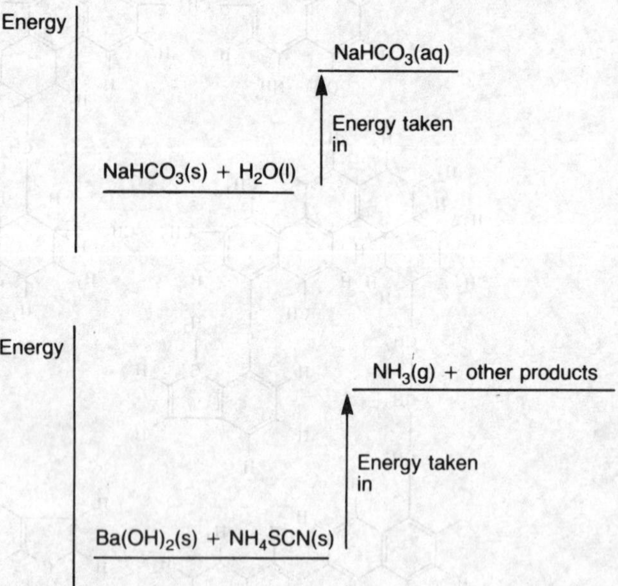

Figure 42.4 *The energy diagram for sodium hydrogencarbonate dissolving in water shows that the solution is higher in energy than the solid and water separately. In this case the change takes in energy from the surroundings. It is an endothermic change. Similarly, the reaction between barium hydroxide and ammonium thiocyanate is also endothermic. (Note: the diagrams are not drawn to scale)*

42.3 Exothermic and endothermic reactions

Reactions that give out heat are called *exothermic* reactions.

Reactions that take in heat are called *endothermic* reactions.

(In giving these definitions we assume that we do not interfere with the reactions, e.g. by compressing gases.)

Endothermic reactions really do occur. This presents us with a problem. If we think about a ball at the top of a hill, we are not surprised if it rolls downwards, so reducing its potential energy. However, we would be immensely surprised if the ball, of its own accord, rolled from the bottom of the hill up to the top. This is just the sort of thing that may seem to be happening in an endothermic reaction. Figure 42.5 summarises exothermic and endothermic reactions.

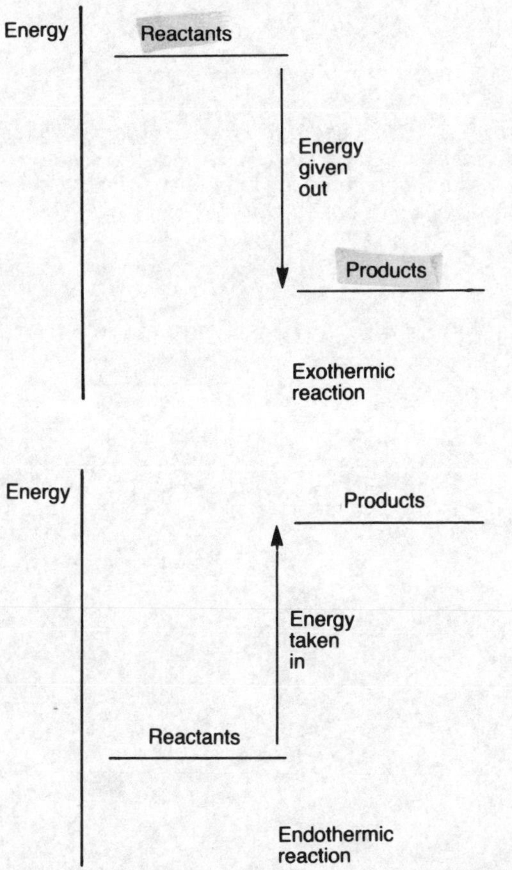

***Figure 42.5** The majority of reactions are exothermic: the products are lower in energy than the reactants. Exothermic reactions give out energy. Some reactions are endothermic: the products are higher in energy than the reactants. Endothermic reactions take in energy*

In the next few units we shall seek an explanation of this and similar puzzles.

42.1 In an exothermic reaction, how do the strengths of the bonds in the reactants compare with the strengths of the bonds in the products?

42.2 Make a similar comparison for the strengths of the bonds involved in an endothermic reaction.

42.3 You would not be the first person to think there is something very strange about endothermic reactions. (We have already said that at one time it was thought that such reactions were impossible.) One student made this comment: 'If heat is taken in during a reaction, surely the temperature of the chemicals should go up, not down.' Can you help the student to understand what is happening? (Hint: look at your answer to question 42.2.)

42.4 Draw an energy diagram for petrol burning in air.

Answers

42.1 The bonds in the products are (overall) stronger than in the reactants. The stronger the bonds that are made, the more energy is released.

42.2 The reverse is true: overall the bonds in the products are weaker than in the reactants.

42.3 The energy taken in is being used in breaking bonds, i.e. it is not getting the chance to appear as heat.

42.4 The diagram is shown in Figure 42.6.

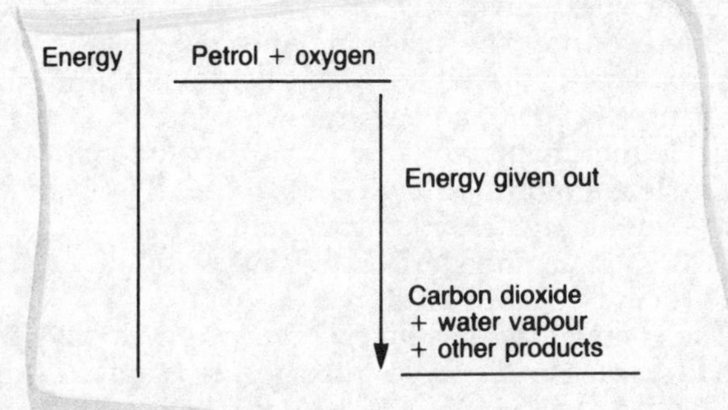

***Figure 42.6** Energy diagram for petrol burning*

UNIT 42 SUMMARY

- Bonds broken mean that heat is taken in.
- Bonds made mean that heat is given out.
- Reactions that give out heat are called exothermic reactions.
- Reactions that take in heat are called endothermic reactions.

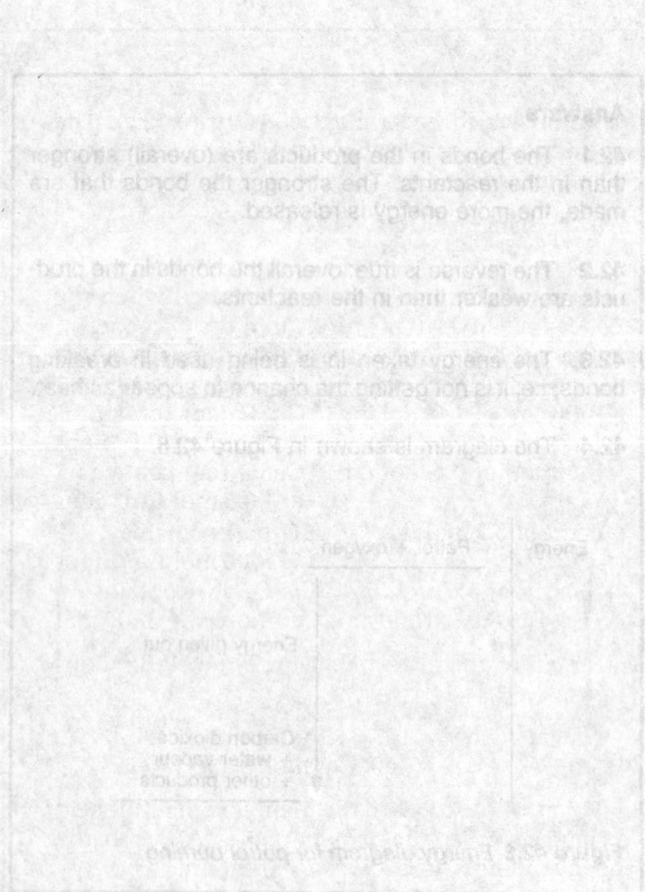

43

Enthalpy

43.1 What is enthalpy?

In the last unit we saw that there are two types of energy changes in chemical reactions: exothermic and endothermic. Here we are going to be more precise and refer to them as *heat* changes. To begin with, we should understand how heat changes are measured. A typical example is determining the heat given out when zinc metal reacts with copper(II) sulphate solution. The reaction that takes place is between zinc atoms and copper(II) ions, Cu^{2+}:

$$Zn(s) + Cu^{2+}(aq) \rightarrow Zn^{2+}(aq) + Cu(s)$$

The experiment is described in panel 43.1 and Figure 43.1. When 1 mol of copper ions is converted into copper metal, approximately 210 kJ of energy is released: the reaction is exothermic. This information allows us to draw up the energy diagram of Figure 43.2.

Panel 43.1

Measuring the heat change when zinc reacts with copper(II) sulphate solution

The reaction that takes place is

$$Zn(s) + CuSO_4(aq) \rightarrow ZnSO_4(aq) + Cu(s)$$

or

$$Zn(s) + Cu^{2+}(aq) \rightarrow Zn^{2+}(aq) + Cu(s)$$

In a typical experiment, we might place 100 cm³ of 0.5 mol dm⁻³ $CuSO_4(aq)$ in an expanded polystyrene beaker, and measure its temperature (Figure 43.1). Enough powdered zinc would be tipped into the solution to make sure that all the Cu^{2+} ions are changed into copper metal. The temperature increases, and we would record the maximum temperature reached. A typical change in temperature is from 18° C to 42° C, i.e. 24° C or 24 K.

Notice that the temperature is measured; we have to calculate the heat change. To do this we need to know the heat capacity, or the specific heat capacity, of the mixture in the beaker. The heat change is given by

$$\text{heat change} = \text{heat capacity} \times \text{change in temperature}$$

or

$$\text{heat change} = \text{mass} \times \text{specific heat capacity} \times \text{change in temperature}$$

In this case we assume that the heat capacity of the mixture in the beaker is equal to that of 100 cm³ of water, which has a mass of 100 g (0.1 kg). The specific heat capacity of water is $4.18\,\text{kJ kg}^{-1}\,\text{K}^{-1}$. Therefore we have

$$\text{heat change} = 0.1\,\text{kg} \times 4.18\,\text{kJ kg}^{-1}\,\text{K}^{-1} \times 24\,\text{K} = 10.03\,\text{kJ}$$

Now, this amount of heat is liberated when the copper ions in 100 cm³ of 0.5 mol dm⁻³ copper(II) sulphate solution are converted into copper metal.

1000 cm³ of 1.0 mol dm⁻³ $CuSO_4(aq)$ contains 1 mol of Cu^{2+} ions

1000 cm³ of 0.5 mol dm⁻³ $CuSO_4(aq)$ contains 0.5 mol Cu^{2+} ions

1 cm³ of 0.5 mol dm⁻³ $CuSO_4(aq)$ contains 0.5/1000 mol Cu^{2+} ions

100 cm³ of 0.5 mol dm⁻³ $CuSO_4(aq)$ contains $100 \times 0.5/1000$ mol Cu^{2+} ions, i.e. 0.05 mol

Therefore, the heat change for 1 mol of Cu^{2+} ions is

$$\text{heat change} = 10.03\,\text{kJ}/0.05\,\text{mol} = 200.6\,\text{kJ mol}^{-1}$$

You will discover in the main text that this heat change is called the *enthalpy change*, ΔH. Also, the convention is to show an exothermic enthalpy change as a negative number. So, finally we have

$$\Delta H = -200.6\,\text{kJ mol}^{-1}$$

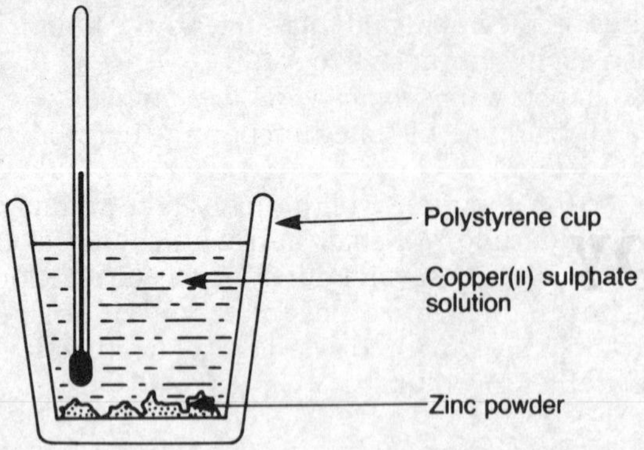

***Figure 43.1** A simple apparatus for determining the enthalpy change in the reaction between zinc and copper(II) sulphate solution*

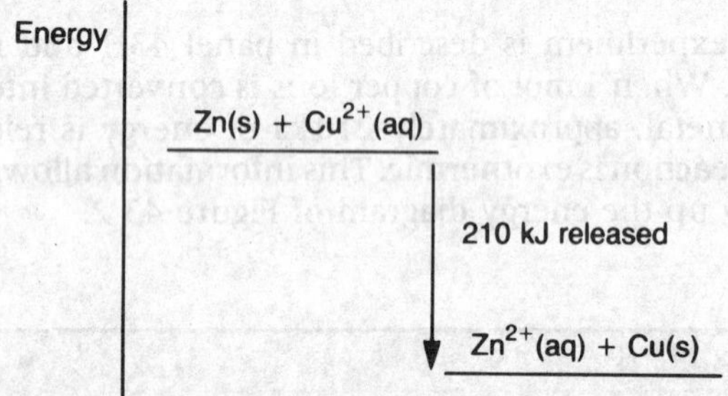

***Figure 43.2** Energy diagram for the reaction between zinc metal and copper ions in solution*

As in the last unit we can see from the diagram that the products of the reaction, $Zn^{2+}(aq)$ and Cu(s), have less energy than the reactants, $Cu^{2+}(aq)$ and Zn(s). Part of the energy stored in the reactants has been lost to the outside world as heat. There is a convention to show when reactants *lose* energy in a reaction. We show the heat change as a *negative* number.

Also, when reactions take place under the ordinary conditions of an open laboratory where the air pressure is constant, the heat change is called the *enthalpy change* of the reaction. That is:

An enthalpy change is a heat change that takes place at constant pressure.

The symbol for enthalpy is H, and a change in enthalpy is shown using the Greek capital letter delta, Δ, in front of the H, like this: ΔH.

We can put these two extra pieces of information together by writing the enthalpy change for the reaction

$$Zn(s) + Cu^{2+}(aq) \rightarrow Zn^{2+}(aq) + Cu(s)$$

as $\Delta H = -210\,\text{kJ mol}^{-1}$.

An even shorter way of writing this is to include the details of the enthalpy change alongside the equation like this:

$$Zn(s) + Cu^{2+}(aq) \rightarrow Zn^{2+}(aq) + Cu(s); \quad \Delta H = -210\,\text{kJ mol}^{-1}$$

43.2 Enthalpy and standard states

Enthalpy values can be measured for many reactions, and you will discover that we can even calculate enthalpy changes for reactions that do not occur. By performing reactions at different pressures, it has been discovered that ΔH changes with pressure. Some reactions have a smaller ΔH at a higher pressure than at a lower pressure; some show the opposite behaviour. In order to make comparisons of ΔH values, it is important that everyone knows what pressure is used. The convention is to choose a pressure of 1 atmosphere (in non SI units), 101.325 kPa in SI units, as the *standard pressure*.

Values of enthalpy changes that are measured at the standard pressure (or corrected to apply to this condition) are called *standard enthalpy changes*. Standard enthalpy changes are given a special symbol: $\Delta H^{\ominus}$.

Similarly, enthalpy values can change with temperature, and it is accepted that whenever possible enthalpy changes should refer to the change taking place at 25°C, i.e. 298 K. When this is done we have yet another special symbol: $\Delta H^{\ominus}(298\,\text{K})$.

For our zinc and copper(II) sulphate reaction, to be precise, we write

$$Zn(s) + Cu^{2+}(aq) \rightarrow Zn^{2+}(aq) + Cu(s); \quad \Delta H^{\ominus}(298\,\text{K}) = -210\,\text{kJ mol}^{-1}$$

However, it can become tedious to keep writing in the temperature. From now on we shall always assume that enthalpies refer to 298 K, so the extra information in brackets will be left out.

Look at the enthalpy changes for these equations:

$$\tfrac{1}{2}N_2(g) + \tfrac{3}{2}H_2(g) \rightarrow NH_3(g); \quad \Delta H^{\ominus} = -46.0\,\text{kJ mol}^{-1}$$
$$N_2(g) + 3H_2(g) \rightarrow 2NH_3(g); \quad \Delta H^{\ominus} = -92.0\,\text{kJ mol}^{-1}$$

The first equation gives the standard enthalpy change for the production of 1 mol of ammonia. The second gives the standard enthalpy change for the production of 2 mol of ammonia. This is the reason why the second value is twice the first. Notice that the units of $\Delta H^{\ominus}$ remain as kJ mol^{-1}. We shall always assume that the $\Delta H^{\ominus}$ value by the side of an equation refers to the quantities shown in the equation. For example,

$$\tfrac{1}{2}H_2(g) + \tfrac{1}{2}Cl_2(g) \rightarrow HCl(g); \quad \Delta H^{\ominus} = -92.3\,\text{kJ mol}^{-1}$$
$$H_2(g) + Cl_2(g) \rightarrow 2HCl(g); \quad \Delta H^{\ominus} = -184.6\,\text{kJ mol}^{-1}$$

In some books you may find, correctly, that these values are called *molar* standard enthalpy changes, and given the symbol $\Delta H^{\ominus}_{m}$. However, we shall not worry about the subscript, m. On the other hand, we shall use subscripts to emphasise special types of enthalpy changes; for example, $\Delta H^{\ominus}_{c}$ will stand for the standard enthalpy change of combustion of a compound.

43.1 $Na(s) + \frac{1}{2}Cl_2(g) \rightarrow NaCl(s)$;

$$\Delta H^{\ominus} = -411 \text{ kJ mol}^{-1}$$

What is the enthalpy change for the following reactions?

(i) $2Na(s) + Cl_2(g) \rightarrow 2NaCl(s)$

(ii) $NaCl(s) \rightarrow Na(s) + \frac{1}{2}Cl_2(g)$

43.3 Enthalpy and state functions

In one of the early units (Unit 2) we talked about energy levels and the changes in potential energy that would take place if we were to travel between the different levels in a coal mine. We agreed to use the ground level at the top of the mine as our zero of potential energy. If we went down the mine our potential energy decreased below zero; it became negative. If we were to travel into the air above the mine, e.g. in a helicopter, our potential energy would increase; it takes a positive value. Now imagine that we undertook two journeys shown in Figure 43.3. In the first journey we go down the mine, return to the surface and then climb up a tower. Finally we arrive on the surface again. In the second journey we start at the surface, climb the tower, return to the surface, go down the mine and then return to the surface.

Notice that in both cases the overall change is zero. Our initial and final states are the same in both cases. It does not matter what happened in between. We can say that the change in potential energy is independent of the history of our movements. A quantity like potential energy that behaves in this way is called a *function of state*, or *state function* for short. The change in its value depends on the initial and final states only, not on what happens between those two states.

It so happens that *enthalpy is a state function*. (Actually it is a special type of state function: a thermodynamic state function.)

To see the importance of this let us take an imaginary chemical journey. We shall start with copper(II) oxide, CuO, and zinc. By several different sets of reactions we shall convert them into copper metal and zinc oxide. The first route is the straightforward one of heating the starting materials together:

$$Zn(s) + CuO(s) \rightarrow ZnO(s) + Cu(s); \quad \Delta H^{\ominus} = -192.8 \text{ kJ mol}^{-1}$$

The second route is more involved. First we shall take the copper(II) oxide and reduce it with hydrogen gas:

$$CuO(s) + H_2(g) \rightarrow Cu(s) + H_2O(g); \quad \Delta H^{\ominus} = -86.6 \text{ kJ mol}^{-1}$$

Then we shall take the steam (water in the gaseous state) and react it with the zinc:

$$Zn(s) + H_2O(g) \rightarrow ZnO(s) + H_2(g); \quad \Delta H^{\ominus} = -106.2 \text{ kJ mol}^{-1}$$

Now if we work out the total enthalpy change for this indirect route, we find it is

$$-86.6 \text{ kJ mol}^{-1} + (-106.2 \text{ kJ mol}^{-1}) = -192.8 \text{ kJ mol}^{-1}$$

This is exactly the same result as the direct route. You might like to check how this happens by following the diagram in Figure 43.4.

Table 43.1 contains a summary of what we now know about enthalpy.

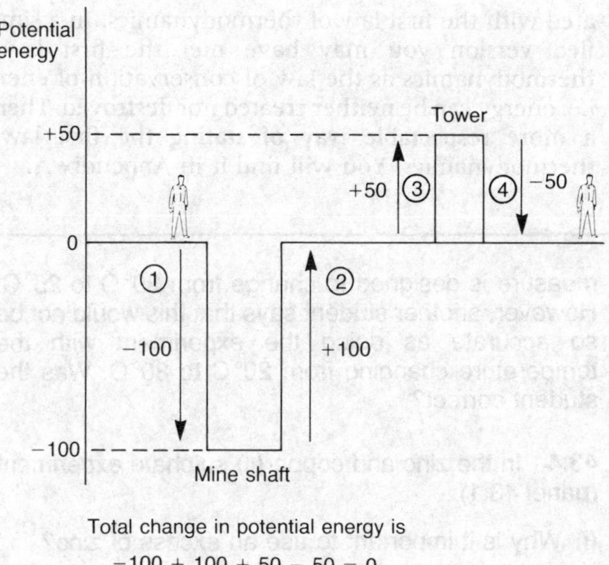

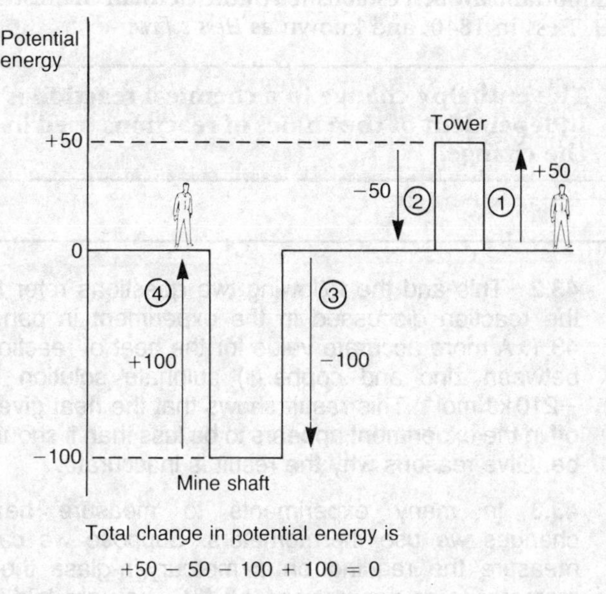

Figure 43.3 *The overall potential energy change for the journey from ground level back to ground level is zero; it does not depend on the route*

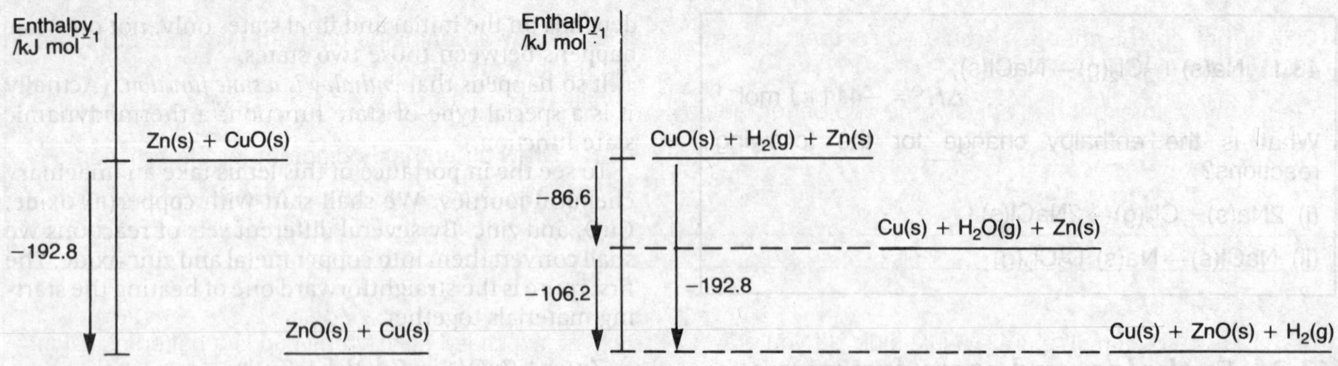

***Figure 43.4** The first diagram shows the enthalpy change for the direct reaction between zinc and copper(II) oxide. In the second diagram, hydrogen is used first to convert the copper(II) oxide into copper. The water given off in this reaction combines with the zinc to give zinc oxide and hydrogen. The two key products, zinc oxide and copper, are the same in both cases. Notice that, in the second diagram, we finish with exactly the 1 mol of hydrogen that we started with. This means that any enthalpy that it contributed at the start has been returned at the end. The net result is as if the hydrogen had not taken part. Also, note that the diagrams show the differences in enthalpy, not the individual values of the levels*

Table 43.1. About enthalpy

An enthalpy change, ΔH, is a heat change that takes place at constant pressure
Enthalpy is a state function, i.e. ΔH does not depend on the history of the chemicals taking part in a reaction
A standard enthalpy change, $\Delta H^{\ominus}$, refers to 101.325 kPa (1 atm) and normally refers to 298 K
Exothermic reaction: ΔH is negative
Endothermic reaction: ΔH is positive

43.4 Hess's law

The example we have just looked at illustrates a most important law first established by the German chemist G. H. Hess in 1840, and known as *Hess's law*:

The enthalpy change in a chemical reaction is independent of the choice of reactions used in the change.

As far as we know there are no exceptions to the law. Actually, it is one of the most useful laws in chemistry. In our calculations on the mine we were concerned with changes in potential energy, and we chose our zero of potential energy to be ground level. Although this seems quite natural, there is nothing to say that we must make this choice. For example, we could decide that a point 100 m up in the air was our zero level. The numbers in Figure 43.3 would then change; but the eventual answer would not change because we were only concerned with *differences* between potential energy values.

A similar situation holds with enthalpy. We are free to choose our zero level of enthalpy. However, experience shows (as it does with potential energy) that some choices make more sense than others. These choices are enshrined in a series of definitions that all chemists are expected to know and use. We shall examine, and apply, these definitions in the next unit. However, before we do so, you should be aware that Hess's law is closely associated with the first law of thermodynamics. In a simplified version you may have met the first law of thermodynamics as the law of conservation of energy; i.e. energy can be neither created nor destroyed. There is a more respectable way of stating the first law of thermodynamics. You will find it in Appendix A.

43.2 This and the following two questions refer to the reaction discussed in the experiment in panel 43.1. A more accurate value for the heat of reaction between zinc and copper(II) sulphate solution is −210 kJ mol^{-1}. This result shows that the heat given off in the experiment appears to be less than it should be. Give reasons why the result is inaccurate.

43.3 In many experiments to measure heat changes we use thermometers. Suppose we can measure the reading on a mercury-in-glass thermometer to an accuracy of ±0.1°C. You are told to carry out an experiment in which the temperature you measure is designed to change from 20°C to 25°C. However, another student says that this would not be so accurate as doing the experiment with the temperature changing from 20°C to 30°C. Was the student correct?

43.4 In the zinc and copper(II) sulphate experiment (panel 43.1):

(i) Why is it important to use an excess of zinc?

(ii) Why must powdered zinc be used, rather than lumps?

(iii) What colour changes would you expect to see during the experiment?

(iv) Why is an expanded polystyrene cup better than, say, a glass beaker?

43.5 Draw an enthalpy diagram (like that of Figure 43.4) for the reaction:

$$Zn(s) + \tfrac{1}{2}O_2(g) \rightarrow ZnO(s); \quad \Delta H^\ominus = -348\,\text{kJ mol}^{-1}$$

43.6 Draw an enthalpy diagram for the reaction:

$$\tfrac{1}{2}N_2(g) + \tfrac{1}{2}O_2(g) \rightarrow NO(g); \quad \Delta H^\ominus = +90.4\,\text{kJ mol}^{-1}$$

Answers

43.1 (i) $-822\,\text{kJ mol}^{-1}$; (ii) $+411\,\text{kJ mol}^{-1}$. If you draw an energy diagram for the reaction you will see why the second answer is positive (endothermic). It also makes sense chemically: if heat is given out when sodium chloride is made, we would have to put heat in to break it apart.

43.2 Some of the heat will be lost into the laboratory. Three ways this can happen are by conduction, convection and radiation. Also, if some of the solution evaporates, heat will be lost from it.

43.3 If the temperature is measured with an accuracy $\pm 0.1°C$, in the worse case the temperature change might be from 19.9°C to 25.1°C. This gives a temperature difference of 5.2°C rather than the 5°C that is recorded. This represents an error of 0.2°C in 5°C, or 4%.

If the measured change was from 20°C to 30°C, the error would be 0.2°C in 10°C; an error of 2%. The student was correct.

43.4 (i) So that all the Cu^{2+} ions are used up.
(ii) The powder reacts quickly; lumps react much more slowly. It is important that the energy is released quickly, so that the temperature rise reflects the amount of heat produced. Think, for example, of the reaction taking place over a period of several hours. The energy released each minute would be so small that the solution would lose it to the atmosphere almost as fast as it was produced. The temperature rise might be as low as 1°C. (If the apparatus was perfectly insulated there would not be the same problem.)
(iii) The solution starts out blue and changes to colourless. At the same time the grey pieces of zinc become covered with a brown layer of copper.
(iv) The expanded polystyrene cup is a better insulator than glass. Thus heat losses are reduced.

43.5 The enthalpy diagram is shown in Figure 43.5.

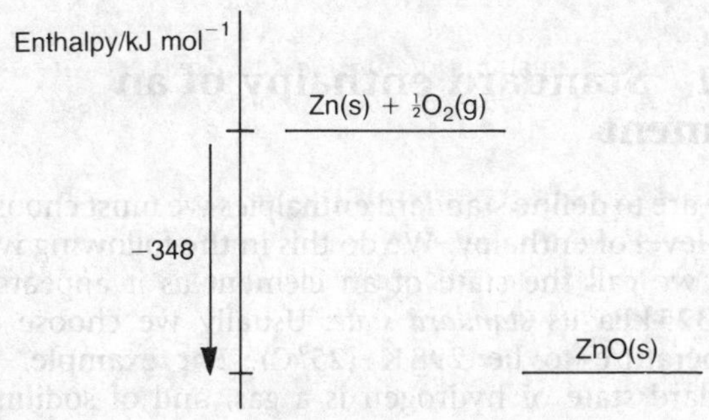

Figure 43.5 *Enthalpy diagram for question 43.5*

43.6 The enthalpy diagram is shown in Figure 43.6.

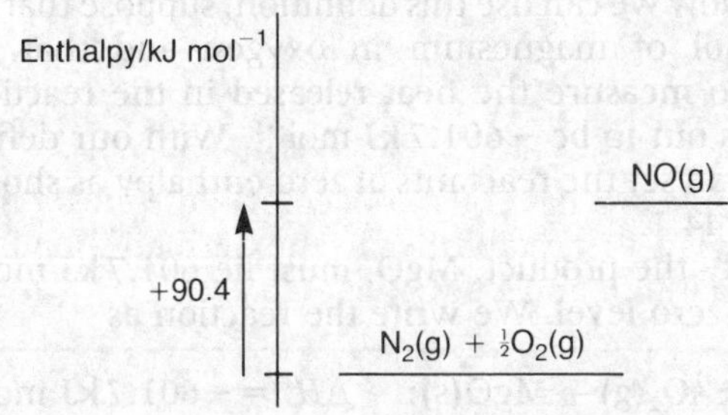

Figure 43.6 *Enthalpy diagram for question 43.6*

UNIT 43 SUMMARY

- Enthalpy is a heat change that takes place at constant pressure.
- Values of enthalpy changes that are measured at the standard pressure (or corrected to apply to this condition) are called *standard* enthalpy changes.
- In S.I. units the standard pressure is 101.325 kPa (1 atmosphere in non S.I. units).
- Enthalpy is a state function; i.e. the change in its value depends on the initial and final states only, not on what happens between those two states.
- Hess's law says that:

  The enthalpy change in a chemical reaction is independent of the choice of reactions used in the change.
- The heat change in a chemical reaction can be calculated using the formula:

$$\text{heat change} = \text{heat capacity} \times \text{change in temperature}$$

or

$$\text{heat change} = \text{mass} \times \text{specific heat capacity} \times \text{change in temperature}$$

44

Standard enthalpies

44.1 Standard enthalpy of an element

If we are to define standard enthalpies we must choose a zero level of enthalpy. We do this in the following way. First we call the state of an element as it appears at 101.325 kPa its *standard state*. Usually we choose the temperature to be 298 K (25° C). For example, the standard state of hydrogen is a gas, and of sodium a solid. We then make our definition:

The enthalpy content of an element in its standard state is zero.

To see how we can use this definition, suppose that we burn 1 mol of magnesium in oxygen and that we manage to measure the heat released in the reaction. This turns out to be $-601.7\,\text{kJ mol}^{-1}$. With our definition, we can set the reactants at zero enthalpy as shown in Figure 44.1.

Similarly the product, MgO, must lie $601.7\,\text{kJ mol}^{-1}$ *below* the zero level. We write the reaction as

$$Mg(s) + \tfrac{1}{2}O_2(g) \rightarrow MgO(s); \quad \Delta H^{\ominus} = -601.7\,\text{kJ mol}^{-1}$$

Notice that we use a fraction ($\frac{1}{2}$) in the equation so that it shows the formation of 1 mol of MgO.

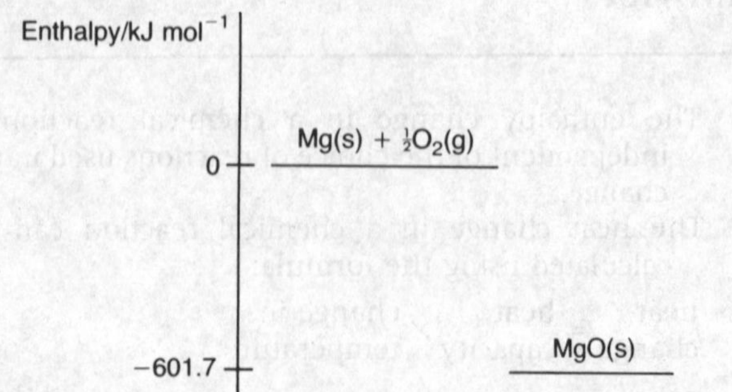

Figure 44.1 Enthalpy diagram for the reaction between magnesium and oxygen

44.2 Standard heats of formation

Indeed, the enthalpy change in this reaction is called the *standard heat of formation* of magnesium oxide. In general, the definition of this quantity is:

The standard heat of formation is the enthalpy change when one mole of the substance is made from its elements in their standard states.

Table 44.1 shows some typical heats of formation for a variety of substances. Notice that heats of formation can be endothermic as well as exothermic. It is useful to show a standard heat of formation by using a subscript f on the $\Delta H^{\ominus}$ symbol. You will have to remember that, unless it is stated otherwise, all values refer to a temperature of 298 K. Thus, in the case of magnesium

Table 44.1. Some standard heats of formation*

Reaction	$\Delta H_f^{\ominus}$/kJ mol^{-1}
$Si(s)+O_2(g) \rightarrow SiO_2(s)$	−910.0
$Ca(s)+\frac{1}{2}O_2(g) \rightarrow CaO(s)$	−635.5
$Na(s)+\frac{1}{2}Cl_2(g) \rightarrow NaCl(s)$	−411.0
$C(s)+O_2(g) \rightarrow CO_2(g)$	−393.5
$H_2(g)+\frac{1}{2}O_2(g) \rightarrow H_2O(l)$	−285.9
$2C(s)+3H_2(g)+\frac{1}{2}O_2(g) \rightarrow C_2H_5OH(l)$	−277.7
$\frac{1}{2}H_2(g)+\frac{1}{2}F_2(g) \rightarrow HF(g)$	−271.1
$H_2(g)+\frac{1}{2}O_2(g) \rightarrow H_2O(g)$	−241.8
$C(s)+2H_2(g)+\frac{1}{2}O_2(g) \rightarrow CH_3OH(l)$	−238.9
$8C(s)+4H_2(g) \rightarrow C_8H_8(l)$	−224.4
$C(s)+\frac{1}{2}O_2(g) \rightarrow CO(g)$	−110.5
$C(s)+2H_2(g) \rightarrow CH_4(g)$	−74.8
$\frac{1}{2}N_2+\frac{3}{2}H_2(g) \rightarrow NH_3(g)$	−46.0
$6C(s)+3H_2(g) \rightarrow C_6H_6(l)$	+49.0
$N_2(g)+2H_2(g) \rightarrow N_2H_4(l)$	+50.6
$2C(s)+2H_2(g) \rightarrow C_2H_4(g)$	+52.3
$2C(s)+H_2(g) \rightarrow C_2H_2(g)$	+226.8

*Carbon, C(s), refers to graphite, not diamond; the value for SiO_2 is only approximate

oxide, the standard heat of formation is $\Delta H_f^\ominus = -601.7\,\text{kJ mol}^{-1}$.

44.1 Draw an enthalpy diagram for the heat of formation of hydrazine, N_2H_4 (see Table 44.1 for data).

44.3 Standard heats of combustion

We have a need for fuels, not only for keeping us warm but also to provide energy for industry and for transport. For example, octane (C_8H_8) is one of the key hydrocarbons in petrol. In a petrol engine the petrol is mixed with air and then a spark from the spark plug causes the mixture to burn (Figure 44.2). The energy released moves the piston, which results in the wheels turning. The energy released when 1 mol of octane burns is called the heat of combustion, $\Delta H_c^\ominus$, of octane. If the change takes place under standard conditions we have:

The standard heat of combustion is the enthalpy change when one mole of the substance is completely burned in oxygen.

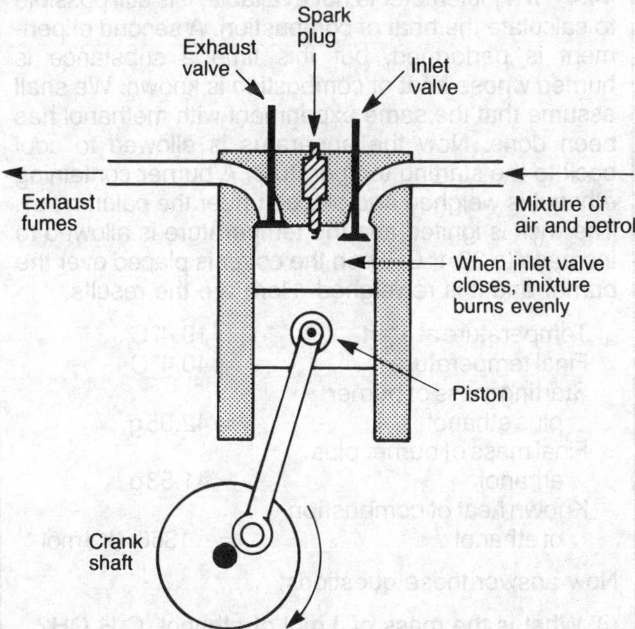

***Figure 44.2** A simplified diagram of the internal combustion engine. Downward motion of the piston pushes the crank shaft (and eventually the wheels) round. The inlet valve and exhaust valve open and close in time with the movement of the piston. The inlet valve allows a mixture of petrol and air into the cylinder. When the piston pushes upwards into the cylinder, it compresses the gases. A spark from the spark plug ignites the gases. Once these have burnt, the exhaust valve opens to let out the spent gases. The cycle then repeats. In a diesel engine, there is no need for a spark plug. When a mixture of diesel fuel and air is compressed by the piston, the mixture burns without the need for a spark*

For octane,

$$2C_8H_{18}(l) + 25O_2(g) \rightarrow 16CO_2(g) + 18H_2O(l);$$

Notice that the water formed is shown as a liquid because the value of $\Delta H_c^\ominus$ refers to 298 K (fairly near room temperature). This value refers to conditions that are not the same as in an engine, but you may understand why octane is such a useful fuel, given the huge amount of energy released when it burns.

The experiment in panel 44.1 and Figure 44.3 describes a method of measuring the heat of combustion in the laboratory.

Panel 44.1

Measuring the heat of combustion of methanol

The apparatus for such an experiment is shown in Figure 44.3. The first step is to weigh the burner when it is about two-thirds full of methanol. It is important to keep the cover over the wick until it is time to ignite the alcohol. Secondly, the temperature of the water in the calorimeter is measured.

With a slow current of air being drawn through the copper spiral, the wick of the burner is lit and the water in the calorimeter gently stirred. When a temperature rise of around 10–20°C has been achieved, the cover is placed over the burner. Finally, the maximum temperature of the water is recorded and the burner reweighed.

The problem that remains is to discover the heat capacity of the apparatus. Unlike the experiment with copper(II) sulphate in panel 43.1, this is not a simple matter. Here there is water, copper and glass present, each with its own heat capacity.

The easiest method of getting round this problem is as follows. We could place an electric heater in the water (once it had returned to room temperature). The heater would be connected to a joulemeter, which measures the number of joules of energy supplied to the calorimeter. We would keep the heater on until the apparatus had reached the same temperature as in the experiment with the alcohol. The joulemeter would tell us how much energy was needed to reproduce the same temperature rise. To see how this works, we shall use the results below.

Starting temperature	= 19.4°C
Final temperature	= 34.6°C
Starting mass of burner plus methanol	= 28.44 g
Final mass of burner plus methanol	= 27.42 g
Thus, mass of methanol burned	= 1.02 g
Starting reading on joulemeter	= 7030 J
Final reading on joulemeter	= 29 020 J
Difference in readings	= 21 990 J

The joulemeter readings tell us that it takes 21 990 J to increase the temperature of the calorimeter from

19.4°C to 34.6°C. Therefore we know that 1.02 g of methanol released 21 990 J when burned. Given that the mass of 1 mol of methanol has a mass of 32 g, we can say that:

energy released when 1 mol methanol is burned
$= 21\,990\,\text{J} \times 32\,\text{g}/1.02\,\text{g}$
$= 689\,882\,\text{J}$

Thus, the heat of combustion of methanol is nearly $-690\,\text{kJ mol}^{-1}$. (Notice that we have included the minus sign now, because the reaction is exothermic.)

The result obtained from a much more accurate experiment is that the standard heat of combustion of methanol is $-726.3\,\text{kJ mol}^{-1}$.

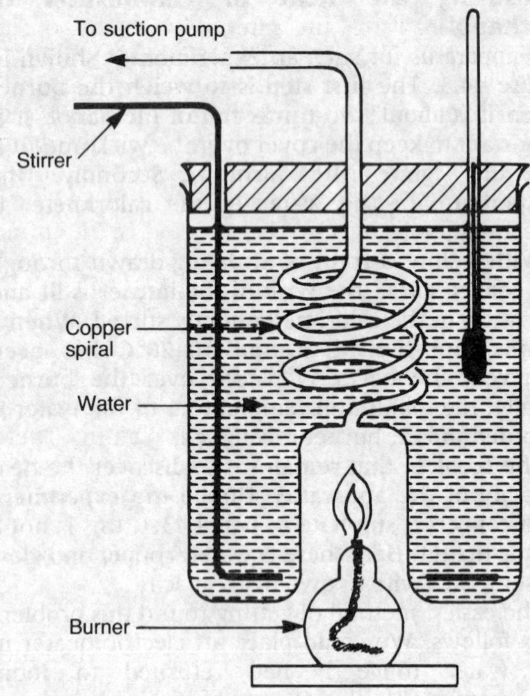

Figure 44.3 *An apparatus for measuring the heat of combustion of a flammable liquid*

44.2 The heat of combustion of butane, C_4H_{10}, is $-2220\,\text{kJ mol}^{-1}$.

(i) Write the equation for the reaction. Remember to use only one mole of butane when you balance the equation.

(ii) Butane can be used as a fuel in gas heaters. Suppose you were to burn 1 kg of butane in your house. How many moles of water would be produced? What is the mass of this amount of water?

(iii) How much heat would be produced?

44.3 This question is about the experiment to measure the heat of combustion of methanol (see panel 44.1).

Clearly there is a considerable error in the experiment. Here is a list of possible sources of error. For each one, say, with reasons, whether you think the error would tend to increase, decrease, or make no difference to the measured value for the heat of combustion. (By 'increase' we mean make the measured result closer to the accepted value.)

(i) The cover is left off the burner *before* it is weighed for the first time.

(ii) The cover is left off the burner *after* it is weighed for the first time.

(iii) The cover is left off the burner after it is used in the experiment, but before it is weighed for the last time.

(iv) The water is not stirred properly.

(v) The thermometer is placed so that its bulb touches the bottom of the glass calorimeter.

(vi) The amount of air drawn through the copper spiral is too low. (When this occurs you often see specks of soot appear on the glass.)

(vii) The flow of air through the copper spiral is very fast.

44.4 If a joulemeter is not available, it is still possible to calculate the heat of combustion. A second experiment is performed, but this time a substance is burned whose heat of combustion is known. We shall assume that the same experiment with methanol has been done. Now the apparatus is allowed to cool back to the starting temperature. A burner containing ethanol is weighed and placed under the calorimeter. The wick is ignited and the temperature is allowed to increase to 30.1° C. Then the cover is placed over the burner and it is reweighed. Here are the results.

Temperature at start	= 19.4°C
Final temperature	= 40.4°C
Starting mass of burner plus ethanol	= 42.55 g
Final mass of burner plus ethanol	= 41.53 g
Known heat of combustion of ethanol	$= -1366.7\,\text{KJ mol}^{-1}$

Now answer these questions:

(i) What is the mass of 1 mol of ethanol, C_2H_5OH?

(ii) What was the mass of ethanol burned in the experiment?

(iii) How many joules of energy are released when this mass of ethanol burns?

(iv) What was the temperature rise in the experiment?

(v) From your answers to (iii) and (iv), calculate the energy required to increase the temperature of the calorimeter by 1° C.

(vi) What was the temperature rise in the methanol experiment?

(vii) How much energy must have been released by the methanol in order to give this temperature rise?

(viii) How many moles of methanol released this energy?

(ix) How much energy would be released if 1 mol of methanol were burned? What is the heat of combustion?

44.4 Enthalpy changes when substances break apart

If any substance is given sufficient energy, the bonds holding the atoms together will break and the atoms will fly apart from one another. We have seen one way of doing this in the mass spectrometer: high energy electrons hit the molecules, causing them to fragment. (However, in the mass spectrometer it is rare for all the bonds to be broken.) The energy involved in the process of turning the substance completely into a gas of atoms is called the atomisation energy or the *heat of atomisation*, $\Delta H^{\ominus}_{at}$. We can define it as follows:

The heat of atomisation is the enthalpy change when one mole of a substance in its standard state is completely changed into atoms in the gaseous state.

For example,

$H_2(g) \rightarrow 2H(g)$; $\Delta H^{\ominus}_{at} = +436\,\text{kJ mol}^{-1}$
$HCl(g) \rightarrow H(g) + Cl(g)$; $\Delta H^{\ominus}_{at} = +431\,\text{kJ mol}^{-1}$
$Fe(s) \rightarrow Fe(g)$; $\Delta H^{\ominus}_{at} = +417.7\,\text{kJ mol}^{-1}$
$Na(s) \rightarrow Na(g)$; $\Delta H^{\ominus}_{at} = +108.4\,\text{kJ mol}^{-1}$

You should not be surprised to see that the values are all positive, i.e. the processes are endothermic. We have to put energy *in* to break bonds.

For iron and sodium, the process of atomisation is a little different in kind from those of hydrogen and hydrogen chloride. For the two metals we are turning a solid already made of atoms (rather than molecules) into a gas of atoms. Also, we have solids turning directly into gases. This type of change is called *sublimation*. For this reason, heats of atomisation of solid elements are sometimes called *heats of sublimation*. For example, we could write

$Na(s) \rightarrow Na(g)$; $\Delta H^{\ominus}_{sub} = +108.4\,\text{kJ mol}^{-1}$

44.5 Bond energies and average bond energies

The atomisation energies of hydrogen and hydrogen chloride can also be given alternative names. In these cases we are actually breaking individual covalent bonds. This leads to the alternative name of *bond enthalpy*, or *bond dissociation enthalpy*, $\Delta H^{\ominus}_{D}$. Table 44.2 provides you with some values of bond enthalpies.

Table 44.2. Examples of bond enthalpies, $\Delta H^{\ominus}_{D}$

Molecule	*Type of covalent bond*	$\Delta H^{\ominus}_{D}$/kJ mol^{-1}
H_2	Single	+436
O_2	Double	+497
N_2	Triple	+945
F_2	Single	+158
Cl_2	Single	+242
Br_2	Single	+193
I_2	Single	+151
HF	Single	+563
HCl	Single	+431
HBr	Single	+366
HI	Single	+299

Often the bond dissociation energies are simply called *bond energies*. The greater the bond energy, the stronger the bond. The strengths of bonds can be found from spectroscopy. We have already met the idea that the vibrations of molecules can be detected in the infrared region of the spectrum. You should not be surprised to learn that the stronger the bond, the harder it is to make it vibrate. By measuring the frequencies of the vibrations, the strength of the bond can be calculated.

You may have noticed that the molecules chosen in Table 44.2 are all relatively simple ones. We have not included molecules with more than two atoms. There is a reason for this. Suppose we want to know the bond energy of each of the four C—H bonds in methane, CH_4. Experiments can be done that cause the four hydrogen atoms to leave the molecule separately. The results are:

$CH_4(g) \rightarrow CH_3(g) + H(g)$; $\Delta H^{\ominus}_{D} = +426\,\text{kJ mol}^{-1}$
$CH_3(g) \rightarrow CH_2(g) + H(g)$; $\Delta H^{\ominus}_{D} = +439\,\text{kJ mol}^{-1}$
$CH_2(g) \rightarrow CH(g) + H(g)$; $\Delta H^{\ominus}_{D} = +451\,\text{kJ mol}^{-1}$
$CH(g) \rightarrow C(g) + H(g)$; $\Delta H^{\ominus}_{D} = +347\,\text{kJ mol}^{-1}$

Clearly the 'bond energy' of a C—H bond depends on the order in which the particular hydrogen atom is lost from the molecule. A similar situation exists for all molecules with more than two atoms: the strengths of the bonds depend on the order in which they are broken. The reason for this is that as soon as one atom is lost, the electrons that remain change their energies. Indeed, the shape of the fragments that remain can be very different to the original molecule. For example, the $CH_3(g)$ fragment is planar whereas the methane molecule from which it came is tetrahedral.

The way in which we get round this difficulty is to define *average bond energies*. In the case of methane, we determine the energy needed to rip all four hydrogen atoms off the carbon atom. This should be the sum of the individual bond energies above:

$CH_4(g) \rightarrow C(g) + 4H(g)$; $\Delta H^{\ominus}_{at} = +1663\,\text{kJ mol}^{-1}$

We then take an average of this value, $+1663/4$ kJ mol^{-1}, or $+416$ kJ mol^{-1}, and call this the average bond

Table 44.3. Some average bond energies

Bond	$\Delta H_D^{\ominus}$/kJ mol^{-1}	*Comment*
N−H	389	In ammonia
O−H	464	In water
C−H	413	Average of many organic compounds
C−C	346	Average of many organic compounds
C=C	598	In ethene, C_2H_4
C=C	611	Average of many alkenes
C≡C	837	In ethyne, C_2H_2
C≡C	835	Average of many alkynes
C−O	358	Average value in alcohols
C=O	745	Average value in ketones
C−F	485	In CF_4
C−Cl	339	Average value in chloroalkanes
C−Br	209	In CBr_4
C−I	218	In iodomethane, CH_3I

energy. You can see that the average value does not necessarily match the energy of any one of the individual bonds. We put up with this as a matter of convenience. From now on we shall use $\Delta H_D^{\ominus}$ to stand for average bond energies. Some typical values are given in Table 44.3.

44.5 Look at the bond enthalpies of the halogens, chlorine, bromine and iodine, in Table 44.2. Which of the halogens would you expect to have the shortest bond, and which the longest bond?

44.6 A student trapped a little of each of the hydrogen halides, HCl, HBr and HI, in separate test tubes. The student heated a platinum wire until it was red hot and put it into one of the test tubes. She then heated the wire again and put it in the second test tube, and so on. In two of the tubes she saw a reaction take place. Which ones were they? What do you think she saw?

44.7 A student said that some of the figures in Table 44.3 must be wrong. In particular he said that: 'Ethene, C_2H_4, contains a double bond between the carbon atoms, and a double bond should be twice the strength of a single bond. The table should show the C=C bond energy in ethene to be about +692 kJ mol^{-1}, not +598 kJ mol^{-1}.' Briefly explain why he was wrong. (Hint: look back to the unit on bonding if necessary.)

44.6 Heats of hydrogenation

Some organic compounds contain double bonds. The simplest example is ethene, C_2H_4. Such compounds are said to be unsaturated; they contain less than the maximum amount of hydrogen. Ethene, for example, can be converted into ethane, C_2H_6. The reaction of adding hydrogen to a double bond is known as hydrogenation. The heat change in a hydrogenation reaction is the *enthalpy of hydrogenation*, $\Delta H_H^{\ominus}$. Its definition is:

The enthalpy of hydrogenation is the heat change when one mole of an unsaturated compound reacts with hydrogen and is completely changed into the corresponding saturated compound.

For example,

$$C_2H_4(g) + H_2(g) \rightarrow C_2H_6(g); \qquad \Delta H_H^{\ominus} = -132\ \text{kJ mol}^{-1}$$

Now compare the value of the heat of hydrogenation of cyclohexene, C_6H_{10}, with that of benzene, C_6H_6:

$$C_6H_{10}(l) + H_2(g) \rightarrow C_6H_{12}(l); \qquad \Delta H_H^{\ominus} = -120\ \text{kJ mol}^{-1}$$

$$C_6H_6(l) + 3H_2(g) \rightarrow C_6H_{12}(l); \qquad \Delta H_H^{\ominus} = -246\ \text{kJ mol}^{-1}$$

In both cases the product is the same, cyclohexane. The structure of benzene is often shown, as in Figure 44.4,

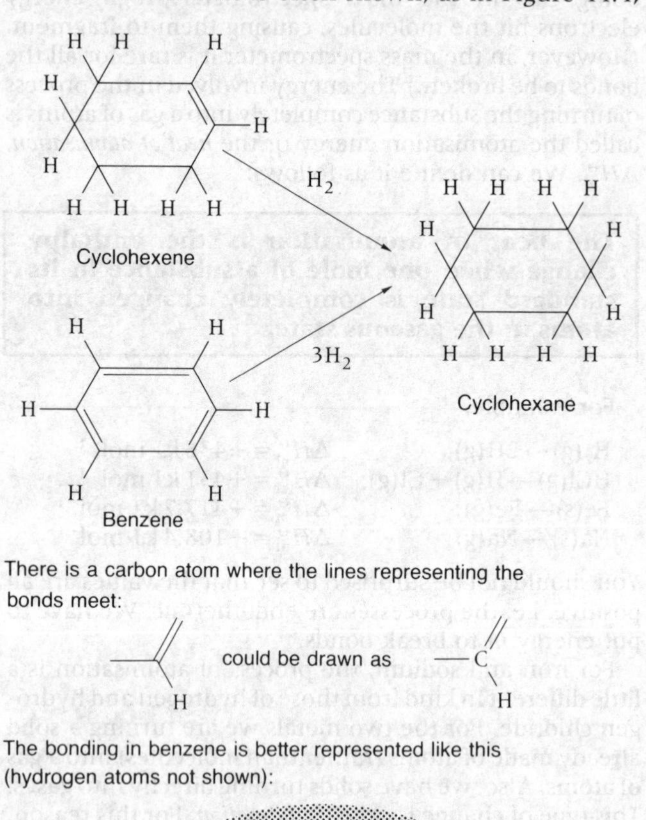

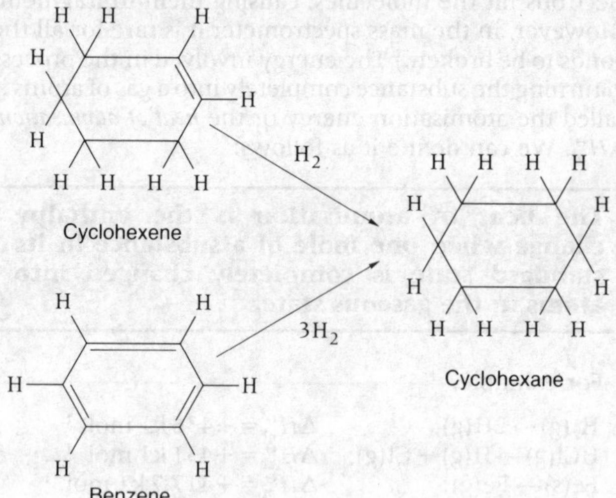

There is a carbon atom where the lines representing the bonds meet:

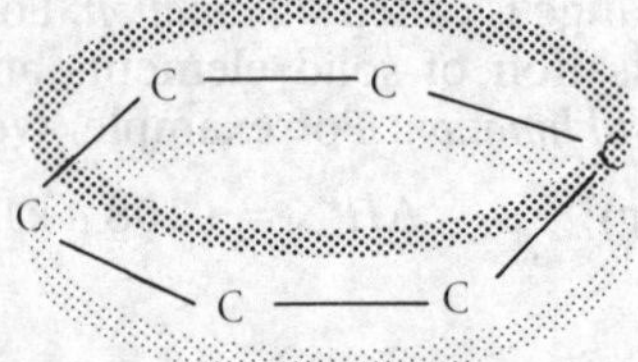

The bonding in benzene is better represented like this (hydrogen atoms not shown):

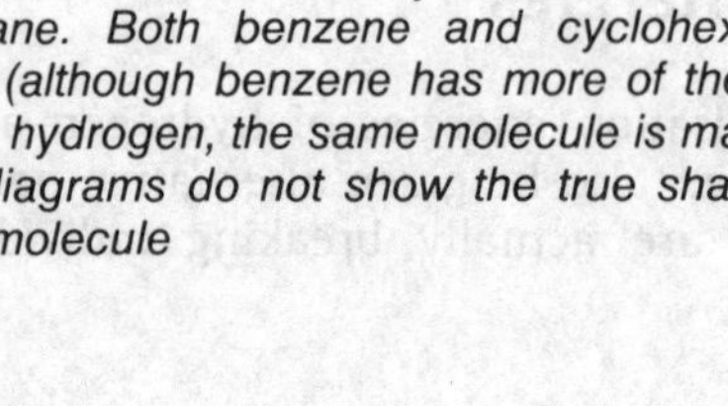

Figure 44.4 The conversions of cyclohexene and benzene into cyclohexane. Both benzene and cyclohexene have double bonds (although benzene has more of them). When they react with hydrogen, the same molecule is made: cyclohexane. The diagrams do not show the true shapes of the three types of molecule

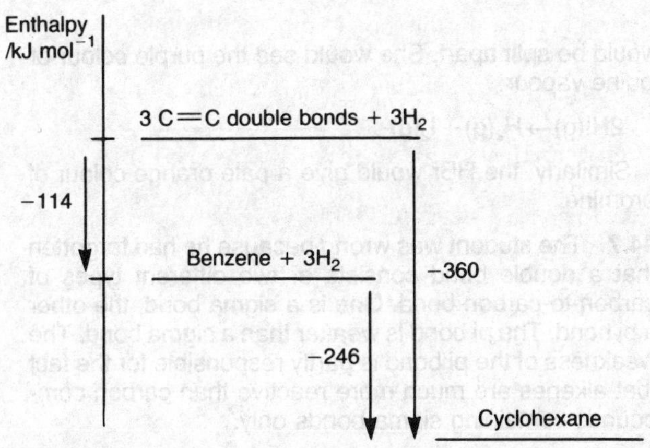

Figure 44.5 The heats of hydrogenation of benzene and of three separate carbon–carbon double bonds of the type in cyclohexene show that benzene is 114 kJ mol^{-1} more energetically stable than if it contained separate double bonds

with three separate double bonds. The fact that the heat of hydrogenation of benzene is not three times that of cyclohexene shows that, as we found in Unit 16, the bonding in benzene is unusual. It consists of a ring of six single bonds and a delocalised pi bond that stretches around the entire ring. In fact, the heats of hydrogenation give us evidence to show that the pi bonding in benzene makes the molecule more energetically stable than if it had three separate double bonds.

If benzene contained three separate double bonds like the double bond in cyclohexene, then we would expect its heat of hydrogenation to be $3\times(-120\,\text{kJ mol}^{-1}) = -360\,\text{kJ mol}^{-1}$. If we put cyclohexane on an enthalpy diagram, then 360 kJ mol^{-1} above it would lie the mythical benzene with three separate double bonds (Figure 44.5). But experiment shows that real benzene lies 246 kJ mol^{-1} above cyclohexane. Therefore (real) benzene lies 114 kJ mol^{-1} *below* the position it would have if there were three separate double bonds. We can say that the delocalisation of the pi electrons in benzene gives the molecule a degree of energetic stability that is not given by completely separate pi bonds. This is a general effect in chemistry:

The greater the spread of charge over a molecule or ion, the greater is the energetic stability of the molecule or ion.

44.8 1,3-Butadiene has a structure that is often shown like this:

$H_2C{=}CH{-}CH{=}CH_2$

Its heat of hydrogenation is −239 kJ mol^{-1}. The heat of hydrogenation of ethene is −132 kJ mol^{-1}. Could there be delocalised pi bonds in 1,3-butadiene?

Answers

44.1 The enthalpy diagram is shown in Figure 44.6.

44.2 (i) $C_4H_{10}(g) + \frac{13}{2}O_2(g) \rightarrow 4CO_2(g) + 5H_2O(g)$

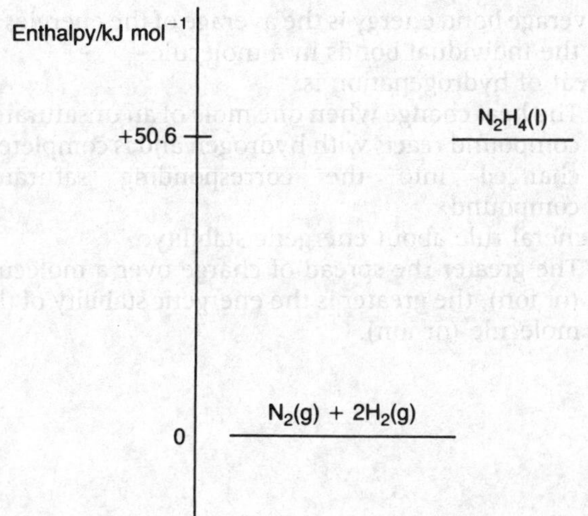

***Figure 44.6** Enthalpy diagram for the formation of hydrazine*

(ii) The mass of 1 mol of butane is 58 g. This produces 5 mol of water, 90 g. Therefore, 1 kg of butane produces $90\,\text{g} \times 1000\,\text{g}/58\,\text{g} = 1551.7\,\text{g}$, or just over 1.55 kg.

(iii) The heat liberated is $2220\,\text{kJ} \times 1000\,\text{g}/58\,\text{g}$, i.e. 37 931 kJ.

44.3 (i) This will make no difference; but it is vital that no methanol evaporates between weighing it and lighting the wick.

(ii) If methanol evaporates after the weighing, then it will seem that more methanol has been burned than is really the case. This will have the effect of lowering the value for the heat of combustion.

(iii) This will have exactly the same effect as in (ii).

(iv) The temperature measured will either be too high or too low (it is most unlikely to be correct). Without knowing the precise position of the thermometer and the nature of the convection currents, we cannot be sure which. If the temperature is too high, then the heat of combustion will be too high, and vice versa.

(v) The glass is likely to be hotter than the water. Thus the temperature recorded will be too high, and the heat of combustion will be too high.

(vi) If there is too little air, then the methanol will not

Answers – contd

burn properly (hence the soot). Not all of the energy of combustion will be released, so the measured value will be too low.

(vii) Here the danger is that the hot gases will escape from the copper spiral before they have conducted their heat into the calorimeter. The heat of combustion will be too low.

44.4 (i) 46 g.

(ii) 1.02 g.

(iii) -1366.7 kJ × 1.02 g/46g = -15.45 kJ.

(iv) 21.0°C.

(v) -30.31 kJ/21°C = -1.44 kJ mol^{-1}

(vi) The rise was 34.6°C − 19.4°C = 15.2°C.

(vii) Energy released = -1.44 kJ $°C^{-1}$ × 15.2°C = -21.89 kJ.

(viii) Number of moles of methanol = 1.02g/32g mol^{-1} = 0.032 mol.

(ix) -684 kJ. The heat of combustion is -684 kJ mol^{-1}.

44.5 The strongest bond should be the shortest, and vice versa. This agrees with the bond length values: Cl_2, 199 pm; Br_2, 228 pm; I_2, 267 pm. You may notice that the other halogen, fluorine, does not fit the pattern. It is thought that the two fluorine atoms are so close together that their lone pairs of electrons tend to repel each other more strongly than in the other halogens. Hence the bond is weaker than expected.

44.6 The strongest bonds are the hardest to break. The HCl tube would not be affected. Especially, the HI would be split apart. She would see the purple colour of iodine vapour:

$$2HI(g) \rightarrow H_2(g) + I_2(g)$$

Similarly, the HBr would give a pale orange colour of bromine.

44.7 The student was wrong because he had forgotten that a double bond consists of two different types of carbon-to-carbon bond. One is a sigma bond, the other a pi bond. The pi bond is weaker than a sigma bond. The weakness of the pi bond is partly responsible for the fact that alkenes are much more reactive than carbon compounds containing sigma bonds only.

44.8 If there were two entirely separate double bonds in 1,3-butadiene, we would expect its heat of hydrogenation to be twice that of ethene, i.e. -264 kJ mol^{-1}. In fact the value is -239 kJ mol^{-1}. This is 25 kJ mol^{-1} less than expected. Thus it appears that the pi bonding in 1,3-butadiene is delocalised, as shown in Figure 44.7.

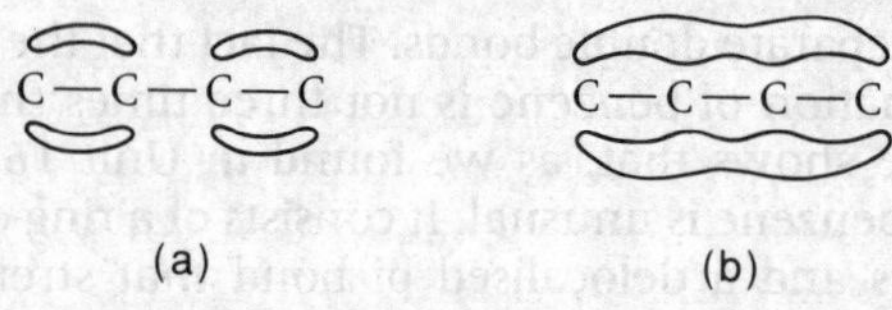

***Figure 44.7** Butadiene, CH_2=CH—CH=CH_2, shown with (a) two separate π orbitals and (b) one delocalised π orbital. (There are three other similar orbitals.) Diagram (b) gives a better impression of the bonding in the molecule. (Note: the hydrogen atoms have been omitted)*

UNIT 44 SUMMARY

- The enthalpy content of an element in its standard state is defined to be zero.
- The standard heat of formation is:
  The enthalpy change when one mole of a substance is made from its elements in their standard states.
- The standard heat of combustion is:
  The enthalpy change when one mole of a substance is completely burned in oxygen.
- The heat of atomisation is:
  The enthalpy change when one mole of a substance in its standard state is completely changed into atoms in the gaseous state.
- Bond energy is the energy needed to break a covalent bond completely.
- Average bond energy is the average of the energies of the individual bonds in a molecule.
- Heat of hydrogenation is:
  The heat change when one mole of an unsaturated compound reacts with hydrogen and is completely changed into the corresponding saturated compound.
- General rule about energetic stability:
  The greater the spread of charge over a molecule (or ion), the greater is the energetic stability of the molecule (or ion).

45

Calculations using Hess's law

45.1 Using heats of formation

Hess's law can be used to calculate all sorts of heat changes. Indeed, as you will discover shortly, it can be used to determine heat changes for reactions that cannot be carried out in the laboratory. If you are to become confident in using the law in a variety of different types of problem, there are two very important ideas that you will need to understand. The first is that, for any reaction, the overall enthalpy change is given by:

enthalpy change of reaction	=	enthalpies of products	−	enthalpies of reactants

If the substances taking part in the reaction and the products are all in their standard states, then we can write this equation in terms of the heats of formation of the reactants and products. This is the second key idea:

enthalpy change of reaction	=	heats of formation of products	−	heats of formation of reactants

or

$$\Delta H^{\ominus}\text{ (reaction)} = \Delta H^{\ominus}_f\text{(products)} - \Delta H^{\ominus}_f\text{(reactants)}$$

To see how this works in a particular case, let us look at the heat change for the following reaction:

$$HCl(g) + NH_3(g) \rightarrow NH_4Cl(s); \qquad \Delta H^{\ominus}\text{ (reaction)}$$

We can look up the heats of formation of each of the chemicals:

$$\tfrac{1}{2}H_2(g) + \tfrac{1}{2}Cl_2(g) \rightarrow HCl(g); \qquad \Delta H^{\ominus}_f = -92.3\text{ kJ mol}^{-1}$$
$$\tfrac{1}{2}N_2(g) + \tfrac{3}{2}H_2(g) \rightarrow NH_3(g); \qquad \Delta H^{\ominus}_f = -46.0\text{ kJ mol}^{-1}$$
$$\tfrac{1}{2}N_2(g) + 2H_2(g) + \tfrac{1}{2}Cl_2(g) \rightarrow NH_4Cl(s); \qquad \Delta H^{\ominus}_f = -315.5\text{ kJ mol}^{-1}$$

Now we can place all three changes on an enthalpy diagram as in Figure 45.1.

Because the enthalpies of formation of elements in their standard states are zero by definition, each of the reactions has a common starting line at 0 kJ mol^{-1}. We can think of making $NH_4Cl(s)$ in two ways. The first is the direct route from its elements (Figure 45.2), illustrated in the third equation above. The second is where the combination $\tfrac{1}{2}N_2(g) + 2H_2(g) + \tfrac{1}{2}Cl_2(g)$ is split into two portions: the first is $\tfrac{1}{2}H_2(g) + \tfrac{1}{2}Cl_2(g)$, which react to make HCl(g); the second is $\tfrac{1}{2}N_2(g) + \tfrac{3}{2}H_2(g)$,

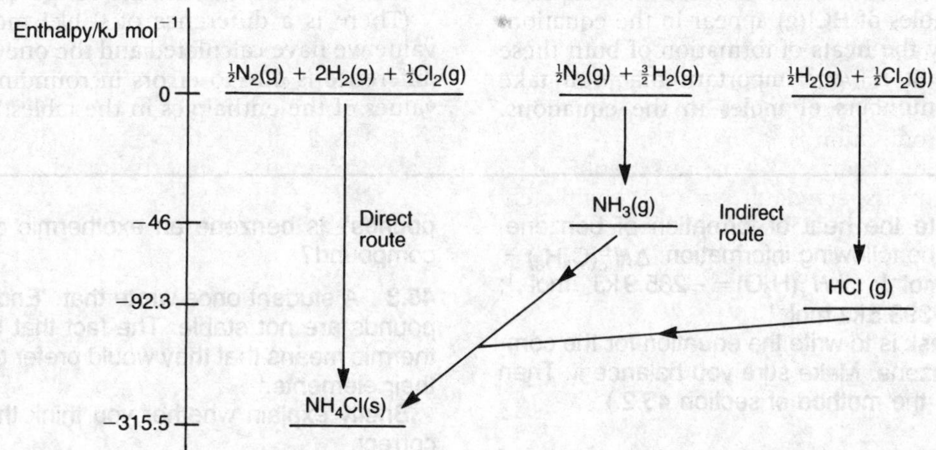

Figure 45.1 *Enthalpy diagrams for direct and indirect routes in making ammonium chloride*

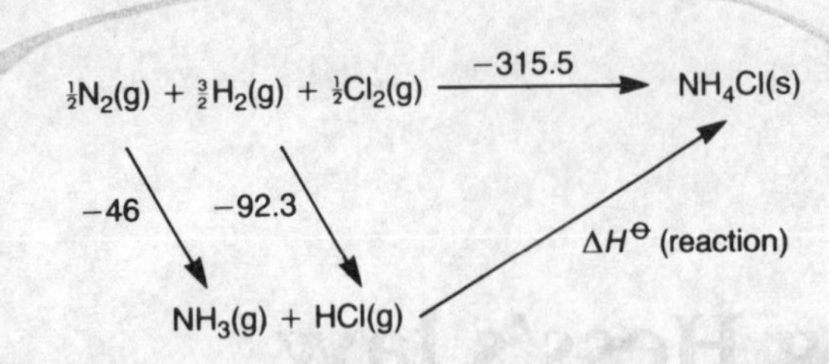

Figure 45.2 Another way of viewing the enthalpy changes in making ammonium chloride. Figures are in kJ mol^{-1}

which combine to give ammonia, $NH_3(g)$. Finally the $HCl(g)$ and $NH_3(g)$ react to produce $NH_4Cl(s)$. This second route is shown in Figure 45.2 as well.

Hess's law tells us that the enthalpy change in arriving at $NH_4Cl(s)$ is the same by the two routes. Therefore the enthalpy change for the reaction we are interested in is the difference between the enthalpy changes for the direct and the indirect routes. This is

$$\Delta H^\ominus \text{ (reaction)} = -315.5\,\text{kJ mol}^{-1} - (-46.0\,\text{kJ mol}^{-1} - 92.3\,\text{kJ mol}^{-1})$$

which gives

$$\Delta H^\ominus \text{ (reaction)} = -177.2\,\text{kJ mol}^{-1}$$

So

$$HCl(g) + NH_3(g) \rightarrow NH_4Cl(s); \quad \Delta H^\ominus \text{ (reaction)} = -177.2\,\text{kJ mol}^{-1}$$

Before going on to other things, let us try one further example, which is a little more complicated. The task is to find the enthalpy change for the reaction:

$$2HI(g) + Cl_2(g) \rightarrow 2HCl(g) + I_2(s); \qquad \Delta H^\ominus \text{ (reaction)}$$

From tables we find that $\Delta H_f^\ominus(HI) = +26.5\,\text{kJ mol}^{-1}$ and $\Delta H_f^\ominus(HCl) = -92.3\,\text{kJ mol}^{-1}$. By definition the heats of formation of $Cl_2(g)$ and $I_2(s)$ are zero. We have the rule,

$$\begin{aligned}\Delta H^\ominus \text{ (reaction)} &= \Delta H_f^\ominus \text{ (products)} - \Delta H_f^\ominus \text{ (reactants)}\\ &= 2\Delta H_f^\ominus \text{ (HCl)} - 2\Delta H_f^\ominus \text{ (HI)}\\ &= 2\times(-92.3\,\text{kJ mol}^{-1}) - 2\times(+26.5\,\text{kJ mol}^{-1})\\ &= -237.6\,\text{kJ mol}^{-1}\end{aligned}$$

The thing to notice here is that because two moles of $HI(g)$ and two moles of $HCl(g)$ appear in the equation, then we multiply the heats of formation of both these molecules by 2. It is very important that you take account of the numbers of moles in the equations. (Sometimes they may be fractions, but the same principle holds.)

45.2 Impossible reactions

Chemistry data books record the heats of formation for a wide variety of compounds. However, you should not think that all the values have actually been measured directly by experiment. Many have been calculated using Hess's law. For example, heats of formation of hydrocarbons cannot be measured directly because hydrogen gas will not combine directly with carbon; yet you will find that the heat of formation of methane is quoted as $-74.9\,\text{kJ mol}^{-1}$:

$$C(s) + 2H_2(g) \rightarrow CH_4(g); \quad \Delta H_f^\ominus(CH_4) = -74.9\,\text{kJ mol}^{-1}$$

This value is obtained by using Hess's law. Reactions for which the enthalpy changes can be measured are the heats of formation of carbon dioxide and water, and the heat of combustion of methane:

$$C(s) + O_2(g) \rightarrow CO_2(g); \quad \Delta H_f^\ominus(CO_2) = -393.5\,\text{kJ mol}^{-1}$$
$$H_2(g) + \tfrac{1}{2}O_2(g) \rightarrow H_2O(l); \quad \Delta H_f^\ominus(H_2O) = -285.9\,\text{kJ mol}^{-1}$$
$$CH_4(g) + 2O_2(g) \rightarrow CO_2(g) + 2H_2O(l); \quad \Delta H_c^\ominus(CH_4) = -890.4\,\text{kJ mol}^{-1}$$

Our task is to combine the information from these three equations in such a way that we discover the heat of formation of methane. We now know that we can write the enthalpy change for the third reaction in terms of heats of formation:

$$\Delta H_c^\ominus(CH_4) = \Delta H_f^\ominus(CO_2) + 2\Delta H_f^\ominus(H_2O) - \Delta H_f^\ominus(CH_4)$$

(Remember that $\Delta H_f^\ominus(O_2)$ is zero.) Putting in our values for the enthalpy changes,

$$\begin{aligned}-890.4\,\text{kJ mol}^{-1} &= -393.5\,\text{kJ mol}^{-1} + 2\times(-285.9\,\text{kJ mol}^{-1}) - \Delta H_f^\ominus(CH_4)\\ &= -965.3\,\text{kJ mol}^{-1} - \Delta H_f^\ominus(CH_4)\end{aligned}$$

so

$$\Delta H_f^\ominus(CH_4) = -74.9\,\text{kJ mol}^{-1}$$

This method can be applied to many other examples, some of which you will find in the questions.

(There is a difference of $0.1\,\text{kJ mol}^{-1}$ between the value we have calculated and the one in the tables. The difference is due to errors in rounding off the various values of the enthalpies in the tables.)

45.1 Calculate the heat of formation of benzene, $C_6H_6(l)$, from the following information: $\Delta H_c^\ominus(C_6H_6) = -3267.6\,\text{kJ mol}^{-1}$; $\Delta H_f^\ominus(H_2O) = -285.9\,\text{kJ mol}^{-1}$; $\Delta H_f^\ominus(CO_2) = -393.5\,\text{kJ mol}^{-1}$.

(Your first task is to write the equation for the combustion of benzene. Make sure you balance it. Then follow through the method of section 45.2.)

45.2 Substances that have an endothermic heat of formation are sometimes called 'endothermic compounds'. Is benzene an exothermic or endothermic compound?

45.3 A student once wrote that: 'Endothermic compounds are not stable. The fact that they are endothermic means that they would prefer to break up into their elements.'

Briefly explain whether you think the student was correct.

45.4 This question concerns an imaginary experiment to determine the enthalpy change of the reaction

$$Na_2CO_3(s) \rightarrow Na_2CO_3 \cdot 10H_2O(s)$$

This is the change of one mole of anhydrous sodium carbonate into one mole of hydrated sodium carbonate crystals.

Distilled water, the usually laboratory apparatus (measuring cylinders, balances and the like), and a supply of the two varieties of sodium carbonate are available. A vacuum flask adapted as shown in Figure 45.3 can also be used.

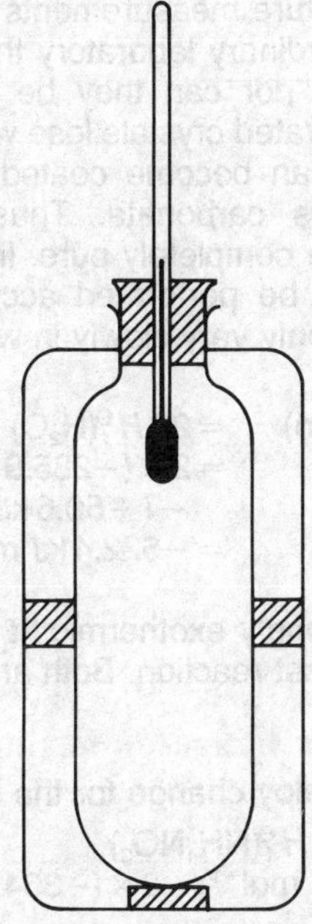

Figure 45.3 Enthalpy changes for reactions in solution can be measured using a Thermos (vacuum) flask. In an experiment the flask is turned upside down so that the liquid inside covers the thermometer bulb

Here is the method; but unfortunately it is muddled. Your task is to put the instructions in the correct order.

(A) Repeat the procedure using 5 g of $Na_2CO_3 \cdot 10H_2O$ crystals.
(B) Take the temperature of the water.
(C) Weigh accurately about 5 g of anhydrous Na_2CO_3 into a clean, dry weighing bottle.
(D) Determine the temperature rise.
(E) Tip the anhydrous Na_2CO_3 into the flask.
(F) Measure out 50 cm^3 of distilled water into a vacuum flask.
(G) Reweigh the weighing bottle.
(H) Calculate the energy released during the reaction.
(I) Measure the maximum temperature reached.

45.5 Assume that the results in the experiment above were:

Temperature *rise* given by 5.0 g anhydrous $Na_2CO_3 = 5.2°C$

Temperature *fall* given by 5.0 g $Na_2CO_3 \cdot 10H_2O = 4.9°C$

Now answer the following questions:

(i) How many moles does 5.0 g anhydrous Na_2CO_3 represent?

(ii) Taking the heat capacity of the 50 cm^3 of the solution to be the same as 50 g of water, calculate the heat released in the experiment. (Specific heat capacity of water = 4.18 kJ kg^{-1} K^{-1}.)

(iii) Calculate the heat change ΔH(anhydrous) where

$Na_2CO_3(s) \rightarrow Na_2CO_3(aq)$; ΔH(anhydrous)

(iv) How many moles does 5.0 g $Na_2CO_3 \cdot 10H_2O$ represent?

(v) Given that 1 mol of the crystals contains 10 mol of water, how many moles of water were in the 5 g of $Na_2CO_3 \cdot 10H_2O$?

(vi) What mass of water is this?

(vii) When the $Na_2CO_3 \cdot 10H_2O$ crystals dissolve in the 50 cm^3 of water in the flask, what volume of water is released from them?

(viii) What is the total volume of water in the flask?

(ix) Calculate the heat change when the $Na_2CO_3 \cdot 10H_2O$ crystals dissolved.

(x) Calculate ΔH(crystals) where

$Na_2CO_3 \cdot 10H_2O(s) \rightarrow Na_2CO_3(aq)$; ΔH(crystals)

(Take care over the sign of the enthalpy change.)

(xi) You should now have the enthalpy changes for the reactions:

$Na_2CO_3(s) \rightarrow Na_2CO_3(aq)$; ΔH(anhydrous)
$Na_2CO_3 \cdot 10H_2O(s) \rightarrow Na_2CO_3(aq)$; ΔH(crystals)

Use Hess's law to estimate the enthalpy change for

$Na_2CO_3(s) \rightarrow Na_2CO_3 \cdot 10H_2O(s)$; ΔH(reaction)

(xii) What might be the main sources of error in the experiment?

45.6 Hydrazine, N_2H_4, is an endothermic compound; its heat of formation is $+50.6$ kJ mol^{-1}. Calculate the enthalpy change for the reaction of burning hydrazine in oxygen:

$$N_2H_4(l) + O_2(g) \rightarrow N_2(g) + 2H_2O(l)$$

Why do you think that hydrazine has had some success as a rocket fuel?

45.7 Ammonium nitrate, NH_4NO_3, is widely used as a fertiliser. Unfortunately it has also found use as an explosive by terrorists. It decomposes according to the equation

$$2NH_4NO_3(s) \rightarrow 2N_2(g) + 4H_2O(g) + O_2(g)$$

(i) What is the energy change in this reaction? You will need the value $\Delta H_f^{\ominus}(NH_4NO_3) = -364.6$ kJ mol^{-1}.

(ii) Why does NH_4NO_3 act as an explosive?

Answers

45.1 $6C(s) + 3H_2(g) \rightarrow C_6H_6(l)$; $\Delta H_f^\ominus(C_6H_6)$

$C_6H_6(l) + \frac{15}{2}O_2(g) \rightarrow 6CO_2(g) + 3H_2O(l)$;
$\Delta H_c^\ominus(C_6H_6) = -3267.6\ \text{kJ mol}^{-1}$

$\Delta H_c^\ominus(C_6H_6) = 6\Delta H_f^\ominus(CO_2) + 3\Delta H_f^\ominus(H_2O) - \Delta H_f^\ominus(C_6H_6)$

$-3267.6\ \text{kJ mol}^{-1} = 6 \times (-393.5\ \text{kJ mol}^{-1}) + 3 \times (-285.9\ \text{kJ mol}^{-1}) - \Delta H_f^\ominus(C_6H_6)$

So $\Delta H_f^\ominus(C_6H_6) = +48.9\ \text{kJ mol}^{-1}$.

45.2 It is endothermic.

45.3 Elsewhere we have said that the use of the word 'stable' can lead to misunderstandings. In this case there is some truth in the student's statement: endothermic compounds do tend to break up. But, they do *not* always do so, nor do they necessarily break into their parent elements. Benzene, for example, will lie in bottles for years without the slightest inclination of decomposing. We shall take up this matter of stability in later units.

45.4 The correct order is C, F, B, E, I, G, D, H, A.

45.5 (i) $M(Na_2CO_3) = 106\ \text{g mol}^{-1}$, so we have $5\ \text{g}/106\ \text{g mol}^{-1}$, or 4.72×10^{-2} mol.

(ii) Heat released
$= 50 \times 10^{-3}\ \text{kg} \times 4.18\ \text{kJ kg}^{-1}\ \text{K}^{-1} \times 5.2\ \text{K} = 1.09\ \text{kJ}$

(iii) Scaling up to 1 mol, $\Delta H(\text{anhydrous}) = -23.11\ \text{kJ mol}^{-1}$. Note the negative sign, showing that the change is exothermic.

(iv) $M(Na_2CO_3{\cdot}10H_2O) = 286\ \text{g mol}^{-1}$, so we have $5\ \text{g}/286\ \text{g mol}^{-1}$, or 1.75×10^{-2} mol.

(v) 0.175 mol of water.

(vi) $0.175\ \text{mol} \times 18\ \text{g mol}^{-1} = 3.15\ \text{g}$.

(vii) $3.15\ \text{cm}^3$.

(viii) Total volume of water $= 53.15\ \text{cm}^3$.

(ix) Heat change
$= 53.15 \times 10^{-3}\ \text{kg} \times 4.18\ \text{kJ kg}^{-1}\ \text{K}^{-1} \times 4.9\ \text{K}$
$= 1.09\ \text{kJ}$

(x) Scaling up to 1 mol of the crystals, we have $\Delta H(\text{crystals}) = +62.3\ \text{kJ mol}^{-1}$. Notice that the reaction was endothermic, so there is a positive sign to the heat change.

(xi) On a diagram the heat changes look like this:

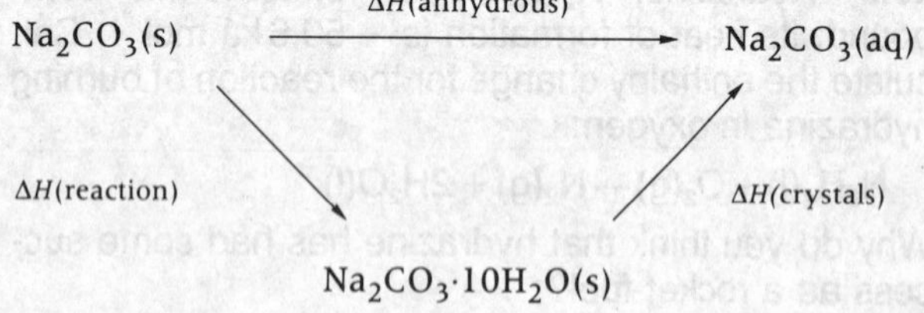

Hess's law tells us that

$\Delta H(\text{reaction}) + \Delta H(\text{crystals}) = \Delta H(\text{anhydrous})$

Putting in our values we find that

$\Delta H(\text{reaction}) + 62.3\ \text{kJ mol}^{-1} = -23.11\ \text{kJ mol}^{-1}$

So

$Na_2CO_3(s) \rightarrow Na_2CO_3{\cdot}10H_2O(s)$;
$\Delta H(\text{reaction}) = -85.41\ \text{kJ mol}^{-1}$

This compares with the tabulated value of $-91.12\ \text{kJ mol}^{-1}$.

(xii) Often temperature measurements are a significant source of error. (Ordinary laboratory thermometers are not very accurate, nor can they be read with great accuracy.) The hydrated crystals lose water easily (they effloresce). They can become coated with a layer of powdery anhydrous carbonate. Thus, the hydrated crystals may not be completely pure. In any event, this experiment cannot be performed accurately because Na_2CO_3 dissolves only very slowly in water.

45.6 $\Delta H^\ominus(\text{reaction}) = 2\Delta H_f^\ominus(H_2O) - \Delta H_f^\ominus(N_2H_4)$
$= 2 \times (-285.9\ \text{kJ mol}^{-1}) - (+50.6\ \text{kJ mol}^{-1})$
$= -622.4\ \text{kJ mol}^{-1}$

The reaction is strongly exothermic. It also happens to be an explosively fast reaction. Both are prime qualities for a rocket fuel.

45.7 (i) The enthalpy change for the reaction is
$4\Delta H_f^\ominus(H_2O) - 2\Delta H_f^\ominus(NH_4NO_3)$
$= 4 \times (-285.9\ \text{kJ mol}^{-1}) - 2 \times (-364.6\ \text{kJ mol}^{-1})$
$= -414.4\ \text{kJ mol}^{-1}$

(ii) Good explosives must decompose rapidly, and produce large changes in volume by releasing gases. Ammonium nitrate does decompose rapidly. It also gives a huge increase in volume. The 2 mol of solid have a volume of the order of some tens of cm^3. The 7 mol of gas produced have a volume of well over 150 000 cm^3. It is the rapid expansion that forces shock waves through the air, which cause the damage we associate with an explosion.

UNIT 45 SUMMARY

- In applying Hess's law we use the equation:

enthalpy change of reaction = enthalpies of products − enthalpies of reactants

or, under standard conditions,

$\Delta H^\ominus(\text{reaction}) = \Delta H_f^\ominus(\text{products}) - \Delta H_f^\ominus(\text{reactants})$

46

Lattice energies

46.1 What is meant by lattice energy?

We know that many substances are composed of ions or, at least, can be thought of in this way (see Unit 18). The ions exist in a three-dimensional array, which we call the lattice. The *lattice energy* is a measure of the energetic stability of the crystal. We should always be careful when speaking of 'stability', and ask 'stable with respect to what?' In this case it is stable with respect to the ions from which it is made when they are present as a gas. We define the *lattice energy*, $\Delta H^{\ominus}_{LE}$, as follows:

The lattice energy is the energy change when one mole of a crystal is formed from its component ions in the gaseous state.

For example, in the case of magnesium oxide the process is

$$Mg^{2+}(g) + O^{2-}(g) \rightarrow MgO(s); \quad \Delta H^{\ominus}_{LE} = -3933\ \text{kJ mol}^{-1}$$

For sodium chloride,

$$Na^{+}(g) + Cl^{-}(g) \rightarrow NaCl(s); \quad \Delta H^{\ominus}_{LE} = -781\ \text{kJ mol}^{-1}$$

Table 46.1 displays some more values of lattice energies.

Table 46.1. Lattice energies of some crystals

Crystal	*Lattice energy* /kJ mol^{-1}	*Crystal*	*Lattice energy* /kJ mol^{-1}
NaF	−915	AgF	−943
NaCl	−781	AgCl	−890
NaBr	−743	AgBr	−877
NaI	−699	AgI	−867

46.2 The Born–Haber cycle

A method, known as the *Born–Haber cycle*, makes use of Hess's law to calculate lattice energies. The best way of understanding the cycle is to see it at work in a particular case. The one we shall choose is potassium fluoride, KF. You will need to consult Figure 46.1, which gives the enthalpy diagram for the cycle.

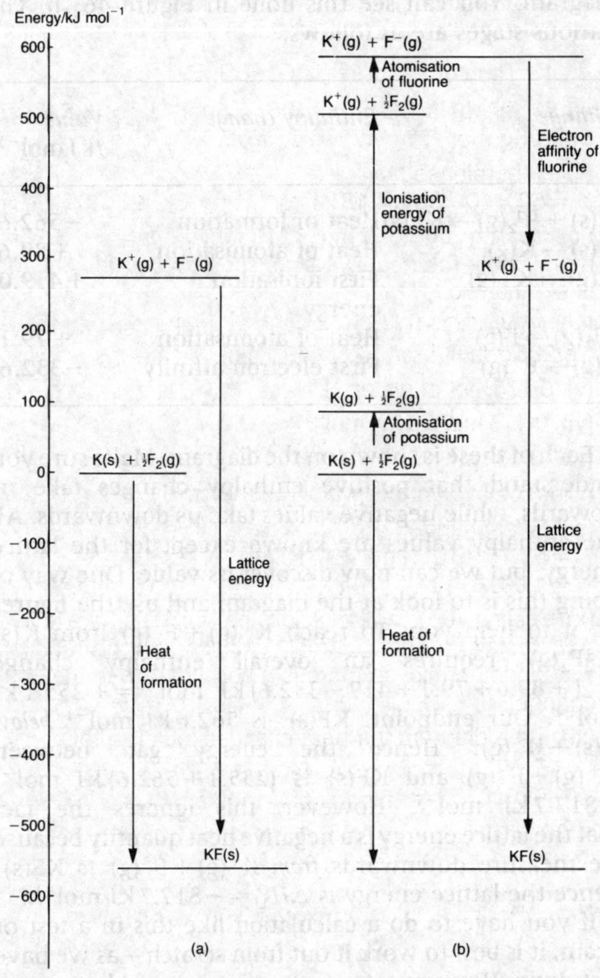

Figure 46.1 Using energy diagrams to calculate the lattice energy of potassium fluoride

One fixed level on the diagram corresponds to the elements in their standard states, K(s) and F_2(g). By definition this gives us our zero level of enthalpy. The second important level is the enthalpy of the crystal in its standard state, KF(s). From tables we find that the heat of formation of KF is $-562.6\,kJ\,mol^{-1}$. Hence the line for KF(s) is $562.6\,kJ\,mol^{-1}$ below that of $K(s)+\frac{1}{2}F_2(g)$. (Notice that the heat of formation refers to the formation of one mole of KF(s), hence the factor of $\frac{1}{2}$ in front of the $F_2(g)$.)

The next thing to realise is that the lattice energy corresponds to the energy change for the process

$$K^+(g)+F^-(g)\rightarrow KF(s)$$

It is this quantity that we are trying to calculate. As the coming together of ions to make a crystal is bound to be an exothermic process, we have placed $K^+(g)+F^-(g)$ some large distance above KF(s).

In the Born–Haber cycle we aim to convert $K(s)+\frac{1}{2}F_2(g)$ into $K^+(g)+F^-(g)$, thereby completing the diagram. You can see this done in Figure 46.1b. The various stages are as follows:

Change	*Enthalpy change*	*Value /kJ mol⁻¹*
$K(s)+\frac{1}{2}F_2(g)\rightarrow KF(s)$	Heat of formation	−562.6
$K(s)\rightarrow K(g)$	Heat of atomisation	+89.6
$K(g)\rightarrow K^+(g)$	First ionisation energy	+419.0
$\frac{1}{2}F_2(g)\rightarrow F(g)$	Heat of atomisation	+79.1
$F(g)\rightarrow F^-(g)$	First electron affinity	−332.6

Each of these is shown on the diagram. Make sure you understand that positive enthalpy changes take us upwards, while negative values take us downwards. All the enthalpy values are known except for the lattice energy, but we can now discover its value. One way of doing this is to look at the diagram and use the figures on it to help you. To reach $K^+(g)+F^-(g)$ from K(s) $+\frac{1}{2}F_2(g)$ requires an overall enthalpy change of $(+89.6+79.1+419-332.6)\,kJ\,mol^{-1}=+255.1\,kJ\,mol^{-1}$. Our endpoint, KF(s), is $562.6\,kJ\,mol^{-1}$ *below* $K(s)+\frac{1}{2}F_2(g)$. Hence the energy gap between $K^+(g)+F^-(g)$ and KF(s) is $(255.1+562.6)\,kJ\,mol^{-1}=817.7\,kJ\,mol^{-1}$. However, this ignores the fact that the lattice energy is a negative heat quantity because we measure downwards *from* $K^+(g)+F^-(g)$ *to* KF(s); hence the lattice energy is $\Delta H^{\ominus}_{LE}=-817.7\,kJ\,mol^{-1}$.

If you have to do a calculation like this in a test or exam, it is best to work it out from scratch – as we have just done. However, if you want, it is possible to use a formula. The formula says that

$$\begin{aligned}-(\text{lattice energy}) = &-(\text{heat of formation})\\ &+\text{heats of atomisation}\\ &+\text{ionisation energies}\\ &+\text{electron affinities}\end{aligned}$$

For example, in the case of potassium fluoride (in units of $kJ\,mol^{-1}$),

$$\begin{aligned}-(\text{lattice energy})&=562.6+89.6+79.1+419-332.6\\&=817.7\end{aligned}$$

Hence, lattice energy $=-817.7\,kJ\,mol^{-1}$.

We shall take a more complicated example now and calculate the lattice energy of aluminium oxide, Al_2O_3, otherwise known as the mineral, corundum. In this case we have to make sure of keeping the correct number of moles of both elements for each of the processes involved in the cycle. To begin with, the equation for the heat of formation is

$$2Al(s)+\frac{3}{2}O_2(g)\rightarrow Al_2O_3(s);\ \Delta H^{\ominus}_f=-1675.7\,kJ\,mol^{-1}$$

Because we are now dealing with two moles of aluminium, we have to take twice the atomisation energy. Also, the aluminium ion is Al^{3+}, so we have to add in contributions from the first, second and third ionisation energies of the element. Owing to 2 mol of aluminium being needed to make 1 mol of aluminium oxide, we need twice the value of each ionisation energy. Similarly, for oxygen we need three times the atomisation energy. Also, because the oxygen ion is O^{2-}, we have to add the first electron affinity of oxygen (which gets us to O^-) and the second electron affinity (to reach O^{2-}). We can list all the changes as before:

Change	*Enthalpy change*	*Value /kJ mol⁻¹*	*Multiply by*
$2Al(s)+\frac{3}{2}O_2(g)\rightarrow Al_2O_3(s)$	Heat of formation	−1675.7	1
$Al(s)\rightarrow Al(g)$	Heat of atomisation	+324.3	2
$Al(g)\rightarrow Al^+(g)$	First ionisation energy	+578	2
$Al^+(g)\rightarrow Al^{2+}(g)$	Second ionisation energy	+1817	2
$Al^{2+}(g)\rightarrow Al^{3+}(g)$	Third ionisation energy	+2745	2
$\frac{1}{2}O_2(g)\rightarrow O(g)$	Heat of atomisation	+249.2	3
$O(g)\rightarrow O^-(g)$	First electron affinity	−141.4	3
$O^-(g)\rightarrow O^{2-}(g)$	Second electron affinity	+790.8	3

You will see these figures used in the Born–Haber cycle of Figure 46.2. If you add up all the heat changes correctly you will find that the lattice energy of aluminium oxide is $-15\,300.1\,kJ\,mol^{-1}$. This large value gives a good indication of the strength with which the aluminium and oxide ions are held together in corundum.

46.1 The equations for the heats of formation of copper(I) oxide, Cu_2O, and copper(II) oxide, CuO, are

$2Cu(s)+\frac{1}{2}O_2(g)\rightarrow Cu_2O(s)$; $\Delta H^{\ominus}_f=-166.7\,kJ\,mol^{-1}$
$Cu(s)+\frac{1}{2}O_2(g)\rightarrow CuO(s)$; $\Delta H^{\ominus}_f=-155.2\,kJ\,mol^{-1}$

The first and second I.E.s of copper are 750 and

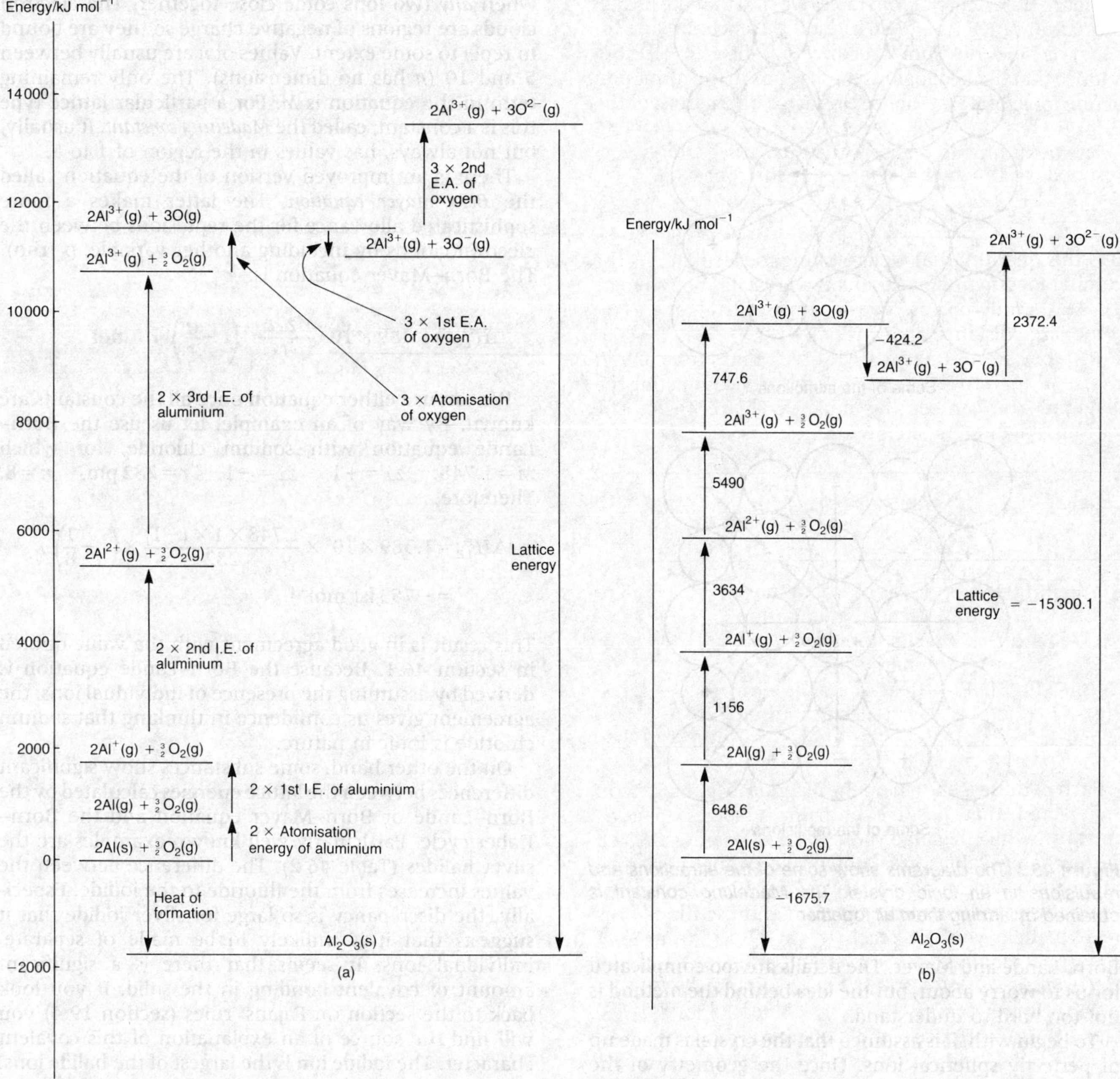

***Figure 46.2** (a) The Born–Haber cycle for aluminium oxide. (b) This diagram is not drawn to scale. It merely shows the values of the energy changes in the Born–Haber cycle*

2000 kJ mol^{-1} respectively; its atomisation energy is 339.3 kJ mol^{-1}.

Draw the Born–Haber cycles and calculate the lattice energies of the two oxides.

46.2 You can see from the figures of section 46.2 that overall the conversion of an oxygen atom into an oxide ion, O^{2-}, is endothermic (-141.4 kJ mol^{-1} $+790.8$ kJ mol^{-1} $= +649.4$ kJ mol^{-1}). Yet the oxide ion is found in many ionic substances. What is the source of the energy that enables oxygen atoms to form oxide ions?

46.3 What do lattice energies tell us?

First, the more negative the value, the greater is the energetic stability of the lattice with respect to it being broken up into separate ions. However, we should be careful not to make the mistake of thinking that the lattice energy tells us whether the substance really is held together by ionic bonds. The values only tell us what would be the energy released *if* the crystal were made from gaseous ions. To some extent it is possible to check the degree of ionic character in a crystal by performing a calculation. The method of calculation was developed by

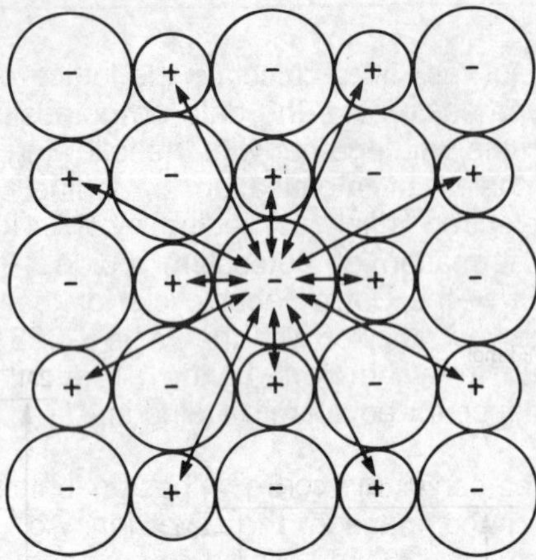

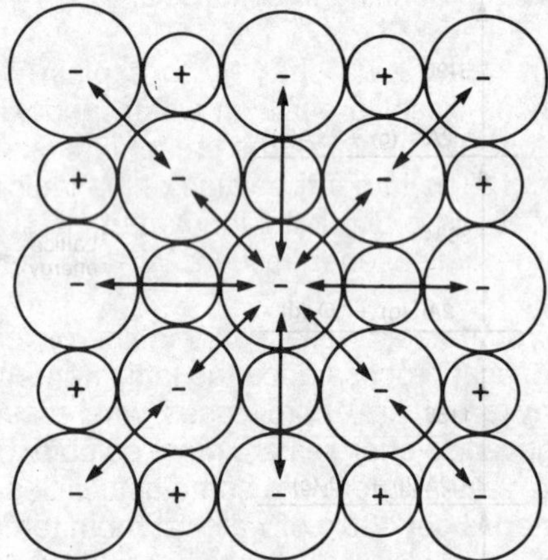

***Figure 46.3** The diagrams show some of the attractions and repulsions in an ionic crystal. The Madelung constant is obtained by adding them all together*

Born, Landé and Mayer. The details are too complicated for us to worry about, but the idea behind the method is not too hard to understand.

To begin with, it is assumed that the crystal is made up of perfectly spherical ions. Once the geometry of the crystal has been determined (e.g. by X-ray diffraction), the distances between the ions are known. The energy of attraction between all oppositely charged ions, and the energy of repulsion between ions of the same charge, are calculated (Figure 46.3). This is the tricky part; but fortunately all the major crystal structures have been done by now. The general result is known as the Born–Landé equation:

$$\Delta H^{\ominus}_{\mathrm{LE}} = 1.389 \times 10^5 \,\frac{Mz_+z_-}{r}\left(1-\frac{1}{n}\right)\ \mathrm{kJ\ mol^{-1}}$$

Here, r is the shortest distance between two oppositely charged ions, measured in picometres (1 picometre, 1 pm $= 10^{-12}$ m); z_+ is the size of the charge on the positive ions, and z_- that on the negative ions; and n is a factor that takes account of the repulsions that occur when *any* two ions come close together. The electron clouds are regions of negative charge so they are bound to repel to some extent. Values of n are usually between 5 and 10 (n has no dimensions). The only remaining term in the equation is M. For a particular lattice type this is a constant, called the *Madelung constant*. It usually, but not always, has values in the region of 1 to 5.

There is an improved version of the equation called the *Born–Mayer equation*. The latter makes a more sophisticated allowance for the repulsions between the electron clouds by including another variable, ϱ (rho). The Born–Mayer equation is:

$$\Delta H^{\ominus}_{\mathrm{LE}} = 1.389 \times 10^5 \,\frac{Mz_+z_-}{r}\left(1-\frac{\varrho}{r}\right)\ \mathrm{kJ\ mol^{-1}}$$

We can use either equation once all the constants are known. By way of an example, let us use the Born–Landé equation with sodium chloride, for which $M = 1.748$, $z_+ = +1$, $z_- = -1$, $r = 282$ pm, $n = 8$. Therefore,

$$\Delta H^{\ominus}_{\mathrm{LE}} = 1.389 \times 10^5 \times \frac{1.748 \times 1 \times (-1)}{282} \times \left(1-\frac{1}{8}\right)$$

$$= -753\ \mathrm{kJ\ mol^{-1}}$$

This result is in good agreement with the value quoted in section 46.1. Because the Born–Landé equation is derived by assuming the presence of individual ions, the agreement gives us confidence in thinking that sodium chloride is ionic in nature.

On the other hand, some substances show significant differences between the lattice energies calculated by the Born–Landé or Born–Mayer equation and the Born–Haber cycle. Particularly well known examples are the silver halides (Table 46.2). The difference between the values increases from the fluoride to the iodide. Especially, the discrepancy is so large for silver iodide that it suggests that it is unlikely to be made of separate, individual ions. It seems that there is a significant amount of covalent bonding in the solid. If you look back to the section on Fajans' rules (section 19.4) you will find the source of an explanation of this covalent character. The iodide ion is the largest of the halide ions. As such it is 'squashy' and polarisable (Figure 46.4). A silver ion might attract the electron cloud around the iodine ion, thus producing a certain amount of covalent bonding.

Table 46.2. Comparison of the lattice energies of the silver halides

Halide	*Lattice energy/kJ mol⁻¹*	
	Born–Haber cycle	*Born–Mayer equation*
AgF	−943	−925
AgCl	−890	−833
AgBr	−877	−808
AgI	−867	−774

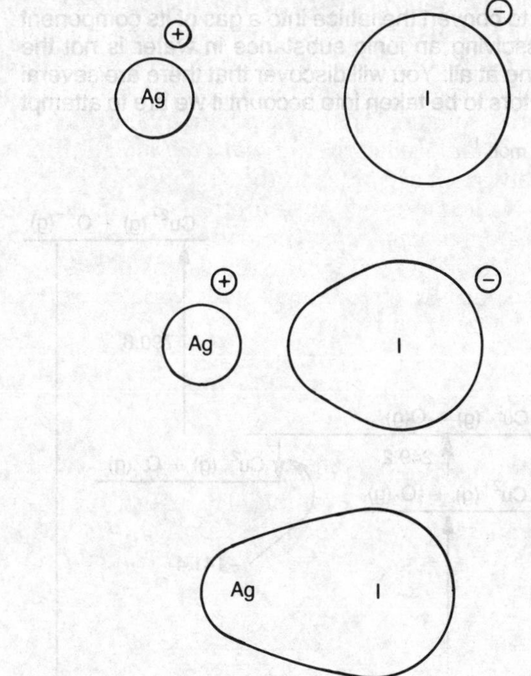

Figure 46.4 *As the silver and iodide ions come closer together, the positive charge on the silver ion attracts the iodine electrons towards it. Eventually the electron clouds of both ions mingle. We say that the silver ion has polarised the iodide ion*

It is wise to be wary of making hard and fast generalisations about the bonding in substances such as silver iodide. For example, along with other 'ionic' solids, silver iodide has a high melting point (558° C) and it does conduct electricity when molten.

46.3 Your task is to calculate the lattice energy of potassium iodide. Use the data on potassium given earlier in the unit together with the following information: enthalpy of atomisation of iodine, 106.6 kJ mol^{-1}; electron affinity of iodine, −295.4 kJ mol^{-1}; heat of formation of potassium iodide, −327.6 kJ mol^{-1}. Draw the Born–Haber cycle for the process. Compare your answer with the value −623 kJ mol^{-1} calculated from the Born–Landé equation. Is there any evidence for covalent bonding in KI?

46.4 The beryllium ion, Be^{2+}, has an ionic radius of 30 pm. (By comparison, the silver ion, Ag^+, has an ionic radius of 126 pm.) Would you expect the Born–Landé equation to give a good estimate of the lattice energy of beryllium chloride, $BeCl_2$? What is the nature of the bonding in solid $BeCl_2$?

46.5 In Unit 59 we shall try to explain why some substances dissolve easily in water, and why others are almost insoluble. For the present, think about this statement: 'The larger the value of the lattice energy, the harder it is to break the ions apart, so substances with large lattice energies are always insoluble in water.'

Can you detect a fallacy in this line of reasoning? (Hint: to what process does the lattice energy refer?)

In any case, are there cases where substances with high lattice energies are more soluble than those with low values? Here are some solubilities in moles of substance per 100 g of water at room temperature: AgF, 1.42; AgCl, 1.35×10^{-6}; NaCl, 0.62; MgO, 2×10^{-5}

Answers

46.1 The Born–Haber cycles are drawn in Figure 46.5. Lattice energies are:

$$\Delta H^{\circ}_{LE}(Cu_2O) = -3243.9\ \text{kJ mol}^{-1}$$
$$\Delta H^{\circ}_{LE}(CuO) = -4143.1\ \text{kJ mol}^{-1}$$

46.2 It is the lattice energy that can be thought of as providing the energy. It is the energy released when the oxide ions are made *together* with the neighbouring positive ions within the solid that determines whether the ion will be formed. Values of the electron affinities (like ionisation energies) refer to changes taking place in a *gas*. This is quite unlike the environment when a solid is being made.

46.3 $\Delta H^{\circ}_{LE} = -647.3$ kJ mol^{-1}. The Born–Haber cycle is given in Figure 46.6. The Born–Mayer equation, which assumes perfect ions to be present, is, like the case of silver iodide, less than that calculated from the Born–Haber cycle. There may be some covalent bonding in KI.

46.4 Look back at Unit 19. There we made the point that the small size of the Be^{2+} ion will polarise a neighbouring negative ion. Covalency results. You will find the structure of solid $BeCl_2$ in Figure 15.4.

46.5 Lattice energies refer to the business of taking *gaseous ions* and converting them into a crystalline lattice. Strictly, the lattice energy tells how energetically favourable this process is. Alternatively, it tells us how hard it is to convert the lattice into a gas of its component ions. Dissolving an ionic substance in water is not the same thing at all. You will discover that there are several other factors to be taken into account if we are to attempt

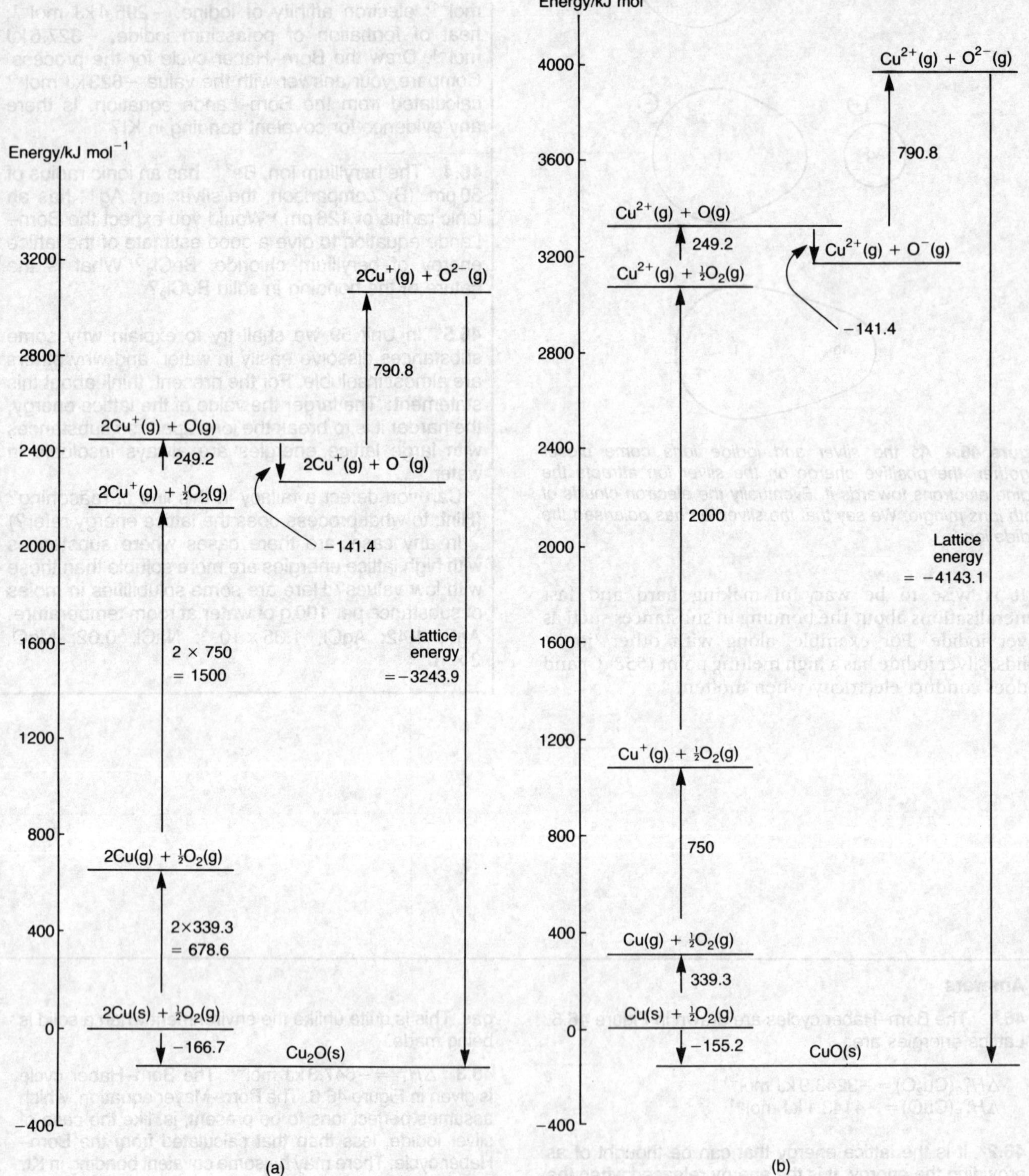

Figure 46.5 *(a) Born–Haber cycle for copper(I) oxide. Check:* $-(\text{lattice energy}) = -(-166.7) + 678.6 + 1500 + 249.2 - 141.4 + 790.8 = 3243.9$*. Therefore, lattice energy* $= -3243.9\ \text{kJ mol}^{-1}$*. (b) Born–Haber cycle for copper(II) oxide. Check:* $-(\text{lattice energy}) = -(-155.2) + 339.3 + 750 + 2000 + 249.2 - 141.4 + 790.8 = 4143.1$*. Therefore, lattice energy* $= -4143.1\ \text{kJ mol}^{-1}$

to explain solubilities. You can see from the figures in the question, together with the lattice energies in the sections above, that there is no simple relationship between lattice energy and solubility. For example, AgF is much more soluble than AgCl even though it has a larger lattice energy than AgCl. There is also the problem of reactions taking place. This happens with MgO, which can produce $Mg(OH)_2$ with water.

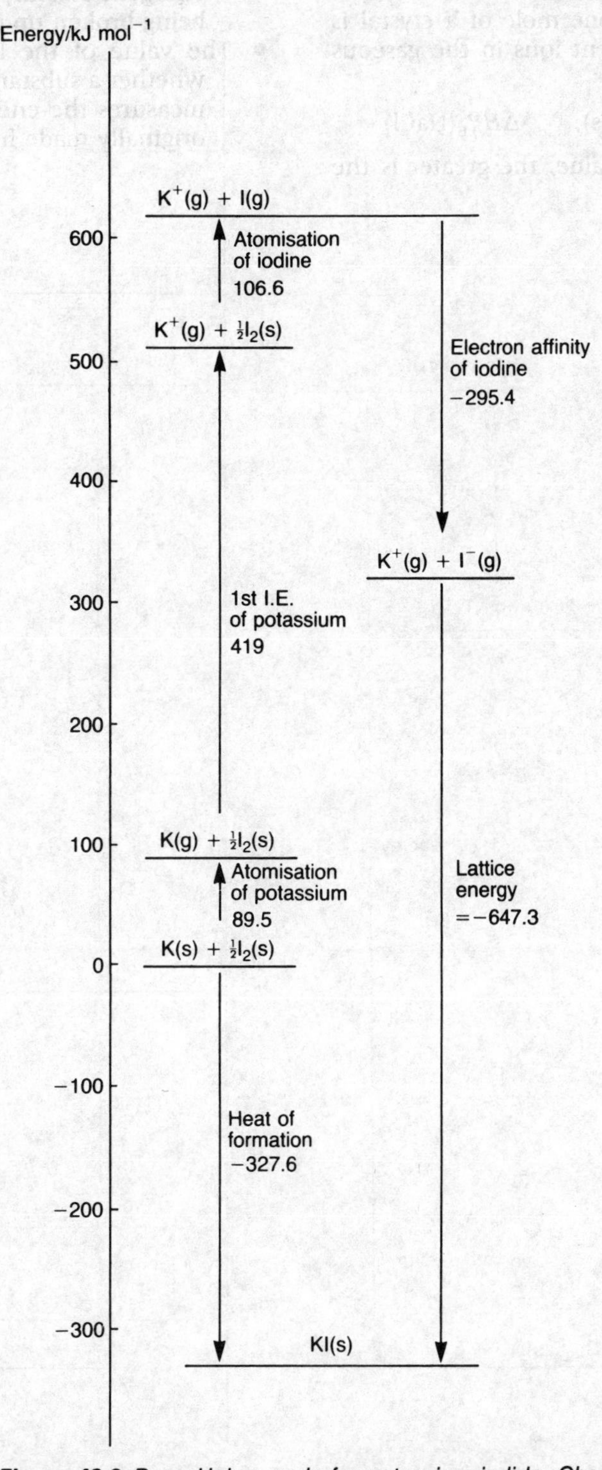

Figure 46.6 *Born–Haber cycle for potassium iodide. Check: −(lattice energy) = −(−327.6) + 89.5 + 419 + 106.6 − 295.4 = 647.3. Therefore, lattice energy = −647.3 kJ mol*$^{-1}$

UNIT 46 SUMMARY

- Lattice energy $\Delta H^{\ominus}_{LE}$ is defined as:
  The energy change when one mole of a crystal is formed from its component ions in the gaseous state. For example,

  $$Na^+(g) + Cl^-(g) \rightarrow NaCl(s); \qquad \Delta H^{\ominus}_{LE}(NaCl)$$

  The more negative the value, the greater is the energetic stability of the lattice with respect to it being broken up into separate ions.
- The value of the lattice energy does not tell us whether a substance is really composed of ions. It measures the energy released *if* the crystal were originally made from gaseous ions.

47

Enthalpy changes in solutions

47.1 Heats of neutralisation

Sodium hydroxide and hydrochloric acid are known as *strong electrolytes*. This means that when dissolved in water their solutions contain only separate ions, i.e. Na^+, OH^-, H^+ and Cl^-. In solution the ions gather about them a sphere of water molecules, called the *hydration sphere*.

In Figure 47.1 notice that the positive ions attract the negatively charged (oxygen) ends of the water molecules towards them. Similarly, the negatively charged ions attract the positively charged (hydrogen) ends of the water molecules.

If the solution is very dilute, the ions are separated by many layers of water molecules and each one behaves as if the other ions were not present. This is said to happen at *infinite dilution*, and it is represented by putting the letters *aq* in brackets after the symbol, e.g. $OH^-(aq)$ or $H^+(aq)$.

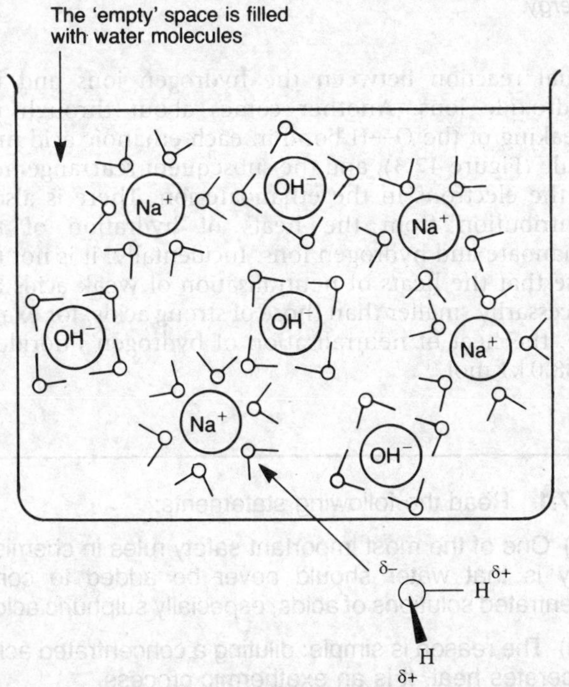

Figure 47.1 Strong electrolytes like sodium hydroxide and hydrochloric acid are completely dissociated into ions in solution. The diagram shows a much exaggerated view of a solution of sodium hydroxide. In reality the water molecules are arranged in three dimensions about the ions.

If you mix solutions of sodium hydroxide and hydrochloric acid, you will find that heat is generated. (*Caution*: *Never* attempt to mix concentrated solutions of acids and alkalis. So much heat can be liberated in a short time that the mixture can be showered over you!) We could write the equation for the reaction as

$$NaOH(aq) + HCl(aq) \rightarrow NaCl(aq) + H_2O(l)$$

But this would be to miss the true source of the heat generated. The sodium and chloride ions begin the reaction separated by water molecules, and this is how they remain at the end of the reaction; they do not react. The reaction is really between the hydroxide ions and the hydrogen ions (Figure 47.2):

$$H^+(aq) + OH^-(aq) \rightarrow H_2O(l)$$

If you prefer, it is possible to write this equation as a reaction between oxonium ions, H_3O^+, and hydroxide ions:

$$H_3O^+(aq) + OH^-(aq) \rightarrow 2H_2O(l)$$

However, nothing of moment is gained by doing this here, so we shall keep to the simpler equation.

The enthalpy change when one mole of hydrogen ions is completely neutralised under standard conditions is called the standard *heat of neutralisation*, $\Delta H^\ominus_n$ (Table 47.1). Its value in the present case is $-57.9\ kJ\ mol^{-1}$, i.e.

$$H^+(aq) + OH^-(aq) \rightarrow H_2O(l); \quad \Delta H^\ominus_n = -57.9\ kJ\ mol^{-1}$$

The definition of the *standard heat of neutralisation* is as follows:

The standard heat of neutralisation is the enthalpy change that takes place when one mole of hydrogen ions from an acid is completely neutralised by an alkali to give an infinitely dilute solution.

Notice that the definition does not talk about one mole of an acid. The reason for this is that one mole of an acid

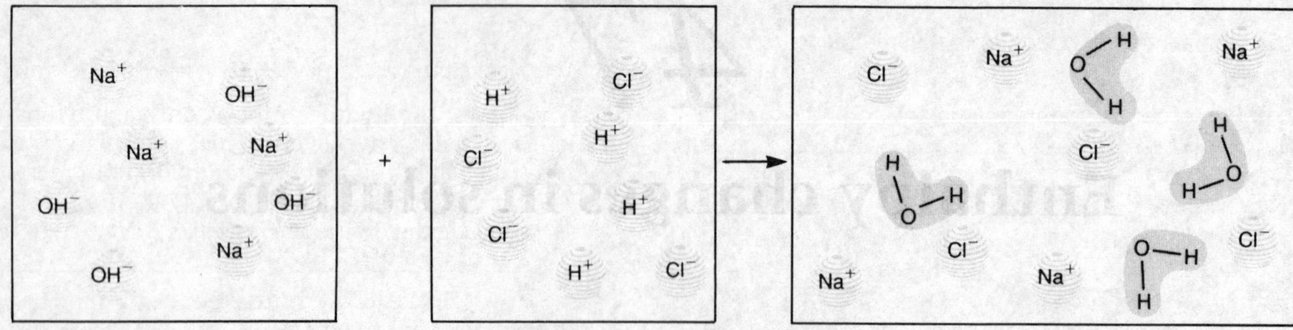

***Figure 47.2** When sodium hydroxide and hydrochloric acid neutralise one another, it is only the hydrogen ions and hydroxide ions that react. They combine to make water. The sodium ions and chloride ions remain surrounded by their hydration spheres. They are sometimes called spectator ions: we can imagine them to be watching the reactions that are taking place.*

Table 47.1. Heats of neutralisation of three strong acids

Acid	$\Delta H_n^{\ominus}$/kJ mol^{-1}
HCl	−57.9
HBr	−57.6
HNO_3	−57.6

like sulphuric acid, H_2SO_4, can give more than one mole of hydrogen ions. A number of different combinations of acids and alkalis have almost the same value for their heats of neutralisation. Examples are the strong electrolytes in Table 47.2. The reaction taking place when they neutralise one another is just the reaction between hydrogen ions and hydroxide ions.

Acids and alkalis that have very different heats of neutralisation are also shown in the table. These are known as *weak electrolytes*. Solutions of weak electrolytes contain molecules of the substance as well as ions. For example, in a dilute solution of ethanoic acid, CH_3COOH, only about 4% of the ethanoic acid molecules exist as ions:

$$\underset{\text{mainly molecules}}{CH_3COOH(aq)} \rightleftharpoons \underset{\text{a very few ions}}{CH_3COO^-(aq) + H^+(aq)}$$

When ethanoic acid reacts with hydroxide ions, there are a number of sources for the heat change. One is the

Table 47.2. Examples of strong and weak electrolytes

	Acids	*Alkalis*
Strong electrolytes	Hydrochloric	Lithium hydroxide
	Nitric	Sodium hydroxide
	Sulphuric*	Potassium hydroxide
Weak electrolytes	Methanoic	Aqueous ammonia
	Ethanoic	

*Only the first dissociation of sulphuric acid is complete; the second is incomplete:

$H_2SO_4(aq) \rightleftharpoons HSO_4^-(aq) + H^+(aq)$ lies far to the right

$HSO_4^-(aq) \rightleftharpoons SO_4^{2-}(aq) + H^+(aq)$ lies to the left

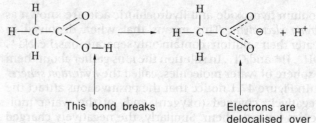

Ethanoic acid Ethanoate ion

This bond breaks

Electrons are delocalised over the carbon and both oxygen atoms

***Figure 47.3** Breaking the O—H bond in ethanoic acid requires energy to be put in. However, delocalisation of the electrons in the ethanoate ion represents a lowering of energy.*

usual reaction between the hydrogen ions and the hydroxide ions. Another comes about through the breaking of the O—H bond in each ethanoic acid molecule (Figure 47.3), and the subsequent rearrangement of the electrons in the ethanoate ion. There is also a contribution from the heats of hydration of the ethanoate and hydrogen ions. Incidentally, it is not the case that the heats of neutralisation of weak acids are necessarily smaller than those of strong acids; for example, the heat of neutralisation of hydrogen fluoride is −68.0 kJ mol^{-1}.

47.1 Read the following statements:

(i) One of the most important safety rules in chemistry is that water should never be added to concentrated solutions of acids, especially sulphuric acid.

(ii) The reason is simple: diluting a concentrated acid liberates heat. It is an exothermic process.

(iii) When water is added, the molecules break up, producing ions. More energy is released as the ions are hydrated by the water molecules than is needed to break the molecules apart.

(iv) The heat liberated is sufficient to boil the water and cause it to spit out of the solution, taking some of the acid with it.

Which of these statements is/are correct?

47.2 Hydration energies

If we were to plunge a mole of gaseous hydrogen ions into water, so that the resulting solution was effectively infinitely dilute, we would discover that a large amount of heat was liberated. The heat change for the process is

Table 47.3. Hydration energies of common ions

Ion	$\Delta H^{\ominus}_{h}$(ion) /kJ mol^{-1}	*Ion*	$\Delta H^{\ominus}_{h}$(ion) /kJ mol^{-1}	*Ion*	$\Delta H^{\ominus}_{h}$(ion) /kJ mol^{-1}
H^+	−1075				
Li^+	−499	Mg^{2+}	−1891	F^-	−457
Na^+	−390	Ca^{2+}	−1562	Cl^-	−384
K^+	−305	Al^{3+}	−4613	Br^-	−351
Ag^+	−464			I^-	−307
NH_4^+	−281			OH^-	−460

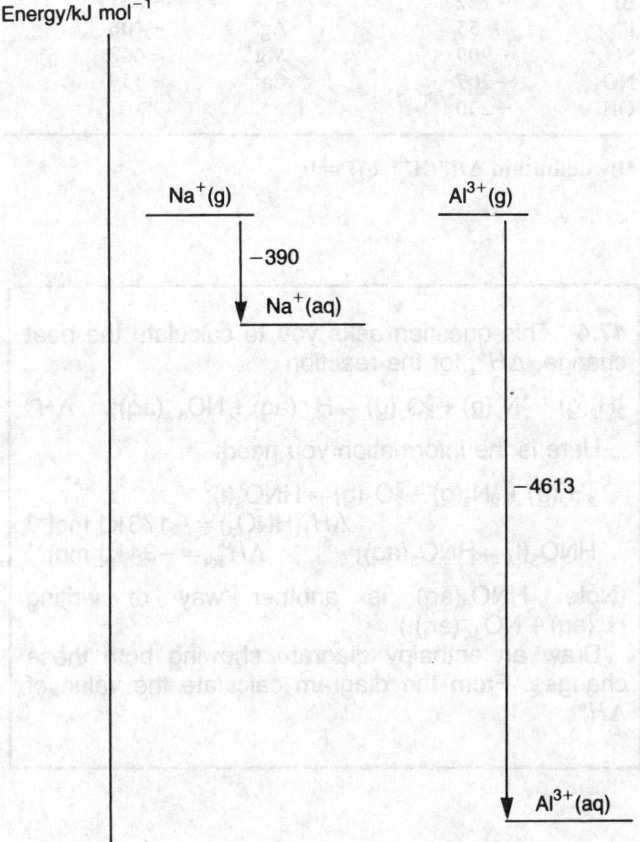

***Figure 47.4** The hydration energy of Al^{3+} is almost 12 times larger than that of Na^+*

known as the *hydration energy*, $\Delta H^{\ominus}_{h}$, of the hydrogen ion:

$$H^+(g) + \text{water} \rightarrow H^+(aq);\ \Delta H^{\ominus}_{h}(H^+) = -1075\,\text{kJ mol}^{-1}$$

(This value for the hydrogen ion is only approximate. Various estimates have been made, some larger and some smaller than this one.) Some hydration energies are shown in Table 47.3 and Figure 47.4.

In general we can define the *hydration energy*, $\Delta H^{\ominus}_{h}$, as:

The hydration energy is the heat change that takes place when one mole of a gaseous ion dissolves in water to give an infinitely dilute solution.

It is interesting to compare these values with the ionic radii of the ions. You will be asked to do this in question 47.2.

47.2 Look up the ionic radii of the ions listed in Table 33.4. Can you find any relation between the ionic radii and the heats of hydration? You might try plotting a graph, either on paper or using a computer. Try to explain any trends that you notice.

47.3 A student made up two solutions by mixing the same volume of dilute hydrochloric acid with two different quantities of water. She called these solutions A and B, and placed 50 cm^3 of each in two polystyrene cups. She invited her friend to measure the temperature of each solution. Both solutions were at 18° C. Then her friend had to add 25 cm^3 of water (again at 18° C) to each cup. The temperature of cup A remained at 18° C; the other increased to 20° C. The friend had to decide which, if either, of the two solutions A and B behaved as if it were infinitely dilute. What should her answer have been?

47.3 Heats of solution

When chemicals dissolve in water there is almost invariably a heat change. It can be hard to predict whether a substance will dissolve exothermically or endothermically. For example, sodium hydroxide dissolves exothermically, while sodium nitrate dissolves endothermically (Figure 47.5). For the present we shall not attempt to explain why these changes take place. It is sufficient to realise that they do take place. We define the *heat of solution*, $\Delta H^{\ominus}_{sol}$, as follows:

The heat of solution is the enthalpy change that takes place when one mole of a substance dissolves in a solvent to give an infinitely dilute solution.

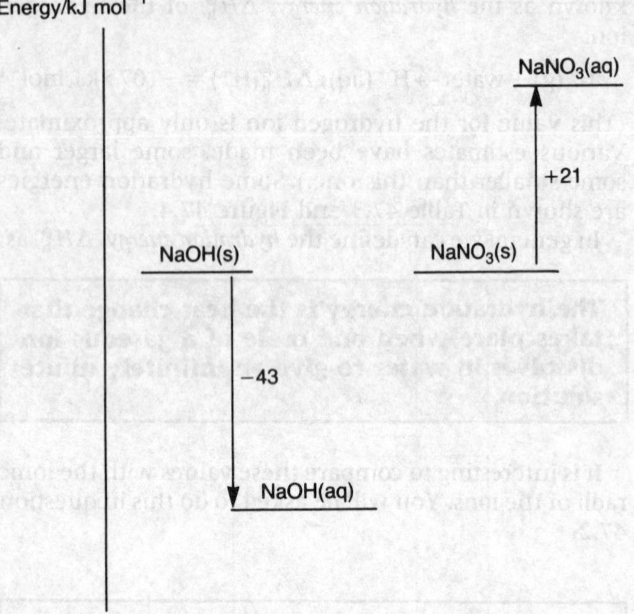

Figure 47.5 The heat of solution of sodium hydroxide is exothermic, while that of sodium nitrate is endothermic

Notice that the definition refers to a solvent. Usually the solvent is water; but it need not be. It is possible to carry out reactions in many other solvents, such as ethanol or liquid ammonia. Also, as in our previous work, the solution produced must be infinitely dilute. Table 47.4 gives some examples.

Table 47.4. Some heats of solution

Change	$\Delta H^{\ominus}_{sol}$/kJ mol^{-1}
$H_2SO_4(l) \rightarrow H_2SO_4(aq)$	−95
$HCl(g) \rightarrow HCl\ (aq)$	−75
$CuSO_4(s) \rightarrow CuSO_4(aq)$	−73
$NaOH(s) \rightarrow NaOH(aq)$	−43
$HNO_3(l) \rightarrow HNO_3(aq)$	−34
$NaCl(s) \rightarrow NaCl(aq)$	+4
$NH_4Cl(s) \rightarrow NH_4Cl(aq)$	+16
$NaNO_3(s) \rightarrow NaNO_3(aq)$	+21

47.4 Enthalpies of formation of ions in solution

In more advanced work in chemistry it is sometimes useful to know the heat change for processes like these:

$$\tfrac{1}{2}H_2(g) + \tfrac{1}{2}Cl_2(g) \rightarrow H^+(aq) + Cl^-(aq); \quad \Delta H^{\ominus} = -167\ \text{kJ mol}^{-1}$$

$$\tfrac{1}{2}H_2(g) + \tfrac{1}{2}N_2(g) + \tfrac{3}{2}O_2(g) \rightarrow H^+(aq) + NO_3^-(aq); \quad \Delta H^{\ominus} = -207\ \text{kJ mol}^{-1}$$

The first represents the formation of one mole of hydrochloric acid, and the second that of nitric acid (both at infinite dilution), from their elements in their standard states. These heat changes can be calculated using Hess's law (see question 47.4). However, we cannot determine the contribution of the formation of the individual ions to the heat changes. For example, in the case of nitric acid the heat change is approximately −207 kJ mol^{-1}, but how much of this is due to the production of $H^+(aq)$ and how much to $NO_3^-(aq)$ it is impossible to say. Faced with this difficulty, chemists have decided to *define* the enthalpy of formation of the hydrogen ion in solution to be zero. When this is done it means that we can tell from the two equations that $\Delta H_f^{\ominus}(Cl^-(aq)) = -167$ kJ mol^{-1} and $\Delta H_f^{\ominus}(NO_3^-(aq)) = -207$ kJ mol^{-1}. Table 47.5 shows values of the heats of formation of common ions.

Table 47.5. Heats of formation of common ions in solution*

Ion	$\Delta H_f^{\ominus}$(ion(aq)) /kJ mol^{-1}	*Ion*	$\Delta H_f^{\ominus}$(ion(aq)) /kJ mol^{-1}
F^-	−332	Li^+	−279
Cl^-	−167	Na^+	−330
Br^-	−122	K^+	−251
I^-	−55	Ag^+	−106
SO_4^{2-}	−909	Mg^{2+}	−462
NO_3^-	−207	Ca^{2+}	−539
OH^-	−230		

*By definition $\Delta H_f^{\ominus}(H^+(aq)) = 0$

47.4 This question asks you to calculate the heat change, $\Delta H^{\ominus}$, for the reaction

$$\tfrac{1}{2}H_2(g) + \tfrac{1}{2}N_2(g) + \tfrac{3}{2}O_2(g) \rightarrow H^+(aq) + NO_3^-(aq); \quad \Delta H^{\ominus}$$

Here is the information you need:

$$\tfrac{1}{2}H_2(g) + \tfrac{1}{2}N_2(g) + \tfrac{3}{2}O_2(g) \rightarrow HNO_3(l); \quad \Delta H_f^{\ominus}(HNO_3) = -173\ \text{kJ mol}^{-1}$$

$$HNO_3(l) \rightarrow HNO_3(aq); \quad \Delta H^{\ominus}_{sol} = -34\ \text{kJ mol}^{-1}$$

(Note: $HNO_3(aq)$ is another way of writing $H^+(aq) + NO_3^-(aq)$.)

Draw an enthalpy diagram showing both these changes. From the diagram calculate the value of $\Delta H^{\ominus}$.

Answers

47.1 All four statements are correct.

47.2 The trend is that the smaller the ionic radius, the greater is the hydration energy. One reason for this is that the water molecules can get closer to the centre of charge, so the attractions are increased.

47.3 Solution A appeared to be infinitely dilute. Adding more water to such a solution cannot cause any further change to the ions in the solution, so there will be no heat change. Solution B gives out heat with the water. This solution cannot be infinitely dilute.

47.4 Figure 47.6 shows the enthalpy diagram.

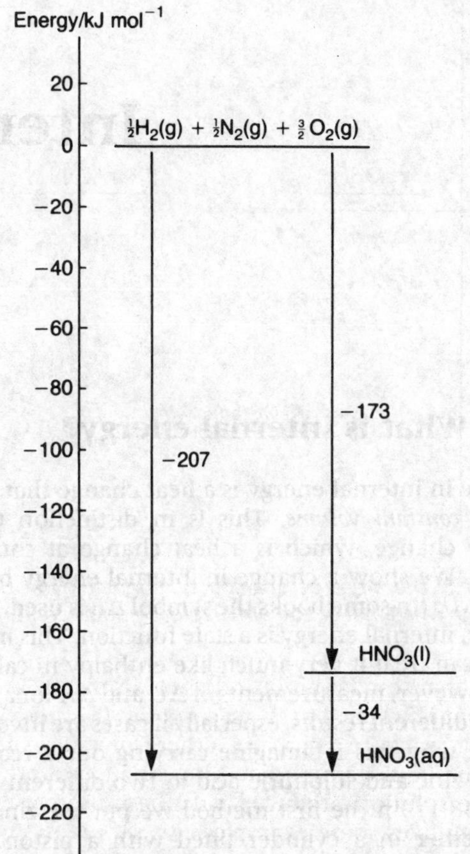

Figure 47.6 *The value of the enthalpy change for the formation of $HNO_3(aq)$ is −207 kJ mol⁻¹*

UNIT 47 SUMMARY

- The standard heat of neutralisation is:
  The enthalpy change that takes place when one mole of hydrogen ions from an acid is completely neutralised by an alkali to give an infinitely dilute solution.
- Hydration energy $\Delta H_h^\ominus$ is:
  The heat change that takes place when one mole of a gaseous ion dissolves in water to give an infinitely dilute solution.
- Heat of solution $\Delta H_{sol}^\ominus$ is:
  The enthalpy change when one mole of a substance dissolves in a solvent to give an infinitely dilute solution.

48

Internal energy

48.1 What is internal energy?

A change in internal energy is a heat change that takes place at *constant volume*. This is in distinction to an enthalpy change, which is a heat change at constant pressure. We show a change in internal energy by the symbol ΔU. (In some books the symbol ΔE is used.) Like enthalpy, internal energy is a state function. This means that we can treat it very much like enthalpy in calculations. However, measurements of ΔU and ΔH for a reaction give different results, especially if gases are involved.

To see why this is, imagine carrying out a reaction between zinc and sulphuric acid in two different ways (Figure 48.1). In the first method we put the zinc and acid together in a cylinder fitted with a piston. The hydrogen given off can push the piston out. When it does this it has to push the air out of the way. This needs energy because *the gas has to do work* in expanding against the air pressure. In the second case the reactants are mixed in a completely enclosed container. Here the volume of the container remains constant. Therefore the hydrogen given off has a constant volume; it does *not* do work like the hydrogen does in the first experiment.

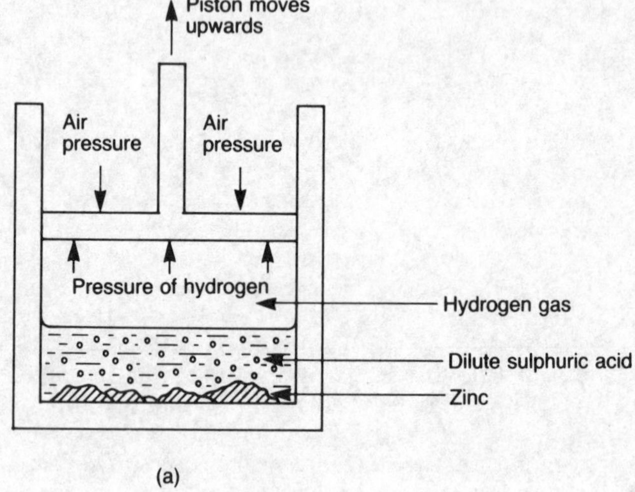

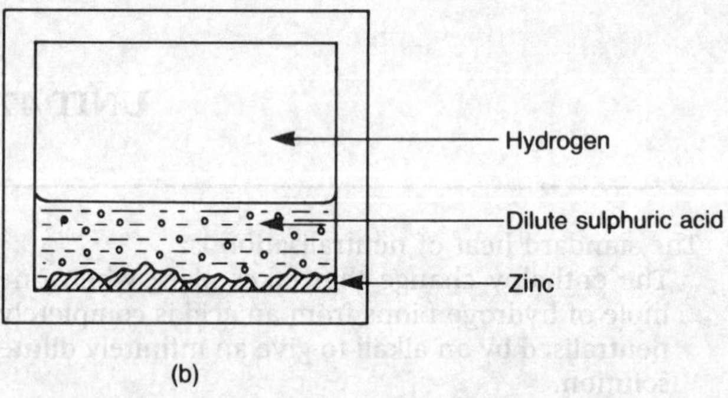

***Figure 48.1** (a) The hydrogen does work in pushing the piston outwards against atmospheric pressure. The volume of the gas changes. (b) The hydrogen given off here does not change its volume. It does not expand against atmospheric pressure, so no work is done*

48.2 Taking account of work

A gas that changes its volume by ΔV when it expands against a pressure p does an amount of work given by $p\Delta V$. The equation that relates ΔH, ΔU and $p\Delta V$ is

$$\Delta H = \Delta U + p\Delta V$$

We can put this in a rather different way by using the ideal gas equation, $pV = nRT$. Suppose we have a set of reactants that has a volume V_r. Then there will be a corresponding number of moles of gas, n_r. Similarly, if the products of the reaction have a volume V_p, then there will be n_p moles of product gas. We have two equations, one for the reactants and one for the products:

$$pV_r = n_rRT \quad \text{and} \quad pV_p = n_pRT$$

As usual we subtract the reactants from the products to give

$$p(V_p - V_r) = (n_p - n_r)RT$$

or,

$$p\Delta V = \Delta nRT$$

This gives us

$$\Delta H = \Delta U + \Delta nRT$$

Now let us see how this works out in an example.

For the reaction between zinc and sulphuric acid,

$$Zn(s) + H_2SO_4(aq) \rightarrow ZnSO_4(aq) + H_2(g); \quad \Delta H^{\ominus} = -151\ \text{kJ mol}^{-1}$$

So, given the enthalpy change, can we work out ΔU? If you look at the equation there is only one gas involved, namely the one mole of hydrogen that is a product of the reaction. This tells us that $\Delta n = 1$, so

$$-151\ \text{kJ mol}^{-1} = \Delta U + 1 \times RT$$

The value of the gas constant, R, is $8.314\ \text{J K}^{-1}\ \text{mol}^{-1}$, and, as usual, the temperature is taken as 298 K. Then,

$$-151\ \text{kJ mol}^{-1} = \Delta U + 1 \times 8.314\ \text{J K}^{-1}\ \text{mol}^{-1} \times 298\ \text{K}$$

Therefore, provided you spot that one of the terms has units of kJ mol^{-1}, and the other J mol^{-1}, we find

$$\Delta U = -151\ \text{kJ mol}^{-1} - 2.5\ \text{kJ mol}^{-1}$$
$$= -153.5\ \text{kJ mol}^{-1}$$

This result is sensible because, when the reaction is done at constant pressure, all the energy goes into increasing the internal energy of the system in the container. None of it is needed to do work. In the open container, some of the available energy is used in doing work by expanding the hydrogen against atmospheric pressure. (The work done is the 2.5 kJ mol^{-1}.)

There are one or two approximations that we have made here. The first is that we assumed that hydrogen behaves as an ideal gas. This is not a bad assumption unless very high pressures and temperatures are used. The second is that we have ignored changes in volumes of the liquids and solids present. For example, one mole of zinc 'disappears' during the reaction. However, this would give a change in volume of a matter of a few tens of cm^3, whereas the volume change produced by the release of one mole of hydrogen is over 22 000 cm^3. Changes in gas volumes far outweigh those for solids or liquids.

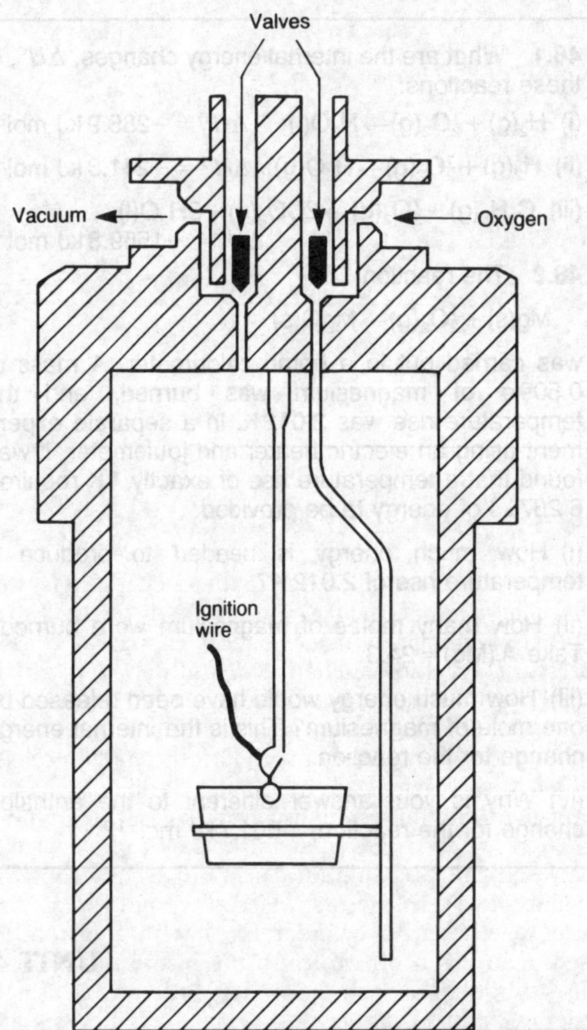

***Figure 48.2** A bomb calorimeter. In practice the calorimeter is immersed in an insulated water bath. Temperature sensors measure the change in temperature of the water. (Diagram taken from: Caldin, E. F. (1958).* Chemical Thermodynamics, *Oxford University Press, Oxford, figure 4(a), p. 43)*

48.3 Measuring internal energy with a bomb calorimeter

If we are to measure a change in internal energy we have to keep the volume of the apparatus constant. A device that does this is called a bomb calorimeter (Figure 48.2). The calorimeter is made of steel and is of great strength, so that it can withstand the vigour of the reactions that take place in it. It has found wide use in measuring heats of combustion. The substance to be burned is weighed and placed in a crucible. The calorimeter is filled with sufficient oxygen at high pressure to ensure the complete combustion of the sample, and the valves are closed to seal the contents from the outside. The calorimeter also contains a platinum wire that can be heated electrically. This is used to ignite the sample in the crucible. The temperature inside the bomb can be measured by electronic sensors.

When all is ready the bomb is immersed in a water bath, which is itself insulated from the surroundings. The temperature rise during the reaction can be measured very accurately, often to within $\pm 10^{-4}$ K. In order to calculate the heat exchange, the heat capacity of the bomb is found by an electrical method. For example, suppose that the temperature rise in a reaction was 1 K. After the reaction is over, the bomb is cooled to its starting temperature and an electric heater used to increase its temperature by 1 K. The energy needed to produce the 1 K temperature rise is easily found by connecting the heater to a joulemeter. The energy supplied is the change in internal energy. Finally the figure has to be scaled up to give ΔU in kJ mol^{-1}.

48.1 What are the internal energy changes, $\Delta U^{\ominus}$, in these reactions:

(i) $H_2(g) + \frac{1}{2}O_2(g) \rightarrow H_2O(l)$; $\Delta H_f^{\ominus} = -285.9\text{ kJ mol}^{-1}$

(ii) $H_2(g) + \frac{1}{2}O_2(g) \rightarrow H_2O(g)$; $\Delta H^{\ominus} = -241.8\text{ kJ mol}^{-1}$

(iii) $C_2H_6(g) + \frac{7}{2}O_2(g) \rightarrow 2CO_2(g) + 3H_2O(l)$; $\Delta H_c^{\ominus} = -1559.8\text{ kJ mol}^{-1}$

48.2 The reaction

$Mg(s) + \frac{1}{2}O_2(g) \rightarrow MgO(s)$

was carried out in a bomb calorimeter. A mass of 0.509 g of magnesium was burned, and the temperature rise was 2.012 K. In a separate experiment using an electric heater and joulemeter, it was found that a temperature rise of exactly 1 K required 6.267 kJ of energy to be provided.

(i) How much energy is needed to produce a temperature rise of 2.012 K?

(ii) How many moles of magnesium were burned? Take $A_r(Mg) = 24.3$.

(iii) How much energy would have been released by one mole of magnesium? This is the internal energy change for the reaction.

(iv) Why is your answer different to the enthalpy change for the reaction, $-601.7\text{ kJ mol}^{-1}$?

Answers

48.1 (i) In this reaction there are 1.5 mol of gas at the beginning, and none at the end. Therefore, $\Delta n = -1.5$. We have $-285.9\text{ kJ mol}^{-1} = \Delta U_f^{\ominus} - 1.5 \times 8.314\text{ J K}^{-1}\text{ mol}^{-1} \times 298\text{ K}$, which gives $\Delta U_f^{\ominus} = -282.2\text{ kJ mol}^{-1}$. In this case the atmosphere does work *on* the mixture because there is a contraction in volume. This represents an *input* of energy into the system, so the enthalpy change is greater than the internal energy change.

(ii) Here, $\Delta n = -0.5$, which leads to $\Delta U = -240.6\text{ kJ mol}^{-1}$.

(iii) This time, $\Delta n = 2 - (1 + \frac{7}{2}) = -2.5$. Therefore, $\Delta U_c^{\ominus} = -1553.6\text{kJ mol}^{-1}$.

48.2 (i) The energy required $= 6.267\text{ kJ} \times 2.012\text{ K}/1\text{ K} = 12.609\text{ kJ}$.

(ii) Number of moles $= 0.509\text{ g}/24.3\text{ g mol}^{-1}$
$= 0.021\text{ mol}$.

(iii) Energy released by one mole is $12.609\text{ kJ} \times 1\text{ mol}/0.021\text{ mol} = 600.43\text{ kJ}$, i.e. $\Delta U = 600.43\text{ kJ mol}^{-1}$.

(iv) During the reaction there is a change in the number of moles of gas (oxygen) of $\Delta n = -\frac{1}{2}$. This leads to the difference in ΔH and ΔU owing to the work done by expansion at constant pressure.

UNIT 48 SUMMARY

- A change in internal energy is a heat change that takes place at constant volume.
- Enthalpy and internal energy are related through the equation

$$\Delta H = \Delta U + \Delta nRT$$

- Internal energy changes are measured with a bomb calorimeter.

49

Entropy

49.1 A first look at entropy

Imagine that we have a sample of a gas trapped in a can at room temperature. Now suppose that we give the molecules of the gas a little extra energy (e.g. by briefly heating the can). On average the energy will cause the molecules:

(i) to move more quickly from one place to another, i.e. there is an increase in *translational* energy;
(ii) to rotate more rapidly, i.e. there is an increase in *rotational* energy;
(iii) to vibrate more violently, i.e. there is an increase in *vibrational* energy.

That is,

energy given to the molecules = increase in translational energy
+increase in rotational energy
+increase in vibrational energy

(Note: we shall ignore the electrons in the molecules, and their energy levels. The electrons will only change their energies if we give molecules a great deal of energy; see Unit 13. Likewise we shall ignore energy levels of the nucleons.)

It is most important that you realise that not every molecule gains the same amount of each of these energies. We say that there is a *spread* of translational, rotational and vibrational energies in a gas. Although we may know the total energy given to the gas, there are many different ways in which the energy can be arranged between the translational, vibrational and rotational energy levels. As the temperature increases, more molecules can reach the higher energy levels, so there is a larger number of arrangements at a higher temperature than there is at a lower temperature.

To see how the number of arrangements can change, let us imagine that we have a large number of molecules, but this time in a crystal. We shall label six of them A to F as in Figure 49.1 and assume that there is a set of vibrational energy levels available to them. (For simplicity we shall assume that the energy levels are evenly spaced.)

If the temperature is very low, the molecules will have the lowest possible energy, which we have shown as E_0 in Figure 49.2. The six dots on the line for E_0 represent this arrangement. Notice that there is only *one* way of organising the molecules if they all have energy E_0. If we give the molecules one extra unit of energy, then only one of the molecules can reach the next highest level, E_1. However, because there are six molecules, there are six ways of arranging them so that one has energy E_1 and five have energy E_0. If we give the molecules another unit of energy, the number of arrangements greatly increases. We could have one molecule with energy E_2, and the other five with E_0; as before, there are six ways of achieving this. Alternatively, two molecules could have energy E_1, with the other four with E_0. There are 15 ways of doing this, thus giving us 21 arrangements all together. You can see that as the total energy increases there is a rapid increase in the number of possible arrangements. (In this case from 1 to 21.) Each arrangement is called a *complexion*. Thus, at a higher temperature, there is a greater number of complexions than at a lower temperature.

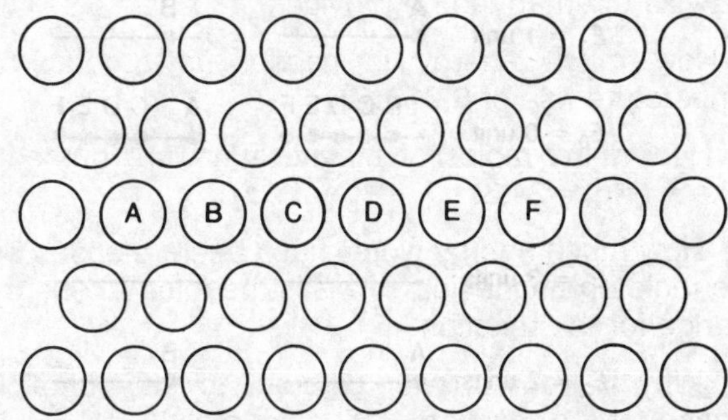

Figure 49.1 *Six of the molecules in a solid, labelled A to F. Even though the molecules are chemically the same, we can tell them apart owing to their different positions*

This brings us to *entropy*:

When the number of complexions increases, we say that entropy increases.

When the number of complexions decreases, we say that entropy decreases.

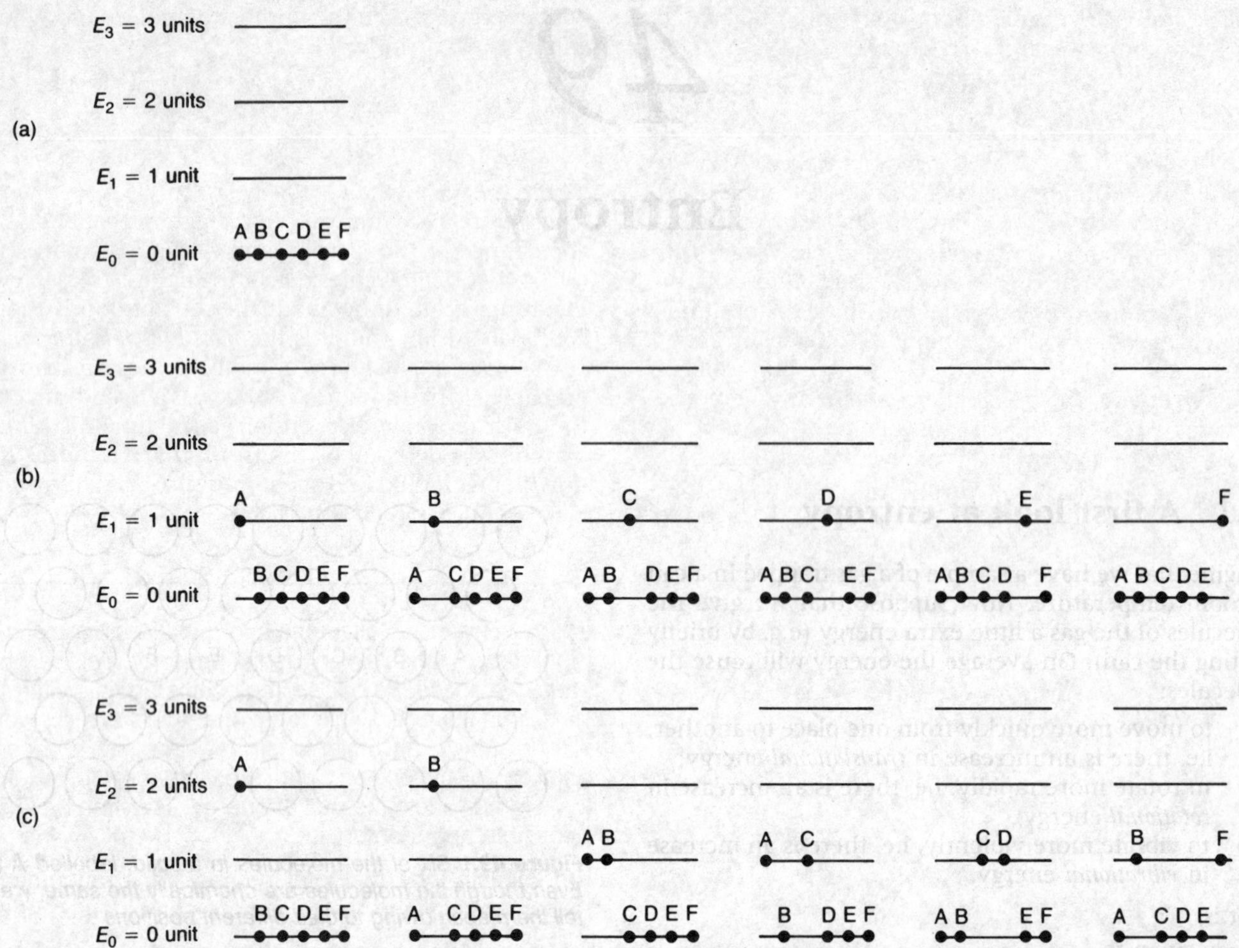

***Figure 49.2** Examples of how molecules can be arranged among energy levels. Each arrangement is called a complexion. (a) There is only one way of arranging the six molecules if they all have the lowest energy. (b) There are six ways of arranging the molecules if they have a total of 1 unit of energy. (c) Some of the 15 ways that the molecules can be arranged so that they have a total of 2 units of energy.*

The person who first made the connection between entropy and the number of complexions was Ludwig Boltzmann. In 1872 he proposed that it was possible to calculate the entropy, S, from the number of complexions, W, using the formula

$$S = k \ln W \qquad \text{Boltzmann's equation}$$

where k is Boltzmann's constant 1.38×10^{-23} J K^{-1}, and ln W means take the natural logarithm of the number of complexions.

In our example, the entropy of the collection of six molecules can be calculated as shown in Table 49.1. The values of the entropies are extremely small. One reason for this is that we are dealing with such a small number of molecules. Another reason is that we are only giving the molecules small amounts of energy. Suppose we had a mole of molecules, i.e. 6×10^{23} of them, with a million units of energy. Then we could have a million molecules with energy E_1, and the remainder with energy E_0. The number of ways of arranging the 6×10^{23} molecules is now very high, running into billions and billions. The entropy calculated from Boltzmann's formula is about 400 J K^{-1}. This would be only one contribution to the total entropy, because there would be many other arrangements of the molecules among the energy levels. Entropies calculated in this way are called *statistical entropies*.

Table 49.1. Arrangements of molecules among energy levels

Energy levels involved	*Number of complexions, W*	*Entropy, S = k ln W/J K^{-1}*
Only E_0	1	0*
E_0, E_1	6	2.47×10^{-23}
E_0, E_1, E_2	21	4.20×10^{-23}

*Note: ln 1 = 0

To summarise our ideas on entropy this far, we can say that entropy is a measure of the number of ways that energy can be shared out among molecules. The greater the number of ways (complexions), the greater is the entropy, and vice versa. The entropy can be calculated from Boltzmann's formula $S = k\ln W$.

49.2 The Boltzmann distribution

Given enough time and ingenuity we could draw diagrams for each of the complexions for a system of molecules with a given total energy. However, this would not itself tell us the actual distribution of the molecules among the energy levels, Some distributions we would guess to be rather unlikely. Think again about a mole of molecules with a total of one million units of energy. We would expect the arrangement where one molecule had all the million units of energy and the rest had none to be extremely unlikely. We would expect (correctly) that the energy would be shared out in a more even way. Fortunately, the puzzle of discovering the most probable distribution has been solved. It is known as the Maxwell–Boltzmann distribution. In symbols the distribution says that if there are N_A molecules with energy E_A, then the number of molecules, N_B, with energy E_B is given by:

$N_B = N_A\exp(-\Delta E/kT)$	**Maxwell–Boltzmann distribution**

where $\Delta E = E_B - E_A$.

In Figure 49.3 you can see a diagram that shows the appearance of the distribution. As you would expect, relatively few molecules reach the highest energy levels. The remarkable thing about the distribution is that, as we have already said, it is the *most probable distribution*.

When a group of atoms or molecules reaches the most probable distribution, their entropy is a maximum. Also, the most probable distribution is the final distribution that the system reaches. This means that it is the distribution that we would find at equilibrium, i.e. when there is no overall change in the system.

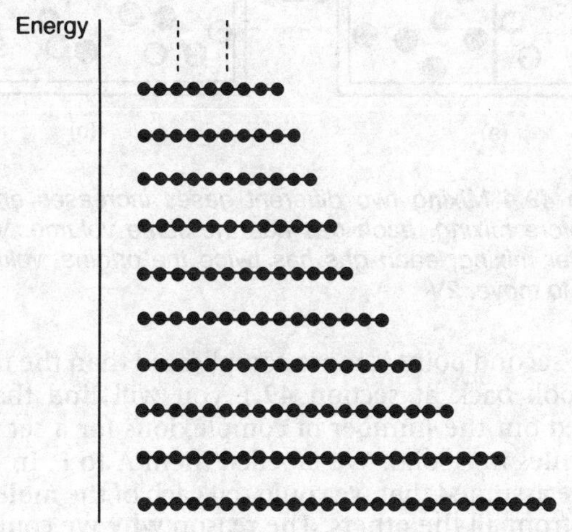

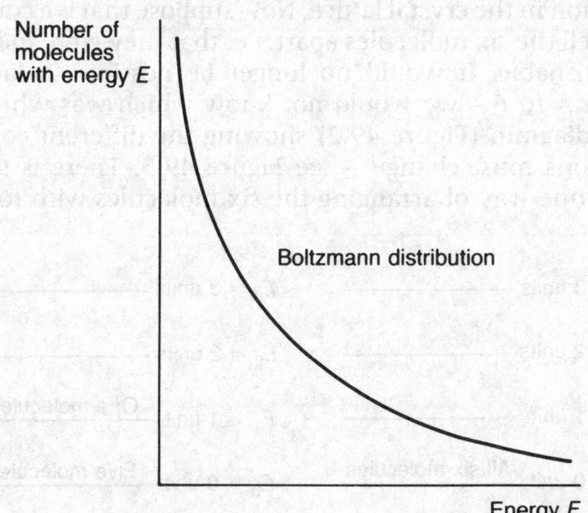

***Figure 49.3** Two ways of looking at the Boltzmann distribution, which is the most probable distribution of atoms or molecules among a set of energy levels*

49.1 Because Boltzmann's formula for entropy uses logarithms, it has a very useful property. To see what it is, we shall take our six molecules again. With one extra unit of energy we know that there are six ways of arranging the molecules. Now imagine a second set of six molecules, with the same set of energy levels and one extra unit of energy. They too have six possible arrangements.

(i) Explain why the total number of arrangements when both sets of molecules are combined is 36.

(ii) Calculate the entropy of the combination.

(iii) Compare your value with that in Table 49.2 for one set of six molecules.

49.2 This question is about the Boltzmann distribution.

Hydrogen chloride has a strong vibration at a frequency of $8652 \times 10^{10}\,s^{-1}$.

(i) Use Planck's equation to calculate the energy gap between the two vibrational energy levels involved. This gives you the value of ΔE in the equation for the Maxwell–Boltzmann distribution.

(ii) What is the value of kT at 298 K?

(iii) Now assume that there are 10^6 molecules in the lower of the two vibrational levels. How many molecules would there be in the higher level?

(iv) Would you expect your answer to be absolutely accurate?

49.3 More about energy levels

We have said that gas molecules have translational, rotational and vibrational energy levels available to them. However, in a solid the molecules are held at particular places in the crystal lattice; they are not free to move about like the molecules in a gas. Neither are they able to rotate freely like gas molecules. Therefore, if we give energy to a solid, the majority of it must go to increasing the vibrations of the molecules in the lattice. By this we mean that the molecules as a whole move about more violently, and that the atoms *in* the molecules vibrate more energetically. The key point to understand is that, compared to a gas, the molecules in a solid have far fewer energy levels available to them. Therefore the number of complexions for a solid is much smaller than that for a gas; and as a result the entropy that we would calculate from Boltzmann's formula would be far less for a solid than for a gas. As you might expect, the entropy of a liquid would be somewhere between that of a gas and a solid.

We now have the pattern of Table 49.2. Please be aware that in drawing up Table 49.2 we are speaking in qualitative terms, and we are not trying to be precise. For example, the number of complexions changes with the number of molecules involved, so it could be that a large amount of a solid might have a higher entropy at room temperature than a much smaller amount of a gas. Similarly, vibrational and rotational energy levels change with the nature of the molecules involved. For example, a gas composed of linear molecules, e.g. CO_2, has fewer vibrational and rotational energy levels available than does a gas of non-linear molecules, e.g. NH_3.

Table 49.2. Comparison of entropies

State	*Number of complexions*	*Entropy*
Solid	Small	Small
Liquid	Medium	Medium
Gas	High	High

49.3 Explain why 'the entropy of a liquid would be somewhere between that of a gas and a solid'.

49.4 Entropy changes and mixing of gases

Now we come to two tricky points about gases, both of which are to do with quantum theory.

Starting with Schrödinger's equation, it can be shown that the translational energy levels available to a gas depend on the volume of the gas. The spacing of the energy levels decreases as the volume increases, and the smaller the gaps between the levels, the easier it is for molecules to occupy them. Let us use some round numbers to illustrate this. Suppose a molecule can have, at most, 100 units of energy. If the gap between levels is 20 units, and the lowest level is at 0 units, then there are six levels (0, 20, 40, 60, 80 and 100) that the molecule can occupy. If, on the other hand, the gap between levels is 5 units, there are now 21 levels that can be occupied. Thus there is a larger number of accessible levels in a large volume, and a smaller number in a small volume. In turn this tells us that *the number of complexions increases if the volume of a gas increases*, and vice versa. Given the link between entropy and the number of complexions expressed in Boltzmann's equation, we can now say that:

An increase in volume of a gas brings with it an increase in entropy.

It is interesting to see what happens if we mix two different gases as shown in Figure 49.4. When the gases are mixed, each has a larger volume to occupy than when it was separate. It is for this reason that the entropy of the mixture is greater than that of the two separate gases.

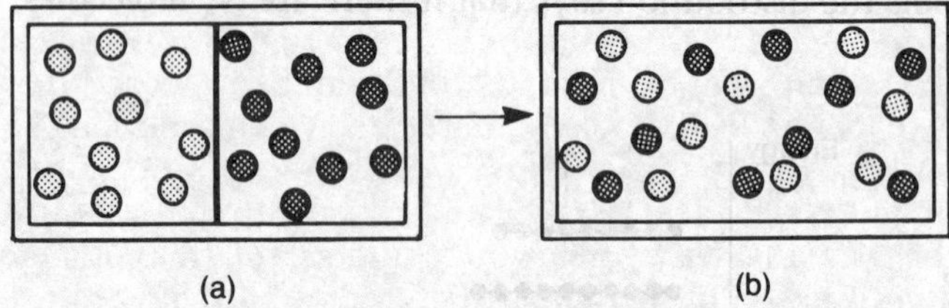

Figure 49.4 *Mixing two different gases increases entropy. (a) Before mixing, each gas has the same volume, V, say. (b) After mixing, each gas has twice the original volume in which to move, 2V*

The second point is more complicated than the first. If you look back at section 49.1 you will find that we worked out the number of complexions for a set of six molecules in a solid. We labelled them A to F. In doing this we assumed that we could tell each of the molecules apart from all the others. The reason why we could distinguish them is that each one had a fixed, identifiable, position in the crystal lattice. Now suppose that we could not tell the six molecules apart, i.e. that they were indistinguishable. It would no longer be possible to label them A to F – we would not know which was which. Our diagram (Figure 49.2) showing the different complexions must change – see Figure 49.5. There is still only one way of arranging the six molecules with total

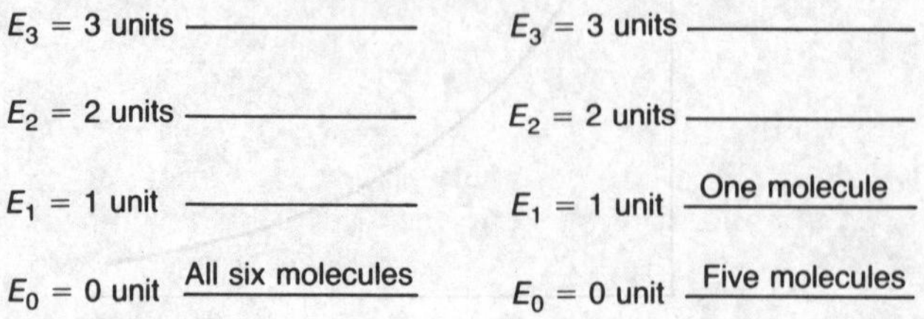

Figure 49.5 *When the six molecules are indistinguishable, there is still only one way they can have the lowest energy. But there is now only one way in which they can have 1 unit of energy*

energy E_0; but there is also only one way in which we can assign the molecules one unit of energy, E_1. Given that the molecules are indistinguishable, it does not matter which molecule has energy E_1, and which have E_0. (Indeed, from a scientific point of view it does not make sense even to ask 'which one has energy E_1?' We have no means of answering the question.) In short, the number of complexions for indistinguishable molecules is markedly different to the number for distinguishable molecules.

This brings us to our key point:

According to quantum theory the molecules in a pure gas are indistinguishable.

For example, according to quantum theory it does not make sense to regard one hydrogen molecule in hydrogen gas as being different *in any way* to another hydrogen molecule. One effect of indistinguishability is that if we mixed two samples of the *same* gas we would find that there is *no change* in entropy. Even though it is correct, this result can be hard to understand. In part, the explanation lies in looking more deeply at our notion of 'mixing'. Given that molecules of the same gas are indistinguishable it does not really make sense to speak about them mixing. It may help you to understand this point if you think about the opposite process: unmixing. If the molecules are different, then we could unmix them, for example by making use of their unequal rates of diffusion. However, we *cannot* unmix molecules of the same gas.

It is possible to distinguish the molecules of a pure substance in a solid because each of them has a unique position in the lattice. The distinguishability of molecules in a liquid is somewhere between that of gases and solids.

These are deep matters, and mysterious in their way, as are any of the other results of quantum theory, such as wavefunctions or electron spins. We shall not pursue the matter further here, but if you study physics or chemistry further you will find out more about such puzzles in books about statistical thermodynamics.

49.4 We have said that there is an increase in entropy when gases mix. There is also a change when a gas expands. For n moles of a perfect gas that expands from a volume V_1 to V_2 at a constant temperature, the change in entropy is

$$\Delta S = nR\ln(V_2/V_1)$$

where R is the gas constant (8.314 J K^{-1} mol^{-1}).

What is the entropy change when the volume of 1 mol of a perfect gas changes from 1 dm^3 to 100 dm^3?

49.5 Entropy and disorder

Water can exist in two different states: solid (ice) and liquid. We know that ice is held together by hydrogen bonds between the water molecules (Figure 49.6a) and that the large amount of hydrogen bonding in (liquid)

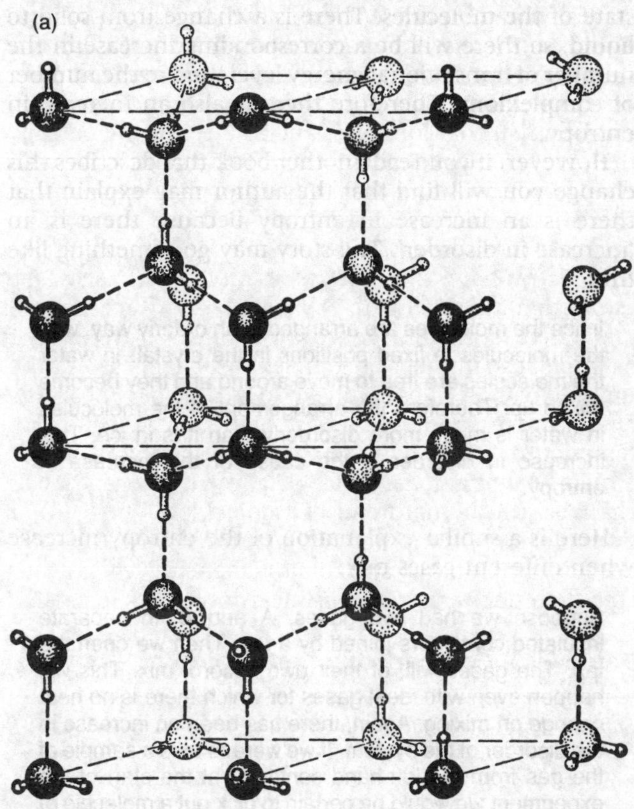

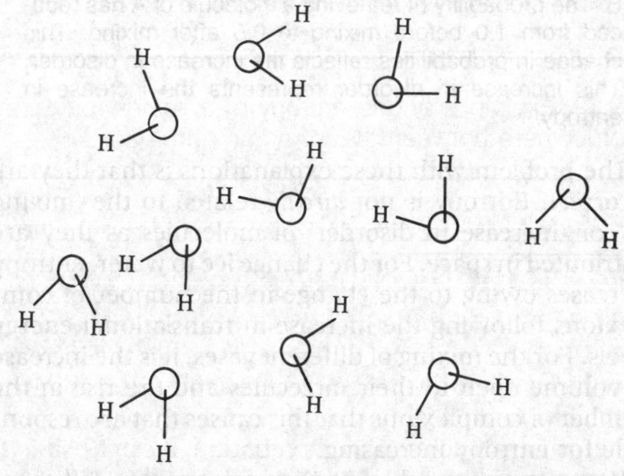

Figure 49.6 (a) How water molecules are arranged in ice. Notice the large amount of empty space in the structure – hence the lower density of ice compared to water. (Diagram taken from: Pauling, L. (1960). The Nature of the Chemical Bond, *3rd edn, Cornell University Press, New York, p. 465, figure 12.6). (b) In liquid water the molecules are no longer held so tightly in position. There is a large number of new translational energy levels open to them. Hence the change ice→water gives an increase in entropy*

water is responsible for its high boiling point. If we heat a cube of ice at 0° C the structure of the solid is disrupted. The ice melts (Figure 49.6b); but if the heat is supplied very slowly the temperature does not change. The water remains at 0° C. We know that some hydrogen bonds have been broken in this process, and that new ones will have been made. However, the main change is in the state of the molecules. There is a change from solid to liquid, so there will be a corresponding increase in the number of translational energy levels and in the number of complexions. Therefore there is also an increase in entropy.

However, if you read another book that describes this change you will find that the author may explain that there is an increase in entropy because there is an 'increase in disorder'. The story may go something like this:

In ice the molecules are arranged in an orderly way, with the molecules in fixed positions in the crystal. In water the molecules are free to move around and they become mixed up. Therefore the arrangement of the molecules in water is much more disorderly than it is in ice. This increase in disorder is the cause of the increase in entropy.

Here is a similar explanation of the entropy increase when different gases mix:

Suppose we had two gases, A and B, in separate insulated containers joined by a tap. Then we open the tap. The gases will, of their own accord, mix. This will happen even with ideal gases for which there is no heat change on mixing. Again, there has been an increase in the disorder of the system. If we were to take a sample of the gas from the left-hand container at the start of the experiment we would be certain to pick out a molecule of A. After the mixing, on average, we would have equal chances of picking out a molecule of A *or* a molecule of B. The probability of retrieving a molecule of A has reduced from 1.0 before mixing to 0.5 after mixing. This change in probabilities reflects the increase in disorder. This increase in disorder represents the increase in entropy.

The problem with these explanations is that they are incorrect. Entropy is not *directly* related to the 'mixing up' or 'increase in disorder' of molecules as they are distributed in space. For the change ice to water, entropy increases owing to the change in the number of complexions following the increase in translational energy levels. For the mixing of different gases, it is the increase in volume open to their molecules and the rise in the number of complexions that this causes that are responsible for entropy increasing.

However, from Table 49.2 we can see that (all other things being equal) if there is a change solid to liquid, or liquid to gas, there *will* be an increase in entropy. The important point to realise is that it is not sensible to explain these changes in terms of the 'order' and 'disorder' of arrangements of molecules in space. It is the change in the number of complexions that we must consider to explain changes in entropy. To calculate the precise change in the number of complexions is not an easy task, and one that we shall not attempt. Instead we shall use a rule of thumb method to help us to predict whether entropy increases or decreases in a chemical change. The rule is outlined in Table 49.3.

Now consider two examples.

Table 49.3. Rules of thumb for predicting entropy changes*

Change	*Entropy change*
Solid to liquid	Increase
Solid to gas	Increase
Liquid to gas	Increase
Liquid to solid	Decrease
Gas to solid	Decrease
Gas to liquid	Decrease

*See text for a discussion of these 'rules'

Example 1

How will the entropy of the reactants and products compare in the change $2Na(s) + Cl_2(g) \rightarrow 2NaCl(s)$?

Here we can see that we start with a solid and gas, and finish with a solid. Owing to the loss of the translational and rotational energy levels available to the chlorine gas, there is likely to be a decrease in entropy. That is, the combination of solid plus gas should have more entropy than a solid only. Calculation shows that this is in fact the case. However, be aware that we have neglected many factors; for example, we do not know how the vibrational energy levels of sodium, chlorine and sodium chloride compare.

Example 2

How will the entropy of the reactants and products compare in the change $H_2(g) + Cl_2(g) \rightarrow 2HCl(g)$?

Here we start with two moles of gas, and finish with two moles of gas. Considering just translational energy levels, we might expect there to be little or no change in entropy. We are not in a position to say what happens to vibrational or rotational energy levels, so we must content ourselves with predicting that the entropy change in the reaction could be very small. Calculation shows that, under standard conditions, there is a small decrease in entropy (about $10\,J\,K^{-1}\,mol^{-1}$.

49.5 In which of these changes would you expect the entropy of the system to increase?

(i) $H_2O(l) \rightarrow H_2O(g)$

(ii) $H_2(g) + \frac{1}{2}O_2(g) \rightarrow H_2O(l)$

(iii) $Mg(s) + 2HCl(aq) \rightarrow MgCl_2(aq) + H_2(g)$

(iv) Haemoglobin(aq) + $O_2(g)$ → Oxyhaemoglobin(aq)

49.6 Reversible and irreversible changes

If you have studied chemistry before you are likely to have met a number of reactions that are called 'reversible' reactions. An example is the reaction of nitrogen and hydrogen to give ammonia:

$$N_2(g) + 3H_2(g) \rightleftharpoons 2NH_3(g)$$

The symbol $\rightleftharpoons$ means that the reaction can go both ways; the ammonia can react back to give nitrogen and hydrogen. In thermodynamics we use the word 'reversible' in rather a different way to this. Here it tells us something about the *way* in which a reaction (or any change) is carried out. For example, we have already said that the change ice to water is very common. In one sense the change is reversible because the ice can change to water, and vice versa. Now let us think about the way that the change might take place.

We could place ice in a beaker and put it over a bunsen flame; very soon liquid water would appear. Compare this with putting the ice in an insulated flask that has a tiny electric heater in it, together with an equally small cooling unit (Figure 49.7). If we connected the heater to a battery through a variable resistance, we could arrange that a current as low as a few millionths of an amp could flow into the heater. This would melt an absolutely tiny amount of ice. Likewise, we could use the cooling circuit for a fleeting instant to withdraw the tiny amount of heat supplied. In this case the change of ice into water, and water into ice, would have been carried out almost perfectly reversibly in the thermodynamic sense. In a perfectly reversible change the ice and water, and their immediate surroundings, would have been returned to their initial states without any change in the rest of the universe. With the beaker of ice over a bunsen, a large change would take place in the surroundings. A significant amount of energy would have been given off by the bunsen, much of which would escape into the atmosphere. Also, there would be no guarantee that the water in the beaker stayed at 0° C while the ice was melting. Here the ice, water and surroundings could only be brought back to their initial states by causing some other change in the surroundings, e.g. by doing work running a refrigerator to refreeze the water.

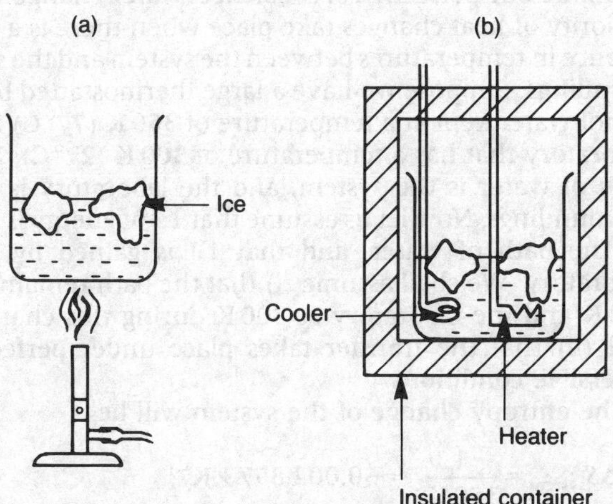

***Figure 49.7** (a) The first method of changing between ice and water is not reversible (in the thermodynamic sense). (b) In the second diagram, the change can be done in a way that is almost perfectly reversible*

In the second case, the change takes place in such a way that the changes in the ice, water and surroundings are extremely small. We could also guarantee that the water from the ice remained at 0° C. This change is much closer to being reversible in the thermodynamic sense.

Here are the two senses of 'reversible':

***Ordinary sense of 'reversible'*: a reaction that can 'go both ways'.**

***Thermodynamic sense of 'reversible'*: a change that takes place in a system and its surroundings so that there is no observable change in the universe.**

For the rest of this unit we shall use the term 'perfectly reversible' to mean a reversible change in the thermodynamic sense. See p. 287 about 'the universe'.

49.7 Some changes are spontaneous, some are not

Changes that take place of their own accord are called *spontaneous changes*. Examples are water evaporating from a puddle, oxygen molecules bonding to the haemoglobin in our blood, and a gas expanding from a region of high to a region of low pressure. You should realise that spontaneous changes like these do not take place under reversible conditions.

Some changes only occur if we *do work* to make them happen. These changes are *not spontaneous*. Examples are a gas at atmospheric pressure liquefying above its normal boiling point, magnesium oxide at room temperature and pressure splitting into magnesium metal and oxygen gas. To understand these points you should appreciate that, in thermodynamics, work is any energy change that is not a heat change. In this sense, we use a battery to do electrical work in pushing a current through the bulb to make it light up, we have to do work in compressing a gas to make it liquefy, and so on.

Spontaneous changes take place without the need to do work.

Non-spontaneous changes only take place when work is done.

One thing that can be confusing about the way we talk about spontaneous changes is that some of them take place only very slowly. For example, coal burning is a spontaneous change. However, at room temperature this change takes place infinitely slowly. To make the reaction go faster we have to ignite the coal. This is not a matter of thermodynamics, but one of kinetics (rates of reactions; see Units 77–79). Many reactions like this are *kinetically* very slow, but we still call them spontaneous reactions.

Thermodynamics is not at all concerned with how fast reactions take place.

49.6 Which of the following are spontaneous changes?

(i) A ball rolling downhill.

(ii) A mixture of nitrogen and oxygen gases changing into separate samples of the two gases.

(iii) Instant coffee granules dissolving in water.

(iv) Petrol burning.

49.8 Entropy and reversible changes

We use the symbol S to stand for entropy and ΔS for a change in entropy. If there is a perfectly reversible change that takes place at a temperature T (measured in kelvins, K), and the heat change is $\Delta H_{\text{reversible}}$, the entropy change in the system is given by

$$\Delta S_{\text{system}} = \frac{\Delta H_{\text{reversible}}}{T}$$

For the change ice → water, $\Delta H_{\text{reversible}} = +6.01\ \text{kJ mol}^{-1}$. This change takes place at 273 K. If the ice melts to water in a reversible way the entropy change within the system is

$$\Delta S_{\text{system}} = \frac{+6.01\ \text{kJ mol}^{-1}}{273\ \text{K}} = +22.0\ \text{J K}^{-1}\ \text{mol}^{-1}$$

Note that the units of entropy change are $\text{J K}^{-1}\ \text{mol}^{-1}$, and that these are *not* the same as enthalpy (which is measured in kJ mol^{-1}).

Now, the heat required to melt the ice must come from somewhere, and in this case we shall simply say that it has come from the surroundings. If the ice/water system has gained 6.01 kJ for each mole of ice converted to water, then the surroundings must have lost 6.01 kJ mol^{-1}. For the surroundings, $\Delta H_{\text{reversible}} = -6.01\ \text{kJ mol}^{-1}$. In our carefully controlled reversible process, the surroundings remain at 273 K as well as the ice and water, so

$$\Delta S_{\text{surroundings}} = \frac{-6.01\ \text{kJ mol}^{-1}}{273\ \text{K}} = -22.0\ \text{J K}^{-1}\ \text{mol}^{-1}$$

For any *reversible* change, not just this one, it is found that:

$$\Delta S_{\text{system}} + \Delta S_{\text{surroundings}} = 0 \qquad \text{(reversible change)}$$

49.7 A change from solid to liquid, or liquid to gas, is called a *change of phase*. If we write the enthalpy change as ΔH_{phase}, then the corresponding entropy change is

$$\Delta S_{\text{phase}} = \frac{\Delta H_{\text{phase}}}{T}$$

The enthalpy change on fusion of mercury is $2.31\ \text{kJ mol}^{-1}$. Fusion is another name for melting. Mercury melts at 234.3 K. What is the entropy change if it melts reversibly?

49.9 Entropy and non-reversible changes

It can be helpful to think about the connection between the heat and entropy changes in a spontaneous change. We know that for a perfectly reversible change $\Delta S_{\text{system}} = \Delta H_{\text{reversible}}/T$. This equation could be written in another way as

$$\Delta S_{\text{reversible}} = \frac{\text{heat change at temperature } T}{T}$$

Unlike our perfectly reversible ice–water change, the majority of heat changes take place when there is a difference in temperatures between the system and the surroundings. Suppose we have a large thermostatted bath of hot water kept at a temperature of 350 K (77°C) in a laboratory that has a temperature of 300 K (27°C). The bath of water is the system, and the laboratory is the surroundings. Now let us assume that 1 J of energy is lost by the bath of water, and that 1 J is gained by the laboratory. We shall assume (i) that the bath remains at 350 K and the laboratory at 300 K during this change, and (ii) that the transfer takes place under perfectly reversible conditions.

The entropy change of the system will be

$$\Delta S_{\text{system}} = \frac{-1\ \text{J}}{350\ \text{K}} \approx -0.002\,857\ \text{J K}^{-1}$$

and of the surroundings will be

$$\Delta S_{\text{surroundings}} = \frac{+1\ \text{J}}{300\ \text{K}} \approx 0.003\,333\ \text{J K}^{-1}$$

There is a negative sign in the formula for ΔS_{system} because the system has *lost* 1 J of energy.

The total entropy change is

$$\Delta S_{\text{system}} + \Delta S_{\text{surroundings}}$$
$$\approx -0.002\,857\ \text{J K}^{-1} + 0.003\,333\ \text{J K}^{-1}$$
$$\approx +0.000\,476\ \text{J K}^{-1}$$

This is one particular example of a general rule. In a spontaneous (non-reversible) change, the total entropy change is always greater than zero. It is always found that:

$$\Delta S_{\text{system}} + \Delta S_{\text{surroundings}} > 0 \quad \text{(non-reversible change)}$$

By way of shorthand we shall call the combination of the system and surroundings 'the universe'. This is not the same universe as astronomers might think of. For example, in the case of ice melting in a laboratory, for all practical purposes the universe will be the laboratory, and its immediate surroundings. Thus we can say that

$$\Delta S_{\text{universe}} > 0 \qquad \text{(non-reversible change)}$$

This result cannot be proved; rather it is a statement of experience. Every non-reversible change that has been investigated shows that the total entropy of the universe is greater after a non-reversible change than it was before the change.

Left to themselves, changes do not occur reversibly, so:

Spontaneous changes always occur with an increase of entropy of the universe.

The next few examples might help to convince you of this.

Example 3

The equation for the reaction of magnesium burning in oxygen is

$$\text{Mg(s)} + \tfrac{1}{2}\text{O}_2\text{(g)} \rightarrow \text{MgO(s)}$$

If we think about the entropy changes in this reaction, it is natural first to consider the system, i.e. the magnesium and oxygen changing into magnesium oxide. This represents a change of a solid plus gas into a solid. The disappearance of the gas should lead us to expect a considerable decrease in the entropy of the system. (Later, we shall be able to show this to be true by calculation.) However, if we now turn our attention to the surroundings, a huge amount of energy has been released. If you have seen magnesium burning you will know that some of this energy goes into light, and much into heat. The heat produces more rapid random motion of the molecules of air in the atmosphere and an increase in the number of complexions. This increase in entropy of the surroundings overcomes the decrease in entropy of the system (Figure 49.8).

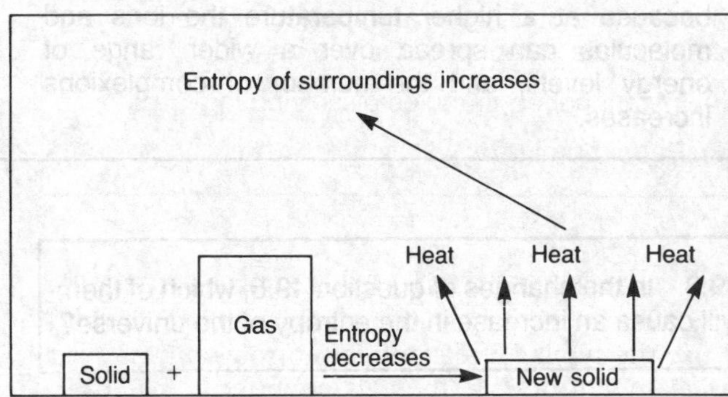

***Figure 49.8** Even though a reaction may appear to produce a decrease in entropy, overall entropy will increase. Often the increase is caused by heat being given off*

Example 4

When a solution of, say, salt in water becomes saturated, a slight loss of water causes crystallisation to occur. Here we are making a solid from a solution, and therefore decreasing the number of complexions owing to the loss of rotational and translational energy levels available to the molecules. However, let us look a little more closely at the system.

First, not all the water molecules in salt water are completely free to move. The ions are surrounded by their hydration spheres of water molecules (see Unit 60). Although the ions themselves can no longer move about so freely when they take up their positions in the crystals, the water molecules released from the hydration spheres become more able to move about (Figure 49.9). Thus there is a decrease in the number of complexions open to the ions, but an increase on the part of the water molecules in the hydration spheres.

Secondly, when solids crystallise from a solution there is a heat change; it is an *exothermic* process. Thus, when the salt crystallises the system is

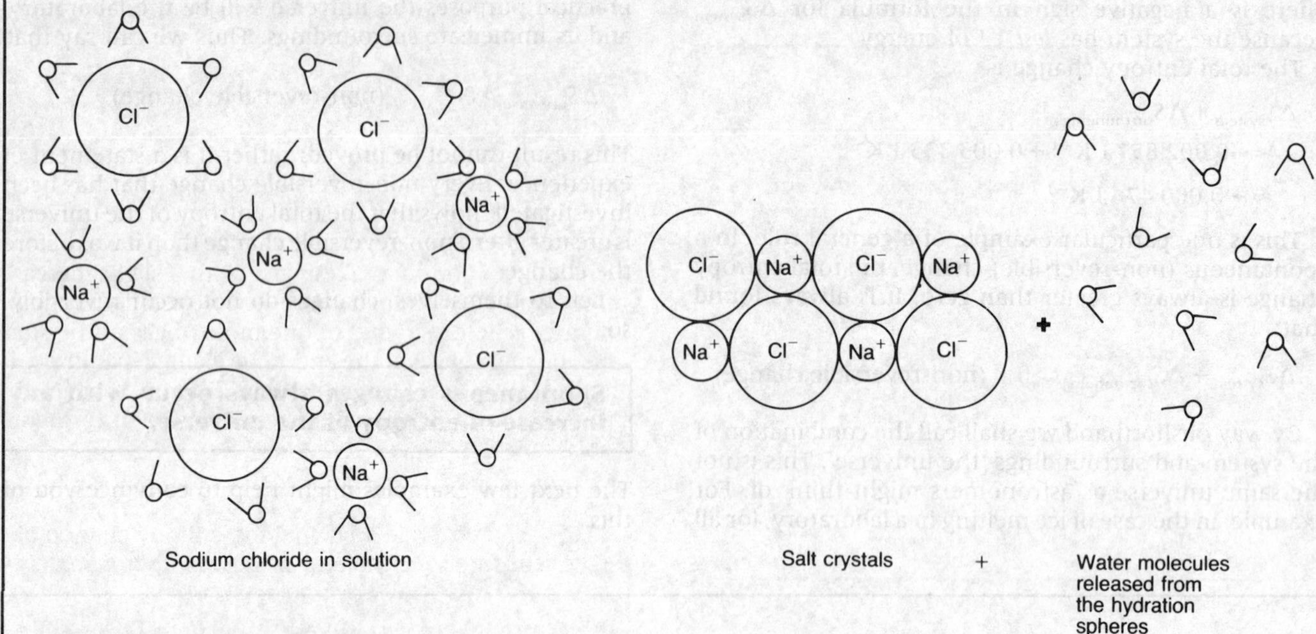

***Figure 49.9** Crystals made in a solution give the impression of entropy decreasing. However, water molecules lost from the hydration spheres provide an increase in entropy. Also, crystallisation usually gives out heat, which tends to increase entropy*

heated, and so are the surroundings. The increase in heat energy brings about an increase in entropy, because at a higher temperature the ions and molecules can spread over a wider range of energy levels, and the number of complexions increases.

Thus we have one major source of entropy decreasing (ions in solution forming crystals), and two sources of entropy increasing (liberation of water molecules in hydration spheres, rise in temperature). When the sums are done, it is found that there is a greater increase than decrease.

49.8 In the changes of question 49.5, which of them will cause an increase in the entropy of the universe?

49.10 Standard entropies

We have seen that the entropy of a solid is less than that of a liquid or gas, and that the number of complexions increases as temperature increases. This suggests that, if we want to reduce the entropy of a substance to a minimum, we should first make sure it is a solid, and then that it is at as low a temperature as possible. The lowest temperature possible is absolute zero, 0 K. So if we had a perfect crystal at 0 K we would expect it to have the lowest entropy possible. In fact, we say that:

The entropy of a perfect crystal at 0 K is zero.

This statement is called the *third law of thermodynamics*.

For example, perfect crystals of hydrogen, of sodium, or of iron are all assumed to have zero entropy at 0 K. Our zero level of entropy is quite unlike the definition of zero levels of enthalpy. For example, the enthalpies of formation of these elements are zero at 298 K and 101.325 kPa.

Actually it is impossible to measure entropy changes right down to 0 K because absolute zero cannot be reached. However, we can get to within a few hundredths of a degree of absolute zero. Another difficulty is that perfect crystals are hard to come by. Perfect means just that: no defects in the arrangements of the atoms, no mixtures of isotopes of any of the atoms, and so on. The entropy of a substance at temperatures just above 0 K can be measured. Estimates are made for the temperatures very close to 0 K. The measurements need not concern us; we can concentrate on the results. They are given the symbol $S^{\ominus}$, and are known as standard entropies. (They can also be called third law entropies.) Some standard entropies are given in Table 49.4.

The figures show that, as we would expect, the entropies of gases tend to be greater than those of liquids, which in turn are greater than those of solids. There are other factors at work though. One is that, if you compare solids, the standard entropy increases as the mass of the substance increases. This is because of the energy contribution to entropy. Heavier atoms, ions, or molecules usually have a greater number of energy levels available to them. Therefore a greater number of complexions can occur; hence entropy increases. Other complications

Table 49.4. Some values of standard entropies, $S^\ominus$

Substance	$S^\ominus$ /J K^{-1} mol^{-1}	*Substance*	$S^\ominus$ /J K^{-1} mol^{-1}
$H_2(g)$	+130.6	C(s) (graphite)	+5.7
$N_2(g)$	+191.4	S(s) (rhombic)	+31.9
$O_2(g)$	+204.9	Na(s)	+51.0
$Cl_2(g)$	+223.0	Zn(s)	+41.4
$I_2(s)$	+116.1	Cu(s)	+33.3
$H_2O(l)$	+70.0	NaCl(s)	+72.4
$H_2O(g)$	+188.7	MgO(s)	+26.8
$CO_2(g)$	+213.6	$CuSO_4{\cdot}5H_2O(s)$	+305.4
NO(g)	+210.5	$Fe_3O_4(s)$	+146.4
$C_6H_6(l)$	+172.8	$C_2H_5OH(l)$	+160.7
$CH_4(g)$	+186.2	$CH_3COOH(l)$	+159.8
$C_2H_4(g)$	+219.5	$CHCl_3(l)$	+201.8
$H^+(aq)$	0.0	$Cl^-(aq)$	+56.5
$Cu^{2+}(aq)$	−98.6	$Br^-(aq)$	+82.4
$Zn^{2+}(aq)$	−106.4	$SO_4^{2-}(aq)$	+20.1

appear when there are different types of bonding. Especially, liquids that are hydrogen bonded tend to have lower entropies than similar liquids that have no hydrogen bonding. (You can think of the hydrogen bonds restricting the motion of the molecules.)

The entropies of ions in solution are calculated using the same convention as for the enthalpy of formation of ions in solution. We *define* the standard entropy of a hydrogen ion in solution as zero, just as we define its enthalpy of formation as zero.

49.11 Calculating entropy changes

Entropy changes can be calculated in much the same way as enthalpy changes. For example, in the reaction

$$H_2(g) + \tfrac{1}{2}O_2(g) \rightarrow H_2O(l)$$

the entropy change is

$$S^\ominus_{\text{Products}} - S^\ominus_{\text{Reactants}}$$
$$= S^\ominus(H_2O(l)) - S^\ominus(H_2(g)) - \tfrac{1}{2}S^\ominus(O_2(g))$$
$$= +70.0 - 130.6 - \tfrac{1}{2}(204.9)\ \text{J K}^{-1}\ \text{mol}^{-1}$$
$$= -102.45\ \text{J K}^{-1}\ \text{mol}^{-1}$$

Notice that the entropy change is negative, which we should expect given that a liquid is made from two gases. Now look at this reaction:

$$\tfrac{1}{2}N_2(g) + \tfrac{1}{2}O_2(g) \rightarrow NO(g)$$

Entropy change is

$$S^\ominus(NO(g)) - \tfrac{1}{2}S^\ominus(N_2(g)) - \tfrac{1}{2}S^\ominus(O_2(g))$$
$$= +210.5 - \tfrac{1}{2}(191.4) - \tfrac{1}{2}(204.9)\ \text{J K}^{-1}\ \text{mol}^{-1}$$
$$= +12.35\ \text{J K}^{-1}\ \text{mol}^{-1}$$

Here is a reaction that takes place with a slight increase in entropy even though there is no overall change in volume. (There is a total of one mole of gas at the start and one mole of gas at the end.) The change in entropy is the result of the gases having different ranges of rotational and vibrational energy levels open to them.

49.9 Trouton's rule says that the entropy change of vaporisation of one mole of a liquid is approximately +85 J K^{-1} mol^{-1}. For example,

$CF_2Cl_2(l) \rightarrow CF_2Cl_2(g)$; $\Delta S_{vap} = +83.6$ J K^{-1} mol^{-1}
$CCl_4(l) \rightarrow CCl_4(g)$; $\Delta S_{vap} = +85.3$ J K^{-1} mol^{-1}
$CS_2(l) \rightarrow CS_2(g)$; $\Delta S_{vap} = +83.6$ J K^{-1} mol^{-1}
$C_6H_6(l) \rightarrow C_6H_6(g)$; $\Delta S_{vap} = +86.9$ J K^{-1} mol^{-1}

Why do you think that these values are very much the same?
(Hint: compare the states of the starting materials and the products.)

49.10 Some substances show much larger entropies of vaporisation than those expected from Trouton's rule:

$H_2O(l) \rightarrow H_2O(g)$; $\Delta S_{vap} = +109.1$ J K^{-1} mol^{-1}
$CH_3OH(l) \rightarrow CH_3OH(g)$;
$\Delta S_{vap} = +104.4$ J K^{-1} mol^{-1}
$C_2H_5OH(l) \rightarrow C_2H_5OH(g)$;
$\Delta S_{vap} = +110.1$ J K^{-1} mol^{-1}

What could be causing these three liquids to show an entropy change that is greater than we might otherwise expect? To help you find the answer, think about this: either the vapour must have a greater entropy than expected, or the liquid have a smaller starting entropy. Which is it? (Hint: think about bonding!)

Answers

49.1 (i) There are 6×6 arrangements in all.

(ii) 4.94×10^{-23} J K^{-1}.

(iii) It is double the value in the table. The entropy for a number of complexions, W_1, is $k \ln W_1$; that for W_2 complexions is $k \ln W_2$. If the two systems are combined the total number of complexions is $W_1 \times W_2$, so the combined entropy is $k \ln(W_1 \times W_2)$. But $k \ln(W_1 \times W_2) = k \ln W_1 + k \ln W_2$. This shows that because of the logarithm in Boltzmann's formula, the entropy of the two combined systems is the sum of the individual entropies. This is the reason why your answer should have been twice that in the table.

49.2 (i) $E = hf = 6.626 \times 10^{-34}$ J s $\times 8652 \times 10^{10}$ s^{-1}
$= 5.733 \times 10^{-20}$ J

(ii) $kT = 1.38 \times 10^{-23}$ J $K^{-1} \times 298$ K $= 4.11 \times 10^{-21}$ J.

(iii) Here, $N_A = 10^6$ and $\Delta E = 5.733 \times 10^{-20}$ J, so
$N_B = 10^6 \times \exp(-5.733 \times 10^{-20}\text{ J}/4.11 \times 10^{-21}\text{ J}) = 0.9$

(iv) For obvious reasons the answer is not completely accurate: we cannot get fractions of molecules. In any case there is a constantly changing situation in the gas. The answer means that, *on average*, there is less than one molecule in a million in the upper vibrational level at room temperature. Very occasionally one or more molecules reach the upper level. This is the usual situation for molecules. Their vibrational energy levels are so far apart that at room temperature they do not have enough energy to reach the higher levels. Almost all of them exist in their ground states.

49.3 Molecules in a solid are not free to move, in gases they are completely free, and in liquids they are partially free. Thus gases have the most energy levels open to them, and solids the least, with liquids in between. Hence the number of complexions, and therefore entropy, follows the same pattern.

49.4 The entropy change is

$\Delta S = 1$ mol $\times 8.314$ J K^{-1} mol$^{-1} \times \ln(100\text{ dm}^3/1\text{ dm}^3)$
$= 38.29$ J K^{-1}

49.5 (i) and (iii). In both of these there is a change in which the amount of gas increases. These changes should produce an increase in entropy. For (ii) and (iv), there is a decrease in the amount of gas, and so there should be a corresponding decrease in entropy.

49.6 (i), (iii) and (iv) do not require us to do work, so they are spontaneous changes.

49.7 $\Delta S_{phase} = \Delta H_{phase}/T = 2.31$ kJ mol^{-1}/234.3 K
$= 9.86$ J K^{-1} mol^{-1}

49.8 In real life the changes will occur under non-reversible conditions, so all four of them will cause the entropy of the universe to increase. It is only under perfectly reversible conditions that the entropy of the universe will not increase.

49.9 In each case we start with one mole of liquid and convert to one mole of gas. The latter has a volume of (about) 24 dm^3 in each case. By comparison the volumes of the liquids are insignificant. Therefore the changes are very similar, and roughly the same entropy increase occurs.

49.10 Each of the liquids has a large amount of hydrogen bonding between the molecules. This means that their molecules are more restricted in their movements. As a consequence they have fewer translational (and rotational) energy levels open to them. When these molecules are released into a vapour they have a correspondingly greater increase in the number of translational energy levels available to them than molecules that were not hydrogen bonded in the liquids. Hence there is a greater increase in entropy than expected from Trouton's rule.

UNIT 49 SUMMARY

- Entropy depends on the number of arrangements of atoms or molecules among energy levels, i.e. the number of complexions.
- The greater the number of complexions open to a system, the greater is the entropy (and vice versa).
- Ordinary sense of 'reversible':
  A reaction that can 'go both ways'.
- Thermodynamic sense of 'reversible':
  A change that takes place in a system and its surroundings so that there is no observable change in the universe.
- Spontaneous changes take place without the need to do work.
- Non-spontaneous changes only take place when work is done.
- Thermodynamics is not at all concerned with how fast reactions take place.
- The Maxwell–Boltzmann distribution

  $N_B = N_A \exp(-\Delta E/kT)$

  is the most probable distribution of molecules among the available energy levels.

50

Free energy

50.1 What is free energy?

To help us answer this question we shall take a careful look at a particular reaction. The one we shall use is

$$Zn(s) + Cu^{2+}(aq) \rightarrow Zn^{2+}(aq) + Cu(s); \quad \Delta H^{\ominus} = -216.7\,\text{kJ mol}^{-1} \quad \Delta S^{\ominus} = -15.9\,\text{J K}^{-1}\,\text{mol}^{-1}$$

If we merely mix zinc metal with copper(II) sulphate solution, the energy of the reaction is not used to any good purpose; a lot of heat is generated, but no work is done. However, in a Daniell cell the reaction can be used to do work (Figure 50.1).

There are many ways in which we can use the cell. One way would be to connect a piece of wire between the positive and negative terminals. If you were to do this, the electrons from the zinc could flow through the wire round to the copper ions. Because the wire has a

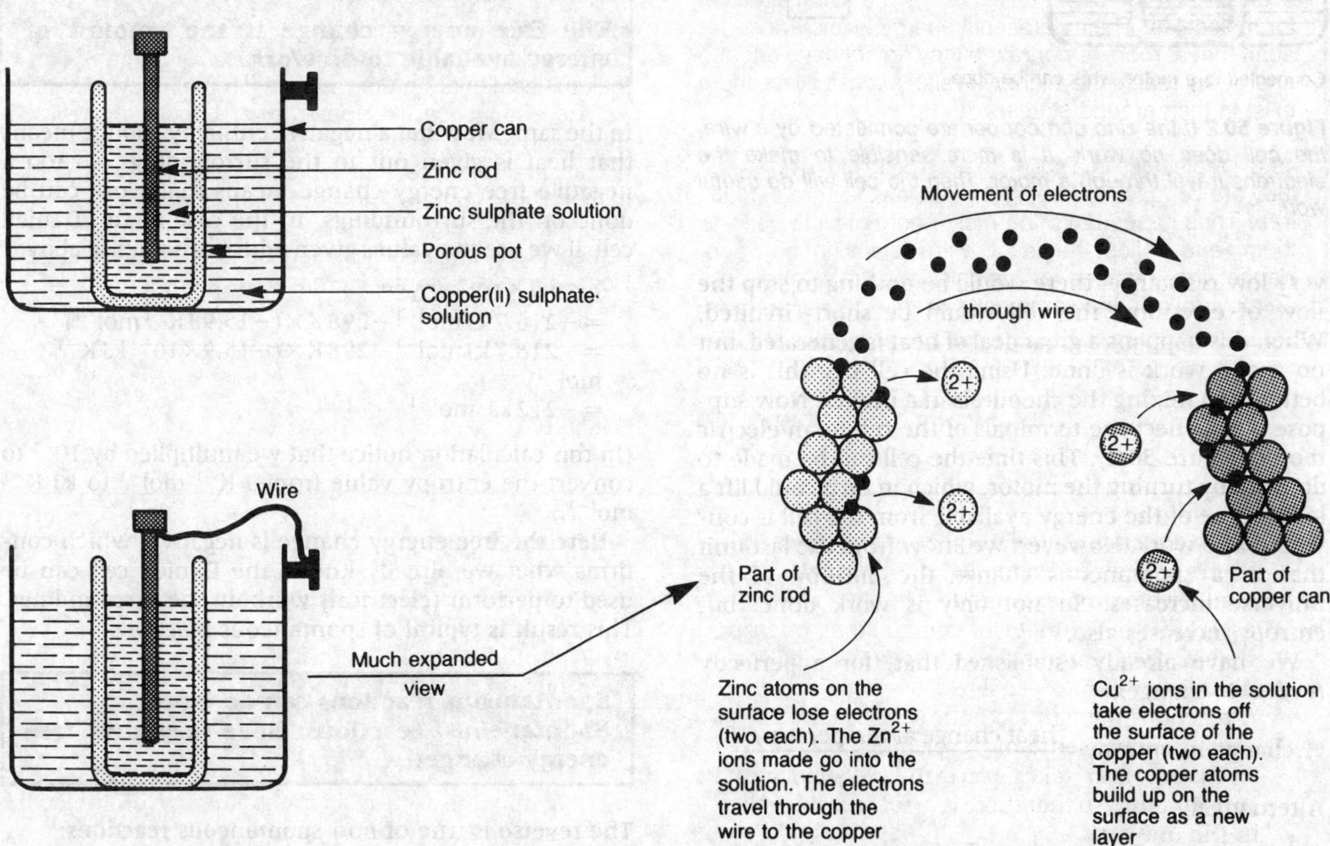

Copper can
Zinc rod
Zinc sulphate solution
Porous pot
Copper(II) sulphate solution
Wire
Much expanded view
Movement of electrons
through wire
2+
Part of zinc rod
Part of copper can
Zinc atoms on the surface lose electrons (two each). The Zn2+ ions made go into the solution. The electrons travel through the wire to the copper
Cu2+ ions in the solution take electrons off the surface of the copper (two each). The copper atoms build up on the surface as a new layer

Figure 50.1 *A Daniell cell consists of a zinc rod dipping into a solution of zinc sulphate, and copper in contact with copper(II) sulphate solution. Often the solutions are kept from mixing by using a porous pot. The same reaction takes place as when zinc is added to copper(II) sulphate solution: $Zn(s) + Cu^{2+}(aq) \rightarrow Zn^{2+}(aq) + Cu(s)$. However, instead of the electrons hopping directly from the zinc to the copper ions, in the cell they would have to travel through the wire connecting the zinc and copper*

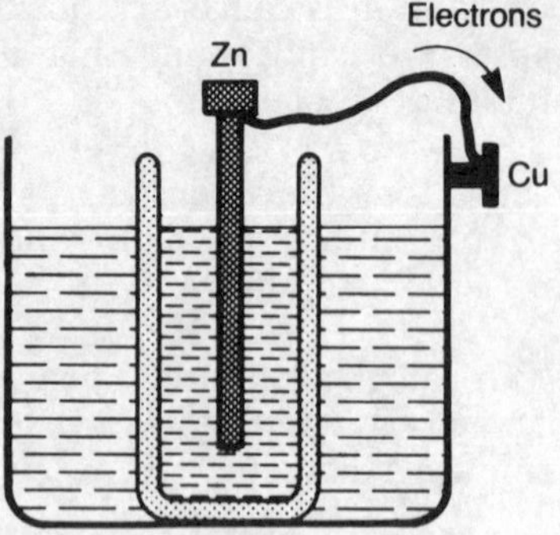

Short-circuited: no useful work, only a lot of heat generated

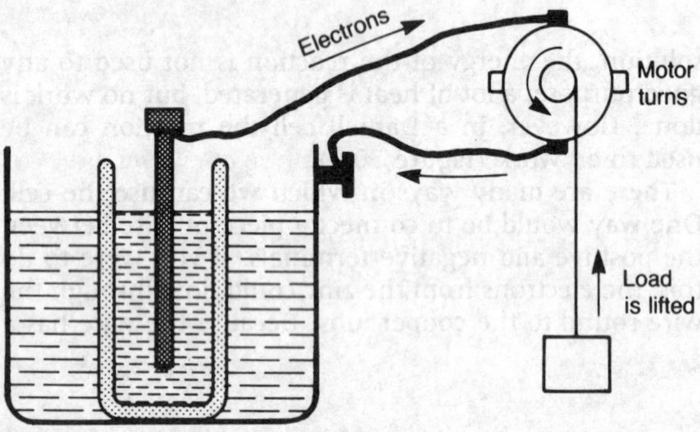

Connected to a motor, work can be done

***Figure 50.2** If the zinc and copper are connected by a wire, the cell does no work. It is more sensible to make the electrons travel through a motor. Then the cell will do useful work.*

very low resistance, there would be nothing to stop the flow of electrons; the cell would be short-circuited. When this happens a great deal of heat is generated, but no useful work is done. Using the cell like this is no better than mixing the chemicals in a beaker. Now suppose we connect the terminals of the cell to an electric motor (Figure 50.2). This time the cell can be made to do work by turning the motor, which in turn could lift a load. Some of the energy available from the cell is converted into work. However, we know from the last unit that in a spontaneous change the entropy of the universe increases. So not only is work done, bu. entropy increases also.

We have already established that, for a perfectly reversible change,

$$\text{change in entropy} = \frac{\text{heat change at temperature } T}{T}$$

Alternatively,

$$\text{heat change at temperature } T = T \times \text{change in entropy}$$

For simplicity we shall write this as

$$\text{heat change} = T\Delta S$$

We can summarise the situation with the Daniell cell in the following way. The available energy change in the reaction can be used to do work; but some of it produces an entropy change:

$$\begin{matrix}\text{energy available} \\ \text{from reaction,} \\ \Delta H\end{matrix} = \begin{matrix}\text{energy that} \\ \text{can do work}\end{matrix} + \begin{matrix}\text{heat change} \\ \text{causing entropy} \\ \text{change } (=T\Delta S)\end{matrix}$$

i.e.

$$\Delta H = \text{energy that can do work} + T\Delta S$$

or,

$$\text{energy that can do work} = \Delta H - T\Delta S$$

There is a special name given to the 'energy that can do work'. It is called the *free energy*, or free energy change, symbol ΔG. Therefore we have

$$\Delta G = \Delta H - T\Delta S$$

Under standard conditions,

$$\Delta G^{\ominus} = \Delta H^{\ominus} - T\Delta S^{\ominus}$$

This is one of the most important equations in chemistry. It says that:

Only part of the energy released in a reaction can be used to do work; the rest is involved in an entropy change.

The free energy change is the amount of energy available to do work.

In the same way that a negative enthalpy change means that heat is given out to the surroundings, so too a negative free energy change means that work can be done on the surroundings. In the case of the Daniell cell, if we use the values given with the equation above,

$$\begin{aligned}\Delta G^{\ominus} &= \Delta H^{\ominus} - T\Delta S^{\ominus} \\ &= -216.7\,\text{kJ mol}^{-1} - 298\,\text{K} \times (-15.9\,\text{J K}^{-1}\,\text{mol}^{-1}) \\ &= -216.7\,\text{kJ mol}^{-1} - 298\,\text{K} \times (-15.9 \times 10^{-1}\,\text{kJ K}^{-1}\,\text{mol}^{-1}) \\ &= -212\,\text{kJ mol}^{-1}\end{aligned}$$

(In this calculation notice that we multiplied by 10^{-3} to convert the entropy value from J K^{-1} mol^{-1} to kJ K^{-1} mol^{-1}.)

Here the free energy change is negative, which confirms what we already know: the Daniell cell can be used to perform (electrical) work on the surroundings. This result is typical of spontaneous reactions:

Spontaneous reactions can do work.
Spontaneous reactions have negative free energy changes.

The reverse is true of non-spontaneous reactions:

Non-spontaneous reactions cannot do work.
Non-spontaneous reactions have positive free energy changes.

Before leaving this section you might like to look at the equation $\Delta G = \Delta H - T\Delta S$ in another way. If we divide through by the temperature, and rearrange, we have

$$-\frac{\Delta G}{T} = -\frac{\Delta H}{T} + \Delta S$$

Each term represents an entropy change. The equation says that

entropy change in the universe = entropy change in the surroundings + entropy change in the system

Table 50.1. Standard free energies of formation for some compounds

Compound	$\Delta G_f^\ominus$ /kJ mol^{-1}	*Compound*	$\Delta G_f^\ominus$ /kJ mol^{-1}
$H_2O(l)$	−237.2	$Li_2CO_3(s)$	−1132.6
$H_2O(g)$	−228.6	$Na_2CO_3(s)$	−1047.7
$NH_3(g)$	−16.7	$CaCO_3(s)$	−1128.8
$CH_4(g)$	−50.8	$BaCO_3(s)$	−1138.9
$CO(g)$	−137.3	$MgO(s)$	−569.4
$CO_2(g)$	−394.4	$Na_2O(s)$	−376.6
$C_2H_4(g)$	+68.1	$Al_2O_3(s)$	−1582.4
$NO(g)$	+86.6	$SiO_2(s)$	−856.0
$NaCl(s)$	−384.0	$BeO(s)$	−581.6
$KCl(s)$	−408.3	$Fe_3O_4(s)$	−1014.2
$CuSO_4{\cdot}5H_2O(s)$	−1879.9	$CuO(s)$	−127.2

50.2 Standard free energies

Free energy is a thermodynamic function of state. Therefore we can use values of standard free energies in calculations in much the same way as we have used standard enthalpies. Table 50.1 lists standard free energies of formation for a range of compounds. Just as with enthalpy, we define:

> **The free energy of formation of an element in its standard state is zero.**

We can also use free energies of formation of ions in aqueous solution (Table 50.2). Here the standard state is defined to be a solution that contains 1 mol of the ion in 1 kg of water. This type of solution is called a 1 molal solution. For many purposes we can assume that a 1 molal solution is the same as a 1 molar (1 mol dm^{-3}) solution.

Table 50.2. Standard free energies of formation for some ions in solution

Ion	$\Delta G_f^\ominus$ /kJ mol^{-1}	*Ion*	$\Delta G_f^\ominus$ /kJ mol^{-1}
$H^+(aq)$	0.0	$Cu^{2+}(aq)$	+65.0
$Cl^-(aq)$	−131.2	$Zn^{2+}(aq)$	−147.1
$Br^-(aq)$	−103.9	$Fe^{3+}(aq)$	−9.7
$Cr_2O_7^{2-}(aq)$	−1257.2	$MnO_4^-(aq)$	−425.0

You might expect by now that the hydrogen ion would have a special role to play; it has. We define the free energy of formation of a 1 molal solution of H^+ to be zero.

Using these values we can calculate the free energy change of a wide variety of reactions. For example, in the reduction of copper(II) oxide by hydrogen,

$$H_2(g) + CuO(s) \rightarrow Cu(s) + H_2O(l)$$

we have

$$\begin{aligned}\Delta G^\ominus &= \Delta G_f^\ominus(Cu(s)) + \Delta G_f^\ominus(H_2O(l)) \\ &\quad - \Delta G_f^\ominus(H_2(g)) - \Delta G_f^\ominus(CuO(s)) \\ &= 0\text{ kJ mol}^{-1} - 237.2\text{ kJ mol}^{-1} \\ &\quad - 0\text{ kJ mol}^{-1} - (-127.2\text{ kJ mol}^{-1}) \\ &= -110\text{ kJ mol}^{-1}\end{aligned}$$

However, if we work out the free energy change for the reaction of aluminium oxide with carbon,

$$Al_2O_3(s) + 3C(s) \rightarrow 2Al(s) + 3CO(g)$$

we get

$$\begin{aligned}\Delta G^\ominus &= 2\Delta G_f^\ominus(Al(s)) + 3\Delta G_f^\ominus(CO(g)) \\ &\quad - \Delta G_f^\ominus(Al_2O_3(s)) - 3\Delta G_f^\ominus(C(s)) \\ &= 0\text{ kJ mol}^{-1} + 3(-137.3\text{ kJ mol}^{-1}) \\ &\quad -(-1582.4\text{ kJ mol}^{-1}) - 0\text{ kJ mol}^{-1} \\ &= -411.9\text{ kJ mol}^{-1} + 1582.4\text{ kJ mol}^{-1} \\ &= +1170.5\text{ kJ mol}^{-1}\end{aligned}$$

These two reactions have very different free energies. In the case of hydrogen reducing copper(II) oxide, the negative value of $\Delta G^\ominus$ tells us that the reaction is spontaneous at 298 K, and that it could do work on the surroundings. On the other hand, the reduction of aluminium oxide by carbon has a positive value for the free energy change. In this case the reaction is not spontaneous. The reaction will not occur unless *we* do work on it.

50.1 Use the values in Table 50.2 to work out the free energy change for the reaction in the Daniell cell. The cell reaction is given in section 50.1.

50.2 Calculate the standard free energy changes for the following reactions. For each one, say whether the reaction is spontaneous (or not). Use the values in Table 50.1.

(i) $C(s) + H_2O(g) \rightarrow CO(g) + H_2(g)$

(ii) $CuO(s) + C(s) \rightarrow Cu(s) + CO(g)$

(iii) $Fe_3O_4(s) + 4C(s) \rightarrow 3Fe(s) + 4CO(g)$

(iv) $CH_4(g) + 2O_2(g) \rightarrow CO_2(g) + 2H_2O(l)$

50.3 Would you expect a cell that uses the reaction

$2Fe^{3+}(aq) + 3Zn(s) \rightarrow 2Fe(s) + 3Zn^{2+}(aq)$

to work?

50.4 Ethene, C_2H_4, is a valuable chemical because it can be made into polyethene. If you were the manager of a chemical plant and someone said they could make ethene out of methane and carbon in a spontaneous reaction, would you believe them? The proposed reaction is

$C(s) + CH_4(g) \rightarrow C_2H_4(g)$

Use the free energy values in Table 50.1 to help you make a decision.

50.3 Free energy values do not tell us how fast a reaction will occur

We have just worked out that the reduction of copper(II) oxide by hydrogen is a spontaneous reaction. It is very important that you take care to understand what this means. In the last unit we said that, in thermodynamics, spontaneous does *not* mean that the reaction will start as soon as we mix the chemicals together. In fact you could put copper(II) oxide and hydrogen gas into a flask, leave them there for a year and you would find they had not reacted. At room temperature they simply will not react. On the other hand, if you heat the oxide so that it reaches several hundred degrees Celsius, and then put hydrogen with it, the reaction takes place very quickly. In a matter of seconds, the black powder is replaced by the pink colour of metallic copper. In fact:

Thermodynamics can tell us nothing about how fast a spontaneous reaction will take place.

However, if we find that the ΔG value for a reaction is positive, we know that the reaction will not take place at all under the conditions to which the ΔG value refers.

50.4 Free energy changes under non-standard conditions

If a reaction does not work at room temperature, one of the first things that we try is to increase the temperature. For example, a strip of magnesium will not burn in air at room temperature; but if part of the magnesium is placed in the flame of a bunsen burner, the reaction takes place immediately.

In general there are two reasons why increasing the temperature has an effect on reactions. First, it *increases the rate* of a reaction. You will discover more about this in Unit 77. For the present you should remember the point we have already made: a spontaneous reaction may not happen at room temperature because it is a very slow reaction. Secondly, a change in temperature can alter the thermodynamics of the reaction. This can happen owing to the presence of the temperature, T, in the equation $\Delta G = \Delta H - T\Delta S$. Zinc carbonate can be kept in bottles at room temperature for years without signs of it decomposing. If you work out the enthalpy, entropy and free energy changes for the reaction where the carbonate gives off carbon dioxide, you will find the following values:

$$ZnCO_3(s) \rightarrow ZnO(s) + CO_2(g);$$
$$\Delta H^{\ominus} = +71\ \text{kJ mol}^{-1}$$
$$\Delta S^{\ominus} = +175.1\ \text{J K}^{-1}\ \text{mol}^{-1}$$
$$\Delta G^{\ominus} = +99.9\ \text{kJ mol}^{-1}$$

The fact that $\Delta G^{\ominus}$ is positive at 298 K tells us that the reaction (in which all the chemicals remain in their standard states) is *not* spontaneous. It does not occur because it is thermodynamically impossible. (Not because it is one of those spontaneous reactions that is very slow.) In data tables it is claimed that zinc carbonate decomposes at around 573 K (300° C). Using our equation $\Delta G = \Delta H - T\Delta S$, we have

$$\Delta G = +71\ \text{kJ mol}^{-1} - 573\ \text{K} \times 175.1 \times 10^{-3}\ \text{kJ K}^{-1}\ \text{mol}^{-1}$$
$$= -29.33\ \text{kJ mol}^{-1}$$

The negative result for ΔG shows that at 573 K the reaction *is* possible. The increase in temperature has caused the reaction to become spontaneous. This change has been brought about thanks to the large entropy change in the reaction. (If the entropy change were about 10 J K^{-1} mol^{-1}, the temperature would have to exceed 7100 K before the reaction became spontaneous.)

A reaction like this, which takes place mainly because of the increase in entropy, is called an *entropy driven* reaction.

You should understand that any reaction that has a positive enthalpy change must be entropy driven if it is to be spontaneous. The combination of a rise in temperature and a large ΔS value can make $T\Delta S$ a large positive number. Hence $-T\Delta S$ becomes a large negative number, which overcomes ΔH (Table 50.3).

It is possible that you may think there has been some cheating here. Are we entitled to use the standard values

Table 50.3. Spontaneous and non-spontaneous reactions

ΔH	ΔS	$-T\Delta S$	ΔG	*Comment*
−ve	+ve	−ve	−ve at all T	Spontaneous at all T
−ve	−ve	+ve	−ve at low T	Spontaneous at low T
			+ve at high T	Non-spontaneous at high T
+ve	+ve	−ve	−ve at high T	Spontaneous at high T; entropy driven
			+ve at low T	Non-spontaneous at low T
+ve	−ve	+ve	+ve at all T	Non-spontaneous at all T

at 298 K for enthalpy and entropy changes in our equation $\Delta G = \Delta H - T\Delta S$ and use any value for the temperature? Strictly, the answer is 'no' because both ΔH and ΔS do change with temperature; but in most cases the predictions we make using the standard values agree with the result obtained when more accurate values are employed. For this reason, in practice, we can often use the standard values at 298 K without too much error. However, in some cases it is necessary to be accurate, especially when reactions take place on the scale used in industry.

50.5 A student said that the standard free energy change for the reaction $Al_2O_3(s) \rightarrow 2Al(s) + \frac{3}{2}O_2(g)$ is $+1582.4\,kJ\,mol^{-1}$. Was he correct? (Consult Table 50.1.)

He also said that, because the value is so large and positive, it proves that it is impossible to get aluminium out of aluminium oxide. Was he correct?

50.6 The thermit reaction has been used to reduce oxides of iron. Under standard conditions the reaction is

$$8Al(s) + 3Fe_3O_4(s) \rightarrow 4Al_2O_3(s) + 9Fe(s)$$

Use Table 50.1 to calculate the free energy change for the reaction. Is it a spontaneous reaction? Would it be safe to mix the aluminium and the oxide, or would you expect an explosion?

50.5 Ellingham diagrams and the extraction of metals

When the Earth was being formed, any metal that was even mildly reactive combined with one or more non-metals. Often the metals combined with oxygen or sulphur. For example, iron is found in Nature in oxide ores such as magnetite, Fe_3O_4; lead is to be found in the mineral cinnabar as lead(II) sulphide, PbS; copper occurs in covellite as copper(II) sulphide, CuS. Some thousands of years ago the discovery was made, presumably by chance, that iron could be obtained from its ore by heating with charcoal (carbon). This was the start of the Iron Age, in which humans discovered how to make tools and weapons that had considerable strength and a long life. Under standard conditions at 298 K a typical reaction is:

$$FeO(s) + C(s) \rightarrow Fe(s) + CO(g)$$

We can think of this reaction as the result of a competition between the iron and carbon for oxygen. If the iron wins the competition then the iron(II) oxide will not be reduced. If carbon wins the competition, then it will steal the oxygen from the iron(II) oxide. In other words, the competition is between

$$2\,Fe(s) + O_2(g) \rightarrow 2FeO(s); \qquad 2\Delta G_f^{\ominus}(FeO(s))$$

and

$$2C(s) + O_2(g) \rightarrow 2CO(g); \qquad 2\Delta G_f^{\ominus}(CO(g))$$

For reasons that you will discover soon, both these equations are written so that they contain 1 mol of oxygen. The free energy changes are then twice the free energies of formation (which refer to the formation of 1 mol of a compound).

The equation we are seeking is

$$FeO(s) + C(s) \rightarrow Fe(s) + CO(g)$$

for which the free energy change is $\Delta G_f^{\ominus}(CO(g)) - \Delta G_f^{\ominus}(FeO(s))$. We know that the reaction will be possible if this is negative. This tells us that $\Delta G_f^{\ominus}(CO(g))$ must be *more negative* than $\Delta G_f^{\ominus}(FeO(s))$. If the reaction

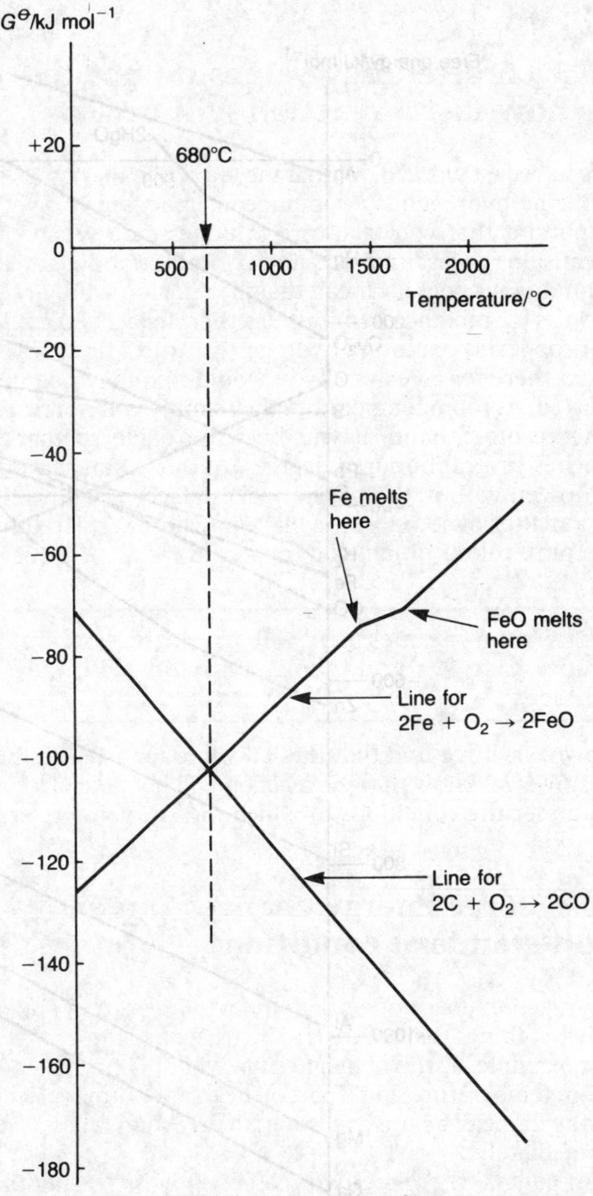

***Figure 50.3** The Ellingham diagram showing how the free energy changes for $2Fe + O_2 \rightarrow 2FeO$ and $2C + O_2 \rightarrow 2CO$ vary with temperature. Note: state symbols have been omitted because, for example, above 1539° C, iron is a liquid, and above 1420° C, iron(II) oxide is also a liquid*

takes place under non-standard conditions, we omit the standard sign ($^{\ominus}$) and say that $\Delta G_f(CO(g))$ must be more negative than $\Delta G_f(FeO(s))$. For example, let us suppose that $\Delta G_f(FeO(s)) = -250\,kJ\ mol^{-1}$, and that $\Delta G_f(CO(g)) = -150\,kJ\ mol$. It follows that

$$\Delta G_f(CO(g)) - \Delta G_f(FeO(s))$$
$$= -150\,kJ\ mol^{-1} - (-250\,kJ\ mol^{-1})$$
$$= +100\,kJ\ mol^{-1}$$

But if $\Delta G_f(FeO(s)) = -150\,kJ\ mol^{-1}$ and $\Delta G_f(CO(g)) = -250\,kJ\ mol^{-1}$, then the free energy change is $-100\,kJ\ mol^{-1}$, and the reduction of the iron(II) oxide can take place. There are equations that allow us to calculate how free energy changes with temperature, but fortunately the work has already been done for us. In the case of our two equations, the values change as shown in the graph of Figure 50.3.

This type of diagram was first described by H. J. T. Ellingham in 1944, and is known as an *Ellingham diagram*. The lines show how the free energy changes for the two reactions change with temperature. The lines cross at about 680° C. Below this temperature FeO is more thermodynamically stable than CO. (ΔG for FeO is more negative than that for CO.) Above this temperature, the reverse is true, and as we have seen the oxide can be reduced by carbon.

In Figure 50.4 there is a more complicated Ellingham diagram. Many more lines are shown. Each line refers to

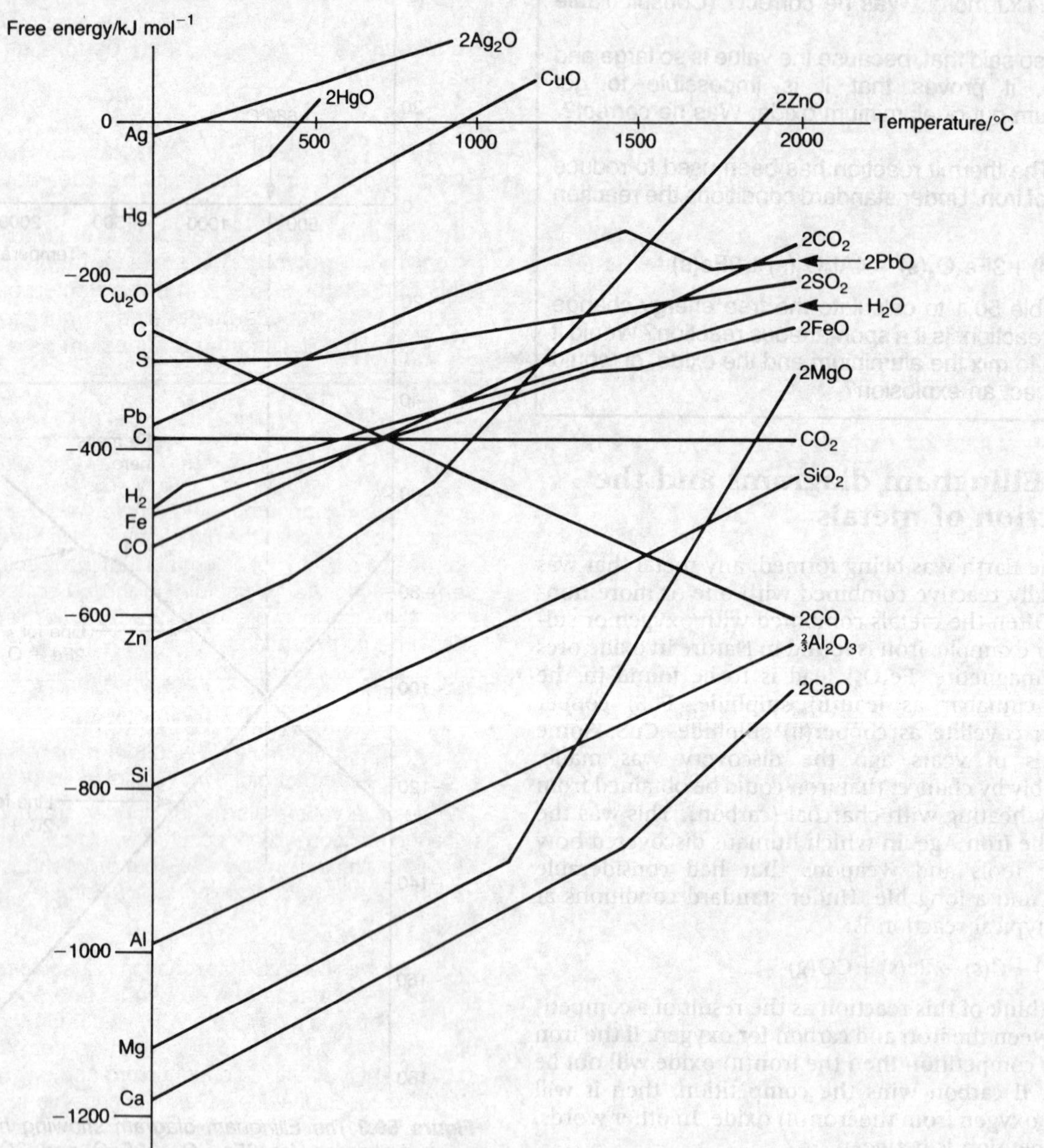

***Figure 50.4** An Ellingham diagram for the reduction of oxides. (Diagram adapted from: Dannatt, C. W. and Ellingham, H. J. T. (1948).* Disc. Faraday Soc. *(No.4), 126; and Ives, D. G. (1972).* Principles of the Extraction of Metals, *Chemical Society, London)*

a reaction in which 1 mol of oxygen is present. For example, in the case of aluminium oxide, the line shows the free energy change for the reaction

$$\tfrac{4}{3}Al(s) + O_2(g) \rightarrow \tfrac{2}{3}Al_2O_3(s)$$

The beauty of an Ellingham diagram is that we only have to look at the relative positions of the lines to decide whether a particular reaction will take place. Here is an example: zinc is a valuable metal, partly owing to its use in galvanising iron. If we wish to reduce zinc oxide, could we use carbon monoxide, and if so, at what temperature will the reaction be spontaneous? You can see from the diagram in Figure 50.4 that the line for the reaction

$$2CO(g) + O_2(g) \rightarrow 2CO_2(g)$$

is *more* negative than that for

$$2Zn(s) + O_2(g) \rightarrow 2ZnO(s)$$

only above 1180°C (approximately). This tells us that carbon monoxide should remove the oxygen from zinc oxide above this temperature. However, it would be unwise to assume that the reaction would actually occur as predicted. We know that predictions from thermodynamics tell us nothing about the rate of a reaction. It might be necessary to use a much higher temperature to make the reaction take place at a reasonable rate.

You may notice that some of the lines on the Ellingham diagram have kinks in them. Usually this is a result of a change of state or a change in structure of a solid. An example is the bend in the line for $2Mg(s) + O_2(g) \rightarrow 2MgO(s)$ at 1117°C; this is the boiling point of magnesium.

50.7 Use the Ellingham diagram in Figure 50.4 to help you answer these questions:

(i) Estimate the minimum temperature at which carbon should reduce lead(II) oxide, PbO, with carbon monoxide as a product.

(ii) Will carbon monoxide reduce aluminium oxide?

(iii) Should iron metal reduce lead(II) oxide? Check your answer by estimating the free energy change at a particular temperature, and performing a calculation.

50.8 If you were running a factory in which carbon was used to reduce magnesium oxide, would carbon monoxide or carbon dioxide be produced? Estimate the minimum temperature at which the reaction would work. What would be the state of the magnesium at this temperature? Given that the whole point of your factory is to produce magnesium, what problems do you face in collecting the magnesium as a solid?

Answers

50.1 $\Delta G^\ominus = \Delta G_f^\ominus(Zn^{2+}(aq)) - \Delta G_f^\ominus(Cu^{2+}(aq))$
$= -147.1\ kJ\ mol^{-1} - (+65.0\ kJ\ mol^{-1})$
$= -212.1\ kJ\ mol^{-1}$

50.2 (i) $\Delta G^\ominus = \Delta G_f^\ominus(CO(g)) - \Delta G_f^\ominus(H_2O(g))$
$= -137.3\ kJ\ mol^{-1} - (-228.6\ kJ\ mol^{-1})$
$= +91.3\ kJ\ mol^{-1}$

(ii) $\Delta G^\ominus = \Delta G_f^\ominus(CO(g)) - \Delta G_f^\ominus(CuO(s))$
$= -137.3\ kJ\ mol^{-1} - (-127.2\ kJ\ mol^{-1})$
$= -10.1\ kJ\ mol^{-1}$

(iii) $\Delta G^\ominus = 4\Delta G_f^\ominus(CO(g)) - \Delta G_f^\ominus(Fe_3O_4(s))$
$= 4(-137.3\ kJ\ mol^{-1}) - (-1014.2\ kJ\ mol^{-1})$
$= +465\ kJ\ mol^{-1}$

(iv) $\Delta G^\ominus = 2\Delta G_f^\ominus(H_2O(l)) + \Delta G_f^\ominus(CO_2(g)) - \Delta G_f^\ominus(CH_4(g))$
$= 2(-237.2\ kJ\ mol^{-1}) + (-394.4\ kJ\ mol^{-1})$
$- (-50.8\ kJ\ mol^{-1})$
$= -818.0\ kJ\ mol^{-1}$

In each of these the $\Delta G_f^\ominus$ values of elements are ignored because they are all zero. Reactions (ii) and (iv) have negative free energy changes. These reactions are spontaneous. Reactions (i) and (iii) have positive values and are not spontaneous.

50.3 The standard free energy change is

$\Delta G^\ominus = 3\Delta G_f^\ominus(Zn^{2+}(aq)) - 2\Delta G_f^\ominus(Fe^{3+}(aq))$
$= 3 \times (-147.1\ kJ\ mol^{-1}) - 2 \times (-9.7\ kJ\ mol^{-1})$
$= -421.9\ kJ\ mol^{-1}$

The reaction is spontaneous, so we would expect the reaction to proceed in the direction given in the equation. However, we could not be certain that the reaction would be fast enough to be useful. On the other hand, reactions involving ions are usually very quick, and these should be no exception.

50.4 Here,
$\Delta G^\ominus = \Delta G_f^\ominus(C_2H_4(g)) - \Delta G_f^\ominus(CH_4(g))$
$= +68.1\ kJ\ mol^{-1} - (-50.8\ kJ\ mol^{-1})$
$= +118.9\ kJ\ mol^{-1}$

The positive value tells us that under standard conditions the reaction will not occur. It would be rather stupid to build a production line at a cost of, perhaps, several million pounds without doing such a simple calculation first!

50.5 He was correct. This reaction is just the reverse of that for the formation of Al_2O_3, so its free energy value has the opposite sign to the $\Delta G_f^\ominus$ value. On the second point he was wrong. It is true that it is not possible to convert Al_2O_3 directly into aluminium and oxygen under standard conditions. However, it is possible to carry out the change by an indirect route under non-standard conditions. This is done in industry, where molten Al_2O_3 undergoes electrolysis (see Unit 85).

50.6 $\Delta G^\ominus = 4\Delta G_f^\ominus(Al_2O_3(s)) - 3\Delta G_f^\ominus(Fe_3O_4(s))$

Answers – contd.

$= 4 \times (-1582.4\,\text{kJ mol}^{-1}) - 3 \times (-1014.2\,\text{kJ mol}^{-1})$
$= -3287\,\text{kJ mol}^{-1}$

The reaction is spontaneous. This does *not* mean that it will take place at room temperature. In fact, the reaction *is* quite violent, but only when it is ignited at several hundred degrees Celsius. However, the free energy value does not tell us this; the only way to find out is to do an experiment (carefully).

50.7 (i) The two lines cross at about 300°C. Above this temperature the reaction favours carbon monoxide rather than the oxide, so the reduction should take place.

(ii) The line for $2CO(g) + O_2(g) \rightarrow 2CO_2(g)$ is above that for aluminium oxide at all temperatures. This means that the gas will *not* reduce the oxide.

(iii) The line for $2Fe(s) + O_2(g) \rightarrow 2FeO(s)$ is below that for lead(II) oxide at all temperatures. This means that iron should remove the oxygen from lead(II) oxide. However, this is not to say that the reaction will be fast enough at low temperatures. At about 600°C, an estimate of the free energy changes for the reactions is:

$2Fe(s) + O_2(g) \rightarrow 2FeO(s); \quad \Delta G(2FeO(s)) = -400\,\text{kJ mol}^{-1}$

$2Pb(s) + O_2(g) \rightarrow 2PbO(s); \quad \Delta G(2PbO(s)) = -250\,\text{kJ mol}^{-1}$

Therefore the free energy change for the reaction

$2PbO(s) + 2Fe(s) \rightarrow 2FeO(s) + 2Pb(s)$

is

$\Delta G(2FeO(s)) - \Delta G(2PbO(s))$
$= -400\,\text{kJ mol}^{-1} - (-250\,\text{kJ mol}^{-1})$
$= -150\,\text{kJ mol}^{-1}$

The sign of the free energy change is negative, which confirms our prediction.

50.8 The lines for MgO and CO cross at about 1600°C. This is the minimum temperature needed for the reaction to be spontaneous. The magnesium would be a gas at this temperature. The problem is that you have to cool the magnesium in order to collect it; but the catch is that once it cools to below 1600°C the production of magnesium oxide becomes the favoured reaction. That is, the magnesium is liable to change back to magnesium oxide. Your only hope, which is the one actually used in such situations, is to cool the magnesium very quickly so that it does not have enough time to change back to the oxide. Again we are as concerned about the rate of a reaction as much as whether it is thermodynamically possible.

UNIT 50 SUMMARY

- Free energy is the energy available to do work.
- Changes in free energy are related to enthalpy, entropy and temperature
  $$\Delta G^{\ominus} = \Delta H^{\ominus} - T\Delta S^{\ominus}$$
- Spontaneous reactions:
  (i) Can do work.
  (ii) Have negative free energy changes.
- The reverse is true of non-spontaneous reactions.
- The standard free energy of formation of an element in its standard state is defined to be zero.
- Free energy values do not tell us how fast a reaction will occur.
- Any reaction that has a positive enthalpy change must be entropy driven if it is to be spontaneous.
- Ellingham diagrams are graphs that show how the free energy change of a series of reactions varies with temperature. They are especially useful in predicting the course of reduction reactions in the extraction of metals from their ores.

51

Equilibrium and free energy*

51.1 What is the effect of concentration and pressure on free energy?

Earlier in this book we mentioned that all reactions can 'go both ways'. However, in many cases the reactants appear not to react at all, or react so well that only products are left at the end of the reaction. We now know how to predict which of these two outcomes is likely by looking at the sign of the free energy change for the reaction. Now we shall discover what thermodynamics has to say about the connection between reactants, products and equilibrium.

First, we shall examine the free energy change for a reaction in more detail. One point that we have ignored up to now is that the standard free energy values we have used refer to *pure* samples of each compound. That is, if we work out the free energy change for the reaction

$$Zn(s) + Cu^{2+}(aq) \rightarrow Zn^{2+}(aq) + Cu(s)$$

we use values that assume that each chemical is separate from all the others. This is not what actually happens in a reaction. It is obvious that, for a reaction to occur, somehow the reactants must interact. Also, it is almost always the case that, during the reaction, the reactants get mixed up with the products. Therefore, to follow the change in free energy during a reaction we must be more careful than merely using standard values.

Since the early days of thermodynamics, chemists have discovered how to take account of the effects of non-standard conditions. We are not going to derive any of the results; rather, our aim is to use and understand them. The most important results are collected in Table 51.1. We shall show the free energy of an ion or a gas on its own as G (rather than ΔG).

Here are some examples to show you the way these formulae work. If we had a 1 mol dm^{-3} solution of zinc ions at 298 K, then from Table 50.2 we have $G^{\ominus}_{Zn^{2+}} = -147.1$ kJ mol^{-1}. Now suppose we have a solution of zinc ions with concentration 0.1 mol dm^{-3}. In this case

Table 51.1. Changes in standard free energies due to non-standard conditions

Condition	*Correction to $G^{\ominus}$*	*Formula**†
Ion not at 1 mol dm^{-3} concentration	$RT\ln\left(\frac{\text{concentration}}{1\text{ mol dm}^{-3}}\right)$	$G = G^{\ominus} + RT\ln[\text{ion}]$
Gas not at 101.325 kPa	$RT\ln\left(\frac{\text{gas pressure}}{101.325\text{ kPa}}\right)$	$G = G^{\ominus} + RT\ln P$
Solid not at 101.325 kPa	None: the influence of pressure on solids is negligible	None
Solid in contact with solution of changing concentration	None: provided some solid is present, changing the amount has no effect (see Unit 35 for an example)	None

*Here we use the symbol [ion] to mean the concentration of the ion written as a number, without its units. We have taken the standard unit of concentration to be 1 mol dm^{-3}. In accurate work the standard should be unit activity, which takes into account such things as ionic interference

†The pressure P means the *partial pressure* of the gas, not the total pressure (see Unit 36). Also, as we have defined it by dividing by the standard pressure (101.325 kPa), P is used without its units. If the pressure is measured in atmospheres (atm) rather than pascals, then the correction to $G^{\ominus}$ is $RT\ln(\text{gas pressure}/1\text{ atm})$

$$[\text{ion}] = \text{concentration of } Zn^{2+}(aq)/1 \text{ mol dm}^{-3}$$

i.e.

$$[Zn^{2+}(aq)] = 0.1$$

and the free energy is

$$G_{Zn^{2+}} = G^{\ominus}_{Zn^{2+}} + RT\ln[Zn^{2+}(aq)]$$
$$= -147.1\text{ kJ mol}^{-1} + RT\ln(0.1)$$
$$= -147.1\text{ kJ mol}^{-1} + 8.314\times10^{-3}\text{ kJ K}^{-1}\text{ mol}^{-1} \times 298\text{ K}\times\ln(0.1)$$
$$= -152.81\text{ kJ mol}^{-1}$$

*This unit is more difficult than most. Check whether your syllabus requires you to cover this work.

This result shows that the free energy changes by about 5.7 kJ mol^{-1} for a 0.1 mol dm^{-3} solution. (Notice that the gas constant, $R = 8.314\,\text{J K}^{-1}\,\text{mol}^{-1}$, is multiplied by 10^{-3} to convert it into kJ K^{-1} mol^{-1}.)

Our second example is to work out the free energy of hydrogen gas at a partial pressure of 202.65 kPa. We have

$$P = \text{gas pressure}/101.325\,\text{kPa} = 2$$

Using

$$G_{H_2} = G^{\ominus}_{H_2} + RT\ln P$$

we obtain

$$G_{H_2} = 0.0\,\text{kJ mol}^{-1} + 8.314 \times 10^{-3}\,\text{kJ K}^{-1}\,\text{mol}^{-1} \times 298\,\text{K} \times \ln(2)$$

$$= +1.72\,\text{kJ mol}^{-1}$$

These two results are not very important by themselves, but they do show us how free energy changes with concentration of an ion or the partial pressure of a gas.

51.2 What is the connection between free energy and equilibrium?

Let us return to the reaction in the Daniell cell. The reaction is

$$Zn(s) + Cu^{2+}(aq) \rightarrow Zn^{2+}(aq) + Cu(s)$$

We assume that the free energy of a solid does not change even though the concentration of the solution in contact with it might vary. Also, in this case we are dealing with elements, for which their standard free energies of formation are defined to be zero. Under non-standard conditions, the free energy of the ions is given by our formula of Table 51.1:

$$G_{Zn^{2+}} = G^{\ominus}_{Zn^{2+}} + RT\ln[Zn^{2+}(aq)]$$
$$G_{Cu^{2+}} = G^{\ominus}_{Cu^{2+}} + RT\ln[Cu^{2+}(aq)]$$

The free energy change of the reaction is

$$G_{Zn^{2+}} - G_{Cu^{2+}}$$
$$= G^{\ominus}_{Zn^{2+}} + RT\ln[Zn^{2+}(aq)] - \{G^{\ominus}_{Cu^{2+}} + RT\ln[Cu^{2+}(aq)]\}$$
$$= G^{\ominus}_{Zn^{2+}} - G^{\ominus}_{Cu^{2+}} + RT\ln[Zn^{2+}(aq)] - RT\ln[Cu^{2+}(aq)]$$

We can write this as

$$\Delta G = \Delta G^{\ominus} + RT\ln\left(\frac{[Zn^{2+}(aq)]}{[Cu^{2+}(aq)]}\right)$$

where $\Delta G^{\ominus} = G^{\ominus}_{Zn^{2+}} - G^{\ominus}_{Cu^{2+}}$. (You will find information about rearranging expressions involving logarithms in Table 51.2.)

We know that while ΔG is negative, the reaction is spontaneous. On the other hand, if ΔG were to become positive, the reaction would not be spontaneous. Instead, the reverse reaction would be spontaneous, and zinc ions would react with copper to give zinc and copper(II) ions. The interesting thing is to ask what would happen if ΔG becomes zero. At this stage, neither the forward nor the reverse action is favoured. This is what happens when equilibrium is achieved:

Table 51.2. Formulae involving logarithms

Rule	*Example*
$\ln A + \ln B = \ln(A \times B)$	$\ln P_A + \ln P_B = \ln(P_A P_B)$
$2\ln A = \ln(A^2)$	$2\ln P_{NO} = \ln P^2_{NO}$
$\ln A - \ln B = \ln(A/B)$	$\ln[Zn^{2+}(aq)] - \ln[Cu^{2+}(aq)] = \ln\left(\frac{[Zn^{2+}(aq)]}{[Cu^{2+}(aq)]}\right)$
If $\ln A = X$ then $A = \exp(X)$	$\ln\left(\frac{[Zn^{2+}(aq)]}{[Cu^{2+}(aq)]}\right) = 59.37$ means that $\frac{[Zn^{2+}(aq)]}{[Cu^{2+}(aq)]} = \exp(59.37) = 6.1 \times 10^{25}$

At equilibrium $\Delta G = 0$

It is most important that you realise that the free energy change here is *not* the *standard* free energy change of the reaction. We have already said that use of the standard values assumes that the chemicals are not really reacting. ΔG is the difference in free energies of the reactants and products corrected for non-standard conditions.

In a reaction that comes to equilibrium the free energy decreases to a minimum, rather than becoming zero. You will find an example in Figure 51.1.

When equilibrium is achieved in the Daniell cell,

$$0 = \Delta G^{\ominus} + RT\ln\left(\frac{[Zn^{2+}(aq)]}{[Cu^{2+}(aq)]}\right)$$

or,

$$\Delta G^{\ominus} = -RT\ln\left(\frac{[Zn^{2+}(aq)]}{[Cu^{2+}(aq)]}\right)$$

Therefore,

$$-147.1\,\text{kJ mol}^{-1} = -8.314 \times 10^{-3}\,\text{kJ K}^{-1}\,\text{mol}^{-1} \times 298\,\text{K} \times \ln\left(\frac{[Zn^{2+}(aq)]}{[Cu^{2+}(aq)]}\right)$$

which gives

$$\ln\left(\frac{[Zn^{2+}(aq)]}{[Cu^{2+}(aq)]}\right) = \frac{-147.1\,\text{kJ mol}^{-1}}{-2.478\,\text{kJ mol}^{-1}}$$

or

$$\ln\left(\frac{[Zn^{2+}(aq)]}{[Cu^{2+}(aq)]}\right) = 59.36$$

You can discover the value of the ratio of the ion concentrations because from this

$$\frac{[Zn^{2+}(aq)]}{[Cu^{2+}(aq)]} = \exp(59.36) = 6.1 \times 10^{25}$$

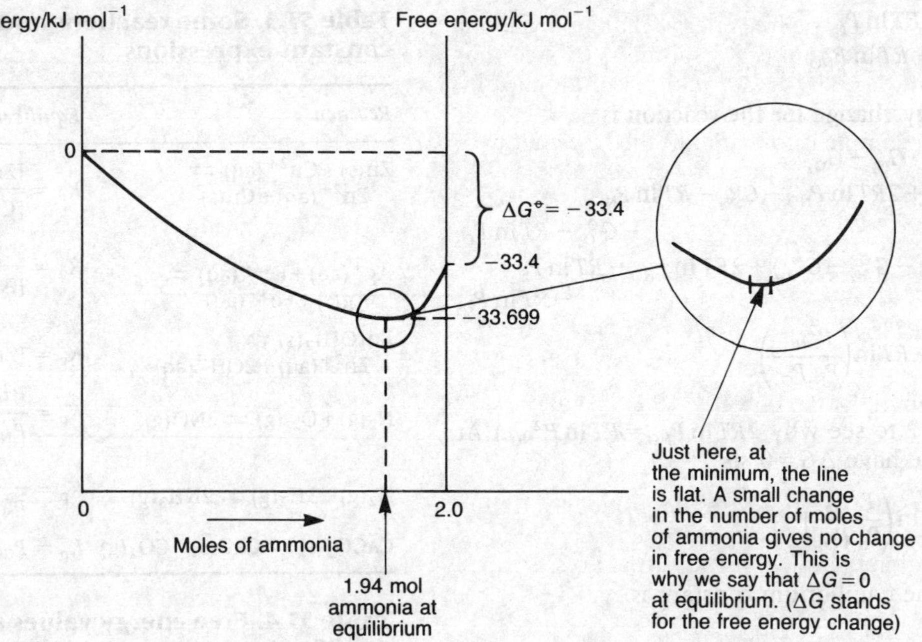

Free energy/kJ mol^{-1}
Free energy/kJ mol^{-1}
0
$\Delta G^{\ominus} = -33.4$
−33.4
−33.699
0
2.0
Moles of ammonia
1.94 mol ammonia at equilibrium
Just here, at the minimum, the line is flat. A small change in the number of moles of ammonia gives no change in free energy. This is why we say that $\Delta G = 0$ at equilibrium. (ΔG stands for the free energy change)

***Figure 51.1** The graph shows how the free energy changes in the reaction $N_2(g) + 3H_2(g) \rightleftharpoons 2NH_3(g)$ (the Haber process). We assume that we start with 1 mol $N_2(g)$ and 3 mol $H_2(g)$. As the reaction proceeds, ammonia is made. At the same time, the free energy decreases, until at equilibrium a minimum is reached. The equilibrium mixture (at 1 atm, 25°C) contains approximately 1.94 mol $NH_3(g)$, 0.03 mol $N_2(g)$ and 0.09 mol $H_2(g)$. (i) The scale of the graph has been exaggerated. (ii) On the left, we start with $N_2(g)$ and $H_2(g)$ alone. Both have $\Delta G_f^{\ominus} = 0$, hence the zero on the scale. (iii) On the right, complete conversion into 2 mol $NH_3(g)$, the figure of -33.4 kJ mol^{-1} is $2 \times \Delta G_f^{\ominus}(NH_3(g))$*

(Again, see Table 51.2 for rules about using logarithms.) This means that the Daniell cell will come to equilibrium when the zinc ion concentration is about 10^{25} greater than the copper(II) ion concentration (Figure 51.2). This happens when for all practical purposes the copper(II) ions have been completely used up. In practice, the quantity of electricity provided by the cell would be negligible long before it had reached true equilibrium.

0.0000
Voltmeter
Many of the zinc atoms have gone into solution
The majority of copper ions have changed into copper metal
The zinc sulphate solution is much more concentrated than at the start
The concentration of the copper(II) sulphate solution becomes extremely low

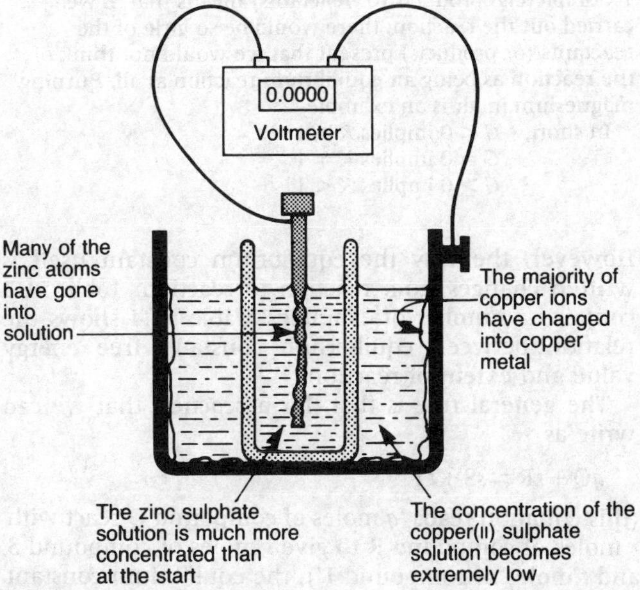

***Figure 51.2** Eventually, after the Daniell cell has been used for a long time, it has a voltage of 0 V. This is when equilibrium has been reached. Calculation shows that $[Zn^{2+}(aq)]$ is more than 10^{25} times greater than $[Cu^{2+}(aq)]$ at equilibrium*

51.3 Equilibrium and equilibrium constants

For the Daniell cell we have

$$\Delta G^{\ominus} = -RT\ln\left(\frac{[Zn^{2+}(aq)]}{[Cu^{2+}(aq)]}\right)$$

The ratio of the concentrations of the ions in this expression is called the *equilibrium constant* for the reaction. We shall write the equilibrium constant as K_c, so

$$\Delta G^{\ominus} = -RT\ln K_c$$

where

$$K_c = \frac{[Zn^{2+}(aq)]}{[Cu^{2+}(aq)]}$$

We have used the c tacked on to the K to show that the equilibrium constant is written using concentrations.

We can also apply our condition for equilibrium to reactions that involve gases. For example,

$$N_2(g) + O_2(g) \rightarrow 2NO(g)$$

The free energies of the gases are:

$$G_{O_2} = G^{\ominus}_{O_2} + RT\ln P_{O_2}$$

$$G_{N_2} = G^\ominus_{N_2} + RT\ln P_{N_2}$$
$$G_{NO} = G^\ominus_{NO} + RT\ln P_{NO}$$

The free energy change for the reaction is

$$\Delta G = 2G_{NO} - G_{N_2} - G_{O_2}$$
$$= 2G^\ominus_{NO} + 2RT\ln P_{NO} - G^\ominus_{N_2} - RT\ln P_{N_2} - G^\ominus_{O_2} - RT\ln P_{O_2}$$
$$= (2G^\ominus_{NO} - G^\ominus_{N_2} - G^\ominus_{O_2}) + 2RT\ln P_{NO} - RT\ln P_{N_2} - RT\ln P_{O_2}$$
$$= \Delta G^\ominus + RT\ln\left(\frac{P^2{}_{NO}}{P_{N_2}P_{O_2}}\right)$$

(See Table 51.2 to see why $2RT\ln P_{NO} = RT\ln P^2{}_{NO}$.) At equilibrium we have $\Delta G = 0$ so

$$\Delta G^\ominus = -RT\ln\left(\frac{P^2{}_{NO}}{P_{N_2}P_{O_2}}\right)$$

In this case, the equilibrium constant is

$$K_p = \frac{P^2{}_{NO}}{P_{N_2}P_{O_2}}$$

Here a p is used as a subscript to the K to show that pressures rather than concentrations are used.

Here is a third example, which involves a mixture of solids and gases:

$$CaCO_3(s) \rightarrow CaO(s) + CO_2(g)$$

We have

$$G_{CO_2} = G^\ominus_{CO_2} + RT\ln P_{CO_2}$$
$$G_{CaO} = G^\ominus_{CaO}$$
$$G_{CaCO_3} = G^\ominus_{CaCO_3}$$

Notice that the free energy of a solid is assumed to be independent of the pressure, so there are no correction terms for CaO or $CaCO_3$. Then we have

$$\Delta G = G_{CaO} + G_{CO_2} - G_{CaCO_3}$$
$$= G^\ominus_{CaO} + G^\ominus_{CO_2} + RT\ln P_{CO_2} - G^\ominus_{CaCO_3}$$
$$= (G^\ominus_{CaO} + G^\ominus_{CO_2} - G^\ominus_{CaCO_3}) + RT\ln P_{CO_2}$$
$$\Delta G = \Delta G^\ominus + RT\ln P_{CO_2}$$

At equilibrium, $\Delta G = 0$ so

$$\Delta G^\ominus = -RT\ln P_{CO_2}$$

In this case the equilibrium constant is very simple:

$$K_p = P_{CO_2}$$

This tells us that if we have a mixture of $CaCO_3$, CaO and CO_2, then the extent of the reaction can be gauged by measuring the pressure of CO_2, often called the *dissociation pressure* of calcium carbonate.

In fact the relation between the standard free energy change and the equilibrium constant is the same for any reaction:

At equilibrium $\quad \Delta G^\ominus = -RT\ln K$

Table 51.3. Some reactions and their equilibrium constant expressions

Reaction	*Equilibrium constant expression*
$Zn(s) + Cu^{2+}(aq) \rightleftharpoons Zn^{2+}(aq) + Cu(s)$	$K_c = \frac{[Zn^{2+}(aq)]}{[Cu^{2+}(aq)]}$
$Ag^+(aq) + Fe^{2+}(aq) \rightleftharpoons Ag(s) + Fe^{3+}(aq)$	$K_c = \frac{[Fe^{3+}(aq)]}{[Ag^+(aq)]\,[Fe^{2+}(aq)]}$
$Zn(OH)_2(s) \rightleftharpoons Zn^{2+}(aq) + 2OH^-(aq)$	$K_c = [Zn^{2+}(aq)]\,[OH^-(aq)]^2$
$N_2(g) + O_2(g) \rightleftharpoons 2NO(g)$	$K_p = \frac{P^2_{NO}}{P_{N_2}P_{O_2}}$
$N_2(g) + 3H_2(g) \rightleftharpoons 2NH_3(g)$	$K_p = \frac{P^2_{NH_3}}{P_{N_2}P^3_{H_2}}$
$CaCO_3(s) \rightleftharpoons CaO(s) + CO_2(g)$	$K_p = P_{CO_2}$

Table 51.4. Free energy values and the position of equilibrium

$\Delta G^\ominus$ /kJ mol^{-1}	*Equilibrium constant**	*At equilibrium*
−100	3.4×10^{17}	Completely products†
−50	5.8×10^{8}	Almost all products
−10	56.6	Rather more products than reactants
−5	7.5	Slightly more products than reactants
0	1.0	Equal amounts of products and reactants
+5	0.1	Slightly more reactants than products
+10	1.8×10^{-2}	Rather more reactants than products
+50	1.7×10^{-9}	Almost all reactants
+100	3.0×10^{-18}	Completely reactants†

*The equilibrium constant is for an imaginary reaction $A \rightleftharpoons B$, for which $K = [B]/[A]$

†'Completely' products (or reactants) means that, if we carried out the reaction, there would be so little of the reactants (or products) present that we would not think of the reaction as being an equilibrium reaction at all. Burning magnesium in air is an example.

In short, $G < 0$ implies $K > 1$
$G = 0$ implies $K = 1$
$G > 0$ implies $K < 1$

However, the way the equilibrium constant itself is written changes from reaction to reaction. Table 51.3 contains a number of examples. Table 51.4 shows the relation between equilibrium constant, free energy value and extent of reaction.

The general rule is that, for a reaction that we can write as

$$qQ + rR \rightleftharpoons sS + tT$$

(this equation reads 'q moles of compound Q react with r moles of compound R to give s moles of compound S and t moles of compound T'), the equilibrium constant is given by

$$K_c = \frac{[S]^s[T]^t}{[Q]^q[R]^r} \quad \text{or} \quad K_p = \frac{P^s_S P^t_T}{P^q_Q P^r_R}$$

K_c or K_p is used depending on whether the compounds are in solution or are gases.

One important thing to remember about using equilibrium constants is that solids do not appear in the formulae. Also, if you look at Table 51.1, you will find that concentrations are divided by 1 mol dm^{-3}, and pressures by the standard pressure. This means that, as we have defined them, the equilibrium constants have no units. There is another convention that is often used which results in equilibrium constants having units. This convention does not make use of thermodynamics, and we shall consider it in the next unit.

51.1 This question is about changes of state, e.g. when liquid turns into vapour, or solid turns into liquid. The free energy of the change is $\Delta G = \Delta H - T\Delta S$. If the change from ice to water is done reversibly (see Unit 49), then the change of state takes place at equilibrium.

(i) What is the value of ΔG at equilibrium?

(ii) What is the connection between ΔH and ΔS at equilibrium?

Where have you met this formula before?

51.2 (i) Write down the expression for the equilibrium constant for the reaction

$$N_2O_4(g) \rightleftharpoons 2NO_2(g); \qquad \Delta G^\ominus = +4.8 \text{ kJ mol}^{-1}$$

(ii) What is the value of the equilibrium constant, K_p, at 298 K?

(iii) Which gas is mainly present at equilibrium?

51.3 (i) Write down the equilibrium constant expression for the reaction

$$N_2(g) + 3H_2(g) \rightleftharpoons 2NH_3(g); \qquad \Delta G^\ominus = -33.4 \text{ kJ mol}^{-1}$$

The reaction is the basis of the Haber process used in industry to make ammonia (see Figure 51.1).

(ii) Calculate K_p and say which gas (or gases) is mainly present at equilibrium.

51.4 Is the following argument correct? Briefly explain your answer.

The standard free energy change of a reaction is -200 kJ mol^{-1}. This means that when the reactants are mixed, they will immediately change into products, and there will be very little of the reactants left.

Answers

51.1 (i) $\Delta G = 0$ at equilibrium.
(ii) $\Delta G = \Delta H - T\Delta S$ gives $\Delta S = \Delta H/T$.
(iii) This is the formula we met in Unit 49 and which we used to calculate entropies of vaporisation.

51.2 (i) $K_p = P_{N_2O_4}/P^2_{NO_2}$.
(ii) Using $\Delta G^\ominus = -RT \ln K_p$ gives
$K_p = \exp[-4.8 \times 10^3 \text{ J mol}^{-1}/(8.314 \text{ J K}^{-1} \text{ mol}^{-1} \times 298 \text{ K})]$
$= 0.144$
(iii) The fact that $\Delta G^\ominus$ is a small positive number tells us that the reactants will be in a slight excess over products: there will be more N_2O_4 than NO_2.

51.3 (i) $K_p = \dfrac{P^2_{NH_3}}{P_{N_2}P^3_{H_2}}$
(ii) Using $\Delta G^\ominus = -RT \ln K_p$ gives
$K_p = \exp[33.4 \times 10^3 \text{ J mol}^{-1}/(8.314 \text{ J K}^{-1} \text{ mol}^{-1} \times 298 \text{ K})]$
$= 7.2 \times 10^5$
(iii) Ammonia will be in excess owing to $\Delta G^\ominus$ being a fairly large negative value.

51.4 It is true that *at equilibrium* the quantity of products would far outweigh the reactants. However, the value of the free energy change does not allow us to predict how fast the reaction will take place. Thermodynamics tells us nothing about rates of reactions. Equilibrium might take years to be achieved, or not be achieved at all in any reasonable time scale.

UNIT 51 SUMMARY

- At equilibrium $\Delta G = 0$ and $\Delta G^\ominus = -RT \ln K_c$ or $\Delta G^\ominus = -RT \ln K_p$ where K_c is the equilibrium constant for the reaction in terms of concentrations, and K_p is in terms of partial pressures.
- For a reaction $q\text{Q} + r\text{R} \rightleftharpoons s\text{S} + t\text{T}$, we have:

$$K_c = \frac{[\text{S}]^s[\text{T}]^t}{[\text{Q}]^q[\text{R}]^r} \quad \text{or} \quad K_p = \frac{P^s_S P^t_T}{P^q_Q P^r_R}$$

52

Chemical equilibrium

52.1 Equilibrium constants

In 1864 two Norwegian chemists, C. M. Guldberg and P. Waage, argued that chemists should

> study the chemical reactions in which the forces which produce new compounds are held in equilibrium by other forces . . . where the reaction is not complete, but partial.

In their work on equilibrium they formulated a law called the *law of mass action*, in which they claimed that each chemical taking part in a reaction had an 'active mass'. Guldberg and Waage said that the forces that they imagined to be controlling reactions were proportional to the product of the active masses of the chemicals. We now recognise their active masses as concentrations.

For a simple reaction like the reaction of an organic acid with an alcohol to give an ester plus water,

$$\text{alcohol} + \text{acid} \rightleftharpoons \text{ester} + \text{water}$$

they were saying that the force making the alcohol and acid react together was proportional to [alcohol] × [acid] (the square brackets mean 'concentration of', with units mol dm^{-3}), i.e.

$$\text{force of forward reaction} = \text{a constant} \times [\text{alcohol}] \times [\text{acid}]$$

Similarly, the force making the ester and water react together was proportional to [ester] × [water], i.e.

$$\text{force of backward reaction} = \text{a constant} \times [\text{ester}] \times [\text{water}]$$

At equilibrium the idea is that the two 'forces' are balanced so we have

$$\text{a constant} \times [\text{alcohol}] \times [\text{acid}] = \text{a constant} \times [\text{ester}] \times [\text{water}]$$

This gives us

$$\frac{\text{a constant}}{\text{a constant}} = \frac{[\text{ester}] \times [\text{water}]}{[\text{alcohol}] \times [\text{acid}]}$$

Because two constants multiplied or divided by one another is also a constant, we can simplify this to give

$$K_c = \frac{[\text{ester}] \times [\text{water}]}{[\text{alcohol}] \times [\text{acid}]}$$

where K_c is called the *equilibrium constant*. The subscript c has been added to show that we are working with concentrations. Usually it is easier to miss out the multiplication signs so we have

$$K_c = \frac{[\text{ester}][\text{water}]}{[\text{alcohol}][\text{acid}]}$$

This expression has been verified many times by careful experimental work. One way of doing this is explained in the following unit.

Please make sure you realise that the concentrations in the expression *must* refer to equilibrium. If you mix ethanol and ethanoic acid together you will have to wait some time before the reaction reaches equilibrium. Only at equilibrium will the expression for the equilibrium constant be correct. It is possible to emphasise this point by writing the concentrations with a subscript 'eq' (short for equilibrium):

$$K_c = \frac{[\text{ester}]_{eq}[\text{water}]_{eq}}{[\text{alcohol}]_{eq}[\text{acid}]_{eq}}$$

However, this can be rather tedious and we shall not use this notation.

The problem with the original law of mass action was that it was hard to predict the correct expression for the equilibrium constant of the majority of reactions. For example, in the reaction

$$2SO_2(g) + O_2(g) \rightleftharpoons 2SO_3(g)$$

we might expect the equilibrium constant to be

$$K_c = \frac{[SO_3(g)]}{[SO_2(g)][O_2(g)]} \quad \textit{wrong}$$

The results of experiment show that

$$K_c = \frac{[SO_3(g)]^2}{[SO_2(g)]^2[O_2(g)]} \quad \textit{correct}$$

Using gases it is easier to measure pressures rather than concentrations, and we can write an equilibrium constant in terms of the partial pressures of the gases

Panel 52.1

Important information on partial pressures of gases

In a mixture of gases, A and B, the total pressure P_T is given by

$$P_T = P_A + P_B$$

where P_A and P_B are the partial pressures of the two gases. These are the pressures that the gases would have if they existed in the container alone.

If there are n_A moles of A and n_B moles of B, then the mole fraction of each gas is

$$x_A = \frac{n_A}{n_A + n_A} \qquad x_B = \frac{n_B}{n_A + n_B}$$

Finally, the partial pressure of each gas is related to the total pressure by the equations

$$P_A = x_A P_T \quad \text{and} \quad P_B = x_B P_T$$

Consider the following example: 1 mol of helium is mixed with 2 mol of neon. The total pressure is 2 atm. What are the partial pressures of the gases?

We have $x_{helium} = \frac{1}{3}$ and $x_{neon} = \frac{2}{3}$. Therefore

$$P_{helium} = \tfrac{1}{3} \times 2\text{ atm} = \tfrac{2}{3}\text{ atm}$$

and

$$P_{neon} = \tfrac{2}{3} \times 2\text{ atm} = \tfrac{4}{3}\text{ atm}.$$

(see panel 52.1 if you have forgotten about partial pressures of gases):

$$K_p = \frac{P^2_{SO_3}}{P^2_{SO_2} P_{O_2}} \quad \textit{correct}$$

In fact the results of many thousands of experiments show that for a general reaction in which q moles of compound Q react with r moles of compound R to give s moles of compound S and t moles of compound T,

$$qQ + rR \rightleftharpoons sS + tT$$

the equilibrium constant is given by

$$K_c = \frac{[S]^s[T]^t}{[Q]^q[R]^r} \quad \text{or} \quad K_p = \frac{P^s_S P^t_T}{P^q_Q P^r_R}$$

K_c or K_p is used depending on whether it is easier to measure concentrations or pressures.

Again, from experiment it turns out that we can ignore solids in writing down equilibrium constants. You can think of the concentration of a solid (which is akin to its density) as a constant value, which will not affect the value of an equilibrium constant. Table 52.1 shows some examples.

You will find other examples of equilibrium reactions, with their constants, in Unit 53. In every case we write the equilibrium constant with the concentrations of the products divided by the concentrations of the reactants.

Table 52.1. Some reactions and their equilibrium constant expressions

Reaction	*Equilibrium constant expression*
$CaCO_3(s) \rightleftharpoons CaO(s) + CO_2(g)$	$K_p = P_{CO_2}$
$H_2(g) + I_2(g) \rightleftharpoons 2HI(g)$	$K_p = \dfrac{P^2_{HI}}{P_{H_2} P_{I_2}}$
$H_2(g) + I_2(s)^* \rightleftharpoons 2HI(g)$	$K_p = \dfrac{P^2_{HI}}{P_{H_2}}$
$AgCl(s) \rightleftharpoons Ag^+(aq) + Cl^-(aq)$	$K_c = [Ag^+(aq)]\,[Cl^-(aq)]$
$Cu^{2+}(aq) + 4Cl^-(aq) \rightleftharpoons CuCl_4^{2-}(aq)$	$K_c = \dfrac{[CuCl_4^{2-}(aq)]}{[Cu^{2+}(aq)]\,[Cl^-(aq)]^4}$

*Notice that the iodine is a solid in this case

52.1 Write down the expression for the equilibrium constant for each of the following reactions:

(i) $CO(g) + 2H_2(g) \rightleftharpoons CH_3OH(g)$

(ii) $C_2H_4(g) + H_2O(g) \rightleftharpoons C_2H_5OH(g)$

(iii) $2Mg(s) + O_2(g) \rightleftharpoons 2MgO(s)$

(iv) $C(s) + O_2(g) \rightleftharpoons CO_2(g)$

(v) $H_2(g) + CO_2(g) \rightleftharpoons H_2O(g) + CO(g)$

(vi) $CH_3COOH(aq) \rightleftharpoons CH_3COO^-(aq) + H^+(aq)$

(vii) $Ce^{4+}(aq) + Fe^{2+}(aq) \rightleftharpoons Ce^{3+}(aq) + Fe^{3+}(aq)$

(viii) $NH_4Cl(s) \rightleftharpoons NH_3(g) + HCl(g)$

(ix) $H_2O(g) + CO(g) \rightleftharpoons H_2(g) + CO_2(g)$

Use K_p or K_c depending on the states of the chemicals.

52.2 Equilibrium constants and their units

There are two ways of tackling equilibrium constants. The way we are dealing with them in this unit is to say that they are determined purely from experiment. If you were to measure the concentrations of the reactants and products in the reaction

$$AgCl(s) \rightleftharpoons Ag^+(aq) + Cl^-(aq)$$

where $K_c = [Ag^+(aq)][Cl^-(aq)]$, your answer for the value of K_c would have to have the units of (concentration)^2, or mol^2 dm^{-6}. Similarly, for the reaction

$$2SO_2(g) + O_2(g) \rightleftharpoons 2SO_3(g)$$

with

$$K_p = \frac{P^2_{SO_3}}{P^2_{SO_2} P_{O_2}}.$$

the units of K_p are those of

$$\frac{(\text{pressure})^2}{(\text{pressure})^2(\text{pressure})} \quad \text{i.e. Pa}^{-1} \text{ or atm}^{-1}$$

Thus, the units of equilibrium constants change depending on the reaction involved.

The second way of treating equilibrium constants is from thermodynamics. In Unit 51 you can discover the connection between the way in which free energy changes in a reaction and the resulting equilibrium. If you use the thermodynamic way of treating equilibrium constants then they are all dimensionless, i.e. they have no units. You will probably find that in the examination course you are following you are expected to state the units of equilibrium constants. This is annoying but it is sensible to make sure you can work out the units.

52.2 For each of the equilibria in question 52.1, write down the units of the equilibrium constant.

52.3 Are equilibrium constants really constant?

To answer this we need to think about changes in four factors that are often used to bring about chemical changes. These are summarised in Table 52.2.

Table 52.2. Influences on equilibrium constants

Change	*Effect on equilibrium constant*
Temperature	Changes
Concentration	No change
Pressure	No change
Catalyst	No change (but equilibrium reached more quickly)

(a) *Temperature*

Equilibrium constants change when temperature changes; but *provided the temperature does not change*, an equilibrium constant really is constant. For example, in the reaction

$$2SO_2(g) + O_2(g) \rightleftharpoons 2SO_3(g)$$

at 298 K, the equilibrium constant is always $K_p = 4 \times 10^{24}$ atm^{-1}. It does not matter whether you mixed the gases in quantities of a few grams of each or several tonnes, always the equilibrium constant has the same value, *provided the temperature is the same.* In the next section we shall discover the ways in which temperature affects equilibrium constants.

(b) *Concentration*

If you change the concentration of the reactants or products in a reaction at equilibrium, the proportions of reactants and products adjust themselves in such a way that K_c does *not* change (provided the temperature does not change). For example, if you add alcohol to the equilibrium

$$\text{alcohol} + \text{acid} \rightleftharpoons \text{ester} + \text{water}$$

for which

$$K_c = \frac{[\text{ester}] \times [\text{water}]}{[\text{alcohol}] \times [\text{acid}]}$$

then some of the extra alcohol reacts to make more ester and water. As a result the increase in [alcohol] is just balanced by the increase in [ester] and [water].

(c) *Pressure*

Equilibrium constants do *not* change when pressure changes. For example, if the sulphur dioxide reaction above is performed at 1 atm or 10 atm then K_p keeps the same value, provided the temperature is 298 K. However, the proportions of reactants and products can change, just as they do when concentrations are changed. In section 52.6 we shall discover how to calculate the extent of the changes that take place.

(d) *Catalysts*

We know that at equilibrium there is no overall change in the proportions of the reactants and products. However, this is not to say that chemical life has come to an end at equilibrium. *The reactions between the chemicals are still taking place.* This fact lies behind the statement that the reactants and products come to a state of *dynamic equilibrium*. The word 'dynamic' implies that there is a lot of activity at equilibrium.

At equilibrium the reactants are changing into products at the same rate as the products are changing back to give reactants. Indeed this is a condition for equilibrium:

$$\text{reactants} \underset{\text{backward reaction}}{\overset{\text{forward reaction}}{\rightleftharpoons}} \text{products}$$

At equilibrium,

rate of forward reaction = rate of backward reaction

We shall deal with rates of reactions in Unit 77. For the present you just need to be aware of the fact that the reactions continue in an equilibrium mixture. If a catalyst is added to the reaction mixture, then the rates of the reactions increase, and equilibrium is achieved more quickly. However, the proportions of the reactants and products at equilibrium do *not* change. For this reason, a catalyst has *no effect* on the value of an equilibrium constant.

52.4 How does temperature affect an equilibrium reaction?

The most direct way of discovering the answer to this question is to do some experiments. In Table 52.3 are

Table 52.3. Variations of equilibrium constants with temperature for two reactions

Reaction $2NO_2(g) \rightleftharpoons N_2O_4(g)$			
T/K	*K*/atm^{-1}	Δ*H*/kJ mol^{-1}	Δ*G*/kJ mol^{-1}
298	0.115	58.0	5.4
350	3.89	57.9	−3.9
400	47.9	57.7	−12.9
450	347	57.6	−21.9
500	1700	57.4	−30.9
550	6030	57.2	−39.9
600	17800	57.1	−48.8

Reaction $N_2(g)+3H_2(g) \rightleftharpoons 2NH_3(g)$			
T/K	*K*/atm^{-2}	Δ*H*/kJ mol^{-1}	Δ*G*/kJ mol^{-1}
298	6.76×10^{5}	−92.4	−33.3
400	4.07×10^{1}	−96.9	−12.3
500	3.55×10^{-2}	−101.3	13.9
600	1.66×10^{-3}	−105.8	31.9
700	7.76×10^{-5}	−110.2	55.1
800	6.92×10^{-6}	−114.6	79.1
900	1.00×10^{-6}	−119.0	103.3

the results of two sets of experiments on the reactions

$$2NO_2(g) \rightleftharpoons N_2O_4(g) \quad \text{and} \quad N_2(g)+3H_2(g) \rightleftharpoons 2NH_3(g)$$

In each case, the gases are allowed to come to equilibrium at a given temperature; then the reaction mixture is analysed in order to find the proportions of each. Given the concentrations, or pressures, of each gas the equilibrium constant can be calculated.

The first reaction is endothermic over the whole temperature range, while the second reaction, the Haber process, is exothermic. For the endothermic reaction, the equilibrium constant increases with temperature. This means that, as the temperature rises, there is proportionately more dinitrogen tetraoxide, N_2O_4, in the equilibrium mixture. On the other hand, in the Haber process, as the temperature rises the equilibrium constant becomes smaller and smaller. Here, the proportion of ammonia decreases as the temperature rises.

These two sets of data are typical of all reactions:

For an endothermic reaction, an increase in temperature favours the products.

For an exothermic reaction, an increase in temperature favours the reactants.

The effect of temperature on an equilibrium is nicely summarised in a famous principle proposed by the French chemist Henri Le Chatelier in 1888. *Le Chatelier's principle* says that:

If a constraint is placed on an equilibrium mixture, then the equilibrium will shift so as to oppose the constraint.

At present we are thinking of 'a constraint' as a change in temperature. Thus the principle says that if the temperature is increased then the equilibrium will shift so as to reduce the temperature. In an *exothermic* reaction the change from reactants to products gives out heat; the reverse change, from products to reactants, absorbs heat:

Exothermic reaction

$$\text{reactants favoured at high temperatures} \;\underset{\text{heat absorbed}}{\overset{\text{heat released}}{\rightleftharpoons}}\; \text{products favoured at low temperatures}$$

Therefore if the temperature is increased, the reaction will shift to the left. As the proportion of reactants increases, more heat is absorbed, which results in the temperature being reduced. The situation with an *endothermic* reaction is different:

Endothermic reaction

$$\text{reactants favoured at low temperatures} \;\underset{\text{heat released}}{\overset{\text{heat absorbed}}{\rightleftharpoons}}\; \text{products favoured at high temperatures}$$

In this case, if the temperature is increased, then the equilibrium will shift to the right, in favour of products. For an endothermic reaction, this is the direction of change that will reduce the temperature.

52.3 Calculate the standard enthalpy changes at 298 K for reactions (i) and (ii) in question 52.1. Then predict what will happen if the temperature of each equilibrium mixture were increased.

You will need the following heats of formation, all in kJ mol^{-1}: $\Delta H^\circ_f(CH_3OH) = -238.9$; $\Delta H^\circ_f(C_2H_5OH) = -277.7$; $\Delta H^\circ_f(C_2H_4) = +52.3$; $\Delta H^\circ_f(H_2O(g)) = -228.6$; $\Delta H^\circ_f(CO) = -110.5$.

52.5 How can the connection between equilibrium constants and temperature be made more exact?

Le Chatelier's principle does not allow us to be exact about the change in an equilibrium. However, it is now known how to predict with some accuracy the change that will take place in an equilibrium constant when temperature changes.

To begin with, look at Table 52.4. The data for the nitrogen dioxide–nitrogen tetraoxide equilibrium illustrate the rule that the enthalpy change for a reac-

Table 52.4. How equilibrium constants change with temperature

Reaction	ΔH	*Temperature change*	*Equilibrium constant*	*Reactants*	*Products*
Exothermic	Negative	Decrease	Increase	Decrease	Increase
		Increase	Decrease	Increase	Decrease
Endothermic	Positive	Increase	Increase	Decrease	Increase
		Decrease	Decrease	Increase	Decrease

tion does not change greatly as the temperature changes. It is a common assumption that enthalpy changes are independent of the temperature. As the data for the Haber process show, this assumption is not always valid; but for the majority of reactions it is quite acceptable. If you had enough time, and the use of a computer, you would be able to discover that there is a definite connection between the equilibrium constant, the standard enthalpy change for the reaction, ΔH, and the temperature, T. The equation which links them is:

$$\ln\left(\frac{K_1}{K_2}\right)=\frac{\Delta H^{\ominus}}{R}\left(\frac{1}{T_2}-\frac{1}{T_1}\right)$$

Here, K_1 is the equilibrium constant measured at temperature T_1, and K_2 that measured at T_2. As usual, ln means the natural logarithm, and R is the gas constant.

This equation has several uses. First, if we know the value of $\Delta H^{\ominus}$ and the equilibrium constant at one temperature, we can calculate the value of the equilibrium constant at a different temperature. Secondly, if we do experiments to discover the values of the equilibrium constants at two different temperatures, then we can work out the size of the enthalpy change. You might like to try your hand at these types of calculation in the questions.

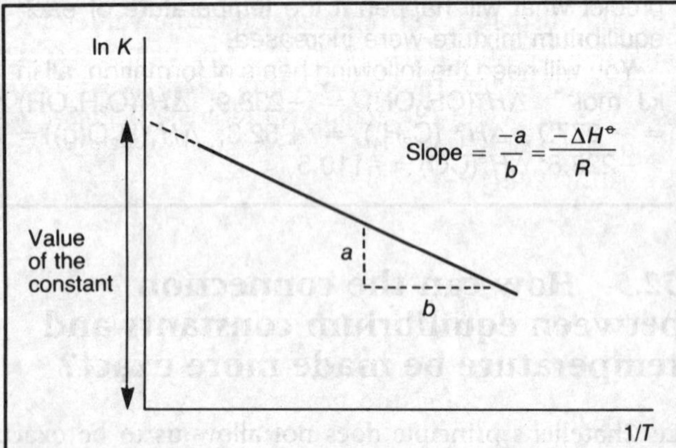

Figure 52.1 A graph of ln K plotted against 1/T is a straight line. The equation of the line is

$$\ln K=-\frac{\Delta H^{\ominus}}{R}\times\frac{1}{T}+\text{constant}$$

The slope of the line allows us to calculate $\Delta H^{\ominus}$, and the intercept on the ln K axis gives the value of the constant

52.4 The equation of the line plotted in Figure 52.1 is

$$\ln K=-\frac{\Delta H^{\ominus}}{R}\times\frac{1}{T}+\text{constant}$$

This is the equation of a straight line if $\ln K$ is plotted against $1/T$. The line will cut the $\ln K$ axis when $1/T=0$. This allows us to measure the value of the constant from the graph. The question is: 'Has the constant any meaning?' Needless to say, it has.

First, write down the equations that link $\Delta G^{\ominus}$ to $\ln K$ (see section 51.3) and to $\Delta H^{\ominus}$ and $\Delta S^{\ominus}$. Then write $\ln K$ in terms of $\Delta H^{\ominus}$ and $\Delta S^{\ominus}$. Compare your result with the equation above.

What does the value of the constant tell us?

52.5 For the reaction

$C(s)+H_2O(g)\rightleftharpoons H_2(g)+CO(g)$

the equilibrium constant has the value 10^{-16} atm^{-1} at 298 K. The value of $\Delta H^{\ominus}$ is $+131.3$ kJ mol^{-1}. Use the equation of section 52.5 to calculate the value of the equilibrium constant at 1000 K.

What do the values of the equilibrium constant tell you about the proportions of reactants and products at the two temperatures?

52.6 For the reaction

$H_2(g)+I_2(g)\rightleftharpoons 2HI(g)$

at 298 K, $K_p=794$, and at 500 K, $K_p=160$. Is the enthalpy change for the reaction endothermic or exothermic? Use the same equation as in question 52.5 to calculate the value of $\Delta H^{\ominus}$.

52.6 Pressure can change the proportions of reactants and products at equilibrium

You might wonder how we can say that a change in pressure does not change the value of an equilibrium constant, yet it can change the proportions of reactants and products. To see how this comes about, look at this reaction:

$Cl_2(g)+PCl_3(g)\rightleftharpoons PCl_5(g)$

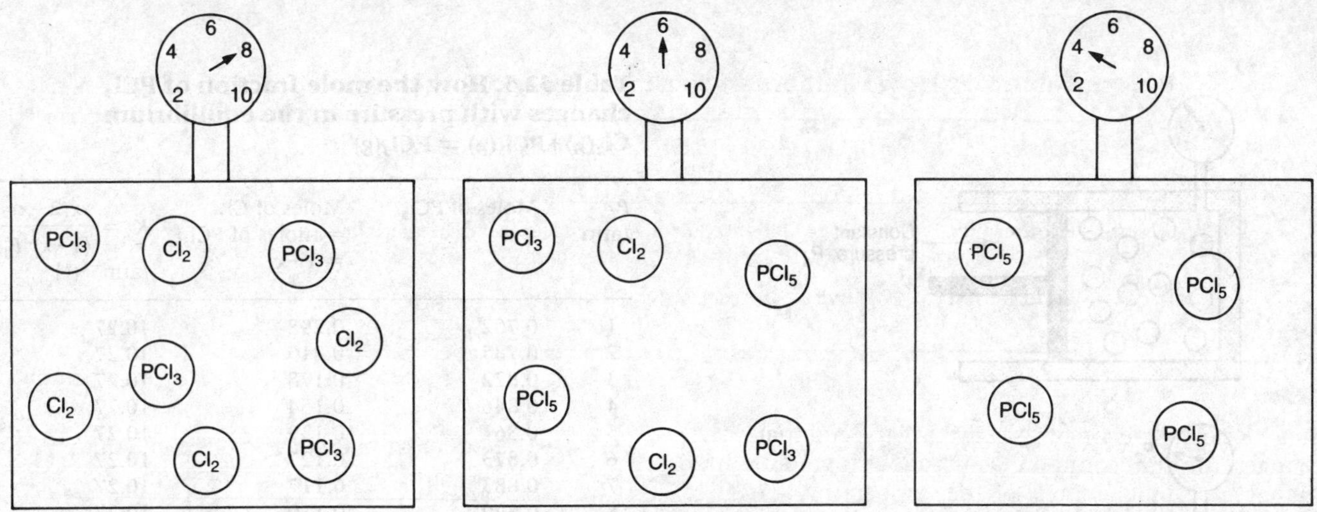

***Figure 52.2** At the start of the reaction between Cl_2 and PCl_3, no PCl_5 has been made. As the reaction proceeds, the number of particles in the box decreases. This causes the pressure to decrease. If all the Cl_2 and PCl_3 were converted into PCl_5 the pressure would go down by one-half. In practice the pressure at equilibrium is somewhere between the two extremes (not necessarily half-way!)*

The equilibrium constant is

$$K_p = \frac{P_{PCl_5}}{P_{Cl_2} P_{PCl_3}}$$

Experiment shows that $K_p = 10.27\,\text{atm}^{-1}$ at about 450 K.

The equation tells us that there must be a connection between the relative amounts of the three gases, because for every 1 mol of PCl_5 that is made, 1 mol of Cl_2 and 1 mol of PCl_3 must have reacted. Let us suppose we allow the reaction to take place in a box fitted with a pressure gauge (Figure 52.2).

We shall also assume that we start the reaction going by mixing 1 mol each of Cl_2 and PCl_3. If the reaction went to completion we would expect to find 1 mol of PCl_5 left. A total of two moles of gas would have been replaced by 1 mol of gas, so in this case we would expect the final pressure inside the cylinder to be half the starting pressure. In fact, the reaction comes to an equilibrium, so the final pressure will not be exactly half the starting pressure; it should be rather greater than this (but less than the starting pressure).

We shall say that the amount of Cl_2 reacted at equilibrium is x mol. Our equation tells us that an equal number of moles of PCl_3 will have reacted, and that the amount of PCl_5 formed will also be x mol. We can summarise this in the following way:

	$Cl_2(g)$	+ $PCl_3(g)$	$\rightleftharpoons$ $PCl_5(g)$
At start	1 mol	1 mol	0 mol
Amount reacted	x mol	x mol	
At equilibrium	$1-x$ mol	$1-x$ mol	x mol
		Total $2-x$ mol	
Mole fraction at equilibrium	$\frac{1-x}{2-x}$	$\frac{1-x}{2-x}$	$\frac{x}{2-x}$
Partial pressure at equilibrium	$\frac{(1-x)P_T}{2-x}$	$\frac{(1-x)P_T}{2-x}$	$\frac{xP_T}{2-x}$

If we put these expressions into the equation for K_p we have

$$K_p = \frac{xP_T/(2-x)}{[(1-x)P_T/(2-x)][(1-x)P_T/(2-x)]}$$

i.e.

$$K_p = \frac{x(2-x)}{(1-x)^2 P_T}$$

With the help of a computer we can solve this equation to discover what happens to x when the total pressure P_T changes. The idea is that we place our 1 mol of Cl_2 and 1 mol of PCl_3 into the cylinder. Then we adjust the cylinder to keep the pressure constant, and allow the system to come to equilibrium. Figure 52.3 shows a graph of the mole fraction, $x/(2-x)$, of PCl_5 plotted against pressure. The graph and Table 52.5 show very clearly that, as the pressure increases, the proportion of PCl_5 also increases, but remember that the value of K_p remains constant. The tendency is for an increase in pressure to favour the formation of PCl_5. As we have already said, when this happens there is a decrease in the number of moles of gas, so pressure will decrease. We can write this in a simple way:

$Cl_2(g) + PCl_3(g)$	$\rightleftharpoons$	$PCl_5(g)$
more moles on this side: 'high pressure' side		fewer moles on this side: 'low pressure' side

We have discovered that, when the pressure is increased by pushing the piston down on the gases, more PCl_5 is made. That is, the equilibrium shifts to the low pressure side. This behaviour is also covered by Le Chatelier's principle. The constraint is the increase in pressure applied to the gases. The response of the equilibrium is to lower the pressure, and it does this by moving to the low pressure side, i.e. the side that has fewer gaseous molecules.

With some thought you should be able to understand

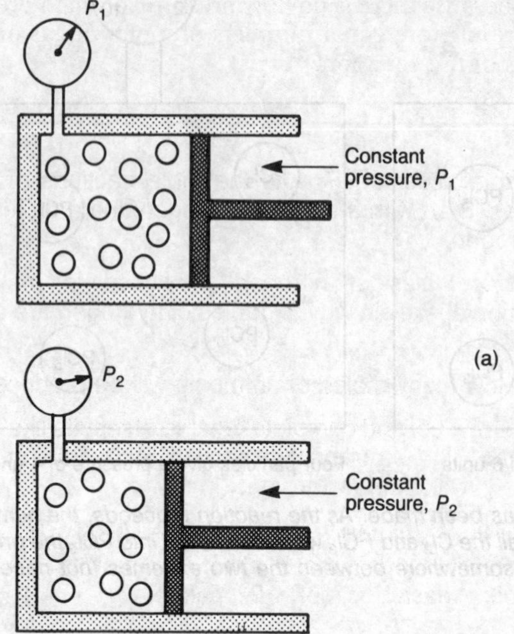

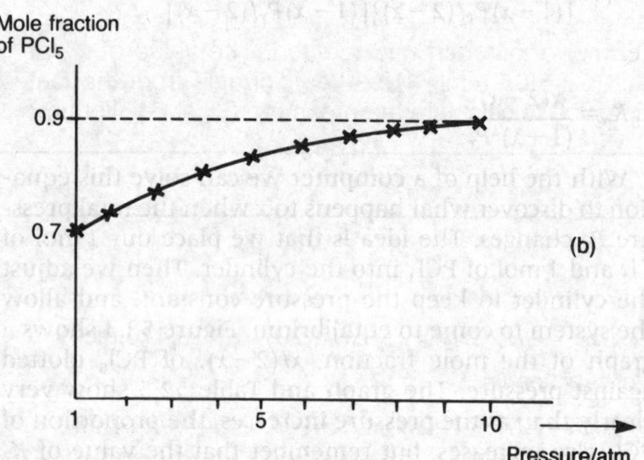

Figure 52.3 (a) As the reaction between Cl_2 and PCl_3 takes place, the number of particles decreases. Unlike the box in figure 52.2, this time we keep the pressure in the cylinder constant by applying a constant pressure to the piston. The volume of the mixture of gases changes until, at equilibrium, the volume remains constant. (b) The mole fraction of PCl_5 in the mixture increases as the pressure increases. Each point on the line corresponds to the mixture of Cl_2, PCl_3 and PCl_5 at equilibrium at the given pressure. (We assume that the temperature is also kept constant)

that if the pressure on the piston were reduced, then the equilibrium will shift in the direction that increases the number of molecules of gas at equilibrium. This is the side that favours PCl_3 and Cl_2.

Before we leave this section we shall think about two other types of gaseous reactions. In the first type there is an increase in the number of moles of gas as the reaction proceeds. A typical example is propane being 'cracked' apart to produce methane and ethene:

Table 52.5. How the mole fraction of PCl_5 changes with pressure in the equilibrium $Cl_2(g)+PCl_3(g) \rightleftharpoons PCl_5(g)$

P_T /atm	Moles of PCl_5 $= x$	Moles of Cl_2 = moles of PCl_3 $= 1-x$	$K_p = \dfrac{x(2-x)}{(1-x)^2 P_T}$ /atm^{-1}(*)
1	0.702	0.298	10.27
2	0.785	0.215	10.27
3	0.822	0.178	10.27
4	0.846	0.154	10.27
5	0.861	0.139	10.27
6	0.873	0.127	10.27
7	0.883	0.117	10.27
8	0.890	0.110	10.27
9	0.897	0.103	10.27
10	0.901	0.099	10.27

*These values have been calculated. Owing to experimental error, it would be most unlikely that measured values would be so consistent

$C_3H_8(g)$	$\rightleftharpoons$	$CH_4(g) + C_2H_4(g)$
fewer moles on this side: 'low pressure' side		more moles on this side: 'high pressure' side

Here an increase in pressure will favour the production of C_3H_8.

Another type of reaction is where there is no change in the number of moles of gas. For example,

$$H_2(g) + Cl_2(g) \rightleftharpoons 2HCl(g)$$

In a reaction like this, a change in pressure has no effect at all on the proportions of the gases at equilibrium. We can prove this by calculating K_p in terms of the mole fractions of the gases:

	$H_2(g)$	+ $Cl_2(g)$	$\rightleftharpoons$ $2HCl(g)$
At start	1 mol	1 mol	0 mol
Amount reacted	x mol	x mol	
At equilibrium	$1-x$ mol	$1-x$ mol	$2x$ mol
		Total 2 mol	
Mole fraction at equilibrium	$\dfrac{1-x}{2}$	$\dfrac{1-x}{2}$	$\dfrac{2x}{2}=x$
Partial pressure at equilibrium	$\dfrac{(1-x)P_T}{2}$	$\dfrac{(1-x)P_T}{2}$	xP_T

If we put these expressions into the equation for K_p we have

$$K_p = \frac{P^2_{HCl}}{P_{H_2}P_{Cl_2}}$$

$$= \frac{(xP_T)^2}{[(1-x)P_T/2][(1-x)P_T/2]}$$

i.e.

$$K_p = \frac{4x^2}{(1-x)^2}$$

The pressure does not appear in this expression, which proves that there is no change in the mole fractions of the gases as the pressure changes. We should expect this because there is no 'low pressure' or 'high pressure' side; there are equal numbers of moles of gas on both sides of the equation.

52.7 Describe what will happen if an equilibrium mixture in each of the following reactions is subjected to a *decrease* in pressure:

(i) $N_2(g)+3H_2(g)\rightleftharpoons 2NH_3(g)$

(ii) $C(s)+2H_2(g)\rightleftharpoons CH_4(g)$

(iii) $CH_4(g)+CO_2(g)\rightleftharpoons 2CO(g)+2H_2(g)$

(iv) $C(s)+O_2(g)\rightleftharpoons CO_2(g)$

52.8 This question asks you to adapt the formula we worked out for K_p in the reaction

$$Cl_2(g)+PCl_3(g)\rightleftharpoons PCl_5(g)$$

in section 52.6. Work through the method in that section, but this time start with a moles of $Cl_2(g)$ and a moles of $PCl_3(g)$ rather than one mole of each. What is the final expression for K_p?

52.9 This is a rather tricky question about the Haber process:

$$N_2(g)+3H_2(g)\rightleftharpoons 2NH_3(g)$$

The objective is to write K_p for the reaction in terms of the total pressure P_T and the mole fractions of the gases. Start with a moles of nitrogen and a moles of hydrogen.

(i) If x moles of nitrogen are used in making ammonia, explain why $3x$ moles of hydrogen are also used.

(ii) How many moles of ammonia will be produced?

(iii) Draw up, and complete, a table of results like that for the other equilibria in section 52.6. Part of the table is done below for you:

	$N_2(g)$ +	$3H_2(g)\rightleftharpoons$	$2NH_3(g)$
At start	a mol	a mol	0 mol
Amount reacted	x mol	$3x$ mol	

What is the expression for K_p?

52.10 A mixture of nitrogen and hydrogen was allowed to come to equilibrium at 400 K. The original amount of each gas was $a=2$ mol. At equilibrium, 0.2 mol of nitrogen had reacted. The value of K_p at 400 K is 40.7 atm^{-2}. Use your formula from the last question to calculate the pressure, P_T, at equilibrium.

Answers

52.1 (i) $K_p=\dfrac{P_{CH_3OH}}{P_{CO}P_{H_2}^2}$; (ii) $K_p=\dfrac{P_{C_2HOH}}{P_{C_2H_4}P_{H_2O}}$;

(iii) $K_p=\dfrac{1}{P_{O_2}}$; (iv) $K_p=\dfrac{P_{CO_2}}{P_{O_2}}$; (v) $K_p=\dfrac{P_{H_2O}P_{CO}}{P_{H_2}P_{CO_2}}$;

(vi) $K_c=\dfrac{[CH_3COO^-(aq)][H^+(aq)]}{[CH_3COOH(aq)]}$;

(vii) $K_c=\dfrac{[Ce^{3+}(aq)][Fe^{3+}(aq)]}{[Ce^{4+}(aq)][Fe^{2+}(aq)]}$;

(viii) $K_p=P_{NH_3}P_{HCl}$; (ix) $K_p=\dfrac{P_{H_2}P_{CO_2}}{P_{H_2O}P_{CO}}$.

In part (vi) K_c is better known as K_a, the acid dissociation constant for ethanoic acid. Notice that the reaction in (ix) is the reverse of that in (v). The expression for the equilibrium constant for (ix) is the K_p for (v) turned upside down. It is important that you write the equilibrium constant expression for the reaction *as written in the chemical equation*.

52.2 (i) atm^{-2}; (ii) atm^{-1}; (iii) atm^{-1}; (iv) none; (v) none; (vi) mol dm^{-3}; (vii) none; (viii) atm^2; (ix) none.
An alternative to atmospheres, atm, is pascals, Pa.

52.3 In reaction (i)

$$\Delta H^\circ=\Delta H_f^\circ(CH_3OH)-\Delta H_f^\circ(CO)=-128.4\text{ kJ mol}^{-1}$$

For reaction (ii)

$$\Delta H^\circ=\Delta H_f^\circ(C_2H_5OH)-\Delta H_f^\circ(C_2H_4)-\Delta H_f^\circ(H_2O(g))$$
$$=+16.4\text{ kJ mol}^{-1}$$

The production of methanol is an exothermic reaction, so Le Chatelier's principle tells us that an increase in temperature will favour the reverse reaction. That is, the proportions of carbon monoxide and hydrogen will increase.

The second reaction is endothermic, so an increase in temperature will favour the forward reaction. There will be an increase in the proportion of ethanol in the mixture.

52.4 The equations are $\Delta G^\circ=-RT\ln K$ and $\Delta G^\circ=\Delta H^\circ-T\Delta S^\circ$. Combining them gives us $-RT\ln K=\Delta H^\circ-T\Delta S^\circ$, or

$$\ln K=-\Delta H^\circ/RT+\Delta S^\circ/R$$

Hence the value of the constant is the standard entropy change divided by the gas constant. By measuring the intercept on the graph, and multiplying by the gas constant, we discover the standard entropy change for the reaction.

Answers – contd.

52.5 Let us put $T_1 = 298\,K$, and $T_2 = 1000\,K$. Then we have

$$\ln\left(\frac{10^{-16}}{K_2}\right) = \frac{131.4\times10^3\,J\,mol^{-1}}{8.314\,J\,K^{-1}\,mol^{-1}}\left(\frac{1}{1000\,K} - \frac{1}{298\,K}\right)$$

$$\ln 10^{-16} - \ln K_2 = \frac{131.4\times10^3}{8.314}\times\left(\frac{298-1000}{1000\times298}\right)$$

$$-36.841 - \ln K_2 = -37.231$$

which gives

$$\ln K_2 = 37.231 - 36.841 = 0.39$$

and

$$K_2 = \exp(0.39) = 1.48$$

We are using the convention that equilibrium constants have units, so the result should be that $K_2 = 1.48\,atm^{-1}$.

This shows that there is a marked change in the balance of the equilibrium. At the low temperature, the equilibrium constant is very small, which means that there will be very little hydrogen and carbon monoxide at equilibrium. At 1000 K circumstances have changed radically and now the products are favoured over the reactants. Notice that the fact that the reaction is endothermic should lead us to expect more products at a higher temperature.

52.6 At the higher temperature, the equilibrium constant is smaller than at the lower temperature. Therefore the products are less favoured at 500 K than at 298 K, and the forward reaction must be exothermic. Put $T_1 = 298\,K$, $T_2 = 500\,K$, $K_1 = 794$, $K_2 = 160$. Then

$$\ln\left(\frac{794}{160}\right) = \frac{\Delta H^\ominus}{8.314\,J\,K^{-1}\,mol^{-1}}\left(\frac{1}{500K} - \frac{1}{298\,K}\right)$$

$$\ln(4.963) = \frac{\Delta H^\ominus}{8.314\,J\,mol^{-1}}\left(\frac{298-500}{500\times298}\right)$$

which means

$$\Delta H^\ominus = -\ln(4.963)\times 8.314\,J\,mol^{-1}\times\frac{500\times298}{202}$$

$$= -9824\,J\,mol^{-1} = -9.82\,kJ\,mol^{-1}$$

52.7 For a decrease in pressure, Le Chatelier's principle tells us that the equilibrium will shift in order to increase the pressure. Therefore we need to look at each equation to discover the side that has the greater number of moles of molecules. For reaction (i) the left-hand side is favoured, so the proportion of ammonia will decrease. Reaction (ii) is similar, as there are two moles of hydrogen on the left-hand side, compared with one mole of methane on the right. Therefore the equilibrium will shift so as to increase the amount of hydrogen. Notice that we do not take the carbon into account because it is present as a solid. Reaction (iii) has twice as many moles on the products side as on the reactants side. Hence, the equilibrium will shift to increase the amount of carbon monoxide and hydrogen. Reaction (iv) is the odd one out here because there are equal numbers of moles of gas on both sides of the equation. Therefore pressure will not change the position of equilibrium. (Again, we do not count the carbon because it is a solid.)

52.8

	$Cl_2(g)$ +	$PCl_3(g)$ $\rightleftharpoons$	$PCl_5(g)$
At start	a mol	a mol	0 mol
Amount reacted	x mol	x mol	
At equilibrium	$a-x$ mol	$a-x$ mol	x mol
		Total $2a-x$ mol	
Mole fraction at equilibrium	$\frac{a-x}{2a-x}$	$\frac{a-x}{2a-x}$	$\frac{x}{2a-x}$
Partial pressure at equilibrium	$\frac{(a-x)P_T}{2a-x}$	$\frac{(a-x)P_T}{2a-x}$	$\frac{xP_T}{2a-x}$

If we put these expressions into the equation for K_p we have

$$K_p = \frac{xP_T/(2a-x)}{[(a-x)P_T/(2a-x)][(a-x)P_T/(2a-x)]}$$

i.e.

$$K_p = \frac{x(2a-x)}{(a-x)^2P_T}$$

52.9 (i) From the equation we know that if 1 mol of nitrogen reacts, then 3 mol of hydrogen also react. Therefore, x mol of nitrogen react with $3x$ mol of hydrogen.

(ii) Again, by looking at the equation you should be able to see that $2x$ mol of ammonia will be made.

	$N_2(g)$ +	$3H_2(g)$ $\rightleftharpoons$	$2NH_3(g)$
At start	a mol	a mol	0 mol
Amount reacted	x mol	$3x$ mol	
At equilibrium	$a-x$ mol	$a-3x$ mol	$2x$ mol
		Total $2a-2x$ mol	
Mole fraction at equilibrium	$\frac{a-x}{2a-2x}$	$\frac{a-3x}{2a-2x}$	$\frac{2x}{2a-2x}$
Partial pressure at equilibrium	$\frac{(a-x)P_T}{2a-2x}$	$\frac{(a-3x)P_T}{2a-2x}$	$\frac{2xP_T}{2a-2x}$

If we put these expressions into the equation for K_p we have

$$K_p = \frac{P^2_{NH_3}}{P_{N_2}P^3_{H_2}}$$

$$K_p = \frac{[2x/(2a-2x)]^2P_T^2}{[(a-x)/(2a-2x)]P_T[(a-3x)/(2a-2x)]^3P_T^3}$$

i.e.

$$K_p = \frac{4x^2(2a-2x)^2}{(a-x)(a-3x)^3P_T^2} = \frac{16x^2(a-x)}{(a-3x)^3P_T^2}$$

52.10 If we substitute the values, we have

$$40.7\,atm^{-2} = \frac{16(0.2)^2(2-0.2)}{(2-0.6)^3P_T^2} = \frac{0.42}{P_T^2}$$

so $P_T = 0.10\,atm$.

UNIT 52 SUMMARY

- Dynamic equilibrium:
  At equilibrium the reactants are changing into products at the same rate as the products are reacting back to give reactants, i.e. rate of forward reaction = rate of backward reaction.
- Le Chatelier's principle says that:
  If a constraint is placed on an equilibrium mixture, then the equilibrium will shift so as to oppose the constraint.
- Examples:
  (i) For an endothermic reaction, an increase in temperature favours the products.
  (ii) For an exothermic reaction, an increase in temperature favours the reactants.
- The value of an equilibrium constant changes only if the temperature changes. Changes in concentration, pressure and the use of a catalyst have no effect; but they will often change the rate at which equilibrium is achieved.
- Partial pressures of gases:
  (i) In a mixture of gases, A and B, the total pressure P_T is given by $P_T = P_A + P_B$, where P_A and P_B are the partial pressures of the two gases. These are the pressures that the gases would have if they existed in the container alone.
  (ii) If there are n_A moles of A and n_B moles of B then the mole fraction of each gas is

$$x_A = \frac{n_A}{n_A + n_B} \qquad x_B = \frac{n_B}{n_A + n_B}$$

  (iii) The partial pressure of each gas is related to the total pressure by the equations $P_A = x_A P_T$ and $P_B = x_B P_T$.

53

Some equilibrium reactions

53.1 What this unit is about

In the sections that follow you will find a number of chemical reactions that are fairly easy to carry out in the laboratory. Each of them involves an equilibrium in which you can see how the proportions of reactants and products change when the equilibrium is disturbed. Often there is a colour change, or a solid appears and disappears. If at all possible you should perform the reactions yourself.

The main thing that you should be able to do as you work through this unit is to apply Le Chatelier's principle to the reactions. For each one there are a number of questions, which ask you to make predictions about how the equilibria change. If you do the experiments you will be able to check your predictions directly; in any case you will find answers at the end of the unit.

On no account should you attempt the experiments without the permission of your teacher or lecturer.

53.2 The bismuth trichloride–water reaction

Bismuth trichloride, $BiCl_3$, is a white powder. It is soluble in water, but will react according to the equation:

$$\underset{\text{colourless}}{BiCl_3(aq)} + H_2O(l) \rightleftharpoons \underset{\text{white powder}}{BiOCl(s)} + 2HCl(aq)$$

If you mix a little of the powder with water in a boiling tube you will see a cloudy white colour. This is due to the insoluble bismuth oxychloride, BiOCl, made when the bismuth trichloride reacts with the water.

> **53.1** What will happen:
> (i) if a few drops of concentrated hydrochloric acid (TAKE CARE!) are added to the tube;
> (ii) if distilled water is added after the acid?

53.3 The chromate(VI)–dichromate(VI) reaction

Potassium dichromate(VI) solution has a beautiful clear orange colour. This is due to the colour of the dichromate(VI) ion, $Cr_2O_7^{2-}(aq)$. Place some of the solution in a boiling tube. In fact there is an equilibrium set up between the dichromate(VI) ions and chromate(VI) ions, $CrO_4^{2-}(aq)$. The latter are yellow in colour:

$$\underset{\text{orange}}{Cr_2O_7^{2-}(aq)} + H_2O(l) \rightleftharpoons \underset{\text{yellow}}{2CrO_4^{2-}(aq)} + 2H^+(aq)$$

> **53.2** What would you expect to see if:
> (i) dilute sodium hydroxide is added to the tube;
> (ii) this is followed by dilute hydrochloric acid?

53.4 The iodine–iodine trichloride reaction

This reaction MUST be carried out in a fume cupboard as it involves chlorine gas, which is highly poisonous.

If chlorine gas is passed over a few crystals of iodine in a U-tube you will first see a dark brown liquid appear. This is iodine monochloride, ICl. Soon afterwards, the liquid is replaced by a yellow solid. This is iodine trichloride, ICl_3. Equilibrium will only be established if the U-tube is detached from the chlorine supply and stoppers put in the ends of the tube:

$$I_2(s) + Cl_2(g) \rightleftharpoons \underset{\text{brown liquid}}{2ICl(l)}$$

$$\underset{\text{brown liquid}}{ICl(l)} + Cl_2(g) \rightleftharpoons \underset{\text{yellow solid}}{ICl_3(s)}$$

> **53.3** What would you expect to see if the stoppers are removed from the tube and it is tilted so that chlorine can escape?

53.5 The iodine–triiodide reaction

Iodine is a black solid, which is almost insoluble in water. On the other hand the triiodide ion, I_3^-, is highly soluble in water. It has a brown colour in water.

Place a few crystals of iodine in water in a boiling tube. Add potassium iodide solution to it drop by drop.

> **53.4** What do you expect to see? Explain what is happening by referring to the equilibrium equation:
>
> $$I_2(s) + I^-(aq) \rightleftharpoons I_3^-(aq)$$
> deep brown

Biologists often call a solution of triiodide ions 'iodine' and use it to test for starch.

Iodine reacts with thiosulphate ions, $S_2O_3^{2-}$, according to the equation:

$$I_2(s) + 2S_2O_3^{2-}(aq) \rightleftharpoons 2I^-(aq) + S_4O_6^{2-}(aq)$$
colourless

> **53.5** What would you expect to happen if you add a few crystals of sodium thiosulphate to the boiling tube containing the iodine and potassium iodide solution?

53.6 The nitrogen dioxide–dinitrogen tetraoxide reaction

Owing to the gases being poisonous, the reactions that follow should only be done in a fume cupboard.

If lead(II) nitrate is heated it gives off a brown gas, which is a mixture of oxygen and nitrogen dioxide, NO_2. If the gases are passed through a dry U-tube surrounded by crushed ice, the nitrogen dioxide condenses to a slightly yellow liquid. The liquid is dinitrogen tetraoxide, N_2O_4, which is colourless when pure. The reason why it is discoloured is that it contains a little of the brown nitrogen dioxide:

$$N_2O_4(l) \rightleftharpoons 2NO_2(g)$$
colourless brown

The enthalpy change for the dissociation of 1 mol of dinitrogen tetraoxide into nitrogen dioxide is +57.2 kJ mol^{-1}.

> **53.6** What should happen if an equilibrium mixture of the gases was warmed?
>
> **53.7** What should happen if an equilibrium mixture of the gases was put into a sealed gas syringe and the plunger pushed in?

53.7 The decomposition of ammonium salts

Ammonium chloride is one of the few compounds that sublimes, i.e. changes directly from a solid into a gas, or rather a mixture of gases:

$$NH_4Cl(s) \rightleftharpoons NH_3(g) + HCl(g)$$

The enthalpy change for the conversion of 1 mol of ammonium chloride into ammonia and hydrogen chloride is + 177.2 kJ mol^{-1}.

> **53.8** Explain why it is that a tube in which ammonium chloride is heated has the appearance shown in the photo in the colour section.

A test for solutions that contain ammonium ions is that they give off ammonia when heated with an alkali, i.e. OH^- ions:

$$NH_4^+(aq) + OH^-(aq) \rightleftharpoons NH_3(g) + H_2O(l)$$

> **53.9** Explain why this reaction is prevented if acid is added to the solution.

53.8 Reactions involving complex ions

You will find information about complex ions in Unit 106. Here you just need to know that they are ions that are not as simple as chloride, sulphate, or nitrate ions. You can follow the production of a complex ion in this reaction.

Add a few drops of sodium chloride solution to a solution of lead(II) nitrate. If you have read Unit 64 on solubility products, you should not be surprised to see a white precipitate of lead(II) chloride:

$$Pb^{2+}(aq) + 2Cl^-(aq) \rightleftharpoons PbCl_2(s)$$

Now add concentrated hydrochloric acid drop by drop (TAKE CARE!).

> **53.10** Explain what you would see in terms of the equilibrium:
>
> $$PbCl_2(s) + 2Cl^-(aq) \rightleftharpoons PbCl_4^{2-}(aq)$$
> white solid pale yellow
>
> **53.11** What should happen if you add more lead(II) nitrate solution?

Here are two other examples in which complex ions play a part. A common test for chloride ions is to add silver nitrate solution in nitric acid. If a white precipitate appears it is likely to be silver chloride. To confirm this, the test is completed by adding aqueous ammonia. The white precipitate should disappear.

53.12 Explain the reasoning behind the test by referring to the following equilibria:

$$Ag^+(aq) + Cl^-(aq) \rightleftharpoons AgCl(s)$$

$$Ag^+(aq) + 2NH_3(aq) \rightleftharpoons \underset{\text{colourless}}{Ag(NH_3)_2^+(aq)}$$

The complex ion $Ag(NH_3)_2^+$ is called the diamminesilver(I) ion.

The second example is the reaction that is often used to test for copper(II) ions. Aqueous ammonia is added, and, if copper(II) ions are present, first a white or very pale blue precipitate is produced, which then dissolves to give a clear royal blue solution.

53.13 Explain this sequence of events in relation to the following reactions:

$$\underset{\text{blue}}{Cu^{2+}(aq)} + 2OH^-(aq) \rightleftharpoons \underset{\text{white solid}}{Cu(OH)_2(s)}$$

$$\underset{\text{blue}}{Cu^{2+}(aq)} + 4NH_3(aq) \rightleftharpoons \underset{\text{royal blue}}{Cu(NH_3)_4^{2+}(aq)}$$

The complex ion $Cu(NH_3)_4^{2+}$ is known as the tetraamminecopper(II) ion.

Answers

53.1 (i) The equilibrium will respond to the increase in hydrochloric acid concentration by shifting so as to decrease the concentration again. The equilibrium therefore shifts to the left. You should see the solution become clear as the white bismuth oxychloride disappears and is replaced by the soluble bismuth trichloride.

(ii) Adding distilled water forces the equilibrium to shift to the right. The white precipitate reappears. You may have to wait about 10 s for this to happen. Remember, an equilibrium will not always respond to changes immediately.

53.2 (i) Addition of dilute alkali will bring about the reaction

$$H^+(aq) + OH^-(aq) \rightarrow H_2O(l)$$

The effect is to reduce the hydrogen ion concentration. Therefore the equilibrium will shift to the right in order to replace those hydrogen ions that have been removed. The solution will become yellow as an excess of CrO_4^{2-} is produced.

(ii) The equilibrium will shift to the left again, with the orange colour of $Cr_2O_7^{2-}(aq)$ returning.

53.3 If chlorine is allowed to escape then the equilibrium involving iodine trichloride will shift to the left in the attempt to replace that which is lost. You should see the yellow colour replaced by the brown colour of iodine monochloride.

53.4 The solution will become orange, then a much deeper brown. If a lot of iodine reacts with the iodide ions you add, then the solution may go almost black. This happens because the equilibrium shifts to the right, in favour of the coloured triiodide ion.

53.5 The effect of the thiosulphate ions is to remove iodine molecules by turning them into iodide ions. Therefore the equilibrium

$$I_2(s) + I^-(aq) \rightleftharpoons I_3^-(aq)$$

moves to the left and the solution will gradually change from being deep brown to being colourless.

53.6 According to Le Chatelier's principle, if heat is applied to the equilibrium reaction then the equilibrium will shift to the side that gives the endothermic reaction. In this case, producing nitrogen dioxide from dinitrogen tetraoxide is the endothermic change. Hence we should expect to see more nitrogen dioxide, and the colour of the mixture should darken.

53.7 In theory the reaction should move to the left, in the direction of the endothermic change, which should give a lighter colour in the syringe. This is the answer you are expected to give. However, if you do this experiment you will be dismayed to find that the colour of the gas darkens. That is, more NO_2 is produced. This is an unfortunate side effect of the nature of the gases in the syringe. When they are suddenly squeezed together, heat is generated. The heating effect wins over the increase in pressure, and temporarily more N_2O_4 molecules change into NO_2 molecules than vice versa. Hence the colour darkens. If the pressure is applied very slowly, or the gases left under pressure for some time, the colour change will be in the direction we expect. Le Chatelier was right!

53.8 The reaction is endothermic in the direction of making ammonia and hydrogen chloride. Therefore, if heat is applied, the equilibrium will shift and increase the amount of these two gases. In the hot part of the tube where there are just the gases there is no white solid. However, further up the tube, where the glass is fairly cold, the equilibrium will shift back in favour of ammonium chloride. This accounts for the white powder to be seen nearer the top of the tube.

53.9 If acid is added, the hydrogen ions and hydroxide ions combine to give water. In effect hydroxide ions are removed from the equilibrium, which then shifts to the left in order to replace them. The left-hand side of the

Answers – contd.

equilibrium favours ammonium ions, so ammonia gas is not released.

53.10 Hydrochloric acid is a source of chloride ions. An increase in their concentration causes the equilibrium to move to the left. We see the white solid dissolve, and the solution turns yellow owing to the increase in concentration of the complex ion.

53.11 Adding more lead(II) nitrate increases the concentration of lead(II) ions. These react with chloride ions to make lead(II) chloride. In effect the concentration of chloride ions is reduced, so the equilibrium shifts to the left. More lead(II) chloride appears, and the yellow colour of the solution fades.

53.12 The solution in contact with the silver chloride contains small amounts of silver ions and chloride ions. When ammonia is added, the silver ions are converted into the complex ion. This has the effect of reducing the concentration of silver ions in the solution above the solid silver chloride. In turn the equilibrium

$$Ag^+(aq) + Cl^-(aq) \rightleftharpoons AgCl(s)$$

shifts to the left so as to replace the silver ions that are lost. We see the result of this as the silver chloride dissolving.

53.13 The white colour is produced by the copper(II) ions reacting with hydroxide ions to make copper(II) hydroxide. When ammonia is added, the free copper(II) ions left in the solution are converted into the complex ion. This decreases the concentration of free copper(II) ions, so the equilibrium

$$Cu^{2+}(aq) + 2OH^-(aq) \rightleftharpoons Cu(OH)_2(s)$$

shifts to the left in order to replace the copper(II) ions. This is the reason why the precipitate is seen to dissolve.

UNIT 53 SUMMARY

- Important equilibrium reactions:

(i) $BiCl_3(aq) + H_2O(l) \rightleftharpoons BiOCl(s) + 2HCl(aq)$
colourless; white

(ii) $Cr_2O_7^{2-}(aq) + H_2O(l) \rightleftharpoons 2CrO_4^{2-}(aq) + 2H^+(aq)$
orange; yellow

(iii) $I_2(s) + Cl_2(g) \rightleftharpoons 2ICl(l)$
black; brown

$ICl(l) + Cl_2(g) \rightleftharpoons ICl_3(s)$
brown; yellow

(iv) $I_2(s) + I^-(aq) \rightleftharpoons I_3^-(aq)$
deep brown

(v) $N_2O_4(l) \rightleftharpoons 2NO_2(g)$
colourless; brown

(vi) $NH_4Cl(s) \rightleftharpoons NH_3(g) + HCl(g)$
white; colourless

(vii) $Pb^{2+}(aq) + 2Cl^-(aq) \rightleftharpoons PbCl_2(s)$
colourless; white

$PbCl_2(s) + 2Cl^-(aq) \rightleftharpoons PbCl_4^{2-}(aq)$
white; yellow

(viii) $Ag^+(aq) + Cl^-(aq) \rightleftharpoons AgCl(s)$
colourless; white

$Ag^+(aq) + 2NH_3(aq) \rightleftharpoons Ag(NH_3)_2^+(aq)$
colourless

(ix) $Cu^{2+}(aq) + 2OH^-(aq) \rightleftharpoons Cu(OH)_2(s)$
blue; white

$Cu^{2+}(aq) + 4NH_3(aq) \rightleftharpoons Cu(NH_3)_4^{2+}(aq)$
blue; royal blue

54

Measuring equilibrium constants

54.1 How can equilibrium constants be measured?

To measure an equilibrium constant in the laboratory there are three key factors to take into account.

(i) The reactants and products of the reaction must actually have come to *equilibrium*. We can test if this has happened by taking small samples out of the reacting mixture at different times and analysing them. When the same result is obtained for successive analyses, then we assume that there is no further overall change in the mixture, i.e. equilibrium has been achieved. There are more sophisticated ways of analysis than actually removing samples from the mixture. For example, if there is a colour change in the reaction, a colorimeter can be used. When there is no further change in colour, we have equilibrium. In a gaseous reaction where there is a change in pressure, all that is needed is to read the pressure gauge. When the reading is steady we know there is equilibrium.

(ii) The *temperature* at which the measurement takes place must be known, and kept constant. This is done by carrying out the reaction in a container whose temperature is kept constant using a thermostat system. However, this can cause difficulties. For example, if a reaction is performed at 800° C, it can be a problem knowing how to carry out the analysis of the equilibrium mixture. There is one standard way of getting round the problem. The idea is to take a sample of the mixture at the high temperature and then stop any further reactions taking place. For all intents and purposes the mixture is then 'frozen' into the same proportions that it had at the high temperature. This process is known as *quenching* the reactions. For example, a reaction mixture at 100° C could be plunged into iced water. At 0° C the reactions are likely to be very slow, thus giving time for the analysis to be carried out.

(iii) The *concentrations*, or *pressure* for gases, must be found. The most common way of measuring a concentration is by performing a titration. However, depending on circumstances, it can be done by using colorimeters or electrochemical cells. For gases, it is sometimes possible to work out the partial pressures of the gases in a mixture if the total pressure is known. In other cases this is not possible and indirect means have to be used. This might involve quenching the reaction mixture and dissolving soluble gases in water. Then the solutions of the gases are analysed, perhaps by titration. If the concentrations of the gases in the solution are known, then it is a brief step to working out their mole fractions.

In the sections that follow, you will find examples of some of the methods we have considered here.

54.2 The ester equilibrium

The equilibrium reaction between ethanoic acid and ethanol was first studied by the French chemist Berthelot in 1862. The reaction is:

$$\underset{\text{ethanoic acid}}{CH_3COOH(l)} + \underset{\text{ethanol}}{C_2H_5OH(l)} \rightleftharpoons \underset{\text{ethyl ethanoate}}{CH_3COOC_2H_5(l)} + \underset{\text{water}}{H_2O(l)}$$

The equilibrium constant is

$$K_c = \frac{[CH_3COOC_2H_5(l)][H_2O(l)]}{[CH_3COOH(l)][C_2H_5OH(l)]}$$

A method that can be used to determine the concentrations is as follows. First, 20.0 cm^3 of ethanol is added to 20 cm^3 of ethanoic acid in a flask, which is then stoppered. The flask is placed in a water bath fitted with a thermostat (Figure 54.1). If the temperature is kept at around 50° C, equilibrium is achieved after some hours. (At lower temperatures, the flask may have to be left for some days before equilibrium is achieved.) A pipette is used to withdraw a 10 cm^3 sample of the equilibrium mixture, and the sample is run into a flask containing iced water.

The concentration of the acid in the flask can be measured by titrating the solution with 1.0 mol dm^{-3} sodium hydroxide solution, using phenolphthalein as

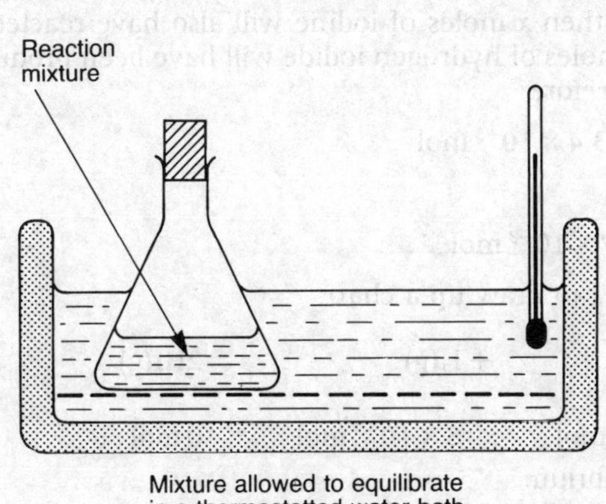
Reaction mixture
Mixture allowed to equilibrate in a thermostatted water bath

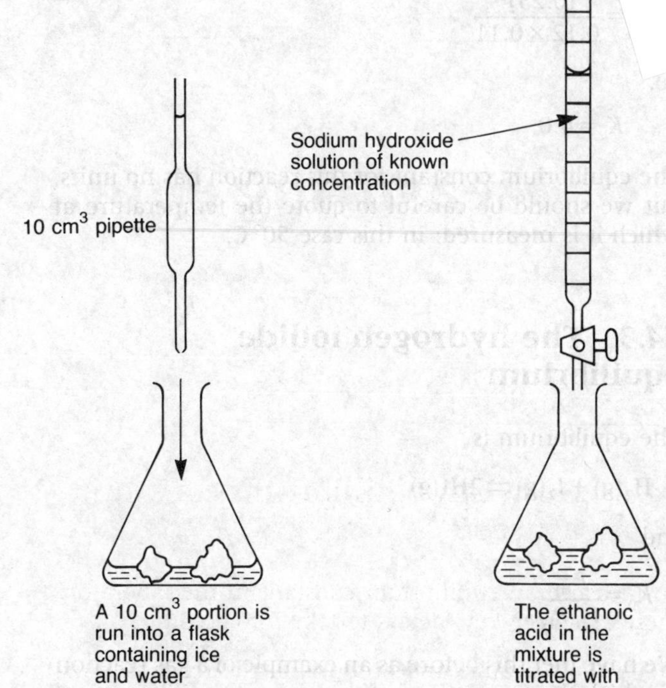
Sodium hydroxide solution of known concentration
10 cm3 pipette
A 10 cm3 portion is run into a flask containing ice and water
The ethanoic acid in the mixture is titrated with alkali

***Figure 54.1** One method for investigating the equilibrium reaction between ethanol and ethanoic acid*

an indicator. A typical result is that 30.0 cm^3 of the sodium hydroxide solution is needed to neutralise the ethanoic acid. Therefore,

number of moles of sodium hydroxide used

$$= \frac{30.0\ cm^3}{1000\ cm^3} \times 1.0\ mol = 0.03\ mol$$

From the equation of the reaction we find that ethanoic acid and sodium hydroxide react in the ratio of 1 mol to 1 mol, so:

number of moles of ethanoic acid in 10 cm^3 = 0.03 mol

The total volume at the start of the reaction was 40 cm^3, and we assume this does not change during the reaction. Therefore,

number of moles of ethanoic acid in equilibrium mixture = 4 × 0.03 mol = 0.12 mol

We can work out the number of moles of ethanoic acid and ethanol we started with by looking up their densities in data tables. The values are:

ethanoic acid, density = 1.049 g cm^{-3}
ethanol, density = 0.789 g cm^{-3}

Remembering that mass = density × volume, we have

mass of ethanoic acid at start
= 1.049 g cm^{-3} × 20.0 cm^3 = 20.98 g

mass of ethanol at start
= 0.789 g cm^{-3} × 20.0 cm^3 = 15.78 g

Then, because $M(CH_3COOH) = 60\ g\ mol^{-1}$, and $M(C_2H_5OH) = 46\ g\ mol^{-1}$

number of moles of ethanoic acid at start

$$= \frac{20.98\ g}{60\ g\ mol^{-1}} = 0.35\ mol$$

number of moles of ethanol at start

$$= \frac{15.78\ g}{46\ g\ mol^{-1}} = 0.34\ mol$$

We are now in a position to follow the pattern of calculation that we used in Unit 52. We know that we started with 0.35 mol of ethanoic acid, and that at equilibrium 0.12 mol remained. Therefore 0.23 mol had reacted. In turn this tells us that 0.23 mol of ethanol were also used up. This leaves 0.11 mol of ethanol at equilibrium.

$CH_3COOH(l)$ +	$C_2H_5OH(l) \rightleftharpoons$	$CH_3COOC_2H_5(l)$ +	$H_2O(l)$
At start			
0.35 mol	0.34 mol	0 mol	0 mol
At equilibrium			
0.12 mol	0.11 mol	0.23 mol	0.23 mol
Concentrations /mol dm^{-3}			
0.12/0.04	0.11/0.04	0.23/0.04	0.23/0.04

Therefore,

$$K_c = \frac{(0.23/0.04\ mol\ dm^{-3})\ (0.23/0.04\ mol\ dm^{-3})}{(0.12/0.04\ mol\ dm^{-3})\ (0.11/0.04\ mol\ dm^{-3})}$$

$$= \frac{(0.23)^2}{0.12 \times 0.11}$$

i.e.

$$K_c = 4.0$$

The equilibrium constant for this reaction has no units, but we should be careful to quote the temperature at which it is measured; in this case 50° C.

54.3 The hydrogen iodide equilibrium

The equilibrium is

$$H_2(g) + I_2(g) \rightleftharpoons 2HI(g)$$

and

$$K_p = \frac{P_{HI}^2}{P_{H_2}P_{I_2}}$$

We have met this before as an example of a gas reaction in which the proportions of the gases at equilibrium are independent of pressure (see Table 52.1). Here it is the way in which this equilibrium can be studied that is of interest.

The German chemist Max Bodenstein investigated the reaction towards the end of the last century. He carried out the reaction with known amounts of hydrogen and iodine in sealed tubes placed in a furnace at around 400° C. The reaction was quenched by opening the tubes under cold water. The hydrogen iodide made during the reaction dissolved in the water. The resulting solution was titrated with alkali, thereby allowing the number of moles of hydrogen iodide present at equilibrium to be established.

Let us assume that the reaction has been carried out and that the results were as follows:

Temperature of experiment tube = 450° C

At start of experiment:
number of moles of hydrogen $= 9 \times 10^{-3}$ mol
number of moles of iodine $= 8 \times 10^{-3}$ mol

At equilibrium:
number of moles of hydrogen iodide $= 13.4 \times 10^{-3}$ mol

If we call x the number of moles of hydrogen that have reacted, then x moles of iodine will also have reacted, and $2x$ moles of hydrogen iodide will have been produced. Therefore,

$$2x = 13.4 \times 10^{-3}\text{ mol}$$

and

$$x = 6.7 \times 10^{-3}\text{ mol}$$

Now we can draw up a chart:

$H_2(g)$	$+ I_2(g)$	$\rightleftharpoons 2HI(g)$
At start		
9×10^{-3} mol	8×10^{-3} mol	0 mol
At equilibrium		
$(9-6.7) \times 10^{-3}$ $= 2.3 \times 10^{-3}$ mol	$(8-6.7) \times 10^{-3}$ $= 1.3 \times 10^{-3}$ mol	13.4×10^{-3} mol
Mole fraction		
$\frac{2.3 \times 10^{-3}\text{ mol}}{17 \times 10^{-3}\text{ mol}}$	$\frac{1.3 \times 10^{-3}\text{ mol}}{17 \times 10^{-3}\text{ mol}}$	$\frac{13.4 \times 10^{-3}\text{ mol}}{17 \times 10^{-3}\text{ mol}}$
$= 0.135$	$= 0.076$	$= 0.788$
Partial pressure		
$0.135P_T$	$0.076P_T$	$0.788P_T$

Thus:

$$K_p = \frac{(0.788P_T)^2}{0.135P_T \times 0.076P_T}$$

i.e. at 450° C,

$$K_p = 60.5$$

The equilibrium constant has no units. Also, notice that the pressure P_T cancels out, which it should do because there are equal numbers of moles of gas on each side of the reaction equation.

54.1 Every 30 minutes, 10 cm³ samples were taken out of a reaction mixture that originally contained 2 mol of ethanoic acid and 2 mol of ethanol. The samples were titrated with sodium hydroxide solution. Look at the graphs in Figure 54.2. Each of them shows volume of sodium hydroxide solution plotted against time. Unfortunately two of the graphs are wrong. Which is the correct graph for the experiment? Explain your choice.

54.2 This question refers to the ester equilibrium of section 54.2.

(i) What was done to quench the reaction?

(ii) Why is it necessary to stopper the reaction flask?

54.3 If you were to mix 2 mol of ethanoic acid with 1 mol of ethanol, and allowed them to come to equilibrium, how many moles of ester would be made?

To answer this question assume $K_c = 4.0$, and call x the number of moles of ester made.

The number of moles of ethanoic acid at equilibrium will be $(2-x)$ mol. What will be the number of moles of each of the other three substances?

You should see from the expression for K_c that the volume of the reaction mixture cancels out, so you can use the number of moles of each substance as a measure of concentration.

Write down the expression for K_c. You will end up

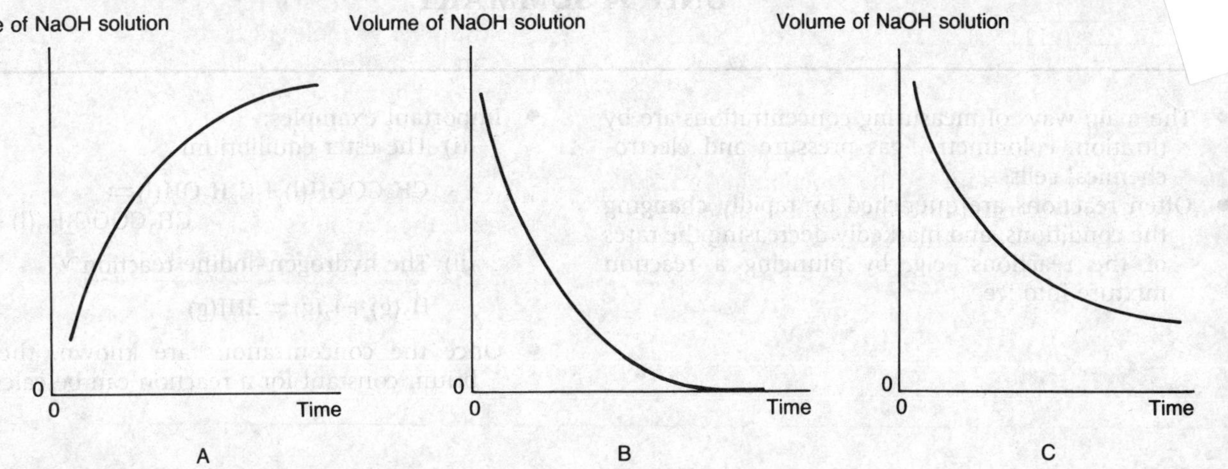

***Figure 54.2** The graphs for question 54.1*

with a quadratic equation to solve. (Only one of the answers makes sense.)

54.4 In the hydrogen iodide equilibrium, if 0.1 mol of hydrogen and 0.1 mol of iodine were allowed to come to equilibrium at 450° C, how many moles of hydrogen iodide would be present at equilibrium? Take K_p as 60.

To answer this question, start by calling $2x$ the number of moles of hydrogen iodide at equilibrium. Then write down:

(i) the number of moles of hydrogen at equilibrium;

(ii) the number of moles of iodine at equilibrium;

(iii) the expression for K_p.

Solve the equation to discover the value of x.

Answers

54.1 Graph C is correct. As the reaction proceeds, the number of moles of ethanoic acid decreases. Therefore the volume of sodium hydroxide used in the titration will decrease. This means that graph A cannot be correct. Graph B claims that the volume of sodium hydroxide decreases to zero. Because this is an equilibrium reaction, there must be ethanoic acid left at equilibrium, hence the volume of sodium hydroxide used cannot be zero and graph B is wrong as well.

54.2 (i) The sample was run into iced water to slow the reactions down.

(ii) Ethanol, ethanoic acid and ethyl ethanoate are all volatile. Without the stopper, much of them would escape from the flask. Equilibrium cannot be achieved if reactants or products are lost from the reaction mixture.

54.3

$$K_c = \frac{[\text{ester}][\text{water}]}{[\text{acid}][\text{alcohol}]} = \frac{x^2}{(2-x)(1-x)} = 4.0$$

Then

$$x^2 = 4(2-x)(1-x)$$
$$= 8 - 12x + 4x^2$$

So

$$3x^2 - 12x + 8 = 0$$

and

$$x = \frac{12 \pm \sqrt{(-12)^2 - 4\times3\times8}}{2\times3}$$

which gives $x = 3.15$ or $x = 0.845$. The first answer must be wrong because we only started with 2 mol of acid, so we certainly could not obtain over 3 mol of ester. Therefore the second answer gives us the number of moles of each substance at equilibrium: acid, 1.155 mol; alcohol, 0.155 mol; ester, 0.845 mol; water, 0.845 mol.

54.4 (i) $(0.1-x)$ mol of hydrogen.

(ii) $(0.1-x)$ mol of iodine.

(iii) $K_p = \frac{(2x)^2}{(0.1-x)^2}$

So

$$4x^2 = 60(0.1-x)^2$$

or

$$56x^2 - 12x + 0.6 = 0$$

Then,

$$x = \frac{12 \pm \sqrt{(-12)^2 - 4\times56\times0.6}}{112}$$
$$= 0.13 \text{ or } 0.079$$

As we started with only 0.1 mol of hydrogen or iodine, if $x = 0.13$ we would have a negative amount of them at equilibrium. This is impossible, so $x = 0.079$ is the correct answer. At equilibrium there will be (approximately) 0.158 mol of hydrogen iodide, and 0.021 mol each of hydrogen and iodine.

UNIT 54 SUMMARY

- The main ways of measuring concentrations are by titration, colorimetry, gas pressure and electrochemical cells.
- Often reactions are quenched by rapidly changing the conditions, and markedly decreasing the rates of the reactions; e.g. by plunging a reaction mixture into ice.
- Important examples:
  (i) The ester equilibrium

$$CH_3COOH(l) + C_2H_5OH(l) \rightleftharpoons CH_3COOC_2H_5(l) + H_2O(l)$$

  (ii) The hydrogen–iodine reaction

$$H_2(g) + I_2(g) \rightleftharpoons 2HI(g)$$

- Once the concentrations are known, the equilibrium constant for a reaction can be calculated.

55

Equilibria between phases

55.1 What is a phase?

A phase can be a solid, a liquid, or a gas. It can also be a solution. The important thing is that in each case every part of the solid, liquid, gas, or solution must be the same as every other part. In short, it must be *homogeneous*. If you were to mix some coal and salt, you would have a mixture of two solids. It is most unlikely that the mixture will be exactly the same in each part. This mixture consists of *two* solid phases. However, if you were to melt a mixture of silver and gold (you would have to be a fairly rich chemist!) and then allow the liquid to solidify, you would find that the solid was homogeneous. Here there would be two elements but only one phase. The solid made is known as a solid solution – it behaves like many solutions made from two liquids.

For much of the time in this unit we shall ignore mixtures, whether they be solid solutions or not, and concentrate on the equilibria between the three phases of a pure substance: solid, liquid and gas.

55.2 How to interpret a phase diagram

A phase diagram is a handy way of summarising a great deal of information. We shall use the phase diagram for water as an example (Figure 55.1 and Table 55.1). A phase diagram like this has a number of lines. Each one summarises the conditions at which equilibrium can be achieved between two of the three phases (Figure 55.2).

(a) *The vapour pressure curve*

The curve TC tells us the combination of temperature and pressure at which water and water vapour can exist at equilibrium (Figure 55.2). For example, at 25°C (298 K) equilibrium is achieved when the vapour pressure of water equals 0.03 atm. If the temperature is kept at 25°C and the vapour pressure is lower than 0.03 atm, then the water will evaporate until the vapour pressure reaches this value. On the other hand, if the vapour

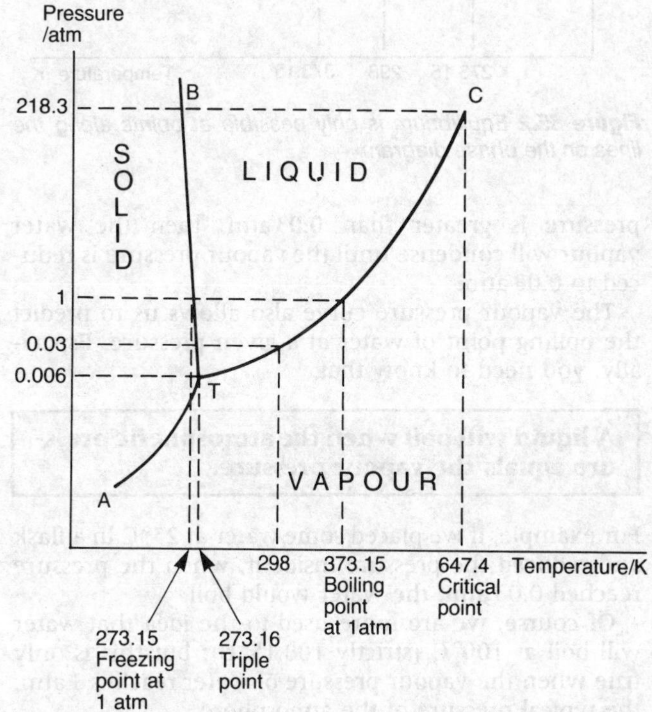

Figure 55.1 *The phase diagram of water. The curves are described in Table 55.1. (Note: the diagram has not been drawn to scale)*

Table 55.1. Equilibrium and the phase diagram of water

	Name	*Equilibrium*
TC	Vapour pressure curve	Water and water vapour
TB	Melting point curve	Ice and water
TA	Sublimation curve	Ice and water vapour
T	Triple point	Ice, water and water vapour
C	Critical point	One indistinguishable phase

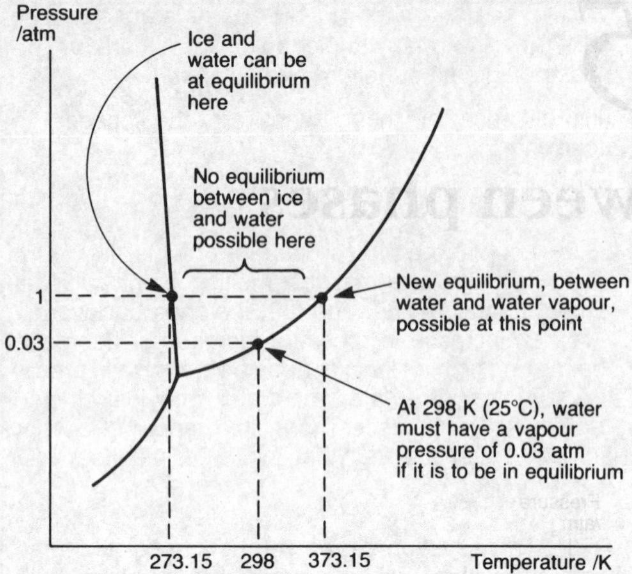
Pressure
/atm
Ice and
water can be
at equilibrium
here
No equilibrium
between ice
and water
possible here
1
0.03
New equilibrium, between
water and water vapour,
possible at this point
At 298 K (25°C), water
must have a vapour
pressure of 0.03 atm
if it is to be in equilibrium
273.15
298
373.15
Temperature /K

***Figure 55.2** Equilibrium is only possible at points along the lines on the phase diagram*

pressure is greater than 0.03 atm, then the water vapour will condense until the vapour pressure is reduced to 0.03 atm.

The vapour pressure curve also allows us to predict the boiling point of water at a given pressure. Especially, you need to know that:

A liquid will boil when the atmospheric pressure equals the vapour pressure.

For example, if we placed some water at 25° C in a flask and reduced the pressure inside it, when the pressure reached 0.03 atm, the water would boil.

Of course, we are more used to the idea that water will boil at 100° C (strictly 100.15° C); but this is only true when the vapour pressure of water reaches 1 atm, the typical pressure of the atmosphere.

(b) *The melting point curve*

Along the curve TB we have pairs of values of temperature and pressure at which ice and water can exist in equilibrium (Figure 55.2). The most famous pair is 0° C (strictly 0.15° C) at 1 atm pressure, which corresponds to the freezing point of water (or the melting point of ice). If we increase the temperature, then on the diagram we move horizontally from left to right. As soon as we move off the curve, equilibrium is no longer possible and, as experience tells us, ice will melt. If we keep moving across the diagram we shall meet the vapour pressure curve, where equilibrium between liquid and vapour can be established.

(c) *The sublimation curve*

Sublimation is the change from solid to vapour, or vapour to solid, without the intermediate change into a liquid. The conditions for an equilibrium between ice and water vapour are shown on the curve AT. The diagram shows that sublimation cannot happen at a temperature above 273.16 K, or at a pressure greater than 0.006 atm.

(d) *The triple point*

The point T (0.006 atm, 273.16 K) is the only place on the diagram where the three phases, ice, water and water vapour, can exist in equilibrium with each other.

(e) *The critical point*

The point C is called the critical point. At this point liquid and vapour become indistinguishable. (Along the vapour pressure curve before the critical point, liquid water has a greater density than water vapour. At the critical point their densities are equal.) Once the critical point is reached, there are no longer two separate phases.

55.3 The phase diagram of sulphur

Sulphur has two allotropes (see Unit 57): rhombic sulphur and monoclinic sulphur. The two differ in their crystal structures. The phase diagram for sulphur is shown in Figure 55.3. The point B is interesting because it is a triple point, but one that involves two solid phases and one vapour phase (rather than solid, liquid and vapour). Here, rhombic and monoclinic sulphur can exist in equilibrium with sulphur vapour. The temperature at B, 95.5° C, is called the *transition temperature* for rhombic and monoclinic sulphur.

However, if you heat rhombic sulphur in the laboratory the transition is unlikely to take place at 95.5° C. It can take a long time for equilibrium to be set up between two solid phases. In the case of sulphur, all but the most careful heating results in rhombic sulphur surviving to 114° C instead of changing into monoclinic sulphur. The rhombic sulphur is said to be in a *metastable* state. It is energetically unstable, but kinetically the change into monoclinic sulphur is very slow. At 114° C a triple point occurs between the metastable rhombic sulphur, liquid sulphur and sulphur vapour. You can see the phase diagram for the metastable system in Figure 55.3b.

55.4 The phase diagram of helium

The phase diagram of helium (Figure 55.4) is remarkable because it shows two liquid phases, called helium I and helium II. The properties of helium II are very odd. For example, if it is put into an open container, it will spontaneously travel up the walls of the container and overflow. There is a triple point between helium I, helium II and helium vapour at 2.17 K and 0.05 atm. This is called the lambda (λ) point of helium.

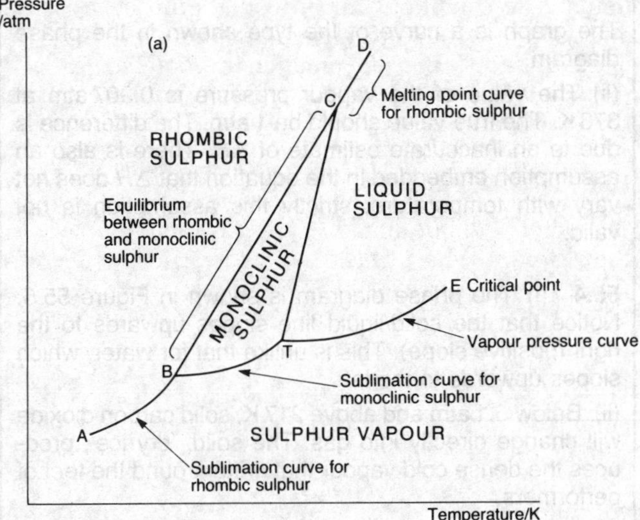

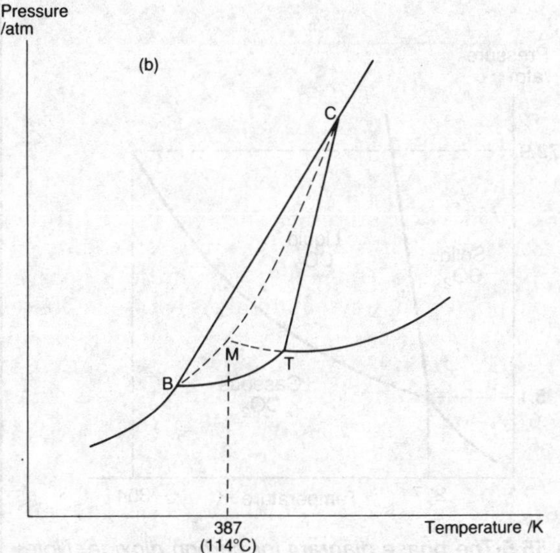

Figure 55.3 *(a) Phase diagram for sulphur. The points B, C and T are: B (368.5 K, 10^{-5} atm); C (428 K, 1290 atm); T (393 K, 3×10^{-5} atm). (b) The phase diagram of sulphur involving the metastable state*

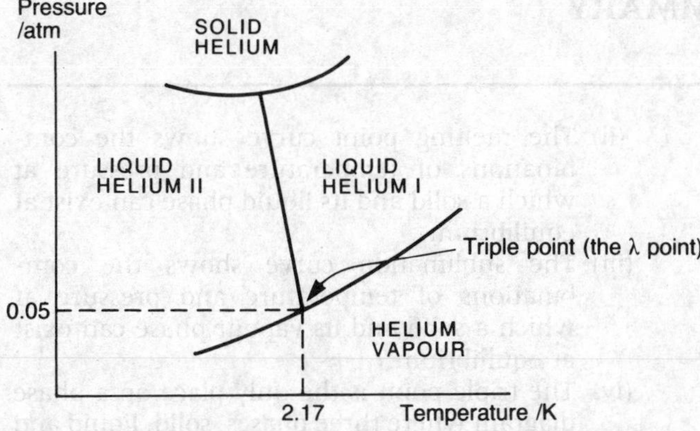

Figure 55.4 *The phase diagram of helium. The diagram is unusual because of the equilibrium between the two liquid forms of helium*

55.1 (i) How many triple points are there in the phase diagrams of helium and sulphur?

(ii) For each of them, what are the phases in equilibrium?

(iii) Will solid helium sublime?

55.2 Look at the phase diagram of water in Figure 55.1. You can see that the melting point curve is almost a straight line, and that it slopes backwards. Does an increase in pressure increase or decrease the melting point of ice, i.e. does an increase in pressure turn ice into water, or water into ice? If you remember Le Chatelier's principle, apply it to your answer, using the fact that ice is less dense than water.

55.3 This question shows you how to calculate the way in which vapour pressures change with temperature.

If we want to change a liquid into a vapour, we have to supply energy. We also know that the vapour pressure of a liquid increases as its temperature increases. The reason is that on average the energy of the molecules increases, so more of them gain enough energy to escape from the surface of the liquid. If ΔH is the energy needed to vaporise 1 mol of liquid, the vapour pressure P at a temperature T is given by

$$P = \text{constant} \times \exp(-\Delta H/RT)$$

With a little mathematics, we can turn this into the following equation

$$\ln\left(\frac{P_1}{P_2}\right) = -\frac{\Delta H}{R}\left(\frac{1}{T_1}-\frac{1}{T_2}\right)$$

(ln is the natural logarithm). This equation (a version of the Clausius–Clapeyron equation) allows us to calculate the vapour pressure of a liquid over a range of temperatures. It assumes that the heat of vaporisation does not change with temperature, which is normally a very reasonable assumption.

(i) For water above about 25° C (298 K), we can estimate ΔH as 42 kJ mol^{-1}. At 298 K the vapour pressure is 0.03 atm. Use these values as T_2 and P_2. Write a computer program to calculate the vapour pressure of water between 298 and 373 K. If you can, use the computer to plot a graph of the results. How does your graph compare with the vapour pressure curve in Figure 55.1? You may prefer to use another version of the equation:

$$P_1 = P_2 \exp\left[-\frac{\Delta H}{R}\left(\frac{1}{T_1}-\frac{1}{T_2}\right)\right]$$

(ii) What value do you get for the vapour pressure of water at 373 K? What value should it be?

55.4 The triple point for carbon dioxide comes at 217 K, 5.1 atm and the critical point is at 304 K,

72.9 atm. Unlike water, carbon dioxide contracts in volume when it changes from a liquid to a solid.

(i) Sketch the phase diagram for carbon dioxide. (Your answer to question 55.2 may help you.)

(ii) Comment on why solid carbon dioxide can be used to produce a cloud of vapour for special effects in films, television shows, pop concerts, etc.

Answers

55.1 (i) For helium there are two, for sulphur three.

(ii) Helium: vapour, helium I, helium II; solid, helium I, helium II. Sulphur: vapour, rhombic, monoclinic; vapour, monoclinic, liquid; liquid, rhombic, monoclinic.

(iii) No; there is no equilibrium line between solid and gaseous helium.

55.2 An increase of pressure takes you up the melting point curve, and backwards along the temperature axis, i.e. the melting point decreases. An increase in pressure turns ice into water. A given mass of ice takes up a greater volume than the same mass of water (both at 0° C). Therefore if there is an equilibrium between them, Le Chatelier's principle tells us that an increase in pressure should cause the equilibrium to shift in the direction of the 'low pressure side' (see section 52.6). This is the side that has the lower volume, in this case water.

55.3 (i) Your program should give the following values:

T/° C	30	40	50	60
T/K	303	313	323	333
P_1/atm	0.04	0.068	0.111	0.178

T/° C	70	80	90	100
T/K	343	353	363	373
P_1/atm	0.277	0.420	0.624	0.907

The graph is a curve of the type shown in the phase diagram.

(ii) The value of the vapour pressure is 0.907 atm at 373 K. The true value should be 1 atm. The difference is due to an inaccurate estimate of ΔH. There is also an assumption embedded in the equation that ΔH does not vary with temperature; strictly this assumption is not valid.

55.4 (i) The phase diagram is shown in Figure 55.5. Notice that the solid/liquid line slopes upwards to the right (positive slope). This is unlike that for water, which slopes upwards to the left.

(ii) Below 5.1 atm and above 217 K, solid carbon dioxide will change directly into gas. The solid, 'dry ice', produces the dense cold vapour that drifts around the feet of performers.

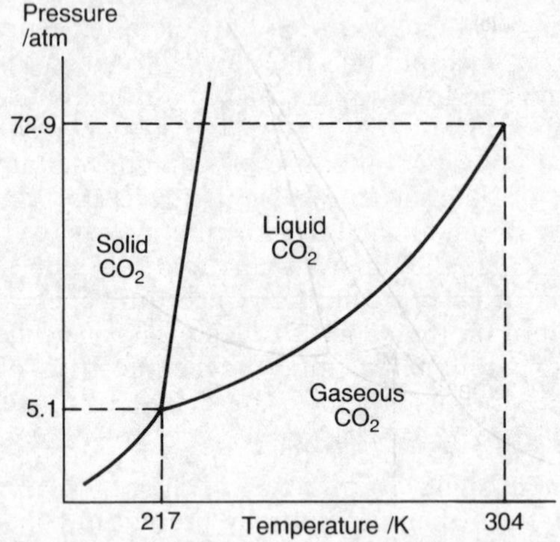

***Figure 55.5** The phase diagram for carbon dioxide. Note: in liquid CO_2 fire extinguishers, the pressure is about 6.7 atm, so that an equilibrium between vapour and liquid can exist at room temperature*

UNIT 55 SUMMARY

- A phase can be a solid, a liquid or a gas. It can also be a solution. In each case, every part of the solid, liquid, gas or solution must be the same as every other part, i.e. homogeneous.
- Phase diagrams often consist of three lines and one point:
  - (i) The vapour pressure curve shows the combinations of temperature and pressure at which a liquid and its vapour can exist at equilibrium. Part of the curve gives the boiling point of the liquid. A liquid will boil when the vapour pressure equals the atmospheric pressure.
  - (ii) The melting point curve shows the combinations of temperature and pressure at which a solid and its liquid phase can exist at equilibrium.
  - (iii) The sublimation curve shows the combinations of temperature and pressure at which a solid and its vapour phase can exist at equilibrium.
  - (iv) The triple point is the only place on a phase diagram where three phases, solid, liquid and vapour, can exist in equilibrium with each other.

56 Chromatography

56.1 What is chromatography?

Chromatography is a method of separating and analysing mixtures. You may have done the simple chromatography experiment illustrated in Figure 56.1. Here, dots of various inks have been placed on a piece of filter paper and the paper stood in a trough of solvent. The solvent may be water, but better results are obtained by using a mixture of ammonia solution and ethanol or butanol. The solvent travels up the paper, dragging the individual dyes in the inks with it. After some minutes the different coloured dyes can be seen separated from one another. Once the paper is dried, the pattern on the paper is called a *chromatogram*.

This experiment illustrates the main features of many types of chromatography. There is a competition at work (Figure 56.2). It is between

(i) the tendency for the dyes to cling to the elements of water that are naturally present in paper, and

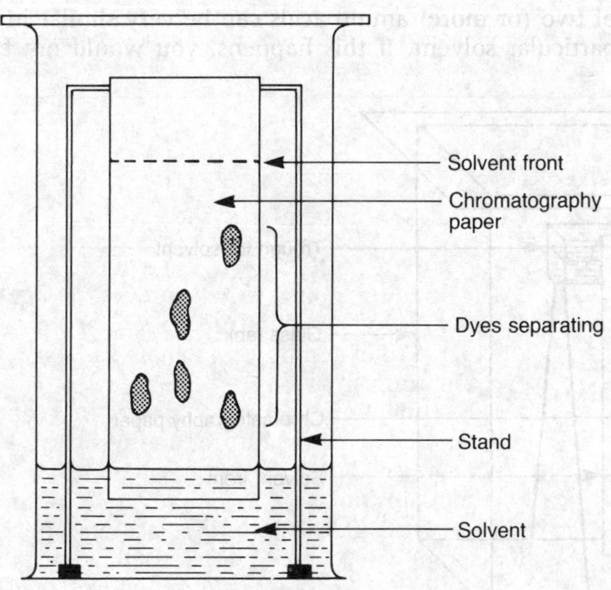

Figure 56.1 *A simple chromatography apparatus. This one uses ascending chromatography*

A sophisticated gas chromatography machine has its output directly analysed by computer.

(ii) the ability of the dyes to dissolve in the solvent as it travels up the paper.

In fact it is a type of *partition* experiment. The major difference between this and the partition experiments we shall look at in Unit 62 is that one of the solvents is invisible, i.e. the water in the molecular structure of the paper.

We say that there is a *partition* between a stationary phase (the water trapped in the paper) and a mobile phase (the solvent). If a dye dissolves more readily in the mobile phase, then it will travel with the solvent. The reason why different dyes travel at different rates up the paper is a result of their different solubilities in the two phases.

We shall now pay closer attention to the five types of chromatography in widespread use.

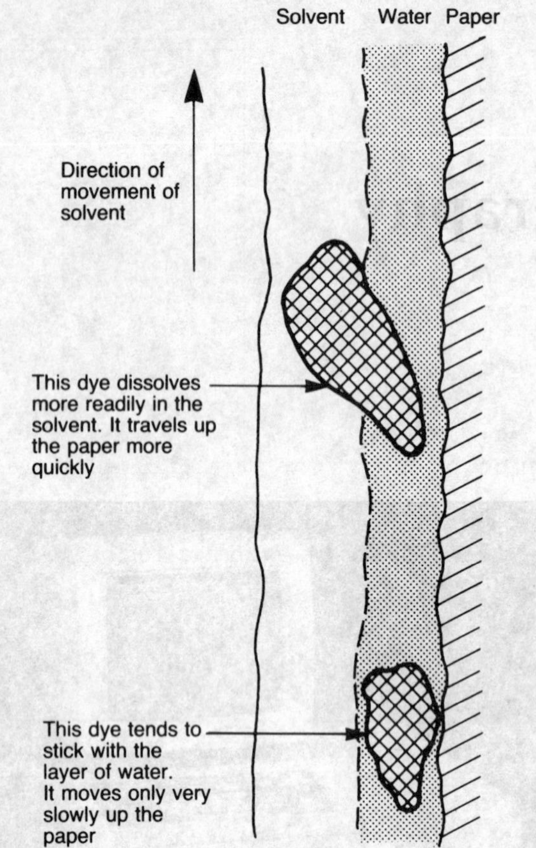
Solvent
Water
Paper
Direction of movement of solvent
This dye dissolves more readily in the solvent. It travels up the paper more quickly
This dye tends to stick with the layer of water. It moves only very slowly up the paper

***Figure 56.2** A much simplified diagram to illustrate the competition between the solvent and water adsorbed on the surface of chromatography paper*

56.2 Paper chromatography

As we have seen, in paper chromatography the partition is between two liquids, although one of them (the water on the paper) is trapped in position by its attraction for the cellulose in paper. In ascending chromatography (see Figure 56.1) the solvent travels up the paper by capillary action. In descending chromatography (Figure 56.3) the solvent travels down the paper, also by capillary action but also helped a little by gravity.

The key to the success of chromatography is that, given the same conditions, i.e. type of paper, solvent and temperature, the same substance will always move at the same rate relative to the solvent. This is shown in Figure 56.4. The three chromatograms have the solvent front and the position of the dye at different distances along the paper. However, in each case the ratio

$$\frac{\text{distance travelled by dye}}{\text{distance travelled by solvent}}$$

is constant. This ratio is the R_f value of the dye. R_f values have been tabulated for a vast range of substances in many different solvents. This allows an 'unknown' component of a mixture to be identified from its chromatogram.

Fortunately paper chromatography is not restricted to analysing coloured compounds. Mixtures of colourless amino acids can be analysed by chromatography. The mixture is spotted on to the paper and left in contact with the solvent. Before the solvent reaches the top of the paper, the experiment is stopped, and the paper dried. Then a developing agent is sprayed on to the paper. A substance called ninhydrin has been widely used for this purpose, but if you come across it, beware: it is carcinogenic. The developer shows the positions of the different acids, so their R_f values can be calculated and compared with values in tables. (Some typical R_f values for amino acids are shown in Table 56.1.) An alternative method is to spot known amino acids on to the paper alongside the mixture, and then the distances travelled by the known and 'unknown' acids can be compared very easily.

A problem that sometimes arises is that the R_f values of two (or more) amino acids can be very similar in a particular solvent. If this happens, you would not be

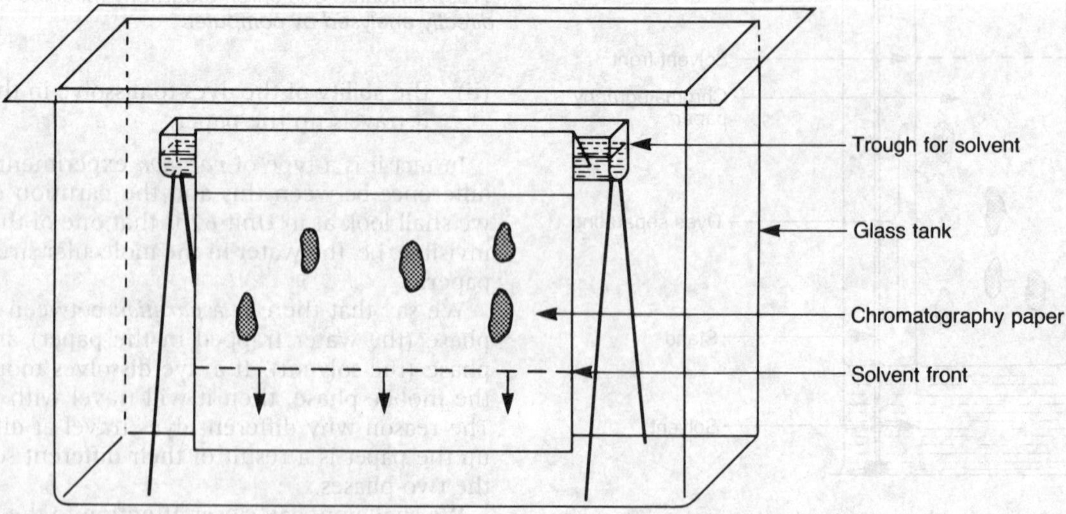
Trough for solvent
Glass tank
Chromatography paper
Solvent front

***Figure 56.3** An apparatus for descending chromatography*

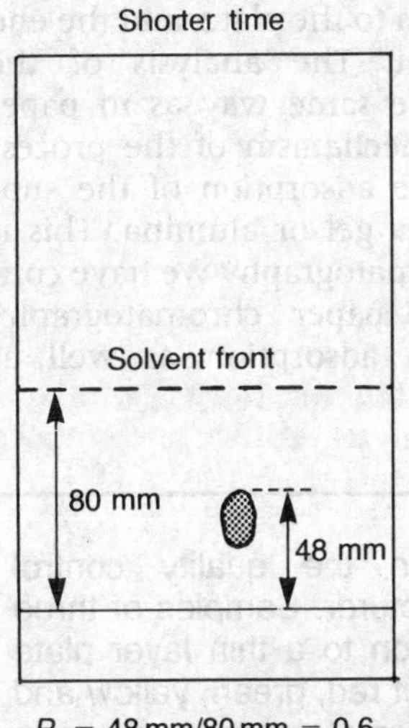

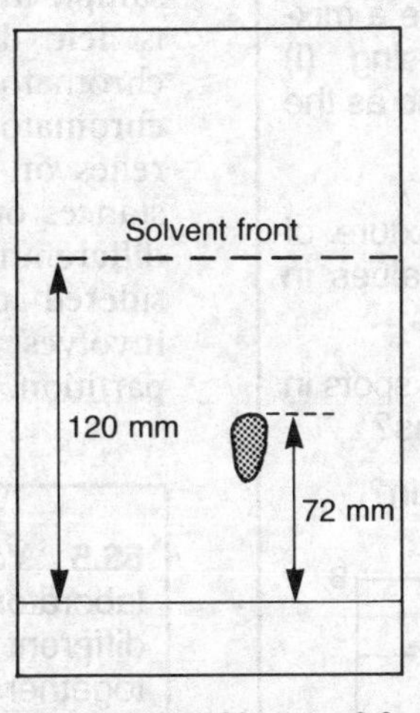

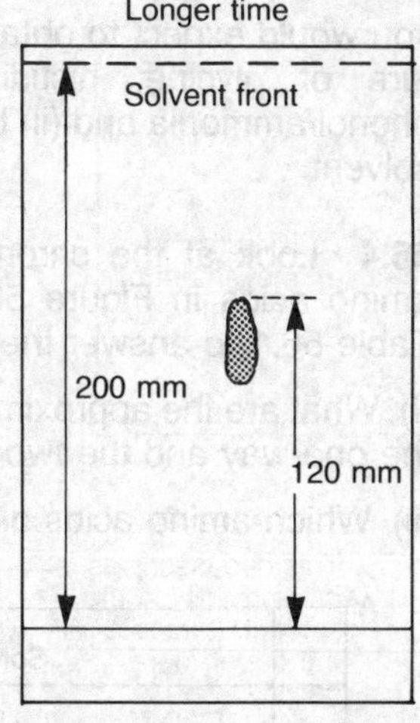

Figure 56.4 *The R_f value tells us the ratio of the distance moved by the solvent to the distance moved by the spot. The positions of the solvent front and the spot will depend on the length of time that the experiment is run*

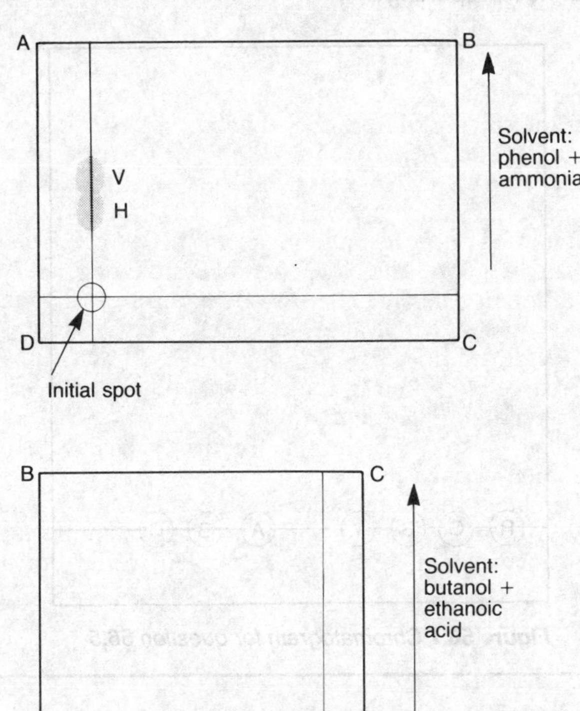

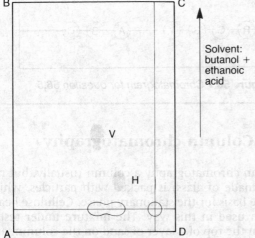

Figure 56.5 *A two-way chromatogram. Chemicals with similar R_f values in one solvent can be separated by running the chromatogram in a second solvent. The paper has to be turned through 90° before the second experiment. In this case valine (V) and histidine (H) have very close R_f values of 0.76 and 0.7 in phenol/ammonia. The spots do not separate properly. However, in butanol/ethanoic acid the R_f values are 0.45 and 0.1 respectively. This time the spots are widely separated*

Table 56.1. R_f values of some amino acids in two solvents*

Amino acid	*Phenol/ammonia*	*Butanol/ethanoic acid*
Alanine	0.55	0.28
Arginine	0.85	0.10
Cystine	0.13	0.05
Glycine	0.41	0.17
Histidine	0.70	0.10
Leucine	0.86	0.61
Serine	0.35	0.16
Valine	0.76	0.45

*Adapted from: Blackburn, S. (1968). *Amino Acid Determination*, Edward Arnold, London, table 10.1, p. 141

able to see separate spots on the developed chromatogram. The way round the problem is to do *two-way chromatography* (Figure 56.5). A chromatogram is produced in the normal way; then the paper is dried and turned through a right angle before it is placed in a second solvent. The second solvent completes the separation.

56.1 A student drew an ink line across a piece of chromatography paper and spotted samples of coloured dyes at several points along it. The paper was then used for ascending chromatography. Why was the student rather foolish?

56.2 A second student wrote that 'in descending chromatography heavier molecules are bound to have higher R_f values than lighter molecules'. Do you agree?

56.3 Draw a diagram showing the chromatograms

you would expect to obtain if you were to use a mixture of glycine, histidine and valine using (i) phenol/ammonia and (ii) butanol/ethanoic acid as the solvent.

56.4 Look at the chromatograms of a mixture of amino acids in Figure 56.6, and use the values in Table 56.1 to answer the following questions:

(i) What are the approximate R_f values of the spots in the one-way and the two-way chromatograms?

(ii) Which amino acids did the mixture contain?

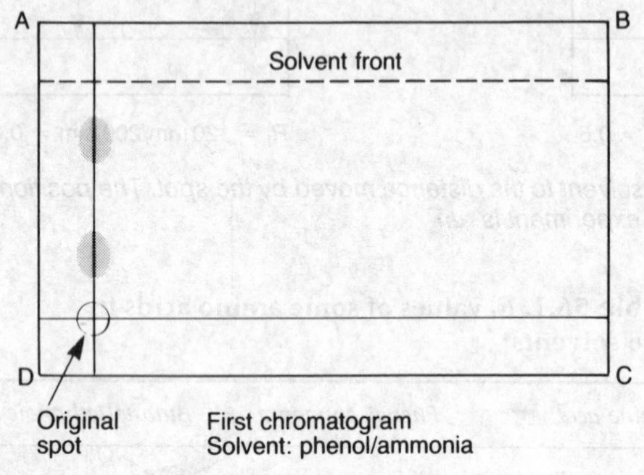

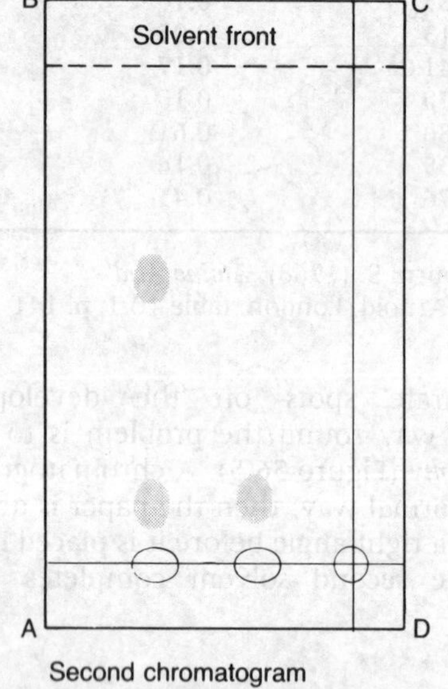

***Figure 56.6** Two-way chromatograms for question 56.4. The diagrams are drawn to scale. Use a ruler to help you measure the R_f values*

56.3 Thin layer chromatography (TLC)

TLC is similar to paper chromatography, but can be more sensitive. A thin layer of, for example, cellulose, silica gel, or alumina is deposited on a glass slide. The sample under test is spotted on to the plate, and the end is left dipping into solvent. The analysis of the chromatogram is done in the same way as in paper chromatography. Here the mechanism of the process relies on the variation in the adsorption of the substances on the cellulose, silica gel or alumina. This is different to the partition chromatography we have considered previously. In fact paper chromatography involves separation through adsorption as well as partition.

56.5 You are working in the quality control laboratory of an ink manufacturer. Samples of three different inks were spotted on to a thin layer plate together with pure samples of red, green, yellow and blue dyes. The resulting chromatogram is shown in Figure 56.7. Which coloured dyes did the three inks contain? Are there any features of the chromatogram that need reporting?

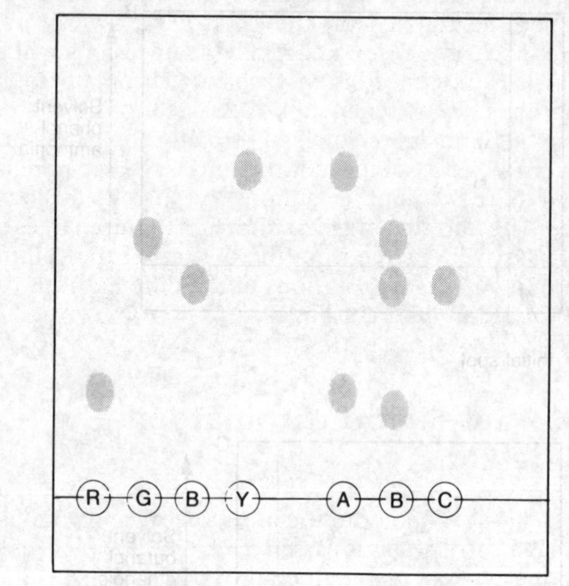

***Figure 56.7** Chromatogram for question 56.5*

56.4 Column chromatography

In column chromatography a column (usually, but not always, made of glass) is packed with particles, which make the basis for the stationary phase. Cellulose beads are often used in this way. The mixture under test is placed on the top of a layer of sand on the column, and a slow stream of solvent, the *eluant*, washes the mixture through it. The sand is there to prevent the particles being disturbed by the liquid. The substance that is the least attracted into the stationary phase is washed out at the bottom of the column first, followed by the remaining components over a period of time. With the right choice of column material and solvent, the components in the mixture can be collected in different flasks, and analysed further if necessary. If you try an experiment like this, you can use a burette filled with alumina; but be sure to mix the alumina with solvent first to make a slurry before putting it into the burette. This ensures that the column is free of air spaces, and also prevents the glass from breaking should the powder expand as it takes up the solvent. If you use a mixture of coloured inks or dyes, you should see the coloured bands work their way down the column. Incidentally, do not let the column dry out.

56.5 Ion exchange chromatography

This is a variation of the column method we have just looked at. The difference is that the column is packed with an *ion exchange resin* (Figure 56.8). This is made of beads of polymer that have charged groups on their surface. In an *anionic* exchange resin, the groups are negatively charged. If positive ions tumble down the column they can be attracted by the negative charges and become trapped on the column. Likewise, in a *cationic* exchange resin, negatively charged ions will be trapped. The essence of ion exchange chromatography is that ions of one type will be attracted to the charges on the column more (or less) strongly than ions of a different type. A solution of the ions to be separated is placed on the top of the column, and the eluant slowly added. The ions that are least attracted to the charges on the beads will emerge from the bottom of the column before the others, so solutions of the different ions can be collected in different flasks.

56.6 Gas–liquid chromatography (GLC)

GLC is a little different to the others because the mobile phase is a gas. The gas is passed over a solid, which, as in the other types of chromatography, acts as a support for the stationary liquid phase. You can see the basic design of a GLC apparatus in Figure 56.9a. An inert solid is used to support the stationary liquid phase, and is packed into a steel coil kept in a thermostatted oven to maintain an even temperature. The sample is injected into the coil through a rubber septum. The temperature of the oven must be high enough to vaporise the sample, which is carried through the coil by a stream of inert gas such as nitrogen. After leaving the coil, the sample, and carrier gas, pass through a detector. This usually works by measuring the thermal conductivity of the gas passing by. The electronics in the detector amplifies the signal and it is sent to a chart recorder. The chart shows a peak for each component in the original mixture (Figure 56.9b). One of the good things about the chart is that the area under each peak is proportional to the amount of the substance present, so the experiment can give us quantitative as well as qualitative information.

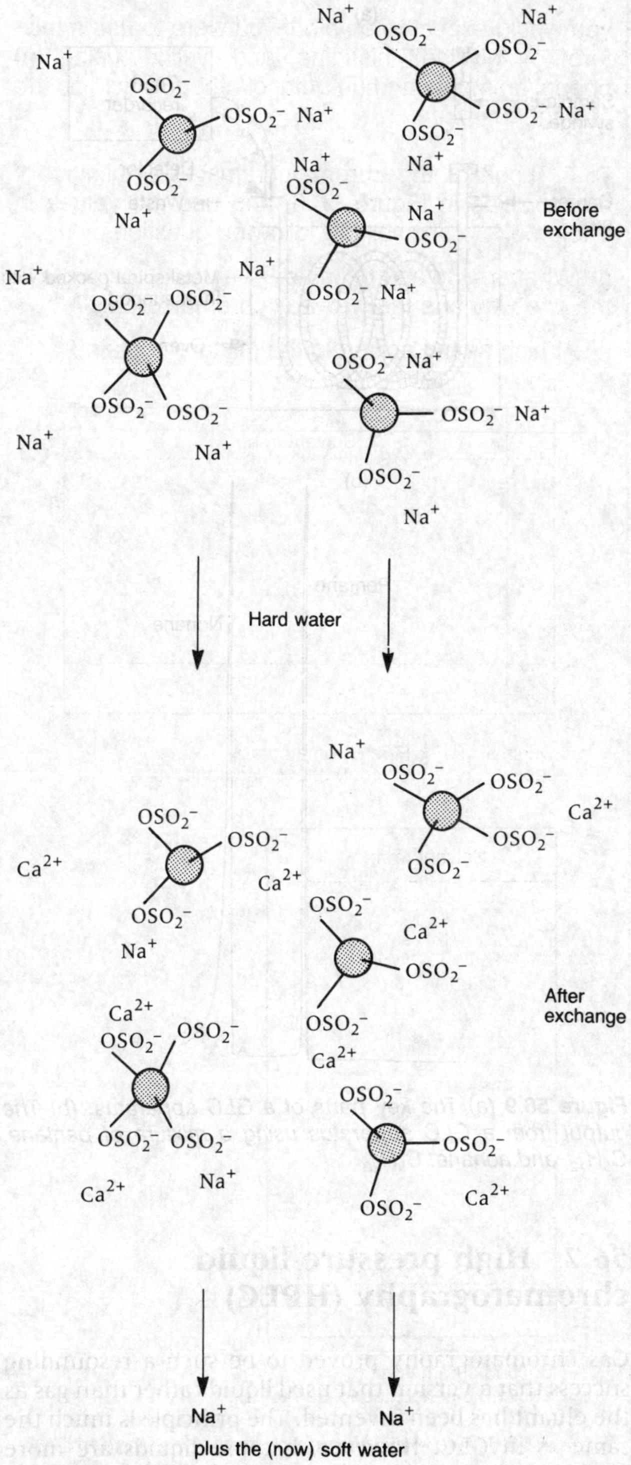

Figure 56.8 *Ion exchange resin. Here Na^+ ions are exchanged for Ca^{2+} ions*

A neat variation on the use of GLC has been used. The output stream from a GLC is fed directly into the input of a mass spectrometer. In this way a mixture can be separated into its components and their mass spectra determined all in one experiment (see photo on p. 161).

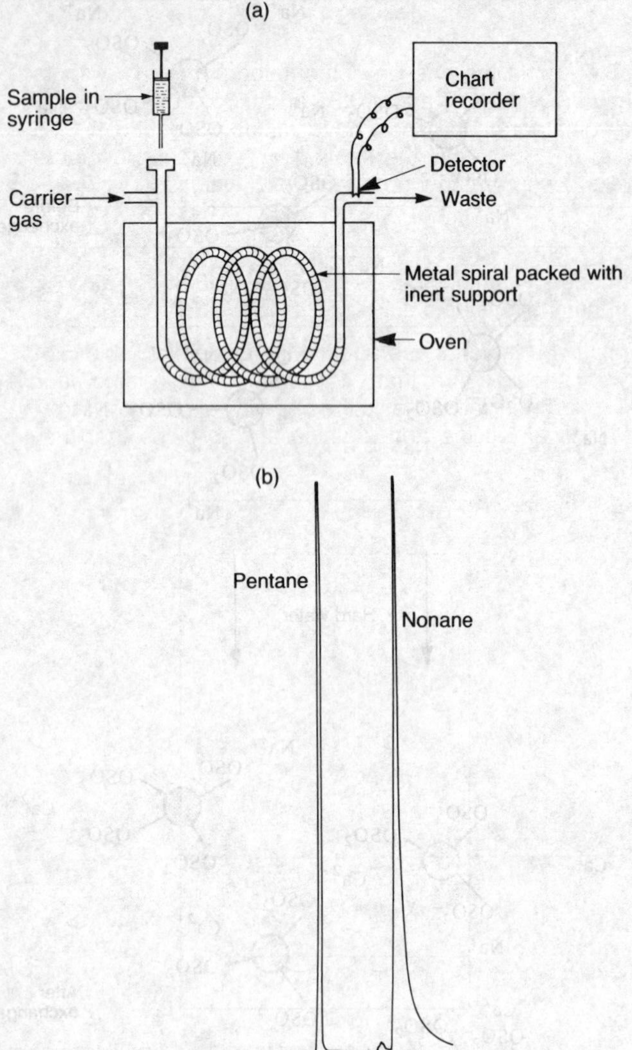

Figure 56.9 (a) The key parts of a GLC apparatus. (b) The output from a GLC apparatus using a mixture of pentane, C_5H_{12}, and nonane, C_9H_{20}

56.7 High pressure liquid chromatography (HPLC)

Gas chromatography proved to be such a resounding success that a version that used liquid rather than gas as the eluant has been invented. The principle is much the same as in GLC. However, because liquids are more viscous than gases, the pressure used to make them pass through a column is greater than in GLC: between 20 and 200 atm. Such high pressures require a strong column, which is often about 25 cm in length. Figure 56.10a shows you the scheme of the process. The molecules coming off the column are detected by an ultraviolet spectrophotometer, and the output appears as a series of peaks very much like the GLC charts (Figure 56.10b). Owing to its accuracy, HPLC has become very widely used in analysis and research.

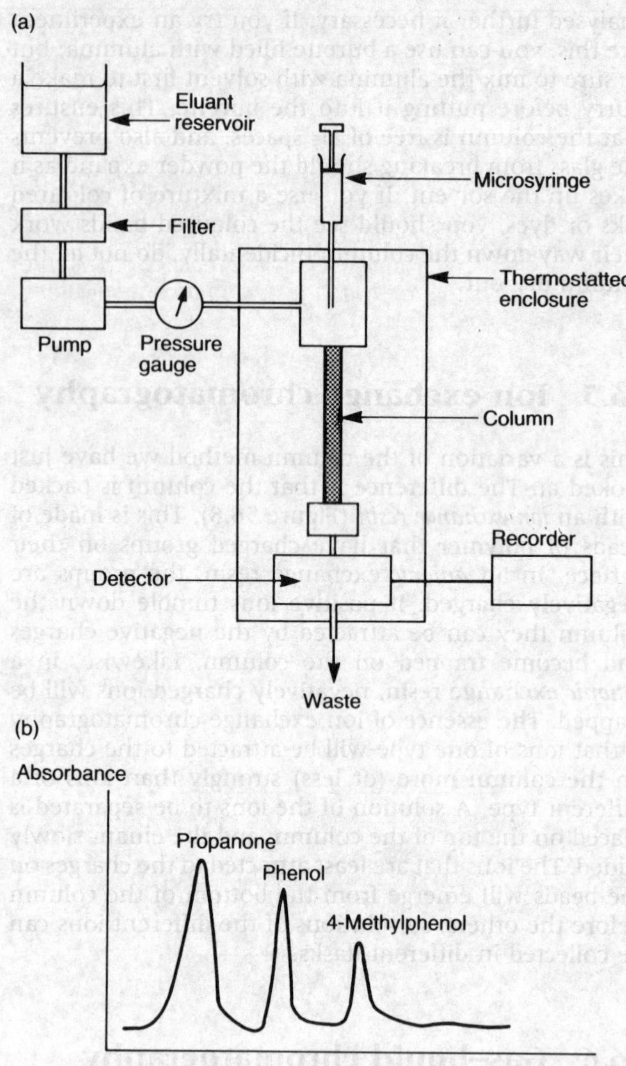

***Figure 56.10** (a) An outline of a high pressure liquid chromatography (HPLC) apparatus, together with (b) a typical output. (Adapted from: Knox, J. H. et al. (1979).* High Performance Liquid Chromatography, *Edinburgh University Press, Edinburgh)*

56.6 The area under the peaks on a GLC chart can be found electronically, but there are other ways of using the charts to find the relative proportions of the components in a mixture. If you were given a chart and asked to work out the proportions of the components from it, what would you do?

Answers

56.1 The dyes in the ink may also travel up the paper and overlap with the dyes under test. A *pencil* line should always be drawn to mark the starting line.

56.2 Chromatography depends on the degree of partition of the molecules between the stationary and mobile phases. A heavy molecule could easily have a smaller R_f value than a lighter molecule. The effects of gravity are insignificant compared with the setting up of equilibrium between the two phases.

56.3 The chromatograms are shown in Figure 56.11.

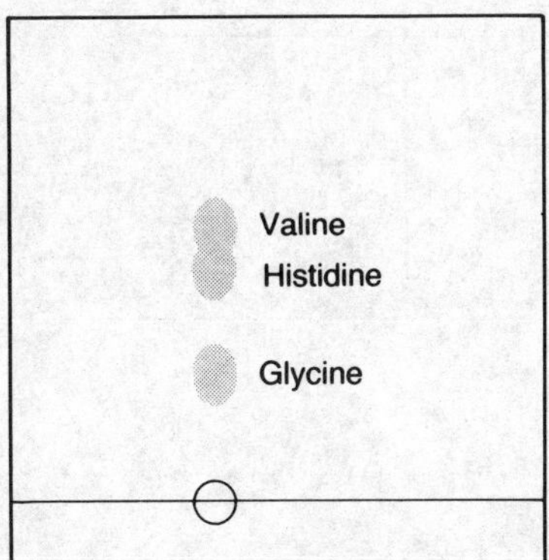

Solvent: phenol/ammonia
The R_f values of valine and histidine are similar. The spots given by these amino acids are likely to overlap

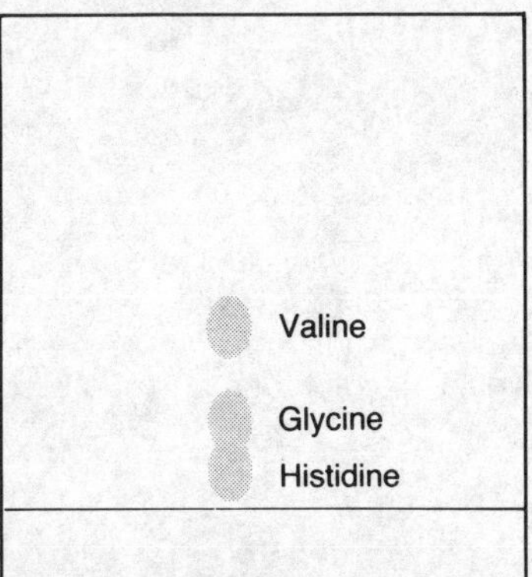

Solvent: butanol/ethanoic acid
In this solvent the R_f values of glycine and histidine mean that they will give overlapping spots

***Figure 56.11** Diagrams for answer to question 56.4*

56.4 (i) In the one-way chromatogram the two spots have R_f values of about 0.85 and 0.35. In the two-way chromatogram the spots have values of about 0.1, 0.15 and 0.6. If we call the spots X, Y and Z as in Figure 56.12, we can draw up a table of R_f values:

	X	*Y*	*Z*
In phenol/ammonia	0.35	0.85	0.85
In butanol/ethanoic acid	0.15	0.1	0.6

(ii) If you match these against the values in Table 56.1 you should find that X = serine, Y = arginine and Z = leucine. Notice that in the one-way experiment the R_f values of leucine and arginine are so close that they appear as one spot.

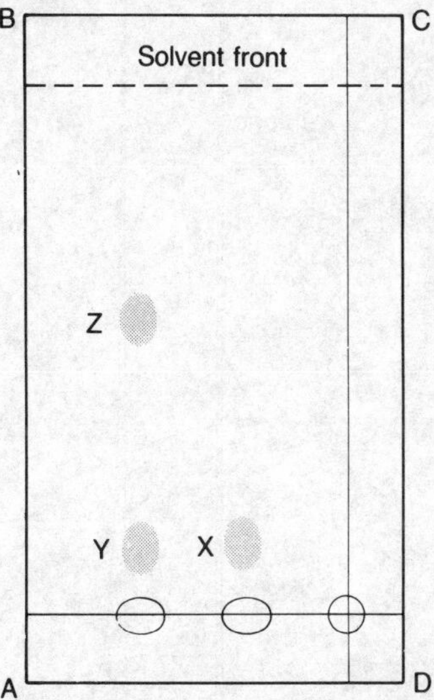

***Figure 56.12** Diagram for answer to question 56.4*

56.5 A contains red and yellow. C contains blue only. The problem is B. It certainly contains blue and green, and it seems as if it might contain red as well. However, the lowest spot is not at the same level as the pure red. It may be that the red dye in sample B is faulty, so that it has a slightly different R_f value; alternatively the spot is showing that an impurity is present. Both possibilities would have to be investigated.

56.6 You might be tempted to ask someone's help, but you might have hit upon the method used before things were automated: cut out the peaks and weigh the pieces of paper. The relative masses will be proportional to their areas, and hence to the quantities of the components present.

UNIT 56 SUMMARY

- Chromatography is a method of separating and analysing mixtures. It is a type of partition experiment.
- Each substance has its own characteristic R_f value for a given mobile and stationary phase. For example, for a dye:

$$R_f \text{ value} = \frac{\text{distance travelled by dye}}{\text{distance travelled by solvent}}$$

- Paper chromatography:
  Partition is between the stationary phase (water on the paper) and the mobile phase (the solvent).
- Column chromatography:
  A column of an inert material has the sample placed on top, and the solvent (the eluant) washes the various components down the column at different rates.
- Ion exchange chromatography:
  The column is packed with an ion exchange resin. This is made of beads of polymer that have charged groups on their surface. In an anionic exchange resin, the groups are negatively charged and trap positive ions. In a cationic exchange resin, negatively charged ions will be trapped.
- Gas–liquid chromatography:
  An inert gas, e.g. nitrogen, is passed over a solid, which acts as a support for the stationary liquid phase. The gas sweeps the sample vapour through the column.

57

Polymorphism and allotropy

57.1 What is polymorphism?

In this unit you will come across a number of new words together with their meanings. You may find it helpful to consult Table 57.1, which summarises the main things you need to know.

Table 57.1. Polymorphism and allotropy

Polymorphism	A substance can exist in two or more forms in the same state
Allotropy	Polymorphism in elements
Enantiotropy	Each allotrope (or polymorph) can be energetically stable
Monotropy	Only one allotrope (or polymorph) is energetically stable
Dynamic allotropy	Two allotropes can exist in equilibrium with each other
Transition temperature	The temperature at which two energetically stable allotropes convert into one another
Metastable	An energetically unstable form of an element or compound appears to be stable owing to a very slow rate of change into the stable form

Some substances can crystallise in two or more forms. For example, mercury(II) iodide can be found as either red or yellow crystals. The two types of crystal are *polymorphs*. We say that mercury(II) iodide exhibits *polymorphism*. The red form is energetically stable below 126° C; the yellow form is energetically stable above 126° C. At 126° C the two forms can change into one another. This temperature is the *transition temperature*. Some examples of polymorphism are shown in Table 57.2.

Calcium carbonate is another chemical that crystallises in two different forms: calcite and aragonite. Both types are widely spread in Nature. For example, marble is an array of small calcite crystals, while Iceland spar is a mineral consisting of large single crystals of calcite. The chalky precipitate made when carbon dioxide reacts with lime water is composed of very fine crystals of calcite. Aragonite is the main building material in corals and the shells of other sea creatures.

Table 57.2. Examples of polymorphism

Mercury(II) iodide	$HgI_2(s)$ red	$\rightleftharpoons$	$HgI_2(s)$ yellow	Transition temperature 126° C
Ammonium chloride	$NH_4Cl(s)$ caesium chloride structure	$\rightleftharpoons$	$NH_4Cl(s)$ sodium chloride structure	Transition temperature 184° C
Iodine monochloride	$ICl(s)$ red, stable	$\rightleftharpoons$	$ICl(s)$ brown, metastable	No transition temperature

Unlike mercury(II) iodide, there is no transition temperature for the change of calcite into aragonite. The reason is that at any temperature calcite is always the energetically stable form of calcium carbonate. Aragonite is always energetically unstable with respect to changing into calcite. However, the *rate* of change of aragonite into calcite is extremely slow. A substance like aragonite, which by rights should not exist because it is energetically unstable, is said to be *metastable*. A metastable state exists only while the rate of change into the energetically stable form is very slow. If aragonite is heated to over 400° C it begins to change into calcite much more quickly than at room temperature. At 450° C the change is even more rapid; at 350° C it is much slower. The temperature of 400° C is *not* a transition temperature. The change of aragonite into calcite is taking place at all temperatures; the change only becomes noticeable at around 400° C.

We have now discovered two types of polymorphism. There are different names for them:

> ***Enantiotropy*: there is a transition temperature.**
>
> ***Monotropy*: there is no transition temperature.**

Marble is an excellent material for many uses, not the least of which is pastry making for the living, and marking the memory of the dead.

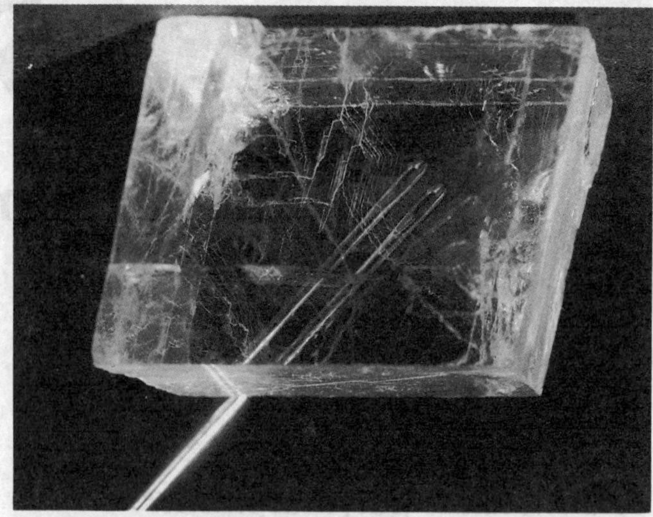

This sample of calcite (Iceland spar) clearly shows the phenomenon of double refraction, where light passing through the crystal is split into two rays.

Table 57.3. Examples of allotropy

Sulphur	$S_8(s)$ rhombic	$\rightleftharpoons$	$S_8(s)$ monoclinic	Transition temperature 95.5° C
Tin	$Sn(s)$ grey	$\rightleftharpoons$	$Sn(s)$ white	Transition temperature 13.2° C
Phosphorus	$(P_4)_n(s)$ red, stable	$\rightleftharpoons$	$P_4(s)$ white, metastable	No transition temperature
Carbon	$C(s)$ graphite, stable	$\rightleftharpoons$	$C(s)$ diamond, metastable	No transition temperature

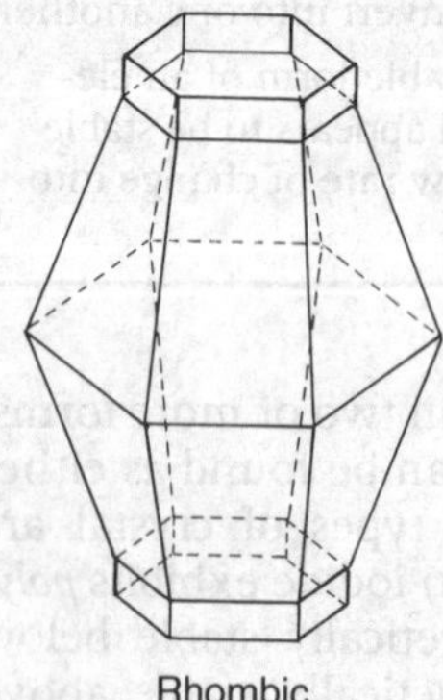

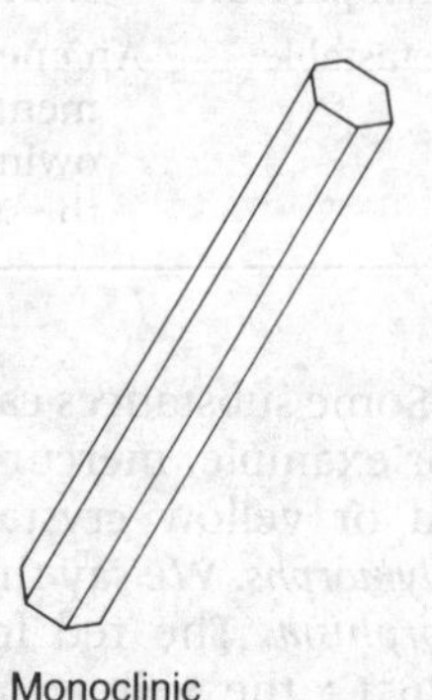

***Figure 57.1** The shapes of crystals of rhombic and monoclinic sulphur. The latter are fine and needle-like*

57.2 What is allotropy?

The short answer to this is that it is polymorphism in elements. Some examples of allotropy are shown in Table 57.3.

Sulphur has two allotropes, called rhombic and monoclinic sulphur. Each type crystallises in a characteristic form (Figure 57.1). They can be distinguished by the shape of their crystals or by measuring their densities. Rhombic sulphur is energetically stable below 95.5° C, and monoclinic sulphur is energetically stable above this temperature. Therefore sulphur is an element that shows enantiotropy (or enantiotropic allotropy).

Phosphorus is an element that displays monotropy. It has three different forms, white, red and black phos-

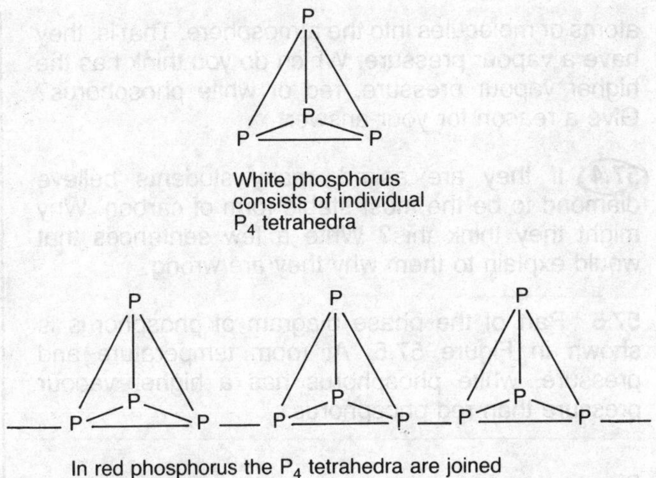
White phosphorus consists of individual P_4 tetrahedra
In red phosphorus the P_4 tetrahedra are joined in long chains

Figure 57.2 The arrangements of phosphorus atoms in red and white phosphorus. The structure of black phosphorus is complicated, with a great deal of interlinking between chains of atoms

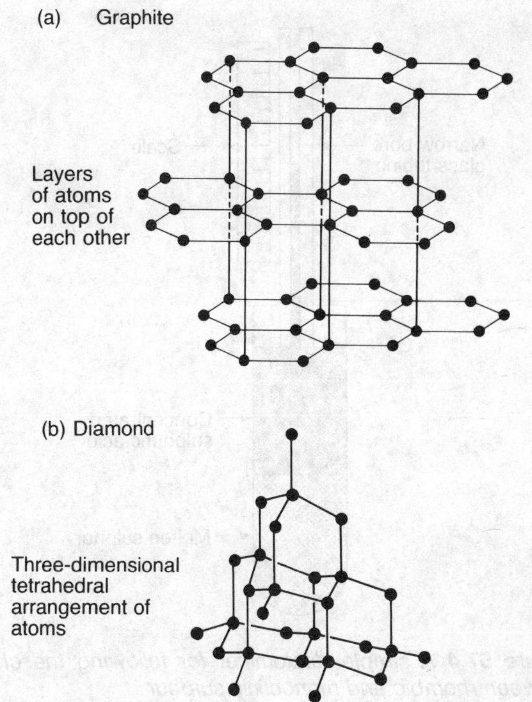
(a) Graphite
Layers of atoms on top of each other
(b) Diamond
Three-dimensional tetrahedral arrangement of atoms

Figure 57.3 The two allotropes of carbon: graphite and diamond

phorus (Figure 57.2). Red phosphorus is always the energetically stable form. White and black phosphorus are metastable forms. White phosphorus is quite common and can be kept in laboratories for years without converting into red phosphorus. (However, it has to be kept under water to prevent it bursting into flame when oxygen in the air reacts with it.) Black phosphorus is made by heating red phosphorus to a high temperature and under high pressure.

Carbon has graphite and diamond as its two allotropes (Figure 57.3). We have discussed their structures in Unit 32. The key things to remember about them is that graphite is much softer than diamond, and that graphite will conduct electricity whereas diamond is an insulator. Graphite has a layer structure, but the carbon atoms in diamond make up a much stronger interconnected three-dimensional lattice.

Oxygen also shows allotropy, but of a special type. In common with a few other elements it has allotropic forms in the same state that can exist in equilibrium with each other. Oxygen, O_2, and trioxygen (ozone), O_3, are the most famous example:

$$3O_2(g) \rightleftharpoons 2O_3(g)$$

Given that all equilibria are dynamic, the change from one allotropic form to the other is also dynamic; hence the name given to the allotropy of oxygen is *dynamic allotropy*. Oxygen will convert into trioxygen when it is irradiated with ultraviolet light. This happens naturally in the upper atmosphere. Trioxygen itself is poisonous, but its presence in the upper atmosphere is essential. It has the ability to absorb much of the harmful ultraviolet radiation from the Sun. You will find more information about the role of trioxygen (ozone) in Unit 99.

The two allotropes of carbon: diamond and graphite.

57.1 The density of rhombic sulphur is 2.07×10^3 kg m^{-3}, and that of monoclinic sulphur is 1.96×10^3 kg m^{-3}. The apparatus shown in Figure 57.4 is used to study the change of rhombic sulphur into monoclinic sulphur. It is a type of *dilatometer*. (A dilatometer measures changes in volumes.) The concentrated sulphuric acid does not react with sulphur, nor does it boil until well above 100° C. Study the diagram and predict:

(i) what happens to the height of sulphuric acid in the

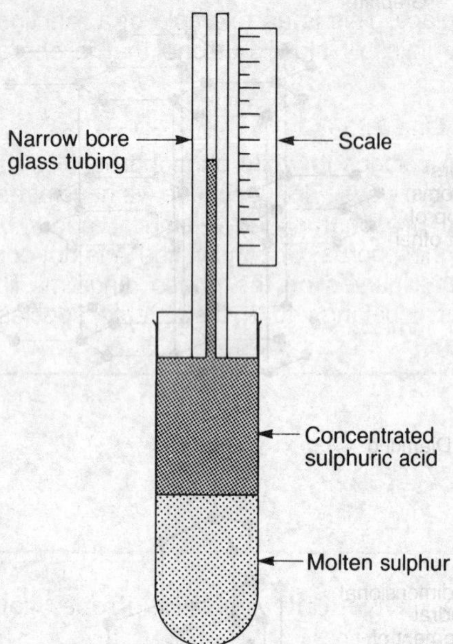

Figure 57.4 A simple dilatometer for following the change between rhombic and monoclinic sulphur

tube when the temperature of the boiling tube is increased from room temperature to about 100° C;

(ii) the shape of a graph of height of liquid in the tube plotted against temperature.

Why is the measuring tube made of capillary tubing (glass tubing of small diameter)?

57.2 Grey tin is considerably more brittle than white tin. Would you recommend making buttons for clothes out of tin?

57.3 All substances have a tendency to lose their atoms or molecules into the atmosphere. That is, they have a vapour pressure. Which do you think has the higher vapour pressure, red or white phosphorus? Give a reason for your answer.

57.4 If they are asked, many students believe diamond to be the most stable form of carbon. Why might they think this? Write a few sentences that would explain to them why they are wrong.

57.5 Part of the phase diagram of phosphorus is shown in Figure 57.5. At room temperature and pressure, white phosphorus has a higher vapour pressure than red phosphorus.

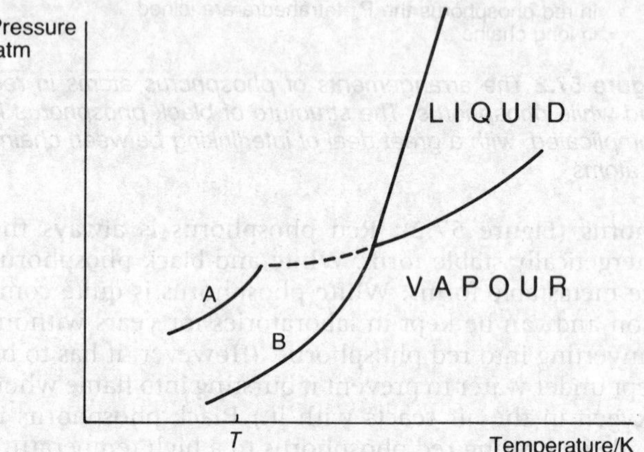

Figure 57.5 *Part of the phase diagram of phosphorus*

(i) At the temperature marked T, which of the lines A and B corresponds to the greater vapour pressure?

(ii) Which of the lines belongs to red phosphorus, and which to white phosphorus?

Answers

57.1 (i) Monoclinic sulphur is less dense than rhombic sulphur, so a given mass of monoclinic sulphur has a greater volume than the same mass of rhombic sulphur. For this reason, at the transition temperature, 95.5° C, the liquid level in the measuring tube rises rapidly.

(ii) The shape of the graph is shown in Figure 57.6.

The tube is narrow so that a small volume change brings about a large increase in height of the liquid – it magnifies the volume change.

57.2 It would not be a good idea. If the temperature falls below the transition temperature, 13.2° C, the buttons might crumble and fall off. It is said that this happened to Napoleon's troops in their winter retreat from Moscow.

57.3 White phosphorus has the greater vapour pressure. It is easier for the separate P_4 molecules in white

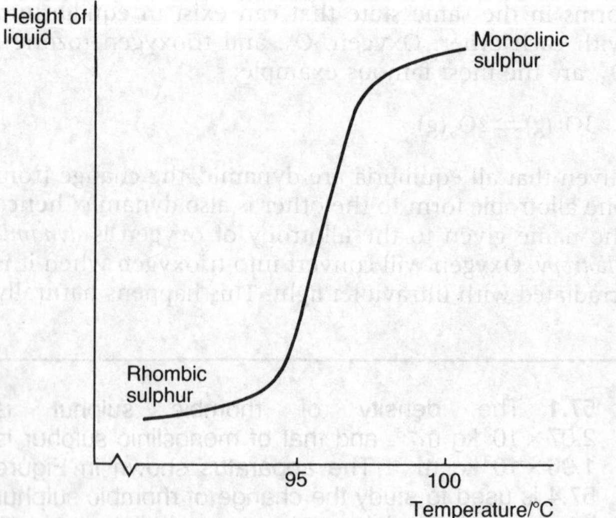

Figure 57.6 *Graph for answer to question 57.1(ii)*

Answers – contd.

phosphorus to escape than for the long chains of joined P_4 units in red phosphorus.

57.4 Diamond is much harder than graphite, and does not burn. Appearances are deceptive though. Graphite *is* the energetically stable form. However, the interlocking tetrahedral arrangement of carbon atoms in diamond means that, if it is to convert into the hexagonal ring structure of graphite, a vast number of bonds have to be broken and new ones made. This is so unlikely to happen that for all intents and purposes the reaction does not take place. This is an example of a reaction that is *kinetically* infinitely slow, but one that is *energetically* possible.

57.5 (i) Line A.

(ii) Line A belongs to white phosphorus. You can work this out in two ways. First, because we have already said that white phosphorus has a higher vapour pressure than red phosphorus. Secondly, line A is not connected to any other curves on the phase diagram. This suggests that it belongs to a metastable species (white phosphorus).

UNIT 57 SUMMARY

- Polymorphism occurs when a substance can exist in two or more forms in the same state.
- Allotropy is polymorphism in elements.
- Enantiotropy applies to cases where each allotrope (or polymorph) is energetically stable.
- Monotropy occurs when only one allotrope (or polymorph) is energetically stable.
- Dynamic allotropy occurs when two allotropes can exist in equilibrium with each other.
- Transition temperature is the temperature at which two energetically stable allotropes convert into one another.
- Metastability is where an energetically unstable form of an element or compound appears to be stable owing to a very slow rate of change into the stable form.
- Elements that have allotropes include carbon (diamond and graphite), sulphur (rhombic and monoclinic) and phosphorus (red and white).

58

Equilibrium between a solid and liquid

58.1 What happens when a liquid freezes?

The particles in a liquid are held together by intermolecular forces. It is the strength of these forces that prevents the liquid from changing completely into a gas. However, the particles have a spread of energies; some have much less energy than the average, some a lot more. It is the particles with more than the average energy that escape into the vapour. One result of the liquid losing these particles is that the average energy of those remaining in the liquid goes down. We feel this as a decrease in the temperature of a liquid when it evaporates.

However, on average the particles in a liquid have sufficient energy to keep them jiggling about and prevent the intermolecular forces from making them stick together permanently. If the average energy of the particles goes down, then the intermolecular forces can win the battle; the particles are attracted strongly together, and we see crystals appear.

The temperature at which a solid turns into a liquid is its melting point. More accurately we should say that the melting point is the temperature at which solid and liquid can exist in equilibrium with each other. Above the melting point, the solid will change completely into liquid. Below the melting point, liquid will change completely into solid.

A typical melting point apparatus. The sample (in a narrow glass tube) is placed in a slot in a heated metal block surrounding the thermometer bulb.

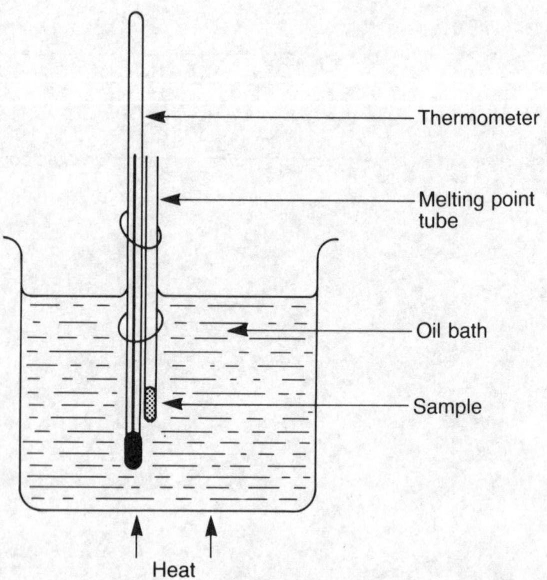

Figure 58.1 *A simple melting point apparatus. If the sample is pure, it should have a sharp melting point*

Every pure substance has its own characteristic melting point. This fact is often used in organic chemistry to identify a compound by measuring its melting point (Figure 58.1).

58.2 Cooling curves

The melting point of a solid can be found by taking the liquid and allowing it to cool. It is interesting to plot a graph of temperature against time in such an experiment (Figure 58.2). The resulting graph is known as a *cooling curve* (Figure 58.3).

At first the temperature decreases steadily, then it remains constant, before finally decreasing again. When molecules in a liquid join together, the intermolecular forces are making bonds between them. Making bonds is an exothermic process and it is the heat given out when crystals are made that stops the temperature falling. The heat released also has the effect of raising the temperature of the liquid. This prevents more crystals appearing until some of the heat is dissipated into the surroundings; then more crystals appear, giving out more heat. Eventually, all the liquid crystallises and the crystals cool to room temperature. Often there is a dip in the cooling curve just before the crystals appear. This dip in temperature is known as *supercooling*. It can happen that the particles in the liquid fail to join up to make crystals; the liquid enters a *metastable state*. (You will find information about such states in Unit 57.) A metastable state is easily disturbed; for example by the liquid being shaken, or a speck of dust entering it. When the first few crystals are made, the energy released causes the temperature to rise rapidly to the normal melting point.

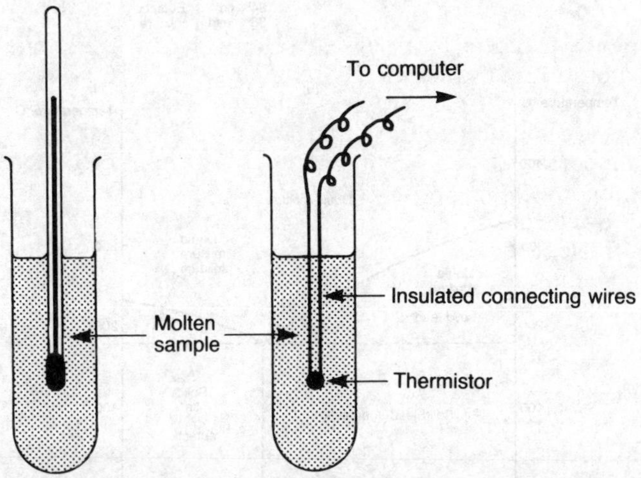

Figure 58.2 *A cooling curve can be measured directly with a mercury-in-glass thermometer. For the experimenter it is less time-consuming to use a thermistor and allow a computer to record the temperature at fixed time intervals (the thermistor has to be calibrated first)*

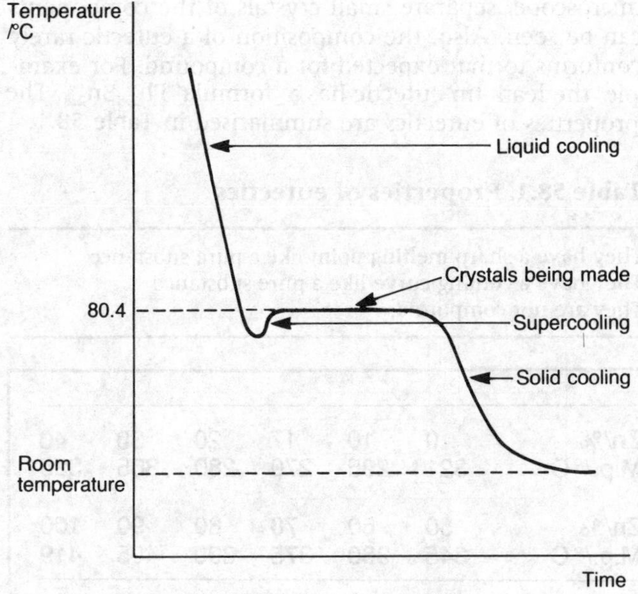

Figure 58.3 *A cooling curve for naphthalene*

58.3 Cooling curves for mixtures

We know that the freezing point of a liquid is depressed if it contains another substance dissolved in it. For example, salt water will freeze below 0°C at atmospheric pressure. Similar depressions occur with other mixtures. One mixture that is very widely used in the electronics industry is solder. Solder is a mixture of tin and lead. (However, if you buy a reel of solder it will almost certainly contain a third substance: the flux. The flux helps to stop the two metals from oxidising when they get hot.) Pure lead melts at 328°C, and pure tin melts at 232°C. However, a mixture of the two melts at a lower temperature than either of them. Solder that contains about twice as much tin as lead, e.g. 10 g tin and 5 g lead, has a cooling curve like that in Figure 58.4a. This cooling curve is exactly the same type as we would find for a pure substance. When the liquid crystallises, the solid made has exactly the same composition as the original mixture. The mixture of (roughly) 64% tin and 36% lead is called the *eutectic* mixture.

Mixtures that do not have the same composition as the eutectic have a cooling curve like that in Figure 58.4b. The big difference is that the curve has a bend in it before the flat portion is reached. If we take a mixture containing 25% tin, the bend occurs at about 270°C. At this temperature, crystals begin to be made. The crystals are pure lead. As the crystals are made, some heat is given out, which makes the mixture cool more slowly. Because the solution loses lead, the liquid remaining becomes richer in tin. Eventually the liquid reaches the eutectic composition (64% tin), at which time the remaining liquid crystallises to give a solid with the eutectic composition. This gives the usual flat part on the cooling curve. The period during which the temperature stays constant while the eutectic crystallises is known as the *eutectic halt*.

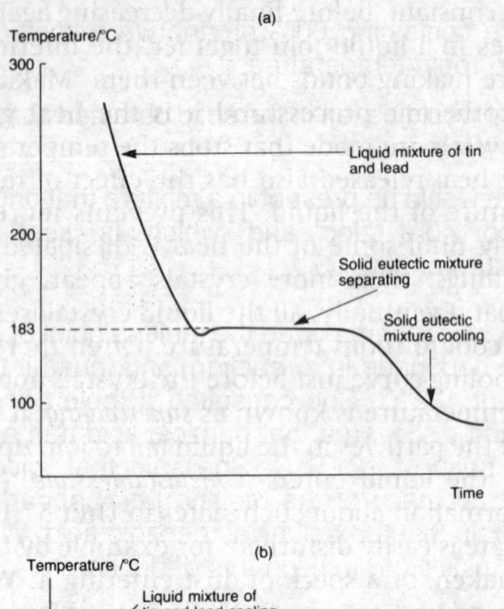

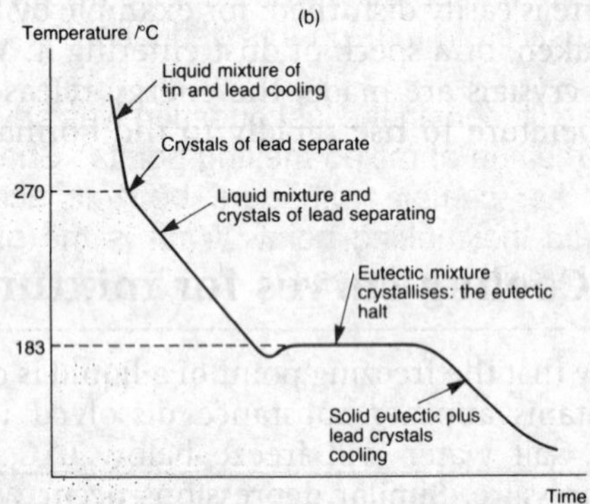

***Figure 58.4** (a) Cooling curve for a mixture of (approximately) 64% tin and 36% lead (by mass). This mixture behaves like a pure substance. It is the eutectic mixture. (b) Cooling curve for a mixture of 25% tin and 75% lead (by mass). At 270° C, lead crystals appear. More lead crystallises until, at 183° C, the eutectic mixture separates*

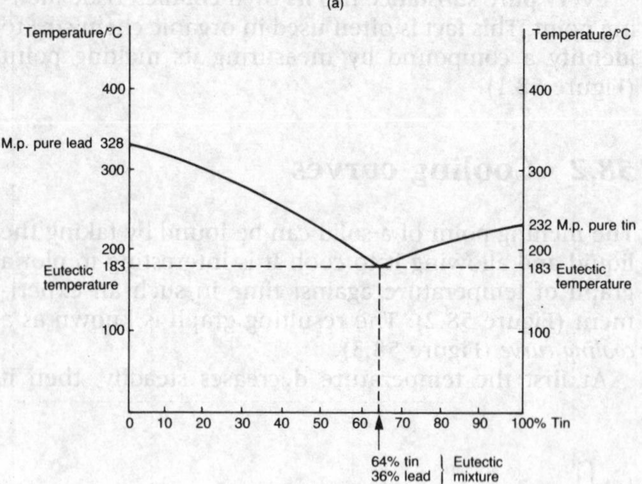

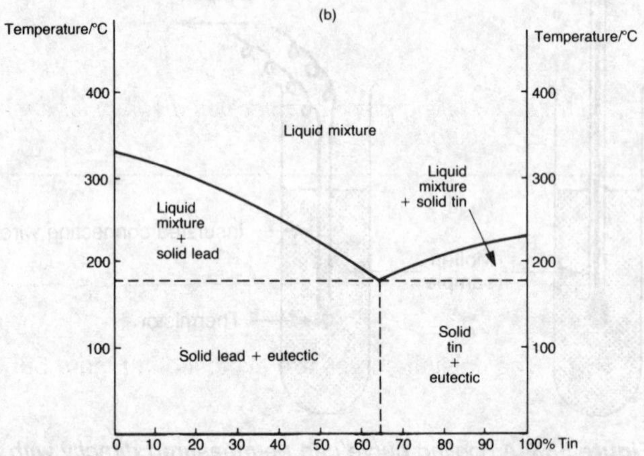

***Figure 58.5** (a) Melting point–composition diagram for mixtures of tin and lead. (b) Composition of the various regions on the tin–lead phase diagram. (This is a simplified diagram, which ignores many details of the complete diagram)*

By changing the proportions of tin and lead, we can discover the temperature at which the bend in the cooling curve occurs for a wide range of mixtures. We can plot this temperature on a melting point–composition graph like that in Figure 58.5a.

Sometimes a diagram like this has labels added to it. For example, Figure 58.5b shows that below the line to the left-hand side of the eutectic there will be solid lead in contact with liquid. In the similar region to the right of the eutectic there will be solid tin in contact with liquid. Below the eutectic temperature, 183° C, only solid is present. To the left of the eutectic the solid will consist of lead and eutectic; to the right of the eutectic the solid will contain tin and eutectic. Eutectics are not chemical compounds. If a eutectic is examined under a microscope, separate small crystals of the components can be seen. Also, the composition of a eutectic rarely conforms to that expected for a compound. For example, the lead–tin eutectic has a 'formula' $Pb_{2.5}Sn_{2.8}$. The properties of eutectics are summarised in Table 58.1.

Table 58.1. Properties of eutectics

They have a sharp melting point like a pure substance
They have a cooling curve like a pure substance
They are not compounds

58.1 Look at the diagram in Figure 58.6. Sketch the cooling curves that you would expect to obtain if you were to use mixtures of composition A, B and C at the temperature shown.

58.2 (i) Use the following information about mixtures of cadmium and zinc to plot a melting point–composition diagram.

Zn/%	0	10	17	20	30	40
M.p./° C	321	295	270	280	305	325

Zn/%	50	60	70	80	90	100
M.p./° C	345	360	375	390	405	419

(ii) Sketch the cooling curve that would be obtained if

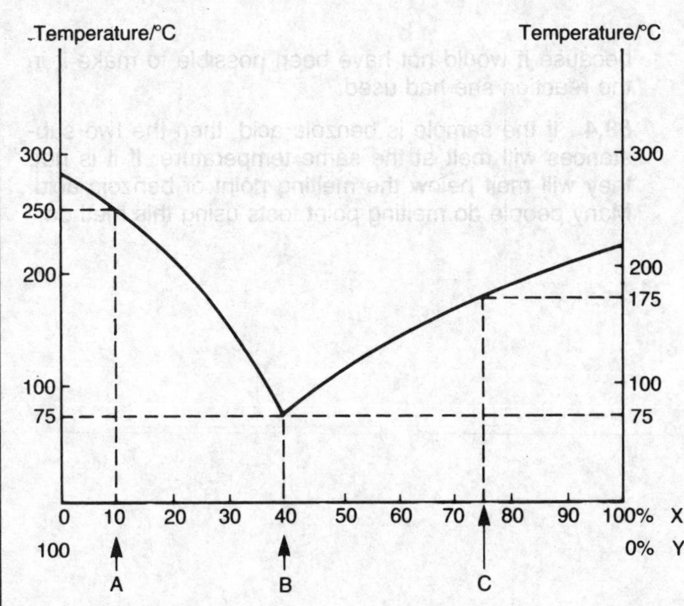

Figure 58.6 *Melting point–composition diagram for a mixture of X and Y (see question 58.1)*

a mixture containing 60% of zinc were cooled from 450° C to room temperature.

(iii) What would be left in the solid obtained at the end of the experiment?

(iv) What would be present in a mixture that originally contained 40% zinc and which is kept at a temperature of 280° C?

58.3 A student measured the melting point of a solid that she had made in a reaction, and found it to melt sharply at 122° C. She consulted a table of melting points and discovered that benzoic acid had a sharp melting point of 121.9° C. She said that, given the limits of accuracy of the melting point apparatus, it was certain that the solid was benzoic acid. Was the student justified in making this deduction?

58.4 The student in the last question was advised to use the 'method of mixed melting points'. She mixed some of her sample with pure benzoic acid, and determined the melting point. What is the principle that lies behind the method?

Answers

58.1 The cooling curves are sketched in Figure 58.7.

58.2 (i) (ii) The answers are shown in Figure 58.8.

(iii) The solid would contain solid zinc and eutectic containing 17% zinc.

(iv) It would contain solid zinc and a liquid containing the remaining zinc and cadmium.

58.3 The sharpness of the melting point suggests that the substance is pure. The only doubt is that it might be a eutectic mixture, which would also have a sharp melting point. Given that the student made the substance, it is extremely unlikely that she would have hit upon a eutectic mixture. Her deduction is reasonable, assuming that no other compound had a similar melting point. Actually, even if another compound were found to have this melting point, it is likely that it could be discounted

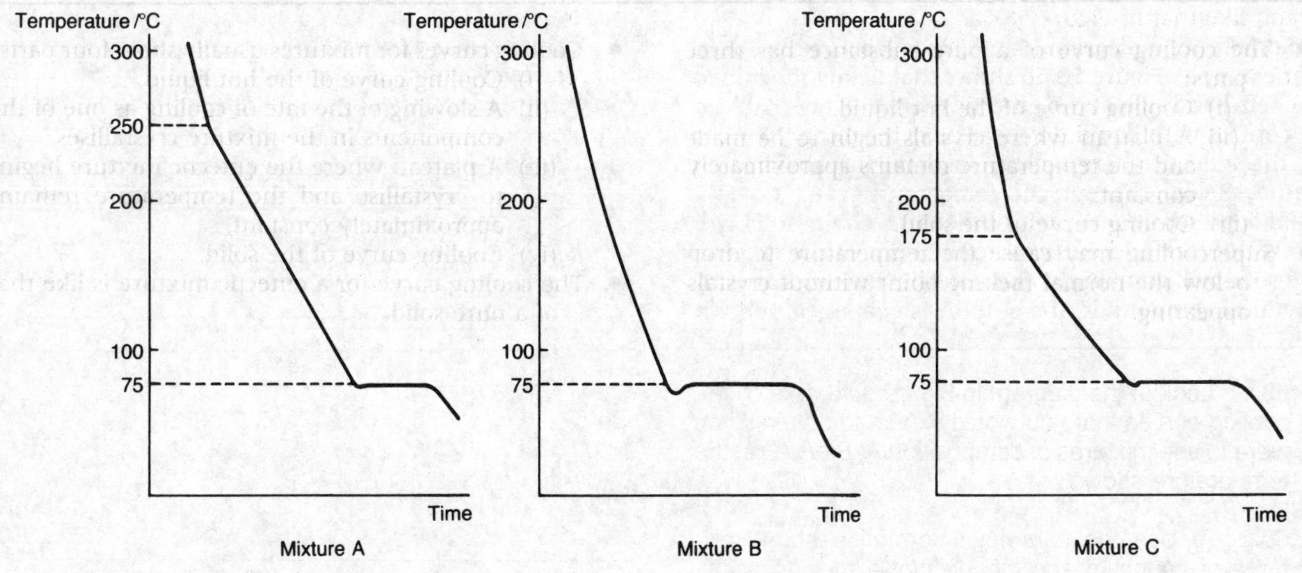

Figure 58.7 *Diagrams for answer to question 58.1*

Answers – contd.

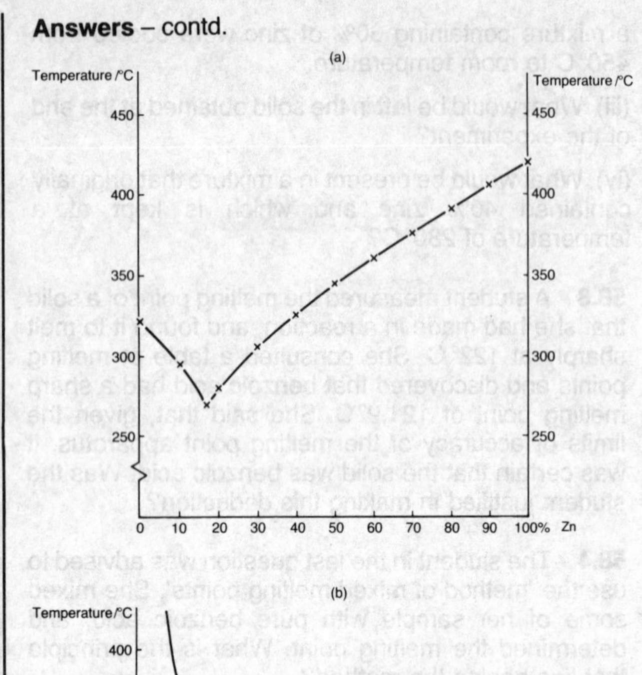

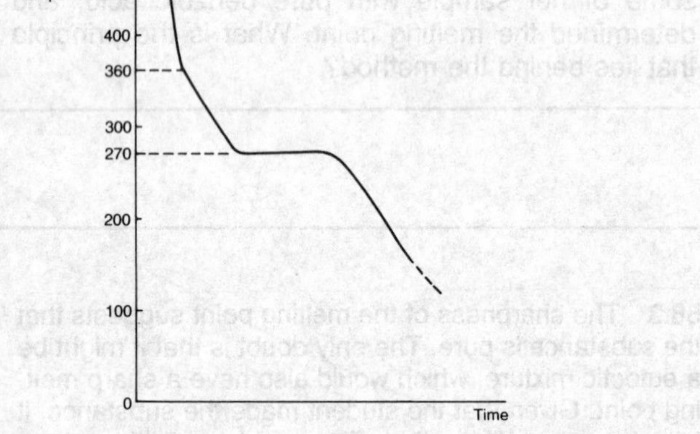

because it would not have been possible to make it in the reaction she had used.

58.4 If the sample is benzoic acid, then the two substances will melt at the same temperature. If it is not, they will melt below the melting point of benzoic acid. Many people do melting point tests using this method.

Figure 58.8 *Diagrams for answer to question 58.2. (a) Melting point–composition diagram for zinc–cadmium mixtures. (b) Cooling curve for mixture of 60% zinc and 40% cadmium*

UNIT 58 SUMMARY

- The cooling curve of a pure substance has three parts:
  - (i) Cooling curve of the hot liquid.
  - (ii) A plateau where crystals begin to be made and the temperature remains approximately constant.
  - (iii) Cooling curve of the solid.
- Supercooling may cause the temperature to drop below the normal melting point without crystals appearing.
- Cooling curves for mixtures usually show four parts:
  - (i) Cooling curve of the hot liquid.
  - (ii) A slowing of the rate of cooling as one of the components in the mixture crystallises.
  - (iii) A plateau where the eutectic mixture begins to crystallise and the temperature remains approximately constant.
  - (iv) Cooling curve of the solid.
- The cooling curve for a eutectic mixture is like that of a pure solid.

59

Solubility of salts in water

59.1 The solubility of a solid in water

The solubility of a solid in water is usually given as the number of grams, or the number of moles, of the solid that will dissolve in 100 g of water at a given temperature. Table 59.1 shows typical values of solubilities at 25° C.

Table 59.1. Solubilities of solids in water at 25° C

Substance	*Solubility*/mol per 100 g water	*Solubility*/g per 100 g water
NaCl	0.615	35.98
NaBr	0.919	94.57
NaI	1.23	184.25
$MgSO_4$	1.83×10^{-1}	22.01
$CaSO_4$	4.66×10^{-3}	0.63
$SrSO_4$	7.11×10^{-5}	0.01
$BaSO_4$	9.43×10^{-7}	2.2×10^{-4}
$NaNO_3$	1.08	91.69
$Ba(NO_3)_2$	3.91×10^{-2}	10.22

The solubilities of ionic crystals often, but not always, increase with temperature, as shown in Figure 59.1. The line for sodium sulphate in Figure 59.1 is odd because it has a kink in it at about 32° C. What is happening is that sodium sulphate changes its nature at this temperature. Below 32.4° C sodium sulphate will exist as crystals containing water of crystallisation, $Na_2SO_4{\cdot}10H_2O$. Above 32.4° C the water of crystallisation is lost, and the salt occurs as anhydrous crystals, Na_2SO_4. Therefore the solubility curve is made up of two parts: that below 32.4° C tells us the solubility of $Na_2SO_4{\cdot}10H_2O$; above 32.4° C we have the solubility curve for Na_2SO_4.

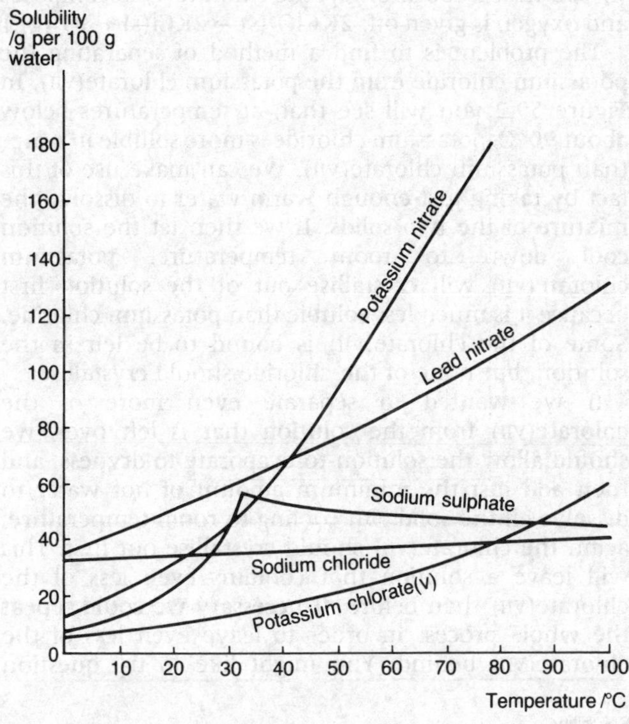

***Figure 59.1** How the solubilities of some salts vary with temperature*

59.1 Your task in this question is to design a method of measuring the solubility of sodium chloride at room temperature. You will need to think about the definition of solubility, what equipment you will have to use, and the measurements you will need to make. Write down the main steps of the method you decide upon. You might find it helpful to discuss this question with another student and decide on a joint answer.

59.2 Once you have done question 59.1, decide how you would change your method to measure the solubility of sodium chloride at 40° C.

59.2 Fractional crystallisation

Marie Curie used fractional crystallisation to separate radium from pitchblende. The method that she used was to remove radium bromide from a solution containing a mixture of radium bromide and barium bromide. The work was extremely slow and laborious and depended on the different solubilities of the two salts in water. We can see how the method works in a simpler example, which you could carry out in a laboratory.

If you heat potassium chlorate(V) very carefully, it changes into potassium chloride and potassium chlorate(VII):

$$4KClO_3(s) \rightarrow KCl(s) + 3KClO_4(s)$$

(If you heat it too strongly, the chlorate(V) decomposes and oxygen is given off: $2KClO_3(s) \rightarrow 2KCl(s) + 3O_2(g)$.)

The problem is to find a method of separating the potassium chloride from the potassium chlorate(VII). In Figure 59.2 you will see that, at temperatures below about 90° C, potassium chloride is more soluble in water than potassium chlorate(VII). We can make use of this fact by taking just enough warm water to dissolve the mixture of the two solids. If we then let the solution cool down to room temperature, potassium chlorate(VII) will crystallise out of the solution first because it is much less soluble than potassium chloride. Some of the chlorate(VII) is bound to be left in the solution, but none of the chloride should crystallise.

If we wanted to separate even more of the chlorate(VII) from the solution that is left over, we should allow the solution to evaporate to dryness, and then add just the minimum amount of hot water to dissolve all the solid. On cooling to room temperature, again the chlorate(VII) should crystallise out first. This will leave a solution that contains even less of the chlorate(VII) than before. If necessary we could repeat the whole process in order to leave even less of the chlorate(VII) behind. You might like to try question 59.3, which will show you how to make an accurate prediction of the success of a series of fractional crystallisations.

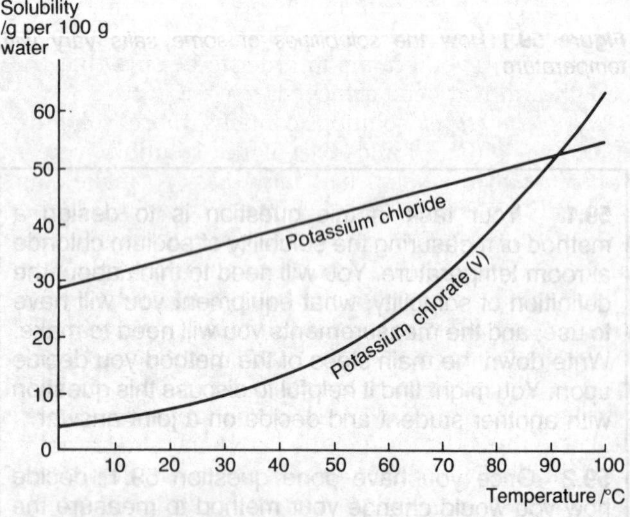

***Figure 59.2** How the solubilities of potassium chloride and potassium chlorate (V) change with temperature*

59.3 This question is designed to show you how to calculate the way to carry out a fractional crystallisation. You will need the information in Table 59.2.

Table 59.2. Solubility data for potassium chloride and potassium chlorate(VII)

	Solubility/g per 100 g water	
	At 25° C	At 50° C
Potassium chloride	35.8	40
Potassium chlorate(VII)	8.6	18

Let us suppose that we heated 8 g of potassium chlorate(V). We should end up with a mixture of 1.1 g of potassium chloride and 6.9 g of potassium chlorate(VII).

(i) How much water at 50° C would be needed to dissolve 6.9 g of potassium chlorate(VII)? Round your answer up to the next whole number. Why round up the answer?

(ii) If this mass of water were actually used, and cooled to 25° C, what is the maximum mass of potassium chlorate(VII) and of potassium chloride that it could contain?

(iii) Does any of the potassium chloride crystallise out?

(iv) What mass of potassium chlorate(VII) would be left as crystals?

(v) What is the percentage of the potassium chlorate(VII) that is left mixed in with the potassium chloride in the solution that remains?

(vi) Is there a better way of doing this experiment that would allow you to use a much smaller volume of water, and therefore improve the separation?

59.3 Crystals that contain water of crystallisation

When a salt has water of crystallisation we say that it has a *hydrate*. A solution has its own vapour pressure owing to the water molecules leaving the surface of the solution and escaping into the air. Hydrates have a vapour pressure owing to some of the water molecules leaving the crystal and escaping into the atmosphere. For many hydrates under normal conditions, there is sufficient moisture in the atmosphere to give rise to an equilibrium in which the numbers of water molecules leaving the hydrate are (on average) balanced by those leaving the atmosphere and joining the crystal. These crystals can remain unchanged in the laboratory for many years.

However, some hydrates have particularly high vapour pressures. These crystals give off their water of crystallisation to a greater or lesser extent, and thereby change their formula. A common example is sodium carbonate decahydrate, $Na_2CO_3 \cdot 10H_2O$, which you will find sold in shops as washing soda crystals. If you look at washing soda crystals you may see that they are translucent inside but covered in a white powder. The white powder is the monohydrate, $Na_2CO_3 \cdot H_2O$, which is produced because of the change

$$Na_2CO_3 \cdot 10H_2O(s) \rightarrow Na_2CO_3 \cdot H_2O(s) + 9H_2O(g)$$

which takes place at room temperature. Hydrates like this, which give off all or some of their water of crystallisation, are said to *effloresce*.

The opposite behaviour to efflorescence is *deliquescence*. Crystals that deliquesce have a vapour pressure lower than that of the water vapour in the atmosphere. An example is calcium chloride, which is often used as a drying agent. If anhydrous calcium chloride, $CaCl_2$, is left on a watch glass in a laboratory, it will turn first into $CaCl_2 \cdot 2H_2O$, then into $CaCl_2 \cdot 4H_2O$, followed by $CaCl_2 \cdot 6H_2O$, and eventually into a pool of liquid, which is a solution of the salt. Some common hydrates are given in Table 59.3.

Table 59.3. Common hydrates and their behaviour

Hydrate	*Efflorescence?*	*Deliquescence?*
$CuSO_4 \cdot 5H_2O$	No	No
$Na_2SO_4 \cdot 10H_2O$	Yes	
$Na_2CO_3 \cdot 10H_2O$	Yes	
$FeCl_3 \cdot 6H_2O$		Yes
$CaCl_2 \cdot 6H_2O$		Yes
$Cu(NO_3)_2 \cdot 9H_2O$		Yes

59.4 Figure 59.3 shows the results of measuring the solubility of calcium chloride over a range of temperatures. Suggest a reason for the shape of the curve.

59.5 A student knew that it was possible to make copper(II) sulphate crystals by (i) adding copper(II) carbonate to dilute sulphuric acid and (ii) warming the resulting solution to drive off some of the water, and then leaving the solution to crystallise. He decided to make copper(II) nitrate crystals by a similar method. The only change he made was to use dilute nitric acid. He left the final solution for several days, but he failed to collect any crystals. Suggest a reason for his failure.

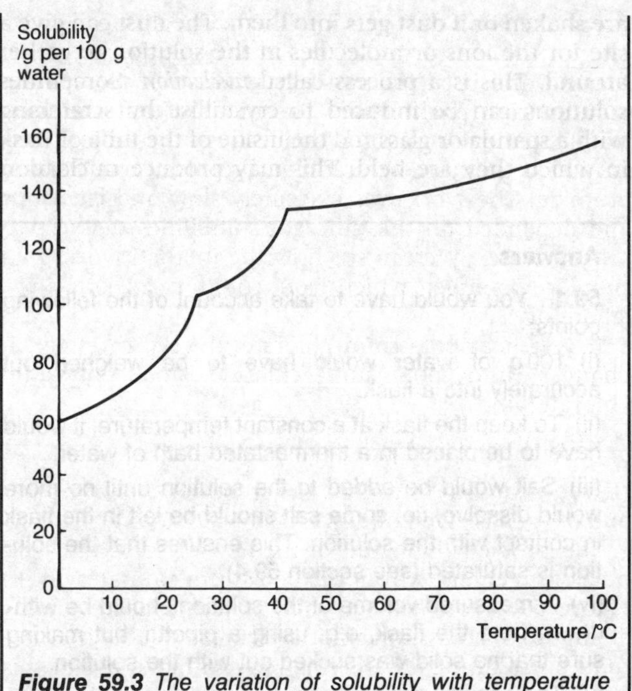

***Figure 59.3** The variation of solubility with temperature for calcium chloride (see question 59.4)*

59.4 Saturated and supersaturated solutions

A solution that contains the maximum amount of a solid dissolved in it at a given temperature is *saturated*. If we are to measure the solubility of a solid, then the solution must be saturated. A solution will be saturated if it remains in equilibrium with the solid dissolved in it. For example, if we took a beaker of water and added copper(II) sulphate to it until there was a little pile of undissolved crystals on the bottom of the beaker, then the solution would be saturated. In practice we have to be rather more careful than this because it may take some time for a solid to dissolve to its maximum amount. For example, it would be wise to leave the solution for several hours in order to be sure that true equilibrium had been achieved.

A *supersaturated* solution contains more solid dissolved in it than could exist if the solution were in contact with the solid. It is fairly easy to make some supersaturated solutions. If you take crystals of sodium thiosulphate, $Na_2S_2O_3 \cdot 5H_2O$, and warm them in a clean test tube, you will find that they appear to melt. Actually they give off their water of crystallisation and the sodium and thiosulphate ions dissolve in this water. If the test tube is handled carefully, the solution in the tube will remain even when it cools back to room temperature. If a small crystal of sodium thiosulphate is added to the cool tube it immediately starts to crystallise (and, incidentally, gives out a lot of heat in the process). The solution was supersaturated; it could not exist in contact with the solid from which it was made.

Often supersaturated solutions will crystallise if they

are shaken or if dust gets into them. The dust can give a site for the ions or molecules in the solution to gather around. This is a process called *nucleation*. Sometimes solutions can be induced to crystallise by scratching with a spatula or glass rod the inside of the tube or flask in which they are held. This may produce nucleation sites on the glass, or the vibrations produced may agitate the solution and induce crystallisation.

A novel case of nucleation in a different context is where clouds are seeded with tiny crystals of silver iodide. The crystals act as nucleation sites for water molecules, which gather together and make raindrops.

Answers

59.1 You would have to take account of the following points:

(i) 100 g of water would have to be weighed out accurately into a flask.

(ii) To keep the flask at a constant temperature, it would have to be placed in a thermostated bath of water.

(iii) Salt would be added to the solution until no more would dissolve, i.e. some salt should be left in the flask in contact with the solution. This ensures that the solution is saturated (see section 59.4).

(iv) A measured volume of the solution should be withdrawn from the flask, e.g. using a pipette, but making sure that no solid was sucked out with the solution.

(v) The sample removed should be analysed. There are two ways of doing this. Either you could perform a silver nitrate titration to discover the number of moles of chloride ion present (and hence the number of moles, and mass, of sodium chloride); or you could carefully evaporate the solution and weigh the sodium chloride left.

(vi) Finally you would scale up the result of your analysis to give the mass of salt in the original 100 g of water.

59.2 Use a different temperature in the thermostat bath, but take care to prevent evaporation of the water in the flask. Another danger that can occur with some solids is that if, say, a cold pipette were used to withdraw a sample, the sudden cooling might cause crystallisation in the pipette.

59.3 (i) $100\,g \times 6.9\,g/18\,g = 38.33\,g$, which rounds up to 39 g. If you use slightly more than 38.33 g you are sure of dissolving all the potassium chlorate(VII). Also, you could be excused for finding it easier to measure out a volume of $39\,cm^3$ using a burette. (We can ignore the change in density of water when it is heated.)

(ii) 39 g of water can contain $8.6\,g \times 39\,g/100\,g = 3.35\,g$ of potassium chlorate(VII). It can contain $35.8\,g \times 39\,g/100\,g = 13.96\,g$ of potassium chloride.

(iii) No. The solution could contain almost 14 g, and it actually contains only 1.1 g.

(iv) $6.9\,g - 3.35\,g = 3.55\,g$ would be left.

(v) $3.55\,g/6.9\,g \times 100\% = 51.45\%$

(vi) Another approach uses the following idea. Instead of dissolving both salts, why not just dissolve the potassium chloride, and leave the potassium chlorate(VII) behind? In this case we need use only the volume of water that would dissolve the 1.1 g of potassium chloride at 25°C. This volume is $100\,g \times 1.1\,g/35.8\,g = 3.07\,g$ of water. We might try using 5 g to be on the safe side, warm it and stir the mixture in with it. The potassium chloride will dissolve and the majority of the chlorate(VII) will be left undissolved. In fact, 5 g of water would contain $8.6\,g \times 5\,g/100\,g = 0.43\,g$ of potassium chlorate(VII) at 25°C. This represents a separation of $6.47\,g/6.9\,g \times 100\% = 93.8\%$. Much better!

59.4 The three parts of the curve correspond to the three different hydrates of calcium chloride: $CaCl_2{\cdot}6H_2O$ (first part), $CaCl_2{\cdot}4H_2O$ (middle part) and $CaCl_2{\cdot}2H_2O$ (last part).

59.5 Copper(II) nitrate is deliquescent, so crystals will not appear under normal conditions in the laboratory.

UNIT 59 SUMMARY

- The solubility of a solid in water is usually given as the number of grams, or the number of moles, of the solid that will dissolve in 100 g of water at a given temperature.
- Fractional crystallisation:
  Dissolve a mixture of two substances in the minimum volume of a warm solvent that will dissolve both substances. Allow to cool. The substance with the lower solubility will crystallise first, leaving the other substance dissolved in the solvent.
- Crystals that contain water of crystallisation:
  A salt that has water of crystallisation has a hydrate.
- Hydrates that have particularly high vapour pressures effloresce, i.e. lose their water of crystallisation to the atmosphere, e.g. $Na_2CO_3{\cdot}10H_2O$.
- Hydrates with particularly low vapour pressures deliquesce, i.e. absorb moisture from the atmosphere, e.g. $CaCl_2$.
- A saturated solution contains the maximum amount of a solid dissolved in it at a given temperature.
- A supersaturated solution contains more solid dissolved in it than could exist if the solution were in equilibrium with the solid.

60
Explaining solubilities

60.1 Why is water a good solvent for ionic crystals?

There are two reasons why water is a good solvent for ionic crystals. The first is that:

Water is a good insulator.

If water molecules come between ions at the edge of a crystal, it weakens the attraction between them. This helps them to float away from the crystal. Also, when the ions are in water, they are surrounded by a layer of water molecules. The layer insulates the ions from one another and prevents them joining together into a crystal again.

Other liquids can act as insulators as well. We can compare how effective they are by looking up values of their *relative permittivity*. (Another name for relative permittivity is dielectric constant.) You will find some values in Table 60.1. The higher the value, the better the insulator.

Table 60.1. The relative permittivities of some liquids

Liquid	*Formula*	*Relative permittivity**
Water	H_2O	80.1
Ethanol	C_2H_5OH	25.7
Ethanoic acid	CH_3COOH	6.2
Benzene	C_6H_6	2.3
Tetrachloromethane	CCl_4	2.3

*Relative permittivity has no units

The second reason why water is a good solvent is that:

Water is a polar molecule with a positive end that can attract negative ions and a negative end that can attract positive ions.

It is the ability of water to gather round both negative and positive ions that makes it such a good solvent for ionic crystals. The layer of water molecules that surrounds the ions is called the *hydration sphere*.

When sodium chloride is put into water, the ions on the outside of the crystal feel two competing influences (Figure 60.1):

(i) the attractions of the oppositely charged ions in the crystal, which tend to stop the outside ions escaping; and
(ii) the attractions between the surrounding water molecules and the outer ions, which tend to pull the ions off the crystal.

One measure of the attractions between the ions in the crystal is the *lattice energy*, ΔH_{LE}. In Unit 46 we

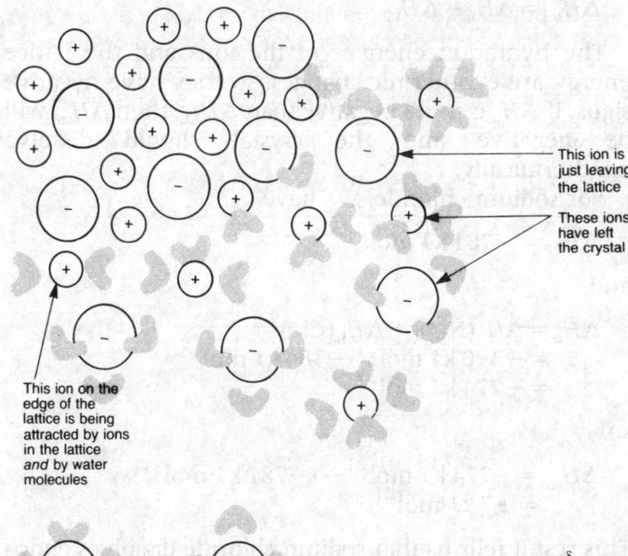
This ion is just leaving the lattice
These ions have left the crystal
This ion on the edge of the lattice is being attracted by ions in the lattice *and* by water molecules
δ–
O
δ+
H
H
δ+

Figure 60.1 Water molecules can attract ions on the outside of a crystal into the bulk of the surrounding water. The hydration spheres surrounding the ions also serve as a layer of insulation that helps to stop the ions joining together again

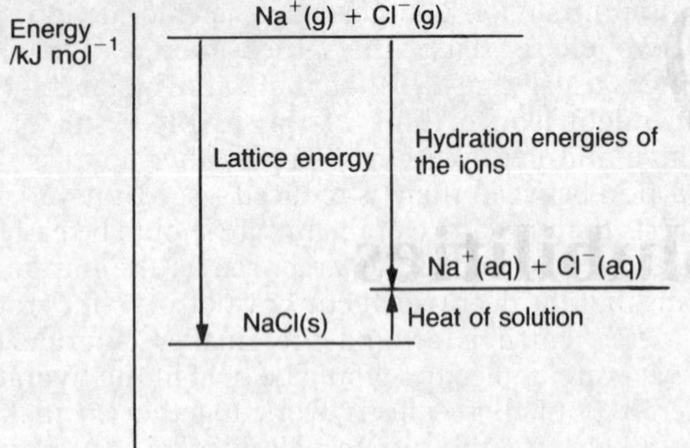

Figure 60.2 *There is an endothermic heat change when sodium chloride dissolves in water. One way of explaining this is to compare the lattice energy with the hydration energies of the ions*

defined the lattice energy to be the enthalpy change when one mole of the crystal is made from its component ions in the gaseous state. It is important to notice that the lattice energy refers to separate ions in a *gas*, not in a solution. A measure of how strongly ions are attracted by water molecules is the *hydration energy*, ΔH_h (Figure 60.2). Approximately, it is the enthalpy change when one mole of an ion in the gaseous state dissolves in water. (You will find the precise definition in Unit 47.) The energy change when one mole of sodium chloride dissolves in water is ΔH_{sol}. You can see from Figure 60.2 that

$$\Delta H_{sol} + \Delta H_{LE} = \Delta H_h$$

or

$$\Delta H_{sol} = \Delta H_h - \Delta H_{LE}$$

The hydration energies of the ions and the lattice energy are exothermic changes, so they have negative signs. If ΔH_h is more negative than ΔH_{LE}, then ΔH_{sol} will be negative and the crystal should dissolve exothermically.

For sodium chloride, we have

$$\Delta H_{LE} = -781 \text{ kJ mol}^{-1}$$

and

$$\begin{aligned}\Delta H_h &= \Delta H_h(\text{Na}^+) + \Delta H_h(\text{Cl}^-)\\ &= -390 \text{ kJ mol}^{-1} - 384 \text{ kJ mol}^{-1}\\ &= -774 \text{ kJ mol}^{-1}\end{aligned}$$

so

$$\begin{aligned}\Delta H_{sol} &= -774 \text{ kJ mol}^{-1} - (-781 \text{ kJ mol}^{-1})\\ &= +7 \text{ kJ mol}^{-1}\end{aligned}$$

This result tells us that sodium chloride dissolves endothermically in water. This is a common result; a great many ionic crystals dissolve endothermically. You can verify this for yourself. Take the temperature of a test tube of water and then tip sodium hydrogencarbonate or potassium nitrate into it. You will find the temperature goes down.

The difficulty this leaves us in is that it appears that ionic crystals dissolve even though it is energetically unfavourable. This is where we turn to thermodynamics for the explanation.

60.2 Entropy changes are important when a crystal dissolves

If we want to decide whether a chemical change will take place, we have to find out the sign of the free energy change, ΔG. If ΔG is negative, then the change should be spontaneous (but remember that this does not tell us how fast the change will take place). In Unit 50 we discovered that

$$\Delta G = \Delta H - T\Delta S$$

where ΔS is the entropy change. Even though ΔH may be positive, it is still possible for ΔG to be negative if the entropy change is large. When crystals dissolve endothermically, it is the entropy change that is responsible for the change taking place (Figure 60.3). The increase in entropy occurs because there is a greater spread of the ions and molecules among the available energy levels, i.e. the number of complexions increases (see Unit 49).

However, we should be careful about oversimplifying where entropy changes are concerned. When an ion leaves a crystal lattice it becomes surrounded by a hydration sphere. The water molecules in the sphere are less free to move than they were in the bulk of the

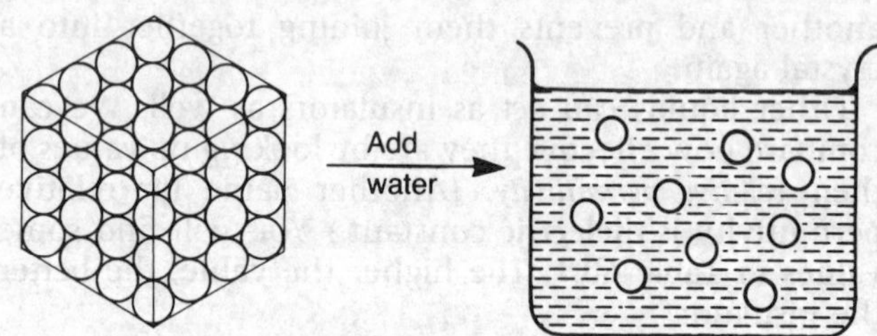

If we concentrate on the particles in the solid, there is an increase in entropy

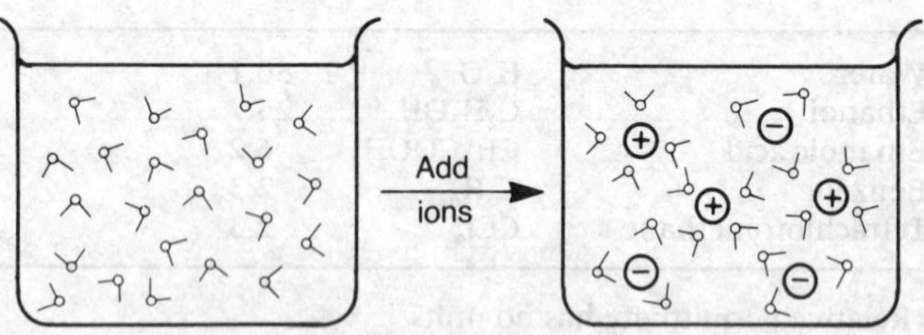

On the other hand, as many of the water molecules gather around the ions making the hydration spheres, there is a decrease in entropy

Figure 60.3 *Two contributions to the entropy change when a solid dissolves in water. (We have not taken account of entropy changes associated with energy absorbed or released in the process)*

water. Indeed, for a small, highly charged ion the hydration sphere may consist of several layers of water molecules. For this reason there may be a reduction in the translational and rotational energy levels open to these water molecules, and a corresponding decrease in entropy. Thus, whether there is an overall increase or decrease in entropy will depend (at least) on the following factors:

(i) change in the number of complexions in the crystal when ions leave;
(ii) change in the number of complexions open to individual ions owing to their release into the liquid; and
(iii) change in the number of complexions owing to the formation of hydration spheres.

Calculating the precise change in the total number of complexions is a fearsome task; fortunately we do not have to attempt it.

60.3 The sizes of the ions in a crystal are important in explaining solubilities

When a crystal is made of small highly charged ions, the lattice energy is usually very high, and it is rare for the enthalpy of solution to be strongly negative. The hydration energies of the ions are not large enough to overcome the lattice energy, so the substance is either insoluble or only very slightly soluble. We can say that the heat of solution would be such a large positive number that, even if the entropy change were positive, the free energy change would remain positive ($\Delta G = \Delta H - T\Delta S$), so the crystal would not dissolve. Table 60.2 contains a summary of factors influencing the solubility of ionic crystals.

We can see the importance of ionic size at work if we compare the solubilities of nitrates and chlorides. The general rule is that, even if the chloride is insoluble, the nitrate will be soluble. Indeed, there is a rule in chemistry that says 'all nitrates are soluble'. The main reason is that the nitrate ion is larger than the chloride ion. This has two effects. First, the lattice energy of a metal nitrate is usually smaller than that of the metal chloride. (You might like to think of this as the result of the positive and negative ions being further apart, so the attraction between them is reduced – see Unit 46.) This suggests that the lattice of the nitrate should be easier to break apart. Secondly, the larger size of the nitrate ion means that the decrease in entropy of the water around it is less than it is around the smaller chloride ion. (Fewer water molecules would be held in the hydration sphere.) Both these effects work together to make it more likely that the nitrate will dissolve. An extreme example is the great *in*solubility of silver chloride, and the great solubility of silver nitrate. However, the nature of the bonding in silver chloride is a complicating factor here (see Unit 46).

Table 60.2. Summary of factors influencing solubilities of ionic crystals

Factor	*Implication*
Lattice energy large	Ions held together very strongly Crystal likely to be insoluble
Lattice energy small	Ions held together weakly Crystal likely to be soluble
Ions large and/or small charge	Lattice energy likely to be small Entropy change likely to be positive ΔG_{sol} will be negative Crystal should be soluble
Ions small and/or high charge	Lattice energy likely to be large Entropy change likely to be negative ΔG_{sol} will be positive Crystal should be insoluble

60.4 Why is water a good solvent for many covalent substances?

It is not only ionic substances that dissolve in water. Many covalent substances dissolve also. However, usually they are of two types.

One type reacts with water rather than dissolves in it. Such a reaction is called a hydrolysis reaction. Hydrogen chloride undergoes hydrolysis:

$$HCl(g) + H_2O(l) \rightarrow H_3O^+(aq) + Cl^-(aq)$$

The second type are usually polar and able to hydrogen bond to water molecules. Organic compounds that dissolve in water are often like this. Typical examples are glucose molecules, $C_6H_{12}O_6$, which have highly electronegative oxygen atoms in them (Figure 60.4). The hydrogen atoms attached to the oxygen atoms

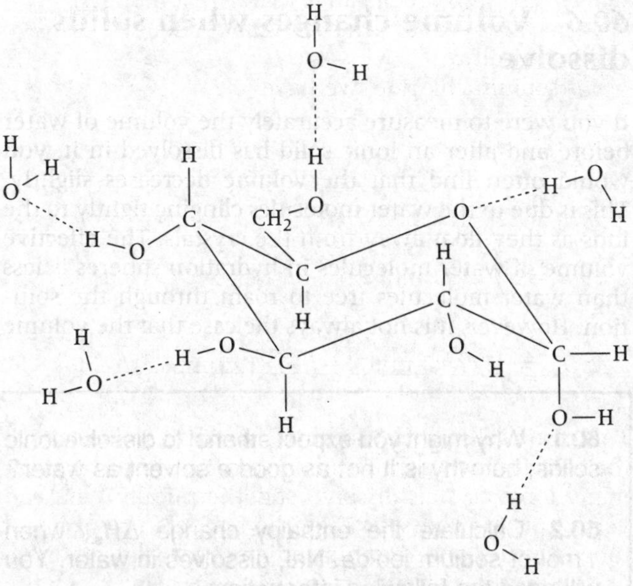

Figure 60.4 *There are many ways in which a glucose molecule can make hydrogen bonds with water molecules*

carry slightly positive charges, just as they do in water molecules.

If covalent molecules are not polar, they are insoluble in water. For example naphthalene, $C_{10}H_8$, is a white solid that is completely insoluble in water.

60.5 Covalent liquids often dissolve covalent solids

There is a saying in chemistry that 'like dissolves like'. Generally this means that an organic liquid will dissolve an organic solid and an inorganic liquid will dissolve an inorganic solid. The most common inorganic liquid is water, and inorganic solids are often ionic. If you have read the preceding sections, you should be able to explain how the saying applies to inorganic substances. Now we shall try to explain why, for example, the organic solid naphthalene will not dissolve in water, even though it will dissolve in the organic liquid benzene.

Naphthalene is not polar, so the molecules in the crystal are held together by van der Waals forces (Figure 60.5). These forces are also responsible for holding benzene molecules together. Van der Waals forces are relatively weak, so it does not require a great deal of energy to move one naphthalene molecule apart from another. Essentially, when naphthalene dissolves in benzene, van der Waals forces in the crystal are swapped for van der Waals forces in the solution. We should expect only a small enthalpy change in such a case; which is what happens. It is rare to find a large enthalpy of solution for an organic solid dissolving in an organic liquid. On the other hand, the entropy change when the solid dissolves should be positive, just as it is for an ionic solid dissolving in water. Indeed, it is the entropy change that drives the process along.

60.6 Volume changes when solids dissolve

If you were to measure accurately the volume of water before and after an ionic solid has dissolved in it, you would often find that the volume decreases slightly. This is due to the water molecules clinging tightly to the ions as they float away from the crystals. The effective volume of water molecules in hydration spheres is less than water molecules free to roam through the solution. However, it is not always the case that the volume decreases. For example, crystals that contain water of crystallisation, e.g. $CuSO_4{\cdot}5H_2O$, release water molecules. In the case of these crystals, 1 mol of the solid would release 5 mol of water, i.e. 90 cm^3.

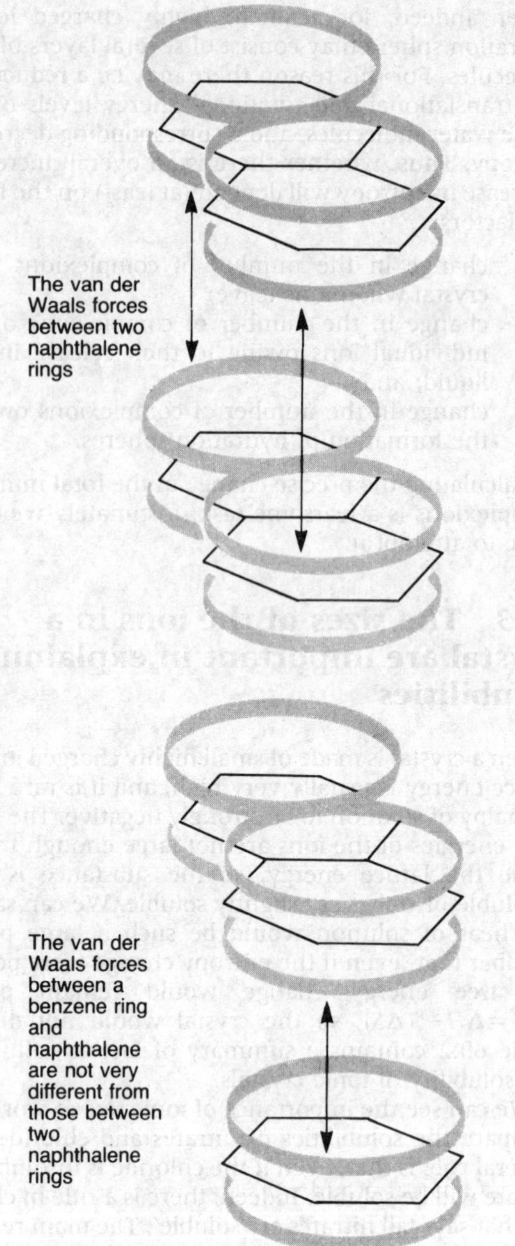

The van der Waals forces between two naphthalene rings
The van der Waals forces between a benzene ring and naphthalene are not very different from those between two naphthalene rings

Figure 60.5 *Naphthalene will dissolve in benzene*

60.1 Why might you expect ethanol to dissolve ionic solids; but why is it not as good a solvent as water?

60.2 Calculate the enthalpy change ΔH_{sol} when 1 mol of sodium iodide, NaI, dissolves in water. You will need the following information:

Lattice energy of NaI $= -699$ kJ mol^{-1}
Hydration energy of Na$^+$ $= -400$ kJ mol^{-1}
Hydration energy of I$^-$ $= -310$ kJ mol^{-1}

(Hint: you may find it useful to draw an enthalpy diagram.)

60.3 Suggest a reason why sodium iodide is more soluble in water than sodium chloride.

60.4 The solubilities of the sulphates of Group II metals (Mg, Ca, Sr, Ba) decrease going down the Group. (You will find the solubilities in Table 59.1.)

(i) Does the ionic radius of the metal ion increase or decrease going down the Group.

(ii) What effect does the change in ionic radius have on the lattice energy of the sulphates, and the hydration energy of the ions?

(iii) Which effect is the more important in explaining the trend in solubilities?

60.5 Here are lattice energies, in kJ mol^{-1}, of two chlorides and two oxides: $MgCl_2$, 2489; MgO, 3933; $CaCl_2$, 2197; CaO, 3523.

(i) Which of each pair would you expect to be the most soluble?

(ii) Suggest a reason why many metal oxides are insoluble in water.

60.6 Predict whether the following substances would be soluble in water, or in benzene (or in both, or in neither) – you may need to refer back to the units on bonding to help you make up your mind: carbon dioxide; aluminium trichloride; iodine; silica; ethanoic acid (CH_3COOH).

Answers

60.1 Ethanol is a polar molecule, with a partially negatively charged oxygen attached to a partially positively charged hydrogen. Ethanol molecules can gather round positive and negative ions like water molecules can. They can *solvate* ions, and form *solvation spheres*. (We speak of hydration spheres only if the solvent is water.) However, the relative permittivity of ethanol is much lower than that of water; ethanol is not such a good insulator. Therefore ions in ethanol find it easier to combine together and make a crystal than they do in water.

60.2 The diagram is drawn in Figure 60.6. This gives

$$\Delta H_{sol} = (-400\,\text{kJ mol}^{-1} - 310\,\text{kJ mol}^{-1}) - (-699\,\text{kJ mol}^{-1}) = -11\,\text{kJ mol}^{-1}$$

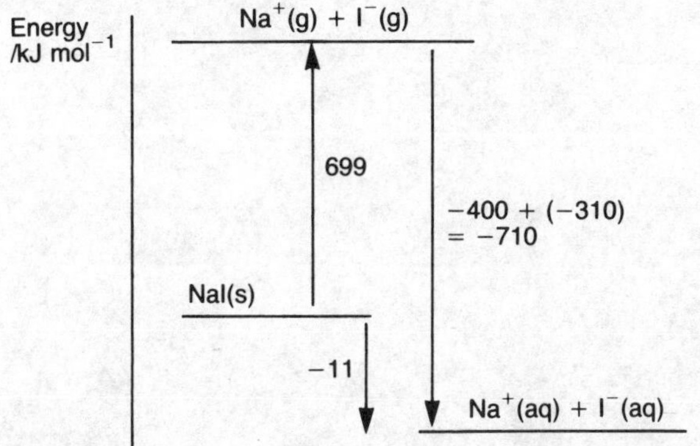

***Figure 60.6** Enthalpy diagram for sodium iodide dissolving in water*

60.3 The lattice energy of sodium chloride is greater than that of sodium iodide by about 82 kJ mol^{-1}. Your answer to question 60.2 should show you that this has the effect of making ΔH_{sol} exothermic. This helps to make ΔG_{sol} negative, even without taking entropy changes into account. (The solubility of sodium chloride relies on entropy changes to make ΔG negative.)

60.4 (i) The ionic radius increases down the Group. (The ionic radius of Ba^{2+} is about twice that of Mg^{2+}.)

(ii) As the size of the ions increases, the lattice energies of the crystals *decrease* going down the Group; this should favour an increase in solubility. The hydration energy of a large ion is less than that of a small ion. Thus the hydration energies decrease down the Group.

(iii) We know that high solubility is favoured by a small lattice energy and a high hydration energy of the ions. In this case even though the lattice is becoming smaller, the hydration energy of the metal ions becomes even smaller. For example, the hydration energies of Ba^{2+} and of SO_4^{2-} are too small to overcome the lattice energy of $BaSO_4$, even though the lattice energy of $BaSO_4$ is considerably smaller than that of $MgSO_4$.

60.5 (i) The chlorides are the more soluble in both pairs.

(ii) The oxide ion is small (its radius is 146 pm), and it has a double negative charge. Both factors lead to large lattice energies of metal oxides, and therefore to insolubility.

60.6 The results are summarised below:

Substance	*Nature*	*Soluble in* Benzene	*Soluble in* Water	*Comment*
CO_2	Covalent	No	Yes	Reacts with water
$AlCl_3$	Covalent	Yes	Yes	Dimers in benzene Reacts with water
I_2	Covalent	Yes	No	
SiO_2	Giant structure	No	No	
CH_3COOH	Covalent	Yes	Yes	Dimers in benzene Dissociates into ions in water

UNIT 60 SUMMARY

- Water is a good solvent for many covalent substances containing highly electronegative elements owing to its ability to make hydrogen bonds.
- Water is a good solvent for ionic crystals because:
  (i) It is a good insulator, so it reduces attractions between ions.
  (ii) It is a polar molecule with a positive end that can attract negative ions, and a negative end that can attract positive ions.
- The hydration sphere is the layer of water molecules that surround ions in water.
- Trends in solubilities can be explained by taking account of:
  (i) The sizes of the ions in a crystal.
  (ii) Entropy changes when a crystal dissolves.
- In general, a substance with a very high lattice energy will be insoluble in water.

61

Mixtures of liquids

61.1 What is the difference between miscible and immiscible liquids?

> **Miscible liquids mix in any proportion.**
>
> **Immiscible liquids do not mix completely; rather, they make two separate layers**

Miscible liquids usually are very similar in their chemical structures. For example, ethanol and water are completely miscible. Their molecules are both polar and contain OH groups that give rise to hydrogen bonding among them. To some extent ethanol and water molecules can mix together without difficulty because of their ability to hydrogen bond with each other. Immiscible liquids have quite different chemical structures. Petrol, which is a mixture of hydrocarbons, is immiscible with water. Hydrocarbon molecules are not polar and are held together by van der Waals forces. They cannot hydrogen bond to water molecules.

There is a range of liquids that are *partially miscible*. Ethoxyethane (ether) and water are partially miscible. Ethoxyethane will dissolve only about 1% of its weight of water; water will dissolve about 6% of ethoxyethane. If you mixed them in proportions greater than these you would find that they separated into two layers.

61.2 Raoult's law and ideal solutions

We tend to think of solutions made by mixing liquids as quite different to solutions made by dissolving a solid in a liquid. However, these two ways of making solutions are quite similar. For example, if we have a little ethanol in a lot of water, we can regard ethanol as the solute, in much the same way as we would describe sugar dissolved in water as the solute. We shall discover in Unit 65 that, when a solid solute dissolves in a solvent, it changes the vapour pressure of the solvent. There is a similar effect when one liquid dissolves in another (i.e. mix together). However, there is a major difference: a solid solute is usually *involatile*, while a liquid solute is volatile. For example, if we were to analyse the vapour above a sugar solution, we would find only water vapour, whereas the vapour above a mixture of ethanol and water always contains both water and ethanol.

Raoult's law says that:

> **The vapour pressure of a solvent in a solution is equal to the vapour pressure of the pure solvent multiplied by its mole fraction in the solution.**

It so happens that for some mixtures of liquid, Raoult's law can be applied separately to each liquid. Suppose we have a mixture of two liquids, A and B. Then Raoult's law says that

$$p_A = N_A \times p^\circ_A$$
$$p_B = N_B \times p^\circ_B$$

where N_A, N_B are the mole fractions, p°_A, p°_B are the vapour pressures of the pure liquids, and p_A, p_B are the vapour pressures above the mixture.

It can be useful to realise that the total vapour pressure above the mixture is

$$p_T = p_A + p_B$$

and that

$$N_A + N_B = 1$$

There are few liquids that obey Raoult's law no matter the proportions in which they are mixed. Those mixtures which do obey the law are called *ideal solutions*. One mixture that is ideal is made from hexane and heptane. The vapour pressures of the two pure liquids are 16 093 Pa and 4655 Pa respectively. It is a simple matter to calculate their vapour pressures above a mixture as the mole fraction of each changes from 0 to 1. A graph of the results is shown in Figure 61.1.

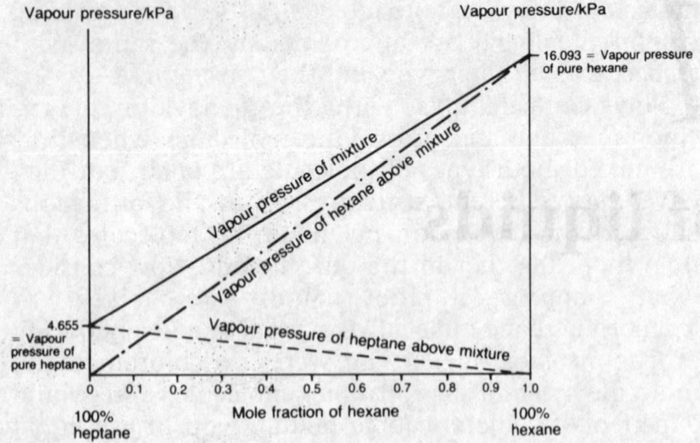

Figure 61.1 *The vapour pressure–composition diagram for a mixture of hexane and heptane. This is the type of diagram we expect for an ideal mixture. The figures refer to a constant temperature of 25° C*

61.3 Solutions that do not obey Raoult's law

The majority of liquid mixtures do not obey Raoult's law. These mixtures are said to show *deviations from ideality*. There are two types of deviation, and you can spot them on a vapour pressure diagram fairly easily. Instead of straight lines on the diagram you will find curves. In one type of deviation, the total vapour pressure curve dips downwards; in the other type the curve loops upwards. The first type is called a *negative deviation* from Raoult's law; the second is a *positive deviation* from Raoult's law. In fact there are two varieties of each deviation. It is possible for the negative deviation curve to slope gently from one side to the other, or to go through a definite minimum. Similarly, a positive deviation may or may not have a maximum in the vapour

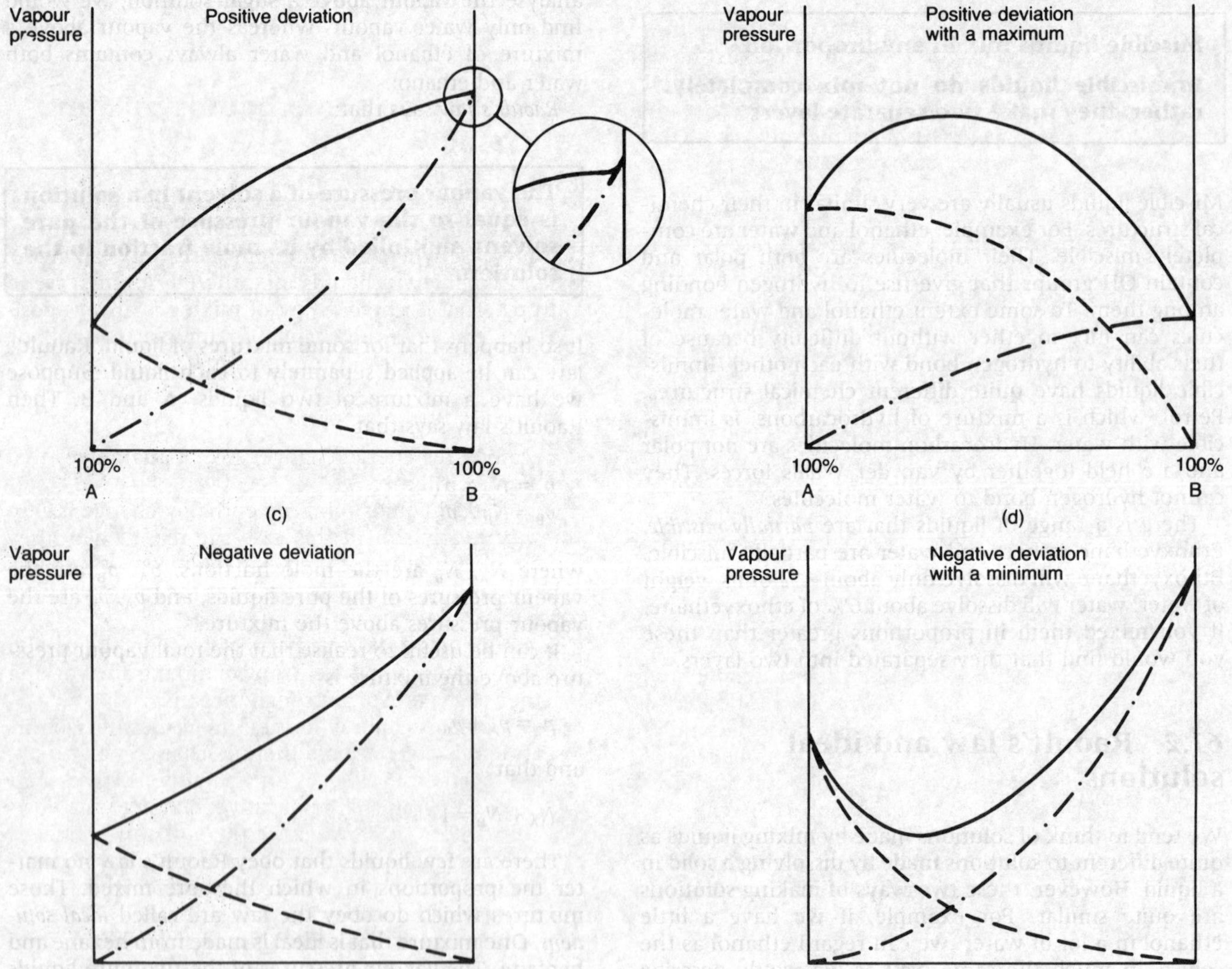

(a) Vapour pressure — Positive deviation — 100% A — 100% B

(b) Vapour pressure — Positive deviation with a maximum — 100% A — 100% B

(c) Vapour pressure — Negative deviation — 100% A — 100% B

(d) Vapour pressure — Negative deviation with a minimum — 100% A — 100% B

Figure 61.2 *The four types of deviation from Raoult's law. Each graph corresponds to readings taken at a constant temperature. Beside diagram (a) is a magnified view of the lines near one of the axes. This shows that the solution containing nearly 100% B and a very little A gives a straight line that obeys Raoult's law. Similar diagrams could be drawn for the other cases*

Table 61.1. Liquid mixtures and Raoult's law

Mixture	*Behaviour*
Hexane/heptane	Ideal
Benzene/methylbenzene	Ideal
Methanol/water	Negative deviation
Trichloromethane/propanone	Negative deviation, with a minimum
Ethanol/water	Positive deviation, with a maximum

pressure curve. The four types are shown in Figure 61.2 and some examples are given in Table 61.1.

If you look carefully at the diagrams you will see that the vapour pressure curves become nearly straight lines when the liquids contain a large amount of one liquid and very little of the other, i.e. when the mixtures can be regarded as dilute solutions. When the solutions are very dilute they obey Raoult's law.

You will find it is sometimes helpful to show two lines on a vapour pressure diagram. One of the lines shows how the vapour pressure changes with the composition of the liquid mixture. This is the line we have already drawn on the diagrams. The second line shows how the composition of the *vapour* changes. The two lines are different because *the vapour is always richer in the more volatile component*. That is, the composition of the vapour is usually different to that of the solution from which it came. Figure 61.3 shows you typical shapes of the two lines for non-ideal mixtures.

The diagrams tell us the composition of the liquid and vapour that are in equilibrium with each other at a particular vapour pressure. For example, in Figure 61.3a, at a vapour pressure p, the liquid has composition D and the vapour has composition C. If you look at the composition scale you can see that, as we would expect, the vapour has a greater proportion of the liquid with the higher vapour pressure.

61.4 Why are there deviations from Raoult's law?

First, let us understand why a mixture of hexane and heptane makes an ideal solution. You should be able to see that the more hexane (or heptane) molecules there are in the mixture, the more likely it is that molecules of hexane (or heptane) will escape into the vapour. Therefore we would expect the vapour pressure of hexane (or heptane) to increase as its mole fraction increases. This is what Raoult's law claims for an ideal solution. However, this line of argument only works because:

forces between hexane molecules
≡ forces between heptane molecules
≡ forces between hexane and heptane molecules
≡ van der Waals forces

This means that if you were a hexane molecule it matters little whether you are surrounded by other hexane molecules or by heptane molecules: the forces holding you in the liquid are approximately the same, with respect to both their type and their strength.

Now compare this with the behaviour of trichloromethane and propanone molecules when they are mixed. Both types of molecule are polar, but they have very different structures. It is the attractions between the dipoles on neighbouring molecules that hold them together in the pure liquids. Now consider what happens if the liquids are mixed. A trichloromethane molecule can bond to a neighbouring propanone molecule. If you were a trichloromethane molecule near to a propanone molecule, you would experience a different force holding you in the liquid than that in pure trichloromethane. It is the strength of this force that reduces the vapour pressure below the ideal value.

You should be able to convince yourself that, in mixtures that show a positive deviation from Raoult's law, the forces that hold the two different types of molecule together in the mixture are weaker than those in the two pure liquids.

61.5 Why do some liquids mix and others not?

In order to understand this section you should first have read Units 49 and 50. There you will find that entropy will increase when two different gases mix. Likewise, when two different liquids mix, there is an increase in entropy. That is, the entropy of mixing is always positive. We can write the changes taking place on mixing as

$$\Delta G_{mix} = \Delta H_{mix} - T\Delta S_{mix}$$

A negative free energy change, ΔG_{mix}, guarantees that two liquids will mix.

When ideal liquids mix, the enthalpy change is zero (or very nearly so). In this case the reason why they mix is solely a result of the positive entropy of mixing. (The situation is extremely similar to the mixing of ideal gases.)

Some liquids mix exothermically. For them, the enthalpy change and the entropy of mixing are working together to make ΔG_{mix} strongly negative.

The problems come when the molecules of two different liquids give an endothermic change when they are put together. If ΔH_{mix} is only slightly positive, then $\Delta H_{mix} - T\Delta S_{mix}$ can still be negative, owing to the positive value of ΔS_{mix}. However, if the enthalpy change is very endothermic, ΔH_{mix} can be a large positive number, which makes $\Delta H_{mix} - T\Delta S_{mix}$ positive. In this case the liquids will be immiscible.

To add a further complication, some liquids are only partially miscible. For them, the enthalpy and entropy changes combine to make ΔG_{mix} negative if only a small amount of one liquid mixes with the other. For example, around room temperature, a little phenol will dissolve in a lot of water, and a little water will dissolve in

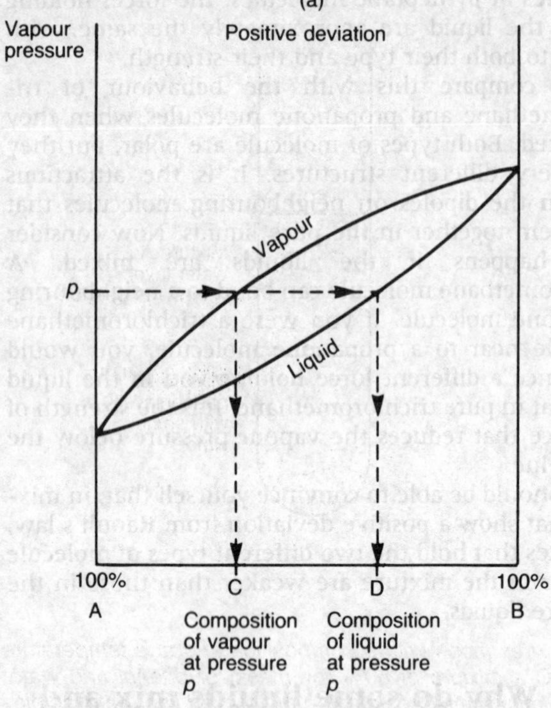

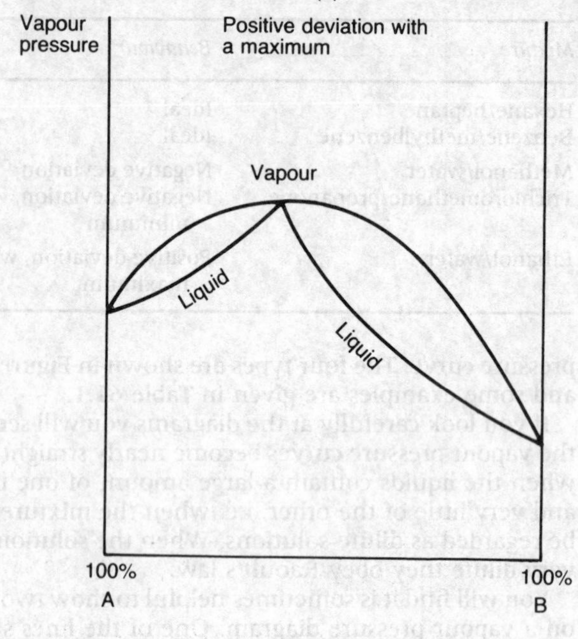

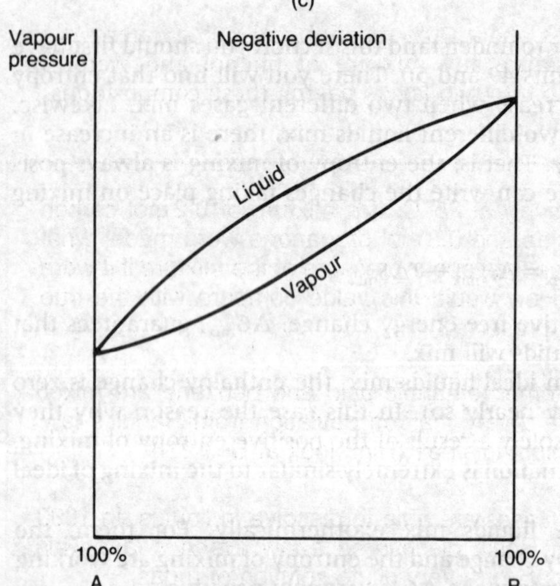

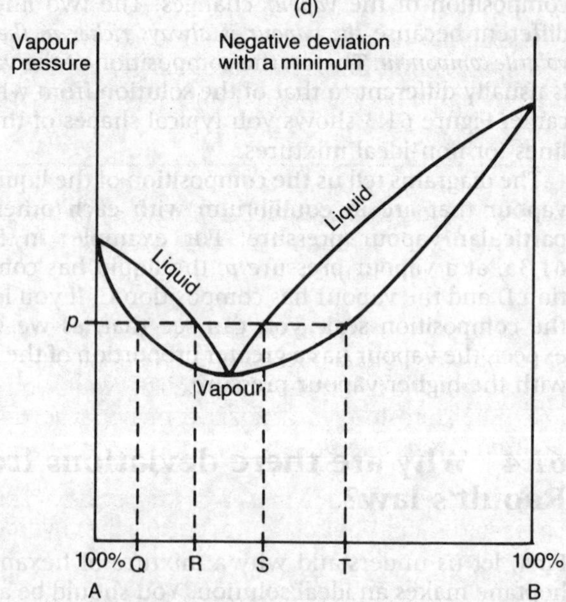

***Figure 61.3** These diagrams show that when there are positive or negative deviations from Raoult's law, the liquid mixture has a different composition to the vapour.* Example 1: *In diagram (a), at pressure p the vapour has composition given by C, and the liquid has composition D. Composition C contains more of the component (A) with the lower vapour pressure, i.e. the more volatile component.* Example 2: *In diagram (d) there are two liquid mixtures that can have a vapour pressure p. Similarly, these mixtures have vapours of different composition as well. The liquids have compositions R and S. They have vapours of compositions Q and T respectively*

a lot of phenol. Here the small increase in ΔS_{mix} is sufficient to overcome the unfavourable ΔH_{mix}. However, if a large proportion of phenol were to dissolve in water, ΔH_{mix} is too endothermic to be overcome by the $T\Delta S_{mix}$ contribution to ΔG_{mix}. On the other hand, we know that if the temperature is high enough it is possible for $T\Delta S_{mix}$ to overcome ΔH_{mix}. In fact this happens at about 66° C for phenol and water. Above this temperature, the two are completely miscible; below it, they form two layers. The temperature at which two partially miscible liquids become completely miscible is called the *upper consolute temperature*.

The way to interpret a diagram like that of Figure 61.4 is to start on the temperature axis and move across

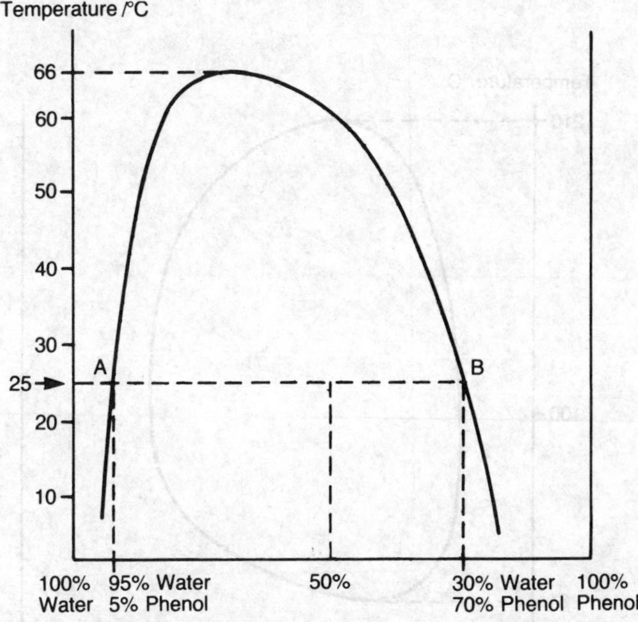

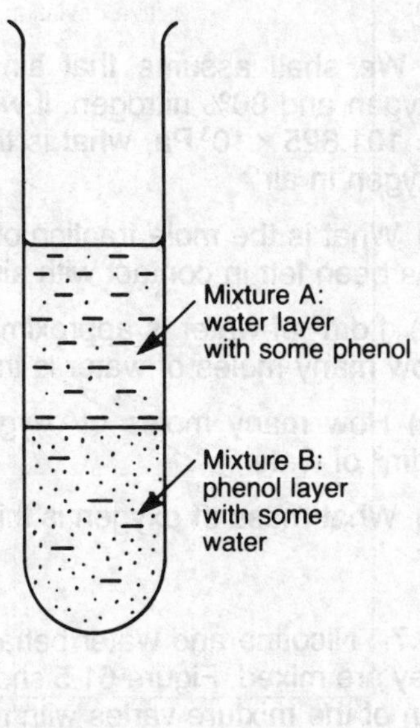

***Figure 61.4** Below 66° C phenol and water are only partially miscible. Mixtures made with a composition and at a temperature inside the curved line will separate into two layers. For example, at 25° C a mixture of 50% (by mass) of phenol and water separates into two layers, A and B. Above 66° C all mixtures are miscible. Similarly mixtures outside the curved line are miscible*

the diagram. For example, at 25° C, two mixtures can exist in equilibrium. These are marked A and B. Mixture A contains 5% phenol and 95% water, while B contains about 70% phenol and 30% water. At this temperature any mixture of phenol and water will separate into two layers having these compositions.

61.1 Would you expect a mixture of (i) hexane and pentane, (ii) propan-1-ol and water to show deviations from Raoult's law?

61.2 In a mixture of trichloromethane and ethyl ethanoate there are strong intermolecular forces between the two types of molecule. Would you expect the mixture to give a positive or negative deviation from Raoult's law?

61.3 Petrol and water are immiscible. You may assume that petrol is made of the hydrocarbon octane.

(i) What type of intermolecular bonding holds octane molecules together?

(ii) What type of intermolecular bonding holds water molecules together?

(iii) Compare the strength of bonds between: two octane molecules, two water molecules, a water molecule and an octane molecule.

(iv) Why is the enthalpy of mixing for these two liquids very positive?

61.4 A mixture of carbon disulphide and propanone shows a positive deviation from Raoult's law. Their vapour pressures are 39 235 Pa and 23 541 Pa respectively at 25° C. If a mixture of 0.2 mol carbon disulphide and 0.8 mol propanone were made, what would be the vapour pressure of the mixture if it were ideal? How would this value compare with the true vapour pressure?

61.5 When ethanoic acid and benzene are mixed there is a very marked deviation from Raoult's law. Why might this be? (Hint: look at Unit 21.)

61.6 Gases are able to dissolve in liquids. In 1803 William Henry discovered a law: *Henry's law*. This says that, for a very dilute solution of a gas,

$$\frac{\text{concentration of molecules in gas}}{\text{concentration of molecules in liquid}} = \text{a constant, } K$$

An alternative way of writing this is

$$\frac{p_A}{N_A} = K$$

where p_A is the partial pressure of the gas, and N_A is the mole fraction of the molecules of gas in the liquid. For oxygen dissolving in water at 25° C, K is about 30×10^4 Pa.

You have decided to keep a goldfish in a rather small tank of volume 1 dm³. How much oxygen is there to keep the fish alive?

(i) We shall assume that air contains about 20% oxygen and 80% nitrogen. If we take air pressure to be 101.325×10^3 Pa, what is the partial pressure of oxygen in air?

(ii) What is the mole fraction of oxygen in water that has been left in contact with air?

(iii) 1 dm^3 of water is approximately 1000 g of water. How many moles of water is this?

(iv) How many moles of oxygen would dissolve in 1 dm^3 of water?

(v) What mass of oxygen is this?

61.7 Nicotine and water behave rather oddly when they are mixed. Figure 61.5 shows how the composition of the mixture varies with temperature.

If you mixed an equal number of moles of nicotine and water and allowed them to come to equilibrium, how many layers will form at (i) 100° C, (ii) 215° C, (iii) 55° C?

What is special about the temperatures 61° C and 210° C?

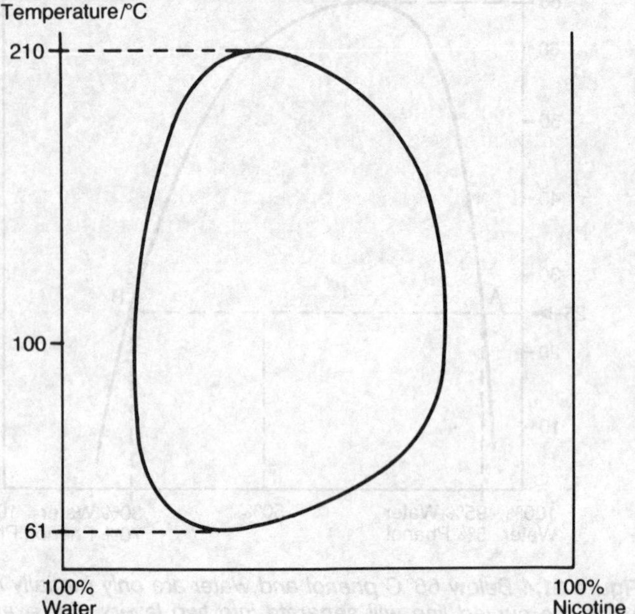

***Figure 61.5** Temperature–composition diagram for mixtures of nicotine and water*

Answers

61.1 (i) No. These are both non-polar hydrocarbons like hexane and heptane.

(ii) Yes. Like ethanol, propan-1-ol is polar, and it can take part in hydrogen bonding. However, without doing an experiment we cannot be sure whether it will give a positive or negative deviation. Actually, like ethanol, it gives a positive deviation with a maximum.

61.2 Negative. The bonding in the mixture will prevent the molecules escaping easily into the vapour.

61.3 (i) Van der Waals forces.

(ii) Hydrogen bonding.

(iii) The order will be water–water > octane–octane > water–octane.

(iv) By mixing the liquids together we would be replacing two stronger types of bond by a weaker type. This is energetically unfavourable, i.e. we would have to put energy *in* to the system in order to break the stronger bonds apart.

61.4 For carbon disulphide,

vapour pressure = 0.2 × 39 325 Pa = 7827 Pa

For propanone,

vapour pressure = 0.8 × 23 541 Pa = 18 833 Pa

The total vapour pressure will be 26 660 Pa. The true vapour pressure will be greater than this because the mixture shows a positive deviation.

61.5 The ethanoic acid molecules dimerise. It is the dimers that change the vapour pressure of the ethanoic acid from what we would otherwise expect.

61.6 (i) $p_{O_2} = 101.325 \times 10^3\ \text{Pa} \times 20/100 = 20.265\ \text{Pa}$.

(ii) Using Henry's law, $20.265\ \text{Pa}/N_{O_2} = 30 \times 10^4\ \text{Pa}$. Then, $N_{O_2} = 6.755 \times 10^{-5}$

(iii) $1000\ \text{g}/18\ \text{g mol}^{-1} = 55.556\ \text{mol}$.

(iv) Let us call n the number of moles of oxygen. Then we have

$$n/(n + 55.556) = 6.755 \times 10^{-5}$$

Rearranging,

$$n = \frac{55.556 \times 6.755 \times 10^{-5}}{1 - 6.755 \times 10^{-5}} = 3.75 \times 10^{-3}$$

(v) $32\ \text{g mol}^{-1} \times 3.75 \times 10^{-3}\ \text{mol} = 0.12\ \text{g}$.

61.7 (i) Two layers, one would contain mostly water, the other mostly nicotine.

(ii), (iii) One layer.

Above 210° C and below 61° C nicotine and water are completely miscible: 210° C is the upper consolute temperature; 61° C is the lower consolute temperature.

UNIT 61 SUMMARY

- Miscible liquids mix in any proportion.
- Immiscible liquids do not mix completely; rather they make two separate layers.
- Raoult's law says that:
  The vapour pressure of a solvent in a solution is equal to the vapour pressure of the pure solvent multiplied by its mole fraction in the solution. In symbols, for two liquids, A and B,

  $p_A = N_A \times p^\circ_A$ and $p_B = N_B \times p^\circ_B$

  and the total vapour pressure is $p_T = p_A + p_B$, where N_A, N_B are the mole fractions, p°_A, p°_B are the vapour pressures of the pure liquids, and p_A, p_B are the vapour pressures above the mixture.
- Ideal solutions obey Raoult's law.
- Non-ideal solutions show deviations from Raoult's law.
- The vapour above a mixture is always richer in the more volatile component, unless it is an azeotropic (constant boiling) mixture.

62

Competition between solvents

62.1 Solvent extraction

You may have done a reaction in which chlorine water is added to a solution of an iodide or bromide. The chlorine oxidises the ions to iodine and bromine respectively. In the case of the iodide, the change from colourless to a murky orange/brown is obvious. (The colour is due to the formation of the triiodide ion, $I_3^-(aq)$.) With the bromide, the change can be less clear. However, if a little of the organic liquid 1,1,1-trichloroethane is added to the reaction mixture, the pale orange colour of bromine collects in the organic layer at the bottom of the tube. If the same organic liquid is shaken with the tube containing the iodine, you will discover that a beautiful purple colour appears. This is due to iodine molecules collecting in the 1,1,1-trichloroethane. What has happened is that the covalent bromine molecules dissolve more readily in the purely covalent organic liquid. We can say that the bromine has been extracted from the aqueous layer into the organic layer. This is the basis of *solvent extraction*. Some substances will dissolve more readily in one liquid rather than another. If a solution containing the substance is shaken with a liquid in which it dissolves more readily, then the substance will separate into the new liquid.

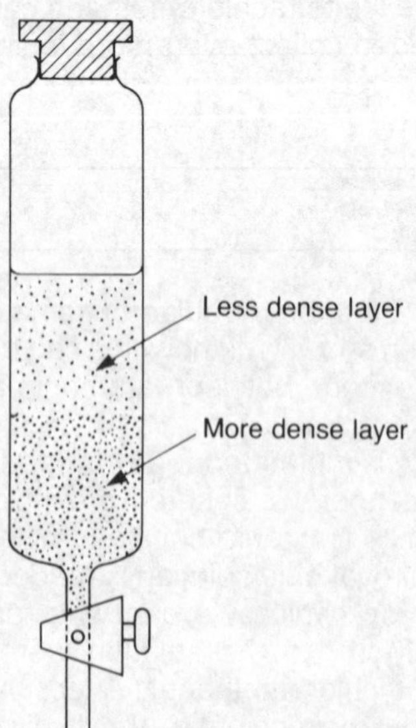

Figure 62.1 *A separating funnel can be used to separate immiscible liquids*

Solvent extraction is an important technique in chemical analysis. Usually it is done by placing the solution and the second liquid into a separating funnel (Figure 62.1). The funnel is stoppered and the two liquids are shaken together. If, as is almost always the case, one of the liquids is organic and volatile (evaporates easily), it is wise to turn the separating funnel upside down and carefully release the pressure of vapour inside by turning the tap to the open position. If you ever do this, be careful. It has been known for the pressure to be so great that drops of liquid may spurt out. (Also, do not forget to hold the stopper on!)

62.2 Solvent extraction is an equilibrium process

Iodine is almost completely insoluble in water, but it does dissolve if iodine ions are present:

$I_2(s)$	$+ I^-(aq) \rightleftharpoons$	$I_3^-(aq)$
insoluble in water, soluble in 1,1,1-trichloroethane		soluble in water, insoluble in 1,1,1-trichloroethane

On the other hand, being ionic, triiodide ions will not dissolve in an organic liquid like 1,1,1-trichloroethane, but covalent iodine molecules will dissolve in it. If we place an aqueous solution of triiodide ions in contact with 1,1,1-trichloroethane, the iodine will transfer from the aqueous layer into the organic layer. This removes iodine molecules from the equilibrium above (which moves to the left). As a result, the brown colour of the triiodide ion fades, and the purple colour of free iodine molecules appears in the organic layer.

To achieve a good separation, we might have to wait for several hours. Also, by gently shaking the two liquids together we can increase their area of contact and improve the chances of transferring iodine molecules. However, it is not a good idea to shake too hard. This can break up the layers into tiny droplets that can take ages to collect back together into separate layers.

62.3 Partition coefficients

If you have read the units on equilibrium (Units 51–55), you will not be surprised to know that there is an equilibrium constant that we can associate with the transfer of a solute between two solvents. The equilibrium constant is called a *partition coefficient*, or sometimes a distribution coefficient. The expression for a partition coefficient looks like this:

$$\text{partition coefficient} = \frac{\text{concentration of solute in first solvent}}{\text{concentration of solute in second solvent}}$$

This expression is known as the *partition law* (or distribution law). Look at the example, which shows you how to use a partition coefficient.

62.4 Why do some results not fit the partition law?

In our work so far we have assumed that the solute (the iodine in our example) remains the same in each solvent. For some solutes this is not always the case. For instance, ethanoic acid can exist as dimers in benzene, whereas it stays as single molecules in water. (We shall ignore the roughly 4% of them that dissociate into ions.) When this happens we have an equilibrium like this:

$$\underset{\text{monomers}}{2CH_3COOH(aq)} \rightleftharpoons \underset{\text{dimers}}{(CH_3COOH)_2(\text{benzene})}$$

Now, in the same way as we have treated other equilibrium expressions, we put

$$K = \frac{\text{concentration of ethanoic acid in benzene}}{(\text{concentration of ethanoic acid in water})^2}$$

With luck you will not have to worry about these complications. Also, the partition law does not work if the solutions involved are highly concentrated.

Example

A solution contains 1 g of iodine dissolved in 20 cm³ of potassium iodide solution. If we shake this solution with 20 cm³ of tetrachloromethane (an organic liquid), how much iodine will be transferred into the tetrachloromethane?

To answer this we need to know that the partition coefficient between tetrachloromethane and water is 85 at 25°C.

We have

$$\frac{\text{concentration of iodine in tetrachloromethane}}{\text{concentration of iodine in water}} = 85$$

Let us say that x g of iodine go into the tetrachloromethane. This will leave $(1-x)$ g of iodine in the water. Therefore we have

$$\frac{x\,\text{g}/20\,\text{cm}^3}{(1-x)\,\text{g}/20\,\text{cm}^3} = 85$$

so,

$$x = 85(1-x)$$

and

$$x = 85/86 = 0.988$$

We should have 0.988 g of iodine in the tetrachloromethane, and 0.012 g left in the water.

If we wanted to collect the iodine, we would have to evaporate the tetrachloromethane carefully. Also, if we wanted to collect even more iodine, we could perform another extraction with the aqueous solution left over.

62.1 Use the value of the partition constant in the example to answer these questions. How much iodine would have been removed from the solution if you had shaken it with

(i) 40 cm³ of tetrachloromethane;

(ii) first, 10 cm³ of tetrachloromethane, and then another 10 cm³ of tetrachloromethane?

In each case compare the effectiveness of the separation with the result we obtained by using 20 cm³ of the solvent.

62.2 The results of partition experiments can be used to work out the formulae of some complex ions. This question shows you how this can be done for the complex ion made between ammonia and copper(II) ions.

First, here is *the method*. 25 cm³ of a 0.2 mol dm⁻³ solution of copper(II) sulphate were mixed with 25 cm³ of 1 mol dm⁻³ ammonia solution. When these solutions mix, a royal blue solution is made. This contains a complex ion, which we can write as $Cu(NH_3)_x{}^{2+}$. The total 50 cm³ of the solution were shaken with 50 cm³ of trichloromethane. After giving time for equilibrium to be achieved, the two solutions were separated. The ammonia was extracted from the trichloromethane. After performing a titration it was found that 0.2×10^{-3} mol of ammonia was present in the trichloromethane.

Now *the calculation*.

(i) Taking the partition coefficient for ammonia between water and trichloromethane as 25, calculate the number of moles of free ammonia in the original 50 cm³ of the royal blue solution.

(ii) What is the total number of moles of ammonia in the trichloromethane and the 50 cm³ of the royal blue solution?

(iii) How many moles of ammonia were present *before* the complex ion was made?

(iv) How many moles of ammonia had been used in joining with the copper(II) ions?

(v) How many moles of copper(II) sulphate had been used?

(vi) Given that every 1 mol of copper(II) sulphate contains 1 mol of copper(II) ions, how many moles of copper(II) ions had been taken?

(vii) What is the ratio of moles of copper(II) ions to moles of ammonia molecules in the complex ion? This is the value of x in the formula $Cu(NH_3)_x^{2+}$.

(viii) What is the formula of the complex ion?

Answers

62.1 (i) $\dfrac{x\,\text{g}/40\,\text{cm}^3}{(1-x)\,\text{g}/20\,\text{cm}^3} = 85$

so $x = 170(1-x)$ and $x = 0.994$.

(ii) $\dfrac{x\,\text{g}/10\,\text{cm}^3}{(1-x)\,\text{g}/20\,\text{cm}^3} = 85$

which gives $x = 0.977$. This leaves 0.023 g of iodine in the 20 cm³ of water. With the second 10 cm³ of solvent, if x g of iodine go into the solvent, $(0.023-x)$ g will be left in the water. Therefore we have

$$\frac{x\,\text{g}/10\,\text{cm}^3}{(0.023-x)\,\text{g}/20\,\text{cm}^3} = 85$$

Then, $2x = 85(0.023-x)$ and $x = 0.0225$.

By using two separate 10 cm³ portions we have separated a total of 0.977 g + 0.0225 g = 0.9995 g. This is better than using one 20 cm³ portion, which only removed 0.988 g. It is also better than using one portion of 40 cm³.

62.2 (i)

$$\frac{\text{number of moles of ammonia in 50 cm}^3\text{ water}}{\text{number of moles of ammonia in 50 cm}^3\text{ trichloromethane}} = 25$$

so

$$\frac{\text{number of moles of ammonia in 50 cm}^3\text{ water}}{0.2 \times 10^{-3}\,\text{mol}} = 25$$

and number of moles of ammonia in 50 cm³ water $= 5 \times 10^{-3}$ mol.

(ii) The total is 5×10^{-3} mol + 0.2×10^{-3} mol = 5.2×10^{-3} mol.

(iii) The original number of moles of ammonia was

$$25\,\text{cm}^3 \times 1\,\text{mol}/1000\,\text{cm}^3 = 25 \times 10^{-3}\,\text{mol}$$

(iv) Therefore 19.8×10^{-3} mol of ammonia had reacted with the copper(II) ions.

(v) $25\,\text{cm}^3 \times 0.2\,\text{mol}/1000\,\text{cm}^3 = 5 \times 10^{-3}$ mol of copper(II) sulphate.

(vi) The ratio of copper(II) ions to ammonia molecules is 5×10^{-3} mol to 19.8×10^{-3} mol, i.e. 1 to 4 (given that the ratio must involve whole numbers).

(vii) The formula is $Cu(NH_3)_4^{2+}$. It is the tetraamminecopper(II) ion.

UNIT 62 SUMMARY

- Solvent extraction:
  A solute can be separated from a solution by shaking the solution with a solvent in which the solute is more soluble; e.g. iodine in potassium iodide solution shaken with 1,1,1-trichloroethane will separate into the latter solvent.
- Partition coefficient

$$= \frac{\text{concentration of solute in first solvent}}{\text{concentration of solute in second solvent}}$$

- Deviations from the partition law occur if there is dissociation or association of the solute; for example,

$$\underset{\text{monomers in water}}{2CH_3COOH} \rightleftharpoons \underset{\text{dimers in benzene}}{(CH_3COOH)_2}$$

63

Distillation

63.1 The boiling points of mixtures

Distillation is a method of separating mixtures of miscible liquids. There are three key ideas that you must know if you are to understand how and why distillation works. The first is that:

A liquid boils when its vapour pressure equals the atmospheric pressure.

The second is that:

The higher the vapour pressure of a liquid, the more volatile is the liquid.

The third, which follows from the first two is:

A liquid with a high vapour pressure will boil at a lower temperature than a liquid with a lower vapour pressure.

The importance of these ideas is that we can use vapour pressure diagrams to tell us how the boiling point of a mixture of liquids will change as the composition of the mixture changes. Instead of plotting vapour pressure against composition, we can plot boiling point against composition. This is done for an ideal mixture in Figure 63.1. If you compare the diagrams in Figure 63.1 you can see that, where the line goes up on a vapour pressure diagram, the line goes down on the boiling point diagram (and vice versa). This has the effect of turning the liquid and vapour composition lines upside down.

There is a right and a wrong way of interpreting a boiling point diagram. The right way is to start on the temperature axis and work across. If we do this in Figure 63.2, starting at temperature *T*, we meet the liquid line at X. Going further to the right, we meet the vapour line at Y. The link between the points X and Y means that:

A liquid with composition X will be in equilibrium with a vapour of composition Y at the temperature *T*.

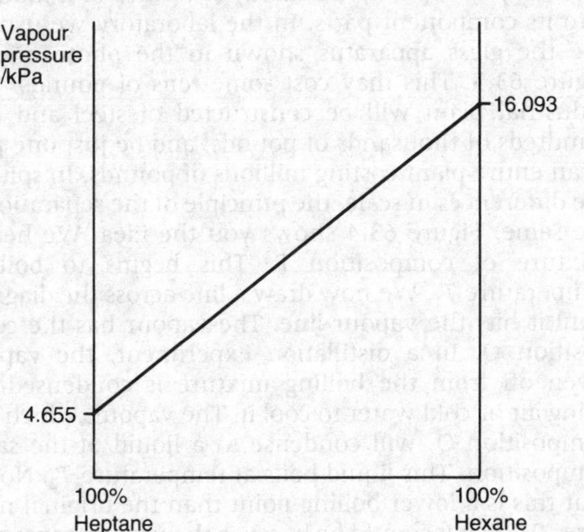

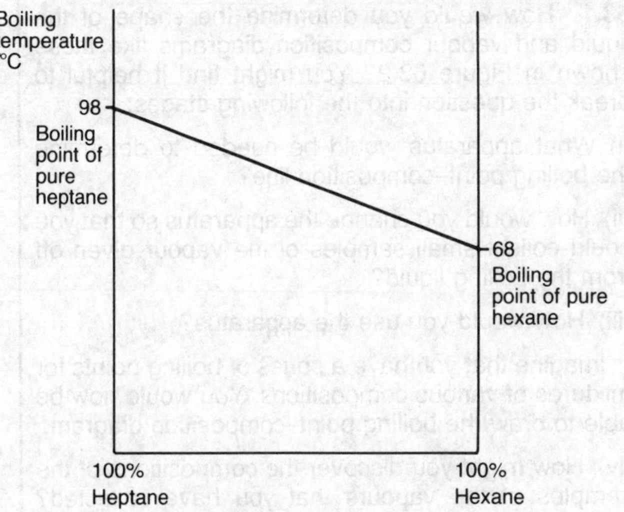

***Figure 63.1** The vapour pressure–composition diagram for a mixture of hexane and heptane slopes in the opposite direction to the boiling point–composition diagram. (Low vapour pressure means high boiling point, and vice versa)*

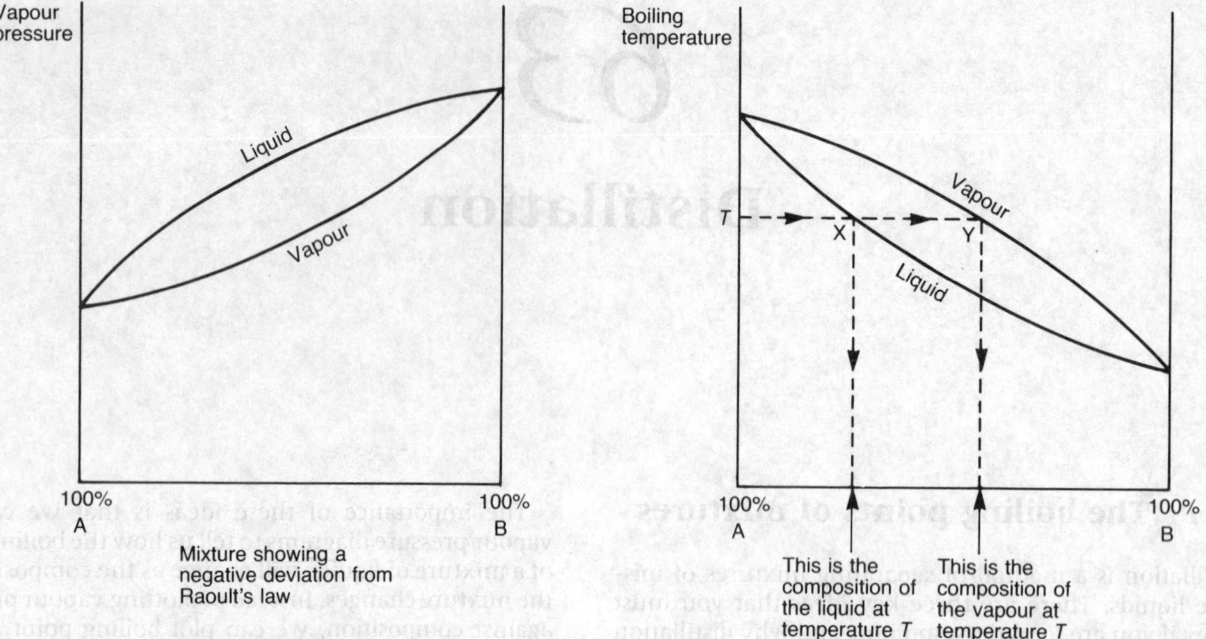

***Figure 63.2** A boiling point–composition diagram for a mixture showing a negative deviation from Raoult's law. It is important to move across the diagram at a given temperature. At T, liquid mixture X is in equilibrium with vapour Y. Notice that Y is richer in the lower boiling point (more volatile) component B*

(The link is often called a tie line.) You can see that the vapour is richer in the more volatile component (the one with the lower boiling point).

Do be careful with boiling point diagrams; if you move upwards instead of across the diagram you will get into a muddle. Also, it is wise to remember that a mixture showing a positive deviation from Raoult's law will have a vapour line that dips *downwards* on a boiling point diagram. Likewise, a negative deviation curves *upwards* on a boiling point diagram. (These are the opposite directions to those on a vapour pressure diagram.)

> **63.1** How would you determine the shape of the liquid and vapour composition diagrams like those shown in Figure 63.2? You might find it helpful to break the question into the following stages:
>
> (i) What apparatus would be needed to determine the boiling point–composition line?
>
> (ii) How would you change the apparatus so that you could collect small samples of the vapour given off from the boiling liquid?
>
> (iii) How would you use the apparatus?
>
> Imagine that you have a series of boiling points for mixtures of various compositions. You would now be able to draw the boiling point–composition diagram.
>
> (iv) How might you discover the compositions of the samples of the vapours that you have collected? (Might there be a problem with the method you suggest?)
>
> (v) Now you should know one method of determining the boiling point–vapour composition line to complete the diagram.

63.2 How distillation works

Distillation is of great importance in the chemical industry and in the laboratory; but the scales of the separation problem are rather different. In a laboratory we might want to separate 20 cm^3 of one liquid from 50 cm^3 of another. On an industrial scale it can be necessary to separate hundreds of tonnes of a mixture into its component parts. In the laboratory we usually use the glass apparatus shown in the photo and in Figure 63.3. This may cost some tens of pounds. The industrial plant will be constructed of steel and cost hundreds of thousands of pounds, and be just one part of an entire plant costing millions of pounds. In spite of the differences in scale, the principle of the separation is the same. Figure 63.4 shows you the idea. We heat a mixture of composition P. This begins to boil at temperature T_1. We now draw a line across the diagram until it hits the vapour line. The vapour has the composition Q. In a distillation experiment, the vapour given off from the boiling mixture is condensed, by using air or cold water to cool it. The vapour, which has composition Q, will condense to a liquid of the same composition. This liquid boils at temperature T_2. Notice that this is a lower boiling point than the original mixture. (Which it should be because the vapour contains a greater amount of the more volatile component.) If this liquid boils, it gives off a vapour of composition R,

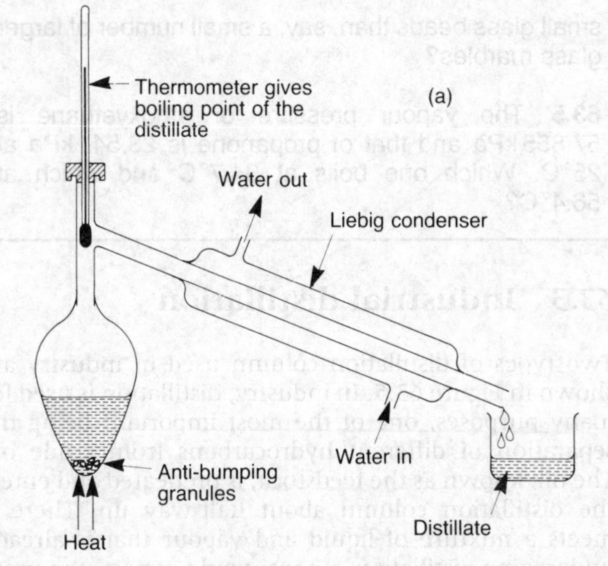

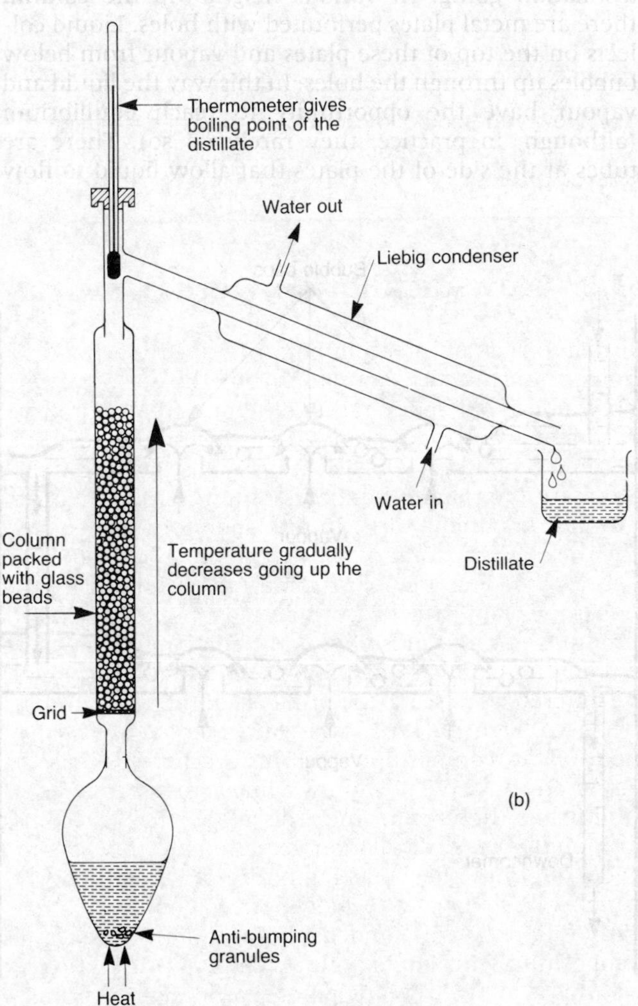

Figure 63.3 *(a) A simple distillation apparatus. (b) A fractional distillation apparatus*

A simple distillation apparatus.

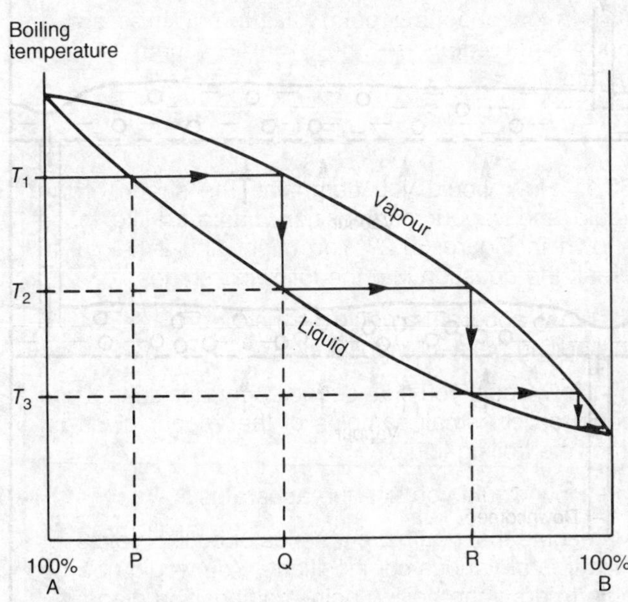

Figure 63.4 *This mixture shows a negative deviation from Raoult's law. The original mixture of composition P boils at T_1. It gives a vapour of composition Q, which boils at the lower temperature T_2, and so on. Eventually the distillate is (almost) pure B*

which condenses to a liquid or even lower boiling point. Eventually the vapour emerging from the distillation apparatus should be pure B. In practice, 100% separation is impossible to achieve.

In order that a distillation separates a mixture efficiently, it is essential that equilibrium is achieved at all places on the fractionating column. If the distillate is heated too quickly, there is insufficient time for equilibrium to be established further up the column. When this happens you can get a short column of liquid travelling up the column. It is pushed up by the large amount of vapour being boiled off from below. This phenomenon is known as logging, and should be avoided if the distillation is to be a success.

63.2 Why is distillation using a Liebig condenser only likely to be a success when separating liquids with very different boiling points?

63.3 In a distillation experiment, we know that the vapour normally becomes richer in the more volatile component. What happens to the composition of the mixture remaining in the flask? Does its boiling point change or remain constant?

63.4 A laboratory fractional distillation column is often filled with glass beads. Why is the column not left empty? Why is it better to use a large number of small glass beads than, say, a small number of larger glass marbles?

63.5 The vapour pressure of ethoxyethane is 57.855 kPa and that of propanone is 23.541 kPa at 25° C. Which one boils at 34.7° C and which at 56.4° C?

63.3 Industrial distillation

Two types of distillation column used in industry are shown in Figure 63.5. In industry, distillation is used for many purposes, one of the most important being the separation of different hydrocarbons from crude oil. The oil, known as the feedstock, is preheated and enters the distillation column about half-way up. There it meets a mixture of liquid and vapour that is already undergoing distillation. As we would expect, the more volatile components rise towards the top, and the less volatile components gravitate downwards. There is a heater at the bottom, which supplies energy to keep the distillation going. At various heights up the column there are metal plates perforated with holes. Liquid collects on the top of these plates and vapour from below bubbles up through the holes. In this way the liquid and vapour have the opportunity to reach equilibrium (although, in practice, they rarely do so). There are tubes at the side of the plates that allow liquid to flow

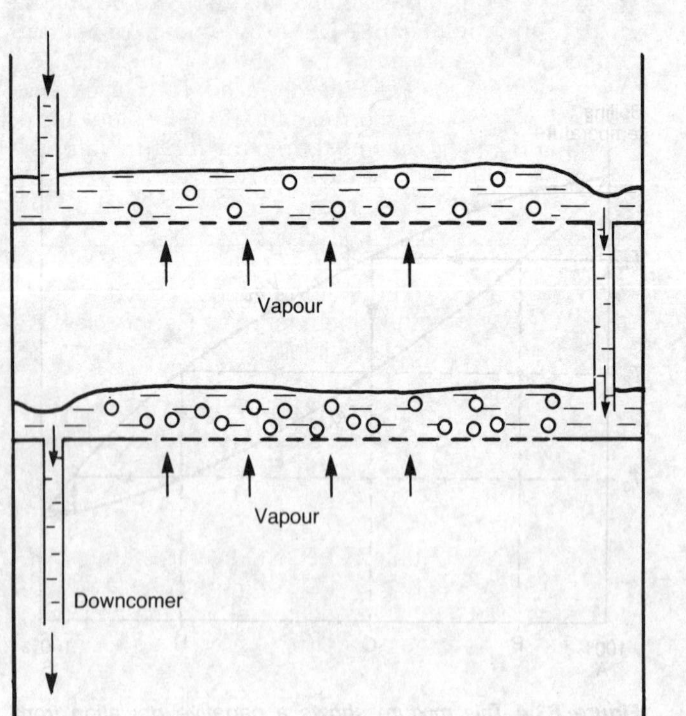

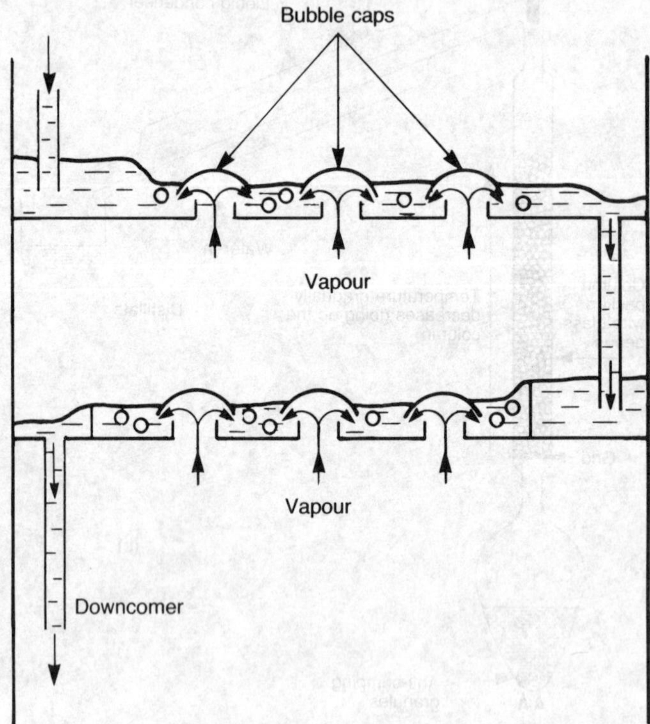

***Figure 63.5** Two designs of an industrial distillation column. On the left the vapours rise up the column, passing through a perforated metal plate into the liquid layer above. On the right is a method that uses 'bubble caps'. Hot vapours from below pass into the upper liquid layers by bubbling through holes in the circular caps*

Part of an oil refinery. The fractionating column is on the left.

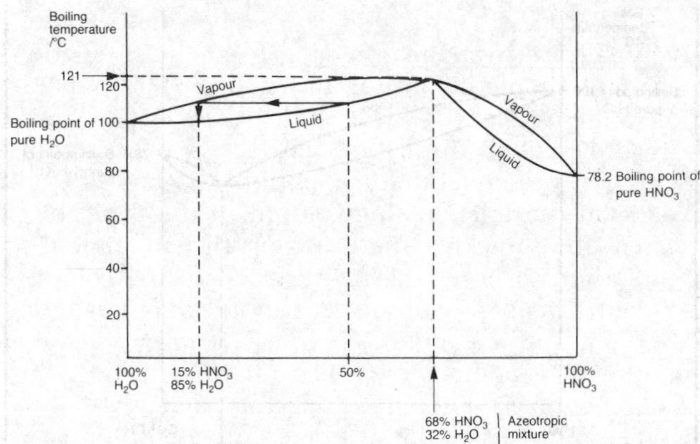

***Figure 63.6** Distillation of a mixture of nitric acid and water will not completely separate them. For example, a 50% mixture gives a vapour containing 15% HNO_3 and 85% H_2O. The liquid remaining in the flask becomes richer in HNO_3. Eventually the flask contains the azeotropic mixture boiling at 121° C*

back down the column. These tubes are the 'downcomers'. When liquid from a downcomer arrives at a lower plate, the higher temperature there brings about evaporation of the more volatile components, which then rise up through the perforated plates above. The less volatile components remain in the liquid and may run down another downcomer to the next plate below. A column like this will be left running indefinitely and a steady state is reached. At various heights up the column the various fractions are tapped off.

63.4 Does distillation always work?

No, it does not if the mixture has a maximum or a minimum in its vapour pressure curve. To see why this is, we shall imagine carrying out a distillation of nitric acid and water. The vapour pressure curve for the mixture shows a minimum for a mixture containing 68% of nitric acid. Therefore the boiling point diagram (Figure 63.6) shows a maximum at this value.

A mixture containing 68% nitric acid and 32% water boils at 121° C. You can see from the diagram that the vapour and liquid lines meet for this mixture; that is, the vapour given off by this mixture also consists of 68% nitric acid and 32% water. Therefore, if we distilled the mixture it would provide a distillate with the same composition. Similarly, the composition of the mixture in the flask would not change; its boiling point is constant.

A mixture that has a constant boiling point is called an *azeotropic* mixture.

If we were to distil a mixture that had a composition of, say, 50% nitric acid, Figure 63.6 shows that we would produce a vapour that contains a greater proportion of water in it. If the distillation continues the distillate would be pure water. The liquid left in the flask would be the azeotropic mixture.

In industry, azeotropic mixtures are a great nuisance. The whole point of distilling a mixture is to be able to separate the components. One way of overcoming the problem is to add another liquid to a mixture. For example, if benzene is added to a mixture of ethanol and water, then an azeotropic mixture does not form. The ethanol can be separated from the mixture (almost) completely pure.

63.6 Is it *always* true that the vapour above a mixture of two liquids that does not obey Raoult's law is richer in the more volatile liquid?

63.7 Figure 63.7 shows the boiling point diagram for a mixture of ethanol and water. What is the result of distilling a mixture containing 50% ethanol and 50% water?

63.8 Figure 63.8 shows the scheme of separation of ethanol and water used in industry. Benzene is added to the ethanol and water mixture during the process. Why is the benzene added?

63.9 Figure 63.9 shows the boiling point diagram for a solution of hydrochloric acid.

(i) What type of deviation from Raoult's law does the solution show?

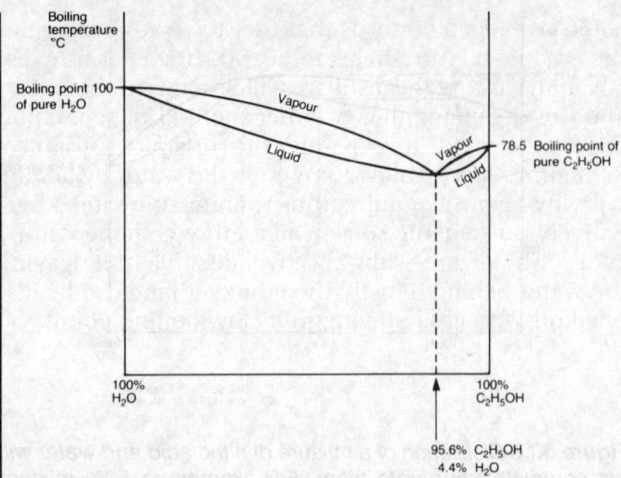

***Figure 63.7** Boiling point–composition diagram for mixtures of ethanol and water. Note: the horizontal scale has been exaggerated to make the diagram more clear*

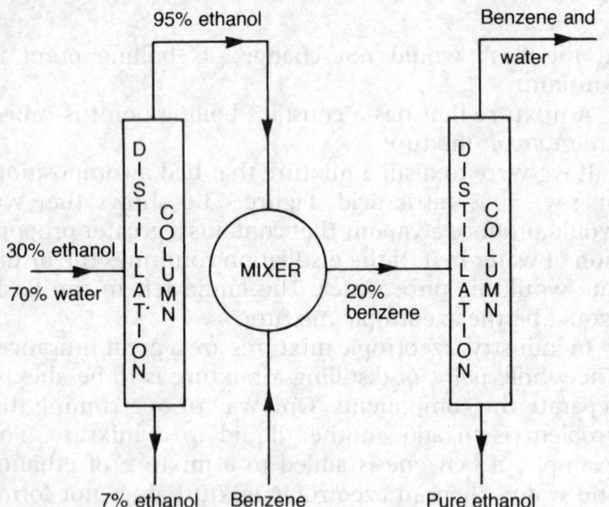

***Figure 63.8** An industrial scheme for separating ethanol and water. (Diagram adapted from: Heaton, C. A. (ed.) (1984).* An Introduction to Industrial Chemistry, *Leonard Hill, Glasgow, figure 5.6, p. 163)*

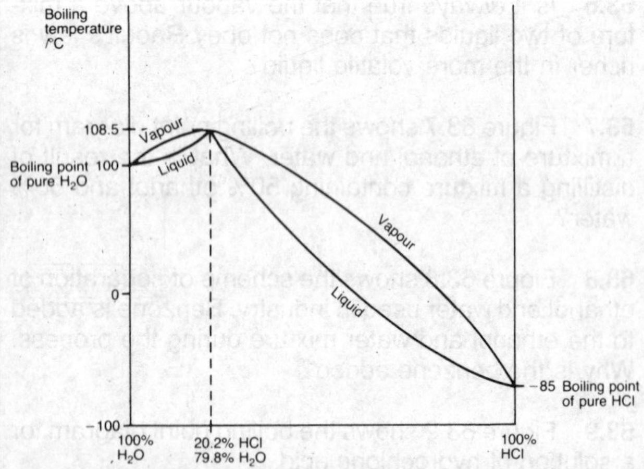

***Figure 63.9** Boiling point–composition diagram for mixtures of hydrogen chloride and water, i.e. hydrochloric acid*

(ii) What would be produced if a solution of hydrochloric acid were distilled?

63.10 Vacuum distillation uses an apparatus illustrated in Figure 63.10.

(i) What happens to the boiling point of a liquid if the pressure above it is reduced?

(ii) Why might vacuum distillation be used?

(iii) An 'air bleed' lets a controlled amount of air into the apparatus. What might be the purpose of the air bleed?

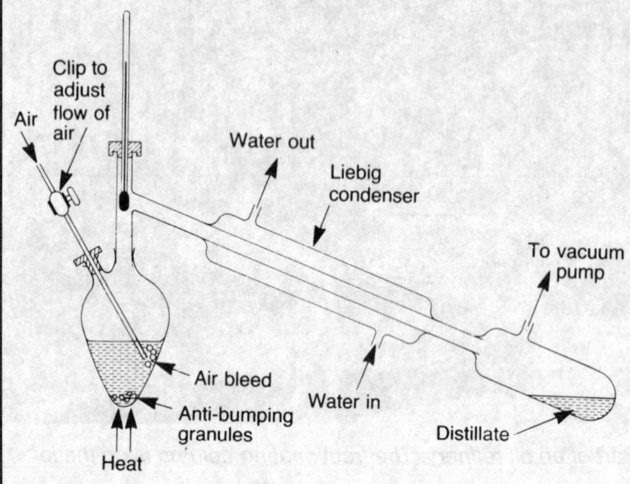

***Figure 63.10** An apparatus for performing distillation at reduced pressure*

63.5 Steam distillation

If two immiscible liquids are kept stirred, the vapour pressure above the mixture is the total of the two separate vapour pressures. For example, octane and water are immiscible. At 25° C, the vapour pressures of octane and water are approximately 3 kPa and 2.3 kPa. The vapour pressure above a mixture of them will be nearly 5.3 kPa. When the mixture is heated, the vapour pressure of both liquids will increase as shown in Figure 63.11. The vapour pressure above the mixture is the sum of the individual vapour pressures. When the total pressure equals the atmospheric pressure, the mixture will boil. However, the diagram shows that this happens at nearly 89° C, a temperature less than the boiling points of either the octane or the water.

It can be useful to pass steam into a distillation mixture that contains an organic liquid (Figure 63.12). Owing to the mixture being organic, the steam is likely to be immiscible with it. The presence of the water in the mixture reduces its boiling point, and the organic liquid will distil at a lower temperature. This is particularly useful if the organic substance is liable to decompose at temperatures near its normal boiling

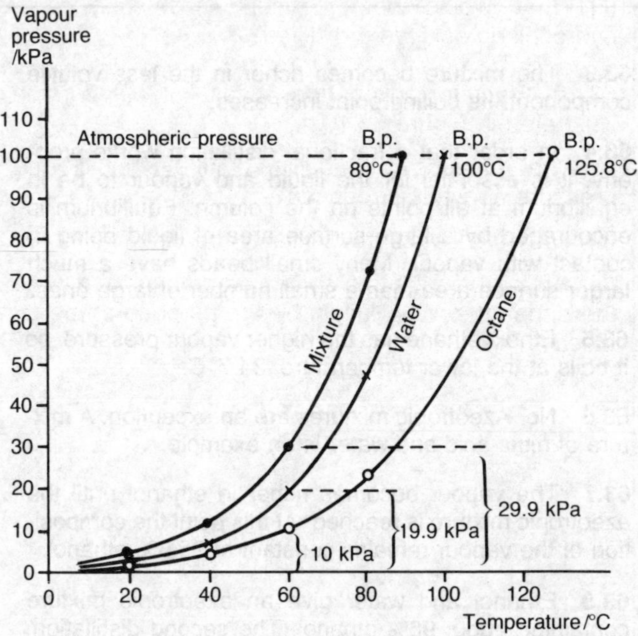

***Figure 63.11** How the vapour pressures of water, octane and a mixture of the two change with temperature*

point. An added bonus is that the steam condensing in the organic mixture helps to heat it. However, the disadvantage is that the distillate will be a mixture of water and the organic liquid. Another method of separation has to be used to separate the organic substance. Sometimes it is possible to remove the water by adding a drying agent like anhydrous sodium sulphate. Alternatively, an organic solvent like ethoxyethane can be added. The organic substance will dissolve in it, leaving the water behind. Finally the ethoxyethane can be distilled off very easily owing to its low boiling point.

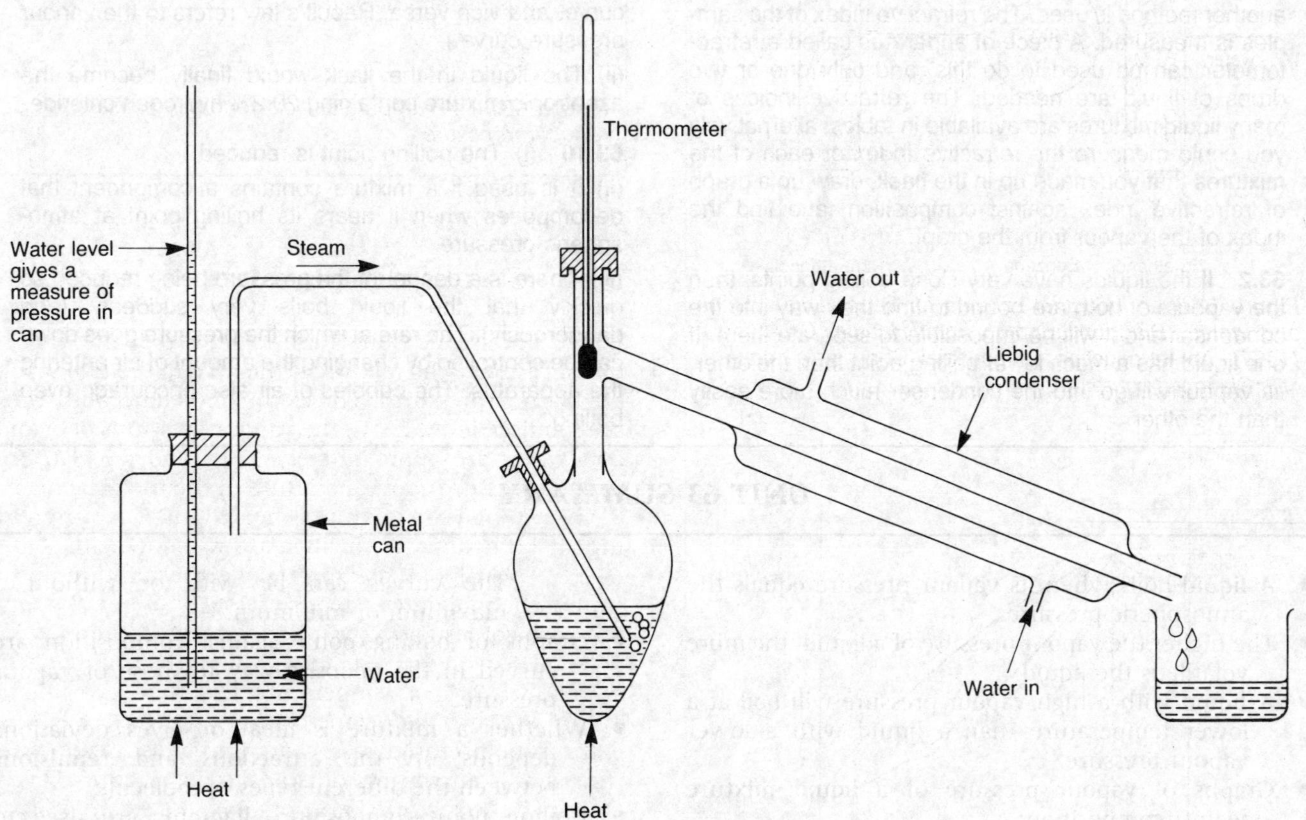

***Figure 63.12** An apparatus for steam distillation*

Answers

63.1 (i) A reflux apparatus fitted with a thermometer to record the boiling point of the liquid.

(ii) Just under the condenser, fit a side arm with a tap.

(iii) Put a known volume of one of the liquids into the flask. Keep the tap under the condenser closed until some of the condensed vapour from the boiling liquid collects; then open the tap and collect the liquid in a labelled container. Measure the boiling point. It is important not to draw off too much liquid because you will change the composition of the liquid in the flask (it becomes richer in the least volatile component). This would cause you to measure an incorrect boiling point. Allow the apparatus to cool and add a measured volume of the second liquid. Repeat the process. Knowing the densities of the two liquids, you would be able to calculate the mole fraction of each in the mixtures you use.

(iv), (v) In principle you could clean out the apparatus and place the first sample of distillate in the flask; then measure its boiling point. From your boiling point–composition diagram, you could read off the composition of the liquid that has the boiling point you measured. This is also the composition of the vapour that you collected. By repeating the process for the other vapour samples, you could draw in the vapour line. The problem is that you may not have a large enough sample to be able to measure its boiling point easily. In practice, another method is used. The refractive index of the samples is measured. A piece of apparatus called a refractometer can be used to do this, and only one or two drops of liquid are needed. The refractive indices of many liquid mixtures are available in tables; alternatively you could measure the refractive index of each of the mixtures that you made up in the flask, draw up a graph of refractive index against composition, and find the index of the vapour from the graph.

63.2 If the liquids have very close boiling points, then the vapours of both are bound to find their way into the condenser and it will be impossible to separate them. If one liquid has a much lower boiling point than the other, its vapour will go into the condenser much more easily than the other.

63.3 The mixture becomes richer in the less volatile component. Its boiling point increases.

63.4 In order that a fractional distillation works properly, it is essential for the liquid and vapour to be in equilibrium at all points on the column. Equilibrium is encouraged by a large surface area of liquid being in contact with vapour. Many small beads have a much larger surface area than a small number of large ones.

63.5 Ethoxyethane has the higher vapour pressure, so it boils at the lower temperature, 34.7°C.

63.6 No. Azeotropic mixtures are an exception. A mixture of nitric acid and water is an example.

63.7 The vapour becomes richer in ethanol until the azeotropic mixture is reached. At this point the composition of the vapour remains constant at 95.6% ethanol.

63.8 Ethanol and water give an azeotropic mixture containing about 96% ethanol. The second distillation, with benzene, allows pure ethanol to be separated.

63.9 (i) The solution shows a *negative* deviation from Raoult's law, but with a minimum in the vapour pressure curve. (Remember that the boiling point shows a maximum when there is a minimum in the vapour pressure curve, and vice versa. Raoult's law refers to the vapour pressure curve.)

(ii) The liquid in the flask would finally become the azeotropic mixture containing 20.2% hydrogen chloride.

63.10 (i) The boiling point is reduced.

(ii) It is used if a mixture contains a component that decomposes when it nears its boiling point at atmospheric pressure.

(iii) There is a danger of the pressure being reduced so quickly that the liquid boils very suddenly (and dangerously). The rate at which the pressure goes down can be controlled by changing the amount of air entering the apparatus. The bubbles of air also encourage even boiling.

UNIT 63 SUMMARY

- A liquid boils when its vapour pressure equals the atmospheric pressure.
- The higher the vapour pressure of a liquid, the more volatile is the liquid.
- A liquid with a high vapour pressure will boil at a lower temperature than a liquid with a lower vapour pressure.
- Graphs of vapour pressure of a liquid mixture against composition:
  - (i) Are straight lines if the mixture obeys Raoult's law.
  - (ii) Are curves if the mixture shows deviations from Raoult's law.
  - (iii) Negative and positive deviations are possible.

  The curves can be with or without a maximum or minimum.
- Graphs of boiling point against composition are curved in the opposite way to those of vapour pressure.
- Whether a mixture is ideal or gives deviations depends on the attractions and repulsions between the different types of molecule.
- Boiling point–composition diagrams are used to explain how liquids are separated by distillation.
- An azeotropic mixture has a constant boiling point and the composition of the vapour above the mixture is the same as that of the liquid.

64

Solubility product

64.1 What is a solubility product?

A solubility product is a special type of equilibrium constant. It tells us about the equilibrium between a solid and the ions it gives in solution. It is important to know that solubility products apply only to solids that are very *insoluble* in water. We shall use silver chloride as an example. Silver chloride is *almost*, but not completely, insoluble in water. The ions it provides are silver, Ag^+, and chloride, Cl^-.

Imagine that we had a supply of silver ions and chloride ions and that we began to add them to a beaker of distilled water. The first few ions in the water merely wander around the beaker surrounded by a layer of water molecules. If we continue to add ions, then gradually their concentration increases until eventually there are so many ions in the water that some of them join together and particles of solid appear (Figure 64.1). If we now add more ions, even more solid is made; the number of ions left in the water does not change. The key thing to realise is that there is a limit to the number of silver and chloride ions that can exist together in the water. We cannot increase their number by adding more solid. In other words:

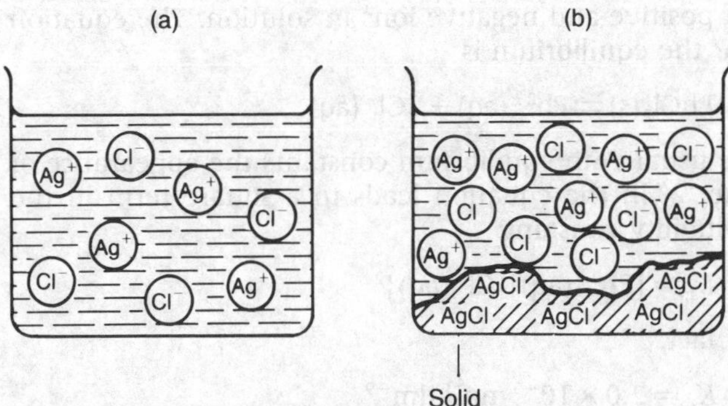

Figure 64.1 There is a limit to the amount of silver chloride that will dissolve in a fixed volume of water. (a) If a very little silver chloride is added to water, it dissolves, i.e. the ions float around surrounded by water molecules. (b) If more silver chloride is added there comes a time when no more will dissolve. A layer of solid lies on the bottom of the beaker

The number of ions in the water will be the same no matter how much solid is in the beaker.

The equilibrium involved is for the reaction

$$AgCl(s) \rightleftharpoons Ag^+(aq) + Cl^-(aq)$$

and we would expect that the equilibrium constant would be

$$K = \frac{[Ag^+(aq)][Cl^-(aq)]}{[AgCl(s)]}$$

However, we have just agreed that the concentrations of the ions are independent of the amount of the solid. For this reason we are entitled to write the equilibrium constant as

$$K_{sp} = [Ag^+(aq)][Cl^-(aq)]$$

Here, the sp added to the K tells us that this equilibrium constant is the *solubility product*. For silver chloride, $K_{sp} = 2.0 \times 10^{-10}\,mol^2\,dm^{-6}$ at 25°C, i.e.

$$[Ag^+(aq)][Cl^-(aq)] = 2.0 \times 10^{-10}\,mol^2\,dm^{-6}$$

Some other solubility products are shown in Table 64.1. (Note that the concentrations in the formulae must be those at equilibrium.)

64.2 Using solubility products to calculate solubilities

It is not too difficult to calculate solubilities from solubility products. We shall use the silver chloride equilibrium as an example:

$$AgCl(s) \rightleftharpoons Ag^+(aq) + Cl^-(aq)$$

The equation shows that each time a silver (or chloride) ion is produced, a particle of silver chloride has dissolved. There is always an equal number of chloride and silver ions (provided no other chemicals are present). Therefore, the concentrations of the ions must be equal, i.e.

$$[Ag^+(aq)] = [Cl^-(aq)]$$

Table 64.1. Solubility products at 25° C

Equilibrium	K_{sp}	*Value*
$AgCl(s) \rightleftharpoons Ag^+(aq) + Cl^-(aq)$	$[Ag^+(aq)][Cl^-(aq)]$	2.0×10^{-10} mol^2 dm^{-6}
$AgIO_3(s) \rightleftharpoons Ag^+(aq) + IO_3^-(aq)$	$[Ag^+(aq)][IO_3^-(aq)]$	2.0×10^{-8} mol^2 dm^{-6}
$Ag_2CrO_4(s) \rightleftharpoons 2Ag^+(aq) + CrO_4^{2-}(aq)$	$[Ag^+(aq)]^2[CrO_4^{2-}(aq)]$	3.0×10^{-12} mol^3 dm^{-9}
$Ag_2S(s) \rightleftharpoons 2Ag^+(aq) + S^{2-}(aq)$	$[Ag^+(aq)]^2[S^{2-}(aq)]$	6.3×10^{-50} mol^3 dm^{-9}
$CuS(s) \rightleftharpoons Cu^{2+}(aq) + S^{2-}(aq)$	$[Cu^{2+}(aq)][S^{2-}(aq)]$	6.3×10^{-36} mol^2 dm^{-6}
$PbS(s) \rightleftharpoons Pb^{2+}(aq) + S^{2-}(aq)$	$[Pb^{2+}(aq)][S^{2-}(aq)]$	1.3×10^{-28} mol^2 dm^{-6}
$ZnS(s) \rightleftharpoons Zn^{2+}(aq) + S^{2-}(aq)$	$[Zn^{2+}(aq)][S^{2-}(aq)]$	1.6×10^{-24} mol^2 dm^{-6}
$HgS(s) \rightleftharpoons Hg^{2+}(aq) + S^{2-}(aq)$	$[Hg^{2+}(aq)][S^{2-}(aq)]$	1.6×10^{-52} mol^2 dm^{-6}
$NiS(s) \rightleftharpoons Ni^{2+}(aq) + S^{2-}(aq)$	$[Ni^{2+}(aq)][S^{2-}(aq)]$	2.0×10^{-26} mol^2 dm^{-6}
$MnS(s) \rightleftharpoons Mn^{2+}(aq) + S^{2-}(aq)$	$[Mn^{2+}(aq)][S^{2-}(aq)]$	1.4×10^{-15} mol^2 dm^{-6}
$BaSO_4(s) \rightleftharpoons Ba^{2+}(aq) + SO_4^{2-}(aq)$	$[Ba^{2+}(aq)][SO_4^{2-}(aq)]$	1.0×10^{-10} mol^2 dm^{-6}
$PbSO_4(s) \rightleftharpoons Pb^{2+}(aq) + SO_4^{2-}(aq)$	$[Pb^{2+}(aq)][SO_4^{2-}(aq)]$	1.6×10^{-8} mol^2 dm^{-6}

Now, because

$$[Ag^+(aq)][Cl^-(aq)] = 2.0 \times 10^{-10}\,\text{mol}^2\,\text{dm}^{-6}$$

we have

$$[Ag^+(aq)]^2 = 2.0 \times 10^{-10}\,\text{mol}^2\,\text{dm}^{-6}$$

so

$$[Ag^+(aq)] = 1.41 \times 10^{-5}\,\text{mol dm}^{-3}$$

In words, this says that the maximum concentration of silver ions in a solution in contact with solid silver chloride is 1.41×10^{-5} mol dm^{-3}. We know from the equilibrium equation that if 1.41×10^{-5} mol of silver ions are present in a litre, then 1.41×10^{-5} mol of silver chloride will have dissolved. Therefore 1.41×10^{-5} mol dm^{-3} is the *solubility* of silver chloride.

Sometimes it is helpful to know the solubility in g dm^{-3}. We calculate this by multiplying the solubility in mol dm^{-3} by the mass of 1 mol of the substance. In the case of silver chloride,

$$\text{solubility} = 1.41 \times 10^{-5}\,\text{mol dm}^{-3} \times 143.5\,\text{g mol}^{-1}$$
$$= 2.02 \times 10^{-3}\,\text{g dm}^{-3}$$

Here is a typical problem involving another barely soluble solid. One way of testing for sulphate ions is to use barium chloride solution. Barium ions and sulphate ions give a white precipitate of barium sulphate, $BaSO_4$. Suppose you separated 10 g of barium sulphate by filtering off the precipitate from a solution, and that you washed the precipitate with a litre (1 dm^3) of distilled water. How much of the precipitate would be lost?

First we start with the equation:

$$BaSO_4(s) \rightleftharpoons Ba^{2+}(aq) + SO_4^{2-}(aq)$$

From Table 64.1 we find $K_{sp} = 1.0 \times 10^{-10}$ mol^2 dm^{-6}, i.e.

$$[Ba^{2+}(aq)][SO_4^{2-}(aq)] = 1.0 \times 10^{-10}\,\text{mol}^2\,\text{dm}^{-6}$$

The equilibrium equation says that there will be an equal number of moles of barium ions and sulphate ions released whenever some barium sulphate dissolves, so

$$[Ba^{2+}(aq)] = [SO_4^{2-}(aq)]$$

Therefore,

$$[Ba^{2+}(aq)]^2 = 1.0 \times 10^{-10}\,\text{mol}^2\,\text{dm}^{-6}$$

and

$$[Ba^{2+}(aq)] = 1.0 \times 10^{-5}\,\text{mol dm}^{-3}$$

We now know that the litre of distilled water will contain 10^{-5} mol of barium ions (assuming that there has been time for equilibrium to be achieved). To produce this number of barium ions, an equal number of particles of barium sulphate must have dissolved, i.e. its solubility is 10^{-5} mol dm^{-3}. The mass of 1 mol of barium sulphate is 233 g. Therefore the mass of barium sulphate that dissolves is 233×10^{-5} g, which is a little more than 0.002 g. This is not a great deal to lose from 10 g.

However, try question 64.6 to see if matters are different if you were trying to wash different masses of barium sulphate.

The next example will allow us to work out the solubility of lead(II) chloride, $PbCl_2$. This substance is an example of a solid that gives different numbers of moles of positive and negative ions in solution. The equation for the equilibrium is

$$PbCl_2(s) \rightleftharpoons Pb^{2+}(aq) + 2Cl^-(aq)$$

As usual with equilibrium constants the appearance of the '2' in the equation leads to a square term in the solubility constant:

$$K_{sp} = [Pb^{2+}(aq)][Cl^-(aq)]^2$$

In fact,

$$K_{sp} = 2.0 \times 10^{-5}\,\text{mol}^3\,\text{dm}^{-9}$$

From the equation, we know that there will be twice as many chloride ions as lead(II) ions in the solution in contact with lead(II) chloride. That is, the concentration of chloride ions is twice that of lead(II) ions, i.e.

$$[Cl^-(aq)] = 2[Pb^{2+}(aq)]$$

(It is easy to get this relation round the wrong way – take care!). Now we have

$$[Pb^{2+}(aq)] \times (2[Pb^{2+}(aq)])^2 = 2.0 \times 10^{-5}\,\text{mol}^3\,\text{dm}^{-9}$$

i.e.

$$4[Pb^{2+}(aq)]^3 = 2.0 \times 10^{-5}\,\text{mol}^3\,\text{dm}^{-9}$$
$$[Pb^{2+}(aq)]^3 = 5.0 \times 10^{-6}\,\text{mol}^3\,\text{dm}^{-9}$$
$$[Pb^{2+}(aq)] = 1.71 \times 10^{-2}\,\text{mol dm}^{-3}$$

The solubility of lead(II) chloride is 1.71×10^{-2} mol dm^{-3}.

64.1 In this and the questions that follow you may need to refer to the values in Table 64.1. What is the solubility in mol dm^{-3} of silver iodate(V), $AgIO_3$?

64.2 What is the solubility in g dm^{-3} of silver chromate(VI), Ag_2CrO_4?

64.3 What is the maximum concentration of chloride ions that could exist in a 0.01 mol dm^{-3} solution of silver nitrate in contact with solid silver chloride?

64.4 You have separated 0.2 g of barium sulphate from a solution. If you washed the precipitate with a litre of distilled water, what mass of barium sulphate would you lose? What percentage loss is this?

64.3 The common ion effect

One of the features of solubility products is that, as they are true equilibrium constants, they only change their values when the temperature changes. Le Chatelier's principle can also be applied to them. For example, suppose we drop a few crystals of silver chloride into a litre of water and allow equilibrium to be achieved. Now let us put 1 mol of sodium chloride into the water. Sodium chloride is quite soluble in water, and will produce 1 mol of sodium ions and 1 mol of chloride ions. The concentration of chloride ions greatly increases. This ion is common to both the silver chloride and the sodium chloride. According to Le Chatelier's principle the silver chloride equilibrium should shift in order to reduce the chloride ion concentration. It will do so by some of the silver ions combining with the extra chloride ions to make solid silver chloride. Therefore we would expect the concentration of silver ions to be less than it was without the added sodium chloride.

We can estimate the new silver ion concentration. The concentration of chloride ions, $[Cl^-(aq)]$, would be 1 mol dm^{-3} owing to the dissolved salt. But we know that

$$[Ag^+(aq)][Cl^-(aq)] = 2.0 \times 10^{-10}\,\text{mol}^2\,\text{dm}^{-6}$$

so

$$[Ag^+(aq)] \times 1\,\text{mol dm}^{-3} = 2.0 \times 10^{-10}\,\text{mol}^2\,\text{dm}^{-6}$$
$$[Ag^+(aq)] = 2.0 \times 10^{-10}\,\text{mol dm}^{-3}$$

Previously we found that for silver chloride on its own, $[Ag^+(aq)] = 1.41 \times 10^{-5}\,\text{mol dm}^{-3}$. The effect of adding the common ion is to make the silver ion concentration about one hundred thousand (10^5) times smaller. This means that the solubility of silver chloride has been reduced by the same amount.

We now have a method of reducing the solubility of silver chloride in water: we add a soluble substance that has an ion in common with the silver chloride.

Having understood this, you might think that if we used a 5 mol dm^{-3}, rather than a 1 mol dm^{-3}, solution of sodium chloride we would reduce the solubility of silver chloride even further. Unfortunately things are not so simple. When the concentration of ions increases beyond a certain level, other effects start to take a part. Especially, the presence of large numbers of ions changes the electric fields in the solution, which in turn influence how ions like Ag^+ and Cl^- join together. The changes that take place are linked to a quantity called the *ionic strength* of a solution. You will find information about ionic strength in more advanced chemistry books. In addition, when silver ions are in solution with large numbers of chloride ions, complex ions such as $AgCl_3^{2-}$ are made. The presence of complex ions leads to the predictions made from solubility product calculations not matching with experiment.

64.5 You have collected a precipitate of lead(II) sulphate, and you want to keep as much of it as you can. Which of the following solutions would you choose to wash the precipitate: potassium nitrate, potassium sulphate, potassium chloride?

64.4 Solubility products tell us when a precipitate will be made

The solubility product for lead(II) sulphate is

$$PbSO_4(s) \rightleftharpoons Pb^{2+}(aq) + SO_4^{2-}(aq); \quad K_{sp} = 1.6 \times 10^{-8}\,\text{mol}^2\,\text{dm}^{-6}$$

This shows that lead(II) ions and sulphate ions can exist together in a solution provided the product of their concentrations is not greater than $1.6 \times 10^{-8}\,\text{mol}^2\,\text{dm}^{-6}$. For example, we could have $[Pb^{2+}(aq)] = 10^{-5}$ mol dm^{-3} and $[SO_4^{2-}(aq)] = 10^{-5}\,\text{mol dm}^{-3}$ without any precipitate appearing. The reason is that $[Pb^{2+}(aq)] \times [SO_4^{2-}(aq)] = 10^{-10}\,\text{mol}^2\,\text{dm}^{-6}$, which is *smaller* than K_{sp}. On the other hand, if $[Pb^{2+}(aq)] = 10^{-5}\,\text{mol dm}^{-3}$ and $[SO_4^{2-}(aq)] = 10^{-2}\,\text{mol dm}^{-3}$, then $[Pb^{2+}(aq)] \times [SO_4^{2-}(aq)] = 10^{-7}\,\text{mol}^2\,\text{dm}^{-6}$. In this case the solubility product is *exceeded* by the product of the concentrations. (Be careful when you look at values of concentrations like this: 10^{-7} is 10 times *larger* than 10^{-8}.) When this happens a precipitate will be produced. Solid lead(II) sulphate will appear until the concentrations of the two ions decrease to a level at which the solubility product is not exceeded. This example is an illustration of a general rule:

A precipitate will appear if the solubility product is exceeded.

However, do not expect predictions always to match with practice. Often ions in solution do not behave independently of one another. Positive ions will tend to stay close to negative ions, and vice versa. Indeed, the formation of *ion-pairs* makes solubility product calculations unreliable.

64.6 A solution was 0.1 mol dm^{-3} in barium ions, Ba^{2+}, and lead(II) ions, Pb^{2+}. If it had drops of sodium sulphate solution added to it, which solubility product would be exceeded first, that of $BaSO_4$ or $PbSO_4$? Which of these substances would be precipitated first?

64.5 Using solubility products in chemical analysis

Over a period of many years, chemists have discovered methods of analysing mixtures of substances. If the analysis is aimed at finding out only which elements or compounds are present, it is called *qualitative analysis*. If it is necessary to discover how much of an element or compound is present, it is called *quantitative analysis*. There is a standard scheme of qualitative analysis that you can find in work such as that by Vogel (see the bibliography at the end of the book).

Several parts of the analysis scheme ask you to pass hydrogen sulphide gas through the solution being analysed. The gas dissolves in water to give sulphide ions, which react with many metal ions to give a precipitate. Sometimes the colour of the precipitate can tell us which metal is present. For example, mercury(II) sulphide, HgS, is black, while manganese(II) sulphide, MnS, is pink. The problem is to arrange things so that in a solution that contains both mercury(II) ions, Hg^{2+}, and manganese(II) ions, Mn^{2+}, each sulphide is precipitated separately from the other.

The way this is done makes use of knowledge of the solubility products of sulphides:

$$MnS(s) \rightleftharpoons Mn^{2+}(aq) + S^{2-}(aq); \quad K_{sp} = 1.4 \times 10^{-15}\ \text{mol}^2\ \text{dm}^{-6}$$

$$HgS(s) \rightleftharpoons Hg^{2+}(aq) + S^{2-}(aq); \quad K_{sp} = 1.6 \times 10^{-52}\ \text{mol}^2\ \text{dm}^{-6}$$

The values show that although both sulphides are barely soluble in water, mercury(II) sulphide is very much less soluble than manganese(II) sulphide. Therefore, if sulphide ions are introduced into a solution containing both Hg^{2+} and Mn^{2+} ions, then mercury(II) sulphide will be precipitated *before* manganese(II) sulphide. The trick is to make the sulphide ion concentration large enough to ensure that the solubility product of mercury(II) sulphide is exceeded but to keep it sufficiently low so the solubility product of manganese(II) sulphide is *not* exceeded. The concentration of sulphide ions is controlled by changing the conditions in the solution to be analysed.

Let us assume that we are analysing a solution that is 0.1 mol dm^{-3} in mercury(II) ions, Hg^{2+}, and 0.1 mol dm^{-3} in manganese(II) ions, Mn^{2+}. The analysis scheme tells us to add a little dilute hydrochloric acid to the solution before bubbling hydrogen sulphide through it. Owing to the hydrochloric acid, the solution has a large number of hydrogen ions present. These ions influence the dissociation of the hydrogen sulphide:

$H_2S(aq)$	$\rightleftharpoons$	$H^+(aq) + HS^-(aq)$	(A)
$HS^-(aq)$	$\rightleftharpoons$	$H^+(aq) + S^{2-}(aq)$	(B)
this side favoured in acid conditions		this side favoured in alkaline conditions	

Le Chatelier's principle tells us that these equilibria will move to the left in order to reduce the concentration of the hydrogen ions.

Therefore, in acid solution there will be relatively few sulphide ions. In fact, in a 0.1 mol dm^{-3} solution of hydrochloric acid, the maximum concentration of sulphide ions is about 1.0×10^{-25} mol dm^{-3}. Thus in our acidified solution we have

$$[S^{2-}(aq)] = 1.0 \times 10^{-25}\ \text{mol dm}^{-3}$$
$$[Hg^{2+}(aq)] = 0.1\ \text{mol dm}^{-3}$$
$$[Mn^{2+}(aq)] = 0.1\ \text{mol dm}^{-3}$$

Therefore,

$$[Hg^{2+}(aq)][S^{2-}(aq)] = 1.0 \times 10^{-26}\ \text{mol}^2\ \text{dm}^{-6}$$

This is about 10^{26} times *larger* than the solubility product of the sulphide ($K_{sp} = 1.6 \times 10^{-52}$ mol^2 dm^{-6}), so mercury(II) sulphide will definitely be precipitated. Also,

$$[Mn^{2+}(aq)][S^{2-}(aq)] = 1.0 \times 10^{-26}\ \text{mol}^2\ \text{dm}^{-6}$$

which is about 10^{11} times *smaller* than the solubility product of manganese sulphide ($K_{sp} = 1.4 \times 10^{-15}$ mol^2 dm^{-6}). Therefore, this sulphide will not be precipitated.

The result is that we would see a black precipitate of mercury(II) sulphide, but no pink precipitate of manganese(II) sulphide.

Having removed (nearly all) the mercury ions you should be able to guess the next step: add an alkali. It is the presence of the hydrogen ions that stops the concentration of sulphide ions becoming large enough to precipitate the manganese(II) ions. If an alkali is added (usually aqueous ammonia), the hydrogen ion concentration is reduced. This causes the two equilibria (A) and (B) to move to the right. The sulphide ion concentration increases and the solubility product of manganese(II) sulphide can be exceeded. We would see a pink solid appear in the reaction tube.

64.7 You have been given a solution that contains equal concentrations of copper(II) ions and lead(II) ions.

(i) If you passed hydrogen sulphide through the solutions, which sulphide would be precipitated first?

(ii) If you wanted to be sure that only one of the sulphides was precipitated, would you add acid or alkali to the solution before bubbling through the hydrogen sulphide? Explain your answer.

64.8 A solution contains equal concentrations of zinc ions and nickel(II) ions. A student decides to pass hydrogen sulphide solution through the solution. What would you expect to happen?

64.9 Say what, if anything, is wrong with this statement: 'The solubility product of copper(II) sulphide is extremely small. This means that the sulphide is almost insoluble in water. It also means that if you mixed copper(II) ions and sulphide ions, they would react together extremely quickly to give a solid.'

Answers

64.1 $AgIO_3(s) \rightleftharpoons Ag^+(aq) + IO_3^-(aq)$;

$$K_{sp} = 2.0 \times 10^{-8}\,\text{mol}^2\,\text{dm}^{-6}$$

$$[Ag^+(aq)][IO_3^-(aq)] = 2.0 \times 10^{-8}\,\text{mol}^2\,\text{dm}^{-6}$$

But, the equation shows us that $[Ag^+(aq)] = [IO_3^-(aq)]$, so

$$[Ag^+(aq)]^2 = 2.0 \times 10^{-8}\,\text{mol}^2\,\text{dm}^{-6}$$

$$[Ag^+(aq)] = 1.4 \times 10^{-4}\,\text{mol dm}^{-3}$$

The equation also shows that for every mole of silver ions that goes into solution a mole of silver iodate(V) must have dissolved. Hence if the number of moles of silver ions in a litre is 1.4×10^{-4} mol, then an equal number of moles of silver iodate(V) must have dissolved, i.e. the solubility is 1.4×10^{-4} mol dm^{-3}.

64.2 We know that

$$Ag_2CrO_4(s) \rightleftharpoons 2Ag^+(aq) + CrO_4^{2-}(aq)$$

$$[Ag^+(aq)]^2[CrO_4^{2-}(aq)] = 3.0 \times 10^{-12}\,\text{mol}^3\,\text{dm}^{-9}$$

The equation shows that there are two silver ions for every chromate(VI) ion. Therefore the concentration of silver ions is twice that of chromate(VI) ions, i.e. $[Ag^+(aq)] = 2[CrO_4^{2-}(aq)]$. This gives

$$(2[CrO_4^{2-}(aq)])^2[CrO_4^{2-}(aq)] = 3.0 \times 10^{-12}\,\text{mol}^3\,\text{dm}^{-9}$$

$$4[CrO_4^{2-}(aq)]^2[CrO_4^{2-}(aq)] = 3.0 \times 10^{-12}\,\text{mol}^3\,\text{dm}^{-9}$$

$$[CrO_4^{2-}(aq)]^3 = 0.75 \times 10^{-12}\,\text{mol}^3\,\text{dm}^{-9}$$

$$[CrO_4^{2-}(aq)] = 9.1 \times 10^{-5}\,\text{mol dm}^{-3}$$

Every chromate(VI) ion that is found in solution comes from one particle of silver chromate(VI) that has dissolved. Therefore, the solubility is also 9.1×10^{-5} mol dm^{-3}. Using the table of atomic masses in Appendix C, you should find that the mass of 1 mol of silver chromate(VI) is 332 g. Hence the solubility in g dm^{-3} is $9.1 \times 10^{-5}\,\text{mol dm}^{-3} \times 332\,\text{g mol}^{-1} = 3.02 \times 10^{-2}\,\text{g dm}^{-3}$

64.3 The solubility product of silver chloride is

$$[Ag^+(aq)][Cl^-(aq)] = 2.0 \times 10^{-10}\,\text{mol}^2\,\text{dm}^{-6}$$

The presence of the silver nitrate solution makes $[Ag^+(aq)] = 0.01$ mol dm^{-3}. Therefore,

$$[Cl^-(aq)] = \frac{2.0 \times 10^{-10}\,\text{mol}^2\,\text{dm}^{-6}}{0.01\,\text{mol dm}^{-3}}$$

$$= 2.0 \times 10^{-8}\,\text{mol dm}^{-3}$$

This is the maximum concentration of chloride ions that can exist in the solution. (We ignore the existence of complex ions.)

64.4 In section 64.2, we worked out the solubility of barium sulphate to be 10^{-5} mol dm^{-3}. This corresponds to a mass of 0.002 g dissolved. The point is that it does not matter whether we wash 10 g or 0.2 g of the sulphate with water, the same mass dissolves. In this case there is a percentage loss of $(0.002\,\text{g}/2\,\text{g}) \times 100\% = 0.1\%$.

64.5 We are looking for a solution that has a *common ion* with the lead(II) sulphate; this is the potassium sulphate solution.

64.6 From Table 64.1 we have $K_{sp} = 1.0 \times 10^{-10}$ mol^2 dm^{-6} for barium sulphate, which is 100 times smaller than $K_{sp} = 1.6 \times 10^{-8}$ mol^2 dm^{-6} for lead(II) sulphate. Therefore the solubility product of barium sulphate will be exceeded first, and this will be the first substance to be precipitated. If the sodium sulphate solution is added continually, then the solubility product of lead(II) sulphate will be exceeded as well, and this will start to precipitate.

64.7 (i) The solubility product of copper(II) sulphide is 10^8 smaller than that of lead(II) sulphide and will be exceeded first. Therefore copper(II) sulphide will be precipitated first.

(ii) It would be necessary to keep the sulphide ion concentration low, so that only the solubility product of copper(II) sulphide will be exceeded. You would have to add dilute acid in order to make sure that the equilibria (A) and (B) in section 64.5 involving hydrogen sulphide lay to the left, thereby keeping the sulphide ion concentration to a minimum.

64.8 The solubility product of nickel(II) sulphide is 100 times smaller than that of zinc sulphide. Therefore nickel(II) sulphide will be precipitated first. However, the values of the solubility products are not so very different and zinc sulphide would be precipitated soon after.

64.9 The statement is correct about the size of the solubility product (see Table 64.1) and about the very low solubility of the sulphide. However, it does not follow from this that the reaction between copper(II) ions and sulphide ions is very fast. We have met this point before: equilibrium constants tell us nothing about the rates of reactions. In fact the ions do react very quickly together, but you discover this from experiment, not from the size of K_{sp}.

UNIT 64 SUMMARY

- If a solid partially dissolves in water, an equilibrium is set up between the solid and the ions. The equilibrium constant for the process is the solubility product. For example,

  $AB_x(s) \rightleftharpoons A^{x+}(aq) + xB^-(aq)$

  $K_{sp} = [A^{x+}(aq)][B^-(aq)]^x$

  (concentrations measured at equilibrium).

- Precipitation of a salt will occur if its solubility product is exceeded.

65

Colligative properties

65.1 What are colligative properties?

A colligative property of a solution is one that depends on the *number of particles* dissolved in it, rather than on the type of particle. There are three colligative properties in which we shall be particularly interested. They are:

(i) *Elevation of boiling point*. For example, a solution of sugar boils at a temperature above 100° C, the normal boiling point of water.
(ii) *Depression of freezing point*. An example of this effect is the fact that salt water freezes at a lower temperature than 0° C, the normal freezing point of water.
(iii) *Osmosis*. This is the name used to explain the observation that water will spontaneously pass through a barrier, such as a cell wall, into a solution. The particles of the solute will not pass through the same barrier.

The first two are somewhat simpler to understand than the last; but strange as it may seem, each of them is linked to the way the vapour pressure of water changes when a solid is dissolved in it. Incidentally, although water is the most common solvent in the world, it is certainly not the only one. We shall use water as our main example, but other solvents behave in similar ways.

65.2 Why does a solute influence the vapour pressure of water?

When a solid dissolves in water, its ions or molecules become surrounded by water molecules: we say that the particles are hydrated. In the case of an ionic solid like sodium chloride, water molecules are attracted to the positive or negative charges on the ions. For a covalent substance like sugar, the attractions are due to the hydrogen bonds made between water and sugar molecules. Owing to the extra attraction that the water molecules feel for the dissolved particles, they find it harder to escape from a solution than from pure water. By comparing the vapour pressure of pure water with the vapour pressure of a solution of an involatile solute (Figure 65.1), we can compare the ease with which water molecules can escape into the vapour. The vapour pressure of a solution is always lower than that of pure water.

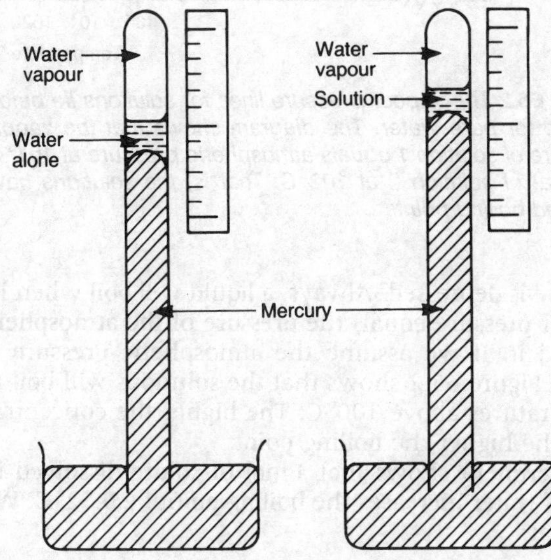

Figure 65.1 *In principle, one method for measuring vapour pressure. The mercury level is depressed less by the vapour of the solution than by water alone. That is, the vapour pressure of the solution is less than that of pure water*

65.3 Elevation of boiling point

In Unit 55, you will find the phase equilibrium diagram of water. The important part of the diagram is reproduced in Figure 65.2. The lines show the equilibrium between liquid and vapour over a range of temperatures. If we were to plot a graph of the vapour pressure of a solution, we should expect the line to lie *below* that of pure water. (At a given temperature, the vapour pressure of the solution is *less* than that of water.) The more concentrated the solution, the more

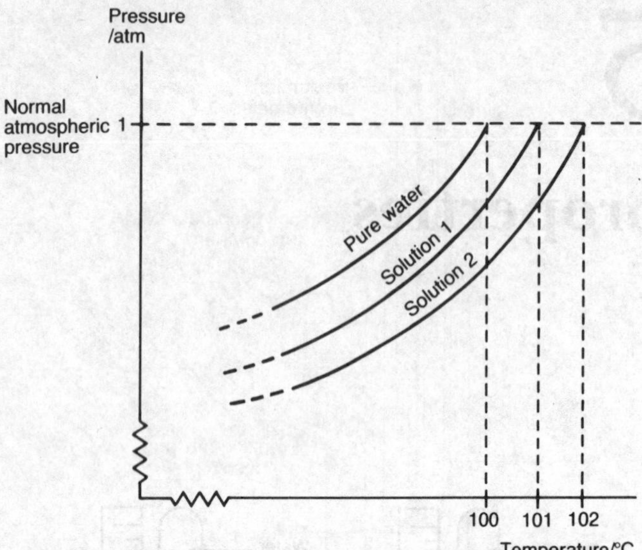

Figure 65.2 The vapour pressure lines for solutions lie below the line for pure water. The diagram shows that the vapour pressure of solution 1 equals atmospheric pressure at 101° C, and that of solution 2 at 102° C. That is, the solutions have elevated boiling points

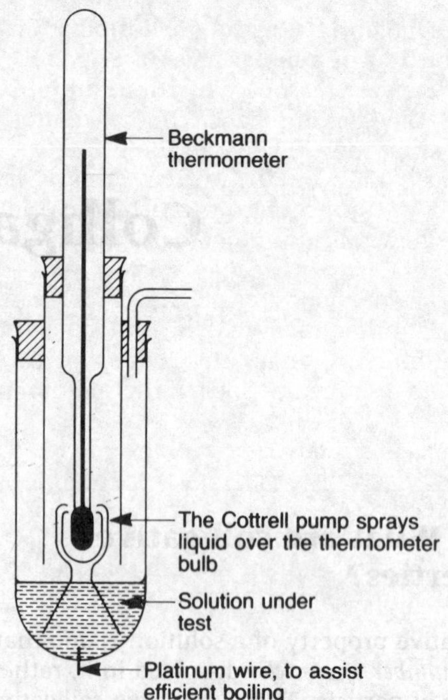

Figure 65.3 The elevation of the boiling point of a liquid can be measured using a method invented by Cottrell. To ensure that equilibrium between the solvent and vapour is achieved, the solution is sprayed over the thermometer bulb. If the bulb is placed directly in the liquid there is a danger that it does not record the temperature of the liquid in contact with vapour, only the temperature of the liquid. The thermometer is a highly accurate type invented by the German chemist Ernst Beckmann. (He did a great deal of work on the colligative properties of liquids in the late 1880s.) The pressure in the apparatus has to be carefully controlled by a system of pumps and manometers. These are not shown in the diagram

the line is depressed. Always, a liquid will boil when its vapour pressure equals the pressure of the atmosphere around it. If we assume the atmospheric pressure is 1 atm, Figure 65.2 shows that the solutions will boil at temperatures above 100° C. The higher the concentration, the higher the boiling point.

Experiment shows that 1 mol of solute dissolved in 1 kg of water increases the boiling point by 0.52° C. We say that:

The elevation of boiling point constant of water is 0.52° C kg mol^{-1}.

Thus, if we were to place 2 mol of solute into 1 kg of water we would expect the boiling point to increase by 1.04° C; 1 mol of solute in 500 g of water should also give an increase of 1.04° C. The way the boiling point of a solution is measured is explained in Figure 65.3.

Every solvent has its own particular boiling point constant – see Table 65.1.

Table 65.1. Elevation of boiling point and depression of freezing point constants

Solvent	*Elevation of boiling point constant /° C kg mol^{-1}*	*Depression of freezing point constant /° C kg mol^{-1}*
Water	0.52	1.86
Ethanol	1.15	1.93
Propanone	1.73	2.71
Benzene	2.64	5.12

65.4 How to make use of the boiling point constant

One of the reasons why the boiling point constants of water and other solvents have been investigated is that, once they are known, the information can be used to determine the molar mass of a compound. For example, if we know that 0.5 g of urea dissolved in 100 g of water increases the boiling point by 0.043° C, we can calculate the molar mass of urea. We shall call M g the mass of 1 mol of urea. It can be helpful to lay out the working like this:

0.5 g in 100 g gives an increase of 0.043° C

0.5 g in 1 kg gives an increase of $0.043° \text{C} \times 100\,\text{g}/10^3\,\text{g} = 0.0043° \text{C}$

1 g in 1 kg gives an increase of $0.0043° \text{C} \times 1\,\text{g}/0.5\,\text{g} = 0.0086° \text{C}$

M g in 1 kg gives an increase of $M \times 0.0086° \text{C}$

But with M g of urea in 1 kg of water the elevation of boiling point should be 0.52° C. Therefore, we have

$$0.0086° \text{C} \times M = 0.52° \text{C}$$

so $M = 60.5$, and the molar mass is 60.5 g mol^{-1}. This compares favourably with the formula $CO(NH_2)_2$ of urea, which gives a molar mass of 60 g mol^{-1}.

There are two reasons why the result of such a calculation may be unreliable. If the solute molecules change when they dissolve in the water, the predicted molar mass may not be correct. This is particularly important if (i) the molecules *dissociate*, e.g. into ions, or (ii) if they *associate* (join together), e.g. some molecules can dimerise (two molecules join to make one larger molecule), and oppositely charged ions can interfere with one another, often making ion-pairs. You will find more information about this in section 65.11 below. Results can also be unreliable if the solution used is not dilute.

> **65.1** You dissolve 18 g of glucose, $C_6H_{12}O_6$, in 1 kg of water in a saucepan. At what temperature will the water boil (assuming 1 atm pressure)?
>
> **65.2** Given that salt is 100% dissociated into separate ions in water, and assuming no ionic interference, how many moles of salt would be needed to give 1 kg of water the same boiling point as in question 65.1?

65.5 Depression of freezing point

Figure 65.4 shows the part of the phase equilibrium diagram of water where ice and water can exist in equilibrium. The diagram shows that the point at which ice can exist in equilibrium with water is at a lower temperature for a solution than it is for pure water. This

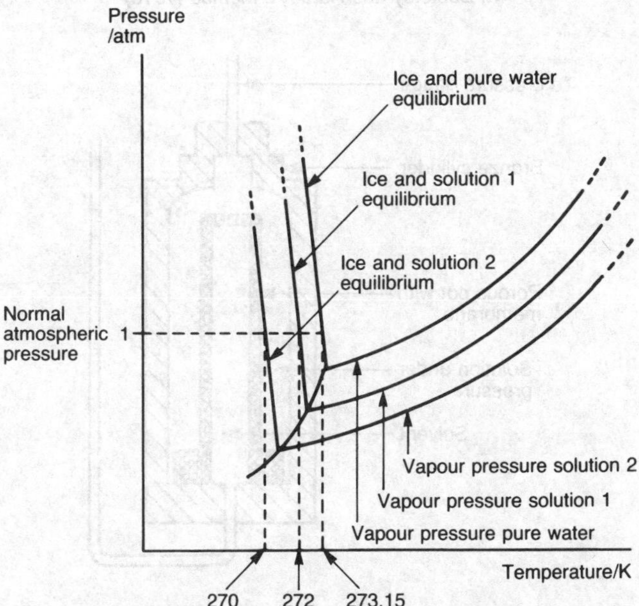

***Figure 65.4** The depression of the vapour pressure of a solution means that ice and solution come to equilibrium below the normal freezing point of water. In this diagram, for example, solution 2 freezes at 270 K, or −3° C*

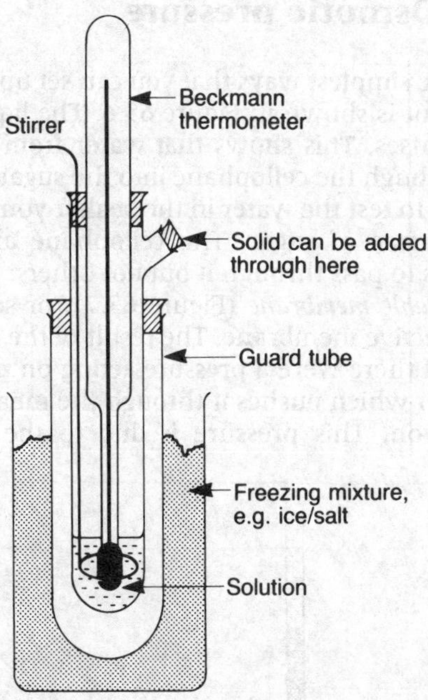

***Figure 65.5** A depression of freezing point apparatus. The guard tube keeps a layer of air between the freezing mixture and the solution in the inner tube. This helps to prevent the solution freezing too rapidly, and perhaps suffering from supercooling. (The details of the thermometer are not shown in the diagram)*

is a result of the lowering of the vapour pressure curve for a solution. Be careful that you realise that the equilibrium involves ice (pure solid water) and water, not the solute particles.

Every solvent has its own depression of freezing point constant. You will find some values in Table 65.1.

Molar masses can be calculated from freezing point measurements in much the same way as for boiling points. The method is explained in Figure 65.5. The same problems can occur if there is association or dissociation.

> **65.3** 0.64 g of an organic compound lowered the freezing point of 100 g of benzene by 0.256° C.
>
> (i) How many moles of the compound were dissolved in the benzene?
>
> (ii) What was the molar mass of the compound?
>
> (iii) Which of the following is the formula for the compound: C_6H_6, C_8H_8, C_8H_{10}, $C_{10}H_8$, $C_{10}H_{10}$? Explain why at least one of these is an impossible answer, irrespective of the molar mass.
>
> **65.4** A student decided to try to lower the freezing point of 1 kg of water to −40° C, and calculated the mass of sodium chloride he would need. His estimate was 21.5 mol of sodium chloride.
>
> (i) Was his estimate correct?
>
> (ii) Would you attempt the experiment yourself?

65.6 Osmotic pressure

One of the simplest ways that you can set up an osmosis experiment is shown in Figure 65.6. The liquid level in the tube rises. This shows that water from the beaker passes through the cellophane into the sugar solution. If you were to test the water in the beaker you would find that it is free of sugar. The cellophane allows some molecules to pass through it but not others; it is called a *semipermeable membrane* (Figure 65.7), or sometimes a perm-selective membrane. The result of the experiment looks as if there were a pressure acting on the water in the beaker which pushes it through the membrane into the solution. This pressure is due to the process of osmosis. One of the key things to remember in osmosis is that:

The *solvent* will pass through a semipermeable membrane from the less concentrated to the more concentrated solution.

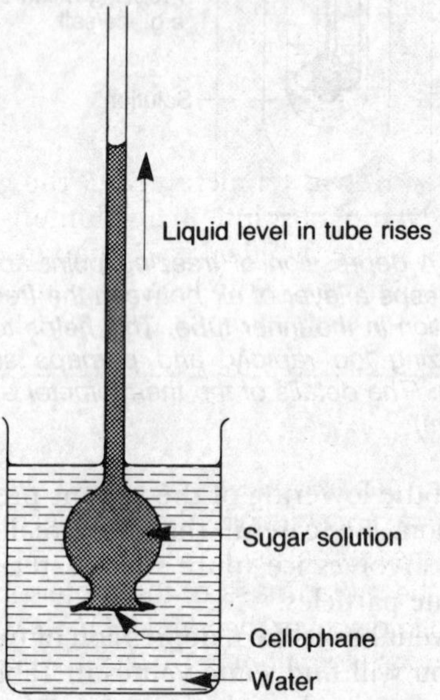

Figure 65.6 *A simple osmosis experiment. Water passes into the sugar solution, causing the liquid level in the tube to rise.*

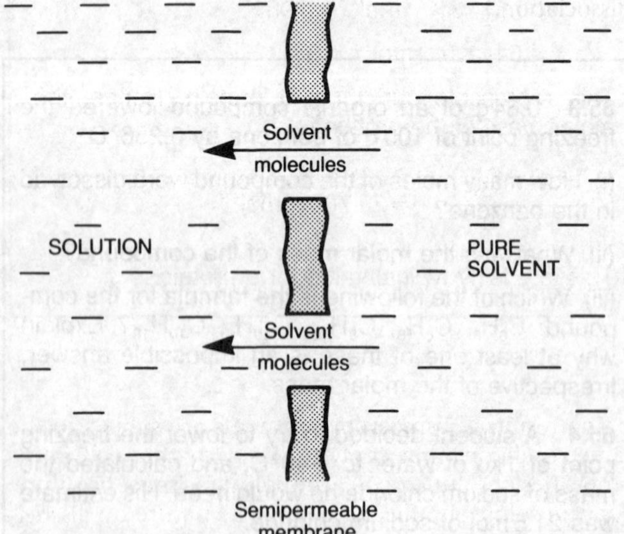

Figure 65.7 *In osmosis, solvent molecules always pass from the less concentrated to the more concentrated solution. Often the movement is from pure solvent to solution*

65.7 Methods of measuring osmotic pressure

A typical way of measuring osmotic pressure is to separate a solution from a solvent by a semipermeable membrane, and then apply a pressure to the solution. If the pressure is adjusted until it equals the osmotic pressure, osmosis will stop. This is the basis for the two types of apparatus illustrated in Figure 65.8.

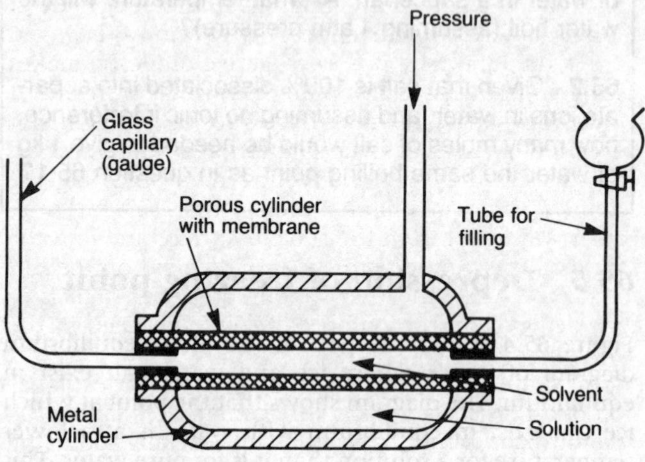

(a) Berkeley and Hartley's method (1916)

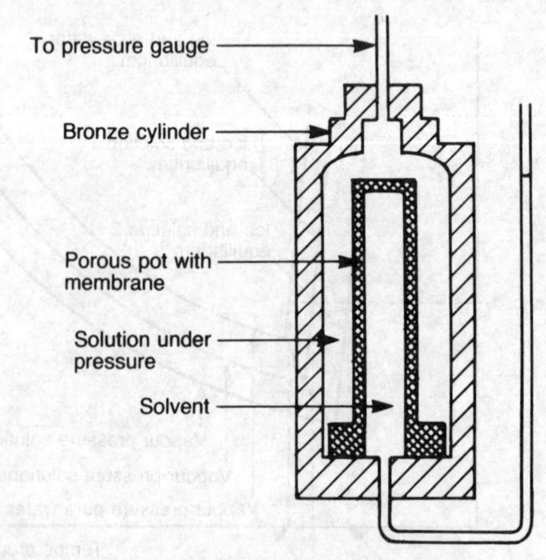

(b) Frazer and Myrick's method (1916)

Figure 65.8 *Two methods of measuring osmotic pressure. (Taken from: Caldin, E. F. (1958).* Chemical Thermodynamics, *Oxford University Press, Oxford, figures 65 and 66)*

65.8 How might we explain osmosis?

One of the first explanations of osmotic pressure was due to van't Hoff in 1886. He suggested, correctly, that solvent molecules in the solution and the pure solvent bombarded the semipermeable membrane. Likewise, he pointed out that, on average, there were more solvent molecules bombarding the membrane on the solvent side than on the solution side. According to van't Hoff we can draw the analogy with a gas and say that the solvent side has the higher 'pressure', so the solvent molecules will travel into the low pressure (solution) side. However, the theory does not work out in detail. (This is in spite of the fact that some of the equations for osmotic pressure are very similar to the gas laws.) In practice solvent molecules interact with the solute particles in a solution. This interaction makes the situation significantly different to the behaviour of gases. A different explanation of why osmosis is linked to pressure, and why it is a colligative property, makes use of our knowledge of vapour pressures (Figure 65.9).

We know that the vapour pressure of a solvent will be greater than that of a solution. The difference in vapour pressures within the narrow pores of the semipermeable membrane means that solvent molecules will travel from the solvent surface and join the solution. The osmotic pressure will depend on the difference between the two vapour pressures, which in turn depends on the number of solute particles in the solution.

You should not think that this is *the* correct explanation of osmosis. Osmosis is very complicated, and a full account of it would have to include details about the effects of the size of the solute and solvent particles, and about the nature of the membrane itself (some of them contain ions, some are covalent).

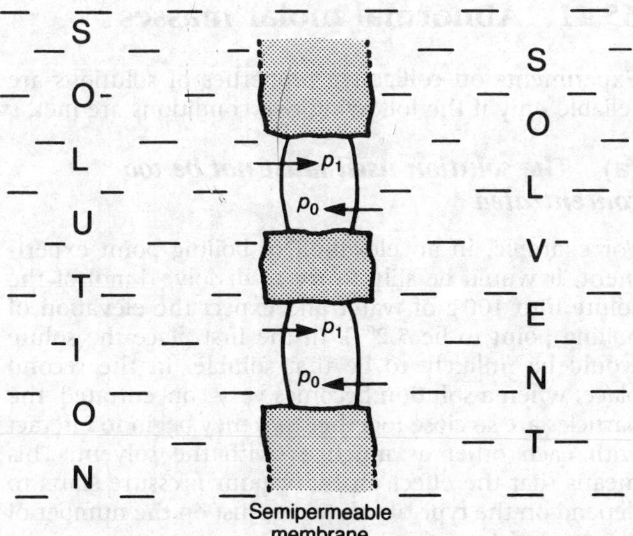

***Figure 65.9** One explanation of osmosis says there are channels through the semipermeable membrane where solvent and solution surfaces come close together. Because the vapour pressure of the solvent, p_0, is greater than that of the solution, p_1, solvent molecules transfer across the gap from the solvent to the solution*

65.9 How to calculate molar masses from osmotic pressure experiments

We have said that a simple explanation of osmosis in terms of treating the solvent and solution as if they were gases is not strictly correct. However, some analogy with a gas is possible. Especially, from thermodynamics, it is possible to prove that the osmotic pressure, Π, of a solution is given by

$$\Pi = \frac{nRT}{V}$$

where T is the Kelvin temperature, R the gas constant and there are n mol of solute in a volume V of solution. This equation is like the ideal gas equation, and we can use it in a similar way. Now look at example 1.

> *Example 1*
>
> 1.1 g of a protein were dissolved in 100 cm³ (100 × 10⁻⁶ m³) of solution. The osmotic pressure at 25°C was measured as 1.15 kPa, i.e. 1150 N m⁻². What was the molar mass of the protein?
>
> We need to discover the value of n, so we start by rearranging the equation:
>
> $$n = \frac{\Pi V}{RT}$$
>
> $$= \frac{1150\,\text{N m}^{-2} \times 100 \times 10^{-6}\,\text{m}^3}{8.314\,\text{J K}^{-1}\,\text{mol}^{-1} \times 298\,\text{K}}$$
>
> $$= 4.64 \times 10^{-5}\,\text{mol}$$
>
> This represents our 1.1 g of protein. Hence, the molar mass of the protein is
>
> $$\frac{1.1\,\text{g}}{4.64 \times 10^{-5}\,\text{mol}} = 23\,700\,\text{g mol}^{-1}$$
>
> This is a fairly typical value for a protein.

The results of osmosis experiments are subject to the same conditions that apply to the two other colligative properties of solutions, i.e. the solutions must be dilute, and the solute should not change its nature by dissociating or associating. In the case of proteins the molecules are so large and liable to interact with one another that strictly our equation $\Pi V = nRT$ is only true in the limit of infinite dilution.

65.5 Haemoglobin is the chemical in blood that is responsible for transporting oxygen from the lungs around the body. A solution containing 1 g of haemoglobin in 100 cm^3 of water had an osmotic pressure of 364 N m^{-2} at 298 K. Estimate the molar mass of haemoglobin.

65.6 If two solutions separated by a perfect semipermeable membrane have the same osmotic pressure, they are said to be *isotonic*. A solution of sugar was isotonic with a solution of an ionic substance, AB. Both solutions had the same volume, and were at the same temperature. If the sugar solution contained 0.2 mol of sugar, estimate the number of moles of AB in the other solution.

65.10 Some examples of osmosis

Perhaps the most important semipermeable membranes are found in living systems. Cell membranes act as semipermeable membranes. For example, if a cell is placed in pure water it will swell. The cytoplasm inside the cell contains dissolved ions and some of the water outside the cell passes through the membrane owing to osmosis. On the other hand, if a cell is placed in a concentrated solution of salt, the cell shrivels. This time the water passes out of the cell into the more concentrated solution around it. Camels have blood cells that are considerably more elastic than those of humans. When a camel takes in a large quantity of water, its blood cells swell owing to water molecules passing into the cells. After many days without water, the cells shrink as water passes out of the cells into the blood stream. Human cells are unable to withstand such changes: hence humans rather than camels are more likely to die as a result of severe drought.

Osmosis has been of great use in *determining molar masses*, especially those of polymers. Even small amounts of a solute can give rise to large osmotic pressures. Small quantities of a polymer, which might have a molar mass of around 100 000 g mol^{-1}, can be dissolved in an organic solvent and give a measurable osmotic pressure. If the same quantity were used in an elevation of boiling point experiment, the rise in temperature could be almost insignificant.

One application of osmosis that has become increasingly important is better known as *reverse osmosis* (Figure 65.10). It is used for water purification. We know that pure water will pass through a semipermeable membrane into a solution. If we apply a pressure equal to the osmotic pressure, we can stop osmosis taking place. However, if we apply a pressure greater than the osmotic pressure, then we will force water *from the solution* to pass into the pure water on the other side of the membrane. Dissolved ions and molecules will remain on the solution side. In this way we have separated pure water from the solution.

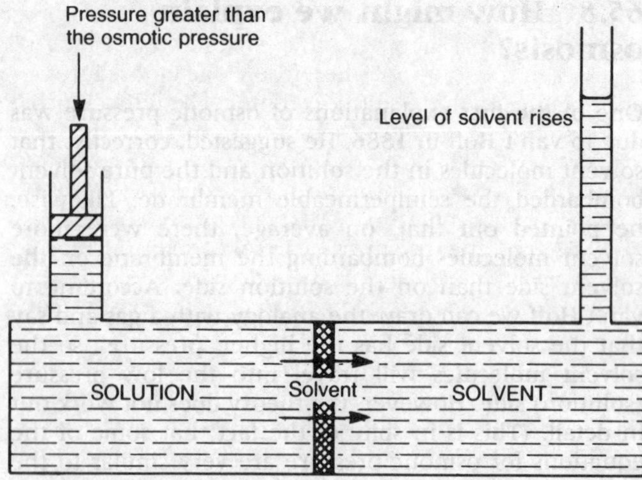

Figure 65.10 *In a reverse osmosis experiment, solvent can be made to move from the solution to the solvent. A pressure greater than the osmotic pressure must be applied to the solution*

Reverse osmosis plants have been set up in parts of the world to separate pure water from sea water. Their effectiveness is also being investigated as a method of purifying water where supplies are contaminated by nitrate, and other varieties of pollution.

65.7 If you were a pathologist faced with the body of a person who died by drowning, how could you tell if the person drowned in sea or fresh water?

65.11 Abnormal molar masses

Experiments on colligative properties of solutions are reliable only if the following two conditions are met.

(a) *The solution used must not be too concentrated*

For example, in an elevation of boiling point experiment, it would be silly to try to dissolve 1 mol of the solute into 100 g of water and expect the elevation of boiling point to be 5.2° C. In the first place the solute would be unlikely to be that soluble. In the second place, when a solution becomes very concentrated, the particles are so close together that they begin to interact with each other as much as with the solvent. This means that the effect on the vapour pressure starts to depend on the type of solute, not just on the number of solute particles.

(b) *The solute must not dissociate or associate*

Ionic compounds that dissolve in water liberate their ions into the solution. For example, if 1 mol of sodium choride, 58.5 g, is dissolved in water, we might expect

1 mol of sodium ions and 1 mol of chloride ions to be released. If this happens there would be 2 mol of particles in the solution. Therefore, if we ignore interactions between ions in solution, 1 mol of sodium chloride in 1 kg of water would be expected to increase the boiling point by $2\times0.52°$ C, or 1.04° C. If we did not know about the dissociation into ions, we would be led to the conclusion that the 2 mol of particles present had a mass of 58.5 g, and that the mass of 1 mol of sodium chloride was 29.25 g. This illustrates the rule that, when there is dissociation into ions, the measured molar mass is *lower* than the true value.

Other substances may not be as extreme as an ionic compound, but may still dissociate slightly into ions. A typical example is a weak acid like ethanoic acid (Figure 65.11), which, in water, takes part in the equilibrium

$$CH_3COOH(aq) \rightleftharpoons CH_3COO^-(aq) + H^+(aq)$$

Often less than 10% of the molecules dissociate into ions, so the measured molar mass is only a little less than the true value.

In an organic solvent like benzene, molecules of ethanoic acid can *dimerise* owing to hydrogen bonding. In this case the number of particles is less than expected if there were no dimerisation. In this case the measured molar mass is *more* than the true value.

To summarise, both dissociation and association give rise to abnormal molar masses.

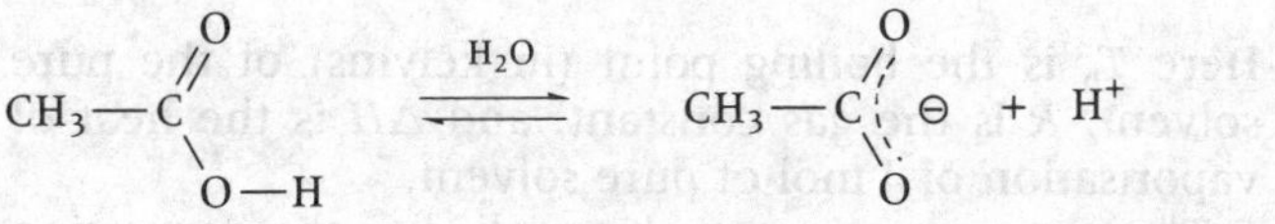

In water, ethanoic acid partially dissociates into ions

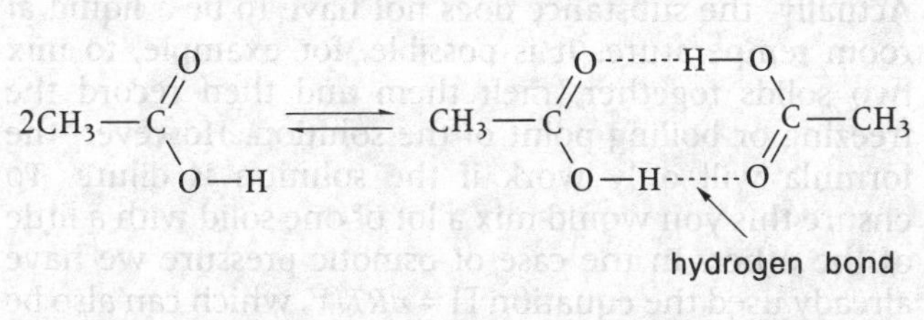

In some solvents, e.g. benzene, ethanoic acid dimerises

***Figure 65.11** Experiments to determine the molar mass of ethanoic acid often lead to abnormal values*

65.12 Calculating the degree of dissociation from abnormal molar masses

Let us imagine a substance that dissociates in solution. We shall call the substance AB and assume that it changes into separate parts, A and B. (A and B might, for example, be positive and negative ions.) If we start with 1 mol, and a fraction x mol dissociates, the total number of moles of particles at equilibrium is $1+x$:

$$AB \rightleftharpoons A + B$$

number of moles $1-x \quad x \quad x \quad$ total $1+x$

The extra number of particles will increase the change in temperature or the osmotic pressure; but this will *decrease* the value of the molar mass.

To see why this is so, let us take an extreme case where the dissociation is complete. If so, $x=1$ and $1+x=2$. Suppose we placed 100 g of a substance into 1 kg of water and measured the elevation of boiling point as 1.04° C. Because the elevation of boiling point constant is 0.52° C kg mol^{-1}, we would say that there were 2 mol of the substance present. Thus we would predict the molar mass to be 100 g/2 mol = 50 g mol^{-1}. This is half the real molar mass.

It is a general rule that:

Dissociation leads to low values for molar masses.

The general rule is that

real molar mass = $(1+x)\times$ measured molar mass

We shall now work through two examples.

Example 2

The osmotic pressure of a solution of potassium chloride containing 0.75 g in 100 cm³ of water was 4.52×10^5 N m^{-2} (452 kPa) at 25°C. What is the predicted molar mass of potassium chloride?

Using the formula

$$n=\frac{\Pi V}{RT}$$

we have

$$n=\frac{4.52\times10^5\,\text{N m}^{-2}\times100\times10^{-6}\,\text{m}^3}{8.314\,\text{J K}^{-1}\,\text{mol}^{-1}\times298\,\text{K}}$$

$$=0.018\,\text{mol}$$

This suggests that 0.75 g of potassium chloride is 0.018 mol, so the mass of 1 mol appears to be 41.7 g. The actual mass of 1 mol of potassium chloride, KCl, is 39 g + 35.5 g = 74.5 g. Using our formula,

$$74.5\,\text{g}=(1+x)\times41.7\,\text{g}$$

$$(1+x)=\frac{74.5\,\text{g}}{41.7\,\text{g}}$$

which gives $x=0.79$.

The fraction x is often expressed as a percentage and is known as the *degree of dissociation*. In this case the degree of dissociation of the potassium chloride is 79% To be more exact, we should call this an *apparent* degree of dissociation. We have ignored ionic interference, especially the presence of ion-pairs.

Example 3

6 g of ethanoic acid was placed in 100 g of benzene. The freezing point depression of the solution was measured as 3.4°C. What is the apparent molar mass of ethanoic acid?

We have,

6 g of acid in 100 g of benzene gives a depression of 3.4°C

6 g of acid in 1 kg of benzene gives a depression of 0.34°C

But we know that 1 mol of substance should depress the freezing point of 1 kg of benzene by 5.12°C. Therefore, we would need 6 g × 5.12°C/0.34°C = 90.4 g of acid to give a depression of 5.12°C. This is the apparent molar mass of ethanoic acid in benzene. It is greater than the real molar mass of the acid, which is 60 g mol^{-1}. The reason is that the acid molecules dimerise in benzene. We have

	CH_3COOH ⇌	$\frac{1}{2}(CH_3COOH)_2$	
number of moles	$1-x$	$x/2$	total $1-x/2$

In this case,

real molar mass = $(1-x/2)$ × measured molar mass

So

$60\ \text{g} = (1-x/2) \times 90.4\ \text{g}$
$(1-x/2) = 0.66$

which gives $x = 0.68$. So 68% of the acid has dimerised.

65.8 Naphthalene is a white organic solid at room temperature. It melts at 80.1°C. Its depression of freezing point constant is 6.5°C kg mol^{-1}. 100 g of naphthalene was melted and 3.94 g of sulphur stirred into it. The sulphur dissolved in the naphthalene. The solution froze at 80.0°C.

(i) What was the depression of freezing point?

(ii) How many grams of sulphur would have depressed the freezing point of 1 kg by this amount?

(iii) What mass of sulphur would have depressed the freezing point of 1 kg by 6.5°C?

(iv) What is the predicted molar mass of sulphur?

(v) Given that $M(S) = 32$ g mol^{-1}, what does this tell you about the sulphur atoms in liquid naphthalene?

65.9 If 1 g of the protein of example 1 in section 65.9, which had a molar mass of 23 700 g mol^{-1}, was dissolved in 100 g of water, what would be the depression of freezing point of the water? Why do people use osmotic pressure measurements for such molecules?

65.10 A solution containing 5.85 g of sodium chloride in 100 g of water had an osmotic pressure of 4.46×10^5 N m^{-2} at 298 K. What is the apparent degree of dissociation of the sodium chloride?

65.13 The thermodynamic explanation of colligative properties

Each of the three colligative properties that we have met is concerned with an equilibrium of one kind or another. In Unit 51 we discovered that a condition for equilibrium in a reaction is that the free energy of the products equals the free energy of the reactants. In symbols, we said that $\Delta G = 0$. A similar relationship holds here, as set out in Table 65.2.

Using the first of these conditions, and more advanced thermodynamics than we can consider here, it is possible to derive an equation for the elevation of boiling point constant, C. The result is

$$C = \frac{RT_b^2}{1000\ \Delta H}$$

Here T_b is the boiling point (in kelvins) of the pure solvent, R is the gas constant, and ΔH is the heat of vaporisation of 1 mol of pure solvent.

The same equation can be applied to the depression of freezing point constant; but this time we should write T_f (the freezing point of pure solvent) instead of T_b, and ΔH becomes the heat of fusion of the pure solvent. Actually, the substance does not have to be a liquid at room temperature. It is possible, for example, to mix two solids together, melt them and then record the freezing or boiling point of the solution. However, the formula will only work if the solution is dilute. To ensure this you would mix a lot of one solid with a little of the other. In the case of osmotic pressure we have already used the equation $\Pi = nRT/V$, which can also be derived from thermodynamics.

Table 65.2. Conditions for equilibrium in colligative properties of solution

Colligative property	*Condition for equilibrium*
Elevation of boiling point	Free energy of pure solvent vapour equals free energy of solvent in solution
Depression of freezing point	Free energy of solvent in solution equals free energy of solid solvent
Osmotic pressure	Free energy of pure solvent equals free energy of solvent in solution

65.14 Raoult's law and solids in solution

The French chemist Francois-Marie Raoult was one of the first to investigate the influence that a solute had on the vapour pressure of a solution. In 1886 he made a discovery that is now known as *Raoult's law*, and which we first met in Unit 61 when discussing mixtures of liquids. In words the law says:

The vapour pressure of a solvent in a solution is equal to the vapour pressure of the pure solvent multiplied by its mole fraction in the solution.

Let us take a solution containing a solvent that we shall label A. We shall write the vapour pressure of *pure* A as p°_A, and of A in the solution as p_A; we shall call its mole fraction N_A. In symbols, Raoult's law is

$$p_A = N_A \times p^\circ_A \quad \text{Raoult's law}$$

For example, at 25° C, the vapour pressure of water, p°_A, is 2261 N m^{-2} (17 mmHg). If we took 1 mol of water (18 cm^3) and dissolved 0.1 mol of sugar in it, the mole fraction of water is

$$N_A = \frac{1\ \text{mol}}{1\ \text{mol} + 0.1\ \text{mol}} = 0.91$$

and

$$p_A = 2261\ \text{N m}^{-2} \times 0.91 = 2058\ \text{N m}^{-2}$$

This tells us that the vapour pressure of water above the sugar solution is lowered by about 10%. Notice that Raoult's law says nothing about the chemical nature of the solute. It is a law that concerns the number of particles of the solute present, not their nature. However, when he first performed his investigations, it was a puzzle to him why some substances gave depressions of vapour pressure that were greater than expected from his formula. Often these were solutions of salts.

65.11 Sodium metal will dissolve in methylbenzene, C_7H_8. The vapour pressure of pure methylbenzene is 2926 N m^{-2} at 25° C. If 1 g of sodium was dissolved in 46 g of the liquid, what would be the new vapour pressure?

65.12 Why do solutions of salts not obey Raoult's law?

Answers

65.1 18 g of glucose represents 0.1 mol. Therefore the boiling point will be raised by 0.1 × 0.52° C = 0.052° C. The new boiling point will be 100.052° C.

65.2 With the salt 100% dissociated, there would be twice as many moles of particles as in the glucose solution. We would need only half the number of moles of salt, i.e. 0.05 mol.

65.3 (i) 1 mol of compound would lower the freezing point of 1 kg of benzene by 5.12° C. The same effect would be given by 0.1 mol in 100 g of benzene. Thus, 0.01 mol would give a depression of 0.512° C, and 0.005 mol a depression of 0.256° C. Hence 0.64 g represents 0.005 mol.

(ii) The molar mass is 0.64 g/0.005 mol = 128 g mol^{-1}.

(iii) The formula is $C_{10}H_8$ (naphthalene). The first, C_6H_6, is the formula of benzene itself. Clearly this cannot depress its own freezing point. Also, the others are liquids at room temperature, so they are volatile solutes. Our work on colligative properties assumes that the solutes are *involatile*.

65.4 (i) 21.5 mol of solute in 1 kg of water should depress the freezing point by 21.5 mol kg^{-1} × 1.86° C kg mol^{-1} = 40° C. It seems that he is correct, but he has forgotten that sodium chloride is ionic and dissociates into free ions in solution. If we assume 100% dissociation, he would only need 10.75 mol of the salt.

(ii) It would be a waste of time: the solubility of salt in water is only about 5 mol kg^{-1}.

65.5 Using the equation $\Pi V = nRT$, or $n = \Pi V/RT$, we have

$$n = \frac{364\ \text{N m}^{-2} \times 100 \times 10^{-6}\ \text{m}^3}{8.314\ \text{J K}^{-1}\ \text{mol}^{-1} \times 298\ \text{K}} = 14.7 \times 10^{-6}\ \text{mol}$$

Thus, 1 g is 14.7 × 10^{-6} mol of haemoglobin, which tells us that the molar mass of haemoglobin is 1 g/(14.7 × 10^{-6} mol), i.e. around 68 000 g mol^{-1}. The reason for this high value is that haemoglobin is a protein.

65.6 With the ionic compound dissociated fully into A^+ and B^- ions, we would obtain two moles of particles from one mole of AB. Therefore we would only need 0.1 mol of AB for the solution to be isotonic with the sugar solution.

65.7 One method would be to look at the size of some of the cells in the body. If the person died in fresh water, owing to the passage of water into them, the cells should have swollen compared to normal.

65.8 (i) The depression was 0.1° C.

(ii) You would need 10 times as much in 1 kg as in 100 g, i.e. 39.4 g.

(iii) To increase the depression from 0.1° C to 6.5° C would require 39.4 g × 6.5 = 256.1 g.

(iv) The predicted molar mass is 256.1 g mol^{-1}.

(v) This corresponds to S_8. Indeed, sulphur is often to be found as rings of eight sulphur atoms (see Unit 100).

Answers – contd.

65.9 1 mol of solute would depress the freezing point of 100 g of water by 0.186°C. 1 g of protein represents about 4×10^{-5} mol. This would give a depression of around 8×10^{-6} °C. This is such a small depression that it would be extremely difficult to measure with sufficient accuracy. Osmotic pressures are easier to measure accurately.

65.10 Using the formula $n=\Pi V/RT$, we have that the number of moles n is

$$n=\frac{4.46\times10^{5}\,\text{N m}^{-2}\times100\times10^{-6}\,\text{m}^{3}}{8.314\,\text{J K}^{-1}\,\text{mol}^{-1}\times298\,\text{K}}=0.18\,\text{mol}$$

Therefore, the molar mass appears to be $5.85\,\text{g}/0.18\,\text{mol}=32.5\,\text{g mol}^{-1}$.

The true molar mass of sodium chloride is 58.5 g mol^{-1}. If we call the apparent degree of dissociation x, we have

$$58.5\,\text{g mol}^{-1}=(1+x)\times32.5\,\text{g mol}^{-1}$$

which gives $x=0.8$, or 80%.

65.11 1 mol of methylbenzene has a mass of 92 g. Thus 46 g represents 0.5 mol. Also, 1 g of sodium represents $1\,\text{g}/23\,\text{g mol}^{-1}=0.043$ mol. We have,

$$\text{mole fraction of methylbenzene}=\frac{0.5\,\text{mol}}{0.5\,\text{mol}+0.043\,\text{mol}}=0.92$$

So

$$\text{vapour pressure above solution}=0.92\times2926\,\text{N m}^{-2}=2694\,\text{N m}^{-2}$$

65.12 Salts are often fully dissociated into ions. For example, 1 mol of potassium chloride dissolved in water would give 2 mol of particles (1 mol of K^+ ions and 1 mol of Cl^- ions). As we found in the other colligative properties, abnormal results are obtained when there is dissociation or association of the particles.

UNIT 65 SUMMARY

- A colligative property of a solution is one that depends on the number, rather than on the types, of particles dissolved in it.
- Elevation of boiling point:
  Each solvent has its own elevation of boiling point constant; e.g. 1 mol of solute dissolved in 1 kg of water increases the boiling point by 0.52°C.
- Depression of freezing point:
  Each solvent has its own depression of freezing point constant; e.g. 1 mol of solute dissolved in 1 kg of benzene will depress the freezing point by 5.12°C.
- Osmosis:
  Osmosis is the process where a solvent passes through a semipermeable membrane from a less concentrated to a more concentrated solution. The pressure needed just to stop the flow of solvent is the osmotic pressure.
- Osmotic pressure Π can be calculated from the formula $\Pi=nRT/V$, where T is the Kelvin temperature, R is the gas constant and n mol of solute are in a volume V of solution.
- All three colligative properties can be used to determine molar masses. Osmotic pressure is best for determining very high molar masses, e.g. those of polymers.
- Abnormal molar masses are obtained if there is association or dissociation of the solute, e.g. ethanoic acid dimers in an organic solvent.

66

Electrochemical cells

66.1 How an equilibrium is set up between a metal and solution

If you were to place a zinc rod into a solution containing zinc ions, an equilibrium would be set up between them. There is a tendency for zinc atoms on the surface of the rod to be attracted into the solution. However, they do not enter the solution as atoms, but as zinc ions, Zn^{2+}. In this guise they can be solvated by water molecules. The electrons left behind when a zinc atom is transformed into a positive ion remain on the rod. As a result the region of solution very close to the rod suffers an increase in positive charge (owing to the extra Zn^{2+} ions), while the rod carries a layer of negative charge (the electrons left behind) – see Figure 66.1.

Other metals dipping into solutions of their ions undergo a similar but opposite change. For them, some of the ions in the solution cling on to the metal and

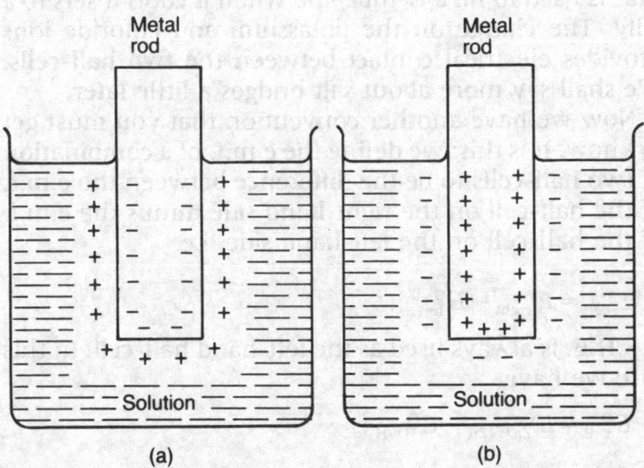

Figure 66.1 *The origin of Helmholtz double layers around a metal rod dipping into a solution. (a) For this metal, the equilibrium $M^{n+}(aq) + ne^- \rightleftharpoons M(s)$ lies to the left. Some of the metal atoms go into solution as positive ions. Electrons remain on the rod. (b) For this metal the equilibrium $M^{n+}(aq) + ne^- \rightleftharpoons M(s)$ lies to the right. Positive ions leave the solution, thus giving the surrounding solution an overall negative charge*

attract electrons out of the rod. This leaves the rod with a positive charge. Because the solution near to the rod loses positive ions, it becomes slightly negatively charged.

An electric double layer is set up. This layer is known as the Helmholtz double layer.

If we call the metal M and we assume that it makes a positively charged ion M^{n+}, the same equilibrium is involved in both cases:

$$M^{n+}(aq) + ne^- \rightleftharpoons M(s)$$

The difference is that for some metals the equilibrium lies to the left (these give extra positive ions into the solution), while for others it lies to the right (these take positive ions out of the solution).

From now on we shall call the metal rods *electrodes*. Whenever there is a separation of positive and negative charges, we should be able to measure a voltage. In this case there should be a voltage between the electrode and the surrounding solution. At first sight it might seem an easy thing to measure this voltage. All we need is a voltmeter and two pieces of wire. One piece we connect to the electrode, the other we dip into the solution. Unfortunately this idea has a flaw in it. As soon as we dip the metal wire into the solution, another equilibrium is set up. This time it is between the metal from which the wire is made and the ions it gives in solution. We have introduced another Helmholtz double layer. The best we can do now is to measure the difference in voltage between the two double layers. This is an unavoidable state of affairs; we cannot directly measure the voltage between the Helmholtz double layer.

This is unfortunate because if we could measure the voltage it would tell us something about how good a metal is at releasing electrons. Metals that release electrons easily are good reducing agents, so by comparing the voltage for each metal we would be able to put them in order of their reducing power.

Given that we are bound to measure a voltage between *two* double layers, the most convenient thing to do is to agree to keep one of them constant and always measure the difference between this one and the others. The system that has been chosen as a standard is the *standard hydrogen electrode*. We shall refer to this as the S.H.E.

66.2 The standard hydrogen electrode

The S.H.E. consists of hydrogen gas bubbling over a platinum electrode immersed in a solution of hydrochloric acid (Figure 66.2). At standard conditions, the hydrogen must be at a pressure of 1 atm (101.325 kPa) and the acid must be 1 mol dm^{-3} in concentration. (Strictly, the acid should be at unit activity, which is approximately 1.18 mol dm^{-3}, but we can ignore the difference.) The temperature should be 25° C (298 K). The platinum electrode is usually coated with finely divided platinum called platinum black. This acts as a catalyst to allow equilibrium between the gas and the solution to be established quickly.

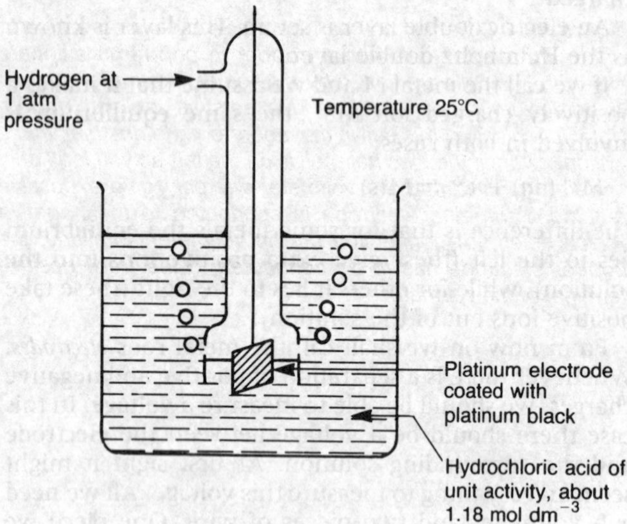

***Figure 66.2** A standard hydrogen electrode (S.H.E.)*

The reaction that takes place in the S.H.E. is

$$2H^+(aq) + 2e^- \rightleftharpoons H_2(g)$$

Under standard conditions the electromotive force, e.m.f., of the S.H.E. is *defined* to be exactly zero volts. A standard e.m.f. is given the symbol $E^\ominus$, so we have

$$E^\ominus_{S.H.E.} = 0.000\ V$$

The more systematic way of writing this is to put

$$E^\ominus_{H^+/H_2} = 0.000\ V$$

66.3 Standard electrode potentials

Having established our standard, we can connect metal electrodes to the S.H.E. and measure the voltage between the two. Figure 66.3 shows an arrangement using a zinc electrode.

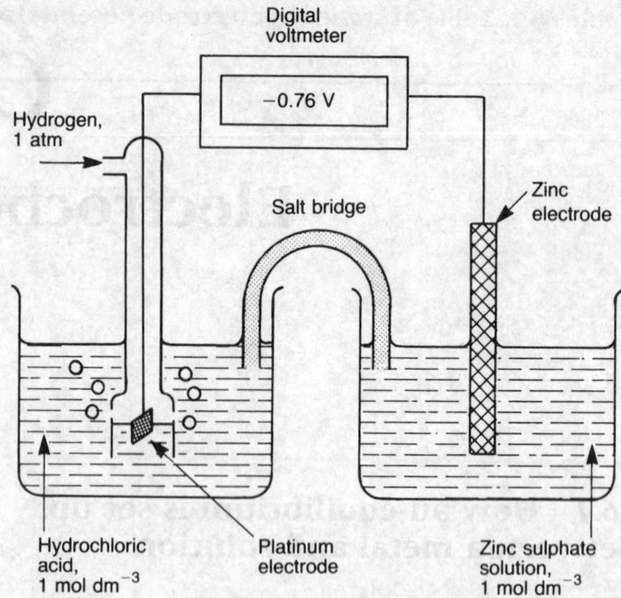

***Figure 66.3** An apparatus to measure the standard electrode potential of zinc. For accurate work the solution should have an activity of 1, rather than a concentration of 1 mol dm^{-3}. The temperature should be 25° C. It is not essential to use a digital voltmeter, but the meter must have a very high resistance*

At standard conditions the zinc should be dipping into a 1 mol dm^{-3} solution of the zinc ions. (Strictly the solution should have an *activity* of 1. Using activities makes an allowance for the way ions influence each other in solution.) The entire arrangement makes up an electrochemical cell, with the S.H.E. making one *half-cell*, and the zinc in a solution of zinc ions the other half-cell. The two half-cells are connected by a *salt bridge*. A typical salt bridge is made by dissolving an ionic substance such as potassium chloride in agar. The warm agar is used to fill a U-tube and when it cools it sets to a jelly. The charge on the potassium and chloride ions provides electrical contact between the two half-cells. We shall say more about salt bridges a little later.

Now we have another convention that you must get to know. It is this: we define the e.m.f. of a combination of two half-cells to be the difference between the e.m.f. of the half-cell on the right-hand side minus the e.m.f. of the half-cell on the left-hand side, i.e.

$$E^\ominus_{cell} = E^\ominus_{right} - E^\ominus_{left}$$

A S.H.E. is always used as the left-hand half-cell. In this case we have

$$E^\ominus_{cell} = E^\ominus_{Zn^{2+}/Zn} - E^\ominus_{H^+/H_2}$$

so

$$E^\ominus_{cell} = E^\ominus_{Zn^{2+}/Zn}$$

because $E^\ominus_{H^+/H_2} = 0\ V$ by definition.

If you were to perform this experiment you would discover that the voltmeter would only give a reading if its negative terminal (the black coloured one) was connected to the zinc. This means that the zinc is *negative*

Table 66.1. Table of standard electrode potentials at 25° C

Reaction	$E^\ominus$/V	
$Li^+(aq)+e^- \rightleftharpoons Li(s)$	−3.03	↑ Strongest reducing agents
$K^+(aq)+e^- \rightleftharpoons K(s)$	−2.92	
$Ca^{2+}(aq)+2e^- \rightleftharpoons Ca(s)$	−2.87	
$Na^+(aq)+e^- \rightleftharpoons Na(s)$	−2.71	
$Mg^{2+}(aq)+2e^- \rightleftharpoons Mg(s)$	−2.37	
$Al^{3+}(aq)+3e^- \rightleftharpoons Al(s)$	−1.66	
$Zn^{2+}(aq)+2e^- \rightleftharpoons Zn(s)$	−0.76	
$Pb^{2+}(aq)+2e^- \rightleftharpoons Pb(s)$	−0.13	
$2H^+(aq)+2e^- \rightleftharpoons H_2(g)$	0.00	
$Cu^{2+}(aq)+2e^- \rightleftharpoons Cu(s)$	+0.34	
$Ag^+(aq)+e^- \rightleftharpoons Ag(s)$	+0.80	↓ Weakest reducing agents

compared to the S.H.E. Indeed, you should find that $E^\ominus_{Zn^{2+}/Zn} = -0.76$ V. This figure is known as the *standard electrode potential* of zinc.

The standard electrode potential of many other half-cells can be measured in a similar way. A cell is made up with the metal dipping into a 1 mol dm^{-3} solution of its ions and connected to a S.H.E. Table 66.1 provides some results.

The more negative the value of the standard electrode potential, the greater is the tendency for a metal to give up its electrons, and the stronger is its reducing power. Conversely, the more positive the value of $E^\ominus$, the greater is the oxidising power.

66.4 Combining half-cells

We can make a Daniell cell by combining zinc and copper half-cells (Figure 66.4). The half-cell with the most negative electrode potential should always be shown as the left-hand half-cell. This is why we have the cell with the zinc half-cell on the left-hand side, and the copper on the right. Therefore,

$$\begin{aligned} E^\ominus_{cell} &= E^\ominus_{right} - E^\ominus_{left} \\ &= E^\ominus_{Cu^{2+}/Cu} - E^\ominus_{Zn^{2+}/Zn} \\ &= +0.34\text{ V} - (-0.76\text{ V}) \\ &= +1.1\text{ V} \end{aligned}$$

As another example we could choose to combine copper and silver half-cells (Figure 66.5). They both have positive standard electrode potentials, but the silver one is more positive than the copper. Alternatively we can say that the copper electrode is more negative than the silver. Therefore, we should show the copper half-cell as the left-hand half-cell. We have

$$\begin{aligned} E^\ominus_{cell} &= E^\ominus_{right} - E^\ominus_{left} \\ &= E^\ominus_{Ag^+/Ag} - E^\ominus_{Cu^{2+}/Cu} \\ &= +0.80\text{ V} - 0.34\text{ V} \\ &= +0.46\text{ V} \end{aligned}$$

The main conventions that you need when working with electrochemical cells are shown in Table 66.2.

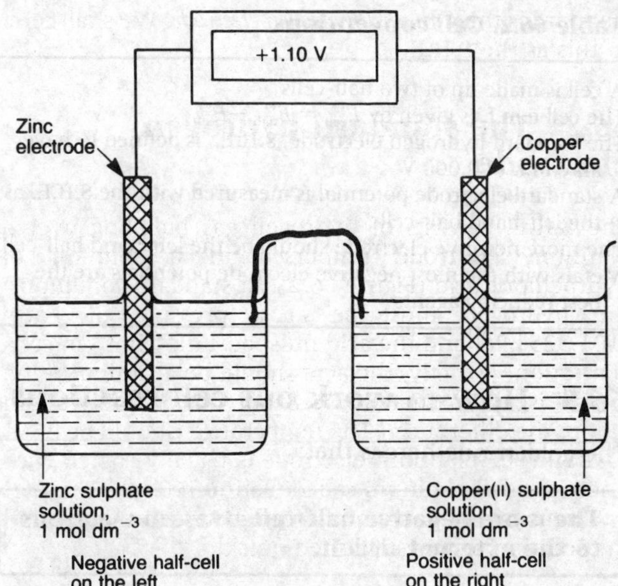

***Figure 66.4** A Daniell cell can be made by joining a zinc in zinc sulphate half-cell with a copper in copper(II) sulphate half-cell. The cells are linked by a piece of filter paper soaked in potassium nitrate solution. This acts as the salt bridge. Note: If you set up this cell in the laboratory, do not think that it will only work if the zinc half-cell is on the left as you look at it! The key thing is that the voltmeter will only give a positive reading if the zinc electrode is connected to the negative (black coloured) connection on the voltmeter. Similarly, the copper electrode has to be connected to the (red) positive terminal of the voltmeter*

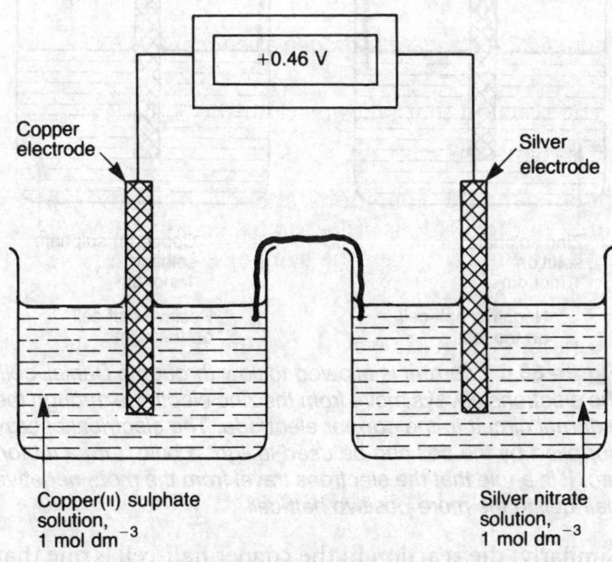

***Figure 66.5** A cell made from copper in copper(II) sulphate and silver in silver nitrate half-cells. Again, we have shown the more negative half-cell on the left of the diagram*

Table 66.2. Cell conventions

A cell is made up of two half-cells
The cell e.m.f. is given by $E^{\ominus}_{cell} = E^{\ominus}_{right} - E^{\ominus}_{left}$
The standard hydrogen electrode, S.H.E., is defined to have an e.m.f. of 0.000 V
A standard electrode potential is measured with the S.H.E. as the left-hand half-cell
The more negative electrode should be the left-hand half-cell
Metals with the most negative electrode potentials are the best reducing agents

66.5 How to work out cell reactions

The golden rule here is that:

The more negative half-cell gives up electrons to the external circuit.

For example, in the Daniell cell, the zinc is the negative electrode, and electrons travel from the zinc through the wire to the positive copper electrode (Figure 66.6). This means that the reaction in the zinc half-cell must be

$$Zn(s) \rightarrow Zn^{2+}(aq) + 2e^-$$

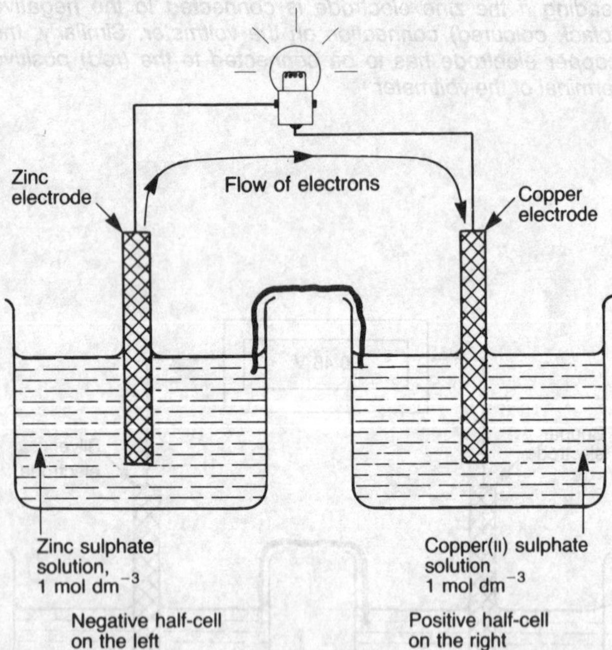

***Figure 66.6** If current is allowed to flow through a Daniell cell, the electrons always move from the zinc electrode through the external circuit to the copper electrode. The electrical energy supplied by the cell can be used to light a bulb, turn a motor, etc. It is a rule that the electrons travel from the more negative half-cell to the more positive half-cell*

Similarly, the reaction in the copper half-cell is one that absorbs the electrons travelling round the circuit. We have

$$Cu^{2+}(aq) + 2e^- \rightarrow Cu(s)$$

The overall equation for the reaction is the sum of these two equations, i.e.

$$Zn(s) + Cu^{2+}(aq) \rightarrow Zn^{2+}(aq) + Cu(s)$$

The way we have written this reaction tells us the *direction* in which the reaction proceeds if we allow electricity to flow through the circuit. As we know, all good things must come to an end, and eventually the voltage of the cell falls to zero. When this happens the reaction has come to a true equilibrium, and for this reason we might write the reaction taking place as an equilibrium reaction like this:

$$Zn(s) + Cu^{2+}(aq) \rightleftharpoons Zn^{2+}(aq) + Cu(s)$$

Let us use the silver and copper half-cell reactions as our second example. Here the copper half-cell is the more negative, so this is the one that gives up electrons to the external circuit. The reaction taking place in this half-cell is

$$Cu(s) \rightarrow Cu^{2+}(aq) + 2e^-$$

In the silver half-cell,

$$Ag^+(aq) + e^- \rightarrow Ag(s)$$

In order to balance the cell reaction we need 2 mol of silver ions to take up the 2 mol of electrons provided by the copper. For this reason the cell reaction is

$$Cu(s) + 2Ag^+(aq) \rightarrow Cu^{2+}(aq) + 2Ag(s)$$

Again, this tells us the direction in which the reaction takes place if we allow electricity to flow. In reality, equilibrium will eventually be set up, so we could equally well write the reaction as

$$Cu(s) + 2Ag^+(aq) \rightleftharpoons Cu^{2+}(aq) + 2Ag(s)$$

66.1 (You will need the data in Table 66.1 in order to answer many of the questions in this unit. Assume standard conditions unless otherwise stated.) You decide to build a cell from lead and copper half-cells.

(i) Which is the negative half-cell?

(ii) Draw a diagram of the cell. (Which half-cell should be drawn on the left-hand side?)

(iii) Write down the reaction that takes place in each half-cell.

(iv) Write down the overall cell reaction in two ways, the first showing the direction that the reaction actually takes, the second showing it as an equilibrium reaction.

66.2 Repeat question 66.1 for a cell made from lead and zinc half-cells.

66.3 Write down the cell reaction for a zinc half-cell combined with a S.H.E. In one equation show the direction that the reaction actually takes, and in another as an equilibrium reaction.

66.6 A quick way of writing cells

At present we either have to write a paragraph saying in words what is present in a cell, or draw a diagram of it. Neither of these options is very convenient, so another method has been invented. To see the method at work, we shall use the Daniell cell as an example. The cell is written*

	negative half-cell		positive half-cell	
Zn(s)	Zn^{2+}(aq), 1 mol dm^{-3}	⁞⁞	Cu^{2+}(aq), 1 mol dm^{-3}	Cu(s)
zinc electrode	1 mol dm^{-3} solution of zinc ions		1 mol dm^{-3} solution of copper ions	copper electrode

The vertical full lines between the symbols mean that there is a change of state present. For example, there is a change in state between the solid electrodes and the solutions in which they sit. The vertical broken lines between the two solutions represent a barrier, such as a porous pot. Sometimes you may see the cell written with a salt bridge between the two half-cells. If the bridge was made of potassium chloride, the cell would be written

$$\mathrm{Zn(s)}\,|\,\mathrm{Zn^{2+}(aq)},\ 1\ \mathrm{mol\ dm^{-3}}\,|\,\mathrm{KCl}\,|\,\mathrm{Cu^{2+}(aq)},\ 1\ \mathrm{mol\ dm^{-3}}\,|\,\mathrm{Cu(s)}$$

A most important half-cell is the S.H.E. If we were to use a S.H.E. to measure the standard electrode potential of lead we could write the cell as

$$\mathrm{Pt(s)}\,|\,\mathrm{H_2(g)},\ 1\ \mathrm{atm}\,|\,\mathrm{H^+(aq)},\ 1\ \mathrm{mol\ dm^{-3}}\ \vdots\vdots\ \mathrm{Pb^{2+}(aq)},\ 1\ \mathrm{mol\ dm^{-3}}\,|\,\mathrm{Pb(s)}$$

Another half-cell that is widely used is called a calomel electrode. This consists of mercury in contact with dimercury(I) chloride (Hg_2Cl_2) dipping into a solution of potassium chloride, which is saturated with the dimercury(I) chloride. The cell reaction is best written

$$\mathrm{Hg_2{}^{2+}(aq) + 2e^- \rightarrow 2Hg(l)}$$

The calomel electrode is often used as a substitute for a S.H.E. The calomel electrode is easier to set up, and its e.m.f. has been measured to a high degree of accuracy. If we want to measure its standard electrode potential we would set up the cell

$$\mathrm{Pt(s)}\,|\,\mathrm{H_2(g)},\ 1\ \mathrm{atm}\,|\,\mathrm{H^+(aq)},\ 1\ \mathrm{mol\ dm^{-3}}\ \vdots\vdots\ \mathrm{Cl^-(aq)},\ 1\ \mathrm{mol\ dm^{-3}}\,|\,\mathrm{Hg_2Cl_2(s)}\,|\,\mathrm{Hg(l)}$$

for which $E^{\ominus}_{\mathrm{Hg_2{}^+/Hg}} = +0.789$ V at 25 °C. The cell also has the virtue of changing its e.m.f. only very slightly as the temperature changes.

66.7 The anode and cathode in a cell

Oxidation occurs when a chemical loses one or more electrons; reduction occurs when a chemical gains one or more electrons. At the negative electrode in the Daniell cell the zinc loses electrons. Therefore oxidation takes place at this electrode. Conversely, reduction takes place at the positive half-cell where the copper(II) ions are converted into copper atoms. The electrode at which *oxidation* takes place is called the *anode.* The electrode at which *reduction* takes place is called the *cathode.* For example, in the Daniell cell, the zinc electrode is the anode and the copper electrode is the cathode.

You should be careful when you use the terms 'anode' and 'cathode'. Often it is said that a cathode carries a negative charge, and an anode a positive charge. This is not in general correct; the anode and cathode should be defined in terms of oxidation and reduction. However, in electrolysis (see Unit 72) it is the case that the electrode at which chemicals are oxidised happens to be the positively charged electrode, and chemicals are reduced at the negative electrode. In *electrolysis,* then, the cathode *is* negatively charged and the anode positively charged. In cells, matters are rather different.

66.4 A cell is made from aluminium and silver half-cells. Which electrode is the cathode, and which the anode?

66.8 More about salt bridges

As we have seen, one type of salt bridge is made by dissolving potassium chloride in agar jelly. A simpler type that you might use is made by allowing a strip of filter paper to soak up an ionic solution, for example potassium nitrate solution. The strip of filter paper can be draped over the sides of two beakers that contain the solutions of the two half-cells.

You should be able to understand why a salt bridge is needed if you think about what would happen if a cell is made up with a bridge missing. If we use the Daniell cell as our example, we know that there will be a Helmholtz double layer in both half-cells. The tendency is for zinc atoms to go into solution, and for copper(II) ions to come out of solution. The solution in the zinc half-cell becomes richer in positive ions. If this positive charge builds up, then the electrons on the zinc electrode are attracted more and more strongly by the solution. In the copper half-cell, the reverse process occurs: positive ions are lost from the solution, so the attraction for electrons is reduced. In this situation electrons will not travel from the zinc to the copper. The cell will not work.

Now let us see what happens if a salt bridge links the two half-cells. In this case, positive and negative ions from the salt bridge can travel into the two solutions. This keeps the charge in balance.

*Normally the cell is written on one line like this:

$$\mathrm{Zn(s)}\,|\,\mathrm{Zn^{2+}(aq)},1\ \mathrm{mol\ dm^{-3}}\ \vdots\vdots\ \mathrm{Cu^{2+}(aq)},\ 1\ \mathrm{mol\ dm^{-3}}\,|\,\mathrm{Cu(s)}$$

but we have arranged this and similar cells so that they fit into one column of text.

66.5 In a cell made from magnesium and lead half-cells, do the electrons move from the lead to the magnesium, or vice versa?

66.6 A student made up a cell from silver and lead half-cells. She decided to use a salt bridge made from filter paper dipped in potassium chloride solution. Why was this a mistake?

66.7 Using the notation we developed in section 66.6, write down the cells made from the following combinations of half-cells: (i) S.H.E. and copper; (ii) zinc and silver; (iii) calomel and copper. In each case work out the e.m.f. of the cell.

66.9 The electrochemical series

Even though you may not have known about electrode potentials before reading this unit, you may have heard of the *reactivity series*. The series attempts to list the elements in order of their reactivities. A number of different reactions have been used to compare the reactivities of the elements. In Table 66.3 you will find a summary of the way Group I and II metals react with water. On the basis of information like this, we can attempt to draw up a provisional table of the relative reactivities of the metals in each group. For example, in Group I the reactivity increases down the Group. This also happens in Group II as well. If we start to compare between the two Groups, we can say that beryllium appears to be the least reactive, closely followed by magnesium. However, it becomes more difficult to compare, say, calcium with lithium. Indeed, there is a good reason why we are unlikely to fit the metals into a respectable order from the information.

The problem with building up a reactivity series is that we can become confused between two important features of chemicals: their energetic stabilities and their kinetic stabilities. By looking at how the metals react with water we are observing how fast they react. Having done this, we tend to assume that the metal that reacts the fastest has the greatest *energetic* tendency to turn into products. However, this is not valid; the rate of a reaction does not tell us about energetics, and vice versa (see Unit 50).

Table 66.3. The reactivity of the Group I and II metals with cold water

Group I	*Nature of reaction*	*Group II*	*Nature of reaction*
Lithium	Steady reaction	Beryllium	No reaction
Sodium	Quite violent	Magnesium	Very slow
Potassium	Violent, ignites	Calcium	Steady reaction
Rubidium	Very violent	Strontium	Steady reaction
Caesium	Explosive	Barium	Steady reaction

The key thing we are seeking in the reactivity series is information, not about rates, but about the energetic stabilities of the elements and their compounds. However, the electrode potentials of the elements give us precisely this information. It is important that you understand that electrode potentials tell us about energetics, not about kinetics. If we draw up a table of the elements in the order of their electrode potentials, we obtain the *electrochemical series*. Part of the series is given in Table 66.4. Notice that it provides some surprises. For example, lithium is at the top, and calcium comes before sodium. The series is useful for predicting the outcome of certain types of reaction, but not all. Especially, the reaction that is being compared is

$$M(s) + xH^+(aq) \rightarrow M^{x+}(aq) + (x/2)H_2(g)$$

For example,

$$Na(s) + H^+(aq) \rightarrow Na^+(aq) + \tfrac{1}{2}H_2(g)$$
$$Ca(s) + 2H^+(aq) \rightarrow Ca^{2+}(aq) + H_2(g)$$

Table 66.4. Part of the electrochemical series

Element	*Comment*
Lithium	↑ Greatest reducing nature
Rubidium	Greatest tendency to form positive ions in solution
Potassium	
Calcium	Most electropositive
Sodium	
Magnesium	
Aluminium	
Zinc	
Iron	
Lead	
HYDROGEN	Elements above hydrogen should displace it from acids. Elements towards the top will displace it from water
Copper	
Iodine*	
Mercury	
Silver	
Bromine*	Least electropositive
Chlorine*	Greatest tendency to form negative ions in solution
Gold	
Fluorine*	↓ Greatest oxidising nature

*The halogens, fluorine, chlorine, bromine and iodine, have been included in the series for completeness

The electrochemical series is a good guide to predicting reactions that take place in solution, but not necessarily otherwise. Especially, we can predict the results of *displacement reactions* in solution. Here is an example: What will happen if magnesium is added to a solution of silver nitrate?

The electrochemical series tells us that

$$Mg(s) + 2H^+(aq) \rightarrow Mg^{2+}(aq) + H_2(g); \quad E^\ominus = -2.37\,V$$
$$Ag(s) + H^+(aq) \rightarrow Ag^+(aq) + \tfrac{1}{2}H_2(g); \quad E^\ominus = +0.80\,V$$

The more negative the electrode potential, the greater is

the reducing nature of the element, i.e. the more likely it is to give up electrons and act as a reducing agent. By comparison, the positive sign of $E^\ominus$ for silver tells us that this metal has little reducing nature. Rather, it is better to regard its ions, Ag^+, as oxidising agents. Thus, if we put magnesium metal into a solution containing silver ions, the magnesium (a good reducing agent) will react with the silver ions (reasonably good oxidising agent):

$$Mg(s) + 2Ag^+(aq) \rightarrow Mg^{2+}(aq) + 2Ag(s)$$

We would see the magnesium dissolve and specks of silver metal take their place. If you do this reaction, you will find that, owing to their size, the silver particles look black. It is possible to grow crystals of silver by a displacement reaction.

There is a general rule about predicting the course of displacement reactions. It is that:

An element higher in the electrochemical series will displace one lower in the series.

66.8 Which of the following should displace hydrogen from an acid: copper, iron, lead, magnesium?

66.9 What do you think of the following statements?

(i) Lithium is at the top of the reactivity series, so it is likely to be extremely violent in its reactions.

(ii) Potassium is a long way above copper in the series, so if we add potassium to copper(II) sulphate solution we would see copper metal displaced.

66.10 With the halogens, we say that chlorine will displace bromine and iodine, bromine will displace iodine, but iodine will not displace either chlorine or bromine. For example, if you mix chlorine dissolved in water with a solution of an iodide, you will see the black colour of iodine appear:

$$Cl_2(aq) + 2I^-(aq) \rightarrow 2Cl^-(aq) + I_2(s)$$

At first sight this seems to go against the rule that elements higher displace those lower in the series. Explain the source of the confusion. (Hint: look closely at this displacement reaction, and the one between magnesium and silver ions.)

66.10 Some useful cells

We make use of electrochemical cells in many ways, especially in batteries, e.g. in digital watches, in transistor radios, in toys, and in cars and lorries. The difference between a battery and a cell is simply that a battery is made up of two or more cells connected together. There are two sorts of battery. Primary batteries cannot be recharged. When they have run down they have to be thrown away. On the other hand, secondary batteries can be recharged.

(a) *Carbon–zinc dry cell*

One of the most common primary batteries is the carbon–zinc dry cell. (We usually call it a battery, but there is only one cell in it.) It has a zinc case surrounding a paste made of water, zinc(II) chloride and ammonium chloride (Figure 66.7). This paste is in contact with a mixture of manganese(IV) oxide and graphite powder in which rests a graphite rod. The changes that take place in the cell are complicated, but the chief reaction is

$$Zn(s) + 2MnO_2(s) + H_2O(l) \rightarrow Zn^{2+}(aq) + Mn_2O_3(s) + 2OH^-(aq)$$

The cell has an e.m.f. of about 1.5 V.

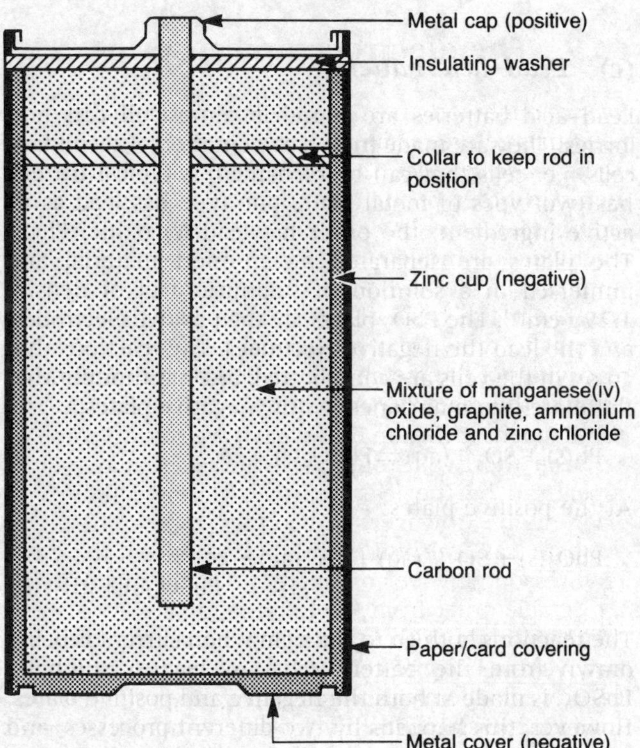

Figure 66.7 *The construction of a typical battery (strictly, a Leclanché primary cell)*

(b) *Silver oxide–zinc cell*

One type of small button-shaped cell that is used in calculators and digital watches consists of a combination of silver(I) oxide, Ag_2O, mixed with potassium or sodium hydroxide, and zinc. The cell has an e.m.f. of around 1.6 V. Provided the cell is used to supply small currents, e.g. a few milliamps, it can have a working life of over a year.

Lithium is also used in button cells, but often for special purposes, e.g. in powering a pacemaker implanted into the chest of a person with heart disease. A combination of nickel and cadmium is another favourite for button cells.

Batteries come in many sizes reflecting their wide range of uses.

A battery-powered vehicle.

(c) *Lead–acid battery*

Lead–acid batteries are found in almost all cars and lorries. They are made from a combination of secondary cells, i.e. cells that can be recharged. A typical battery has two types of metal plate; one type has lead as its active ingredient, the other has lead(IV) oxide, PbO_2. The plates are separated by an inert material and immersed in a solution of sulphuric acid of density 1.25 g cm^{-3}. The PbO_2 plates are the positive electrodes, and the lead the negative electrodes. The reactions that go on in the cells are complicated, but it is thought that there are two main ones. At the negative plates:

$$Pb(s) + SO_4^{2-}(aq) \rightleftharpoons PbSO_4(s) + 2e^-$$

At the positive plates:

$$PbO_2(s) + SO_4^{2-}(aq) + 4H^+(aq) + 2e^- \rightleftharpoons PbSO_4(s) + 2H_2O(l)$$

The reactions both go to the right when current is being drawn from the battery. That is, lead(II) sulphate, $PbSO_4$, is made at both the negative and positive plates. However, this happens by two different processes, and for each mole of $PbSO_4$ made two moles of electrons travel through the external circuit. These are the electrons that, for example, make the lights, indicators and a car radio work.

When a car or lorry moves, an electric current is generated by the alternator. This current is passed into the battery in the direction that forces the two reactions to go to the left. That is, the $PbSO_4$ is decomposed. In theory, at least, the charging and discharging can go on indefinitely. However, in practice, this is not so. The sulphuric acid decomposes, and has to be replaced; and in time the plates themselves change their structure. Eventually the battery becomes much less efficient and has to be changed. One of the worst things that can happen to a car battery is for it to spend most of its time in a discharged state. This causes so much $PbSO_4$ to build up that it is almost impossible to remove. A typical car battery provides a voltage of 12 V. This is not a large voltage, but the battery can provide a large current, e.g. over 10 A, without being destroyed.

(d) *Fuel cells*

A fuel cell is a primary cell of a special type. The chemicals that produce electricity are constantly replaced as soon as they are used. The most well known type of fuel cell generates electricity from hydrogen and oxygen using platinum electrodes and a solution of an alkali. A simple version can be set up in a laboratory as shown in Figure 66.8a. Practical fuel cells have a different design (Figure 66.8b). At the negative electrode, electrons are released through the reaction

$$2H_2(g) + 4OH^-(aq) \rightarrow 4H_2O(l) + 4e^-$$

The electrons released travel to the positive terminal where oxygen is used up:

$$O_2(g) + 2H_2O(l) + 4e^- \rightarrow 4OH^-(aq)$$

Overall the change is

$$2H_2(g) + O_2(g) \rightarrow 2H_2O(l)$$

Not only does the cell produce a reliable supply of electricity, it also produces water. Both features have given hydrogen–oxygen fuel cells a use in space exploration. Other fuel cell systems have been investigated using different electrolytes and reactants. One of the aims of the research has been to find a system that could be used to power cars and other vehicles. There has been some success, with some experimental cars travelling at over 80 km h^{-1}. However, the economics of fuel cells mean that they cannot as yet compete with petrol as a fuel.

> **66.11** The zinc is the negative terminal of the zinc–carbon cell. Should we call it the anode or the cathode?

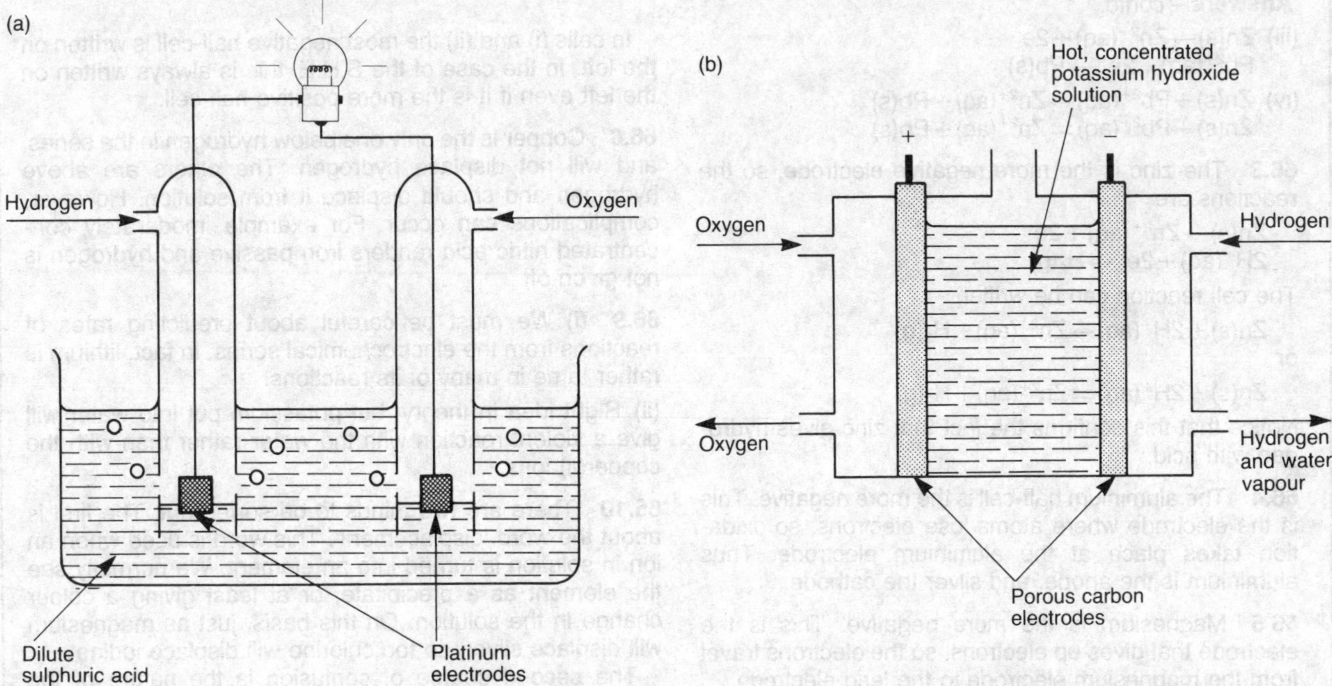

***Figure 66.8** (a) A simple fuel cell, which can be made in the laboratory. (b) The essentials of a hydrogen–oxygen fuel cell*

Answers

66.1 (i) $E^{\ominus}_{Pb^{2+}/Pb}$ is more negative than $E^{\ominus}_{Cu^{2+}/Cu}$; therefore, the lead is the negative half-cell.

(ii) The cell is drawn in Figure 66.9.

(iii) The negative half-cell gives up electrons to the external circuit, so the reactions are

$$Pb(s) \rightarrow Pb^{2+}(aq) + 2e^-$$
$$Cu^{2+}(aq) + 2e^- \rightarrow Cu(s)$$

(iv) The reaction takes place in the direction

$$Pb(s) + Cu^{2+}(aq) \rightarrow Pb^{2+}(aq) + Cu(s)$$

As an equilibrium equation we have

$$Pb(s) + Cu^{2+}(aq) \rightleftharpoons Pb^{2+}(aq) + Cu(s)$$

66.2 (i) The zinc is the negative half-cell.

(ii) The cell is drawn in Figure 66.10.

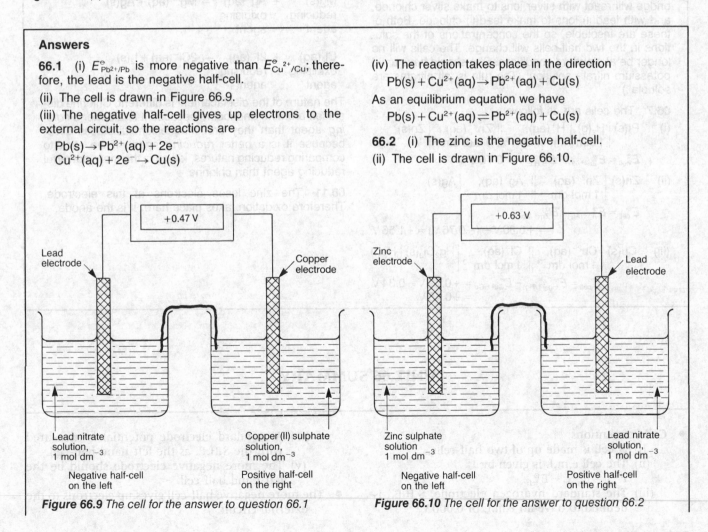

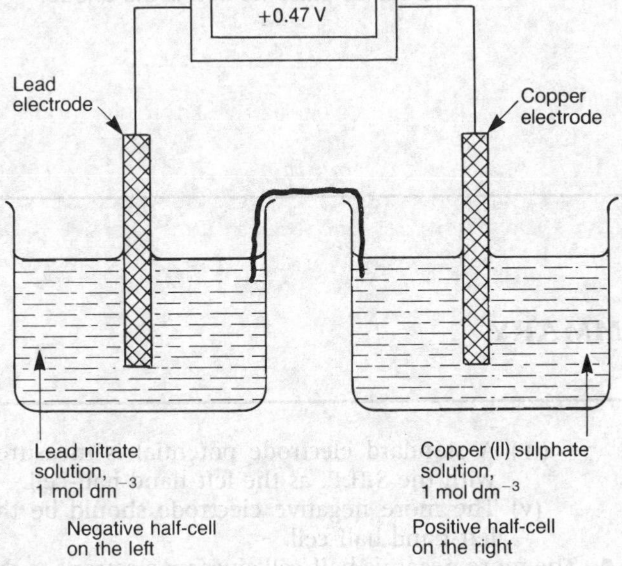

+0.47 V
Lead electrode
Copper electrode
Lead nitrate solution, 1 mol dm^{-3}
Copper (II) sulphate solution, 1 mol dm^{-3}
Negative half-cell on the left
Positive half-cell on the right

***Figure 66.9** The cell for the answer to question 66.1*

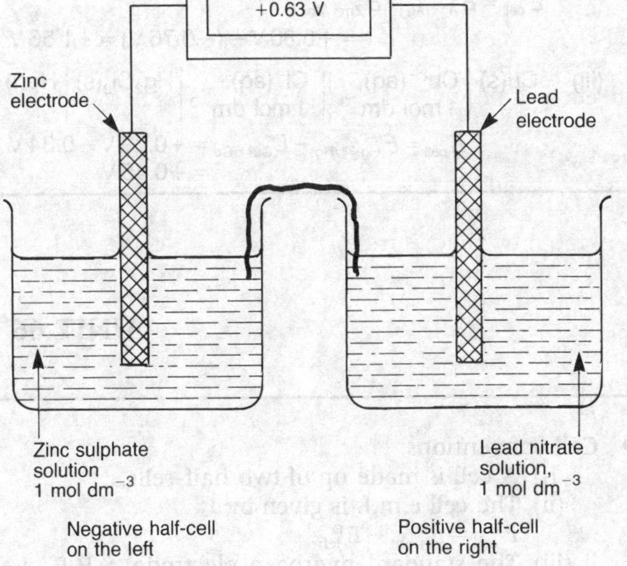

+0.63 V
Zinc electrode
Lead electrode
Zinc sulphate solution 1 mol dm^{-3}
Lead nitrate solution, 1 mol dm^{-3}
Negative half-cell on the left
Positive half-cell on the right

***Figure 66.10** The cell for the answer to question 66.2*

Answers – contd.

(iii) $Zn(s) \rightarrow Zn^{2+}(aq) + 2e^-$
$Pb^{2+}(aq) + 2e^- \rightarrow Pb(s)$

(iv) $Zn(s) + Pb^{2+}(aq) \rightarrow Zn^{2+}(aq) + Pb(s)$
$Zn(s) + Pb^{2+}(aq) \rightleftharpoons Zn^{2+}(aq) + Pb(s)$

66.3 The zinc is the more negative electrode, so the reactions are

$Zn(s) \rightarrow Zn^{2+}(aq) + 2e^-$
$2H^+(aq) + 2e^- \rightarrow H_2(g)$

The cell reaction can be written

$Zn(s) + 2H^+(aq) \rightarrow Zn^{2+}(aq) + H_2(g)$

or

$Zn(s) + 2H^+(aq) \rightleftharpoons Zn^{2+}(aq) + H_2(g)$

Notice that this confirms the fact that zinc gives hydrogen with acid.

66.4 The aluminium half-cell is the more negative. This is the electrode where atoms lose electrons, so oxidation takes place at the aluminium electrode. Thus aluminium is the anode, and silver the cathode.

66.5 Magnesium is the more negative. This is the electrode that gives up electrons, so the electrons travel from the magnesium electrode to the lead electrode.

66.6 The problem is that the chloride ions from the salt bridge will react with silver ions to make silver chloride, and with lead(II) ions to make lead(II) chloride. Both of these are insoluble, so the concentrations of the solutions in the two half-cells will change. The cells will no longer be at standard conditions. She should have used potassium nitrate solution. (The rule is 'all nitrates are soluble'.)

66.7 The cells are as follows:

(i) Pt(s) | $H_2(g)$, 1 atm | $H^+(aq)$, 1 mol dm^{-3} ¦¦ $Zn^{2+}(aq)$, 1 mol dm^{-3} | Zn(s)

$E^{\ominus}_{cell} = E^{\ominus}_{Zn^{2+}/Zn} - E^{\ominus}_{S.H.E.} = -0.76\,V$

(ii) Zn(s) | $Zn^{2+}(aq)$, 1 mol dm^{-3} ¦¦ $Ag^+(aq)$, 1 mol dm^{-3} | Ag(s)

$E^{\ominus}_{cell} = E^{\ominus}_{Ag^+/Ag} - E^{\ominus}_{Zn^{2+}/Zn}$
$= +0.80\,V - (-0.76\,V) = +1.56\,V$

(iii) Cu(s) | $Cu^{2+}(aq)$, 1 mol dm^{-3} ¦¦ $Cl^-(aq)$, 1 mol dm^{-3} | $Hg_2Cl_2(s)$ | Hg(l)

$E^{\ominus}_{cell} = E^{\ominus}_{Hg_2^{2+}/Hg} - E^{\ominus}_{Cu^{2+}/Cu} = +0.79\,V - 0.34\,V$
$= +0.45\,V$

In cells (i) and (ii) the most negative half-cell is written on the left. In the case of the S.H.E. this is always written on the left even if it is the more positive half-cell.

66.8 Copper is the only one below hydrogen in the series, and will not displace hydrogen. The others are above hydrogen and should displace it from solution. However, complications can occur. For example, moderately concentrated nitric acid renders iron passive and hydrogen is not given off.

66.9 (i) We must be careful about predicting rates of reactions from the electrochemical series. In fact, lithium is rather tame in many of its reactions.

(ii) Right idea in theory; but potassium put into water will give a violent reaction with the water rather than with the copper(II) ions.

66.10 There are two things to be sorted out. The first is about the word 'displacement'. This word is used when an ion in solution is turned into an element. We normally see the element as a precipitate, or at least giving a colour change in the solution. On this basis, just as magnesium will displace silver, so too chlorine will displace iodine.

The second source of confusion is the nature of the changes taking place in the two reactions:

$Mg(s)$	$+ Ag^+(aq)$	$\rightarrow Mg^{2+}(aq) + Ag(s)$
reducing agent	oxidising agent	
$Cl_2(aq)$	$+ 2I^-(aq)$	$\rightarrow 2Cl^-(aq) + I_2(s)$
oxidising agent	reducing agent	

The nature of the displacement is different. Chlorine displaces bromine and iodine because it is a better *oxidising* agent than they are. Magnesium displaces silver because it is a better *reducing* agent. If we stick to comparing reducing natures, iodine *is* the more powerful reducing agent than chlorine.

66.11 The zinc loses electrons at this electrode. Therefore oxidation takes place here. It is the anode.

UNIT 66 SUMMARY

- Cell conventions:
  (i) A cell is made up of two half-cells.
  (ii) The cell e.m.f. is given by
  $E^{\ominus}_{cell} = E^{\ominus}_{right} - E^{\ominus}_{left}$.
  (iii) The standard hydrogen electrode, S.H.E., is defined to have an e.m.f. of 0.000 V.
  (iv) A standard electrode potential is measured with the S.H.E. as the left-hand half-cell.
  (v) The more negative electrode should be the left-hand half-cell.
- The more negative half-cell gives up electrons to the external circuit.

- Metals with the most negative electrode potentials are the best reducing agents.
- The electrochemical series, or reactivity series, is a list of elements in the order of their reducing power. In displacement reactions, an element higher in the series will displace a lower element from solution; e.g.

$$Zn(s) + Cu^{2+}(aq) \rightarrow Zn^{2+}(aq) + Cu(s)$$

67

Cells and concentration changes

67.1 How cell e.m.f.s change with concentration

You may remember that under standard conditions the concentrations of ions in a cell have to be 1 mol dm^{-3} (strictly, unit activity). The reason is that cell e.m.f.s change when the concentrations of the ions change. You can see how this happens for yourself if you set up a Daniell cell and change the concentration of the solution in either the zinc or the copper half-cell. For example, you might keep the zinc ion concentration fixed at 1 mol dm^{-3}, and use solutions of copper(II) sulphate with concentrations varying between 1 and 10^{-6} mol dm^{-3}. (The easiest way of doing this is by gradually diluting the 1 mol dm^{-3} solution.) Table 67.1 provides some typical results.

Table 67.1. How the e.m.f. of a Daniell cell varies as the concentration of copper(II) ions changes*

Concentration of $Cu^{2+}(aq)$/mol dm^{-3}	E_{cell}/V	$E_{Cu^{2+}/Cu}$/V
1.0	1.1	0.340
0.1	1.070	0.310
0.01	1.041	0.281
0.001	1.011	0.251
0.000 1	0.982	0.222
0.000 01	0.953	0.193
0.000 001	0.923	0.163

*The zinc ion concentration is constant at 1 mol dm^{-3}. In this cell we have $E_{cell} = E_{Cu^{2+}/Cu} - E^{\ominus}_{Zn^{2+}/Zn}$ and $E^{\ominus}_{Zn^{2+}/Zn} = -0.76$ V. Notice that we do not write the standard sign for E_{cell} and $E_{Cu^{2+}/Cu}$ because the concentration is not kept at 1 mol dm^{-3}

You might like to plot a graph to show how $E_{Cu^{2+}/Cu}$ varies with the concentration of copper(II) ions, $[Cu^{2+}(aq)]$. This is best done using a computer. You would find that a straight line graph is obtained if $E_{Cu^{2+}/Cu}$ is plotted against $\ln[Cu^{2+}(aq)]$ or $\lg[Cu^{2+}(aq)]$. Such a graph is shown in Figure 67.1.

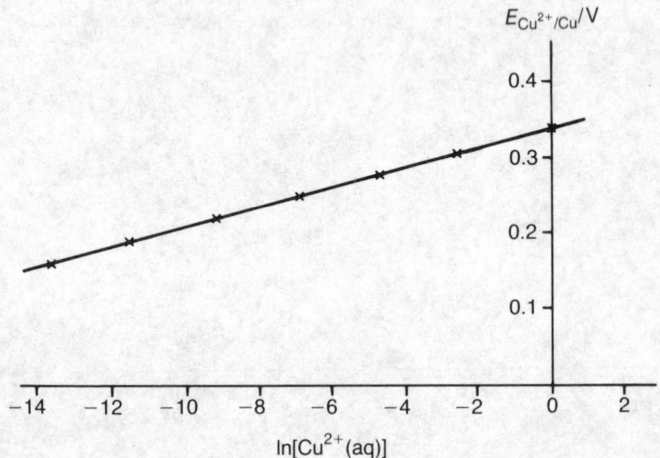

Figure 67.1 *A graph of $E_{Cu^{2+}/Cu}$ against $\ln[Cu^{2+}(aq)]$ shows how the electrode potential changes as the concentration of Cu^{2+} ions varies*

We are not in a position to prove it, but the equation for the line is

$$E_{Cu^{2+}/Cu} = E^{\ominus}_{Cu^{2+}/Cu} + \frac{RT}{2F}\ln[Cu^{2+}(aq)]$$

where R is the gas constant, T the Kelvin temperature and F the faraday of electricity. The presence of the '2' is due to the fact that 2 mol of electrons are transferred if 1 mol of copper(II) ions are converted into copper metal.

In a general reaction

$$M^{n+}(aq) + ne^- \rightleftharpoons M(s)$$

n moles of electrons are transferred and the equation becomes

$$E_{M^{n+}/M} = E^{\ominus}_{M^{n+}/M} + \frac{RT}{nF}\ln[M^{n+}(aq)]$$

which is known as the *Nernst equation*.

If you put in the values of R and F and take $T = 298$ K, we have

$$E_{M^{n+}/M} = E^{\ominus}_{M^{n+}/M} + \frac{0.026}{n}\ln[M^{n+}(aq)]$$

where we are using natural logarithms. Alternatively,

$$E_{M^{n+}/M} = E^\ominus_{M^{n+}/M} + \frac{0.059}{n} \lg[M^{n+}(aq)]$$

if we use logarithms to the base 10.

For convenience the units (volts) of the constants $0.026/n$ and $0.059/n$ have not been written into the equations. Either of these equations is extremely useful. One reason is that, as you will find in the next section, each can be used to determine equilibrium constants.

67.2 How to work out equilibrium constants from cell e.m.f.s

Let us use the Daniell cell, and apply our new equation to each half-cell. If we put $n=2$, and $0.059/2=0.029$, we have

$$E_{Cu^{2+}/Cu} = E^\ominus_{Cu^{2+}/Cu} + 0.029 \lg[Cu^{2+}(aq)]$$
$$E_{Zn^{2+}/Zn} = E^\ominus_{Zn^{2+}/Zn} + 0.029 \lg[Zn^{2+}(aq)]$$

Now, we know that

$$E_{cell} = E_{Cu^{2+}/Cu} - E_{Zn^{2+}/Zn}$$

so

$$E_{cell} = E^\ominus_{Cu^{2+}/Cu} + 0.029 \lg[Cu^{2+}(aq)] - E^\ominus_{Zn^{2+}/Zn} - 0.029 \lg[Zn^{2+}(aq)]$$
$$= E^\ominus_{Cu^{2+}/Cu} - E^\ominus_{Zn^{2+}/Zn} + 0.029\{\lg[Cu^{2+}(aq)] - \lg[Zn^{2+}(aq)]\}$$

i.e.

$$E_{cell} = E^\ominus_{cell} - 0.029 \lg\left(\frac{[Zn^{2+}(aq)]}{[Cu^{2+}(aq)]}\right)$$

From this equation we can calculate the e.m.f. of a Daniell cell with any concentration of zinc ions and copper(II) ions.

Now let us think about what happens to a Daniell cell if we use it to do some electrical work. For example, we could connect it to a small electric motor. We know that after some time the motor will stop. We would say that the cell had run down (just as an ordinary battery wears out). When this happens $E_{cell}=0$ and there is no overall transfer of electricity from one half-cell to the other. When there is no overall change taking place in a chemical reaction, *equilibrium has been established*. That is, we can write a condition for equilibrium in a cell reaction:

At equilibrium $\quad E_{cell} = 0$

Returning to the Daniell cell, this condition tells us that

$$0 = E^\ominus_{cell} - 0.029 \lg\left(\frac{[Zn^{2+}(aq)]}{[Cu^{2+}(aq)]}\right)$$

So

$$E^\ominus_{cell} = 0.029 \lg\left(\frac{[Zn^{2+}(aq)]}{[Cu^{2+}(aq)]}\right)$$

If you have read Unit 51 you will recognise that the equilibrium constant for the Daniell cell reaction

$$Cu^{2+}(aq) + Zn(s) \rightarrow Cu(s) + Zn^{2+}(aq)$$

is

$$K_c = \frac{[Zn^{2+}(aq)]}{[Cu^{2+}(aq)]}$$

Therefore we have

$$E^\ominus_{cell} = 0.029 \lg K_c$$
$$\lg K_c = 1.1\ V/0.029\ V$$
$$K_c = \text{antilog}(1.1/0.029) = 1.94 \times 10^{37}$$

This large value tells us that the equilibrium lies almost entirely in favour of copper metal and zinc ions.

We can generalise our work on the Daniell cell to include any combination of cell reactions. The recipe is shown in panel 67.1.

Panel 67.1

Establishing equilibrium constants from e.m.f.s

Stage 1 Write down the cell reaction.
Stage 2 Write down the value of n, the number of moles of electrons transferred.
Stage 3 Work out $E^\ominus_{cell}$.
Stage 4 Write down the equilibrium constant for the reaction.
Stage 5 Put $E^\ominus_{cell} = \frac{0.059}{n} \lg K_c$
Stage 6 Calculate $K_c = \text{antilog}(nE^\ominus_{cell}/0.059)$
Stage 7 Put in the units of K_c.

Example 1
The cell

$$Cu(s)\,|\,Cu^{2+}(aq)\,\vdots\vdots\,Ag^{+}(aq)\,|\,Ag(s)$$

has $E^\ominus_{Ag^{+}/Ag} = +0.80\ V$ and $E^\ominus_{Cu^{2+}/Cu} = +0.34\ V$. The cell reaction is

$$2Ag^{+}(aq) + Cu(s) \rightarrow 2Ag(s) + Cu^{2+}(aq)$$

for which $n=2$. Also,

$$E^\ominus_{cell} = E^\ominus_{Ag^{+}/Ag} - E^\ominus_{Cu^{2+}/Cu} = +0.46\ V$$

and

$$K_c = \frac{[Cu^{2+}(aq)]}{[Ag^{+}(aq)]^2}$$

Panel – cont.

Finally,

$$K_c = \text{antilog}(2 \times 0.46/0.059) = 3.9 \times 10^{15}\ \text{mol}^{-1}\ \text{dm}^3$$

Example 2

The cell

$$Pt(s)\ \Big|\ \begin{matrix} Fe^{3+}(aq), \\ Fe^{2+}(aq) \end{matrix}\ \Big\Vert\ \begin{matrix} Cr^{3+}(aq), \\ Cr_2O_7^{2-}(aq), H^+(aq) \end{matrix}\ \Big|\ Pt(s)$$

has $E^\ominus_{Cr_2O_7^{2-}/Cr^{3+}} = +1.33\ \text{V}$ and $E^\ominus_{Fe^{3+}/Fe^{2+}} = +0.77\ \text{V}$. The cell reaction is

$$6Fe^{2+}(aq) + Cr_2O_7^{2-}(aq) + 14H^+(aq) \rightarrow 6Fe^{3+}(aq) + 2Cr^{3+}(aq) + 14H_2O(l)$$

for which $n = 6$. Also,

$$E^\ominus_{cell} = E^\ominus_{Cr_2O_7^{2-}/Cr^{3+}} - E^\ominus_{Fe^{3+}/Fe^{2+}} = +0.56\ \text{V}$$

and

$$K_c = \frac{[Fe^{3+}(aq)]^6[Cr^{3+}(aq)]^2}{[Fe^{2+}(aq)]^6[Cr_2O_7^{2-}(aq)][H^+(aq)]^{14}}$$

Finally,

$$K_c = \text{antilog}(6 \times 0.56/0.059) = 8.9 \times 10^{56}\ \text{mol}^{-13}\ \text{dm}^{39}$$

Here the units are those of (concentration)^8 divided by (concentration)^{21}, i.e. (concentration)$^{-13}$.

The value of K_c is so large that for all intents and purposes all the iron(II) ions would be converted into iron(III) ions.

Note: Your calculator may not cope with finding the antilog($6 \times 0.56/0.059$), i.e. antilog(56.949). If not, you might know that this antilog is the same as $10^{56.949}$. We can write this as $10^{56} \times 10^{0.949}$. You will find that $10^{0.949} = 8.89$. Hence our answer is about 8.9×10^{56}.

In a redox half-cell like $Pt(s)|Fe^{3+}(aq), Fe^{2+}(aq)$, the cell e.m.f. is given by

$$E_{Fe^{3+}/Fe^{2+}} = E^\ominus_{Fe^{3+}/Fe^{2+}} + 0.059\ \lg\left(\frac{[Fe^{3+}(aq)]}{[Fe^{2+}(aq)]}\right)$$

If the reaction involves the transfer of n mol of electrons (rather than 1 mol as in this case) we have to divide the factor 0.059 by n. Notice that if we compare iron(III) ions with iron(II) ions, the iron(III) ions are the oxidised form, and the iron(II) ions are the reduced form of the ions. This might help you to see why there is a general way of writing down the e.m.f. of a half-cell, like this:

$$E_{ox/red} = E^\ominus_{ox/red} + \frac{0.059}{n}\ \lg\left(\frac{[\text{oxidised form}]}{[\text{reduced form}]}\right)$$

Warning: some people prefer to write this equation as

$$E_{ox/red} = E^\ominus_{ox/red} - \frac{0.059}{n}\ \lg\left(\frac{[\text{reduced form}]}{[\text{oxidised form}]}\right)$$

so when you consult other books, make sure you know which version is being used.

In some half-cells, hydrogen ions appear, for example in the reaction

$$\underset{\text{Oxidised form}}{Cr_2O_7^{2-}(aq) + 14H^+(aq)} + 6e^- \rightarrow \underset{\text{reduced form}}{2Cr^{3+}(aq) + 7H_2O(l)}$$

In such cases the hydrogen ions are included as one of the 'oxidised forms'. In this case,

$$E_{Cr_2O_7^{2-}/Cr^{3+}} = E^\ominus_{Cr_2O_7^{2-}/Cr^{3+}} + \frac{0.059}{6}\ \lg\left(\frac{[Cr_2O_7^{2-}(aq)][H^+(aq)]^{14}}{[Cr^{3+}(aq)]^2}\right)$$

You can also see that we obey the same rules as when writing down equilibrium constants. That is, we raise the concentrations to the appropriate power given by the number of moles in the equation. In addition, the convention is that we ignore the concentration of water when the reactions take place in aqueous solution.

67.1 Write down the equation that shows how the e.m.f. of the cell

$$Ce(s)|Ce^{3+}(aq) \Vert Cr^{3+}(aq)|Cr(s)$$

changes as the concentrations of chromium(III) and cerium(III) ions change.

67.2 Given that $E^\ominus_{Cr^{3+}/Cr} = -0.41\ \text{V}$ and $E^\ominus_{Ce^{3+}/Ce} = -2.33\ \text{V}$, calculate the value of the equilibrium constant for the reaction

$$Ce(s) + Cr^{3+}(aq) \rightleftharpoons Ce^{3+}(aq) + Cr(s)$$

67.3 We discovered that the e.m.f. of a Daniell cell is given by

$$E_{cell} = E^\ominus_{cell} - 0.029\ \lg\left(\frac{[Zn^{2+}(aq)]}{[Cu^{2+}(aq)]}\right)$$

We also know that $E^\ominus_{cell} = +1.1\ \text{V}$.

(i) Calculate E_{cell} when $[Zn^{2+}(aq)] = 2.0\ \text{mol dm}^{-3}$ and $[Cu^{2+}(aq)] = 0.5\ \text{mol dm}^{-3}$.

(ii) What is E_{cell} when $[Zn^{2+}(aq)] = 0.4\ \text{mol dm}^{-3}$ and $[Cu^{2+}(aq)] = 0.1\ \text{mol dm}^{-3}$. Before reaching for your calculator, take a careful look at the formula for E_{cell} and your answer to (i). Do you need to do the calculation?

67.4 Write down the expression for the cell e.m.f. for the reaction

$$MnO_4^-(aq) + 8H^+(aq) + 5e^- \rightarrow Mn^{2+}(aq) + 4H_2O(l)$$

Briefly explain why the oxidising power of manganate(VII) ions is quite sensitive to the concentration of hydrogen ions in the solution.

67.5 The cell

$$Ni(s)\,|\,Ni^{2+}(aq),\ 1\ mol\ dm^{-3}\ \vdots\vdots\ Pb^{2+}(aq)\,|\,Pb(s)$$

is made up. The nickel(II) ion concentration is kept at 1 mol dm^{-3} but the concentration of lead(II) ions in the other half-cell is changed. The e.m.f. of the cell is measured, and the results are found to be as follows:

$[Pb^{2+}(aq)]$/mol dm^{-3}	10^{-1}	10^{-2}	10^{-3}	10^{-4}	10^{-5}	10^{-6}
E_{cell}/V	0.091	0.061	0.032	0.002	−0.028	−0.057

(i) Plot a graph of E_{cell} against lg$[Pb^{2+}(aq)]$ using the axes arranged as shown in Figure 67.2.

You can use this graph to work out the standard e.m.f. of the cell, and the equilibrium constant for the reaction. Here is the method.

The cell reaction is

$$Pb^{2+}(aq) + Ni(s) \rightarrow Pb(s) + Ni^{2+}(aq)$$

for which

$$E_{cell} = E^{\ominus}_{cell} - \frac{0.059}{2}\lg\left(\frac{[Ni^{2+}(aq)]}{[Pb^{2+}(aq)]}\right)$$

(ii) Rewrite the equation for this cell, in which $[Ni^{2+}(aq)] = 1$.

(iii) At standard conditions, we know that $[Pb^{2+}(aq)] = 1$. What is the value of lg$[Pb^{2+}(aq)]$ at standard conditions?

(iv) What is the relation between E_{cell} and $E^{\ominus}_{cell}$ at standard conditions?

(v) Show how you can extend (extrapolate) the line on your graph to measure $E^{\ominus}_{cell}$. What value do you get?

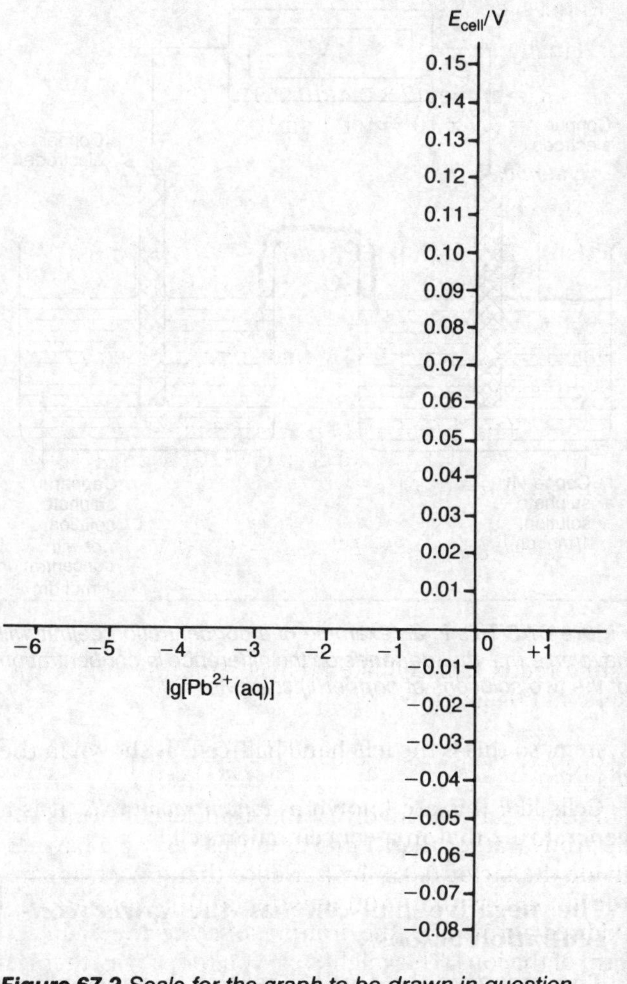

Figure 67.2 *Scale for the graph to be drawn in question 67.5*

(vi) We also know that, *at equilibrium*, $E_{cell} = 0$. What is the value of lg$[Pb^{2+}(aq)]$ when this happens? What is the value of $[Pb^{2+}(aq)]$ at equilibrium?

(vii) Write down the expression for the equilibrium constant, K_c, of the reaction. You should now know the values of the concentrations, so calculate the value of K_c.

67.3 Concentration cells

We have discovered the way in which cells change their e.m.f.s when concentrations change. Now look at the cell in Figure 67.3. At first sight we might expect a cell made from two half-cells both containing copper electrodes dipping into solutions of copper(II) ions to have a zero e.m.f.; but this is true only if the concentrations of the two solutions are identical. If the concentrations are different, then there *will* be an e.m.f. The reaction in the cell takes place in order to reduce the difference in concentrations. Equilibrium is achieved when the two concentrations are equal: the higher concentration is reduced, and the lower concentration is increased.

In the half-cell where the original concentration of copper(II) ions is low, the reaction increases the concentration of copper(II) ions by the reaction

$$Cu(s) \rightarrow Cu^{2+}(aq) + 2e^-$$
(lower concentration reaction)

In the other half-cell, the reaction converts the copper(II) ions into copper metal. That is, the reaction is

$$Cu^{2+}(aq) + 2e^- \rightarrow Cu(s)$$
(higher concentration reaction)

It is the first reaction that gives up electrons to the

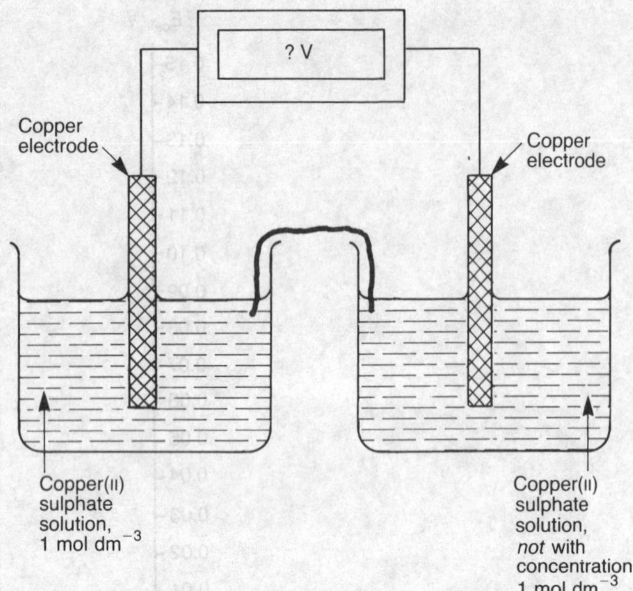

Figure 67.3 *This is an example of a concentration cell. It will have an e.m.f. that depends on the difference in concentration of the two solutions of copper(II) sulphate*

system, so this is the left-hand half-cell, as shown in the diagram.

Cells like this are known as *concentration cells*. It is a general rule that in a concentration cell:

> **The negative half-cell has the lower concentration of ions.**
>
> **The positive half-cell has the higher concentration of ions.**
>
> **The cell reaction proceeds in the direction that equalises the concentrations in the half-cells.**

67.6 A cell is made by linking two half-cells each containing a silver electrode dipping into 1 mol dm^{-3} silver nitrate solution. What will be E_{cell}? Some sodium chloride solution is added to one of the half-cells. What happens to E_{cell}. What reactions take place in the negative half-cell and in the positive half-cell?

67.4 pH and the glass electrode

We know that the e.m.f. of a cell changes as the concentration of the ions in the cell changes. A glass electrode is an electrode system that changes its e.m.f. as the concentration of *hydrogen ions* varies. A typical arrangement for a glass electrode is shown in Figure 67.4.

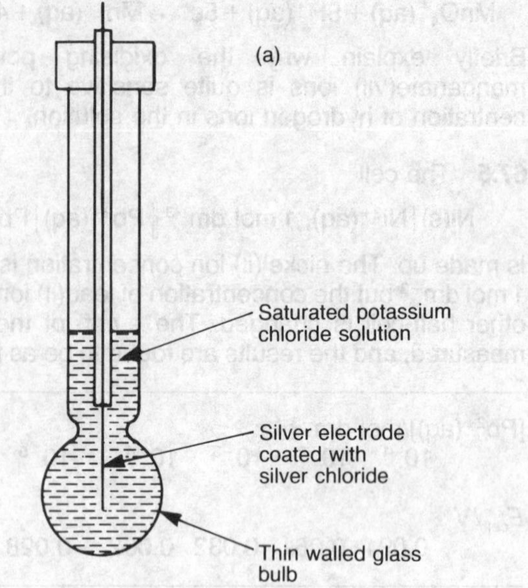

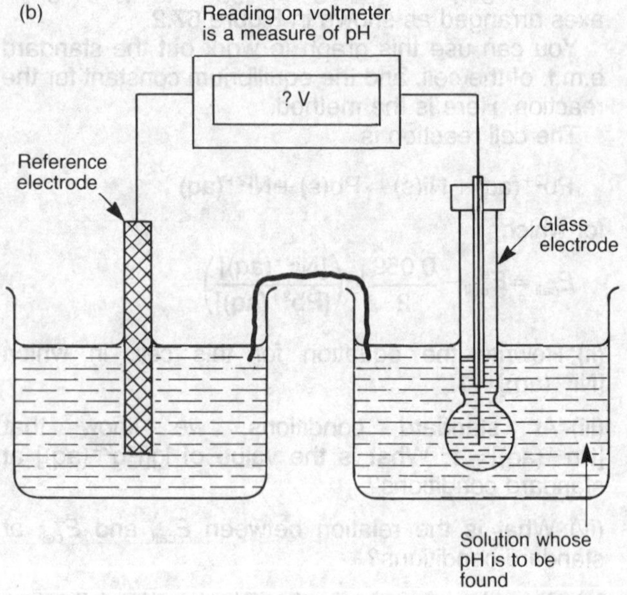

Figure 67.4 *(a) A simple glass electrode. (b) The glass electrode must be used together with another half-cell*

The electrode consists of a silver wire coated with silver chloride dipping into a saturated solution of potassium chloride. If this electrode is placed into a solution containing hydrogen ions, an e.m.f. is set up across the surface of the glass bulb.

The e.m.f. of a glass electrode is given by an equation like this:

$$E = \text{constant} + 0.059 \lg[H^+(aq)]$$

The definition of pH is

$$\text{pH} = -\lg[H^+(aq)]$$

so

$$E = \text{constant} - 0.059\text{pH}$$

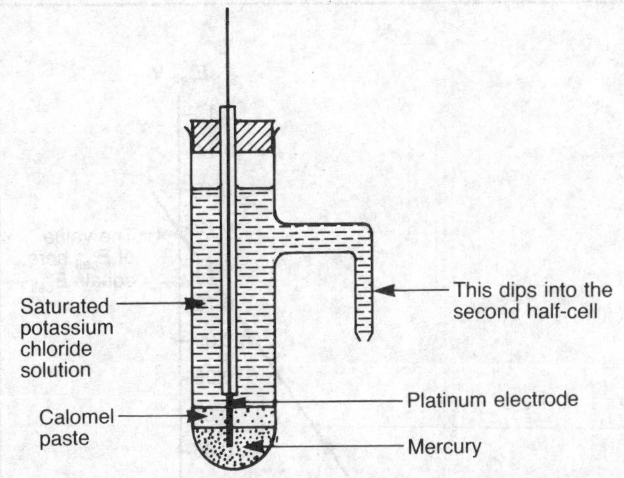

***Figure 67.5** A calomel cell consists of a platinum electrode dipping into mercury in contact with calomel (dimercury(I) chloride, Hg_2Cl_2) and potassium chloride solution. Usually the solution is saturated with potassium chloride. The cell has an e.m.f. of 0.246 V at 25° C*

In other words, the e.m.f. of a glass electrode is a direct measure of the pH of the solution in which it is put.

If we are to determine the e.m.f. we need to complete the cell using another reference electrode. Often, but not always, this is a calomel half-cell, which consists of a platinum electrode in contact with mercury, dimercury(I) chloride and a solution of potassium chloride (Figure 67.5).

Usually it is more convenient to use a *combination electrode*. A typical one is shown in the photo and in Figure 67.6. The idea behind a combination electrode is that the glass electrode and a reference half-cell are arranged in one piece of equipment. The e.m.f. of the cell can be measured using a digital voltmeter; but more often the e.m.f. is converted into a pH reading using a pH meter.

In practice, it is quite difficult for a pH meter to measure pH very accurately. One reason for this is that the glass electrode tends to change its e.m.f. over a period of time; it is also affected by changes in temperature. However, for everyday use it is ideal. Before it is used the electrode should always be placed in a buffer solution (see Unit 75) whose pH is known. The reading on the pH meter can then be adjusted accordingly.

> **67.7** The pH of a solution of hydrochloric acid was found to be 1.5. What was the hydrogen ion concentration?

A typical pH meter and electrode.

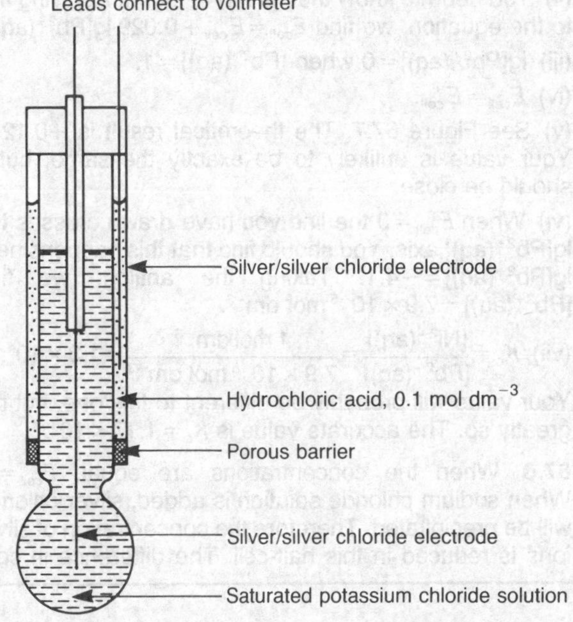

***Figure 67.6** One type of combination electrode for measuring pH*

Answers

67.1 $E_{cell} = E^{\ominus}_{cell} - \frac{0.059}{3} \lg\left(\frac{[Ce^{3+}(aq)]}{[Cr^{3+}(aq)]}\right)$

67.2 We use

$$E^{\ominus}_{cell} = \frac{0.059}{3} \lg\left(\frac{[Ce^{3+}(aq)]}{[Cr^{3+}(aq)]}\right) = \frac{0.059}{3} \lg K_c$$

So

$$\lg K_c = \frac{3 \times E^{\ominus}_{cell}}{0.059}$$

Also,

$$E^{\ominus}_{cell} = E^{\ominus}_{Cr^{3+}/Cr} - E^{\ominus}_{Ce^{3+}/Ce} = -0.41\,V + 2.33\,V = +1.92\,V$$

Putting this value into the equation gives us the result $K_c = 4.2 \times 10^{97}$ (no units).

67.3 (i) $E_{cell} = +1.1 - 0.029 \lg(2/0.5) = +1.082\,V$.

(ii) We do not need to do another calculation. The formula for E_{cell} shows that its value depends on the logarithm of the *ratio* of the two concentrations. The ratio in part (i) is 2.0:0.5, or 4:1. The ratio 0.4:0.1 is also 4:1; so E_{cell} remains the same, 1.082 V.

67.4 $E_{MnO_4^-/Mn^{2+}} = E^{\ominus}_{MnO_4^-/Mn^{2+}}$

$$+\frac{0.059}{5} \lg\left(\frac{[MnO_4^-(aq)][H^+(aq)]^8}{[Mn^{2+}(aq)]}\right)$$

The expression shows that the e.m.f. depends on $\lg[H^+(aq)]^8$, which is equal to $8 \lg[H^+(aq)]$. Therefore, the e.m.f., and hence the oxidising power, changes appreciably when $[H^+(aq)]$ changes.

67.5 (i) The graph is shown in Figure 67.7.

(ii) You need to know that $\lg(1/x) = -\lg(x)$. Applying this to the equation, we find $E_{cell} = E^{\ominus}_{cell} + 0.029 \lg[Pb^{2+}(aq)]$.

(iii) $\lg[Pb^{2+}(aq)] = 0$ when $[Pb^{2+}(aq)] = 1$.

(iv) $E_{cell} = E^{\ominus}_{cell}$.

(v) See Figure 67.7. The theoretical result is +0.12 V. Your value is unlikely to be exactly the same, but it should be close.

(vi) When $E_{cell} = 0$ the line you have drawn crosses the $\lg[Pb^{2+}(aq)]$ axis. You should find that this happens near $\lg[Pb^{2+}(aq)] = -4.1$. Taking the antilog, we find $[Pb^{2+}(aq)] = 7.9 \times 10^{-5}\,mol\,dm^{-3}$.

(vii) $K_c = \frac{[Ni^{2+}(aq)]}{[Pb^{2+}(aq)]} = \frac{1\,mol\,dm^{-3}}{7.9 \times 10^{-5}\,mol\,dm^{-3}} = 1.3 \times 10^4$.

Your value will probably be different to this one, but not greatly so. The accurate value is $K_c = 1.17 \times 10^4$.

67.6 When the concentrations are equal, $E_{cell} = 0$. When sodium chloride solution is added, silver chloride will be precipitated. Therefore the concentration of silver ions is reduced in this half-cell. The difference in concentrations means that E_{cell} is no longer zero. The reaction in the half-cell with the lower concentration of silver ions will be

$$Ag(s) \rightarrow Ag^+(aq) + e^-$$

because this will increase the concentration again. This reaction gives up electrons to the system, so this is the negative half-cell. In the positive half-cell the reaction will be

$$Ag^+(aq) + e^- \rightarrow Ag(s)$$

because this removes silver ions from the solution, and lowers the concentration.

67.7 $1.5 = -\lg[H^+(aq)]$, so $[H^+(aq)] = \text{antilog}(-1.5)$, i.e. $[H^+(aq)] = 3.2 \times 10^{-2}\,mol\,dm^{-3}$.

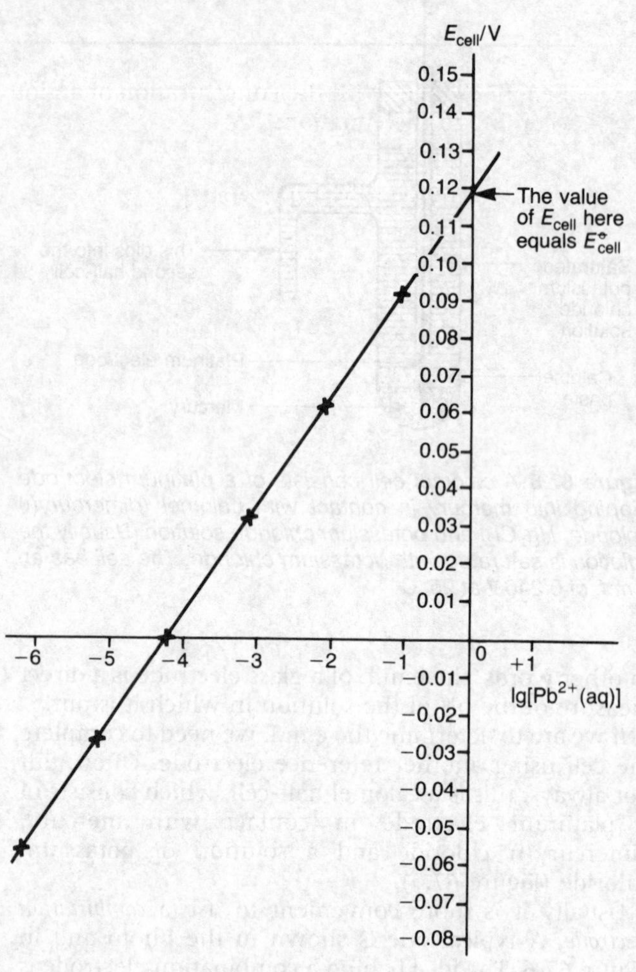

***Figure 67.7** The graph for the answer to question 67.5*

UNIT 67 SUMMARY

- Cell e.m.f. changes with the concentration of an ion according to the equation:

$$E_{M^{n+}/M} = E^{\ominus}_{M^{n+}/M} + \frac{RT}{nF}\ln[M^{n+}(aq)]$$

or

$$E_{M^{n+}/M} = E^{\ominus}_{M^{n+}/M} + \frac{0.026}{n}\ln[M^{n+}(aq)]$$

or

$$E_{M^{n+}/M} = E^{\ominus}_{M^{n+}/M} + \frac{0.059}{n}\lg[M^{n+}(aq)]$$

- The glass electrode has an e.m.f. that changes with hydrogen ion concentration, and is used to measure pH: $E = \text{constant} - 0.059\text{pH}$, where $\text{pH} = -\lg[H^+(aq)]$.
- Establishing equilibrium constants from e.m.f.s:
  - (i) Write down the cell reaction.
  - (ii) Write down the value of n, the number of moles of electrons transferred.
  - (iii) Work out $E^{\ominus}_{cell}$.
  - (iv) Write down the equilibrium constant for the reaction.
  - (v) Put $E^{\ominus}_{cell} = (0.059/n)\lg K_c$.
  - (vi) Calculate $K_c = \text{antilog}(nE^{\ominus}_{cell}/0.059)$.
  - (vii) Put in the units of K_c.

68

Corrosion

68.1 An example of corrosion

We can think of corrosion occurring whenever a metal surface is destroyed by being converted into a compound. The most common example is iron turning to rust. There is a connection between corrosion of iron and electrochemical cells. To see what this connection is, we shall start by looking at another example of corrosion. This is the wearing away of zinc in acid.

The electrode potentials that we drew up in Table 66.1 tell us the relative reducing (and oxidising) powers of the metals. We know, for example, that, because $E^\ominus_{Zn^{2+}/Zn} = -0.76\,V$, zinc should reduce hydrogen ions and give off hydrogen from an acid:

$$Zn(s) + 2H^+(aq) \rightarrow Zn^{2+}(aq) + H_2(g)$$

Similarly, because $E^\ominus_{Cu^{2+}/Cu} = +0.34\,V$, copper should not be able to release hydrogen from an acid. If you were to put a few zinc granules or a zinc rod into dilute sulphuric acid, you would find hydrogen is given off, but only very slowly. If you were to add copper turnings, or a copper strip, to another sample of the acid, no hydrogen at all would be given off. Both observations confirm the predictions from cell e.m.f. values.

An interesting thing happens if you put the zinc rod and the copper strip into the same solution of acid and connect them with a conducting wire (Figure 68.1). Hydrogen is given off very rapidly from the copper. What happens is this: In the same way as in a conventional cell, the electrons travel round the external circuit to the copper. At the copper, hydrogen ions from the acid are reduced. The reactions are

at the zinc	$Zn(s) \rightarrow Zn^{2+}(aq) + 2e^-$
at the copper	$2H^+(aq) + 2e^- \rightarrow H_2(g)$

The overall reaction is the same as if the copper were absent:

$$Zn(s) + 2H^+(aq) \rightarrow Zn^{2+}(aq) + H_2(g)$$

The reason why the hydrogen appears at the copper is complicated, and to do with a phenomenon known as *overpotential* (or overvoltage). We shall talk about overpotential in Unit 72 on electrolysis; for the present we shall just accept that it is easier for hydrogen to be given off from the copper.

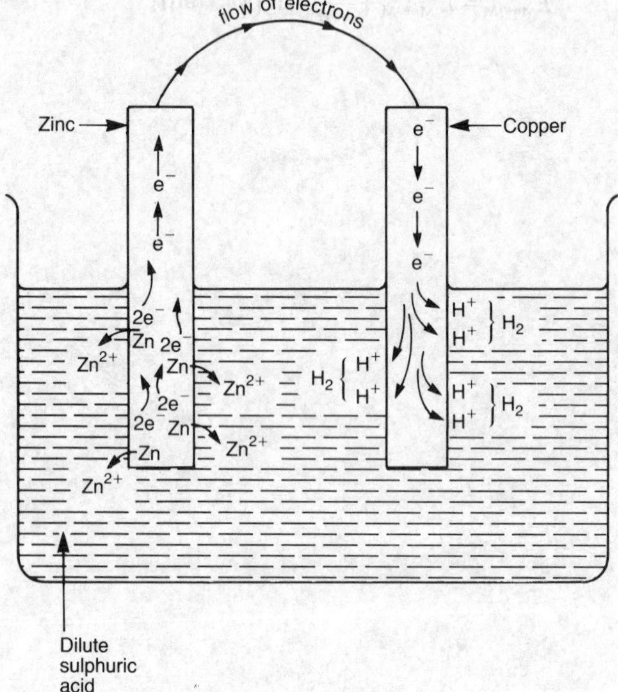

Figure 68.1 *When a strip of zinc is connected to a strip of copper, and the two strips are placed into acid, hydrogen is given off from the copper. The zinc dissolves, and the electrons 'lost' travel round to the copper. At the copper, hydrogen ions in the acid combine with the electrons to make hydrogen gas*

This simple experiment shows that zinc will be corroded much more quickly in acid if it is connected to copper. In fact we do not need to join the zinc and copper by a wire. It is easier to place them directly in contact. This is what happens in the laboratory preparation of hydrogen. Zinc granules are placed in dilute sulphuric acid. A little copper(II) sulphate is added, which has the effect of increasing the rate at which hydrogen is given off. Often it is said that the copper(II) sulphate is acting as a catalyst; but this is not strictly true. Rather, what happens is that a little of the zinc displaces copper from the solution:

$$Zn(s) + Cu^{2+}(aq) \rightarrow Zn^{2+}(aq) + Cu(s)$$

The copper coats portions of the zinc, and provides the path for the hydrogen to be given off. Instead of the electrons wandering round an external circuit, they pass directly from the zinc to the copper coating.

68.2 The rusting of iron

You may have performed some simple experiments to show that iron rusts only when there is water and oxygen present. Rust is a complicated material that contains various types of hydrated iron(III) oxide, $Fe_2O_3{\cdot}xH_2O$. (The number of moles of water, x, varies.) Iron begins to rust at places on its surface where there is an impurity, or where the iron lattice has imperfections. At these points some iron atoms produce iron(II) ions in solution. (We saw this type of behaviour in the work on electrode potentials, in Unit 66.) The reaction is

$$Fe(s) \rightarrow Fe^{2+}(aq) + 2e^-$$

which shows that the iron suffers an oxidation. You may remember that an electrode where oxidation occurs is called the *anode*. As the iron(II) ions move away from the anode region they meet hydroxide ions and produce iron(II) hydroxide:

$$Fe^{2+}(aq) + 2OH^-(aq) \rightarrow Fe(OH)_2(s)$$

It is the dissolved oxygen that oxidises the iron(II) hydroxide to the complicated substance we call rust:

$$Fe(OH)_2(s) + \text{dissolved oxygen} \rightarrow \text{rust, } Fe_2O_3{\cdot}xH_2O$$

In the water there are hydrogen ions, especially if the water is at all polluted by gases such as sulphur dioxide. At a neighbouring point on the surface of the iron the hydrogen ions take up the electrons liberated from the anode area:

$$2H^+(aq) + 2e^- \rightarrow H_2(g)$$

This is a process of reduction, so we can call the place where it occurs the *cathode*. The hydrogen produced at the cathode also reacts with dissolved oxygen to make water.

Figure 68.2 illustrates the fact that iron rusts at the anodic area. If a drop of water covers an iron surface, the anodic region will be found near the centre of the drop, and the cathode at the edges. One reason for this is that there will be more oxygen dissolved from the air near the edges of the drop. Therefore, *initially* more rust will be made at the edges than at the centre. The layer of rust at the edges tends to prevent further corrosion taking place there. However, nearer the centre of the drop, where there is less oxygen, the iron(II) ions have time to float away from the surface, and rust particles are not made directly at the surface. This means the surface does not become coated with rust, so further corrosion can take place. This is why even a small break in the paintwork of a car can, in time, produce an enormous amount of corrosion under the paint some distance from the original blemish: the greatest amount of corrosion occurs some distance from the region where the most oxygen is available.

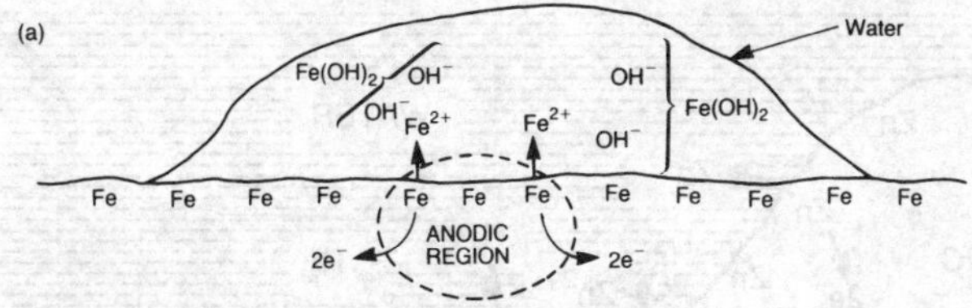

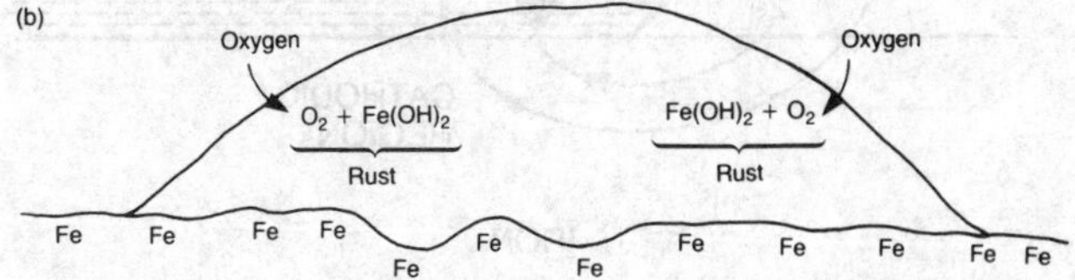

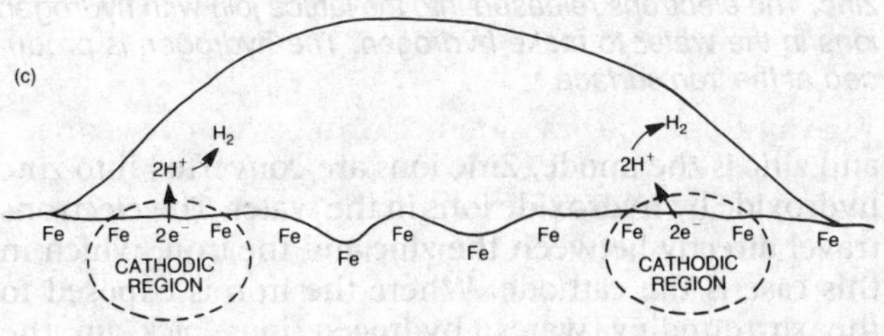

Figure 68.2 *Three stages in the rusting of iron. (a) Fe^{2+} ions go into the water and make $Fe(OH)_2$ with OH^- ions present in the water. Each Fe^{2+} ion leaves $2e^-$ in the metal lattice. (b) At the surface of the drop there is more oxygen dissolved. Here rust is made. Where Fe atoms have made Fe^{2+}, holes appear in the lattice. (c) The electrons released combine with H^+ ions in water to give H_2 gas*

68.3 How does a layer of zinc prevent iron rusting?

If iron is dipped into molten zinc (at about 450° C) it gains a layer of zinc over its surface. Iron with its layer of zinc is said to be galvanised. There are two reasons why the zinc prevents the iron rusting away. The first, most obvious, reason is that it prevents water or oxygen reaching the iron. The second, more interesting, reason is that even if the zinc becomes partially worn away, it still prevents rusting. Figure 68.3 will give you an idea of why this happens.

A somewhat similar situation arises to the zinc and copper that we met in section 68.1. In that case the copper was not worn away; rather, it provided a path for the reaction of zinc with hydrogen ions to give off hydrogen successfully. So it is with zinc and iron. Zinc has a more negative electrode potential than iron. (The values are $E^\ominus_{Zn^{2+}/Zn} = -0.76$ V, $E^\ominus_{Fe^{2+}/Fe} = -0.44$ V.) Therefore, zinc will react according to the equation

$$Zn(s) \rightarrow Zn^{2+}(aq) + 2e^-$$

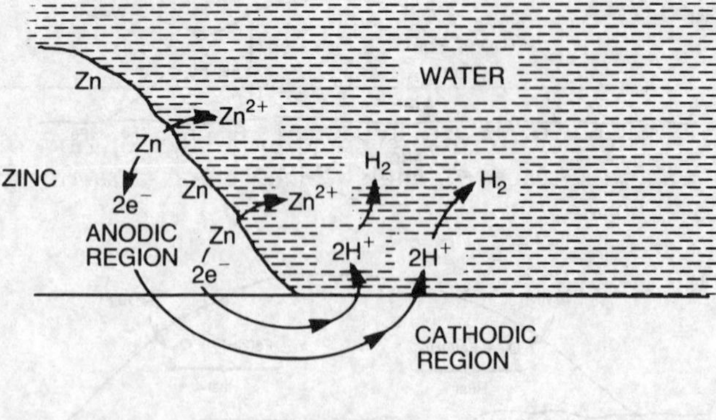

***Figure 68.3** A layer of zinc prevents iron from rusting. Instead of Fe^{2+} ions going into solution, Zn^{2+} ions are lost from the zinc. The electrons released into the lattice join with hydrogen ions in the water to make hydrogen. The hydrogen is produced at the iron surface*

and zinc is the anode. Zinc ions are converted into zinc hydroxide by hydroxide ions in the water. The electrons travel directly between the zinc and the iron, which in this case is the cathode. Where the iron is exposed to the surrounding water, hydrogen ions pick up the electrons:

$$2H^+(aq) + 2e^- \rightarrow H_2(g)$$

The point is that the iron remains unaffected; it is protected from corrosion.

68.4 Why does tin protect iron from corrosion?

The enormous variety of 'tin cans' that are used for preserving foodstuffs, beer and so on shows that tin is very handy for protecting iron or steel. It is possible to plate steel with a very thin layer of tin much more easily than it is to plate with zinc. Also, tin is less reactive than zinc, so it is less likely to dissolve in liquids stored in the cans.

However, tin is not so effective as zinc in preventing corrosion. The electrode potentials are $E^{\ominus}_{Fe^{2+}/Fe} = -0.44\,V$, $E^{\ominus}_{Sn^{2+}/Sn} = -0.14\,V$. The iron is the more negative, so it behaves like the zinc in the previous example. The iron becomes the anode, at which the reaction

$$Fe(s) \rightarrow Fe^{2+}(aq) + 2e^-$$

takes place. This tells us that the iron will dissolve. That is, it will corrode and the iron(II) ions go on to make rust. You can see that tin only protects iron provided the tin is not holed. Zinc continues to protect iron even if it is holed.

68.1 Why do you think the zinc on galvanised iron is sometimes called a *sacrificial anode*?

68.2 Explain why blocks of magnesium can be attached to the hulls of ships or attached to iron pipes with the aim of preventing rusting. ($E^{\ominus}_{Mg^{2+}/Mg} = -2.37\,V$.)

68.3 Why is it that, given enough time, corrosion will always defeat the protection applied to iron?

68.4 Let us do a very rough calculation on corrosion. Suppose a car contains 100 kg of steel (iron), and that 1000 cars are rusting away in a dump. Assume the formula of rust is $Fe_2O_3{\cdot}3H_2O$. What is the mass of rust made when all the cars have completely rusted away?

Answers

68.1 You should now know that the zinc acts as an anode. The zinc is worn away before the iron; therefore it is 'sacrificed' instead of the iron.

68.2 Because magnesium has a more negative electrode potential than iron, it behaves in the same way as zinc. The magnesium will wear away before the iron.

68.3 Eventually the layer of zinc on a piece of iron will be worn away owing to the reaction taking place at its surface. Once this happens, the iron will rust away. Even if the zinc is not holed, eventually it will be worn away through use and the iron exposed. Similarly, paint will eventually be worn away owing to weathering. Decay and corruption get iron, and us all, in the end!

68.4 One mole of $Fe_2O_3{\cdot}3H_2O$ contains $2 \times 56\,g = 112\,g$ of iron, $6 \times 16\,g = 96\,g$ of oxygen, and $6 \times 1\,g = 6\,g$ of hydrogen. Total, 214 g. Therefore, 1 g of iron would produce $(1\,g/112\,g) \times 214\,g = 1.911\,g$ of rust. In other words, the mass of rust produced from 10^{-3} kg of iron is 1.911×10^{-3} kg. Thus, we have that the mass of rust from 100 kg of steel is $1.911 \times 10^{-3}\,kg \times 100\,kg/10^{-3}\,kg = 191.1\,kg$. From 1000 cars, there will be 191.1×10^3 kg, a significant pollution problem!

UNIT 68 SUMMARY

- Rusting of iron is an example of corrosion. Rusting takes place in the presence of air (oxygen) and water. Rusting occurs at the anodic region:
  - (i) $Fe(s) \rightarrow Fe^{2+}(aq) + 2e^-$
  - (ii) $Fe^{2+}(aq) + 2OH^-(aq) \rightarrow Fe(OH)_2(s)$
  - (iii) $Fe(OH)_2(s) + \text{dissolved oxygen} \rightarrow \text{rust}(Fe_2O_3{\cdot}xH_2O)$
- Rusting of iron is prevented by a layer of zinc, or other reactive metal, which acts as a sacrificial anode.

69

Cells and thermodynamics

69.1 The link between free energy and cell e.m.f.s

In Unit 66 we discovered that a Daniell cell is a method for making the chemical reaction between zinc and copper(II) sulphate solution do useful work:

$$Zn(s) + Cu^{2+}(aq) \rightarrow Zn^{2+}(aq) + Cu(s); \quad \Delta G^{\ominus} = -212.1\ \text{kJ mol}^{-1}$$

We said that the free energy change in the reaction tells us how much work can be done by the cell. Indeed, we can link the free energy change to the cell electromotive force (e.m.f.). The e.m.f. measured when the chemicals in the cell are at standard conditions is the *standard e.m.f.*, $E^{\ominus}$. The connection between $E^{\ominus}$ and $\Delta G^{\ominus}$ for the Daniell cell is

$$\Delta G^{\ominus} = -2FE^{\ominus}$$

Here F is the faraday of electricity, and has a value 9.649×10^4 C mol^{-1}. It tells us the quantity of charge carried by 1 mol of electrons. The $2F$ in the equation represents the charge carried by 2 mol of electrons transferred between the zinc and copper(II) ions.

In general a cell reaction can involve n mol of electrons being transferred. In this case,

$$\Delta G^{\ominus} = -nFE^{\ominus}$$

There are several uses for this equation. If we know the value of $\Delta G^{\ominus}$, we can calculate $E^{\ominus}$; alternatively if we measure $E^{\ominus}$ we can discover the size of $\Delta G^{\ominus}$. Examples of each method follow in the next two sections.

69.2 Calculating standard e.m.f.s from free energy values

We shall calculate the e.m.f. of a cell in which the reaction is

$$Cu(s) + 2Ag^+(aq) \rightarrow Cu^{2+}(aq) + 2Ag(s); \quad \Delta G^{\ominus} = -89.2\ \text{kJ mol}^{-1}$$

Here 2 mol of silver ions, Ag^+, are converted into 2 mol of silver atoms. Therefore, 2 mol of electrons must be transferred, and we have $n=2$ in our equation $\Delta G^{\ominus} = -nFE^{\ominus}$. So

$$-89.2 \times 10^3\ \text{J mol}^{-1} = -2 \times 9.649 \times 10^4\ \text{C mol}^{-1} \times E^{\ominus}$$

Then

$$E^{\ominus} = \frac{-89.2 \times 10^3\ \text{J mol}^{-1}}{-2 \times 9.649 \times 10^4\ \text{C mol}^{-1}} = +0.462\ \text{V}$$

Notice that in this calculation we converted the $\Delta G^{\ominus}$ value from kJ mol^{-1} to J mol^{-1}. Also we made use of the fact that units of J C^{-1} are the same as volts, V.

We can check this result by working out the cell e.m.f. from the electrode potentials $E^{\ominus}_{Cu^{2+}/Cu} = +0.34$ V and $E^{\ominus}_{Ag^+/Ag} = +0.80$ V. If we apply the method we used in Unit 66, we have

$$\begin{aligned} E^{\ominus}_{cell} &= E^{\ominus}_{right} - E^{\ominus}_{left} \\ &= E^{\ominus}_{Ag^+/Ag} - E^{\ominus}_{Cu^{2+}/Cu} \\ &= +0.80\ \text{V} - 0.34\ \text{V} \\ &= +0.46\ \text{V} \end{aligned}$$

(You may remember that the more negative half-cell is on the left. In this case, the copper half-cell is more negative, i.e. less positive, than the silver half-cell.) The two results are in good agreement.

The next example will show you what happens in a reaction that has a positive $\Delta G^{\ominus}$. We consider the reaction

$$Pb(s) + Zn^{2+}(aq) \rightarrow Pb^{2+}(aq) + Zn(s); \quad \Delta G^{\ominus} = +122.9\ \text{kJ mol}^{-1}$$

Again, $n=2$, so

$$122.9 \times 10^3\ \text{J mol}^{-1} = -2 \times 9.649 \times 10^4\ \text{C mol}^{-1} \times E^{\ominus}$$

$$E^{\ominus} = \frac{122.9 \times 10^3\ \text{J mol}^{-1}}{-2 \times 9.649 \times 10^4\ \text{C mol}^{-1}} = -0.637\ \text{V}$$

This time the cell e.m.f. turns out to be negative in sign. This is another way of telling us that the reaction as we have written it cannot take place. We already know that a reaction with a positive free energy change cannot be a spontaneous reaction. So a proposed cell that produces a negative $E^{\ominus}$ also means that the reaction cannot take place.

Instead, the reaction must occur in the opposite

direction to the one we have written down. That is, if we made a cell from Pb^{2+}/Pb and Zn^{2+}/Zn half-cells, the reaction that would actually take place is

$$Pb^{2+}(aq) + Zn(s) \rightarrow Pb(s) + Zn^{2+}(aq)$$

Now, $\Delta G^{\ominus} = -122.9\,\text{kJ mol}^{-1}$ and $E^{\ominus} = +0.637\,\text{V}$.

69.3 Calculating free energy values from standard e.m.f.s

If you were to measure $E^{\ominus}$ of the Daniell cell you would find it to be 1.1 V. Using the equation $\Delta G^{\ominus} = -nFE^{\ominus}$ we find

$$\begin{aligned}\Delta G^{\ominus} &= -2 \times 9.649 \times 10^4\,\text{C mol}^{-1} \times 1.1\,\text{V}\\ &= -212.3 \times 10^3\,\text{C V mol}^{-1}\\ &= -212.3\,\text{kJ mol}^{-1}\end{aligned}$$

Here we have used the fact that Coulomb volts, C V, and the joule, J, are equivalent units. The value we have calculated is in good agreement with the value calculated from the values in data tables which we quoted at the start of section 69.1.

69.1 (i) How many moles of electrons are transferred when 1 mol of zinc is converted into zinc ions in the Daniell cell?

(ii) Use your answer and the equation $\Delta G^{\ominus} = -nFE^{\ominus}$ to calculate $E^{\ominus}$ for the cell. How does your result compare with the accepted value, 1.1 V?

69.2 Here is a reaction which tells us that potassium will liberate hydrogen from acid (please do *not* try this – the reaction is extremely dangerous):

$$2K(s) + 2H^+(aq) \rightarrow 2K^+(aq) + H_2(g); \quad \Delta G^{\ominus} = -566.4\,\text{kJ mol}^{-1}$$

(i) Calculate the corresponding cell e.m.f.

(ii) If you attempted to make up this cell, what would you use as the half-cells?

(iii) What is the connection between your answers and the standard electrode potential of potassium, which is $E^{\ominus}_{K^+/K} = -2.92\,\text{V}$?

(iv) Is there anything that strikes you as odd about the potassium half-cell?

69.3 A student said that under standard conditions the reaction

$$2Cr^{3+}(aq) + 3Cd(s) \rightarrow 2Cr(s) + 3Cd^{2+}(aq)$$

would take place at 298 K. Explain why the student was wrong.

(i) To answer this question, first work out $\Delta G^{\ominus}$ for the reaction. You will need the values $\Delta G^{\ominus}(Cd^{2+}) = -77.6\,\text{kJ mol}^{-1}$ and $\Delta G^{\ominus}(Cr^{3+}) = -204.9\,\text{kJ mol}^{-1}$.

(ii) Now decide on your answer from the sign of $\Delta G^{\ominus}$.

(iii) Having realised his error, the student wrote down the reaction showing the correct direction:

$$2Cr(s) + 3Cd^{2+}(aq) \rightarrow 2Cr^{3+}(aq) + 3Cd(s)$$

What is $\Delta G^{\ominus}$ now?

(iv) How many moles of electrons are transferred in this reaction?

(v) Calculate $E^{\ominus}$ for a cell that used this reaction.

(vi) Calculate $E^{\ominus}$ given $E^{\ominus}_{Cd^{2+}/Cd} = -0.40\,\text{V}$ and $E^{\ominus}_{Cr^{3+}/Cr} = -0.74\,\text{V}$. How do the two results compare?

69.4 The standard electrode potential of aluminium can be measured in the cell

$$Pt(s) \mid \underset{1\,\text{atm}}{H_2(g),} \mid \underset{1\,\text{mol dm}^{-3}}{H^+(aq),} \;\vdots\vdots\; \underset{1\,\text{mol dm}^{-3}}{Al^{3+}(aq),} \mid Al(s)$$

The result is $E^{\ominus}_{cell} = E^{\ominus}_{Al^{3+}/Al} = -1.66\,\text{V}$. Which of these two reactions actually takes place at the aluminium electrode: (a) $Al^{3+}(aq) + 3e^- \rightarrow Al(s)$ or (b) $Al(s) \rightarrow Al^{3+}(aq) + 3e^-$?

Answers

69.1 (i) Two.

(ii) $E^{\ominus} = \dfrac{-212.1 \times 10^3\,\text{J mol}^{-1}}{-2 \times 9.649 \times 10^4\,\text{C mol}^{-1}} = 1.1\,\text{V}$

Excellent agreement.

69.2 (i) $E^{\ominus} = \dfrac{-566.4 \times 10^3\,\text{J mol}^{-1}}{-2 \times 9.649 \times 10^4\,\text{C mol}^{-1}} = 2.94\,\text{V}$

(ii) One of them might be expected to consist of a potassium electrode in $1\,\text{mol dm}^{-3}$ solution of potassium ions (but see below). The other would be a S.H.E., where the reaction

$$2H^+(aq) + 2e^- \rightarrow H_2(g)$$

takes place.

(iii) Given that one of the cells is a S.H.E., the e.m.f. of the cell should be related to the standard electrode potential of potassium. The sign is different because of the convention of measuring electrode potentials with the S.H.E. as the left-hand electrode.

(iv) The problem is imagining a half-cell that has potassium in an *aqueous* solution of potassium ions. You should know that potassium reacts violently with water. In other words it is not possible to set up this half-cell. This illustrates the fact that many of the $E^{\ominus}$ values that you will find in data tables have not been determined directly. Often they are found by indirect means; for example, by combining results from other cells and $\Delta G^{\ominus}$

Answers – contd.

values, or in this case by using potassium amalgams.

69.3 (i)

$$\Delta G^\ominus = 3\Delta G^\ominus(Cd^{2+}) - 2\Delta G^\ominus(Cr^{3+})$$
$$= 3(-77.6\,\text{kJ mol}^{-1}) - 2(-204.9\,\text{kJ mol}^{-1})$$
$$= -232.8\,\text{kJ mol}^{-1} + 409.8\,\text{kJ mol}^{-1}$$
$$= +177\,\text{kJ mol}^{-1}$$

(ii) The positive value of $\Delta G^\ominus$ tells us that the reaction is *not* spontaneous as the student has written it down; that is, the reaction will take place in the opposite direction. However, notice that if standard conditions for reactants and products did not apply, e.g. if the student mixed only Cr^{3+}(aq) and Cd(s), then the reaction would take place as written until a position of equilibrium was reached.

(iii) $\Delta G^\ominus = -177\,\text{kJ mol}^{-1}$.

(iv) Six.

(v) $E^\ominus = \dfrac{-177 \times 10^3\,\text{J mol}^{-1}}{-6 \times 9.649 \times 10^4\,\text{C mol}^{-1}} = +0.306\,\text{V}$

(vi) The chromium electrode gives up electrons, so this is the negative, left-hand half-cell. Therefore we have

$$E^\ominus_{\text{cell}} = E^\ominus_{\text{right}} - E^\ominus_{\text{left}}$$
$$= E^\ominus_{Cd^{2+}/Cd} - E^\ominus_{Cr^{3+}/Cr}$$
$$= -0.40\,\text{V} - (-0.74\,\text{V})$$
$$= +0.34\,\text{V}$$

The difference is due to uncertainties in the values of the free energies of formation of the two ions.

69.4 The negative value for the aluminium electrode tells us that this is the electrode that gives up electrons to the external circuit. Therefore it is reaction (b) that takes place. The overall cell reaction is

$$Al(s) + 3H^+(aq) \rightarrow Al^{3+}(aq) + (3/2)H_2(g)$$

or

$$2Al(s) + 6H^+(aq) \rightarrow 2Al^{3+}(aq) + 3H_2(g)$$

UNIT 69 SUMMARY

- The link between free energy and cell e.m.f. is $\Delta G^\ominus = -nFE^\ominus$, where F is the faraday of electricity and n is the number of moles of electrons transferred.
- A reaction with a negative e.m.f. cannot occur; a reaction with a positive e.m.f. can occur (but may take place very slowly).

70

Redox potentials

70.1 Standard redox potentials

We know that the more negative the standard electrode potential of a metal, the stronger is its reducing power. That is, the better the metal is at releasing its electrons and turning into positive ions. A metal like sodium, which easily forms Na^+ ions, is a case in point. Actually, sodium ions show little tendency to gain electrons. That is, they are not very good oxidising agents. Thus, another way of looking at a metal with a very negative $E^\ominus$ is to say that the more negative the value, the weaker is the oxidising power of the metal's ions. Conversely, the more positive its value of $E^\ominus$, the weaker is the reducing power of the metal, and the stronger is the oxidising power of its ions. An $E^\ominus$ value therefore tells us about the balance between a reducing agent and an oxidising agent. We can write a reaction taking place in any half-cell as

$$\text{oxidising agent} + \text{electrons} \rightleftharpoons \text{reducing agent}$$

For example, a zinc half-cell fits this pattern:

$$Zn^{2+}(aq) + 2e^- \rightleftharpoons Zn(s)$$

Now, there are many types of oxidising and reducing agents in which chemists are interested. Some of them involve non-metals like chlorine and fluorine. Others involve ions of the same element but which have different oxidation states; for example iron(II) and iron(III) (Fe^{2+} and Fe^{3+}), iodate(V) and iodide (IO_3^- and I^-). A method has been established that allows us to measure the e.m.f. of a half-cell that involves changes between pairs of ions like these. A typical example is shown connected to a S.H.E. in Figure 70.1.

The electrode is made of platinum, which provides the path for electrons to travel into, or out of, the solution. If we were to connect this half-cell to a standard hydrogen electrode and measure the cell e.m.f., we would find that $E^\ominus_{cell} = +0.77$ V. This value is known as the *standard redox potential* of the iron(III)/iron(II) system, which we shall write $E^\ominus_{Fe^{3+}/Fe^{2+}}$. (The word 'redox' comes from an abbreviation of 'reduction and oxidation'. An electrode potential is a particular type of redox potential.) The fact that $E^\ominus_{Fe^{3+}/Fe^{2+}} = +0.77$ V

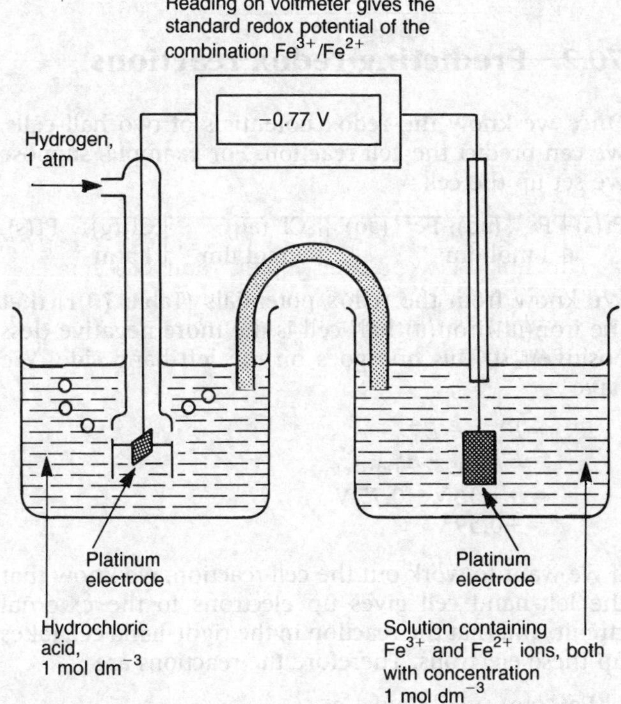

***Figure 70.1** Measuring the standard redox potential of the combination Fe^{3+} and Fe^{2+}*

means that the S.H.E. is the negative half-cell. Therefore the reaction taking place in the S.H.E. is

$$H_2(g) \rightarrow 2H^+(aq) + 2e^-$$

The electrons given up by the hydrogen gas travel round to the iron(III)/iron(II) half-cell. There they are taken up by the iron(III) ions:

$$Fe^{3+}(aq) + e^- \rightarrow Fe^{2+}(aq)$$

The overall cell reaction is

$$2Fe^{3+}(aq) + H_2(g) \rightarrow 2Fe^{2+}(aq) + 2H^+(aq)$$

In this case the iron(III) ions are behaving as oxidising agents, and hydrogen gas as a reducing agent.

Some standard redox potentials are shown in Table 70.1.

Table 70.1. Some standard redox potentials

Reaction	$E^\ominus$/V	*Comment*
$Cr_2O_7^{2-}(aq)+14H^+(aq)+6e^- \rightleftharpoons 2Cr^{3+}(aq)+7H_2O(l)$	+1.33	Dichromate(VI) in acid
$MnO_4^-(aq)+8H^+(aq)+5e^- \rightleftharpoons Mn^{2+}(aq)+4H_2O(l)$	+1.51	Manganate(VII) in acid
$MnO_4^-(aq)+4H^+(aq)+3e^- \rightleftharpoons MnO_2(s)+2H_2O(l)$	+1.59	Manganate(VII) in alkali
$2IO_3^-(aq)+12H^+(aq)+10e^- \rightleftharpoons I_2(s)+6H_2O(l)$	+1.20	
$Co^{3+}(aq)+e^- \rightleftharpoons Co^{2+}(aq)$	+1.84	
$Ce^{4+}(aq)+e^- \rightleftharpoons Ce^{3+}(aq)$	+1.45	
$Fe^{3+}(aq)+e^- \rightleftharpoons Fe^{2+}(aq)$	+0.77	
$Fe(CN)_6^{3-}(aq)+e^- \rightleftharpoons Fe(CN)_6^{4-}(aq)$	+0.36	Complex ions change $E^\ominus$
$Cu^{2+}(aq)+e^- \rightleftharpoons Cu^+(aq)$	+0.15	
$Cl_2(aq)+2e^- \rightleftharpoons 2Cl^-(aq)$	+1.36	
$Br_2(aq)+2e^- \rightleftharpoons 2Br^-(aq)$	+1.07	
$I_2(aq)+2e^- \rightleftharpoons 2I^-(aq)$	+0.54	I_2 present as I_3^-

70.2 Predicting redox reactions

Once we know the redox potentials of two half-cells, we can predict the cell reaction. For example, suppose we set up the cell

$$Pt(s) \mid Fe^{3+}(aq),\ Fe^{2+}(aq),\ 1\ mol\ dm^{-3} \ \vdots\vdots\ Cl^-(aq),\ 1\ mol\ dm^{-3} \mid Cl_2(g),\ 1\ atm \quad Pt(s)$$

We know from the redox potentials (Table 70.1) that the iron(III)/iron(II) half-cell is the more negative (less positive); so this one goes on the left-hand side. We have

$$\begin{aligned} E^\ominus_{cell} &= E^\ominus_{right} - E^\ominus_{left} \\ &= E^\ominus_{Cl_2/Cl^-} - E^\ominus_{Fe^{3+}/Fe^{2+}} \\ &= +1.36\ V - 0.77\ V \\ &= +0.59\ V \end{aligned}$$

If we want to work out the cell reaction, we know that the left-hand cell gives up electrons to the external circuit, and that the reaction in the right-hand cell takes up these electrons. Therefore the reactions are

$$Fe^{2+}(aq) \rightarrow Fe^{3+}(aq) + e^-$$
$$Cl_2(g) + 2e^- \rightarrow 2Cl^-(aq)$$

Overall the balanced reaction is

$$2Fe^{2+}(aq) + Cl_2(g) \rightarrow 2Fe^{3+}(aq) + 2Cl^-(aq)$$

As before (section 66.5), we can show this reaction as an equilibrium if we wish:

$$2Fe^{2+}(aq) + Cl_2(g) \rightleftharpoons 2Fe^{3+}(aq) + 2Cl^-(aq)$$

70.3 Predicting reactions in the laboratory from redox potentials

Redox potentials are very useful, not so much as sources of electricity in cells, but because they allow us to make predictions about reactions in general. The reaction we have just looked at is a case in point. From the cell reaction we worked out, we know that chlorine gas should oxidise iron(II) ions into iron(III) ions. If you were to bubble the gas through a solution of iron(II) ions, for example iron(II) sulphate solution, you would discover that the reaction does indeed take place.

The chief difference is that it is unlikely that you would be using standard conditions; but fortunately changes in concentration and temperature have to be quite large before cell e.m.f.s change markedly. Also, it so happens that because redox reactions involve ions, the reactions tend to be fast. This is one time when we can use thermodynamic data (which is what cell e.m.f.s are) without worrying over much that reactions will not occur because they are too slow.

The key to making correct predictions from redox potentials (Table 70.2) is to compare $E^\ominus$ values, and to recognise that:

The more negative half-cell will contain the reducing agent.

The more positive half-cell will contain the oxidising agent.

Table 70.2. Using redox potentials to predict reactions

Half-cell with the most negative $E^\ominus$; this gives $E^\ominus_{left}$	Contains the reducing agent, i.e. chemical with the lowest oxidation number
Half-cell with the most positive $E^\ominus$; this gives $E^\ominus_{right}$	Contains the oxidising agent, i.e. chemical with the highest oxidation number
Combine the half-cell reactions	So that the oxidising agent reacts with the reducing agent. Balance the equation
Calculate $E^\ominus_{cell} = E^\ominus_{right} - E^\ominus_{left}$	If $E^\ominus_{cell}$ is much less than 0.6 V, your predictions may not agree with experiment

However, there is one proviso. Experience shows that if two redox potentials differ by much less than 0.6 V, the predictions made may not be valid in practice. This was first noticed by W. M. Latimer in 1952, who was particularly concerned with chemicals that might cause water to decompose. He used the 0.6 V figure as a rule of thumb, and others have adopted the same figure for reactions that are quite different to those in which he was interested.

You do not have to be too fussy about the '0.6 V rule', but if $E^\ominus$ values differ by only 0.1 or 0.2 V, then your predictions may well be wrong. Here is an example where we assume the rule works. The problem is as follows: What, if anything, would you expect to see if an acidified solution of potassium iodate(V), KIO_3, was added to potassium iodide solution?

First, it is as well to say that both these solutions are colourless. Now we look at the table of redox potentials (Table 70.1). We find $E^\ominus_{IO_3^-/I_2} = +1.20\,V$ and $E^\ominus_{I_2/I^-} = +0.54\,V$. Here the iodate(V) half-cell contains the oxidising agent. To decide which of the chemicals in a half-cell is the oxidising agent, you look for the one with the highest oxidation state. In this case the choice is between iodate(V) and the element iodine. By definition the oxidation state of an element is zero; so the iodate(V) is the oxidising agent. The cell e.m.f. would be $E^\ominus_{IO_3^-/I_2} - E^\ominus_{I_2/I^-} = +0.66\,V$.

Conversely, in the other half-cell we look for the reducing agent. This will be the chemical that is best able to lose electrons. Clearly it is the iodide ion. (If an iodine atom were to lose an electron it would turn into an I^+ ion, which does not exist.)

We can now write down the reactions that should take place:

$$2IO_3^-(aq) + 12H^+(aq) + 10e^- \rightarrow I_2(aq) + 6H_2O(l)$$
$$2I^-(aq) \rightarrow I_2(aq) + 2e^-$$

The balanced equation is

$$IO_3^-(aq) + 6H^+(aq) + 5I^-(aq) \rightarrow 3I_2(aq) + 3H_2O(l)$$

The product of the reaction is iodine, so we would expect to see a dark brown colour appear in the solution. This would be due to I_3^- ions made when the liberated iodine joins with any iodide ions remaining. You might also see black powdery specks of solid iodine float about. As the cell e.m.f. is above 0.6 V we would expect our predictions to be matched by experiment, as indeed they are.

70.4 Redox titrations

Titrations are one of the methods we can use to discover the precise concentrations of solutions. A typical titration involves adding a solution from a burette to another solution in a flask. The endpoint of the titration is found by watching a colour change take place. This is the method used in the examples we discussed in Unit 40. However, a problem arises when a suitable indicator cannot be found, or when the colour changes involved are unclear. In these cases redox potentials may sometimes come to the rescue.

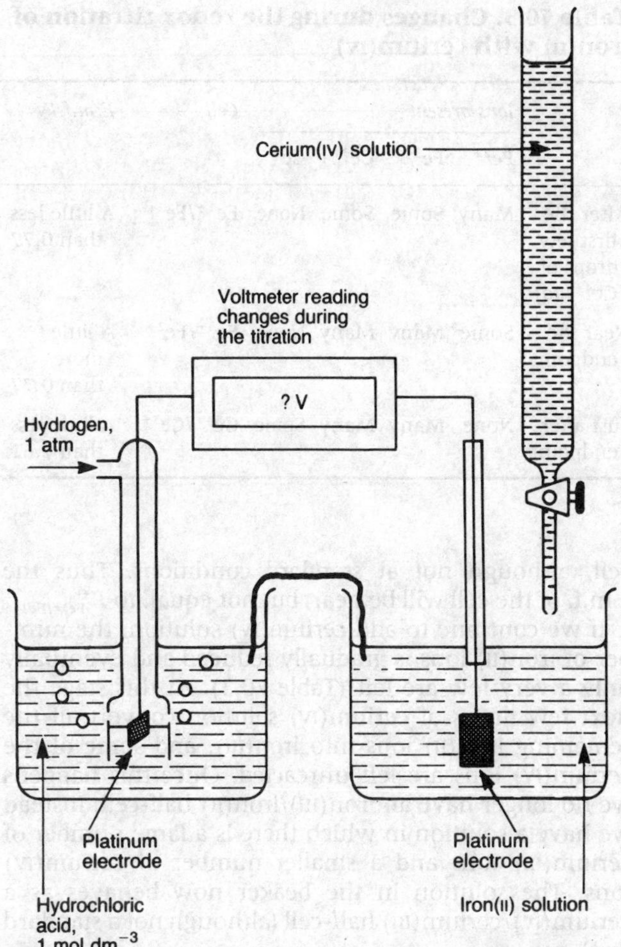

***Figure 70.2** A redox titration using cerium(IV) ions to determine the concentration of iron(II) ions. It is not necessary to use a S.H.E. as the reference electrode. Another type of half-cell will do, provided it has a constant e.m.f. However, the cell e.m.f. will not then correspond to standard values*

A particularly well known example (Figure 70.2) is a method of discovering the concentration of iron(II) ions in a solution by titrating them with a solution of cerium(IV). The redox potentials that are of interest here are $E^\ominus_{Fe^{3+}/Fe^{2+}} = +0.77\,V$ and $E^\ominus_{Ce^{4+}/Ce^{3+}} = +1.61\,V$. These tell us that cerium(IV) ions are the oxidising agents, and iron(II) ions are the reducing agents. They should react according to the equation

$$Fe^{2+}(aq) + Ce^{4+}(aq) \rightarrow Fe^{3+}(aq) + Ce^{3+}(aq)$$

Now imagine that we know the concentration of the cerium(IV) ion solution in the burette. We want to measure the concentration of the iron(II) solution. If we add just one drop of the cerium(IV) solution from the burette, some of the iron(II) ions will be oxidised. As a consequence the beaker would now contain a large number of unreacted iron(II) ions, but also some iron(III) ions as well. All of the cerium(IV) ions added would have been converted to cerium(III). The solution in the beaker now represents an iron(III)/iron(II) half-

Table 70.3. Changes during the redox titration of iron(II) with cerium(IV)

	Ions present				Cell	E.m.f./V
	Fe^{2+}	Fe^{3+}	Ce^{3+}	Ce^{4+}		
After the first few drops of Ce^{4+}(aq)	Many	Some	Some	None	Fe^{3+}/Fe^{2+}	A little less than 0.77
Near the endpoint	Some	Many	Many	None	Fe^{3+}/Fe^{2+}	A little more than 0.77
Just after endpoint	None	Many	Many	Some	Ce^{4+}/Ce^{3+}	A little less than 1.61

cell, although not at standard conditions. Thus the e.m.f. of the cell will be near, but not equal, to $E^{\ominus}_{Fe^{3+}/Fe^{2+}}$.

If we continue to add cerium(IV) solution, the number of iron(II) ions is gradually reduced and eventually only a very few are left (Table 70.3). At this stage the next few drops of cerium(IV) solution convert all the remaining iron(II) ions into iron(III), and some of the cerium(IV) ions are left unreacted. Once this happens we no longer have an iron(III)/iron(II) half-cell. Instead we have a solution in which there is a large number of cerium(III) ions and a smaller number of cerium(IV) ions. The solution in the beaker now behaves as a cerium(IV)/cerium(III) half-cell (although not a standard one).

Just before all the iron(II) ions are converted into iron(III) we have a cell with an e.m.f. of around +0.77 V. After all the iron(II) ions are oxidised, we have

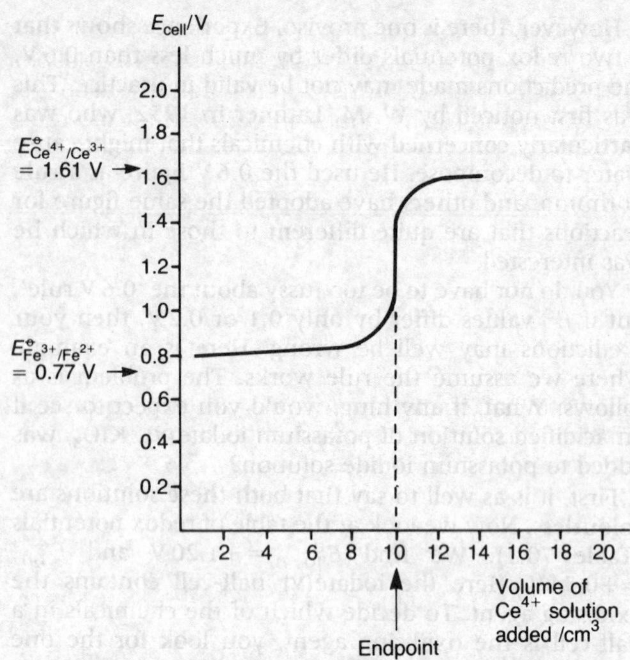

Figure 70.3 A typical graph of results obtained in a redox titration of Fe^{2+} ions with Ce^{4+} ions. The endpoint occurs when the line becomes (almost) vertical, in this case corresponding to 10 cm^3 of the Ce^{4+} solution

a cell with an e.m.f. of about +1.61 V. This rapid rise in e.m.f. occurs with the addition of just one drop of cerium(IV) solution. You should be able to understand why a graph of cell e.m.f. against volume of cerium(IV) solution added looks like that of Figure 70.3. The endpoint of the titration can be read from the graph and the concentration of the iron(II) solution calculated in the usual way.

70.1 (i) What is the e.m.f. of the cell

Pt(s) | Fe^{3+}(aq), Fe^{2+}(aq), 1 mol dm^{-3} ⁞⁞ $Cr_2O_7^{2-}$(aq), Cr^{3+}(aq), 1 mol dm^{-3}, H^+(aq) | Pt(s)

(ii) Write a balanced equation for the cell reaction.

70.2 Manganate(VII) ions can react in two different ways depending on the concentration of hydrogen ions in the solution. If the solution is rich in hydrogen ions, they react to make manganese(II) ions, Mn^{2+}(aq). If there are few hydrogen ions, we say the reaction occurs in alkaline conditions and manganese(IV) oxide, MnO_2, is made. What will be the e.m.f. of a cell made from a standard iodine/iodide half-cell and a standard manganate(VII) half-cell (i) in acid conditions and (ii) in alkaline conditions? In each case write down the cell reaction.

70.3 When an ion is converted into a complex ion, the redox potential changes. You can see this in the case of the e.m.f. of the iron(III)/iron(II) system (+0.77 V) and the hexacyanoferrate(III)/hexacyanoferrate(II) system (+0.36 V). The cyanide ion is said to *stabilise the oxidation state* of the iron. If you were to make up a cell

Pt(s) | $Fe(CN)_6^{3-}$(aq), $Fe(CN)_6^{4-}$(aq), 1 mol dm^{-3} ⁞⁞ Fe^{3+}(aq), Fe^{2+}(aq), 1 mol dm^{-3} | Pt(s)

what would be the e.m.f., and what would be the cell reaction?

70.4 The cell shown below was set up

Pt(s) | Fe^{3+}(aq), Fe^{2+}(aq), 1 mol dm^{-3} ⁞⁞ Br^-(aq), 1 mol dm^{-3} | Br_2(l) | Pt(s)

What would be the cell e.m.f.?

If potassium cyanide solution were added to the left-hand half-cell (with due care!), what would you expect to happen to the e.m.f. of the cell?

70.5 Imagine you were given a solution of potassium dichromate(VI) in a beaker, and a solution of iron(II) sulphate in a burette. You do not know the concentration of dichromate(VI) ions, but the concentration of the iron(II) solution is known. Your task is to carry out a redox titration using the two solutions in order to determine the concentration of dichromate(VI) ions. Write an equation for the reaction that takes place in the titration. Draw a diagram of the apparatus you would use and sketch a graph showing how the e.m.f. changes in the course of the titration.

Answers

70.1 (i) $E^{\ominus}_{cell} = E^{\ominus}_{Cr_2O_7^{2-}/Cr^{3+}} - E^{\ominus}_{Fe^{3+}/Fe^{2+}}$
$= +1.33\,V - 0.77\,V$
$= +0.56\,V$

(ii) The dichromate(VI) ion is the oxidising agent, and iron(II) the reducing agent. Therefore the cell reaction is

$$6Fe^{2+}(aq)\ Cr_2O_7^{2-}(aq) + 14H^+(aq) \rightarrow 6Fe^{3+}(aq) + 2Cr^{3+}(aq) + 7H_2O(l)$$

70.2 In acid conditions,

$E^{\ominus}_{cell} = E^{\ominus}_{MnO_4^-/Mn^{2+}} - E^{\ominus}_{I_2/I^-} = +1.51\,V - 0.54\,V = +0.97\,V.$

The reaction is

$$2MnO_4^-(aq) + 10I^-(aq) + 16H^+(aq) \rightarrow 2Mn^{2+}(aq) + 5I_2(s) + 8H_2O(l)$$

In alkaline conditions,

$E^{\ominus}_{cell} = E^{\ominus}_{MnO_4^-/MnO_2} - E^{\ominus}_{I_2/I^-} = +1.59\,V - 0.54\,V = +1.04\,V.$

The reaction is

$$2MnO_4^-(aq) + 6I^-(aq) + 8H^+(aq) \rightarrow 2MnO_2(aq) + 3I_2(s) + 4H_2O(l)$$

70.3 $E^{\ominus}_{cell} = E^{\ominus}_{Fe^{3+}/Fe^{2+}} - E^{\ominus}_{Fe(CN)_6^{3-}/Fe(CN)_6^{4-}}$
$= +0.77\,V - 0.36\,V = +0.41\,V$

The reaction is

$$Fe(CN)_6^{4-}(aq) + Fe^{3+}(aq) \rightarrow Fe(CN)_6^{3-}(aq) + Fe^{2+}(aq)$$

70.4 $E^{\ominus}_{cell} = E^{\ominus}_{Br_2/Br^-} - E^{\ominus}_{Fe^{3+}/Fe^{2+}}$
$= +1.07\,V - 0.77\,V = +0.30\,V$

If cyanide ions are added, the left-hand half-cell would change its e.m.f. to $E^{\ominus}_{Fe(CN)_6^{3-}/Fe(CN)_6^{4-}} = +0.36\,V$. There fore the e.m.f. would change to +0.71 V.

70.5 After one drop of iron(II) solution is added the beaker will contain a mixture of $Cr_2O_7^{2-}$, Cr^{3+} and Fe^{3+} ions. The e.m.f. will be near to $E^{\ominus}_{Cr_2O_7^{2-}/Cr^{3+}} = +1.33\,V$. At the end of the titration there will be Cr^{3+}, Fe^{2+} and Fe^{3+} ions. The e.m.f. will be near to $E^{\ominus}_{Fe^{3+}/Fe^{2+}} = +0.77\,V$. The reaction is:

$$6Fe^{2+}(aq) + Cr_2O_7^{2-}(aq) + 14H^+(aq) \rightarrow 6Fe^{3+}(aq) + 2Cr^{3+}(aq) + 7H_2O(l)$$

The apparatus would be like that in Figure 70.2. The graph is shown in Figure 70.4.

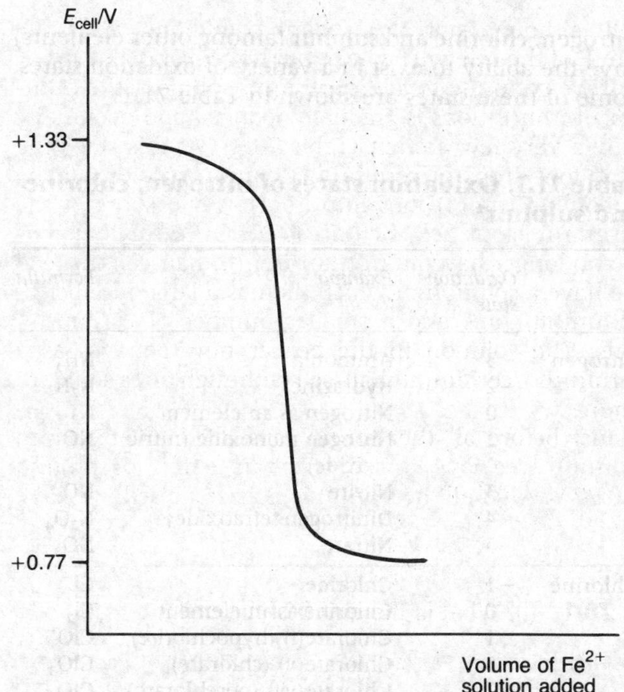

Figure 70.4 *Graph for answer to question 70.5*

UNIT 70 SUMMARY

- The standard redox potential is measured against a standard hydrogen electrode (see Figure 70.1).
- In a reaction involving two redox systems:
  (i) The more negative half-cell will contain the reducing agent.
  (ii) The more positive half-cell will contain the oxidising agent.
- Reactions whose half-cell redox potentials differ by 0.6 V or more tend to go to completion, i.e. the equilibrium lies in favour of the products of the reaction.
- The endpoint of some titrations can be found by e.m.f. measurements.
- The half-cell with the most negative $E^{\ominus}$ contains the reducing agent.
- The half-cell with the most positive $E^{\ominus}$ contains the oxidising agent.

71

Redox charts

71.1 What is a redox chart?

Nitrogen, chlorine and sulphur (among other elements) have the ability to exist in a variety of oxidation states. Some of these states are shown in Table 71.1.

Table 71.1. Oxidation states of nitrogen, chlorine and sulphur*

	Oxidation state	*Example*	*Formula*
Nitrogen	−3	Ammonia	NH_3
	−2	Hydrazine	N_2H_4
	0	Nitrogen as an element	N_2
	2	Nitrogen monoxide (nitric oxide)	NO
	3	Nitrite	NO_2^-
	4	Dinitrogen tetraoxide†	N_2O_4
	5	Nitrate	NO_3^-
Chlorine	−1	Chloride	Cl^-
	0	Chlorine as an element	Cl_2
	1	Chlorate(I) (hypochlorite)	ClO^-
	5	Chlorate(V) (chlorate)	ClO_3^-
	7	Chlorate(VII) (perchlorate)	ClO_4^-
Sulphur	−2	Sulphide	S^{2-}
	0	Sulphur as an element	S or S_8
	2	Thiosulphate	$S_2O_3^{2-}$
	4	Sulphite	SO_3^{2-}
	6	Sulphate	SO_4^{2-}

*Not all the oxidation states are shown
†Also nitrogen dioxide, NO_2

In a redox chart we link the various oxidation states of an element to standard redox potentials. For example, Figures 71.1–71.3 show the diagrams for nitrogen, chlorine and sulphur. Diagrams like these summarise a lot of information, and allow us to make predictions about whether particular reactions will take place.

71.2 How to use redox charts

Before we discover how to use the charts, let us try to answer this question: 'Will a solution of nitric acid oxidise copper metal to copper(II) ions and give off nitrogen dioxide?' We have to recognise that a solution of nitric acid is a mixture of nitrate ions and hydrogen ions. With this established, we can answer the question in the same way as in previous units. We start by asking which e.m.f. is the more negative (less positive), and we know that this is the one that gives up electrons. In this case $E^\ominus_{Cu^{2+}/Cu} = +0.34\,V$ and $E^\ominus_{NO_3^-/N_2O_4} = +0.80\,V$, so the copper half-cell will provide electrons:

$$Cu(s) \rightarrow Cu^{2+}(aq) + 2e^-$$

We now know that the other half-cell will contain the oxidising agent (which gains the electrons), in this case the nitrate ions:

$$2NO_3^-(aq) + 4H^+(aq) + 2e^- \rightarrow N_2O_4(g) + 2H_2O(l)$$

Given that the two $E^\ominus$ values differ by less than 0.6 V, we should be cautious about saying that the reaction will definitely take place under non-standard conditions, but we can be fairly sure it will. (We do not know how fast though!) To round things off it is sensible to write down the overall equation for the reaction:

$$Cu(s) + 2NO_3^-(aq) + 4H^+(aq) \rightarrow Cu^{2+}(aq) + N_2O_4(g) + 2H_2O(l)$$

If you try this reaction, you will see brown fumes of nitrogen dioxide, NO_2, gas being given off owing to the dissociation of dinitrogen tetraoxide (see section 53.6).

With a little practice you should be able to predict whether a given reaction will take place simply by looking at a redox chart. An important point to realise is that, if you move from left to right on the chart, this is the direction in which electrons are gained; for example in a change from copper(II) ions to copper metal (oxidation state 0) the copper gains electrons. Similarly, a movement from right to left represents a loss of electrons. We shall place the information about the copper(II)/copper redox system on a modified redox chart, as shown in Figure 71.4. You can see arrows representing the movement of electrons in the reactions. The

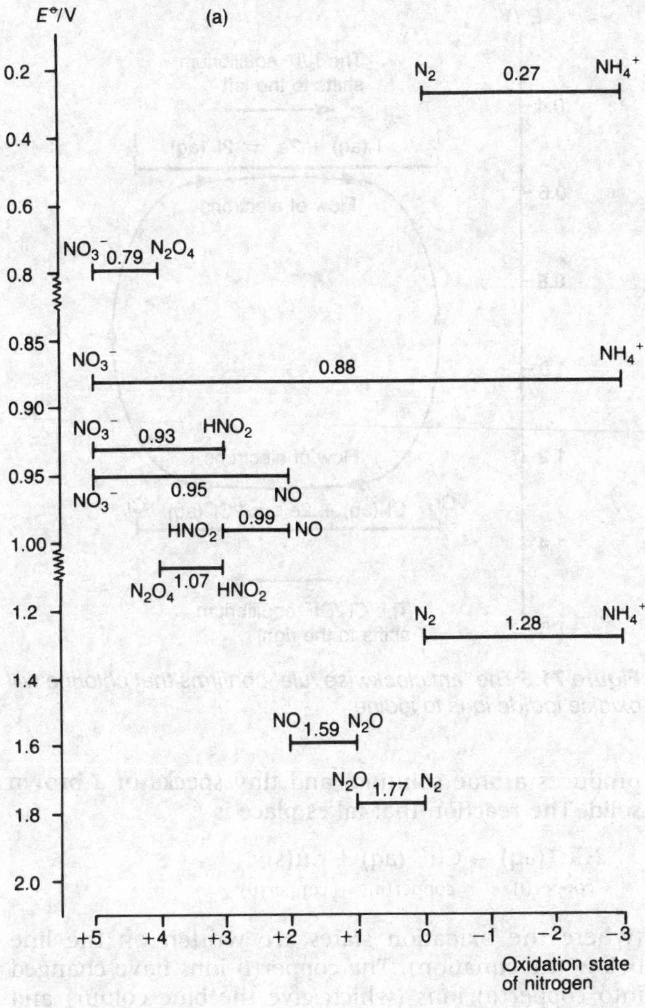

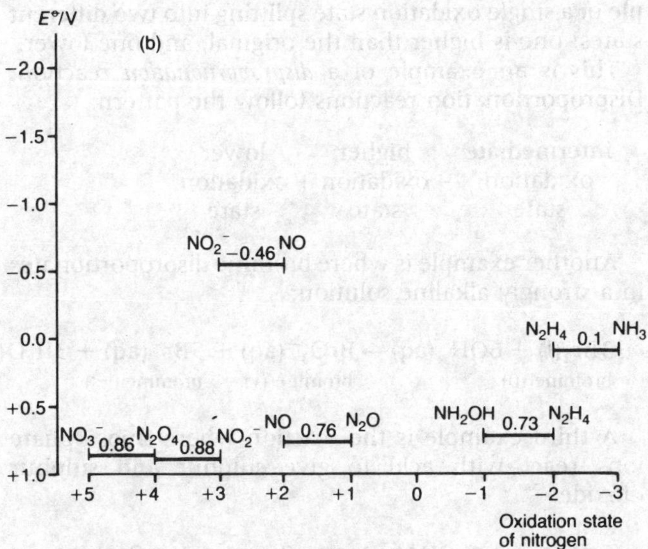

Figure 71.1 *The redox charts for nitrogen: $E^{\ominus}$ values are for (a) acidic conditions and (b) alkaline conditions. Notice that (i) the diagrams show the $E^{\ominus}$ scale becomes more positive downwards, (ii) higher oxidation states are to the left, lower to the right, and (iii) the scale between $E^{\ominus} = 0.8$ and 1.0 V in (a) has been expanded to show the data more clearly*

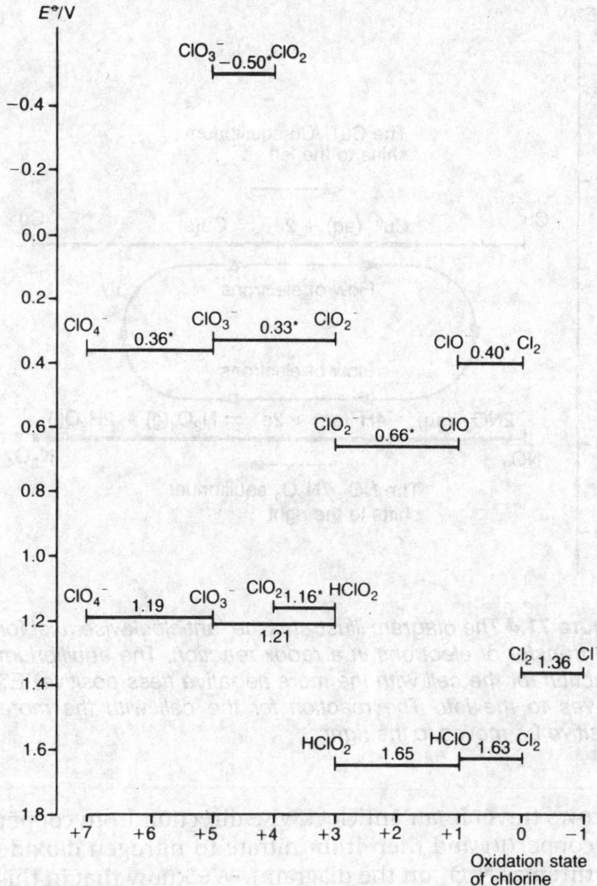

Figure 71.2 *Redox chart for chlorine. Values without asterisks refer to acid conditions; those with asterisks refer to alkaline conditions*

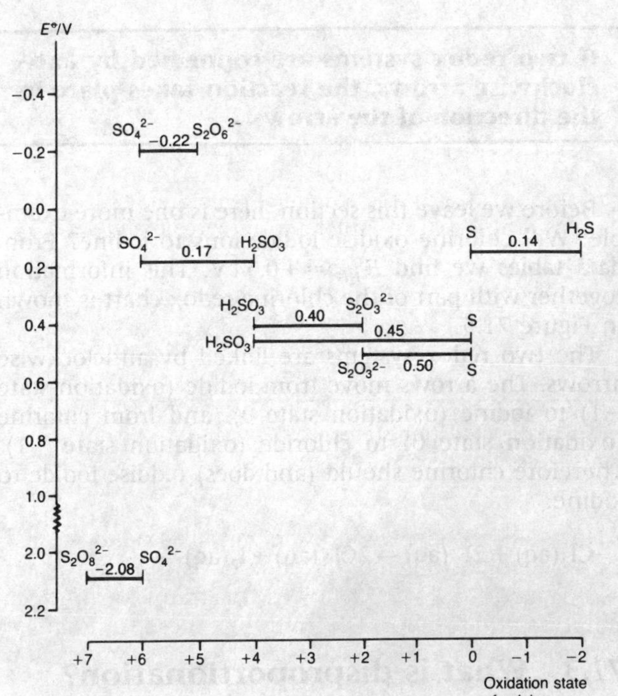

Figure 71.3 *Redox chart for sulphur. $E^{\ominus}$ values refer to acidic conditions*

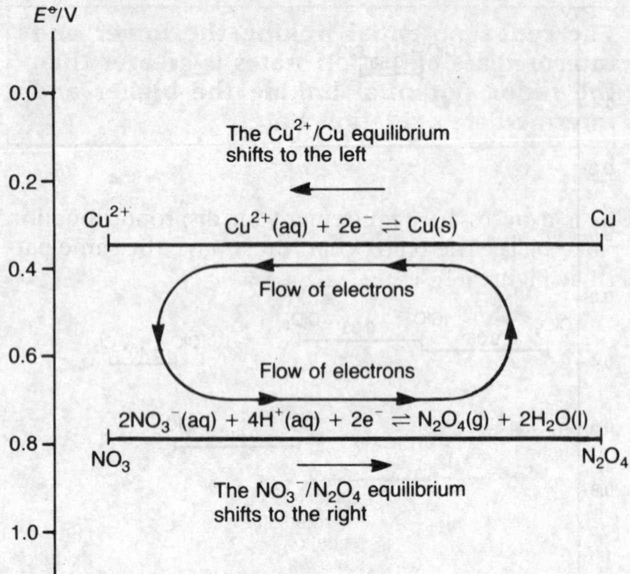

Figure 71.4 The diagram illustrates the 'anticlockwise rule' for the transfer of electrons in a redox reaction. The equilibrium reaction for the cell with the more negative (less positive) E$^\ominus$ moves to the left. The reaction for the cell with the more positive E$^\ominus$ moves to the right

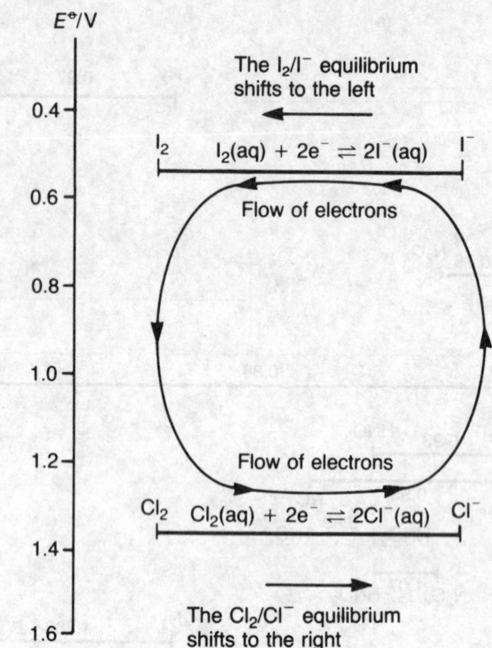

Figure 71.5 The 'anticlockwise rule' confirms that chlorine will oxidise iodide ions to iodine

arrows travel in an anticlockwise direction from copper to copper(II) and then from nitrate to nitrogen dioxide (written as N_2O_4 on the diagram). We know that in this reaction the arrows show the correct direction for the changes.

This is a general rule:

If two redox systems are connected by anticlockwise arrows, the reaction takes place in the direction of the arrows.

Before we leave this section, here is one more example: Will chlorine oxidise iodide ions to iodine? From data tables we find $E^\ominus_{I_2/I^-} = +0.54\,V$. This information together with part of the chlorine redox chart is shown in Figure 71.5.

The two redox systems are linked by anticlockwise arrows. The arrows move from iodide (oxidation state −1) to iodine (oxidation state 0), and from chlorine (oxidation state 0) to chloride (oxidation state −1). Therefore chlorine should (and does) oxidise iodide to iodine:

$$Cl_2(aq) + 2I^-(aq) \rightarrow 2Cl^-(aq) + I_2(aq)$$

71.3 What is disproportionation?

If you put a little copper(I) sulphate, Cu_2SO_4, in a test tube of water you will discover that the white powder produces a blue solution, and tiny specks of a brown solid. The reaction that takes place is

$$\underset{\text{copper(I)}}{2Cu^+(aq)} \rightarrow \underset{\text{copper(II)}}{Cu^{2+}(aq)} + \underset{\text{copper(0)}}{Cu(s)}$$

(where the oxidation states are written on the line below the equation). The copper(I) ions have changed into copper(II) ions (which give the blue colour) and copper metal (the brown solid). Here we have an example of a single oxidation state splitting into two different states; one is higher than the original, and one lower.

This is an example of a *disproportionation* reaction. Disproportionation reactions follow the pattern:

$$\begin{matrix}\text{intermediate} & & \text{higher} & & \text{lower}\\ \text{oxidation} & \rightarrow & \text{oxidation} & + & \text{oxidation}\\ \text{state} & & \text{state} & & \text{state}\end{matrix}$$

Another example is where bromine disproportionates in a strongly alkaline solution:

$$\underset{\text{bromine (0)}}{3Br_2(l)} + 6OH^-(aq) \rightarrow \underset{\text{bromine (V)}}{BrO_3^-(aq)} + \underset{\text{bromine (−I)}}{5Br^-(aq)} + 3H_2O(l)$$

A third example is the reaction where thiosulphate ions react with acid to give sulphur and sulphur dioxide:

$$\underset{\text{sulphur (II)}}{S_2O_3^{2-}(aq)} + 2H^+(aq) \rightarrow \underset{\text{sulphur (0)}}{S(s)} + \underset{\text{sulphur (IV)}}{H_2SO_3(aq)}$$

It is interesting to see the redox potentials for these reactions shown on a redox chart (Figure 71.6).

You might discover that there is a pattern to the charts:

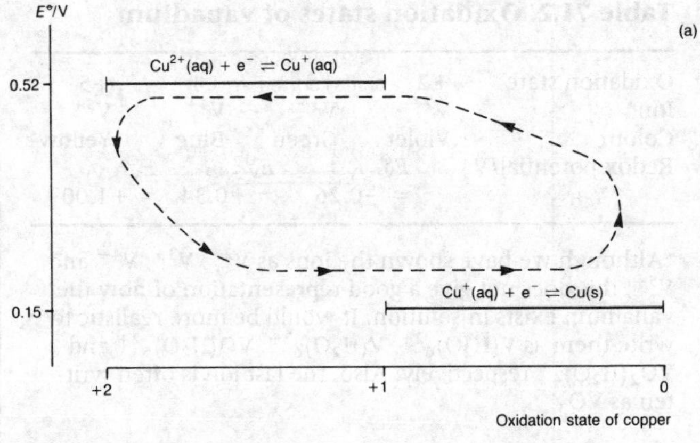

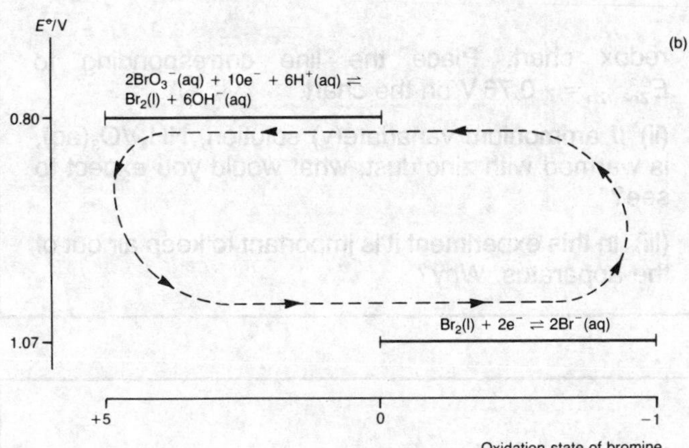

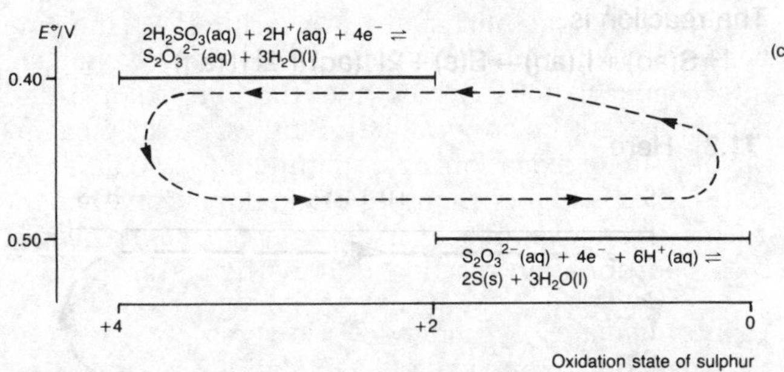

Figure 71.6 *Redox diagrams for three disproportionations. Note: the diagrams are not drawn to scale. (a) The 'anticlockwise rule' confirms that Cu^+ can disproportionate to Cu and Cu^{2+}. (b) The 'anticlockwise rule' shows that Br_2 should disproportionate to BrO_3^- and Br^-. (c) Again, the 'anticlockwise rule' establishes that $S_2O_3^{2-}$ will disproportionate into H_2SO_3 (i.e. SO_2 in acid solution) and S*

The redox potential linking the lower and intermediate oxidation states is greater than the redox potential linking the higher and intermediate oxidation states.

This is a necessary requirement for disproportionation to take place. The redox chart must have the same pattern as Figure 71.7.

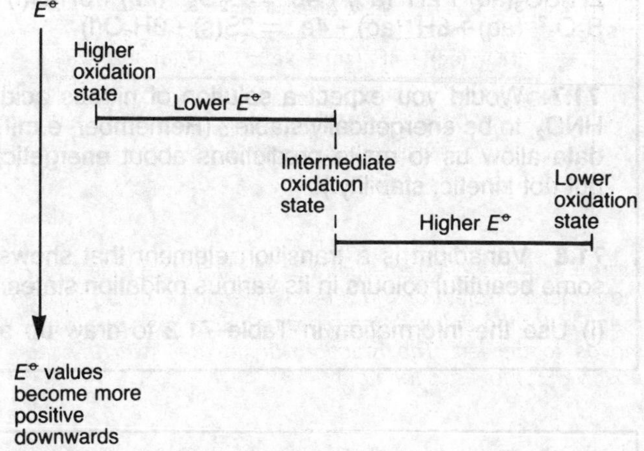

Figure 71.7 *The pattern of the oxidation state diagram in a disproportionation reaction*

We can see how this works out in practice by using the copper(I) disproportionation as an example. We have $E^\ominus_{Cu^{2+}/Cu^+} = +0.15\,V$ and $E^\ominus_{Cu^+/Cu} = +0.52\,V$. This tells us that if we made a cell from these two half-cells, the copper(II)/copper(I) half-cell would be the more negative half-cell. This is the half-cell that gives up electrons, so the reaction will be

$$Cu^+(aq) \rightarrow Cu^{2+}(aq) + e^-$$

On the other hand, in the other half-cell, these electrons will be taken up in the reaction

$$Cu^+(aq) + e^- \rightarrow Cu(s)$$

The overall reaction is

$$2Cu^+(aq) \rightarrow Cu(s) + Cu^{2+}(aq)$$

which is the equation for the disproportionation.

(You will need to use the data in Tables 66.1 and 70.1 together with the redox charts above to answer most of these questions. In questions 71.1 to 71.4 work out equations for reactions that you think will take place.)

71.1 Will chlorate(I) (hypochlorite) ions oxidise iodide ions to iodine?

71.2 Will hydrogen sulphide oxidise iodide ions to iodine?

71.3 What happens, if anything, if solutions of chlorine and hydrogen sulphide are mixed?

71.4 When nitric acid reacts with copper, as well as the reaction we considered there is another that can take place. What is it?

71.5 In acid conditions, $E^{\ominus}_{BrO_3^-/Br_2} = +1.52\,V$. Will bromine disproportionate to bromide and bromate(V) in acid? Briefly explain how you decide on your answer.

71.6 Follow through the working on the copper(I) disproportionation and apply the same reasoning to the disproportionation of thiosulphate. Write down the half-cell reactions and the overall reaction. You will need to know that the equilibria involved in the half-cells are

$$2H_2SO_3(aq) + 2H^+(aq) + 4e^- \rightleftharpoons S_2O_3^{2-}(aq) + 3H_2O(l)$$
$$S_2O_3^{2-}(aq) + 6H^+(aq) + 4e^- \rightleftharpoons 2S(s) + 3H_2O(l)$$

71.7 Would you expect a solution of nitrous acid, HNO_2, to be energetically stable? (Remember, e.m.f. data allow us to make predictions about energetic, but not kinetic, stability.)

71.8 Vanadium is a transition element that shows some beautiful colours in its various oxidation states.

(i) Use the information in Table 71.2 to draw up a redox chart. Place the line corresponding to $E^{\ominus}_{Zn^{2+}/Zn} = -0.76\,V$ on the chart.

(ii) If ammonium vanadate(V) solution, $NH_4VO_3(aq)$, is warmed with zinc dust, what would you expect to see?

(iii) In this experiment it is important to keep air out of the apparatus. Why?

Table 71.2. Oxidation states of vanadium

Oxidation state	+2	+3	+4	+5
Ion*	V^{2+}	V^{3+}	V^{4+}	V^{5+}
Colour	Violet	Green	Blue	Yellow
Redox potential/V	$E^{\ominus}_{V^{3+}/V^{2+}} = -0.26$		$E^{\ominus}_{V^{4+}/V^{3+}} = +0.34$	$E^{\ominus}_{V^{5+}/V^{4+}} = +1.00$

*Although we have shown the ions as V^{2+}, V^{3+}, V^{4+} and V^{5+}, this does not give a good representation of how the vanadium exists in solution. It would be more realistic to write them as $V(H_2O)_6^{2+}$, $V(H_2O)_6^{3+}$, $VO(H_2O)_5^{2+}$ and $VO_2(H_2O)_4^+$ respectively. Also, the last ion is often written as VO_3^-

Answers

71.1 Yes they will. The relevant part of the redox chart should look like this:

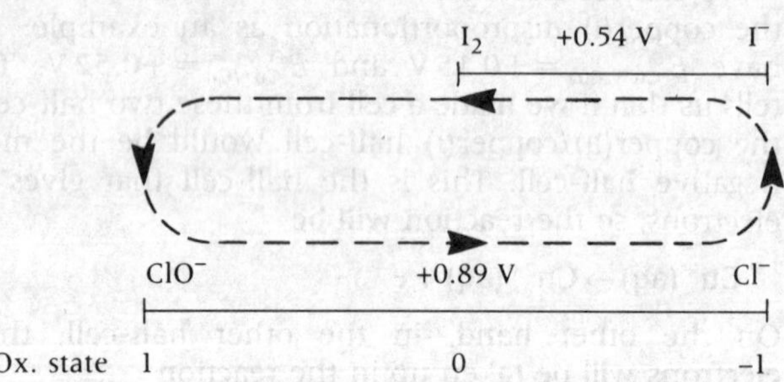

The reaction is

$$ClO^-(aq) + 2I^-(aq) + 2H^+(aq) \rightarrow Cl^-(aq) + I_2(aq) + H_2O(l)$$

71.2 The chart in this case is

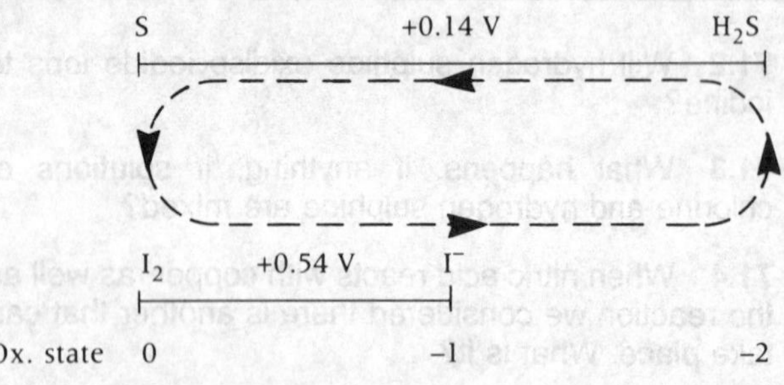

Here the arrows show that this reaction will *not* occur. Rather, hydrogen sulphide will reduce iodine to iodide. The reaction is

$$H_2S(aq) + I_2(aq) \rightarrow S(s) + 2I^-(aq) + 2H^+(aq)$$

71.3 Here

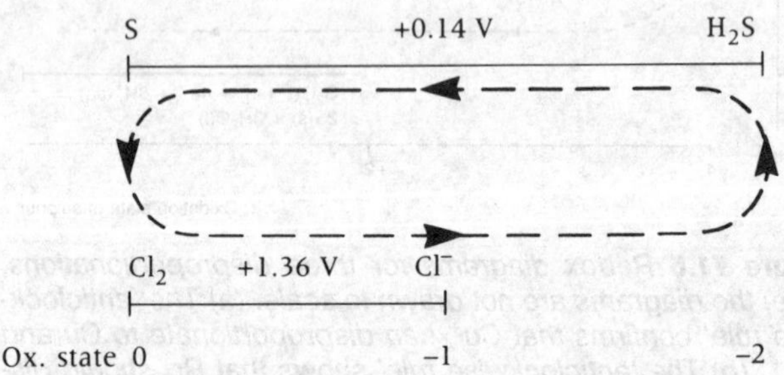

The chart shows that chlorine will oxidise the hydrogen sulphide. A yellow deposit of sulphur will be made:

$$Cl_2(g) + H_2S(aq) \rightarrow S(s) + 2Cl^-(aq) + 2H^+(aq)$$

71.4 The redox chart shows that the acid can react to give nitrous acid. The half-cell reaction is

$$NO_3^-(aq) + 3H^+(aq) + 2e^- \rightarrow HNO_2(aq) + H_2O(l)$$

But the nitrous acid can further react to produce nitrogen monoxide:

$$HNO_2(aq) + H^+(aq) + e^- \rightarrow NO(g) + H_2O(l)$$

Overall,

$$NO_3^-(aq) + 4H^+(aq) + 3e^- \rightarrow NO(g) + 2H_2O(l)$$

Answers – contd.

If we combine this with

$Cu(s) \rightarrow Cu^{2+}(aq) + 2e^-$

we have the final reaction

$3Cu(s) + 2NO_3^-(aq) + 8H^+(aq) \rightarrow 3Cu^{2+}(aq) + 2NO(g) + 4H_2O(l)$

71.5 The redox chart now looks like this:

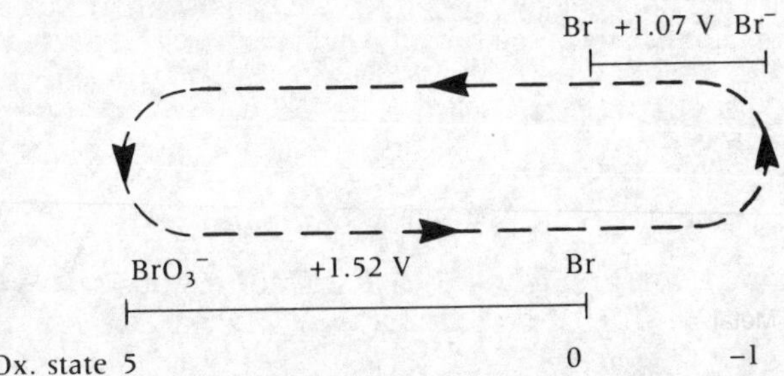

In this case disproportionation will *not* occur because $E^\ominus_{Br_2/Br^-}$ is less than $E^\ominus_{BrO_3^-/Br_2}$. If you think about the values of the redox potentials, the bromine/bromide will be the negative half-cell, which means that the reaction taking place is

$2Br^-(aq) \rightarrow Br_2(l) + 2e^-$

In the bromine/bromate(V) half-cell the reaction is

$2BrO_3^-(aq) + 12H^+(aq) + 10e^- \rightarrow Br_2(l) + 6H_2O(l)$

Hence the overall reaction is

$BrO_3^-(aq) + 5Br^-(aq) + 6H^+(aq) \rightarrow 3Br_2(l) + 3H_2O(l)$

This shows that bromine is the favoured product in acid solution and that it will not disproportionate.

71.6 $E^\ominus_{S_2O_3^{2-}/S} = +0.52\,V$ and $E^\ominus_{H_2SO_3/S_2O_3^{2-}} = +0.40\,V$. These values tell us that the negative half-cell contains the H_2SO_3 and $S_2O_3^{2-}$. The reaction taking place will be the one that gives up electrons:

$S_2O_3^{2-}(aq) + 3H_2O(l) \rightarrow 2H_2SO_3(aq) + 2H^+(aq) + 4e^-$

In the other half-cell the thiosulphate is the oxidising agent and the reaction is

$S_2O_3^{2-}(aq) + 6H^+(aq) + 4e^- \rightarrow 2S(s) + 3H_2O(l)$

If we combine the two equations, we have

$S_2O_3^{2-}(aq) + 2H^+(aq) \rightarrow H_2SO_3(aq) + S(s)$

which is the equation for the disproportionation.

71.7 If you look at the redox chart for nitrogen you will find that nitrous acid should disproportionate. It is linked to nitrogen monoxide (the lower oxidation state) at $E^\ominus = +0.93\,V$, and to nitrate (the higher oxidation state) by $E^\ominus = +0.8\,V$. The two e.m.f.s are not the usual 0.6 V apart that we normally take to be our guiding line for confident predictions; but in fact a solution of nitrous acid does decompose slowly according to the reaction

$3HNO_2(aq) \rightarrow HNO_3(aq) + 2NO(g) + H_2O(l)$

71.8 (i) Your chart should look like this:

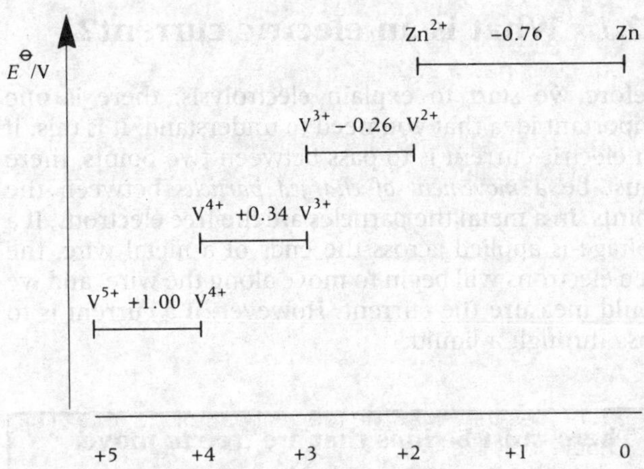

(ii) $E^\ominus_{Zn^{2+}/Zn}$ is sufficiently negative for zinc to reduce all the oxidation states of vanadium. Alternatively, you could say that the redox potentials of vanadium are all sufficiently positive for the oxidation states to oxidise zinc to zinc ions. Therefore you should expect to see the pale yellow colour of the ammonium vanadate(V) change to blue, then to green, and finally to violet.

(iii) Oxygen in air can oxidise the lower oxidation states back to vanadium(V).

UNIT 71 SUMMARY

- Rule for using redox charts:
  If two redox systems are connected by anticlockwise arrows, the reaction takes place in the directions of the arrows.
- Disproportionation reactions follow the pattern:

  intermediate oxidation state → higher oxidation state + lower oxidation state

  e.g.

  $2Cu^+(aq) \rightarrow Cu^{2+}(aq) + Cu(s)$
  copper(I) → copper(II) + copper(0)

- On a redox chart a necessary requirement for disproportionation to take place is that:
  The redox potential linking the lower and intermediate oxidation states is greater than the redox potential linking the higher and intermediate oxidation states.

72

Electrolysis

72.1 What is an electric current?

Before we start to explain electrolysis, there is one important idea that you need to understand. It is this: if an electric current is to pass between two points, there must be a *movement of charged particles* between the points. In a metal the particles are the free electrons. If a voltage is applied across the ends of a metal wire, the free electrons will begin to move along the wire, and we could measure the current. However, if a current is to pass through a liquid:

There must be ions that are free to move.

Water itself is only very slightly dissociated into hydrogen and hydroxide ions, so pure water does not conduct very well. However, if we dissolve sodium chloride in water, the large number of free sodium and chloride ions allows the solution to conduct very easily. Sodium chloride itself will conduct if it is molten. In this case the crystal structure is broken down, freeing the ions to move about.

In Figure 72.1 you can see diagrams representing the movement of ions through a liquid. We have shown the positive ions moving towards the negative electrode, and the negative ions moving towards the positive electrode. However, our diagrams are much exaggerated; ions do not whizz from one side of the liquid to the other. Instead, there is a gradual drift of the ions in the two directions. A large current flows if there are a large number of ions present, all moving slowly, rather than a few ions moving at great speeds.

72.1 In which of the following cases will the bulb in Figure 72.2 light up: when the beaker contains (i) ethanol, (ii) sugar dissolved in water, (iii) sodium hydroxide solution, (iv) copper(II) sulphate solution, (v) molten sugar, (vi) molten potassium chloride, (vii) solid magnesium oxide?

(a) Metal

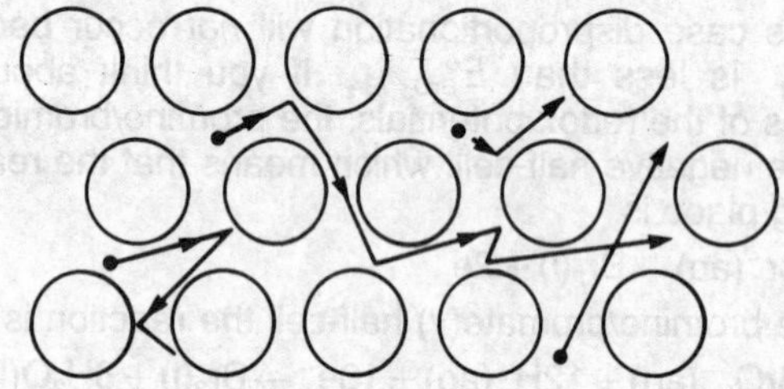

(b) Ionic solution

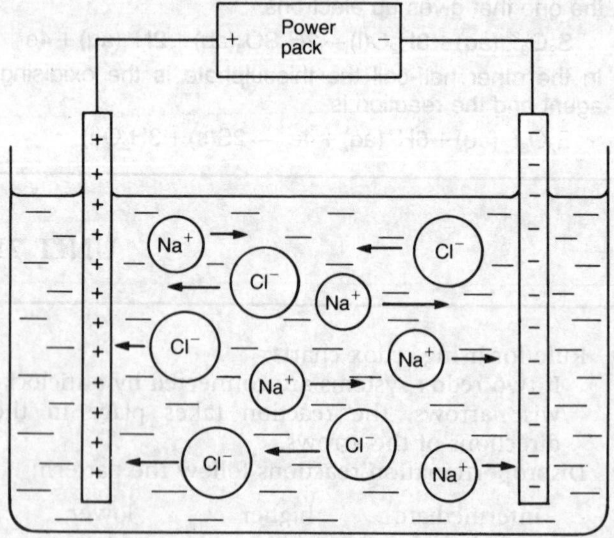

***Figure 72.1** Much exaggerated views of a metal and a solution of an ionic substance conducting an electric current. (a) In a metal, an electric current is the movement of electrons. (b) In a solution of an ionic substance, the electric current is the movement of ions*

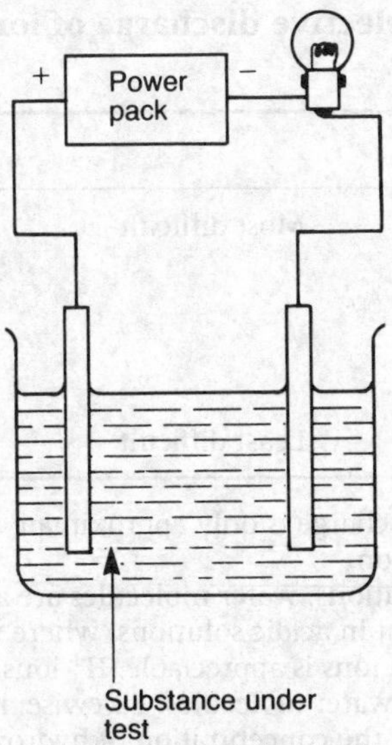

Figure 72.2 Apparatus for question 72.1

72.2 Two electrolysis cells are set up as shown in Figure 72.3. What happens?

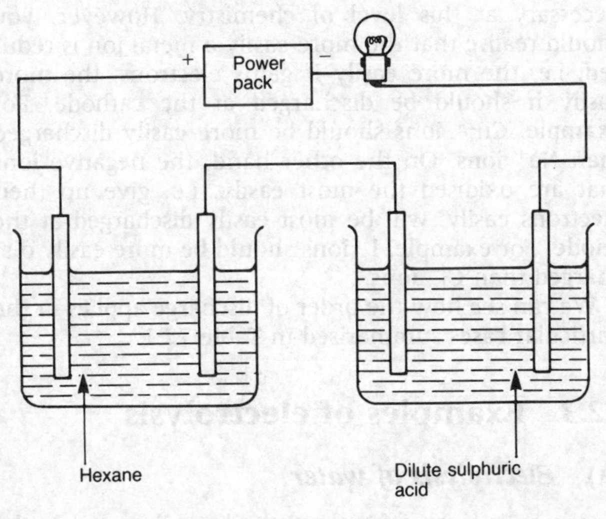

Figure 72.3 An electrolysis cell containing hexane in series with another containing dilute sulphuric acid (see question 72.2)

72.2 What happens during electrolysis?

In an electrolysis experiment a current is passed through a solution containing ions, or a molten salt, called the *electrolyte*. The negative electrode is coated with electrons, some of which can be stolen by positive ions that come close to the electrode. A typical example is the reaction

$Na^+ + e^- \rightarrow Na$

which takes place in molten sodium chloride (Figure

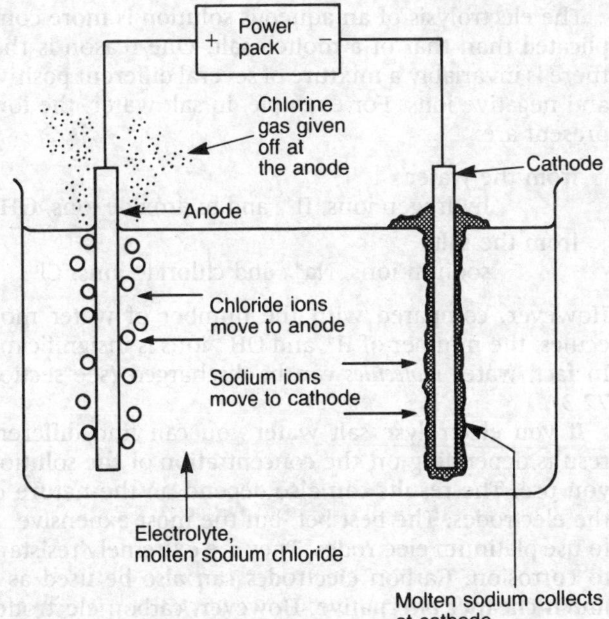

***Figure 72.4** In the electrolysis of molten sodium chloride, sodium ions travel to the cathode and sodium metal is liberated:*

$Na^+ + e^- \rightarrow Na$

Chloride ions move to the anode, and chlorine is given off:

$2Cl^- - 2e^- \rightarrow Cl_2$

(Note: if this experiment were being done in the laboratory, special safety measures would have to be taken to deal with the sodium and the poisonous chlorine)

72.4). This is a reaction in which the sodium ion is reduced (it gains an electron). In fact, in an electrolysis experiment:

Reduction always takes place at the negative electrode.

This electrode is called the *cathode*.

On the other hand, negative ions are attracted to the positive electrode, where they are oxidised (lose electrons), e.g.

$Cl^- - e^- \rightarrow Cl$

followed by

$2Cl \rightarrow Cl_2$

Therefore we have:

Oxidation always takes place at the positive electrode.

This electrode is called the *anode*.

We can summarise the results of the experiment by saying that sodium is *discharged* at the cathode, and chlorine is discharged at the anode.

The electrolysis of an aqueous solution is more complicated than that of a molten salt. One reason is that there is invariably a mixture of several different positive and negative ions. For example, in salt water, the ions present are:

from the water

hydrogen ions, H^+, and hydroxide ions, OH^-

from the salt

sodium ions, Na^+, and chloride ions, Cl^-

However, compared with the number of water molecules, the number of H^+ and OH^- ions is insignificant. In fact, water *molecules* can be discharged (see section 72.3).

If you electrolyse salt water you can find different results depending on the concentration of the solution you use. The results can also depend on the nature of the electrodes. The best bet, but the most expensive, is to use platinum electrodes. They are extremely resistant to corrosion. Carbon electrodes can also be used as a much cheaper alternative. However, carbon electrodes suffer corrosion quite easily. If you were gradually to increase the voltage across the cell and measure the current passing through the electrolyte, you would find that the current remains very small until, at a certain voltage, it rises very quickly (Figure 72.5). This is when the electrolysis starts. The minimum voltage causing electrolysis to take place is the *decomposition voltage*.

If you have read Unit 66 you will know that an electrode placed into a solution will set up an electrode potential. The decomposition voltage is at least equal to the combination of the two electrode potentials at the anode and cathode. Once electrolysis is under way, there are significant changes in the concentrations of the ions near the electrodes. This effect increases the decomposition voltage, so that it is larger than that which we might calculate from electrode potentials. The amount of this 'extra voltage' is called the *over-voltage*. If we are to predict which ions will be discharged during an electrolysis, we need to know their over voltages. You will be pleased to know that this is not necessary at this level of chemistry. However, you should realise that the more easily a metal ion is reduced, i.e. the more easily it gains electrons, the more easily it should be discharged at the cathode. For example, Cu^{2+} ions should be more easily discharged than Na^+ ions. On the other hand, the negative ions that are oxidised the most easily, i.e. give up their electrons easily, will be most easily discharged at the anode. For example, I^- ions should be more easily discharged than Cl^- ions.

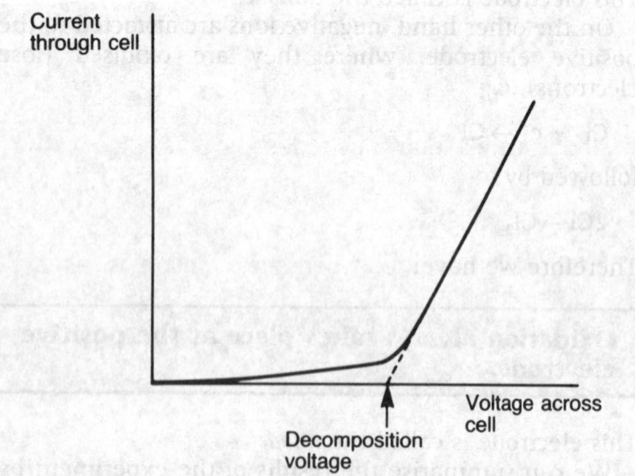

***Figure 72.5** How the current through an electrolysis cell varies with voltage*

Table 72.1. Selective discharge of ions during an electrolysis*†

At the cathode		*At the anode*
Na^+	Most difficult	F^-
Al^{3+}		SO_4^{2-}
Zn^{2+}		NO_3^-
Pb^{2+}		Cl^-
H^+		Br^-
Cu^{2+}		I^-
Ag^+	Least difficult	OH^-

*The order of discharge is only approximate and changes with concentration

†In aqueous solutions, water molecules are always available for discharge. But in acidic solutions, where the concentration of hydrogen ions is appreciable, H^+ ions are discharged in preference to water molecules. Likewise, in alkaline solutions, where the concentration of hydroxide ions is appreciable, OH^- ions are discharged in preference to water molecules. The reactions are:

anode $4OH^-(aq) - 4e^- \rightarrow 2H_2O(l) + O_2(g)$

cathode $2H^+(aq) + 2e^- \rightarrow H_2(g)$

We can see how the order of discharge applies in the particular cases summarised in Table 72.1.

72.3 Examples of electrolysis

(a) *Electrolysis of water*

Hydrogen is given off at the cathode, and oxygen at the anode (Figure 72.6). Although in principle these gases could be produced by the discharge of hydrogen and hydroxide ions respectively, in practice water molecules react:

at the anode $2H_2O(l) - 4e^- \rightarrow 4H^+(aq) + O_2(g)$

at the cathode $2H_2O(l) + 2e^- \rightarrow 2OH^-(aq) + H_2(g)$

or $4H_2O(l) + 4e^- \rightarrow 4OH^-(aq) + 2H_2(g)$

You can see from the equations that the release of 1 mol of oxygen needs 4 mol of electrons to be transferred. In an electrolysis, equal numbers of electrons must be lost from the cathode as gained at the anode. Thus 4 mol of electrons must be picked up by water molecules from the cathode. Therefore 2 mol of hydrogen gas will be given off for every 1 mol of oxygen. This reflects the ratio of the two elements in the formula of water, H_2O. Sometimes dilute sulphuric acid is added to water before electrolysis. This boosts the conductivity of the

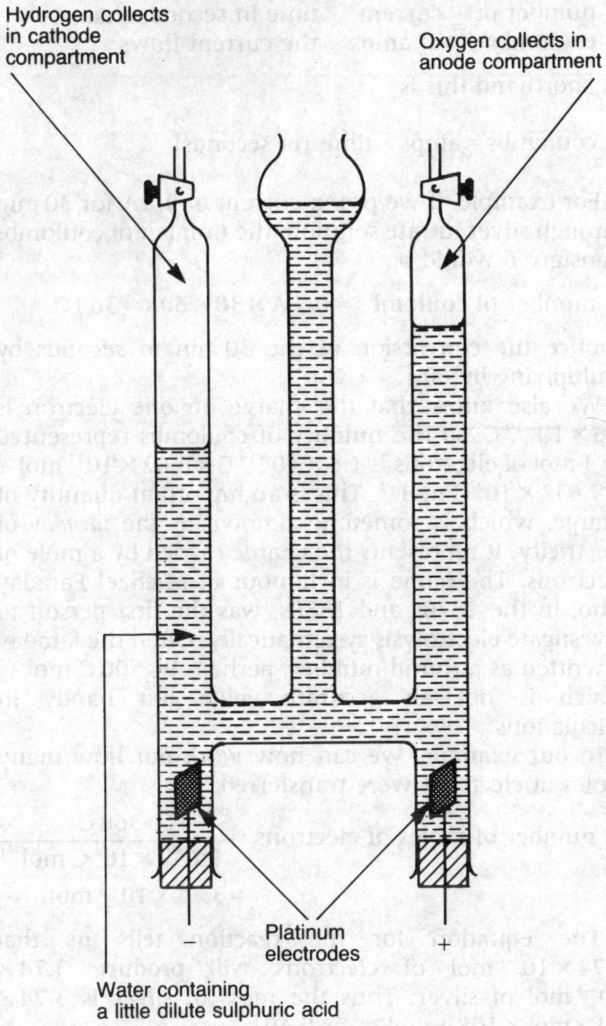

Figure 72.6 A Hofmann voltameter often used for the electrolysis of water

solution by increasing the number of ions present. It also means that hydrogen ions are discharged at the cathode through the reaction:

$$2H^+(aq) + 2e^- \rightarrow H_2(g)$$

Sulphate ions are resistant to oxidation and are not discharged at the cathode.

(b) *Electrolysis of copper(II) sulphate solution*

We shall think about two ways of carrying out the electrolysis. The first uses two inert electrodes, platinum or carbon for example. The other method uses electrodes made from copper. In both cases we have the same set of ions and molecules present:

from water	H_2O molecules
from copper(II) sulphate	Cu^{2+} and $SO_4{}^{2-}$

With inert electrodes

In this case, H_2O molecules and Cu^{2+} ions are preferentially discharged:

at the anode	$2H_2O(l) - 4e^- \rightarrow 4H^+(aq) + O_2(g)$
at the cathode	$Cu^{2+}(aq) + 2e^- \rightarrow Cu(s)$

This is, perhaps, the simplest example of the basis of *electroplating*. Copper metal is liberated at the cathode. If the conditions are right, the copper will cling to the cathode, thereby plating it.

In industry, electroplating is very important. Cutlery can be silver plated, and many of the shiny decorative parts of cars and bicycles are chromium plated. To plate a metal accurately the surface must be thoroughly clean and treated so that the plated metal coats it evenly. The objects to be plated are made the cathode in an electrolysis bath. The length of time they spend in the electrolyte and the current flowing determine the thickness of the plating.

With copper electrodes

It is easier for copper metal to lose electrons (be oxidised) than it is for water molecules to lose them. Instead of oxygen being given off, the copper from the anode changes into copper(II) ions:

at the anode	$Cu(s) - 2e^- \rightarrow Cu^{2+}(aq)$
at the cathode	$Cu^{2+}(aq) + 2e^- \rightarrow Cu(s)$

You can see from these two equations that the anode will gradually be worn away while the cathode becomes coated with copper. The cathode will gain a mass of copper equal to that lost from the anode.

72.3 Briefly explain why equal numbers of electrons must be lost from the cathode as gained at the anode during an electrolysis.

72.4 A little litmus is placed in the acidified water in the compartments around the anode and cathode in a Hofmann voltameter (see Figure 72.6), and the electrolysis is started.

(i) What colour will the litmus be at the start of the experiment?

(ii) Explain why the litmus gradually changes colour in one of the compartments.

72.5 When copper(II) sulphate solution is electrolysed using platinum electrodes, the blue colour of the solution gradually fades.

(i) Why is this?

(ii) After some time, when the solution is almost colourless, bubbles appear at the cathode. Why do they appear, and what are they?

72.6 When does an electrolysis of copper(II) sulphate using copper electrodes stop?

72.7 What would you expect to see if you were to carry out an electrolysis of (i) moderately concentrated hydrochloric acid, (ii) very dilute hydrochloric acid, (iii) dilute sodium hydroxide? In each case write down the reactions that should take place at the anode and cathode. (Make use of Table 72.1 to help you decide.)

72.8 Use the information in Table 72.1 to predict the products of the electrolysis of concentrated salt water. Write down equations to show the reactions at the anode and cathode. What happens as the electrolysis continues?

72.4 How to calculate the mass of a substance liberated in electrolysis

If we electrolyse silver nitrate solution, the reactions that take place at the electrodes are:

at the anode $2H_2O(l) - 4e^- \rightarrow 4H^+(aq) + O_2(g)$
at the cathode $Ag^+(aq) + e^- \rightarrow Ag(s)$

Let us take a closer look at the cathode reaction. The problem we are going to solve is to work out how many grams of silver will be deposited at the cathode if a current of 0.2 A is passed for 30 min through the electrolysis cell (Figure 72.7). As with any chemical equation we can interpret it in terms of the numbers of moles of particles reacting:

$$\underset{1\,\text{mol}}{Ag^+(aq)} + \underset{1\,\text{mol}}{e^-} \rightarrow \underset{1\,\text{mol}}{Ag(s)}$$

First we calculate the number of coulombs of charge transferred by the current. This is given by the formula

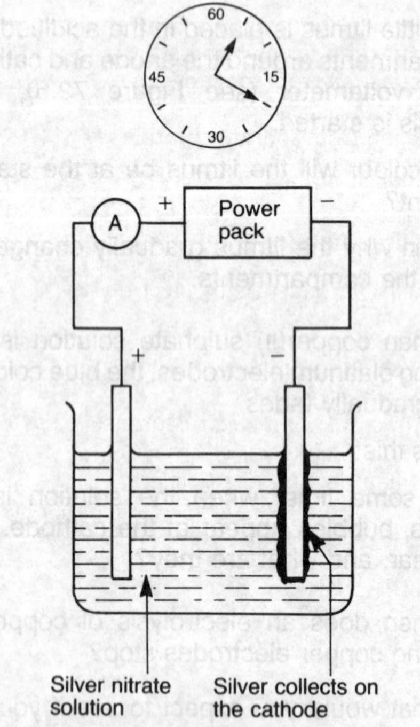

Figure 72.7 For the accurate electrolysis of silver nitrate solution, an ammeter and clock are needed

$$\text{number of coulombs} = \text{current in amps} \times \text{time in seconds that the current flows}$$

In shorthand this is

$$\text{coulombs} = \text{amps} \times \text{time (in seconds)}$$

For example, if we pass a current of 0.2 A for 30 min through silver nitrate solution, the number of coulombs transferred would be

$$\text{number of coulombs} = 0.2\,\text{A} \times 30 \times 60\,\text{s} = 360\,\text{C}$$

(Notice the conversion of the 30 min to seconds by multiplying by 60.)

We also know that the charge on one electron is 1.6×10^{-19} C, so the number of coulombs represented by 1 mol of electrons is $1.6 \times 10^{-19}\,\text{C} \times 6.02 \times 10^{23}\,\text{mol}^{-1} = 9.632 \times 10^4\,\text{C mol}^{-1}$. This is an important quantity of charge, which is sometimes known as the *faraday* of electricity. It represents the charge carried by a mole of electrons. The name is in honour of Michael Faraday who, in the 1870s and 1880s, was the first person to investigate electrolysis systematically. Often the faraday is written as a round number, perhaps 96 500 C mol^{-1}, which is not an accurate value but handy in calculations.

In our example, we can now work out how many moles of electrons were transferred:

$$\text{number of moles of electrons} = \frac{360\,\text{C}}{9.632 \times 10^4\,\text{C mol}^{-1}} = 3.74 \times 10^{-3}\,\text{mol}$$

The equation for the reaction tells us that 3.74×10^{-3} mol of electrons will produce 3.74×10^{-3} mol of silver. Thus the mass of silver is $3.74 \times 10^{-3}\,\text{mol} \times 108\,\text{g mol}^{-1}$, or 0.40 g.

Here is another example. If a current of 0.1 A is passed for 10 hours through acidified water at room temperature, what volume of oxygen will be released? We shall take the faraday as 96 500 C mol^{-1}.

Stage 1 The equation

at the anode

$$\underset{4\,\text{mol}}{4H_2O(l)} - \underset{4\,\text{mol}}{4e^-} \rightarrow \underset{4\,\text{mol}}{4H^+(aq)} + \underset{24\,\text{dm}^3\text{ at room temp.}}{O_2(g)}$$

Thus we know that 4 mol of electrons will release 24 dm^3 of oxygen.

Stage 2 The number of coulombs passed

$$\text{number of coulombs} = 0.1\,\text{A} \times 10 \times 60 \times 60\,\text{s} = 3600\,\text{C}$$

Stage 3 The number of moles of electrons

$$\text{number of moles of electrons} = \frac{3600\,\text{C}}{96\,500\,\text{C mol}^{-1}} = 0.0373\,\text{mol}$$

Stage 4 The final answer

$$\text{volume of oxygen released} = 24\,\text{dm}^3 \times \frac{0.0373\,\text{mol}}{4\,\text{mol}} = 0.224\,\text{dm}^3$$

72.9 Faraday announced two laws of electrolysis that, not surprisingly, became known as Faraday's laws. In modern terms we can write them as:

(A) The mass of a substance liberated in an electrolysis is proportional to the quantity of electricity passed.

(B) If the same quantity of electricity is passed through different electrolytes, the mass of the substances liberated will be inversely proportional to the charges on the ions.

The first law is another way of saying that the greater the number of moles of electrons transferred, the greater the mass of the products. To see how the second law works, answer the following question.

Two electrolysis cells were connected in series as shown in Figure 72.8. A current of 0.25 A was passed through the silver nitrate solution for 20 min.

(i) What current passed through the other electrolysis cell?

(ii) Write down the cathode reactions in each cell.

(iii) How many moles of silver were deposited on the cathode?

(iv) How many moles of copper were deposited on the cathode?

(v) Briefly explain how your answers relate to Faraday's second law.

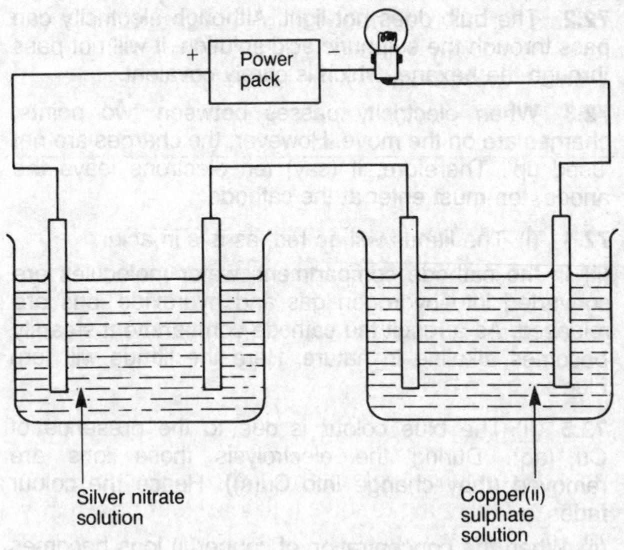

***Figure 72.8** An electrolysis cell containing silver nitrate solution in series with another cell containing copper(II) sulphate solution (see question 72.9)*

72.5 Why is electrolysis used in industry?

The very reactive metals of Groups I and II, and some others, like aluminium, are often found in Nature combined with halogens or oxygen. These compounds are energetically very stable and difficult to break apart. One of the few ways that the reactive metals can be isolated is by electrolysis. The extraction of sodium from sodium chloride and aluminium from aluminium oxide are examples.

Electrolysis is also used to decompose compounds, and to convert them into more useful and valuable chemicals. The conversion of salt water into chlorine and sodium hydroxide is one example, which we shall examine in Unit 84.

A third use of electrolysis is in the purification (refining) of metals like gold or copper. Here the electrolysis is carefully controlled so that only the metal ions are discharged at a cathode. A summary of these uses of electrolysis in industry is given in Table 72.2.

Table 72.2. Uses of electrolysis in industry

Process	*Energy needed /kW h kg^{-1}*
Aluminium extraction from alumina	18
Magnesium extraction from magnesium chloride	25
Sodium extraction from sodium chloride	15
Copper electrolytic refining	0.2
Gold electrolytic refining	0.3
Lead electrolytic refining	0.2
Sodium hydroxide manufacture by electrolysis of brine	3
These values can be compared with non-electrolytic processes:	
Phosphorus extraction in an electric furnace	10
Steel manufacture in an electric furnace	6
Silicon carbide manufacture in an electric furnace	8

Answers

72.1 It will light up in (iii), (iv) and (vi). These contain ions that are free to move. (i), (ii) and (v) are covalent, so contain no ions. (vii) is ionic, but in the solid the ions are not free to move.

72.2 The bulb does not light. Although electricity can pass through the sulphuric acid solution, it will not pass through the hexane, which is purely covalent.

72.3 When electricity passes between two points, charges are on the move. However, the charges are not 'used up'. Therefore, if (say) ten electrons leave the anode, ten must enter at the cathode.

72.4 (i) The litmus will go red, as it is in acid.

(ii) In the cathode compartment, water molecules are converted into hydrogen gas and hydroxide ions are released. As a result the cathode compartment steadily becomes alkaline in nature. Here the litmus will turn blue.

72.5 (i) The blue colour is due to the presence of $Cu^{2+}(aq)$. During the electrolysis these ions are removed (they change into Cu(s)). Hence the colour fades.

(ii) When the concentration of copper(II) ions becomes very small, water molecules begin to be discharged. The bubbles are hydrogen.

72.6 When the anode has been worn away so much that it no longer dips properly into the electrolyte.

72.7 (i) Hydrogen and chlorine are given off:

at the anode $2Cl^-(aq) - 2e^- \rightarrow Cl_2(g)$
at the cathode $2H^+(aq) + 2e^- \rightarrow H_2(g)$

(ii) Hydrogen and oxygen are given off. When the chloride ion concentration is very low, water molecules begin to be discharged at the anode. While the solution remains acidic, hydrogen ions are likely to be discharged in preference to water molecules, but eventually the latter molecules will be discharged:

at the anode $4H_2O(l) - 4e^- \rightarrow 4H^+(aq) + O_2(g)$
at the cathode $2H^+(aq) + 2e^- \rightarrow H_2(g)$
and later $2H_2O(l) + 2e^- \rightarrow 2OH^-(aq) + H_2(g)$

(iii) Hydrogen and oxygen are given off:

at the anode $4OH^-(l) - 4e^- \rightarrow 2H_2O(l) + O_2(g)$
at the cathode $2H_2O(l) + 2e^- \rightarrow 2OH^-(aq) + H_2(g)$

72.8 Chloride ions are discharged at the anode, and water molecules at the cathode:

at the anode $2Cl^-(aq) - 2e^- \rightarrow Cl_2(g)$
at the cathode $2H_2O(l) + 2e^- \rightarrow 2H_2(g) + 2OH^-(aq)$

Chloride ions are removed from the solution, and eventually water molecules will be discharged, giving off oxygen.

72.9 (i) 0.25 A, the same as through the first cell.

(ii) $Ag^+(aq) + e^- \rightarrow Ag(s)$; $Cu^{2+}(aq) + 2e^- \rightarrow Cu(s)$.

(iii) The number of coulombs passed $= 0.25\,A \times 20 \times 60\,s = 300\,C$. This represents $300\,C/96\,500\,C\,mol^{-1} = 3.11 \times 10^{-3}$ mol. Therefore the number of moles of silver deposited is also 3.11×10^{-3} mol.

(iv) If you look at the two cathode equations you can see that for every mole of electrons passed you get 1 mol of silver and 0.5 mol of copper. Therefore we would get $0.5 \times 3.11 \times 10^{-3}\,mol = 1.56 \times 10^{-3}$ mol of copper.

(v) With a little thought you should realise that if aluminium ions, Al^{3+}, were being discharged we would get one-third as many moles, i.e. 3.11×10^{-3} mol/3. Now you should see that the number of moles of ion discharged depends on 1/(charge on the ion). This is what Faraday's second law says.

UNIT 72 SUMMARY

- An electric current is the movement of charged particles. In solution, the positive and negative ions carry the current. For conduction to take place, ions must be free to move.
- In an electrolysis experiment:
  (i) Positive ions are discharged at the cathode, negative ions at the anode.
  (ii) Reduction always takes place at the negative electrode, the cathode; oxidation takes place at the anode.
- The mass of a substance liberated in electrolysis can be calculated using the equation:

$$\text{number of coulombs} = \text{current in amps} \times \text{time in seconds that the current flows}$$

The number of coulombs represented by 1 mol of electrons is approximately $96\,500\,C\,mol^{-1}$, the faraday of electricity.

73

Conductivity of solutions

73.1 How do we measure conductivity?

We know that a solution will conduct electricity if it contains ions that are free to move. In the last unit we used this fact to explain the results of electrolysis experiments. If we want to study the way ions conduct, then electrolysis can be a nuisance, largely because the ions are constantly being removed from the solution. Electrolysis can be avoided if, instead of keeping the electrodes permanently positively or negatively charged, we repeatedly change the charge on them. This is achieved by using an alternating voltage. A conductivity cell (see Figure 73.1) contains two platinum electrodes bonded into the glass walls of the cell. In use, the cell is placed into a solution and the electrodes are

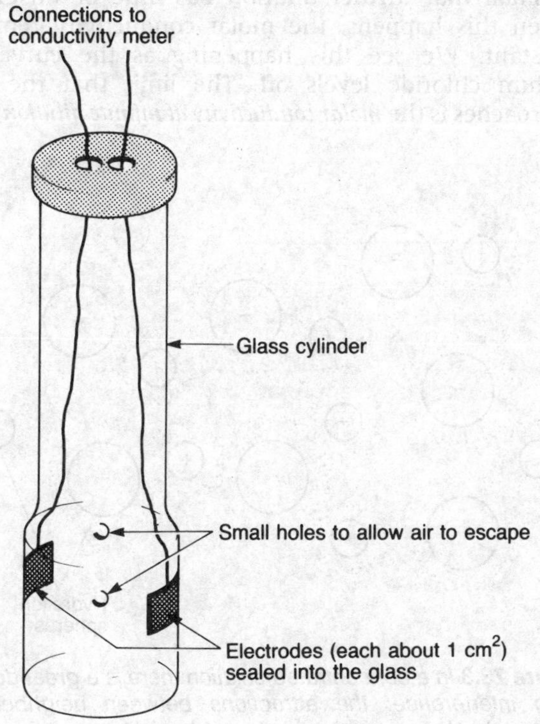

Figure 73.1 *A conductivity cell*

connected to a conductivity meter. The electronics in the meter is designed to connect an alternating voltage to the cell, and at the same time to measure the *resistance* of the solution between the electrodes.

The higher the resistance, the lower the conductivity, and vice versa. In other words, the conductivity is proportional to 1/resistance. With some thought you should appreciate that if there is a greater length of solution between the electrodes, then the resistance will increase. On the other hand, if we keep the distance between the electrodes fixed, but increase their area, then the resistance should decrease. (This is exactly the same behaviour that we find with metals. If you increase the length of a metal wire, its resistance increases, but a wire of greater cross-sectional area will have a lower resistance than one of smaller area.) Now we can define the conductivity $\varkappa$ (the Greek letter pronounced 'kappa') as

$$\varkappa = \frac{1}{R} \times \frac{l}{A}$$

Thus, if we know the dimensions of the cell (l and A) and we take the reading from the conductivity meter, we can calculate the conductivity. If you actually use a conductivity meter, take care to look at the units in which it reads. It should give readings of $1/R$, known as the *conductance*. Resistance is measured in ohms, Ω, so conductance has units of ohm^{-1}. It has become more common to use the siemens, S, as the unit instead of ohm^{-1}. Your meter may give results in ohm^{-1} or S.

For example, a conductivity meter gave a reading of 0.011 S when a conductivity cell having $l = 1$ cm and $A = 1$ cm^2 was dipped into a solution of 0.1 mol dm^{-3} sodium chloride. What was the conductivity? We have $1/R = 0.011$ S so

$$\varkappa = 0.011\text{ S} \times \frac{1\text{ cm}}{1\text{ cm}^2}$$

or

$$\varkappa = 0.011\text{ S cm}^{-1}\ (0.011\text{ ohm}^{-1}\text{ cm}^{-1})$$

In practice we do not normally attempt to measure l and A for a conductivity cell. Rather, the cell is calibrated against a solution of known concentration and the ratio l/A, called the *cell constant*, is stated by the manufacturer. You will find more details about this in question 73.1. Also, if we were strict about using SI units, $\varkappa$ should be quoted in $S\ m^{-1}$. However, it is much more common to give the results in $S\ cm^{-1}$.

73.2 Molar conductivities

We now know how to measure the conductivity of a solution; but apart from listing a whole series of such measurements, we are not much further on. The problem is that if we are to compare conductivities, we should compare like with like. For this reason we make use of *molar conductivities.* The molar conductivity is the conductivity that we would expect the solution to have if it were to contain 1 mol of the substance. We write the molar conductivity as Λ (the Greek letter capital 'lambda') and put

$$\Lambda = \varkappa V_m$$

where V_m is the volume that would contain 1 mol of substance. V_m is called the (molar) *dilution*. It has units $cm^3\ mol^{-1}$.

For example, in our $0.1\ mol\ dm^{-3}$ solution of sodium chloride, the volume that would contain 1 mol of the salt is $10\ dm^3$. (The $0.1\ mol\ dm^{-3}$ solution contains 0.1 mol in $1\ dm^3$, so $10\ dm^3$ would be needed if we wanted 1 mol.) Owing to the units we are using for conductivity, we must write the volume in cm^3, in this case $10\,000\ cm^3$. Then,

$$\Lambda = 0.011\ S\ cm^{-1} \times 10\,000\ cm^3\ mol^{-1} = 110\ S\ cm^2\ mol^{-1}$$

We could perform a series of experiments on sodium chloride solutions of different concentrations, measure their conductivities, and calculate the molar conductivity each time. Figure 73.2 shows you the result of such a series of experiments, but with the results plotted on a graph. Be sure to notice that the graph has molar conductivity plotted against dilution (not concentration). You can compare this with a second series of results for ethanoic acid.

These two lines are typical of their kind. You should know that sodium chloride is a *strong electrolyte*, i.e. it is completely dissociated into ions in water. However, ethanoic acid is a *weak electrolyte*, i.e. it is only partially dissociated into ions. We can explain the shapes of the graphs in the following way.

(a) *Strong electrolytes*

In a concentrated solution of a strong electrolyte there are vast numbers of ions, but they are very close together. Indeed, owing to the attractions between the opposite charges, a positive ion will, on average, find itself surrounded by a sphere of negative ions. Similarly, a negative ion will be surrounded by positive ions. Each ion *interferes* with its neighbours. Therefore, if a positive ion attempts to move in one direction under the influence of the electric field between the plates in a conductivity cell, the surrounding negative ions will hold it back. Likewise the negative ions are restrained by the positive ions. Now, if we dilute the solution (increase the dilution), the ions are, on average, further apart and the amount of interference between them decreases (Figure 73.3). This is why the molar conductivity of a strong electrolyte increases with dilution. To set against this is the fact that, as the dilution increases, there comes a time when the amount of interference is so small that further dilution has little or no effect. When this happens, the molar conductivity remains constant. We see this happening as the curve for sodium chloride levels off. The limit that the line approaches is the *molar conductivity at infinite dilution*, Λ^∞.

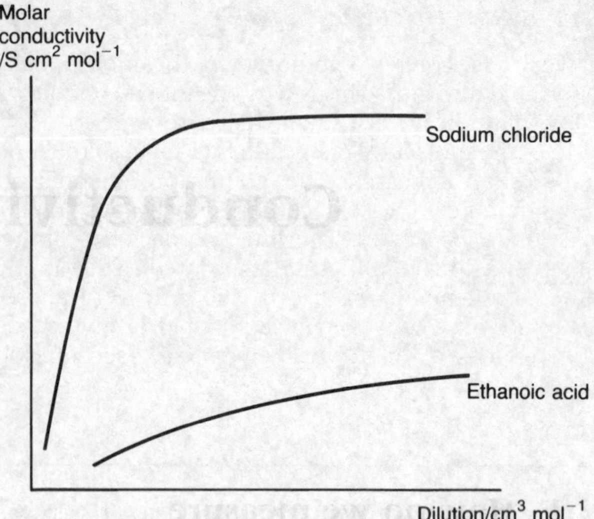

Figure 73.2 *Graph of molar conductivity versus dilution for a strong electrolyte (sodium chloride) is markedly different to that for a weak electrolyte (ethanoic acid). Note: the lines have not been drawn to the same scale*

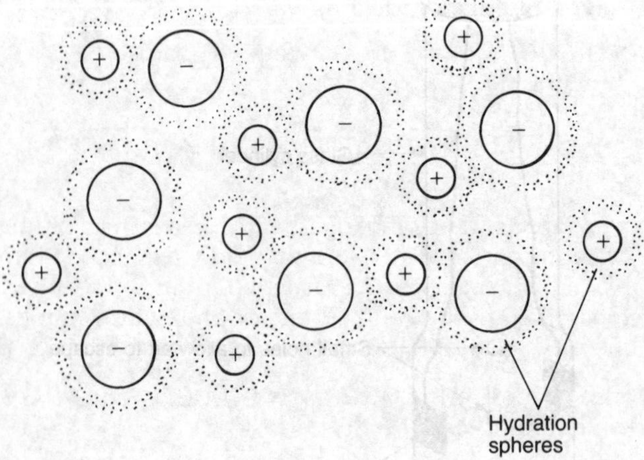

Figure 73.3 *In a concentrated solution there is a great deal of ionic interference: the attractions between neighbouring oppositely charged ions are strong. In a dilute solution, ions are much further apart and have less influence on each other*

(b) *Weak electrolytes*

In weak electrolytes a minority of the molecules are dissociated into ions. This is why the molar conductivity at low dilution is very small. As more water is added, more of the molecules dissociate into ions, so the molar conductivity increases. The graph for ethanoic acid shows that the increase in conductivity is not so rapid as for strong electrolytes. The line approaches a limiting value very slowly, and attempts to predict the limiting value that it might reach can give only very approximate answers. However, it is possible to give a good estimate for Λ^∞ of a weak electrolyte (see question 73.3).

> **73.1** The cell constant of a conductivity cell was stated as $0.215\,\text{cm}^{-1}$. The conductance of a $0.001\,\text{mol dm}^{-3}$ solution of potassium nitrate was found to be 6.6×10^{-4} S.
>
> (i) What is the conductivity of the solution?
>
> (ii) What result does this give for the molar conductivity of potassium nitrate?

73.3 Molar conductivities and the degree of dissociation

When the conductivities of solutions were first investigated some 100 years ago, the difference between strong and weak electrolytes had not been established. The ratio Λ/Λ^∞ was called the *degree of dissociation*. We now know that Λ/Λ^∞ does *not* tell us about the degree of dissociation of strong electrolytes. Rather, the ratio is an indication of the amount of ionic interference in the solution. However, for weak electrolytes the ratio does give a measure of the degree of dissociation.

We shall call K_a the equilibrium constant for the dissociation of ethanoic acid in water:

$$CH_3COOH(aq) \rightleftharpoons CH_3COO^-(aq) + H^+(aq)$$

i.e.

$$K_a = \frac{[CH_3COO^-(aq)][H^+(aq)]}{[CH_3COOH(aq)]}$$

Let us suppose that 1 mol of ethanoic acid is in a volume V of solution. The acid is only partially dissociated into ions and we shall say that at equilibrium a fraction, α (alpha), is converted into ethanoate and hydrogen ions. Then we have the following pattern of concentrations:

Concentration at equilibrium /mol dm^{-3}	$CH_3COOH(aq)$	$\rightleftharpoons CH_3COO^-(aq)$	$+\ H^+(aq)$
	$\frac{1-\alpha}{V}$	$\frac{\alpha}{V}$	$\frac{\alpha}{V}$

This means that

$$K_a = \frac{(\alpha/V)(\alpha/V)}{(1-\alpha)/V}$$

or

$$K_a = \frac{\alpha^2}{(1-\alpha)V}$$

Now, if we put $\alpha = \Lambda/\Lambda^\infty$ we find

$$K_a = \frac{(\Lambda/\Lambda^\infty)^2}{(1-\Lambda/\Lambda^\infty)V}$$

This gives us a way of calculating an equilibrium constant from conductivity measurements. This formula was first given by Wilhelm Ostwald in 1888, and is known as *Ostwald's dilution law*.

> **73.2** A $0.001\,\text{mol dm}^{-3}$ solution of ethanoic acid was found to have a molar conductivity of $14.3\,\text{S cm}^2\,\text{mol}^{-1}$. Use this value together with $\Lambda^\infty(CH_3COOH) = 390.7\,\text{S cm}^2\,\text{mol}^{-1}$ to calculate
>
> (i) the degree of dissociation of the acid,
>
> (ii) the equilibrium constant.

73.4 How individual ions contribute to conductivities

In 1874 the German chemist Friedrich Kohlrausch pointed out that there was good evidence to suggest that:

The conductivity of a solution is the sum of individual contributions from the positive and negative ions.

This is a statement of *Kohlrausch's law of independent ionic mobilities*.

For example, if we write the molar conductivities of individual ions as λ (the Greek lower-case letter 'lambda') we should have

$$\Lambda^\infty(NaCl) = \lambda_{Na^+} + \lambda_{Cl^-} \qquad \Lambda^\infty(KCl) = \lambda_{K^+} + \lambda_{Cl^-}$$

The individual λ values are the *ionic molar conductivities*. Table 73.1 lists some values.

We can use these values to estimate the molar conductivities of various salts. For example,

Table 73.1. Values of ionic molar conductivities

Ion	Λ/S cm^2 mol^{-1}	*Ion*	Λ/S cm^2 mol^{-1}
H^+	349.8	OH^-	198.3
Li^+	38.7	F^-	55.4
Na^+	50.1	Cl^-	76.3
K^+	73.5	Br^-	78.1
Ag^+	61.9	I^-	76.8
Ca^{2+}	119.0	NO_3^-	71.5
Mg^{2+}	106.2	SO_4^{2-}	159.6
Cu^{2+}	107.2	CO_3^{2-}	138.6

$$\Lambda^{\infty}(\text{NaCl}) = \lambda_{\text{Na}^+} + \lambda_{\text{Cl}^-} = (50.1 + 76.3)\ \text{S cm}^2\ \text{mol}^{-1}$$
$$= 126.4\ \text{S cm}^2\ \text{mol}^{-1}$$

The figures in Table 73.1 show some surprising results. The value for the hydrogen ion is remarkably high. If we are to explain this we should first remind ourselves what happens when a more typical ion, say a sodium ion, moves through water. The ion carries with it an atmosphere of water molecules (Figure 73.4). This molecular baggage slows it down and impedes its progress through the solution.

Hydrogen ions appear to conduct so much better than sodium ions because of some subterfuge. They employ a different method of getting about: they indulge in molecule hopping (Figure 73.5). Hydrogen ions, which are really protons, attach themselves to lone pairs on the water molecules. A proton on one water molecule can very easily find itself on a neighbouring molecule simply by swapping from one lone pair to another. The result is that conduction takes place by protons being passed from one molecule to another. The conduction process is something like the knocking down of giant layouts of dominoes. The wave of movement along the line of dominoes is the result of large numbers of small movements, just as the conduction by protons in water is the result of many small changes in the arrangements of the protons.

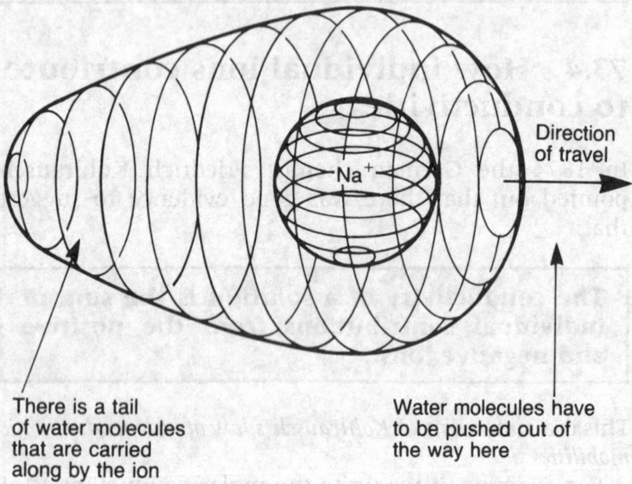

Na^+
Direction of travel
There is a tail of water molecules that are carried along by the ion
Water molecules have to be pushed out of the way here

Figure 73.4 The atmosphere of water molecules around a moving ion is unsymmetrical

Positive charge starts here

Positive charge finishes here

Figure 73.5 Swapping of hydrogen atoms between water molecules gives the impression that a proton (hydrogen ion, H^+) travels very quickly through a solution

73.3 This question is about calculating the molar conductivity at infinite dilution of the weak electrolyte ammonium hydroxide, NH_4OH, more properly known as aqueous ammonia. The molar conductivities of three strong electrolytes were measured, values in S cm^2 mol^{-1}: NaCl, 126.4; NaOH, 248.4; NH_4Cl, 149.8.

(i) We can write these in terms of the individual ionic molar conductivities. Write down the three equations. (One of them is already done for you in the text.)

(ii) Try to spot how the three equations can be combined so that λ_{Na^+} and λ_{Cl^-} cancel out. This should allow you to complete the equation $\lambda_{\text{NH}_4^+} + \lambda_{\text{OH}^-} = \ldots$. This is the answer to the question.

73.4 Use your answer to question 73.3 and the data in Table 73.1 to find the value of $\lambda_{\text{NH}_4^+}$.

73.5 The lithium ion has a radius of 68 pm. By comparison the radius of a sodium ion is 98 pm. In spite of its smaller size, the lithium ion has a smaller molar conductivity than the sodium ion. You might think this surprising because it seems to make sense that the smaller the ion, the more easily it will travel through a solution. Why then does the lithium ion travel less easily than a sodium ion?

73.6 Experiment shows that, for strong electrolytes, a graph of Λ against $\sqrt{\text{concentration}}$ (i.e. $\sqrt{c}$) is a straight line, provided the concentration is not too large. This provides a way of determining Λ^{∞}. Plot this type of graph using the following results for sodium hydroxide solutions:

c(NaOH)/mol dm^{-3}	0.01	0.04	0.09	0.16	0.25	0.36
Λ/S cm^2 mol^{-1}	238	230	224	217	210	202

(i) What is the dilution when $\sqrt{c} = 0$?
(ii) Use your graph to estimate the value of Λ^{∞} for sodium hydroxide.

73.5 How can we make use of conductivity measurements?

We have discovered that conductivity measurements can give us some insights into the nature of solutions of strong and weak electrolytes. It is possible to make practical use of this knowledge. If ions are removed from a solution, then the conductivity of the solution will decrease. A conductivity apparatus would show that the conductance (1/resistance) of the solution should decrease. We can make use of this fact by performing a *conductimetric titration*. We shall look at the result of titrating a strong acid with a strong alkali, e.g. hydrochloric acid and sodium hydroxide.

The conductivity cell is placed in the sodium hydroxide and hydrochloric acid is added from a burette in the normal way. Initially, the conductance will be high because the free sodium and hydroxide ions conduct easily. However, when the first few drops of hydrochloric acid are added, some of the hydroxide ions are removed owing to the neutralisation

$$H^+(aq) + OH^-(aq) \rightarrow H_2O(l)$$

Because this removes ions from the solution, the conductance should decrease; but we should not forget that along with the added hydrogen ions come chloride ions in the hydrochloric acid. Adding chloride ions will tend to increase the conductance. However, if you look at Table 73.1 you will see that chloride ions conduct less than half as well as hydroxide ions. The overall result is that the conductance goes down. The decrease in conductance continues until the endpoint of the titration. At the endpoint all but a very few hydroxide ions have been neutralised by the hydrogen ions. With the next drop of acid added, the hydrogen ions from the acid remain in the solution. We know that hydrogen ions will contribute hugely to the conductance, so the effect of their addition, together with the chloride ions that accompany them, means that the conductance increases. The result is that we obtain a graph like that in Figure 73.6. This type of graph can be drawn by hand, but it is far easier to connect the conductivity meter to a graph recorder or computer and record the results automatically.

Titrations of other combinations of weak and strong acids and alkalis can also be followed, but the graphs can be less easy to interpret.

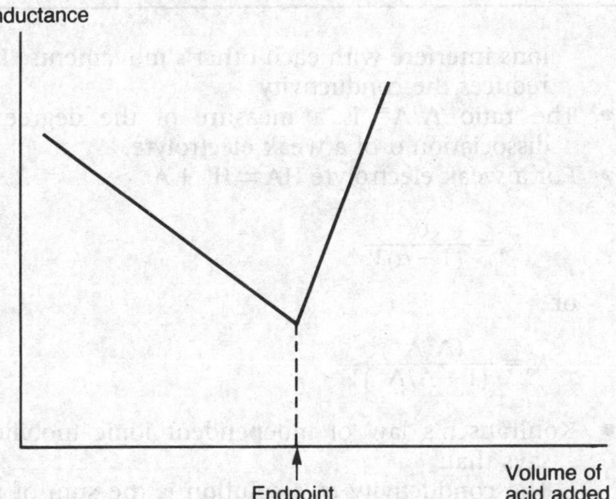

Figure 73.6 *Graph of conductance versus volume of acid added in a titration of sodium hydroxide with hydrochloric acid.*

73.7 The graph of a conductimetric titration is shown in Figure 73.7. It corresponds to the addition of a strong alkali, sodium hydroxide, to a weak acid, ethanoic acid. Explain the shape of the graph. (The molar conductivity of an ethanoate ion, CH_3COO^-, is 41 S cm^2 mol^{-1}.)

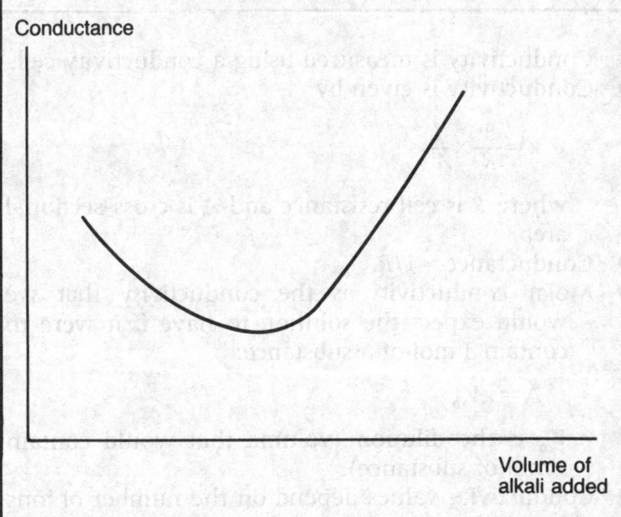

Figure 73.7 Graph for question 73.6

Answers

73.1 (i) Conductivity = conductance × cell constant
$= 1.42 \times 10^{-4}$ S cm^{-1}

(ii) Molar conductivity = conductivity × molar dilution
$= 1.42 \times 10^{-4}$ S cm^{-1} $\times 1\,000\,000$ cm^3 mol^{-1}
$= 142$ S cm^2 mol^{-1}

73.2 (i) $\alpha = 14.3$ S cm^2 mol^{-1}/390.7 S cm^2 mol^{-1}
$= 0.037$.

(ii) $K_a = \dfrac{(0.037)^2}{(1-0.037)\times 10^3} = 1.4\times 10^{-5}$ mol dm^{-3}

73.3 (i) $\lambda_{Na^+} + \lambda_{Cl^-} = 126.4$

$\lambda_{Na^+} + \lambda_{OH^-} = 248.4$

$\lambda_{NH_4^+} + \lambda_{Cl^-} = 149.8$

Each has units S cm^2 mol^{-1}, which for convenience we shall omit in the working.

(ii) We want to end up with the value of $\lambda_{NH_4^+} + \lambda_{OH^-}$, so

Answers – cont.

we need to cancel out the contributions from the sodium and chloride ions. We can do this by taking

$$(\lambda_{NH_4^+} + \lambda_{Cl^-}) + (\lambda_{Na^+} + \lambda_{OH^-}) - (\lambda_{Na^+} + \lambda_{Cl^-}) = 149.8 + 248.4 - 126.4$$

which gives the result

$$\lambda_{NH_4^+} + \lambda_{OH^-} = 271.8\ \mathrm{S\ cm^2\ mol^{-1}}$$

73.4 We have $\lambda_{OH^-} = 198.3\ \mathrm{S\ cm^2\ mol^{-1}}$, so $\lambda_{NH_4^+} = 73.5\ \mathrm{S\ cm^2\ mol^{-1}}$.

73.5 The lithium ion is a very dense centre of charge, and water molecules are attracted to it extremely strongly. The ion carries several layers of water molecules around it, which greatly increase the effective size of the ion. Hence it does not conduct so well as a sodium ion.

73.6 (i) The dilution is infinitely large. Λ becomes equal to Λ^∞ when $\sqrt{c} = 0$.

(ii) Your graph should give an approximately straight line, which extends back to hit the Λ axis near $245\ \mathrm{S\ cm^2\ mol^{-1}}$. This is the (approximate) value of $\Lambda^\infty(\mathrm{NaOH})$.

73.7 Ethanoic acid is only partially ionised in solution so the conductivity is not very large at the start.

$$CH_3COOH(aq) \rightleftharpoons CH_3COO^-(aq) + H^+(aq)$$

When sodium hydroxide is added, many of the hydrogen ions react to make water. Thus hydrogen ions are removed from the solution; but sodium ions are added, and there are more ethanoate ions in the solution. Overall this brings about a lowering of the conductivity because the molar conductivities of the sodium and ethanoate ions are much lower than that of the hydrogen ions that are lost. Once all (or nearly all) the ethanoic acid molecules have had their hydrogen ions neutralised, the conductivity shows a marked increase. This is because there are now free hydroxide ions in the solution, which have a fairly high molar conductivity.

UNIT 73 SUMMARY

- Conductivity is measured using a conductivity cell.
- Conductivity is given by

$$\varkappa = \frac{1}{R} \times \frac{l}{A}$$

where R is cell resistance and A is cross-sectional area.

- Conductance $= 1/R$.
- Molar conductivity is the conductivity that we would expect the solution to have if it were to contain 1 mol of a substance:

$$\Lambda = \varkappa V_m$$

V_m is the dilution (volume that would contain 1 mol of substance).

- Conductivity values depend on the number of ions in solution.
- A strong electrolyte is completely dissociated into ions.
- A weak electrolyte is only partially dissociated into ions.
- In a concentrated solution of a strong electrolyte the ions interfere with each other's movements. This reduces the conductivity.
- The ratio Λ/Λ^∞ is a measure of the degree of dissociation α of a weak electrolyte.
- For a weak electrolyte $HA \rightleftharpoons H^+ + A^-$

$$K_a = \frac{\alpha^2}{(1-\alpha)V}$$

or

$$K_a = \frac{(\Lambda/\Lambda^\infty)^2}{(1-\Lambda/\Lambda^\infty)V}$$

- Kohlrausch's law of independent ionic mobilities says that:
The conductivity of a solution is the sum of the individual contributions from the positive and negative ions; e.g.

$$\Lambda^\infty(\mathrm{NaCl}) = \lambda_{Na^+} + \lambda_{Cl^-} \qquad \Lambda^\infty(\mathrm{KCl}) = \lambda_{K^+} + \lambda_{Cl^-}$$

- Conductivities can be used to find the endpoints in titrations.

74

Acids and bases

74.1 Early ideas about acids

It has been known for well over 300 years that acids have a sour taste and react strongly with a wide variety of substances, such as metals. Similarly, bases were known to react with acids, and alkalis to have a soapy feel to them. The early chemists found it difficult to decide upon a reason why acids had a set of properties in common. One of the more successful ideas was that 'acids contain oxygen', a view for which the great French chemist Antoine Lavoisier was primarily responsible. Unfortunately for Lavoisier, and for the advance of chemistry, Lavoisier was held to be responsible for a great deal more than his ideas on acids. He was guillotined during the French revolution on 8 May 1794. The connection between oxygen and acidic properties is valid for a number of common acids such as sulphuric acid (H_2SO_4) and nitric acid (HNO_3), but, for example, it does not fit hydrochloric acid (HCl).

Antoine Lavoisier before his untimely end at the hands of the executioner.

The search for the common factor in acids came to a head during the 1830s when the German chemist Justus von Liebig (of Liebig condenser fame) wrote:

> Acids are . . . hydrogen compounds in which the hydrogen may be replaced by metals.

His and many others' work on acids has led to the following standard definition of an acid in introductory chemistry books:

An acid will (i) give hydrogen with a metal, (ii) neutralise a base to give a salt and water only, and (iii) give carbon dioxide with carbonates.

This summarises a great deal of information about the properties of acids, but does not tell us anything about their chemical structures except that they contain hydrogen as one of their elements.

74.2 Acids give hydrogen ions in solution

A significant advance was made in the study of acids when it was found that solutions of acids conducted electricity extremely well. This piece of experimental evidence tells us that acidic solutions contain *ions*. Indeed, the link between Liebig's observation about acids and the presence of ions makes the following proposal particularly appealing:

Acids provide hydrogen ions, H^+(aq), in solution.

The simplest way of explaining this is to suggest that

when a molecule like hydrogen chloride dissolves in water, it dissociates into ions:

$$HCl(g) + water \rightarrow H^+(aq) + Cl^-(aq)$$

However, there is considerable evidence to show that the active ingredient of an acidic solution is not a simple hydrogen ion, $H^+(aq)$; rather, it is the *oxonium ion*, $H_3O^+(aq)$. (Oxonium ions are also known as hydronium ions.) We now believe that when hydrogen chloride dissolves in water there is a chemical reaction:

$$HCl(aq) + H_2O(l) \rightarrow H_3O^+(aq) + Cl^-(aq)$$

Much the same sort of thing happens with the other common acids, as shown in Figure 74.1.

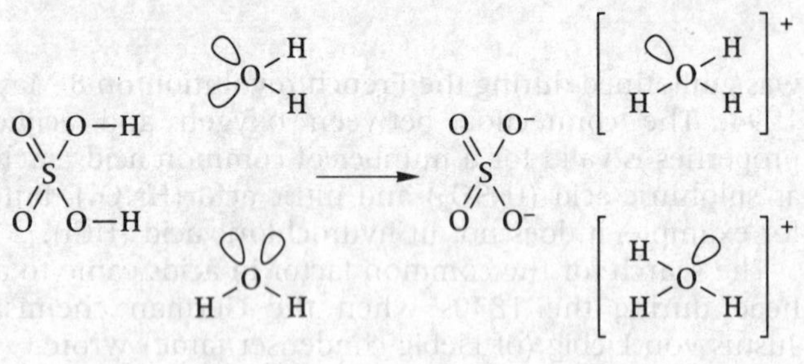

$$H_2SO_4 + 2H_2O \longrightarrow SO_4^{2-} + 2H_3O^+$$

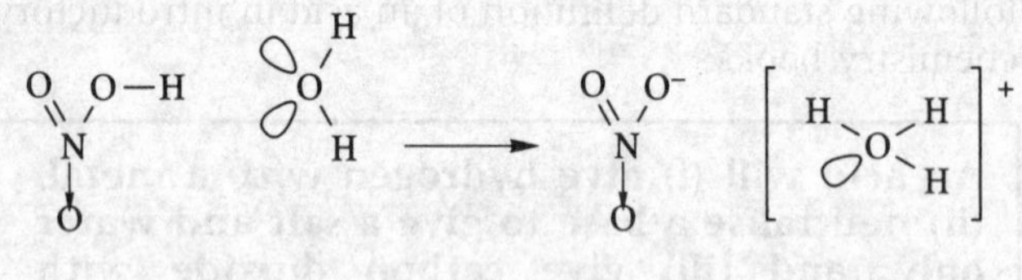

$$HNO_3 + H_2O \longrightarrow NO_3^- + H_3O^+$$

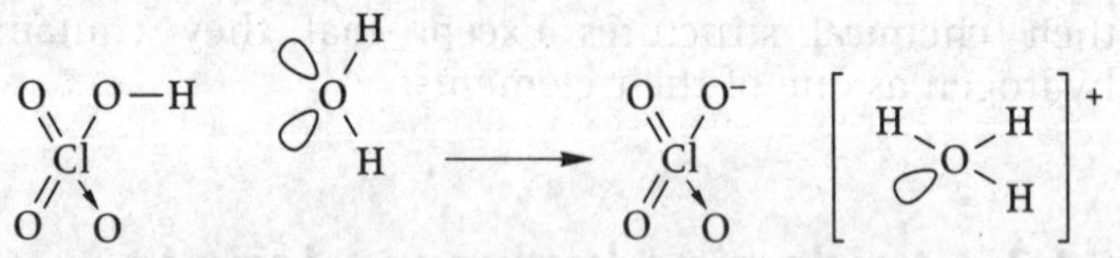

$$HClO_4 + H_2O \longrightarrow ClO_4^- + H_3O^+$$

Figure 74.1 *When sulphuric, nitric and chloric(VII) acids mix with water, oxonium ions (H_3O^+) are made*

74.3 The Brønsted theory of acids and bases

One of the problems with the last definition of acids is that it is rather restrictive. For one thing it has become common for chemists to carry out reactions in solvents other than water. These *non-aqueous* solvents include liquid ammonia and liquid sulphur dioxide. We would find it hard to accept that acids of one type or another cannot exist in these solvents; but we cannot apply a definition of acid behaviour that refers to oxonium ions in water to them.

It was in 1923 that the Danish chemist J. N. Brønsted provided a new definition of an acid and of a base:

Acids are proton donors.

Bases are proton acceptors.

This fits with our earlier definition, but can be applied to many other areas of chemistry as well. For example, when hydrogen chloride reacts with water, the hydrogen chloride can be said to donate a proton to a water molecule. The proton becomes bonded to one of the lone pairs on a water molecule.

We can apply Brønsted's idea of an acid to a reaction that would not fit our previous ideas about acids. For example, in liquid ammonia, hydrogen chloride and ammonia molecules react in this way:

$$HCl(a) + NH_3(a) \rightarrow NH_4^+(a) + Cl^-(a)$$

Here we have written an 'a' in brackets to show that the different ions and molecules are surrounded by the solvent molecules, in this case ammonia rather than water. The hydrogen chloride is again acting as an acid, but because it is donating a proton to an ammonia molecule (Figure 74.2), *not* because it is producing oxonium ions.

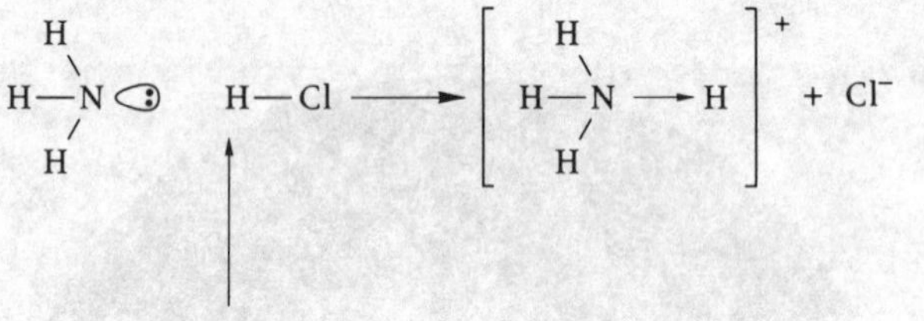

This proton will be donated to the ammonia molecule

Figure 74.2 *Hydrogen chloride acts as a Brønsted acid when it reacts with ammonia*

We can also see how Brønsted's definition can be applied to bases. When a water molecule reacts with hydrogen chloride it accepts a proton and turns into an oxonium ion. Therefore, in this reaction the water is acting as a base. Similarly, an ammonia molecule is a base when it reacts with hydrogen chloride.

If a metal oxide or hydroxide dissolves in water, an alkali is made. Alkalis such as sodium hydroxide or potassium hydroxide are often used in laboratories. It is the hydroxide ions they contain that are the Brønsted bases. One of the simplest reactions in chemistry is the neutralisation of an 'acid' by a 'base', which in an introductory chemistry book might be written as

$$HNO_3(aq) + NaOH(aq) \rightarrow NaNO_3(aq) + H_2O(l)$$

Really the nitric acid solution is a mixture of oxonium ions and nitrate ions:

$$HNO_3(aq) + H_2O(l) \rightarrow H_3O^+(aq) + NO_3^-(aq)$$

The sodium hydroxide solution is a mixture of sodium ions and hydroxide ions:

$$NaOH(aq) \rightarrow Na^+(aq) + OH^-(aq)$$

The overall reaction between the two solutions is

$$H_3O^+(aq) + OH^-(aq) \rightarrow 2H_2O(l)$$

Here the oxonium ion donates a proton to the hydroxide ion (Figure 74.3). Alternatively we can say that the hydroxide ion accepts a proton from the oxonium ion. Thus, in this reaction the hydroxide ion is a Brønsted base.

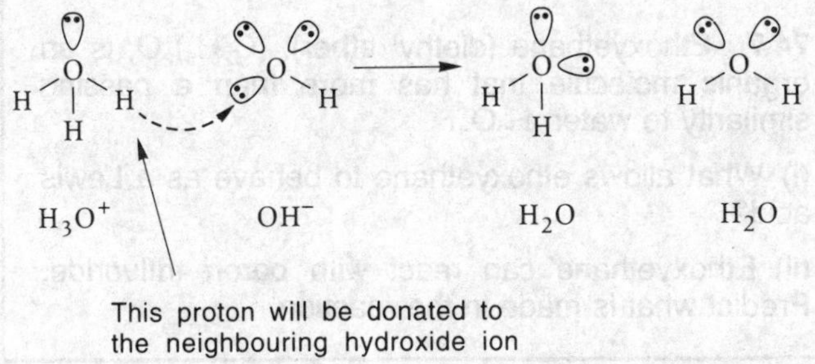

H_3O^+ OH^- H_2O H_2O

This proton will be donated to the neighbouring hydroxide ion

***Figure 74.3** In the reaction between a hydroxide ion and an oxonium ion, the former is a Brønsted base and the latter a Brønsted acid*

This theory of acid and base behaviour is often called the Brønsted–Lowry theory. However, it was Brønsted who was really responsible for the theory; the contribution of the chemist T. Lowry was not so important, and we shall simply speak about 'Brønsted acids' or 'Brønsted bases'.

74.1 Write down the equation for the reaction that takes place when sulphuric acid is neutralised by potassium hydroxide solution.

74.2 In the reaction between sodium hydride and water:

$$H^-(aq) + H_2O(l) \rightarrow OH^-(aq) + H_2(g)$$

is the water acting as a Brønsted acid, or is it a base?

74.3 In pure ethanol, C_2H_5OH, the following equilibrium can exist with ammonium ions:

$$NH_4^+(e) + C_2H_5OH(l) \rightleftharpoons NH_3(e) + C_2H_5OH_2^+(e)$$

where (e) means that the chemicals are surrounded by ethanol molecules. Does the ethanol behave as a Brønsted acid?

74.4 The Lewis theory of acids and bases

The American G. N. Lewis was a very influential chemist who decided that an even more general theory of acids and bases was possible. His definition (proposed in 1923) was that:

Acids are electron pair acceptors.

Bases are electron pair donors.

We can see how this idea fits with a neutralisation reaction such as that between oxonium ions and hydroxide ions. In Figure 74.3 the diagram shows the transfer of a proton onto one of the lone pairs on the hydroxide ion. We can interpret this in a different way by saying that the hydroxide ion donates one of its lone pairs to the proton. This makes the hydroxide ion a Lewis base. The proton accepts the lone pair, so it is the Lewis acid.

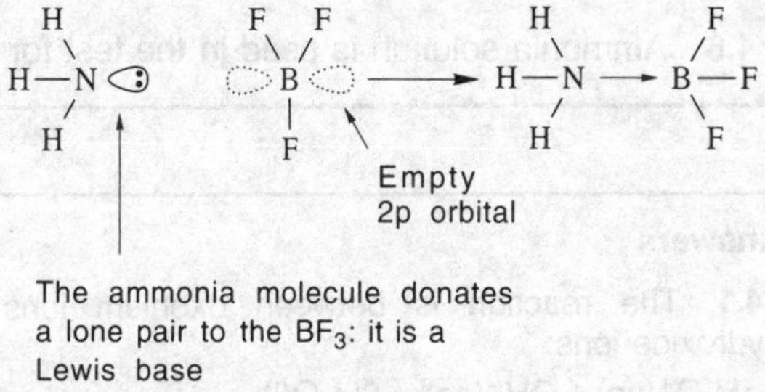

Empty 2p orbital

The ammonia molecule donates a lone pair to the BF_3: it is a Lewis base

***Figure 74.4** The reaction between ammonia and boron trifluoride can be thought of as a reaction between a Lewis base and Lewis acid*

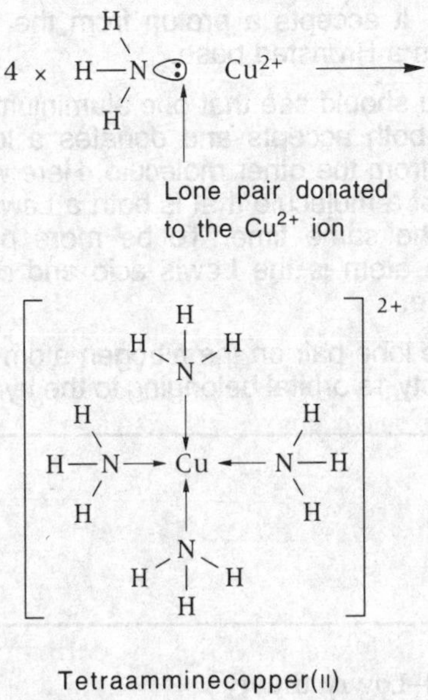

Lone pair donated to the Cu^{2+} ion

Tetraamminecopper(II)

***Figure 74.5** When the tetraamminecopper(II) ion is made, the ammonia molecules act as Lewis bases: each one donates a lone pair to the copper(II) ion. (Two water molecules also bonded to the Cu^{2+} ion are not shown)*

Now look at the reaction between ammonia and boron trifluoride illustrated in Figure 74.4. The lone pair on the ammonia molecule is donated to the empty p orbital on the boron atom (see Unit 15). The ammonia is acting as a Lewis base, and the boron trifluoride is a Lewis acid.

Lewis's theory can be applied to a wide range of reactions that we would not otherwise think of being related to acids and bases. An example is the reaction in which we test for copper(II) ions by adding ammonia solution (Figure 74.5). A deep blue clear solution is produced owing to the production of the tetraamminecopper(II) complex ion, $Cu(NH_3)_4^{2+}(aq)$. This ion is formed by each of the four ammonia molecules donating its lone pair to d orbitals on the copper(II) ion. Here the ammonia molecules are Lewis bases, and the copper(II) ion is a Lewis acid.

74.4 If you look at Unit 15 you will find an explanation of why aluminium trichloride can be found as dimers, Al_2Cl_6. After reading the explanation, say whether aluminium trichloride is a Lewis acid or base (or is it both?).

74.5 Describe the reaction between ammonia molecules and hydrogen ions:

$$NH_3(aq) + H^+(aq) \rightarrow NH_4^+(aq)$$

in terms of Lewis acids and bases.

74.6 Ammonia solution is used in the test for silver ions (section 101.7). The final stage in the reaction is

$$2NH_3(aq) + Ag^+(aq) \rightarrow Ag(NH_3)_2^+(aq)$$

What is the Lewis acid, and base, in this reaction?

74.7 Ethoxyethane (diethyl ether), $(C_2H_5)_2O$, is an organic molecule that has more than a passing similarity to water, H_2O.

(i) What allows ethoxyethane to behave as a Lewis acid?

(ii) Ethoxyethane can react with boron trifluoride. Predict what is made in the reaction.

Answers

74.1 The reaction is between oxonium ions and hydroxide ions:

$$H_3O^+(aq) + OH^-(aq) \rightarrow 2H_2O(l)$$

74.2 The water molecule loses a proton, so it is a Brønsted acid. The hydride ion takes the proton, so it is a Brønsted base.

74.3 No. It accepts a proton from the ammonium ion, so it is a Brønsted base.

74.4 You should see that one aluminium trichloride molecule both accepts and donates a lone pair of electrons from the other molecule. Here we have an example of a molecule that is both a Lewis acid and base at the same time. To be more precise, the aluminium atom is the Lewis acid and chlorine the Lewis base.

74.5 The lone pair on the nitrogen atom is donated to the empty 1s orbital belonging to the hydrogen ion. Therefore the ammonia is a Lewis base and the hydrogen ion is a Lewis acid.

74.6 The silver ion accepts the lone pairs from the ammonia molecules. Therefore the silver ion is the Lewis acid, and ammonia the base.

74.7 (i) The ether has two lone pairs on the oxygen, like water.

(ii) The reaction makes a product very much like that between ammonia and boron trifluoride. The ether donates one of its lone pairs to the empty p orbital on the boron atom. Thus the ether is a Lewis base, and the boron trifluoride a Lewis acid. You might also notice that boron trifluoride cannot be regarded as a Brønsted acid (it has no protons to donate). However, as we know, it can be a Lewis acid (electron pair acceptor). Lewis theory is more powerful than Brønsted theory because Lewis theory encompasses a greater variety of possibilities.

UNIT 74 SUMMARY

- Brønsted–Lowry theory:
  Acids are proton donors.
  Bases are proton acceptors.
- Lewis theory:
  Acids are electron pair acceptors.
  Bases are electron pair donors.

75

Strong and weak acids

75.1 What is the difference between strong and weak acids?

Typically we think of hydrochloric, nitric and sulphuric acids as strong acids. By saying that they are strong acids we usually mean that the acid molecules are almost *completely dissociated into ions* in solution (Table 75.1). For example, the equilibria

$$HCl(aq) + H_2O(l) \rightleftharpoons Cl^-(aq) + H_3O^+(aq)$$
$$H_2SO_4(aq) + H_2O(l) \rightleftharpoons HSO_4^-(aq) + H_3O^+(aq)$$
$$HNO_3(aq) + H_2O(l) \rightleftharpoons NO_3^-(aq) + H_3O^+(aq)$$

all lie far to the right.

On the other hand, weak acids have equilibria that are more balanced in favour of the undissociated molecules (Table 75.1). Examples are ethanoic acid, phosphoric(V) acid and hydrogen sulphide:

$$CH_3COOH(aq) + H_2O(l) \rightleftharpoons CH_3COO^-(aq) + H_3O^+(aq)$$
$$H_3PO_4(aq) + H_2O(l) \rightleftharpoons H_2PO_4^-(aq) + H_3O^+(aq)$$
$$H_2S(aq) + H_2O(l) \rightleftharpoons HS^-(aq) + H_3O^+(aq)$$

You should be careful not to confuse the meaning of 'strong' and 'concentrated' when talking about acids (see Table 75.1). As we have said, strength refers to the degree of dissociation of the acid molecules into ions. However, concentration refers to the number of moles of the acid in a given volume of water. For example, if we dissolve 10 mol of sulphuric acid in 1 litre of solution, we would have a concentrated strong acid. If we dissolved just 0.001 mol of the acid in 1 litre of solution we would have a dilute solution of a strong acid. Similarly, 10 mol of ethanoic acid in 1 litre of solution would make a concentrated solution of a weak acid. If we put 0.001 mol of ethanoic acid in 1 litre of solution we would have a dilute weak acid.

Shortly you will discover how we can make our ideas on strong and weak acids rather more exact. Instead of thinking about how particular molecules behave in water, we shall take a broader view and compare the ability of acids to donate protons.

Table 75.1. The differences between strong and weak acids

Strong acids	are completely dissociated into ions
Weak acids	are partially dissociated into ions
Concentrated acids	have many moles of acid in a litre of solution
Dilute acids	have few moles of acid in a litre of solution

> **75.1** A student saw a bottle marked 'Acid: pH = 5' on the label. He said to his friend that the bottle must contain a very weak acid. Was he correct?

75.2 Conjugate acids and bases

For an acid to show its acidic nature it has to react with a base (and vice versa). This means that we can only decide whether a chemical is an acid or a base by looking at the particular reaction in which it is involved. If we do this for the reaction between ammonia and water, we have:

$NH_3(aq)$	+	$H_2O(l)$	$\rightleftharpoons$	$NH_4^+(aq)$	+	$OH^-(aq)$
base X gains a proton		acid Y donates a proton		acid X donates a proton		base Y gains a proton

If we concentrate on the forward reaction, a water molecule is a Brønsted acid because it donates a proton to an ammonia molecule. On the other hand, if we look at the reverse reaction, the ammonium ion can donate a proton to a hydroxide ion. This makes the ammonium ion an acid and the hydroxide ion a base.

You can see that an acid on the left-hand side of the equation turns into a base on the right-hand side, and vice versa. An acid and base pair like water and hydroxide ion is called a *conjugate acid and base*. Similarly, an ammonium ion and an ammonia molecule make another conjugate acid and base pair. We have shown the conjugate pairs by labelling them as X and Y below the equation.

Here is another example:

$$HCl(g) + H_2O(l) \rightleftharpoons Cl^-(aq) + H_3O^+(aq)$$

HCl(g)	+	$H_2O(l)$	⇌	$Cl^-(aq)$	+	$H_3O^+(aq)$
acid X donates a proton		base Y gains a proton		base X gains a proton		acid Y donates a proton

Now compare this reaction with the previous one. The water acts as an acid with ammonia, but as a base with hydrogen chloride. In other words, it would be silly of us to say that 'water is an acid' or 'water is a base' in absolute terms; it all depends on the reaction.

It so happens that hydrogen chloride is a stronger acid than water, but water is a stronger acid than ammonia. Alternatively, ammonia is a stronger base than water, and water is a stronger base than hydrogen chloride.

75.2 Label the conjugate acids and bases in these reactions:

(i) $S^{2-}(aq) + H_3O^+(aq) \rightleftharpoons HS^-(aq) + H_2O(l)$

(ii) $N_2H_4(aq) + H_2O(l) \rightleftharpoons N_2H_5^+(aq) + OH^-(aq)$

(iii) $NH_2^-(aq) + H_2O(l) \rightleftharpoons NH_3(aq) + OH^-(aq)$

(iv) $CH_3COOH(aq) + H_2O(l) \rightleftharpoons CH_3COO^-(aq) + H_3O^+(aq)$

75.3 The ionic product of water

Water molecules take part in an equilibrium reaction

$$2H_2O(l) \rightleftharpoons H_3O^+(aq) + OH^-(aq)$$

The equilibrium equation says that two water molecules can react to make two different ions. This reaction is sometimes called the *autoionisation* of water.

A simpler way of representing the equilibrium is

$$H_2O(l) \rightleftharpoons H^+(aq) + OH^-(aq)$$

The equilibrium constant is given a special symbol and name. Its symbol is K_w and it is known as the *ionic product* of water:

$$K_w = [H_3O^+(aq)][OH^-(aq)]$$

or

$$K_w = [H^+(aq)][OH^-(aq)]$$

At 298 K, the value of K_w is 10^{-14} mol² dm⁻⁶.

Because it is a little more simple, we shall generally use the second of the two equations.

Normally we would write the equilibrium constant like this:

$$K_c = \frac{[H^+(aq)][OH^-(aq)]}{[H_2O(l)]}$$

or

$$K_c[H_2O(l)] = [H^+(aq)][OH^-(aq)]$$

But the concentration of water is for all intents and purposes constant, and a constant multiplied by a constant is another constant, so we can put

$$K_c[H_2O(l)] = K_w$$

Hence the absence of $[H_2O(l)]$ from the ionic product of water.

If water is pure, the equilibrium equation shows us that there are equal numbers of hydrogen and hydroxide ions. This means that the concentrations of the two types of ion are equal:

$$[H^+(aq)] = [OH^-(aq)]$$

So

$$[H^+(aq)]^2 = 10^{-14}\ \text{mol}^2\ \text{dm}^{-6}$$
$$[H^+(aq)] = 10^{-7}\ \text{mol dm}^{-3}$$

According to the definition of pH (p. 404), we have

$$\text{pH} = -\lg[H^+(aq)] = -\lg(10^{-7})$$

i.e.

$$\text{pH} = 7$$

This is the pH of pure water, which defines our standard of pH for a neutral solution.

If we add hydrogen ions to water, e.g. by pouring in hydrochloric acid, so that the hydrogen ion concentration increases to 0.1 mol dm⁻³ at equilibrium, then

$$\text{pH} = -\lg(10^{-1}) = 1$$

This shows us that:

The pH of an acidic solution is less than 7.

On the other hand, if we pour alkali into water, the water equilibrium will shift to the left in order to 'mop up' the added hydroxide ions. That is, the concentration of hydrogen ions will decrease. If we assume that in an alkali like sodium hydroxide solution the concentration of hydroxide ions is 0.1 mol dm⁻³ (10^{-1} mol dm⁻³) we shall have

$$[H^+(aq)] \times 10^{-1}\ \text{mol dm}^{-3} = 10^{-14}\ \text{mol}^2\ \text{dm}^{-6}$$

so

$$[H^+(aq)] = 10^{-13}\ \text{mol dm}^{-3}$$

and

$$\text{pH} = 13$$

This shows us that:

The pH of an alkaline solution is more than 7.

If we add hydrogen ions to water, the equilibrium will shift to the left and hydroxide ions will combine with some of the added hydrogen ions. However, as is always the case with equilibrium constants, provided the temperature does not change, K_w will keep the same value. If the concentration of hydrogen ions at equilibrium changes to 0.01 mol dm^{-3} (10^{-2} mol dm^{-3}), we shall have

$$10^{-2}\ \text{mol dm}^{-3} \times [OH^-(aq)] = 10^{-14}\ \text{mol}^2\ \text{dm}^{-6}$$

so

$$[OH^-(aq)] = 10^{-12}\ \text{mol dm}^{-3}$$

In the majority of cases the solutions we use in chemistry vary in pH between 0 and 14, as shown in Table 75.2.

Table 75.2. How pH varies with hydrogen ion concentration

$[H^+(aq)]$/mol dm^{-3}	pH	*Conditions*
1.0	0	Highly acidic
10^{-1}	1	
10^{-2}	2	
10^{-3}	3	
10^{-4}	4	Slightly acidic
10^{-5}	5	
10^{-6}	6	
10^{-7}	7	Neutral
10^{-8}	8	
10^{-9}	9	
10^{-10}	10	Slightly alkaline
10^{-11}	11	
10^{-12}	12	
10^{-13}	13	
10^{-14}	14	Highly alkaline

75.3 What is the concentration of hydrogen ions and hydroxide in:

(i) a 0.01 mol dm^{-3} solution of hydrochloric acid,

(ii) a 0.25 mol dm^{-3} solution of hydrochloric acid?

75.4 Like all equilibrium constants, the ionic product of water changes its value as the temperature changes. At 25°C we know that $K_w = 10^{-14}$ mol^2 dm^{-6}. At 65°C, its value changes to $K_w = 2.92 \times 10^{-14}$ mol^2 dm^{-6}.

(i) Is the dissociation of water into ions an exothermic or an endothermic process?

(ii) What is $[H^+(aq)]$ at 65°C?

(iii) What is the pH of water at 65°C?

(iv) What pH corresponds to a neutral solution at 65°C?

75.4 Acid dissociation equilibrium constants

A typical weak acid is ethanoic acid, CH_3COOH. In water, an equilibrium is set up as some of the ethanoic acid molecules dissociate into ions:

$$CH_3COOH(aq) \rightleftharpoons CH_3COO^-(aq) + H^+(aq)$$

Alternatively we could write this as

$$CH_3COOH(aq) + H_2O(l) \rightleftharpoons CH_3COO^-(aq) + H_3O^+(aq)$$

but the first equation is easier to use.

The equilibrium constant for the reaction is called the *acid dissociation constant* of ethanoic acid, K_a. As you might expect by now,

$$K_a = \frac{[CH_3COO^-(aq)][H^+(aq)]}{[CH_3COOH(aq)]}$$

The value of K_a for ethanoic acid is 1.7×10^{-5} mol dm^{-3} at 25°C.

Table 75.3 shows you values of K_a for a number of acids. The larger the value of K_a, the stronger is the acid. In much the same way as we find it simpler to use a pH scale that provides us with whole number figures, so it is with acid dissociation constants. We define the pK_a of an acid by

$$pK_a = -\lg K_a$$

According to this definition:

The smaller the value of pK_a, the stronger the acid.

Table 75.3. Table of acid dissociation constants, and pK_a values*

Acid	*Equilibrium*	K_a/mol dm^{-3}	pK_a
Ethanoic	$CH_3COOH(aq) \rightleftharpoons CH_3COO^-(aq) + H^+(aq)$	1.8×10^{-5}	4.7
Benzoic	$C_6H_5COOH(aq) \rightleftharpoons C_6H_5COO^-(aq) + H^+(aq)$	6.3×10^{-5}	4.2
Methanoic	$HCOOH(aq) \rightleftharpoons HCOO^-(aq) + H^+(aq)$	1.6×10^{-4}	3.8
Chloroethanoic	$CH_2ClCOOH(aq) \rightleftharpoons CH_2ClCOO^-(aq) + H^+(aq)$	1.3×10^{-3}	2.9
Dichloroethanoic	$CHCl_2COOH(aq) \rightleftharpoons CHCl_2COO^-(aq) + H^+(aq)$	5.0×10^{-2}	1.3
Trichloroethanoic	$CCl_3COOH(aq) \rightleftharpoons CCl_3COO^-(aq) + H^+(aq)$	2.3×10^{-1}	0.7

*Values of K_a are at 25°C

Each of the equilibria in Table 75.3 has the same pattern. It is

acid ⇌ conjugate base + hydrogen ion

There are many more acids and conjugate bases than are shown in the table. If you are willing to use a short-hand way of writing down the information, you will find the order of acid and base strengths for a much wider range of chemicals in Table 75.4. The information in the table shows you that there is pattern to the connection between an acid and its conjugate base, and vice versa:

> **The weaker the acid, the stronger the conjugate base.**
>
> **The stronger the acid, the weaker the conjugate base.**

Table 75.4. Table of acid and base strengths*

Acid	*Conjugate base*	K_a/mol dm^{-3}	pK_a
$HClO_4$	ClO_4^-	Very large	Small
HI	I^-	Very large	Small
HBr	Br^-	Very large	Small
HCl	Cl^-	Very large	Small
H_2SO_4	HSO_4^-	Very large	Small
HNO_3	NO_3^-	Very large	Small
H_3O^+	H_2O	Very large	Small
H_2SO_3	HSO_3^-	1.7×10^{-2}	1.8
HSO_4^-	SO_4^{2-}	1.2×10^{-2}	1.9
H_3PO_4	$H_2PO_4^-$	7.5×10^{-3}	2.1
HF	F^-	7.0×10^{-4}	3.2
HNO_2	NO_2^-	4.5×10^{-4}	3.3
CH_3COOH	CH_3COO^-	1.8×10^{-5}	4.7
H_2CO_3	HCO_3^-	4.2×10^{-7}	6.4
H_2S	HS^-	1.0×10^{-7}	7.0
HSO_3^-	SO_3^{2-}	5.6×10^{-8}	7.3
NH_4^+	NH_3	5.6×10^{-10}	9.3
HCN	CN^-	4.0×10^{-10}	9.4
HCO_3^-	CO_3^{2-}	4.8×10^{-11}	10.3
HPO_4^{2-}	PO_4^{3-}	4.4×10^{-13}	12.4
H_2O	OH^-	1.0×10^{-14}	14.0
CH_3OH	CH_3O^-	Very small	Large
NH_3	NH_2^-	Very small	Large

*Adapted from: Jensen, W. (1980). *The Lewis Acid–Base Concepts*, Wiley, New York, p. 53

75.5 What makes an acid strong?

There are four main things that a chemical needs in its favour if it is to behave as a strong Brønsted acid.

The first factor is that:

> **The ion it makes must be energetically stable.**

For this to happen it should be possible for the charge on the ion to be spread out rather than concentrated in one place. (We discussed examples of these 'resonance stabilised' ions in section 14.7.)

A similar state of affairs helps us to understand why organic compounds such as ethanoic acid are acidic in water. The negative charge on the ethanoate ion, CH_3COO^-, is spread over three atoms, as shown in Figure 75.1.

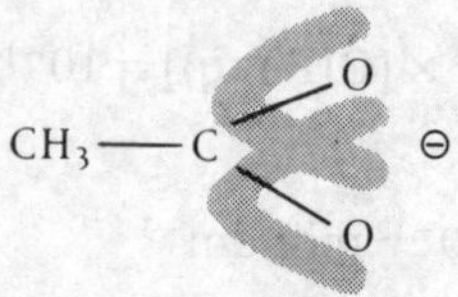

***Figure 75.1** The charge on an ethanoate ion, CH_3COO^-, is spread over two oxygen and one carbon atoms. This delocalisation of charge contributes to the energetic stability of the ion*

The second factor is that:

> **Once the ion is made, it should not easily change back into the molecule from which it came.**

The best way of ensuring this is to have it surrounded by a layer of insulating material. The effectiveness of the insulating power of a liquid is its relative permittivity (also called the dielectric constant): the higher the relative permittivity, the greater the insulating ability. It so happens that water has a very high relative permittivity of about 80 (Figure 75.2). It is this value that is partly responsible for the strengths of hydrochloric, sulphuric and nitric acids in water.

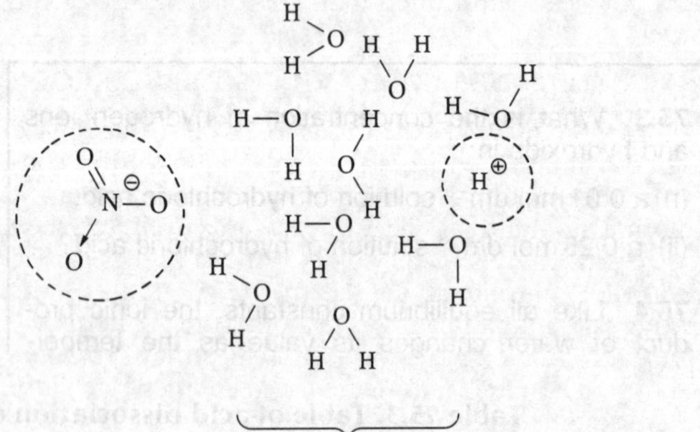

The water molecules between nitrate and hydrogen ions act as a layer of insulation. The layer keeps the ions apart

***Figure 75.2** Water is a solvent with a high relative permittivity*

The third factor is that:

> **The nature of the parent molecule, or ion, should encourage the loss of a proton.**

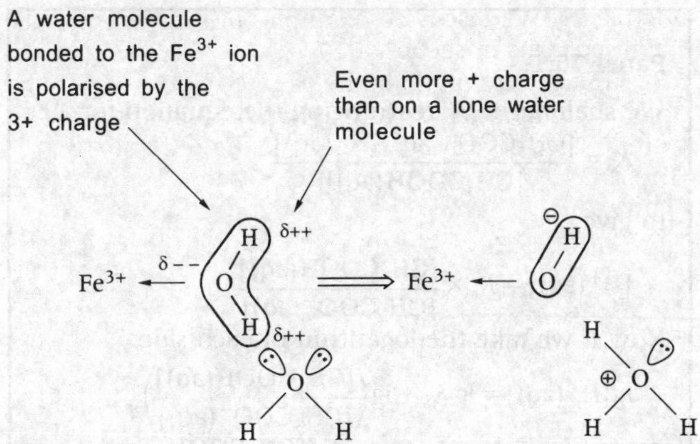

Overall: $Fe(H_2O)_6{}^{3+} + H_2O \longrightarrow Fe(H_2O)_5(OH)^{2+} + H_3O^+$

***Figure 75.3** One way of explaining why solutions of iron(III) salts in water are acidic*

We can see this happening in the case of some rather unusual Brønsted acids. The complex ion, hexaaquaferrate(III), $Fe(H_2O)_6{}^{3+}$, is produced when many iron(III) compounds are dissolved in water. It is the presence of this ion that makes solutions of iron(III) salts slightly acidic (Figure 75.3). The equilibrium

$$Fe(H_2O)_6{}^{3+}(aq) + H_2O(l) \rightleftharpoons Fe[(H_2O)_5OH]^{2+}(aq) + H_3O^+(aq)$$

is set up. Here the charge on the central iron atom is so large that it polarises the water molecules that are attached to it. This weakens the bonds between the hydrogen and oxygen atoms, and one of the protons can be donated to a neighbouring (solvent) water molecule.

In Table 75.3 you can see that the strengths of ethanoic acids substituted with chlorine change in the order

$$CCl_3COOH > CHCl_2COOH > CH_2ClCOOH > CH_3COOH$$

Chloroethanoic acid, $CH_2ClCOOH$, is a stronger acid than ethanoic acid. Part of the explanation for this concerns the highly electronegative chlorine atom. A chlorine atom attracts electrons towards itself, so when the negative ion is made, some of the charge is spread over the chlorine atom (Figure 75.4). Indeed, the greater the number of chlorine atoms, the greater is the spread of charge. We have seen before that spreading charge over an ion leads to increased energetic stability; so we might expect that the formation of CCl_3COO^- would be more favoured than CCl_2HCOO^-, and so on, with CH_3COO^- the least favoured. However, the enthalpy change for the production of CCl_3COO^- is endothermic, while that for CH_3COO^- is exothermic. This does not match our prediction. The reason is a little complicated, and we must turn to thermodynamics for help:

$$CH_3COOH(aq) \rightarrow CH_3COO^-(aq) + H^+(aq); \quad \Delta H^\ominus = -0.4\,\text{kJ mol}^{-1} \quad \Delta S^\ominus = -9\,\text{J K}^{-1}\,\text{mol}^{-1}$$

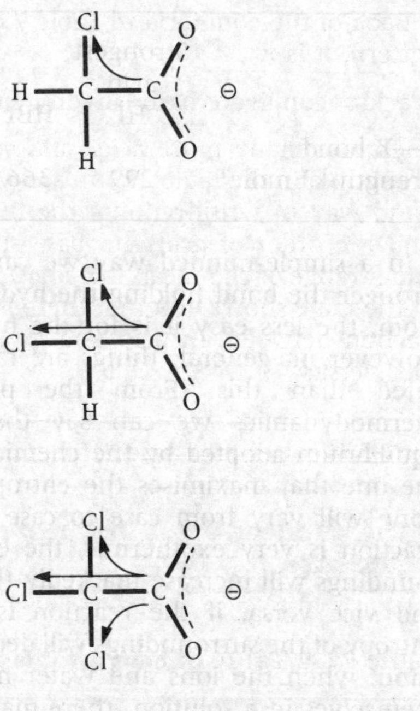

***Figure 75.4** The highly electronegative chlorine atoms help to spread charge over the negative ions made from the chloroethanoic acids*

$$CCl_3COOH(aq) \rightarrow CCl_3COO^-(aq) + H^+(aq); \quad \Delta H^\ominus = +4\,\text{kJ mol}^{-1} \quad \Delta S^\ominus = +8\,\text{J K}^{-1}\,\text{mol}^{-1}$$

Owing to the way the charge is spread over CCl_3COO^-, the ion represents a less attractive centre to water molecules than does a CH_3COO^- ion. The more localised charge in CH_3COO^- leads to a greater hydration energy for this ion, and a correspondingly more negative value of $\Delta H^\ominus$. On the other hand, there is an increase in entropy for the production of CCl_3COO^- ions, and a decrease for the production of CH_3COO^-. A major reason for this lies in differences in the hydration spheres around the ions. Assuming that water molecules are more strongly attracted to CH_3COO^- ions, they will be more tightly held, and thereby suffer a greater loss of movement (and a corresponding loss of translational energy levels open to them). If you use the equations $\Delta G^\ominus = \Delta H^\ominus - T\Delta S^\ominus$ and $\Delta G^\ominus = -RT\ln K$, you will find that the value of the equilibrium constant for CH_3COOH is about 10^{-5} whereas that for CCl_3COOH is nearly 2. Thus, CH_3COOH is only partially dissociated into ions, and is a weak acid, while CCl_3COOH is a strong acid.

The fourth factor is that:

The bond holding the hydrogen atom should not be too strong.

A particular example of this is the order of acidity of the hydrogen halides, which correlates with the order of the bond strengths:

	Strongest acid HI	HBr	HCl	Weakest acid HF
H—X bond strength/kJ mol^{-1}	299	366	431	569

In a simple-minded way we can imagine that the stronger the bond holding the hydrogen to the halide atom, the less easy it is for the hydrogen to be lost. However, in general, things are rather more complicated than this. From the point of view of thermodynamics we can say that the position of equilibrium adopted by the chemicals in a reaction is the one that maximises the entropy. The way this is done will vary from case to case. For example, if a reaction is very exothermic, the entropy of the surroundings will increase markedly (by a factor $-\Delta H/T$); and vice versa, if the reaction is endothermic, the entropy of the surroundings will decrease. On the other hand, when the ions and water molecules rearrange themselves in a solution, there may be an increase or decrease in the spatial disorder of the particles; it can be hard to tell without doing a detailed calculation. The actual position of equilibrium will be the one in which the entropy changes associated with the enthalpy change and the spatial arrangement of the particles are balanced to give the maximum entropy. For this reason it is unwise to pick on any single factor and claim that it is *the* reason why an acid is weak or strong.

75.5 Why might it be more sensible to write sulphuric acid as $SO_2(OH)_2$ and nitric acid as NO_2OH rather than their usual formulae?

75.6 Explain why solutions containing aluminium ions, Al^{3+}, are often acidic. (Hint: it is thought that the ion $Al(H_2O)_6^{3+}$ (aq) is present.)

75.6 What is the connection between pH and pK_a?

If you look at the formula for K_a of ethanoic acid, you should be able to see that the greater the value of $[CH_3COO^-(aq)]$ and $[H^+(aq)]$, the larger is the value of K_a. That is, the more the ethanoic acid molecules dissociate into ions, the more acidic the solution becomes. This being the case, we should be able to find a link between K_a and pH. This is done in panel 75.1. The result is that

$$\mathrm{pH} = \mathrm{p}K_a - \lg\left(\frac{[\text{acid}]}{[\text{base}]}\right)$$

where, in the case of ethanoic acid, the acid is $CH_3COOH(aq)$ and the base is $CH_3COO^-(aq)$. The interesting thing about this formula is that the pH of a solution of a weak acid depends on the *ratio* of the acid and base forms.

Panel 75.1

We shall begin by rearranging the equation for K_a:

$$K_a = \frac{[CH_3COO^-(aq)][H^+(aq)]}{[CH_3COOH(aq)]}$$

to give

$$[H^+(aq)] = K_a \times \frac{[CH_3COOH(aq)]}{[CH_3COO^-(aq)]}$$

Now if we take the logarithm of each side,

$$\lg[H^+(aq)] = \lg K_a + \lg\left(\frac{[CH_3COOH(aq)]}{[CH_3COO^-(aq)]}\right)$$

$$-\lg[H^+(aq)] = -\lg K_a - \lg\left(\frac{[CH_3COOH(aq)]}{[CH_3COO^-(aq)]}\right)$$

so

$$\mathrm{pH} = \mathrm{p}K_a - \lg\left(\frac{[CH_3COOH(aq)]}{[CH_3COO^-(aq)]}\right)$$

If we call $CH_3COOH(aq)$ the *acid* and $CH_3COO^-(aq)$ the *base*, the general equation is

$$\mathrm{pH} = \mathrm{p}K_a - \lg\left(\frac{[\text{acid}]}{[\text{base}]}\right)$$

To see how this works, we shall answer the following question: What is the pH of a solution that in 1 dm^3 contains (i) 0.1 mol of ethanoic acid and 0.2 mol of sodium ethanoate, (ii) 0.2 mol of ethanoic acid and 0.4 mol of sodium ethanoate?

We shall need to use our formula, but we also need to understand that sodium ethanoate is a salt of ethanoic acid. It is an ionic solid, which produces sodium ions, Na^+, and ethanoate ions, CH_3COO^-, in water:

$$CH_3COONa(aq) \rightarrow CH_3COO^-(aq) + Na^+(aq)$$

If it is put into a solution already containing ethanoic acid, the equilibrium

$$CH_3COOH(aq) \rightleftharpoons CH_3COO^-(aq) + H^+(aq)$$

will shift to the left. (This is an example of the common ion effect; see section 64.3.) However, because there are so many ethanoate ions from the sodium ethanoate, the equilibrium will lie almost entirely to the left. That is, to a good approximation all the ethanoic acid is in the form of molecules. Likewise, there are so many ethanoate ions that even if a few of them combine with hydrogen ions to make ethanoic acid molecules, the concentration of ethanoate ions does not change greatly. For this reason in part (i) of the question we have

$$[CH_3COOH(aq)] = 0.1\ \text{mol dm}^{-3}$$
$$[CH_3COO^-(aq)] = 0.2\ \text{mol dm}^{-3}$$

and in part (ii)

$$[CH_3COOH(aq)] = 0.2\ \text{mol dm}^{-3}$$
$$[CH_3COO^-(aq)] = 0.4\ \text{mol dm}^{-3}$$

If we take the two solutions side by side, we have

(i) $pH = 4.8 - lg(0.1/0.2)$
$= 4.8 - lg(0.5)$
$= 4.5$

(ii) $pH = 4.8 - lg(0.2/0.4)$
$= 4.8 - lg(0.5)$
$= 4.5$

The pH values of both solutions are the same because the *ratios* of the acid and base forms are the same.

75.7 A litre ($1\,dm^3$) of $0.5\,mol\,dm^{-3}$ solution of ethanoic acid has 0.2 mol of sodium ethanoate added to it.

What was the pH of the solution (i) before the salt was added, (ii) after it was added?

Explain the pH change by referring to the influence that the added ethanoate ions have on the equilibrium for the dissociation of the acid.

75.7 Base dissociation constants and pK_b

Sometimes people like to concentrate on the behaviour of bases, rather than on acids. For example, ammonia can take part in the equilibrium

$$NH_3(aq) + H_2O(l) \rightleftharpoons NH_4^+(aq) + OH^-(aq)$$

for which the equilibrium constant, the *base dissociation constant*, is

$$K_b = \frac{[NH_4^+(aq)][OH^-(aq)]}{[NH_3(aq)]}$$

As in our definition of K_a, we assume that the concentration of water remains constant, so that it need not appear in the expression. We define pK_b in much the same way;

$$pK_b = -lg\, K_b$$

A dilute solution of ammonia has a pK_b of around 4.8. Organic chemists are often interested in pK_b values because of the importance of compounds such as the amines. For example, methylamine, CH_3NH_2, has $K_b = 4.4 \times 10^{-4}\,mol\,dm^{-3}$ and $pK_b = 2.4$. We shall refer to these values again in Unit 122.

In passing, it can be useful to know that there is a connection between pK_a and pK_b values for a conjugate acid–base pair. In water at 25°C

$$[H^+(aq)][OH^-(aq)] = 10^{-14}\,mol^2\,dm^{-6}$$

Taking the logarithm of both sides,

$$lg[H^+(aq)] + lg[OH^-(aq)] = -14$$
$$-lg[H^+(aq)] - lg[OH^-(aq)] = 14$$

i.e.

$$pK_a + pK_b = 14$$

75.8 Just as we define pH by $-lg[H^+(aq)]$, so we can define a measure of the hydroxide ion concentration by

$$pOH = -lg[OH^-(aq)]$$

(i) What is the pOH of water at 25°C?

(ii) The way that pH and pOH are defined means that $pH + pOH = 14$ at 25°C. Draw up a table like Table 75.2, but put in two more columns labelled $[OH^-(aq)]$ and pOH. Put the missing values into your table.

75.8 How to work out the degree of dissociation of a weak acid

The degree of dissociation of a weak acid is the fraction of the number of moles of the acid that are converted into ions. We know that a weak acid dissolved in water largely consists of molecules; relatively few of the molecules dissociate into ions. Let us suppose that we put 1 mol of ethanoic acid into a volume $V\,dm^3$ of solution. We shall assume that x mol of the molecules dissociate. The equation tells us that for each mole of ethanoic acid that dissociates an equal number of moles of ethanoate ions and of hydrogen ions are produced:

	$CH_3COOH(aq)$	$\rightleftharpoons CH_3COO^-(aq)$	$+\ H^+(aq)$
At start	1 mol	0 mol	0 mol
At equilibrium	$1-x$ mol	x mol	x mol
Concentration /mol dm^{-3}	$\frac{1-x}{V}$	$\frac{x}{V}$	$\frac{x}{V}$

Putting these concentrations into the formula for K_a we have

$$K_a = \frac{(x/V)(x/V)}{(1-x)/V}$$

i.e.

$$K_a = \frac{x^2}{(1-x)V} \quad \text{Ostwald's dilution law}$$

The units of K_a are $mol\,dm^{-3}$. This formula was first derived by the German chemist Wilhelm Ostwald in 1888. It is known as *Ostwald's dilution law*. The law fits any weak acid, HA, like ethanoic acid, that dissociates according to the pattern

$$HA(aq) \rightleftharpoons A^-(aq) + H^+(aq)$$

We know that for a weak acid the fraction x is small. In most cases it is less than 0.1 (or 10%); often it is much smaller. This allows us to make an approximation. We put $1 - x \approx 1$; in which case,

$$K_a = \frac{x^2}{V}$$

or

$$x = \sqrt{K_a V}$$

This is the approximate version of Ostwald's dilution law.

Now let us take a particular example, and estimate the degree of dissociation of a solution of ethanoic acid. In our working we said that V was the volume of solution that contained 1 mol of the acid. For a 0.1 mol dm^3 solution, there will be 1 mol of acid in 10 dm^3, i.e. $V = 10$ dm^3. Therefore,

$$x = \sqrt{1.7 \times 10^{-5} \times 10} = 0.013 \text{ mol}$$

This tells us that the acid is approximately 1.3% dissociated into ions. (See question 75.12, and its answer, if you are worried about the units in this calculation.)

> **75.9** The pH of a solution of methanoic acid and sodium methanoate was 4.6. What was the ratio of [HCOOH(aq)] and [HCOO$^-$(aq)] in the solution?
>
> **75.10** Use the approximate Ostwald's dilution law to estimate the pH of a 0.1 mol dm^{-3} solution of chloroethanoic acid.
>
> **75.11** Only do this question if you can solve a quadratic equation. Repeat question 75.10 but this time use the accurate dilution law to calculate the degree of dissociation, x. Then calculate the pH using pH $= -\lg(x/V)$. Compare your result with that from question 75.10.
>
> **75.12** Explain why the units of x remain as moles even if it looks from the equation $x = \sqrt{K_a V}$ that they are $\sqrt{\text{mol dm}^{-3}\text{ dm}^3}$, i.e. $\sqrt{\text{mol}}$ or mol$^{1/2}$.

75.9 How to work out the pH of a weak acid

If you look at the working in the last section, you will see that the concentration of hydrogen ions is x/V mol dm^{-3}. This gives us our method of calculating the pH. In fact, to a good approximation, for a weak acid HA

$$\text{pH} = -\lg\left(\frac{x}{V}\right)$$

However, from the approximate version of Ostwald's dilution law we have

$$x = \sqrt{K_a V}$$

This means that

$$\text{pH} = -\lg\left(\frac{\sqrt{K_a V}}{V}\right)$$

or

$$\text{pH} = -\lg(\sqrt{K_a/V})$$

For example, what is the pH of a 0.2 mol dm^{-3} solution of methanoic acid? From Table 75.3 we find that for this acid $K_a = 1.6 \times 10^{-4}$ mol dm^{-3}. V is the volume of solution that contains 1 mol of the acid. For a 0.2 mol dm^{-3} solution, there are 0.2 mol in 1 dm^3, so there will be 1 mol in 5 dm^3. Therefore we have $V = 5$ dm^3 and

$$\text{pH} = -\lg(\sqrt{1.6 \times 10^{-4}/5}) = 2.25$$

75.10 Buffer solutions

A buffer solution keeps its pH approximately constant when small amounts of an acid or alkali are added (Table 75.5). There are two types of buffer:

> **Acidic buffers keep the pH below 7.**
>
> **Alkaline buffers keep the pH above 7.**

Table 75.5. Buffer solutions

Type	*Use*	*Made from*
Acidic buffer	Fixes an acidic pH, i.e. pH <7	Weak acid plus salt of weak acid
Alkaline buffer	Fixes an alkaline pH, i.e. pH >7	Weak alkali plus salt of weak alkali

(a) *Acidic buffer solutions*

Earlier we found that a mixture of ethanoic acid and sodium ethanoate has a pH below 7. In fact we found that a mixture for which $[CH_3COOH(aq)] = 0.1$ mol dm^{-3} and $[CH_3COO^-(aq)] = 0.2$ mol dm^{-3} had a pH of 4.5. There are two processes at work that are responsible for setting this pH:

Partial dissociation into ions

$$\underset{\text{In the majority}}{CH_3COOH(aq)} \rightleftharpoons CH_3COO^-(aq) + H^+(aq) \quad \text{(A)}$$

Complete dissociation into ions

$$CH_3COONa(aq) \rightarrow \underset{\text{In the majority}}{CH_3COO^-(aq)} + Na^+(aq) \quad \text{(B)}$$

We said that, in accord with Le Chatelier's principle, equilibrium (A) is forced over far to the left by the ethanoate ions from the sodium ethanoate. Let us see what happens if we add alkali or acid to the mixture.

Adding alkali

Hydroxide ions from the alkali will react with the hydrogen ions in the solution:

$$OH^-(aq) + H^+(aq) \rightarrow H_2O(l)$$

Removal of hydrogen ions will shift equilibrium (A) to the right. The shift provides hydrogen ions, which are available to react with further hydroxide ions. We say that the hydroxide ions are 'mopped up' by the hydrogen ions. In this way the added alkali does not markedly change the pH.

On the other hand, if we add a large amount of alkali, virtually all the ethanoic acid molecules will dissociate into ions. None are left to provide hydrogen ions, so the buffer will no longer work.

Adding acid

This time, the buffer has to mop up extra hydrogen ions from the acid. It is the large number of ethanoate ions (from the sodium ethanoate) that do this. Equilibrium (A) shifts to the left, removing the majority of the added hydrogen ions and thereby keeping the pH approximately constant.

It is not only a mixture of ethanoic acid and sodium ethanoate that acts as an acidic buffer. It is a common feature of almost any mixture of a weak acid and a salt of the weak acid.

(b) *Alkaline buffer solutions*

An alkaline buffer can be made by mixing a weak alkali and a salt of the weak alkali. A typical example is a mixture of aqueous ammonia (otherwise known as ammonium hydroxide) and ammonium chloride, NH_4Cl. In aqueous ammonia nearly all the ammonia molecules remain unreacted; they exist in solution solvated by water molecules. Only a minority react giving hydroxide ions:

$$\underset{\text{In the majority}}{NH_3(aq)} + H_2O(l) \rightleftharpoons NH_4^+(aq) + OH^-(aq) \quad \text{(C)}$$

$$NH_4Cl(aq) \rightarrow \underset{\text{In the majority}}{NH_4^+(aq)} + Cl^-(aq) \quad \text{(D)}$$

Adding acid

We can imagine the hydrogen ions to be mopped up in two different ways. We could say that they react with the hydroxide ions from equilibrium (C). This would displace the equilibrium to the right, replenishing the supply of hydroxide ions. Alternatively, and more importantly, free ammonia molecules can react with the hydrogen ions to make ammonium ions:

$$NH_3(aq) + H^+(aq) \rightarrow NH_4^+(aq)$$

In both cases the pH would remain approximately constant, until all the ammonia molecules have reacted.

Adding alkali

The added hydroxide ions are mopped up by the ammonium ions:

$$NH_4^+(aq) + OH^-(aq) \rightarrow NH_3(aq) + H_2O(l)$$

Again, this will keep the pH almost constant, until the supply of ammonium ions is exhausted.

75.13 What will be the pH of a buffer solution made from a mixture of 0.1 mol dm^{-3} ethanoic acid and 0.3 mol dm^{-3} sodium ethanoate?

75.14 What will be the pH of a buffer solution made from a mixture of 0.1 mol dm^{-3} aqueous ammonia and 0.1 mol dm^{-3} ammonium chloride? To find the answer, go through the following stages:

(i) In the formula

$$pH = pK_a - \lg\left(\frac{[\text{acid}]}{[\text{base}]}\right)$$

what is the acid in the mixture, and what is the base?

(ii) What is the value of the logarithm term?

(iii) Given that the pK_b for ammonia is 4.75, what is the pK_a?

(iv) What is the pH of the mixture?

75.15 Repeat the previous question but with a mixture of 0.2 mol dm^{-3} aqueous ammonia and 0.1 mol dm^{-3} ammonium chloride

75.16 You have been asked to make a buffer solution with a pH of approximately 5.

(i) Which chemicals would you use?

(ii) What should be their concentrations?

75.17 A student calculated that she could make up a buffer solution with an alkaline pH by mixing ammonium ions and ammonia molecules in the ratio 1 to 3. She decided to mix 50 cm^3 of solutions of 0.001 mol dm^{-3} of ammonium chloride and 0.003 mol dm^{-3} aqueous ammonia. A friend told her this was not a very good idea. Why was the friend correct?

75.18 Here is an extract from a book on A Level biology. It concerns the influence of the kidney on the pH of blood:

> Hydrogencarbonate and phosphate buffers in the blood prevent excess hydrogen ions (H^+), produced by metabolic activity, from decreasing the pH of the blood. Carbon dioxide released into the blood during respiration is regulated by this system and prevented from causing changes in plasma pH prior to its excretion from the lungs. Excessive changes in blood chemistry which would change the plasma pH from its normal level of 7.4, however, are counteracted by the distal convoluted tubule. This excretes hydrogen ions and retains hydrogencarbonate ions if the pH falls, and excretes bicarbonate ions and retains hydrogen ions if the pH rises. This may produce changes in the pH of the urine from 4.5 to 8.5. A fall in pH also stimulates the kidney cells to produce the

base ion ammonia (NH_4^+) which combines with acids brought to the kidney and is then excreted as ammonium salts.

(i) What is the normal pH of blood?

(ii) Explain how hydrogencarbonate and phosphate ions, PO_4^{3-}, act as buffers and help to prevent the pH of blood decreasing.

(iii) What is the difference between bicarbonate and hydrogencarbonate ions?

(iv) What do you think of the description of the ion NH_4^+ as 'the base ion ammonia'?

(v) In what sense do ammonium ions 'combine with acids'?

Answers

75.1 It is possible that he was correct because we might expect a weak acid to give a pH in this region. However, it is possible that the bottle contained a very dilute solution of a strong acid, like sulphuric acid. The pH alone does not tell us whether a solution contains a strong or weak acid; pH depends on concentration.

75.2 (i) $\underset{\text{base X}}{S^{2-}(aq)} + \underset{\text{acid Y}}{H_3O^+(aq)} \rightleftharpoons \underset{\text{acid X}}{HS^-(aq)} + \underset{\text{base Y}}{H_2O(l)}$

(ii) $\underset{\text{base X}}{N_2H_4(aq)} + \underset{\text{acid Y}}{H_2O(l)} \rightleftharpoons \underset{\text{acid X}}{N_2H_5^+(aq)} + \underset{\text{base Y}}{OH^-(aq)}$

(iii) $\underset{\text{base X}}{NH_2^-(aq)} + \underset{\text{acid Y}}{H_2O(l)} \rightleftharpoons \underset{\text{acid X}}{NH_3(aq)} + \underset{\text{base Y}}{OH^-(aq)}$

(iv) $\underset{\text{acid X}}{CH_3COOH(aq)} + \underset{\text{base Y}}{H_2O(l)} \rightleftharpoons \underset{\text{base X}}{CH_3COO^-(aq)} + \underset{\text{acid Y}}{H_3O^+(aq)}$

75.3 (i) We have $[H^+(aq)] = 0.01\ \text{mol dm}^{-3}$, so

$$0.01\ \text{mol dm}^{-3} \times [OH^-(aq)] = 10^{-14}\ \text{mol}^2\ \text{dm}^{-6}$$
$$[OH^-(aq)] = 10^{-12}\ \text{mol dm}^{-3}$$

(ii) Using the same method, $[H^+(aq)] = 0.25\ \text{mol dm}^{-3}$ and $[OH^-(aq)] = 4 \times 10^{-14}\ \text{mol dm}^{-3}$.

75.4 (i) As K_w is larger at the higher temperature, Le Chatelier's principle tells us that the forward reaction must be endothermic.

(ii) We have $[H^+(aq)][OH^-(aq)] = 2.92 \times 10^{-14}\ \text{mol}^2\ \text{dm}^{-6}$, and, as at 25°C, $[H^+(aq)] = [OH^-(aq)]$. Therefore, $[H^+(aq)]^2 = 2.92 \times 10^{-14}\ \text{mol}^2\ \text{dm}^{-6}$. This gives $[H^+(aq)] = 1.71 \times 10^{-7}\ \text{mol dm}^{-3}$.

(iii) $\text{pH} = -\lg(1.71 \times 10^{-7}) = 6.77$.

(iv) 6.77 is the neutral pH. Note that this proves that water is not always neutral at pH = 7.

75.5 The hydrogen atoms are bonded to oxygen atoms, which is not shown by the formulae H_2SO_4 and HNO_3. We use these formulae largely for reasons of history, and because they show clearly the number of replaceable hydrogen atoms.

75.6 The reason is very much the same as for $Fe(H_2O)_6^{3+}$. The aluminium ion is highly charged, which leads to the polarisation of the water molecules and the loss of a proton.

75.7 (i) We have $\text{pH} = -\lg(\sqrt{K_a/V})$. Here, with a 0.5 mol dm^{-3} solution we need 2 dm^3 for 1 mol to be present, so $V = 2\ \text{dm}^3$. Also, $K_a = 1.7 \times 10^{-5}\ \text{mol dm}^{-3}$. This gives pH = 2.54.

(ii) After the sodium ethanoate is added we must use

$$\text{pH} = \text{p}K_a - \lg\left(\frac{[\text{acid}]}{[\text{base}]}\right)$$

with $[\text{acid}] = 0.5\ \text{mol dm}^{-3}$ and $[\text{base}] = 0.2\ \text{mol dm}^{-3}$. Putting in the values we find

$$\text{pH} = 4.8 - \lg(0.5/0.2) = 4.4$$

The pH has increased, which tells us that there are fewer hydrogen ions in the solution than before. In accord with Le Chatelier's principle, the addition of ethanoate ions causes the dissociation equilibrium to shift to the left. This is the direction that removes hydrogen ions, as they join with ethanoate ions to make ethanoic acid molecules.

75.8 (i) pOH = 7 because $[OH^-(aq)] = 10^{-7}\ \text{mol dm}^{-3}$.

(ii) The values you should find are:

$[H^+(aq)]$ /mol dm^{-3}	1	10^{-1}	10^{-2}	...	10^{-12}	10^{-13}	10^{-14}
$[OH^-(aq)]$ /mol dm^{-3}	10^{-14}	10^{-13}	10^{-12}	...	10^{-2}	10^{-1}	1
pOH	14	13	12	...	2	1	0

75.9 We have

$$\text{pH} = \text{p}K_a - \lg\left(\frac{[HCOOH(aq)]}{[HCOO^-(aq)]}\right)$$

i.e.

$$4.6 = 3.8 - \lg\left(\frac{[HCOOH(aq)]}{[HCOO^-(aq)]}\right)$$

$$\lg\left(\frac{[HCOOH(aq)]}{[HCOO^-(aq)]}\right) = -0.8$$

$$\frac{[HCOOH(aq)]}{[HCOO^-(aq)]} = \text{antilog}(-0.8) = 0.15$$

This shows that there must be between six and seven times more methanoate ions than methanoic acid.

75.10 Here, $K_a = 1.3 \times 10^{-3}\ \text{mol dm}^{-3}$ and the volume that contains 1 mol is 10 dm^3. Hence, $\text{pH} = -\lg(1.3 \times 10^{-3}/10) = 1.94$. Clearly this solution is markedly acidic.

75.11 Now,

$$1.3 \times 10^{-3} = \frac{x^2}{(1-x)10}$$

so

$$x^2 + 0.013x - 0.013 = 0$$

$$x = \frac{-0.013}{2} \pm \frac{\sqrt{(0.013)^2 + 4 \times 1 \times 0.013}}{2}$$

Answers – contd.

which means

$x = 0.108$ or $x = -0.121$

The negative value has no meaning so we can put

$pH = -\lg(0.108/10) = 1.97$

The approximate formula overestimates the degree of dissociation of the acid.

75.12 The approximation was that we replace $1 - x$ by 1, so putting in the units,

$$K_a \text{ mol dm}^{-3} = \frac{(x \text{ mol})^2}{(1 \text{ mol}) V \text{ dm}^3}$$

Rearranging we have

$$(x \text{ mol})^2 = K_a \text{ mol dm}^{-3} (1 \text{ mol}) V \text{ dm}^3$$

i.e.

$$x \text{ mol} = \sqrt{K_a V \text{ mol}^2} = \sqrt{K_a V} \text{ mol}$$

and the units agree.

75.13 The ratio of [acid] to [base] is 1/3, so $pH = 4.8 - \lg(0.33) = 5.3$.

75.14 (i) NH_4^+ is the acid (proton donor); NH_3 is the base (proton acceptor).

(ii) Zero; the ratio is 1 and $\lg(1) = 0$.

(iii) We have $pK_a + pK_b = 14$, so $pK_a = 9.25$.

(iv) It is also 9.25.

75.15 Now, $pH = 9.25 - \lg(1/2) = 9.55$.

75.16 (i) A weak acid and its salt, e.g. ethanoic acid and sodium ethanoate.

(ii) We have

$$5 = 4.8 - \lg\left(\frac{[CH_3COOH(aq)]}{[CH_3COO^-(aq)]}\right)$$

so

$$\frac{[CH_3COOH(aq)]}{[CH_3COO^-(aq)]} = \text{antilog}(-0.2) = 0.63$$

This is a ratio of nearly 2 to 3. Provided the concentrations are in this ratio, it does not matter about their precise values. (This assumes we do not choose 'silly' concentrations that are so high that the substances would not dissolve properly, or so low that they would only mop up extremely small amounts of acid or alkali.) We might choose $[CH_3COOH(aq)] = 0.2 \text{ mol dm}^{-3}$ and $[CH_3COO^-(aq)] = 0.3 \text{ mol dm}^{-3}$.

75.17 Although it is the ratio of the two forms that fixes the pH, we also need sufficient free ammonia molecules and ammonium ions to react with the acid or alkali added. If solutions of such small concentrations were used, the buffer would not work very well. For example, even a small amount of a dilute laboratory acid could convert all the ammonia molecules into ammonium ions. Any more acid added would lower the pH. A more sensible mixture would use concentrations of 0.1 mol dm^{-3} and 0.3 mol dm^{-3}.

75.18 (i) 7.4.

(ii) They mop up hydrogen ions by way of equilibria such as

$$HCO_3^-(aq) + H^+(aq) \rightleftharpoons H_2CO_3(aq)$$

and

$$PO_4^{3-}(aq) + H^+(aq) \rightleftharpoons HPO_4^{2-}(aq)$$

(iii) None. Bicarbonate is the old name for hydrogen-carbonate.

(iv) It is an ammonium ion, not ammonia. It cannot act as a base, i.e. it cannot accept protons, nor can it donate a lone pair because the lone pair on the nitrogen already carries an extra proton. There has been a mistake in naming the ion. However, it is made from a base – ammonia.

(vi) The ion cannot combine with a hydrogen ion. It will make salts with negative ions such as Cl^-, SO_4^{2-}, NO_3^-. However, these salts are soluble (even in urine) so the ammonium ion should not be said to combine with these negative ions in urine. Rather we should say that the ammonium ion is excreted along with the negative ions from the acids.

UNIT 75 SUMMARY

- Strong acids and bases are completely dissociated into ions.
- Weak acids and bases are partially dissociated into ions.
- Characteristics of strong acids:
  - (i) The ion it makes must be energetically stable. Once the ion is made, it should not easily change back into the molecule from which it came.
  - (ii) The nature of the parent molecule, or ion, should encourage the loss of a proton.
  - (iii) The bond holding the hydrogen atom should not be too strong.
- Conjugate acids and bases:
  A chemical that behaves as an acid (base) on one side of an equation and turns into a base (acid) on the other side of the equation is a conjugate acid–base pair. For example,

$$\underset{\text{acid X}}{HCl(aq)} + \underset{\text{base Y}}{H_2O(l)} \rightleftharpoons \underset{\text{base X}}{Cl^-(aq)} + \underset{\text{acid Y}}{H_3O^+(aq)}$$

- A weak acid has a strong conjugate base.
- A strong acid has a weak conjugate base.
- Water autoionises $2H_2O(l) \rightleftharpoons H_3O^+(aq) + OH^-(aq)$.
- The ionic product of water is

$$K_w = [H_3O^+(aq)]\,[OH^-(aq)]$$

or

$$K_w = [H^+(aq)][OH^-(aq)]$$

At 25° C, $K_w = 10^{-14}\ mol^2\ dm^{-6}$.

- At 25° C the pH of pure water is 7.
- Alkalis have pH > 7, acids have pH < 7.
- The acid dissociation constant for $HA(aq) \rightleftharpoons H^+(aq) + A^-(aq)$ is

$$K_a = \frac{[H^+(aq)][A^-(aq)]}{[HA(aq)]}$$

- Acids are given pK_a values: $pK_a = -\lg K_a$. The smaller the value of pK_a, the stronger the acid.
- Connection between pH and pK_a:
  For 'acid' ⇌ 'base' + H^+

$$pH = pK_a - \lg\left(\frac{[acid]}{[base]}\right)$$

  e.g. $CH_3COOH(aq) \rightleftharpoons CH_3COO^-(aq) + H^+(aq)$

$$pH = pK_a - \lg\left(\frac{[CH_3COOH(aq)]}{[CH_3COO^-(aq)]}\right)$$

- Base dissociation constants and pK_b: $pK_b = -\lg K_b$. A strong base has a small pK_b.
- Ostwald's dilution law:
  For a weak acid $HA(aq) \rightleftharpoons H^+(aq) + A^-(aq)$, the law is

$$K_a = \frac{x^2}{(1-x)V}$$

  where x is the degree of dissociation. To a good approximation, $x = \sqrt{K_a V}$.

- The pH of a weak acid is $pH = -\lg(\sqrt{K_a/V})$.
- Buffer solutions:
  (i) A buffer solution keeps its pH approximately constant when small amounts of an acid or alkali are added.
  (ii) Acid buffers keep the pH below 7. Acid buffers consist of a weak acid and a salt of the acid, e.g. CH_3COOH, $CH_3COO^-Na^+$.
  (iii) Alkaline buffers keep the pH above 7. Alkaline buffers consist of a weak alkali and a salt of the weak alkali, e.g. $NH_3(aq)$, $NH_4{}^+Cl^-$.
- pH of a buffer can be calculated using

$$pH = pK_a - \lg\left(\frac{[acid]}{[base]}\right)$$

- Differences between strong and weak acids (or alkalis):
  (i) Strong acids (or alkalis) are completely dissociated into ions.
  (ii) Weak acids (or alkalis) are partially dissociated into ions.
- Differences between dilute and concentrated acids (or alkalis):
  (i) Concentrated acids (or alkalis) have many moles in a litre of solution.
  (ii) Dilute acids (or alkalis) have few moles in a litre of solution.

76

Neutralisation and titrations

76.1 Salt hydrolysis

We can think of salts being made in the four ways shown in Table 76.1. If you make a solution of each of the four salts mentioned in the table and measure the pH, you should find the pattern in Table 76.2. The change in pH is due to *hydrolysis*. Hydrolysis means that there has been a *reaction with water*.

Table 76.1. Four ways of making salts*

Combination		*Salt*
Strong acid+strong base		
e.g. $HCl(aq)+NaOH(aq)$	$\rightarrow$	$NaCl(aq) + H_2O(l)$ sodium chloride
Strong acid+weak base		
e.g. $HCl(aq)+NH_3(aq)$	$\rightarrow$	$NH_4Cl(aq)$
or $HCl(aq)+NH_4OH(aq)$	$\rightarrow$	$NH_4Cl(aq) + H_2O(l)$ ammonium chloride
Weak acid+strong base		
e.g. $CH_3COOH(aq)+NaOH(aq)$	$\rightarrow$	$CH_3COONa(aq)+H_2O(l)$ sodium ethanoate
Weak acid+weak base		
e.g. $CH_3COOH(aq)+NH_3(aq)$	$\rightarrow$	$CH_3COONH_4(aq)$
or $CH_3COOH(aq)+NH_4OH(aq)$	$\rightarrow$	$CH_3COONH_4 + H_2O(l)$ ammonium ethanoate

*All the salts are completely dissociated into ions in solution, e.g. $CH_3COONH_4(aq) \rightarrow CH_3COO^-(aq)+NH_4^+(aq)$

Table 76.2. The results of salt hydrolysis

Salt made from	*Example*	*Nature of solution*
Strong acid+strong base	$NaCl$	Neutral
Strong acid+weak base	NH_4Cl	Acidic
Weak acid+strong base	CH_3COONa	Alkaline
Weak acid+weak base	CH_3COONH_4	Almost neutral

76.2 Salts of a strong acid and a strong base

For a salt like sodium chloride we know (see Unit 60) that the water molecules help to break up the crystal lattice, and that the molecules surround the ions, producing a hydration sphere around them. It is arguable whether this counts as a hydrolysis reaction because the water molecules are not broken up by their interactions with the ions. For this reason the number of hydrogen and hydroxide ions does not change, and the pH remains constant.

76.3 Salts of a strong acid and a weak base

When ammonium chloride dissolves in water, an equilibrium is set up in which the ammonium ions undergo hydrolysis:

$$\underset{\text{acid}}{NH_4^+(aq)} + \underset{\text{base}}{H_2O(l)} \rightleftharpoons NH_3(aq) + H_3O^+(aq)$$

Essentially what is happening here is that the ammonium ion is showing its ability to act as a Brønsted acid. It is donating a proton to a water molecule, which in turn is acting as a base. You can see from Table 75.4 that this corresponds with the order of their pK_a values.

This behaviour is typical of the salt of a strong acid and a weak base. The cation (positive ion) in the salt is a stronger acid than water, so in solution the water acts as a base and oxonium ions are made. It is the presence of the extra oxonium ions that makes the solution acidic.

76.4 Salts of a weak acid and a strong base

Our example is sodium ethanoate. If we place this salt in water, it produces free ions in solution:

$$CH_3COONa(aq) \rightarrow Na^+(aq) + CH_3COO^-(aq)$$

which is followed by hydrolysis of the ethanoate ions:

$$\underset{\text{base}}{CH_3COO^-(aq)} + \underset{\text{acid}}{H_2O(l)} \rightleftharpoons CH_3COOH(aq) + OH^-(aq)$$

The water molecules act as Brønsted acids and the ethanoate ions are Brønsted bases. (Alternatively, we could say that ethanoate ions are stronger bases than water molecules.) The presence of the hydroxide ions made in the equilibrium is responsible for the solution having an alkaline pH (greater than 7).

76.5 Salts of a weak acid and a weak base

Here our example is ammonium ethanoate. The salt produces free ions:

$$CH_3COONH_4(aq) \rightarrow CH_3COO^-(aq) + NH_4^+(aq)$$

Now we have a real competition set up. There are two hydrolysis reactions

$$CH_3COO^-(aq) + H_2O(l) \rightleftharpoons CH_3COOH(aq) + OH^-(aq)$$

$$NH_4^+(aq) + H_2O(l) \rightleftharpoons NH_3(aq) + H_3O^+(aq)$$

If the first reaction wins over the second, the solution will be alkaline; if the second wins over the first, the solution will be acidic. In this particular case the base strength of ethanoate ions compared to water and the acid strength of ammonium ions compared to water move both equilibria slightly to the right-hand side. There is a similar tendency to produce hydroxide and oxonium ions. Therefore the solution is approximately neutral, with a pH of nearly 7. This is typical of salts of weak acids and weak bases.

76.6 Endpoints in titrations depend on the strength of the acid and base

At the end of a titration of a base with an acid, the solution will contain one of the types of salt that we have just talked about. If, for example, we titrated a solution of sodium hydroxide with ethanoic acid, the final solution will contain sodium ethanoate. You should now realise that if you were to measure the pH of the solution when the acid and alkali had just neutralised each other, it would not be pH = 7 (Table 76.3). Rather, the pH would be a little on the alkaline side because of the hydrolysis reaction

$$CH_3COO^-(aq) + H_2O(l) \rightleftharpoons CH_3COOH(aq) + OH^-(aq)$$

Table 76.3. The pH at the endpoint of a titration

Acid	*Base*	pH *at endpoint*
Strong	Strong	7
Strong	Weak	<7
Weak	Strong	>7
Weak	Weak	≈7

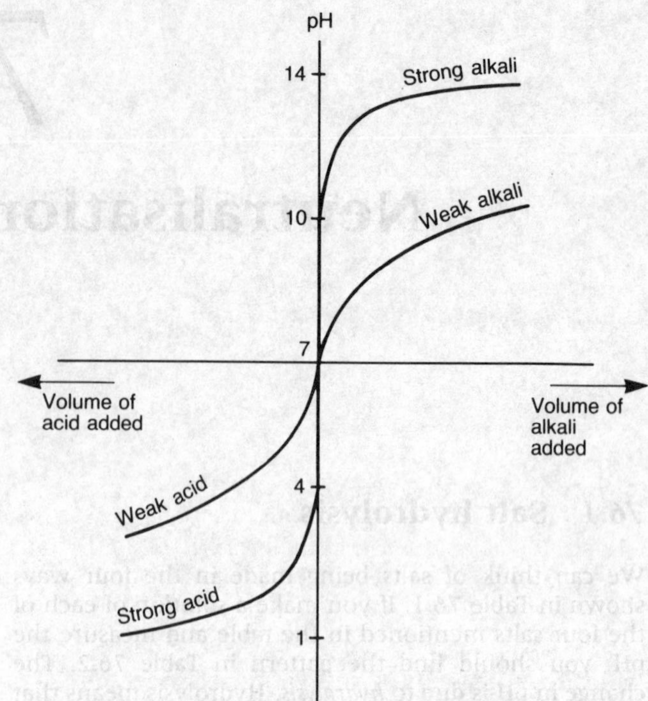

***Figure 76.1** Idealised pH profiles for titrations between strong and weak acids and alkalis*

In fact the only time we should expect the pH to be 7 at neutralisation is when we titrate a strong base with a strong acid, for example, sodium hydroxide with hydrochloric acid.

Figure 76.1 summarises how the pH changes for the combinations of acids and bases in Table 76.3.

76.7 Indicators

An indicator is a weak acid that happens to change its colour depending on the pH of the solution in which it exists. A very common indicator is phenolphthalein. It is pink in alkali and colourless in acid.

For the present we shall represent any indicator as HA, which takes part in the equilibrium

$$\underset{\text{one colour}}{HA(aq)} \rightleftharpoons \underset{\text{another colour}}{A^-(aq)} + H^+(aq)$$

In the case of phenolphthalein,

$$\underset{\text{colourless}}{HA(aq)} \rightleftharpoons \underset{\text{pink}}{A^-(aq)} + H^+(aq)$$

so that in acid, when the equilibrium lies to the left, the indicator is clear; but in alkali, when the equilibrium lies to the right, it is pink.

The pH of a solution of an indicator is given by applying the formula that we used in the previous unit:

$$pH = pK_a - \lg\left(\frac{[\text{acid}]}{[\text{base}]}\right)$$

or

$$pH = pK_{in} - \lg\left(\frac{[HA(aq)]}{[A^-(aq)]}\right)$$

Here we have used pK_{in} instead of pK_a to show that we are talking about indicators.

From Table 76.4, for phenolphthalein we have $pK_{in} = 9.2$. If we put 25 cm³ of 1 mol dm⁻³ sodium hydroxide in a flask, it will have a pH of 14. If we add a few drops of phenolphthalein indicator, we can calculate the ratio of the acid and base forms of the indicator:

$$14 = 9.2 - \lg\left(\frac{[HA(aq)]}{[A^-(aq)]}\right)$$

$$\frac{[HA(aq)]}{[A^-(aq)]} = 1.6 \times 10^{-5}$$

Table 76.5 illustrates the changes in [HA(aq)] and $[A^-(aq)]$ for a range of pH. The pink anion, A^-, far outweighs the colourless acid, HA, until the pH reaches 9.2, i.e. $\lg\{[HA(aq)]/[A^-(aq)]\} = 0$. At this point $[HA(aq)] = [A^-(aq)]$ and the colour will be mid-way between a clear pink and colourless. This means that if we were to add 1 mol dm^{-3} hydrochloric acid to the alkali, the indicator will remain pink until the pH of the solution decreases to a little below 9.2. If we did this as a titration experiment, we would see the colour change as the endpoint. Notice that the endpoint is *not* at pH = 7, which is what it should be for the titration of a strong base with a strong acid. Not all of the hydroxide ions would have been neutralised when we stopped adding the acid.

Now imagine performing the same experiment but this time using methyl red as the indicator. This indicator has a pK_{in} of 5.1. Above this pH it is yellow, below it is red. If we added this indicator to the alkali in the flask, it would be yellow. It would stay yellow until the pH dropped to around 5.1. Here the two coloured forms would have equal concentrations and the solution would appear orange. With the addition of a little more acid, the pH would drop to below 5.1 and the solution would be red. We would take the orange colour as the endpoint. However, the solution would not be at pH = 7 at the endpoint. This time we would have added too many hydrogen ions.

The point of this is that:

The endpoint we see in a titration depends on the indicator.

If we are to be accurate in determining the endpoint of a titration, we should choose an indicator that has a pK_{in} equal, or near, to the pH at the endpoint.

Table 76.4. pK_{in} values and colour changes for some indicators

Indicator	pK_{in}	pH *range*	*Colour range*
Congo red	4.0	3.0 to 5.0	Blue to red
Methyl red	5.1	4.2 to 6.3	Red to yellow
Litmus*	–	5.0 to 8.0	Red to blue
Cresol red	8.2	7.2 to 8.8	Yellow to red
Phenolphthalein	9.2	8.3 to 10	Colourless to pink

*The pK_{in} of litmus is uncertain

Table 76.5. How the colour of phenolphthalein changes with pH

pH	$\frac{[HA(aq)]}{[A^-(aq)]}$	*Colour*
13*	1.6×10^{-4}	Pink
12	1.6×10^{-3}	Pink
11	1.6×10^{-2}	Pink
10	1.6×10^{-1}	Pink
9.2	1.0	Pale pink (endpoint)
9	1.6	Colourless
8	1.6×10^{1}	Colourless
7	1.6×10^{2}	Colourless
6	1.6×10^{3}	Colourless
5	1.6×10^{4}	Colourless
4	1.6×10^{5}	Colourless
3	1.6×10^{6}	Colourless
2	1.6×10^{7}	Colourless
1	1.6×10^{8}	Colourless

*At very high pH, phenolphthalein loses its colour

76.1 Hydrogen sulphide can be regarded as a weak acid in water. What would you expect the pH of a solution of sodium sulphide, Na_2S, to be?

76.2 Carbonic acid, H_2CO_3, is a weak acid. In water it takes part in the equilibrium:

$$H_2CO_3(aq) + H_2O(l) \rightleftharpoons HCO_3^-(aq) + H_3O^+(aq)$$

Would you expect the pH for a solution of sodium carbonate (Na_2CO_3) to be >7, 7 or <7?

76.3 Which indicator would you choose if you were to perform a titration that gives a pH = 5.0 at the endpoint?

76.4 What would be the colour of cresol red in a solution of (i) 0.1 mol dm⁻³ sodium hydroxide; (ii) 0.1 mol dm⁻³ hydrochloric acid?

Answers

76.1 It should be alkaline, pH > 7.

76.2 Sodium carbonate is the salt of a strong base (sodium hydroxide) and a weak acid. Therefore we would expect its solution to have a pH > 7. A solution of the carbonate is noticeably alkaline.

76.3 From Table 76.3, methyl red has a $pK_{in} = 5.1$ and a colour change that covers the range.

76.4 (i) Red; (ii) yellow.

UNIT 76 SUMMARY

- Salt hydrolysis occurs when a salt reacts with water; e.g. the salt of a strong acid and weak base gives an acidic solution (see Table 76.2).
- Endpoints in titrations depend on the strength of the acid and base because the salt made in the titration may take part in hydrolysis.
- Indicators are weak acids that change their colours depending on the pH of the solution in which they exist.
- pH of an indicator is related to its acid dissociation constant:

$$\text{pH} = \text{p}K_{in} - \lg\left(\frac{[\text{HA(aq)}]}{[\text{A}^-(\text{aq})]}\right)$$

77

Rates of reactions

77.1 Why do we study the rates of reactions?

In thermodynamics we have discovered a method of finding out if a reaction should, or should not, take place. The trick is to work out the free energy change in the reaction. If the change is negative, then the reaction can occur; it is a spontaneous reaction. If the change is positive, the reaction cannot take place. However, thermodynamics does not tell us *how fast* a spontaneous reaction will be. For example, at room temperature the free energy change for diamond reacting with oxygen to make carbon dioxide is negative. Thermodynamics says that this reaction can take place, yet we do not see diamond rings burning away on people's fingers. On the other hand, the reaction between white phosphorus and oxygen is also spontaneous, and takes place very easily. In fact, white phosphorus has to be kept under water to keep oxygen away from it. If it is put in air, it ignites. Here we have an example of a spontaneous reaction that does take place rapidly.

Thermodynamics cannot tell us which spontaneous reactions will take place slowly, and which quickly. To find the explanation is one reason why chemists study the rates of reactions.

The study of reaction rates is also known as *reaction kinetics* (or chemical kinetics). Someone who does research in reaction kinetics will make many measurements of the speed of reactions. Once the measurements are made, the next stage will be to try to explain the observations. The explanation is called the *mechanism* of the reaction. Among other things, the mechanism helps us imagine how new bonds are made and old ones broken. This type of insight into chemical reactions is interesting in its own right, but it is also potentially very powerful. For example, it can help us to design new drugs and ways of making other important chemicals more efficiently.

From now on we shall normally assume that the reactions we meet are all spontaneous. That is, we shall assume that thermodynamics says that the reactions can take place. Our task will be to explain why the reactions are fast, or why they are slow. There is an enormous difference between the rates of reactions. Explosions and flames are examples of reactions that take place very quickly. The reactions that take place when you cook bread or meat in an oven are relatively slow.

77.2 What makes reactions take place?

There is one observation that is so obvious that it might seem unnecessary to mention it: two chemicals will only react if they come into contact. Put in a slightly different way we can say that:

The reactants must collide together.

We can also be sure that:

The more particles there are in a given volume, the more likely they are to collide and react together.

This gives us a clue as to why the rates of reactions often change when the concentrations of the reactants change.

Unfortunately it is not easy to say just what counts as a collision. When two atoms come close together, the electric fields of the electron clouds interact with one another. It is the disturbance caused by the electron clouds that starts the reaction between them. The problem is to discover how close the atoms have to be for the disturbance to be significant. One rule of thumb is to say that the atoms have to be no further apart than the sum of their van der Waals radii (Figure 77.1).

Not only must there be a collision:

The reactants must have the right energy.

This is especially true for reactions between covalent substances. If a new substance is to be made, new bonds must be formed. Also, one or more of the original bonds

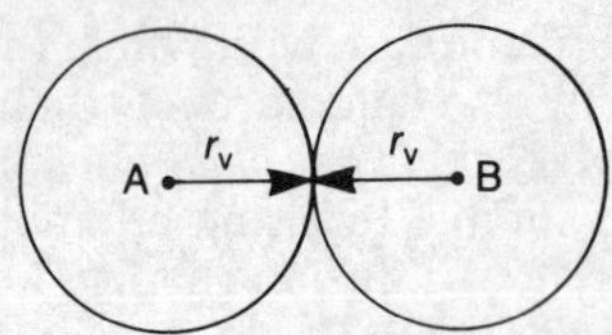

We can think of a collision taking place when the van der Waals radii of two atoms or molecules touch

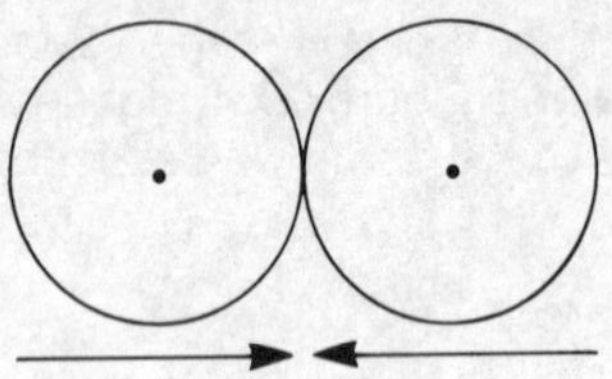

A head-on collision

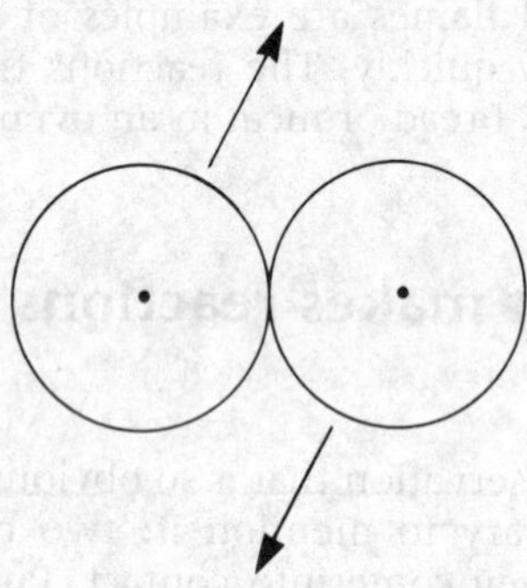

A glancing collision

***Figure 77.1** For two particles to react they must collide, but whether a reaction does occur may depend on the directions in which they are moving*

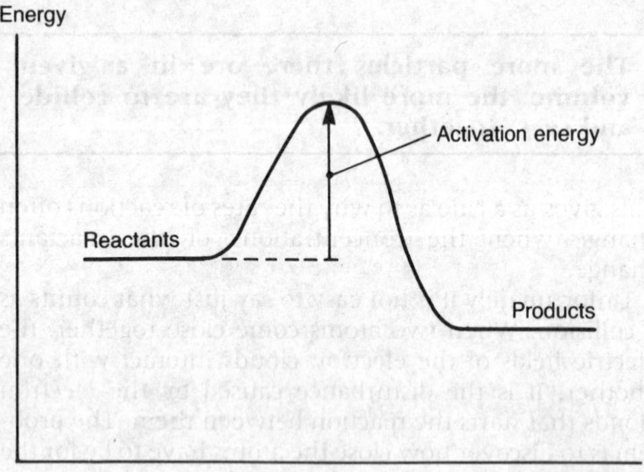

***Figure 77.2** The activation energy is the minimum energy that the reactants must have before they can change to products*

has to break. Breaking bonds needs energy. If the molecules collide only weakly, they may not have enough energy to break the necessary bonds. (Alternatively, bonds that we do not want to break may be disrupted instead!)

We can use a diagram, Figure 77.2, to show the minimum energy that chemicals must have if they are to react. The minimum energy needed to make a reaction take place is called the *activation energy*. Reactions that take place easily at room temperature have fairly low activation energies; reactions that require higher temperatures have higher activation energies.

77.1 Ions of opposite charge always have a tendency to combine together.

(i) Why are reactions between ions in solutions usually very much faster than reactions between covalent substances.

(ii) How do the activation energies of ionic reactions compare with those of reactions between covalent substances?

(iii) Estimate the order of magnitude of activation energies of covalent reactions.

(iv) Why is it possible to carry out many inorganic reactions in test tubes or flasks at room temperature, while organic reactions usually have to be heated for long periods of time?

77.2 You might think that the more energy the reactants have, the better it is. For the most part you would be right; but sometimes too much energy can be a disadvantage. To see why this is, let us imagine a hydrogen atom and a chlorine atom coming together with a total energy of 10×10^{-19} J. We know that hydrogen and chlorine atoms can stick together to make hydrogen chloride:

$$H(g) + Cl(g) \rightarrow HCl(g)$$

The strength of the bond in hydrogen chloride is about 7×10^{-19} J.

(i) Why is it that, in this case, the molecule is likely to fall apart almost as soon as it is made?

(ii) Now suppose that the reaction is done in a flask that contains nitrogen molecules. There is now a better chance that the two atoms will give a molecule of hydrogen chloride that does not break up. Why is this?

77.3 What can prevent reactions taking place?

You should be able to give two answers to this question. A reaction will not take place (i) if the particles do not collide, or (ii) if their energy is less than the activation energy. We have said that it is not always obvious what counts as a collision, but there is evidence that the way that some molecules approach each other is extremely important. If they approach in one way, they react; if they approach in a different way, they do not react. Such a thing happens in the reaction between hydrox-

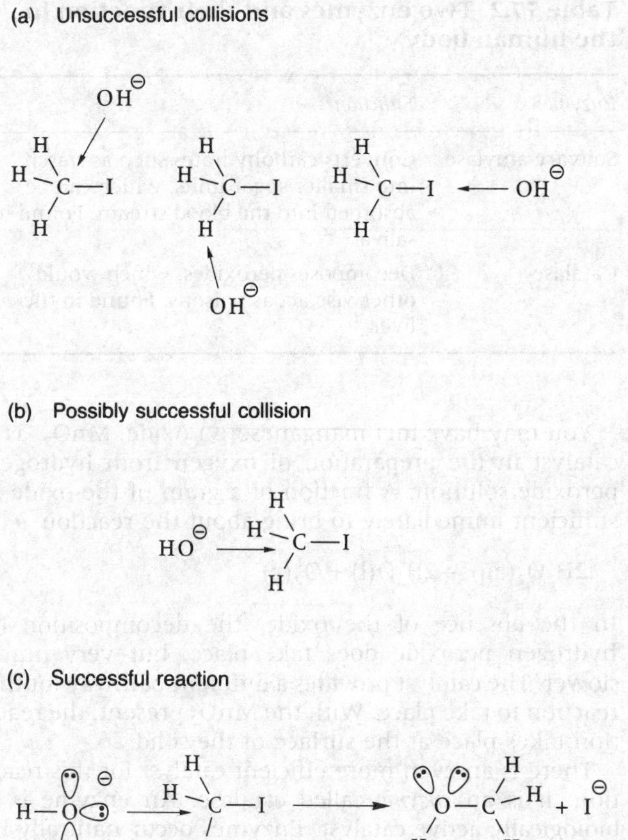

(a) Unsuccessful collisions

(b) Possibly successful collision

(c) Successful reaction

$OH^- + CH_3I \longrightarrow CH_3OH + I^-$

***Figure 77.3** Different views of the reaction between iodomethane and hydroxide ions. (a) Three of the many types of collision that are unsuccessful. (b) This collision may be successful–the direction of approach is correct, but the energy has to be right as well. (c) Two views of a successful reaction. Notice that the chemical equation tells us nothing about the way the reaction takes place*

ide ions and iodomethane (Figure 77.3). We will discover later that the two types of particle normally have to collide in the very particular way shown in Figure 77.3.

If the hydroxide ion meets the iodomethane at a different angle, for example if it bumps into one of the hydrogen atoms, the reaction fails. When reactions are influenced by the shapes of the molecules, we say that there is a *steric factor* in the reaction. In some cases the atoms, or groups of atoms, in a molecule can hinder the course of a reaction. If a group is particularly large, then it can get in the way of an attacking molecule or ion. If this happens, we say that the reaction suffers from *steric hindrance*.

The progress of a reaction that takes place in a solution can also be influenced by the solvent. For example, if two molecules or ions in water are to react, they have to find a way through the surrounding layers of water molecules. The speed with which the molecules react might be limited by the ease with which they can travel through the water. A measure of their movement through the water is their *rate of diffusion*. If the solvent is changed, for example by using ethanol rather than water, then the rate of diffusion changes and the rate of the reaction changes.

77.3 Suggest a reason why 2-iodo-2-methylpropane, shown in Figure 77.4, does not react with hydroxide ions in the same way as iodomethane.

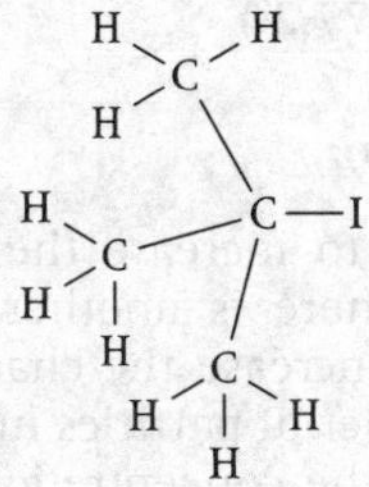

***Figure 77.4** The shape of 2-iodo-2-methylpropane $(CH_3)_3CI$*

77.4 Why do reactions between ions like Ag^+ and Cl^- not suffer from steric hindrance?

77.4 How can we make reactions go faster?

There are four ways that we can do this, which you will find listed in Table 77.1. We shall consider them one by one.

Table 77.1. Factors that change rates of reactions

Factor	*Comment*
Temperature	At a higher temperature: (i) more molecules have an energy greater than the activation energy; (ii) there are more collisions. Both increase the rate of reaction
Concentration	The higher the concentration, the greater the number of collisions, and the greater the rate of reaction
Surface area	The greater the surface area of a solid, the greater the area open to reaction
Catalyst	A catalyst provides a different pathway for a reaction, which has a lower activation energy than the original route. Therefore, at a given temperature, more molecules can react than when the catalyst is absent

(a) *Temperature*

The most well known method of making reactions go faster is to heat the reactants. Heat increases the average speed of molecules. This has two results. First, the greater their energy, the more likely it is that bonds will break, thereby allowing new ones to be made. We can put this in a different way by saying that:

The higher the temperature, the greater is the chance of the reactants having an energy greater than the activation energy of the reaction.

Secondly, the greater their speed, the more likely the particles are to collide, and so the greater the chance of reaction. However, it is possible for reactants to have too much energy. (If you would like to find out why this is, see question 77.2.)

(b) *Concentration*

If we do not wish to increase the temperature of a reaction mixture, there is another way of speeding things up. We can increase the chance of collision by increasing the number of particles in the mixture. That is, we can increase the concentration of the reactants. Again, the world of atoms and molecules has some surprises for us. Some reactions do *not* go faster if we increase concentrations. You will find out why in section 81.3.

(c) *Surface area*

There is a convenient way of speeding up reactions that involve solids. All that is necessary is to use a powder rather than large lumps of the solid. For example, marble chips react with hydrochloric acid giving off carbon dioxide. The hydrogen ions in the acid attack the carbonate ions at the surface of the chips. By grinding the chips to a powder, the surface area in contact with the acid is greatly increased. The more the surface area, the greater the chance of the hydrogen ions attacking the carbonate ions; hence the rate of reaction increases.

(d) *Catalysts*

In industry, time means money, and the speed with which reactions take place is of great importance. For example, if one company can make a drug faster than another, that company has a greater chance of making a profit on its sales. If success could be achieved simply by heating or increasing concentrations, then every company would be equally successful. Clearly, life is not so simple, one reason being that too much heat can destroy the substance that is being made. A more subtle approach is to find a *catalyst* for a reaction:

An *ideal catalyst* will increase the speed of a reaction without itself being destroyed during the reaction.

In fact the majority of catalysts are not ideal. Eventually they lose their ability to catalyse a reaction. We shall discuss reasons for this later (section 81.6).

Table 77.2. Two enzymes and their function in the human body

Enzyme	*Function*
Salivary amylase	Converts carbohydrates such as starch into smaller sugar units, which can be absorbed into the blood stream. Found in saliva
Catalase	Decomposes peroxides, which would otherwise act as poisons. Found in the liver

You may have met manganese(IV) oxide, MnO_2, as a catalyst in the preparation of oxygen from hydrogen peroxide solution. A fraction of a gram of the oxide is sufficient immediately to bring about the reaction

$$2H_2O_2(aq) \rightarrow 2H_2O(l) + O_2(g)$$

In the absence of the oxide, the decomposition of hydrogen peroxide does take place, but very much slower. The catalyst provides a different pathway for the reaction to take place. With the MnO_2 present, the reaction takes place at the surface of the solid.

There is an even more efficient catalyst for this reaction. It is an *enzyme* called catalase. An enzyme is a biologically active catalyst. Enzymes occur naturally in our bodies (Table 77.2), and in the bodies of other living things. There are two main types of catalyst:

***Homogeneous catalysts* are in the same state as the reactants.**

***Heterogeneous catalysts* are not in the same state as the reactants.**

Manganese(IV) oxide is an example of a heterogeneous catalyst. It is a solid, whereas the hydrogen peroxide it decomposes is a solution. Enzymes that are to be found at work in cell reactions are in solution, like the chemicals with which they react. Enzymes are homogeneous catalysts.

Before we leave this section, it is important that you realise the influence that catalysts have on equilibrium reactions. The key points are:

A catalyst does not change the position of equilibrium; it increases the rate of the backward reaction as well as the forward reaction.

By providing a lower activation energy, it is easier for the reactants to surmount the energy barrier (Figure 77.5), but so too is it easier for the products to revert to reactants. For this reason a catalyst does not change the position of equilibrium; but it will mean that equilibrium is achieved more rapidly.

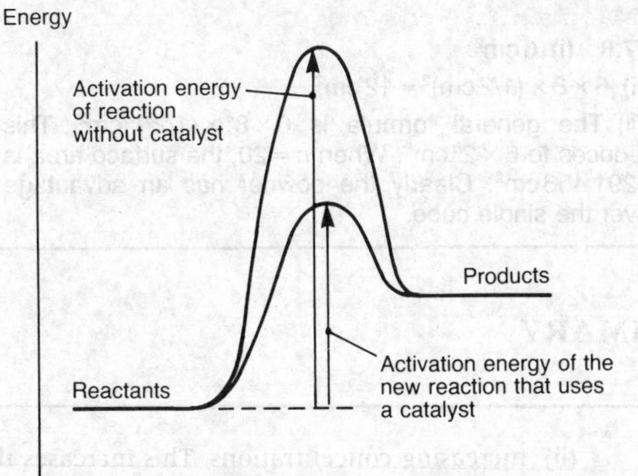

Figure 77.5 *The change of reactants to products has a lower activation energy if a catalyst is used*

77.5 If you were in charge of a chemical company, why would you prefer to find a catalyst that works at room temperature rather than heat a reaction to 200° C?

77.6 How would you show that manganese(IV) oxide is a catalyst for the decomposition of hydrogen peroxide? (Hint: there are two parts to this; you have to show that it speeds up the reaction, and that it is not destroyed.)

77.7 A student attempted this definition of a catalyst: 'It is a substance that speeds up a reaction without taking part in the reaction.' What is wrong with the definition?

77.8 This question is about surface area.

(i) If you had a cube of marble with sides exactly 1 cm in length, what is the total surface area?

(ii) Now imagine that you cut the cube into eight identical smaller cubes. Each of these cubes has sides of length 0.5 cm. What is the total surface area now?

(iii) If you like mathematical puzzles, work out a general formula for the total surface area if each of the eight new cubes are split into eight more, and these into eight more, and so on for *n* times. Use your formula to work out the total surface area after 20 splits. This would be a very powdery sample of marble chips.

Answers

77.1 (i) Oppositely charged ions do not need very much energy to make them react because it is not necessary to break bonds.

(ii) Ionic reactions have much smaller activation energies.

(iii) In covalent reactions, covalent bonds must be broken. Therefore we would expect the activation energies to be of the same order as the strengths of covalent bonds, i.e. some hundreds of kJ mol^{-1}.

(iv) Inorganic reactions often involve reactions between ions. Organic reactions are usually reactions between covalent compounds in which bonds have to be broken. This requires a significant amount of energy; hence the need for heating.

77.2 (i) If the two atoms do stick together, their total energy is greater than the energy needed to break the bond between them. The outcome is that the molecule breaks up and the atoms fly apart.

(ii) If the collision is to be successful, there has to be a way for the hydrogen chloride molecule to lose energy before it has time to break apart. This can happen if it collides with a molecule of nitrogen. The molecule can give up some of its energy to the nitrogen molecule, which will move off faster than it was moving before.

It can also happen that gaseous reactions are influenced by the collisions of the molecules with the walls of the container.

77.3 The methyl groups get in the way of the hydroxide ion. That is, they cause steric hindrance. However, there is another effect at work here; see section 81.5.

77.4 The ions are perfectly symmetrical.

77.5 To raise the temperature requires heat to be generated. This can be very costly and is best avoided. Other costs are involved as well; for example, there has to be a method of cooling the products.

77.6 If you try this reaction, be careful! Solutions of hydrogen peroxide come in different concentrations. A reasonable concentration to use is a '20 volume' solution. Do *not* use a solution labelled '100 volume'. This solution is too concentrated, and could explode. It is obvious that the reaction is quicker with the manganese(IV) oxide. To be strict you should show that the gas given off is oxygen, e.g. by collecting some in a test tube and showing that it ignites a glowing splint. The more interesting thing is to show that the oxide is not used up in the reaction. This requires two things: We have to show (i) that the same mass is present at the beginning and end of the reaction; (ii) that the oxide is chemically unchanged. The powder should be weighed before the reaction. After the reaction it should be filtered off, washed, dried and reweighed. Within the limits of experimental error, the masses should be the same. In order to show that it is chemically unchanged, we should analyse it. The way of doing this would depend on the apparatus available; but it could be done by titration.

77.7 In chemistry, as in any science, it is best to avoid

Answers – contd.

magical ideas. If the catalyst does not take part in the reaction, how could it have an effect? Catalysts *do* take part in a reaction. Indeed they may change their chemical nature during the reaction; but at the end they should have the same formula and chemical properties that they had at the start.

77.8 (i) 6 cm^2.

(ii) $6 \times 8 \times (1/2\,cm)^2 = 12\,cm^2$.

(iii) The general formula is $6 \times 8^n \times (1/2^n)^2\,cm^2$. This reduces to $6 \times 2^n\,cm^2$. When $n = 20$, the surface area is 6291 456 cm^2. Clearly the powder has an advantage over the single cube.

UNIT 77 SUMMARY

- Conditions for a reaction to take place:
  - (i) The reactants must collide together.
  - (ii) The more particles there are in a given volume, the more likely they are to collide and react.
  - (iii) The reactants must have the right energy.
- Activation energy is the minimum energy that the reactants need to change into products.
- Reactions may not take place because:
  - (i) They are thermodynamically impossible.
  - (ii) The reactants have an energy less than the activation energy.
  - (iii) The reactants do not collide with the right geometry, i.e. there is steric hindrance.
- Rates are increased by:
  - (i) Increasing the temperature. This increases the chance of reactants having an energy greater than the activation energy.
  - (ii) Increasing concentrations. This increases the chances of the reactant molecules colliding.
  - (iii) Increasing the surface area (for reactions that involve solids). This gives more sites for the reaction to take place.
  - (iv) Using a catalyst.
- Catalysts provide a new route for a reaction that has a lower activation energy than in the absence of the catalyst.
- Homogeneous catalysts are in the same state as the reactants, e.g. an enzyme in solution.
- Heterogeneous catalysts are not in the same state as the reactants, e.g. solid MnO_2 in hydrogen peroxide solution.
- A catalyst does not change the position of equilibrium; it increases the rate of the backward reaction to the same extent as the forward reaction.

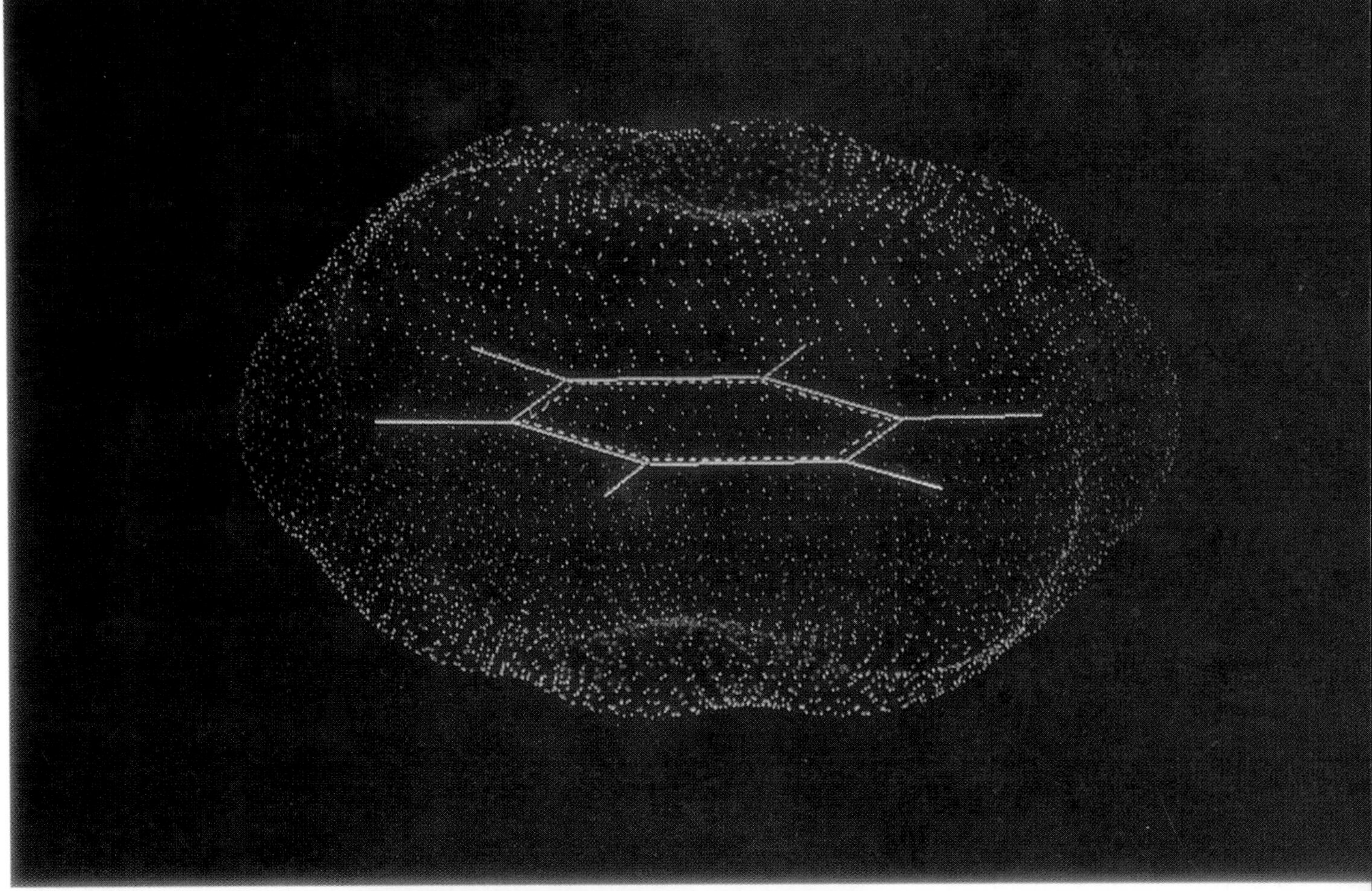

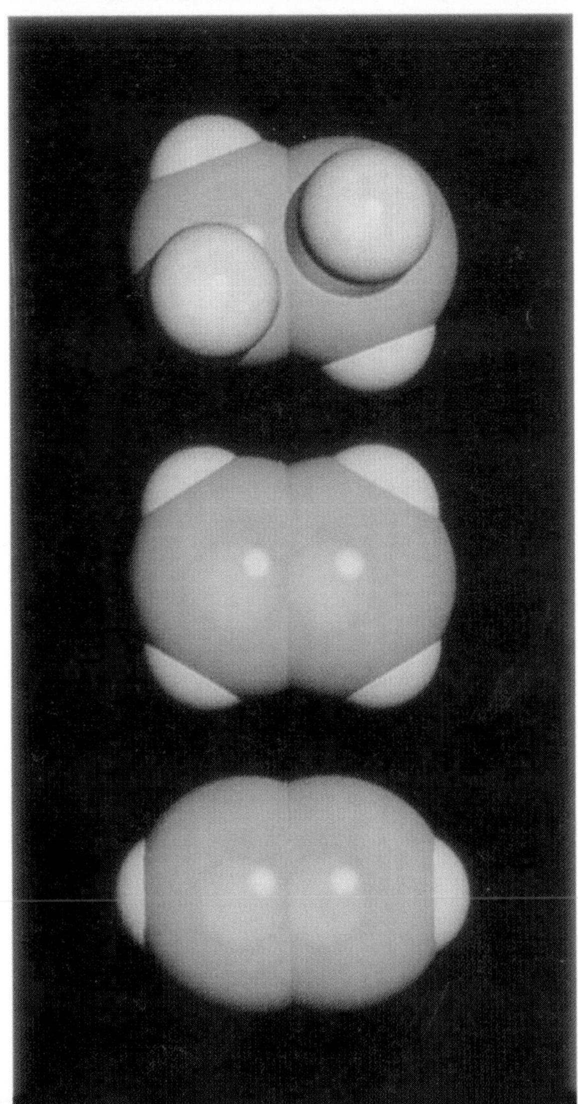

These images were drawn by a modern computer molecular graphics system. The colours in the top photograph indicate the degree of positive and negative charge around a benzene ring. The red areas indicate positive charge, and the blue negative, with the other colours showing variation in positive or negative charge. Note that the hydrogen atoms (not shown) occur near the red regions, and the blue spreads in the region of the pi clouds. See Unit 16.

The lower photograph shows space-filling models of ethane, C_2H_6, ethene, C_2H_4, and (at the bottom) ethyne, C_2H_2. They give a good idea of the relative amounts of space taken up by the carbon and hydrogen atoms. See Unit 16. (Photographs provided by the Molecular Graphics Unit, Trinity College, Dublin. The assistance of Loctite (Ireland) Ltd, is gratefully acknowledged.)

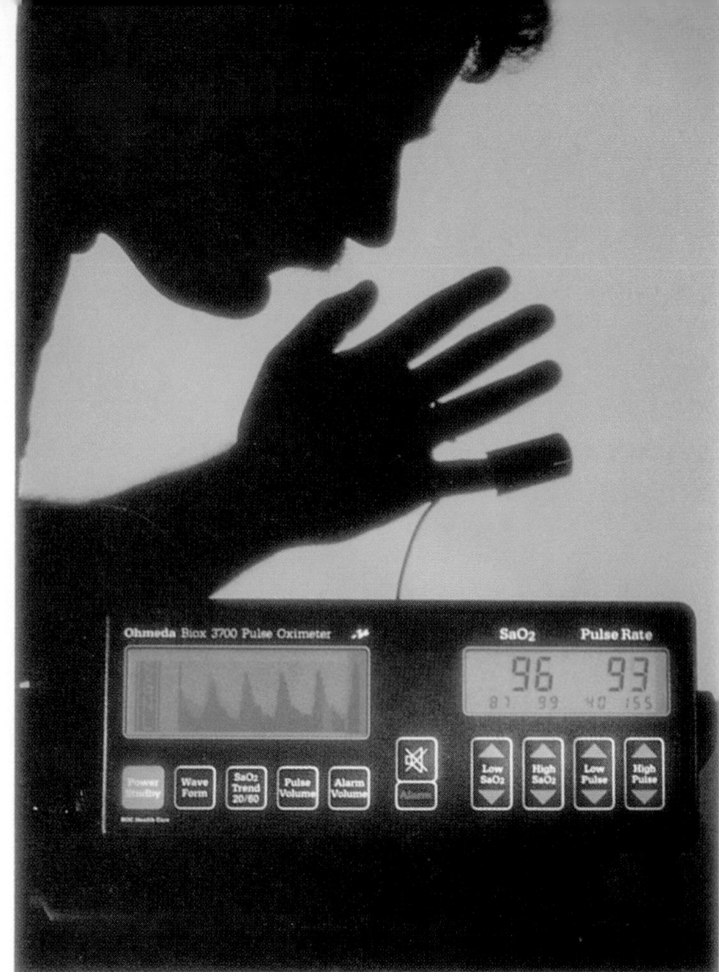

Top left When solid iodine (black) is heated, the I_2 molecules move much further apart in the gas. The separated molecules give a characteristic purple colour. See Unit 20.

Top right The displays from these LCDs are indicating a patient's pulse rate and blood oxygen level. LCDs consist of molecules with a special blend of physical properties. See Unit 23.

Bottom This superb image of a stained glass window at Canterbury Cathedral shows the beauty of a liquid masquerading as a solid. See Unit 23.

Top This beautiful pattern was produced by a white laser light passing through a diffraction grating. It illustrates the wave nature of light. See Unit 30.

Bottom left The patient in the background is having a brain scan taken by n.m.r. The patient's head is surrounded by a large electromagnet. You can see the image produced by the scan in the foreground. See Unit 28.

Bottom right The Tyndal effect. Blue light from the bright white lamp behind a solution of a sulphur sol has been scattered off to the sides. This leaves the lamp looking orange. See Unit 23.

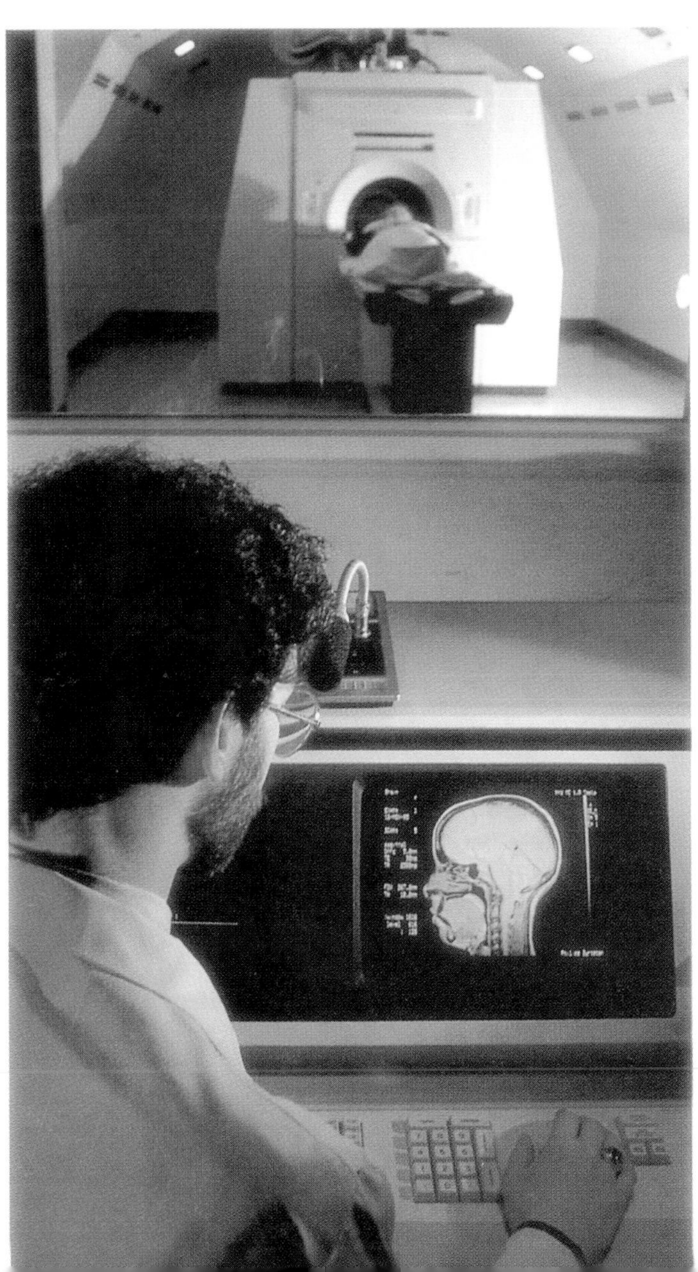

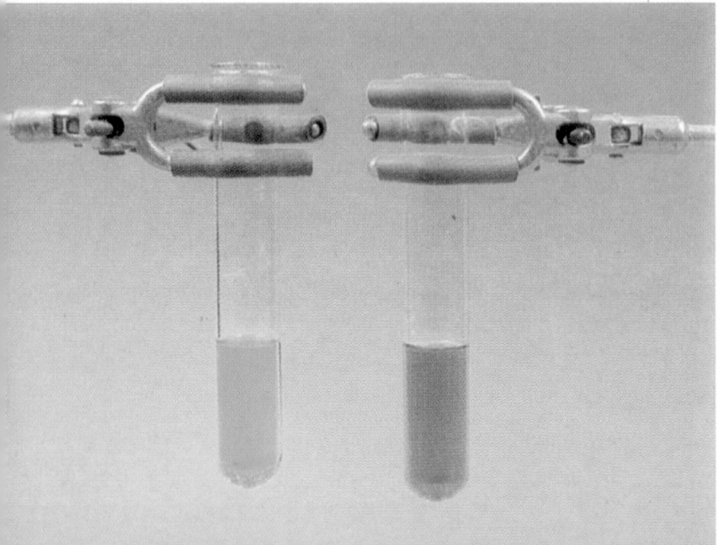

Titrations are important in chemistry. The **top** photograph shows three stages in an acid–base titration using screened methyl orange as indicator. Alkaline on the left, end point at centre, overshoot (acidic) on right. The **middle left** photograph shows the end point approaching in an iodine/thiosulphate titration using starch as an indicator. The blue/black colour of the iodine and starch is just fading to clear. See Unit 39. **Middle right** A tube containing ammonium chloride just after heating. Towards the middle of the tube ammonium chloride has dissociated into ammonia and hydrogen chloride (colourless). Nearer the top, where it is much colder, the two gases have recombined to produce solid ammonium chloride again. See Unit 53. **Bottom** Chromate(VI), CrO_4^{2-}, and dichromate(VI), $Cr_2O_7^{2-}(aq)$, at equilibrium. On the left in alkaline conditions CrO_4^{2-} ions (yellow) predominate. On the right, in acid, $Cr_2O_7^{2-}$ (orange) ions are in the majority.

Top Copper(II) ions in water, $Cu^{2+}(aq)$, are a much lighter blue (left) than when ions are in aqueous ammonia (right). With ammonia, the complex ions $Cu(NH_3)_4^{2+}(aq)$ are present. See Unit 53.
Middle left The result of a simple ascending chromatography experiment with felt tip pens. The green ink is a mixture of blue and yellow dyes. The 'yellow' ink contains the same yellow dye, and a purple dye. See Unit 56.
Middle right The result of a partition experiment in which a solution of I_2 and KI is shaken with 1,1,1-trichloroethane. An equilibrium is set up in which the majority of iodine molecules dissolve in the lower organic layer. This layer takes on the purple colour of free I_2 molecules. See Unit 62.
Bottom The iron nails have been left in a gel containing a mixture of potassium hexacyanoferrate(III) and phenolphthalein. The red areas indicate where rusting is most advanced. See Unit 68.

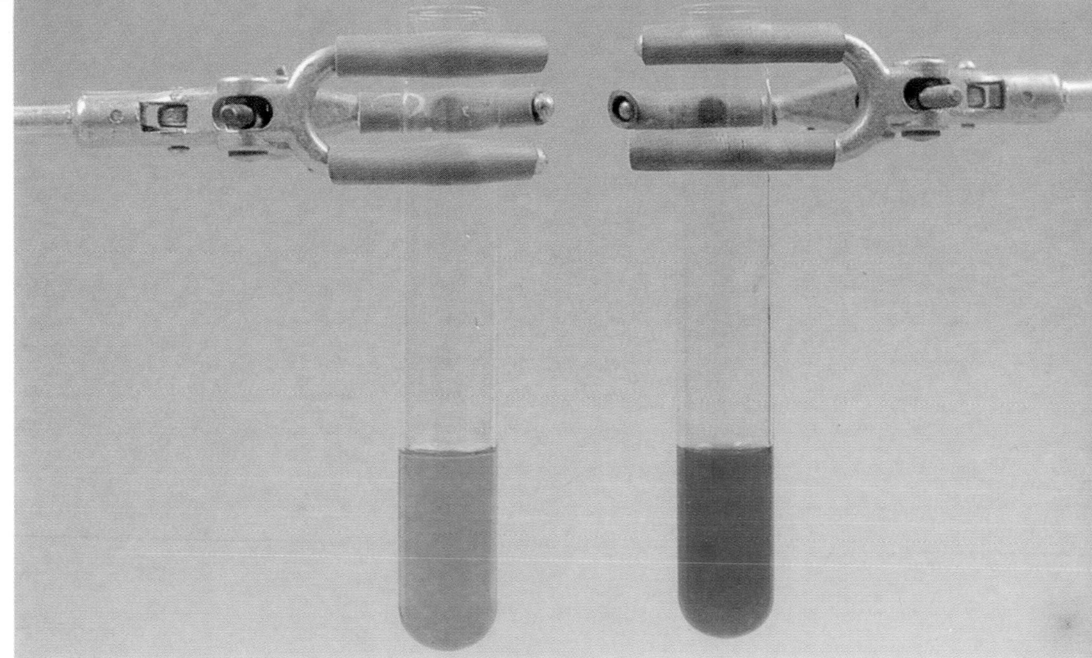

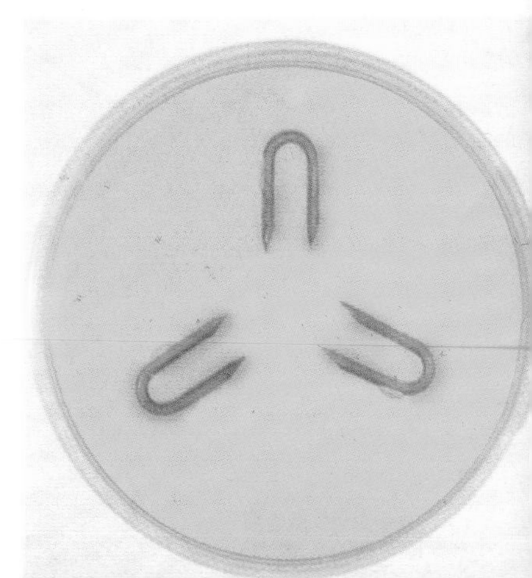

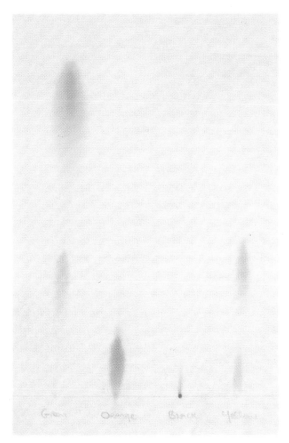

A selection of catalysts used in the oil industry, and other areas of the chemical industry.

Molten iron and steel are of little use until they are cast into moulds, as is happening here in an iron foundry. See Unit 85.

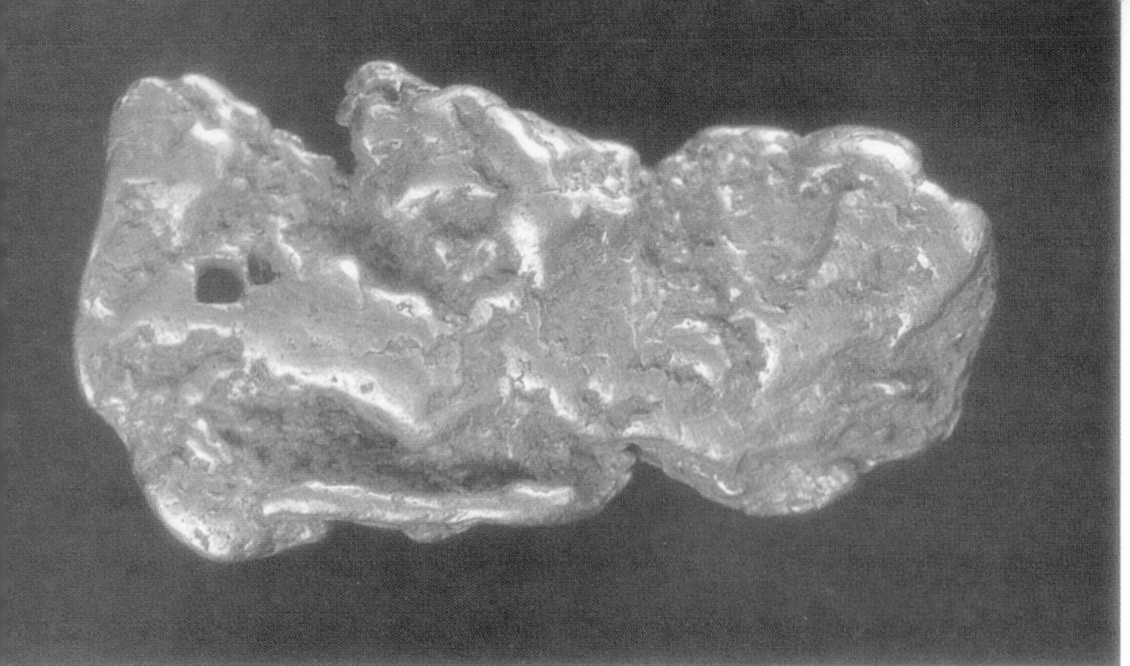

The relative unreactivity of gold, silver and platinum allow them to be dug directly from the ground, although samples of these sizes are rare. The beauty of the metals is not matched by the conditions down the mines, like this gold mine in Saudi Arabia. See Unit 85.

Right. Clearing of tropical rain forest may have a marked effect on the world's climate. See Unit 91. The three photographs show parts of the rain forest in Malaysia before, during and after clearing.

The solutions below show the attractive colours of many transition metal compounds. From the left the colours are due to chromium(III) (in $K_2Cr_2O_7(aq)$), manganese(VII) (in $KMnO_4(aq)$, cobalt(III) (in $CoCl_3(aq)$), nickel(II) (in $NiSO_4(aq)$), and copper(II) (in $CuSO_4(aq)$). See Unit 105 (and Unit 25).

Top left. Samples of ruby (red) and sapphire (blue) crystals. Ruby contains small amounts of chromium ions, sapphire contains iron, cobalt or titanium ions. Large ruby crystals are artificially grown in order to make lasers. Both minerals are based on a corundum structure. See Unit 94.

Middle right. A sample of the mineral Blue John, an elegant variety of the mineral fluorspar, CaF_2. See Unit 93.

Middle left and bottom left and right. Quartz, opal and amethyst are based on the same formula SiO_2 and are framework silicates. The colours of opal and amethyst are due to small quantities of impurities such as manganese. See Unit 96 for more about silicates.

Middle left. Carbon dioxide fire extinguishers produce clouds of cold, dense vapour in use. See Unit 95.

Top right. The characteristic haze of photochemical smog covering Los Angeles, USA. See Unit 97.

Bottom right. The excess growth of algae (an algal bloom) like that shown here on the Basingstoke canal in the UK has been encouraged by excess nitrate in water. See Unit 97.

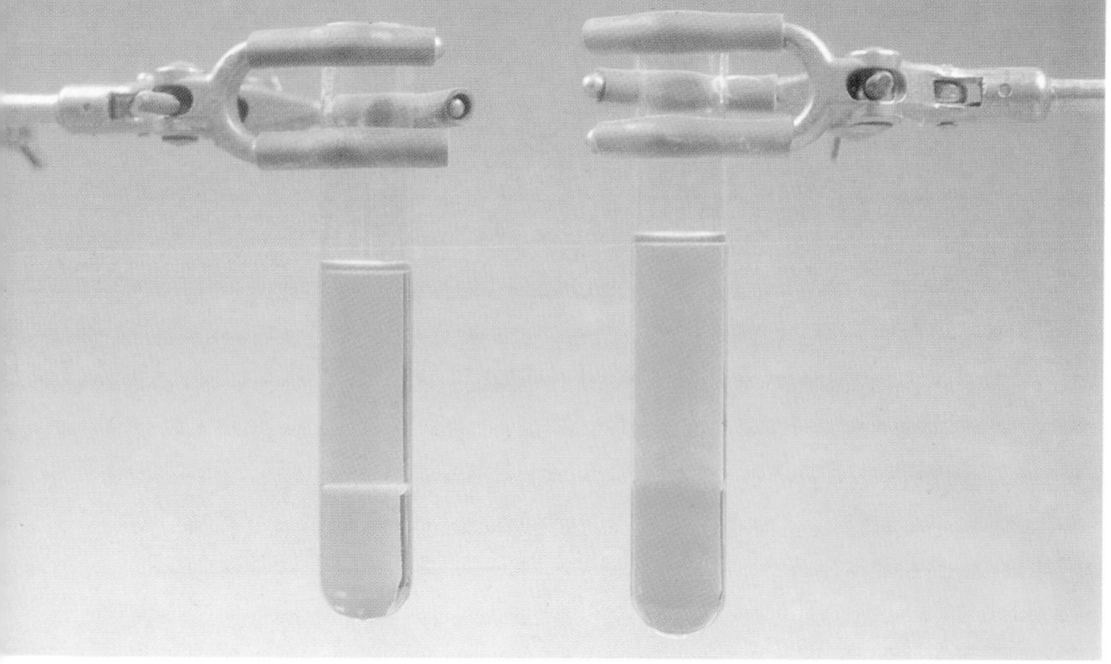

Top. These tubes show the result of adding 1,1,1-trichloroethane to a solution of bromine in water (right) and iodine in water (left). This is a good way of testing for bromine and iodine. See Unit 101.

Middle and bottom left. The models in the upper photograph show the shape of the mirror image forms of lactic acid. The lower photograph is a computer image of the same pair of isomers. The computer has drawn the molecules in a ball-and-stick fashion. The hydrogen atoms are not shown. See Unit 110 for information about mirror images.

Bottom right. Sulphur at the bottom of the tube has been warmed and a few drops of fuming nitric acid have been added. The brown fumes of nitrogen dioxide above the sulphur are a sure sign that the sulphur has been oxidised by the acid. See Unit 97.

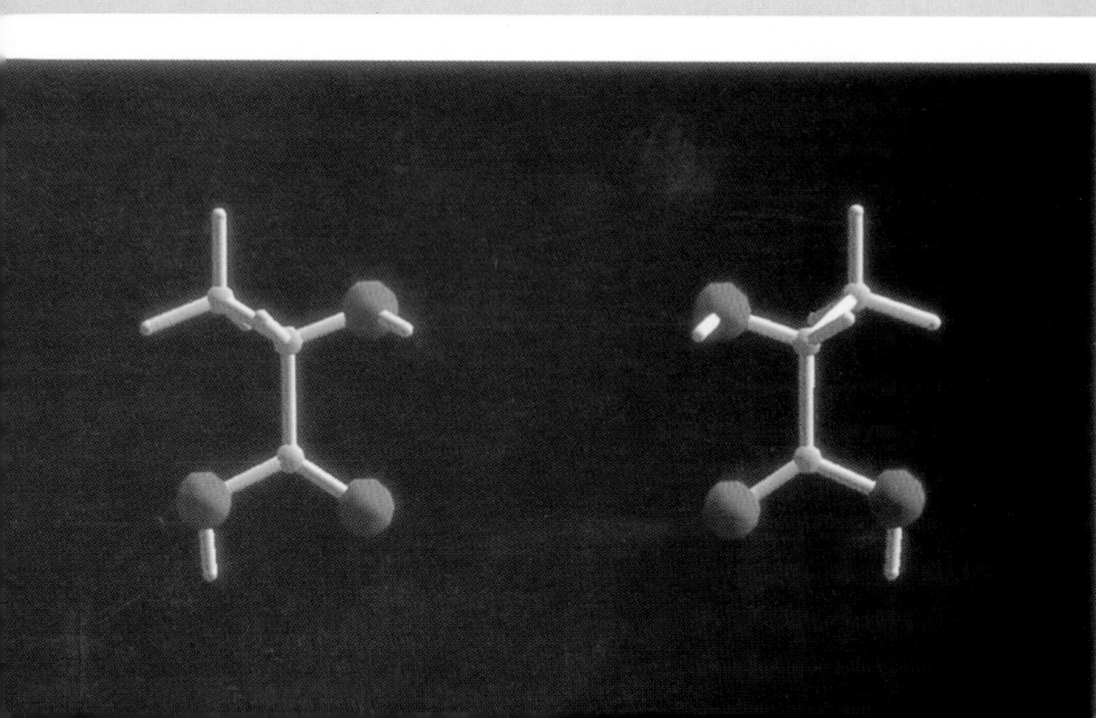

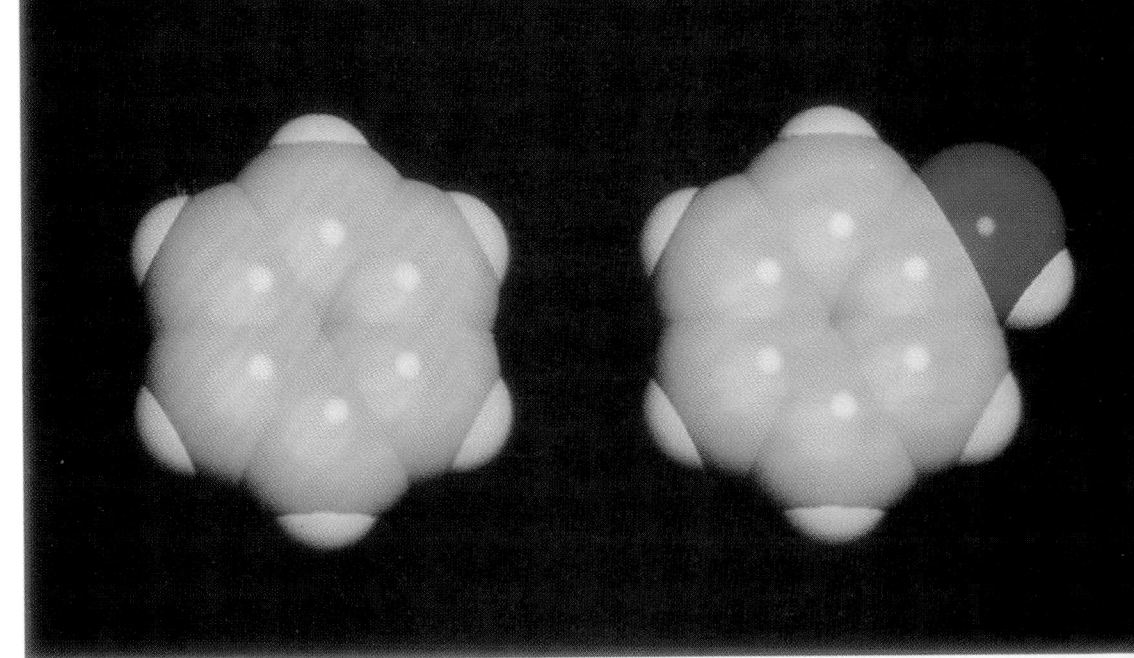

Top. These images drawn by computer represent space-filling models of benzene C_6H_6 (left) and phenol C_6H_5OH (right). They give a good idea of the relative amounts of space taken up by the carbon and hydrogen atoms. See Unit 117 for information about phenol.

Middle. Neon lights in Piccadilly circus.

Bottom left. Brightly coloured clothes are partly the result of research in organic chemistry. See Unit 122.

Bottom right. The results of a successful silver mirror test (left) and a Fehling's test (right) for an aldehyde. See Unit 118.

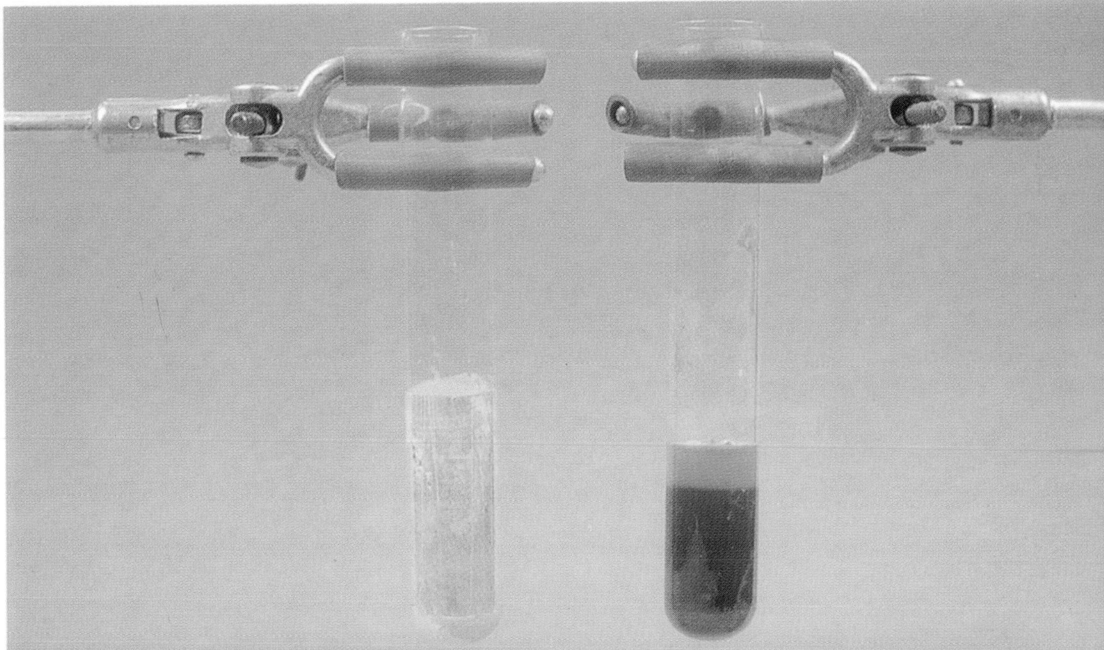

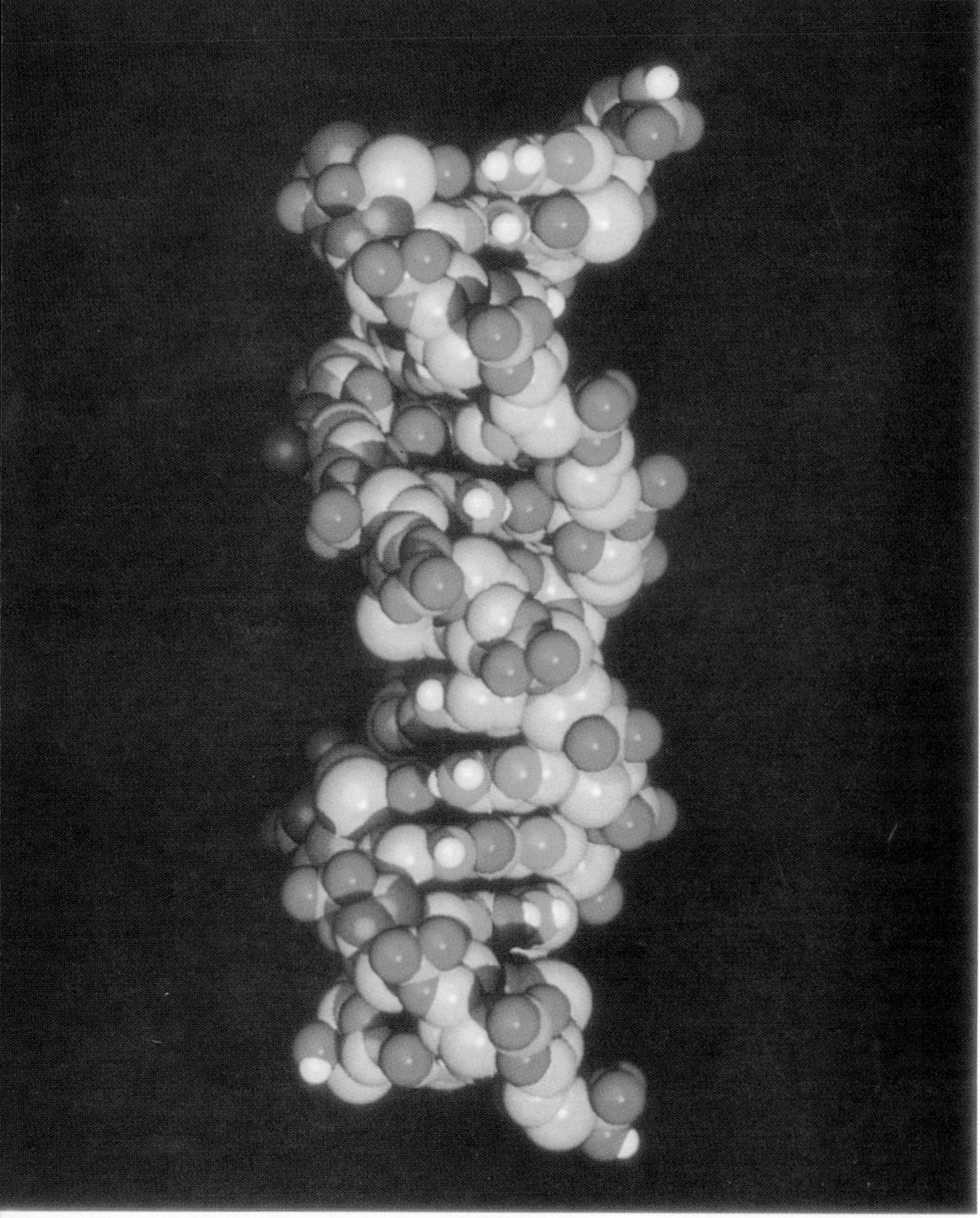

Left. A computer-drawn representation of a fragment of DNA. You should be able to see the two strands of the helix winding around each other. See Unit 124 for information about DNA.

Bottom left. This computer-drawn image represents the structure of an enzyme which happens to have two active sites. The blue, yellow, and red regions are the two substrate molecules which fit in the active sites. The bonds between atoms of the enzyme are shown by short lines. Red lines indicate carbon–oxygen bonds; blue lines represent carbon–nitrogen bonds.

Bottom right. The third image is a magnified view of the region around the substrate. The substrate is held in the active site by hydrogen bonds. If you look carefully at the arrangement of the bonds you should be able to spot several peptide links (—CONH—). See Unit 123 for information about peptide links and enzymes.

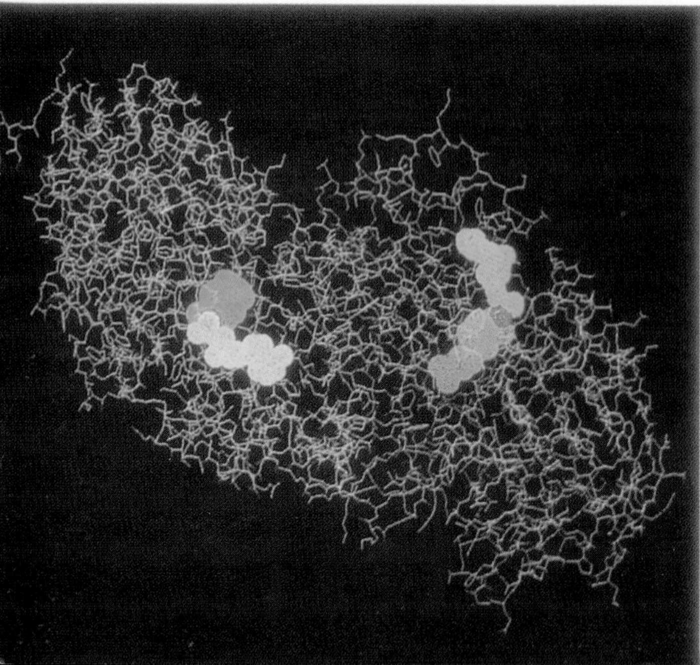

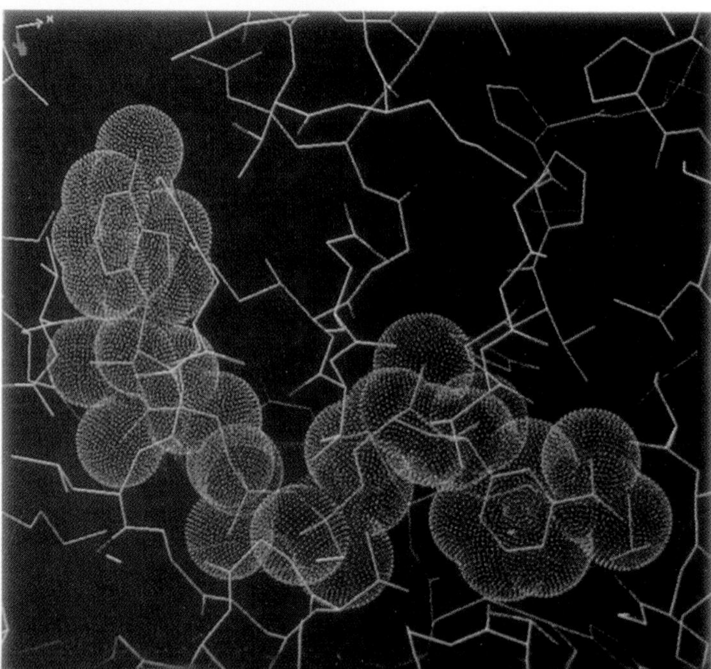

Top. You might like to count the number of ways in which these climbers rely on nylon for their survival. See Unit 127.

Bottom. Although most detergents are biodegradable, some can give precipitates with metal ions, producing a scum like this on a river in the Peak District, UK. See Unit 129.

Foam fire fighting, emulsion paints, and mayonnaise make use of surfactants to preserve their colloidal nature. See Unit 129 (and Unit 23).

78

Two theories of reaction rates

78.1 Collision theory

We have already met the main ideas behind collision theory. They are that a reaction occurs if the particles involved in the reaction collide together, and if they have the right energy. We shall deal with the collisions and energy requirements separately.

(a) *Collisions*

We can give each reaction a *collision frequency*, which will be given the symbol Z. If the average speed of the molecules is known, it is possible to estimate the value of Z. A typical value for 1 mol of particles is 10^{13} collisions every second in a volume of $1\,cm^3$, i.e. $Z = 10^{13}\,cm^3\,mol^{-1}\,s^{-1}$. However, we have said that not all collisions are effective because the particles often have to meet at a particular angle. We can allow for this by multiplying Z by a *steric factor*, P. We shall write the effective number of collisions as N where

$$N = PZ$$

Because the rate depends on the number of collisions, we have

rate is proportional to N, i.e. to PZ

> **78.1** The steric factor, P, is a number. What are its maximum and minimum values?

(b) *Energy*

Rates of reactions increase as temperature increases. However, the way the rate increases is not simple. The increase is given by an exponential factor, called the *Arrhenius factor*:

rate is proportional to $\exp(-E_a/RT)$

Here, E_a is the activation energy of the reaction, R is the gas constant and T the Kelvin temperature. The activation energy is the minimum energy the particles need in order to react.

We can put our two requirements about collisions and energy together in one equation. Any individual reaction will have its own particular values for P, Z and E_a. This means that, at a given temperature, the two factors N and $\exp(-E_a/RT)$ will be constant. This allows us to define the *rate constant*, k, for a reaction as

$$k = PZ\exp(-E_a/RT)$$

An equation just like this was established from experiment by Arrhenius. He wrote the rate constant as

$$k = A\exp(-E_a/RT) \qquad \text{Arrhenius equation}$$

The difference is that we have used collision theory to give an explanation of what his constant, A, might mean.

We can use the Arrhenius equation to help us measure the activation energy of a reaction. If we take the natural logarithm of both sides, we have

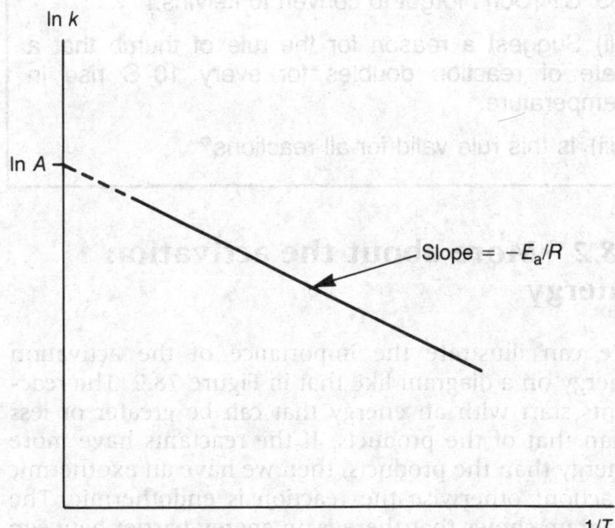

Figure 78.1 A graph of ln k against 1/T is a straight line. The equation of the line is

$$\ln k = \ln A - \frac{E_a}{R} \times \frac{1}{T}$$

$$\ln k = \ln A - \frac{E_a}{RT}$$

or

$$\ln k = \ln A - \frac{E_a}{R} \times \frac{1}{T}$$

A graph of ln k against $1/T$ should be a straight line (Figure 78.1). The slope will be $-E_a/R$, and the intercept on the ln k axis will give the value of ln A, from which we can find the value of A.

78.2 Here are some data for the reaction between hydrogen and iodine, making hydrogen iodide. k is the rate constant.

Temperature/K	500	550	600	650	700
k/cm^3 mol^{-1} s^{-1}	6.81 $\times 10^{-4}$	2.64 $\times 10^{-2}$	0.56	7.31	66.67

(i) Plot a graph of ln k against $1/T$. You will have to be careful with the scales, especially $1/T$. Try putting the scale in multiples of 10^{-3}, and do not necessarily start the $1/T$ scale at zero.

(ii) Measure the slope of the line. The slope $= -E_a/R$. Hence calculate the activation energy. Your answer should be given in kJ mol^{-1}.

78.3 Many reactions that take place around room temperature have activation energies around 50 kJ mol^{-1}.

(i) What is the value of $\exp(-E_a/RT)$ at 25° C and at 35° C? (Don't forget to convert to kelvins.)

(ii) Suggest a reason for the rule of thumb that a rate of reaction doubles for every 10° C rise in temperature.

(iii) Is this rule valid for all reactions?

78.2 More about the activation energy

We can illustrate the importance of the activation energy on a diagram like that in Figure 78.2. The reactants start with an energy that can be greater or less than that of the products. If the reactants have more energy than the products, then we have an exothermic reaction; otherwise the reaction is endothermic. The diagram shows that there is an energy barrier between the reactants and products. If the reactants are to change into products, they have to get over the energy barrier. That is, they must gain at least the activation energy.

The diagram we drew in Figure 35.4, which shows the spread of energies among gas molecules, allows us to understand why rates increase with temperature. Figure 78.3 tells us that, at a higher temperature, the energy distribution curve stretches out. The shaded areas give the proportion of molecules that have an energy equal to or greater than the activation energy. The area increases at the higher temperature. That is, more molecules can get over the energy barrier at a higher temperature than at a lower temperature.

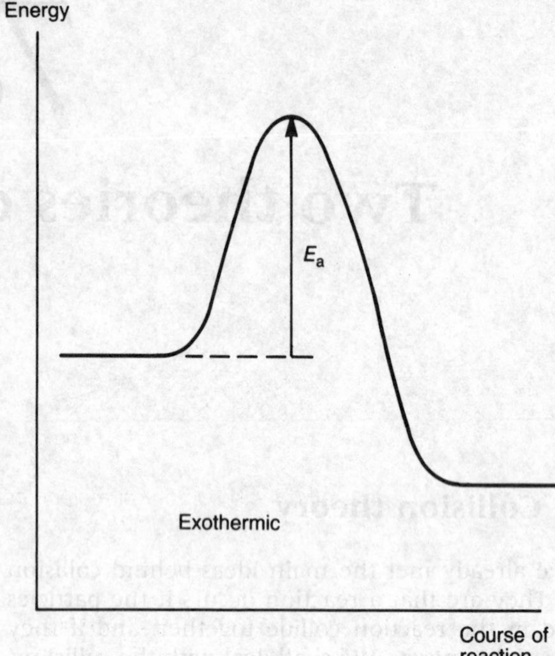

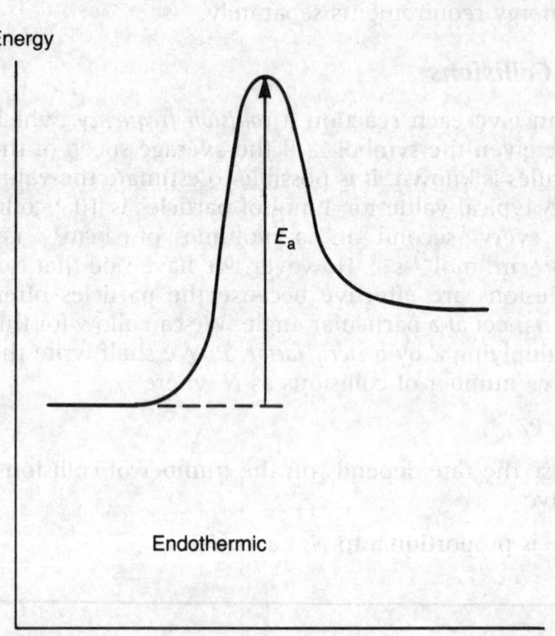

Figure 78.2 Energy diagrams for exothermic and endothermic reactions, showing the activation energies for the forward reactions

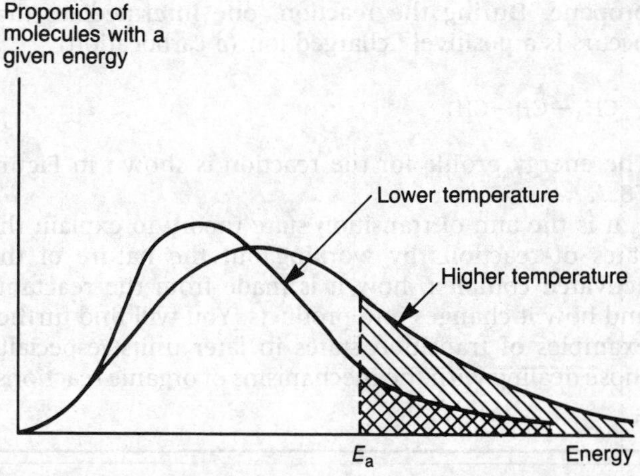

***Figure 78.3** At higher temperatures the number of molecules with energy greater than the activation energy increases*

78.3 Catalysts and activation energy

Catalysts increase the rate of a reaction without the necessity of increasing the temperature. They do this by providing a different route for the reaction to take place. We say that the *mechanism* of the reaction is different in the presence of the catalyst. The key thing is that the new mechanism has a lower activation energy than the uncatalysed reaction (Figure 78.4). With the decrease in the activation energy, many more reactant particles are able to surmount the new energy barrier and turn into products.

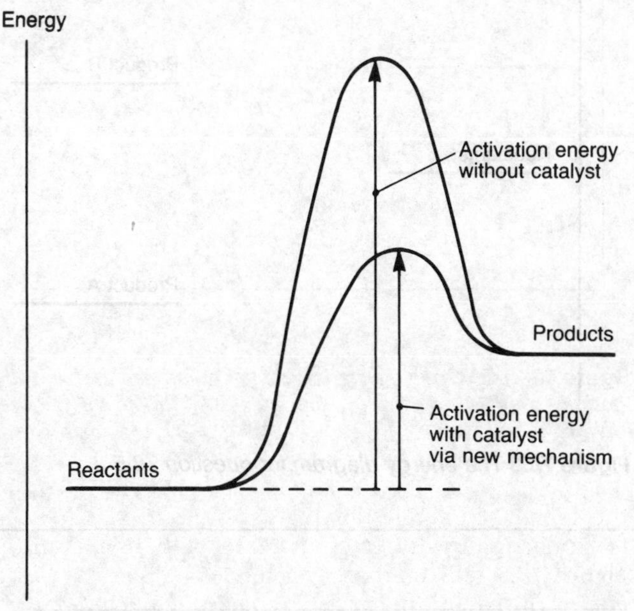

***Figure 78.4** A catalyst lowers the activation energy of a reaction by providing a new mechanism*

78.4 A student wrote the following explanation of how a catalyst works: 'When ethene and hydrogen react to give ethane, the molecules of the two gases must collide. Nickel catalyses the reaction. It does this by lowering the activation energy of this collision reaction between the two molecules.'

Can you find the error that suggests that the student does not really understand how catalysts work?

78.4 Transition state theory

Transition state theory explains rates of reactions in a rather different way to collision theory. In transition state theory we concentrate on what happens to the reactants when they are about to change into products. This change takes place at the top of the energy barrier, so this is called the *transition state region* (Figure 78.5).

When a reactant molecule, or combination of molecules, is changing into products, some of its old bonds are breaking, and new bonds are being made. When the reactants are in this state of change they make up the *activated complex*. The activated complex does not always change into products; it can equally well change back into the reactants.

One example is the reaction between a hydrogen atom and a hydrogen molecule. The transition state is linear, with the two bonds somewhere between being made and being broken (see Figure 78.6). If the energy possessed by the transition state is concentrated in bond A, then it changes back into reactants; if it concentrates in bond B, then it makes products.

It can happen that the activated complex changes into an intermediate that is more energetically stable

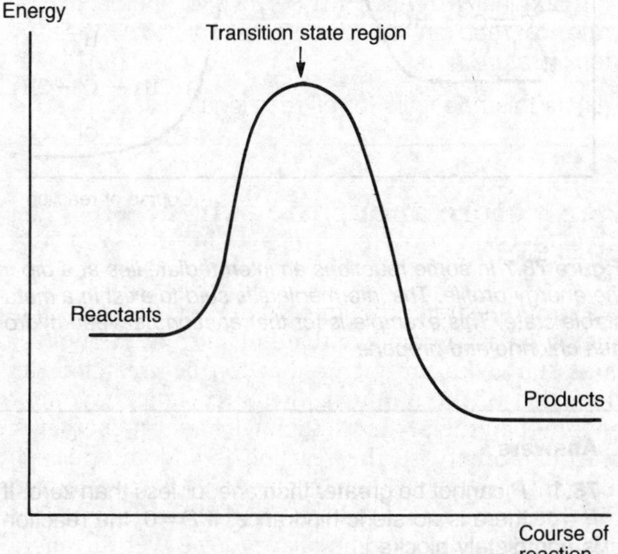

***Figure 78.5** The transition state lies at the top of the energy profile*

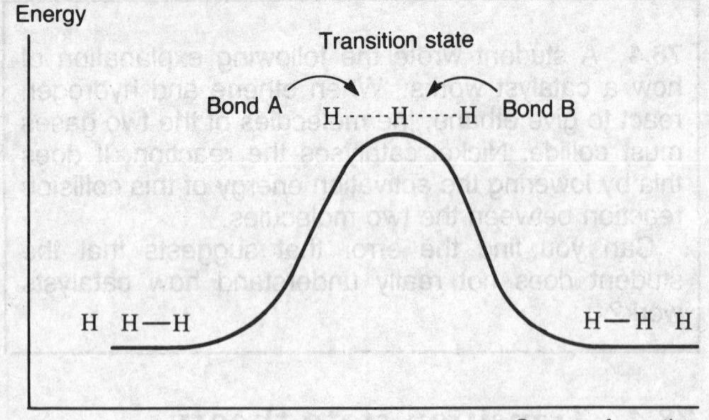

Figure 78.6 The reaction between a hydrogen atom and a hydrogen molecule involves a linear transition state (see text)

than the activated complex. The intermediate may last for sufficiently long time to allow it to be isolated, but this is rare. More often it is possible to spot an intermediate by virtue of its spectrum. The intermediate may change into another activated complex before finally being converted into products. An example of this occurs in the reaction between hydrogen chloride and propene. During the reaction, one intermediate that occurs is a positively charged ion (a carbocation)

$$CH_3-\overset{+}{C}H-CH_3$$

The energy profile for the reaction is shown in Figure 78.7.

It is the aim of transition state theory to explain the rates of reactions by working out the nature of the activated complex, how it is made from the reactants and how it changes into products. You will find further examples of transition states in later units, especially those dealing with the mechanisms of organic reactions.

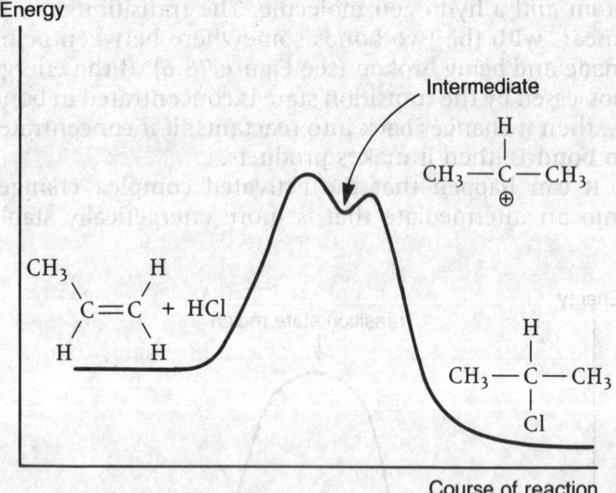

Figure 78.7 In some reactions an intermediate lies at a dip in the energy profile. The intermediate is said to exist in a metastable state. This example is for the reaction between hydrogen chloride and propene

78.5 A student looked at the energy diagram of Figure 78.8. It applies to a reaction that, under the same reaction conditions, can give two products, A and B. The student wrote the following: 'Product A is more energetically stable than product B. Therefore if we did this reaction in the laboratory, A would be made much faster than B, and we would obtain nearly all A as the product.'

Was the student correct? Give reasons for your answer.

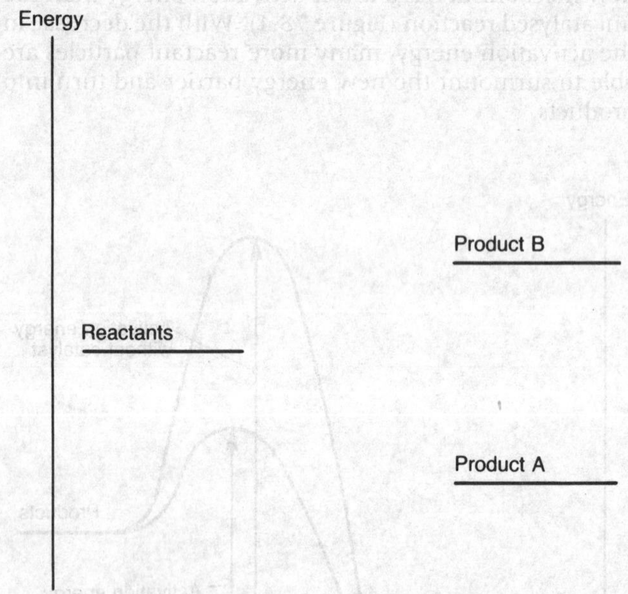

Figure 78.8 The energy diagram for question 78.5

Answers

78.1 P cannot be greater than one, or less than zero. If $P=1$, there is no steric hindrance. If $P=0$, the reaction is completely blocked.

78.2 (i) The values of ln k and $1/T$ are shown below and are plotted in Figure 78.9.

ln k	−7.29	−3.63	−0.58	1.99	4.20
$(1/T)/K^{-1}$	2.00×10^{-3}	1.82×10^{-3}	1.67×10^{-3}	1.54×10^{-3}	1.43×10^{-3}

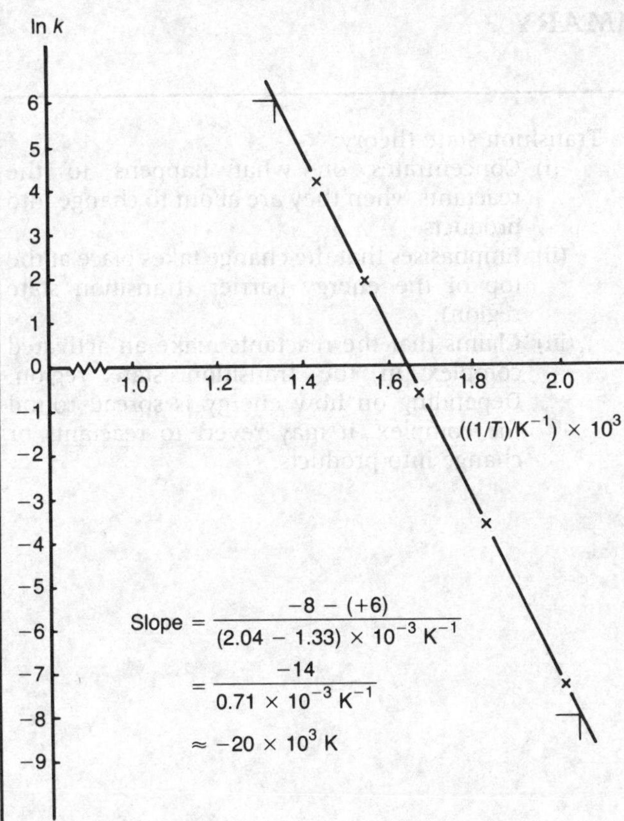

Figure 78.9 *Graph for answer to question 78.2*

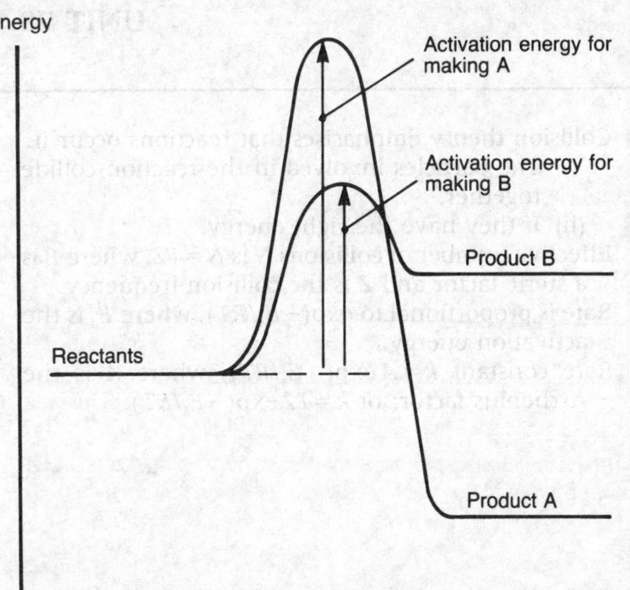

Figure 78.10 *Diagram for answer to question 78.5*

(ii) The slope is -20×10^3 K, so we have

$$E_a=20\times10^3\,\text{K}^{-1}\times8.314\,\text{J K}^{-1}\,\text{mol}^{-1}=160.6\,\text{kJ mol}^{-1}$$

Just as a matter of interest, the collision frequency is around 10^{14} cm^3 mol^{-1} s^{-1}.

78.3 (i)

$$\exp[-50\,000\,\text{J mol}^{-1}/(8.314\,\text{J K}^{-1}\,\text{mol}^{-1}\times298\,\text{K})]=1.72\times10^{-9}$$

and

$$\exp[-50\,000\,\text{J mol}^{-1}/(8.314\,\text{J K}^{-1}\,\text{mol}^{-1}\times308\,\text{K})]=3.31\times10^{-9}$$

(ii) For this 10°C rise in temperature the exponential factor has almost doubled. This means that the rate will have almost doubled. Hence the rule.

(iii) No. The ratio changes as the activation energy changes.

78.4 The student is right that nickel does catalyse this reaction. But it is not the 'collision reaction between the two molecules' that is involved. The catalyst does not lower the activation energy of *this* process. The catalyst provides an entirely different route for the reaction to take place. Now the reaction takes place at the surface of the nickel. It is this reaction that has a lower activation energy than the separate reaction between the gases on their own.

78.5 If we are thinking of the reaction in which they both turn back to products, the student was correct in saying that A is more energetically stable than B. Unfortunately, the diagram does not show the activation energies for the two reaction pathways. You can see from Figure 78.10 that the activation energy for making A could be much higher than that for B. For this reason, B would be made faster than A. We have no reason to think that B will change into A, so the product will be nearly all B. (Of course, in another case the student might be right; A might have the lower activation energy path.)

The moral of this is that the most energetically favourable product is *not* always the one that is made the most rapidly, or in the greatest amounts.

Another complicating issue that we have ignored is the nature of the transition states in the two reactions. This can have a marked influence on the rate at which different products are made.

UNIT 78 SUMMARY

- Collision theory emphasises that reactions occur if:
  - (i) The particles involved in the reaction collide together.
  - (ii) If they have the right energy.
- Effective number of collisions N is $N = PZ$, where P is a steric factor and Z is the collision frequency.
- Rate is proportional to $\exp(-E_a/RT)$, where E_a is the activation energy.
- Rate constant $k = A\exp(-E_a/RT)$, where A is the Arrhenius factor; or $k = PZ\exp(-E_a/RT)$.
- Transition state theory:
  - (i) Concentrates on what happens to the reactants when they are about to change into products.
  - (ii) Emphasises that the change takes place at the top of the energy barrier (transition state region).
  - (iii) Claims that the reactants make an activated complex in the transition state region. Depending on how energy is spread round the complex, it may revert to reactants or change into products.

79

Measuring the rates of reactions

79.1 An example of measuring a rate

To measure the rate of a chemical reaction, we must find out the change in the number of particles of a reactant that is disappearing or of a product that is being made. We must also record the time taken for the change to take place.

Suppose we decide to measure the rate at which hydrogen peroxide solution decomposes in the presence of a catalyst. The equation for the reaction is

$$2H_2O_2(aq) \rightarrow 2H_2O(l) + O_2(g)$$

There are three different types of molecule in the reaction, and we could put

$$\text{rate of disappearance of } H_2O_2 = \frac{\text{number of molecules of } H_2O_2 \text{ lost}}{\text{time taken}}$$

or

$$\text{rate of appearance of } H_2O = \frac{\text{number of molecules of } H_2O \text{ produced}}{\text{time taken}}$$

or

$$\text{rate of appearance of } O_2 = \frac{\text{number of molecules of } O_2 \text{ produced}}{\text{time taken}}$$

Fortunately we do not have to try to count the actual number of molecules of hydrogen peroxide, water, or oxygen. We can measure a quantity that is directly related to the number of molecules: their *concentrations*.

At this stage common sense must take a part. We should decide which measurements would be the easiest to make. In this case, the oxygen can be collected the most easily, so it is the third equation that we should use. For a gas, the concentration is proportional to its volume at constant pressure and temperature, or its pressure at a constant volume and temperature. Thus we can put

$$\text{rate of appearance of } O_2 = \frac{\text{volume of } O_2 \text{ produced}}{\text{time taken}}$$

We could set up an apparatus like that in Figure 79.1a, and measure the volume of oxygen collected every 10 s or so. If the volume of oxygen given off is plotted against time, a graph like that of Figure 79.1b is

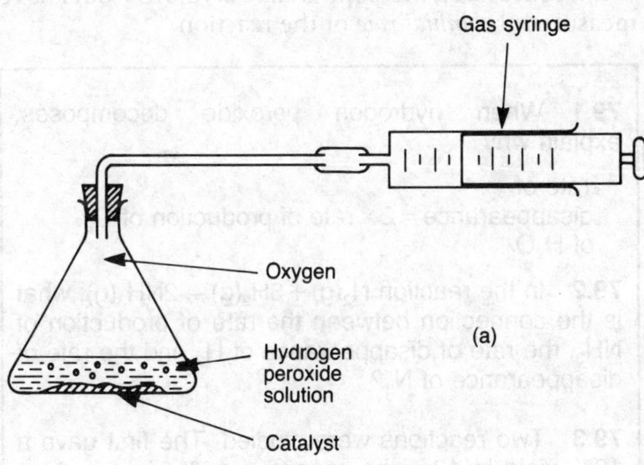

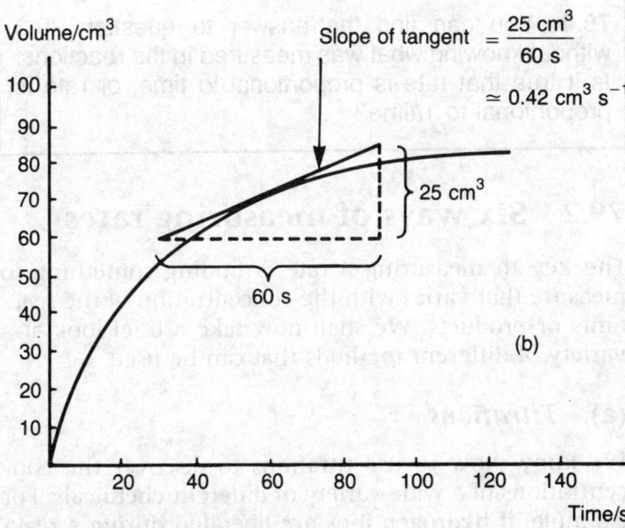

Figure 79.1 *(a) An apparatus for measuring the rate of decomposition of hydrogen peroxide. (b) Graph of results from an experiment like that shown in part (a)*

obtained. An alternative way of producing this graph is to connect the pen of a chart recorder to the plunger of the gas syringe. The pen will then produce the graph automatically.

You can see from the graph that the oxygen is given off very quickly at the start. This is where the curve is the steepest. As time goes on, the curve becomes less steep, until at about 120 s it levels off. At this stage the reaction has stopped. We can measure the rate at which oxygen is evolved at any time by finding out how steep the curve is. One such measurement has been done in Figure 79.1b at time 60 s. The slope is found by drawing a tangent to the curve at time 60 s. This involves a certain amount of estimation if you do it by hand and eye. (There are more accurate methods, which make use of advanced mathematics and computers.) We have,

slope of line = $0.42\ cm^3\ s^{-1}$

i.e. rate of appearance of oxygen is $0.42\ cm^3\ s^{-1}$ at time 60 s.

If we measured the slope at time zero, we would have measured the *initial rate* of the reaction.

79.1 When hydrogen peroxide decomposes, explain why

rate of disappearance of H_2O_2 = 2 × rate of production of O_2

79.2 In the reaction $N_2(g) + 3H_2(g) \rightarrow 2NH_3(g)$, what is the connection between the rate of production of NH_3, the rate of disappearance of H_2 and the rate of disappearance of N_2?

79.3 Two reactions were studied. The first gave a 10% yield in 10 s, the second a 10% yield in 20 s. Which had the higher rate?

79.4 You can find the answer to question 79.3 without knowing what was measured in the reactions. Is it true that rate is proportional to time, or rate is proportional to 1/time?

79.2 Six ways of measuring rates

The key to measuring a rate is finding something to measure that varies with the concentration of the reactants or products. We shall now take a brief look at a variety of different methods that can be used.

(a) *Titrations*

We know how to use titrations to discover the concentrations of a wide variety of different chemicals. For example, if hydrogen ions are liberated during a reaction, the course of the reaction can be followed by titrating a sample of the reaction mixture with an alkali. The experiment in panel 79.1 and Figure 79.2 gives you

Panel 79.1

An experiment to study the rate of reaction between iodine and propanone

The reaction between iodine and propanone, CH_3COCH_3, takes place slowly at room temperature:

$$CH_3COCH_3(aq) + I_2(aq) \rightarrow CH_3COCH_2I(aq) + H^+(aq) + I^-(aq)$$

However, the reaction is catalysed by hydrogen ions. The course of the reaction can be followed by using a colorimeter, but here we shall describe a method that involves titrations. The approach is outlined below. (If you perform the experiment, you may use solutions of different concentrations.)

(i) Solutions of 0.05 mol dm^{-3} iodine, 1 mol dm^{-3} propanone and dilute sulphuric acid are made up and placed in a thermostatted water bath to come to a constant temperature.

(ii) 25 cm^3 of the acid and 25 cm^3 of the propanone solution are mixed in a conical flask, also kept in the water bath. Now 25 cm^3 of the iodine solution are added, and a clock is started.

(iii) Every five minutes or so (the time interval does not have to be exact), 10 cm^3 of the reaction mixture are removed using a small pipette and drained into another flask containing 20 cm^3 of 0.5 mol dm^{-3} sodium hydrogencarbonate solution. The time at which the 10 cm^3 is run in is recorded. This time *does* have to be known accurately.

(iv) The iodine in the flask is now titrated with sodium thiosulphate solution, using starch as an indicator. (See Unit 40 for details.)

The purpose of the hydrogencarbonate is to neutralise the acid in the 10 cm^3 of reaction solution. Once the hydrogen ions are neutralised, the reaction stops, and the titration gives a measure of the amount of iodine remaining in the mixture at the time it was run into the hydrogencarbonate. Stopping the reaction in this way is an example of *quenching* a reaction.

(v) Another 10 cm^3 of reaction mixture are withdrawn, and treated in the same way. The procedure is repeated at least five or six times.

(vi) The volume of thiosulphate solution used in each of the titrations is proportional to the concentration of iodine present. A graph of volume against time looks like that in Figure 79.2.

The graph is unusual in one respect: it is a straight line. In nearly all rate experiments we obtain curved lines. This reaction is an exception. It is telling us that the rate of the reaction is constant: a straight line has a constant slope. With a little thought you will realise why this is unusual. It is telling us that although iodine is being used up in the reaction, the rate remains unchanged. That is,

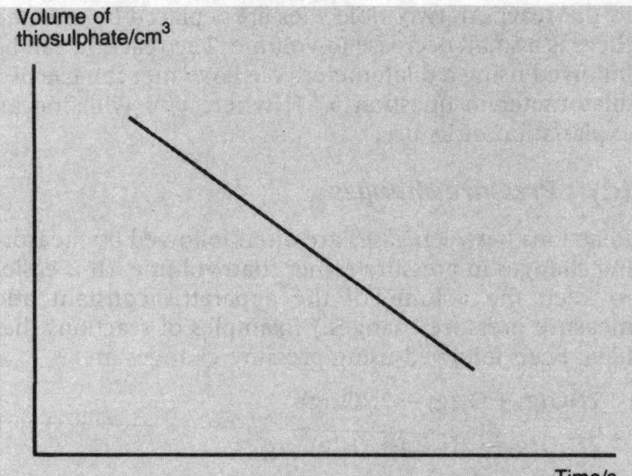

***Figure 79.2** The straight line shows that this reaction has a constant rate. That is, even though iodine is used up in the reaction, its change in concentration has no effect on the rate*

the rate is independent of the amount of iodine present (assuming of course that there is *some* iodine present to react). Normally, we would expect that with fewer iodine molecules present, there would be fewer collisions, and hence fewer reactions in a given time. This reaction appears not to work like that. You will discover the reason why in section 81.3, where we will discuss the mechanism of the reaction.

Note: Take care how you dispose of the products of this reaction. CH_3COCH_2I is a powerful lachrymator (makes you cry).

a more detailed method of how the course of one reaction can be followed using a series of titrations. One interesting feature of the experiment is that it uses a technique called *quenching*. A reaction is quenched when it is brought to a halt abruptly. In panel 79.1, the example is a reaction catalysed by acid. Samples of the reaction mixture are run into a solution of a hydrogencarbonate. This immediately neutralises the acid, thus bringing the reaction to a halt. Then the mixture can be analysed to see how much of the reactants remain. In other cases, reactions can be stopped by cooling them rapidly, e.g. by plunging the reactants into ice.

(b) *Colour changes*

Many chemicals are coloured, and the intensity of their colour varies with their concentration. For example, thiosulphate ions, $S_2O_3^{2-}$, react with hydrogen ions to produce sulphur:

$$\underset{\text{colourless}}{S_2O_3^{2-}(aq)} + 2H^+(aq) \rightarrow \underset{\text{yellow}}{2S(s)} + \underset{\text{colourless}}{SO_2(aq)} + H_2O(l)$$

The progress of the reaction can be followed by measuring the intensity of the yellow colour. Provided we do not need very accurate results, no special equipment is needed for this reaction. You can see why if you try question 79.7.

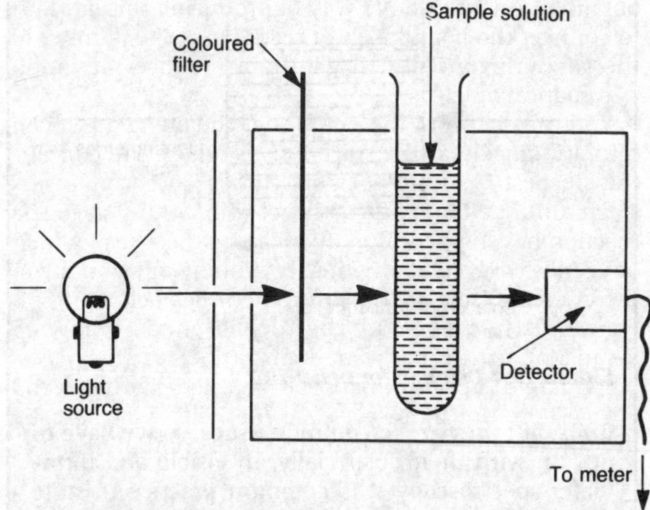

***Figure 79.3** Block diagram of a colorimeter*

However, a more accurate method of following a reaction by a colour change is to use a *colorimeter* (Figure 79.3). If the colorimeter is to be used successfully, it is necessary to use light of the correct colour. This is the colour that is absorbed by the chemical, not the colour you see. For example, solutions containing copper(II) ions are blue. This is because they absorb red light. For this reason, if we were following a reaction involving copper(II) ions, we should use a red filter.

The detector in a colorimeter does not necessarily respond in a simple way to light coming through solutions of different concentrations. For example, if the colorimeter recorded a value of 100 units for a 10^{-3} mol dm^{-3} solution of copper(II) ions, it would not necessarily measure 50 units for a 2×10^{-3} mol dm^{-3} solution. For this reason it is essential to calibrate a colorimeter before using it. The Beer–Lambert law governs the way light is absorbed by solutions. Look at panel 79.2 and Figure 79.4 if you want to find out about the law.

Panel 79.2

Beer–Lambert law

Imagine a beam of light passing through a solution as shown in Figure 79.4. The light enters the solution with intensity I_0 and emerges with intensity I. We shall assume that the solution has concentration c mol dm^{-3}, and the light passes through a length l cm.

The Beer–Lambert law says that

$$\varepsilon cl = \lg\left(\frac{I_0}{I}\right)$$

Here ε is known as the extinction coefficient. (The Greek symbol is pronounced 'epsilon'.) The units of ε are dm^3 mol^{-1} cm^{-1}. These are rather unfortunate

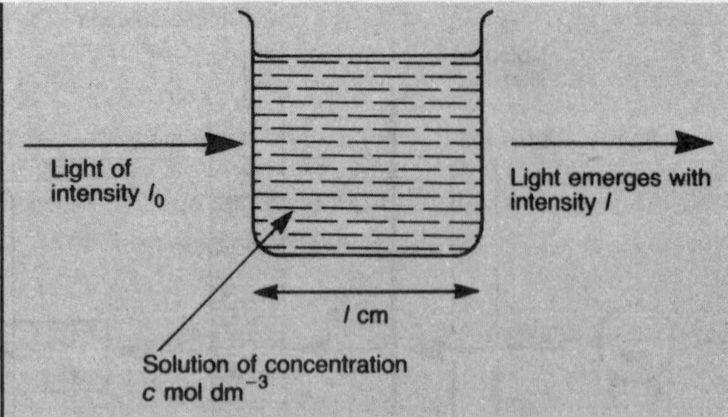

Figure 79.4 *Diagram for panel 79.2*

units, but they are in common usage, so we have to put up with them. Especially, in visible and ultraviolet spectroscopy it is common practice to state values of the extinction coefficients for the absorption bands of a molecule, or part of a molecule. For example, alkenes often have extinction coefficients of the order of 16 000 dm^3 mol^{-1} cm^{-1}. Copper(II) ions in water have a value nearer 10 dm^3 mol^{-1} cm^{-1}.

We can rearrange the equation in this way:

$$\frac{I}{I_0}=10^{-\varepsilon cl}$$

Armed with a calculator, we can discover what happens to the intensity of light passing through a 1 cm length of 1 mol dm^{-3} copper(II) sulphate solution. We have

$$\frac{I}{I_0}=10^{-10\times1\times1}=10^{-10}$$

That is, the intensity of light emerging from the solution is *very* much less than the light entering. Now suppose we halve the concentration. This time we find that $I/I_0=10^{-5}$, so the intensity of light getting through is 100 000 times greater than before.

(c) *Volume changes*

We have already seen how to measure volume changes when gases are given off in a reaction. Some reactions involving liquids also show volume changes. An example is the reaction between 2-methylpropene and water:

$$(CH_3)_2C{=}CH_2+H_2O\rightarrow(CH_3)_3COH$$

In the reaction, two molecules are replaced by one and there is a small decrease in volume. The reaction can be followed using a dilatometer. We have met the use of a dilatometer in question 57.1, where you will find an explanation of its use.

(d) *Pressure changes*

Reactions between gases are often followed by measuring changes in pressure rather than volume. (It is easier to keep the volume of the apparatus constant and measure pressure changes.) Examples of reactions that have been followed using pressure changes are

$$2NO(g)+O_2(g)\rightarrow2NO_2(g)$$

$$2N_2O(g)\rightarrow2N_2(g)+O_2(g)$$

Notice that in both cases there is a change in the number of moles of gas.

(e) *Conductivity changes*

Ions take part in many reactions. Solutions containing ions conduct electricity, so if there is an increase in the concentration of ions, the conductivity will increase. On the other hand, if the concentration of ions decreases, the conductivity will decrease. In some cases conductivity measurements can be used even if there is no change in the overall number of ions. An example is the reaction between an ester such as ethyl ethanoate, $CH_3COOC_2H_5$, and hydroxide ions:

$$CH_3COOC_2H_5(aq)+OH^-(aq)\rightarrow CH_3COO^-(aq)+C_2H_5OH(aq)$$

Each time an ethanoate ion, CH_3COO^-, is made, a hydroxide ion is used up. As a consequence there is no change in the total number of ions. However, ethanoate ions have much smaller conductivities than hydroxide ions, so the reaction involves a gradual decrease in conductivity.

(f) *Rotation of the plane of polarised light*

In Unit 110 you will find that some molecules rotate the plane of polarised light. The amount of rotation can be measured using a polarimeter. The reaction of sucrose with water is an example. In the reaction, sucrose changes into a mixture of glucose and fructose. This brings about a change in the amount of rotation. The rotation can be measured at various time intervals. A graph of angle of rotation plotted against time allows the rate of the reaction to be determined.

79.5 Look at the equations for the reactions below, and suggest the best method for measuring the rate of the reaction. If you think more than one method is possible, say so.

(i) $5C_2O_4^{2-}(aq)+2MnO_4^-(aq)+16H^+(aq)\rightarrow 10CO_2(g)+2Mn^{2+}(aq)+8H_2O(l)$

(ii) $MnO_4^-(aq)+8H^+(aq)+5Fe^{2+}(aq)\rightarrow Mn^{2+}(aq)+5Fe^{3+}(aq)+4H_2O(l)$

(iii) $N_2(g)+3H_2(g)\rightarrow2NH_3(g)$

(iv) $H_2O_2(aq)+2I^-(aq)+2H^+(aq)\rightarrow2H_2O(l)+I_2(aq)$

(v) $C_6H_5NH_2+CH_3I\rightarrow[C_6H_5NH_2CH_3]^++I^-$

79.6 The rate of reaction between marble chips (calcium carbonate) and hydrochloric acid can be determined in several ways. Two methods are illustrated in Figure 79.5.

(i) Sketch the graph of volume of carbon dioxide given off against time, in method A.

(ii) On the same sketch, draw in the line/curve that you would expect if you used acid that was twice as concentrated as before. In both reactions, all the marble chips are used up before the syringe is completely full.

(iii) When the gas syringe is being connected, the marble chips are in the small test tube, and not directly in contact with the acid. Why is this?

(iv) Sketch the graph you would expect if you were to plot the mass recorded by the top pan balance against time, in method B.

(v) Why is there cotton wool in the mouth of the flask?

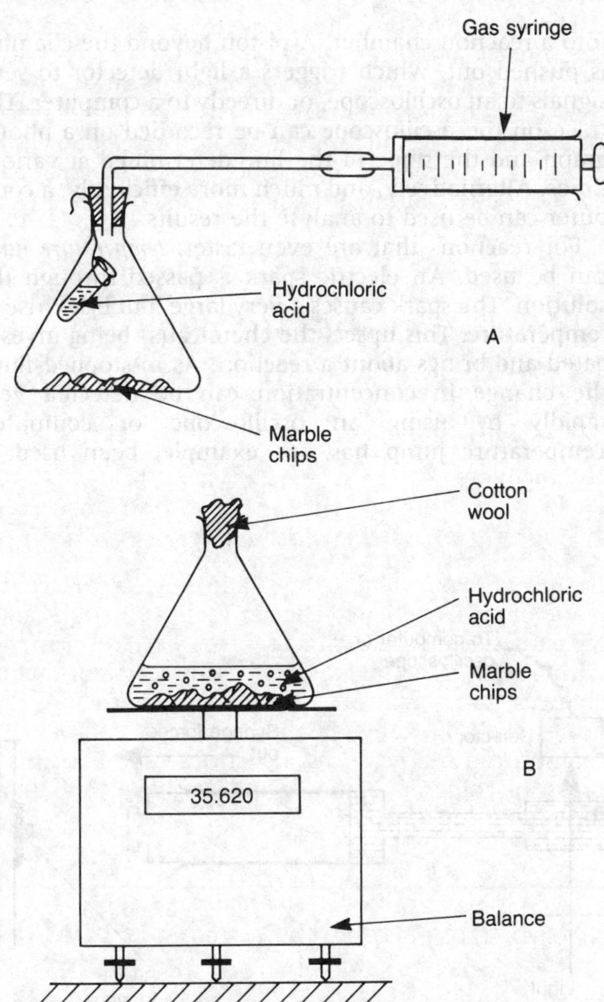

Figure 79.5 Two methods of following the rate of reaction between marble chips and hydrochloric acid (see question 79.6)

(vi) Sketch the graph you would expect if you were to plot the mass of carbon dioxide given off against time, in method B.

(vii) On the same sketch as in (iv), show the results you would expect if you used smaller marble chips in the experiment. Assume that the same mass of marble chips is used in both experiments and that they are all used up.

79.7 The reaction between thiosulphate ions and hydrogen ions is very easy to study. A beaker containing 25 cm^3 of 0.1 mol dm^{-3} sodium thiosulphate solution is placed over a cross drawn on a piece of paper. Then 5 cm^3 of a dilute solution of nitric acid is added. You would start timing as soon as the acid is added. Gradually the amount of sulphur in the solution increases. Eventually there is so much sulphur that it is no longer possible to see the cross through the solution. The time taken for the cross to disappear is noted. Then the experiment is repeated but using sodium thiosulphate solutions of different concentrations. Each time recorded shows how long it took for the same amount of sulphur to be made in each experiment.

Here are some results.

Concentration of thiosulphate /mol dm^{-3}	0.01	0.02	0.04	0.08	0.1
Time taken/s	98	51	24	12	10

(i) Plot a graph of time (horizontally) against the concentration of sodium thiosulphate (vertically).

(ii) For which solution is the rate the smallest? Explain how your graph gives you the answer.

(iii) Plot a graph of concentration of sodium thiosulphate (vertically) against 1/time (horizontally). Is the graph a curve or a straight line (within the limits of experimental error)?

(iv) You should realise that 1/time is a measure of the rate of the reaction. How does the rate change as the concentration of the thiosulphate solution changes?

(v) Is the rate proportional to $[S_2O_3^{2-}(aq)]$, to $[S_2O_3^{2-}(aq)]^2$, or to $[S_2O_3^{2-}(aq)]^3$?

79.8 The hydrolysis of the ester, ethyl ethanoate, can be speeded up by reacting it with alkali rather than water alone:

$$CH_3COOC_2H_5(aq) + OH^-(aq) \rightarrow CH_3COO^-(aq) + C_2H_5OH(aq)$$

One method of following the course of the reaction is outlined below. The method is not quite right. The questions that follow will ask you to find out what is wrong.

First, 50 cm^3 of an aqueous solution of 0.01 mol

dm^{-3} ethyl ethanoate is mixed with 50 cm^3 of 0.01 mol dm^{-3} sodium hydroxide solution. The mixture is swirled together and placed in a thermostat bath. Every five minutes 10 cm^3 of the reaction mixture is removed using a pipette. The 10 cm^3 of solution is run into a conical flask and titrated with a 0.01 mol dm^{-3} solution of nitric acid. The volume of acid run in is a measure of how much sodium hydroxide had been used up. From the titration results, it is possible to follow the course of the reaction.

(i) What absolutely vital instructions have been missed out?

(ii) Where/when should these instructions appear?

(iii) Titrating the reaction mixture with acid is not the best method. A better approach is to run the mixture into a flask already containing enough acid to neutralise all of the hydroxide ions. Then the acid left over is titrated with another solution of sodium hydroxide of known concentration. Why is this, more elaborate, method likely to give better results? (Hint: quenching!)

79.9 Iron(III) ions react with thiocyanate ions, CNS^-, to give a blood red complex ion, $Fe(CNS)^{2+}$. If you were to attempt to follow the reaction in a colorimeter, what colour filter would you use?

79.10 The reaction between hydrogen and iodine has been studied very extensively. It takes place readily at temperatures around 300° C:

$$H_2(g) + I_2(g) \rightarrow 2HI(g)$$

Your task is to suggest a method of carrying out the reaction, and of discovering the concentration of hydrogen iodide made at various times from the start of the reaction. You might like to know that the reaction virtually ceases at room temperature. Also, hydrogen iodide is strongly acidic in water.

79.3 Measuring the rates of very fast reactions

The methods of measuring rates that we have discussed so far are fine provided the reactions are fairly slow. If two chemicals completely react in, say, 0.01 s, we have a problem in measuring the rate. For example, we could not mix them by pouring one solution into another; by the time they had finished mixing the reaction would be over.

There are a number of methods that have been developed to study very fast reactions. One is called *stopped-flow* (Figure 79.6). In a stopped-flow experiment the reactants are mixed very quickly by squeezing them into a reaction chamber. A piston beyond the chamber is pushed out, which triggers a light detector to send signals to an oscilloscope, or directly to a computer. The trace on the oscilloscope can be recorded on a photograph and the slope of the line determined at various times. Alternatively, and much more efficiently, a computer can be used to analyse the results.

For reactions that are even faster, *temperature jump* can be used. An electric spark is passed through the solution. The spark causes a very large, but brief, rise in temperature. This upsets the chemical(s) being investigated and brings about a reaction. As in stopped-flow, the change in concentration can be detected very rapidly by using an oscilloscope or computer. Temperature jump has, for example, been used to

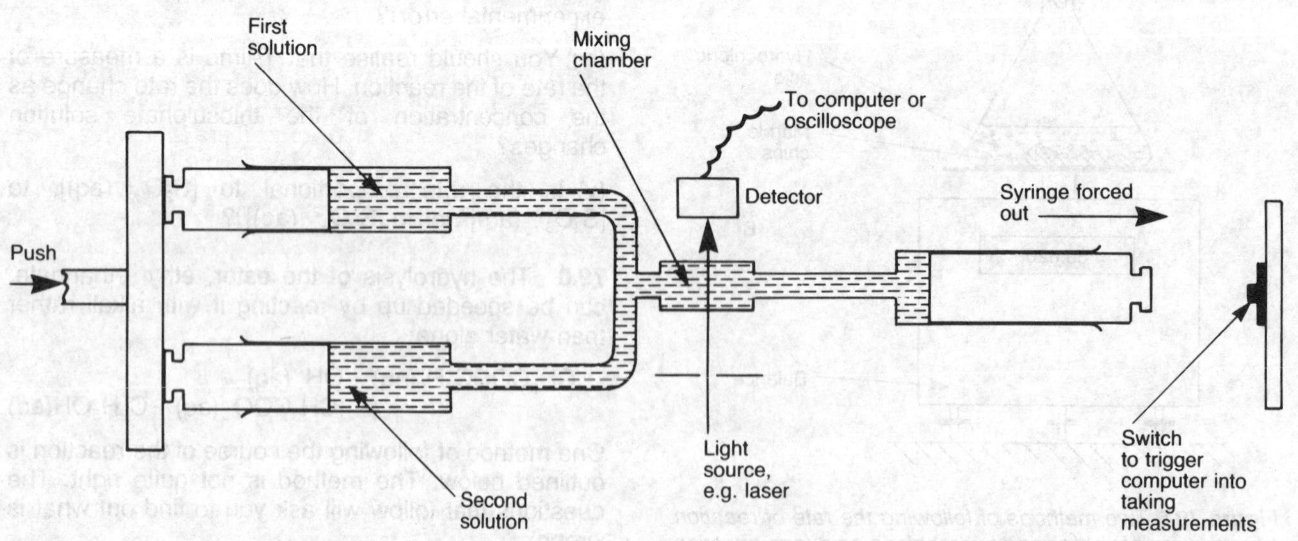

***Figure 79.6** A stopped-flow apparatus*

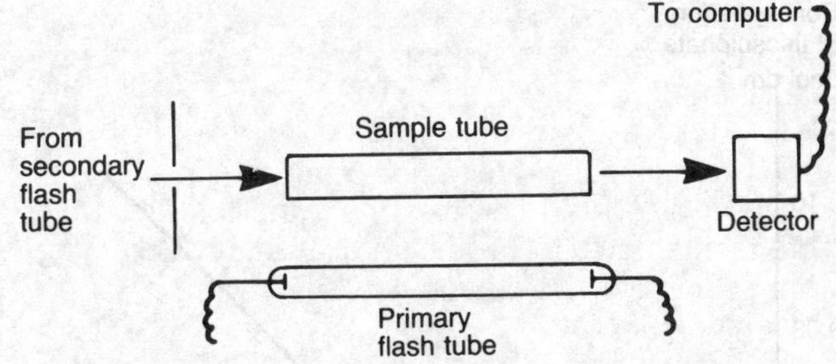

Figure 79.7 *In a flash photolysis experiment, the sample is subjected to an intense flash of light from the primary flash tube. This causes chemical change in the sample. Some thousandths of a second (or less) later, a light beam from the secondary flash tube passes through the sample. The degree of absorption of the beam depends on the species present in the sample tube. The absorption is measured by the detector*

investigate the rate at which the two strands in DNA zip together.

A third method, called *flash photolysis* (Figure 79.7), can measure rates of reactions that are extremely fast. In this case, a very short, but intense, flash of light passes into the reaction mixture. After an equally brief period of time, another flash of light passes through the mixture. The molecules produced in the reaction absorb some of the light from the second flash. By taking a photograph, the spectrum of the molecules can be recorded. The intensity of the lines in the spectrum gives a measure of the concentration of the molecules. If the time interval between the first and second flashes is changed, the intensity of the lines in the spectrum changes. In this way a series of experiments allows the way the concentration of the molecules changes with time to be found.

Answers

79.1 From the equation you will see that 1 mol of O_2 is produced when 2 mol of H_2O_2 decompose. Therefore, H_2O_2 will be lost twice as quickly as O_2 is made.

79.2 Rate of production of NH_3

$$= 2 \times \text{rate of disappearance of } N_2$$
$$= \tfrac{2}{3} \times \text{rate of disappearance of } H_2$$

79.3 The first (in 10 s). The shorter the time, the faster the rate.

79.4 Rate is proportional to 1/time.

79.5 To answer this it is best to know that manganate(VII) ions, MnO_4^-, are purple in solution, Mn^{2+} ions are very pale pink, Fe^{2+} are pale green, Fe^{3+} are yellow-brown, I_2 and I^- ions together are deep brown.

(i) A colorimeter could be used, or the volume of CO_2 given off could be measured. The latter approach has the disadvantage that CO_2 is somewhat soluble in water, so measurements of gas volume at the start of the experiment will be in error.

(ii) A colorimeter is best. The change in the intense colour of MnO_4^- is easily detected.

(iii) Gas pressure.

(iv) Conductivity measurements or a colorimeter could be used. Alternatively, thiosulphate titrations can be done to determine the change in iodine concentration. If the titration method is chosen, samples of the reaction mixture should be quenched. (There is also an alternative method, known as the Harcourt–Esson reaction, that you may meet.)

(v) Conductivity.

79.6 (i), (ii) The graph is shown in Figure 79.8. With the more concentrated acid, the reaction will be faster, and the line steeper. Notice that, because the marble chips are used up each time, the total amount of carbon dioxide must be the same.

(iii) If the marble chips and acid start to react before the syringe is connected, it is not possible to get an accurate measurement of the initial volume of carbon dioxide.

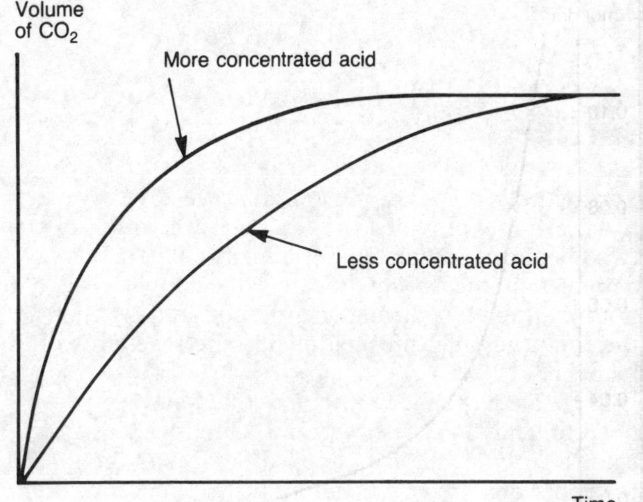

Figure 79.8 *The graphs for answer to question 79.6(i) and (ii)*

(iv) The graph is given in Figure 79.9. Take care to realise that the mass of the flask must decrease.

(v) When the marble chips react there is effervescence. As bubbles of carbon dioxide rise out of the acid and burst, they might throw small amounts of solution out of the flask. This would give inaccurate readings for the mass of gas given off. The cotton wool prevents droplets of solution escaping, but allows carbon dioxide through.

(vi) The graph would be similar to that in Figure 79.8.

(vii) The smaller marble chips will have the greater surface area, so the reaction will be faster.

79.7 (i) The graph is plotted in Figure 79.10.

(ii) The 0.01 mol dm^{-3} solution. Here the slope of the graph is the smallest.

(iii) The values of 1/time are, in s^{-1}, 0.010, 0.020, 0.042, 0.083 and 0.100. The graph is a straight line, as shown in Figure 79.11.

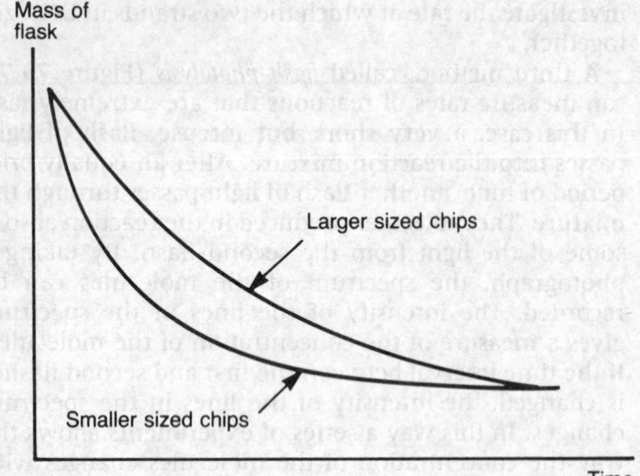

Figure 79.9 *Graph for answer to question 79.6(iv) and (vii)*

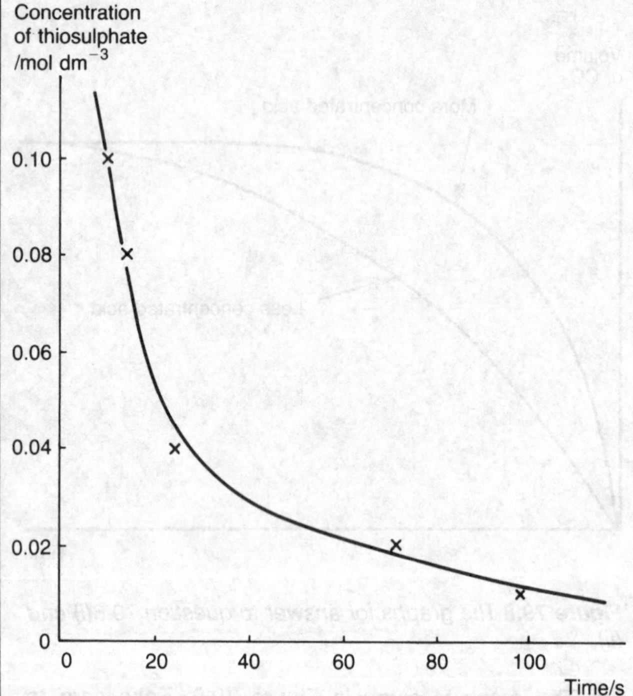

Figure 79.10 *Graph for answer to question 79.7(i)*

(iv) From the second graph we can see that the rate increases as the concentration increases.

(v) The fact that the graph is a straight line tells us that rate is proportional to [$S_2O_3^{2-}$(aq)]. If it were one of the other two possibilities, the graph would be a curve. A reaction that is directly proportional to the concentration of one of the reactants is said to be *first order* in that reactant.

Actually there is a slight 'cheat' in this method. Once the 5 cm^3 of acid is added, the thiosulphate is diluted from 25 cm^3 to 30 cm^3. Therefore all of the concentrations stated are slightly different. For example, the 0.01 mol dm^{-3} solution becomes about 0.008 mol dm^{-3}. You can try adapting all the values if you wish.

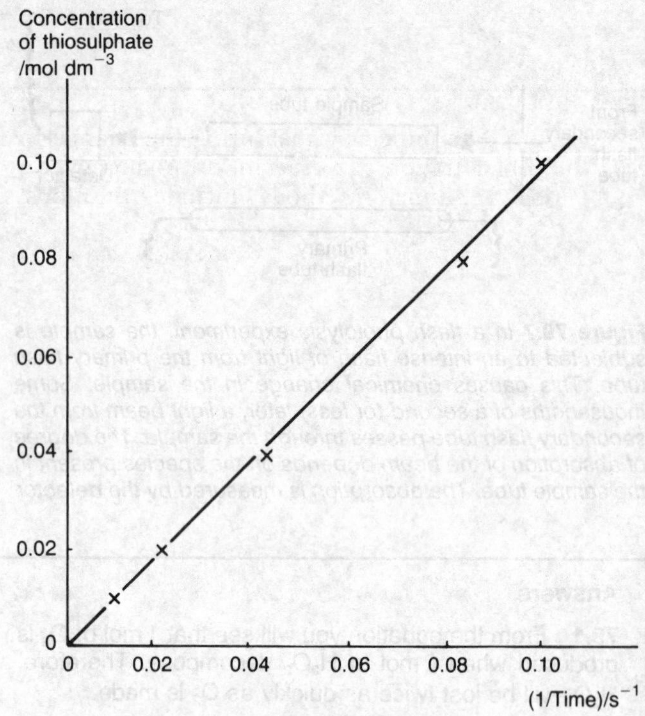

Figure 79.11 *Graph for answer to question 79.7(iii). Note that 1/time is a measure of the rate of reaction*

79.8 (i) There is no mention of recording the time.

(ii) A clock should be started when the reactants are mixed. The time at which the 10 cm^3 portions are titrated should be noted.

(iii) If the reaction mixture is titrated with acid, the reaction between the alkali and ester does not finish until all the alkali is neutralised. (If the mixture were run into a flask containing ice, the situation would be improved. The ice would help to quench the reaction.) By running the mixture into acid, the hydroxide ions are immediately removed and the reaction is quenched.

79.9 As the complex reflects red light, it absorbs in the blue region of the spectrum. Therefore you would use a blue filter.

79.10 The reaction can be performed by sealing known quantities of the reactants into steel tubes. The tubes can be placed in a furnace/oven kept at the required temperature. At known time intervals the tubes can be withdrawn from the furnace. When they come into contact with air at room temperature they quickly cool and quench the reaction. The tubes can be opened under a known volume of water. Like hydrogen chloride, hydrogen iodide is very soluble in water. The acidic solution can be titrated with an alkali in order to discover its concentration, and thereby the quantity of hydrogen iodide made in the reaction.

Notice that because there is no change in the number of molecules during the reaction, volume or pressure changes cannot be used to follow the course of the reaction.

UNIT 79 SUMMARY

- Rates are determined by measuring the change in the concentration of a reactant or product over a period of time. Methods include titrations, pressure measurements (for gases), colour changes and mass changes.

80

Rate laws

80.1 What is a rate law?

The usual pattern for reactions is that they start off fast and gradually slow down to a stop. You should realise that the reason they slow down is that the reactants are being used up. Therefore their concentrations decrease, and the number of collisions also decreases. Eventually there is so little left that collisions cease. A rate law is a way of expressing this behaviour in a more precise way.

We might think that if we doubled the concentration of a reactant we would automatically double the rate; but this is not always so. Sometimes the rate will double, but sometimes it may increase by a factor of four; indeed sometimes it may not increase at all, or increase in an apparently weird fashion.

A very common rate law is one where the rate is directly proportional to concentration. If we write one of the reactants as A, and its concentration as [A], we have

$$\text{rate} \propto [\text{A}]$$

or

$\text{rate} = k[\text{A}]$	First-order rate law

This is called the first-order rate law. Here k is the *rate constant*. Every reaction has its own particular rate constant. Like equilibrium constants, rate constants will only change their values with temperature. For this reason, whenever the value of a rate constant is quoted, the temperature should also be given. In this unit we shall assume that, unless stated otherwise, rate constants are measured at 20° C.

Other rate laws are

$\text{rate} = k[\text{A}]^2$	Second-order rate law
$\text{rate} = k[\text{A}]^3$	Third-order rate law

Some reactions have a zeroth-order rate law. In this case,

$$\text{rate} = k[\text{A}]^0$$

or

$\text{rate} = k$	Zeroth-order rate law

Zeroth-order reactions do not occur very often. You might think that they should not happen at all because the law says that the rate of the reaction does not depend on the concentration of the reactant. However, we saw in panel 79.1 that the reaction between iodine and propanone is zeroth order with respect to iodine.

Some units of rate constants are given in Table 80.1.

Table 80.1. The units of rate constants

Order	*Units of rate constant**
Zeroth	$\text{mol dm}^{-3}\ \text{s}^{-1}$
First	s^{-1}
Second	$\text{dm}^3\ \text{mol}^{-1}\ \text{s}^{-1}$
Third	$\text{dm}^6\ \text{mol}^{-2}\ \text{s}^{-1}$

*Usually concentrations are measured in mol dm^{-3}, and time in seconds. However, time is sometimes measured in other units, e.g. minutes, hours, days, or even years for very slow reactions

The majority of reactions involve two or more different chemicals reacting together. If we call the reactants A, B, C, etc., then the reaction might be first order with respect to A, first order with respect to B and second order with respect to C. The overall rate law for the reaction will be

$$\text{rate} = k[\text{A}][\text{B}][\text{C}]^2$$

and the overall order of the reaction is *four* $(1+1+2)$.

For a general reaction in which we write the orders as x, y and z, we have

$$\text{rate} = k[\text{A}]^x[\text{B}]^y[\text{C}]^z$$

The *overall* order of the reaction is $x+y+z$.

Incidentally, orders are not always whole numbers. However, you are most unlikely to meet reactions that have fractional orders.

80.1 What is the equation that tells us how rate constants vary with temperature?

80.2 Suppose that a reaction has the rate law rate $= k[A]^2[B][C]^2$. What is the overall order?

80.3 A reaction involves two chemicals, A and B. The reaction is second order in A and zeroth order in B. Write down the rate law for the reaction.

80.2 How can we discover the rate law?

The first thing to do is to use one of the methods of the last unit to follow the course of a reaction. The rate at which hydrogen peroxide, H_2O_2, solution decomposes can be increased by adding a little copper(II) sulphate. Instead of collecting the oxygen given off, the concentration of the hydrogen peroxide can be measured by titrating samples of the solution with potassium manganate(VII), $KMnO_4$, solution. Here is a typical set of results obtained by withdrawing 20 cm^3 samples every 5 min.

Time/min	0	5	10	15	20	25	30
Vol. of $KMnO_4/cm^3$	24.0	18.7	14.6	11.3	8.8	6.9	5.4

The results are shown plotted on the graph in Figure 80.1a.

The rate of the reaction at any time is given by the slope of the line. The values of the rates are

Time/min	0	5	10	15
Rate/cm^3 min^{-1}	−1.2	−0.93	−0.73	−0.57

Time/min	20	25	30
Rate/cm^3 min^{-1}	−0.44	−0.34	−0.27

(The figures have a negative sign because the line curves downwards.) As we expect, the rate decreases as the H_2O_2 is used up. At each of the times, the volume of $KMnO_4$ is directly proportional to the concentration of H_2O_2. We can see how the rate depends on the concentration by plotting another graph. This is the graph in Figure 80.1b. Clearly this is a straight line, which tells us that

$$\text{rate} \propto [H_2O_2]$$

or

$$\text{rate} = k[H_2O_2]$$

We have discovered that the decomposition of hydrogen peroxide is a *first-order reaction*.

We can use the same graph to calculate the value of the rate constant. We know that $k = \text{rate}/[H_2O_2]$. This is the slope of the line, which equals 0.05 min^{-1}, i.e. $k = 0.05$ min^{-1}.

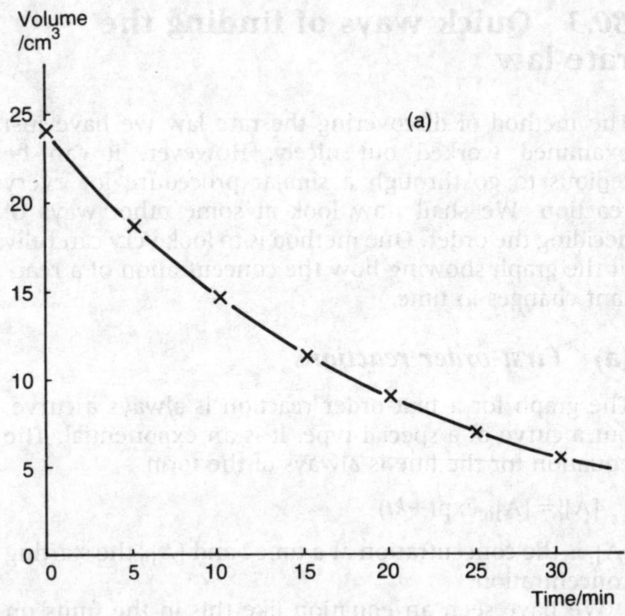

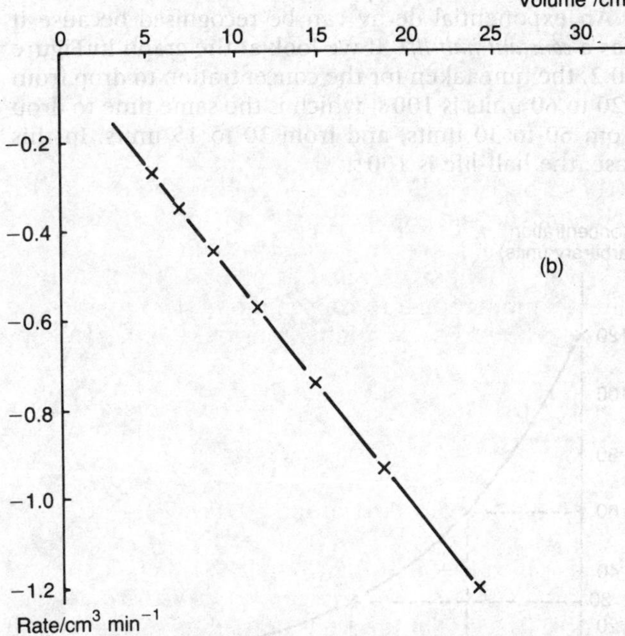

***Figure 80.1** (a) Graph of volume of potassium manganate(VII) solution against time. (b) Graph of rate against volume of potassium manganate(VII) solution*

80.4 A student wrote down this sentence in an essay: 'The rate constant for a reaction always has units of time^{-1}, for example s^{-1} or min^{-1}.' Was the student correct?

80.3 Quick ways of finding the rate law

The method of discovering the rate law we have just examined worked out nicely. However, it can be tedious to go through a similar procedure for every reaction. We shall now look at some other ways of deciding the order. One method is to look very carefully at the graph showing how the concentration of a reactant changes in time.

(a) *First-order reactions*

The graph for a first-order reaction is always a curve, but a curve of a special type. It is an exponential. The equation for the line is always of the form

$$[A]_t = [A]_0 \exp(-kt)$$

$[A]_t$ is the concentration at a time t and $[A]_0$ the starting concentration.

We have seen an equation like this in the units on radioactive decay. Indeed, we can think of radioactive decay as a particular type of first-order reaction.

An exponential decay can be recognised because it has a *constant half-life*. If we look at the graph in Figure 80.2, the time taken for the concentration to drop from 120 to 60 units is 100 s, which is the same time to drop from 60 to 30 units, and from 30 to 15 units. In this case, the half-life is 100 s.

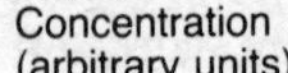

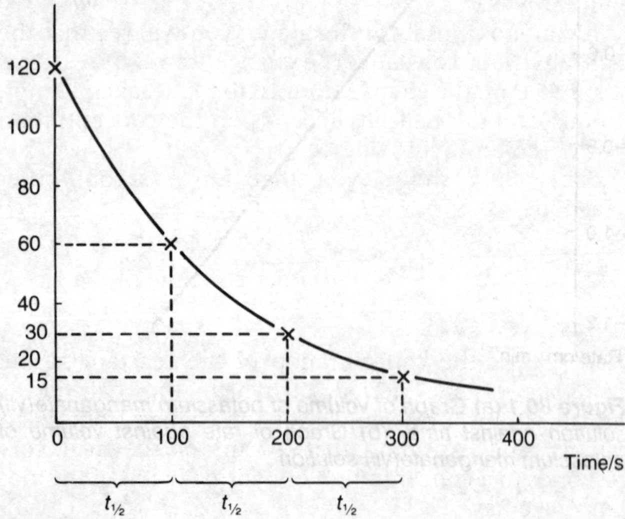

***Figure 80.2** An exponential decay has a constant half-life; in this case 100 s*

Panel 80.1 shows you that there is a simple connection between the half-life, $t_{1/2}$, of a first-order reaction and the rate constant. It is

$$t_{1/2} = \frac{0.693}{k} \qquad \text{First-order reaction only}$$

Panel 80.1

The mathematics of rate laws

First-order reactions

Suppose we have a first-order reaction in which a substance A changes into products. We shall write the starting concentration of A as a. After the reaction has started, some of it will have changed into products. We shall say that after time t a concentration x has 'disappeared'. We can show the information like this:

	A	$\rightarrow$	products
At start	a		0
At time t	$a-x$		x

For a first-order reaction we know that

rate of formation of products = the rate constant × concentration of reactant

If we use calculus, we can write the rate of formation of products as dx/dt, so that at time t

$$\frac{dx}{dt} = k(a-x)$$

Rearranging,

$$k\,dt = \frac{dx}{(a-x)}$$

Now we have to integrate:

$$\int k\,dt = \int \frac{dx}{(a-x)}$$

The result is

$$kt = \ln\left(\frac{a}{a-x}\right) \qquad (1)$$

Alternatively, we have

$$\frac{a}{(a-x)} = \exp(kt)$$

or

$$(a-x) = a\exp(-kt)$$

In the main text this equation has been written

$$[A]_t = [A]_0 \exp(-kt)$$

Any one of these equations can be used to find the value of the rate constant. For example, if we rearrange equation (1) we find

$$\ln(a) - \ln(a-x) = kt$$

If we plot a graph of $\ln(a-x)$ against t we should obtain a straight line. The slope is $-k$, from which we can calculate the value of the rate constant.

The half-life of a first-order reaction occurs when $x = a/2$. Putting this into equation (1) shows that

$$kt_{1/2} = \ln 2$$

or

$$t_{1/2}=\frac{0.693}{k} \qquad \text{First-order reaction}$$

Second-order reactions

We shall deal with two possibilities. There may be one reactant, for which the rate law is $k[A]^2$; or two reactants, with the law $k[A][B]$. In the first case, the rate of the reaction will be given by

$$\frac{dx}{dt}=k(a-x)^2$$

Then

$$k\,dt=\frac{dx}{(a-x)^2}$$

which gives

$$kt=\frac{x}{a(a-x)} \qquad \text{or} \qquad kt=\frac{1}{a-x}-\frac{1}{a}$$

A graph of $x/a(a-x)$ or $1/(a-x)$ plotted against t should give a straight line of slope k.

The half-life of the reaction occurs when $x=a/2$. Then we have

$$t_{1/2}=\frac{1}{ka} \qquad \text{Second-order reaction}$$

If there are two reactants involved, we shall assume that the concentration of B starts as b, and changes to $b-x$ at time t. Similarly, the concentration of A is initially a and changes to $a-x$. During the reaction we have

$$\frac{dx}{dt}=k(a-x)(b-x)$$

Rearranging, we have

$$k\,dt=\frac{dx}{(a-x)(b-x)}$$

The integration of the right-hand side can be done by the method of parts. The result is

$$kt=\frac{1}{a-b}\ln\left(\frac{b(a-x)}{a(b-x)}\right)$$

Unless you are doing a particularly advanced chemistry course you will not need to use this equation.

(b) *Second-order reactions*

Graphs of concentration against time for a second-order reaction are also curves. However, they are not exponentials, and do not have a constant half-life. A typical graph is shown in Figure 80.3, which shows the results of the reaction of the ester, ethyl ethanoate, with sodium hydroxide. 25 cm^3 portions of the reaction mixture are withdrawn at fixed time intervals and titrated with dilute acid. The volume of the acid used is a measure of the concentration of sodium hydroxide remaining at the given time. The results have been idealised so that you can see the method of working more easily. Real experimental results rarely work out quite so well.

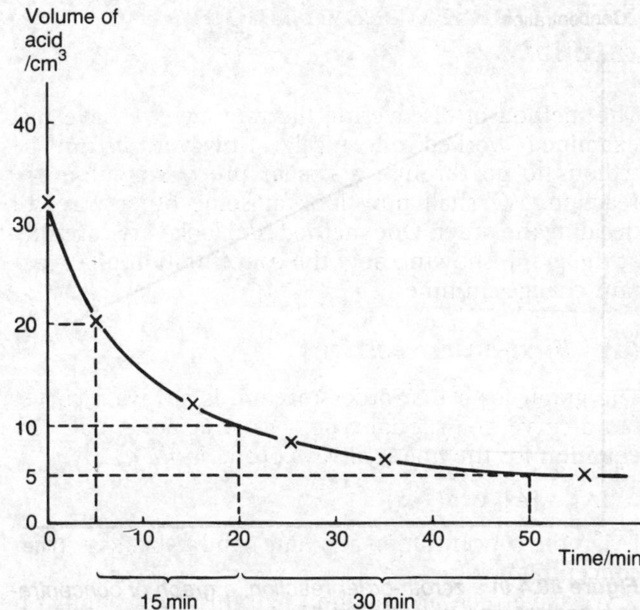

***Figure 80.3** A second-order reaction does not have a constant half-life. In this case the change from 20 to 10 cm³ takes 15 min. If this were a first-order reaction, the change from 10 to 5 cm³ should also take 15 min; rather it takes 30 min*

If you look closely at the graph, you will see that the half-life is not constant. The change from 20 to 10 cm^3 takes 15 min, the change from 10 to 5 cm^3 takes 30 min. In this case the half-life depends on the concentration of the sodium hydroxide.

Panel 80.1 shows you that for a second-order reaction:

$$t_{1/2}=\frac{1}{k[A]_t} \qquad \text{Second-order reaction}$$

Here $[A]_t$ is the concentration of the reactant at the *beginning* of the period in which the half-life is measured. In our example, for the change from 20 to 10 cm^3, and assuming that 20 cm^3 of the acid corresponds to a concentration of hydroxide ion of 0.1 mol dm^{-3}, we have

$$15\text{ min}=\frac{1}{k\times 0.1\text{ mol dm}^{-3}}$$

which gives

$$k=0.67\text{ dm}^3\text{ mol}^{-1}\text{ min}^{-1}$$

Similarly, for the period from 10 to 5 cm^3,

$$30\text{ min}=\frac{1}{k\times 0.05\text{ mol dm}^{-3}}$$

which gives the same value for k.

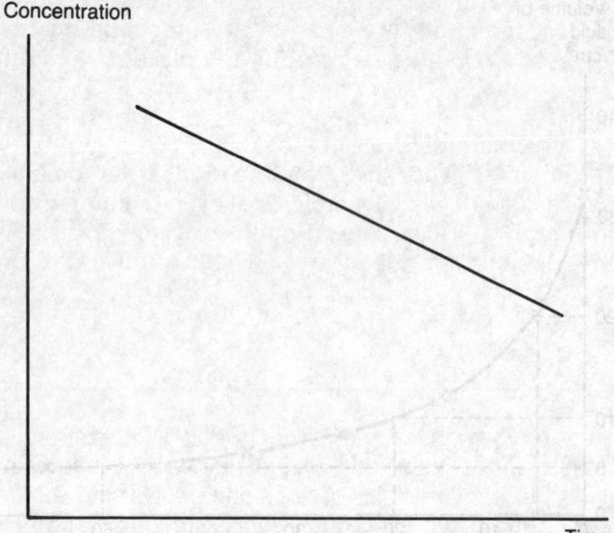

Figure 80.4 In a zeroth-order reaction, a graph of concentration against time is a straight line (compare Figure 79.2). In both these graphs we assume that the concentration of one of the reactants is being measured

(c) *Zeroth-order reactions*

It is easy to spot a zeroth-order reaction because the rate stays constant even though the reactant is being used up. This behaviour shows up on a graph of concentration against time as a straight line (Figure 80.4).

The slope of the line is constant, which means that the rate is constant. You will find an explanation of how zeroth-order reactions come about in the next unit.

80.5 Look carefully at the graphs in Figure 80.5 and discover the orders of the reactions. They might be zeroth, first or second order.

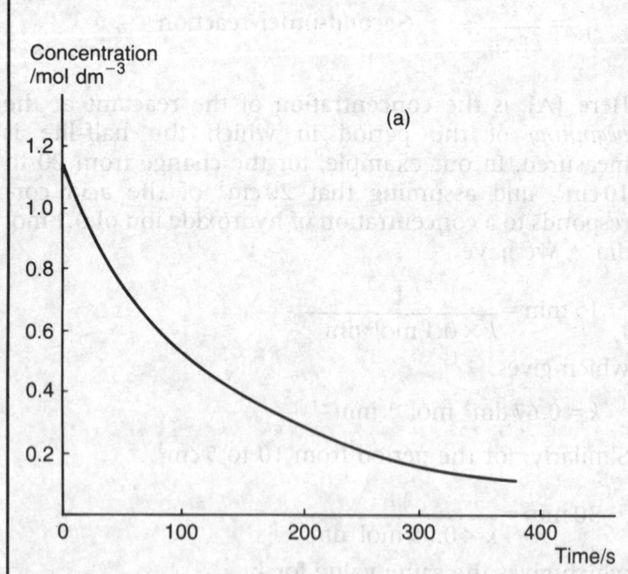

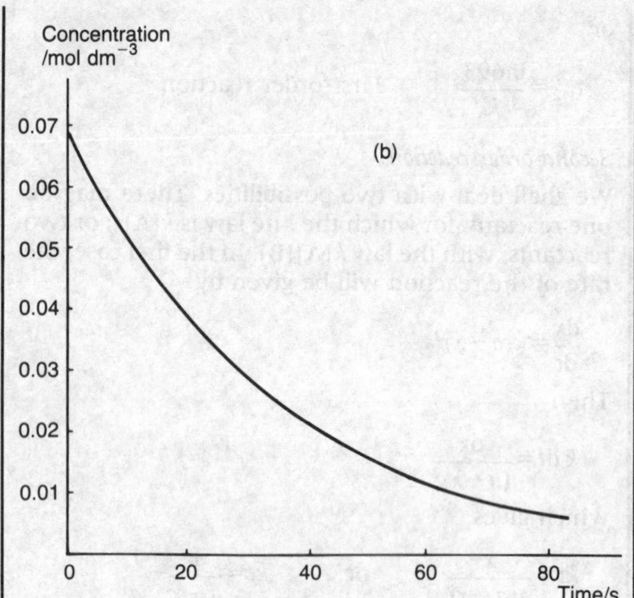

Figure 80.5 Graphs for question 80.5

80.6 Draw two axes of a graph. The vertical axis should be labelled 'rate of reaction'. The horizontal axis should be labelled 'concentration of reactant'. (The units and scales are unimportant.) On the graph, sketch lines that show how the rate varies with concentration for (i) a zeroth-order reaction, (ii) a first-order reaction, (iii) a second-order reaction.

80.4 The contribution of individual orders to the overall rate law

Even if we know that a reaction is second order overall, we do not necessarily know the orders with respect to the individual reactants. There is a method that can help us out of the difficulty. The reaction is performed a number of times, and the initial rate measured. (The initial rate can be found from a graph, as in section 80.2.) However in each experiment one of the reactants has its concentration changed. The series of results can be put into a chart, as shown in Table 80.2. Here we assume that there are two reactants, A and B, combining to make a product, C. We can represent the reaction as

$$A + B \rightarrow C$$

Table 80.2. Some initial rates of reaction for a reaction between A and B

Experiment	[A] /mol dm^{-3}	[B] /mol dm^{-3}	*Initial rate* /mol dm^{-3} s^{-1}
1	0.1	0.1	0.02
2	0.1	0.2	0.04
3	0.2	0.1	0.04
4	0.2	0.2	0.08

The initial rate of production of C has been measured. If we look at experiments 1 and 2, we see that [A] remains constant while [B] doubles. We can also see that the rate doubles. Clearly A cannot be responsible for the change, so it must be caused by the change in [B]. A reaction whose rate doubles if the concentration of the reagent doubles must be a first-order reaction, i.e.

$$\text{rate} \propto [B]$$

To discover how the rate changes with [A] we need to find two experiments in which [A] changes but [B] remains constant. Experiments 1 and 3 are suitable. Here, as [A] doubles, the rate also doubles. Therefore the reaction is also first order in A. Combining the two results, we have the rate law for the reaction:

$$\text{rate} = k[A][B]$$

It is a second-order reaction overall.

(You may have realised that the numbers in the table were deliberately kept simple. Real experimental results do not always fit a pattern quite so readily; you may have to look for the nearest whole number for the orders.)

80.7 Table 80.3 gives the initial rate for a reaction between two chemicals X and Y giving a product, Z. (The results are subject to a little experimental error.)

(i) What is the order with respect to X?

(ii) What is the order with respect to Y?

(iii) What is the overall order, and the rate law?

Table 80.3. Initial rates of reaction for a reaction between X and Y

Experiment	[X] /mol dm^{-3}	[Y] /mol dm^{-3}	*Initial rate* /mol dm^{-3} s^{-1}
1	0.01	0.02	0.12
2	0.01	0.03	0.12
3	0.04	0.07	1.90
4	0.03	0.09	1.10

80.8 Under certain conditions the reaction between thiosulphate ions and hydrogen ions is first order in each of them, i.e. rate $= k[S_2O_3^{2-}][H^+]$. A student measured the initial rate of the reaction four times using the combinations of solutions shown in Table 80.4. Write down the actual concentrations of both ions in each experiment, and hence determine the value of the rate in terms of k. (Hint: you will have to think carefully about the difference between concentration and volume.)

Table 80.4. Data for question 80.8

Experiment	*Solution of thiosulphate ions*		*Solution of hydrogen ions*	
	Concentration /mol dm^{-3}	*Volume* /cm^3	*Concentration* /mol dm^{-3}	*Volume* /cm^3
A	0.1	25	0.01	25
B	0.1	50	0.01	50
C	0.1	100	0.01	100
D	0.1	100	0.01	25

Answers

80.1 The Arrhenius equation, $k = A\exp(-E_a/RT)$.

80.2 Five (2 + 1 + 2).

80.3 Rate $= k[A]^2$.

80.4 No. The statement is true for first-order reactions, but not for others. See Table 80.1.

80.5 In the second graph you should find that there is a constant half-life of about 23 s. Therefore the curve is an exponential and the reaction is first order. The first graph does not have a constant half-life. Neither is it a straight line, hence it is neither first nor zeroth order. At this level of chemistry we can assume it is a second-order reaction.

80.6 Your graph should look like Figure 80.6. For a zeroth-order reaction, the rate is constant even though the concentration changes. Therefore we have a horizontal line. In a first-order reaction, the rate is directly proportional to the concentration. This gives a

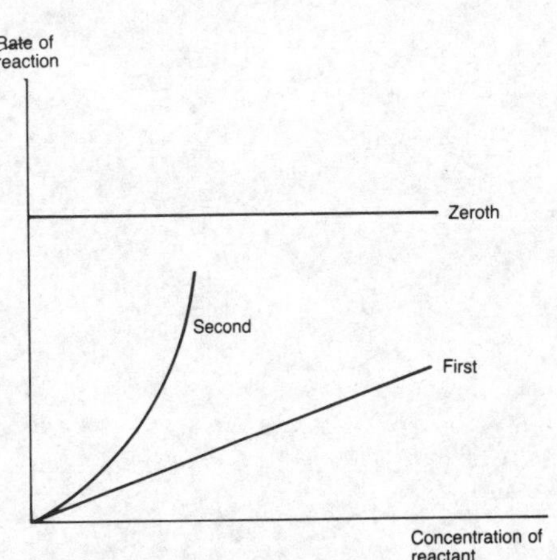

Figure 80.6 *The graph for answer to question 80.6. (This question was based on: Lowry, R. S. and Ferguson, H. J. C. (1975).* Chemistry: An Integrated Approach, *Pergamon, Oxford, figure 17.2, p. 195)*

Answers – contd.

straight line at an angle (like a graph of $y=x$ or $y=2x$, etc.). The angle is unimportant; it depends on the rate constant. A second-order reaction depends on the square of concentration. This means that the line is a curve.

80.7 (i), (ii) The key to this question is to notice from experiments 1 and 2 that while [X] is constant and [Y] changes, the rate does *not* change. This tells us that the rate is independent of [Y], i.e. it is zeroth order in Y. Therefore, we can ignore the [Y] in finding the order with respect to X. Comparing either experiment 1 or 2 with experiment 3 shows that as [X] increases by 4, the rate goes up by about 16 times. That is, the reaction is second order in X, i.e. the rate depends on $[X]^2$. If you compare experiment 4 with either 1 or 2 you will find the effect of trebling [X] is to increase the rate by a factor of 9, which again tells us that the reaction is second order in X.

(iii) The overall order is second (2+0), and the rate law is rate $= k[X]^2$.

80.8 The key thing to remember is that the rate will change if the *concentrations* of the reagents change. In experiments A, B and C the concentrations of the thiosulphate and hydrogen ions remain the same, although they are half the values stated in the table. For example, in experiment A, when the two solutions are mixed, the total volume becomes 50 cm^3. This is twice the volume of each of the separate solutions, so their concentrations are halved. The same thing happens in experiments B and C. However, in experiment D, the total volume is 125 cm^3. The concentration of the thiosulphate ions will go down by a factor of 100/125. The concentration of hydrogen ions will be reduced by a factor 25/125. Hence, because the reaction is first order in both reactants, the rates will be:

experiments A, B, C

$$\text{rate} = k \times (0.1/2)(0.01/2) = k \times 2.5 \times 10^{-4}$$

experiment D

$$\text{rate} = k \times (0.1 \times 100/125)(0.01 \times 25/125)$$
$$= k \times 1.6 \times 10^{-4}$$

Units of rate in both cases are mol $dm^{-1} s^{-1}$.

UNIT 80 SUMMARY

- A rate law is of the form: rate $= k[A]^x[B]^y[C]^z$, where [A], [B], [C] are concentrations of the reactants, and x, y, z are the orders of the reaction with respect to A, B, C. The overall order $= x+y+z$.
- Zeroth-order reaction: rate $= k$, independent of concentration.
- First-order reaction: rate $= k[A]$.
- Second-order reaction: rate $= k[A][B]$ or $k[A]^2$ or $k[B]^2$.
- Third-order reaction: rate $= k[A][B][C]$, or $k[A]^2[B]$ or $k[A]^3$, etc.
- First-order reactions:
  - (i) Have constant half-life, $t_{1/2} = 0.693/k$.
  - (ii) Show exponential change with time, $[A]_t = [A]_0 \exp(-kt)$.

81

Reaction mechanisms

81.1 What is a reaction mechanism?

The mechanism of a reaction is the explanation of *how* a reaction takes place. For example, we might find out which bonds are broken, what happens in the transition state, and whether the reaction takes place in one, or more than one, stage. Often it is possible to think of several mechanisms for a single reaction. The task of the chemist is to perform experiments that will help to discover which mechanism gives the better explanation. One of the fascinations of studies of mechanisms is that molecules appear to have the remarkable facility to change the way they react depending on circumstances. For example, a mechanism that explains the reactions of gases at moderate pressures will not fit at low pressures; a mechanism for a reaction in water may not explain the same reaction if it is carried out in another solvent.

Working out a mechanism for a reaction can be very challenging, and fascinating for those people who like puzzles. However, it is not only the intrinsic interest of mechanisms that drives chemists to study them. Advances in biochemistry, medicine and industrial chemistry often rely on an understanding of mechanisms to produce new chemicals, or to make known chemicals more efficiently.

81.2 Bonds can break in two ways

There are two ways a covalent bond can break. They are called *heterolysis* and *homolysis*.

(a) *Heterolysis*

This is when one of the atoms gains both electrons forming the bond. This atom now has one more electron than it started with, and becomes negatively charged. The other atom is left with one less electron than it started with, and becomes positively charged. (We assume that the covalent bond was made by each atom supplying one electron.) We can show heterolysis like this:

$$A \overset{\bullet}{\times} B \longrightarrow A^+ + B\overset{\bullet}{\times}^-$$

or like this:

$$A \overset{\bullet}{\times} B \longrightarrow A\overset{\bullet}{\times}^- + B^+$$

All other things being equal, the atom that has the negative charge will be the most electronegative of the two.

An example of heterolysis is where 2-methyl-2-iodopropane undergoes the change

$$(H_3C)_3C\overset{\bullet}{\times}I \longrightarrow (H_3C)_2\overset{\oplus}{C}CH_3 + I\overset{\bullet}{\times}^{\ominus}$$

(b) *Homolysis*

Homolysis is a more 'democratic' way of bond breaking. Here both atoms keep one of the two electrons. As a result they end up as neutral atoms:

$$A \overset{\bullet}{\times} B \longrightarrow A\cdot + B\times$$

The electron left over on each atom is not paired with another electron. Atoms like this are called *free radicals*. We shall show a free radical by putting a single dot next to the symbol of the atom, like this: X· . Free radicals are very reactive. Owing to its unpaired electron, it often seems that a radical's one purpose in life is to react with other atoms or molecules.

The study of free radicals has a long history. One of the earliest methods of detecting them was invented by the German chemist Paneth in 1929. He showed that, if free radicals were passed over a thin layer of lead, the layer would disappear. The apparatus he used is illustrated in Figure 81.1.

Tetramethyl-lead(IV), $Pb(CH_3)_4$, was carried in to the apparatus by a stream of gas. When the tube was heated, a layer of lead appeared on the glass. He proposed that this was due to the tetramethyl-lead(IV) undergoing homolysis:

$$Pb(CH_3)_4(g) \rightarrow Pb(s) + 4CH_3\cdot(g)$$

methyl radicals

If the position of heating was moved closer to the entrance to the apparatus, a new layer of lead appeared at the point of heating. However, equally interesting

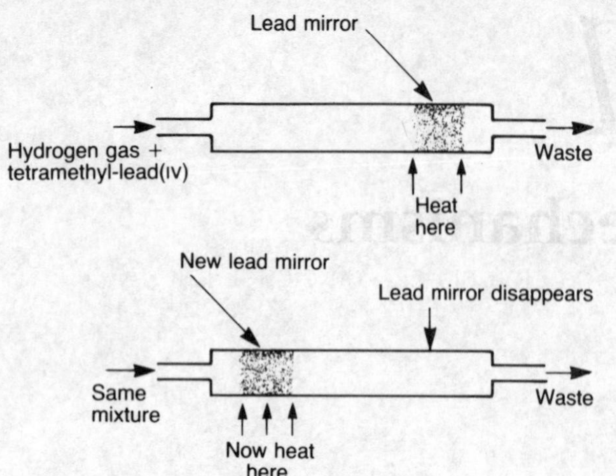

***Figure 81.1** The experiment performed by F. Paneth in 1929, which provided evidence for the existence of free radicals*

was the fact that the first layer disappeared. This was the result of the methyl radicals recombining with the lead:

$$Pb(s) + 4CH_3\cdot(g) \rightarrow Pb(CH_3)_4(g)$$

There are more sophisticated ways of detecting radicals now. One of the most important is electron spin resonance spectroscopy.

> **81.1** Two bond energies are sometimes quoted for the bond in a chlorine molecule: 242 kJ mol^{-1} and 1150 kJ mol^{-1}. Which do you think refers to the homolytic fission and which to the heterolytic fission? Do tables of bond energies refer to homolysis or heterolysis?

81.3 The slowest step in a reaction governs the rate

A reaction that appears straightforward from its chemical equation often turns out to contain some surprises in its mechanism. A good example is the reaction of iodine with propanone. The chemical equation is

$$CH_3COCH_3(aq) + I_2(aq) \rightarrow CH_3COCH_2I(aq) + HI(aq)$$

This tells us that one mole of propanone will react with one mole of iodine to give one mole of iodopropanone and one mole of hydrogen iodide. Please be sure to notice that the equation gives us absolutely no information about how fast the reaction takes place. Nor does it tell us anything about the mechanism. It is a golden rule that:

> **The chemical equation tells us nothing definite about the rate or mechanism of a reaction.**

Looking at the equation, it is tempting to think that the reaction of iodine with propanone takes place by molecules of iodine colliding with molecules of propanone. If so, we would expect the rate to change if we changed the concentrations of either of the reactants. We might predict the rate law to be

$$\text{rate} = k[CH_3COCH_3(aq)][I_2(aq)]$$

However, the experimental evidence is that

$$\text{rate} = k[CH_3COCH_3(aq)]$$

That is, the rate is independent of the concentration of iodine. For example, if the temperature is kept constant, the rate of the reaction is the same if we use 0.01 mol dm^{-3} or 0.1 mol dm^{-3} iodine solution. We shall now consider a mechanism that can explain the observations.

A nuclear magnetic resonance spectrometer detects the presence of hydrogen atoms in a molecule. The spectrometer shows that a sample of propanone contains hydrogen atoms attached to carbon atoms (which is what we expect). However, it also shows that a small proportion of molecules have a hydrogen atom attached to the oxygen atom. The reason for this is thought to be that, of its own accord, propanone exists in two forms (called *tautomers*), which are in equilibrium with each other:

$$\underset{\text{keto form}}{CH_3-\overset{\overset{\displaystyle O}{\|}}{C}-CH_3} \rightleftharpoons \underset{\text{enol form}}{CH_3-\overset{\overset{\displaystyle OH}{|}}{C}=CH_2}$$

The molecule with a hydrogen atom bonded to the oxygen atom has a double bond. It is well known that such molecules (e.g. alkenes) react rapidly with halogens, and it is believed that it is the enol form that reacts with iodine to give the final products:

$$CH_3-\overset{\overset{\displaystyle OH}{|}}{C}=CH_2 + I_2 \longrightarrow CH_3-\overset{\overset{\displaystyle O}{\|}}{C}-CH_2I + HI$$

Thus there are two stages in the reaction. The first is the keto form of propanone changing into the enol form. This takes place relatively slowly. Once it is made, the enol form reacts rapidly with iodine. This is a much faster reaction:

stage I	keto form → enol form	slow step
stage II	enol form + iodine → products	fast step

The next thing to understand is that:

> **The slowest step in a reaction determines the rate.**

We can see why this is by comparing this reaction with the way a computer works. The central processor might execute five million instructions each second, but it might take one second to type in a single instruction. So the effective rate would be one instruction each second.

If the computer relies on receiving instructions from the keyboard, it would be pointless buying a new computer that executed ten million instructions each second. The rate of performing instructions would still be limited by the rate of typing: the slowest step in the process.

Returning to our reaction, the conversion of the keto to the enol form of propanone is the slowest, rate determining, step. Adding more iodine has no effect on the rate because it cannot increase the rate at which the enol form is made. However, if we increase the concentration of propanone, the greater is the concentration of the enol form, and the more product will be made. This is why the rate depends on the concentration of propanone.

81.2 The reaction between hydrogen and bromine is

$H_2(g) + Br_2(g) \rightarrow 2HBr(g)$

A student predicted that the rate law would be

rate $= k[H_2(g)][Br_2(g)]$

Was the student justified in making this prediction?

81.3 The same student discovered a reaction that had the following pattern of stages involving the molecules A, B, C and D:

stage 1	$A \rightarrow B + C$	fast reaction
stage 2	$B + C \rightarrow D$	slow reaction

Which is the more likely to be the rate law: (i) rate $= k[A]$, or (ii) rate $= k[B][C]$?

81.4 Free radical reactions

Reactions between gases often involve free radicals. An example is the reaction between chlorine and a hydrocarbon like ethane. A mixture of chlorine and ethane can be kept for long periods of time at room temperature, provided it is guarded from sunlight. If sunlight, or even better (or worse, depending on your point of view) ultraviolet light, enters the mixture, there is an immediate explosion. When a reaction is sensitive to ultraviolet light it is a sure sign that free radicals are involved. The ultraviolet light has the effect of bringing about the homolytic fission (i.e. breaking) of bonds. This is the *initiation* step of the reaction. Once free radicals are let loose, the reaction proceeds very rapidly. These radicals can attack other molecules, which give rise to new radicals, which then go on to give further reactions, and so on. This is the *propagation* stage. From time to time the free radicals combine to give normal molecules. The removal of radicals from the reaction eventually brings the reaction to an end. This is the *termination* stage. We can show each of these three stages using some sample reactions:

Initiation

$Cl_2 \rightarrow 2Cl\cdot$
$CH_3CH_3 \rightarrow 2CH_3\cdot$

Propagation

$CH_3CH_3 + Cl\cdot \rightarrow CH_3CH_2Cl + H\cdot$
$CH_3CH_3 + CH_3\cdot \rightarrow CH_4 + CH_3CH_2\cdot$
$CH_3CH_2Cl + Cl\cdot \rightarrow CH_2ClCH_2Cl + H\cdot$
$CH_2ClCH_2Cl + Cl\cdot \rightarrow CH_2ClCHCl_2 + H\cdot$
$Cl_2 + H\cdot \rightarrow HCl + Cl\cdot$

Termination

$CH_3CH_2\cdot + H\cdot \rightarrow CH_3CH_3$
$CH_3CH_2\cdot + Cl\cdot \rightarrow CH_3CH_2Cl$
$CH_3\cdot + Cl\cdot \rightarrow CH_3Cl$

The contents of the reaction flask (assuming it survives the explosion) will contain a range of chloroalkanes in which the hydrogen atoms of ethane have been *substituted* by chlorine atoms. A reaction like this is called a *chain reaction* because one reaction is linked to another like the links in a chain.

Free radicals are involved in many of the chemical reactions that occur in the Earth's atmosphere. Especially, they are involved in the way in which chlorofluorocarbons (CFCs) interact with ozone (trioxygen) in the stratosphere. One of the CFCs to be found in aerosol propellants is known commercially as Freon-12. Its formula is CF_2Cl_2. Ultraviolet light can break the carbon–chlorine bonds:

$$CF_2Cl_2 \xrightarrow{hf} \cdot CF_2Cl + Cl\cdot$$

The chlorine radicals then attack ozone molecules:

$$O_3 + Cl\cdot \rightarrow ClO\cdot + O_2$$

However, ozone is also disrupted by ultraviolet light, which provides a supply of free oxygen atoms:

$$O_3 \xrightarrow{hf} O_2 + O$$

These take part in the reaction

$$ClO\cdot + O \rightarrow O_2 + Cl\cdot$$

It is this last reaction that makes CFCs so dangerous to the ozone layer. It regenerates a chlorine radical, which can react with another ozone molecule, thus repeating the entire cycle. The production of one chlorine radical from a CFC can be responsible for destroying many ozone molecules.

81.4 Free radical reactions can be controlled by adding *inhibitors*. These are molecules that combine readily with free radicals. Suggest a reason why an inhibitor added to a mixture of ethane and chlorine results in very little hexachloroethane, C_2Cl_6, being formed.

81.5 In the reaction of ethane with chlorine, try to explain why:

(i) the reaction $Cl\cdot + Cl\cdot \rightarrow Cl_2$ has little part to play as a means of chain termination;

(ii) CH_3CH_2Cl is more likely to react with a chlorine radical to make CH_2ClCH_2Cl than CH_3CHCl_2.

81.6 Use the values of bond strengths in Tables 44.2 and 44.3 to explain why the reaction

$$C_2H_6 \rightarrow C_2H_5\cdot + H\cdot$$

does not take place in the halogenation of ethane.

81.7 In recent years there has been a great deal of concern about the amount of lead compounds that are entering the atmosphere. Among other things, lead accumulates in the bodies of young children and can cause mental retardation. One of the chief sources of lead pollution is petrol. An additive that has been added to petrol by petrol companies is tetraethyl-lead(IV), $Pb(C_2H_5)_4$. Why do you think it has been added?

81.8 In his pioneering work on mass spectroscopy, F. W. Aston made the following comments on p. 129 of the second edition of his book *Mass Spectra and Isotopes* published in 1942:

> Carbon and its hydrides form well-marked groups of reference lines which were of the greatest value in developing the scale of mass . . . The second or C_2 group 24–C_2, 25–C_2H also appears frequently, derived from hydrocarbons in the wax and grease used in the joints of the apparatus . . . The higher groups C_3 and C_4 appear, for some obscure reason, when metallic methyls and carbonyls are present.

What is the 'obscure reason' of which Aston was unaware?

81.5 Mechanisms of the hydrolysis of halogenoalkanes

If iodomethane, CH_3I, reacts with hydroxide ions, it is converted into methanol, CH_3OH. The chemical equation is

$$OH^- + CH_3I \rightarrow CH_3OH + I^-$$

The rate law is found to be

$$\text{rate} = k[CH_3I][OH^-]$$

The hydroxide ion is not only negatively charged, it carries three lone pairs of electrons. Ions or molecules with one or more lone pairs very often seek out centres of positive charge. They are called *nucleophiles*. Hydroxide ions are powerful nucleophiles, and the attack by a hydroxide ion on iodomethane is an example of a nucleophilic attack. One of the lone pairs on the hydroxide ion begins to make a bond to the carbon atom, and at the same time the carbon to iodine bond begins to weaken. Mid-way through the process, a transition state is formed like that shown in Figure 81.2.

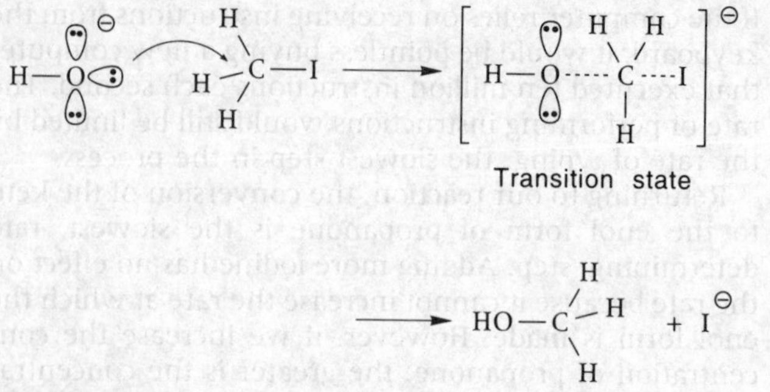

H—O⊖ + H₃C—I → [H—O····C····I]⊖ Transition state → HO—CH₃ + I⊖

***Figure 81.2** The broken lines in the transition state show bonds that are in the process of making or breaking. If the C—OH bond strengthens, then products will be made. If, on the other hand, it weakens and the C—I bond strengthens, then the reactants will be made again*

This transition state is made from two molecules (we shall use the word 'molecule' to stand for any reacting particle, be it an atom, ion or true molecule). A single step reaction that has a transition state made from two molecules is said to have a *molecularity* of 2.

In some cases the transition state breaks apart, returning to reactant molecules. In other cases the iodine leaves the transition state as an iodide ion, leaving the OH group firmly bonded to the carbon atom. This conversion of the transition state into products is assisted by virtue of the iodine ion being a *good leaving group*. Iodine tends to leave a molecule more easily than, say, a chlorine atom partly because the carbon–iodine bond is relatively weak, and partly because the iodide ion often fits neatly into the surrounding solvent molecules.

The result of the reaction is that the iodide atom is substituted by an OH group. We now have three pieces of information about this reaction: it involves a *s*ubstitution, a *n*ucleophilic attack and has a molecularity of 2. This is summarised by calling the reaction an S_N2 *reaction*.

Now compare this with the reaction of 2-iodo-2-methylpropane, $(CH_3)_3CI$, with sodium hydroxide. The equation for the reaction is not unlike the previous one:

$$OH^- + (CH_3)_3CI \rightarrow (CH_3)_3COH + I^-$$

However, the rate law is

$$\text{rate} = k[(CH_3)_3CI]$$

The fact that the rate does not depend on the concentration of hydroxide ions tells us that hydroxide ions cannot take part in the rate determining step.

The 2-iodo-2-methylpropane molecule spontaneously ionises. The positive ion produced is called a *carbocation*. (Carbocations were once called carbonium ions.) The formation of the carbocation is the slow step in the reaction (Figure 81.3). Therefore the ionisation step determines the rate of the reaction. Once the carbocation appears in the solution, it can be attacked quickly by neighbouring negatively charged hydroxide ions.

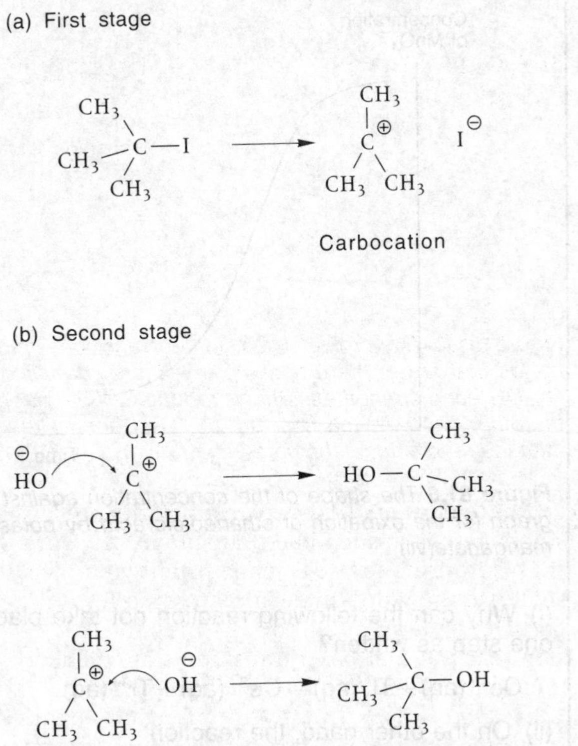

(a) First stage

$$(CH_3)_3C{-}I \longrightarrow (CH_3)_3C^{\oplus} \quad I^{\ominus}$$

Carbocation

(b) Second stage

$$HO^{\ominus} + (CH_3)_3C^{\oplus} \longrightarrow HO{-}C(CH_3)_3$$

$$(CH_3)_3C^{\oplus} + {}^{\ominus}OH \longrightarrow (CH_3)_3C{-}OH$$

***Figure 81.3** The mechanism of the reaction between hydroxide ions and 2-iodo-2-methylpropane. (a) The first stage is the autoionisation of the 2-iodo-2-methylpropane. (b) The second stage is attack on the carbocation by hydroxide ions. This can take place from either side of the carbocation. In this example the same product is made; in other cases, optical isomers are formed*

This result of the reaction is still a *s*ubstitution of an iodide ion by an OH group. Similarly it involves a *n*ucleophilic attack by hydroxide ions. However, the transition state consists of just one species, so the molecularity is *1*. All this is summed up by calling this an *S_N1 reaction*.

> **81.9** The transition state in the S_N1 reaction we considered involves a negative ion separating from a positive ion (carbocation). Suggest a reason why the rate of an S_N1 reaction like this is much faster if it is done in a polar rather than a non-polar solvent.

81.6 The influence of catalysts

You should know that catalysts provide an alternative pathway for a reaction, and that the new route has a lower activation energy than the original reaction. In this section we shall take a closer look at how some catalysts achieve this feat. In Unit 78 we said that there are two broad categories of catalyst: *heterogeneous* and *homogeneous*. Solids are heterogeneous catalysts. The reactions they catalyse take place on their surfaces. A good example is the reaction between ethene and hydrogen:

$$C_2H_4(g) + H_2(g) \rightarrow C_2H_6(g)$$

This reaction is catalysed by nickel. At particular sites on the surface of a piece of nickel the atoms are arranged in such a way that the π cloud of electrons can overlap with an empty d orbital (Figure 81.4). (Nickel is a transition metal, and these metals often have empty d orbitals; see Unit 105.) The ethene molecule is held to the surface, where it reacts with a hydrogen molecule.

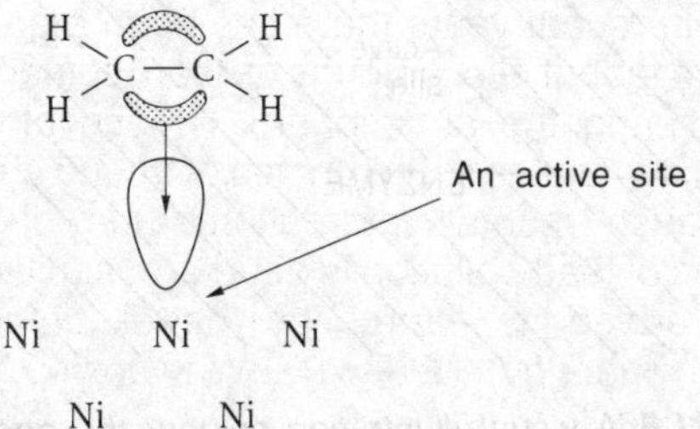

***Figure 81.4** Ethene molecules can bond through their π electrons. Vacant d orbitals on transition elements such as nickel can bond to ethene molecules. The π orbital on an ethene molecule overlaps with the d orbital*

The places on the surface where the geometry is just right for the molecules to sit are called *active sites*. The effectiveness of a solid catalyst is increased if it is present as a powder. A powder has a much larger surface area than a large lump. By increasing the surface area, the number of active sites is increased.

Enzymes are extremely efficient biologically active catalysts. They are homogeneous catalysts, reacting in solution in body fluids. Enzymes are proteins, which, from a distance, appear as a long tangled chain of atoms consisting mainly of carbon, hydrogen, nitrogen and oxygen. On closer inspection, using X-ray diffraction, the structure of an enzyme shows up. The geometry is always very complicated, but a major feature that they have in common is a region into which only molecules of a very particular shape and size will fit. This region is the *active site* of the enzyme. Generally, only *one* type of molecule will fit the active site. This means that enzymes are much more specific than other catalysts. For example, only hydrogen peroxide molecules will fit the active site of catalase. The molecule that fits the active site is called the *substrate*. Figure 81.5 will give you a visual impression of how enzymes work.

Enzymes have a feature in common with many other catalysts. They can be *poisoned*. A catalyst is poisoned if its active site(s) become clogged by an unwanted molecule. Hydrogen sulphide is a very efficient poison for metal catalysts, and metal ions will often poison enzymes. A great deal of money has to be spent in industry to ensure that reactants are free of poisons before they are admitted to the reaction chamber containing a catalyst. Also, enzymes are particularly susceptible to damage from too much heat. They are not designed to work at temperatures much above body temperature, 37° C. As the temperature rises, the struc-

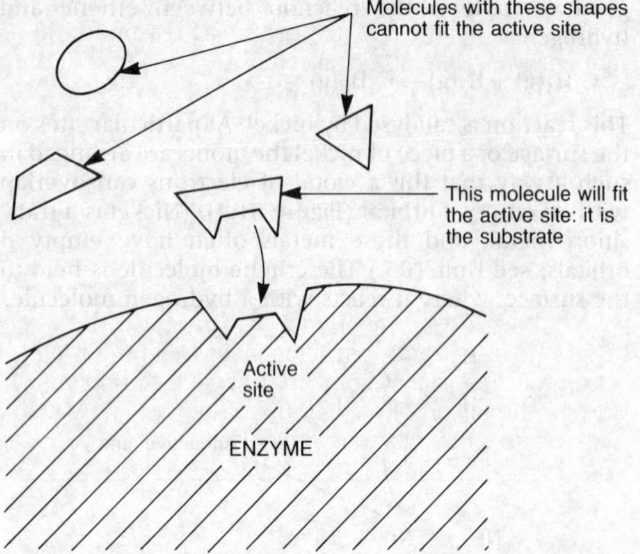
Molecules with these shapes cannot fit the active site
This molecule will fit the active site: it is the substrate
Active site
ENZYME

Figure 81.5 *A visual illustration of how the geometry of an active site will only fit one type of substrate (in most cases)*

ture of the protein chain around the active site changes. Very soon the change becomes irreversible. The delicate geometry of the atoms that hold the substrate in position is wrecked, and the enzyme stops working; it is said to be denatured. In living things, changes of this nature will lead to death.

81.10 Imagine a reaction that only takes place when molecules of a gas are in contact with the surface of a solid.

(i) Why is it that the reaction is likely to be zeroth order with respect to the gas?

(ii) Will the pressure of the gas have any influence on the order of the reaction?

81.11 The oxidation of ethanedioic acid, $C_2O_4H_2$, by manganate(VII) ions, MnO_4^-, can be followed in a colorimeter or by titration. The graph of concentration of MnO_4^- plotted against time looks like that in Figure 81.6.

(i) Describe how the rate changes during the reaction.

(ii) Does the graph fit one of the simple rate laws?

(iii) Can you suggest a reason for the shape of the graph.

(Hint: Transition metal ions are able to change their oxidation states quite easily. This allows them to behave as catalysts in redox reactions, i.e. reactions in which electrons are lost or gained.)

81.12 Thallium has two major oxidation states, corresponding to the ions Tl^+ and Tl^{3+}. Cerium exists as Ce^{3+} or Ce^{4+}.

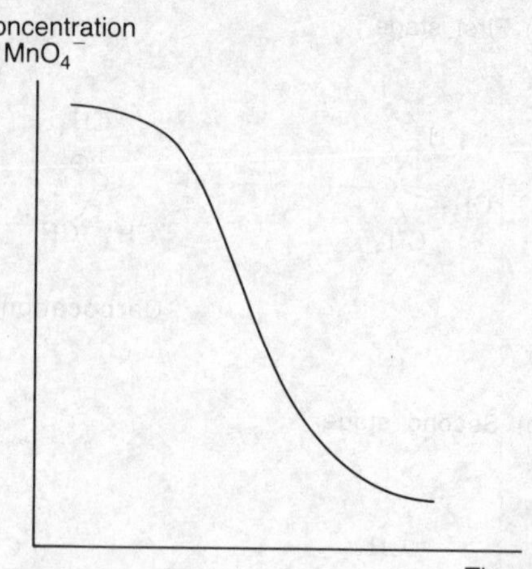
Concentration of MnO_4^-
Time

Figure 81.6 *The shape of the concentration against time graph for the oxidation of ethanedioic acid by potassium manganate(VII)*

(i) Why can the following reaction not take place in one step as written?

$$Ce^{4+}(aq) + Tl^{+}(aq) \rightarrow Ce^{3+}(aq) + Tl^{3+}(aq)$$

(ii) On the other hand, the reaction

$$2Ce^{4+}(aq) + Tl^{+}(aq) \rightarrow 2Ce^{3+}(aq) + Tl^{3+}(aq)$$

can occur. Assuming the reaction takes place in one step, why is the reaction likely to be very slow? (Hint: think about the collisions that have to take place.)

(iii) Manganese can exist in solution as Mn^{2+}, Mn^{3+} and Mn^{4+} ions. Try to work out how Mn^{2+} ions can catalyse the reaction in (ii). You might like to know that Ce^{4+} can oxidise Mn^{2+} and Mn^{3+} ions, and Mn^{4+} can oxidise Tl^+ ions.

81.13 It has been said that the role of the chlorine radical in the destruction of ozone is an excellent example of catalysis. Do you agree?

81.7 The kinetics of enzyme reactions

Enzyme reactions are so important that it is sensible to know something of their kinetics. The first thing that you will discover if you use an enzyme in a reaction is that the rate increases with the concentration of the enzyme. Similarly, the rate increases with the substrate concentration, but only up to a certain point. This behaviour is shown in Figure 81.7.

There is a limit to the rate of the reaction. The reason for this behaviour is that the active sites become saturated with substrate molecules. When, on average, all the available active sites have substrate molecules in place, adding more substrate to the solution will have no effect.

Enzyme reactions are also sensitive to pH. Usually there is an optimum pH at which the rate is a maxi-

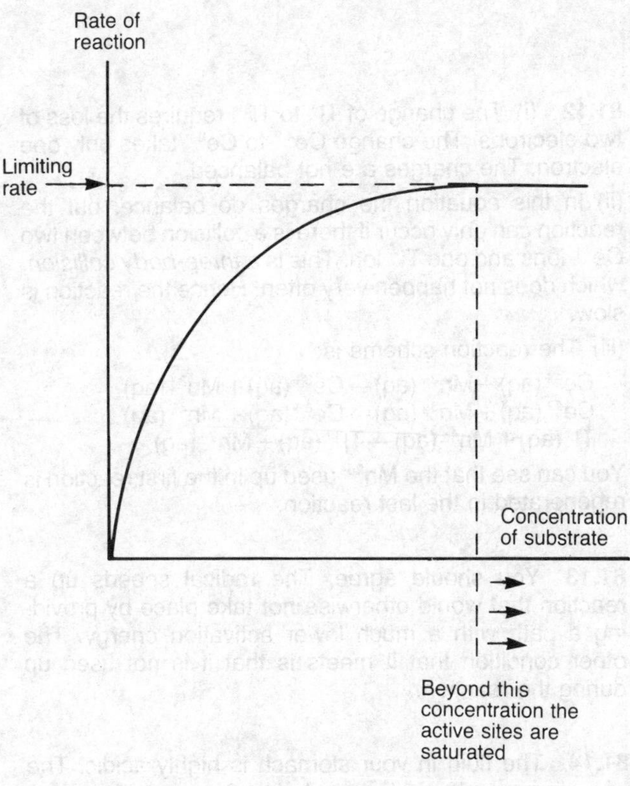

Figure 81.7 *How the rate of an enzyme reaction varies with the concentration of substrate molecules*

mum. If the pH is increased or decreased from the optimum value, the rate decreases. The reason for this is that enzymes, like other proteins, are built from amino acids. These acids have the ability to lose or gain protons. (You will find out why in Unit 123.) If an enzyme gains a proton, its charge increases by +1; if it loses a proton, its charge increases by −1. Even small changes in charge around the active site can prevent the substrate entering or leaving.

81.14 The enzyme pepsin is involved in the breakdown of food in the stomach. Estimate the optimum pH for the action of pepsin. (If you do not know how your stomach works, ask a biologist.)

Answers

81.1 The smaller value is for the homolytic fission. Heterolytic fission requires a process very much like ionisation to occur. This requires a great deal of energy. The tables refer to homolysis.

81.2 No. It is not right to predict a rate law from the chemical equation. You might be surprised by the actual rate law:

$$\text{rate} = k_1[H_2][Br_2]^{3/2}/(k_2[Br_2] + [HBr])$$

(The mechanism involves free radicals.)

81.3 Stage 2 is the rate determining step, so we would expect

$$\text{rate} = k[B][C]$$

81.4 The inhibitor will react with free radicals more easily than the other molecules. It will prevent the propagation stage becoming too elaborate. Because there are initially a lot of ethane molecules and chlorine radicals, it is quite likely that C_2H_5Cl molecules will form, but as the inhibitor gets to work, few radicals will be left to convert C_2H_5Cl into $C_2H_4Cl_2$ and virtually none will live long enough to make C_2Cl_6.

81.5 (i) The chlorine molecule must have had enough energy to split apart in the first place. So, unless the chlorine radicals lose some energy, e.g. by collision with other molecules, they will promptly fly apart again.

(ii) If you were an incoming chlorine radical you would 'see' three hydrogen atoms at one end, and two at the other. On this basis you would have a 3:2 chance of reacting to make CH_2ClCH_2Cl rather than CH_3CHCl_2. This ignores other effects such as the size and electronegativity of the chlorine atom at one end.

81.6 The bond strengths in kJ mol^{-1} are: C—C, 346; Cl—Cl, 342; C—H, 413. Thus the C—H bond needs more energy to break.

81.7 Like $Pb(CH_3)_4$, tetraethyl-lead(IV) converts into radicals when it is heated. The presence of radicals in the air and petrol vapour mixture in the pistons improves the rate of reaction. Therefore it gives better performance. Fortunately, most car engines have now been designed to use lead-free petrol.

81.8 The fragments of higher relative molecular mass (the C_3 and C_4) probably came about through the production of free radicals, such as $CH_3\cdot$, from the metallic methyls. The free radicals would have combined with other carbon hydrides to give a variety of more complicated molecules.

81.9 The carbocations and iodide ions can be solvated by polar molecules (very much like an ionic substance dissolving in water). The solvation encourages the formation of the ions, so there are more of them in a polar solvent. This results in the rate increasing. A non-polar solvent cannot solvate the ions, so does nothing to favour the S_N1 reaction.

Answers – contd.

81.10 (i) The rate is likely to be controlled by the number of active sites on the surface of the solid, not the concentration of the gas.

(ii) However, at very low pressures, it may be that not all the active sites are occupied. If so, we would expect an increase in pressure (concentration) of the gas to increase the rate. The reaction would be likely to be first order in the gas at low pressure.

81.11 (i) The rate is slow at the beginning and then greatly speeds up, until it becomes slow again near the end of the reaction.

(ii) No.

(iii) This graph is typical of reactions in which the products, or intermediates, catalyse the reaction. We say that the reaction is autocatalysed. In this case manganese ions in a number of different oxidation states are produced in the reaction. As with other transition metals, these oxidation states can assist in the transfer of electrons, and hence in the oxidation of the ethanedioic acid. Initially, there are few of the intermediate oxidation states present; hence the reaction is slow. After a while, those that are made catalyse the reaction, which produces even more of them, which increases the rate even more; and so on.

81.12 (i) The change of Tl^+ to Tl^{3+} requires the loss of two electrons. The change Ce^{4+} to Ce^{3+} takes only one electron. The charges are not balanced.

(ii) In this equation the charges do balance, but the reaction can only occur if there is a collision between two Ce^{4+} ions and one Tl^+ ion. This is a *three-body collision*, which does not happen very often. Hence the reaction is slow.

(iii) The reaction scheme is:

$$Ce^{4+}(aq) + Mn^{2+}(aq) \rightarrow Ce^{3+}(aq) + Mn^{3+}(aq)$$
$$Ce^{4+}(aq) + Mn^{3+}(aq) \rightarrow Ce^{3+}(aq) + Mn^{4+}(aq)$$
$$Tl^{+}(aq) + Mn^{4+}(aq) \rightarrow Tl^{3+}(aq) + Mn^{2+}(aq)$$

You can see that the Mn^{2+} used up in the first reaction is regenerated in the last reaction.

81.13 You should agree. The radical speeds up a reaction that would otherwise not take place by providing a path with a much lower activation energy. The other condition that it meets is that it is not used up during the reaction.

81.14 The fluid in your stomach is highly acidic. The enzyme works best at around pH = 2.

UNIT 81 SUMMARY

- The mechanism of a reaction is the explanation of how a reaction takes place.
- There are two ways in which a covalent bond can break:
  - (i) Heterolysis: one of the atoms gains both electrons forming the bond.
  - (ii) Homolysis: both atoms keep one of the two electrons forming the bond.
- Free radicals are made in homolysis. These are atoms or groups with an unpaired electron. Free radicals are extremely reactive.
- Free radicals are involved in chain reactions, which occur in three steps: initiation, propagation, termination.
- The slowest step in a reaction governs the rate.
- The chemical equation tells us nothing definite about the order or mechanism of a reaction.
- Before changing into products, reactants form a transition state.
- The molecularity of a reaction is the number of species forming the transition state.
- Hydrolysis of halogenoalkanes takes place in two ways:
  - (i) S_N1, i.e. unimolecular nucleophilic substitution (one species in the transition state).
  - (ii) S_N2, i.e. bimolecular nucleophilic substitution (two species in the transition state).
- S_N1 reactions have carbocations as transition states. (Carbocations are organic groups with a positive charge.)
- Heterogeneous catalysts exist in a different state to the reactants.
- Homogeneous catalysts exist in the same state as the reactants.
- Enzymes act as homogeneous catalysts. Reactions take place at the active site of an enzyme. Only molecules of particular shapes (substrate molecules) fit the active site. This explains why enzymes only catalyse specific reactions.

Part B

INDUSTRIAL CHEMISTRY

82

The chemical industry

82.1 Why is the chemical industry important?

You can look at the chemical industry from many points of view. Some people think of it in terms of huge factories or oil refining plants giving out smoke and polluting the environment. Others see it in terms of facts and figures, profits and losses. The people who work in the industry see it as the source of their livelihoods. Whatever one's view it would be hard to exaggerate the importance of the industry. In our daily lives we cannot help but make use of chemicals. They are in the food we eat, or rather we should say that chemicals *are* the food we eat. They are the clothes we wear, the medicines we take and the immense variety of articles that we use.

This large chemical plant near Bombay in India can process 225 000 tonnes of naphtha per year. The naphtha is converted into ethene, propanone, PVC, and many other chemicals.

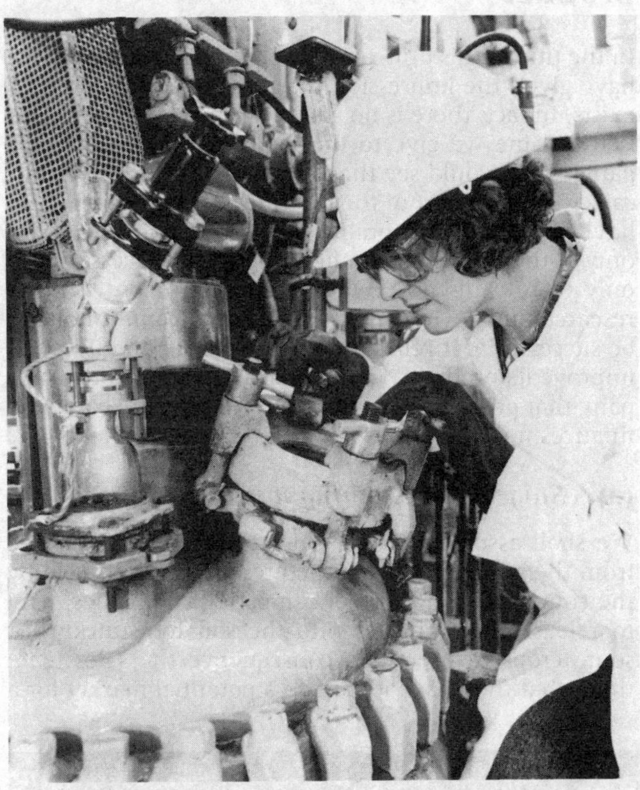

A small batch reactor used for manufacturing fine chemicals in a pilot plant. The technician is monitoring a scaled-up chemical reaction.

The properties of chemicals have been exploited by humans over thousands of years. Sometimes our knowledge of their behaviour has been put to good use, sometimes to bad; and often the effects of their use have been entirely unexpected. Whatever your view of the industry as a whole, it is impossible to avoid its influence, on individuals, on the environment and on the economy of a country. One of the signs of the economic development of a country is the state of its chemical industry. One reason for this is that the industry can take essentially simple, and often cheap, raw materials and turn them into much more valuable items. A particularly good example is the Haber process. This exploits the free supply of nitrogen in the atmosphere and converts it into ammonia, and then into fertilisers, upon which the efficient supply of food has come to rely.

Often it is the poorer nations that are the sources of the original chemicals, i.e. the *feedstock*. Traditionally these nations have exported the chemicals for processing in the sophisticated chemical plants of developed countries. The developed nations make the most money out of this arrangement because the final product can be sold at a much greater profit than the feedstock. It is for this reason that underdeveloped countries have tried to develop their own chemical industries.

82.2 The stages in producing a new product

In the title to this unit, and the previous paragraphs, we have given the impression that 'the' chemical industry exists. In fact, there is no single chemical industry. This is the name we give to the many thousands of companies that would see themselves as processing chemicals as a major part of their business. However, they all have one thing in common: they can remain successful only if they generate profits. Profits are necessary not only to reward those who invest money but to fund research and development. A company cannot hope to be successful if it relies on old technology and does not improve its products. Let us take an example of a company that produces fertilisers and see how the company finances might work.

(a) *Stage 1: researching a new product*

We shall assume that the sales team have discovered from their customers that the present fertilisers sold by the company, and those of competing companies, tend to release their nitrates into the soil too quickly for some crops to use. As a consequence the sales team think that they have identified a potential market for a new, slow release fertiliser. The size of the market is investigated and is thought large enough to warrant the development of a new slow release fertiliser.

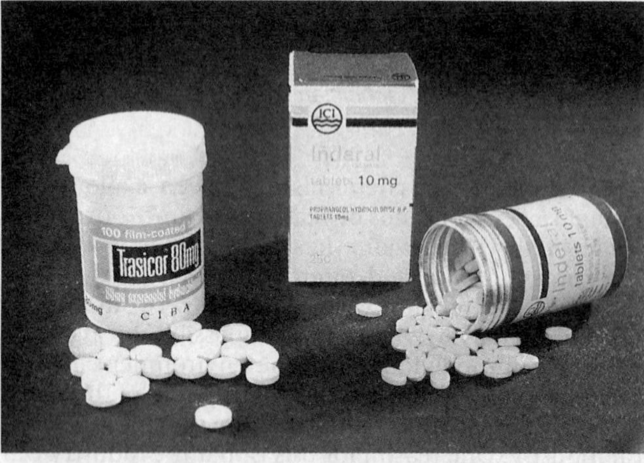

Two of the drugs used for controlling blood pressure. The manufacture of heart, and blood related, drugs is a multi-million pound business.

The research chemists are likely to spend some years on developing a fertiliser that fits, or nearly fits, the specification.

This assumes that they are successful, an outcome that is by no means certain. In other words, there is a definite risk in the venture. The money spent on the research may come to nothing. However, a wise company will not be researching only one product at a time. If it employs high quality staff, it is unlikely to fail in all its ventures.

(b) *Stage 2: moving to a pilot study*

The research done at the laboratory bench must be scaled up to a level that more closely matches the way the fertiliser will be finally manufactured. At this stage, and in the design of the final plant, the knowledge and experience of the chemical engineers is of crucial importance. They will need to calculate the amounts of feedstock required to give a specific yield of fertiliser, the cost of supplying the energy needed in the manufacture, the size of pumps, tubes, heaters, coolers and a myriad other things that have to be taken into account.

(c) *Stage 3: the decision to go ahead*

This is the stage at which the most difficult decision has to be taken. It is likely that it has taken five years since the plan to produce a new fertiliser was adopted. If an entirely new chemical plant has to be built to make the fertiliser, it may not be in operation for another two or three years. There will be the capital cost of building the plant, and on-going running costs to be taken into account. Also, the company has to be reasonably sure that the market for the product will be strong after the plant is built. This is no easy thing to decide. For example, feedstock costs might rise unpredictably, as they did some years ago when the oil producing countries all put up the price of oil. Similarly it is likely that other chemical companies are planning to produce slow release fertilisers. If there is strong competition for similar products, the price that the company can charge will be forced down, as will their potential profits. Here, again, there is an unavoidable degree of risk that has to be taken. Only experience and good information from analysts, whose job it is to predict the trends in economics and political climate, can reduce the level of risk to one that is regarded as acceptable.

(d) *Stage 4: making and selling the product*

Long before production is under way the sales team will be preparing potential customers for the arrival of the new fertiliser. They have to inform existing and potential customers of the qualities of the new product, and encourage them to try it. The skills of the sales force are as important as the more scientific ones of the chemists and chemical engineers. There is little point in produc-

The farmer is loading a fertiliser spreader. The numbers on the bag indicate that the fertiliser contains 20% nitrogen, 10% phosphorus, and 10% potassium.

ing thousands of tonnes of fertiliser each week if no one knows it exists. However, no amount of salesmanship will persuade a customer to keep buying the fertiliser if it is not effective. The quality of the product will finally decide the fate of the whole exercise.

(e) *Stage 5: review*

This is where we go back to the beginning. Reports on the fertiliser will be obtained from customers, and new or different needs identified. The whole cycle may begin on a new product. However, it could be that the review of the operation shows that there have been misjudgements, or just bad luck, and that the fertiliser cannot be sold at a profit. In this case production may cease. It is not certain that it will be stopped, even if it is making a loss, because the company may not want to lose its customers to another company. It can be best to keep the present customers so that they will buy the next, more profitable, product.

82.3 The economics of production

When a company considers starting a new manufacturing plant, the managers must carefully consider the economics of the plant. We can think of the plant in a simple way as a process that has a number of inputs and outputs. Among the key inputs are the raw materials, energy and support services. The support services will include labour, laboratory services (e.g. for quality control), security and fire services. It is a mistake to think that the only output is the major product, in this case the fertiliser. Other chemicals will be made by side reactions, and often energy is released. Usually the energy is trapped as steam at high temperature and pressure. As such it can be recycled to run electrical generators, pumps and the like. The side products will be purified and sold, provided there is a market for them. It is wasteful to run a plant that produces side products which cannot be sold. Indeed, it can be more economic to change the conditions in the production of the major product so that undesirable side reactions are suppressed, even if this means that the yield of the major product is reduced.

We can split the costs of production into two: fixed costs and variable costs. Here are examples of each:

Fixed costs	*Variable costs*
Labour	Raw materials
Maintenance	Energy
Safety	Packaging
Laboratory services	Transport
Management	Licences and patents
Depreciation	

The key difference between the two is that:

Variable costs change with the amount of product made.

Fixed costs do not change with the amount of product made.

For example, the company might employ 500 people at the plant, including laboratory, maintenance, secretarial and security staff, managers and accountants. These people will be employed for a whole year no matter whether the plant works at 100% or 50% of its capacity. On the other hand, the cost of raw materials might be cut by half if the plant works at only 50% of its capacity. Similarly, the company might have to pay another firm for the use of one of its patented reactions. The charge for this will usually depend on the quantity of chemical made by the process. This is another variable cost.

Depreciation is a cost which, unless you are in business, you might not think about. Suppose the plant costs £20 million to build and that it has a useful life of ten years. In effect the company will have suffered a loss of this £20 million during this time. Each year the plant is worth less than the previous year. The annual loss in value is the depreciation. There are several ways of calculating depreciation rates, but 20% per year is common.

To see how the economics works, let us imagine a much simplified case where the fertiliser plant involves the sums below. Only two fixed and two variable costs have been included. One extra, and a crucial one, which you will see towards the bottom of the table, is the return on capital. This is the sum that the company expects to earn over the costs of running the plant and depreciation. We can think of this as the profit. Normally a company will look upon the profit as a percentage of the money it has invested in the plant. The percentage has to be high enough to give the shareholders a reasonable return on the capital they have invested, and to fund the research and development of further products. We shall assume that the company requires a return of 15%.

Fertiliser manufacture, year 1

Capital cost £20 million; depreciation at 20% each year.
Return on capital at 15%.
Production at 100% capacity: 100 000 tonnes fertiliser.

Costs	*Sum*/£ millions
Labour	1
Depreciation	4
Raw materials	10
Energy	2
Subtotal	17
Return on capital	3
Total	20

$$\text{Price per tonne} = \frac{£20\ 000\ 000}{100\ 000} = £200$$

82.1 We appear to have worked out the price that the company must charge for its fertiliser if it is to trade profitably.

(i) Suppose that there are problems with the plant, which means that it works at only 60% of its capacity. What should the new price of the fertiliser be?

(ii) During the 1970s there was a marked increase in the cost of oil, owing to price rises imposed by the Gulf States. This had an influence on both raw material and energy costs. Assume that raw material costs double and energy costs increase five-fold compared to the figures we have used. What should be the selling price of the fertiliser in the first year?

(iii) What will be the depreciation charge in the third year of production? Assume that inflation has increased the other costs by 10% compared to the first year. What should be the price of the fertiliser?

82.4 Cash flow in the production cycle

There can be a delay of many years from the first stages of manufacturing a new product to the time when it finally comes on to the market. During this time the company will be spending money. It will find this money either by using profits from previous years, or by borrowing money from a bank that specialises in lending to chemical companies. Whichever choice is made, there is an expense involved. If the company borrows the money, it has to pay interest to the bank; if it uses its own money, it loses the interest it would have gained by investing it. The company will be willing to bear this loss for a number of years if it believes that the product will produce profits.

One of the main things that a company must do while it is developing its new products is to take out *patents*. A patent is a detailed description of the product and its method of manufacture. Most countries have a law that says that, once a patent is registered, another company or individual cannot use the method described in the patent to make the same product. In this way the company can protect itself from all the work and costs involved in research and development being used by another company. A company will also take out a copyright on a brand name to prevent imitations being sold under the same name.

However, patents have a finite lifetime, often 15 to 20 years. Once the patent has run out, other companies can enter the market using the methods developed by the original company. It is at this stage that the competition to sell a product becomes fierce. The competition drives down the price of the product as companies lower prices to persuade consumers to buy it. If the company does not make sufficient profits in the time the patent lasts, it is most unlikely to do so afterwards. Also, even while the patent is in operation, competing companies may develop very similar products with features that the original lacked. This is very common in the pharmaceutical industry, where relatively small changes can be made to molecules while maintaining the essential body chemistry.

You will find in Figure 82.1 a way of seeing how the economics of production varies through the life of a project. A negative cash flow means the company is

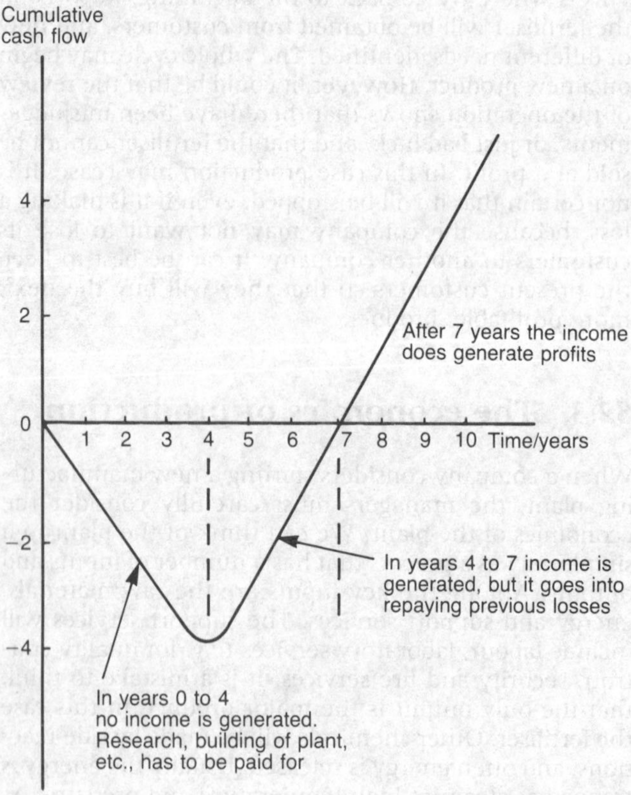

***Figure 82.1** How cash flow changes during the life of a project. (Adapted from: Heaton, C. A. (ed.) (1984).* An Introduction to Industrial Chemistry, *Leonard Hill, Glasgow, figure 4.4, p. 128)*

paying out more money than it is getting in. In the figure the graph reaches a minimum at four years. This is the time taken for research, development and construction of the plant. Only after this time is there a product to sell. Gradually the graph climbs upwards as profits are made. You can think of the profits being used to reduce the overdraft run up in the first four years. Only after seven years does the graph rise to show a positive cash flow. This is where true profits are made; the overdraft has been paid off. This happy situation only lasts for another eight years. Fifteen years from the start the patents have run out, and competition brings a decline in profits.

The price of a pharmaceutical, or any chemical, must have built into it not only the actual cost of production, but an element to pay for the years in which the product was being developed. Pharmaceutical companies are often accused of selling their drugs at inflated prices. No doubt in some cases they do so, but given the amount of testing that has to be done before a new drug can be released on to the market, the price might have to cover ten years of development work (and fund the development of yet another new product).

82.5 Running a chemical plant

There are many different types of chemical plant, but they usually use one of two methods of production. Either the chemical is made continuously, or it is made in batches. Continuous reactors are best when there is known to be a large and dependable demand for a product. Oil refineries work on a continuous basis. Crude oil is fed into the distillation towers, and the various products are directed into the catalytic crackers, polymerisation reactors and so on. Compare this with a speciality chemicals firm that makes small amounts of chemicals for research establishments in industry or universities. This type of firm may only sell 100 kg of an organic reagent each year. The chemical would be made in small batches, perhaps around 10 kg a month.

Clearly the economics and physical scale of batch and continuous methods will be different, but they have many features in common. In particular, safety is of absolute importance, as is quality control.

With the advances in automation it is possible to run a huge chemical plant with no more than a dozen workers. Temperature and pressure changes can be

Cleaning the site of the Bhopal disaster, in which at least 2500 people died.

measured by instruments directly connected to computers. The computers can be programmed to control pumps, heaters and the like so that the plant is kept running under the best conditions.

The way the reactors are controlled has a direct bearing on safety. Dangerous situations can be caused if the sensors respond too slowly, or not at all. Especially, exothermic reactions that are not cooled properly can increase their rate of reaction extremely quickly. If gases are produced, a sudden rise in pressure may fracture pipes and cause fires or explosions. Similarly, if the plant is not regularly inspected for metal fatigue, leaks can give rise to a poisonous cloud of gas escaping into the atmosphere, or to an explosion taking place.

Two accidents, one in India at Bhopal in 1984, the other in England at Flixborough in 1974, illustrate the damage that can be caused if something goes wrong. At Bhopal a cloud of poisonous gas released from a chemical works proved fatal to a large number of people in the surrounding area, and caused severe harm to many more. The cause of the accident has not been finally decided. There is evidence that the company was to blame for lack of care in monitoring the running of the plant, but the company claims that the accident was the result of sabotage. At Flixborough, caprolactam was made for use in Nylon manufacture. A leak in a pipe allowed vapour to escape into the atmosphere. The loss of vapour was not detected until too late and the entire plant was destroyed in a huge explosion.

82.6 Designing a chemical plant

The design of a chemical plant is sometimes as much an art as a science. The overall aim is to increase production while minimising costs, and at the same time keeping a good margin for safety. It is the chemical engineer who has the task of balancing a number of criteria to ensure the most efficient running. For example, chemicals tend to react faster at high temperatures. However, if the reaction is exothermic and involves an equilibrium, a high temperature will hinder the formation of products. Often a compromise must be reached. Even if a high temperature is best for chemical reasons, for reasons of economy it may be best to work at a lower temperature. It may cost more to provide the energy to increase the temperature than is returned by the profit on the sale of the extra chemical produced.

Similarly, gaseous reactions may be most effective at high pressures, but it is far more costly to build a plant to withstand high pressures. Indeed, a high pressure plant is also more expensive to run.

Energy costs are one of the most important variables in the design and running of a plant. Large chemical sites are often run as *integrated* concerns. This means that, for example, the heat from an exothermic reaction in one part of the plant may be used to produce steam that drives turbines, compressors or pumps used in another part of the plant. Likewise an endothermic reaction may be used to cool fluid, which in turn cools gases from an exothermic reaction.

82.2 Why is it more expensive to run a plant at high pressures?

82.3 Hydrogen is a feedstock for many industrial processes, not the least of which is the Haber process. Why is the hydrogen invariably made on the site rather than transported from another chemical plant? (Other chemicals, e.g. sulphur, are transported, so there must be something special about hydrogen that makes it uneconomic.)

82.7 Energy and mass balances

There are two guiding principles that must hold true for the changes that take place in a chemical process. They are as follows:

(a) *Energy balance*

The total energy put in to the process must equal the total energy taken out. This is just the law of conservation of energy being restated in a different way. You should realise that it can be quite tricky doing the sums to take account of all the bond energies, the heat changes during the reactions and the energy requirements to raise steam, run the pumps and so on. However, this type of calculation has to be done if the overall energy requirements of the plant are to be costed.

(b) *Mass balance*

The total masses of the reactants should equal the total masses of the products. This is true for the entire process, and for each individual stage. In previous units we have done calculations in which we find out how many moles of products can be obtained from a given number of moles of reactants. In the chemical industry such calculations are extremely important because the design of the plant depends upon them, as do calculations of profitability. Also, the mass balance can help to solve problems that crop up during the analysis of the various processes.

82.4 One of the most important aspects of designing a chemical plant is deciding where to put it. This question asks you to think about some of the issues involved when a hypothetical company, Dream Chemical Co., seeks a place to build a new plant.

Dream Chemical Co. has a problem. It started life as a paint manufacturer, but in recent years it has suffered from intense competition as new companies have entered the market. The company needs to establish a new range of products, and believes that its future lies in making polymers using oil as a feedstock. It is willing to invest several tens of millions of pounds in building a plant on a completely new site.

After a lengthy period of surveying possible locations, the company believes that a plant close to the town of Abitinland would be suitable. The map in Figure 82.2 describes the location.

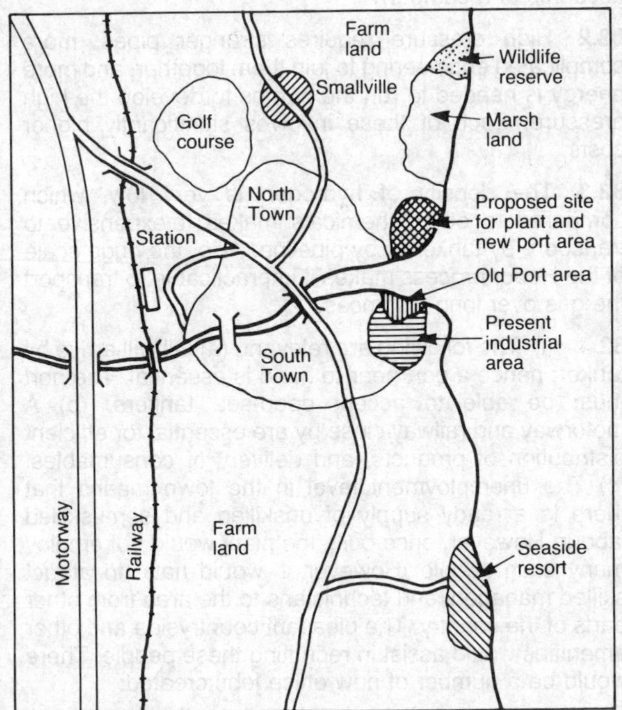

Figure 82.2 *The environment of the town of Abitinland*

Information about the town of Abitinland

Population 25 000.

History: Once a thriving industrial town based on small ship building and fishing. Ship building ceased with the decline in world markets during the 1960s and 1970s. Fishing has also declined.

Present: Unemployment is high, about 15% among both males and females. Many young people leave the area in search of work. The quaintness of parts of the town and the neighbouring unspoilt countryside has meant considerable numbers of retired people have come to live in the area. It is also used as a dormitory town by commuters working in the city of Frantic 15 miles south.

(i) Imagine you were one of the directors of Dream Chemical Co. Explain why the chosen site would be suitable for the new plant.

(ii) The local newspaper wants to interview you. What would be the main points you would use to persuade the readers to support the project?

(iii) You are now the newspaper reporter. What questions would you put to the director?

(iv) Several groups in the town are very much against the plant. Why would people be worried about it? What objections might be made? Which groups of people would make the main objections?

(v) Which groups of people might be in favour of the plant?

(vi) What benefits do *you* think the plant would bring to the town?

(vii) What reasons would *you* give for opposing the plant?

(viii) What further information would you want before finally deciding?

82.8 Continuous and batch processing

In some parts of the chemical industry, e.g. sulphuric acid manufacture, it it known that there is nearly always a large and constant demand for a product. Given the need to produce thousands of tonnes of product each week, a chemical plant is designed to work continuously, with the minimum of human intervention. Parts of the plant will only be shut down in cases of emergency, or for essential maintenance. Such plants use *continuous flow* reactors. The aim is to automate the working of a continuous flow plant. In this way labour costs are minimised. However, to construct a continuous flow plant will often require huge capital expenditure.

Continuous flow is only really suitable for processes where the reactants are gases or liquids. In these cases problems over mixing are relatively easy to overcome. For example, in reactions between solids and liquids it can be extremely difficult to design efficient mixers that will prevent solid matter from settling out.

At the opposite extreme to continuous processing there is *batch processing*. Here, relatively small amounts of a chemical (perhaps some tens or hundreds of kilograms) are made in individual reactors. Batch processing is useful, and may be essential, where there is a demand for relatively small quantities of chemicals of very high purity. It is easier to control the reaction conditions in a small reactor and to clean it thoroughly between batches. Also, a small reactor can be made from specialised materials, e.g. very high grade steel or polymers, which would be unsuitable, or prohibitively expensive, for larger-scale continuous reactors. One disadvantage of batch processing is that it is more labour intensive than continuous processing. Batch processing is the method used to make small quantities of chemicals for research, pharmaceuticals, dyes and (increasingly) biochemical products.

Answers

82.1 (i) The production is now 60 000 tonnes, a change of 60%. The fixed costs will remain the same, but the energy and raw materials costs will change by 60%. Thus, we have:

Costs	*Sum*/£ millions
Labour	1
Depreciation	4
Raw materials	6
Energy	1.2
Subtotal	12.2
Return on capital	3
Total	15.2

$$\text{Price per tonne} = \frac{£15\,200\,000}{60\,000} = £254$$

The price has increased by about 25%. This reflects the fact that it is often the fixed costs that determine the price of a chemical rather than the variable costs.

(ii)

Costs	*Sum*/£ millions
Labour	1
Depreciation	4
Raw materials	20
Energy	10
Subtotal	35
Return on capital	3
Total	38

$$\text{Price per tonne} = \frac{£38\,000\,000}{100\,000} = £380$$

This is a huge increase in price. Such price rises did take place in the 1970s, which brought about a significant rise in inflation and a recession in world trade.

(iii) After the first year of production the plant is worth £20 million × 80% = £16 million; after the second year it is worth £16 million × 80% = £12.8 million. The depreciation is £16 million − £12.8 million = £3.2 million.

Costs	*Sum*/£ millions
Labour	1.1
Depreciation	3.2
Raw materials	11
Energy	2.2
Subtotal	17.5
Return on capital	3
Total	20.5

$$\text{Price per tonne} = \frac{£20\,500\,000}{100\,000} = £205$$

It appears that the price stays roughly constant. In fact such a result can be deceptive because the £205 in year three is worth 10% less than £205 in the first year, i.e. about £185. In terms of the first year the price has actually dropped, and so has the true return to the company. Inflation can have a great influence on the accounts of a company.

82.2 High pressure requires stronger pipes, more complicated engineering to join them together, and more energy is needed to run the pumps to develop the high pressure. Each of these involves significantly higher costs.

82.3 The density of hydrogen is very low, which compared to other chemicals makes it expensive to transport, by tanker or by pipeline. Also, the huge scale of the Haber process makes it impracticable to transport the gas over long distances.

82.4 (i) The following are relevant: (a) Oil will arrive by tanker; hence a port near to hand is essential. The port must be able to accept deep-sea tankers. (b) A motorway and railway close by are essential for efficient distribution of products, and delivery of consumables. (c) The unemployment level in the town means that there is a ready supply of unskilled and semi-skilled labour. However, once built, the plant would not employ many such people. However, it would have to attract skilled managers and technicians to the area from other parts of the country. The pleasant countryside and other amenities would assist in recruiting these people. There would be a number of new office jobs created.

(ii) You might mention new jobs, e.g. in the port as well as the plant; the boost to the local economy through secondary services such as house building, increased trade for shops, garages, hotels, haulage companies, etc.

(iii) Questions might include: how many jobs, and of what kind for the local people; the level of pollution the plant might cause; dangers of oil spillage in the port; the effect on the neighbouring wildlife reserve and marshes; the effect on the trade of the holiday resort further down the coast; effects on people in neighbouring villages of increased traffic? How would lorries reach the motorway and/or station? It is clear that a new road would be needed – which route would it take?

(iv) The commuters and people who have retired to the area are unlikely to see any benefits for them: they came to the town because of its quietness and semi-rural location. People in the northern half of the town have always been further away from the traditional industrial area. They are likely to see the development as radically changing the area in which they live. Those on the northern edge of the town and the residents of Smallville suspect that the new road is bound to go near them. (They would be correct in this – it could not be routed through the built-up areas in the town itself.) Conservation groups would be most concerned about the effects on wildlife in the river, in the sea and in the marsh land. Residents of the seaside resort would be worried that the plant could discourage holiday makers.

(v) Those people who hope to be employed at the plant. The owners of small (and large) businesses that would increase their trade. The Government might welcome

Answers – contd.

the plant on the basis that it might lead to significant export business. Politicians in power would welcome a decrease in the unemployment rate. Those who have always lived in the town might see the plant as a way of encouraging young people and their families to remain in the area.

(vi), (vii) Only you know the answers to these!

(viii) You would be right to expect facts and figures relating to the issues outlined above. For example, precise numbers of jobs, route of the new road, precautions to be taken against pollution, and measures to deal with pollution if it occurs. As a chemist you might also want details of the chemical processes in the plant so that you can judge the dangers of the types of chemical being used and made.

UNIT 82 SUMMARY

- Stages in producing a new product:
  Research, pilot study, decision to scale up, making and selling, review of activity.
- Economics of production:
  Must account for fixed costs (e.g. labour, maintenance, safety services, laboratory services, management, depreciation) and variable costs, which depend on the quantity of product manufactured (e.g. raw materials, energy, packaging, transport, licences and patents).
- It is normal for a plant to move into profitability only after several years of production.
- In the running of a plant there must be an energy balance (total energy in = total energy out) and a mass balance (total mass of reactants = total mass of product and side products).
- Continuous flow processing:
  (i) Is used for making large quantities of chemicals for which there is a steady demand.
  (ii) Allows savings to be made on labour and buying chemicals in bulk.
  (iii) Often involves large capital costs.
  (iv) Mainly suitable for reactions of liquids and gases.
- Batch processing:
  (i) Is used for making relatively small quantities of specialised chemicals, e.g. dyes, research chemicals, pharmaceuticals.
  (ii) Allows fine control of conditions to produce chemicals of high purity.
  (iii) Is suitable for reactions between solids and liquids requiring efficient stirring.
  (iv) Is often more labour intensive than continuous processing.

83

Chemical processes

83.1 Examples of modern chemical manufacture

In the next four units we are going to look at how some of the most important chemicals are made. In particular, we shall take six examples:

(i) sulphuric acid manufacture;
(ii) ammonia manufacture;
(iii) nitric acid manufacture;
(iv) the chlor-alkali industry;
(v) the extraction of metals;
(vi) the oil industry.

In this unit we shall deal with the first three.

83.2 Manufacture of sulphuric acid

The majority of sulphur is used in sulphuric acid manufacture. The scale of this industry is remarkable. For example, in the USA over 10 000 000 tonnes of sulphur are converted into sulphuric acid each year. It has been estimated that in 1990 the total output of sulphuric acid plants in Europe could be as much as 200 000 tonnes *per day*. The quantity of sulphuric acid made or consumed by a country has been used as a measure of the state of its economy. If the economy is thriving, then industry needs huge quantities of the acid. Table 83.1 shows some of its uses. If the economy is in decline, the use of the acid also declines.

Table 83.1. The uses of sulphuric acid

Making superphosphate fertiliser
Making ammonium sulphate fertiliser
Processing of metal ores
Manufacture of detergents
Manufacture of paper
Manufacture of Rayon and other polymers
Manufacture of paints and pigments
Electrolyte in heavy duty batteries
Industrial treatment of metals
Laboratory reagent

The acid is manufactured by the *contact process* (Figure 83.1). There are three main stages in the process:

(1) burning sulphur to make sulphur dioxide;
(2) converting sulphur dioxide and oxygen into sulphur trioxide;
(3) absorbing sulphur trioxide in sulphuric acid to give highly concentrated sulphuric acid (oleum).

We shall deal with each stage in turn. It is the second stage that is the most interesting from a chemical point of view.

(a) *Stage 1: making sulphur dioxide*

Before passing into the burning chamber, air is dried by passing it through concentrated sulphuric acid. Liquid sulphur is burnt at jets as it is sprayed into the chamber. A highly exothermic reaction takes place:

$$S(l) + O_2(g) \rightarrow SO_2(g); \qquad \Delta H^{\ominus} = -298\,\text{kJ mol}^{-1}$$

This reaction is so exothermic that the energy released is more than sufficient to supply the energy requirements of the entire plant. This is done by using the heat of the reaction to raise steam at high pressure. Steam is one of the most important commodities in a modern chemical plant. It can be used to power pumps and to provide heat for reactions. For example, in the sulphuric acid plant, steam is used to keep the stock of sulphur molten and to drive the pumps that force the gases through the plant. In some countries the excess energy from sulphuric acid plants is used in local houses and offices for heating. It has been estimated that the energy supplied by the plant each day is equivalent to the burning of over 35 000 tonnes of oil.

(b) *Stage 2: catalytic conversion*

The key part of the method is the catalytic conversion of sulphur dioxide and oxygen into sulphur trioxide:

$$2SO_2(g) + O_2(g) \rightleftharpoons 2SO_3(g); \quad \Delta H^{\ominus} = -197\,\text{kJ mol}^{-1}$$

If you apply Le Chatelier's principle to this reaction you should realise that the production of sulphur trioxide is favoured by (i) a low temperature and (ii) a high press-

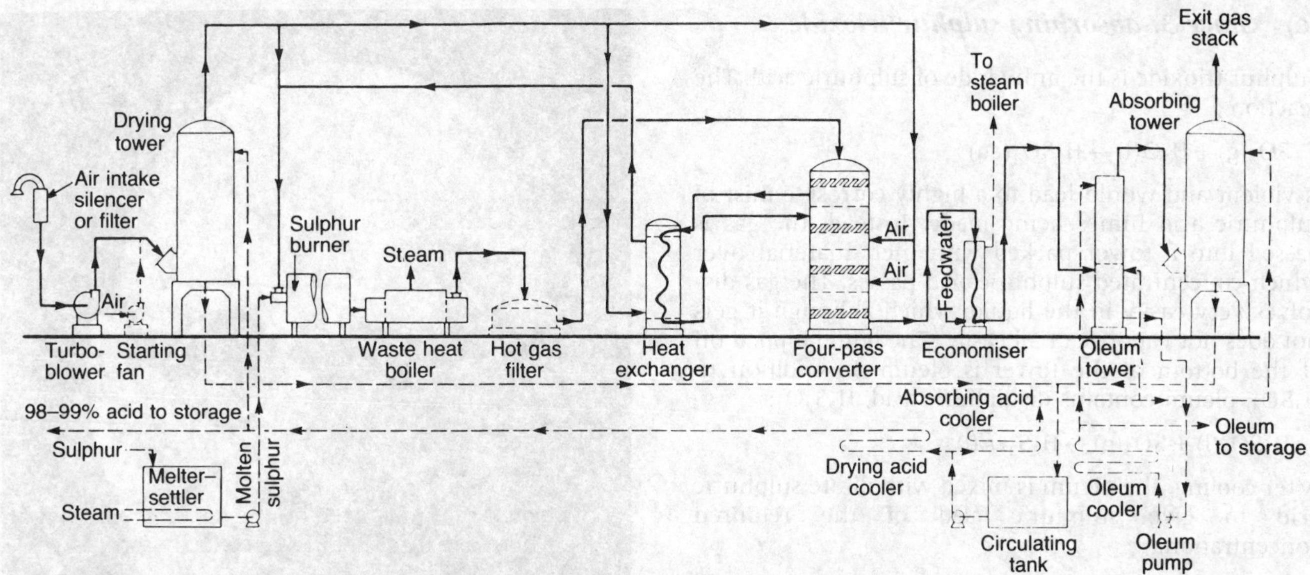

***Figure 83.1** A flowchart for a sulphuric acid plant using the contact process. (Taken from: Austin, G. T. (1984).* Shreve's Chemical Process Industries, *5th edn, McGraw-Hill, New York, figure 19.3, p. 330)*

ure. So the maximum equilibrium yield should be obtained by cooling to a low temperature, and squeezing the gases together at a high pressure. As always in industry theory has to be tempered by economics. First, it may not be economic to wait for true equilibrium to be established. Secondly, if the temperature is lowered too much, the reactions will be so slow that the yield of sulphur trioxide is minuscule. Thirdly, it is costly to build a chemical plant to work at high pressures.

The problem over increasing the rate of reaction is overcome by using a catalyst. The main one is made of vanadium(V) oxide, V_2O_5, which is combined with other materials as a support. Usually the catalyst is produced in the shape of hollow cylinders. This gives a reasonable surface area while at the same time allowing a good flow of gas through the catalyst. The equilibrium constant for the reaction at 400° C is eight times larger than at 500° C, and 40 times larger than at 600° C. Even so, experience shows that a reaction temperature of 550° C is the best. At this temperature the forward reaction is fast, but the reverse reaction is still slow. Indeed, the reaction is good enough to give over 70% conversion on passing through the catalyst.

The method of passing the gases through the catalytic converter is crucial. To achieve more than 70% conversion the mixture of gases must be passed through a catalyst bed more than once (Figure 83.2). However, the reaction making sulphur trioxide is highly exothermic and, as we have seen, the higher the temperature, the less favoured is the production of the gas. For this reason, after passing through a catalyst bed for the first time, the exit gases are cooled by taking them through a heat exchanger. Then they enter the second catalyst chamber, and so on. Four passes ensure about 98% conversion into sulphur trioxide.

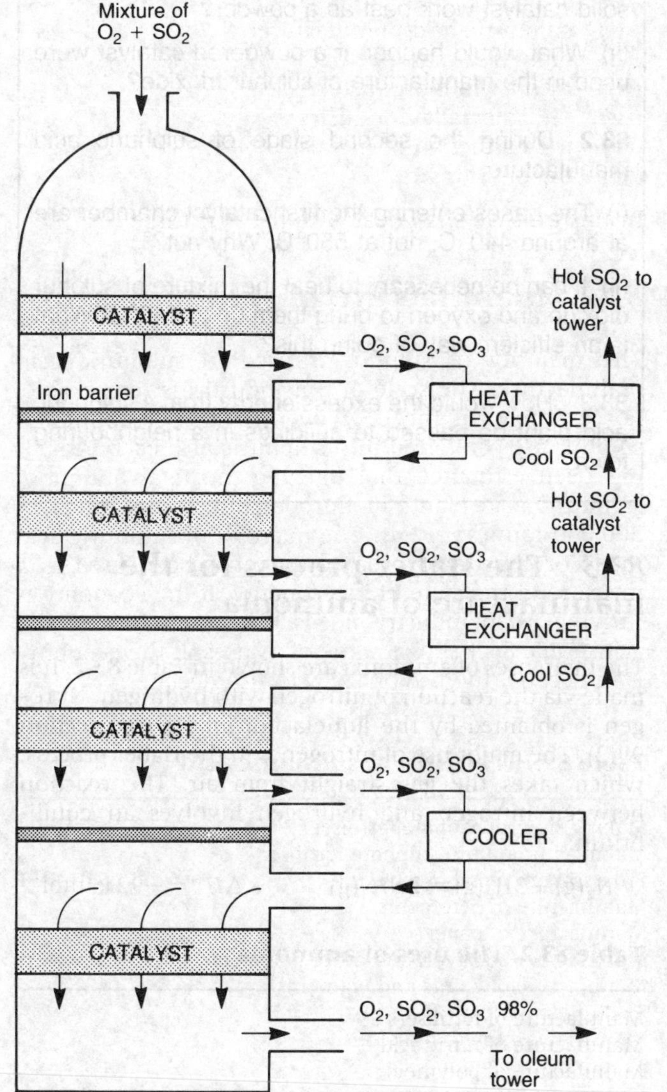

***Figure 83.2** A four-pass catalytic converter in making sulphur trioxide. (Data and diagram adapted from: Austin, op. cit.)*

(c) *Stage 3: absorbing sulphur trioxide*

Sulphur trioxide is the anhydride of sulphuric acid. The reaction

$$SO_3(g) + H_2O(l) \rightarrow H_2SO_4(aq)$$

is violent and would lead to a highly corrosive mist of sulphuric acid fumes being made. Instead, the gas is passed into a tower packed with inert material over which concentrated sulphuric acid passes. The gas dissolves very easily in the liquid, which although it gets hot does not vaporise at all easily. The liquid tapped off at the bottom of the tower is oleum. In addition to H_2SO_4, oleum contains disulphuric acid, $H_2S_2O_7$:

$$H_2SO_4(l) + SO_3(g) \rightarrow H_2S_2O_7(l)$$

After cooling, the oleum is mixed with dilute sulphuric acid to give sulphuric acid of the required concentration.

83.1 (i) Why, ignoring practical matters, should a solid catalyst work best as a powder?

(ii) What would happen if a powdered catalyst were used in the manufacture of sulphur trioxide?

83.2 During the second stage of sulphuric acid manufacture:

(i) The gases entering the first catalyst chamber are at around 440° C, not at 550° C. Why not?

(ii) It can be necessary to heat the mixture of sulphur dioxide and oxygen to bring them up to 440° C. What is an efficient way of doing this?

83.3 How would the excess energy from a sulphuric acid plant be passed to buildings in a neighbouring town?

'In 1911, at the age of forty-two, Fritz Haber was appointed the first director of the newly founded Kaiser Wilhelm Institute for Physical Chemistry and Electrochemistry. He had already achieved international eminence, principally for his discovery of a process by which nitrogen could be fixed from the air. The task of building up the institute was interrupted by the Great War, during which Haber placed himself at the service of the state. He developed and introduced a new weapon, poison gas, and supervised its first – and devastating – use at Ypres in April 1915. After the war, Haber's institute became one of the world's greatest scientific centres. In 1933, the anti-Jewish decrees of the Nazi regime made his position untenable, and he resigned. A year later he died in exile.' (Extract taken from p.50 of Dreams and Delusions *by Fritz Stern, Weidenfeld and Nicolson, London 1988.)*

83.3 The Haber process for the manufacture of ammonia

The main uses of ammonia are shown in Table 83.2. It is made via the reaction of nitrogen with hydrogen. Nitrogen is obtained by the liquefaction of air (see section 99.2). The major use of nitrogen is in the Haber process, which takes the gas straight from air. The reaction between nitrogen and hydrogen involves an equilibrium:

$$N_2(g) + 3H_2(g) \rightleftharpoons 2NH_3(g); \qquad \Delta H^{\ominus} = -92\,\text{kJ mol}^{-1}$$

Table 83.2. The uses of ammonia

Manufacture of fertilisers
Manufacture of nitric acid
Manufacture of polymers

The way the equilibrium proportion of ammonia varies with temperature and pressure is shown in Figure 83.3. (We assume that hydrogen and nitrogen are originally mixed in the ratio 3 to 1.) The graph shows that, as we expect, the greatest yield of ammonia occurs at low temperatures and high pressures. However, a low temperature decreases the rate of reaction, so it can be more profitable to work the plant at a higher temperature even though the maximum yield of ammonia is not obtained. Similarly, a plant that must withstand very high pressures will be much more expensive to build and run than one which works at a lower pressure. It is economical to use a moderate pressure even though the maximum yield of ammonia is not obtained. Most plants use pressures between 15 and 30 MPa (150 and 300 atm) and a temperature around

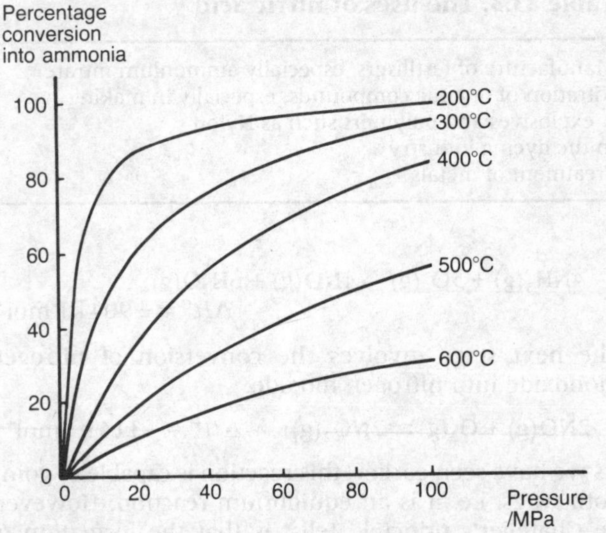

***Figure 83.3** The graph shows that the percentage of ammonia in an equilibrium mixture of N_2, H_2 and NH_3 is greatest at low temperatures and high pressures*

500° C, which gives a conversion rate of around 15% to 25%.

The Haber process involves three main stages (Figure 83.4):

(1) supply and purification of the reacting gases;
(2) compression of the gases and conversion into ammonia;
(3) recovery of the ammonia.

We shall examine each stage in turn.

(a) *Stage 1: supply and purification of the gases*

The source of hydrogen is naphtha (a mixture of hydrocarbons) from the oil industry, or natural gas. Sulphur compounds are removed from the hydrocarbons by passing them over zinc oxide or activated charcoal. Then they undergo a two-stage process, known as *primary* and *secondary re-forming,* in which they are reacted with steam over a nickel catalyst. The result of primary re-forming is that carbon monoxide and hydrogen are produced. For example,

$$CH_4(g) + H_2O(g) \rightarrow CO(g) + 3H_2(g)$$

Secondary re-forming involves mixing the products of the primary re-forming with air and then carrying out the *shift reaction*. This increases the amount of hydrogen in the mixture by use of the reaction:

$$CO(g) + H_2O(g) \rightleftharpoons CO_2(g) + H_2(g)$$

The shift reaction, introduced by Bosch, was an improvement on the original process; hence the name 'Haber–Bosch process' is sometimes used instead of 'Haber process'.

(b) *Stage 2: compression and conversion*

Most of the carbon dioxide is removed from the products of the re-forming stage by washing with potassium carbonate solution and by absorbing the gas in a variety of chemicals. Any remaining carbon monoxide and carbon dioxide is converted into methane in the *methanator*. This is a vital stage in the process because it prevents the iron catalyst in the ammonia converter being poisoned. (The catalyst is not affected by methane.) Now the gases are compressed and passed through a tower packed with a catalyst. This is mainly iron, but other chemicals are added to improve performance. These substances are called *promoters*. Commonly used promoters are aluminium oxide, zirconium oxide and potassium oxide. Promoters do not necessarily take a direct part in the reaction. Often they improve the stability of the catalyst and increase its porosity, thereby allowing a greater surface area to be

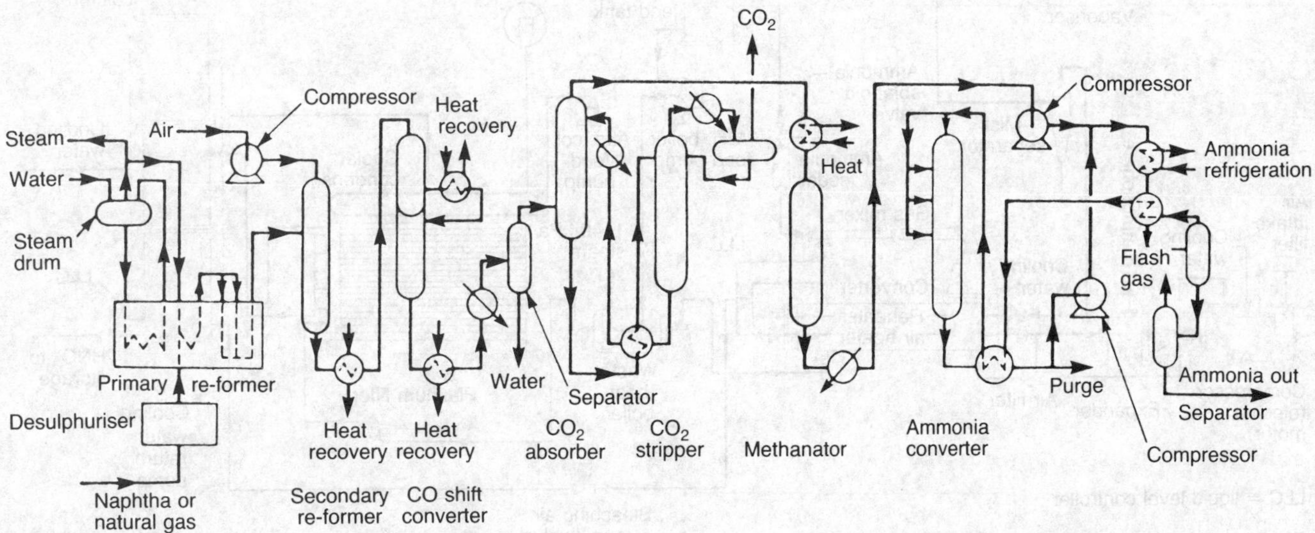

***Figure 83.4** A block diagram of ammonia manufacture; see the text for a description of the main stages. (Taken from: Austin, op. cit., figure 18.3, p. 306)*

used. Haber process catalysts are easily poisoned, especially by sulphur compounds and carbon monoxide. It is for this reason that the nitrogen and hydrogen have to be thoroughly purified before they are used.

It is quite an art designing an efficient converter. The catalyst is arranged on perforated trays and the gases pass downwards through them. Beneath each tray the emerging gases, which are at a higher temperature than before they went through the catalyst, are cooled by passing through heat exchangers containing unreacted gases.

(c) *Stage 3: recovery of ammonia*

On emerging from the converter the gases are cooled and the pressure reduced. This causes most of the ammonia to liquefy. If necessary, the gases can be cooled below 0° C to remove even more ammonia. The unreacted gases, plus a little ammonia, are recycled. Ammonia is usually stored, and transported, as a liquid in steel tanks.

83.4 The manufacture of nitric acid

The main uses of nitric acid are shown in Table 83.3. In industry nitric acid is made in a process that relies on the catalytic oxidation of ammonia (Figure 83.5). Air containing about 10% ammonia, at around 230° C and 900 kPa (9 atm), is passed through a metal gauze made of platinum (about 90%) and rhodium (about 10%). The reaction gives nitrogen monoxide as the main product:

Table 83.3. The uses of nitric acid

Manufacture of fertilisers, especially ammonium nitrate
Nitration of organic compounds, especially in making explosives and polymers such as Nylon
In the dyeing industry
Treatment of metals

$$4NH_3(g) + 5O_2(g) \rightarrow 4NO(g) + 6H_2O(g); \quad \Delta H^{\ominus} = -904\,\text{kJ mol}^{-1}$$

The next stage involves the conversion of nitrogen monoxide into nitrogen dioxide:

$$2NO(g) + O_2(g) \rightleftharpoons 2NO_2(g); \quad \Delta H^{\ominus} = -114\,\text{kJ mol}^{-1}$$

As we have seen earlier, this reaction is capable of going both ways, i.e. it is an equilibrium reaction. However, Le Chatelier's principle tells us that the formation of nitrogen dioxide will be encouraged by a low temperature. Given that the catalytic conversion is highly exothermic, it follows that the gases have to be cooled before the nitrogen monoxide and the unreacted oxygen in the air will give a good yield of nitrogen dioxide. In practice the reaction goes almost completely in favour of nitrogen dioxide if the temperature is kept below 150° C. After cooling, the gases are washed with both water and dilute nitric acid. This is the stage at which nitric acid is produced. Under the conditions used the reaction is

$$3NO_2(g) + H_2O(l) \rightleftharpoons 2HNO_3(aq) + NO(g)$$

The acid solution contains between 50% and 60% HNO_3. It is often contaminated by unreacted nitrogen

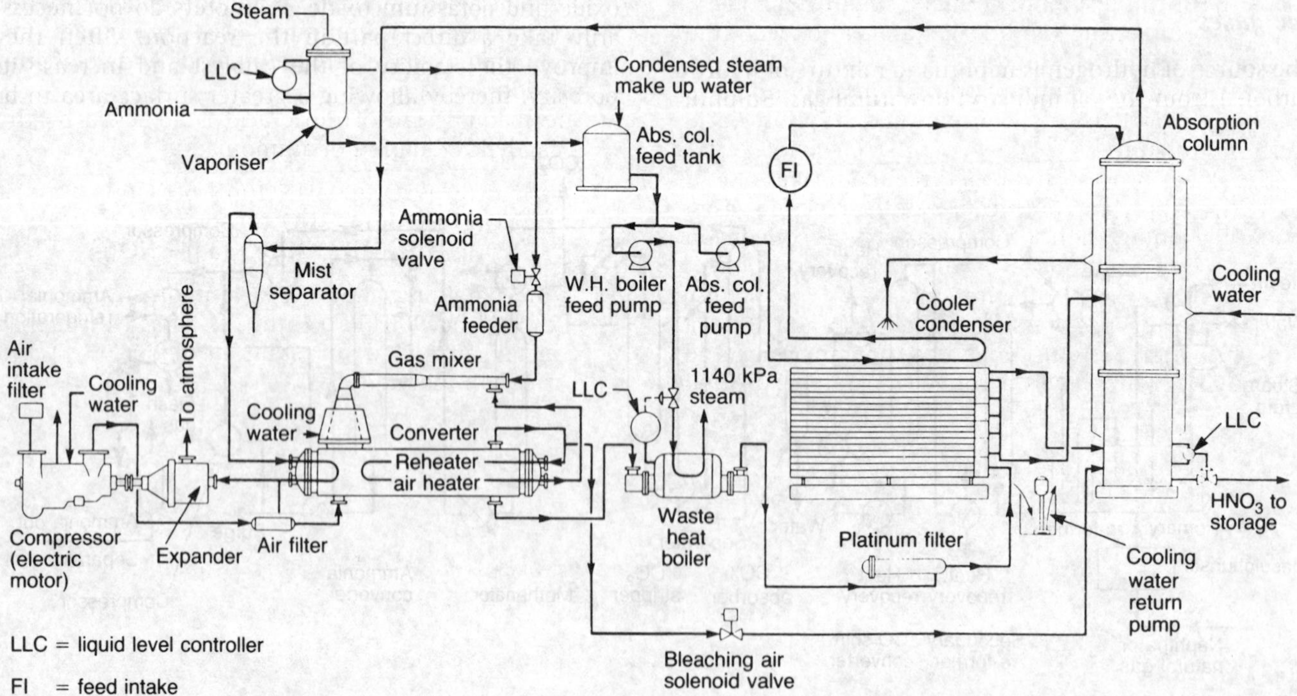

***Figure 83.5** Block diagram of nitric acid manufacture. (Adapted from: Austin, op.cit., figure 18.8)*

dioxide, which can be removed by passing the acid down a tower through which air is blown. If highly concentrated nitric acid is required, the dilute acid is passed through a tower containing anhydrous magnesium nitrate. The anhydrous salt absorbs much of the water, giving a liquid that is 95% HNO_3.

83.4 There is a side reaction when ammonia and oxygen combine in the first stage of nitric acid manufacture. It occurs when the nitrogen monoxide that has been made itself begins to react with ammonia.

$$4NH_3(g) + 6NO(g) \rightarrow 5N_2(g) + 6H_2O(g)$$

This is highly undesirable.

(i) Why is it undesirable?

(ii) Explain how adjustment of the flow rate of the gases through the catalyst can prevent the reaction taking place.

83.5 What do you think is done with the nitrogen monoxide given off when nitrogen dioxide and water react?

Answers

83.1 (i) The powder will have a large surface area and therefore proportionately more active sites.

(ii) Assuming that it does not get blown out of the catalyst chamber, it would be compacted into a hard mass by the pressure of gas, and the gases would not be able to get through it.

83.2 (i) They are heated by the energy released during the reaction. If they were at the higher temperature before entering the chamber, then the temperature rise would bring about a reduction in yield of the product.

(ii) Pre-heat them using the heat of the product gases by passing the two through a heat exchanger.

83.3 By passing steam along insulated pipes. Steam pipes are the chemical industry's energy highways.

83.4 (i) It will lower the yield of nitrogen monoxide, and therefore of nitric acid.

(ii) If the flow rate is kept just right, all the ammonia is converted into nitrogen monoxide, leaving none for the side reaction. If the flow rate is too fast, the gases pass too quickly across the catalyst. This leaves ammonia free to react with nitrogen monoxide.

83.5 It is recycled.

UNIT 83 SUMMARY

- Manufacture of sulphuric acid:
  (i) Burning sulphur to make sulphur dioxide.
  (ii) Converting sulphur dioxide and oxygen into sulphur trioxide.
  (iii) Absorbing sulphur trioxide in sulphuric acid to give highly concentrated sulphuric acid (oleum).
- The Haber process involves three main stages:
  (i) Supply and purification of the reacting gases.
  (ii) Compression of the gases and conversion into ammonia.
  (iii) Recovery of the ammonia.
  Most plants use pressures between 15 and 30 MPa (150 and 300 atm) and a temperature around 500° C, which gives a conversion rate of around 15% to 25%. Iron is the main catalyst; other chemicals are added to improve performance (promoters). Commonly used promoters are aluminium oxide, zirconium oxide and potassium oxide.
- The manufacture of nitric acid is achieved by the catalytic oxidation of ammonia:

  $$4NH_3(g) + 5O_2(g) \rightarrow 4NO(g) + 6H_2O(g)$$
  $$2NO(g) + O_2(g) \rightleftharpoons 2NO_2(g)$$
  $$3NO_2(g) + H_2O(l) \rightleftharpoons 2HNO_3(aq) + NO(g)$$

  Air containing about 10% ammonia, at around 230° C and 900 kPa (9 atm), is passed through a metal gauze made of platinum (about 90%) and rhodium (about 10%).

84

The chlor-alkali industry

84.1 What is the chlor-alkali industry?

This is the name given to a group of three related industries that produce chlorine, sodium hydroxide and sodium carbonate. These three chemicals are used in huge quantities in a vast number of different chemical processes, some of which are shown in Table 84.1. In industry, sodium carbonate is known as soda ash. Chlorine and sodium hydroxide are made from the electrolysis of sodium chloride. The way that soda ash is obtained depends on where in the world the chemical plant is to be set up. In some areas, especially in the USA, there are huge deposits of a mineral called trona. This is a mixed carbonate and hydrogencarbonate of sodium: $Na_2CO_3{\cdot}NaHCO_3{\cdot}2H_2O$. It can be completely converted into the carbonate by heating, and after some purification it is ready for use. In Europe where there are no major supplies of trona, soda ash is made by the ammonia–soda process, also known as the Solvay process. We shall now look in greater detail at how the three major chlor-alkali chemicals are made.

84.2 The production of chlorine and sodium hydroxide

Chlorine and sodium hydroxide are both made by the electrolysis of brine (salt water). There are three methods in large-scale use. We shall deal with each of them in turn. The initial stage is to obtain sodium chloride from deposits of rock salt. Rock salt can be mined directly, but more often water is pumped into the deposits, and the salt removed as brine. The resulting solution can be purified (see question 84.2). If solid sodium chloride is wanted, it can be produced by crystallising it out from the solution.

(a) *The mercury cell*

Brine is continuously passed into a cell that has graphite anodes and a moving layer of mercury as the cathode (Figure 84.1). As usual, chloride ions are discharged in preference to the hydroxide ions in water. However, in this cell sodium ions are discharged in preference to water or hydrogen ions owing to the use of mercury as the cathode rather than another material. Sodium actually reacts with the mercury, making an amalgam. The amalgam travels with unused mercury out of the cell into a chamber containing water. It is at this stage that sodium hydroxide is produced:

Table 84.1. The uses of chlorine, sodium hydroxide and sodium carbonate (soda ash) in the UK*

Chlorine		*Sodium hydroxide*		*Soda ash*	
Used in	*Percentage of total*	*Used in*	*Percentage of total*	*Used in*	*Percentage of total*
Solvents	22	Inorganic chemicals	21	Glass containers	34
PVC	18	Organic chemicals	17	Sodium phosphate	12
Paper products	11	Paper products	14	Other glass products	11
Chloromethanes	10	Aluminium industry	7	Alkaline cleaners	5
Inorganic chemicals	8	Soap	4	Paper products	4

*Table adapted from: Heaton, C. A. (ed.) (1986). *The Chemical Industry*, Blackie, Glasgow, table 3.2, p. 132

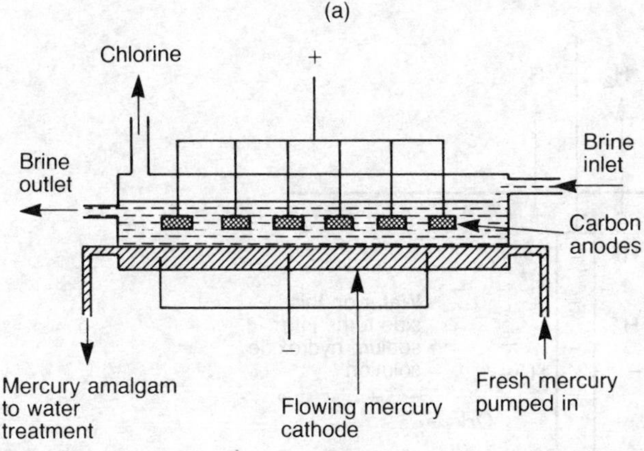

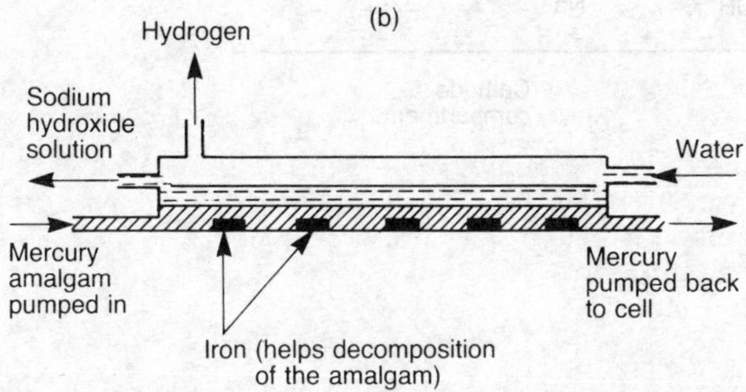

***Figure 84.1** The mercury cell method for making sodium hydroxide and chlorine. (a) The mercury cell where sodium amalgam and chlorine are made. (b) The soda cell where sodium hydroxide is made from the sodium amalgam*

$$2NaHg + 2H_2O(l) \rightarrow 2Na^+(aq) + 2OH^-(aq) + 2Hg(l) + H_2(g)$$

The chlorine given by the anode reaction:

$$2Cl^-(aq) - 2e^- \rightarrow Cl_2(g)$$

is not completely pure owing to it being mixed with oxygen and water vapour. The latter can be removed by drying the gas with concentrated sulphuric acid. Once this is done, the chlorine is liquefied under pressure and sold. Alternatively, in some cases, the chlorine can be taken from the cell and reacted with hydrogen to make hydrogen chloride. This is absorbed in water and the resulting hydrochloric acid sold.

The use of mercury cells has declined rapidly. This is because of the damage that mercury, and some of its compounds, can cause if they escape into the environment. The amount of mercury escaping into the atmosphere around a mercury cell plant is always carefully controlled, but almost inevitably some mercury enters the sodium hydroxide solution or is lost in effluent. This happens very easily if the water used in the process contains organic matter. Mercury reacts with many organic molecules and it is now established that organomercury compounds find their way into the food chain of animals. In Japan, mercury cell plants have been banned by law. This was one consequence of the deaths or severe illness of over 120 fishermen and members of their families between 1953 and 1960 at Minamata Bay. The people were poisoned by eating fish and other seafood that had accumulated large amounts of mercury in their bodies. The sea in the area was badly contaminated with mercury compounds, although from a plastics factory rather than a mercury cell plant.

(b) *The diaphragm cell*

In a diaphragm cell the anode and cathode are separated in two compartments by a diaphragm made of asbestos. The anode is made from titanium, sometimes with a coating of platinum, and the cathode is made from steel. In Figure 84.2 you can see two diagrams. The first is simplified so that you can understand the purpose of the diaphragm; the second gives a more realistic impression of the construction of the cell.

In the anode compartment chlorine is given off through the reaction:

$$2Cl^-(aq) - 2e^- \rightarrow Cl_2(g)$$

At the cathode hydrogen is discharged:

$$2H_2O(l) + 2e^- \rightarrow 2OH^-(aq) + H_2(g)$$

As the discharge equation shows, hydroxide ions are released and therefore the solution becomes increasingly alkaline. (Also, see the answer to question 72.4.) The overall result is that the brine loses its chloride ions and becomes richer in hydroxide ions. We are left with a solution of sodium hydroxide. At least we should be; but life is not that simple. Several things can go wrong. First, chlorine reacts with hydroxide ions. In the cold, chlorate(I) (hypochlorite) ions are produced:

$$Cl_2(g) + 2OH^-(aq) \rightarrow OCl^-(aq) + Cl^-(aq) + H_2O(l)$$

Secondly, if hydroxide ions reach the anode, they can be discharged. If this happens, oxygen is given off, which contaminates the chlorine and makes the isolation of pure chlorine more difficult.

To avoid these problems, the brine in the anode compartment is kept at a slightly higher pressure than in the cathode compartment. This makes it less likely that the solution around the cathode will reach the anode. The asbestos membrane keeps the two solutions apart while allowing ions to move between them, thus keeping the current flowing. The sodium hydroxide solution drawn off from the cathode compartment contains a large amount of salt. The solution is partially evaporated and allowed to cool. Owing to its lower solubility, sodium chloride crystallises first. The liquid left contains about 50% sodium hydroxide by weight, together with a little sodium chloride.

A variation on the diaphragm cell is the membrane cell. Here, in place of asbestos, an ion exchange material is used. The idea is to allow only sodium ions to move between the compartments. In theory this should stop the chlorine reacting with hydroxide ions, and hydroxide ions being discharged at the cathode. However, in practice it is very difficult to obtain perfect operation of the ion exchange membrane.

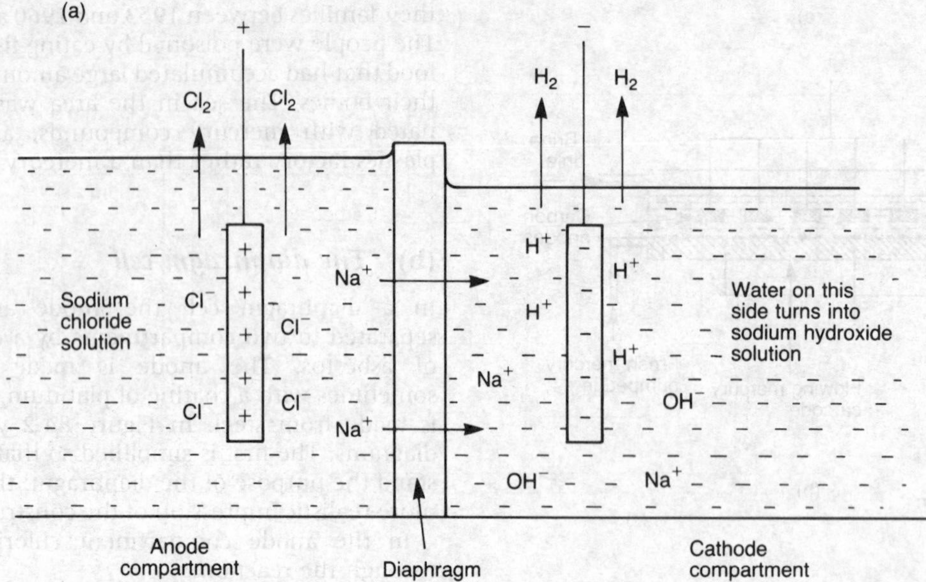

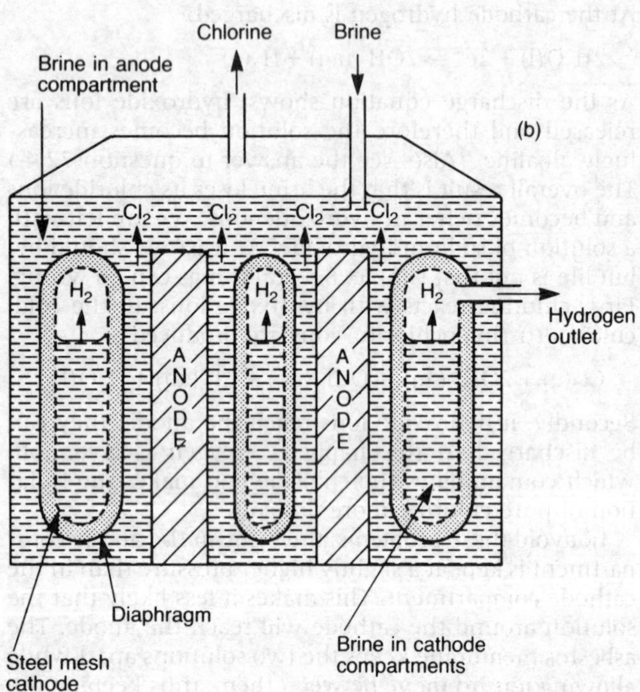

***Figure 84.2** (a) The basis of the diaphragm cell for making sodium hydroxide and chlorine. Sodium ions can pass through the diaphragm into the cathode compartment. There they mix with hydroxide ions, which remain from the decomposition of water. The liquid level in the anode compartment is greater than in the cathode compartment. This keeps the direction of flow of liquid in the direction anode to cathode. (b) How the anode and cathode compartments are arranged in a diaphragm cell. Notice that the level of brine in the anode compartment is higher than in the cathode compartments. The cathode compartments are similar to one another. Only one has an outlet for hydrogen shown. (Adapted from: Thompson, R. (ed.) (1977).* The Modern Inorganic Chemicals Industry, *The Chemical Society, London, figure 3, p. 119)*

84.1 There is a by-product of the mercury cell, which we have not mentioned, but which can be sold to help increase the profitability of the process. What is it?

84.2 Two stages that can be used in purifying brine are: (i) adding barium salts, (ii) adding sodium carbonate. Which ions are removed by these means? (Hint: you are looking for ions that give precipitates.)

84.3 The ammonia–soda (Solvay) process

It is possible to summarise the manufacture of sodium carbonate in the equation

$$CaCO_3(s) + 2NaCl(s) \rightarrow Na_2CO_3(s) + CaCl_2(s)$$

The equation says that calcium carbonate, i.e. limestone, will react with sodium chloride to make sodium carbonate and calcium chloride. The problem with this equation is that it cannot be carried out in practice.

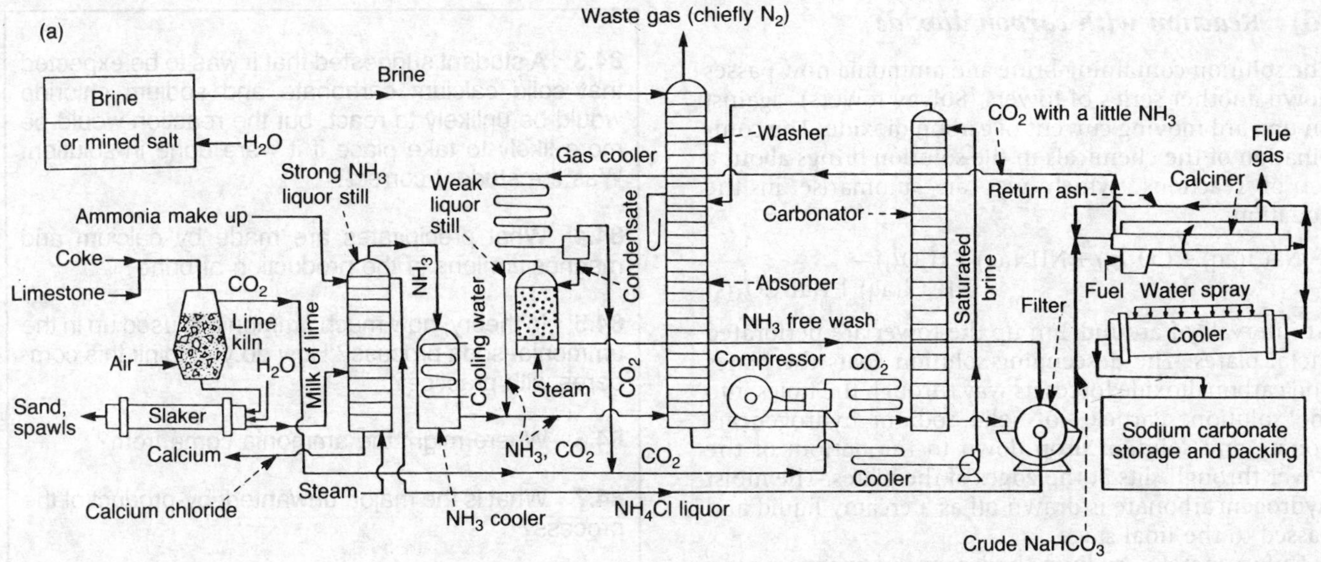

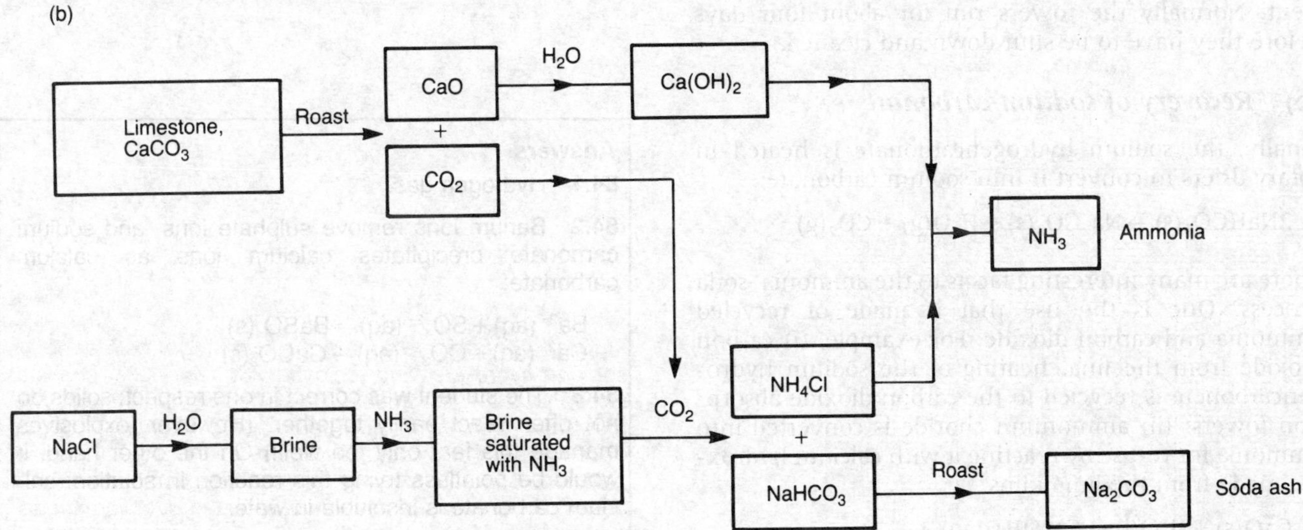

***Figure 84.3** (a) The Solvay process. (Diagram taken from: Heaton, C. A. (1986).* The Chemical Industry, *Blackie, Glasgow, figure 3.5.) (b) Key stages in the ammonia–soda process*

Limestone and sodium chloride are the starting materials, but a somewhat tortuous route is taken to produce sodium carbonate. The main stages are summarised in Figure 84.3. Here are brief details of them.

(a) *Roasting of limestone*

The limestone is mixed with coke and heated in kilns, through which a supply of air passes. The limestone gives off carbon dioxide, and calcium oxide (lime) remains:

$$CaCO_3(s) \rightarrow CaO(s) + CO_2(g)$$

The purpose of the coke and air is to generate energy as well as more carbon dioxide through the reaction

$$C(s) + O_2(g) \rightarrow CO_2(g)$$

(b) *Production of brine*

Saturated brine is obtained by dissolving salt in water. Before it can be used it has to be freed of calcium and magnesium ions. These two ions can cause precipitates to be made, which have the same effect as the furring up of boiler pipes by hard water, i.e. magnesium and calcium carbonates can be deposited. This is prevented by adding carbonate and hydroxide ions to the brine.

(c) *Saturation of brine with ammonia*

The brine is passed down a tower through which ammonia is passed. This saturates the brine with ammonia.

(d) *Reaction with carbon dioxide*

The solution containing brine and ammonia now passes down another series of towers (Solvay towers), against an upward moving current of carbon dioxide. The combination of the chemicals in the solution brings about a set of reactions, which we can summarise in the equation:

$$NaCl(aq) + CO_2(g) + NH_3(aq) + H_2O(l) \rightarrow NH_4Cl(aq) + NaHCO_3(s)$$

At intervals of around 1 m up the tower are perforated metal plates. The descending solution coats the plates and carbon dioxide forces its way through the holes into the solution. Particles of solid sodium hydrogencarbonate and solution drop down to the bottom of the tower through slits at the edges of the plates. The moist hydrogencarbonate is drawn off as a creamy liquid and passed to the final stage.

Unfortunately, sodium hydrogencarbonate crystals gradually block the towers, making the process inefficient. Normally the towers run for about four days before they have to be shut down and cleaned.

(e) *Recovery of sodium carbonate*

Finally, the sodium hydrogencarbonate is heated in rotary driers to convert it into sodium carbonate:

$$2NaHCO_3(s) \rightarrow Na_2CO_3(s) + H_2O(g) + CO_2(g)$$

There are many interesting facets to the ammonia–soda process. One is the use that is made of recycled ammonia and carbon dioxide. For example, (i) carbon dioxide from the final heating of the sodium hydrogencarbonate is recycled to the carbon dioxide absorption towers; (ii) ammonium choride is converted into ammonia for re-use by reacting it with calcium hydroxide made from the lime kilns:

$$CaO(s) + H_2O(l) \rightarrow Ca(OH)_2(aq)$$

$$Ca(OH)_2(aq) + 2NH_4Cl(aq) \rightarrow CaCl_2(aq) + 2H_2O(l) + 2NH_3(g)$$

The temperature of the various stages has to be carefully controlled. For example, in the Solvay towers the reactions that take place are exothermic; but if the temperature rises too far, the reverse reaction takes place at a significant rate, regenerating sodium chloride. For this reason, the Solvay tower has a water cooling system built into it.

84.3 A student suggested that it was to be expected that solid calcium carbonate and sodium chloride would be unlikely to react, but the reaction would be more likely to take place if it were done in solution. Was the student correct?

84.4 What precipitates are made by calcium and magnesium ions in the production of brine?

84.5 In theory, how much ammonia is used up in the ammonia–soda process? How do you think this compares with practice?

84.6 Where might the ammonia come from?

84.7 What is the major, unwanted, by-product of the process?

Answers

84.1 Hydrogen gas.

84.2 Barium ions remove sulphate ions, and sodium carbonate precipitates calcium ions as calcium carbonate:

$$Ba^{2+}(aq) + SO_4^{2-}(aq) \rightarrow BaSO_4(s)$$

$$Ca^{2+}(aq) + CO_3^{2-}(aq) \rightarrow CaCO_3(s)$$

84.3 The student was correct in one respect: solids do not often react easily together. (However, explosives manage this feat only too well!) On the other hand, it would be pointless trying this reaction in solution: calcium carbonate is insoluble in water.

84.4 Calcium and magnesium carbonates are possible (these are also made when hard water is boiled), as is magnesium hydroxide.

84.5 None; but in practice there are always losses owing to the gas being so soluble in the solutions used.

84.6 The Haber process.

84.7 Calcium chloride. There is no appreciable market for this chemical.

UNIT 84 SUMMARY

- The production of chlorine and sodium hydroxide is done by the electrolysis of brine in two types of cell:

  (i) The mercury cell

  cathode $2NaHg(s) + 2H_2O(l) \rightarrow 2Na^+(aq) + OH^-(aq) + 2Hg(l) + H_2(g)$

  anode $2Cl^-(aq) - 2e^- \rightarrow Cl_2(g)$

  (ii) The diaphragm cell

  anode $2Cl^-(aq) - 2e^- \rightarrow Cl_2(g)$

  cathode $2H^+(aq) + 2e^- \rightarrow H_2(g)$

- In both cells, a solution of sodium hydroxide remains, and is separated.
- The ammonia–soda process is used to manufacture sodium carbonate. The process is summarised in the equation

$$CaCO_3(s) + 2NaCl(s) \rightarrow Na_2CO_3(s) + CaCl_2(s)$$

The change takes place in five stages:

(i) Roasting of limestone.
(ii) Production of brine.
(iii) Saturation of brine with ammonia.
(iv) Reaction with carbon dioxide

$$NaCl(aq) + CO_2(g) + NH_3(aq) + H_2O(l) \rightarrow NH_4Cl(aq) + NaHCO_3(s)$$

(v) Recovery of sodium carbonate

$$2NaHCO_3(s) \rightarrow Na_2CO_3(s) + H_2O(g) + CO_2(g)$$

85

The extraction of metals

85.1 The methods of extraction

There are four main ways in which metals are extracted from their ores (Table 85.1). The simplest, which is far from typical, occurs for only a few metals such as gold and platinum. These unreactive elements can be found in the ground uncombined with other elements. Hence the occurrence of gold mines in some areas of the world, especially southern Africa.

The second method removes the metals from their sulphide ores by a combination of roasting to turn them into oxides, followed by reduction by carbon. This is a method used for a number of the transition elements and, especially, the B metals such as zinc, lead and mercury.

Thirdly, we have metals that occur chiefly as oxides. Extraction here relies on the oxide being reduced by carbon. The extraction of iron is the most famous example.

Finally, we have the most reactive elements in Groups I, II and III. The problem with these metals is that their compounds (often chlorides or oxides) are extremely hard to break down by chemical means. Here the extraction is done by electrolysis.

In many cases there is more than one method that could be used. The choice made will depend on a number of factors, but the economics of the different processes will usually decide the issue. For example, where there is a relatively cheap supply of electricity, an electrolytic method may be favoured over a chemical method of reduction. Where electricity is expensive, the chemical method may win.

In the next four sections we shall briefly review these four methods of extraction.

Before we go into the detail of some of the processes, you should realise that none of the methods of extraction are without cost. This does not mean just an economic cost; there are human and environmental costs as well. Any type of mining is dangerous, but the record of accidents in gold mines in South Africa is far worse than it should be. Many men have died in the mines. The roasting of sulphide ores produces sulphur dioxide. For many years there were few controls on the amount of this highly acidic gas that could be allowed to escape into the atmosphere. Many countries have now introduced tight regulations aimed at preventing this source of pollution. However, safety and the equipment necessary for reducing sulphur dioxide emissions are expensive. We should not be surprised if we have to pay more for metals in the future.

Table 85.1. Methods of extraction of the metals

Method	*Type of metal*
Mining the pure metal	Noble metals such as silver, gold and platinum
Roasting the sulphide, and reduction of the oxide	Some transition metals, but especially the B metals
Reduction of the oxide	Some transition metals, especially iron
Electrolysis of molten solid	Reactive elements of Groups I, II and III, e.g. sodium, magnesium and aluminium

85.2 Extracting the noble metals

On the face of it the method is simple: dig a hole and take out the lumps of metal. This is what a gold mine is for. Unfortunately, the chances of finding large pieces of gold (nuggets) are extremely small. Rather the gold is present as tiny fragments mixed in with large quantities of other material. The solids removed from the mine are milled to a powder, and then the gold is recovered by a flotation method, or by a large-scale variation of the traditional panning method. Panning is the method used by gold prospectors. The mixture of earth and rock suspected of containing gold is swilled with water. Owing to the greater density of the gold particles, they tend to lie on the bottom of the pan, while the other solid particles are washed away. Sometimes chemical methods are also used to remove gold. For example, in the presence of oxygen, gold will give a soluble complex cyanide, $Au(CN)_2^-$, with cyanide ions. After separation, the solution of the complex will deposit gold if zinc is added to it. The final stage in gold refining is to melt the metal and cast it into ingots. The ingots are sold on the open market, or hoarded by governments to prove how wealthy their countries are.

85.3 Reducing sulphide ores

The techniques used in the extractions depend on a number of factors, especially thermodynamic ones. We shall take the extraction of mercury, zinc, lead, copper and nickel as examples. Their sulphide ores are listed in Table 85.2.

Table 85.2. Some sulphide ores

Metal	*Ore*
Copper	Copper pyrites, $CuFeS_2$ (also known as fool's gold); chalcocite, Cu_2S; covellite, CuS
Lead	Galena, PbS
Mercury	Cinnabar, HgS
Nickel	Pentlandite, $Fe_9Ni_9S_{16}$
Zinc	Zinc blende, ZnS

The treatment of sulphide ores tends to follow a similar pattern:

(i) crushing;
(ii) froth flotation;
(iii) roasting in air.

Once the ore is crushed and broken into finer particles, the separation of the mineral from the other components in the ore is done by *froth flotation*. In this method the impure mineral is mixed with water to which a number of other chemicals may be added. The mixture is strongly agitated so that it froths. The particles of the mineral adhere to the surface of the bubbles, which together float to the surface. The bubbles and their mineral coating are removed and the mineral allowed to separate. The chemicals added to the water act on the interface between the mineral particles, water and air. Essentially they are surfactants of one type or another. Sometimes the pH of the solution has to be adjusted, and ions added that adhere to the mineral particles, thereby making them more attractive to water molecules.

Roasting of sulphide ores is done to convert the sulphide into an oxide. To understand the reason from the point of view of thermodynamics, you will need to understand Ellingham diagrams. In section 50.5 we found the conditions at which carbon would reduce a metal oxide. The test is whether the free energy change for the reaction is negative at a particular temperature. An Ellingham diagram allows us to find this out by looking at graphs rather than performing calculations. Figure 85.1 shows an Ellingham diagram for a number of sulphides.

If we use carbon to reduce a sulphide, we would expect to get carbon disulphide, CS_2, as the product; if we use hydrogen, hydrogen sulphide, H_2S, will be the

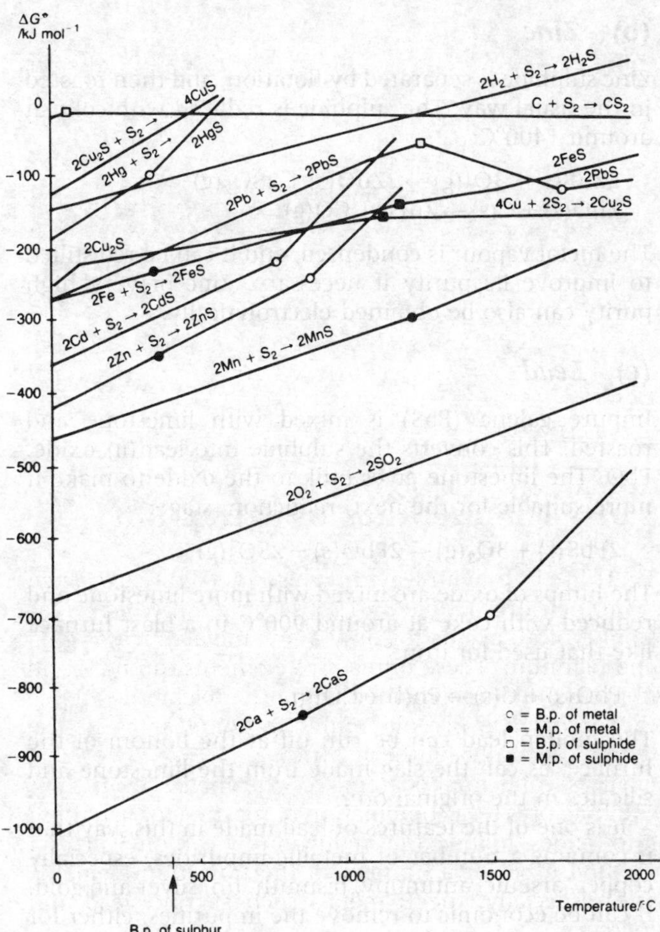

***Figure 85.1** The Ellingham diagram for a number of sulphides. (Adapted from: Dannatt, C. W. and Ellingham, H. J. T. (1948).* Disc. Faraday Soc. *126–39)*

product. You can see from the diagram that the line for CS_2 crosses that for CuS at around 500° C. The line for H_2S only crosses the line for HgS (at about 300° C). None of the other lines are crossed by CS_2 or H_2S. Therefore, the use of carbon or hydrogen is hopeless as a method of extracting the other elements. Hence we need to convert the sulphides into oxides, which we know can be reduced by hydrogen or carbon.

(a) *Mercury*

The efficient roasting of an ore requires the careful design of a furnace, and control of the amount of air (oxygen) let into it. In the case of mercury the process is very simple. This is because the mercury(II) oxide made in the reaction

$$2HgS(s) + 3O_2(g) \rightarrow 2HgO(s) + 2SO_2(g)$$

immediately decomposes into mercury (a vapour at the temperature of the furnace) and oxygen:

$$2HgO(s) \rightarrow 2Hg(g) + O_2(g)$$

The final stage in isolating mercury is to condense the vapour.

(b) *Zinc*

Zinc sulphide is separated by flotation, and then roasted in the usual way. The sulphide is reduced with coke at around 1400°C:

$$2ZnS(s) + 3O_2(g) \rightarrow 2ZnO(s) + 2SO_2(g)$$
$$ZnO(s) + C(s) \rightarrow Zn(s) + CO(g)$$

The metal vapour is condensed, and it can be redistilled to improve its purity if necessary. Zinc of very high purity can also be obtained electrolytically.

(c) *Lead*

Impure galena (PbS) is mixed with limestone and roasted. This converts the sulphide into lead(II) oxide, PbO. The limestone gives bulk to the oxide to make it more suitable for the next, reduction, stage:

$$2PbS(s) + 3O_2(g) \rightarrow 2PbO(s) + 2SO_2(g)$$

The lumps of oxide are mixed with more limestone and reduced with coke at around 900°C in a blast furnace like that used for iron:

$$PbO(s) + C(s) \rightarrow Pb(l) + CO(g)$$

The molten lead can be run off at the bottom of the furnace, as can the slag made from the limestone and silicates in the original ore.

It is one of the features of lead made in this way that it contains a number of metallic impurities, especially copper, arsenic, antimony, bismuth, tin, silver and gold. It can be economic to remove the impurities, either for their own intrinsic value, or because lead of high purity is in demand.

(d) *Copper*

Unlike lead sulphide, which is completely converted into an oxide, after flotation copper pyrites is roasted only to the extent necessary to convert the iron content into an oxide:

$$2CuFeS_2(s) + 4O_2(g) \rightarrow Cu_2S(s) + 2FeO(s) + 3SO_2(g)$$

The mixture of Cu_2S and FeO is mixed with sand and roasted again. This removes the iron as liquid slag, and the Cu_2S (together with some FeS) is left as a molten mass.

The next stage is to run it off into another converter, add more sand, and then blast air through it. Some of the sulphide is converted into copper(I) oxide, Cu_2O. The main reaction liberating the copper is

$$Cu_2S(s) + 2Cu_2O(s) \rightarrow 6Cu(s) + SO_2(g)$$

Owing to its nobbly look the product is known as blister copper. In order to obtain pure copper the blister copper can be used as the anode in an electrolysis cell, using copper(II) sulphate solution as the electrolyte. Look at section 72.3 to see how this works.

(e) *Nickel*

After the sulphide ore is concentrated it is roasted with silica. This removes much of the iron as a slag. The remaining mixture of iron and nickel oxides is reduced with water gas (see section 90.2). The next stage is a novel one: carbon monoxide is passed over the impure nickel at about 60° C and nickel carbonyl, $Ni(CO)_4$, is produced. The carbonyl is volatile and after it is removed from the reaction chamber it is heated to well above 100° C when it promptly decomposes into nickel and carbon monoxide. The nickel produced in this way is of high purity. The added advantage is that the carbon monoxide can be recycled.

85.1 Is the reason for the lack of reducing power of carbon when it converts into CS_2 that ΔG for the reaction $C + 2S \rightarrow CS_2$ is too negative or too positive?

85.2 (i) Calculate the free energy changes for these reactions:

$$2CuS(s) + C(s) \rightarrow 2Cu(s) + CS_2(l)$$
$$2CaS(s) + C(s) \rightarrow 2Ca(s) + CS_2(l)$$
$$2CuS(s) + 3O_2(g) \rightarrow 2CuO(s) + 2SO_2(g)$$

$\Delta G_f^\ominus(CuS) = -49$ kJ mol^{-1}; $\Delta G_f^\ominus(CS_2) = 63.6$ kJ mol^{-1}; $\Delta G_f^\ominus(CaS) = -1320.5$ kJ mol^{-1}; $\Delta G_f^\ominus(CuO) = -127.2$ kJ mol^{-1}; $\Delta G_f^\ominus(SO_2) = -300.4$ kJ mol^{-1}.

(ii) Which of them are spontaneous under standard conditions?

(iii) What do you notice about the value of $\Delta G_f^\ominus(CS_2)$ compared to $\Delta G_f^\ominus(SO_2)$?

(iv) Why are the reactions not carried out at standard conditions?

85.4 Reducing an oxide ore

The most important example of the reduction of an oxide ore is in the extraction of iron. The chief iron ore is haematite, Fe_2O_3. Reduction of the ore takes place in a blast furnace (Figure 85.2), which is often about 30 m high and 8 m in diameter at its widest point. The furnace is charged with a mixture of limestone, coke and iron ore. Air is introduced under pressure near the bottom of the furnace, where the coke combines with the oxygen to make carbon monoxide. This is an exothermic process, which helps to provide energy to keep the furnace going. Temperatures around 1500 to 2000° C are reached. It is the carbon monoxide that plays the largest part in the reduction of the ore, which takes place towards the top of the furnace:

$$Fe_2O_3(s) + 3CO(g) \rightarrow 2Fe(l) + 3CO_2(g)$$

The reason for adding the limestone to the furnace charge is that the carbonate decomposes to give calcium oxide. This highly basic material reacts with parts of the ore that contain silica, to give calcium silicate. This silicate is the chief component of the molten slag that is tapped off near the bottom of the furnace:

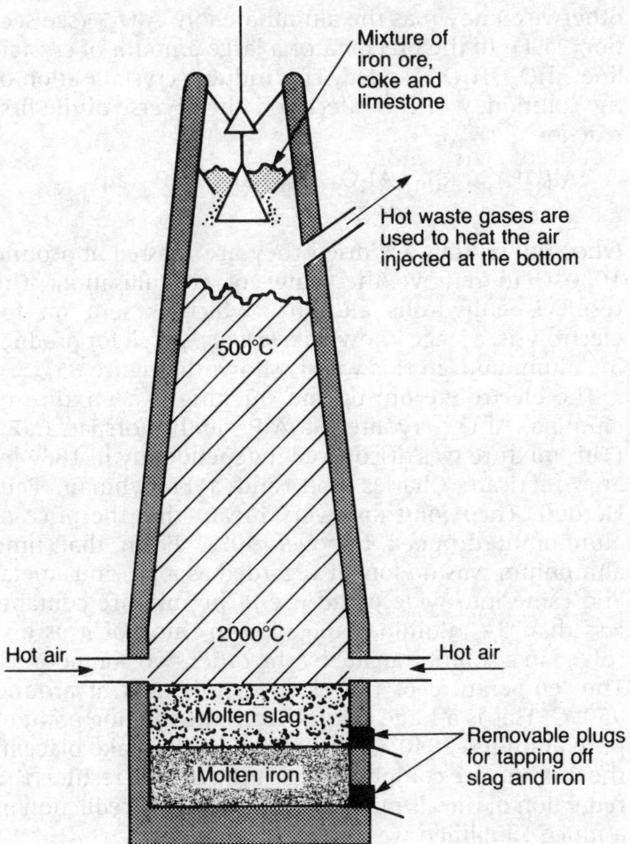

Figure 85.2 The basic design of a blast furnace for extracting iron from iron ore

$$CaO(s) + SiO_2(s) \rightarrow CaSiO_3(l)$$

The liquid iron run off at the bottom can be cast into moulds called pigs; hence the term pig iron. It is not particularly useful because it contains a great many impurities. Given the importance of steel in industries such as car manufacture, the bulk of the molten iron is turned into steel.

The most common method of making steel now is to blast oxygen through the impure molten iron. The oxygen oxidises impurities such as carbon and phosphorus to oxides, which escape from the melt either as gases or by being absorbed into slag. There are many qualities of steel, each having a different set of characteristics to the others. It is the amount of carbon mixed with the iron that largely determines the nature of the steel, e.g. its tensile strength and malleability. Small amounts of other substances, such as manganese, can also be added to give desirable qualities.

Once the steel making industry employed hundreds of thousands of workers in Europe. Now the number is measured in tens of thousands. Like many industries, steel making has become highly automated.

> **85.3** It is possible to identify an 'iron cycle' of the same kind as a water or nitrogen cycle. Suggest some stages in the cycle.

85.5 The extraction of reactive metals

We shall look at two processes. The first is for the extraction of sodium and the second is for the extraction of aluminium.

(a) *The Downs process for the extraction of sodium from sodium chloride*

The electrolysis is carried out in a Downs cell. The sodium chloride is mixed with calcium chloride in a ratio of about 2 to 3. The melting point of the mixture is about 600° C (around 200° C lower than that of pure sodium chloride). A diagram of the Downs cell is shown in Figure 85.3.

Sodium is discharged at the steel cathode, and chlorine released at the graphite anode:

at the anode	$2Cl^- - 2e^- \rightarrow Cl_2$
at the cathode	$Na^+ + e^- \rightarrow Na$

A large current is passed through the cell, but at a low voltage. This has the effect of both discharging the sodium effectively and heating the mixture so that it does not crystallise.

The sodium collects in inverted troughs above the cathode ring, and can be drawn off when necessary. The demand for metallic sodium is declining as lead-free petrol is becoming more widely used. The reason is that sodium is a vital ingredient in making 'anti-knock' compounds like tetraethyl-lead(IV), $Pb(C_2H_5)_4$. This compound is a ready source of free radicals, which aid the smooth burning of petrol. (See section 81.4 for more information on free radicals.) Until relatively

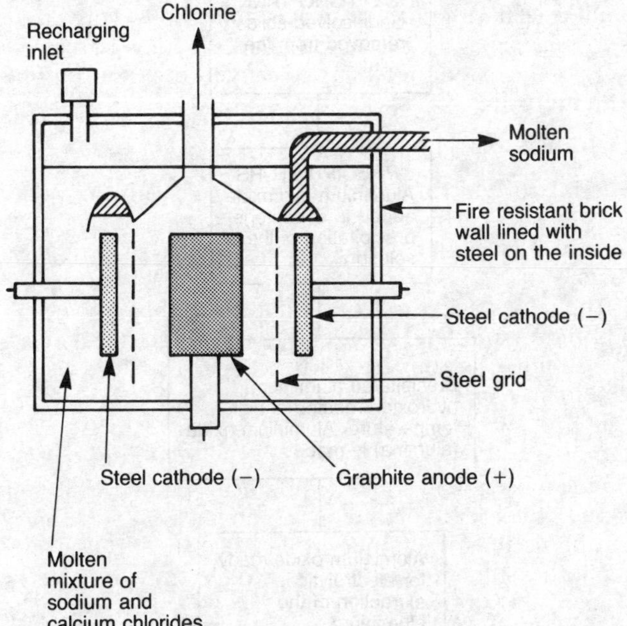

Figure 85.3 A Downs cell for extracting sodium from sodium chloride. The cell is circular, with the steel cathode making a continuous ring around the carbon anode

recently nearly 80% of sodium production was used in this way.

(b) *The extraction of aluminium from bauxite*

Bauxite is the major ore of aluminium, consisting of up to 60% aluminium oxide, Al_2O_3, commonly known as alumina. It is pure alumina that is needed, and the unwanted material in the ore has to be removed. Figure 85.4 outlines the method. It is a process that gives a large quantity of waste, and an equally large problem of how to deal with it. The waste is a slurry with a mud-like consistency and red-brown in colour owing to the presence of iron(III) oxide.

The method makes use of the amphoteric nature of aluminium. Aluminium oxide in the ore dissolves in sodium hydroxide solution at over 40 atm pressure and around 250° C:

$$\underset{\text{in bauxite}}{Al_2O_3(s)} + 2OH^-(aq) + 3H_2O(l) \rightarrow 2Al(OH)_4^-(aq)$$

The resulting solution contains the $Al(OH)_4^-$ ion,

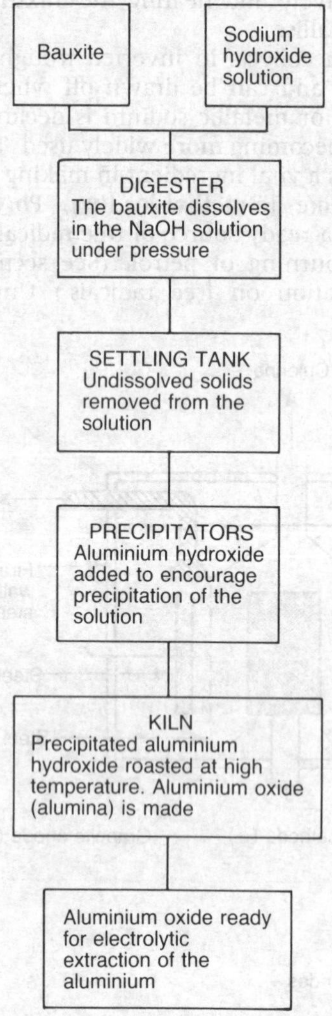

Figure 85.4 *Flowchart for the production of aluminium oxide (alumina)*

otherwise known as the aluminate ion, AlO_2^- (see section 94.1). In the precipitator a large amount of crystalline $Al_2O_3{\cdot}3H_2O$ is added. This induces crystallisation of the solution, which is effectively the reverse of the first reaction:

$$2Al(OH)_4^-(aq) \rightarrow \underset{\text{pure}}{Al_2O_3{\cdot}3H_2O(s)} + 2OH^-(aq)$$

Once the crystals are dried they are roasted at around 1000° C to remove the water of crystallisation. The result is anhydrous alumina, which is sent on for electrolysis, a stage known as *smelting*. A cell for producing aluminium in this way is shown in Figure 85.5.

The electrolyte during the smelting is a mixture of alumina, Al_2O_3, cryolite, Na_3AlF_6, and fluorspar, CaF_2. (This mixture was discovered independently in 1886 by an American, Charles Hall, and a Frenchman, Paul Heroult. Their joint discovery meant that the price of aluminium dropped by over 90%. From that time aluminium was no longer regarded as a precious metal and came into widespread use.) The mixture contains less than 5% alumina, and we can think of it as dissolved in a solution made by the other two compounds. The temperature of the electrolyte is kept at around 950° C. This is a huge change from the melting point of pure alumina, 2040° C. The reactions that take place in the mixture are complicated, but the overall result is the reduction of the alumina. We can write the reduction in a much simplified way as

$$Al^{3+} + 3e^- \rightarrow Al$$

The carbon anode burns away owing to its reaction with oxygen liberated from the alumina. For each kilogram of aluminium extracted, over 0.5 kg of the anodes is burnt away. On the one hand, this is a nuisance because it means that the anodes have to be replaced from time to time, which adds to the manufacturing costs. On the other hand, the energy released is a significant factor in driving the whole process on.

Molten aluminium is tapped from the smelter and kept in a secondary furnace (called the reverbatory

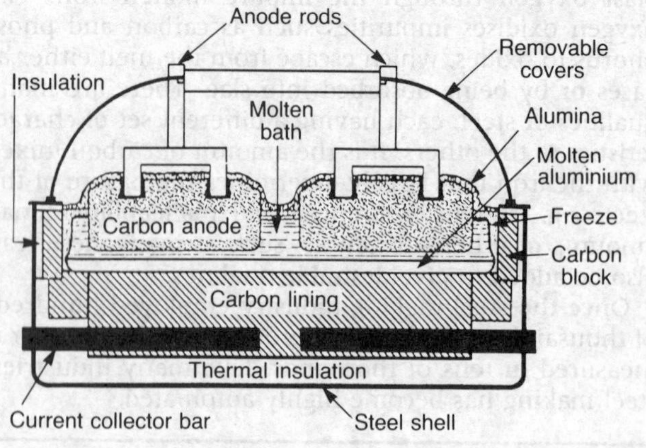

Figure 85.5 *Design of a cell for producing aluminium by the electrolysis of alumina. (Source: Kirk, R. E. and Othmer, D. F. (1985).* Concise Encyclopaedia of Chemical Technology, *Wiley, New York, p. 77)*

This is the site of an aluminium smelter at Lynemouth in the UK. Notice the closeness of the plant to the power station in the background.

One result of the resistance of aluminium to corrosion is the ease with which it is recycled.

furnace) until it is cast into ingots. Aluminium is a valuable commodity owing to the combination of strength it can give to alloys together with resistance to corrosion. Aluminium alloys are widely used in aircraft, ships, ladders and, more mundanely, dustbins. The metal also finds use in cooking foil and in television aerials. In fact aluminium does corrode slightly, giving a layer of aluminium oxide on its surface. However, once the layer is there it protects the remaining aluminium from oxidising any further.

85.4 In the Downs cell, why are the anodes made from graphite rather than steel?

85.5 If the temperature of the electrolyte in the Downs cell increases far above 600°C, the sodium dissolves in the molten electrolyte rather than lying on top of it. If this happens current still passes through the cell, but the electrolysis stops, i.e. production of sodium and chlorine ceases. What might be the reason for this? (Hint: sodium is a metal.)

85.6 The power supplied by a current of I amps at a voltage V is given by: power $= I \times V$ (units are watts, W).

(i) What is the power supplied to 100 aluminium cells, each passing 40 000 A at 5 V? Give your answer in kilowatts, kW (1 kW = 1000 W).

(ii) Electricity companies sell electricity by the 'unit'. One 'unit' is a kilowatt-hour, kW h. To calculate the number of 'units', simply multiply the number of watts by the number of hours. How many units does the smelter use in one day?

(iii) It needs approximately 15 000 kW h to produce 1 tonne of aluminium. What mass of aluminium will the smelter give each day?

(iv) Find out the price of a 'unit' of electricity used in your home. If the company paid the same price as you, what would it cost to supply electricity to the smelter each day?

(v) Why is it that companies prefer to site smelters in mountainous regions, e.g. in parts of Norway and Canada, unless a government induces them to set up in another area, perhaps by offering cheap electricity?

(vi) Why might a government offer an inducement like this?

(vii) What other factors would a company take into account before deciding on where to site a smelter?

85.7 If you look at the formulae of cryolite and fluorspar you should be able to suggest a dangerous by-product that can be made in an aluminium smelter. What is it? Why is it so dangerous?

Answers

85.1 It is positive. A reaction that has a positive free energy change at a given temperature cannot be spontaneous at that temperature.

85.2 (i) The free energy changes are, respectively, 161.6, 2704.6, −502.8, all in kJ mol^{-1}.

(ii) Only the third is spontaneous.

(iii) It is positive. This is the reason why the first two reactions will not take place.

(iv) First, the Ellingham diagram shows that the reactions often become spontaneous at a higher temperature even if they are not spontaneous at a lower temperature. Secondly, the rate of the reactions will be faster at a higher temperature.

85.3 The cycle might be: iron oxides→Fe→iron and steel products→rusting→iron oxides.

Almost 750 million tonnes of iron and steel are made in the world each year. Clearly this rate of extraction cannot go on for ever; but relatively little attention is paid to the virtues of recycling iron and steel products.

85.4 The chlorine given off will attack hot steel giving iron(III) chloride. Carbon is much more resistant to attack by chlorine.

85.5 Sodium conducts electricity very well. Current passes directly through the sodium, so the sodium, anode and cathode behave almost as if they were one length of conducting wire. Charge cannot build up on the two electrodes, so electrolysis stops.

85.6 (i) Power = 40 000 A × 5 V × 100 = 2000 kW.

(ii) 2000 kW × 24 h = 48 000 kW h or units.

(iii) 1 tonne × 48 000 kW h/15 000 kW h = 3.2 tonnes.

(iv) Using a round number of 10 p per unit, the cost is in the region of £4800. Actually industry can negotiate cheaper prices for electricity than for home use.

(v) Hydroelectric power stations are often situated in mountainous regions. These generate electricity relatively cheaply by allowing water falling under gravity to turn turbines. The smelters make use of the cheaper electricity.

(vi) A smelter brings employment to an area, not only to those working in the plant but also to other people who supply goods and services to the plant and workforce. (It can help to get politicians elected if they reduce unemployment.)

(vii) Among the more important ones are: (i) close access to a port so that bauxite can be imported or aluminium exported; (ii) easy access to a good network of roads and/or railways so that other raw materials, and finished aluminium, can be transported easily to and from the smelter; (iii) if the bauxite is being converted into alumina at the same site, there must be waste pits available where the red mud, and other waste products, can be stored.

85.7 Fluoride ions can be discharged at the anode, giving fluorine, F_2. This is a highly reactive gas, which easily reacts with other chemicals. It has been known for fluorine and fluorides to escape from smelters and cause damage to animal and plant life in the surrounding area.

UNIT 85 SUMMARY

- Methods of extraction of metals include:
  - (i) Direct mining, e.g. of gold.
  - (ii) Removal of metals from their sulphide ores by a combination of roasting to turn them into oxides, followed by reduction by carbon.

    e.g. $2PbS(s) + 3O_2(g) \rightarrow 2PbO(s) + 2SO_2(g)$
    galena

    $PbO(s) + C(s) \rightarrow Pb(l) + CO(g)$

    Treatment of sulphide ores follows the pattern: crushing, froth flotation, roasting in air.
  - (iii) Reduction of metal oxide ores, often by carbon or carbon monoxide. This is especially important for iron in the blast furnace.

    $Fe_2O_3(s) + 3CO(g) \rightarrow 2Fe(l) + 3CO_2(g)$
    haematite

- The most reactive elements in Groups I, II and III are extracted by electrolysis:
  - (i) Aluminium is extracted from bauxite (Al_2O_3) by electrolysis of a molten mixture of Al_2O_3, Na_3AlF_6, CaF_2.

    $Al^{3+} + 3e^- \rightarrow Al$
  - (ii) Sodium is extracted by the electrolysis of a molten mixture of NaCl and $CaCl_2$ in a Downs cell.

    $Na^+ + e^- \rightarrow Na$

86

The oil industry

86.1 Why is the oil industry important?

The oil industry is important because it is the major source of the world's energy and chemicals. The products range from petrol and other fuels for transport and oil heating systems to polymers and detergents. Millions of tonnes of oil are extracted each year and processed in refineries and other chemical plants. We could not possibly cover all the chemical processes in which oil is involved. Instead, we shall concentrate on three of them. They all involve the direct treatment of oil and the simpler organic compounds that can be made from it.

First, you should know the origin of oil. Essentially it is the product of the decay of the bodies of countless tiny sea creatures that have been trapped under layers of rock (Figure 86.1). Usually the oil is accompanied by methane, otherwise known as natural gas.

There are many areas on the Earth where oil can be found. Under land, oil and gas is relatively easy to extract, but removing deposits from under the sea poses difficult technological problems. New methods of extraction have had to be developed in the seas around Britain, particularly in the North Sea. Once the oil is taken from the wells, it is transported to the refineries. This is best done by pipeline, but generally involves moving it around the world by massive oil tankers. If these tankers are holed in accidents, they invariably cause severe problems of pollution.

Once the oil arrives at the refineries, the interesting chemistry begins.

We have discussed the theory of how, or why, distillation works in Unit 63. We find in section 111.2 that crude oil can be split into a number of fractions ranging from tarry substances of very high boiling point to gaseous molecules of low boiling point (see Table 111.2). Some of the fractions have immediate uses, but most require further treatment. The demand for the different fractions is not uniform, nor do they necessarily contain molecules of exactly the right type. We shall look at two examples of how the fractions are treated to turn them into substances with more desirable characteristics.

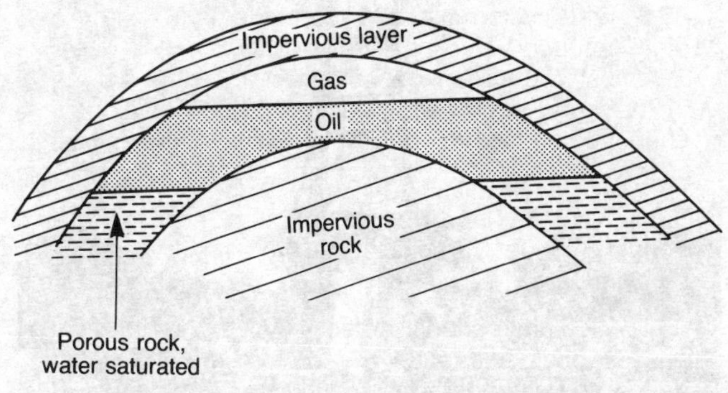

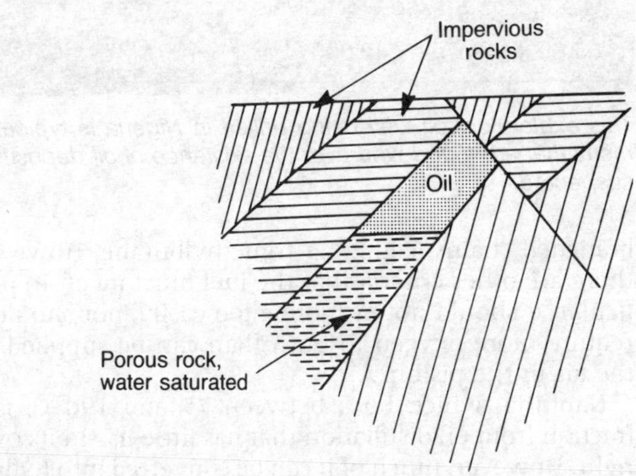

Figure 86.1 *Two of the many ways in which oil may be found trapped underground. The diagram on the right shows oil trapped in a fault*

If petrol engines in cars are to work properly, the fuel must burn evenly rather than exploding suddenly. If the fuel does explode, the engine is said to suffer from knocking. This leads to a loss of power, so it is wasteful of the fuel, and it can cause damage to the engine. The *octane number* of a fuel is a measure of how resistant it is to knocking. A fuel with a high octane number will cause less knocking than a fuel with a low octane number. Experiment shows that aromatic hydrocarbons have high octane ratings, as do hydrocarbons with

This exploratory oil well being drilled in Nigeria is typical of many that are found wherever the existence of oil deposits is suspected.

As the value of oil has increased, it has become economically worthwhile to develop oil fields at sea. This offshore platform is in the North Sea.

branched chains, e.g. 2,2,3-trimethylbutane. However, there are other criteria that the fuel must meet. In particular, it should not evaporate too easily, nor should it require more oxygen to burn than can be supplied by the air in the pistons.

Naphtha, which boils between 75 and 190° C, is a fraction from oil distillation that has little use in its own right. However, much of it can be converted into hydrocarbons with a high octane number by a process called *catalytic re-forming.* A fraction of much higher boiling point (gas oil), much of which is used for diesel fuel, can be changed to hydrocarbons of shorter chain length by *catalytic cracking.*

86.1 Why should fuel for cars not evaporate too easily?

86.2 Catalytic re-forming

In catalytic re-forming, naphtha is mixed with hydrogen and passed over a catalyst. A high pressure of up to 40 atm is needed, and the gases must be heated to over 450° C. The catalyst used is often a mixture of platinum and aluminium oxide. The reactions that take place depend on the type of hydrocarbon in the naphtha. Some of them are converted into aromatics, and some straight-chain hydrocarbons rearrange into branched-chain hydrocarbons. Both these changes give products with increased octane numbers. For example,

$$CH_3CH_2CH_2CH_2CH_2CH_3 \longrightarrow CH_3CH_2CH(CH_3)CH_2CH_3$$

$$CH_3CH_2CH_2CH_2CH_2CH_2CH_3 \longrightarrow C_6H_5{-}CH_3 + 4H_2$$

However, some hydrocarbons split apart giving small molecules, which are of no use for petrol.

There is another variety of re-forming that has nothing to do with making petrol, but a lot to do with making ammonia. The process is *steam re-forming.* In this

The scene of one of the world's worst oil spillages. The tanker Valdez spilled over ten million tonnes of oil in Prince William Sound, Alaska, in March 1989, causing environmental damage from which the area has still not recovered.

case naphtha, or another hydrocarbon feedstock, is reacted with steam at a high temperature over a nickel catalyst. Eventually the hydrocarbon yields up its hydrogen, which is then used in the Haber process. You will find details of the changes that take place in Unit 83.

> **86.2** The conversions that take place in re-forming tend to break more carbon–hydrogen bonds than are made in the products. Is catalytic re-forming an exothermic or endothermic process?

86.3 Catalytic cracking

Catalytic cracking takes long-chain hydrocarbons and breaks them into smaller ones. The method is to pass the hydrocarbons at around 500° C over a catalyst mixture of silica and aluminium oxide, or of zeolites (see section 91.6). The hydrocarbons are in contact with the catalyst for a very short time – less than ten seconds.

The mechanisms of re-forming and cracking are complicated, but often they involve carbocations, which are produced on the catalyst and then rearrange.

Part of the Shell oil refinery at Ellesmere Port in the UK. The central area of the photograph is dominated by the catalytic cracker plant.

> **86.3** What might be the reason for the conversion of
>
> $$CH_3-CH_2-\overset{+}{C}H-CH_2-CH_2-CH_3$$
>
> into
>
> $$CH_3-CH_2-\underset{\underset{CH_3}{|}}{\overset{+}{C}}-CH_2-CH_3$$
>
> (Hint: see Unit 112.)
>
> **86.4** How might the products of the cracking be separated?

86.4 Thermal cracking

Thermal cracking has been used for many years as a way of converting alkanes into alkenes. The cracking is done by the apparently simple method of heating the alkanes to a high temperature. However, the process is not quite so simple in practice. Typically, the alkanes are brought to a temperature of around 800° C and then rapidly cooled to half that temperature in the space of a second. This can only be done by quickly moving the gases through tubes heated in a furnace and then into a heat exchanger. There is invariably a mixture of different products, but ethene is the most favoured product. The cracking takes place through a free radical mechanism. (See Unit 81 for details of these reactions.)

Ethene is valuable because it is a key starting material for the preparation of a large number of other chemicals; so too are other alkenes (see Figure 86.2).

> **86.5** What is the name we give to the process by which a reaction rate is decreased by quickly lowering the temperature, or some other method?

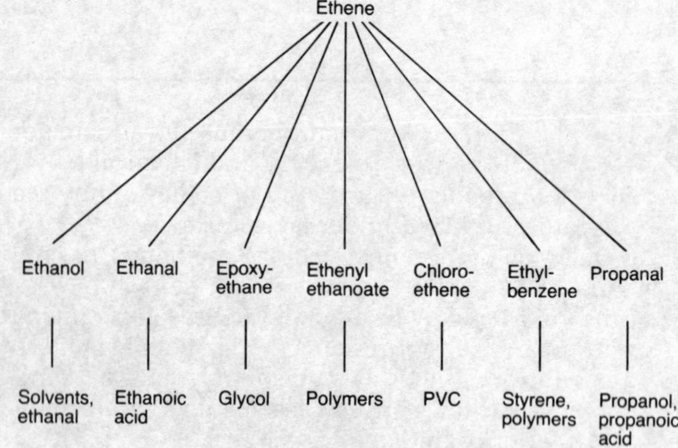

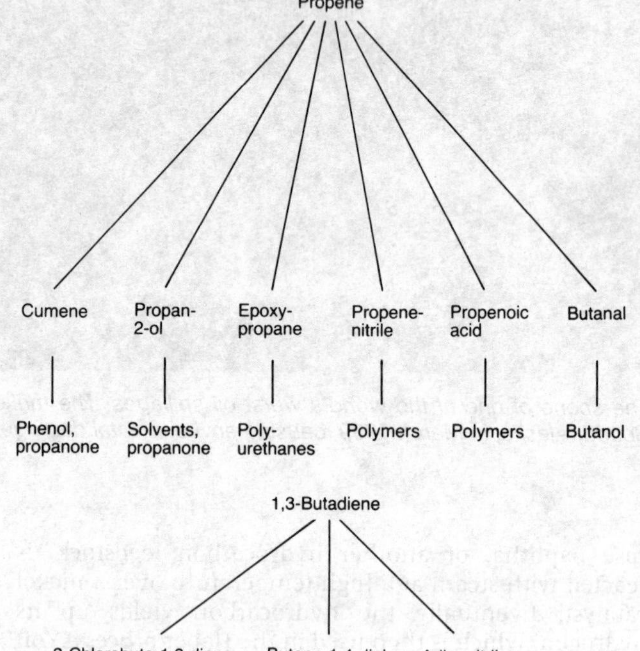

***Figure 86.2** Chemicals that can be made from alkenes. (Adapted from: Heaton, C. A. (1984).* An Introduction to Industrial Chemistry, *Leonard Hill, Glasgow, p. 336)*

> **Answers**
>
> **86.1** It would be dangerous to fill up on a hot day! Also, if the petrol were to vaporise in the fuel lines, a bubble of vapour would prevent the fuel flowing properly.
>
> **86.2** It is endothermic. Carbon–hydrogen bonds are strong, and require significant amounts of energy to break them. This energy is not retrieved by, for example, making the π bonds in a double bond.
>
> **86.3** The second carbocation is energetically stabilised by the presence of the methyl group on the carbon carrying the positive charge.
>
> **86.4** Distillation.
>
> **86.5** The reaction is 'quenched'.

UNIT 86 SUMMARY

- The oil industry is important because it is the major source of the world's energy and chemicals.
- Oil is the product of the decay of bodies of tiny sea creatures trapped under layers of rock.
- Usually oil is accompanied by methane (natural gas).
- Crude oil is split by distillation into fractions ranging from tarry substances of very high boiling point to gaseous molecules of low boiling point.
- Catalytic cracking converts gas oil into hydrocarbons of shorter chain length.
- Steam re-forming reacts naphtha with steam at a high temperature over a nickel catalyst a releases hydrogen, which is used in the Ha process.
- Catalytic re-forming converts naphtha (a fraction boiling between 75 and 190° C) into hydrocarbons with high octane numbers.
- Thermal cracking can be used to convert alkanes into alkenes by heating the alkanes to a high temperature.

Part C

INORGANIC CHEMISTRY

87

The Periodic Table

87.1 The origin of the Periodic Table

Chemists have long tried to find patterns in the properties of the elements. Some were discovered fairly readily; for example, elements were classified as metals or non-metals, and many of their compounds as acids, alkalis, or salts. However, it was widely believed that there had to be an underlying reason for the patterns. One of the first suggestions was due to Prout. Prout's hypothesis was that all elements were made from a whole number of hydrogen atoms. (Be careful here: an 'atom' in Prout's time was a very different thing to our understanding of the word.) According to him the atomic masses of the elements should be a whole number of times that of hydrogen, i.e. they should be integers. Unfortunately, from Prout's point of view, the results of experiments showed that the atomic masses of many elements were not integers.

However, as more elements were discovered, and their atomic masses determined, the search for patterns among the masses continued. Döbereiner drew attention to the fact that there were groups of three elements that not only had chemical properties in common, but also showed trends in the way their atomic masses changed. Some examples are shown in Table 87.1.

Observations like this explained little, but were intriguing, and began a search for other connections between the chemical properties of elements and their atomic masses. A major attempt at making a link was made by Newlands in 1864 (Table 87.2). He grouped elements into sets of eight and claimed that every eighth element in the pattern was chemically similar. Newlands' *law of octaves* was largely ignored, or at best treated with mild amusement.

The first thorough attempt at relating chemical properties to atomic masses was made by the Russian

Table 87.1. Some of Döbereiner's triads

Element	*Atomic mass*	*Comment*
Lithium	7.0	The difference between the values is nearly 16
Sodium	23.0	
Potassium	39.2	
Calcium	40.1	The difference between the values is around 48 and 50
Strontium	87.6	
Barium	137.4	
Chlorine	35.5	The difference between the values is around 45 and 47
Bromine	80.0	
Iodine	126.9	

Table 87.2. Examples of Newlands' octaves*

	No.		*No.*		*No.*		*No.*		*No.*
H	1	F	8	Cl	15	Co & Ni	22	Br	29
Li	2	Na	9	K	16	Cu	23	Rb	30
G	3	Mg	10	Ca	17	Zn	24	Sr	31
Bo	4	Al	11	Cr	18	Y	25	Ce & Le	32
C	5	Si	12	Ti	19	In	26	Zr	33
N	6	P	13	Mn	20	As	27	Di & Mo	33
O	7	S	14	Fe	21	Se	28	Ro & Ru	35

*This is part of a table that John Newlands presented in a talk he gave to the Chemical Society on 9 March 1866. The talk was entitled 'The Law of Octaves, and the Causes of Numerical Relations among the Atomic Weights'. (You might like to work out which elements G, Bo, etc., stand for.) Here is part of an account of the talk:

> The author claims the discovery of a law according to which the elements analogous in their properties exhibit peculiar relationships, similar to those subsisting in music between a note and its octave . . .. Professor G. F. Foster humorously enquired of Mr. Newlands whether he had ever examined the elements according to the order of their initial letters?

Newlands was not at all happy about the credit that went to Mendeléeff over the discovery of the periodic law. In 1884 Newlands wrote:

> Having been the first to publish the existence of the periodic law more than nineteen years ago, I feel, under existing circumstances, compelled to assert my priority in this matter . . .. As a matter of simple justice, and in the interest of all true workers in science, both theoretical and practical, it is right that the originator of any proposal or discovery should have the credit of his labour.

PERIODIC SYSTEM OF THE ELEMENTS IN GROUPS AND SERIES.

SERIES	GROUPS OF ELEMENTS								
	0	I	II	III	IV	V	VI	VII	VIII
1	—	Hydrogen H 1·008	—	—	—	—	—	—	
2	Helium He 4·0	Lithium Li 7·03	Beryllium Be 9·1	Boron B 11·0	Carbon C 12·0	Nitrogen N 14·04	Oxygen O 16·00	Fluorine F 19·0	
3	Neon Ne 19·9	Sodium Na 23·05	Magnesium Mg 24·3	Aluminium Al 27·0	Silicon Si 28·4	Phosphorus P 31·0	Sulphur S 32·06	Chlorine Cl 35·45	
4	Argon Ar 38	Potassium K 39·1	Calcium Ca 40·1	Scandium Sc 44·1	Titanium Ti 48·1	Vanadium V 51·4	Chromium Cr 52·1	Manganese Mn 55·0	Iron Fe 55·9; Cobalt Co 59; Nickel Ni 59 (Cu)
5		Copper Cu 63·6	Zinc Zn 65.4	Gallium Ga 70·0	Germanium Ge 72·3	Arsenic As 75	Selenium Se 79	Bromine Br 79·95	
6	Krypton Kr 81·8	Rubidium Rb 85·4	Strontium Sr 87·6	Yttrium Y 89·0	Zirconium Zr 90·6	Niobium Nb 94·0	Molybdenum Mo 96·0	—	Ruthenium Ru 101·7; Rhodium Rh 103·0; Palladium Pd 106·5 (Ag)
7		Silver Ag 107·9	Cadmium Cd 112·4	Indium In 114·0	Tin Sn 119·0	Antimony Sb 120·0	Tellurium Te 127	Iodine I 127	
8	Xenon Xe 128	Caesium Cs 132·9	Barium Ba 137·4	Lanthanum La 139	Cerium Ce 140	—	—	—	— — —
9		—	—	—	—	—	—	—	
10	—	—	—	Ytterbium Yb 173	—	Tantalum Ta 183	Tungsten W 184	—	Osmium Os 191; Iridium Ir 193; Platinum Pt 194·9 (Au)
11		Gold Au 197·2	Mercury Hg 200·0	Thallium Tl 204·1	Lead Pb 206·9	Bismuth Bi 208	—	—	
12	—	—	Radium Rd 224	—	Thorium Th 232	—	Uranium U 239		
HIGHER SALINE OXIDES	R	R_2O	RO	R_2O_3	RO_2	R_2O_5	RO_3	R_2O_7	RO_4
HIGHER GASEOUS HYDROGEN COMPOUNDS					RH_4	RH_3	RH_2	RH	

***Figure 87.1** Mendeléeff's Periodic Table of 1905*

chemist Dimitri Mendeléeff. In 1869 he published a table that formed the basis of the Periodic Table that we now use. A version that he published in 1905 is shown in Figure 87.1. The claim was made that:

> the properties of the elements vary in relation to their atomic masses.

This statement became known as the periodic law. However, Mendeléeff was well aware that there was at least one anomaly in the table. You will see that he quotes the atomic mass of argon as 38. However, the experimental evidence was that the true value was about 39.6. Mendeléeff was so convinced that the periodic law was correct that he changed the figure to one which would fit the law. The reason he gave was:

> . . . argon represents a slight discrepancy . . .. This leads one to think that argon still includes some other gas of high density in admixture with it.

In other words, he thought that the measurements of the atomic mass of argon were wrong because there was an impurity present. The anomaly would not, however, go away. It was joined by other exceptions to the periodic law; for example, cobalt (58.9) and nickel (58.7), and tellurium (127.6) and iodine (126.9) were in the reverse order of their relative atomic masses.

We now know that the reason for the anomalies was that the periodic law as Mendeléeff set it out is not correct. It was Moseley who showed that the position of an element in the Periodic Table depended on its *atomic number* not on its atomic mass. The correct *periodic law* is:

The properties of the elements vary in relation to their atomic numbers.

(You might need to look at Unit 3 for information about the work of Moseley and atomic number.)

87.1 What do you think about Mendeléeff's attitude to the atomic mass of argon?

87.2 The modern Periodic Table

The modern Periodic Table (Figure 87.2) differs in several respects to Mendeléeff's table. The most obvious difference is that it is stretched out. No longer are there two columns of elements in the Groups, nor are there so many rows. The two columns are separated into two sets of Groups recognised by the letters A and B after them. The rows, which Mendeléeff called series, are now called Periods. There are three short and four long

Dimitri Mendeléeff, looking suitably Russian.

Periods. The long Periods show the elements that we now call the transition metals. In Periods 6 and 7 are to be found the lanthanides and actinides, many of which were not known in Mendeléeff's time. Although it can be useful to distinguish the A Group from the B Group elements, we shall only do so when we discusss the B metals. These are the metals that lie by the side of the transition elements – especially Group IIB – or at the bottom of the other B Groups. For the most part, as earlier in the book, we shall leave out the A and B labels. For example, we shall normally refer to the elements lithium to francium as the Group I metals rather than Group IA metals and the elements carbon to lead will be Group IV, not Group IVB.

Sandwiched between Group II and III are the transition, or d-block, elements. These are all metals, some of which you will be familiar with owing to their widespread uses, e.g. chromium, iron, nickel, platinum. The transition metals have many properties in common, e.g. they often give coloured compounds, and make complexes rather easily. You will find out more about them in Unit 105.

Writing the Periodic Table in the way it is normally done, there are two sets of elements that are not shown in their rightful positions. These are the lanthanides and actinides. The lanthanides start at lanthanum (atomic number 57) and fit in the gap up to hafnium (atomic number 72). The actinides appear in a similar position in the Period below the lanthanides. These elements have, respectively, the 4f and 5f orbitals filling. Their chemistry is complicated owing to the large number of oxidation states that they can adopt. Some of them have been isolated from nuclear reactions in remarkably small quantities. (In some cases literally no more than would fit on the head of a pin.) The American chemist G. T. Seaborg and his coworkers were responsible for developing extremely accurate techniques for dealing with such small quantities. The actinides coming after uranium are called the transuranic elements. Their tendency to be radioactive makes dealing with them even more of a problem. We shall make life a little easier by ignoring them henceforth.

87.2 In the modern Periodic Table the elements in Groups IB and IIB are shown in the d block. This block is the place where the transition elements are found. Why do you think some chemists argue that the Group IB and IIB elements should not be considered as d-block elements?

87.3 The Periodic Table and electron structures

In Unit 12 we discovered that the quantum theory gives us a neat account of the electron structures of the elements. Here we can relate the filling of electron shells to the position of the elements in the Periodic Table. Figure 87.3 illustrates the orbitals that are being used in the various parts of the table. The table splits into four main regions depending on the type of orbitals that are being filled. The regions are: s block, p block, d block and f block.

87.4 The Periodic Table, metals and non-metals

The majority of the elements in the table are metals, with about 20 being non-metals. The metals are to be found to the left of the zig-zag line in Figure 87.4, and the non-metals to the right. However, it is not always helpful to try to classify an element as either a metal or a non-metal. Many elements, particularly those close to the zig-zag line, show the properties of both categories. These are the *metalloids*: boron, silicon, germanium, arsenic and tellurium. A particularly important property of silicon and germanium is that they are semiconductors.

In Table 87.3 are gathered the typical properties of metals and non-metals. Metals that show these properties to the fullest extent are to be found in Groups I and II. These are the *s-block* metals. Especially, the metals to the bottom of Group I are the most powerful reducing agents. This is a result of the outermost s electron being extremely well shielded from the nuclear charge. The

GROUPS

(a)

PERIODS	IA	IIA	IIIA	IVA	VA	VIA	VIIA	← VIII	VIII	VIII →	IB	IIB	IIIB	IVB	VB	VIB	VIIB	0
1	1 H																	2 He
2	3 Li	4 Be											5 B	6 C	7 N	8 O	9 F	10 Ne
3	11 Na	12 Mg											13 Al	14 Si	15 P	16 S	17 Cl	18 Ar
4	19 K	20 Ca	21 Sc	22 Ti	23 V	24 Cr	25 Mn	26 Fe	27 Co	28 Ni	29 Cu	30 Zn	31 Ga	32 Ge	33 As	34 Se	35 Br	36 Kr
5	37 Rb	38 Sr	39 Y	40 Zr	41 Nb	42 Mo	43 Tc	44 Ru	45 Rh	46 Pd	47 Ag	48 Cd	49 In	50 Sn	51 Sb	52 Te	53 I	54 Xe
6	55 Cs	56 Ba	57 La	72 Hf	73 Ta	74 W	75 Re	76 Os	77 Ir	78 Pt	79 Au	80 Hg	81 Tl	82 Pb	83 Bi	84 Po	85 At	86 Rn
7	87 Fr	88 Ra	89 Ac															

Lanthanides	58 Ce	59 Pr	60 Nd	61 Pm	62 Sm	63 Eu	64 Gd	65 Tb	66 Dy	67 Ho	68 Er	69 Tm	70 Yb	71 Lu
Actinides	90 Th	91 Pa	92 U	93 Np	94 Pu	95 Am	96 Cm	97 Bk	98 Cf	99 Es	100 Fm	101 Md	102 No	103 Lr

(b)

GROUPS

Key: Atomic number / Symbol / Name / Relative atomic mass

PERIODS	I (s block)	II (s block)	d block										III (p block)	IV	V	VI	VII	0
1	1 H Hydrogen 1.0																	2 He Helium 4.0
2	3 Li Lithium 6.9	4 Be Beryllium 9.0											5 B Boron 10.8	6 C Carbon 12.0	7 N Nitrogen 14.0	8 O Oxygen 16.0	9 F Fluorine 19.0	10 Ne Neon 20.2
3	11 Na Sodium 23.0	12 Mg Magnesium 24.3											13 Al Aluminium 27.0	14 Si Silicon 28.1	15 P Phosphorus 31.0	16 S Sulphur 32.1	17 Cl Chlorine 35.5	18 Ar Argon 39.9
4	19 K Potassium 39.1	20 Ca Calcium 40.1	21 Sc Scandium 45.0	22 Ti Titanium 47.8	23 V Vanadium 50.9	24 Cr Chromium 52.0	25 Mn Manganese 54.9	26 Fe Iron 55.9	27 Co Cobalt 58.9	28 Ni Nickel 58.7	29 Cu Copper 63.5	30 Zn Zinc 65.4	31 Ga Gallium 69.7	32 Ge Germanium 72.6	33 As Arsenic 74.9	34 Se Selenium 79.0	35 Br Bromine 79.9	36 Kr Krypton 83.8
5	37 Rb Rubidium 85.5	38 Sr Strontium 87.6	39 Y Yttrium 88.9	40 Zr Zirconium 91.2	41 Nb Niobium 92.9	42 Mo Molybdenum 95.9	43 Tc Technetium (99)	44 Ru Ruthenium 101.1	45 Rh Rhodium 102.3	46 Pd Palladium 106.4	47 Ag Silver 107.9	48 Cd Cadmium 112.4	49 In Indium 114.8	50 Sn Tin 118.7	51 Sb Antimony 121.8	52 Te Tellurium 127.6	53 I Iodine 114.8	54 Xe Xenon 131.3
6	55 Cs Caesium 132.9	56 Ba Barium 137.3	57 La Lanthanum 138.9	72 Hf Hafnium 178.5	73 Ta Tantalum 181.0	74 W Tungsten 183.9	75 Re Rhenium 186.2	76 Os Osmium 190.2	77 Ir Iridium 192.2	78 Pt Platinum 195.1	79 Au Gold 197.0	80 Hg Mercury 200.6	81 Tl Thallium 204.4	82 Pb Lead 207.2	83 Bi Bismuth 209.0	84 Po Polonium (210)	85 At Astatine (210)	86 Rn Radon (222)
7	87 Fr Francium (223)	88 Ra Radium (226)	89 Ac Actinium (227)	104 Unq Unnil-quadium (261)	105 Unp Unnil-pentium (262)	106 Unh Unnil-hexium (263)												

f block

Lanthanides	58 Ce Cerium 140.1	59 Pr Praseo-dymium 140.9	60 Nd Neodymium 144.2	61 Pm Promethium (147)	62 Sm Samarium 150.4	63 Eu Europium 152.0	64 Gd Gadolinium 157.3	65 Tb Terbium 158.9	66 Dy Dysprosium 162.5	67 Ho Holmium 164.9	68 Er Erbium 167.3	69 Tm Thulium 168.9	70 Yb Ytterbium 173.0	71 Lu Lutetium 175.5
Actinides	90 Th Thorium 232.0	91 Pa Protactinium (231)	92 U Uranium 238.1	93 Np Neptunium (237)	94 Pu Plutonium (242)	95 Am Americium (243)	96 Cm Curium (247)	97 Bk Berkelium (245)	98 Cf Californium (251)	99 Es Einsteinium (254)	100 Fm Fermium (253)	101 Md Mendelevium (256)	102 No Nobelium (254)	103 Lr Lawrencium (257)

***Figure 87.2** (a) The modern version of the Periodic Table showing the A and B groups. The atomic number is shown above each element's symbol. (b) The Periodic Table using a simpler notation for the groups. This is the table we shall normally use*

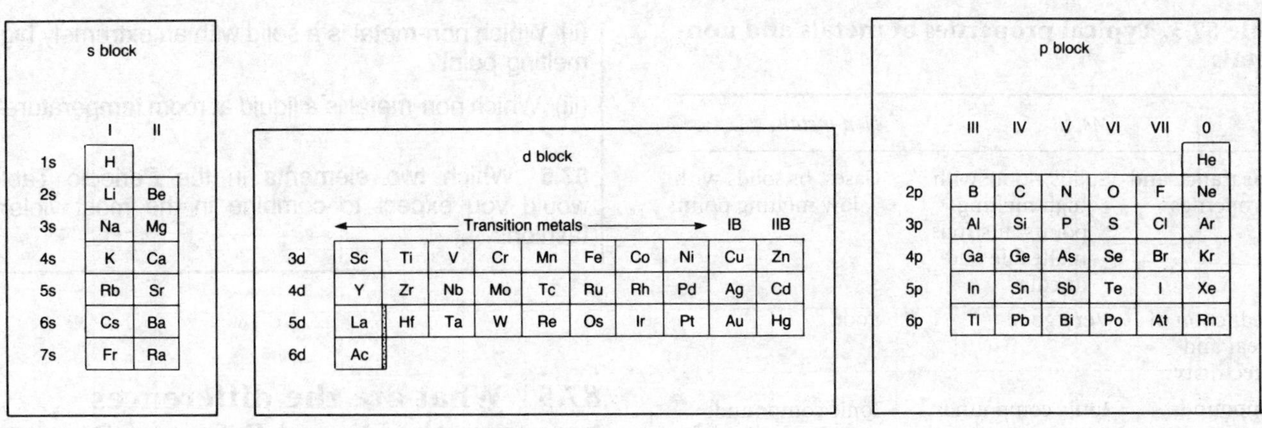

f block

Lanthanides 4f	Ce	Pr	Nd	Pm	Sm	Eu	Gd	Tb	Dy	Ho	Er	Tm	Yb	Lu
Actinides 5f	Th	Pa	U	Np	Pu	Am	Cm	Bk	Cf	Es	Fm	Md	No	Lr

***Figure 87.3** The four main blocks in the Periodic Table showing the orbitals that are being filled*

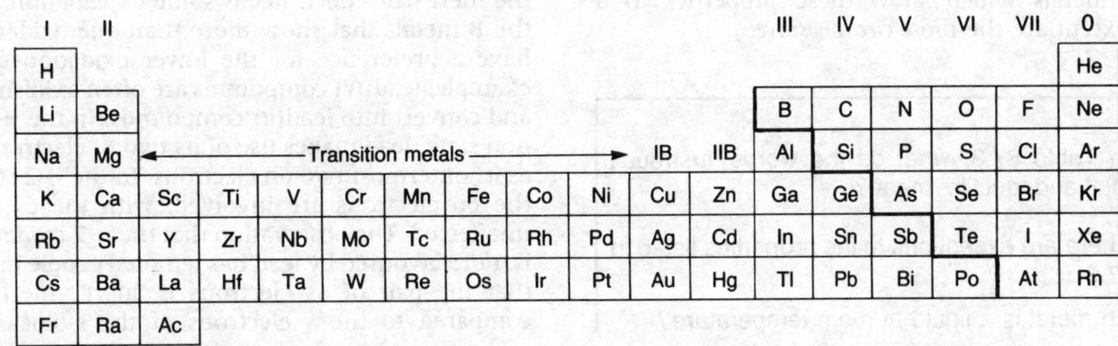

***Figure 87.4** A slightly shorter version of the Periodic Table. The heavy black line marks the division between those elements normally regarded as metals (on the left) and those thought of as non-metals (on the right)*

electron is only weakly held to the atom, so it is easily lost. The Group I metals react with water to give strong alkalis; they are known as the *alkali metals*. The metals in Group II tend to make weaker alkalis, and are known as the *alkaline earth metals*.

The *halogens*, in Group VII, show the most complete set of properties of non-metals. Fluorine, at the top of the Group, is the most powerful oxidising agent. It has a nuclear charge that is not very well shielded by the seven electrons it possesses. Fluorine will readily take an electron from a metal and make a fluoride ion, F^-.

Going across a Period there is a point at which the properties of the elements change from being primarily metallic to primarily non-metallic. You can see that this change-over point lies further to the right the lower down the table you go. Indeed it is true to say that:

> **Metallic nature increases going down any Group.**

This is summarised in Figure 87.5. The reason for this is to do with *shielding*. The further down a Group an element finds itself, the more protons it has in its nucleus, but the more electrons there are surrounding the nucleus. We saw in Unit 13 that the evidence of ionisation potentials is that shielding wins over the effect of increasing nuclear charge. Thus, going down a Group,

Table 87.3. Typical properties of metals and non-metals

	Metals	Non-metals
Appearance and properties	Solids, some with high melting points; lustrous, malleable and ductile	Gases, or solids with low melting points
Conduction of heat and electricity	Very good	Poor
Compounds	Ionic compounds with non-metals; alloys with other metals	Ionic compounds with metals; covalent compounds with other non-metals
Charge on ions	Positive	Negative
Chemical nature	Reducing agents	Oxidising agents
Electro-negativity	Low	High

the outermost electrons become progressively easier to remove. In other words, the tendency to make positive ions, and to behave as reducing agents, increases. We say that metals which show these properties to a marked extent are the most *electropositive*.

87.3 In Table 87.3, what do the words 'lustrous', 'malleable' and 'ductile' mean?

87.4 There are exceptions to the properties listed in Table 87.3.

(i) Which metal is a liquid at room temperature?

(ii) Which non-metal is a solid with an extremely high melting point?

(iii) Which non-metal is a liquid at room temperature?

87.5 Which two elements in the Periodic Table would you expect to combine in the most violent fashion?

87.5 What are the differences between the A and B Groups?

First, you can see from Figure 87.6 that the majority of the A Group elements are metals, and the majority of the B Group elements are non-metals. The most interesting differences between the A and B Groups come with the elements known as the B metals. These are shown highlighted in Figure 87.6.

In the later units we shall discuss the individual properties of these metals. For the moment you might like to look at Table 87.4, which summarises the key differences between the B metals and the other metals in the Periodic Table.

You may find that the last point in the table, about the inert pair effect, needs some explanation. Some of the B metals that show more than one oxidation state have a preference for the lower oxidation state. For example, lead(IV) compounds are often oxidising agents and convert into lead(II) compounds. In the +4 oxidation state, lead makes use of its two 6s electrons as well as its outermost two 6p electrons. In the +2 state, only the 6p electrons are involved, with the 6s electrons unaffected. The observation that the +2 oxidation state is more favoured by lead has tempted people into saying that the pair of 6s electrons is 'inert' (inert, that is, compared to the s electrons of the s-block metals);

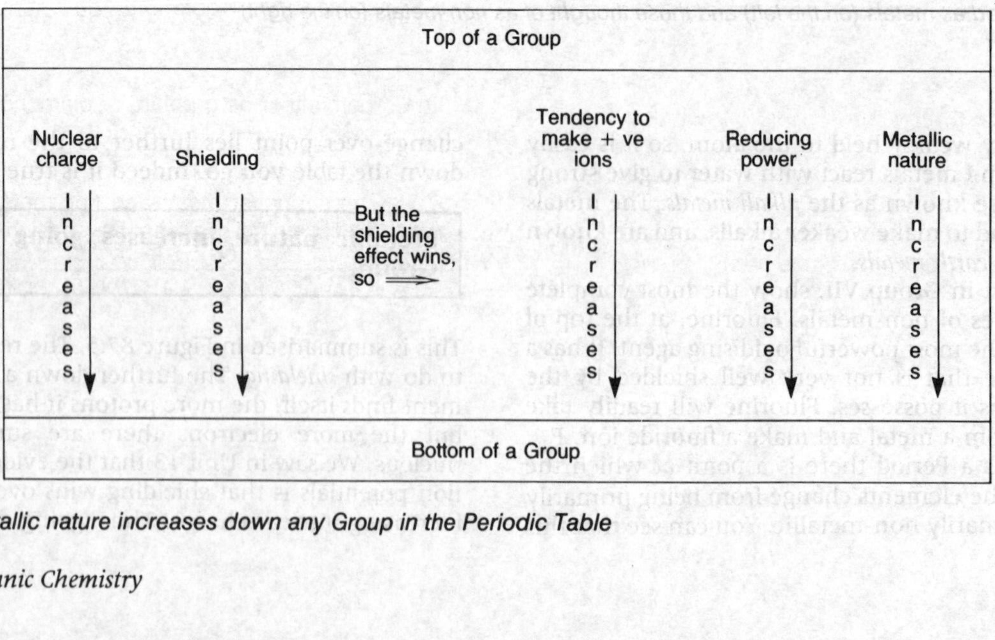

***Figure 87.5** Metallic nature increases down any Group in the Periodic Table*

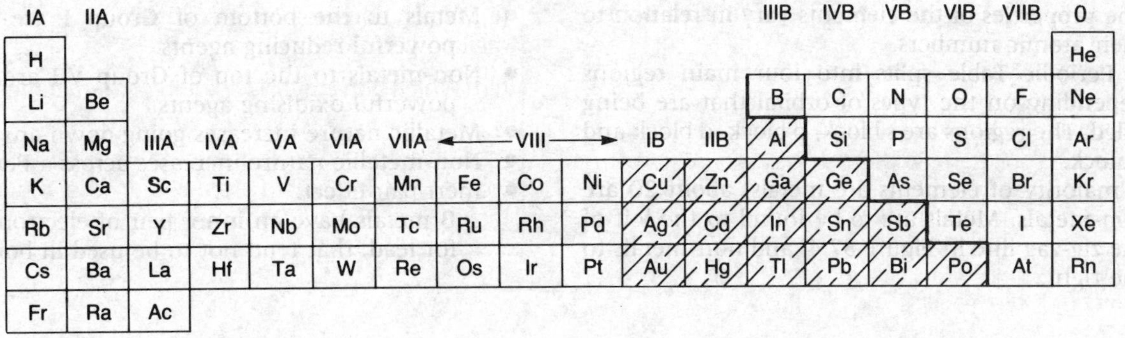

IA	IIA	IIIA	IVA	VA	VIA	VIIA	←VIII	VIII	VIII→	IB	IIB	IIIB	IVB	VB	VIB	VIIB	0
H																	He
Li	Be											B	C	N	O	F	Ne
Na	Mg											Al	Si	P	S	Cl	Ar
K	Ca	Sc	Ti	V	Cr	Mn	Fe	Co	Ni	Cu	Zn	Ga	Ge	As	Se	Br	Kr
Rb	Sr	Y	Zr	Nb	Mo	Tc	Ru	Rh	Pd	Ag	Cd	In	Sn	Sb	Te	I	Xe
Cs	Ba	La	Hf	Ta	W	Re	Os	Ir	Pt	Au	Hg	Tl	Pb	Bi	Po	At	Rn
Fr	Ra	Ac															

***Figure 87.6** The B metals in the Periodic Table are shown shaded*

Table 87.4. Comparison of properties of s-block and B metals

Property	*Example*
B metals are less reactive than the s-block metals	Potassium violent with water; silver and gold totally unreactive
B metals are weaker reducing agents, e.g. their $E^{\ominus}$ values are less negative than the s-block metals	$E^{\ominus}_{Na^+/Na} = -2.71$ V $E^{\ominus}_{Ag^+/Ag} = +0.8$ V
B metals show a greater tendency to form complex ions than s-block metals	Aluminium forms $Al(OH)_6^{3-}$ ions; similar s-block ions not made
B metals are 'softer' (more easily polarised) and tend to give compounds with a greater degree of covalency than s-block metals	$AlCl_3$ predominantly covalent; KCl ionic
B metals may show more than one oxidation state	Sn^{2+}, Sn^{4+}; Pb^{2+}, Pb^{4+}; Tl^{+}, Tl^{3+}
B metals show the so-called inert pair effect	B metals at the bottom of their Group tend not to use their outer s electrons in bonding (also, see text)

hence the term 'inert pair effect'. However, these s electrons are not really inert. Rather it seems that the bonds made by the B metals in their higher oxidation state are weaker than the bonds made in their lower oxidation states. Hence, once they are made, the compounds tend to break apart more easily.

Answers

87.1 It is tempting to think that he was 'fiddling' the results. However, if you put yourself in his position you might adopt the same attitude as he did. First, the noble gases had been discovered only very recently (argon was discovered in 1894). Little was known about it except that it was very unreactive. The possibility that another unreactive gas was mixed in with it was not impossible. Secondly, the methods used to determine atomic masses were not always reliable. There was the real possibility of error. Given that the vast majority of the elements fitted his scheme, it must have seemed very likely that the experimental results were at fault.

87.2 In the d block, the 3d, 4d, or 5d orbitals are filling. The properties of the transition elements are a result of them having unfilled d orbitals. However, the IB and IIB elements have full d orbitals. Indeed, these elements have s orbitals filling. This is one reason why some chemists think them misplaced tacked on to the end of the transition elements. However, the chemical properties of the IB metals make it sensible to include them among the transition metals. The IIB metals are best excluded.

87.3 Lustrous ≡ shiny; malleable ≡ able to be beaten into shapes; ductile ≡ able to be drawn into wires.

87.4 (i) Mercury.
(ii) Carbon, either as graphite or diamond.
(iii) Bromine.

87.5 The strongest metal and non-metal are likely to give the most violent reaction, i.e. caesium and fluorine.

UNIT 87 SUMMARY

- Mendeléeff published a table (in 1869) that formed the basis of the modern Periodic Table.
- Moseley showed that the position of an element in the Periodic Table depended on its atomic number.
- The periodic law says that:

The properties of the elements vary in relation to their atomic numbers.

- The Periodic Table splits into four main regions depending on the types of orbital that are being filled. The regions are s block, p block, d block and f block.
- The majority of elements are metals; about 20 are non-metals. Metals are to be found to the left of the zig-zag line in Figure 87.4, and non-metals to the right.
- Metals to the bottom of Group I are the most powerful reducing agents.
- Non-metals to the top of Group VII are the most powerful oxidising agents.
- Metallic nature increases going down any Group.
- Non-metallic nature increases across a Period.
- Inert pair effect:
  B metals have an inner pair of electrons, e.g. $6s^2$ for lead, that tend not to be used in bonding.

88

Periodicity of physical properties

88.1 Periodicity of ionisation energies

The periodic law says that the properties of the elements vary with their atomic numbers. Periodicity is the study of the variation in the properties, which can be both physical and chemical. We have already seen how electron structures and the division between metals and non-metals change in the Periodic Table. Now we shall concentrate on the variation in some other characteristics of the elements. We begin with ionisation energies, or rather return to them. Figure 88.1 repeats the graph in Figure 13.4, which shows the periodicity of ionisation energies of the elements hydrogen to neon, and extends it to include many more elements.

The peaks are always the noble gases, and the troughs the alkali metals (Group I). Notice that the ionisation energies tend to decrease down a Group and to increase across a Period. If you have read Unit 13 you should be able to explain these trends using the ideas that:

(i) Down a Group the shielding of outer by inner electrons overcomes the influence of the increasing nuclear charge. Thus, the outer electron is progressively more easy to remove as we go down a Group.

(ii) Across a Period the reverse is true; increasing nuclear charge has a greater effect than shielding. For this reason the outer electron of an atom is less easily lost as we go across a Period. Shielding is only important once a complete set of orbitals (an electron shell) has been filled.

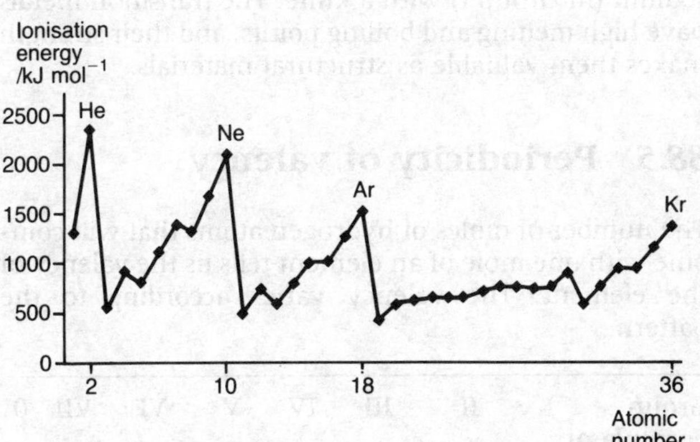

***Figure 88.1** The ionisation energies of the elements hydrogen to krypton*

88.1 Use the data in Appendix B to draw a graph of second ionisation energy against atomic number for the elements hydrogen to potassium. Explain the main differences between your graph and Figure 88.1.

88.2 Periodicity of atomic volume

The atomic volume of an element is the volume occupied by one mole of atoms of the element when it is a solid. The atomic volume is a guide to the size of the atoms. If the radius of an atom increases, then we would expect the atomic volume to increase. Figure 88.2 shows that again there is a series of peaks and

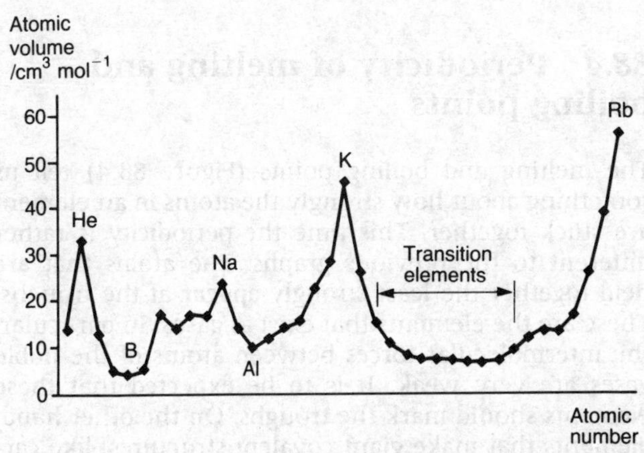

***Figure 88.2** Atomic volumes of the elements hydrogen to rubidium*

troughs, with the peaks appearing at the alkali metals (apart from the first at helium).

88.2 Atomic volume is not a direct measure of the size of atoms. Why not?

88.3 Periodicity of atomic radius

The graph of atomic radius plotted against atomic number (Figure 88.3) shows some similarity to that of atomic volume. Again the alkali metals are found at the peaks, but this time the halogens are at the troughs. The contraction we see across a Period occurs for much the same reason as the increase in ionisation energy. With increasing nuclear charge, the electrons are held more tightly by the nucleus. Once a new shell of electrons is made (at the noble gases) there is an expansion of the atomic radius.

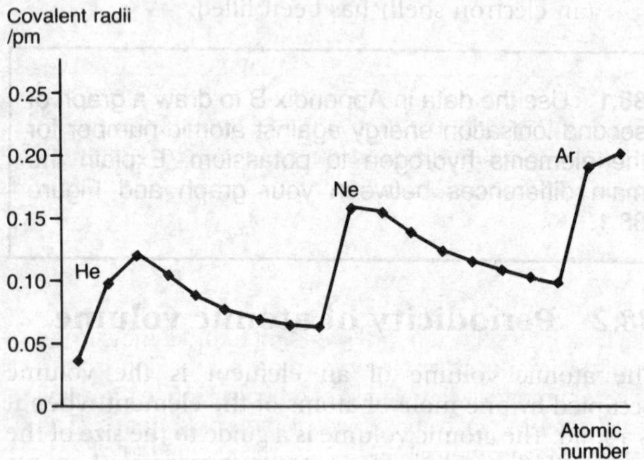

***Figure 88.3** Covalent radii of the elements hydrogen to potassium. In the case of the noble gases, van der Waals radii have been plotted*

88.4 Periodicity of melting and boiling points

The melting and boiling points (Figure 88.4) tell us something about how strongly the atoms in an element are stuck together. This time the periodicity is rather different to the previous graphs. The atoms that are held together the least strongly appear at the troughs. These are the elements that exist as gases. In particular, the intermolecular forces between atoms of the noble gases are very weak. It is to be expected that these elements should mark the troughs. On the other hand, elements that make giant covalent structures, like carbon, or metallic structures, like the transition elements, appear as peaks. Notice that atoms of the alkali metals

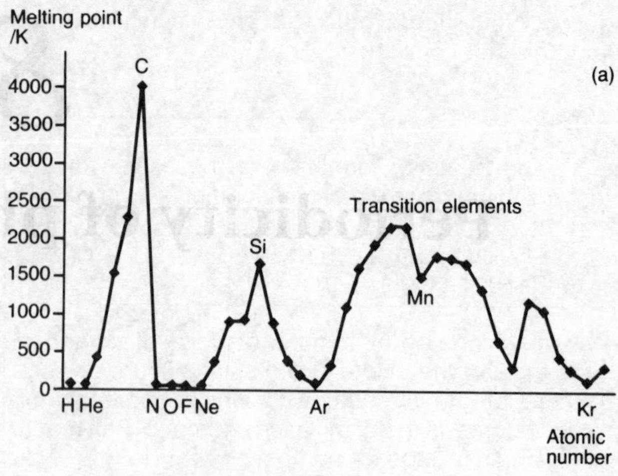

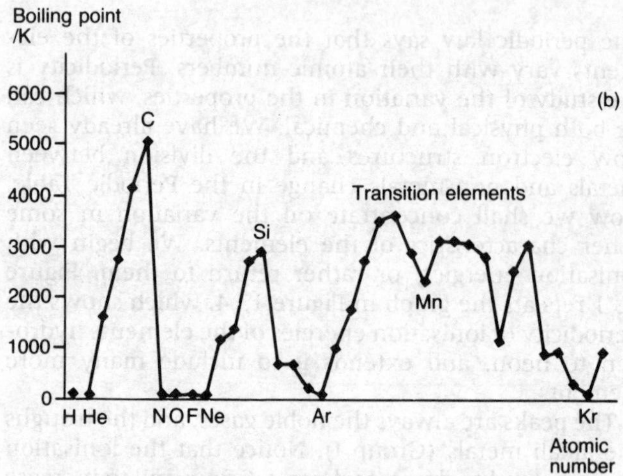

***Figure 88.4** (a) Melting points of the elements hydrogen to rubidium. Note that carbon (graphite) and silicon, with giant covalent lattices, have very high melting points. (b) Boiling points of the elements hydrogen to rubidium*

are only weakly bound together. This matches with the fact that it is possible to cut samples of potassium or sodium (in Group I) with a knife. The transition metals have high melting and boiling points, and their strength makes them valuable as structural materials.

88.5 Periodicity of valency

The number of moles of hydrogen atoms that will combine with one mole of an element tells us the valency of the element. The valency varies according to the pattern:

Group	I	II	III	IV	V	VI	VII	0
Formula of hydride	LiH	BeH_2	BH_3	CH_4	NH_3	H_2O	HF	
Valency	1	2	3	4	3	2	1	0

However, you should note that the valency of many elements is not constant.

88.3 The heats of formation of the oxides of the Period sodium to argon are, in kJ mol^{-1}:

Na_2O	MgO	Al_2O_3	SiO_2	P_4O_{10}	SO_3	Cl_2O_7
−416	−602	−1676	−911	−2984	−395	+250

Divide each one by the number of moles of oxygen in the formula of the oxide. The resulting figure gives a measure of the strength with which one mole of oxygen atoms is held by each element. Plot each figure against atomic number. What is the link between the graph (or the figures) and the structures of the oxides?

88.6 Periodicity of electronegativity

Electronegativity is a measure of the tendency of an element to attract electrons to itself. When electronegativity is plotted against atomic number (Figure 88.5), the strongest non-metals, the halogens, appear at the peaks. The alkali metals mark the troughs. This is largely a result of a new shell of electrons starting with the noble gases. The Group I metals have their nuclei quite strongly shielded. Hence they show little tendency to gain new electrons. The electronegativities of the transition elements, like their ionisation energies, do not change greatly one from another.

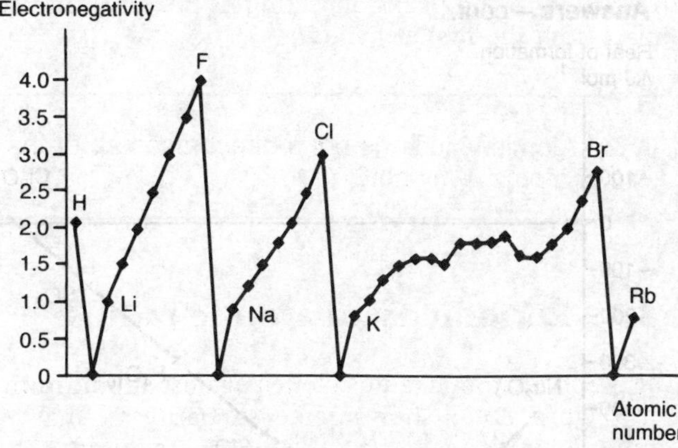

Figure 88.5 *Electronegativities of the elements hydrogen to rubidium. The electronegativities of the noble gases have been set at zero*

88.4 Why is it not strictly correct to consider electronegativity values as physical properties of elements?

Answers

88.1 The graph is drawn in Figure 88.6. The alkali metals now come at the peaks. Once they have lost an electron they gain a noble gas structure. Removing an electron from such a structure means breaking in to a more energetically stable set of orbitals. Hence the alkali metal ions M^+ take the place of the noble gases. The pattern of the other elements is similarly shifted.

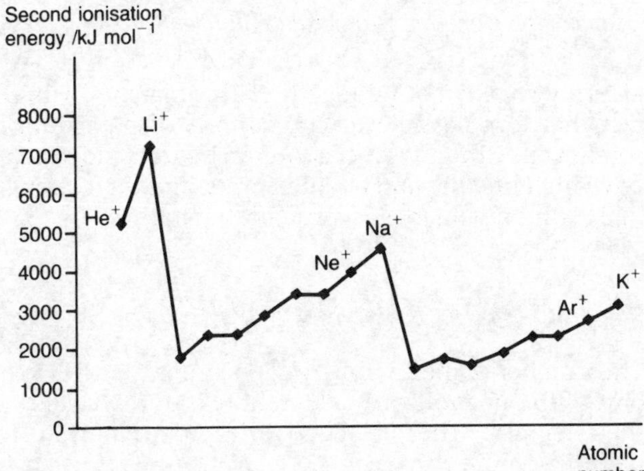

Figure 88.6 *The second ionisation energies of the elements hydrogen to potassium. Note that (i) hydrogen has no second ionisation energy; (ii) the Group I metals are now at the peaks. The ions Li^+, Na^+, K^+ have noble gas electron structures*

88.2 Atoms can pack together in different crystal structures. This means that, for example, atoms that pack in a very open structure will have a large atomic volume; slightly larger atoms that pack in a tighter arrangement will have a smaller atomic volume. This is the reverse pattern to their sizes.

88.3 The graph of Figure 88.7 shows that oxygen is most tightly bound to magnesium. This corresponds to the highly ionic nature of magnesium oxide. The weakest bonding is in Cl_2O_7, which happens to be a covalent molecule. Notice though that SiO_2 is closer to MgO than to Cl_2O_7 even though SiO_2 is also covalent. Remember, it is *not* true to say that 'ionic bonds are strong and covalent bonds are weak'. The figures reflect the differences in structure of the substances: MgO, a giant ionic lattice; SiO_2, a giant covalent lattice (see section 96.2); Cl_2O_7, independent molecules. P_4O_{10} has an unusual structure; see section 98.5.

Answers – cont.

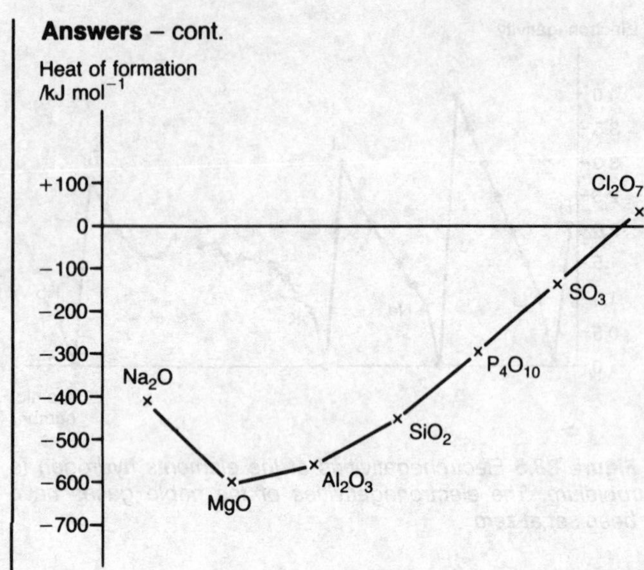

88.4 We discussed this point in Unit 19. We cannot measure electronegativities because they have been invented by chemists, particularly Linus Pauling. They are not properties of atoms. However, the values have been conjured from measurements we can make, e.g. ionisation potentials.

Figure 88.7 *Heats of formation plotted as answer to question 88.3*

UNIT 88 SUMMARY

- Periodicity is the study of the variation in chemical and physical properties of the elements.
- Key points:
  - (i) Down a Group, shielding of outer by inner electrons overcomes the influence of increasing nuclear charge; the outer electron(s) is (are) progressively more easy to remove.
  - (ii) Across a Period, increasing nuclear charge has a greater effect than shielding; the outer electron(s) is (are) less easily lost.
  - (iii) Shielding is only important once a complete set of orbitals (an electron shell) has been filled.
  - (iv) Ionisation energies decrease down a Group and increase across a Period.
- Periodicity of ionisation energy, atomic volume, etc., are illustrated in Figures 88.1 to 88.7.

89

Periodicity of chemical properties

89.1 How this unit is arranged

In this unit much of the information presented to you is in the form of charts. You will find little discussion of the properties and reactions that are mentioned. The place to look for the detail is in the separate units that follow.

There are three ways in which the periodicity of chemical properties are usually discussed. The first compares the properties of elements going down a Group. The second compares them going across a Period. The third is a comparison of elements that are on a diagonal line traversing two Groups and two Periods. We shall adopt each of these approaches in turn.

89.2 How do properties change down a Group?

We have said a little about this in the previous unit. The key point is that (Table 89.1):

Metallic nature increases down a Group.

Owing to shielding, atoms towards the bottom of a Group lose one or more of their outer electrons more easily than atoms nearer the top. This happens even in the Groups to the right of the Periodic Table, which we normally associate with non-metals. For example, in Group V the non-metals nitrogen and phosphorus are near the top, but by the time we reach bismuth at the bottom, distinct metallic character is present.

Table 89.1. Changes in chemical properties down a Group

Shielding of outer electrons	Metallic nature	Ionic character of compounds	Basic nature of oxides
Increases	Increases	Increases	Increases

89.3 How do properties change across a Period?

Across a Period the number of protons in the nucleus increases, as do the number of electrons. This also happens down a Group; but the key difference is that across a Period a new shell of electrons is not completed until the noble gas at the end of the period is reached. Complete shells of electrons screen the outer electrons from the full attraction of the nucleus. As we go across a Period the efficiency of screening is not so great. Indeed, the pattern is for the increasing nuclear charge to hold the electrons more tightly. (You should know by now that this is the reason why the ionisation energies of the elements increase across a Period.)

As a consequence, the elements become harder to ionise, and they also tend to attract electrons towards them. Thus we see a change from the metals (which give positive ions) on the left of a Period to the non-metals (which give negative ions) on the right. With this change goes a change in the nature of the hydrides, oxides and chlorides of the elements. These changes are summarised in Figures 89.1 to 89.4.

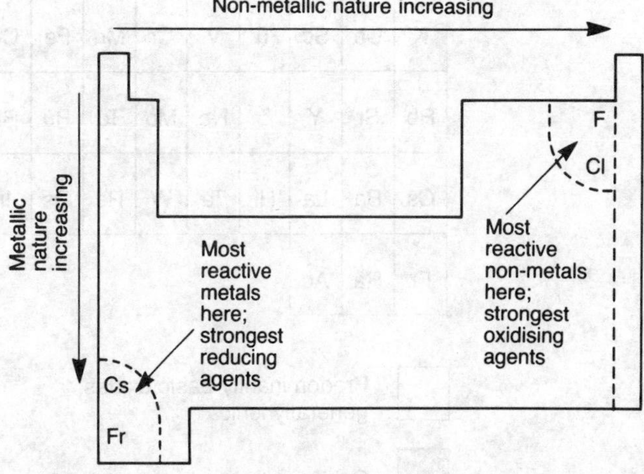

Figure 89.1 How metallic and non-metallic behaviour change in the Periodic Table

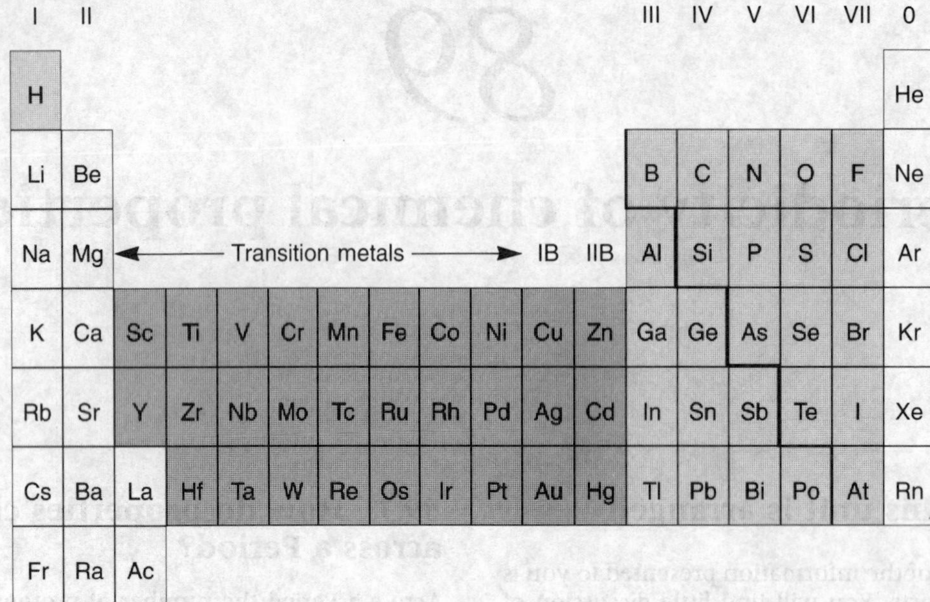

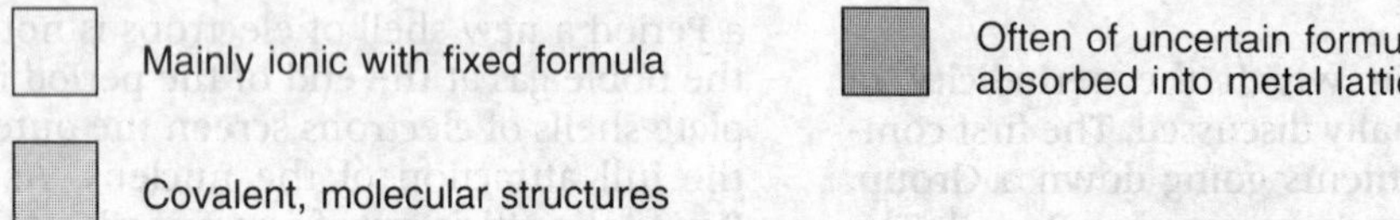

Figure 89.2 *The nature of hydrides of the elements*

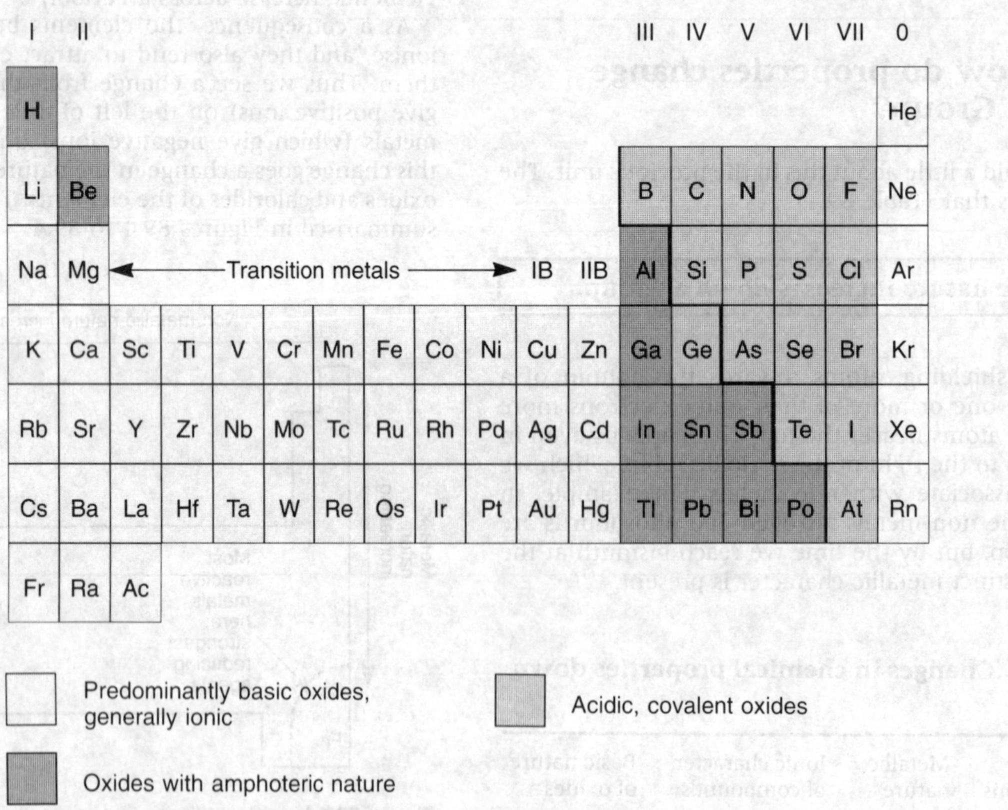

Figure 89.3 *The nature of oxides of the elements*

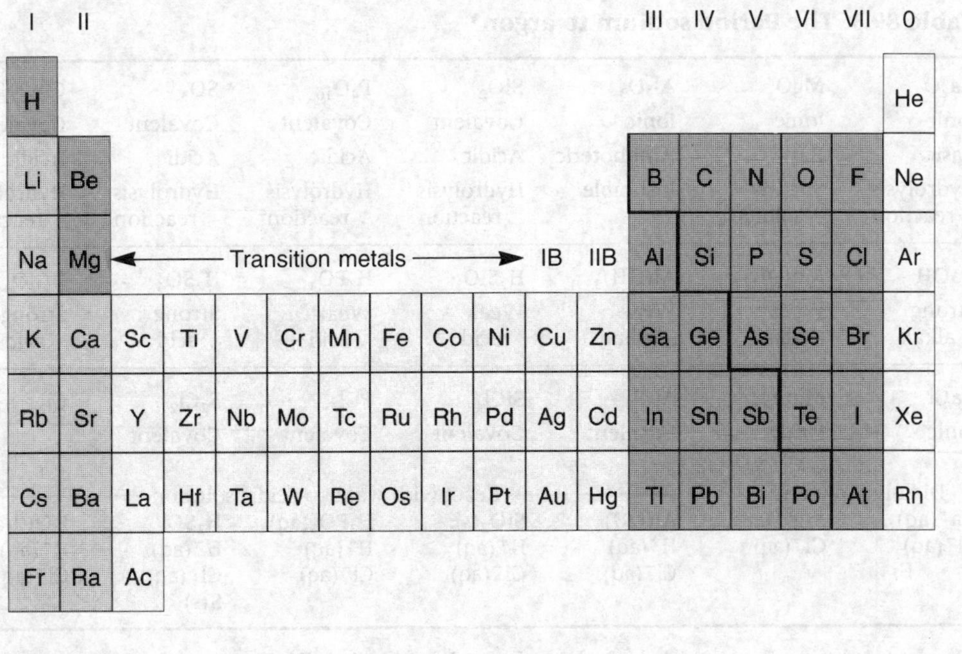

Chlorides that are mainly ionic

Mainly covalent chlorides

Chlorides often occur in complexes

Figure 89.4 *The nature of chlorides of the elements*

Table 89.2. The Period lithium to neon*†

Li_2O	BeO	B_2O_3	CO_2	NO_2	O_2	F_2O
Ionic	Covalent/ ionic	Covalent	Covalent	Covalent	Covalent	Covalent
Basic	Amphoteric	Acidic	Acidic	Acidic	Neutral	Acidic
Hydrolysis reaction	Insoluble	Slightly soluble	Hydrolysis reaction	Hydrolysis reaction	Slightly soluble	Hydrolysis reaction
$LiOH$	$Be(OH)_2$	$B(OH)_3$	H_2CO_3	HNO_3	H_2O	HF
Strong alkali	Amphoteric	Weak acid	Weak acid	Strong acid	Amphoteric‡	Weak acid
$LiCl$	$BeCl_2$	BCl_3	CCl_4	NCl_3	Cl_2O_7	ClF
Ionic	Covalent	Covalent	Covalent	Covalent	Covalent	Covalent
Dissolves	Dissolves	Hydrolysis	No reaction	Hydrolysis	Hydrolysis	Hydrolysis
$Li^+(aq)$ $Cl^-(aq)$	$Be^{2+}(aq)$ $Cl^-(aq)$	$B(OH)_3$ $H^+(aq)$ $Cl^-(aq)$		$NH_3(aq)$ $HOCl(aq)$	$H^+(aq)$ $ClO_4^-(aq)$	$HF(aq)$ $HOCl(aq)$

*Be careful about taking the labels 'ionic' and 'covalent' too literally. The majority of compounds show a mix of both extreme types of bonding

†The properties listed here are only examples of the reactions undergone by the oxides and chlorides

‡Sometimes water is described as being amphiprotic rather than amphoteric

You might like to look at the way the oxides, hydroxides and chlorides of the elements in the Periods lithium to neon (Table 89.2) and sodium to argon (Table 89.3) compare with one another. (It is likely that your examination syllabus particularly requires you to know about sodium to argon.)

Table 89.3. The Period sodium to argon*

Na_2O	MgO	Al_2O_3	SiO_2	P_4O_{10}	SO_3	Cl_2O_7
Ionic	Ionic	Ionic	Covalent	Covalent	Covalent	Covalent
Basic	Basic	Amphoteric	Acidic	Acidic	Acidic	Acidic
Hydrolysis reaction	Slightly soluble	Insoluble	Hydrolysis reaction	Hydrolysis reaction	Hydrolysis reaction	Hydrolysis reaction
$NaOH$	$Mg(OH)_2$	$Al(OH)_3$	H_2SiO_3	H_3PO_4	H_2SO_4	$HClO_4$
Strong alkali	Weak alkali	Weak alkali	Weak acid	Weak acid	Strong acid	Strong acid
$NaCl$	$MgCl_2$	$AlCl_3$	$SiCl_4$	PCl_3	S_2Cl_2	Cl_2
Ionic	Partly covalent	Covalent	Covalent	Covalent	Covalent	
Dissolve in water		←React with water→acidic solution→				
$Na^+(aq)$ $Cl^-(aq)$	$Mg^{2+}(aq)$ $Cl^-(aq)$	$Al(OH)_3$ $H^+(aq)$ $Cl^-(aq)$	$SiO_2(s)$ $H^+(aq)$ $Cl^-(aq)$	$H_3PO_3(aq)$ $H^+(aq)$ $Cl^-(aq)$	H_2SO_3 $H^+(aq)$ $Cl^-(aq)$ $S(s)$	$HOCl(aq)$ $H^+(aq)$ $Cl^-(aq)$

*Be careful about taking the labels 'ionic' and 'covalent' too literally. The majority of compounds show a mix of both extreme types of bonding

There are two elements that make life difficult when we want to generalise about the Period lithium to neon (Table 89.2). They are beryllium and boron. (They also tend to give exceptions to the trends in their Groups.) Given their positions in Group II and III respectively, we would expect them to be metals, to give ionic compounds and to give basic oxides. They do none of these things. The main reason is that, if they were to exist as ions, their sizes would be extremely small. The ionic radius of Be^{2+} is 30 pm, and of B^{3+} is only 16 pm. These ions are so small that they represent extremely dense centres of positive charge, and they would polarise any negative ions that approach them. If you can recall Fajans' rules (Table 19.4) you will understand why this leads to covalency.

You can also see changes taking place across the Periods in the way the oxides behave with water. To the left of the Periods the oxides give hydroxides, and to the right they give acids. For example, in the Period lithium to neon we have the change from amphoteric beryllium hydroxide, $Be(OH)_2$, to strongly acidic nitric acid, HNO_3. However, if we show how the atoms are bonded together in hydroxides and acids, we find that they are more similar than we might otherwise expect. Look at Figure 89.5. In each case the hydrogen atoms are bonded to the oxygen atoms. Molecules that we regard as acids tend to give up hydrogen atoms (as hydrogen ions) to water molecules. For example,

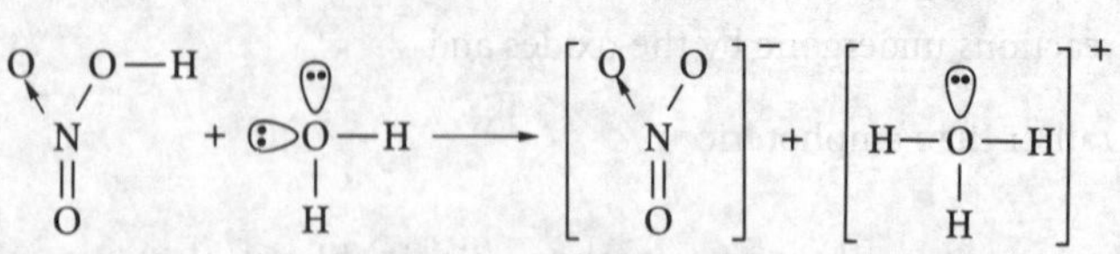

$$HNO_3(aq) + H_2O(l) \longrightarrow NO_3^-(aq) + H_3O^+(aq)$$

The reason why they do this is complicated, but the process is certainly helped if the negative ion produced (in this case NO_3^-) is energetically stable. In the nitrate ion and sulphate ion there is a considerable degree of electron delocalisation, which, as we said in Unit 14, leads to just this energetic stabilisation. However, many other things (such as entropy changes and kinetic factors) have to be taken into account if we are to give a really satisfactory explanation of the way in which a molecule with OH groups will behave in water. Fortunately we can leave this task to more advanced books.

The shapes of the chlorides of the elements in the two Periods lithium to neon and sodium to argon are summarised in Figures 89.6 and 89.7.

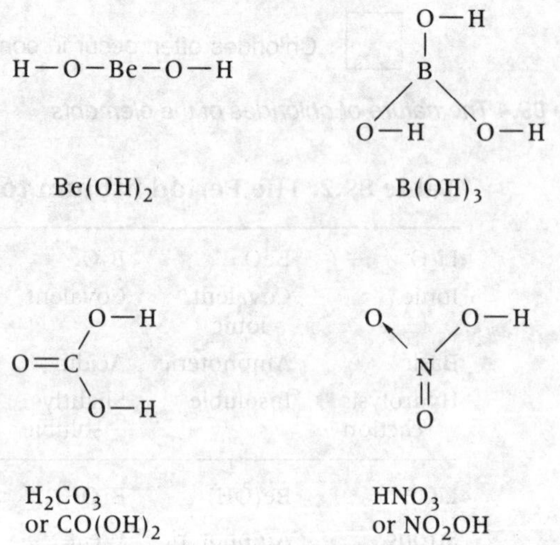

H—O—Be—O—H $Be(OH)_2$ | $B(OH)_3$ | H_2CO_3 or $CO(OH)_2$ | HNO_3 or NO_2OH

***Figure 89.5** Two hydroxides, $Be(OH)_2$ and $B(OH)_3$, and two acids, H_2CO_3 and HNO_3, are structurally similar. They all have OH groups in them*

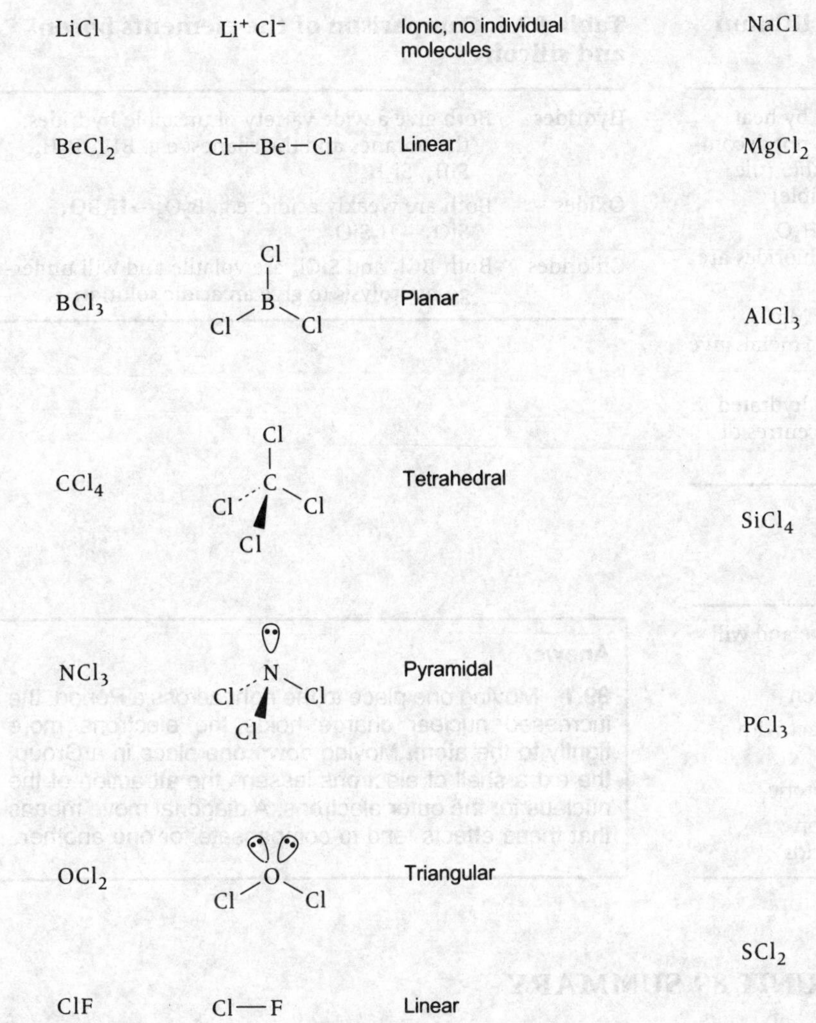

Figure 89.6 *The shapes of chlorides of elements lithium to neon*

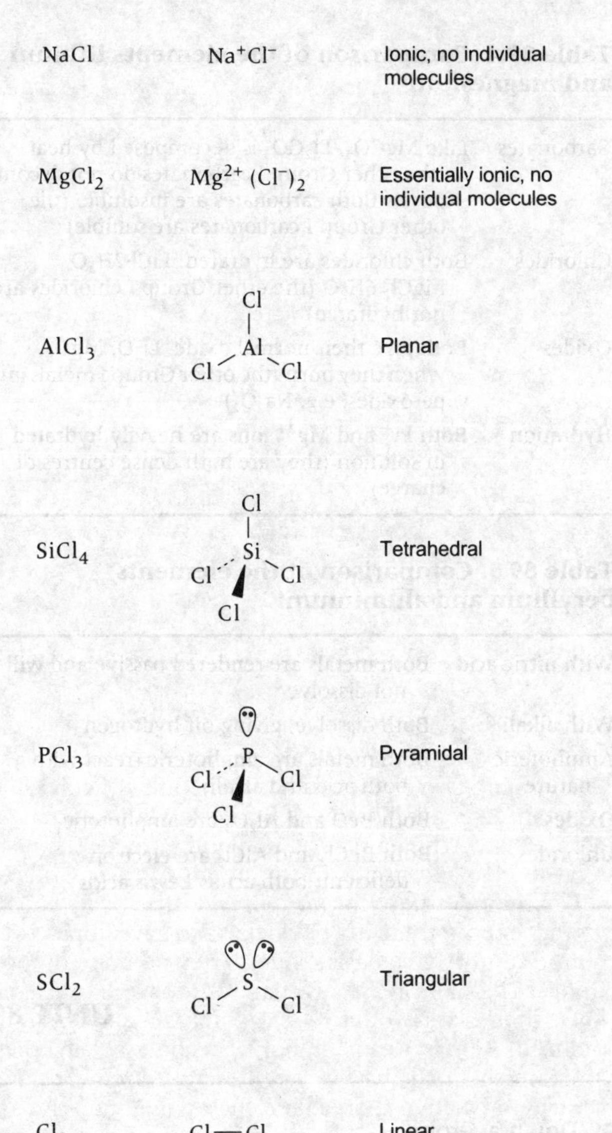

Figure 89.7 *The shapes of chlorides of elements sodium to argon*

89.4 Diagonal relationships between some elements

We know that metallic nature increases down a Group, and that non-metallic nature increases across a Period. If we take a diagonal route across the Periodic Table (Figure 89.8), these two trends might be expected to cancel one another out.

Indeed, it is the case that some elements on a diagonal do tend to show similarities. The pairs that we shall consider are (i) lithium and magnesium, (ii) beryllium and aluminium, and (iii) boron and silicon. You will find the similarities summarised in Tables 89.4 to 89.6.

> **89.1** Give a short explanation of diagonal relationships in the Periodic Table in terms of changes in nuclear charge and shielding of electrons.

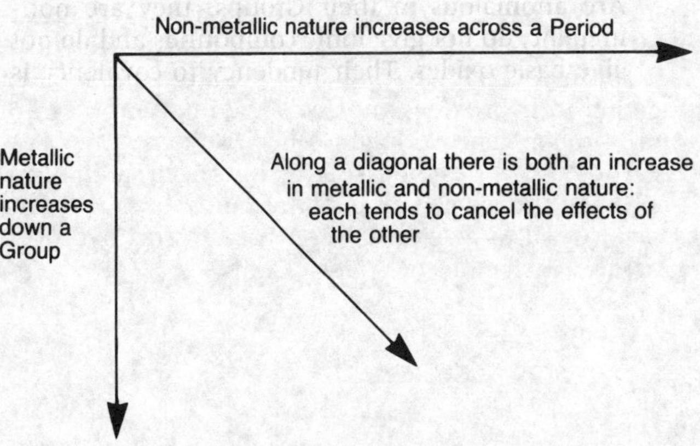

Figure 89.8 *Why neighbouring elements that lie diagonally to one another have similar properties*

Table 89.4. Comparison of the elements lithium and magnesium

Carbonates	Like $MgCO_3$, Li_2CO_3 is decomposed by heat (the other Group I carbonates do not decompose). Both carbonates are insoluble (the other Group I carbonates are soluble)
Chlorides	Both chlorides are hydrated: $LiCl{\cdot}2H_2O$, $MgCl_2{\cdot}6H_2O$ (the other Group I chlorides are not hydrated)
Oxides	Both give their normal oxide, Li_2O, MgO, when they burn (the other Group I metals give peroxides, e.g. Na_2O_2)
Hydration	Both Li^+ and Mg^{2+} ions are heavily hydrated in solution (they are both dense centres of charge)

Table 89.5. Comparison of the elements beryllium and aluminium

With nitric acid	Both metals are rendered passive and will not dissolve
With alkali	Both dissolve, giving off hydrogen
Amphoteric nature	Both metals are amphoteric (react with both acid and alkali)
Oxides	Both BeO and Al_2O_3 are amphoteric
Chlorides	Both $BeCl_2$ and $AlCl_3$ are electron deficient; both act as Lewis acids

Table 89.6. Comparison of the elements boron and silicon

Hydrides	Both give a wide variety of unstable hydrides: the boranes and the silanes, e.g. BH_4, B_2H_6, SiH_4, Si_2H_6
Oxides	Both are weakly acidic, e.g. $B_2O_3 \rightarrow H_3BO_3$, $SiO_2 \rightarrow H_2SiO_3$
Chlorides	Both BCl_3 and $SiCl_4$ are volatile and will undergo hydrolysis to give an acidic solution

Answer

89.1 Moving one place to the right across a Period, the increased nuclear charge holds the electrons more tightly to the atom. Moving down one place in a Group, the extra shell of electrons lessens the attraction of the nucleus for the outer electrons. A diagonal move means that these effects tend to compensate for one another.

UNIT 89 SUMMARY

- Down a Group:
  Metallic nature, ionic nature of compounds and basic nature of oxides all increase.
- Across a Period:
  Non-metallic nature, tendency to covalency and acidic nature of oxides all increase.
- Beryllium and boron:
  Are anomalous in their Groups; they are non-metallic, do not give ionic compounds and do not give basic oxides. Their tendency to covalency is explained by the intense polarising power of their very small ions.
- Diagonal relationships are shown by:
  (i) Lithium and magnesium.
  (ii) Beryllium and aluminium.
  (iii) Boron and silicon.
  The similarities are partly due to the cancelling out effect of moving one place to the right along a Period (non-metallic nature increasing) and one place down a Group (metallic nature increasing).

90

Hydrogen and hydrides

90.1 The element

Although air contains almost no free hydrogen, hydrogen atoms are very abundant in Nature. One reason for this is that they are to be found in water, which is widely distributed over the Earth; another is that, combined with carbon, they are found in all living matter. Hydrogen is also to be found in space. It plays a crucial role in stars (such as our Sun) in nuclear fusion reactions. Information about hydrogen is summarised in Table 90.1.

Table 90.1. Information about hydrogen

Relative atomic mass	1.008
Electron structure	1s
Ionisation energy	1312 kJ mol^{-1}
Electron affinity	−72 kJ mol^{-1}
Molecular formula	H_2
Melting point	14 K (−259° C)
Boiling point	20 K (−253° C)
Density at s.t.p.	0.09 g dm^{-3}
Bond energy, H—H	436 kJ mol^{-1}
Bond length, H—H	74 pm
Colourless, odourless, tasteless	

Hydrogen has three isotopes: ${}^{1}_{1}H$ (protium, H), ${}^{2}_{1}H$ (deuterium, D) and ${}^{3}_{1}H$ (tritium, T). Deuterium occurs naturally but only to the extent of 0.015%. Tritium can be made by causing the nuclear reaction:

$${}^{2}_{1}H + {}^{2}_{1}H \rightarrow {}^{3}_{1}H + {}^{1}_{1}H$$

Tritium is radioactive, decaying by beta emission.

90.1 What is the equation for the nuclear reaction that takes place when tritium undergoes beta decay? What is produced in the reaction?

90.2 The mass spectrum of a sample of hydrogen gas has a strong peak corresponding to a mass to charge ratio (*m/e*) value of 2. However, there are other lines at higher *m/e* values. Why is this? How many peaks would you expect? What would their *m/e* values be?

90.2 The large-scale extraction of hydrogen

One of the vital uses of hydrogen is in the manufacture of ammonia by the Haber process. We followed the working of the process in Unit 83. Here we shall mention that a very important source of hydrogen for the process is natural gas, methane (Table 90.2). The key idea is to react methane with steam at a high pressure (35 atm) and temperature (800° C) in the presence of a catalyst (nickel). A mixture of carbon monoxide, carbon dioxide and hydrogen results:

$$CH_4(g) + H_2O(g) \rightarrow CO(g) + 3H_2(g)$$
$$CO(g) + H_2O(g) \rightarrow CO_2(g) + H_2(g)$$

The carbon monoxide and carbon dioxide are removed, leaving the hydrogen for further reaction.

Hydrogen can also be obtained from the oil refining industry. It is made in many reactions that involve cracking long-chain hydrocarbons into smaller molecules (see section 86.3), e.g.

$$C_6H_{12}(g) \rightarrow C_6H_6(g) + 3H_2(g)$$

It is possible to make hydrogen by the *Bosch reaction*. The process takes place in three stages.

(i) *Stage 1.* Steam is passed over white hot coke:

$$H_2O(g) + C(s) \rightarrow \underbrace{CO(g) + H_2(g)}_{\text{water gas}}$$

(ii) *Stage 2.* The mixture of carbon monoxide and hydrogen, known as water gas, is mixed with

Table 90.2. The manufacture and uses of hydrogen

Manufacture	*Uses*
From methane	Making ammonia in the Haber process
Cracking of hydrocarbons	Production of margarines from vegetable oils
Electrolysis	Welding
Bosch reaction	Fuel cells

more steam and passed over an iron catalyst. Only the carbon monoxide reacts:

$$H_2O(g) + CO(g) \rightarrow CO_2(g) + H_2(g)$$

(iii) *Stage 3.* Under pressure the carbon dioxide is dissolved in water, thus leaving the hydrogen available for further use.

A method that is still used where either supplies of methane are limited, or where electricity is relatively cheap, is electrolysis. This can be a direct electrolysis of water (on a suitably large scale), or as a by-product of the electrolysis of brine. The electrolysis of water is not as simple as it might seem. The main problem is that the hydrogen can become contaminated by impurities given off at the cathode. It can also mix with oxygen that diffuses through the electrolyte from the anode. If particularly pure hydrogen is needed, the cathode gas has to be purified.

Apart from the desire to obtain hydrogen, the electrolysis of water is carried out in order to make heavy water, D_2O. This is water that consists of two atoms of deuterium rather than ordinary hydrogen. Heavy water is often used in chemical research.

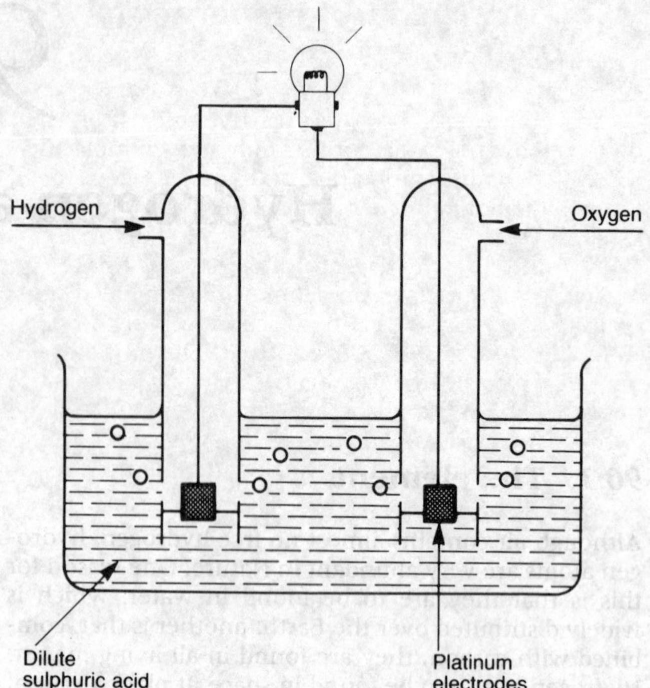

***Figure 90.1** A fuel cell that can be made in the laboratory*

90.3 Before natural gas can be used to make hydrogen, it has to be purified. Especially, sulphur compounds must not be allowed through. Why?

90.3 The uses of hydrogen

Over 20 million tonnes of hydrogen are produced each year. Almost 50% is used in the Haber process to make ammonia (Table 90.2). In addition to the Haber process, hydrogen finds large-scale use in the hydrogenation of vegetable oils to make margarine. The oils are said to be unsaturated. This means that they contain double bonds between carbon atoms. In the presence of a nickel catalyst, the double bonds take up hydrogen:

$$\gt C{=}C\lt \xrightarrow{H_2} -\overset{H}{\underset{|}{\overset{|}{C}}}-\overset{H}{\underset{|}{\overset{|}{C}}}-$$

Hydrogen has also been used in welding. The gas is passed through an electric arc, which splits the molecules into atoms. When the atoms recombine to produce molecules, a great deal of heat is generated. This heat is used to melt and fuse metal surfaces together. A bonus of the process is that because it does not use oxygen, oxidation of the metals is prevented.

One use of hydrogen that has been thoroughly researched in recent years is its potential use as a fuel. When hydrogen burns in air it produces significant amounts of energy, and it has the virtue of being pollution free. Cars have been built that use hydrogen as a fuel rather than petrol. It might be thought that carrying hydrogen around could be dangerous, but it can be absorbed by a number of metal alloys, which are perfectly safe.

Hydrogen–oxygen fuel cells are useful devices for converting the energy of the reaction

$$2H_2(g) + O_2(g) \rightarrow 2H_2O(l)$$

into electrical energy. You can see a diagram of a fuel cell in Figure 90.1. Hydrogen and oxygen gas are brought together over two electrodes, which can catalyse the reaction between them. The electrolyte can be an acid or an alkali, depending on the type of cell. The virtue of the fuel cell is that it produces electricity with only water as the side product. The cells can operate with high power outputs and efficiencies greater than those of conventional ways of generating electricity, e.g. in oil burning power stations. Fuel cells have been used in space vehicles, where they have the virtue of being reliable, efficient and of relatively small size compared to conventional electric cells.

90.4 The free energy change for the reaction powering a hydrogen–oxygen fuel cell is about $-240\,\text{kJ mol}^{-1}$. What is the e.m.f. of the cell? (Hint: see Unit 69.)

90.5 Work out the standard enthalpy changes for the reaction:

$$H_2O(g) + C(s) \rightarrow CO(g) + H_2(g)$$

You will need the following information: $\Delta H_f^\circ(H_2O(g)) = -241.8\,\text{kJ mol}^{-1}$; $\Delta H_f^\circ(CO(g)) = -110.5\,\text{kJ mol}^{-1}$.

Why is it that air has to be blown through the coke from time to time if the reaction is to be kept going?

90.4 The chemical properties of hydrogen

Free hydrogen atoms are too reactive to exist on their own, and hydrogen gas consists of hydrogen molecules, H_2. Many of the properties of hydrogen have been known for a long time. The most important of them are listed in Table 90.3.

The fact that hydrogen and oxygen make an explosive mixture has had some unfortunate results. On the large scale the destruction of the air ship Hindenburg in 1937 was spectacular. The possibility of explosion exists when hydrogen is made on a large scale in the laboratory, and the experiment should be done with great care. The standard method (Figure 90.2) is to mix dilute sulphuric acid with zinc granules:

$$Zn(s) + 2H^+(aq) \rightarrow Zn^{2+}(aq) + H_2(g)$$

Copper(II) sulphate crystals are usually added. A displacement reaction takes place, which gives the zinc a thin layer of copper metal. An electrochemical cell is set up, which greatly increases the rate of evolution of hydrogen.

Hydrogen from a cylinder can be safely burnt at a jet. It burns with a pale blue flame. If the hydrogen is burnt at the mouth of a glass tube, the flame may appear yellow owing to contamination from sodium in the glass. The same reaction occurs as in an explosion:

$$H_2(g) + \tfrac{1}{2}O_2(g) \rightarrow H_2O(g); \quad \Delta H^{\ominus} = -285.9\ \text{kJ mol}^{-1}$$

Table 90.3. Chemical properties of hydrogen

Forms *hydrides* with many elements: hydrides of non-metals are covalent, e.g. CH_4, NH_3, H_2O, HCl hydrides of reactive metals are ionic, e.g. Na^+H^-, $Ca^{2+}(H^-)_2$
Forms hydrogen bonds with highly electronegative atoms, e.g. in liquid HF, H_2O
Explodes with oxygen if ignited (gives a 'pop' with a lighted splint): $2H_2(g) + O_2(g) \rightarrow 2H_2O(g)$
A reducing agent; will remove the oxygen from many oxides: $CuO(s) + H_2(g) \rightarrow Cu(s) + H_2O(g)$
Liberated from acids by many metals: $Zn(s) + 2H^+(aq) \rightarrow Zn^{2+}(aq) + H_2(g)$ This is the basis of the laboratory preparation of the gas
Hydrogen can exist as positive ions, $H^+(aq)$ or $H_3O^+(aq)$, in water. Hydrogen ions are the active agents in aqueous acids

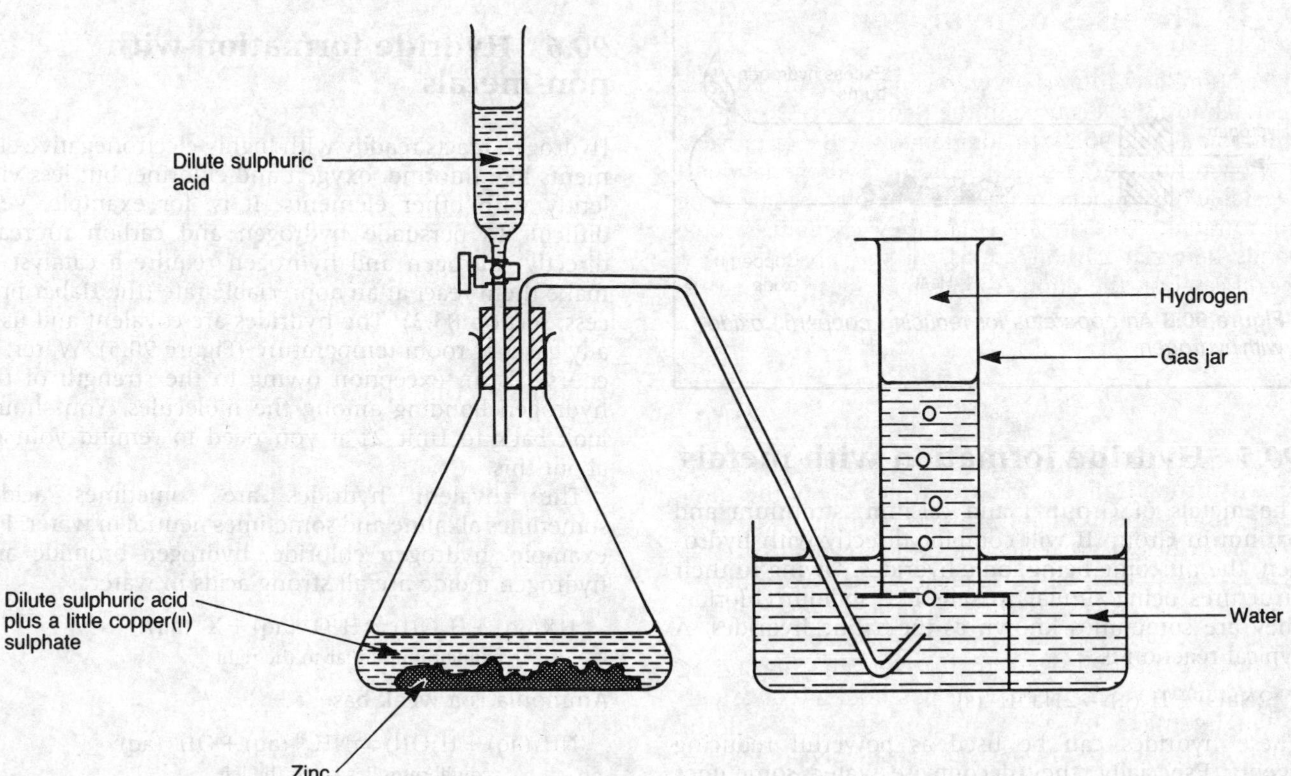

***Figure 90.2** A simple apparatus for preparing hydrogen. If the gas must be dried before it is collected, it can be passed through concentrated sulphuric acid. However, it must not then be collected over water!*

90.6 The reaction between hydrogen and oxygen can be started by ultraviolet light. What does this suggest about the mechanism of the reaction?

90.7 (i) For the most powerful explosion, hydrogen and oxygen should be mixed in a particular proportion. What is it?

(ii) If hydrogen is made from zinc and dilute sulphuric acid in a test tube, there is a loud pop with a lighted splint soon after the reaction starts. However, if there is a delay of some minutes before doing the test, no pop is heard even though many bubbles of gas can be seen. Why does the test not work?

90.8 Copper(II) oxide can be reduced by hydrogen using the apparatus shown in Figure 90.3. The oxide has to be hot to start the reaction, but once it starts it is sufficiently exothermic to keep going without further heating. A student performed the experiment using 2.0 g of the oxide. As soon as all the oxide had changed colour to orange, the hydrogen supply was turned off and air allowed into the tube. When it was cool enough the tube was reweighed and the mass of the product found to be 1.7 g. (The molar masses are: $M(\text{Cu}) = 64\text{ g mol}^{-1}$; $M(\text{O}) = 16\text{ g mol}^{-1}$.)

(i) What is the equation for the reaction.

(ii) What should have been the mass of the product?

(iii) What had gone wrong in the experiment?

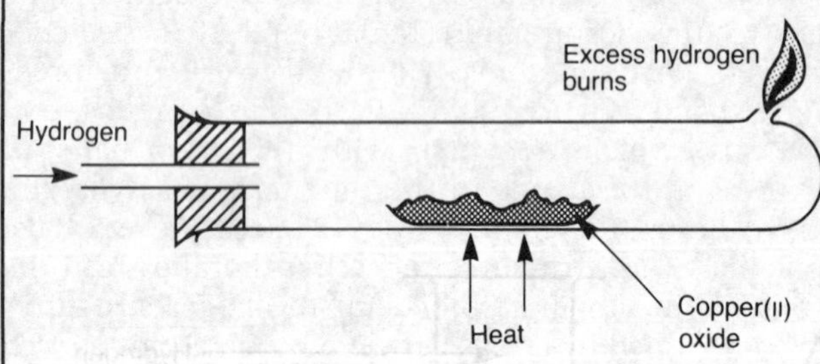

Figure 90.3 An apparatus for reducing copper(II) oxide with hydrogen

90.5 Hydride formation with metals

The metals of Group I and calcium, strontium and barium in Group II will combine directly with hydrogen, the outcome being ionic hydrides. Owing to their structures being similar to salts like sodium chloride, they are sometimes known as the saline hydrides. A typical reaction is

$$2\text{Na(s)} + \text{H}_2\text{(g)} \rightarrow 2\text{Na}^+\text{H}^-\text{(s)}$$

These hydrides can be used as powerful reducing agents. Especially, they decompose water, sometimes violently:

$$\text{Na}^+\text{H}^-\text{(s)} + \text{H}_2\text{O(l)} \rightarrow \text{Na}^+\text{(aq)} + \text{OH}^-\text{(aq)} + \text{H}_2\text{(g)}$$

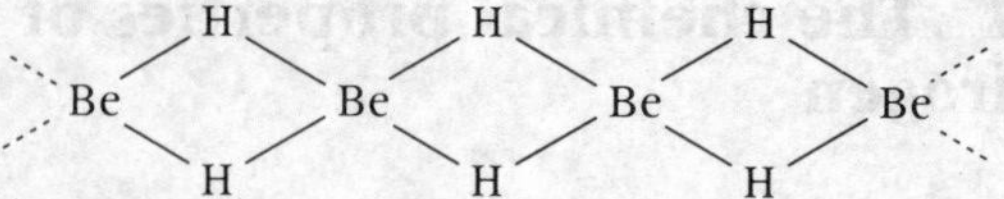

Figure 90.4 The chain structure in solid beryllium hydride

With transition elements, hydrogen behaves somewhat oddly. Although true compounds can occur, for example copper forms CuH, it is more common for hydrogen to be absorbed into the crystal structures of the solids. This can happen because hydrogen molecules are small enough to squeeze into the spaces between the metal atoms; hence they are called the *interstitial hydrides*. They do not have a fixed formula, which is summed up by saying that they are *non-stoichiometric*. The actual formula can vary with temperature and pressure of the hydrogen. For example, palladium hydride can vary in composition between $\text{PdH}_{0.1}$ and $\text{PdH}_{0.6}$.

The hydrides of beryllium and magnesium are believed to be predominantly covalent, and to exist in chains (Figure 90.4).

90.9 Briefly explain why aluminium hydride, AlH_3, would be expected to bond with a hydride ion. (Look back at Unit 14 if you are stuck.)

90.6 Hydride formation with non-metals

Hydrogen reacts readily with highly electronegative elements like fluorine, oxygen and chlorine, but less violently with other elements. It is, for example, very difficult to persuade hydrogen and carbon to react directly; nitrogen and hydrogen require a catalyst to make them react at an appreciable rate (the Haber process, section 83.3). The hydrides are covalent and usually gases at room temperature (Figure 90.5). Water, of course, is an exception owing to the strength of the hydrogen bonding among the molecules. You should look back to Unit 21 if you need to remind yourself about this.

The covalent hydrides are sometimes acidic, sometimes alkaline and sometimes neutral in water. For example, hydrogen chloride, hydrogen bromide and hydrogen iodide are all strong acids in water:

$$\text{HX(aq)} + \text{H}_2\text{O(l)} \rightleftharpoons \text{H}_3\text{O}^+\text{(aq)} + \text{X}^-\text{(aq)}$$

equilibrium lies far to the right

Ammonia is a weak base:

$$\text{NH}_3\text{(aq)} + \text{H}_2\text{O(l)} \rightleftharpoons \text{NH}_4{}^+\text{(aq)} + \text{OH}^-\text{(aq)}$$

equilibrium lies far to the left

Methane, CH_4, is only very slightly soluble and does not react with water.

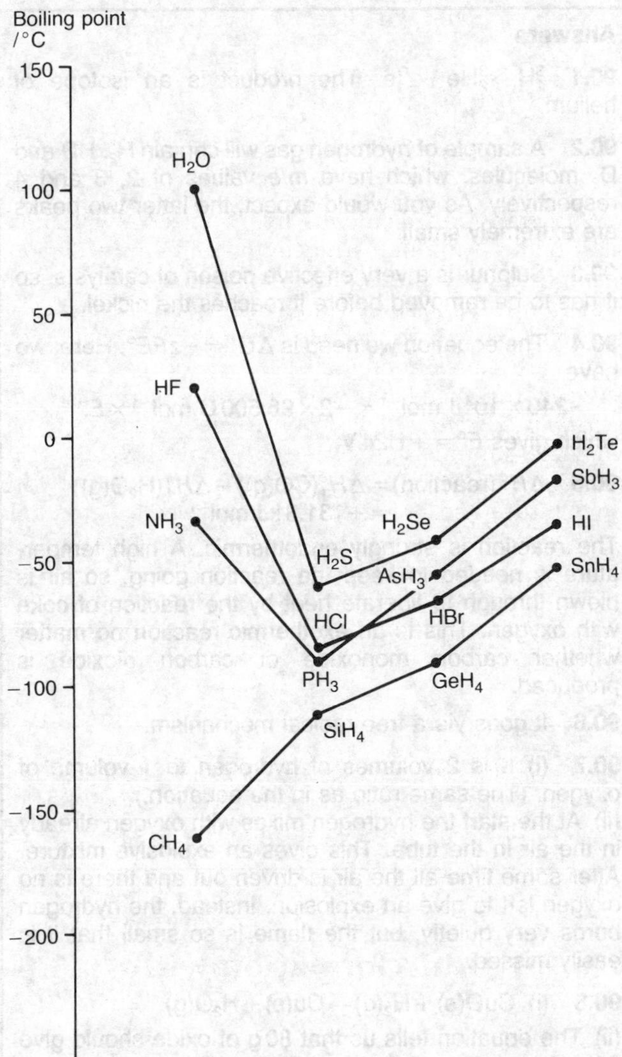

Figure 90.5 *Boiling points for hydrides of elements in Groups IV, V, VI and VII*

> **90.10** $E^{\ominus}$ for a standard hydrogen electrode (S.H.E.) is defined to be exactly 0 V. This value implies that hydrogen should reduce any redox system that has a positive $E^{\ominus}$. For example, $E^{\ominus}_{Br_2/Br^-} = +1.09$ V.
>
> (i) What should be the cell reaction if this half-cell is combined with a S.H.E.?
>
> (ii) If hydrogen is bubbled through a solution of bromine, nothing happens. Why might this be?

90.7 Some unusual hydrides

You are almost certain to have used the simpler hydrides, like hydrogen chloride or ammonia, or their solutions in your chemistry course. However, you may not have met the hydrides of boron before. These hydrides provided a severe shock for theories of chemical bonding when they were first investigated. There are many boron hydrides (Table 90.4), but we shall concentrate on the simplest: diborane, B_2H_6.

Table 90.4. Some of the hydrides of boron

Name	*Formula*	*Comment*
Diborane	B_2H_6	Easily hydrolysed; highly flammable in air
Tetraborane	B_4H_{10}	Rather less reactive than diborane
Hexaborane-10	B_6H_{10}	Similar to tetraborane
Decaborane	$B_{10}H_{14}$	Little reaction with air or water
Icosaborane-16	$B_{20}H_{16}$	Like decaborane

If we count the electrons available for bonding we have one each from six hydrogen atoms, and there are three electrons in the valence shell of each boron (B: $1s^22s^22p$), making 12 electrons in all. The essential problem about diborane is this: the X-ray structure of diborane shows that there are two hydrogen atoms attached to each boron atom, and two more shared between the boron atoms. Therefore it appears that there are eight bonds, for which we should need 16 electrons. Clearly the numbers do not fit. There appear to be too few electrons to account for the number of bonds. A molecule, like diborane, for which this is true is called an *electron deficient* molecule.

One solution to the puzzle is to use molecular orbital theory. Each bridging hydrogen atom is imagined to be held to the boron atom by a bond that stretches between all three atoms. The bond is called a three-centre bond (Figure 90.6). Each one contains two electrons, which, together with the four pairs of electrons in the bonds to the four terminal hydrogen atoms, brings the total to the 12 electrons we have available. The structures of other boranes can be explained in similar fashion, but the larger structures are complicated by bonds between boron atoms as well as between the boron and hydrogen atoms.

A second hydride that is rather unusual is *lithium tetrahydridoaluminate(III)*, $LiAlH_4$. (It has the alternative name lithium aluminium hydride.) This hydride can be made by reacting lithium hydride with aluminium trichloride in ethoxyethane (ether):

$$4LiH + AlCl_3 \rightarrow LiAlH_4 + 3LiCl$$

It is a white ionic solid, which has remarkable powers as a reducing agent. The AlH_4^- ion is the active reducing agent. One of the problems with it is that it will react violently with water, even in small amounts. It finds its main use in organic chemistry. For example, it will reduce acid, aldehyde and ketone groups to alcohols, but leave any double bonds alone. The following conversions are typical:

(i) ethanoic acid to ethanol,

$$CH_3COOH \rightarrow CH_3CH_2OH$$

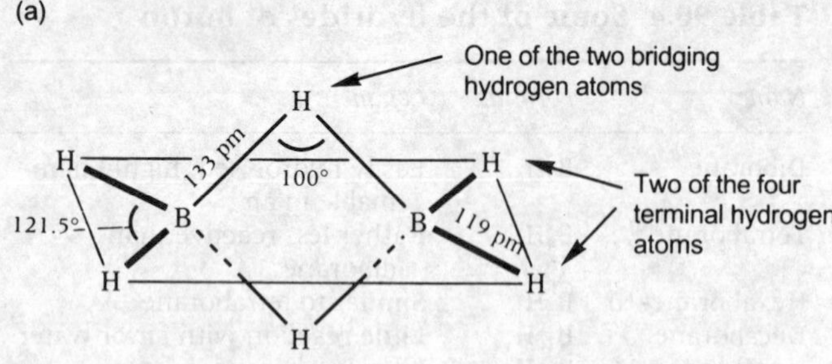

(b)

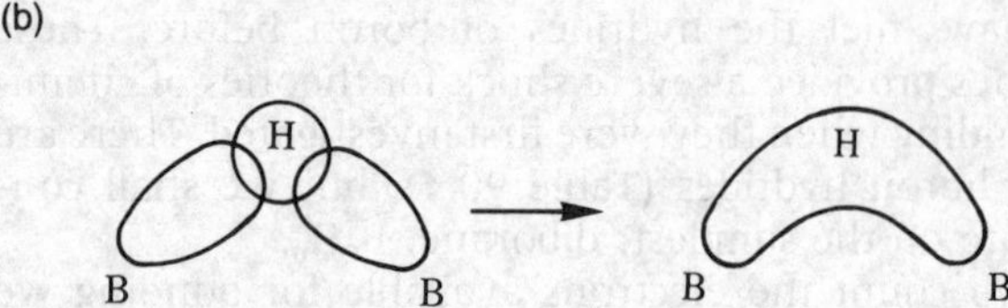

***Figure 90.6** (a) The structure of diborane, B_2H_6. (b) The bridging hydrogen atoms have a 1s orbital, which can overlap with one orbital on each boron atom. A three-centre bond results*

(ii) ethanal to ethanol,

$$CH_3CHO \rightarrow CH_3CH_2OH$$

(iii) propanone to propan-2-ol,

$$(CH_3)_2CO \rightarrow (CH_3)_2CH_2OH$$

In addition it will convert nitriles (organic compounds that contain CN groups) to amines, and amides to amines. For example, ethanonitrile changes to ethylamine,

$$CH_3CN \rightarrow CH_3CH_2NH_2$$

and ethanamide changes to ethylamine,

$$CH_3CONH_2 \rightarrow CH_3CH_2NH_2$$

In some reactions sodium tetrahydridoborate(III), $NaBH_4$, behaves similarly to $LiAlH_4$. The main difference between them is that $NaBH_4$ is a less powerful reducing agent.

90.11 Write down the formula of the molecule made when $LiAlH_4$ reacts with $CH_2{=}CHCOOH$.

90.12 $LiAlH_4$ will reduce chlorides. It is found that 1 mol of it reacts completely with 1 mol of silicon(IV) chloride, $SiCl_4$. Two of the products are 1 mol of lithium chloride and 1 mol of aluminium trichloride. The third product is a gaseous hydride of silicon. Discover its formula by working out the equation for the reaction.

90.13 Suggest a way of making phosphine, PH_3, starting with phosphorus trichloride, PCl_3.

Answers

90.1 ${}^3_1H \rightarrow {}^3_2He + {}^{0}_{-1}e$. The product is an isotope of helium.

90.2 A sample of hydrogen gas will contain H_2, HD and D_2 molecules, which have *m/e* values of 2, 3 and 4 respectively. As you would expect, the latter two peaks are extremely small.

90.3 Sulphur is a very effective poison of catalysts, so it has to be removed before it reaches the nickel.

90.4 The equation we need is $\Delta G^\ominus = -zFE^\ominus$. Here, we have

$$-240 \times 10^3\,J\,mol^{-1} = -2 \times 96\,500\,C\,mol^{-1} \times E^\ominus$$

which gives $E^\ominus = +1.24\,V$.

90.5 $\Delta H^\ominus(\text{reaction}) = \Delta H_f^\ominus(CO(g)) - \Delta H_f^\ominus(H_2O(g)) = +131.3\,kJ\,mol^{-1}$

The reaction is strongly endothermic. A high temperature is needed to keep the reaction going, so air is blown through to liberate heat by the reaction of coke with oxygen. This is an exothermic reaction no matter whether carbon monoxide or carbon dioxide is produced.

90.6 It goes via a free radical mechanism.

90.7 (i) It is 2 volumes of hydrogen to 1 volume of oxygen. (The same ratio as in the equation.)
(ii) At the start the hydrogen mixes with oxygen already in the air in the tube. This gives an explosive mixture. After some time all the air is driven out and there is no oxygen left to give an explosion. Instead, the hydrogen burns very quietly, but the flame is so small that it is easily missed.

90.8 (i) $CuO(s) + H_2(g) \rightarrow Cu(s) + H_2O(g)$
(ii) The equation tells us that 80 g of oxide should give 64 g of copper; so 2.0 g should produce 1.6 g of copper.
(iii) The result shows that the product has a greater mass than expected. One possibility is that some of the copper(II) oxide was left unreacted. Also, it is likely that by letting air into the tube before it was cold, some of the hot copper reacted with oxygen and changed back to oxide.

90.9 Like aluminium trichloride, there is an empty orbital on the aluminium, which can accept a lone pair of electrons. The hydride ion has the necessary pair of electrons.

90.10 (i) $H_2(g) + Br_2(aq) \rightarrow 2H^+(aq) + 2Br^-(aq)$
(ii) The reaction is kinetically blocked. Largely this is because of the strength of the bond in the hydrogen molecule. In other words, there is a large activation energy to the reaction.

90.11 $CH_2{=}CHCH_2OH$. The double bond is not affected. The acid group is converted to an alcohol.

90.12 $LiAlH_4 + SiCl_4 \rightarrow LiCl + AlCl_3 + SiH_4$

90.13 One possibility is to react phosphorus trichloride with lithium tetrahydridoaluminate(III):

$$3LiAlH_4 + 4PCl_3 \rightarrow 3LiCl + 3AlCl_3 + 4PH_3$$

UNIT 90 SUMMARY

- Hydrogen:
  (i) Is much less dense than air.
  (ii) Is a good reducing agent.
  (iii) Is highly flammable.
- Laboratory preparation:

  Zinc + dilute sulphuric acid + trace copper(II) sulphate

  $Zn(s) + 2H^+(aq) \rightarrow Zn^{2+}(aq) + H_2(g)$

- Manufacture:
  (i) From methane at 35 atm, 800° C, Ni catalyst

  $CH_4(g) + H_2O(g) \rightarrow CO(g) + 3H_2(g)$
  $CO(g) + H_2O(g) \rightarrow CO_2(g) + H_2(g)$

  (ii) Bosch process, reacting steam and carbon or carbon monoxide at high temperature plus Fe catalyst

  $H_2O(g) + C(s) \rightarrow CO(g) + H_2(g)$
  $H_2O(g) + CO(g) \rightarrow CO_2(g) + H_2(g)$

Reactions

- With oxygen:

  $2H_2(g) + O_2(g) \rightarrow 2H_2O(g)$

  This reaction used in fuel cells to generate electricity.
- A reducing agent:

  e.g. $CuO(s) + H_2(g) \rightarrow Cu(s) + H_2O(l)$

- Hydrogenation:
  Converts alkenes to alkanes (Ni catalyst), e.g.

  $H_2C{=}CH_2 + H_2(g) \rightarrow H_3C{-}CH_3$

- With reactive metals:
  Ionic hydrides made, e.g.

  $2Na(s) + H_2(g) \rightarrow 2Na^+H^-(s)$

- Haber process:
  Used to make ammonia

  $N_2(g) + 3H_2(g) \rightleftharpoons 2NH_3(g)$

- With boron:
  Electron deficient hydrides exist, e.g. B_2H_6.

91

Water

91.1 What is special about water?

Water played a crucial part in the origin of life and it still has an essential role in maintaining plant and animal life. Plants depend on water for the transfer of nutrients and for photosynthesis. Owing to the presence of water in cells and body fluids such as blood, human beings are approximately 60% water. Nearly all the processes essential for life depend on reactions that take place in an aqueous solution, be it the division of DNA in a cell, the digestion of foodstuffs in the stomach, or the transport of oxygen around the body. Given the importance of water, it is not surprising that men and women can survive very much longer without food than they can without water.

Historically, the availability of water supplies has determined where villages, towns and cities are sited. Nomadic peoples, and animals, may travel hundreds of miles over the course of a year following the seasonal variation in rainfall. A lack of good quality drinking water, and water for sanitation, brings deadly illnesses such as typhoid.

Scenes like this, of flooding in Bangladesh, will become even more common if the worst predictions of the results of global warming come true.

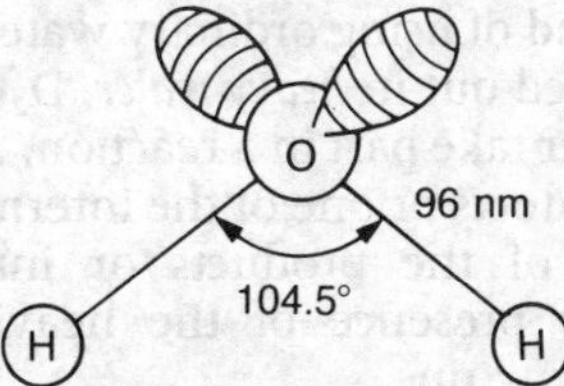

Figure 91.1 A water molecule has a bond angle of 104.5° and bond length of 96 nm. According to valence bond theory it also has two lone pairs of electrons

All these factors, and many more, make water a substance of great importance. From a strictly chemical point of view the remarkable thing about water is the amount of hydrogen bonding there is, both in the solid (ice) and in the liquid. If it were not for the fact that hydrogen bonds are of intermediate strength (stronger than van der Waals bonds but weaker than ordinary ionic or covalent bonds) then life as we know it could not exist and the world would be without rivers, lakes or seas.

We have talked about how hydrogen bonding comes about, and the effects it has, in Unit 21. For example, you should know that in many ways water is anomalous when it is compared to the other hydrides of elements in the same Group as oxygen. The solubility of many salts is due in no small measure to the polarity of water molecules. The attraction of the negatively charged oxygen atoms allows them to congregate around positive ions; the positively charged hydrogen atoms can gather round negative ions. This is the process of *hydration*. If you look at Unit 60 you will find that we discussed solubility largely as a competition between the magnitude of the lattice energy of a solid and the hydration energies of its ions or molecules.

According to valence bond theory each water molecule has two lone pairs of electrons (Figure 91.1). Often one of the lone pairs can be used in dative covalent bonding. An important example is the ability of a water molecule to bond to a proton in making the oxonium ion:

H—O—H + H^+ (1s orbital) ⟶ [H_3O]$^+$

$$H_2O(l) \quad + \quad H^+(aq) \longrightarrow H_3O^+(aq)$$

The colour of many transition metal ions in water is due to the ability of water molecules to bond to the ions. Transition metal ions often have d orbitals available, which can be used in dative covalent bonding with water molecules. For example, the colour of copper(II) sulphate in water is due to the presence of $Cu(H_2O)_4{}^{2+}$ ions (Figure 91.2). Molecules (or other species with lone pairs) that bond with transition metal ions are called *ligands*. This gives us another property of water: its molecules can be ligands.

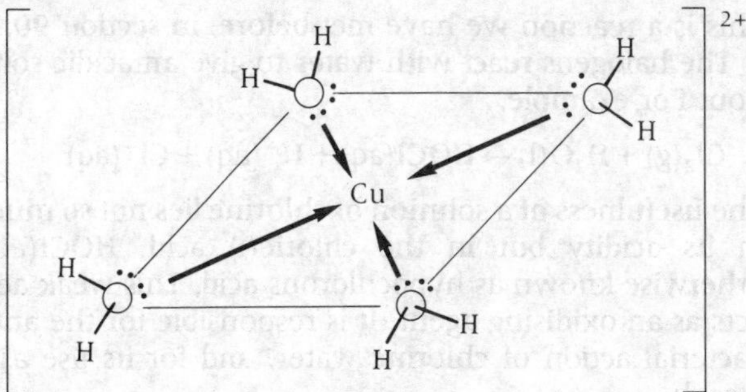

***Figure 91.2** The $Cu(H_2O)_4{}^{2+}$ ion*

91.1 What does molecular orbital theory have to say about the presence of lone pairs in a water molecule? (Look back at section 16.8.)

91.2 Some chemical reactions of water

There are two main types of reaction of water. They are reactions with metals and with non-metals. A third type is reactions with compounds.

(a) *With metals*

The way metals react with water can give us a measure of their reactivities. The most reactive metals are the alkali metals in Group I. Each of them reacts with cold water, giving off hydrogen and leaving an alkaline solution. A typical reaction is

$$2K(s) + 2H_2O(l) \rightarrow 2K^+(aq) + 2OH^-(aq) + H_2(g)$$

The reactivity increases down the Group. The Group II metals react in a similar way but less violently. (Beryllium does not react at all.) However, the hydroxides of the Group II metals are much less soluble than those of Group I.

Some of the transition metals react with hot water or steam to give an oxide. For example, if steam is passed over heated iron, hydrogen is released and an oxide is left:

$$3Fe(s) + 4H_2O(l) \rightarrow Fe_3O_4(s) + 4H_2(g)$$

Water plays an important part in the rusting of iron, the details of which you will find in section 68.2.

(b) *With non-metals*

The typical reaction with non-metals is for little to happen. Elements such as carbon, sulphur and phosphorus normally do not react with water. Carbon, usually in the guise of coke, when it is white hot will react with steam. The product is called water gas:

$$C(s) + H_2O(g) \rightarrow CO(g) + H_2(g)$$

This is a reaction we have met before, in section 90.2.

The halogens react with water to give an acidic solution. For example,

$$Cl_2(g) + H_2O(l) \rightarrow HOCl(aq) + H^+(aq) + Cl^-(aq)$$

The usefulness of a solution of chlorine lies not so much in its acidity but in the chloric(I) acid, HOCl(aq), otherwise known as hypochlorous acid. This weak acid acts as an oxidising agent. It is responsible for the antibacterial action of chlorine water, and for its use as a bleach.

(c) *With compounds*

We have already discussed why salts will often dissolve in water, some of them suffering hydrolysis. You had best look back at Unit 76 if you have forgotten this. Similarly, in Units 74 and 75 we met many instances where compounds of non-metals react to give acidic or alkaline solutions. Here a few equations might remind you of the possibilities.

Solutions of carbonates are slightly alkaline:

$$CO_3^{2-}(aq) + H_2O(l) \rightleftharpoons HCO_3^-(aq) + OH^-(aq)$$

A solution of ammonia is a weak alkali:

$$NH_3(aq) + H_2O(l) \rightleftharpoons NH_4^+(aq) + OH^-(aq)$$

A solution of carbon dioxide is weakly acidic:

$$CO_2(g) + H_2O(l) \rightleftharpoons H_2CO_3(aq) \rightleftharpoons HCO_3^-(aq) + H^+(aq)$$

Hydrogen chloride gives a strongly acidic solution:

$$HCl(g) + H_2O(l) \rightarrow H_3O^+(aq) + Cl^-(aq)$$

91.2 We have said that some oxides can show the properties of both acids and bases. These are the amphoteric oxides. Water is an amphoteric oxide. It shows this behaviour when it reacts with hydrogen chloride and with ammonia.

(i) Write down equations for the two reactions.

(ii) Identify where water is acting as an acid and where it is a base.

(iii) Which theory of acid and base behaviour have you used?

91.3 Why is it that ethanol, C_2H_5OH, and glucose, $C_6H_{12}O_6$, are both very soluble in water?

91.3 Heavy water

Deuterium, ^2_1H or D for short, is one of the isotopes of hydrogen. It has twice the mass of an ordinary hydrogen atom (protium), but like all isotopes of an element it has the same chemical properties. However, its extra mass makes a deuterium atom react less quickly than ordinary hydrogen, ^1_1H. Deuterium atoms are often used in chemistry to discover the mechanism of a reaction. Especially, instead of using ordinary water, H_2O, a reaction can be carried out in *heavy water*, D_2O. If hydrogen atoms from water take part in a reaction, they should be found in the products or one of the intermediates. If the mass spectrum of the products or intermediates is taken, then the presence of the heavier deuterium atoms should show up.

It so happens that D_2O does not undergo electrolysis as easily as H_2O. This allows heavy water to be obtained as a product of the electrolysis of water. Apart from its use in the study of chemical reactions, heavy water has been widely used in nuclear reactors. It is a fairly efficient moderator. That is, it can lower the energies of fast neutrons.

91.4 Ammonia gas, NH_3, can easily dissolve in heavy water.

(i) Write down the equation for the equilibrium that is set up.

(ii) If the solution is warmed and the gas produced is dried before being passed into a mass spectrometer, there is a large peak at $m/e = 17$, and a smaller one at 18. What causes the two peaks?

(iii) What does the experiment show about the equilibrium?

91.5 Some pure ordinary water, H_2O, is mixed with heavy water, D_2O. How many different molecules and ions could appear in the mixture once equilibrium is established? What are their formulae?

91.6 Write down the equation for the reaction of sodium with heavy water.

91.4 The water cycle

It has been estimated that the total volume of water that falls to the Earth's surface each year is about 496 000 km^3, i.e. approaching 500×10^{12} tonne. About one quarter of this precipitation (a general term for water falling as rain, snow, etc.) occurs over land, the rest over the seas. The precipitation is balanced by evaporation of an equal amount of water. (A nice example of the rule that what goes up must come down!) The changes involved in the continuous process of precipitation and evaporation is called the *water cycle* (Figure 91.3).

Evaporation mainly takes place from the sea (about 425×10^{12} tonne each year). On land, much water evaporates from rivers and lakes; but a great deal returns to the atmosphere by the loss of water from the leaves of plants. This is the process of *transpiration*. With the large amount of rain forest that is being cut down in some countries, changes in climate may be caused by

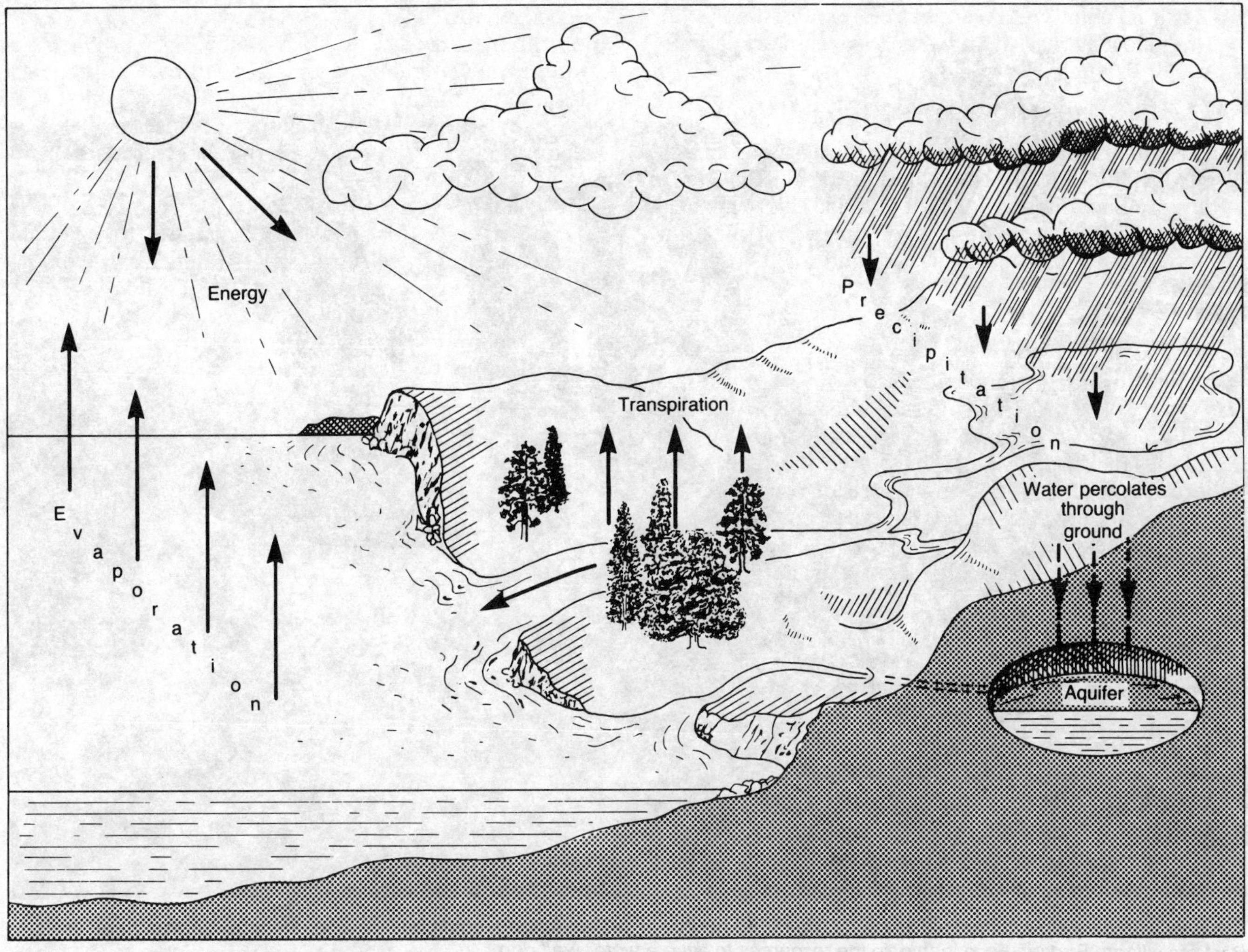

***Figure 91.3** The water cycle. About 875 km^3 of water evaporates from oceans, and about 160 km^3 from the land. Over 775 km^3 of water falls as rain over oceans, more than 260 km^3 over land, and 100 km^3 flows into the oceans from rivers. Much water is present as clouds and invisible water vapour in the air. (Data taken from: Allaby, M. (1986).* Ecology Facts, *Hamlyn, London)*

the reduction in transpiration. This is in addition to the increase in soil erosion that takes place when forest is cleared. There is, of course, evaporation from all other surfaces that get wet, such as roads, fields and washing hung out to dry. Some precipitation escapes evaporation by finding its way through the surface layers of rock and soil to underground chambers, where it may remain for thousands of years. The chambers are known as *aquifers,* and they are a useful source of water where wells can be sunk sufficiently deeply to reach them.

91.7 At a temperature of 15°C the energy absorbed when water changes from liquid to gas is about 2500 kJ kg^{-1}.

(i) Estimate the energy used in the evaporation of water over land and sea each year.

(ii) When water vapour condenses to rain drops, energy is released. Around 125×10^{12} tonne of precipitation takes place over land each year. How much energy is released?

91.5 Water pollution

When rain drops fall through the atmosphere they dissolve small quantities of gases in the atmosphere. Where there is little air pollution, the gases are mainly nitrogen, oxygen and a little carbon dioxide. Although small in its amount, the carbon dioxide does make the water very slightly acidic owing to the production of weak carbonic acid. Rain falling in a thunderstorm is more acidic than normal. The energy of the lightning is sufficient to dissociate nitrogen molecules, which then combine with oxygen to give oxides such as nitrogen

It is only with the help of charities such as Oxfam that people in many African communities, like the one shown here in Baskare village, Burkina Faso, can gain the resources to have a water well dug.

dioxide. Indeed, rain in a thunderstorm is very dilute nitric acid.

As the rain percolates through soil and rock it dissolves minerals. Depending on the geology of the catchment area for water, reservoirs and aquifers can contain high amounts of dissolved salts. Especially, in regions where there is chalk, $CaCO_3$, the water contains calcium ions and hydrogencarbonate ions owing to the reaction

$$CaCO_3(s) + H^+(aq) \rightarrow Ca^{2+}(aq) + HCO_3^-(aq)$$

Magnesium ions can appear by a similar means where dolomite, a mineral containing $MgCO_3$ and $CaCO_3$, occurs.

Over the last few years the concentrations of sulphate and nitrate ions in water have greatly increased in areas that are intensively farmed. This is partly due to the widespread use of fertilisers such as ammonium sulphate and ammonium nitrate. It is the nitrate that is the main cause of worry because in some circumstances it is able to give rise to nitrite ions. Nitrite ions are known carcinogens. It remains to be seen whether populations that drink water contaminated by nitrate ions will show a higher incidence of cancers in years to come.

The use of machines to spread chemically manufactured fertilisers has led to over-use, and problems with water purity.

In most industrialised areas of the world the air contains significant quantities of the oxides of carbon, nitrogen and sulphur. A major source of nitrogen oxides in the atmosphere is the burning of fuel in inter-

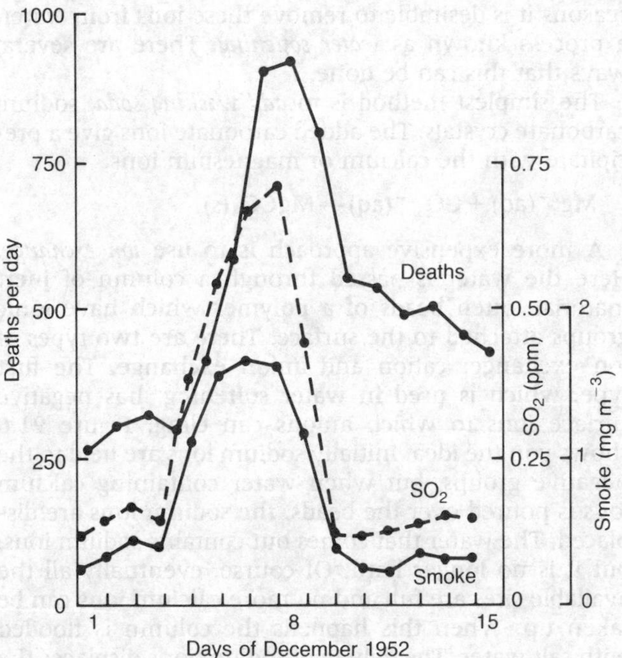

Figure 91.4 *The graphs show how the increased air pollution in a London fog of 1952 caused a marked increase in the death rate. (Taken from: White, I. D. et al. (1987).* Environmental Systems, *Allen and Unwin, London, figure 24.18)*

nal combustion engines, e.g. in cars and lorries. Carbon dioxide and sulphur dioxide are produced in large quantities by the burning of fossil fuels, e.g. in open coal fires, oil central heating systems and power stations; such burning can cause a health risk (Figure 91.4). The smoke from power stations is usually sent into the air from very tall chimneys. For the people who live close to the power stations this is all to the good; but the acidic oxides can travel hundreds or thousands of miles in the winds higher in the atmosphere. The oxides then give rise to *acid rain* in regions far from the power station. The deaths of huge areas of forest in Germany and parts of Scandinavia has been blamed on power stations in Britain, many of which have inefficient purification systems for the effluent sent to the chimneys.

Acid rain also has a marked effect on the ecology of lakes and rivers. A small change in pH can greatly affect the ability of fish to breed. Some parts of Scotland and Scandinavia have suffered almost complete loss of salmon from rivers where the pH has decreased. Acid rain can also leach minerals from rocks and soil which are unaffected by normal rain water. For example, some inland lakes now have much higher concentrations of aluminium ions than a few years ago.

These trees in the USA show the characteristic loss of foliage which is the mark of damage by acid rain.

91.6 Water treatment

As we have seen, water can contain different ions depending on the nature of the area in which it is found. Normally it will also contain small amounts of organic matter, such as particles of clay and decaying vegetation suspended in it. The particles are often of a colloidal size and can be precipitated by the addition of aluminium salts. However, if the addition is not controlled properly, the aluminium can itself end up in the water supply as a pollutant. Larger particles can be removed by passing the water through beds of sand and

Sprinkler beds contain particles which provide a large surface area upon which bacteria live and digest much of the harmful matter in sewage.

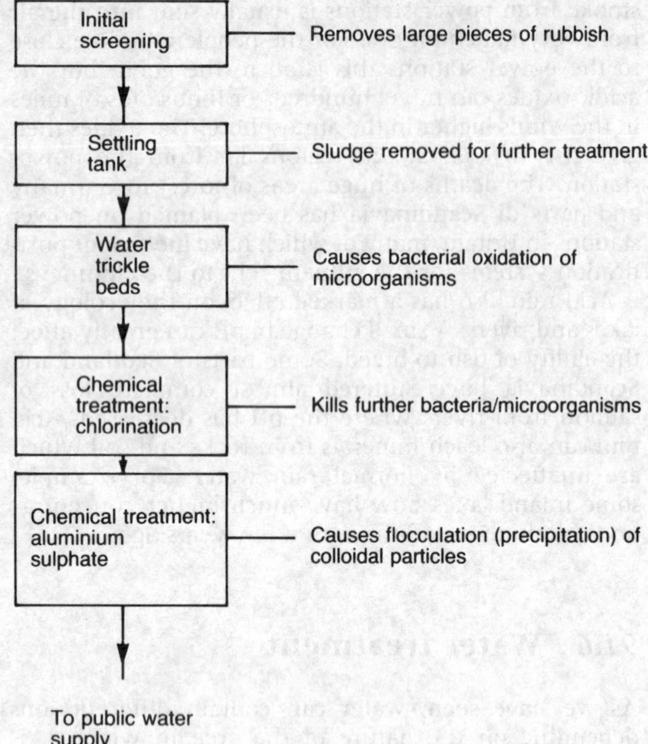
Initial screening
Removes large pieces of rubbish
Settling tank
Sludge removed for further treatment
Water trickle beds
Causes bacterial oxidation of microorganisms
Chemical treatment: chlorination
Kills further bacteria/microorganisms
Chemical treatment: aluminium sulphate
Causes flocculation (precipitation) of colloidal particles
To public water supply

Figure 91.5 *The key stages in the purification of water*

gravel that act as filters (Figure 91.5). Before it is fed to the public water supply, chlorine is added in small quantities in order to oxidise harmful bacteria. In some countries fluoride is also added because there is evidence that it can help prevent tooth decay, particularly among children.

Water that contains calcium and magnesium ions is called *hard water*. When these ions are accompanied by hydrogencarbonate ions, the water contains *temporary hardness*. It is called temporary because the calcium and magnesium ions can be removed from the water by boiling. The hydrogencarbonate ions decompose on heating, producing carbon dioxide and carbonate ions. The carbonate ions give precipitates with the metal ions:

$$2HCO_3^-(aq) \rightarrow CO_3^{2-}(aq) + H_2O(l) + CO_2(g)$$
$$Mg^{2+}(aq) + CO_3^{2-}(aq) \rightarrow MgCO_3(s)$$

When the metal ions are present with chloride or sulphate ions, the water is *permanently hard*. Permanent hardness cannot be removed by boiling.

Hard water has several unwanted properties. In the first place, it gives a scum with soap. Soaps are ionic compounds containing a long hydrocarbon chain with a —COO^- group on the end. This group is the remnant of an organic acid that has its hydrogen removed. In a solid soap it is found with a sodium or potassium ion. A typical soap particle is sodium stearate, $C_{17}H_{35}COO^-Na^+$. A particle like this is easily soluble in water, but with calcium or magnesium ions the stearate ion forms an insoluble solid. Not only is this a waste of soap, but the scum it makes is unpleasant. For both reasons it is desirable to remove these ions from water, a process known as *water softening*. There are several ways that this can be done.

The simplest method is to *add washing soda*, sodium carbonate crystals. The added carbonate ions give a precipitate with the calcium or magnesium ions:

$$Mg^{2+}(aq) + CO_3^{2-}(aq) \rightarrow MgCO_3(s)$$

A more expensive approach is to use *ion exchange*. Here the water is passed through a column of inert material, often beads of a polymer which have ionic groups attached to the surface. There are two types of ion exchange: cation and anion exchange. The first type, which is used in water softening, has negative surface ions to which anions can cling. Figure 91.6 shows you the idea. Initially sodium ions are held to the negative groups, but when water containing calcium ions is poured over the beads, the sodium ions are displaced. The water that comes out contains sodium ions, but it is no longer hard. Of course, eventually all the available sites are full and no more calcium ions can be taken up. When this happens the column is flooded with salt water. The deluge of sodium ions displaces the calcium ions and then the column is ready to be used again.

A similar method to using an ion exchange column is to use *zeolites*. Zeolites are cage-like structures made from silicates (Figure 91.7). They have empty spaces in their structures into which ions can fit. As with ordinary ion exchange, sodium ions are the normal residents in the holes. When hard water passes over the zeolite, the calcium ions displace the sodium ions. The zeolite is regenerated by swamping it with salt water.

There is another reason why magnesium and calcium ions should be removed from water. If hard water is boiled the calcium or magnesium carbonates that are precipitated produce a layer of scale. The presence of scale in a kettle can be annoying, but in hot water pipes in the home or in industry it leads to two problems. First, it takes more energy to heat water in a tank that has a layer of scale on it. This can greatly increase the cost of heating. Secondly, it becomes very much harder for water to pass round the system. This can overload pumps and reduce efficiency. Eventually pipes can become completely blocked or 'furred up'.

The concentration of ions such as Ca^{2+} and Mg^{2+} that cause hardness in water can be found by titration.

Ethylenediaminetetraacetic acid (EDTA; more correctly named 1,2-bis[bis(carboxymethyl)amino]ethane) has an anion with long tentacle-like groups that can wrap round a metal ion. In principle there are six sites that can be used in bonding, but they are not always used. For example, with Ca^{2+} ions only four bonds are made. Figure 91.8 shows you the idea. (The calcium ion makes a complex with the EDTA anion – a process we normally associate with transition metals.) An indicator is added to the sample of water that is to be titrated. The indicator changes colour in the presence of Mg^{2+} or Ca^{2+} ions. Often a solution of Erichrome Black T is used, but this will only work if the water solution is made alkaline. To ensure the solution remains alkaline, a buf-

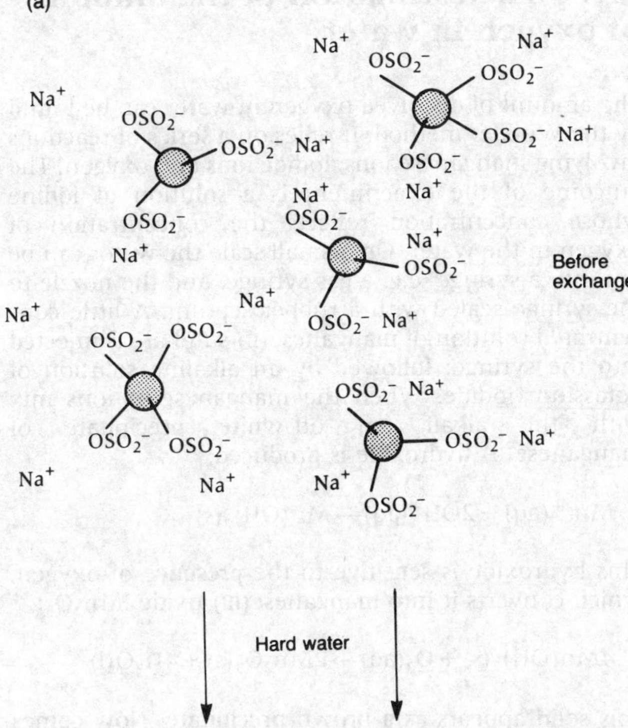

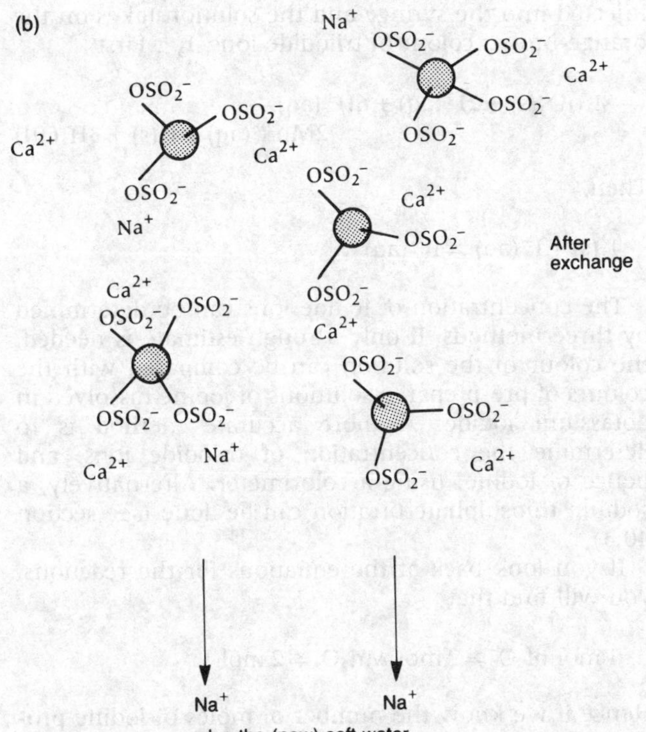

Figure 91.6 *(a) Part of an ion exchange resin. The beads carry SO_3^- ions, together with Na^+ ions close by. (b) After hard water is passed over the resin, most of the Ca^{2+} ions in the water are held on the beads. Na^+ ions are washed off the beads*

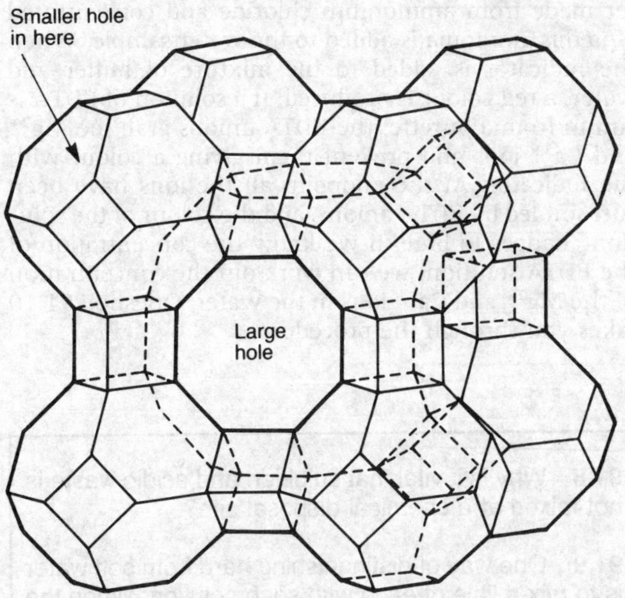

Figure 91.7 *The cage structure of zeolite, with formula $Na_{12}(Al_{12}Si_{12}O_{48})\cdot 27H_2O$. The structure is based on a combination of cubes and octahedra. There is a large hole in the centre, and smaller ones inside the other frameworks, in which atoms, molecules or ions can be trapped. (Adapted from: Wells, A. F. (1950).* Structural Inorganic Chemistry, *2nd edn, Clarendon Press, Oxford, figure 23.25)*

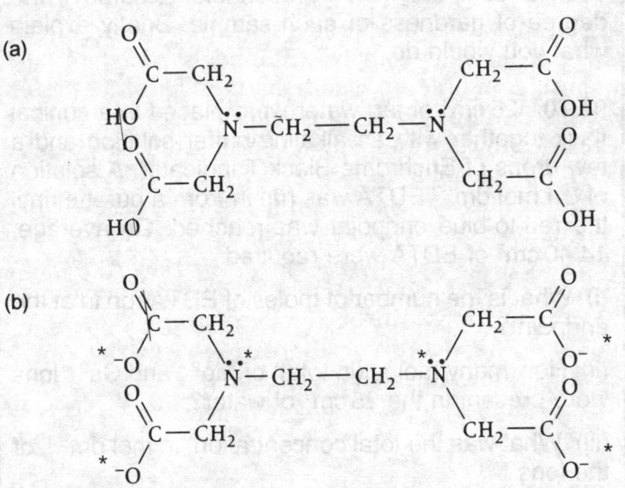

Figure 91.8 *How EDTA works. (a) A molecule of EDTA. (b) There are six possible sites that an $EDTA^{4-}$ ion can use in bonding. Note that two of these are lone pairs on the nitrogen atoms. (c) The complex made by $EDTA^{4-}$ with a Ca^{2+} ion*

fer made from ammonium chloride and concentrated aqueous ammonia is added to the water sample. When the indicator is added to the mixture of buffer and water, a red colour is produced. If a solution of EDTA is run in from a burette, the EDTA anions grab the Mg^{2+} and Ca^{2+} ions and prevent them giving a colour with the indicator. At the endpoint all the ions have been surrounded by EDTA anions, and the colour of the solution changes to blue. If we know the concentration of the EDTA solution, we can work out the concentration of the Mg^{2+} and Ca^{2+} ions in the water. Question 91.10 takes you through the procedure.

91.8 Why is it vital that sulphide and acidic waste is not mixed at a chemical disposal site?

91.9 One way of distinguishing hard from soft water is to mix a little of each with soap solution. When the mixture is shaken, the soft water will give a lather; the hard water will not give a lather until much more soap solution is added.

You have been given a soap solution together with the usual apparatus found in a chemical laboratory. You have also been given three samples of water. Your task is to design an experiment that would allow you to compare (with reasonable accuracy) the degree of hardness of each sample. Briefly explain what you would do.

91.10 25 cm^3 of tap water were placed in a conical flask together with an alkaline buffer solution and a few drops of Erichrome Black T indicator. A solution of 0.1 mol dm^{-3} EDTA was run in from a burette until the red-to-blue endpoint was reached. On average, 14.40 cm^3 of EDTA were required.

(i) What is the number of moles of EDTA run in at the endpoint?

(ii) How many moles (in total) of Mg^{2+} and Ca^{2+} ions were present in the 25 cm^3 of water?

(iii) What was the total concentration, in mol dm^{-3}, of the ions?

(iv) Assume that 50% of the ions were Ca^{2+} ions. What mass of chalk, $CaCO_3$, would provide these ions in the water? $M(CaCO_3) = 100$ g mol^{-1}.

(v) Assume the water came from a reservoir holding 10^6 tonnes of water. What mass of $CaCO_3$ had been leached out of the rock structures in the area? Density of water = 1 g cm^{-3} or 1 kg dm^{-3}; 1 tonne ≡ 1000 kg.

91.11 Water that is fit for drinking is called *potable* water. Try a little research of your own to discover the source of potable water in your area. What ions or other chemicals does your local water contain?

91.7 The estimation of the amount of oxygen in water

The amount of dissolved oxygen in water can be found by the Winkler method. It relies on a series of reactions involving manganese ions, iodide ions and oxygen. The outcome of the experiment is a solution of iodine whose concentration reflects the concentration of oxygen in the water. On a small scale the water can be put into a syringe, e.g. a gas syringe, and the nozzle to the syringe sealed with a rubber septum. A little concentrated solution of manganese(II) sulphate is injected into the syringe, followed by an alkaline solution of potassium iodide. When the manganese(II) ions mix with the alkali, an off-white precipitate of manganese(II) hydroxide is produced:

$$Mn^{2+}(aq) + 2OH^-(aq) \rightarrow Mn(OH)_2(s)$$

This hydroxide is sensitive to the presence of oxygen, which converts it into manganese(III) oxide, Mn_2O_3:

$$4Mn(OH)_2(s) + O_2(aq) \rightarrow 2Mn_2O_3(s) + 4H_2O(l)$$

This solid appears as a brown precipitate. Now comes the last part of the process. Manganese(III) is sufficiently oxidising in its nature to convert iodide ions into iodine. However, it will only do so in acidic conditions. Once the precipitation reaction is finished, sulphuric acid is injected into the syringe and the solution takes on the orange-brown colour of triiodide ions, I_3^-. First,

$$Mn_2O_3(s) + 2I^-(aq) + 6H^+(aq) \rightarrow 2Mn^{2+}(aq) + I_2(s) + 3H_2O(l)$$

Then,

$$I_2(s) + I^-(aq) \rightleftharpoons I_3^-(aq)$$

The concentration of iodide ions can be determined by three methods. If only a rough estimate is needed, the colour of the solution can be compared with the colours of pre-prepared solutions of iodine dissolved in potassium iodide. A more accurate method is to determine the concentration of triiodide ions, and hence of iodine, using a colorimeter. Alternatively, a sodium thiosulphate titration can be done (see section 40.3).

If you look back at the equations for the reactions, you will find that

$$1 \text{ mol of } O_2 \equiv 2 \text{ mol } Mn_2O_3 \equiv 2 \text{ mol } I_2$$

Hence if we know the number of moles of iodine produced, we also know the number of moles of oxygen molecules that were in the original water sample.

Answers

91.1 The lone pairs are not to be found in molecular orbital theory. This just goes to show that we should not mistake the results of mathematical theories as a direct picture of 'reality'.

91.2 (i), (ii) $\underset{\text{base}}{H_2O(l)}+HCl(g)\rightarrow H_3O^+(aq)+Cl^-(aq)$

$\underset{\text{acid}}{H_2O(l)}+NH_3(aq)\rightleftharpoons NH_4{}^+(aq)+OH^-(aq)$

(iii) In the first equation water is a proton acceptor, so using the Brønsted theory it is a base. For the opposite reason, water is a Brønsted acid in the second equation.

91.3 Their solubility is due to hydrogen bonding (Unit 21).

91.4 (i) $D_2O(l)+NH_3(aq)\rightleftharpoons NH_3D^+(aq)+OD^-(aq)$

(ii) As this is an equilibrium the NH_3D^+ ion can react with the OD^- like this:

$NH_3D^+(aq)+OD^-(aq)\rightarrow NH_2D(aq)+HDO(l)$

The NH_2D can be given off as a gas (just like NH_3). This gives rise to the peak at 18 and NH_3 to the peak at 17.

(iii) It is dynamic.

91.5 In ordinary water you might remember that an equilibrium is set up:

$2H_2O(l)\rightleftharpoons H_3O^+(aq)+OH^-(aq)$

Another way of writing this is

$H_2O(l)+H_2O(l)\rightleftharpoons H_3O^+(aq)+OH^-(aq)$

If one of the pair of water molecules is D_2O, we can have

$H_2O(l)+D_2O(l)\rightleftharpoons H_2DO^+(aq)+OH^-(aq)$

or

$H_2O(l)+D_2O(l)\rightleftharpoons D_2HO^+(aq)+OD^-(aq)$

If both molecules are D_2O we have

$2D_2O(l)\rightleftharpoons D_3O^+(aq)+OD^-(aq)$

An OD^- ion can combine with an H^+ ion, or an OH^- ion with a D^+ ion to give HDO molecules. Therefore we can have three different molecules and five different types of ion.

91.6

$2Na(s)+2D_2O(l)\rightarrow 2Na^+(aq)+2OD^-(aq)+D_2(g)$

91.7 (i) To convert 500×10^{12} tonne of liquid water to vapour requires

$500\times10^{12}\times10^3\,kg\times2500\,kJ\,kg^{-1}=1.25\times10^{21}\,kJ$

This energy is absorbed and leads to a lowering of temperature.

(ii) $125\times10^{12}\times10^3\,kg\times2500\,kJ\,kg^{-1}=0.31\times10^{21}\,kJ$

This energy is released, and thereby tends to increase the temperature of the atmosphere.

91.8 Sulphides can react with acid to give off very poisonous hydrogen sulphide gas, e.g.

$Na_2S(s)+2H^+(aq)\rightarrow 2Na^+(aq)+H_2S(g)$

One of the properties of hydrogen sulphide is that it can be smelled in very small quantities; but once someone begins to be poisoned, he or she loses sensitivity to the smell. Accidents have occurred at disposal sites when work people have died as a result of such poisoning.

91.9 The soap solution can be put in a burette and a pipette used to measure out a known volume of each water sample into separate flasks. The soap solution is added in the standard method during a titration. However, instead of looking for a colour change in an indicator, the flask is shaken to see if a permanent lather is produced. Once the lather is achieved the volume of soap solution used is recorded. The harder the water, the more soap solution will be needed.

91.10 (i) There were

$$\frac{14.4\,cm^3}{1000\,cm^3}\times0.1\,mol\,dm^{-3}=14.4\times10^{-4}\,mol$$

(ii) 14.4×10^{-4} mol in $25\,cm^3$; the ratio is 1 EDTA anion to each ion.

(iii) We scale up from $25\,cm^3$ to $1000\,cm^3$, i.e. multiply by 40. The concentration is $57.6\times10^{-3}\,mol\,dm^{-3}$.

(iv) There are 28.8×10^{-3} mol of Ca^{2+} ions in $1\,dm^3$. Given that 1 mol of Ca^{2+} ions comes from 1 mol of $CaCO_3$, the amount of $CaCO_3$ is also 28.8×10^{-3} mol, i.e. $28.8\times10^{-3}\,mol\times100\,g\,mol^{-1}=2.88\,g$.

(v) 10^6 tonne of water represents 10^9 kg, or $10^9\,dm^3$. The mass of $CaCO_3$ leached is 2.88×10^9 g, or 2880 tonnes. This provides one more example of the huge scale upon which natural processes take place.

91.11 This will depend on your own locality.

UNIT 91 SUMMARY

- Water:
  - (i) Essential for living systems (see Figure 91.3 for the water cycle).
  - (ii) A good solvent for ionic and covalent compounds.
  - (iii) A good ligand with transition metal ions.
- Hydrogen bonding is responsible for the high melt ing and boiling points of water.
- Hard water
  - (i) Contains magnesium ions, Mg^{2+}, and calcium ions, Ca^{2+}, which give precipitates (scum) with soap, and deposits of insoluble magnesium and calcium carbonates after hard water is boiled.
  - (ii) Hardness in water can be removed by passing water through an ion exchange column.

- The Winkler method is used to estimate the proportion of dissolved oxygen in water.

Reactions

- Water autoionises:

$$2H_2O(l) \rightarrow H_3O^+(aq) + OH^-(aq)$$

- With reactive metals:
  Hydrogen released, alkaline solution left;

$$\text{e.g. } 2K(s) + 2H_2O(l) \rightarrow 2K^+(aq) + 2OH^-(aq) + H_2(g)$$

- With halogens:
  Acidic solutions made;

$$\text{e.g. } Cl_2(g) + H_2O(l) \rightarrow HOCl(aq) + H^+(aq) + Cl^-(aq)$$

- Hydrolysis reactions:

$$\text{e.g. } HCl(g) + H_2O(l) \rightarrow H_3O^+(aq) + Cl^-(aq)$$

$$NH_3(g) + H_2O(l) \rightarrow NH_4^+(aq) + OH^-(aq)$$

$$CO_3^{2-}(aq) + H_2O(l) \rightarrow HCO_3^-(aq) + OH^-(aq)$$

92

Group I

92.1 The nature of the elements

The elements of Group I are all metals. Indeed, from a chemist's point of view they make an excellent set because they have a large number of properties in common. Lithium is the only member of the Group that is not completely typical. Table 92.1 provides you with some of the physical data about the elements and Table 92.2 gives their uses.

The negative values of their standard redox potentials should tell you that they are all good reducing agents. Alternatively, we can say that they are all highly electropositive metals. Indeed, the tendency for them to lose their outermost electron and change into a positive ion is the most important feature of their chemistry. The main reason why they do this is that the outer s electron is very well shielded by the inner electrons. The s electron feels only a fraction of the nuclear charge. As we go down the Group, shielding wins over the effect of the increasing numbers of protons in the nucleus. Caesium, for example, is a much more powerful reducing agent than sodium. The metals are so reactive that in Nature they are always found combined with other elements. Especially, they exist as chlorides, nitrates, sulphates and carbonates.

The exception to the rule that the reducing power of the elements increases down the Group appears to be lithium. It has a more negative electrode potential than sodium, potassium or rubidium. The reason for the anomaly lies in the nature of the lithium ion in water. The order of the ionisation energies agrees with our notion that the further you go down the Group, the more easily electrons are lost from the atoms. However,

Table 92.2. Uses of the elements in Group I

*Element**	*Main uses*
Lithium	In small, long-life batteries, e.g. for use in digital watches, calculators and computers
	In the reducing agents LiH and $LiAlH_4$
	Specialist chemicals in a wide range of industries, e.g. making glass, organic chemicals
Sodium	Liquid sodium has been used for heat transfer in nuclear power stations
	As a reducing agent in the manufacture of some elements, e.g. titanium
	In alloys
	In batteries
Potassium	Manufacture of KO_2 for oxygen generators

*The other metals have but few uses

Table 92.1. Physical properties of the elements in Group I*

Symbol	*Lithium* Li	*Sodium* Na	*Potassium* K	*Rubidium* Rb	*Caesium* Cs
Electron structure	(He)2s	(Ne)3s	(Ar)4s	(Kr)5s	(Xe)6s
Electronegativity	1.0	0.9	0.8	0.8	0.7
I.E./kJ mol^{-1}	520	513	419	400	380
Melting point/°C	181	98	63	39	29
Boiling point/°C	1331	890	766	701	685
Atomic radius/pm	123	157	203	216	235
Ionic radius/pm	68	98	133	148	167
Principal oxid. no.	+1	+1	+1	+1	+1
$E^{\ominus}_{M^+/M}$/V	−3.03	−2.71	−2.92	−2.93	−3.08

*The last element in the Group, francium, is omitted. It is not at all common, and its chemistry is of little importance

in solution, the product is a metal ion in water, surrounded by its hydration sphere. Table 92.1 shows that the lithium ion has by far the smallest ion. This results in it being a very dense centre of positive charge. It attracts and holds water molecules to it very strongly. Indeed, its hydration energy is huge: almost −500 kJ mol^{-1}. (This is about 110 kJ mol^{-1} greater than the next largest, for the sodium ion.) The large hydration energy is responsible for the ease with which a lithium ion will be made in solution. The electrode potential of lithium reflects this tendency for lithium to convert into a hydrated ion, rather than its inherent ability as a reducing agent. If lithium takes part in reactions that do not involve water, then it does show less reducing power than the other members of the Group.

It is difficult to convert Group I metal ions into neutral atoms, so if we need to obtain the pure metal we have to use electrolysis. Sodium is by far the most widely used of the metals, and it is made by the electrolysis of sodium hydroxide in the Downs process. You will find details of the process in Unit 85. It was Humphry Davy who in 1807 first isolated pure potassium and sodium by using electrolysis.

The pure metals are silvery white and, apart from lithium, soft and easy to cut. However, they rapidly tarnish in air giving a layer of oxide, peroxide, or sometimes superoxide. They will also react violently with water. For both reasons they are kept under a layer of oil.

92.2 Reactions with oxygen

Lithium oxidises less rapidly than the other metals, but they all give ionic oxides and peroxides. In a plentiful supply of oxygen the reactions can be violent. (You will find more information about different types of oxide in Unit 99.) A typical reaction is:

$$2K(s) + O_2(g) \rightarrow K_2O_2(s)$$

As we should expect with metallic oxides, they are basic; indeed very strongly so. They dissolve in water to give strongly alkaline solutions containing hydroxide ions. For example,

$$Na_2O(s) + H_2O(l) \rightarrow 2Na^+(aq) + 2OH^-(aq)$$
$$2Na_2O_2(s) + 2H_2O(l) \rightarrow 4Na^+(aq) + 4OH^-(aq) + O_2(g)$$

One use of potassium superoxide, KO_2, is for generating oxygen. It has the ability to absorb carbon dioxide, while giving out oxygen at the same time:

$$4KO_2(s) + 2CO_2(g) \rightarrow 2K_2CO_3(s) + 3O_2(g)$$

This property has been made use of in breathing equipment, e.g. for mountaineers, in submarines and in spacecraft.

92.3 Reactions with water

Lithium, sodium and potassium all float on water. Lithium reacts only slowly, but sodium and potassium react more quickly. Hydrogen is given off and the solution remaining is alkaline. You may have seen an experiment in which sodium darts across the surface of water. If it sticks to the side of the container it may even burst into flame along with the hydrogen released. Potassium almost always ignites soon after being placed on water. It too rushes around over the surface. The reactions of rubidium and caesium with water are best not attempted. Explosions result! The reaction for sodium is:

$$2Na(s) + 2H_2O(l) \rightarrow 2Na^+(aq) + 2OH^-(aq) + H_2(g)$$

92.4 The hydroxides

The hydroxides of the Group I metals are among the strongest bases known. They exist as ionic solids and are very soluble in water; except, that is, for lithium hydroxide, which is slightly soluble. (The solubility of LiOH in water is about 130 g dm^{-3}, the others are greater than 400 g dm^{-3}.) Lithium hydroxide is also the only one that will convert to an oxide on heating.

Probably you will have used a solution of sodium hydroxide as a source of hydroxide ions. For example, in neutralising acids,

$$OH^-(aq) + H^+(aq) \rightarrow H_2O(l)$$

converting ammonium ions into ammonia,

$$OH^-(aq) + NH_4^+(aq) \rightarrow NH_3(g) + H_2O(l)$$

or precipitating insoluble hydroxides of metals such as iron,

$$Fe^{3+}(aq) + 3OH^-(aq) \rightarrow \underset{\text{iron(III) hydroxide}}{Fe(OH)_3(s)}$$

Another use for hydroxides, especially potassium hydroxide, is to absorb carbon dioxide. This happens in the cold, and a carbonate results:

$$2OH^-(aq) + CO_2(g) \rightarrow CO_3^{2-}(aq) + H_2O(l)$$

92.1 Write the equation for the action of heat on LiOH.

92.2 Which indicator would you use for titrating sodium hydroxide solution with (i) dilute hydrochloric acid, (ii) a solution of ethanoic acid?

92.3 Why should an alkali never (or almost never) be put into a burette?

92.5 The carbonates and hydrogencarbonates

The carbonates are all soluble in water, and their hydrogencarbonates exist as solids. The exception once again is lithium, which does not give a hydrogencarbonate. This pair of properties is different to the corresponding compounds of the Group II metals. For example, their carbonates are insoluble, and their hydrogencarbonates only exist in solution.

If you heat one of the carbonates you will not find a great deal happening: they do not decompose, except that is for lithium carbonate. On the other hand, the hydrogencarbonates do decompose, giving off carbon dioxide and water vapour, e.g.

$$2NaHCO_3(s) \rightarrow Na_2CO_3(s) + H_2O(g) + CO_2(g)$$

Sodium carbonate is a useful substance. It may be that you have some in your home. It is sold as washing soda crystals, $Na_2CO_3{\cdot}10H_2O$. In water it gives a slightly alkaline solution owing to salt hydrolysis (see Unit 76):

$$CO_3^{2-}(aq) + H_2O(l) \rightarrow HCO_3^-(aq) + OH^-(aq)$$

In industry sodium carbonate has a much more important role. It is one of the key participants in the chlor-alkali industry, where it is known as soda or soda ash. It is made in huge quantities by the Solvay process. You will find details in Unit 84. The overall change that takes place is

$$CaCO_3 + 2NaCl \rightarrow Na_2CO_3 + CaCl_2$$

but this hides a number of intermediate steps involving ammonia and carbon dioxide (among other things). The majority of sodium carbonate is used in glass making.

Both the carbonates and hydrogencarbonates react readily with acids, giving off carbon dioxide and water. For example,

$$CO_3^{2-}(s) + 2H^+(aq) \rightarrow CO_2(g) + H_2O(l)$$
$$HCO_3^-(s) + H^+(aq) \rightarrow CO_2(g) + H_2O(l)$$

The ease with which hydrogencarbonates give off carbon dioxide is made use of in fire extinguishers and baking powders. See Unit 95 for details.

92.4 (i) What would you expect to happen if you heated washing soda crystals?

(ii) Why are these crystals used in bath salts (together with a little colouring and perfume)?

92.6 The halides

All the metals give fluorides, chlorides, bromides and iodides. Apart from caesium they have the same crystal structure as sodium chloride: the rock salt structure (Figure 92.1). We have met this structure before in Unit 32. The positive metal ions and the negative halide ions each have a coordination number of 6. The structure of the caesium halides is different. Here the coordination number of the ions is 8. If you look back at Unit 32 you will find that we explained this in terms of the ratio of the radii of the caesium and halide ions. In simple terms, the caesium ion is large enough for eight other ions to fit round it without bumping into one another.

There are many deposits of sodium chloride around the world. Often they are the result of the evaporation of seas and lakes. Rock salt mines are a source of sodium

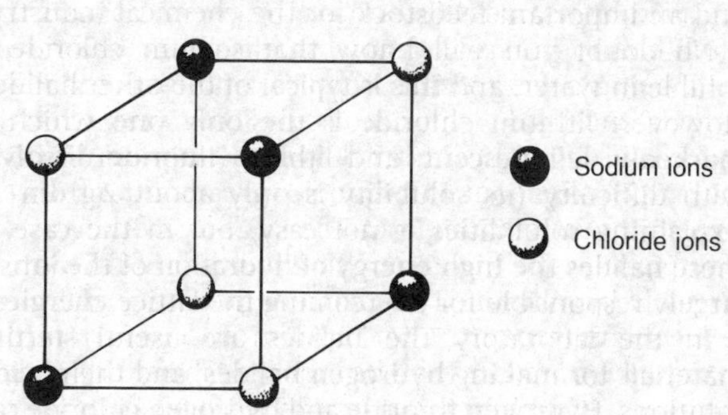

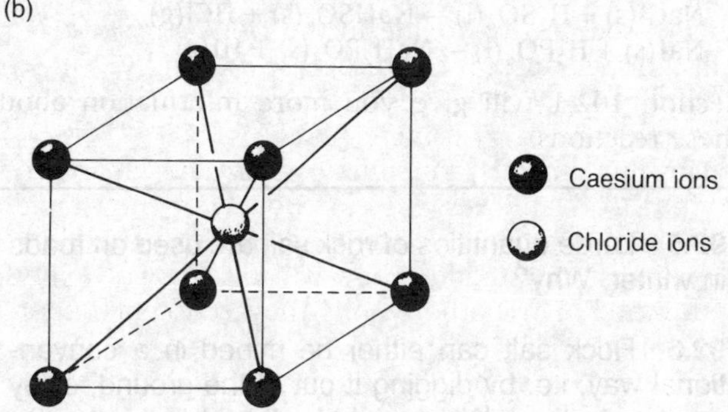

***Figure 92.1** (a) The sodium chloride (rock salt) structure and (b) the caesium chloride structure*

An age-old method of salt manufacture is to allow salt water to be evaporated by the heat of the sun. This particular scene is near Lanzarote in the Canary Islands.

chloride, which is both an essential mineral for health and an important feedstock for the chemical industry.

No doubt you will know that sodium chloride is soluble in water, and this is typical of the other halides. However, lithium chloride is the only one which is markedly deliquescent, and lithium fluoride dissolves with difficulty (its solubility is only about 2 g dm^{-3}). Explaining solubilities is not easy, but in the case of these halides the high energy of hydration of the ions is largely responsible for overcoming the lattice energies.

In the laboratory the halides are useful starting materials for making hydrogen halides, and their acidic solutions. Hydrogen fluoride and hydrogen chloride can be prepared by warming concentrated sulphuric acid with sodium fluoride or chloride. To make hydrogen bromide or iodide, the sodium salt must be reacted with an acid that has less oxidising power than sulphuric acid, usually phosphoric(V) acid:

$$NaCl(s) + H_2SO_4(l) \rightarrow NaHSO_4(s) + HCl(g)$$
$$NaI(s) + H_3PO_4(l) \rightarrow NaH_2PO_4(s) + HI(g)$$

Section 102.1 will give you more information about these reactions.

92.5 Large quantities of rock salt are used on roads in winter. Why?

92.6 Rock salt can either be mined in a conventional way, i.e. by digging it out of the ground, or by another method. What might be the other method?

92.7 The Solvay process is the name of an industrial process that makes use of large quantities of salt. What is made in the process?

92.8 (i) Why is it that lithium salts have a greater degree of covalent character than the other halides of the Group?

(ii) Which of LiCl, LiBr, LiI would you expect to have the most covalent character? (Hint: Fajans' rules.)

92.9 Why is it that although the lithium ion, Li^+, is far smaller than the other metal ions, it moves through a solution less rapidly than the others? (Hint: hydration spheres.)

92.10 Suggest a reason why lithium fluoride has the lowest solubility of the Group I metal halides.

92.7 The nitrates and nitrites

Sodium nitrate, $NaNO_3$, and sodium nitrite, $NaNO_2$, are the most important salts.

(a) *Nitrates*

Sodium nitrate can be obtained from deposits in Chile. These deposits of 'Chile saltpetre' contain large amounts of iodates. The latter provide the world's main source of iodine. Sodium nitrate can also be made by neutralising nitric acid with sodium carbonate. The salt is valuable because it is used as a fertiliser. In common with all other nitrates, sodium nitrate is soluble in water, so the nitrate ions are readily available to plants. However, for the same reason much of the nitrate put on soil is washed away by rain. One consequence is that the over-use of nitrate fertilisers is responsible for the pollution of water supplies by nitrate ions.

Chemically, the Group I nitrates are a little different to those of other metals. In particular, when they are heated, they give off oxygen and change into a nitrite, e.g.

$$2KNO_3(s) \rightarrow 2KNO_2(s) + O_2(g)$$

Nitrates of the Group II metals and others, like copper, give off nitrogen dioxide and decompose into an oxide, e.g.

$$2Ca(NO_3)_2(s) \rightarrow 2CaO(s) + 4NO_2(g) + O_2(g)$$

Perhaps we might expect that lithium nitrate might be an exception, and so it is. It decomposes like the majority of nitrates of other Groups.

Most nitrates are energetically stable. However, the nitrogen in a nitrate ion is in a high oxidation state (+5) and the ions contain a high percentage of oxygen. With the right chemicals (or wrong, depending on your point of view), the ions will show a considerable ability to act as oxidising agents. Especially, potassium nitrate mixed with sulphur and carbon is used as gun powder. The mixture will explode when ignited by a spark. The explosion is due to the very speedy release of large volumes of nitrogen and carbon dioxide:

$$2KNO_3(s) + S(s) + 3C(s) \rightarrow K_2S(s) + N_2(g) + 3CO_2(g)$$

Sodium or potassium nitrate can be used to make nitric acid in the laboratory. Nitric acid is much more volatile than concentrated sulphuric acid, and we can make it by heating this acid with the nitrate:

$$NaNO_3(s) + H_2SO_4(l) \rightarrow NaHSO_4(s) + HNO_3(g)$$

The main difference between this and the preparation of hydrogen chloride is that the nitric acid fumes must be passed through a Liebig condenser in order to collect the liquid.

(b) *Nitrites*

There are two large-scale uses of nitrites. Sodium nitrite is used in the manufacture of dyes. This is a result of its ability to take part in diazotisation reactions with aromatic amines. You will find details of these reactions in Unit 122. The other large-scale use is as an anti-oxidant in foodstuffs. Meat products such as paté, sausages, hamburgers and bacon, as well as raw meat sold in supermarkets, often has sodium nitrite (and sometimes sodium nitrate) added to it. Although the shelf life of the products is increased, it is known that nitrites can be converted into very dangerous carcinogenic compounds in acids. It is no comfort to realise that our stomachs are full of an acidic solution! There are good reasons for not eating too many meat products treated with nitrates and nitrites.

92.11 Write the equation for the decomposition of lithium nitrate, $LiNO_3$.

92.12 Estimate the change in volume when 2 mol of KNO_3 reacts with 1 mol of S and 3 mol of C.

92.8 The sulphates, hydrogen sulphates and sulphites

All the members of the Group give sulphates, SO_4^{2-}, and hydrogensulphates, HSO_4^-. They are all soluble in water. This fact, like the solubility of the carbonates, is a marked difference to the sulphates of Group II.

Sulphites, such as sodium sulphite, Na_2SO_3, are more reactive than either sulphates or hydrogensulphates. For example, if you warm a sulphite with an acid, you will find sulphur dioxide is given off:

$$SO_3^{2-}(aq) + 2H^+(aq) \rightarrow SO_2(g) + H_2O(l)$$

Another reaction that you may come across is the conversion of sodium sulphite into sodium thiosulphate, $Na_2S_2O_3$. This change is performed by boiling a solution of sodium sulphite with powdered sulphur:

$$SO_3^{2-}(aq) + S(s) \rightarrow S_2O_3^{2-}(aq)$$

Sodium thiosulphate is used as 'hypo' in photography. In the laboratory it is used in iodine titrations (see section 40.3). The reaction with iodine is

$$I_2(s) + 2S_2O_3^{2-}(aq) \rightarrow S_4O_6^{2-}(aq) + 2I^-(aq)$$

92.13 How might you show that sulphur dioxide is given off in a reaction?

92.9 The hydrides

All the hydrides of the Group are ionic, with the metal being positive and the hydrogen being negative. As you may know, it is most unusual for hydrogen to make an ion other than the positively charged hydrogen ion, H^+. Indeed, hydride ions are very reactive. In water they immediately react, giving off hydrogen:

$$Li^+H^-(s) + H_2O(l) \rightarrow Li^+(aq) + OH^-(aq) + H_2(g)$$

In organic chemistry, lithium tetrahydridoaluminate(III) (otherwise known as lithium aluminium hydride), $LiAlH_4$, is a very useful reducing agent. It can be made by reacting lithium hydride with aluminium trichloride, and contains Li^+ and AlH_4^- ions. It is the latter ions that supply the hydride ions which perform the reduction. You will find examples of its reactions in the units on organic chemistry, and in Unit 90. For example, it will reduce amides to amines, $RCONH_2 \rightarrow RCH_2NH_2$. Also, see section 90.7.

92.14 (i) How many electrons does a hydride ion possess?

(ii) What is its electron structure?

(iii) What does this tell you about the statement that all noble gas structures are very stable?

92.15 What is special about aluminium trichloride that allows it to bond with a hydride ion?

Answers

92.1 $2LiOH(s) \rightarrow Li_2O(s) + H_2O(l)$

92.2 Hydrochloric acid is a strong acid. A good strong acid/strong base indicator is screened methyl orange. For ethanoic acid (a weak acid) and a strong base, phenolphthalein is best.

92.3 It gives a deposit of a carbonate with carbon dioxide in the air, which can jam the tap.

92.4 (i) The crystals dissolve in their own water of crystallisation and then steam is given off.

(ii) The carbonate ions give a deposit of $CaCO_3$ with Ca^{2+} ions often found in hard water.

92.5 They lower the freezing point of water, thus preventing ice from forming (see section 65.5).

92.6 Water passed into the deposits will dissolve the salt. After pumping out, the salt is crystallised out.

92.7 Sodium carbonate.

92.8 (i) The small size of Li^+ gives it a huge polarising power. This leads to covalency.

(ii) LiI. The iodide is larger and more polarisable (see Fajans' rules in Unit 19).

92.9 The dense charge of Li^+ attracts several layers of water molecules around it. They increase the effective size of the ion, thus slowing it down. See section 73.4.

92.10 The small size of both the Li^+ and F^- ions leads to a very large lattice energy, which means that the crystal is very hard to break apart.

92.11 $4LiNO_3(s) \rightarrow 2Li_2O(s) + 4NO_2(g) + O_2(g)$

92.12 The volume of the solids will be some tens of cm^3. Four moles of gas at room temperature have a volume of 96 dm^3. Hence the expansion is enormous.

92.13 Sulphur dioxide is a reducing agent. A standard test is to show that it turns orange acidified potassium dichromate(VI) solution a green colour; or acidified potassium manganate(VII) from purple to colourless.

92.14 (i) Two. (ii) $1s^2$. (iii) It is wrong.

92.15 $AlCl_3$ is electron deficient. It can accept a pair of electrons into one of its empty orbitals. See Unit 15.

UNIT 92 SUMMARY

- The Group I metals:
  - (i) Are all good reducing agents (highly electropositive), with reducing power increasing down the Group. (Lithium is an exception, owing to the very small size of the Li^+ ion.)
  - (ii) Make ionic compounds with non-metals.
- Manufacture:
  Isolated by electrolysis of molten salts.

Reactions

- With water:
  Vigorous reaction, hydrogen given off, alkaline solution remains;

  e.g. $2Na(s) + 2H_2O(l) \rightarrow 2Na^+(aq) + 2OH^-(aq) + H_2(g)$
- With oxygen:
  Peroxides made;

  e.g. $2K(s) + O_2(g) \rightarrow K_2O_2(s)$
- With halogens:
  Ionic salts made;

  e.g. $2Na(s) + Cl_2(g) \rightarrow 2Na^+Cl^-(s)$

Compounds

- Oxides:
  Basic, dissolve in water to make strong alkalis.
- Hydroxides:
  - (i) Strong alkalis in water; give ammonia with ammonium salts;

    e.g. $NH_4^+(aq) + OH^-(aq) \rightarrow NH_3(g) + H_2O(l)$
  - (ii) Give precipitates with some metal ions;

    e.g. $Fe^{3+}(aq) + 3OH^-(aq) \rightarrow Fe(OH)_3(s)$
- Hydrides:
  Are ionic, give hydrogen with water;

  e.g. $Li^+H^-(s) + H_2O(l) \rightarrow Li^+(aq) + OH^-(aq) + H_2(g)$
- Carbonates:
  - (i) Soluble in water.
  - (ii) Give carbon dioxide with acids;

    e.g. $Na_2CO_3(s) + 2H^+(aq) \rightarrow 2Na^+(aq) + CO_2(g) + H_2O(l)$
  - (iii) Do not give carbon dioxide when heated.
- Halides:
  React with concentrated sulphuric acid, e.g. a method of making HCl(g)

  $NaCl(s) + H_2SO_4(l) \rightarrow NaHSO_4(s) + HCl(g)$
- Nitrates:
  - (i) Give oxygen but not nitrogen dioxide when heated;

    e.g. $2KNO_3(s) \rightarrow 2KNO_2(s) + O_2(g)$
  - (ii) Can be used to make nitric acid using concentrated sulphuric acid;

    $NaNO_3(s) + H_2SO_4(l) \rightarrow NaHSO_4(s) + HNO_3(l)$
- Sulphates:
  All soluble in water.
- Sulphites:
  Give sulphur dioxide when warmed with acids;

  e.g. $Na_2SO_3(s) + 2H^+(aq) \rightarrow 2Na^+(aq) + SO_2(g) + H_2O(l)$
- Thiosulphates:
  - (i) Sodium thiosulphate can be made by boiling a solution of sodium sulphite, Na_2SO_3, with sulphur;

    $SO_3^{2-}(aq) + S(s) \rightarrow S_2O_3^{2-}(aq)$
  - (ii) Thiosulphates deposit sulphur with acids (a common experiment in rates of reactions).
  - (iii) Thiosulphate solutions are used in iodine titrations (iodine decolourised);

    $2S_2O_3^{2-}(aq) + I_2(aq) \rightarrow S_4O_6^{2-}(aq) + 2I^-(aq)$

93

Group II

93.1 The nature of the elements

The elements of Group II are metals. They show the properties we would expect, e.g. they are good reducing agents, they give ionic compounds, their oxides and hydroxides are basic, and they give hydrogen with acids. The alkaline nature of the elements is responsible for them being known as the alkaline earth metals. Their properties and uses are summarised in Tables 93.1 and 93.2. The exception to the common pattern is the first member, beryllium. One reason why beryllium is different is that its electrons are not strongly shielded from its nucleus. The radius of the Be^{2+} ion is extremely small, and it represents a very dense centre of positive charge. Fajans' rules remind us that such an ion would have an immense polarising power. This ability to draw electrons towards itself is responsible for the covalency of many of its compounds. For example, we saw in Unit 17 that beryllium chloride, $BeCl_2$, is a covalent, linear molecule. Beryllium also has a higher electronegativity than the other elements. This tells us that the compounds it makes with non-metals should have less ionic character. Another feature of the chemistry of beryllium is that in solution its compounds tend to suffer from hydrolysis, and some are amphoteric rather than completely basic.

Table 93.2. Uses of the elements in Group II

Element	*Main uses*
Beryllium	As a moderator in nuclear reactors
Magnesium	In alloys of many kinds—it lends strength with little increase in weight; hence its use in aircraft structures
Calcium	In biological systems it is essential for the healthy growth of bones Its carbonate is used in manufacturing cement, and in the alkali industry
Strontium	Few uses, although its radioactive isotope $^{90}_{38}Sr$ is well known (and feared) because it is produced in nuclear fall-out
Barium	In some alloys with lead and calcium $BaSO_4$ is used in medicine as 'barium meal', which patients swallow—the sulphate is relatively opaque to X-rays so it shows particularly well on X-ray photographs

For example, magnesium is often used in the laboratory to liberate small quantities of hydrogen:

$$Mg(s) + 2H^+(aq) \rightarrow Mg^{2+}(aq) + H_2(g)$$

Table 93.1. Physical properties of the elements in Group II*

	Beryllium	*Magnesium*	*Calcium*	*Strontium*	*Barium*
Symbol	Be	Mg	Ca	Sr	Ba
Electron structure	(He)$2s^2$	(Ne)$3s^2$	(Ar)$4s^2$	(Kr)$5s^2$	(Xe)$6s^2$
Electronegativity	1.5	1.2	1.0	1.0	0.9
1st I.E./kJ mol^{-1}	899	738	590	550	500
2nd I.E./kJ mol^{-1}	1800	1500	1100	1100	1000
Melting point/°C	1283	650	850	770	710
Boiling point/°C	2477	1117	1492	1367	1637
Atomic radius/pm	106	140	174	191	198
Ionic radius/pm	30	65	94	110	134
Principal oxid. no.	+2	+2	+2	+2	+2
$E^{\ominus}_{M^{2+}/M}$/V	−1.85	−2.37	−2.87	−2.89	−2.90

*The last element in the Group, radium, is omitted. It is not common, but is famous for its radioactive nature and its discovery by Mme Curie

Even if it is coated with a thin layer of oxide, the metal will still react because the oxide dissolves in the acid. If beryllium is coated with oxide it will not react at all. When it is pure, reaction does take place, especially if it is finely powdered. Hydrogen is given off, but the Be^{2+} ion is heavily hydrated and exists as $Be(H_2O)_4{}^{2+}$. Here the water molecules act as ligands by bonding to the ion through one of their lone pairs. It is characteristic of beryllium that it gives complexes of the kind we would normally associate with transition metals. The other metals sometimes give complexes, but much less readily than beryllium.

Beryllium will dissolve in alkali. This is something that magnesium and the other metals in the Group will not do:

$$Be(s) + 2OH^-(aq) \rightarrow BeO_2{}^{2-}(aq) + H_2(g)$$

The product, $BeO_2{}^{2-}$, is the beryllate ion, which is better represented in solution as the tetrahydroxoberyllate(II) ion, $Be(OH)_4{}^{2-}$. However, several other types of ion are usually present as well. In its amphoteric behaviour it resembles aluminium in Group III.

Like the Group I metals, the reactivity of the elements makes it difficult to extract them by chemical means. Magnesium is the most important member of the Group and it is extracted by the electrolysis of magnesium chloride, $MgCl_2$.

Beryllium is hard to extract. Partly this is because its minerals are not widely distributed in Nature. The most common method is to convert minerals such as beryl, $Be_3Al_2Si_6O_{18}$, into beryllium chloride and reduce the chloride with magnesium metal.

Warning: Do not attempt to perform reactions with beryllium compounds. They are intensely poisonous. One way in which they poison is by blocking the reactivity of enzymes and other biologically active systems, e.g. by taking the place of magnesium ions.

93.1 Explain why the ionisation potentials decrease going down the Group.

93.2 Beryllium gives a compound with the following percentage composition: Be, 6.1%; N, 37.8%; Cl, 48%; H, 8.1%. One mole of the compound had a mass of 148 g. $M(Be) = 9\text{ g mol}^{-1}$.

(i) What is the molecular formula of the compound?

(ii) In water, 1 mol of the compound reacts with 2 mol of silver ions. Suggest a structural formula for the compound, and explain how the atoms are arranged.

93.3 Do you know of a biologically important molecule in which magnesium atoms are held in position by organic groups?

93.4 A student suggested that calcium should be made if calcium oxide is reacted with aluminium powder. Was the student correct?

You will need to use the following free energies of formation: $\Delta G_f^\circ(CaO) = -604.2\text{ kJ mol}^{-1}$; $\Delta G_f^\circ(Al_2O_3) = -1582.4\text{ kJ mol}^{-1}$.

93.2 The oxides and hydroxides

Beryllium oxide, BeO, is more like the oxide of aluminium in Group III rather than the oxides of the other elements in Group II. It has a high degree of covalency, which is lacking in the other oxides. It is insoluble in water and it will dissolve only with great difficulty in acids. The reactivity of BeO depends on its treatment. If it is heated to a high temperature (about 800° C) it becomes almost completely inert.

The other oxides will dissolve in water with increasing ease down the Group. The resulting solutions are slightly alkaline owing to reactions between the oxides and water, e.g.

$$MgO(s) + H_2O(l) \rightleftharpoons Mg^{2+}(aq) + 2OH^-(aq)$$
$$CaO(s) + H_2O(l) \rightleftharpoons Ca^{2+}(aq) + 2OH^-(aq)$$

We have to be a little careful here. You may recognise a solution of calcium and hydroxide ions as 'lime water'. Lime water is famous for giving a milky precipitate with carbon dioxide. It is normally treated with much less care than the caustic alkalis of Group I metals such as sodium hydroxide. The reason is not that the hydroxide ions it contains are any the less reactive than those in sodium hydroxide. Rather, there are far fewer of them in solution. Calcium hydroxide, like the other hydroxides in the Group, is only partially soluble in water. You might like to compare the solubilities in Table 93.3. The values tell us that solubility increases down the Group. We can understand this trend if we remember one of the most important factors in explaining trends in solubility: high solubility often correlates with low lattice energy and vice versa. Also, we know that a high lattice energy is given by ionic substances that contain small highly charged ions, and covalent substances with giant molecular lattices. As we go down the Group the size of the metal ion increases. We can claim that this is the chief reason for the lattice energy decreasing, and the solubility increasing. However, a word of warning: if you read Unit 60 you will find that we have to take entropy changes into account if we are to give a thorough explanation of solubilities.

Table 93.3. The solubilities of the Group II hydroxides

Hydroxide	*Solubility at 25° C/mol per 100 g water*
$Be(OH)_2$	Highly insoluble
$Mg(OH)_2$	2.0×10^{-5}
$Ca(OH)_2$	1.5×10^{-3}
$Sr(OH)_2$	3.4×10^{-3}
$Ba(OH)_2$	1.5×10^{-2}

93.5 Write the equation for the reaction between carbon dioxide and calcium hydroxide solution.

93.6 Apart from lattice energy, what other energy change is important in accounting for solubilities?

93.7 0.2 g of magnesium ribbon was placed in a crucible and heated with the lid on until the magnesium began to burn fiercely. At the end of the experiment there was 0.3 g of a white powder left. Show that this result does *not* agree with the equation

$$2Mg(s) + O_2(g) \rightarrow 2MgO(s)$$

What might have gone wrong?

93.3 The halides

The chlorides are much the most common of the halides, so we shall concentrate on them.

We have discussed the bonding in beryllium chloride before in Units 15 and 17. The important things to know about this chloride is that isolated molecules are linear, while the solid is composed of chains of linked molecules (Figure 93.1). The bonding is very much like that in aluminium trichloride. Lone pairs on some of the chlorine atoms are used in bonding with empty orbitals on the beryllium atoms. The chlorides of the other metals have a greater degree of ionic character. Unlike the Group I chlorides, they easily react with water to give hydrates (Table 93.4). Anhydrous calcium chloride is deliquescent and widely used as a drying agent.

The elements all give fluorides, bromides and iodides as well as chlorides. They are all soluble in water, but the fluorides are much less soluble than the others; e.g. the solubility of magnesium fluoride is little more than 10^{-4} mol per 100 g of water at 18°C. We shall seek an explanation of this in section 93.6.

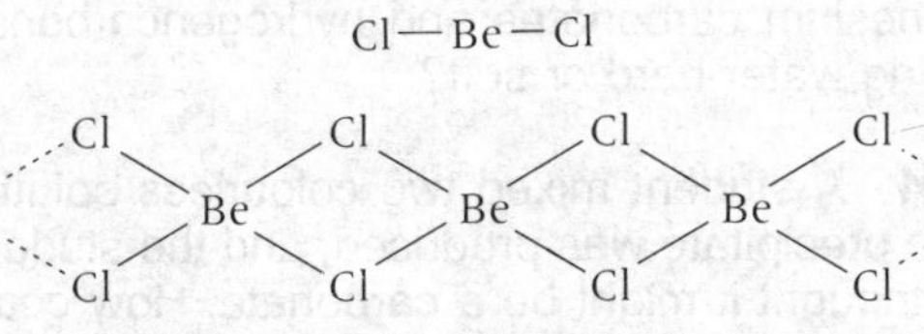

***Figure 93.1** The structures of single $BeCl_2$ molecules and the chains that exist in solid $BeCl_2$*

Table 93.4. The chlorides of Group II

Chloride		
Anhydrous	*Hydrated*	*Solubility at 18°C** /mol per 100 g water
$BeCl_2$	$BeCl_2{\cdot}4H_2O$	0.90
$MgCl_2$	$MgCl_2{\cdot}6H_2O$	0.59
$CaCl_2$	$CaCl_2{\cdot}6H_2O$	0.66
$SrCl_2$	$SrCl_2{\cdot}6H_2O$	0.32
$BaCl_2$	$BaCl_2{\cdot}2H_2O$	0.18

*The figures give the solubilities of the anhydrous salts, apart from beryllium chloride

93.8 Suggest other ways of writing the formulae $BeCl_2{\cdot}4H_2O$ and $MgCl_2{\cdot}6H_2O$.

93.9 Beryllium makes the complex ion BeF_4^{2-}. Predict the shape of this ion, and suggest the types of orbital used in bonding by the beryllium atom.

93.4 The carbonates and hydrogencarbonates

The Group II carbonates are different to those of the alkali metals of Group I in two major respects. First, they are only very slightly soluble in water, with the solubility decreasing down the Group. Secondly, they are decomposed by heat, giving off carbon dioxide and leaving an oxide. For example,

$$MgCO_3(s) \rightarrow MgO(s) + CO_2(g)$$

The ease of decomposition decreases down the Group. These properties are summarised in Table 93.5.

Table 93.5. Solubility and decomposition temperature of the carbonates*

Carbonate	*Solubility at 25° C* /mol per 100 g water	*Decomposition temperature/° C*
$MgCO_3$	1.5×10^{-4}	400
$CaCO_3$	1.3×10^{-5}	900
$SrCO_3$	7.4×10^{-6}	1280
$BaCO_3$	9.1×10^{-6}	1360

*Data for $BeCO_3$ are not available

Calcium carbonate in the form of chalk or limestone is particularly important, both in Nature and in industry. You can find information about them in Unit 84.

Chalk is one Group II carbonate ($CaCO_3$) that is widely found in nature.

Concrete is one of the world's most common building materials. Unfortunately it is rare for concrete to be used in such an attractive way as in the Law Courts building in Liverpool shown here.

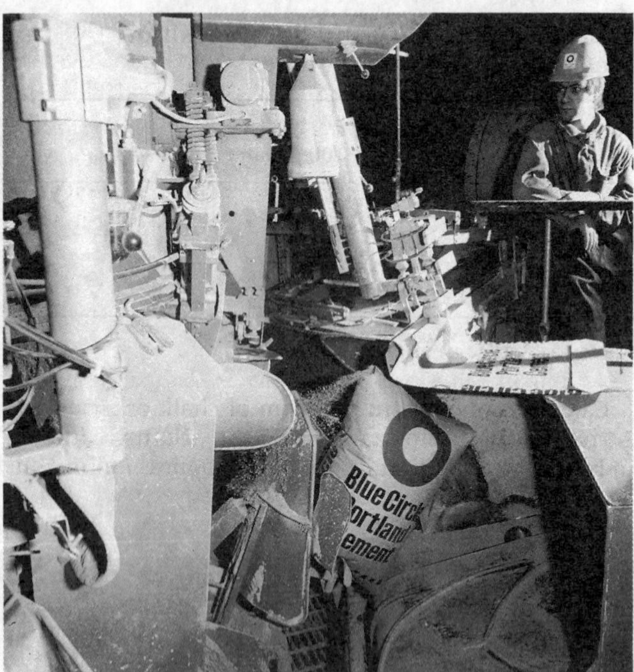

Cement powder being loaded into bags.

One way of explaining the trend in decomposition is to relate it to the size of the metal ion. The smaller the ion, the greater is its polarising power. This suggests that a beryllium ion would have the greatest ability to distort carbonate ions, pulling electron density from the oxygen atoms towards it. Likewise, barium ions would have the least tendency to distort carbonate ions. In addition, if we look at the products of the reaction, we know that carbon dioxide is given off in each case. This is a common factor, so it is unlikely to give us help in explaining the decompositions. However, the metal oxide is different for each reaction. Given that a large lattice energy is encouraged by small highly charged ions close together, we should not be surprised to find that the lattice energies of the oxides follow the order

$$BeO > MgO > CaO > SrO > BaO$$

largest lattice energy ... smallest lattice energy

Therefore, with $BeCO_3$ we have carbonate ions already highly distorted, and a product of the reaction that is energetically very favoured. Both factors encourage decomposition of the carbonate. At the other extreme, $BaCO_3$ has carbonate ions that are not highly polarised, and an oxide product that is not so energetically favoured. The other carbonates fall nicely in order between the two extremes. You will find an explanation of the trend in solubilities in section 93.6.

Finally, another observation that marks out the elements of this Group from the alkali metals of Group I is that those metals possess solid hydrogencarbonates. The hydrogencarbonates of the alkaline earth metals only exist in solution.

93.10 Is BeO ionic?

93.11 Strictly, if we are to explain the decomposition of the carbonates we should refer to the free energies of the reactions. Why, in these reactions, will we not go far wrong in concentrating on enthalpy changes rather than free energies?

93.12 What do you understand by the term *dissociation pressure* of calcium carbonate?

93.13 What is the importance of calcium and magnesium carbonates and hydrogencarbonates in making water hard or soft?

93.14 A student mixed two colourless solutions. A white precipitate was produced, and the student said she thought it might be a carbonate. How could you find out if she was right?

93.5 The sulphates

The solubilities of the sulphates decrease down the Group (Table 93.6). We discussed the reasons for this trend in Unit 60. You will also find a brief comment about it in the following section.

Beryllium, magnesium and calcium sulphates are often found as hydrated crystals, e.g. $BeSO_4{\cdot}4H_2O$, $MgSO_4{\cdot}7H_2O$, $CaSO_4{\cdot}2H_2O$. The crystals of magnesium sulphate have a rather unfortunate reputation. They are better known as Epsom salts, and at one time they were widely used as a laxative in medicine. Crystals of $CaSO_4{\cdot}2H_2O$ are found in Nature as the mineral gyp-

Table 93.6. The solubilities of Group II sulphates

Sulphate	*Solubility at 25° C*/mol per 100 g water
$BeSO_4$	3.79×10^{-1}
$MgSO_4$	1.83×10^{-1}
$CaSO_4$	4.66×10^{-3}
$SrSO_4$	7.11×10^{-5}
$BaSO_4$	9.43×10^{-7}

sum. Anhydrous calcium sulphate also occurs naturally as anhydrite.

If you have had a broken bone set in plaster you can thank gypsum for your recovery. When gypsum is heated to just under 100° C it loses three quarters of its water of crystallisation. The powder remaining is plaster of Paris, which can be represented by the formula $(CaSO_4)_2 \cdot H_2O$. When water is mixed with it, gypsum crystals are produced again, but this time they set to a hard, solid mass. In surgery the dehydrated gypsum is often embedded in bandages which are wrapped around the damaged limb. The speed with which the plaster sets can be controlled by adding other chemicals to it.

We can make use of the insolubility of barium sulphate in the test for a sulphate. In its simplest form, the test is to add barium chloride solution to the suspected sulphate. If sulphate ions are present, a white precipitate of barium sulphate is made:

$$Ba^{2+}(aq) + SO_4^{2-}(aq) \rightarrow BaSO_4(s)$$

However, this way of doing the test is not to be trusted because, for example, if carbonate ions are present there will also be a precipitate (of barium carbonate). To avoid such confusion it is best to add dilute hydrochloric acid to the solution before adding barium chloride.

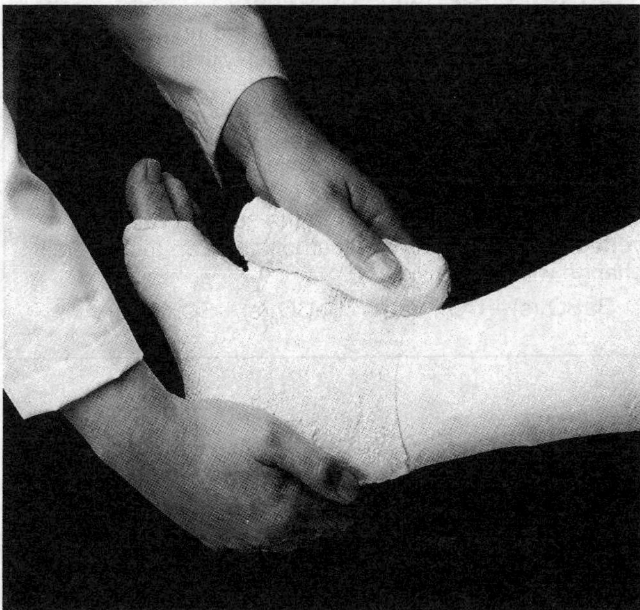

A common sight in hospital casualty departments: bandages impregnated with plaster of Paris are used to set broken bones.

93.15 Barium phosphate is also insoluble in water. However, a solution of a phosphate will not give a precipitate with barium chloride solution provided dilute acid is added first. What might be the explanation for this? (Hint: weak acids.)

93.16 The solubility products of barium sulphate and barium carbonate are 1×10^{-10} mol^2 dm^{-6} and 5.5×10^{-10} mol^2 dm^{-6} respectively. What would happen, if anything, if (i) solid barium carbonate were boiled with a solution containing sulphate ions, (ii) solid barium sulphate were boiled with a solution containing carbonate ions?

93.6 Explaining trends in solubilities

You should read Unit 60 for a more detailed explanation of trends in solubilities. If you have already read that unit you should know that many of the trends can be explained in terms of a competition between two opposing tendencies:

(i) The higher the lattice energy, the harder it is to break a crystal apart, so the less likely it is to dissolve.

(ii) The higher the hydration energy of the ions, the greater is the tendency for the crystal to dissolve.

In the case of the relative insolubilities of the fluorides of the Group II elements compared to the other halides, we can claim that this is a result of the higher lattice energies of the fluorides, compared to the chlorides or other halides. Fortunately the claim is backed up by experimental evidence: the lattice energies of the fluorides are between 300 and 600 kJ mol^{-1} greater than the other halides.

The *decreasing* solubility of the carbonates down the Group (Table 93.7) is not explained by the trend in

Table 93.7. Trends in solubilities in Group II

	Chlorides	*Carbonates*	*Sulphates*	*Hydroxides*
Be	Most soluble ↑	Most soluble ↑	Most soluble ↑	Least soluble ↓
Mg				
Ca				
Sr				
Ba	Least soluble	Least soluble	Least soluble	Most soluble

lattice energies, which also decrease down the Group. Rather the trend follows the order of the hydration energies of the metal ions (Be^{2+} having the greatest and Ba^{2+} the least). However, this is another occasion on which we have to take great care. You may have seen in Unit 60 that it is not really respectable to explain solubilities without taking account of entropy changes. Fortunately we do not have to track down all the entropy changes that take place when small portions of these carbonates dissolve, but we can be quite sure that they play a significant part in determining the trend down the Group.

Answers

93.1 The outer electrons are increasingly well shielded from the nucleus by the inner shells of electrons.

93.2 (i) If you follow through the method of Unit 37 you should find that the molecular formula is $BeN_4H_{12}Cl_2$.
(ii) The reaction with silver ions suggests that the 2 mol of chlorine is present as chloride ions. We know that nitrogen and hydrogen are often to be found together in ammonia, so we can guess that the formula is $Be(NH_3)_4Cl_2$, or $[Be(NH_3)_4]^{2+}(Cl^-)_2$. The four ammonia molecules act as ligands. Compare this with some of the complexes in Unit 105.

93.3 Chlorophyll is the compound.

93.4 The equation is

$$3CaO(s) + 2Al(s) \rightarrow 3Ca(s) + Al_2O_3(s)$$
$$\Delta G^\ominus(\text{reaction}) = \Delta G_f^\ominus(Al_2O_3) - 3\Delta G_f^\ominus(CaO) = +230.2\ \text{kJ mol}^{-1}$$

The positive sign tells us that the reaction cannot occur under standard conditions. However, the student would be pleased to know that under non-standard conditions, e.g. at high temperatures, the free energy change is negative and the reaction takes place. This is the method used to extract calcium in industry.

93.5 $CO_2(g) + Ca^{2+}(aq) + 2OH^-(aq) \rightarrow CaCO_3(s) + H_2O(l)$

93.6 The solvation energies of the ions.

93.7 The equation shows that 2 mol, i.e. 48 g, of magnesium should give 2 mol, i.e. 80 g, of magnesium oxide. Therefore, 0.2 g of magnesium should give $80\ g \times 0.2\ g/48\ g = 0.33\ g$ of the oxide. Perhaps some of the oxide escaped as smoke, or the magnesium did not completely react, or the magnesium may have made magnesium nitride instead.

93.8 The clue to this is realising that the water molecules can act as ligands: $[Be(H_2O)_4]^{2+}(Cl^-)_2$, $[Mg(H_2O)_6]^{2+}(Cl^-)_2$.

93.9 The electron structure of Be^{2+} is $1s^2$. The ion can make four bonds if it makes use of its empty 2s and 2p orbitals. We can think of them as four sp^3 hybrids. As there are no lone pairs, and only four bond pairs to the four fluorine ions, electron repulsion theory predicts that the BeF_4^{2-} ion should be tetrahedral in shape. It is.

93.10 No. But covalent, as well as ionic, substances have lattice energies.

93.11 One mole of each carbonate gives off 1 mol of gas. Thus the entropy changes for each of the reactions will be approximately the same. Therefore, changes in free energies between the reactions will be governed by the enthalpy changes.

93.12 Look back to section 51.3 for this.

93.13 When slightly acidic rain water percolates through carbonate rocks, some of the rock dissolves. Ca^{2+} and Mg^{2+} ions are dissolved in the water. It is these ions which give scum with soap, or make scale when hard water is boiled.

93.14 Add dilute nitric acid. If it is a carbonate, carbon dioxide would be given off.

93.15 When acid is added to a solution containing phosphate ions, the equilibrium

$$3H^+(aq) + PO_4^{3-}(aq) \rightleftharpoons H_3PO_4(aq)$$

is driven to the right. This reduces the number of free PO_4^{3-} ions that are available to react with the Ba^{2+} ions.

93.16 The values of the solubility products show that $BaSO_4$ is *less soluble* than $BaCO_3$. (The smaller the solubility product, the less soluble is the solid.) Therefore, in (i) there will be no change; but in (ii) over a period of time the free barium ions in the solution will be converted into solid barium carbonate, i.e. the overall change will be

$$BaSO_4(s) + CO_3^{2-}(aq) \rightarrow BaCO_3(s) + SO_4^{2-}(aq)$$

UNIT 93 SUMMARY

- The Group II metals:
  - (i) Are all good reducing agents.
  - (ii) Make ionic compounds.
  - (iii) Make oxides and hydroxides that are less soluble in water than those of Group I.
  - (iv) Give hydrogen with water and acids.
  - (v) Beryllium is an exception in the Group. Especially, owing to the small size of its ion, Be^{2+} (high polarising power), its compounds are covalent.
- Manufacture:
  Isolated by electrolysis of molten salts.

- Solubilities:
  - (i) Of chlorides, sulphates and carbonates decrease down the Group.
  - (ii) Of hydroxides increase down the Group.

Reactions

- With water:
  Less vigorous reaction than Group I, hydrogen given off, alkaline solution remains;

  e.g. $Ca(s) + 2H_2O(l) \rightarrow Ca(OH)_2(s) + H_2(g)$

  (Magnesium only reacts well with steam.)
- With oxygen:
  Oxides made;

  e.g. $2Mg(s) + O_2(g) \rightarrow 2MgO(s)$
- With halogens:
  Ionic salts made. Beryllium an exception; $BeCl_2$ is covalent.

Compounds

- Oxides:
  Basic, partially soluble in water giving alkaline solutions.
- Hydroxides:
  Calcium hydroxide solution, i.e. lime water, used to test for carbon dioxide ('lime water goes milky');

  $$Ca(OH)_2(aq) + CO_2(g) \rightarrow CaCO_3(s) + H_2O(l)$$
- Carbonates:
  Only partially soluble in water, give carbon dioxide with acids and when heated;

  e.g. $CaCO_3 + 2H^+(aq) \rightarrow 2Ca^{2+}(aq) + CO_2(g) + H_2O(l)$

  $CaCO_3(s) \rightarrow CaO(s) + CO_2(g)$
- Halides:
  - (i) Are often hydrated, e.g. $CaCl_2{\cdot}6H_2O$. Anhydrous calcium chloride is used as a drying agent; it is deliquescent.
  - (ii) Barium chloride solution is used to test for sulphates, gives a white precipitate of barium sulphate;

    $Ba^{2+}(aq) + SO_4{}^{2-}(aq) \rightarrow BaSO_4(s)$
- Nitrates:
  Give oxygen and nitrogen dioxide when heated;

  e.g. $2Ba(NO_3)_2(s) \rightarrow 2BaO(s) + 4NO_2(g) + O_2(g)$
- Sulphates:
  - (i) Are not as soluble as Group I sulphates.
  - (ii) Solubility decreases down the Group.
  - (iii) Gypsum, $CaSO_4{\cdot}2H_2O(l)$ used to make plaster of Paris; $(CaSO_4)_2{\cdot}H_2O$.

94

Group III

94.1 The nature of the elements

This Group marks the beginning of the p-block elements. In the following Groups the elements show definite non-metallic nature. For example, carbon, nitrogen and oxygen all tend to gain electrons rather than lose them. (It is the metals that give up electrons to make positive ions.) The compounds of boron are mainly covalent, and it clearly shows non-metallic properties. Going down the Group to the next period we reach aluminium, which is a metal. However, both boron and aluminium are amphoteric. That is, the elements, and their oxides, will react with both acids and alkalis. A summary of their properties and uses is shown in Tables 94.1 and 94.2.

Examples of their amphoteric nature are the reactions of boron and aluminium with alkali. These reactions are often written:

$$2B(s) + 2OH^-(aq) + 2H_2O \rightarrow \underset{\text{metaborate ions}}{2BO_2^-(aq)} + 3H_2(g)$$

$$2Al(s) + 2OH^-(aq) + 2H_2O \rightarrow \underset{\text{aluminate ions}}{2AlO_2^-(aq)} + 3H_2(g)$$

Table 94.2. Uses of the elements in Group III

*Element**	*Main uses*
Boron	As a neutron absorber in nuclear reactors In boron nitride, BN, as an extremely hard abrasive material
Aluminium	Widely used in alloys where strength and lightness are needed together, e.g. in aircraft manufacture In making cooking utensils In packaging and cooking foils As $Al_2(SO_4)_3$ in water purification As $Al(OH)_3$ in foam fire extinguishers and as a mordant in dyeing
Gallium	As a semiconductor, e.g. with phosphorus and arsenic in light emitting diodes.

*Indium and thallium have few uses

but the ions are better represented as complex ions, e.g.

$$[Al(OH)_4(H_2O)_2]^- \quad \text{or} \quad Al(OH)_6^{3-}$$

In common with other reactive metals, aluminium will give off hydrogen with hydrochloric or sulphuric

Table 94.1. Physical properties of the elements in Group III*

Symbol	*Boron* B	*Aluminium* Al	*Gallium* Ga	*Indium* In	*Thallium* Tl
Electron structure	(He)$2s^22p$	(Ne)$3s^23p$	(Ar)$3d^{10}4s^24p$	(Kr)$4d^{10}5s^25p$	(Xe)$4f^{14}5d^{10}6s^26p$
Electronegativity	2.0	1.5	1.6	1.7	1.8
1st I.E./kJ mol^{-1}	801	578	580	560	590
2nd I.E./kJ mol^{-1}	2400	1800	2000	1800	2000
3rd I.E./kJ mol^{-1}	3700	1600	3000	2700	2900
Melting point/°C	2027	659	30	256	304
Boiling point/°C	3927	2447	2237	2047	1467
Atomic radius/pm	88	126	126	150	155
Ionic radius/pm	16	45	62	81	95
Principal oxid. no.	+3	+3	+3	+3,+1	+1
$E^{\ominus}_{M^{3+}/M}$/V		−1.66	−0.56	−0.38	+2.18
$E^{\ominus}_{M^{+}/M}$/V					−0.34

*Boron does not have a simple electrode potential for the change $B^{3+}(aq) + 3e^- \rightleftharpoons B(s)$. The $E^{\ominus}$ values for Al and Ga are in acid solution, the others in basic solution

acids. But it will not react with nitric acid. This acid is said to render the surface of aluminium passive. Amorphous boron does not give hydrogen with sulphuric or nitric acids. Instead, these acids are reduced, e.g.

$$2B(s) + 6HNO_3(aq) \rightarrow 2H_3BO_3(aq) + 6NO_2(g)$$

orthoboric acid

Boron, aluminium and gallium all show an oxidation number of +3 in their compounds; but indium and especially thallium prefer an oxidation number of +1. Here we have an example of the so-called inert pair effect, about which we spoke in section 87.5. This refers to the tendency of elements towards the bottom of the B Groups not to lose their outer pair of s electrons.

One of the main reasons why boron does not make ionic compounds lies in the extremely small size of the B^{3+} ion. With an ionic radius of only 16 pm, the ion is such a dense centre of charge that if it did exist it would polarise any neighbouring ion. That is, it would attract electron density towards itself and lead to electrons being shared between the atoms.

Pure boron can be obtained as either a crystalline solid or a fine amorphous powder. When crystalline it is extremely hard, and largely inert. In contrast, the powder will react with non-metals. For example, it gives the oxide B_2O_3, nitride BN and chloride BCl_3. We shall return to a description of boron trichloride later.

Aluminium is far more reactive, although if it is left in air for all but a short time it becomes coated with a layer of aluminium oxide, Al_2O_3. This oxide protects the aluminium from further attack. The layer is so useful that in industry it is purposely increased by an electrolytic process called *anodising*.

The aluminium is made the anode in an electrolyte of sulphuric, phosphoric, or chromic acid. A voltage from 10 to 500 V may be used. The mechanism of anodising is complicated, but the result is a layer of aluminium oxide whose thickness lies between 0.25×10^{-6} and 150×10^{-6} m. A coloured layer can be produced either by adding chemicals to the electrolyte or by immersing the anodised layer in a dye.

Aluminium is widely used in alloys where, like magnesium, it is valued for the strength it can add with little increase in mass. The metal can be rolled into thin sheets that have a wide variety of uses. Especially, cooks will be familiar with it as baking foil. The importance of aluminium as a metal makes it worth extracting from its main ore, bauxite, which also has the formula Al_2O_3. We saw how this is done in Unit 85. It is an indication of how strongly the aluminium is bonded to oxygen that electrolysis has to be used rather than a strictly chemical method.

In recent years aluminium has been under suspicion as a possible cause of Alzheimer's disease. This disease induces senility in relatively young men and women. The disease causes them to lose their memory and they can no longer look after themselves. Needless to say, it is not small particles of the solid that are blamed; rather it is the presence of aluminium ions that can occur in foodstuffs or water supplies. However, as yet the link between the disease and aluminium has not been proved.

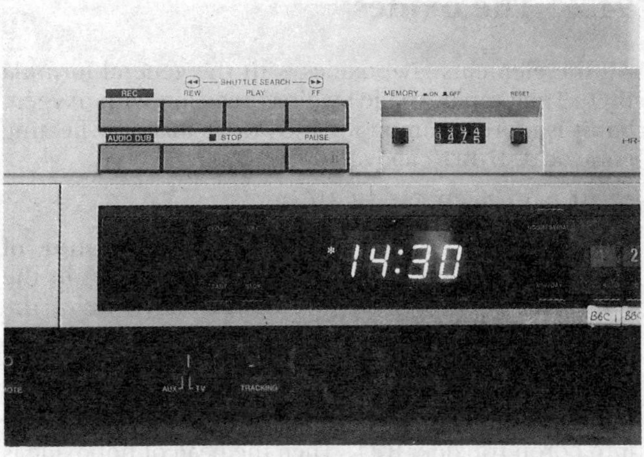

Light emitting diodes are used in displays in many types of electrical equipment, including video recorders like that shown here.

The other elements in the Group are less important than boron or aluminium, so we shall say little about them. However, gallium does have one important use when it is combined with arsenic and phosphorus. Gallium arsenic phosphide gives out light when a voltage is placed across it. The substance is used in light emitting diodes (LEDs).

94.1 You should know that the oxides of non-metals are acidic, and the oxides of metals are basic. Would you expect boron to be more acidic or more basic in its reactions than aluminium?

94.2 What evidence is there from Table 94.1 that thallium has a greater tendency to give Tl^+ ions in solution rather than Tl^{3+} ions?

94.3 $E^{\ominus}_{Al^{3+}/Al} = -1.66$ V; $E^{\ominus}_{SO_4^{2-}/SO_2} = +0.17$ V. What, if anything, would happen if you reacted aluminium with sulphuric acid? If you think a reaction would take place, write down the equation.

94.4 Boron nitride has a layer structure rather like graphite. Remind yourself of the structure of graphite, and then write out the structure of part of a layer of boron nitride.

94.5 Aluminium has a carbide, Al_4C_3. It reacts with water to give a colourless gas, which does not react with bromine. What might be the gas? Write an equation for the reaction.

94.6 The standard free energies of formation of B_2O_3 and MgO are -1194 kJ mol^{-1} and -569 kJ mol^{-1} respectively. Should it be possible to prepare boron by reacting B_2O_3 with magnesium?

94.2 The oxides

All the elements give oxides with the general formula E_2O_3. They can be made by direct reaction with oxygen, but it is more common for B_2O_3 to be made by heating boric acid, H_3BO_3, above 100° C:

$$2H_3BO_3(s) \rightarrow B_2O_3(s) + 3H_2O(g)$$

An interesting example of the amphoteric nature of B_2O_3 is shown by its reaction with basic oxides in the *borax bead test.* (Borax is the traditional name of the substance that should really be called disodium tetraborate-10-water, $Na_2B_4O_7{\cdot}10H_2O$. However, for the present we shall continue to refer to it as borax.) In this test a little borax is heated alone, which converts it into boron trioxide, B_2O_3. Then the bead of hot oxide is touched on a sample of a metal oxide, and the two heated in a bunsen flame. Depending on the metal present a bead of a characteristic colour is produced. For example, cobalt oxide gives a blue bead, copper oxide a red bead and iron a green bead. A typical reaction is

$$CoO(s) + B_2O_3(s) \rightarrow Co(BO_2)_2(s)$$

The product is an example of a metaborate. There are several different types of structures for metaborates. They contain chains of boron and oxygen atoms rather than separate BO_2^- ions.

We have said that borax crystals have the empirical formula $Na_2B_4O_7{\cdot}10H_2O$. However, the crystals contain $B_4O_5(OH)_4^{2-}$ ions shown in Figure 94.1. Borax is used in laboratories as a primary standard in titrations. Strong acids convert it into boric acid, H_3BO_3, which is only very weak. The reaction is usually written

$$B_4O_7^{2-}(aq) + 2H^+(aq) + 5H_2O(l) \rightarrow 4H_3BO_3(aq)$$

Boric acid does not itself release hydrogen ions in solution. Rather, it accepts hydroxide ions; thereby an excess of hydrogen ions exists which makes its solution slightly acidic.

Aluminium oxide also shows amphoteric properties, dissolving in both acid and alkali:

$$Al_2O_3(s) + 6H^+(aq) \rightarrow 2Al^{3+}(aq) + 3H_2O(l)$$
$$Al_2O_3(s) + 6OH^-(aq) + 3H_2O(l) \rightarrow 2Al(OH)_6^{3-}(aq)$$

Aluminium oxide occurs in Nature in several minerals, the most important of which is bauxite. This is the mineral from which aluminium is extracted by electrolysis (see section 85.5). Another variety of Al_2O_3 is corundum. This is a particularly hard mineral, and it is used as an abrasive. Corundum can be made in the laboratory by heating powdered aluminium oxide to a high temperature. If you have an eye for beauty you might be more impressed by the minerals in the photos in the colour section.

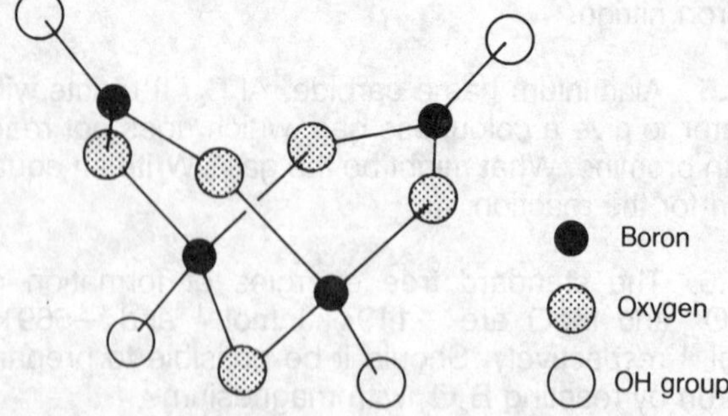

***Figure 94.1** The structure of the $B_4O_5(OH)_4^{2-}$ ion*

Like magnesium oxide, aluminium oxide has a very large enthalpy (and free energy) of formation. This suggests that aluminium will remove the oxygen from other metal oxides, which indeed it does. The most famous example of this is the thermit reaction. Here, a combination of powdered magnesium and aluminium is mixed with a metal oxide. The reaction needs energy to make it start, but once begun the reaction is rapid and highly exothermic. For example,

$$Fe_2O_3(s) + 2Al(s) \rightarrow 2Fe(s) + Al_2O_3(s); \quad \Delta H^{\ominus} = -854\ \text{kJ mol}^{-1}$$

The thermit reaction can be done in the laboratory, but it has found practical use in two rather different ways. A constructive use was when molten iron made by the thermit reaction was once used to plug holes in broken tram lines. A destructive use of the thermit reaction is in incendiary bombs. Those who like to design such weapons regard the thermit reaction as admirable not only because it gives out a lot of heat, but also because it cannot be put out by water.

94.7 Rewrite the equation

$$B_4O_7^{2-}(aq) + 2H^+(aq) + 5H_2O(l) \rightarrow 4H_3BO_3(aq)$$

showing the reaction as one that involves the $B_4O_5(OH)_2^{2-}$ ion instead of $B_4O_7^{2-}$. Does it matter very much which equation is used?

94.8 The endpoint of a borax–acid titration is at about pH = 4. Which indicator would you use in the titration?

94.9 (i) The formula of boric acid does not represent its structure. What is its formula?

(ii) The formula could be written in a different way. What is it?

(iii) How might you classify 'boric acid' if this formula were used?

94.10 Why can the thermit reaction not be stopped by water like an ordinary fire?

94.11 Hot aluminium oxide will catalyse the decomposition of ethanol, C_2H_5OH. A colourless gas is given off, which decolourises bromine water. What are the products of the reaction?

94.3 The hydroxides

The hydroxide of boron is $B(OH)_3$, but earlier we wrote its formula as H_3BO_3 and called it boric acid (Figure

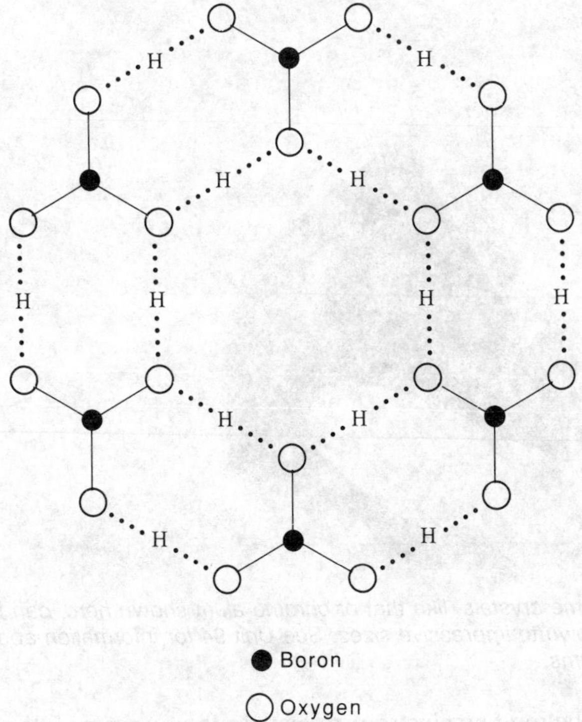

Figure 94.2 The structure of boric acid, H_3BO_3, has planar BO_3 groups linked by hydrogen bonds

94.2). This just goes to show that the structures of many acids and alkalis are similar. (You should look back at Unit 74 to remind yourself about the structures of acids such as HNO_3 and H_2SO_4.)

If you add hydroxide ions to a solution of an aluminium salt, you will find that a gelatinous white precipitate of aluminium hydroxide, $Al(OH)_3$, is produced:

$$Al^{3+}(aq) + 3OH^-(aq) \rightarrow Al(OH)_3(s)$$

The precipitate will dissolve in both acid and alkali:

$$Al(OH)_3(s) + 3H^+(aq) \rightarrow Al^{3+}(aq) + 3H_2O(l)$$
$$Al(OH)_3(s) + 3OH^-(aq) \rightarrow Al(OH)_6{}^{3-}(aq)$$

Aluminium hydroxide has two important uses. Fire extinguishers can be made that contain aluminium sulphate together with the usual carbonate and acid. When the extinguisher is used, aluminium hydroxide is produced:

$$2Al^{3+}(aq) + 3CO_3{}^{2-}(aq) + H_2O(l) \rightarrow 2Al(OH)_3(s) + 3CO_2(g)$$

The hydroxide has the virtue of stabilising the foam, which covers the fire. A second use is in dyeing. Particles of the hydroxide are able to attach themselves to the fibres in cloth. The hydroxide is able to absorb dye molecules much more efficiently than the fibres alone. A substance which, like aluminium hydroxide, assists in the dyeing of a fabric is called a *mordant*.

> **94.12** Why is it that solutions of many aluminium salts are acidic in water? (Hint: see Unit 76.)

94.4 The halides

The elements all give halides with the general formula EX_3. For example, BF_3, $AlCl_3$, $GaBr_3$. However, there are two complicating factors. The first, which we shall come to in a moment, is that some of the halides dimerise, e.g. aluminium trichloride gives Al_2Cl_6. The second, which we shall largely ignore, is that below aluminium other formulae are found, e.g. GaI_2, which often hide some complicated structures.

Boron trichloride and aluminium trichloride are famous for the bonding they contain, and for the shapes of their molecules. You will find details about them in Unit 17. However, in Figure 94.3 you can see the shapes of the isolated molecules, and of the dimer that aluminium trichloride makes.

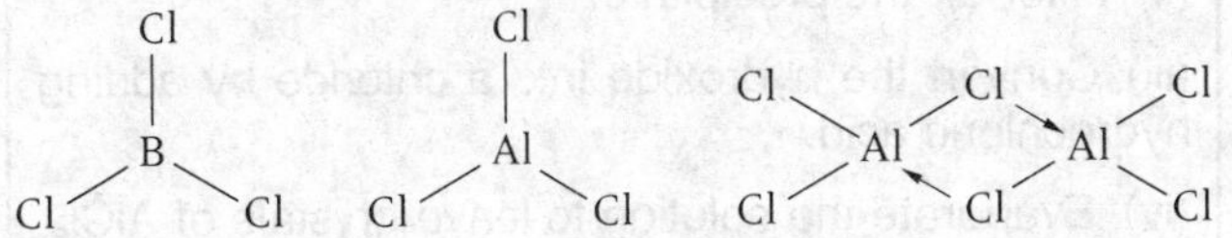

***Figure 94.3** The shapes of BCl_3, $AlCl_3$ and the dimer Al_2Cl_6*

Both BCl_3 and $AlCl_3$ are prone to hydrolysis. This is characteristic of many chlorides, but very different to tetrachloromethane, CCl_4, which will not hydrolyse. The reason for the difference lies in the electron deficient nature of BCl_3 and $AlCl_3$. Both boron and aluminium have more p orbitals in their outer shell than are used in bonding to the three chlorine atoms. We can imagine that the hydrolysis reaction starts by a water molecule donating one of its pairs to the empty orbital (Figure 94.4). This disrupts the arrangement of the electron clouds in the molecules, and the reaction has begun. We can write the equation in two ways. The first is a simple version, the second rather more accurate:

$$AlCl_3(s) + 3H_2O(l) \rightarrow Al(OH)_3(aq) + 3HCl(aq)$$
$$AlCl_3(s) + 6H_2O(l) \rightarrow Al(H_2O)_6{}^{3+}(aq) + 3Cl^-(aq)$$

Tetrachloromethane cannot react in this way because it has no empty orbitals with the right range of energies to accept a lone pair from a water molecule.

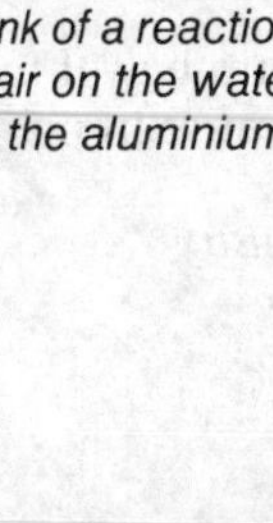

***Figure 94.4** We can think of a reaction between H_2O and $AlCl_3$ starting when a lone pair on the water molecule overlaps with an empty 2p orbital on the aluminium atom*

94.13 Gallium gives a chloride whose molar mass in the vapour state is approximately 352 g mol^{-1}. What is the likely formula of the chloride? M(Ga) = 69.7 g mol^{-1}; M(Cl) = 35.5 g mol^{-1}.

94.14 A solution of a thallium compound had some sodium chloride solution added to it. A white insoluble chloride of thallium was made, which was found to contain about 15% of chlorine. What is the likely formula of the chloride? M(Tl) = 204.4 g mol^{-1}.

94.15 A student suggested making aluminium trichloride by this recipe:

(i) Add sodium hydroxide solution to aluminium sulphate solution.

(ii) Filter off the precipitate.

(iii) Convert the hydroxide into a chloride by adding hydrochloric acid.

(iv) Evaporate the solution to leave crystals of $AlCl_3$.

Why will this method not work? What method must be used to make the chloride?

94.16 Explain why (i) BF_3 can react with ammonia to give a compound of formula BF_3NH_3; (ii) 1 mol of $AlCl_3$ will combine with 1 mol of ethoxyethane, $(C_2H_5)_2O$.

94.17 $AlCl_3$ is used in the Friedel–Crafts reaction in organic chemistry. Look up this reaction (if you need to) and give an example of it; explain what the connection is between the example and *Lewis acids*.

Some crystals, like that of chrome alum shown here, can be grown to impressive sizes. See Unit 94 for information about alums.

94.5 The sulphates

Aluminium sulphate and the alums are the most widely known of the sulphates. You may come across aluminium sulphate as a white crystalline material, $Al_2(SO_4)_3{\cdot}18H_2O$, but more interesting is the mixed sulphate of aluminium and potassium known as potash alum, $KAl(SO_4)_2{\cdot}12H_2O$. The crystals of this alum are octahedral and translucent. They are isomorphic with the violet crystals of chrome alum, $KCr(SO_4)_2{\cdot}12H_2O$. That is, the two varieties have exactly the same crystal form. Indeed a crystal of potash alum in a saturated solution of chrome alum will grow a layer of chrome alum over it. Other alums include ammonia alum (ammonium aluminium sulphate), $NH_4Al(SO_4)_2{\cdot}12H_2O$, and iron alum (iron(III) ammonium sulphate), $NH_4Fe(SO_4)_2{\cdot}12H_2O$.

94.6 The hydrides

Boron makes a large number of hydrides. The bonding in them is unusual, because in many cases there appear to be too few electrons to explain the number of bonds present. For example, diborane, B_2H_6, has the structure shown in Figure 94.5a. We have discussed this compound in section 90.7. Here we shall just say that the two hydrogen atoms that bridge between the boron atoms are involved in three-centre bonds. These bonds consist of orbitals that contain two electrons in the nor-

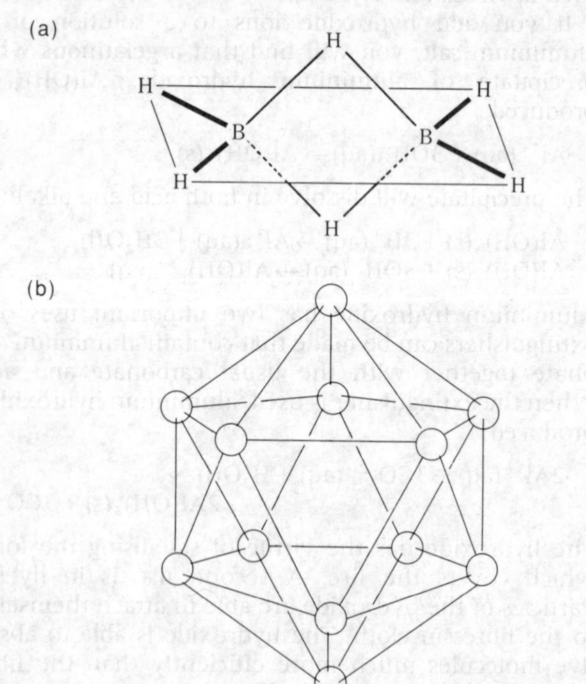

Figure 94.5 *(a) The structure of diborane, B_2H_6. (b) The $B_{12}H_{12}^{2-}$ ion has the shape of an icosahedron. Only the boron atoms are shown. (Adapted from: Muetterties, E. L. (1967).* The Chemistry of Boron and its Compounds, *Wiley, New York, p. 39)*

Table 94.3. Differences between $NaBH_4$ and $LiAlH_4$

Class of organic compound	Reaction with $NaBH_4$	Reaction with $LiAlH_4$
Aldehyde	Reduced	Reduced
Ketone	Reduced	Reduced
Acid	No effect	Reduced
Ester	No effect	Reduced
Amide	No effect	Reduced
Nitrile	No effect	Reduced

mal way, but the orbitals spread over three atoms rather than two. Boron and hydrogen can also give a large number of ionic hydrides with remarkable structures, e.g. $B_{12}H_{12}^{2-}$ has the shape of an icosahedron (Figure 94.5b).

Some of the hydrides made by boron and aluminium have useful properties. In particular, sodium tetrahydridoborate(III), $NaBH_4$, and lithium tetrahydridoaluminate(III), $LiAlH_4$, are widely used in organic chemistry as reducing agents (Table 94.3). These hydrides contain BH_4^- and AlH_4^- ions respectively. We can think of them as sources of hydride ions, H^-, which are powerful reducing agents. However, $LiAlH_4$ is more powerful than $NaBH_4$. See Unit 90 and the units on organic chemistry for more information on them.

Answers

94.1 Being nearer the top of the Group, we would expect boron to show more non-metallic nature than aluminium; so it should be more acidic in nature than aluminium. (It is.)

94.2 $E^{\ominus}_{Tl^+/Tl}$ is more negative than $E^{\ominus}_{Tl^{3+}/Tl}$, which suggests that thallium has a greater tendency to turn into Tl^+ in solution.

94.3 The aluminium is capable of reducing the acid to sulphur dioxide. The two half-equations are

$$Al^{3+}(aq) + 3e^- \rightarrow Al(s)$$

$$SO_4^{2-}(aq) + 2e^- + 4H^+(aq) \rightarrow SO_2(g) + 2H_2O(l)$$

They can be combined by taking three times the second and subtracting twice the first:

$$2Al(s) + 3SO_4^{2-}(aq) + 12H^+(aq) \rightarrow 3SO_2(g) + 6H_2O(l) + 2Al^{3+}(aq)$$

94.4 The structure is shown in Figure 94.6.

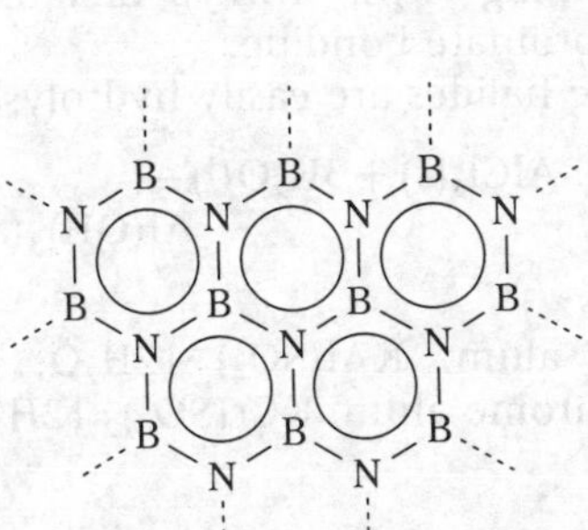

Figure 94.6 Part of a layer of boron nitride. The circles in the ring stand for delocalised π electrons. The structure of the compound is similar to that of graphite shown in Figure 95.2. However, there are marked differences in properties. For example, boron nitride is white and does not conduct electricity

94.5 It is methane. The equation is

$$Al_4C_3(s) + 12H_2O(l) \rightarrow 4Al(OH)_3(s) + 3CH_4(g)$$

94.6 The equation is

$$B_2O_3(s) + 3Mg(s) \rightarrow 2B(s) + 3MgO(s)$$

The free energy change is

$$3\Delta G_f^{\ominus}(MgO) - \Delta G_f^{\ominus}(B_2O_3) = -513\,kJ\,mol^{-1}$$

The negative sign shows us that the reaction should be spontaneous. As usual, though, the two reactants have to be heated to start the reaction.

94.7 $B_4O_5(OH)_2^{2-}(aq) + 2H^+(aq) + 4H_2O(l) \rightarrow 4H_3BO_3(aq)$

No, it does not; the molar ratio of the ion to hydrogen ions is the same in both cases.

94.8 Screened methyl orange.

94.9 (i) H_3BO_3.
(ii) Boric acid could be written $B(OH)_3$.
(iii) It looks like a hydroxide.

94.10 In an ordinary fire the reactions are kept going by the material reacting with oxygen in the air. Water not only cools the fire, but also keeps oxygen out. In the thermit reaction, the oxygen involved is in the metal oxide, so keeping atmospheric oxygen out has no effect. (Also, at the temperatures of the thermit reaction (above 1000° C), water will give off hydrogen with aluminium.)

94.11 Ethene and water (see section 112.2).

94.12 The $Al(H_2O)_6^{3+}$ ion can lose protons (see section 75.5).

94.13 You should guess that the chloride might be GaCl, $GaCl_2$, $GaCl_3$, or perhaps Ga_2Cl_6. By trial and error you should find that Ga_2Cl_6 is correct. You might have guessed this by analogy with Al_2Cl_6 and because the molar mass is high.

94.14 15% is not a high proportion of chlorine. Also, if you read the first section you will find that there is a hint that thallium tends to give compounds in which its oxidation number is +1. The chloride is TlCl.

94.15 Aluminium chloride is hydrolysed by water so it cannot be crystallised from solution. The chloride is made by direct combination of aluminium and chlorine.

Answers – cont.

94.16 (i) Like aluminium in $AlCl_3$, BF_3 is electron deficient. The boron can accept a pair of electrons from the nitrogen atom in ammonia.

(ii) Ethoxyethane has two lone pairs on the oxygen atom. One of them can be used in bonding to the boron atom, as in the case of ammonia.

94.17 A methyl group can be substituted in a benzene ring by reacting benzene with a combination of $AlCl_3$ and chloromethane, CH_3Cl. This happens by the chlorine of the CH_3Cl bonding with the $AlCl_3$, leaving a methyl cation, CH_3^+. This is an electrophile, which attacks the benzene ring. See section 113.6 for more information.

UNIT 94 SUMMARY

- The Group III metals:
  - (i) Show non-metallic character, e.g. BCl_3 and $AlCl_3$ are covalent.
  - (ii) Boron and aluminium are amphoteric, i.e. the elements and their oxides will react with both acids and alkalis.
  - (iii) B^{3+} ion is extremely small, thus leading to covalency (Fajans' rules).
- Manufacture:
  Aluminium isolated by electrolysis of molten bauxite, Al_2O_3.

Reactions

- With oxygen:
  - (i) Oxides made;

    e.g. $2Al(s) + 3O_2(g) \rightarrow 2Al_2O_3(s)$
  - (ii) Aluminium powder is used in the thermit reaction to remove oxygen from (i.e. reduce) iron(III) oxide;

    $Fe_2O_3(s) + 2Al(s) \rightarrow 2Fe(s) + Al_2O_3(s)$
- With halogens:
  Aluminium makes aluminium trichloride, $AlCl_3$, which occurs as dimers, Al_2Cl_6;

  $2Al(s) + 3Cl_2(g) \rightarrow Al_2Cl_6(s)$

Compounds

- Oxides:
  - (i) Basic, but insoluble in water.
  - (ii) Amphoteric nature shown by B_2O_3 and Al_2O_3;

    e.g. $Al_2O_3(s) + 6H^+(aq) \rightarrow 2Al^{3+}(aq) + 3H_2O(l)$

    $Al_2O_3(s) + 6OH^-(aq) + 3H_2O(l) \rightarrow 2Al(OH)_6{}^{3-}(aq)$
- Hydroxides:
  - (i) The hydroxide of boron, $B(OH)_3$, is better classed as boric acid, H_3BO_3.
  - (ii) Gelatinous white $Al(OH)_3$ is insoluble in water. It is made by adding alkali to a solution containing Al^{3+} ions, but dissolves in excess alkali.
- Hydrides:
  - (i) Boron forms many electron deficient hydrides, e.g. B_2H_6. These hydrides contain hydrogen atoms bridging between boron atoms.
  - (ii) Sodium tetrahydridoborate(III), $NaBH_4$, and lithium tetrahydridoaluminate(III), $LiAlH_4$, are used as reducing agents in organic chemistry; $LiAlH_4$ is the more vigorous.
- Halides:
  - (i) Aluminium trichloride, $AlCl_3$, dimerises, forming Al_2Cl_6 with a mix of covalent and coordinate bonding.
  - (ii) The halides are easily hydrolysed;

    e.g. $AlCl_3(s) + 3H_2O(l) \rightarrow Al(OH)_3(aq) + 3HCl(aq)$
- Sulphates:
  Potash alum, $KAl(SO_4)_2{\cdot}12H_2O$, is isomorphic with chrome alum, $KCr(SO_4)_2{\cdot}12H_2O$.

95

Carbon

95.1 Why is carbon important?

The normal valency of carbon is four. It is most important that you can explain why it is that carbon can make four covalent bonds. Do read Unit 17 if you have to remind yourself of the explanation.

The properties and uses of carbon are listed in Tables 95.1 and 95.2. Carbon is an especially important element because it shows the property of *catenation*. This means that its atoms can join together to make chains. This property is shown in the millions of carbon compounds that are either naturally occurring or have been made for the first time in laboratories. Indeed, there are so many of them that they are best studied as a separate branch of chemistry: organic chemistry. In this unit we shall summarise the chemistry of the simple carbon compounds, e.g. the gases carbon monoxide and carbon dioxide, and the carbonates. However, the main reason why carbon is one of the most important of elements is that life is based upon it. The molecules that are responsible for the growth and development of living organisms, such as vitamins, proteins, enzymes, hormones and DNA, are structures built from chains of carbon atoms. Owing to the key part that carbon plays in maintaining life, it is as well that you know about the *carbon cycle*. The cycle is represented in Figure 95.1.

The atmosphere acts as a reservoir of carbon dioxide. During photosynthesis plants convert the gas into sugars, and then into more complicated molecules. Animals that consume the plants then incorporate many of the carbon compounds into their own structures, or use them as a source of energy. Carbon dioxide is released back into the atmosphere in many ways. Some is breathed out by animals as a breakdown product of respiration, and some is released when organic matter decays. (You count as organic matter!) Another source of carbon dioxide in the atmosphere is the burning of fuels such as wood, peat, coal and oil. The majority of carbon dioxide released in this way is caused by humans: to keep warm, to cook food, to run cars and lorries, and to use in industry.

In previous centuries the proportion of carbon dioxide in the atmosphere has increased fairly slowly; but in the last 20 years the increase has been much more rapid. It appears that humans are releasing more carbon dioxide through the burning of fuels than can be absorbed by plants or dissolved in the oceans. One consequence of this build-up of carbon dioxide is the *greenhouse effect*. Visible and ultraviolet light from the Sun strikes the Earth's surface as photons of relatively short wavelength. Radiation is emitted from the Earth's surface in the infrared region of the spectrum, and it is of a much longer wavelength. Carbon dioxide is capable of absorbing a significant amount of this radiation, so the more of the gas present, the less energy escapes into space. The result is that the temperature of the atmosphere rises. The average temperature of the atmosphere does appear to be rising, and it may have marked effects on the climate. The precise influence is hard to analyse because the weather system is so complicated; but if the rise continues, dramatic changes are sure to take place. For example, a small rise in the average

Table 95.1. Information about carbon

Relative atomic mass, A_r(C)	12
Electron structure	$1s^22s^22p^2$
Ionisation energy	1086 kJ mol^{-1}
Electronegativity	2.5
Bond energy (C—C, average)	346 kJ mol^{-1}
Bond length (C—C, average)	154 pm
Two allotropes: diamond and graphite	

Table 95.2. Uses of carbon

Diamond	Gem stone
	In industry for cutting, milling and drilling
Graphite	Reducing agent in the extraction of metals
	Electrodes in electrolytic extraction of elements
	Moderator in nuclear reactors
	In very high strength carbon fibres
Activated charcoal	To adsorb gases and other chemicals
Charcoal	As a fuel

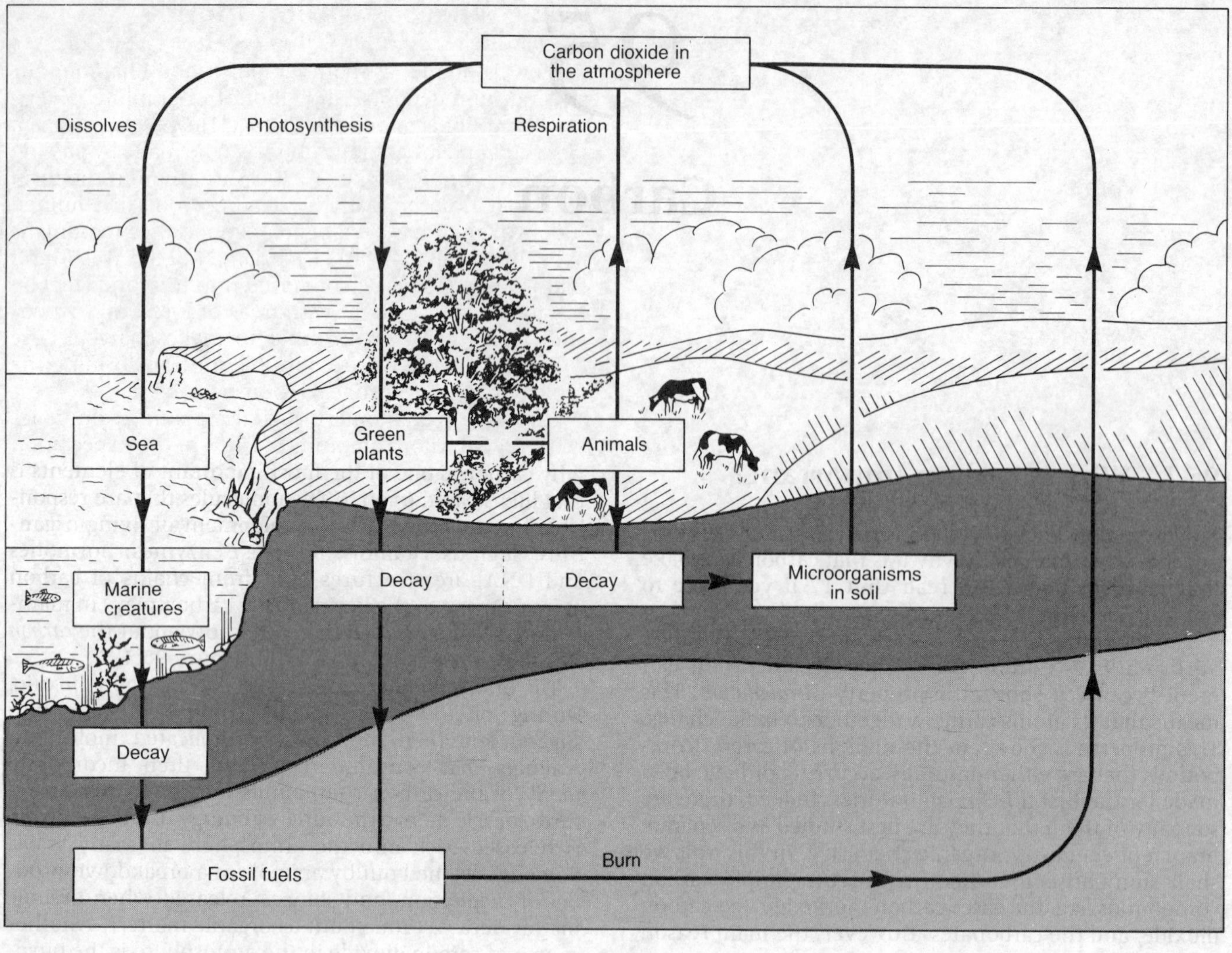

Figure 95.1 The carbon cycle

temperature of the polar regions will cause a massive melting of the ice caps. Given that the majority of the water on Earth is locked up as ice in these caps, its release into the oceans will cause a rise of sea level of many feet. Cities like London or New York will be flooded. Perhaps of more importance is that regions of the world in which food is grown may turn into deserts; or alternatively they may become swamped by rain levels now associated with the tropics.

Carbon possesses two famous allotropes: diamond and graphite (Figure 95.2). You will find details of them in Units 32 and 57. Contrary to appearances, graphite is the more thermodynamically stable allotrope of carbon. This is in spite of the fact that graphite is much softer than diamond, and that it burns much more easily. The difference in properties is due to the difference in bonding. Diamond has its carbon atoms joined in an interlocking network of tetrahedra. It is very hard to break diamond apart, either physically or chemically, because of the vast number of bonds that have to be broken. On the other hand graphite has a layer structure in which the atoms are joined in interlocking networks of hexagons. The hexagonal layers can slide over one another.

The two allotropes of carbon, diamond and graphite, have very different properties and values.

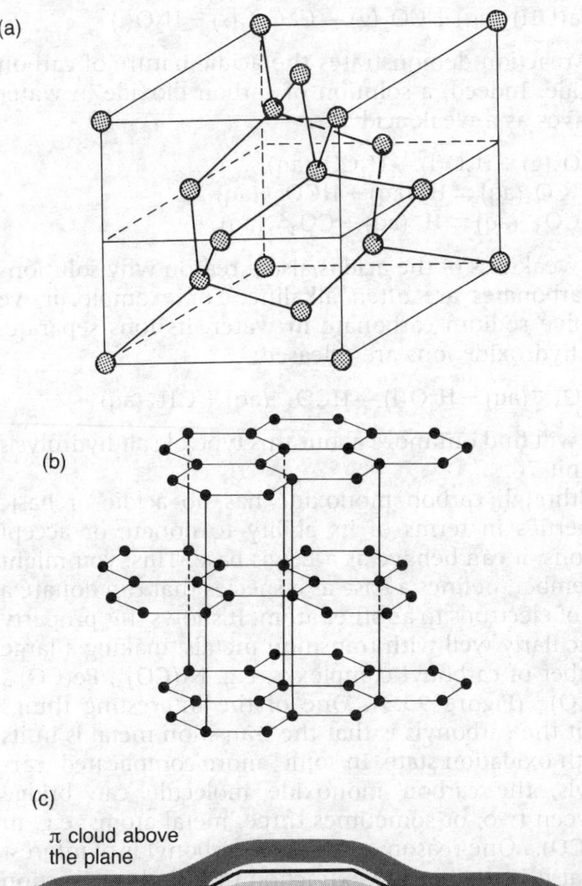

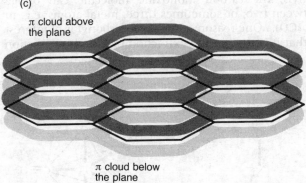

***Figure 95.2** Structures of (a) diamond and (b) graphite. In graphite there is a delocalised π cloud of electrons parallel to the planes of carbon atoms*

95.1 What is one explanation of the bonding in methane, CH_4?

95.2 What happens to the infrared energy absorbed by molecules in the atmosphere?

95.3 (i) What type of bonding holds the layers together in graphite?

(ii) Why will graphite conduct electricity well in a direction parallel to the planes of hexagons, but not at all well in a direction perpendicular to the planes?

(iii) What is the name we give to crystals, or substances, that show different properties in different directions?

95.2 Where is carbon found?

Carbon is found as both graphite and diamond in underground deposits. The amount of graphite is very small and not economic to extract. However, there is a large demand for graphite and it can be made by passing electricity through coke at 2700° C. Carbon in the form of charcoal can be made by heating wood in a limited supply of air. It has been of great importance to humans over thousands of years. Especially, once it was found that iron ore could be converted into iron and steel by reacting it with carbon, vast areas of forest and woodland were cut down in order to make charcoal. The charcoal industry was responsible for transforming the ecology of many European countries.

The value of diamonds is such that mining companies will shift enormous amounts of earth in the expectation of finding them. Native diamonds have to be cut and polished before they make good gem stones. The smaller, less well formed, specimens can be used as industrial diamonds, e.g. in cutting and milling machines. However, it is now common for industrial grade diamonds to be made artificially by heating graphite at high pressures and temperatures.

95.3 Carbon dioxide and carbon monoxide

Carbon monoxide and carbon dioxide are the only two gaseous oxides in Group IV. Carbon dioxide is denser than air; carbon monoxide is less dense. Both can be produced when organic matter burns, depending on the amount of oxygen present. For example, if coke burns in a plentiful supply of air,

$$C(s) + O_2(g) \rightarrow CO_2(g)$$

but in a limited supply of air,

$$2C(s) + O_2(g) \rightarrow 2CO(g)$$

Both these reactions are exothermic and take place in furnaces used in reducing metal ores. Generally in such places it is desirable to make carbon monoxide because it is a reducing agent and will, for example, remove the oxygen from a metal oxide. Units 50 and 85 are the places to find out more about this.

The two gases also occur in the exhausts from car and lorry engines. Many countries now have laws that regulate the amount of carbon monoxide that should be emitted from these engines.

Carbon dioxide is used in many fire extinguishers (Table 95.3). There are two types. In water based extinguishers a sealed bottle of acid is immersed in a solution of a hydrogencarbonate. When the plunger on

Table 95.3. Uses of carbon dioxide

In fire extinguishers
Making fizzy drinks, e.g. champagne, lemonade, colas
Dry ice, solid CO_2, is used in show business for making mists

the extinguisher is struck, the bottle bursts, allowing the acid and hydrogencarbonate to mix. Carbon dioxide is given off in a watery spray (or in a foam if other chemicals have been added).

A second type contains pure carbon dioxide under pressure. The gas given out covers the fire and prevents oxygen in the air from reacting with the hot materials. If you use this type of extinguisher you will find that the gas given out is very cold. This is a well known effect in thermodynamics (the Joule–Kelvin effect) and takes place when a gas expands from a region of high to a region of low pressure. If the gas cools sufficiently, it will make crystals of CO_2, i.e. solid CO_2, also known as dry ice.

In the laboratory carbon monoxide is best made by dehydrating methanoic acid or sodium methanoate with concentrated sulphuric acid:

$$HCOOH - H_2O \rightarrow CO$$

You may have seen carbon dioxide made in the traditional way by reacting dilute hydrochloric acid with marble chips:

$$CaCO_3(s) + 2H^+(aq) \rightarrow Ca^{2+}(aq) + CO_2(g) + H_2O(l)$$

Both CO and CO_2 are poisonous, odourless, colourless gases. Carbon dioxide is heavier than air. Carbon monoxide acts as a poison by acting as a ligand on the iron atom in haemoglobin. Once it has combined with the iron it tends to stay there, so it prevents oxygen molecules being taken up. The blood of victims of carbon monoxide poisoning is a brilliant red-pink colour rather than the dull red of normal blood. Carbon monoxide is the dangerous component of coal gas, and is produced when, for example, the flues of coal or oil burners become blocked. Carbon dioxide kills people by entering the lungs and preventing sufficient oxygen being absorbed.

You should know how to test for carbon dioxide: it gives a white precipitate with lime water ('lime water goes milky'). The cloudiness is due to a precipitate of calcium carbonate:

The cold vapour escaping from dry ice (solid carbon dioxide) is responsible for the clouds of 'mist' seen at many rock concerts.

$$Ca(OH)_2(aq) + CO_2(g) \rightarrow CaCO_3(s) + H_2O(l)$$

This reaction demonstrates the acidic nature of carbon dioxide. Indeed, a solution of carbon dioxide in water behaves as a weak acid:

$$CO_2(g) + H_2O(l) \rightarrow H_2CO_3(aq)$$
$$H_2CO_3(aq) \rightleftharpoons H^+(aq) + HCO_3^-(aq)$$
$$HCO_3^-(aq) \rightleftharpoons H^+(aq) + CO_3^{2-}(aq)$$

The weakness of the acid is also a reason why solutions of carbonates are often alkaline. For example, if we dissolve sodium carbonate in water, its ions separate, and hydroxide ions are released:

$$CO_3^{2-}(aq) + H_2O(l) \rightarrow HCO_3^-(aq) + OH^-(aq)$$

You will find out more about this type of salt hydrolysis in Unit 76.

Although carbon monoxide has no acidic or basic properties in terms of its ability to donate or accept protons, it can behave as a Lewis base. This, you might remember, defines a base as a species that can donate a pair of electrons to another atom. It shows this property particularly well with transition metals, making a large number of carbonyl complexes, e.g. $Ni(CO)_4$, $Fe(CO)_5$, $Cr(CO)_6$ (Figure 95.3). One of the interesting things about the carbonyls is that the transition metal is in its zeroth oxidation state. In some, more complicated, carbonyls, the carbon monoxide molecule can bridge between two, or sometimes three, metal atoms, e.g. in $Fe_2(CO)_9$. One reason why nickel carbonyl is of interest is that it is used in the extraction of nickel; see section 85.3.

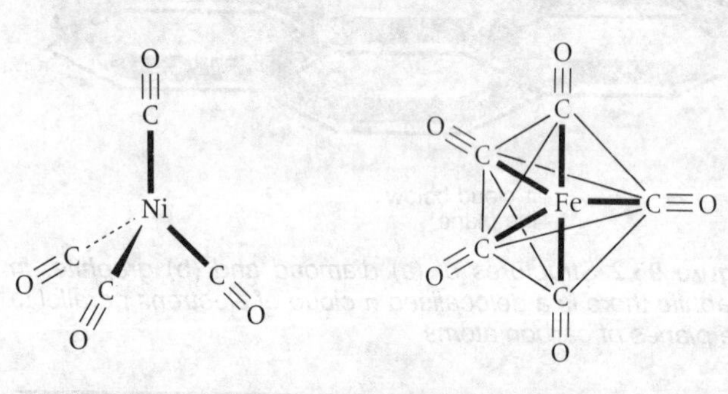

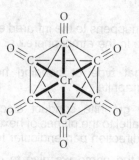

Cr(CO)6: octahedral

Figure 95.3 *The structures of three transition metal carbonyl compounds*

95.4 Every year some people die by being in a room containing a faulty heater that uses coal, gas, or oil. How might the deaths occur?

95.5 Describe the bonding in CO and CO_2. What is the shape of the CO_2 molecule?

95.6 Why does the precipitate redissolve if excess carbon dioxide is passed through lime water?

95.7 If you had a mixture of carbon monoxide and carbon dioxide, how would you find out the relative proportions of the two gases in the mixture?

95.8 In the carbonyls of Figure 95.3, each carbonyl donates two electrons to the transition metal ion.

(i) How many electrons does each of the metals have in its zeroth oxidation state?

(ii) How many electrons in total are donated by the carbon monoxide molecules?

(iii) What is special about the total number of electrons that the metals now have?

(iv) Predict the formula of molybdenum carbonyl. (The atomic number of molybdenum, Mo, is 42.)

These limestone figures at Wells Cathedral in Somerset show the unfortunate effects of hundreds of years of atmospheric pollution.

95.4 The importance of carbonates

Carbonates (Table 95.4), together with silicates, are some of the most important geological minerals. Calcium carbonate, $CaCO_3$, occurs in a variety of limestones, including chalk. One of the characteristics of limestone is that it is dissolved by acids, even weakly acidic rain water. Among other things this is why limestone deposits are often riddled by caves, and why water that comes from aquifers in chalky areas is hard. We can write the reaction that takes place as

$$CaCO_3(s) + H^+(aq) \rightarrow Ca^{2+}(aq) + HCO_3^-(aq)$$

Chalk has been made from the shells of tiny sea creatures and the bodies of algae. It is a lot softer than other limestones, some of which have been subjected to high temperatures and pressures during changes in the Earth's crust.

Table 95.4. Carbonate minerals

Name	*Formula*	*Comment*
Calcite	$CaCO_3$	A pure variety is Iceland spar. It shows the property of double refraction
Aragonite	$CaCO_3$	Similar to calcite, but with a different crystal structure. Gradually changes into calcite
Dolomite	$CaCO_3{\cdot}MgCO_3$	More resistant to acid than other limestones. Found as mountains, e.g. 'the Dolomites' in Italy
Siderite	$FeCO_3$	An important ore of iron
Malachite	$CuCO_3{\cdot}Cu(OH)_2$	A copper ore with a characteristic green colour

95.9 Explain why a solution containing Ca^{2+}(aq) and HCO_3^-(aq) ions is said to be hard.

95.10 What is wrong with this statement: 'water is often hard because it has calcium carbonate dissolved in it'?

95.11 In recent years limestone rocks have been dumped (on purpose, and legally) in a number of lakes in Scandinavia, Germany and Great Britain. What might be the reason for this?

95.12 Why are there no mountains made of the Group I metal carbonates, e.g. Na_2CO_3, K_2CO_3?

95.13 What is wrong with this description of an

experiment: 'a little nitric acid was added to a solution of barium carbonate and the carbon dioxide given off turned lime water milky'?

95.14 Explain why it is that a solution of washing soda crystals (i) is alkaline, (ii) gives hydrogen if it is heated with aluminium.

95.5 Carbon disulphide

Carbon disulphide, CS_2, is a poisonous, volatile liquid with a most unpleasant smell. It has a marked ability to dissolve sulphur and rubber. It can be used to make crystals of rhombic sulphur by dissolving powdered sulphur in it, and allowing the liquid to evaporate slowly. However, it is better to use an organic solvent such as methylbenzene for the purpose. Carbon disulphide can be made by reacting sulphur vapour with carbon at very high temperatures:

$$C(s) + 2S(s) \rightarrow CS_2(l); \qquad \Delta H_f^{\ominus} = +88 \text{ kJ mol}^{-1}$$

The enthalpy change is strongly positive, so we can call carbon disulphide an endothermic compound. With this piece of knowledge you should expect that it would be quite likely to break apart easily, which it does. It is explosive in its reactions with a number of chemicals.

95.15 A mixture of CS_2 vapour and nitrogen monoxide, NO, gives a vivid blue flame when ignited. A yellow solid is left afterwards. Predict the products of the reaction, and write the equation.

95.16 Why, given its endothermic heat of formation, can you *expect* that CS_2 would decompose easily but you cannot be certain?

Answers

95.1 sp^3 hybridisation. See Unit 17 for details.

95.2 It makes the molecules vibrate more rapidly.

95.3 (i) Van der Waals bonding.

(ii) If you look at Figure 95.2c you will see that the delocalised orbitals in graphite lie parallel to the planes. Electrons can move along the planes making use of these orbitals. Conduction is good parallel to the planes. There is no overlap of orbitals perpendicular to the planes, so conduction is poor in this direction.

(iii) They are anisotropic.

95.4 If the flue to the heater becomes blocked, or there is insufficient ventilation, the fumes of CO and CO_2 build up in the room. Unless the person lies on the floor, it is the CO that kills.

95.5 There is a triple bond in CO, and two double bonds in CO_2 (see section 14.2). CO_2 is linear.

95.6 As the gas dissolves, the solution becomes acidic. The insoluble $CaCO_3$ is converted into soluble calcium hydrogencarbonate, $Ca(HCO_3)_2$.

95.7 One method is to measure their total volume, and then pass them through a solution of an alkali. (Potassium hydroxide is very good.) The CO_2 will be absorbed, so by measuring the residual volume of CO their proportions can be found.

95.8 (i) Ni has 28, Fe has 26 and Cr has 24. (These are the same as their atomic numbers.)

(ii) Each donates two electrons, so 8 go to Ni, 10 to Fe and 12 to Cr.

(iii) The totals are 36 for each metal. This is the number of electrons belonging to the noble gas krypton. It is common for the transition metals to make carbonyls with a total number of electrons equal to that of a noble gas.

(iv) The noble gas following molybdenum is xenon. This has 54 electrons. The difference of 12 electrons can be made up from six CO molecules. The formula is $Mo(CO)_6$.

95.9 The Ca^{2+} ions give precipitates (scum) with soaps. On heating the HCO_3^- ions revert to CO_3^{2-}, which gives a precipitate with Ca^{2+} ions. (This is the scale/fur in kettles and boilers.)

95.10 It contains only extremely small amounts of $CaCO_3$ through the solid dissolving in water of its own accord. Mainly it contains the products of the reaction between $CaCO_3$ and slightly acidic rain water.

95.11 Many lakes and waterways have become acidic owing to the effects of acid rain. The limestone is used to neutralise the acid. The treatment can be successful, but is not always so.

95.12 They are all soluble, so even if they were made millions of years ago, they would have soon dissolved away when it rained!

95.13 Barium carbonate is almost insoluble in water, so the solution could not have contained this carbonate. See section 93.4.

95.14 (i) Salt hydrolysis is responsible.

(ii) Aluminium is amphoteric and will give hydrogen with solutions containing H^+ or OH^- ions (see section 94.1).

95.15 You should have predicted that the nitrogen is likely to be released as N_2, and that the solid is sulphur. The equation is

$$2NO(g) + CS_2 \rightarrow 2S(s) + N_2(g) + CO_2(g)$$

95.16 We know that endothermic compounds are energetically unstable; but they may be *kinetically* stable. That is, the reaction may have a large activation energy.

UNIT 95 SUMMARY

- The element:
  - (i) Carbon is a non-metal.
  - (ii) Carbon atoms show the property of catenation, i.e. they can bond with each other to form chains.
  - (iii) Carbon compounds form the basis of biologically active molecules.
  - (iv) Carbon has two allotropes: diamond and graphite.
  - (v) Graphite is the most energetically stable of the two.
- Manufacture:
  Charcoal (graphite) is made by heating wood in the absence of air; diamond occurs naturally, but can be made by heating graphite at a high temperature and pressure.

Reactions

- A reducing agent:
  Will reduce many metal oxides, especially useful in the extraction of iron in the blast furnace.
- With water:
  Takes part in the Bosch reaction: see Unit 90.
- With oxygen:
  Produces carbon monoxide or carbon dioxide depending on the quantity of oxygen present;

$$C(s) + O_2(g) \rightarrow CO_2(g)$$
$$2C(s) + O_2(g) \rightarrow 2CO(g)$$

Compounds

- Oxides:
  - (i) Carbon dioxide is acidic in water;

$$CO_2(g) + H_2O(l) \rightarrow HCO_3^-(aq) + H_3O^+(l)$$

  - (ii) Carbon dioxide turns lime water milky.
  - (iii) Carbon monoxide is a neutral oxide; but it can act as a ligand to transition metal ions, e.g. $Fe(CO)_5$.
- Hydrides:
  A vast number of hydrides exist (CH_4, C_2H_6, etc.), which are the subject of organic chemistry.
- Halides:
  Tetrachloromethane, CCl_4, is used as a solvent. Unlike many other chlorides of non-metals it will not undergo hydrolysis. See Unit 96.

96

Group IV

96.1 The nature of the elements

Carbon and silicon show many of the properties that are characteristic of non-metals; but as we move down the Group, the metallic nature of the elements increases. For example, carbon and silicon give acidic oxides, whereas those of germanium, tin and lead are amphoteric, although some lead oxides are definitely basic. There is a change in the nature of the bonding down the Group as well. Covalency dominates until, as we would expect with metals, tin and lead make some ionic compounds.

The physical properties and uses are listed in Tables 96.1 and 96.2.

The normal valency of the elements is four; but apart from carbon, the elements can make more than four bonds. This is because they make use of a set of d orbitals in bonding. The d orbitals are not those listed in Table 96.1 (which are full of electrons). Rather they are the empty d orbitals of the outer electron shell, e.g. the 3d set for silicon and the 4d set for germanium (Figure 96.1). The availability of d orbitals is responsible for the ability of the elements, except carbon, to make complex ions such as SiF_6^{2-}. Here silicon can provide a maximum of four unpaired electrons by making use of one electron in each of the 3s and 3p orbitals. To make the extra two bonds, two of the 4d orbitals are used. In fact the bonds in the SiF_6^{2-} ion are a mixture of 3s, 3p and 4d orbitals. If we use the theory of hybridisation, which we discussed in Unit 17, we can describe the bonding orbitals as a set of d^2sp^3 hybrids.

Another feature of the chemistry of the Group is that some carbon compounds are less reactive than the corresponding compounds of the other members of the Group. For example, tetrachloromethane, CCl_4, will not react with water at all easily, whereas silicon tetrachloride, $SiCl_4$, will. As you will see in section 96.5, this too is a result of the elements (except carbon) making use of an empty set of d orbitals.

Table 96.2. Uses of the elements in Group IV

Element	*Main uses*
Silicon	As a semiconductor in transistors and other electronic components In silicone waxes and polymers As silicates, in the ceramics and glass industries
Germanium	As a semiconductor
Tin	In alloys As a protective coating for iron or steel
Lead	In alloys and water pipes (this use is much in decline) In petrol additives (also in decline) In car batteries

Table 96.1. Physical properties of the elements in Group IV

Symbol	*Carbon* C	*Silicon* Si	*Germanium* Ge	*Tin* Sn	*Lead* Pb
Electron structure	(He)$2s^22p^2$	(Ne)$3s^23p^2$	(Ar)$3d^{10}4s^24p^2$	(Kr)$4d^{10}5s^25p^2$	(Xe)$5d^{10}6s^26p^2$
Electronegativity	2.5	1.8	1.8	1.8	1.8
I.E./kJ mol^{-1}	1086	786	760	710	720
Melting point/°C	3550 diamond	1410	940	232 white	328
Boiling point/°C	4830 diamond	2680	2830	2690 white	1751
Atomic radius/pm	77	117	122	140	154
Principal oxid. no.	+4	+4	+2, +4	+2, +4	+2, +4

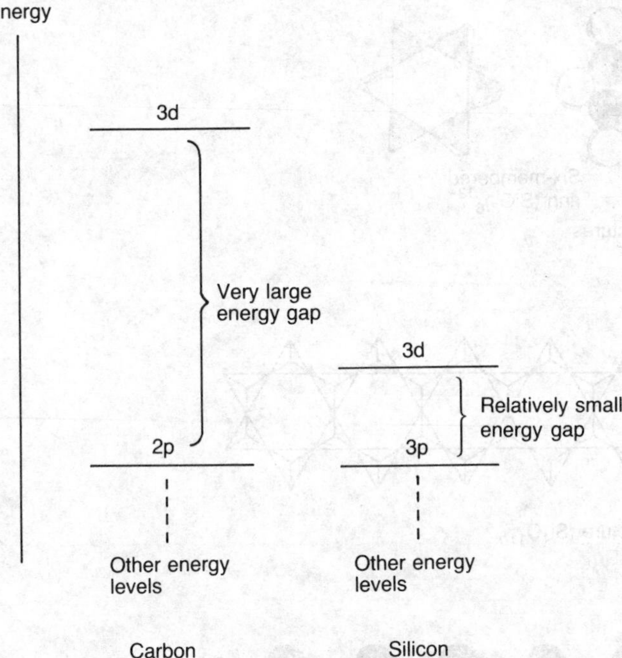

Figure 96.1 *The diagram illustrates the large difference between the 2p and 3d energy levels for carbon. The carbon 3d orbitals are so high in energy that they cannot be used in bonding. The 3p to 3d gap for silicon is relatively small. Silicon can use the 3d orbitals in bonding. (Note: the diagram is not to scale)*

> **96.1** (i) Which theory other than valence bond theory could be used to explain the bonding in SiF_6^{2-}?
>
> (ii) Predict the shape of this ion.

96.2 The importance of silicon

Silicon is one of the most abundant of elements, being the essential ingredient of a large number of minerals that make up the Earth's surface. Sand, clay and the stuff we called 'earth' is mainly a mixture of compounds of silicon and oxygen. The majority of the compounds consist of silicates, in which silicon and oxygen make giant three-dimensional structures. They are all based on the same basic building block made from one silicon atom and four oxygen atoms at the corners of a tetrahedron. Figure 96.2 illustrates the more important structures, and examples of minerals in which they occur.

The name 'silica' covers an entire group of minerals, which have the general formula SiO_2, the most common of which is quartz. Quartz is a framework silicate with SiO_4 tetrahedra arranged in spirals. The spirals can turn in a clockwise or anticlockwise direction – a feature that results in there being two mirror image, optically active, varieties of quartz.

In recent years silicon and silicates have been studied from a new point of view. It has been suggested that the first primitive forms of life on Earth may have been based on silicon rather than carbon. This suggestion cannot be discounted out of hand because the silicates show that these minerals have some ability to replicate and develop their structures into long chains. However, clearly carbon won the competition (if such it was) owing to its ability to make a wider variety of more flexible structures.

Silicates are also used as the basis of ceramics. Ceramics are much better electrical and thermal insulators than metals, and have greater rigidity, hardness and temperature stability than organic polymers. Following a great deal of research, new ceramic materials have been developed that contain, for example, borides, carbides and nitrides. They have found an increasing number of uses, e.g. glasses for covering solar panels, parts of turbines and internal combustion engines, and refractory brick linings for high temperature furnaces.

> **96.2** Talc, $Mg_3Si_4O_{10}(OH)_2$, is the softest mineral. It has a smooth, greasy touch. It is used in talcum powder. Muscovite, $KAl_2(Si_3Al)O_{10}(OH)_2$, is one of the micas, which split into thin layers extremely easily. Both minerals have layer structures. Which type of force holds the layers together?

96.3 The extraction of the elements

(a) *Silicon*

Silicon is the most important element used in semiconductors such as transistors and diodes. Without a supply of pure silicon it would be impossible to make the range of high quality computers, calculators, telephones, radios, etc., upon which modern industrial societies have come to rely. Crude silicon can be obtained by reducing silica (sand) with coke:

$$SiO_2(s) + 2C(s) \rightarrow Si(s) + 2CO(g)$$

The product is contaminated by silicon carbide, SiC_2. This carbide is also known as carborundum. It is extremely hard. The bits of steel drills are often impregnated with carborundum in order to reduce the wear on them.

Much better quality silicon is produced by reducing silicon tetrachloride with hydrogen:

$$SiCl_4(l) + 2H_2(g) \rightarrow Si(s) + 4HCl(g)$$

However, even silicon made in this way must be subjected to further purification if it is to be used in making semiconductors. The method used is called zone refining (see Figure 96.3). A cylinder of impure silicon is drawn very slowly (no faster than 1 cm per hour) through a small furnace. The key to understanding zone refining is to think about it as a variety of fractional

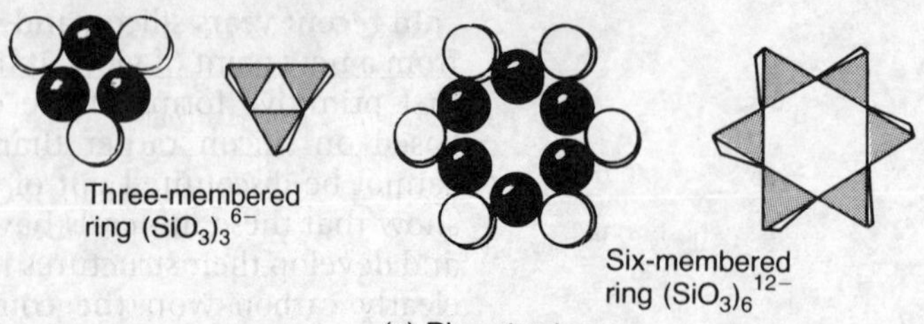

(a) Ring structures

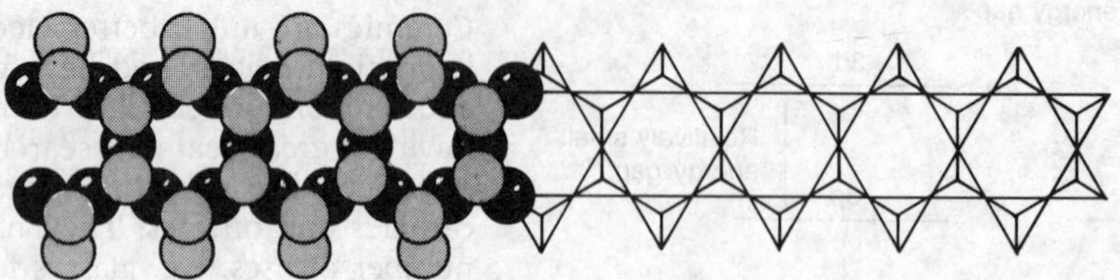
(b) Double chain structure $(Si_4O_{11})_n^{6-}$

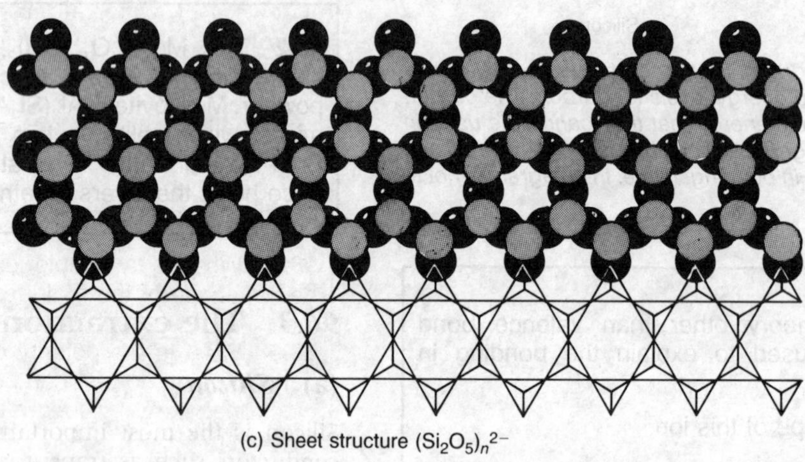
(c) Sheet structure $(Si_2O_5)_n^{2-}$

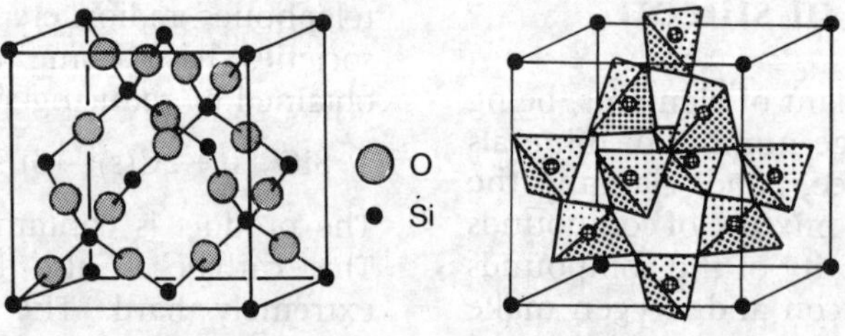

(d) Framework structure (SiO_2)

***Figure 96.2** The structures of four types of silicates. (Taken from: Sorrel, C. A. and Sandstrom, E. F. (1977).* The Rocks and Minerals of the World, *Collins, London, p. 157)*

Examples		
Topaz	$Al_2SiO_4(OH)_2F_2$	*Tetrahedral units*
Beryl	$Be_3Al_2Si_6O_{18}$	*Six-membered rings*
Tremolite	$Ca_2Mg_5Si_8O_{22}(OH)_2F_2$	*Double chains*
Talc	$Mg_3Si_4O_{10}(OH)_2$	*Sheets*
Quartz	SiO_2	*Framework*

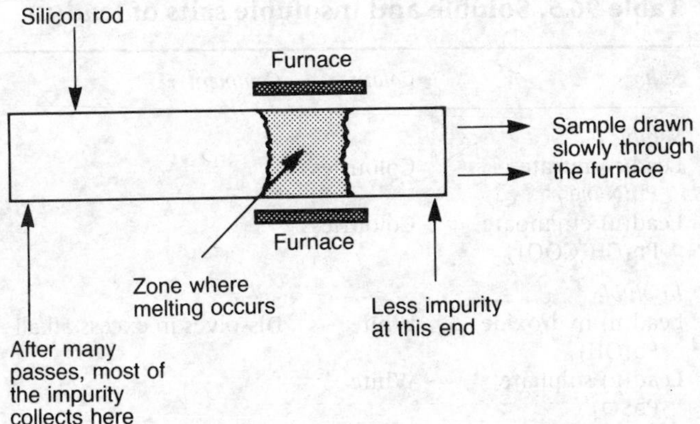

Figure 96.3 Zone refining. The sample is passed through the furnace many times. The impurities collect at one end of the sample rod. (Note: the furnace is cylindrical)

crystallisation. Inside the furnace the solid melts; and as the rod moves through it, the part that emerges begins to cool. It so happens that the pure silicon crystallises from the solution (of molten silicon plus impurities) more easily than the impurities. Therefore the liquid in the furnace tends to retain the impurities and the rod leaving the furnace is of higher purity than before. The best results (impurities less than 10^{-6}%) are obtained by zone refining the rod many times.

(b) *Germanium*

Germanium is isolated as a side product from zinc and copper refining. Impure germanium compounds are converted into the tetrachloride by reacting them with hydrogen chloride. Then the chloride is hydrolysed with water and the resulting oxide reduced by hydrogen or carbon. Germanium for the semiconductor industry will also be zone refined.

(c) *Tin*

The chief mineral containing tin is cassiterite, SnO_2. It can be reduced by coke in much the same way as in the iron blast furnace. Impurities, e.g. lead, can be removed by electrolysis.

(d) *Lead*

Lead is found mainly as galena, its sulphide mineral PbS. Essentially, the sulphide is converted into an oxide and then reduced with carbon. You will find details of the method in Unit 85.

> **96.3** Write equations for the conversion of $GeCl_4$ into GeO_2 by water, and the reduction of the oxide by hydrogen.

96.4 The hydrides

All the elements give hydrides. Carbon, of course, gives an immense number, but silicon and germanium also show a wide variety (see Table 96.3). The geometries of the hydrides follow those of methane, and are based on a tetrahedral arrangement around the central atom.

Table 96.3. The major hydrides of Group IV

Element	*Hydrides*
Carbon	CH_4 (methane), C_2H_2 (ethyne), C_2H_4 (ethene), C_2H_6 (ethane), C_3H_8, and many, many more
Silicon	SiH_4 (silane), Si_2H_6, Si_3H_8, . . ., Si_6H_{14}
Germanium	GeH_4 (germane), Ge_2H_6, Ge_3H_8, . . ., Ge_9H_{20}
Tin	SnH_4 (stannane), Sn_2H_6
Lead	PbH_4 (plumbane)

The carbon hydrides will not ignite in air unless a flame is put to them. Apart from silane, SiH_4, the silicon hydrides are less well behaved. For example, Si_3H_8 is spontaneously flammable in air:

$$Si_3H_8(l) + 5O_2(g) \rightarrow 3SiO_2(s) + 4H_2O(l)$$

Like the carbon hydrides, silicon hydrides are not hydrolysed by water alone. However, traces of alkali will convert them into hydrated silica, $SiO_2{\cdot}nH_2O$, and hydrogen gas. Carbon hydrides are not hydrolysed by alkali.

The hydrides of tin and lead are not very important and we shall ignore them.

> **96.4** What is a simple explanation for the tetrahedral shape of the hydrides?
>
> **96.5** What is the polarity of (i) a carbon–hydrogen bond, (ii) a carbon–silicon bond? (See Table 96.1 for electronegativity values; the electronegativity of hydrogen is 2.1.)

96.5 The halides

The halides are listed in Table 96.4. Once again there is a tendency for the elements to make four bonds, and

Table 96.4. The major halides of Group IV

Element	*Typical halides**	*Complex halides*
Carbon†	CCl_4	None; d orbitals are needed
Silicon	$SiCl_4$	SiF_6^{2-}
Germanium	$GeCl_4$, $GeCl_2$	GeF_6^{2-}, $GeCl_6^{2-}$
Tin	$SnCl_4$, $SnCl_2$	SnF_6^{2-}, $SnCl_4^{2-}$, $SnCl_6^{2-}$
Lead	$PbCl_4$, $PbCl_2$	$PbCl_4^{2-}$, $PbCl_6^{2-}$

*For the simple halides only the chlorides are shown. Similar compounds are given with fluorine, bromine and iodine; except that $PbBr_4$ and PbI_4 do not exist
†As in the case of the hydrides, carbon forms many halides, e.g. C_2Cl_6, C_2F_4. Silicon has a similar, but less marked, tendency to make a variety of halides

with a tetrahedral arrangement. As with the hydrides, there is a marked difference in the hydrolysis reactions of tetrachloromethane and silicon tetrachloride. CCl_4 will not react with water, but $SiCl_4$ is immediately converted into silica:

$$SiCl_4(l) + 2H_2O(l) \rightarrow SiO_2(s) + 4H^+(aq) + 4Cl^-(aq)$$

We can explain the difference by assuming that one of the lone pairs on a water molecule can overlap with one of the empty 3d orbitals on the silicon atom. If you look back at Unit 16 you will find that we made the point that efficient overlap can only occur between orbitals that have not only the right shape (or symmetry) but also similar energies. (An orbital is not merely a region of three-dimensional space, it has the added dimension of energy.) The 3d orbitals of carbon are much higher in energy than those of silicon, so bonding cannot occur between them and a water molecule. Once electron density is fed into the silicon atom, the chlorine atoms can detach themselves by converting into chloride ions, and the $SiCl_4$ is destroyed.

The metallic nature of tin is shown by the way it dissolves in hydrochloric acid, giving off hydrogen. The solution that remains contains tin(II), Sn^{2+}, ions. These ions are good reducing agents, a property that is made use of in organic chemistry in the reduction of nitrobenzene to phenylamine (see section 122.2 for details).

The halides of lead show some interesting characteristics. Lead(IV) chloride, $PbCl_4$, decomposes very easily into lead(II) chloride and chlorine:

$$PbCl_4(s) \rightarrow PbCl_2(s) + Cl_2(g)$$

The corresponding bromides and iodides are too unstable to have any life of their own. We can relate these observations to the tendency of lead(IV) compounds to act as oxidising agents. For example, we can interpret the equation we have just looked at as an example where two changes take place:

(i) lead(IV) takes electrons
$$Pb^{4+} + 2e^- \rightarrow Pb^{2+}$$

(ii) chloride loses electrons
$$2Cl^- - 2e^- \rightarrow Cl_2$$

Given that iodide ions and bromide ions are less resistant to oxidation than chloride ions, we can appreciate why PbI_4 and $PbBr_4$ do not exist.

The reason why lead(IV) acts as an oxidising agent can be related to the inert pair effect. The B metals at the bottom of their Group have a pair of s electrons (6s in the case of lead), which tend not to be used in bonding. In the higher oxidation state, lead(IV), these electrons are involved in bonding; in the lower oxidation state, lead(II), they are not used.

On the other hand, from silicon downwards the elements all give one or more complex ions, e.g. SiF_6^{2-}. In these octahedral complexes the elements do make use of their outer s electrons, e.g. the 6s, 6p and 6d orbitals are used by lead.

Lead(II) chloride is very insoluble in water and you will see it precipitate as a white solid if you add chloride ions to a solution of lead(II) nitrate. Similarly, lead(II) iodide is insoluble in water, but this substance is a beautiful orange-yellow colour. Both of them are more soluble in hot water than in cold. In fact the majority of lead(II) salts are insoluble in water (see Table 96.5).

Table 96.5. Soluble and insoluble salts of lead(II)

Salts	*Colour*	*Comment*
Soluble		
Lead(II) nitrate, $Pb(NO_3)_2$	Colourless	
Lead(II) ethanoate, $Pb(CH_3COO)_2$	Colourless	
Insoluble		
Lead(II) hydroxide, $Pb(OH)_2$	White	Dissolves in excess alkali
Lead(II) sulphate, $PbSO_4$	White	
Lead(II) chloride, $PbCl_2$	White	Soluble in hot water
Lead(II) iodide, PbI_2	Orange	Soluble in hot water
Lead(II) sulphide, PbS	Black	Soluble in hot nitric acid. Converted to white $PbSO_4$ by hydrogen peroxide
Lead(II) chromate(VI), $PbCrO_4$	Yellow	Soluble in ammonia and ethanoic acid solution

Lead shows the ability to make a complex with chloride ions. If ice cold concentrated hydrochloric acid has lead(IV) oxide added to it, yellow hexachloroplumbate(IV) ions, $PbCl_6^{2-}$, are made:

$$PbO_2(s) + 6Cl^-(aq) + 4H^+(aq) \rightarrow PbCl_6^{2-}(aq) + 2H_2O(l)$$

Lead(II) also gives an analogous complex ion.

Tetrachloroplumbate(II) can be made by dissolving lead(II) oxide in concentrated hydrochloric acid:

$$PbO(s) + 4Cl^-(aq) + 2H^+(aq) \rightarrow PbCl_4^{2-}(aq) + 2H_2O(l)$$

96.6 Why is it reasonable to think that the release of chloride ions from $SiCl_4$ is a favourable process?

96.7 One problem with making crystals of tin(II) chloride is that they are easily hydrolysed by warm water. Instead of dissolving tin in hydrochloric acid, how else might the anhydrous chloride be made?

96.8 Use the redox potentials below to decide if Sn^{2+} ions will (i) reduce Fe^{3+} to Fe^{2+}; (ii) reduce Fe^{2+} to Fe.

(iii) Is it possible to convert Sn^{2+} ions to Sn^{4+} ions using $Cr_2O_7^{2-}$ ions? In each case, if you think a reaction is possible, write the equation.

$E^{\ominus}_{Sn^{2+}/Sn} = -0.14\,V$; $E^{\ominus}_{Sn^{4+}/Sn^{2+}} = +0.15\,V$;

$E^{\ominus}_{Fe^{3+}/Fe^{2+}} = +0.77\,V$; $E^{\ominus}_{Fe^{2+}/Fe} = -0.44\,V$;
$E^{\ominus}_{Cr_2O_7^{2-}/Cr^{3+}} = +1.33\,V$.

96.9 Explain why we know that lead(IV) is acting as an oxidising agent in the change

$$PbCl_4(s) \rightarrow PbCl_2(s) + Cl_2(g)$$

96.10 A student was given a colourless solution and was told to add a little sodium chloride solution to it. A cloudy white precipitate was made. What conclusion should the student draw about the nature of the colourless solution?

96.6 The oxides

The oxides of Group IV are shown in Table 96.6. The oxides of carbon and silicon are predominantly covalent, but the chief oxide of silicon, SiO_2, unlike the small gaseous molecules CO and CO_2, has a giant molecular structure that is better represented by the formula $(SiO_2)_n$. GeO_2 is found with two different crystal structures and SnO_2 with three. The most important of them is the rutile structure, which we saw in Figure 32.10. This is also the structure of PbO_2. The melting points of these oxides show what a great difference there is in the bonding when compared with that in carbon dioxide.

The oxides of silicon and lead are more important than those of germanium and tin, so for the most part we will concentrate on the former rather than the latter.

Carbon and silicon oxides are definitely acidic. For example, silica behaves like carbon dioxide when it reacts with an alkali. The alkali has to be hot and concentrated if it is in solution; alternatively the silica can be heated with pellets of potassium hydroxide or sodium hydroxide, e.g.

$$SiO_2(s) + 2OH^-(aq) \rightarrow SiO_3^{2-}(aq) + H_2O(l)$$

Depending on whether KOH or NaOH is used, the product will be potassium or sodium silicate.

Silica will also react with metal carbonates, giving off carbon dioxide:

$$SiO_2(s) + Na_2CO_3(s) \rightarrow Na_2SiO_3(s) + CO_2(g)$$

Silicates are not destroyed by hydrogen ions as are carbonates. Rather, if you were to add dilute acid to

Table 96.6. The oxides of Group IV

Element	*Oxides*	*Nature*	*Melting point/° C*
Carbon	CO, CO_2	Acidic	CO_2: −56
Silicon	SiO_2	Acidic	SiO_2: 1610
Germanium	GeO, GeO_2	Amphoteric	GeO_2: 1116
Tin	SnO, SnO_2	Amphoteric	SnO_2: 1127
Lead	PbO, PbO_2, Pb_3O_4	Basic/ amphoteric	PbO_2: decomposes at 300° C

sodium silicate solution you would find the solution turning to a gel. It is colloidal and an example of hydrated silica, $SiO_2{\cdot}nH_2O$, often with $n = 2$. If the product is heated carefully it loses much of its water and gives a lumpy solid. The solid is *silica gel*, which is widely used as a drying agent. You may, for example, see small sachets of it in boxes containing electrical equipment such as videos and radios. It has the ability to lose the water it absorbs if it is heated, so the gel can be recycled.

Solutions of sodium silicate are sold as *water glass*. Water glass was once used for preserving eggs (a layer of insoluble calcium silicate is made, which keeps out air and bacteria). The solution can also be used to grow 'crystal gardens'.

The oxygen can be removed from silica by reacting it with a reactive metal like magnesium. It is possible to do this in the laboratory by heating a mixture of *dry* sand and magnesium powder in a *dry* boiling tube. The reaction is exothermic and takes place readily. Two reactions can occur, depending on the proportions of silica and magnesium:

$$SiO_2(s) + 2Mg(s) \rightarrow 2MgO(s) + Si(s)$$
$$SiO_2(s) + 4Mg(s) \rightarrow 2MgO(s) + 2Mg_2Si(s)$$

The second gives magnesium silicide, Mg_2Si. The silicon made is amorphous (i.e. without a consistent crystal structure), and if it is made as a very fine powder it is very reactive. For example, it will readily revert to SiO_2 with oxygen, and combine directly with fluorine and chlorine, e.g.

$$Si(s) + 2F_2(g) \rightarrow SiF_4(l)$$

It will also react with steam, giving off hydrogen:

$$Si(s) + 2H_2O(g) \rightarrow SiO_2(s) + 2H_2(g)$$

You may notice that this reaction is one that is also performed by many metals.

As we descend the Group, the basic character of the oxides increases. The oxides of germanium and tin are amphoteric rather than distinctly basic. For example, tin(II) oxide will dissolve in both acid and alkali:

$$SnO(s) + 2H^+(aq) \rightarrow Sn^{2+}(aq) + H_2O(l)$$
$$SnO(s) + 4OH^-(aq) + H_2O(l) \rightarrow Sn(OH)_6^{4-}(aq)$$

(a) *Glass*

Silica, in the form of sand, has one very important use: it is used to make glass. Glasses of one kind or another are found in various geological deposits. Glass has been made by humans for around 6000 years. Although glass gives every appearance of being a solid, its structure is best regarded as belonging to a supercooled liquid containing a mixture of silicates, e.g. $CaSiO_3$, Na_2SiO_3. There are tetrahedra of silicon and four oxygen atoms bonded together, but the arrangement is not regular, as it should be in a true solid. Indeed, we have mentioned before that over long periods of time glass will flow (see section 23.5).

The essential ingredients for making glass are silica, SiO_2, and an alkaline substance, although a wide variety of chemicals can be added to give glasses of

The manufacture of plate glass by the float process was invented by the Pilkington company in the UK.

different characteristics, e.g. colour and strength. A typical mix consists of sand, limestone, sodium carbonate, metal oxides such as PbO and MgO, and coke. In modern processes, recycled glass is also added. Molten glass is formed if the mixture is heated to about 1500°C. The way the glass is treated depends on its eventual use. It can be blown by hand to make fine articles, or blown automatically to make mass produced items such as milk bottles. Much of the glass used for shop, office and house windows is made by a float process. Here the liquid glass flows onto a bath of liquid tin. The tin gives a smooth surface for the glass, and by heating the glass from above and below a more uniform structure to the glass is obtained. The float process gives very high quality plate glass.

(b) *Oxides of lead*

There are three oxides of lead: lead(II) oxide, PbO; lead(IV) oxide, PbO_2; and Pb_3O_4. This last oxide is best considered as a combination of the other two, i.e. $2PbO{\cdot}PbO_2$. For this reason it can be called dilead(II) lead(IV) oxide. However, a more friendly name is 'red lead'.

Lead(II) oxide

Lead(II) oxide, also known as litharge, is a yellow-orange solid that is easily reduced, e.g. by heating with carbon. It is amphoteric:

$$PbO(s) + 2H^+(aq) \rightarrow Pb^{2+}(aq) + H_2O(l)$$
$$PbO(s) + 2OH^-(aq) + H_2O(l) \rightarrow Pb(OH)_4{}^{2-}(aq)$$

The crystal structure of the oxide shows that it has a considerable amount of covalent character. The repeating unit in the crystal is a square-based pyramid with lead at one apex, and four oxygen atoms at the other corners. You can see the pattern in Figure 96.4.

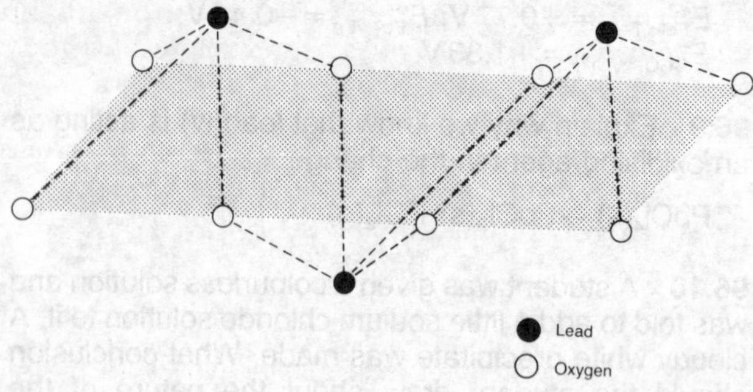

Figure 96.4 The layer structure of lead(II) oxide, PbO

Lead(IV) oxide

Lead(IV) oxide is a dark brown solid. Given that lead is showing its highest oxidation state in this oxide, we might expect it to behave as an oxidising agent; and so it does. Here are two examples, involving hot concentrated hydrochloric acid and sulphur dioxide:

$$PbO_2(s) + 4HCl(aq) \rightarrow PbCl_2(s) + 2H_2O(l) + Cl_2(g)$$
$$PbO_2(s) + SO_2(g) \rightarrow PbSO_4(s)$$

When the oxide is heated it also shows a tendency to convert to the lower oxidation state. It is one of the few oxides that give off oxygen on heating:

$$2PbO_2(s) \rightarrow 2PbO(s) + O_2(g)$$

It also gives off oxygen if it is heated with concentrated sulphuric acid:

$$2PbO_2(s) + 2H_2SO_4(aq) \rightarrow 2PbSO_4(s) + 2H_2O(l) + O_2(g)$$

Unlike PbO the oxide will not simply dissolve in an acid, although it will dissolve in concentrated alkali:

$$PbO_2(s) + 2OH^-(aq) + 2H_2O(l) \rightarrow Pb(OH)_6{}^{2-}(aq)$$

Dilead(II) lead(IV) oxide

This oxide, Pb_3O_4, can be made by heating lead(II) oxide in air. Its crystal structure shows that it is predominantly covalent and composed of a combination of two types of lead atom. One type is bonded to six oxygen atoms, the other to three oxygen atoms. However, as far as its chemistry is concerned, it sometimes behaves like a mixture of PbO and PbO_2. For example, if Pb_3O_4 is heated we find that oxygen is given off:

$$2Pb_3O_4(s) \rightarrow 6PbO(s) + O_2(g)$$

We can imagine that this occurs in a different way:

$$2(2PbO{\cdot}PbO_2) \equiv 4PbO + 2PbO_2$$

Of this combination only the PbO_2 is affected by heat:

$$2PbO_2(s) \rightarrow 2PbO(s) + O_2(g)$$

The overall change is the same as the first equation.

This pattern is not always maintained. For example, when it reacts with sulphuric acid, oxygen is given off, but the other main product is lead(II) sulphate. On its own, lead(II) oxide will not react with the acid. See the answer to question 96.13 for the reason. With hot dilute nitric acid, Pb_3O_4 gives a precipitate of lead(IV) oxide:

$$Pb_3O_4(s) + 4HNO_3(aq) \rightarrow PbO_2(s) + 2Pb(NO_3)_2(aq) + 2H_2O(l)$$

This is one way of making PbO_2.

96.11 Silica will react in a similar way with metal sulphates (and phosphates) as it does with carbonates, giving a solid residue and a gas. 1 mol of silica reacts with 1 mol of sodium sulphate, Na_2SO_4. Write the equation for the reaction.

96.12 Why does powdered silicon react much more quickly with steam than a lump of silicon?

96.13 If you were to attempt to dissolve lead(II) oxide in acid, which acid would you choose?

96.14 Explain why the reactions with hydrochloric acid and sulphur dioxide show the oxidising nature of PbO_2.

96.15 Predict the result of reacting Pb_3O_4 with concentrated hydrochloric acid.

96.7 Organic compounds of the elements

As we said at the beginning of this unit, we shall not concern ourselves here with the organic chemistry of carbon. On the other hand, the other elements all give compounds with carbon or carbon compounds that we can classify as organic in nature. We shall consider just a few examples.

(a) *Organo-silicon compounds*

Among the most important organic compounds of silicon are the silicones. A typical silicone has a chain of repeating units like this:

```
  CH3     CH3     CH3
   |       |       |
—Si—O—Si—O—Si—O—
   |       |       |
  CH3     CH3     CH3
```

$$-Si(CH_3)_2-O-Si(CH_3)_2-O-Si(CH_3)_2-O-$$

Typically the chains may be built of several thousand monomer units. In this chain the monomer is $-Si(CH_3)_2-O-$. They can be made by the hydrolysis of organo-silicon compounds such as $Si(CH_3)_2Cl_2$, or in general SiR_2Cl_2 where R is an organic group.

The reason why silicones are useful depends on the fact that they are kinetically and energetically stable. Their sheer size together with the non-polar organic side chains make them immiscible with water. They are widely used as sealants and greases, where their water repellent properties are extremely useful. (It may be that a burette you use may have its tap lubricated with silicone grease.) Their ability to repel water also makes them a suitable material for treating fabrics to be used in rain wear. Others are used in waxes and polishes. Some silicones exist as crosslinked polymers. These can be hard, and resistant to wear. They find uses in insulating electrical equipment.

By changing the side chains, and using a mixture of different starting materials, the length and nature of the chain can be changed. For example, when $Si(CH_3)_2Cl_2$ loses its two chlorine atoms in hydrolysis there are two sites per molecule that can be used in bonding. This allows a chain to grow using oxygen atoms to link the silicon atoms. If we were to use $Si(CH_3)_3Cl$ as a starting material, it could not make a chain any longer than two units long. There is only one chlorine to lose, so each molecule can make but one link to another.

On the other hand, this molecule has a use if we mix it with $Si(CH_3)_2Cl_2$. When the $Si(CH_3)_3Cl$ reacts, it will stop the polymer chain growing. For example, we could get

```
      CH3     CH3     CH3     CH3
       |       |       |       |
CH3—Si—O—Si—O—Si—O—Si—CH3
       |       |       |       |
      CH3     CH3     CH3     CH3
```

$$Si(CH_3)_3-O-Si(CH_3)_2-O-Si(CH_3)_2-O-Si(CH_3)_3$$

By changing the proportions of $Si(CH_3)_3Cl$ and $Si(CH_3)_2Cl_2$ we can control the length of the chains.

On the other hand, if we use $SiCH_3Cl_3$ as a starting material the chain can grow in three places. This gives the opportunity for crosslinking to take place. For example, we might obtain

```
      CH3     CH3
       |       |
  —O—Si—O—Si—O—
       |       |
       O       O
       |       |
  —O—Si—O—Si—O—
       |       |
      CH3     CH3
```

Some specialist adhesives are made by mixing two silicone-based materials, which react together when mixed to give a crosslinked polymer.

(b) *Organo-lead compounds*

The most famous, or infamous, organic compound of lead is tetraethyl-lead(IV), $Pb(C_2H_5)_4$. We have discussed this compound before for two reasons. First, it has been used as a petrol additive. It allows petrol to burn more smoothly, but at the expense of polluting the world with tens of thousands of tonnes of lead each year. Secondly, and related to its use in petrol, is its ability to break into free radicals. You will find more details about both these matters in Units 81 and 86.

96.16 What would be the structure of the silicone molecule made from $Si(CH_3)_3Cl$?

96.17 One type of silicone adhesive uses a polymer that has two OH groups left on the ends of the chain, e.g.

$$HO—Si(CH_3)_2—[O—Si(CH_3)_2]_n—O—Si(CH_3)_2—OH$$

It has been found that this kind of polymer reacts easily with an organo-silicon molecule that contains ethanoate groups, CH_3COO. Which of these three molecules:

$CH_3COOSi(CH_3)_3$
$(CH_3COO)_2Si(CH_3)_2$
$(CH_3COO)_3SiCH_3$

would you choose to add to the hydroxy polymer in order to make a strong adhesive? Briefly explain your choice.

96.8 Sulphides

You will find a list of the sulphides of the Group in Table 96.7. You are unlikely to come across many of them.

Table 96.7. The sulphides of Group IV

Element	*Sulphides*
Carbon	CS_2
Silicon	SiS_2
Germanium	GeS, GeS_2
Tin	SnS, SnS_2
Lead	PbS, PbS_2

We described some of the properties of carbon disulphide in the previous unit. Here, only tin(II) sulphide and lead(II) sulphide need concern us. They are precipitated from solutions by hydrogen sulphide. Tin(II) sulphide, SnS, is brown, but rapidly converts into yellow tin(IV) sulphide, SnS_2. Lead(II) sulphide, PbS, is black. In the days when many paints contained white pigments based on lead compounds, the paints would be discoloured by hydrogen sulphide present in the air of industrial towns and cities. The white colour could be recovered by washing with hydrogen peroxide solution. This has the ability to oxidise the sulphide to sulphate:

$$\underset{\text{black}}{PbS(s)} + 4H_2O_2(aq) \rightarrow \underset{\text{white}}{PbSO_4(s)} + 4H_2O(l)$$

Answers

96.1 (i) Molecular orbital theory. (ii) Octahedral.

96.2 Van der Waals forces.

96.3 $GeCl_4(l) + 2H_2O(l) \rightarrow GeO_2(s) + 4HCl(aq)$
$GeO_2(s) + 2H_2(g) \rightarrow Ge(s) + 2H_2O(l)$

96.4 Electron repulsion theory says that if there are four bonds and no lone pairs, the repulsions will be minimised if the bonds are at the tetrahedral angle.

96.5 (i) The hydrogen is slightly positive and the carbon slightly negative.
(ii) The silicon is slightly positive and the hydrogen atoms slightly negative.

96.6 Chloride ions, Cl^-, are kinetically and energetically stable in water and they can be solvated by water molecules, so they making good leaving groups in the reaction.

96.7 React tin with hydrogen chloride gas. This is the same approach needed to make anhydrous iron(II) chloride.

96.8 (i) If Sn^{2+} ions are to act as reducing agents they must gain electrons. This means they will convert into tin atoms, so we look at the values of $E^\ominus_{Sn^{2+}/Sn}$ and $E^\ominus_{Fe^{3+}/Fe^{2+}}$ to decide. $E^\ominus_{Sn^{2+}/Sn}$ is much more negative than $E^\ominus_{Fe^{3+}/Fe^{2+}}$ so the reduction should take place. The reaction is

$$Sn^{2+}(aq) + 2Fe^{3+}(aq) \rightarrow Sn^{4+}(aq) + 2Fe^{2+}(aq)$$

(ii) This time $E^\ominus_{Fe^{2+}/Fe}$ is more negative than $E^\ominus_{Sn^{2+}/Sn}$ so the reduction will not take place.

(iii) $E^\ominus_{Cr_2O_7^{2-}/Cr^{3+}}$ is much more positive than $E^\ominus_{Sn^{4+}/Sn^{2+}}$ so the oxidation should take place. The reaction is

$$Cr_2O_7^{2-}(aq) + 3Sn^{2+}(aq) + 14H^+(aq) \rightarrow 2Cr^{3+}(aq) + 3Sn^{4+}(aq) + 7H_2O(l)$$

It helps to remember that $Cr_2O_7^{2-}$ ions are 'six-electron oxidising agents' (see section 41.7) so 1 mol of $Cr_2O_7^{2-}$ will react with 3 mol of Sn^{2+}.

96.9 It gains electrons.

96.10 First, the student should realise that, because sodium salts are soluble in water, it is the chloride ions that are giving the precipitate. There might be Pb^{2+} ions in the solution, but equally there might be Ag^+ ions. One way to distinguish them is to warm the solution: $PbCl_2$ dissolves in hot water. Alternatively, AgCl dissolves in ammonia solution.

96.11 $SiO_2(s) + Na_2SO_4(s) \rightarrow Na_2SiO_3(s) + SO_3(g)$

96.12 It has a greater surface area.

96.13 Nitric acid. This is because the lead(II) nitrate made is soluble in water. If sulphuric acid is used, an insoluble layer of $PbSO_4$ clings to the surface of the powder and stops the reaction. Likewise, $PbCl_2$ prevents the reaction with dilute hydrochloric acid.

96.14 The lead changes from lead(IV) to lead(II). This represents a gain of electrons, and therefore an oxidation of the other reactant.

Answers – cont.

96.15 We would expect the acid to be oxidised, with chlorine given off, and the oxide to be converted into $PbCl_2$:

$$Pb_3O_4(s) + 8HCl(aq) \rightarrow 3PbCl_2(s) + 4H_2O(l) + Cl_2(g)$$

96.16 The structure is

```
     CH3      CH3
     |        |
CH3—Si—O—Si—CH3
     |        |
     CH3      CH3
```

$Si(CH_3)_3—O—Si(CH_3)_3$

96.17 $(CH_3COO)_3SiCH_3$. This should give the cross-linking necessary for strength. (Compare $SiCH_3Cl_3$ above.)

UNIT 96 SUMMARY

- The Group IV elements:
  - (i) Metallic nature increases down the Group: silicon is a non-metal; silicon and germanium are semiconductors; tin and lead show definite metallic properties.
  - (ii) Silicon is found combined with oxygen in a wide range of rocks and minerals (silicates) whose structures are based upon SiO_4 tetrahedra.
  - (iii) Silicon is of key importance in making semiconductors for the electronics and computer industries.
- Extraction:
  - (i) Silicon is obtained by reducing silicon tetrachloride with hydrogen;

    $$SiCl_4(l) + H_2(g) \rightarrow Si(s) + 4HCl(g)$$
  - (ii) Tin is isolated by the reduction of SnO_2 with carbon (coke).
  - (iii) Lead is made from its sulphide, galena;

    $$2PbS(s) + 3O_2(g) \rightarrow 2PbO(s) + 2SO_2(g)$$
    $$PbO(s) + C(s) \rightarrow Pb(s) + CO(g)$$

Reactions

- With oxygen:
  Oxides are formed;

  e.g. $Si(s) + O_2(g) \rightarrow SiO_2(s)$
- With halogens:
  Chlorides are made;

  e.g. $Si(s) + 2Cl_2(g) \rightarrow SiCl_4(l)$

Compounds

- Oxides:
  - (i) The oxides are predominantly covalent.
  - (ii) Silica, SiO_2, will undergo hydrolysis with alkali, showing an acidic nature expected of a non-metal oxide. GeO, SnO and PbO are amphoteric;

    e.g. $PbO(s) + 2H^+(aq) \rightarrow Pb^{2+}(aq) + H_2O(l)$
    $PbO(s) + 2OH^-(aq) + H_2O(l) \rightarrow Pb(OH)_4{}^{2-}(aq)$
  - (iii) Lead(IV) oxide, PbO_2, and dilead(II) lead(IV) oxide, Pb_3O_4, show oxidising properties;

    e.g. $PbO_2(s) + 4HCl(aq) \rightarrow PbCl_2(s) + H_2O(l) + Cl_2(g)$

    Pb_3O_4 behaves like a combination of lead(II) and lead(IV) oxides (PbO and PbO_2).
  - (iv) Silica can be reduced by reacting with magnesium;

    $$SiO_2(s) + 2Mg(s) \rightarrow Si(s) + 2MgO(s)$$

    Other oxides can be reduced by carbon;

    $$PbO(s) + C(s) \rightarrow Pb(s) + CO(g)$$
- Chlorides:
  Silicon tetrachloride (like tetrachloromethane) is a volatile liquid at room temperature and pressure. It will undergo hydrolysis (tetrachloromethane will not). This is the result of silicon having 3d orbitals that are much lower in energy than those of carbon and can be used in reactions.
- Sulphides:
  Tin(II) sulphide, SnS (brown), and lead(II) sulphide, PbS (black), are precipitated by hydrogen sulphide from solutions containing Sn^{2+} or Pb^{2+} ions.
- Organic:
  All the elements make a range of compounds with organic groups.
  - (i) Tetraethyl-lead(IV), $Pb(C_2H_5)_4$, is used as anti-knock in petrol.
  - (ii) The silicones contain chains of $—Si(CH_3)_2—O—$ groups, and are used as lubricants and adhesives.

97

Nitrogen

97.1 The element

The properties of nitrogen are summarised in Table 97.1. Nitrogen makes up almost 78% of the atmosphere, and is therefore the most common gas. The fact that there is so much nitrogen about tells us something about its chemistry. That is, it is particularly unreactive. Most of the oxygen and other gases that may have been produced when the Earth was being made combined with other elements to give us the solid and liquid matter that we see around us. For example, nearly all the hydrogen combined with oxygen to make the vast quantities of water on and around the Earth's surface. Nitrogen is different because there is a triple bond between the atoms in a nitrogen molecule. This gives the molecule a very high bond strength, so it is correspondingly hard to break apart. (The bond energy of N_2 is over twice as large as either H_2 or O_2.) However, nitrogen will react directly with some metals. For example, burning magnesium will continue to burn in nitrogen, giving white magnesium nitride, Mg_3N_2:

$$3Mg(s) + N_2(g) \rightarrow Mg_3N_2(s)$$

Nitrides are ionic, containing the N^{3-} ion.

Although nitrogen molecules are almost inert, nitrogen atoms can bond readily to many other atoms, mainly the non-metals hydrogen, oxygen and carbon. It shows a valency of three, e.g. in ammonia, NH_3, and amines like methylamine, CH_3NH_2. The most important compounds of nitrogen are in living things, e.g. amino acids and proteins. Among other things, the high electronegativity of nitrogen allows it to take part in hydrogen bonding and, for example, help to keep the strands of DNA together. The main classes of organic compounds that contain nitrogen are amines, amides, amino acids and proteins, and nitriles. You will find each type discussed in the units on organic chemistry.

Table 97.1. Information about nitrogen

Relative atomic mass, A_r(N)	14
Electron structure	$1s^2 2s^2 2p^3$
Ionisation energy	1402 kJ mol^{-1}
Electronegativity	3.0
Molecular formula	N_2
Melting point	63 K (−210°C)
Boiling point	77 K (−196°C)
Bond energy	945 kJ mol^{-1}
Bond length	110 pm
Colourless, odourless, tasteless	

97.2 Nitrogen, ammonia and fertilisers

The extraction and uses of nitrogen are given in Table 97.2. Nitrogen is isolated by the liquefaction of air – a process that we discussed in Unit 83. The conversion of nitrogen into ammonia through the equilibrium reaction

$$N_2(g) + 3H_2(g) \rightleftharpoons 2NH_3(g)$$

is one of the most important industrial chemical processes in the world. This is because ammonia is a feedstock for the manufacture of nitric acid and fertilisers. You can find details about the industrial processes concerned in Unit 83.

The most important fertilisers are urea, $(NH_2)_2CO$, ammonium sulphate, $(NH_4)_2SO_4$, ammonium nitrate, NH_4NO_3, and monoammonium phosphate, $NH_4H_2PO_4$. These are either used on their own or in conjunction with other chemicals, often to make NPK fertilisers. These are designed to release nitrogen (N), phosphorus (P) and potassium (K) into the soil.

Urea is made by the direct combination of ammonia

Table 97.2. The extraction and uses of nitrogen

Extraction	*Uses*
Liquefaction of air Nitrogen fixation in the Haber process	Provides an inert atmosphere for food storage and metal working When liquid, as a refrigerant, e.g. for frozen foods Manufacture of ammonia, and then fertilisers, nitric acid and other nitrogen-containing chemicals

with carbon dioxide at 180° C and a pressure of around 140 atm:

$$2NH_3(g) + CO_2(g) \rightarrow NH_2CONH_2(g) + H_2O(g)$$

Ammonium nitrate is made on an industrial scale by continuously mixing nitric acid and ammonia. If the proportions are kept properly balanced, the resulting solution will crystallise if it is dropped through a tower against a counter-current of air. The granules of the nitrate are removed, mixed with drying agents and packed ready for distribution.

Ammonium sulphate can be made in a similar manner, but using sulphuric acid of course.

> **97.1** If ammonium nitrate decomposes rapidly, the reaction
>
> $$2NH_4NO_3(s) \rightarrow 2N_2(g) + O_2(g) + 4H_2O(g)$$
>
> takes place.
>
> (i) Calculate the enthalpy change for the reaction. The heats of formation of $NH_4NO_3(s)$ and $H_2O(g)$ are $-365.6\,kJ\,mol^{-1}$ and $-241.8\,kJ\,mol^{-1}$ respectively.
>
> (ii) Explain why this is the basis for the use of the 'fertiliser' as an explosive.

97.3 The place of nitrogen in Nature

Over the course of millions of years of evolution, some microorganisms have developed methods of capturing nitrogen from the atmosphere and converting it into useful compounds. This process is called *nitrogen fixation*. The microorganisms manage to fix nitrogen through a complicated system of biochemical reactions involving an enzyme, nitrogenase, and adenosine triphosphate (ATP). Nitrogenase has active sites in which iron and molybdenum atoms are involved. It first converts nitrogen into ammonia, which is then used to make more complicated molecules.

Some plants fix nitrogen by use of *Rhizobium* bacteria, which are often found in the root system. Peas and other legume plants are particularly good at fixing nitrogen in this way. The virtue of this system is that such plants provide their own fertiliser. The only large-scale method that chemists have developed to fix nitrogen also involves ammonia; it is the Haber process, which we discussed earlier. However, the Haber process is extremely inefficient when compared to the way nitrogenase works. Nonetheless the demand for ammonia has remained high, largely because of the part that the gas plays in the manufacture of nitrogenous fertilisers. The increasing demand for efficiency in farming has meant that farmers have often been persuaded to take two or more crops each year from a given piece of land. By itself the land cannot supply the nutrients that the crops need, so fertilisers have to be added to the soil. Unfortunately, much of the fertiliser is wasted because rain washes it out of the soil before it can be used by the crops. Recently, it has been found that some water supplies have been contaminated by nitrogenous fertilisers. This has had the effect of encouraging the uncontrolled growth of algae and other water plants. It has also meant that nitrate ions have collected in drinking water. There is some evidence that links nitrate ions with cancer in humans, so for several environmental reasons the over-use of nitrogenous fertilisers is being discouraged.

Nitrogen is also fixed by chemical reactions in the atmosphere, particularly in thunderstorms. Here the energy released by lightning converts nitrogen into nitrogen oxides and nitric acid, which falls to earth in the rain. However, the proportion of nitrogen in the atmosphere is not continually decreasing because that lost by fixation is replaced by the decomposition of nitrogenous compounds by bacteria. This process is called bacterial denitrification. The balance between the removal and return of nitrogen to the atmosphere gives us the nitrogen cycle of Figure 97.1.

97.4 Ammonia and hydrazine

(a) *Ammonia*

We have discussed the bonding in ammonia in Units 14 and 17. Here we shall just summarise the key points. Ammonia is a tetrahedral molecule, with three bond pairs and one lone pair (Figure 97.2). The lone pair is responsible for decreasing the H—N—H bond angles to 107° (as compared with the perfect tetrahedral angle of 109°28′). The lone pair is involved in most of the reactions of ammonia and of amines. It can be used in coordinate bonding, for example in combining with a hydrogen ion to make an ammonium ion:

1s

$$H^+ \quad + \quad NH_3 \longrightarrow NH_4^+$$

Similarly it is responsible for ammonia's ability to act as a ligand with transition metal ions, e.g.

$$Cu^{2+}(aq) + 4NH_3(aq) \rightarrow [Cu(NH_3)_4]^{2+}(aq)$$

tetraamminecopper(II)
(royal blue colour)

Ammonia is extremely soluble in water, but its solution is only a weak alkali. Although it is sometimes labelled ammonium hydroxide, it is better called aqueous ammonia. By far the majority of ammonia molecules in water remain intact. Only a few react with the solvent:

$$NH_3(aq) + H_2O(l) \rightleftharpoons NH_4^+(aq) + OH^-(aq)$$

There are many salts that contain ammonium ions, e.g. ammonium chloride, NH_4Cl, and those in the previous section, which we found were used as fertilisers. Ammonium chloride is famous for changing

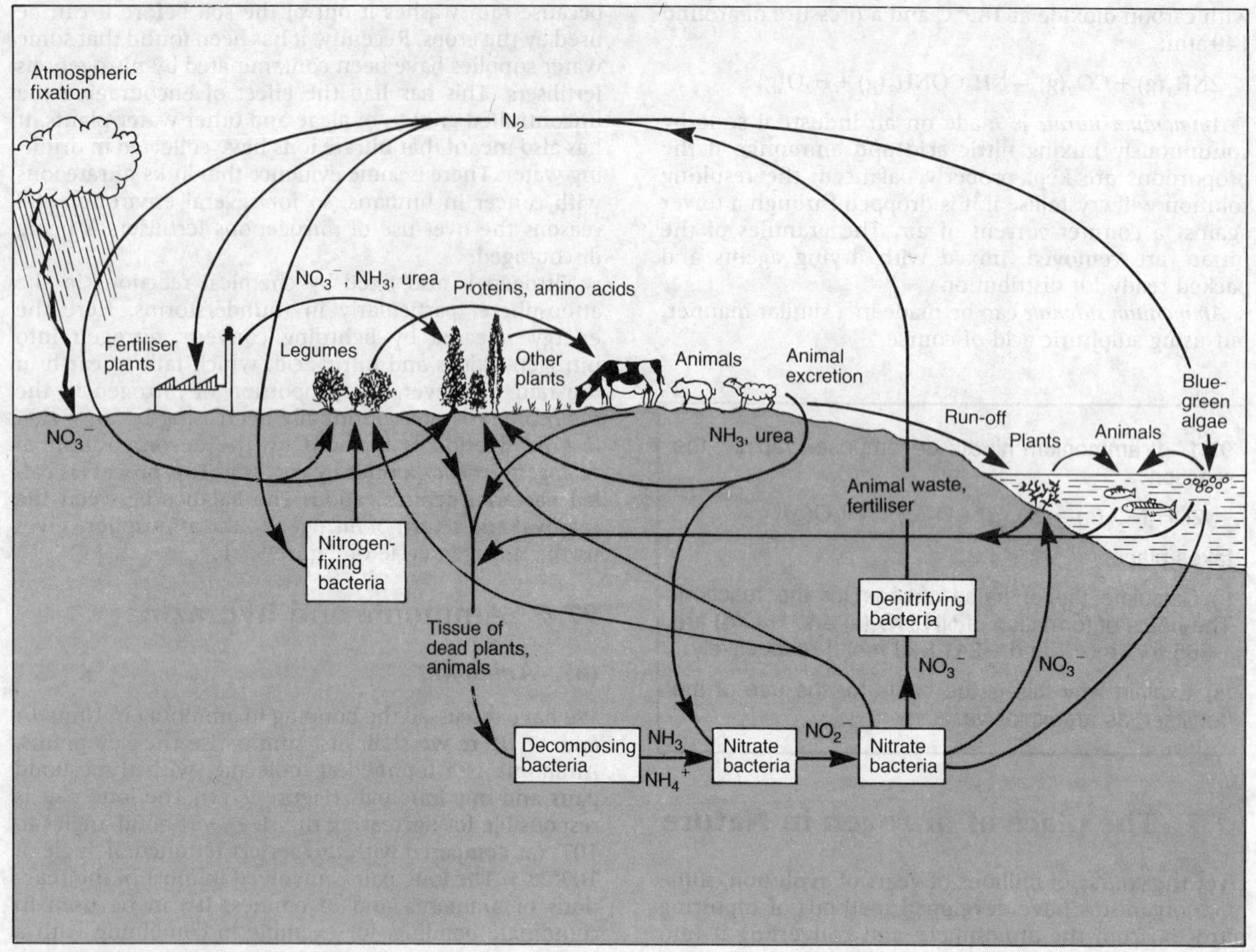

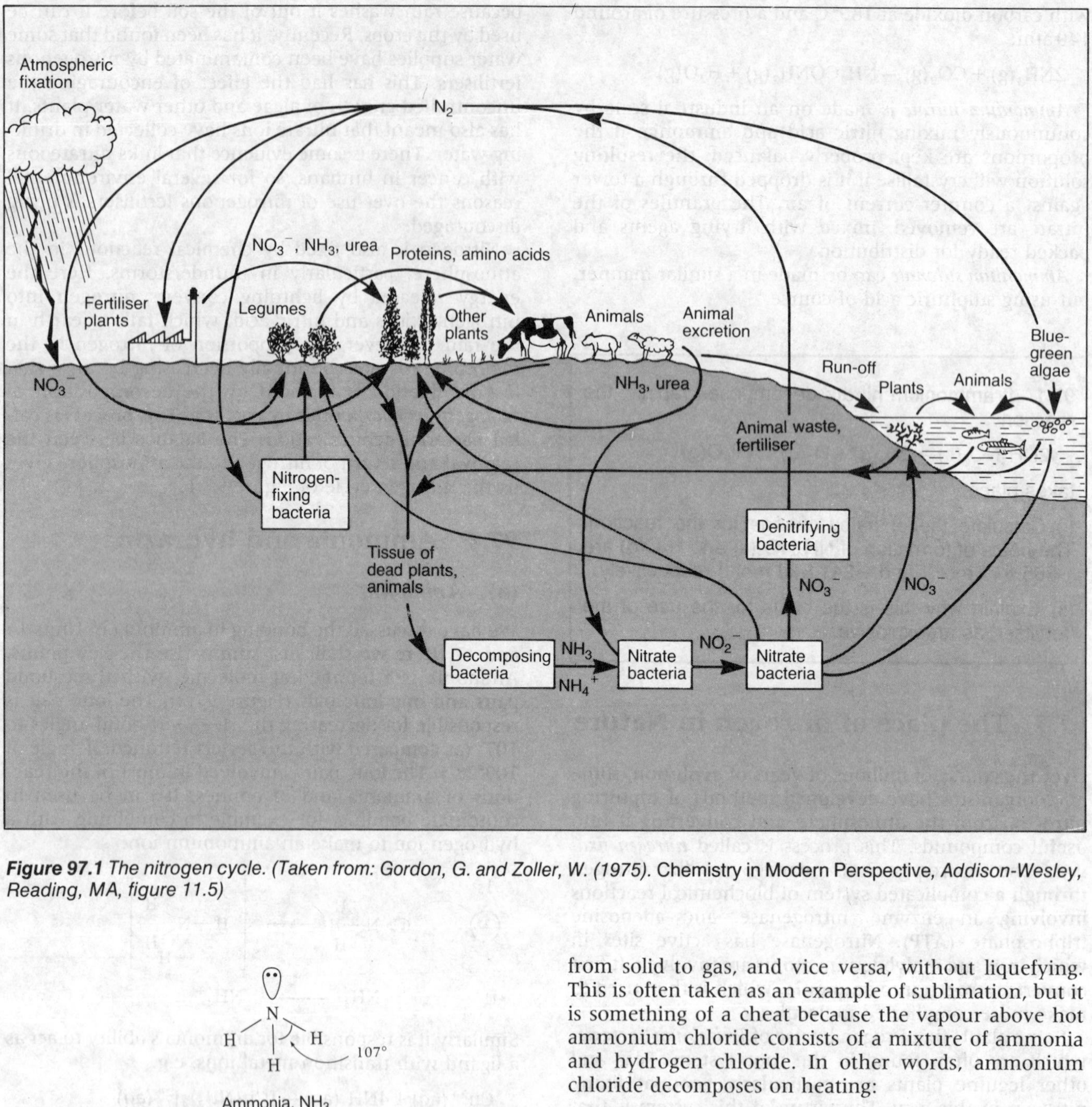

Figure 97.1 *The nitrogen cycle. (Taken from: Gordon, G. and Zoller, W. (1975).* Chemistry in Modern Perspective, *Addison-Wesley, Reading, MA, figure 11.5)*

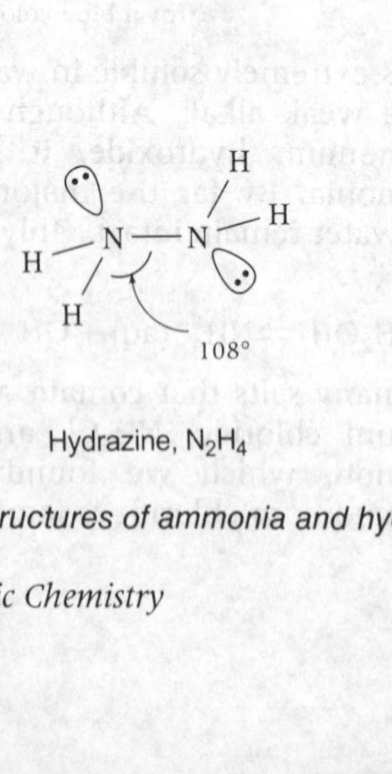

Ammonia, NH_3 (107°)

Hydrazine, N_2H_4 (108°)

Figure 97.2 *The structures of ammonia and hydrazine*

from solid to gas, and vice versa, without liquefying. This is often taken as an example of sublimation, but it is something of a cheat because the vapour above hot ammonium chloride consists of a mixture of ammonia and hydrogen chloride. In other words, ammonium chloride decomposes on heating:

$$NH_4Cl(s) \rightleftharpoons NH_3(g) + HCl(g)$$

Ammonia is a reducing agent. This is shown by the way it will remove oxygen from a number of metal oxides. A good example is the reduction of hot copper(II) oxide:

$$3CuO(s) + 2NH_3(g) \rightarrow 3Cu(s) + N_2(g) + 3H_2O(l)$$

(b) *Hydrazine*

Hydrazine has the formula N_2H_4 (Figure 97.2). It is a gas at room temperature, but it readily dissolves in water, and its solution can be used to show many of its reactions. In particular, it is a powerful reducing agent; for

This Messerschmitt ME163 Komet was one of the early jet planes developed in Germany towards the close of the Second World War. These planes used hydrazine as a fuel. They had the unfortunate habit of exploding and killing the pilot.

example, if you drop a little aqueous hydrazine into a test tube containing silver nitrate solution you will see a silver mirror on the glass:

$$4Ag^+(aq) + N_2H_4(aq) \rightarrow 4Ag(s) + N_2(g) + 4H^+(aq)$$

Hydrazine, together with hydrogen peroxide, has been used as a rocket fuel. We might expect a vigorous reaction when a good reducing agent meets a good oxidising agent, but in this case the reaction is particularly violent:

$$N_2H_4(l) + 2H_2O_2(l) \rightarrow N_2(g) + 4H_2O(g); \quad \Delta H^\ominus(298\,K) = -642\,kJ\,mol^{-1}$$

One reason for this is that hydrazine is an endothermic compound, i.e. it has a positive heat of formation, so when it breaks up into its elements heat should be given out. (Even though its hydrogen is converted into water in the reaction, this only adds to the exothermic nature of the reaction.) In addition, the products of the reaction are gases, which give an explosive edge to the process.

97.2 Why does silver chloride dissolve in aqueous ammonia?

97.3 (i) Why is ammonia a polar molecule?

(ii) Why does it show a large deviation from ideal gas behaviour?

(iii) Why does ammonia have no difficulty in dissolving in water?

97.4 Sketch an apparatus that would allow you to pass ammonia over hot copper(II) oxide, and collect the water as well as the nitrogen given off.

97.5 Suggest a reason why you would expect hydrazine to dissolve easily in acids.

97.6 What would you expect to see if hydrazine solution were added to copper(II) sulphate solution?

97.5 Nitrogen oxides

The oxides of nitrogen that we shall consider are listed in Table 97.3. The oxides show the wide range of oxidation numbers that can be assigned to nitrogen, ranging from +1 in N_2O to +5 in N_2O_5. However, all the oxides are essentially covalent compounds. Except for N_2O_5, which is an unstable colourless solid, they are all gases at room temperature.

Dinitrogen oxide, N_2O, has something of a chequered history. It has been widely used as an anaesthetic. Many operations, and visits to the dentist, have been rendered (almost) painless by its use. It is also known as laughing gas, owing to its ability to induce laughter in people when it is breathed in small quantities. Among certain groups of people in Victorian times this property of the gas was used as a source of entertainment, which we would now describe as drug abuse. Less harmful is the use of the gas as a propellant in producing whipped cream from a can. Dinitrogen oxide also happens to be one of the few colourless gases that will support combustion.

Nitrogen monoxide, NO, is an odd-electron molecule (see section 16.7). Alternatively, we can say that it is a free radical. In either event, the odd electron makes the gas highly reactive. Nitrogen monoxide will not survive long in air because it reacts with oxygen (which has two unpaired electrons) to give brown fumes of nitrogen dioxide:

$$\underset{\text{colourless}}{2NO(g)} + O_2(g) \rightarrow \underset{\text{brown}}{2NO_2(g)}$$

Nitrogen dioxide, NO_2, is also an odd-electron molecule, but it is not given to reacting with oxygen. However, it will combine with itself to give dinitrogen tetraoxide:

$$2NO_2(g) \rightleftharpoons N_2O_4(g)$$

This is an equilibrium reaction that is influenced by both pressure and temperature. If you want to remind yourself about the details of the equilibrium, look at section 53.6. Nitrogen dioxide will often support combustion. This happens if the temperature reaches above 150°C when the gas decomposes:

$$2NO_2(g) \rightarrow 2NO(g) + O_2(g)$$

It is the presence of the oxygen that aids the combustion. Many hot metals will even decompose the nitrogen monoxide, giving nitrogen as one of the products.

Dinitrogen tetraoxide, N_2O_4, solidifies at −11.2°C, and is colourless. As the temperature increases, the proportion of brown NO_2 increases and the colour of the liquid darkens. At around 140°C the mixture is almost entirely NO_2.

Dinitrogen trioxide, N_2O_3, has no significant claim to fame. It melts at a little below −100°C, and promptly decomposes. Such is life.

Dinitrogen pentaoxide, N_2O_5, is made when concentrated nitric acid is dehydrated. Therefore we can regard it as the anhydride of nitric acid. However, its formula N_2O_5 belies the nature of the solid, which is ionic and consists of nitryl cations, NO_2^+, and nitrate, NO_3^-, ions.

97.7 Apart from N_2O, which other colourless gas supports combustion?

97.8 Write an equation for the reaction of burning magnesium with nitrogen dioxide.

97.6 Nitrogen oxides and air pollution

Collectively, nitrogen oxides are often given the symbol NO_x. Two of them, nitrogen monoxide and nitrogen dioxide, are of special importance in environmental

Table 97.3. The oxides of nitrogen

Name	*Formula*	*Preparation*
Dinitrogen oxide (nitrous oxide)	N_2O	Heat ammonium nitrate $NH_4NO_3(s) \rightarrow N_2O(g) + 2H_2O(g)$
Nitrogen monoxide (nitric oxide)	NO	Add copper turnings to 5 mol dm^{-3} nitric acid $3Cu(s) + 8HNO_3(aq) \rightarrow 3Cu(NO_3)_2(aq) + 2NO(g) + 4H_2O(l)$
Nitrogen dioxide	NO_2	Heat lead(II) nitrate $2Pb(NO_3)_2(s) \rightarrow 2PbO(s) + 4NO_2(g) + O_2(g)$
Dinitrogen tetraoxide	N_2O_4	Cool nitrogen dioxide $N_2O_4(g) \underset{\text{low temp}}{\overset{\text{high temp}}{\rightleftharpoons}} 2NO_2(g)$
Dinitrogen trioxide	N_2O_3	Combine NO and NO_2 $NO(g) + NO_2(g) \rightarrow N_2O_3(g)$
Dinitrogen pentaoxide	N_2O_5	Dehydrate nitric acid with P_2O_5 $2HNO_3(l) - H_2O(l) \rightarrow N_2O_5(s)$

chemistry. They are responsible for a considerable amount of air pollution. They are given off in car exhaust fumes and when fossil fuels are burned, as well as being made during thunderstorms. In each case nitrogen monoxide is made when nitrogen and oxygen in air react at a high temperature:

$$N_2(g) + O_2(g) \rightarrow 2NO(g)$$

and then the nitrogen monoxide goes on to make nitrogen dioxide. Of the two, it is the nitrogen dioxide that is the more unpleasant. Not only does it give rise to acid rain, it also takes part in photochemical reactions, which results in the photochemical smogs enveloping cities such as Los Angeles. The photons making up sunlight can cause the NO_2 molecules to fall apart, releasing oxygen atoms:

$$NO_2(g) \xrightarrow{hf} NO(g) + O(g)$$

Oxygen atoms are extremely reactive and will attack other molecules, especially those in car exhaust fumes. For example, hydrocarbons that escape combustion can be changed into aldehydes. The oxygen atoms can also react with oxygen molecules to make trioxygen (ozone, O_3).

Nitrogen dioxide is also involved in the production of one of the most unpleasant of all chemicals present in photochemical smog. It is known as PAN (peroxyacetyl nitrate):

$$CH_3—C(=O)—O—O—NO_2$$

Between them, PAN, the aldehydes, ozone and nitrogen dioxide make a most unpleasant mix. They irritate eyes and lungs, and generally make breathing difficult.

97.7 The chemistry of nitric acid

You will find the industrial manufacture of nitric acid described in Unit 83.

Nitric acid, HNO_3, can be made in the laboratory by warming sodium nitrate with concentrated sulphuric acid. Nitric acid is more volatile than sulphuric acid, and is given off as a vapour:

$$NaNO_3(s) + H_2SO_4(l) \rightarrow NaHSO_4(s) + HNO_3(g)$$

The vapour condenses to a yellow fuming liquid ('fuming nitric acid'). It takes on this colour owing to nitrogen dioxide made during the reaction being absorbed by the acid. It is colourless when pure. On heating it decomposes at high temperatures, giving off steam, oxygen and nitrogen dioxide.

Nitric acid is both a very strong acid in water, and a vigorous oxidising agent.

In water, as we would expect for a strong acid, the equilibrium

$$HNO_3(aq) + H_2O(l) \rightarrow NO_3^-(aq) + H_3O^+(aq)$$

lies far to the right. The acid is a good source of hydrogen ions and shows many of the properties of acids, e.g. it neutralises a base, and gives carbon dioxide with carbonates or hydrogencarbonates. However, it does not always give hydrogen with metals. The reason is that its oxidising power wins over its action as an acid. In fact it is only with extremely dilute nitric acid that magnesium will behave in its typical manner and give off hydrogen.

(a) *The oxidising power of nitric acid*

To appreciate fully the varieties of reaction that can occur, you will benefit from reading about redox reactions in Unit 41. Here is a list of the major half-reactions that may take place:

$$2NO_3^-(aq) + 4H^+(aq) + 2e^- \rightarrow 2NO_2(g) + 2H_2O(l); \quad E^\ominus = +0.80\,V$$

$$NO_3^-(aq) + 4H^+(aq) + 3e^- \rightarrow 2NO(g) + 2H_2O(l); \quad E^\ominus = +0.95\,V$$

$$NO_3^-(aq) + 10H^+(aq) + 8e^- \rightarrow NH_4^+(aq) + 3H_2O(l); \quad E^\ominus = +0.88\,V$$

With metals

Given that $E^\ominus_{Cu^{2+}/Cu} = +0.34\,V$, we can see that copper will reduce nitric acid. (Copper has the more negative redox potential.) In principle each of the three half-reactions could take place; in practice the first predominates if concentrated nitric acid is used. The overall reaction is

$$Cu(s) + 4H^+(aq) + 2NO_3^-(aq) \rightarrow Cu^{2+}(aq) + 2NO_2(g) + 2H_2O(l)$$

On the other hand, if the concentrated acid is diluted by about 50%, nitrogen monoxide is released:

$$3Cu(s) + 8H^+(aq) + 2NO_3^-(aq) \rightarrow 3Cu^{2+}(aq) + 2NO(g) + 4H_2O(l)$$

With non-metals

The pattern is for concentrated nitric acid to oxidise a non-metal to a high oxidation state, and give off brown fumes of nitrogen dioxide at the same time. Fuming nitric acid gives the most vigorous reaction. Be warned: these reactions can be violent, and nitrogen dioxide is very poisonous. Typical reactions are

$$S(s) + 6HNO_3(l) \rightarrow H_2SO_4(aq) + 6NO_2(g) + 2H_2O(l)$$
$$I_2(s) + 10HNO_3(l) \rightarrow 2HIO_3(aq) + 10NO_2(g) + 4H_2O(l)$$
$$P(s) + 5HNO_3(l) \rightarrow H_3PO_4(aq) + 5NO_2(g) + H_2O(l)$$

97.9 Sketch an apparatus that you could use to collect liquid nitric acid made in the reaction between $NaNO_3$ and H_2SO_4.

97.10 Explain how the equation

$$Cu(s) + 4H^+(aq) + 2NO_3^-(aq) \rightarrow Cu^{2+}(aq) + 2NO_2(g) + 2H_2O(l)$$

was obtained from the half-equations given earlier in this section.

97.11 Zinc is a sufficiently good reducing agent ($E^{\ominus}_{Zn^{2+}/Zn} = -0.76$ V) to give ammonium ions in its reaction with nitric acid. Write the equation for the reaction.

97.12 A reasonably safe reaction using fuming nitric acid is to drop it onto warm sawdust. What do you think happens?

97.13 Nitric acid will also oxidise ions in solution. For example Fe^{2+} to Fe^{3+}, and sulphite, SO_3^{2-}, to sulphate, SO_4^{2-}.

(i) With Fe^{2+}, nitrogen monoxide is given off. Write the equation. Why would you still see brown fumes evolved?

(ii) With SO_3^{2-}, nitrogen dioxide is given off. Write the equation.

97.8 Nitrates

There are five things you should know about nitrates.

(i) There is a rule in chemistry that says that all nitrates are soluble. This is the reason why, for example, if you want a solution of silver ions you will use a solution of silver nitrate; most other silver salts are insoluble in water. (For once this is a rule that has no exceptions.)

(ii) Nitrates of Group I metals decompose in a different way to other nitrates. They give off oxygen and turn into nitrites, e.g.

$$2KNO_3(s) \rightarrow 2KNO_2(s) + O_2(g)$$

(iii) Nearly all other nitrates give off oxygen and nitrogen dioxide when they are heated. The metal oxide is left. For example,

$$2Pb(NO_3)_2(s) \rightarrow 2PbO(s) + 4NO_2(g) + O_2(g)$$
$$2Cu(NO_3)_2(s) \rightarrow 2CuO(s) + 4NO_2(g) + O_2(g)$$

You should take care if you heat lead(II) nitrate. It crackles and the crystals fly into pieces once they start to give off the gases. Copper(II) nitrate is less tiresome, but it contains a large amount of water of crystallisation. When it is heated it might seem to melt; actually it is dissolving in the water of crystallisation. Reactions like these are best done in a fume cupboard, owing to the danger of inhaling nitrogen dioxide.

(iv) Two exceptions to the last pattern are the nitrates of mercury and silver. These metals have oxides that are themselves destroyed by heat and they decompose to mercury and silver respectively.

(v) Ammonium nitrate decomposes to give dinitrogen oxide; see Table 97.3.

97.9 Nitrous acid and nitrites

Nitrous acid has the formula HNO_2, but it can also be thought of as a mixture of nitrite ions, NO_2^-, and hydrogen ions in water. The acid cannot exist in its own right free from water. It appears as a pale blue solution when a nitrite is dissolved in dilute hydrochloric acid. In order to prevent the solution decomposing it must be kept below 5° C. The main use of the acid is in organic chemistry where, among other things, it is used in making dyes. You can find details in Unit 122.

Unlike nitric acid, nitrous acid tends to react as either an oxidising or a reducing agent. As a reducing agent, it will decolourise acidified potassium manganate(VII) solution:

$$\underset{\text{purple}}{2MnO_4^-(aq)} + 6H^+(aq) + 5NO_2^-(aq) \rightarrow \underset{\text{colourless}}{2Mn^{2+}(aq)} + 5NO_3^-(aq) + 3H_2O(l)$$

As an oxidising agent it will, for example, oxidise Fe^{2+} to Fe^{3+}:

$$2Fe^{2+}(aq) + 4H^+(aq) + 2NO_2^-(aq) \rightarrow 2Fe^{3+}(aq) + 2NO(g) + 2H_2O(l)$$

We can think of these two reactions in terms of the redox reactions:

(i) as an oxidising agent

$$2HNO_2(aq) + 2H^+(aq) + 2e^- \rightarrow 2NO(g) + 2H_2O(l); \quad E^{\ominus} = +0.99\text{ V}$$

(ii) as a reducing agent

$$NO_3^-(aq) + 3H^+(aq) + 2e^- \rightarrow HNO_2(aq) + H_2O(l); \quad E^{\ominus} = +0.94\text{ V}$$

In the first reaction, the acid is acting as an oxidising agent, taking electrons from the chemical with which it reacts. The second shows what will happen if the acid is oxidised by another chemical: it is converted into nitrate ions. The acid will behave as a reducing agent if it becomes involved with a half-reaction that has a redox potential more positive than +0.94 V. This is the case with acidified manganate(VII) ions, for which $E^{\ominus}_{MnO_4^-/Mn^{2+}} = +1.51$ V. However, $E^{\ominus}_{Fe^{3+}/Fe^{2+}} = +0.77$ V, so in this case nitrous acid will be the oxidising agent and Fe^{2+} will be the reducing agent.

97.14 Nitrous acid is able to oxidise sulphite ions, SO_3^{2-}, to sulphate, SO_4^{2-}. Write the equation for the reaction.

97.10 Nitrogen halides

The most important halides are NF_3 (a gas) and NCl_3 (an oily liquid). Nitrogen trifluoride is almost inert, but the trichloride is easily hydrolysed:

$$NCl_3(l) + 3H_2O(l) \rightarrow NH_3(aq) + 3HOCl(aq)$$

NCl_3 can be made by passing chlorine into a solution of ammonium chloride:

$$NH_4Cl(aq) + 3Cl_2(g) \rightarrow NCl_3(l) + 4HCl(aq)$$

It is not a good idea to try this reaction because NCl_3 has an unfortunate tendency to explode.

Both NBr_3 and NI_3 can be obtained in a similar way but combined with ammonia, as in $NI_3{\cdot}NH_3$. The latter compound is also explosive.

Answers

97.1 (i) Heat of reaction

$$= \Delta 4H_f^\ominus(H_2O(g)) - \Delta H_f^\ominus(NH_4NO_3)$$
$$= -761.6\ \text{kJ mol}^{-1}$$

(ii) Not only is the reaction highly exothermic, the change is from a solid of negligible volume to a mixture of gases of large volume. It is the sudden, violent, expansion of the gases that represents the explosion.

97.2 The soluble complex ion $Ag(NH_3)_2{}^+$ is made (see section 53.8).

97.3 (i) The nitrogen pulls electron density towards itself, and away from the hydrogen atoms. Thus the nitrogen carries a slight negative charge, and the hydrogen atoms a slight positive charge. The separation of charge gives rise to the dipole moment.

(ii) Owing to the dipole moment, there are strong intermolecular forces between the molecules.

(iii) It can hydrogen bond with water molecules.

97.4 Figure 97.3 shows the sketch.

97.5 Hydrazine has two lone pairs. These can be protonated, in much the same way as the lone pair on the nitrogen in ammonia is protonated in acid.

97.6 A copper mirror is produced and the blue colour of the solution fades.

97.7 Oxygen.

97.8 $4Mg(s) + 2NO_2(g) \rightarrow 4MgO(s) + N_2(g)$

97.9 A simple distillation apparatus using all glass apparatus should be used, as in Figure 115.5, except that the vessel containing the nitric acid distillate should be cooled.

97.10 We can produce the equation by noting that the conversion

$$Cu(s) \rightarrow Cu^{2+}(aq) + 2e^-$$

represents the loss of 2 mol of electrons. The first nitric acid half-equation involves the gain of 2 mol of electrons. Hence, all we have to do is to add the two half-equations.

97.11 $4Zn(s) + 10H^+(aq) + NO_3{}^-(aq) \rightarrow 4Zn^{2+}(aq) + 3H_2O(l) + NH_4{}^+(aq)$

97.12 The sawdust is oxidised, with brown fumes of nitrogen dioxide being given off. It may burst into flame.

97.13 (i) $3Fe^{2+}(aq) + 4H^+(aq) + NO_3{}^-(aq) \rightarrow 3Fe^{3+}(aq) + 2H_2O(l) + NO(g)$

The nitrogen monoxide will react with oxygen in the air to give brown nitrogen dioxide.

(ii) $SO_3{}^{2-}(aq) + 2H^+(aq) + 2NO_3{}^-(aq) \rightarrow SO_4{}^{2-}(aq) + H_2O(l) + 2NO_2(g)$

97.14 $SO_3{}^{2-}(aq) + 2H^+(aq) + 2NO_2{}^-(aq) \rightarrow SO_4{}^{2-}(aq) + 2NO(g) + H_2O(l)$

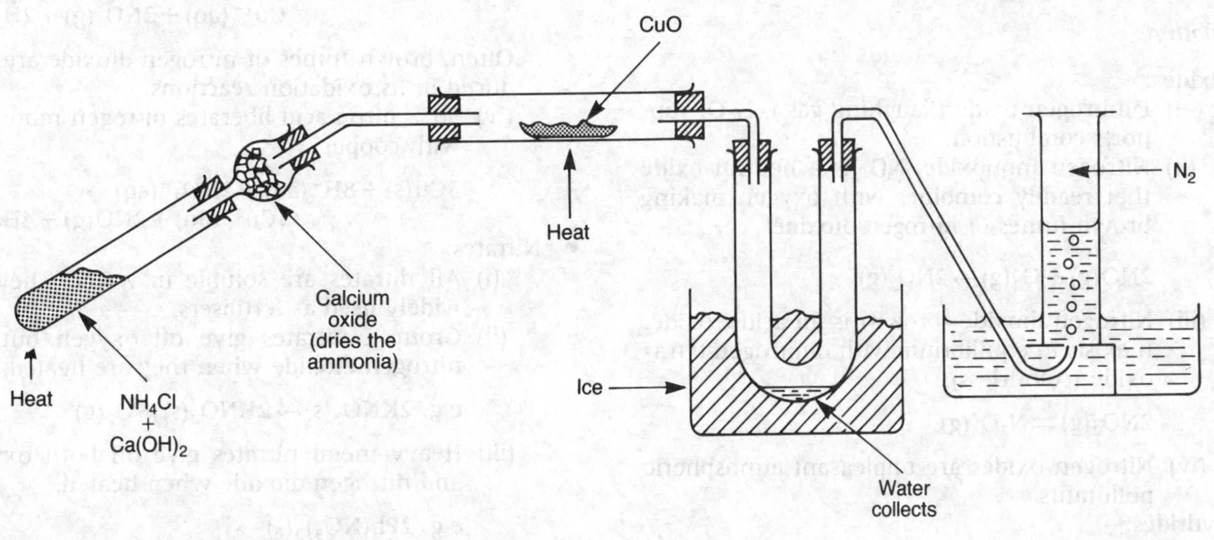

Figure 97.3 One method in answer to question 97.4

UNIT 97 SUMMARY

- Nitrogen:
  - (i) Makes up almost 78% of the atmosphere, and is the most common gas.
  - (ii) Shows very few reactions, mainly as a result of the very high N≡N bond strength.
  - (iii) Is used in the Haber process to make ammonia;

    $N_2(g) + 3H_2(g) \rightleftharpoons 2NH_3(g)$

    Conditions: pressures between 15 and 30 MPa (150 and 300 atm), temperature around 500° C, iron catalyst with a promoter (e.g. aluminium oxide, zirconium oxide, potassium oxide).
  - (iv) Is fixed by microorganisms, i.e. converted direct from the atmosphere into biologically active compounds. (Also, see the nitrogen cycle of Figure 97.1.)
- Isolation:

  By the liquefaction of air followed by fractional distillation.

Reactions

- With burning magnesium:

  An ionic nitride is made;

  $3Mg(s) + N_2(g) \rightarrow Mg_3N_2(s)$
- With hydrogen:

  Makes ammonia in the Haber process;

  $N_2(g) + 3H_2(g) \rightleftharpoons 2NH_3(g)$

Compounds

- Oxides:
  - (i) Dinitrogen oxide ('laughing gas'), N_2O, supports combustion.
  - (ii) Nitrogen monoxide, NO, is a neutral oxide that readily combines with oxygen making brown fumes of nitrogen dioxide;

    $2NO(g) + O_2(g) \rightarrow 2NO_2(g)$
  - (iii) Nitrogen dioxide (brown) is an acidic oxide. It exists in equilibrium with dinitrogen tetraoxide (colourless);

    $2NO_2(g) \rightleftharpoons N_2O_4(g)$
  - (iv) Nitrogen oxides are unpleasant atmospheric pollutants.
- Hydrides:

  Ammonia, NH_3
  - (i) Has a lone pair of electrons, which can be protonated by hydrogen ions to give the ammonium ion;

    $NH_3(aq) + H^+(aq) \rightarrow NH_4^+(aq)$

    Ammonium ions are found in a variety of ammonium salts. These give off ammonia when warmed with alkali.
  - (ii) Owing to its lone pair, an ammonia molecule can act as a ligand with transition metal ions, e.g. in making $Cu(NH_3)_4^{2+}$.
  - (iii) Ammonia is a reducing agent;

    e.g. $3CuO(s) + 2NH_3(g) \rightarrow 3Cu(s) + N_2(g) + 3H_2O(l)$

  Hydrazine, N_2H_4
  - (i) Is an endothermic compound and a vigorous reducing agent;

    e.g. $4Ag^+(aq) + N_2H_4(aq) \rightarrow 4Ag(s) + N_2(g) + 4H^+(aq)$
  - (ii) With hydrogen peroxide, it is used as a rocket fuel.
- Nitric acid, HNO_3:
  - (i) Made by warming a mixture of concentrated sulphuric acid and sodium nitrate;

    $NaNO_3(s) + H_2SO_4(l) \rightarrow NaHSO_4(s) + HNO_3(g)$
  - (ii) Is a strong acid in water;

    $HNO_3(l) + H_2O(l) \rightarrow H_3O^+(l) + NO_3^-(aq)$

    and will, for example, give CO_2 with carbonates.
  - (iii) Shows oxidising ability when concentrated;

    e.g. $S(s) + 6HNO_3(l) \rightarrow H_2SO_4(aq) + 6NO_2(g) + 2H_2O(l)$

    $Cu(s) + 4H^+(aq) + 2NO_3^-(aq) \rightarrow Cu^{2+}(aq) + 2NO_2(g) + 2H_2O(l)$

    Often, brown fumes of nitrogen dioxide are produced in its oxidation reactions.
  - (iv) 50% nitric acid liberates nitrogen monoxide with copper;

    $3Cu(s) + 8H^+(aq) + 2NO_3^-(aq) \rightarrow 3Cu^{2+}(aq) + 2NO(g) + 4H_2O(l)$
- Nitrates:
  - (i) All nitrates are soluble in water. They are widely used as fertilisers.
  - (ii) Group I nitrates give off oxygen but not nitrogen dioxide when they are heated;

    e.g. $2KNO_3(s) \rightarrow 2KNO_2(s) + O_2(g)$
  - (iii) Heavy metal nitrates give off both oxygen and nitrogen dioxide when heated;

    e.g. $2Pb(NO_3)_2(s) \rightarrow 2PbO(s) + 4NO_2(g) + O_2(g)$
  - (iv) Silver and mercury nitrates decompose to the metal rather than oxide.
  - (v) Ammonium nitrate decomposes to give dinitrogen oxide;

    $2NH_4NO_3(s) \rightarrow 2N_2O(g) + 4H_2O(g)$

- Nitrous acid, HNO_2:
  Can act as both an oxidising and reducing agent, e.g. oxidises Fe^{2+} to Fe^{3+}, and will reduce (decolourise) potassium manganate(VII) solution.

- Halides:
  Nitrogen trichloride, NCl_3, is easily hydrolysed;

$$NCl_3(l) + 3H_2O(l) \rightarrow NH_3(aq) + 3HOCl(aq)$$

98

Group V

98.1 The nature of the elements

In this unit we shall see how the properties of the elements in Group V change as we go down the Group. You will not find details of the chemistry of nitrogen here; the previous unit is the place to find out about nitrogen.

Nitrogen and phosphorus show the typical properties of non-metals. For example, they are poor conductors of heat and electricity and give acidic oxides. Their compounds are predominantly covalent. However, bismuth at the bottom of the Group shows definite metallic properties, e.g. it conducts electricity and makes salts such as bismuth nitrate, $Bi(NO_3)_3$. This trend is typical of the behaviour of elements in all the Groups of the Periodic Table: metallic nature increases going down a Group. This is also reflected in the electronegativities of the elements. Nitrogen has the greatest tendency to attract electrons, antimony and bismuth the least. The properties and uses of the elements are summed up in Tables 98.1 and 98.2.

As you might expect then, the trend down the Group is a move from covalent bonding to ionic bonding, with the majority of compounds showing a mix of each. That is, many of the bonds made by the elements are polar.

Phosphorus, arsenic and antimony have allotropes. However, only the allotropes of phosphorus (red and white phosphorus) are of importance. We have met these in Unit 57, so look there if you want to remind yourself about them.

Table 98.2. Uses of the elements in Group V

Element	*Main uses*
Nitrogen	Manufacture of ammonia, fertilisers and nitric acid
Phosphorus	In phosphoric acid and phosphate fertilisers Rust preventatives Matches, flares, fireworks and explosives
Arsenic	In alloys The manufacture of semiconductors, e.g. light emitting diodes Agricultural insecticides
Antimony	Treatment of parasitic diseases, in insecticides Antimony sulphide is used in fireworks
Bismuth	In alloys* In medicines

*Alloys of bismuth often have melting points between 50 and 250° C. This makes them useful in fire safety devices. For example, part of the valve in a water sprinkler can be made of a bismuth alloy. When a fire causes the temperature to rise the valve will open automatically as the alloy melts

Table 98.1. Physical properties of the elements in Group V

Symbol	*Nitrogen* N	*Phosphorus* P	*Arsenic* As	*Antimony* Sb	*Bismuth* Bi
Electron structure	$(He)2s^22p^3$	$(Ne)3s^23p^3$	$(Ar)3d^{10}4s^24p^3$	$(Kr)4d^{10}5s^25p^3$	$(Xe)5d^{10}6s^26p^3$
Electronegativity	3.0	2.1	2.0	1.9	1.9
I.E./kJ mol^{-1}	1402	1012	950	830	700
Melting point/° C	−210	597 red 44 white	817	630	272
Boiling point/° C	−204	431 red 281 white	613	1637	1559
Atomic radius/pm	74	110	121	141	152
Principal oxid. no.	+3,+5	+3,+5	+3,+5	+3,+5	+3*

* Bismuth will show an oxidation number of +5, but it is not common

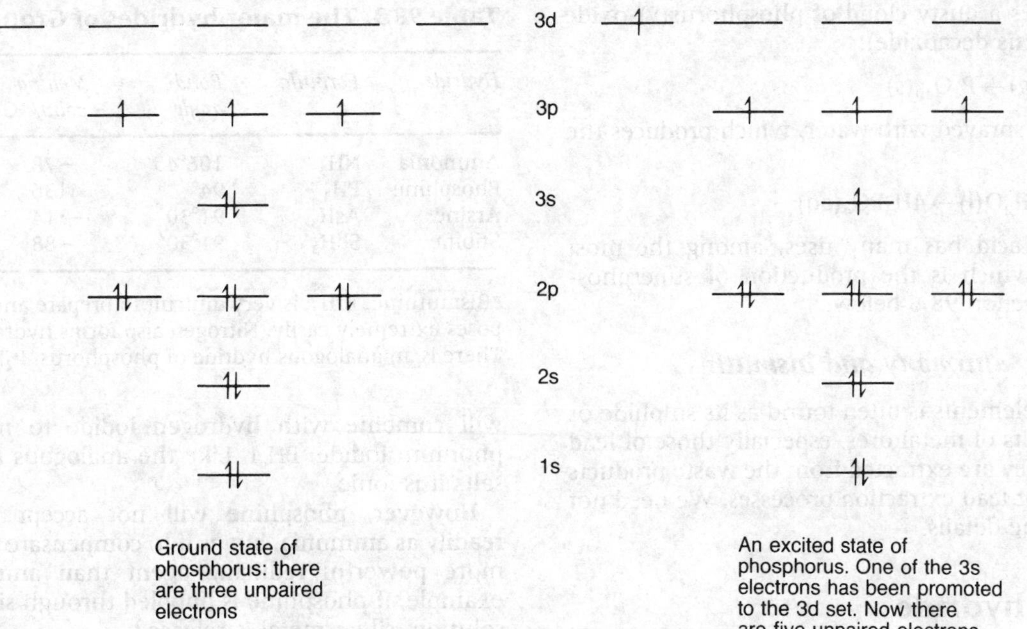
3d
3p
3s
2p
2s
1s
Ground state of phosphorus: there are three unpaired electrons
An excited state of phosphorus. One of the 3s electrons has been promoted to the 3d set. Now there are five unpaired electrons

***Figure 98.1** One way of explaining how phosphorus can make three or five covalent bonds*

Phosphorus and the other members of the Group can make use of d orbitals in their bonding. This is because the energy of these orbitals is not a lot greater than those of the other valence electrons. For example, phosphorus can make use of its 3s, 3p and the empty 3d orbitals. If we imagine that the pair of 3s electrons can be parted, and that one of the five valence electrons is promoted to a 3d orbital, then we would expect that phosphorus could make a maximum of five single covalent bonds (see Figure 98.1). If the 3s electrons are not split, then phosphorus should make three covalent bonds. Indeed, three and five are the favoured valencies of the Group V elements (Figure 98.2). The exception is nitrogen, whose 3d orbitals are far too high in energy to be used in bonding.

$CH_3-CH_2-O-C(=O)-CH-S-P(=S)(-O-CH_3)-O-CH_3$
$CH_3-CH_2-O-C(=O)-CH_2$

Malathion

$O_2N-C_6H_4-O-P(=S)(-O-CH_2-CH_3)-O-CH_2-CH_3$

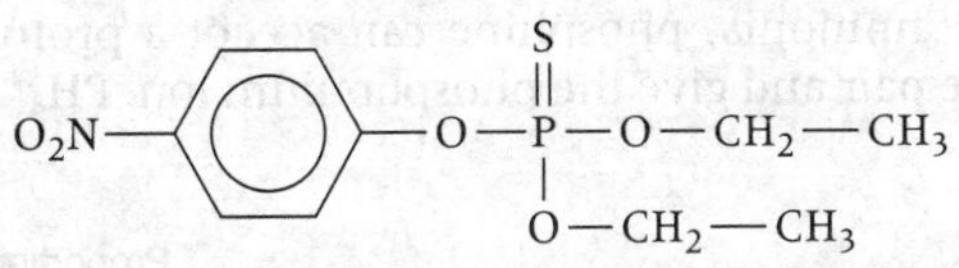

Parathion

***Figure 98.2** Two organic phosphorus insecticides in which phosphorus is showing a valency of five*

98.1 Does the polarisability of the atoms increase or decrease going down the Group? Briefly explain your answer.

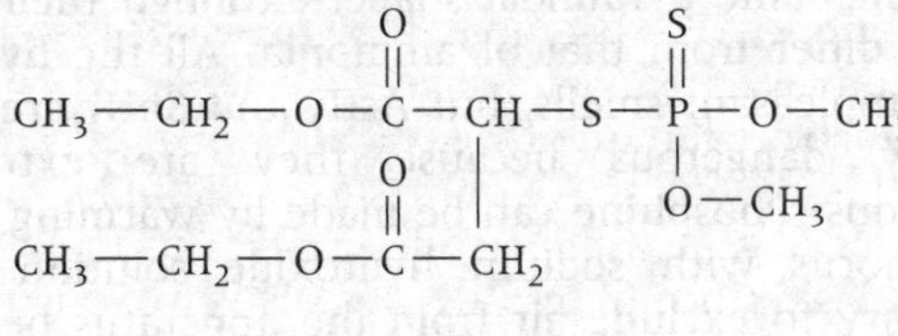

98.2 The extraction of the elements

(a) *Phosphorus*

Fluorapatite, $CaF_2{\cdot}3Ca_3(PO_4)_2$, is the chief ore of phosphorus. The phosphorus is removed from the ore by first grinding it to remove large lumps, and then heating it in a mixture with sand (silica, SiO_2) and coke (carbon). The reactions take place at around 1500°C. This very high temperature is reached by using an electric arc furnace (see Figure 98.3). Be careful that you do not think of this as an electrolysis. Current is not passed through the chemicals, it is only used to heat them. The key reaction is

$$2Ca_3(PO_4)_2 + 6SiO_2 + 10C \rightarrow 6CaSiO_3 + 10CO + P_4$$

The phosphorus vapour is allowed to escape from the furnace and is condensed by passing it into water spraying towers. The product is white phosphorus, which can be sold as it stands or first converted into red phosphorus. The conversion is done by heating white phosphorus at 400°C for some hours (or at a lower temperature for a longer time).

The chief reason for extracting the phosphorus is to convert it into phosphoric(V) acid, H_3PO_4 (Figure 98.3). This is done by burning red phosphorus in excess air, which produces a dusty cloud of phosphorus(V) oxide (tetraphosphorus decaoxide):

$$P_4(s) + 5O_2(g) \rightarrow P_4O_{10}(s)$$

The fumes are sprayed with water, which produces the acid:

$$P_4O_{10}(s) + 6H_2O(l) \rightarrow 4H_3PO_4(aq)$$

Phosphoric(V) acid has many uses, among the most important of which is the production of superphosphates – see section 98.6 below.

(b) *Arsenic, antimony and bismuth*

Each of these elements is often found as its sulphide or oxide in deposits of metal ores, especially those of lead and copper. They are extracted from the waste products of the copper or lead extraction processes. We need not worry about the details.

98.3 The hydrides

Just as nitrogen makes ammonia, NH_3, so the other elements give similar hydrides (Table 98.3). They all have the same pyramidal shape, although their bond angles differ from that of ammonia. All the hydrides have unpleasant smells, but AsH_3 and SbH_3 are additionally dangerous because they are extremely poisonous. Phosphine can be made by warming white phosphorus with sodium hydroxide solution. It is necessary to exclude air from the apparatus because, although pure PH_3 will not burn unless ignited, it is often contaminated with P_2H_4, which is spontaneously flammable. The equation is

$$P_4(s) + 3OH^-(aq) + 3H_2O(l) \rightarrow PH_3(g) + 3H_2PO_2^-(aq)$$

Like ammonia, phosphine can accept a proton onto its lone pair and give the phosphonium ion, PH_4^+, and it will combine with hydrogen iodide to make phosphonium iodide, PH_4I. Like the analogous ammonium salts it is ionic.

Table 98.3. The major hydrides of Group V*

Hydride	*Formula*	*Bond angle*	*Melting point/°C*	*Boiling point/°C*
Ammonia	NH_3	106°45′	−78	−33.5
Phosphine	PH_3	94°	−136	−87
Arsine	AsH_3	91°30′	−114	−55
Stibine	SbH_3	91°30′	−88	−18

*Bismuthine, BiH_3, is very difficult to prepare and decomposes extremely easily. Nitrogen also forms hydrazine, N_2H_4. There is an analogous hydride of phosphorus, P_2H_4

However, phosphine will not accept protons as readily as ammonia, but as if to compensate it is a much more powerful reducing agent than ammonia. For example, if phosphine is bubbled through silver nitrate solution, silver metal is released:

$$PH_3(g) + 6Ag^+(aq) + 3H_2O(l) \rightarrow H_3PO_3(aq) + 6Ag(s) + 6H^+(aq)$$

One of the characteristics of the hydrides of arsenic, antimony and bismuth is that they are decomposed by heat (AsH_3 the least and BiH_3 the most easily). This property has been used in an important test for arsenic called Marsh's test. The substance thought to contain arsenic is placed in a mixture of zinc and sulphuric acid. The hydrogen given off converts any arsenic into AsH_3. The gases from the reaction flask are led through a heated glass tube. If AsH_3 is present, a black deposit of solid arsenic will be seen. The reason why this test has been widely used is the unfortunate tendency of some people to murder their acquaintances by poisoning them with arsenic. Marsh's test has been a cornerstone

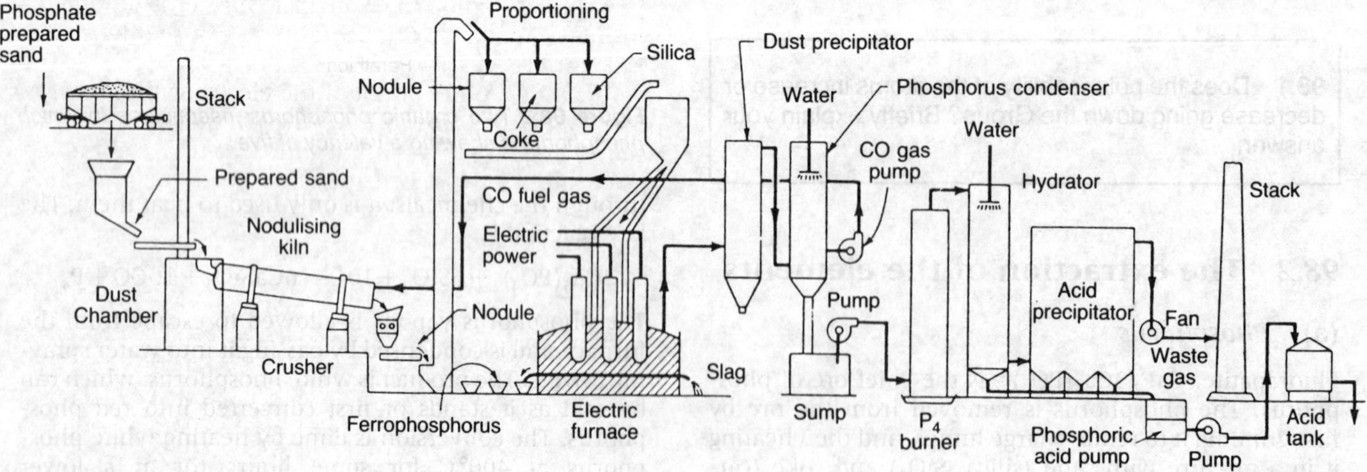

***Figure 98.3** An outline of the manufacture of phosphoric(V) acid. In order to produce 1 tonne of 85% H_3PO_4, the following materials and utilities are needed: phosphate rock (35.6% P_2O_5), 1000 kg; silica rock, 320 kg; coke, 377 kg; iron, depends on ferrophosphorus requirements; electricity, 13 840 MJ; direct labour (est.), 0.5–1 work hours. (Taken from Austin, G. T. (1984).* Shreve's Chemical Process Industries, *5th edn, McGraw-Hill, New York)*

of forensic science. However, fashions in murder change and the use of arsenic is a little behind the times now.

98.2 Look at the values of the bond angles in Table 98.3.

(i) Why do the molecules all have a tetrahedral shape?

(ii) Explain the change in the bond angle going from NH_3 to AsH_3. (Hint: look back at Unit 17, and also take notice of the electronegativities of the elements.)

98.3 (i) Briefly describe how you would make and collect phosphine.

(ii) What is special about the changes in oxidation number of phosphorus in the reaction?

98.4 When phosphine burns in air, phosphorus(V) oxide, P_4O_{10}, is produced. What else do you think is made? Write the equation for the reaction.

98.5 Phosphine will also reduce Cu^{2+} ions, but this time phosphoric(V) acid, H_3PO_4, is formed rather than phosphonic acid, H_3PO_3. Write the equation for the reaction.

98.6 Why is it likely that phosphine and chlorine would react? Predict what will be made in the reaction.

98.7 What would you expect to happen if (i) NH_4Cl and (ii) PH_4I are warmed with sodium hydroxide solution?

98.8 Predict the outcome of heating PH_4I.

98.4 The halides and oxohalides

The major halides that the elements make are listed in Table 98.4. You can see that they all give trihalides and all but bismuth give one or more pentahalides. Of these the phosphorus chlorides are by far the most important, and we shall use them as examples.

Table 98.4. The principal halides of Group V

Element	*Trihalides*	*Pentahalides*
Nitrogen	NF_3, NCl_3, NBr_3, NI_3	None
Phosphorus	PF_3, PCl_3, PBr_3, PI_3	PF_5, PCl_5, PBr_5
Arsenic	AsF_3, $AsCl_3$, $AsBr_3$, AsI_3	AsF_5
Antimony	SbF_3, $SbCl_3$, $SbBr_3$, SbI_3	SbF_5, $SbCl_5$
Bismuth	BiF_3, $BiCl_3$, $BiBr_3$, BiI_3	BiF_5

(a) *The trihalides*

The trihalides are covalent and can be made by reacting the element and halogen directly together. For example, to make phosphorus trichloride, chlorine can be passed over molten white phosphorus:

$$P_4(l) + 6Cl_2(g) \rightarrow 4PCl_3(l)$$

The product is a fuming oily liquid. The reason why it fumes in air is that it reacts with water:

$$PCl_3(l) + 3H_2O(l) \rightarrow H_3PO_3(aq) + 3HCl(aq)$$

When the water is present as water vapour, the two acids form misty fumes.

Phosphorus trichloride can be used to prepare one of the oxochlorides of phosphorus: phosphorus trichloride oxide, $POCl_3$. This is done by warming the liquid with potassium chlorate(V):

$$3PCl_3(l) + KClO_3(s) \rightarrow 3POCl_3(l) + KCl(s)$$

$POCl_3$ is another unpleasant fuming liquid, but in industry it is widely used in the manufacture of organic phosphate esters. You will find it is often produced when PCl_3 or PCl_5 react.

Although bismuth trichloride is not as well known as phosphorus trichloride, we have had reason to refer to it elsewhere (see section 53.2). The reason is that it too is hydrolysed by water, but an equilibrium is set up:

$$\underset{\text{colourless}}{BiCl_3(aq)} + H_2O(l) \rightleftharpoons \underset{\text{white}}{BiOCl(s)} + 2HCl(aq)$$

The bismuth(III) chloride oxide, BiOCl, is a white insoluble powder. The equilibrium can be shifted to one side or the other by adding water or concentrated hydrochloric acid.

(b) *Pentahalides*

Phosphorus pentachloride is the most well known of the pentahalides. It is a pale yellow solid, whose structure belies its formula, PCl_5. In fact the solid consists of pairs of PCl_4^+ and PCl_6^- ions. The former is tetrahedral in shape, the latter octahedral. You can see the shapes in Figure 98.4.

If you do a quick count of the electrons that must be involved in bonding in PCl_6^- or PCl_5 you will find that the 3s and 3p orbitals are insufficient to accommodate them all. As we said earlier, the 3d orbitals of phosphorus can also be used in bonding. If we assume

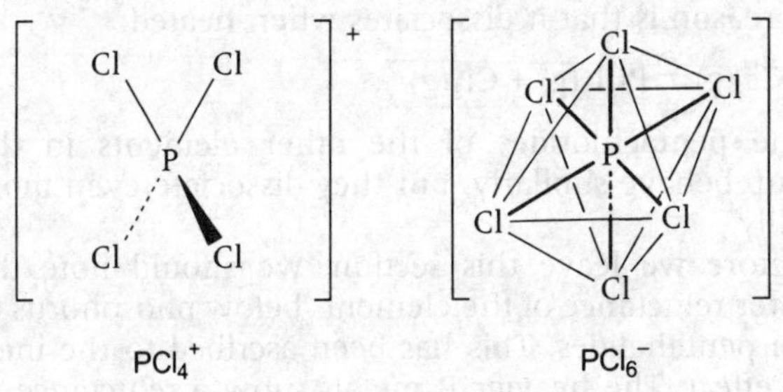

Figure 98.4 *The two types of ion present in solid PCl_5*

hybridisation to occur, the octagonal shape can be obtained by using a set of d^2sp^3 hybrids, and the trigonal bipyramid using dsp^3 hybrids.

To make the chloride, you can pass chlorine into an ice-cooled glass container into which phosphorus trichloride is dropped:

$$PCl_3(l) + Cl_2(g) \rightarrow PCl_5(s)$$

Phosphorus pentachloride also fumes in air. It too reacts with water. If water is in short supply the reaction is

$$PCl_5(s) + H_2O(l) \rightarrow POCl_3(l) + 2HCl(aq)$$

If water is in excess,

$$PCl_5(s) + 4H_2O(l) \rightarrow H_3PO_4(aq) + 5HCl(g)$$

Indeed, in the units on organic chemistry you will find that we shall speak of a use for PCl_5 as a test for the presence of OH groups. If OH groups are present, white fumes of HCl will be given off. At the same time the OH group is replaced by Cl. For example,

$$CH_3-CH_2-OH + PCl_5 \longrightarrow CH_3-CH_2-Cl + POCl_3 + HCl$$

$$\underset{\text{ethanol}}{C_2H_5OH} + PCl_5 \longrightarrow C_2H_5Cl + POCl_3 + HCl$$

$$CH_3-C(=O)OH + PCl_5 \longrightarrow CH_3-C(=O)Cl + POCl_3 + HCl$$

$$\underset{\text{ethanoic acid}}{CH_3COOH} + PCl_5 \longrightarrow CH_3COCl + POCl_3 + HCl$$

It will also react with aldehydes and ketones, but no HCl is given off:

$$CH_3-C(=O)H + PCl_5 \longrightarrow CH_3-CHCl_2 + POCl_3$$

$$\underset{\text{ethanal}}{CH_3CHO} + PCl_5 \longrightarrow CH_3CHCl_2 + POCl_3$$

Phosphorus pentachloride has one other facet to its nature that we have looked at before (see section 52.6). If you were to measure the molar mass of its vapour you would find that, depending on the temperature, it appears to be anywhere between 104 and 208 g mol^{-1}. The reason is that it dissociates when heated:

$$PCl_5(g) \rightleftharpoons PCl_3(g) + Cl_2(g)$$

The pentachlorides of the other elements in the Group behave similarly, but they dissociate even more readily.

Before we leave this section, we should note the greater reluctance of the elements below phosphorus to form pentahalides. This has been ascribed to the inert pair effect. The heavier B metals show a reluctance to use their outer s electrons in bonding. For example, these are the 6s electrons for bismuth. If these electrons are not used, the elements will make molecules with only three bonds.

98.9 Sketch an apparatus that you could use to make PCl_3. What precautions would you have to take (i) on account of the phosphorus, (ii) to stop the product being hydrolysed.

98.10 Predict the shape of (i) PCl_3, (ii) $POCl_3$ and draw dot-and-cross diagrams to represent the bonding in them.

98.11 In the gaseous state, PCl_5 can exist as individual, covalent, molecules. In one sentence explain why the shape of the molecule is a trigonal bipyramid, as shown in Figure 98.5.

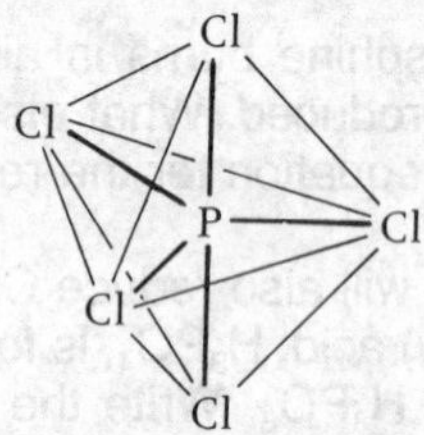

Figure 98.5 An isolated PCl_5 molecule

98.12 Suggest a reason why nitrogen does not give NF_5 or NCl_5.

98.13 The ability of PCl_5 to replace OH groups by chlorine atoms extends to its reaction with sulphuric and nitric acids. Draw the structures of these two acids (see Figure 74.1 if you are stuck), and draw diagrams of the molecules that are left after the reaction.

98.5 The oxides

The oxides of the elements are shown in Table 98.5. We have dealt with the oxides of nitrogen in the previous unit, so we shall ignore them here. The oxides of phosphorus were once given the formulae P_2O_3 and P_2O_5 (hence their old names of phosphorus trioxide and

Table 98.5. The oxides of Group V

Element	*Oxides*	*Trend*
Nitrogen	N_2O, NO, N_2O_3, NO_2, N_2O_4, N_2O_5	↑ Acidic
Phosphorus	P_4O_6, P_4O_{10}	
Arsenic	As_4O_6, As_4O_{10}	Amphoteric
Antimony	Sb_4O_6, Sb_4O_{10}	
Bismuth	Bi_2O_3	↓ Basic

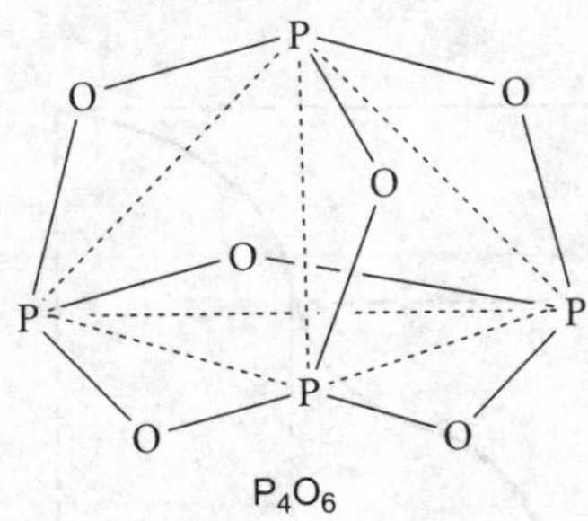

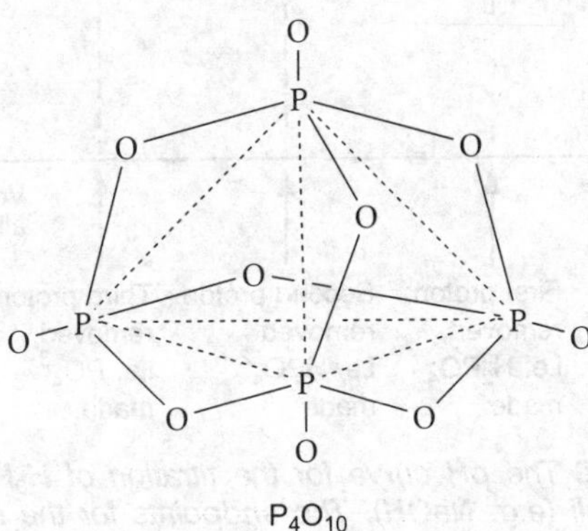

Figure 98.6 The structures of P_4O_6 and P_4O_{10}

phosphorus pentoxide) but this was before their structures had been found using X-ray diffraction. The basic building block of both of them is a tetrahedron of phosphorus atoms (Figure 98.6). The oxygen atoms in phosphorus(III) oxide, P_4O_6, act as bridges between the corners of the tetrahedron, as if the edges had been plucked outwards. In phosphorus(V) oxide, P_4O_{10}, each phosphorus atom is also bonded to an extra oxygen atom.

The oxides of phosphorus react vigorously with water to give acidic solutions:

$$P_4O_6(s) + 6H_2O(l) \rightarrow \underset{\text{phosphonic acid}}{4H_3PO_3}$$

$$P_4O_{10}(s) + 6H_2O(l) \rightarrow \underset{\text{phosphoric(v) acid}}{4H_3PO_4}$$

Phosphorus(V) oxide has such an affinity for water that it finds use as a dehydrating agent. For example, it will dehydrate nitric acid, releasing the acid anhydride, N_2O_5:

$$P_4O_{10}(s) + 4HNO_3(l) \rightarrow \underset{\text{metaphosphoric acid}}{4HPO_3(l)} + 2N_2O_5(s)$$

It can also be a useful reagent in organic chemistry, for example in converting amides into nitriles.

Given that we know that nitrogen and phosphorus are definitely non-metallic in character, we should expect them to give acidic oxides, However, as we go down the Group, we know that metallic nature increases, and this should give a greater tendency for the oxides to be basic. In fact the oxides of arsenic and antimony show amphoteric properties, i.e. partly acidic and partly basic properties. For example, arsenic(III) oxide will dissolve in both alkali and concentrated acid:

$$As_4O_6(s) + 12OH^-(aq) \rightarrow 4AsO_3^{3-}(aq) + 6H_2O(l)$$
$$As_4O_6(s) + 12HCl(aq) \rightarrow 4AsCl_3(aq) + 6H_2O(l)$$

The oxide of bismuth is definitely basic in nature. A good example is the way it obeys the simple rule that a base plus an acid gives a salt plus water:

$$Bi_2O_3(s) + 6HNO_3(aq) \rightarrow Bi(NO_3)_2(aq) + 3H_2O(l)$$

Indeed, bismuth is alone in the Group in giving a stable nitrate, sulphate and carbonate. In this respect it is showing the typical behaviour of a metal.

> **98.14** Use your knowledge of bonding to suggest how each of the phosphorus atoms can bond to an extra oxygen atom in P_4O_{10}.

98.6 The oxoacids

The oxoacids of phosphorus are by far the most important, and there is a remarkable range of them. Table 98.6 lists their names and formulae. The structure of phos-

Table 98.6. The oxoacids of phosphorus

Name	*Formula*	*Bonding*
Phosphoric(V) (orthophosphoric) acid	H_3PO_4	$(HO)_3P{=}O$
Phosphonic (phosphorus) acid	H_3PO_3	$(HO)_2HP{=}O$
Phosphinic (hypophosphorus) acid	H_3PO_2	$(HO)H_2P{=}O$
Phosphinous acid	H_3PO	$(HO)H_2P$
Pyrophosphoric acid	$H_4P_2O_7$	$HO{-}P(=O)(OH){-}O{-}P(=O)(OH){-}OH$
Tripolyphosphoric acid	$H_5P_3O_{10}$	$HO{-}P(=O)(OH){-}O{-}P(=O)(OH){-}O{-}P(=O)(OH){-}OH$

Table 98.6. (*cont.*)

Name	*Formula*	*Bonding*
Tetrapolyphosphoric acid	$H_6P_4O_{13}$	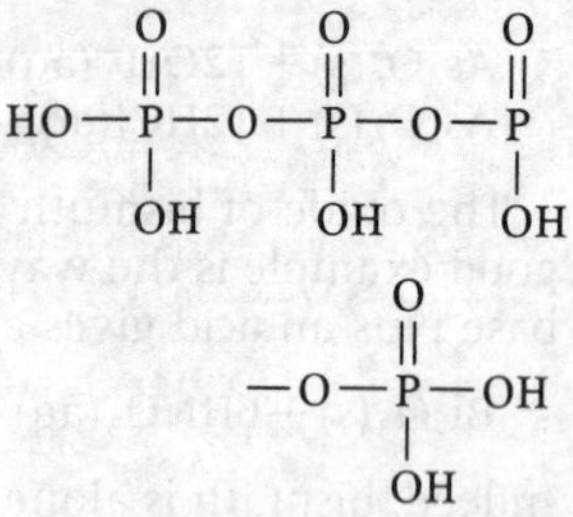 HO—P(=O)(OH)—O—P(=O)(OH)—O—P(=O)(OH)—O—P(=O)(OH)—OH
Pyrophosphonic acid	$H_4P_2O_5$	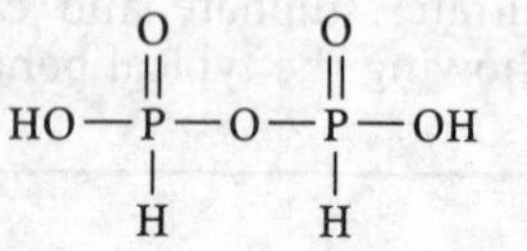 HO—P(=O)(H)—O—P(=O)(H)—OH
Metaphosphoric acid	HPO_3	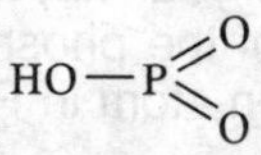 HO—P(=O)=O
Trimetaphosphoric acid	$H_3P_3O_9$	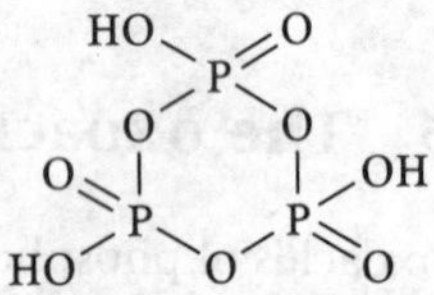 cyclic: three HO—P(=O) units joined by —O— bridges in a six-membered P—O ring

phoric(V) acid is shown in Figure 98.7. Fortunately you will not have to remember any but the first two or three. However, this should not prevent you from admiring the structures of the others.

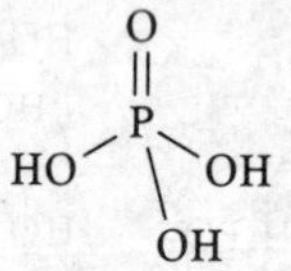

O
||
P
HO OH
OH

***Figure 98.7** The structure of phosphoric(V) acid, H_3PO_4, is a distorted tetrahedron*

The first point to understand about these acids is that the hydrogen atoms directly attached to oxygen atoms can usually be lost from the molecule, but those bonded to the phosphorus atoms cannot. This means that, for example, phosphoric(V) acid is a triprotic (or tribasic) acid. In a titration with alkali, the pH changes as shown in Figure 98.8.

The graph shows that the first hydrogen is completely removed at pH = 5, the second at pH = 10, and the third at pH = 13.

The salts made by crystallising the solution at each stage are sodium dihydrogenphosphate(V), NaH_2PO_4, disodium hydrogenphosphate(V), Na_2HPO_4, and trisodium phosphate(V), Na_3PO_4. Salts like NaH_2PO_4 and Na_2HPO_4 that contain hydrogen are often known as acid salts. A salt like Na_3PO_4 *can* be categorised as a neutral salt. However, these names should not be taken too literally. If you were to dissolve a sample of each of

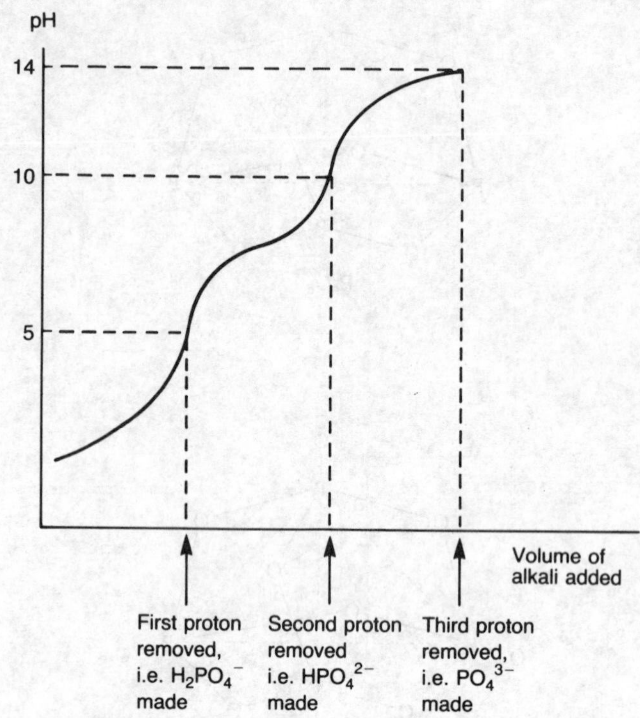

***Figure 98.8** The pH curve for the titration of H_3PO_4 with a strong alkali (e.g. NaOH). The endpoints for the removal of successive protons are not sharp. This is characteristic of a weak acid. (Compare the weak acid part of Figure 76.1)*

them in water, you would find that NaH_2PO_4 does give an acidic solution owing to the equilibrium

$$H_2PO_4^-(aq) + H_2O(l) \rightleftharpoons HPO_4^{2-}(aq) + H_3O^+(aq)$$

lying over to the right-hand side. However, with Na_2HPO_4 the equilibrium is

$$HPO_4^{2-}(aq) + H_2O(l) \rightleftharpoons H_2PO_4^-(aq) + OH^-(aq)$$

That is, the solution of this 'acid' salt is really slightly alkaline. Likewise, a solution of 'neutral' Na_3PO_4 is also alkaline:

$$PO_4^{3-}(aq) + H_2O(l) \rightleftharpoons HPO_4^{2-}(aq) + OH^-(aq)$$

98.7 The uses of phosphate salts

Some phosphate salts have great importance in agriculture. They are a source of phosphorus, which is essential for the healthy growth of plants. The element is used, for example, in building the phosphate groups of DNA, and the biochemically important substance adenosine triphosphate (ATP). Originally, bone ash was used as a source of phosphate, but the ash suffers the same problem as the mineral fluorapatite: the phosphates they contain are released into the soil only very slowly. In the 1830s and 1840s it was discovered that the rate of release was greatly improved by treating the ash or rock with sulphuric acid. This remains the method used to treat fluorapatite today. The more soluble phosphate salts that can be made in the process are known as superphosphates (Figure 98.9).

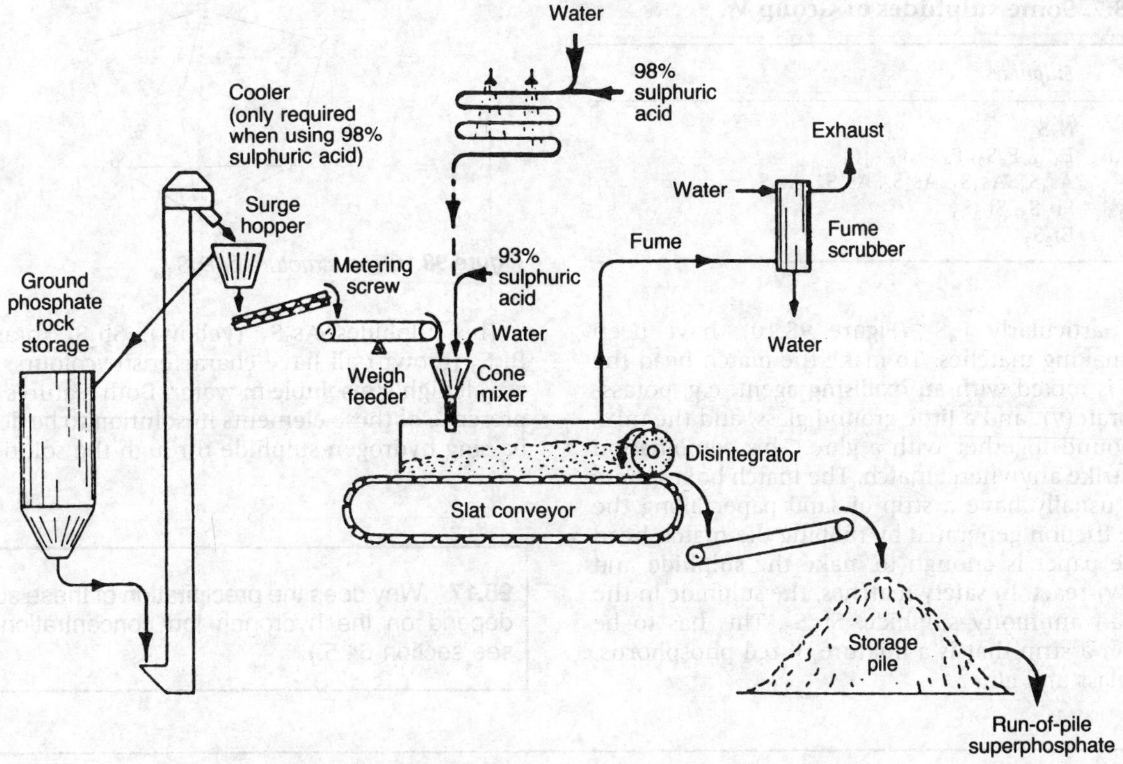

***Figure 98.9** An outline of superphosphate manufacture. (Taken from: Austin, G. T. (1984).* Shreve's Chemical Process Industries, *5th edn, McGraw-Hill, New York, figure 16.3, p. 275)*

The fluorapatite rock is ground and mixed with concentrated sulphuric acid. It takes about an hour for the mixture to pass along a slowly moving conveyor, by which time the crucial reactions have finished. The most important of them is

$$Ca_3(PO_4)_2(s) + 2H_2SO_4(l) + 4H_2O(l) \rightarrow Ca(H_2PO_4)_2(s) + 2CaSO_4(s)$$

At the end of the conveyor, the product is broken into small pieces and is ready for distribution.

The mixture of the much more soluble calcium dihydrogenphosphate(V), $Ca(H_2PO_4)_2$, and anhydrite, $CaSO_4$, is sold as 'superphosphate'. The market for phosphate fertiliser is far larger than that for elemental phosphorus. About 90% of fluorapatite goes in fertiliser manufacture, and only 10% in extracting phosphorus.

The calcium fluoride in the mineral releases hydrogen fluoride with the sulphuric acid, which itself reacts to give various side products. The gaseous waste products are removed by washing with water in the fume scrubber.

Superphosphate is also made by reacting fluorapatite, or other phosphate rock, with phosphoric(V) acid:

$$Ca_3(PO_4)_2(s) + 4H_3PO_4(l) \rightarrow 3Ca(H_2PO_4)_2(s)$$

Cooks might be particularly interested in some salts of phosphorus because they are ingredients of baking powders. For example hydrated calcium dihydrogenphosphate(V), $Ca(H_2PO_4)_2{\cdot}H_2O$, mixed with sodium hydrogencarbonate and starch makes a good baking powder. When the temperature is high enough the salt and the hydrogencarbonate give off carbon dioxide:

$$3Ca(H_2PO_4)_2(s) + 8NaHCO_3(s) \rightarrow Ca_3(PO_4)_2(s) + 4Na_2HPO_4(s) + 8H_2O(l) + 8CO_2(g)$$

Other acid phosphorus salts used in baking powder are NaH_2PO_4, KH_2PO_4 and $Na_2H_2P_2O_7$.

Phosphoric(V) acid is useful in the preparation of the hydrogen halides, especially HBr and HI. The acid has little oxidising power, and is not very volatile. When it is heated with potassium bromide or iodide the hydrogen halide is released uncontaminated with the impurities that result from using sulphuric acid. (Also, see section 102.1.)

98.15 The product $Ca(H_2PO_4)_2$ is known as triple superphosphate. Why does it command a higher price than ordinary superphosphate?

98.16 Classify each of the acids in Table 98.6 according to how many protons can (in principle) be lost from their molecules.

98.8 The sulphides

Phosphorus and the other members of the Group give a number of sulphides (Table 98.7). Sulphides of phos-

Table 98.7. Some sulphides of Group V

Element	*Sulphides*
Nitrogen	N_4S_4
Phosphorus	P_4S_3, P_4S_5, P_4S_7, P_4S_{10}
Arsenic	As_4S_4, As_4S_3, As_4S_6, As_2S_5, As_2S_3
Antimony	Sb_2S_5, Sb_2S_3
Bismuth	Bi_2S_3

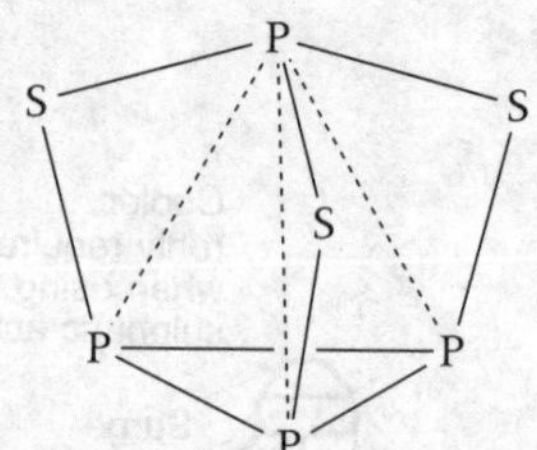

Figure 98.10 The structure of P_4S_3

phorus, particularly P_4S_3 (Figure 98.10), have been used in making matches. To make the match head the sulphide is mixed with an oxidising agent, e.g. potassium chlorate(V), and a little ground glass, and the mixture is bound together with a glue. This combination gives a 'strike anywhere' match. The match boxes these come in usually have a strip of sand paper along the side. The friction generated by rubbing the match head along the paper is enough to make the sulphide and chlorate(V) react. In safety matches, the sulphide in the head is an antimony sulphide, Sb_2S_3. This has to be rubbed on a strip that is a mixture of red phosphorus, ground glass and glue.

The sulphides As_2S_3 (yellow), Sb_2S_3 (orange) and Bi_2S_3 (brown) all have characteristic colours, and they are all highly insoluble in water. Both features allow the presence of these elements in solution to be detected by passing hydrogen sulphide through the solution.

98.17 Why does the precipitation of these sulphides depend on the hydrogen ion concentration? (Hint: see section 64.5.)

Answers

98.1 It increases. Going down the Group, the atoms become larger and more polarisable ('squashy') because the outer electrons are increasingly well shielded from the nucleus.

98.2 (i) This arrangement minimises the repulsions between one lone pair and three bond pairs.

(ii) The nitrogen atom pulls its lone pair of electrons very strongly towards itself. (Note its high electronegativity.) This makes the lone pair a very dense centre of negative charge, which in turn repels the bond pairs strongly. This tends to reduce the H—N—H bond angles. By comparison the lone pair on the antimony atom is much less tightly held to the atom. The diffuse charge means that the bond pairs of electrons are less strongly repelled, so the bond angle is greater. Given that arsenic and antimony have identical electronegativities, we might expect the bond angle to be similar. Phosphorus is in between nitrogen and arsenic, and the bond angle is correspondingly intermediate in value.

98.3 (i) The main thing that you should realise is that air must be removed from the apparatus before the alkali and phosphorus are allowed to meet. This can be done by passing carbon dioxide, or nitrogen, through the flask and then allowing alkali to pour into the reaction flask. The phosphine can be collected in a gas jar over water in the time honoured manner.

(ii) The phosphorus changes from 0 to -3 (in PH_3) and $+1$ (in $H_2PO_2^-$). This is a disproportionation reaction.

98.4 Water.

$$4PH_3(g) + 8O_2(g) \rightarrow P_4O_{10}(s) + 6H_2O(l)$$

98.5 $PH_3(g) + 4Cu^{2+}(aq) + 4H_2O(l) \rightarrow H_3PO_4(aq) + 4Cu(s) + 8H^+(aq)$

98.6 Chlorine is a good oxidising agent, so when it meets a good reducing agent a vigorous reaction can be expected. The chlorine removes the hydrogen, giving fumes of hydrogen chloride. The phosphorus and chlorine give phosphorus trichloride. (You might not have known which chloride phosphorus makes, but you should have predicted that *a* chloride would be made.) The reaction is

$$PH_3(g) + 3Cl_2(g) \rightarrow PCl_3(l) + 3HCl(g)$$

98.7 (i) Ammonia is given off.

(ii) By analogy, phosphine is given off.

98.8 It dissociates:

$$PH_4I(s) \rightleftharpoons PH_3(g) + HI(g)$$

(Compare NH_4Cl.)

98.9 The apparatus is sketched in Figure 98.11.

98.10 The diagrams are shown in Figure 98.12.

98.11 This shape minimises the repulsions.

98.12 If it is to make these compounds it would have to use the 3d set of orbitals. These are far too high in energy for them to be used by nitrogen, and others in the same Period. Also, see section 96.5.

98.13 The diagrams are drawn in Figure 98.13.

98.14 Each of the phosphorus atoms in P_4O_6 is bonded to three oxygen atoms. This leaves a lone pair over on each phosphorus, which can give a coordinate bond with an oxygen atom.

98.15 It contains no anhydrite, $CaSO_4$, so each kilogram is richer in fertiliser.

Answers – cont.

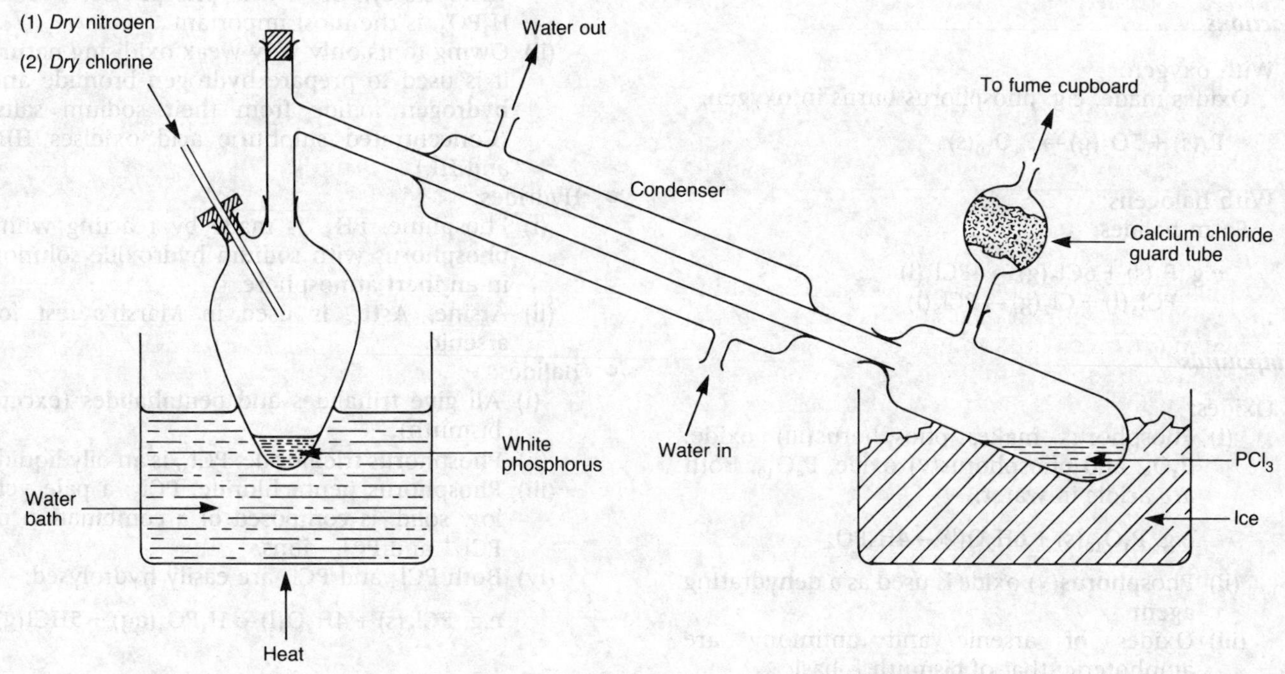

Figure 98.11 *One apparatus for preparing PCl_3. Dry nitrogen (or CO_2) is passed through the apparatus to remove air. The $CaCl_2$ guard tube prevents moisture in the air entering the apparatus*

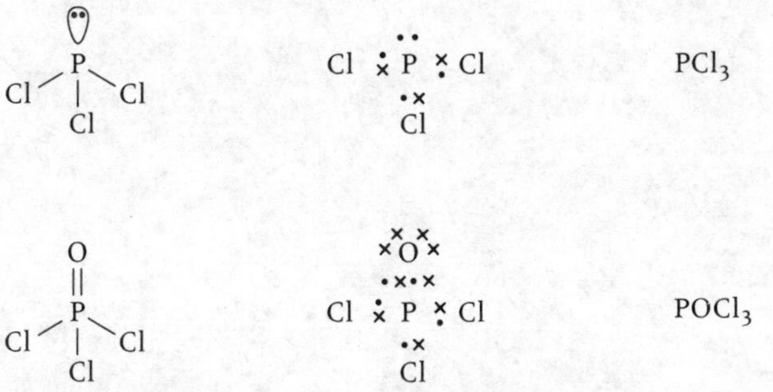

PCl_3

$POCl_3$

Figure 98.12 *Diagrams of PCl_3 and $POCl_3$*

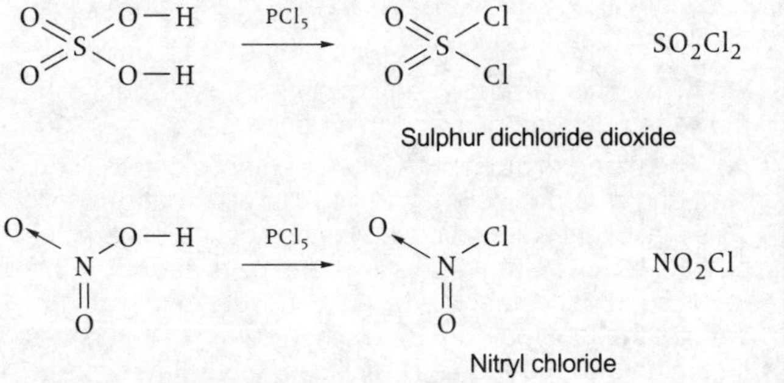

$$H_2SO_4 \xrightarrow{PCl_5} SO_2Cl_2$$

Sulphur dichloride dioxide

$$HNO_3 \xrightarrow{PCl_5} NO_2Cl$$

Nitryl chloride

Figure 98.13 *Diagrams for answer to question 98.13*

98.16 We only count the hydrogen atoms attached to oxygen atoms. Going down the list in order: 3, 2, 1, 1, 4, 5, 6, 2, 1, 3.

98.17 This is because of the different solubility products of the sulphides. Addition of hydrogen ions suppresses the production of S^{2-} ions, so in acidic solution $[S^{2-}]$ is very low and only the most insoluble sulphides will precipitate.

UNIT 98 SUMMARY

- The Group V elements:
  - (i) Metallic nature increases down the Group.
  - (ii) Phosphorus and following elements can make use of d orbitals in bonding, and show several valencies.
  - (iii) Phosphorus (red and white), arsenic and antimony have allotropes.
- Extraction:
  - (i) Phosphorus is extracted by heating fluorapatite, $CaF_2{\cdot}3Ca_3(PO_4)_2$, with sand (silica, SiO_2) and coke (carbon) in an electric arc furnace;

$$2Ca_3(PO_4)_2 + 6SiO_2 + 10C \rightarrow 6CaSiO_3 + 10CO + P_4$$

(ii) The other elements are extracted by reducing their oxides or sulphides.

Reactions

- With oxygen:
  Oxides made, e.g. phosphorus burns in oxygen;

  $$P_4(s) + 5O_2(g) \rightarrow P_4O_{10}(s)$$

- With halogens:
  Form halides;

  e.g. $P_4(s) + 6Cl_2(g) \rightarrow 4PCl_3(l)$
  $PCl_3(l) + Cl_2(g) \rightarrow PCl_5(l)$

Compounds

- Oxides:
  (i) Phosphorus makes phosphorus(III) oxide, P_4O_6, and phosphorus(V) oxide, P_4O_{10}. Both are acidic in water;

  e.g. $P_4O_{10}(s) + 6H_2O(l) \rightarrow 4H_3PO_4$

  (ii) Phosphorus(V) oxide is used as a dehydrating agent.
  (iii) Oxides of arsenic and antimony are amphoteric; that of bismuth is basic.
- Oxoacids:
  (i) Phosphorus makes a series of oxoacids (see Table 98.6), of which phosphoric(V) acid, H_3PO_4, is the most important.
  (ii) Owing to its only very weak oxidising nature it is used to prepare hydrogen bromide and hydrogen iodide from their sodium salts. (Concentrated sulphuric acid oxidises HBr and HI.)
- Hydrides:
  (i) Phosphine, PH_3, is made by reacting white phosphorus with sodium hydroxide solution in an inert atmosphere.
  (ii) Arsine, AsH_3, is used in Marsh's test for arsenic.
- Halides:
  (i) All give trihalides and pentahalides (except bismuth).
  (ii) Phosphorus trichloride, PCl_3, is an oily liquid.
  (iii) Phosphorus pentachloride, PCl_5, a pale yellow solid, is composed of a combination of PCl_4^+ and PCl_6^- ions.
  (iv) Both PCl_3 and PCl_5 are easily hydrolysed;

  e.g. $PCl_5(s) + 4H_2O(l) \rightarrow H_3PO_4(aq) + 5HCl(g)$

99

Oxygen and oxides

99.1 The element

Oxygen exists as diatomic molecules, O_2, and constitutes approximately 20.8% of air. It has three isotopes. $^{16}_{8}O$ is the main one, with an abundance of nearly 99.8%. The others, are $^{17}_{8}O$ (0.04%) and $^{18}_{8}O$ (0.2%). The most important use of oxygen is in keeping animals, including the human variety, alive through its activity in respiration. Its slight solubility in water is essential to fish and other aquatic life.

Another virtue of oxygen is that it supports combustion, especially of organic substances such as coal, oil and wood. We rely on the combustion of fuels to provide heat, electricity and transportation.

Information about oxygen is summarised in Table 99.1. Oxygen has an allotrope: trioxygen or ozone, O_3. The importance of ozone has become widely recognised. It is present in the upper atmosphere where it absorbs a good deal of ultraviolet radiation from the Sun. The ozone layer has suffered damage owing to the widespread use of chlorofluorocarbons (CFCs) in aerosols.

Table 99.1. Information about oxygen

Relative atomic mass, A_r(O)	16
Electron structure	$1s^22s^22p^4$
Ionisation energy	1314 kJ mol^{-1}
First electron affinity	-141.4 kJ mol^{-1}
Second electron affinity	$+790.8$ kJ mol^{-1}
Molecular formula	O_2
Bond energy	497 kJ mol^{-1}
Bond length	121 pm
Melting point	54 K (−219° C)
Boiling point	90 K (−183° C)
Solubility* in water at s.t.p.	8.6 cm^3 dm^{-3}
Colourless, odourless, tasteless	

*This is the solubility of oxygen from air in contact with water. Pure oxygen dissolves to the extent of about 49 cm^3 dm^{-3} at s.t.p.

99.2 The large-scale extraction of oxygen

Oxygen is obtained by the fractional distillation of air. This is achieved by forcing air under pressure through a nozzle. The air expands into a region of lower pressure, which cools the gas. (This is known as the Joule–Thomson effect.) The cooled air circulates around the expansion tubes, cooling the air even more. Eventually a point is reached when the air condenses to a liquid. It consists of a mixture of nitrogen, oxygen and noble gases. The mixture can be separated by allowing the liquid to increase in temperature. Oxygen boils less easily than the other gases, so it evaporates last of all. Once the other gases have evaporated, liquid oxygen can be stored in insulated containers, or allowed to vaporise and kept in cylinders under pressure.

Some manufacturing plants operate a more elaborate system, which allows both nitrogen and oxygen to be liquefied. It is rather more difficult to effect the separation of the two liquids from liquid air rather than to allow the nitrogen to escape. Although they use a more tricky process, such plants have the benefit of being able to change the proportions of the two gases in order to meet varying demand.

Liquid oxygen is pale blue in colour and, owing to an oxygen molecule having two unpaired electrons, it is strongly paramagnetic. Molecular orbital theory, but not valence bond theory, has a neat explanation of this.

99.1 You might be surprised to discover that even reactive metals like sodium do not react with liquid oxygen. What explanation (from reaction kinetics) can you give for this lack of reactivity?

99.3 The uses of oxygen

The uses of oxygen are shown in Table 99.2. Oxygen is of immense importance in medicine. Patients with respiratory problems can be given an oxygen enriched

Table 99.2. The extraction and uses of oxygen

Extraction	*Uses*
Liquefaction of air	Medical uses in aiding respiration Breathing by divers, astronauts, etc. Oxy-acetylene welding Rocket fuels

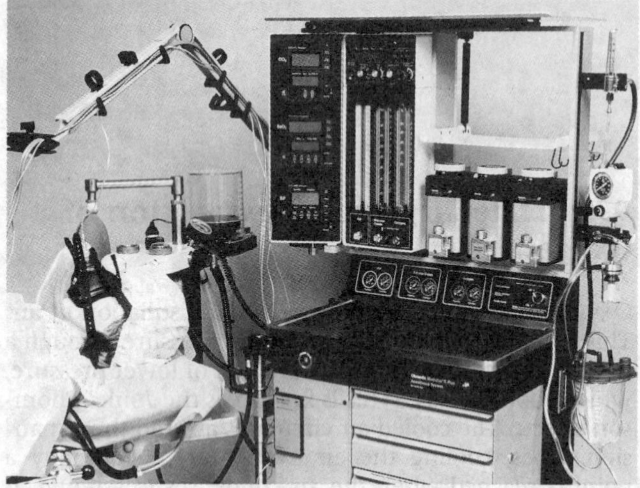

A supply of pure oxygen is essential to the survival of some patients in hospital. The volume of gas given to the patient has to be carefully monitored using equipment like that shown here.

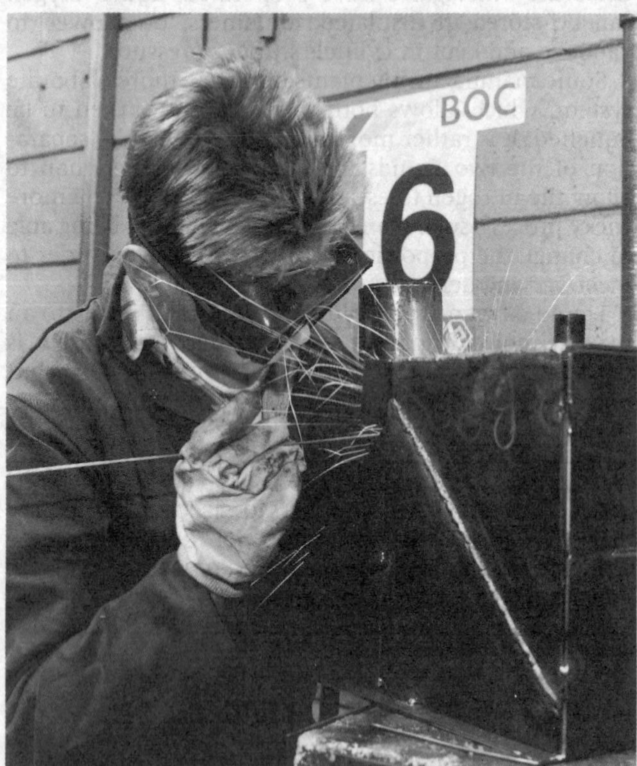

Oxy-acetylene welding is an essential part of many manufacturing processes.

Liquid oxygen is one component of the fuel that lifts the Space Shuttle into orbit around the Earth.

atmosphere to breathe. In operations, the supply of oxygen and anaesthetic have to be carefully balanced.

Divers need a supply of oxygen, but not too much. Often they breathe oxygen greatly diluted with helium, a mixture that results in their voices taking on a high pitched squeaky sound.

Oxygen has found much use in rocketry and space flight. Apart from the needs of the astronauts, liquid oxygen is widely used as the oxidant in the fuel mixture.

Owing to the highly exothermic nature of the reaction, oxygen and ethyne (acetylene) are used in oxy-acetylene welding:

$$C_2H_2(g) + \tfrac{5}{2}O_2(g) \rightarrow 2CO_2(g) + H_2O(g); \quad \Delta H^{\ominus} = -1255.6\,\text{kJ mol}^{-1}$$

99.2 Hydrazine, N_2H_4, is known as an endothermic compound because its heat of formation is positive: $\Delta H_f^{\ominus} = +50.6\,\text{kJ mol}^{-1}$. It reacts with oxygen according to the equation

$N_2H_4(g) + O_2(g) \rightarrow N_2(g) + 2H_2O(g)$

At 25°C hydrazine is a liquid. Neglecting the heat needed to convert it into a gas, estimate the enthalpy change in the reaction.

99.4 The place of oxygen in Nature

Oxygen is constantly being used up. Living things use it to generate energy through respiration. Humans and other mammals take in oxygen through their lungs, where it passes into the blood and combines with haemoglobin. Haemoglobin is a protein that has an iron atom held by a ring of carbon atoms called a haem group (Figure 99.1). An oxygen molecule can bond to the iron sufficiently strongly that it can be carried round the body, but not so strongly that the oxygen cannot be removed. Indeed, the oxygen is given up to the various tissues as the blood passes through the labyrinth of capillaries.

A simple way in which we can represent the chemical change of respiration is

$$C_6H_{12}O_6 + 6O_2 \rightarrow 6CO_2 + 6H_2O; \quad \Delta H^{\ominus} = -2820\,\text{kJ mol}^{-1}$$

Here we have used glucose to represent the conversion of carbohydrate into carbon dioxide and water. These two products of respiration are breathed out. The energy released is essential to keep us alive. Respiration is a rather important type of combustion reaction.

Oxygen is also used up by more obvious types of combustion. Burning coal, peat, or wood in a fire, or oil in central heating boilers, converts the carbon and other elements into oxides. Oxides of nitrogen and carbon are responsible for producing acid rain. Carbon dioxide plays a large part in the greenhouse effect. For the present we shall concentrate on the explanation of how it is that the proportion of oxygen in the atmosphere stays constant. The reason is that oxygen is constantly being returned to the atmosphere by the process of *photosynthesis*, which occurs in green plants.

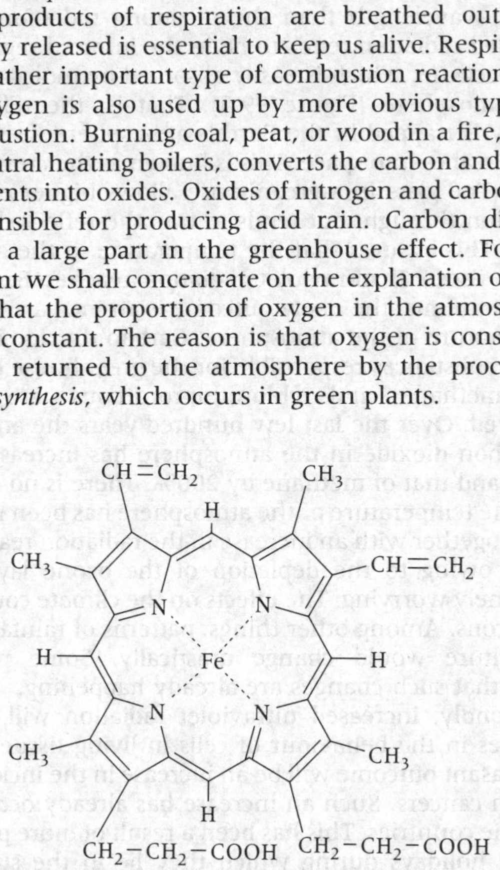

Figure 99.1 *A single haem group. In haemoglobin, haem groups are attached to a protein molecule*

Photosynthesis takes place through a complicated series of reactions in which *light energy* from the Sun and *chlorophyll* are essential components. Chlorophyll exists in two varieties called chlorophyll *a* (Figure 99.2) and chlorophyll *b*. Both are large organic molecules that contain magnesium.

The visible spectrum of chlorophyll (Figure 99.3) confirms that the molecule absorbs strongly in the red and blue-violet regions of the visible spectrum. The light that is not absorbed is, of course, primarily in the green region. When photons with the right wavelength strike chlorophyll, the energy is given to an electron, which is able to escape and start a highly complicated chain of reactions. The conversion of carbon dioxide

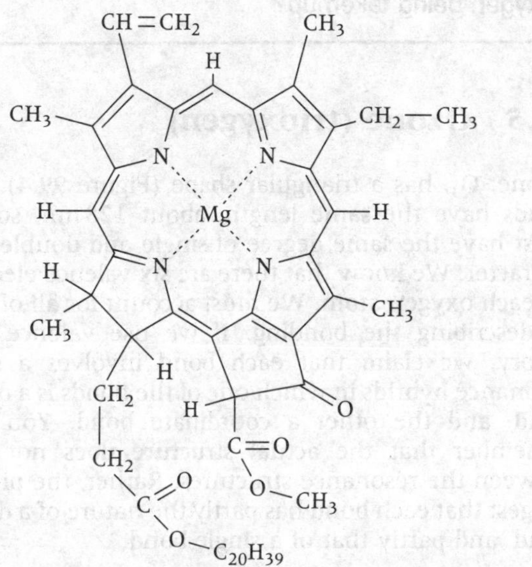

Figure 99.2 *The structure of chlorophyll a. Notice the similarity to the structure of haem (Figure 99.1)*

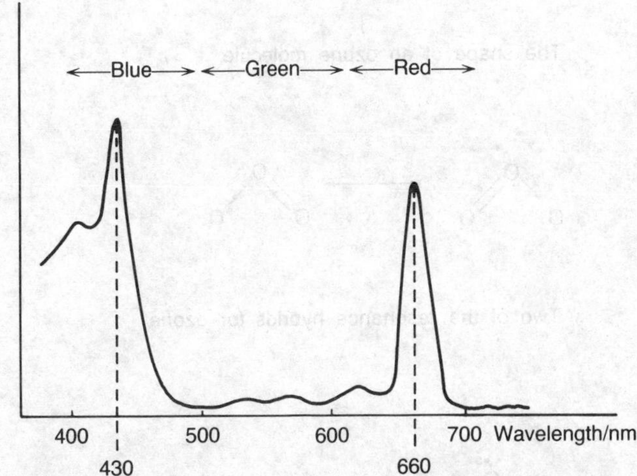

Figure 99.3 *The spectrum of chlorophyll a. The spectrum of chlorophyll b is similar, with peaks near 450 and 640 nm. There is strong absorption in the blue and red regions of visible light*

and water into carbohydrate takes place according to the equation

$$6CO_2 + 6H_2O + \text{light energy} \rightarrow C_6H_{12}O_6 + 6O_2$$

The overall change in photosynthesis is the reverse of respiration.

99.3 Carbon monoxide and cyanide ions are highly poisonous. A sign that someone has been poisoned by either of these two chemicals is that the person's blood changes colour. They both have the effect of preventing oxygen being taken up by the blood stream. What might happen to haemoglobin to stop oxygen being taken up?

99.5 Ozone (trioxygen)

Ozone, O_3, has a triangular shape (Figure 99.4). Both bonds have the same length, about 128 nm, so they must have the same degree of single and double bond character. We know that there are six valence electrons on each oxygen atom. We must account for all of them in describing the bonding. If we use valence bond theory, we claim that each bond involves a set of resonance hybrids in which one of the bonds is a double bond, and the other a coordinate bond. You must remember that the actual structure does not swap between the resonance structures. Rather, the pictures suggest that each bond has partly the nature of a double bond, and partly that of a single bond.

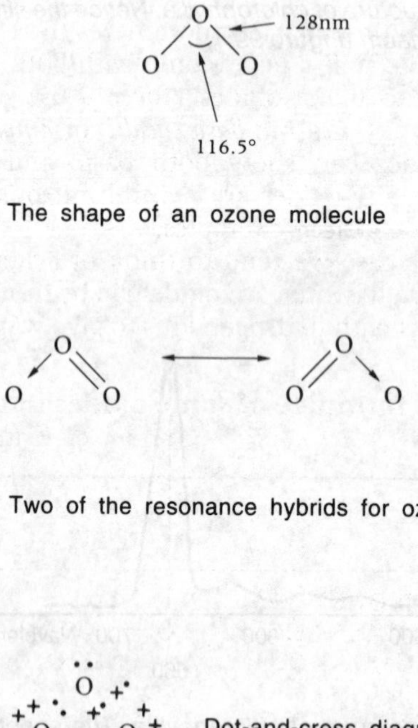

128nm

116.5°

The shape of an ozone molecule

Two of the resonance hybrids for ozone

Dot-and-cross diagram for the hybrid on the left

Figure 99.4 The structure of an ozone (trioxygen) molecule

In the laboratory, ozone can be made by passing oxygen through a strong electric field. An equilibrium is set up:

$$3O_2(g) \rightleftharpoons 2O_3(g)$$

Ozone is only a metastable allotrope, always having a tendency to convert back into oxygen. It is a vigorous oxidising agent, often reacting with the evolution of oxygen. For example,

$$2I^-(aq) + H_2O(l) + O_3(g) \rightarrow I_2(s) + 2OH^-(aq) + O_2(g)$$
$$S^{2-}(aq) + 2O_3(g) \rightarrow SO_4^{2-}(aq) + O_2(g)$$

Some 30 km above the Earth's surface oxygen molecules can be split apart by ultraviolet light from the Sun. Some of the atoms join with other oxygen molecules to make ozone:

$$O_2(g) + O(g) \rightarrow O_3(g)$$

This reaction has been of extreme importance in the maintenance of life on Earth. The reason is that ozone has the ability to absorb ultraviolet radiation. This is radiation of short wavelength, and therefore of high energy. Other molecules in the atmosphere also absorb electromagnetic radiation, but none of them absorb ultraviolet radiation to a useful extent. If too much ultraviolet radiation reaches Earth, two things happen.

First, the energy balance of the Earth will be upset. The radiation that is reflected from the Earth's surface, which includes rocks, trees and animals, etc., has a longer wavelength than the incoming radiation. The reflected radiation tends to be in the infrared region of the spectrum, which is easily absorbed by molecules in the atmosphere (Figure 99.5). That is, the reflected energy is trapped in the Earth's atmosphere; less than 10% escapes into space. This is known as the *greenhouse effect*. (The glass in a greenhouse allows higher energy radiation through, but tends to trap the reflected radiation. This ensures that the temperature in the greenhouse rises.) If ultraviolet radiation reaches Earth in large amounts, the likely outcome is an increase in the temperature of the atmosphere. Carbon dioxide is one of the substances responsible for the greenhouse effect, but methane and chlorofluorocarbons are also involved. Over the last few hundred years the amount of carbon dioxide in the atmosphere has increased by 25%, and that of methane by 200%. There is no doubt that the temperature of the atmosphere has been rising. This, together with an increase in the radiation reaching Earth owing to the depletion of the ozone layer, is extremely worrying. The effects on the climate could be disastrous. Among other things, patterns of rainfall and agriculture would change drastically. Some people think that such changes are already happening.

Secondly, increased ultraviolet radiation will bring changes in the behaviour of cells in living tissue. One unpleasant outcome will be an increase in the incidence of skin cancers. Such an increase has already occurred in some countries. This has been a result of more people taking holidays during which they lie in the sun for many hours each day. The longer the time spent in the sun, the more ultraviolet radiation hits the skin, and the

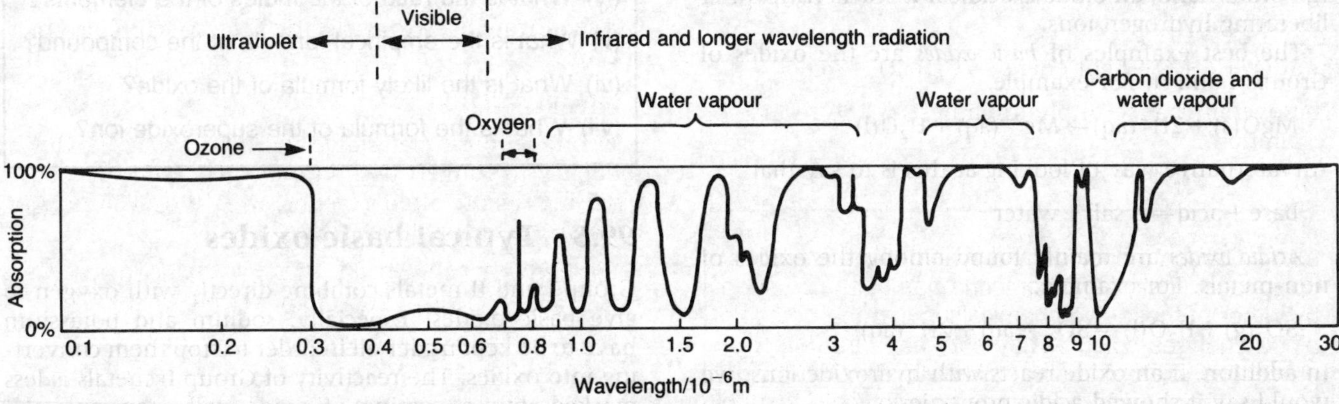

***Figure 99.5** The peaks on this graph show those parts of the spectrum which are absorbed by oxygen, ozone, water vapour and carbon dioxide. (Adapted from: White, I. D. et al. (1987).* Environmental Systems, *Allen and Unwin, London, figure 3.6, p. 47)*

more likely is it that changes in the skin take place.

In 1985 researchers noticed that a gap in the ozone layer appeared above the Antarctic. This hole in the ozone layer was at first thought to be just one of the many fluctuations that take place in the Earth's atmosphere from time to time. However, it has been shown that it is mainly due to the presence of chlorofluorocarbons (CFCs) reacting with ozone. CFCs are gases that are easily liquefied, and in most conditions they are unreactive molecules. Both properties allow them to be used in aerosols, for example in deodorant sprays, paint sprays and furniture polishes, in refrigerators and so on. The problem is that they *do* react with ozone. When the CFCs diffuse into the ozone layer the ozone is removed faster than it can be replaced. The dangers caused by CFCs have now been recognised, and many manufacturers are finding different chemicals to use instead. However, it is certain that the decline in their use will have come too late for many future sufferers from skin cancer. Whether it has come too late to prevent irreversible changes in climatic conditions is less clear.

99.4 Why can molecules in the atmosphere absorb infrared radiation? What happens to the energy supplied by the radiation?

99.6 Ozonolysis

Ozone has a use in organic chemistry. In the right conditions it has the effect of breaking apart molecules with double bonds. The method is known as *ozonolysis*. Essentially, the alkene reacts with ozone to give an unstable ozonide. If the ozonide is treated with dilute acid it breaks up. We can show the result of an ozonolysis experiment on an alkene like this:

$$>C{=}C< \longrightarrow >C\overset{O}{\diagup\diagdown}C< \text{ (with } O{-}O \text{ bridge)} \longrightarrow >C{=}O \;+\; O{=}C<$$

As you can see, an oxygen atom is joined on to each carbon atom. The molecules made will be aldehydes or ketones. In Unit 118 you will discover how the nature of these types of molecule can be determined. Once this is done the point of ozonolysis becomes clear: it allows us to find out where the double bond was in the original molecule.

99.5 An alkene was used in an ozonolysis experiment. One mole of the alkene was found to react with four moles of ozone. What does this tell you about the alkene?

99.7 There are four types of oxide

The one chemical property that dominates the chemistry of oxygen is its ability to combine with both metals and non-metals to make oxides (Table 99.3). Oxides can be of four types: *neutral, basic, acidic,* or *amphoteric*. Amphoteric oxides can show both basic and acidic properties. Not many oxides are neutral: nitrous oxide and carbon monoxide are examples.

As is often the case we tend to think of acidity and basicity in relation to water. An oxide will be thought to be basic if it reacts with hydrogen ions to give water. On

Table 99.3. The formulae of some oxides in the Periodic Table*

Group I	*Group II*	*Group III*	*Group IV*	*Group V*	*Group VI*	*Group VII*
Li_2O	BeO	B_2O_3	CO_2	N_2O_5	O_2	F_2O
Na_2O	MgO	Al_2O_3	SiO_2	P_4O_{10}	SO_2	Cl_2O
K_2O	CaO	Ga_2O_3	GeO_2	As_2O_3	SeO_2	Br_2O
Rb_2O	SrO	In_2O_3	SnO	Sb_2O_3	TeO_2	I_2O_5
Cs_2O	BaO	Tl_2O	PbO	Bi_2O_3	PoO_2	

*Not all oxides are shown. Especially, nitrogen has many oxides. There are no noble gas oxides

the other hand, an oxide is acidic if it reacts with water liberating hydrogen ions.

The best examples of *basic oxides* are the oxides of Groups I and II. For example,

$$MgO(s) + 2H^+(aq) \rightarrow Mg^{2+}(aq) + H_2O(l)$$

An alternative way of looking at this is to say that

base + acid → a salt + water

Acidic oxides are mainly found among the oxides of non-metals. For example,

$$SO_3(g) + H_2O(l) \rightarrow SO_4{}^{2-}(aq) + 2H^+(aq)$$

In addition, if an oxide reacts with hydroxide ions, we would say it showed acidic properties.

Aluminium oxide is an example of an *amphoteric oxide*. It shows basic properties by reacting with hydrogen ions in the usual way:

$$Al_2O_3(s) + 6H^+(aq) \rightarrow 2Al^{3+}(aq) + 3H_2O(l)$$

However, it also dissolves in alkali in a reaction that we can write as

$$Al_2O_3(s) + 6OH^-(aq) + 3H_2O(l) \rightarrow 2Al(OH)_6{}^{3-}(aq)$$

or

$$Al_2O_3(s) + 2OH^-(aq) + 5H_2O(l) \rightarrow 2[Al(OH)_4(H_2O)_2]^-(aq)$$

Sometimes the product ions are written as the aluminate ion, $AlO_2{}^-$.

Many non-metals also exist in combination with oxygen as ions; for example sulphate ions, $SO_4{}^{2-}$, and nitrate ions, $NO_3{}^-$. Such ions are called *oxoanions*. Oxoanions are often thermodynamically and kinetically stable. As such they exist in salts and minerals of many types, and in solutions of acids such as sulphuric and nitric acids. It is wise to know something of the bonding in these ions. Make sure you have read Unit 14, which explains the key points.

99.6 Zinc oxide, ZnO, is amphoteric. It dissolves in alkali to give the ion $Zn(OH)_4{}^{2-}$.

(i) What is the equation for the reaction?

(ii) What is the equation for the reaction of the oxide with hydrogen ions?

99.7 Oxides and peroxides are not the only types of compound that metals can make with oxygen. *Superoxides* are also possible.

Here is some information that you should use to work out the formula of sodium superoxide: 1.15 g of sodium reacted with oxygen at a high pressure gives 2.75 g of a white powder, sodium superoxide.

(i) What mass of oxygen was combined with the sodium?

(ii) How many moles of oxygen *atoms* is this?

(iii) How many moles of sodium were used?

(iv) What is the ratio of the moles of the elements?

(v) What is the empirical formula of the compound?

(vi) What is the likely formula of the oxide?

(vii) What is the formula of the superoxide ion?

99.8 Typical basic oxides

Group I and II metals combine directly with oxygen to give basic oxides. Especially, sodium and potassium have to be kept under oil in order to stop them converting into oxides. The reactivity of Group II metals is less marked, but a coating of oxide will soon give the otherwise shiny metal surfaces a dull grey appearance. Some, like magnesium, burn violently in air. Typical reactions are

Group I $\quad 4Na(s) + O_2(g) \rightarrow 2Na_2O(s)$
Group II $\quad 2Mg(s) + O_2(g) \rightarrow 2MgO(s)$

However, if the Group I metals are heated with oxygen they make *peroxides*, which contain $O_2{}^{2-}$ ions:

$$2Na(s) + O_2(g) \rightarrow \underset{\text{sodium peroxide}}{Na_2O_2(s)}$$

The Group II oxides can be converted into peroxides by heating them in oxygen; for example,

$$2BaO(s) + O_2(g) \rightarrow 2BaO_2(s)$$

The oxides are generally ionic, although, as is often the case in its reactions, beryllium at the top of Group II is an exception. Beryllium oxide, BeO, is covalent.

The Group I oxides dissolve in water to give strongly alkaline solutions:

$$Na_2O(s) + H_2O(l) \rightarrow 2Na^+(aq) + 2OH^-(aq)$$

The Group II oxides react less vigorously with water giving hydroxides that are only partially soluble in water and weakly alkaline. For example,

$$MgO(s) + H_2O(l) \rightleftharpoons Mg(OH)_2(s)$$
$$Mg(OH)_2(s) \rightleftharpoons Mg^{2+}(aq) + 2OH^-(aq)$$

The solubility product of magnesium hydroxide is small, which shows that there are very few hydroxide ions in solution. However, the solubilities of the hydroxides do increase down the Group.

99.9 Typical acidic oxides

The oxides of sulphur and phosphorus are typical acidic oxides in that they all react with water to give acidic solutions; e.g.

$$SO_2(g) + H_2O(l) \rightarrow SO_3{}^{2-}(aq) + H^+(aq)$$
sulphurous acid

$$SO_3(g) + H_2O(l) \rightarrow SO_4{}^{2-}(aq) + 2H^+(aq)$$
sulphuric acid

$$P_4O_{10}(s) + 4H_2O(l) \rightarrow H_3PO_4(aq) \rightleftharpoons 2PO_4{}^{3-}(aq) + 6H^+(aq)$$
phosphoric(V) acid

Nitrogen dioxide, NO_2, is acidic, but nitrogen monoxide, NO, and dinitrogen oxide, N_2O, are neutral:

$$2NO_2(g) + H_2O(l) \rightarrow NO_2^-(aq) + NO_3^-(aq) + 2H^+(aq)$$

The resulting solution is a mixture of nitrous, HNO_2, and nitric, HNO_3, acids.

Some metals can give acidic oxides. Usually they are transition metals, and have oxides that have a particularly high proportion of oxygen in them. An example is manganese(VII) oxide,

$$Mn_2O_7(s) + H_2O(l) \rightarrow 2MnO_4^-(aq) + 2H^+(aq)$$

The solution contains the purple manganate(VII) ion.

99.8 Oxides that react with water to give acids can be called *acid anhydrides*. It is possible to work out the formula of an anhydride by subtracting the formula of water from the formula of the acid. For example, sulphur trioxide is the anhydride of sulphuric acid: $H_2SO_4 - H_2O = SO_3$. For an acid like hypochlorous acid, HClO, we have to write the change as $2HClO - H_2O = Cl_2O$. The anhydride is chlorine monoxide. What is the anhydride of (i) carbonic acid, H_2CO_3; (ii) perchloric acid, $HClO_4$; (iii) nitric acid, HNO_3?

99.9 At one time, before the poisonous properties of lead were realised, paints contained lead compounds. Especially, lead(II) carbonate, $PbCO_3$, was used as a white pigment. Unfortunately, owing to air often being polluted by acids and sulphides, the pigment was converted to black lead(II) sulphide, PbS. A dilute solution of hydrogen peroxide can be used to remove the black discoloration by oxidising the sulphide to sulphate. What is the equation for the reaction?

99.10 Peroxides

The most important peroxide is hydrogen peroxide, H_2O_2 (Figure 99.6). When pure, it is a colourless liquid, but it is too dangerous to use in this form in the laboratory. Instead, it is kept in solution with water. Often the concentrations of the solutions are given as a number of 'volumes'. This gives a measure of the volume of oxygen that would be given off from a given volume of solution. For example, a 100 volume solution would give approximately 100 cm³ of oxygen from 1 cm³ of solution.

The equation for the decomposition is

$$2H_2O_2(aq) \rightarrow 2H_2O(l) + O_2(g)$$

and, as we found in Unit 77, it can be catalysed by a variety of substances, especially manganese(IV) oxide. The easiest way of making oxygen in the laboratory is to add this oxide to hydrogen peroxide solution.

A solution of hydrogen peroxide is very slightly acidic through the reaction

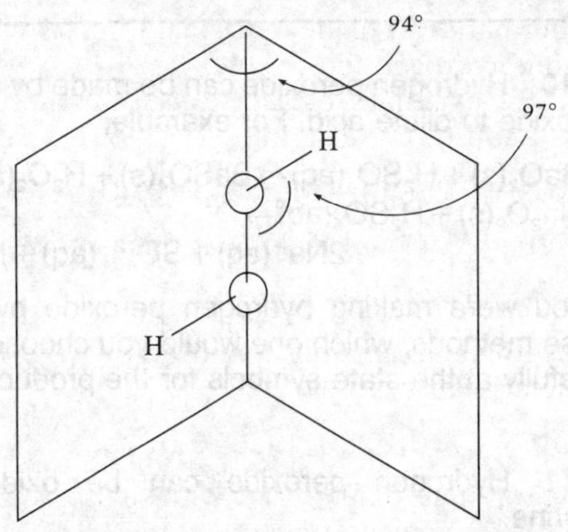

Figure 99.6 One way of explaining the shape of an H_2O_2 molecule. The hydrogen atoms would lie on the pages of a partly opened book, and the oxygen atoms along the spine

$$H_2O_2(aq) + H_2O(l) \rightleftharpoons H_3O^+(aq) + HO_2^-(aq)$$

It is possible to regard peroxides as salts of hydrogen peroxide.

Apart from its use in making oxygen, hydrogen peroxide is a useful oxidising agent. At one time it was widely used as a crude type of bleach for hair. This gave rise to women (usually) who had their hair bleached being called 'peroxide blondes'. However, as far as more mundane matters of chemistry are concerned, hydrogen peroxide can react in two ways. In acid it gives rise to a redox potential of +1.77 V, but in alkali the potential can drop to as low as +0.22 V. This behaviour means that:

In acid, hydrogen peroxide is an oxidising agent.

However, in alkaline conditions some reagents are able to oxidise hydrogen peroxide because they have a redox potential greater than +0.22 V. Therefore:

In alkali, hydrogen peroxide is a reducing agent.

Here are some examples.

As an oxidising agent

$$2I^-(aq) + H_2O_2(aq) + 2H^+(aq) \rightarrow I_2(s) + 2H_2O(l)$$
iodide → iodine

$$2Fe^{2+}(aq) + H_2O_2(aq) + 2H^+(aq) \rightarrow 2Fe^{3+}(aq) + 2H_2O(l)$$
iron(II) → iron(III)

As a reducing agent

$$2Fe(CN)_6^{3-}(aq) + H_2O_2(aq) + 2OH^-(aq) \rightarrow 2Fe(CN)_6^{4-}(aq) + 2H_2O(l) + O_2(g)$$
hexacyanoferrate(III) → hexacyanoferrate(II)

$$2MnO_4^-(aq) + 5H_2O_2(aq) + 6H^+(aq) \rightarrow 2Mn^{2+}(aq) + 8H_2O(l) + 5O_2(g)$$
manganate(VII) → manganese(II)

99.10 Hydrogen peroxide can be made by adding a peroxide to dilute acid. For example,

$$BaO_2(s) + H_2SO_4(aq) \rightarrow BaSO_4(s) + H_2O_2(aq)$$
$$Na_2O_2(s) + H_2SO_4(aq) \rightarrow 2Na^+(aq) + SO_4^{2-}(aq) + H_2O_2(aq)$$

If you were making hydrogen peroxide by one of these methods, which one would you choose? (Look carefully at the state symbols for the products.)

99.11 Hydrogen peroxide can be oxidised by chlorine.

(i) What ion does chlorine turn into when it has been reduced?

(ii) What is the equation for the reaction?

99.12 Design an apparatus that could be used to make oxygen from hydrogen peroxide solution. Your apparatus should allow the oxygen to be given off in controlled amounts.

99.13 At one time oxygen was made by heating barium oxide in air. Provided the temperature was not too high, barium peroxide was made. The product was then heated much more strongly, which caused the peroxide to decompose. We can show the reactions as involving an equilibrium

$$2BaO(s) + O_2(g) \rightleftharpoons 2BaO_2(s)$$

Some time later it was discovered that oxygen could be made from the peroxide more easily by adjusting the pressure in the apparatus. What changes in pressure would you make during the reaction?

Answers

99.1 At the temperature of liquid oxygen (less than 90 K) the sodium and oxygen have insufficient energy to get over the energy barrier.

99.2

$$\Delta H^\ominus(\text{reaction}) = 2\Delta H_f^\ominus(H_2O) - \Delta H_f^\ominus(N_2H_4) = -534.2\text{ kJ mol}^{-1}$$

99.3 Carbon monoxide and cyanide ions are able to bond more strongly to the iron atom in haemoglobin than can oxygen. If you were to breathe in carbon monoxide for any length of time, your haemoglobin would become saturated with carbon monoxide molecules rather than oxygen. As a result all the body processes that rely on a supply of oxygen gradually cease. Death is the result.

99.4 Infrared radiation has the right amount of energy to excite the vibrations of molecules (see Unit 24). The energy increases the vibrational energy of the molecules.

99.5 One mole of ozone is absorbed for each double bond, so there are four double bonds in the alkene.

99.6 (i) $ZnO(s) + 2OH^-(aq) + H_2O(l) \rightarrow Zn(OH)_4^{2-}(aq)$
(ii) $ZnO(s) + 2H^+(aq) \rightarrow Zn^{2+}(aq) + H_2O(l)$

99.7 (i) 2.75 g − 1.15 g = 1.60 g.

(ii) 1.60 g/16 g mol^{-1} = 0.1 mol of oxygen atoms.

(iii) 1.15 g/23 g mol^{-1} = 0.05 mol of sodium atoms.

(iv) 2 mol oxygen to 1 mol sodium.

(v) NaO_2.

(vi) Usually we need to know the relative molecular mass in order to work out the molecular formula from the empirical formula. In this case we have the simplest whole number ratio of the atoms. If NaO_2 is not the correct formula, we would have to consider Na_2O_4, Na_3O_6, etc. All these are most unlikely, so we are left with NaO_2 as the molecular formula.

(vii) Because sodium always forms the Na^+ ion, the superoxide ion has the formula O_2^-.

99.8 (i) CO_2, carbon dioxide

(ii) $2HClO_4 - H_2O = Cl_2O_7$, dichlorine heptaoxide

(iii) $2HNO_3 - H_2O = N_2O_5$, dinitrogen pentaoxide.

99.9

$$\underset{\text{sulphide}}{S^{2-}(aq)} + 2H_2O_2(aq) + 4H^+(aq) \rightarrow \underset{\text{sulphate}}{SO_4^{2-}(aq)} + 4H_2O(l)$$

99.10 The advantage of the first reaction is that the barium sulphate is highly insoluble in water and can be filtered off. This leaves a fairly pure solution of hydrogen peroxide behind. To set against this is that the insoluble sulphate can form on the surface of the barium peroxide. This will prevent the acid reacting, so bringing the reaction to a halt before all the peroxide is used up. In the second reaction all the barium peroxide can be used up because the products are all soluble. However, the disadvantage is that the solution will be contaminated with sodium and sulphate ions.

99.11 (i) Chloride ion, Cl^-.

(ii) $$\underset{\text{chlorine}}{Cl_2(g)} + H_2O_2(aq) + 2OH^-(aq) \rightarrow \underset{\text{chloride}}{2Cl^-(aq)} + 2H_2O(l) + O_2(g)$$

99.12 The apparatus of Figure 90.2 would be suitable.

99.13 If we use Le Chatelier's principle, we can see that the decomposition of the peroxide is favoured by a *low* pressure. Therefore, after the peroxide is made, the pressure in the apparatus should be reduced.

UNIT 99 SUMMARY

- Oxygen:
  - (i) Has two allotropes, O_2, and trioxygen (ozone), O_3.
  - (ii) Is essential to life.
  - (iii) Is released into the atmosphere through photosynthesis in green plants.
  - (iv) Is slightly soluble in water, essential for aquatic life.
  - (v) Is an oxidising agent.
  - (vi) Supports combustion.
- Laboratory preparation:
  By the decomposition of hydrogen peroxide using manganese(IV) oxide as a catalyst;

  $$2H_2O_2(aq) \rightarrow 2H_2O(l) + O_2(g)$$

- Isolation:
  By the liquefaction of air followed by fractional distillation.

Reactions

- With hydrogen:

  $$2H_2(g) + O_2(g) \rightarrow 2H_2O(g)$$

  This reaction is used in fuel cells to generate electricity.
- With metals and non-metals:
  Oxides made, e.g. magnesium, carbon and sulphur burn in oxygen;

  $$2Mg(s) + O_2(g) \rightarrow 2MgO(s)$$
  $$C(s) + O_2(g) \rightarrow CO_2(g)$$
  $$S(s) + O_2(g) \rightarrow SO_2(g)$$

- Combustion reactions:
  Among the most important is the burning of organic matter, e.g. wood, coal, oil and natural gas. Carbon dioxide and water vapour are released.
- Photosynthesis:
  The conversion of carbon dioxide and water into carbohydrate and oxygen using light energy, and chlorophyll as a catalyst;

  $$6CO_2 + 6H_2O + \text{light energy} \rightarrow C_6H_{12}O_6 + 6O_2$$

- Respiration:
  A variety of combustion reaction that releases energy for use by living systems;

  $$C_6H_{12}O_6 + 6O_2 \rightarrow 6CO_2 + 6H_2O + \text{energy}$$

Compounds

- Oxides:
  - (i) The oxides of metals are basic, e.g. CaO. Group I oxides dissolve to give highly alkaline solutions;

    e.g. $Na_2O(s) + H_2O(l) \rightarrow 2Na^+(aq) + 2OH^-(aq)$
  - (ii) The oxides of non-metals are acidic;

    e.g. $SO_3(g) + H_2O(l) \rightarrow SO_4^{2-}(aq) + 2H^+(aq)$
  - (iii) Some oxides are neutral, e.g. CO.
  - (iv) Some oxides are amphoteric, e.g. Al_2O_3 dissolves in both acid and alkali;

    $$Al_2O_3(s) + 6H^+(aq) \rightarrow 2Al^{3+}(aq) + 3H_2O(l)$$
    $$Al_2O_3(s) + 6OH^-(aq) + 3H_2O(l) \rightarrow 2Al(OH)_6^{3-}(aq)$$
- Water:
  An extremely abundant oxide that is essential for life, and a good solvent.
- Oxoanions:
  Occur in a wide range of compounds, e.g. sulphate, SO_4^{2-}, nitrate, NO_3^-, carbonate, CO_3^{2-}, manganate(VII), MnO_4^-, chlorate(VII), ClO_4^-.
- Peroxides:
  - (i) Examples are barium peroxide, BaO_2, sodium peroxide, Na_2O_2, and hydrogen peroxide, H_2O_2. All are vigorous oxidising agents and decompose, giving off oxygen.
  - (ii) Hydrogen peroxide is used to prepare oxygen;

    $$2H_2O_2(aq) \rightarrow 2H_2O(l) + O_2(g)$$
  - (iii) H_2O_2 acts as an oxidising agent in acidic conditions, and as a reducing agent in alkaline conditions.
- Trioxygen (ozone)
  - (i) The ozone layer in the upper atmosphere controls the amount of ultraviolet light reaching the Earth's surface. The layer is in danger of being destroyed by chlorofluorocarbons.
  - (ii) Trioxygen is an oxidising agent;

    e.g. $S^{2-}(aq) + O_3(g) \rightarrow SO_4^{2-}(aq) + O_2(g)$
- Ozonolysis:
  Is important in organic chemistry. Alkenes are converted into mixtures of aldehydes and/or ketones; e.g.

$$RR'C{=}CR''R''' \xrightarrow[\text{(ii) } H^+]{\text{(i) } O_3} RR'C{=}O + O{=}CR''R'''$$

100

Group VI

100.1 The nature of the elements

You will find a summary of the important physical properties of the elements in Table 100.1, and their uses are shown in Table 100.2. We have discussed the chemistry of oxygen in some detail in the previous unit. Here we shall concentrate on the other elements in the Group, especially sulphur. As is common with the first member of a Group, the properties of oxygen are not necessarily typical of the Group as a whole. For example, oxygen is the only gas among them, and has by far the highest electronegativity. Oxygen tends to bond with nearly every element in the Periodic Table, which cannot be said of the other members of the Group. Similarly, oxygen will make ionic compounds with the most reactive metals, whereas unless they react with a Group I metal, the sulphides, selenides, etc., are normally covalent (even though they may be polar). There is the usual tendency for metallic nature to increase going down the Group. However, polonium, right at the bottom of the Group, which displays the most metallic nature, is hardly a pleasant element to study: it is radioactive. One indication of its metallic nature is that it makes an ionic oxide, PoO_2. Polonium is the only B metal in the Group.

Sulphur and selenium possess allotropes, with those of sulphur being the most important. The structure of, and relationship between, rhombic and monoclinic sulphur was discussed in Unit 57. You should look there for details about them. However, just to remind you, both allotropes are built of puckered rings of eight sulphur atoms. (Selenium has a similar structure.)

Another major difference to oxygen comes about through the use of d orbitals in bonding. In many sulphur compounds the bonds to sulphur are shorter than expected. This suggests a degree of double bond character, which can occur if sulphur makes use of its empty 3d orbitals as well as its s and p orbitals. Similarly, apart from oxygen the elements can make up to six covalent bonds by using d orbitals, e.g. sulphur in sulphates and sulphur hexafluoride, SF_6. (The empty 3d orbitals

Table 100.2. Uses of the elements in Group VI

Element	*Main uses*
Oxygen	Aids to breathing
Sulphur	Sulphuric acid manufacture Fertilisers Explosives, dyes, polymers, detergents and myriad other chemical processes
Selenium	In some alloys The manufacture of light sensitive resistors and semiconductors Medicines
Tellurium	Alloys Semiconductors In photocopiers
Polonium	Little or no commercial use

Table 100.1. Physical properties of the elements in Group VI

Symbol	*Oxygen* O	*Sulphur* S	*Selenium* Se	*Tellurium* Te	*Polonium* Po
Electron structure	(He)$2s^22p^4$	(Ne)$3s^23p^4$	(Ar)$3d^{10}4s^24p^4$	(Kr)$4d^{10}5s^25p^4$	(Xe)$5d^{10}6s^26p^4$
Electronegativity	3.5	2.5	2.4	2.1	
I.E./kJ mol^{-1}	1314	1000	950	830	700
Melting point/°C	−219	114.5	217	450	254
Boiling point/°C	−183	444.6	685	1390	962
Atomic radius/pm	74	104	117	137	164
Principal oxid. no.	−2	−2,+4,+6	−2,+4,+6	−2,+4,+6	+2,+4

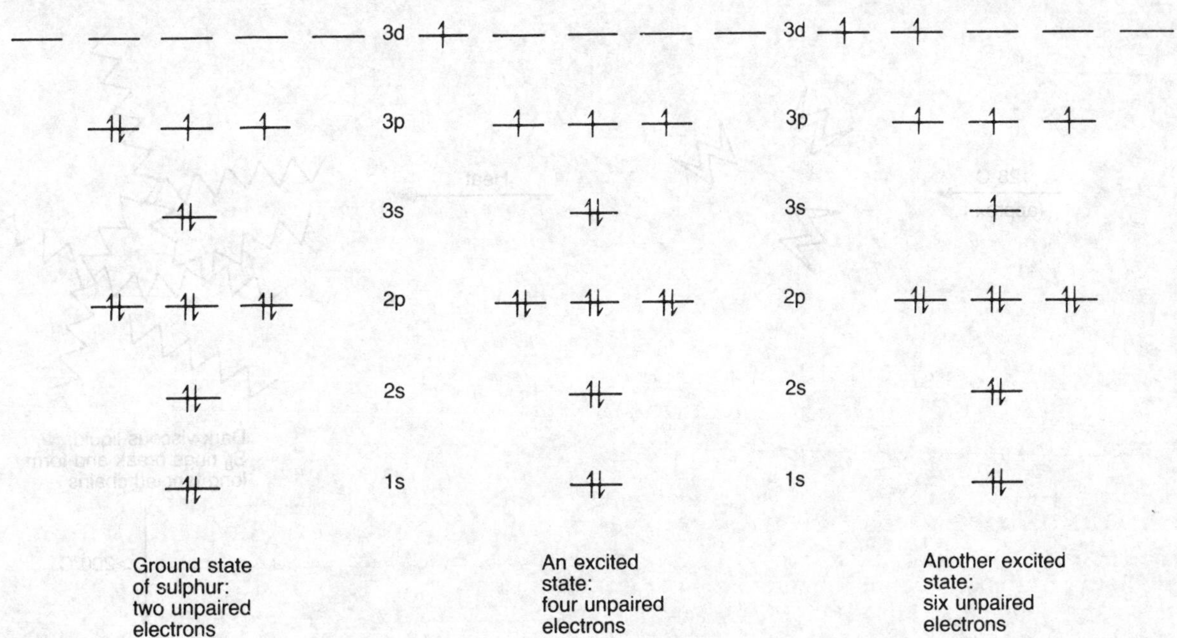

Figure 100.1 *Ways in which sulphur can have two, four or six unpaired electrons, and then make two, four or six covalent bonds*

belonging to oxygen are too high in energy to be used in bonding.)

In fact there are three possibilities for sulphur in using its valence electrons together with its 3d orbitals. Let us assume that electrons can be promoted between the 3s, 3p and 3d sets while keeping the order of energies of the orbitals constant (this is not really possible; see section 17.4 on hybridisation). Then sulphur can have two, four, or six unpaired electrons (Figure 100.1). This is reflected in the common oxidation states of the element (Figure 100.2), and especially in the nature of its halides (see Tables 100.1 and 100.5). The other members of Group VI also have d orbitals available for them to use in bonding.

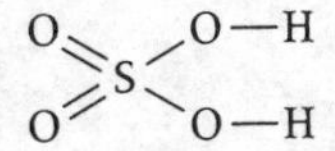

$$\begin{array}{c} O \\ \| \\ \end{array} S(=O)_2(OH)_2$$

Figure 100.2 *The structure of sulphuric acid shows sulphur making six bonds to the four oxygen atoms. This number of bonds occurs when sulphur uses its 3d orbitals in bonding*

> **100.1** What is wrong with this statement: 'oxygen forms the oxide ion, O^{2-}, in many compounds in order that it can gain the noble gas structure of neon'?
>
> **100.2** One isotope of polonium, $^{218}_{84}Po$, decays by alpha emission with a half-life of about 3 min. What is the product of its decay?

100.2 The action of heat on sulphur

If you heat sulphur in a test tube fairly quickly, you will find that the yellow solid changes into a pale orange, mobile (i.e. runny) liquid. This happens at around 128°C. Even at this temperature some of the S_8 rings are breaking apart. Although the change from rhombic to monoclinic sulphur takes place at 96.5°C (the transition temperature, see Unit 57), you cannot see this change take place, and in any case rapid heating does not allow an equilibrium to be set up between the two allotropes. On further heating the colour darkens, and the liquid becomes more viscous. The increase in viscosity is due to many S_8 rings breaking apart, and the sulphur atoms joining to make long chains up to 10^6 atoms long. The chains become entangled and cannot slide over one another at all easily. Viscosity is a maximum near 200°C. Eventually the liquid becomes almost black in colour and mobile again as many chains break apart to give smaller molecules. Although sulphur will not boil until 444°C, fumes of sulphur will be given off. If you do this experiment, take care: the hot fumes may well catch fire, giving a blue flame and pungent fumes of sulphur dioxide. If you pour the almost black liquid into cold water, an orange/brown solid is produced. This solid is called *plastic sulphur*, and is elastic. Plastic sulphur is *not* an allotrope of sulphur. It consists of a tangle of long chains of sulphur atoms. Gradually the solid loses its rubbery feel; it becomes hard and takes on the yellow colour of rhombic sulphur to which all of it eventually converts. The key stages in the process are shown in Figure 100.3.

100.3 The extraction of sulphur

Sulphur is found in many minerals, especially combined with B metals like copper, tin, mercury and lead. Sulphur can be obtained as a by-product of the extraction of these metals from their ores. However, this is a costly and involved process. Some deposits of oil and

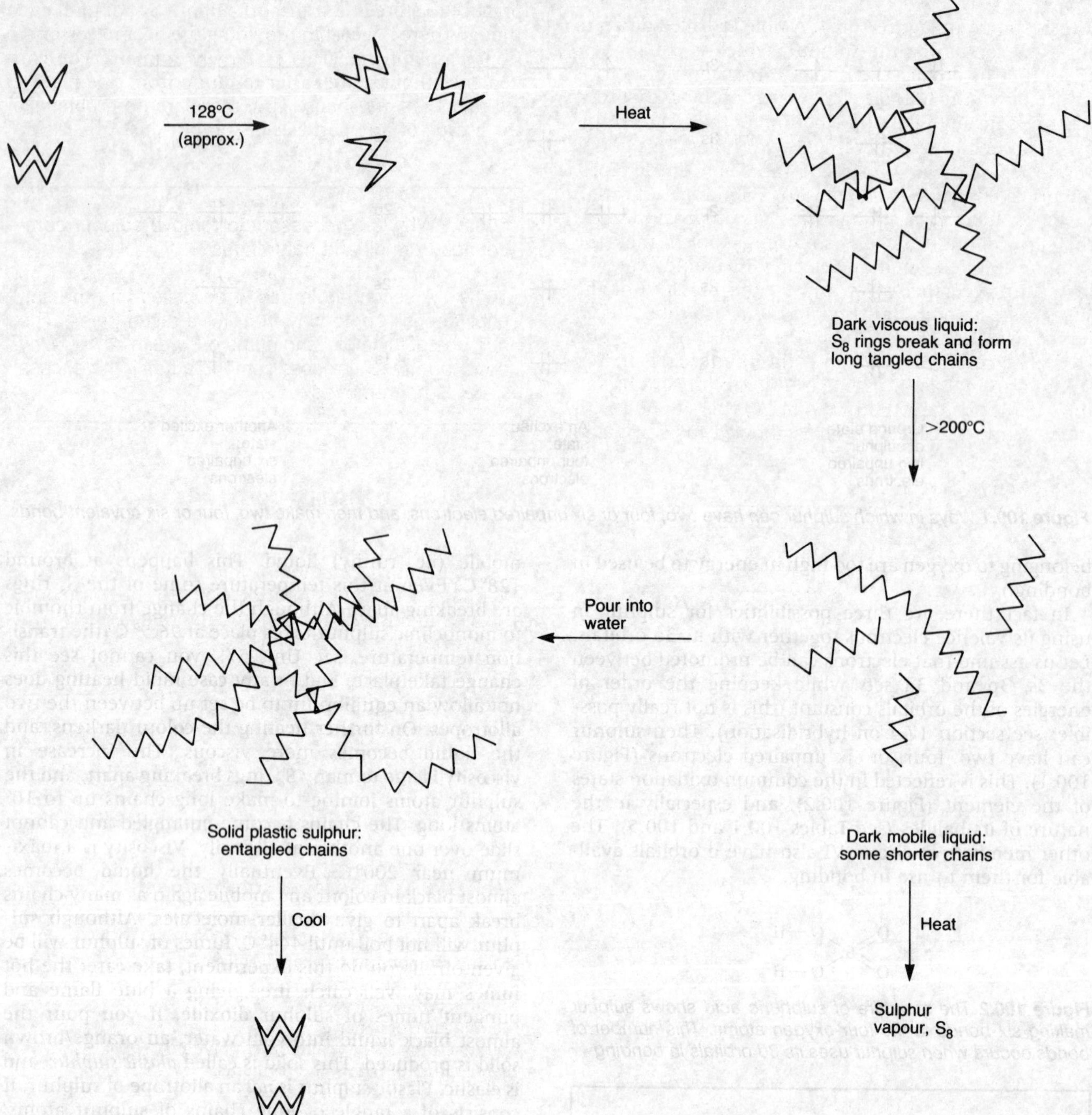

***Figure 100.3** The action of rapid heating on sulphur*

natural gas contain a significant amount of sulphur, particularly in the form of hydrogen sulphide. Owing to the necessity of removing all traces of sulphur compounds before the oil and gas can be converted into anything useful, some oil refineries are able to sell the sulphur they have to extract. It is far easier to extract sulphur directly out of the ground using a method invented by Hermann Frasch about 100 years ago. In certain parts of the world, especially USA, Poland and Iraq, there are huge deposits of elemental sulphur buried underground. Often the sulphur is mixed with other minerals, and although it is possible to dig the mixture out and separate the sulphur, Frasch developed a better method.

(a) *The Frasch process*

This is shown in Figure 100.4. A hole is drilled down to the rock containing the sulphur, which is usually less than 1000 m down. Then a set of concentric tubes is placed down the hole. The lower part of the widest tube has holes through it and the bottom of the tube terminates in a metal surround drilled with holes. This grid is connected to the second of the three concentric pipes. Superheated water at about 160°C is pumped through the outer tube. Even though the water cools as it enters the surrounding rock, it is sufficiently hot to melt the sulphur. Molten sulphur mixed with some water is forced through the lower grid by the pressure of the superheated water and rises up the inner tube. About half-way up the second tube, the third tube ends and feeds hot compressed air into the mixture of molten sulphur and water. This makes the mixture froth, and the bubbles rise up the tube, taking the sulphur with them. On the surface the air is allowed to escape and

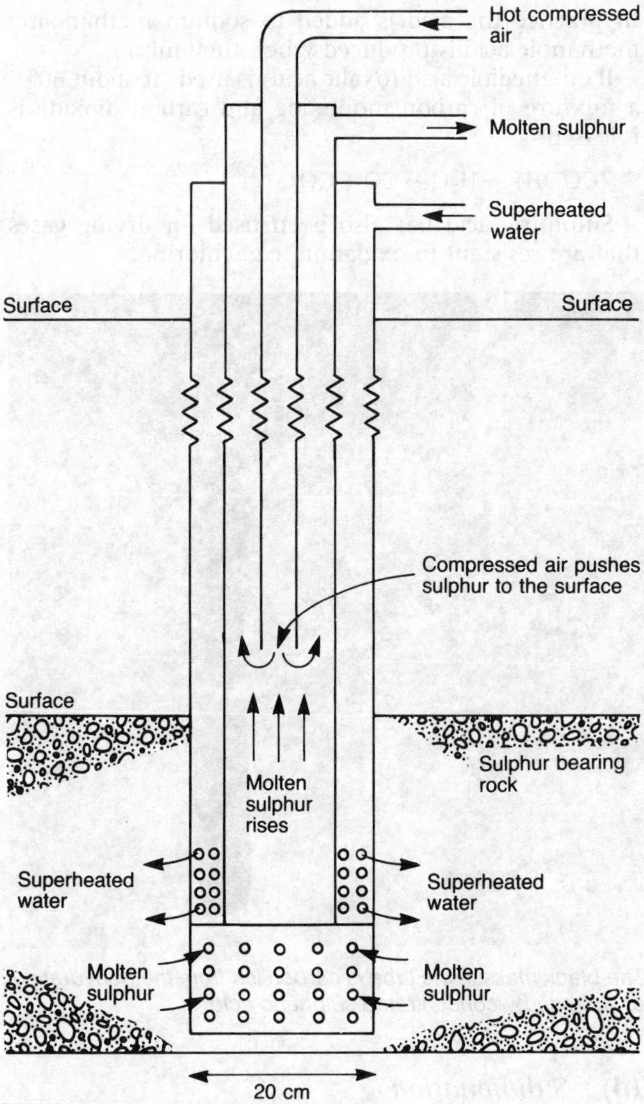

Figure 100.4 *The Frasch process for extracting sulphur*

the sulphur is stored, usually as a liquid. It is common practice to store and transport sulphur as a liquid, even though there is a cost in providing the heat necessary to stop it solidifying. This is largely a matter of convenience; liquids are easier to pump from one place to another than are solids. Also, there are no problems of the escape of fine particles of sulphur dust.

100.3 Why is it necessary to remove sulphur compounds from oil and natural gas?

100.4 A second hole has to be drilled into the sulphur deposit some way from the Frasch pipes. The purpose of this hole is to pump out waste water. Why does the Frasch process come to a halt if the excess water is not removed?

100.4 Sulphuric acid

The majority of sulphur is used to make sulphuric acid. You will find the method of manufacture described in Unit 83. The uses of sulphuric acid are shown in Table 100.3. Sulphuric acid has four different aspects to its chemistry:

(i) in dilute solution it behaves like a typical strong acid;
(ii) when concentrated it shows some oxidising ability;
(iii) when concentrated it is a good dehydrating agent;
(iv) it is a sulphonating agent in organic chemistry.

Table 100.3. The uses of sulphuric acid

Making superphosphate fertiliser
Making ammonium sulphate fertiliser
Processing of metal ores
Manufacture of detergents
Manufacture of paper
Manufacture of Rayon and other polymers
Manufacture of paints and pigments
Electrolyte in heavy duty batteries
Industrial treatment of metals
Laboratory reagent

(a) *As a strong acid*

Sulphuric acid is regarded as a strong acid in water. It dissociates in two stages:

$$H_2SO_4(aq) + H_2O(l) \rightarrow HSO_4^-(aq) + H_3O^+(aq)$$
$$HSO_4^-(aq) + H_2O(l) \rightleftharpoons SO_4^{2-}(aq) + H_3O^+(aq)$$

Only the first dissociation is complete; the second is partial.

When it is *dilute* it shows all the usual properties of

acids. For example, it will give hydrogen with metals above hydrogen in the activity series, e.g.

$$Zn(s) + H_2SO_4(aq) \rightarrow ZnSO_4(aq) + H_2(g)$$

or

$$Zn(s) + 2H_3O^+(aq) \rightarrow Zn^{2+}(aq) + H_2(g) + 2H_2O(l)$$

When reacting in this way, the sulphate ion remains intact.

A mixture of concentrated nitric and sulphuric acids is used as a *nitrating mixture* in organic chemistry. When the two acids are mixed an equilibrium is set up, the active ingredient of which is the nitryl cation (nitronium ion), NO_2^+:

$$HNO_3 + 2H_2SO_4 \rightarrow NO_2^+ + H_3O^+ + 2HSO_4^-$$

The nitryl cation is a sufficiently good electrophile to attack a benzene ring.

(b) *As an oxidising agent*

The acid shows its oxidising nature when it is *concentrated*. For example, it cannot be used to prepare hydrogen bromide from sodium bromide. This is because it can oxidise the hydrogen bromide released:

$$2HBr(g) + H_2SO_4(l) \rightarrow Br_2(l) + SO_2(g) + 2H_2O(l)$$

(You will find details of this and similar reactions in Unit 101 on the halogens.)

The oxidising reaction is a feature of the sulphate ion, in which sulphur has the high oxidation state (or number) of +6. We have said before that high oxidation states lead to oxidation reactions because the element involved tends to take electrons and revert to a lower oxidation state.

A variety of possibilities exist for the way it reacts, of which the most important follow:

(i) Sulphur dioxide given off

$$SO_4^{2-}(aq) + 4H^+(aq) + 2e^- \rightarrow H_2SO_3(aq) + H_2O(l)$$

or

$$SO_4^{2-}(aq) + 4H^+(aq) + 2e^- \rightarrow SO_2(g) + 2H_2O(l)$$

(ii) Sulphur deposited

$$SO_4^{2-}(aq) + 8H^+(aq) + 6e^- \rightarrow S(s) + 4H_2O(l)$$

(iii) Hydrogen sulphide given off

$$SO_4^{2-}(aq) + 10H^+(aq) + 8e^- \rightarrow H_2S(g) + 4H_2O(l)$$

If you look at the number of electrons involved in each of these changes, you should realise that it is harder to remove six or eight electrons from an atom or ion than to remove two. The first change, where SO_2 is given off, will occur unless the acid is reacting with something that can easily lose electrons. That is, we expect sulphur or hydrogen sulphide only when there is a good reducing agent reacting with the acid. Hydrogen bromide and hydrogen iodide are two of the more common substances that will give these changes; see section 102.1.

Normally the hot, concentrated acid reacts as in the following examples:

$$Cu(s) + 2H_2SO_4(aq) \rightarrow CuSO_4(aq) + 2H_2O(l) + SO_2(g)$$
$$S(s) + 2H_2SO_4(aq) \rightarrow 2H_2O(l) + 3SO_2(g)$$
$$C(s) + 2H_2SO_4(aq) \rightarrow CO_2(g) + 2H_2O(l) + 2SO_2(g)$$

(c) *As a dehydrating agent*

Concentrated sulphuric acid will remove the elements of water from a wide variety of organic compounds. A reaction that you might see performed is the addition of a few drops of the concentrated acid to sugar (glucose). The sugar becomes very hot and froths, leaving a black mass of carbon:

$$C_6H_{12}O_6 - 6H_2O \rightarrow 6C$$

In organic chemistry the acid is used to convert alcohols into alkenes (and vice versa; see section 112.2).

Its dehydrating action on methanoic acid can be used as a method of preparing carbon monoxide:

$$\underset{\text{methanoic acid}}{HCOOH} - H_2O \rightarrow CO$$

In practice the acid is added to sodium methanoate; methanoic acid is produced when they mix.

If ethanedioic acid (oxalic acid) is used, at about 60° C a mixture of carbon monoxide and carbon dioxide is released:

$$(COOH)_2 - H_2O \rightarrow CO + CO_2$$

Sulphuric acid has also been used for drying gases that are resistant to oxidation, e.g. chlorine.

The black mass in the tube is carbon left from the dehydration of sucrose by concentrated sulphuric acid.

(d) *Sulphonation*

Please look at section 113.6 for information about this.

100.5 Apart from those listed above, what other properties are typical of strong acids?

100.6 Which of nitric acid and sulphuric acid is the stronger Brønsted acid, i.e. which donates a proton to the other?

100.7 Here is some information about redox potentials: $E^\ominus_{Cu^{2+}/Cu} = +0.34$ V; $E^\ominus_{Zn^{2+}/Zn} = -0.76$ V; $E^\ominus_{SO_4^{2-}/H_2SO_3} = +0.17$ V; $E^\ominus_{SO_4^{2-}/H_2S} = +0.3$ V; $E^\ominus_{SO_4^{2-}/S} = +0.36$ V.

(i) Why do these figures show that copper should *not* be oxidised by sulphuric acid, under standard conditions?

(ii) What is an explanation of why the figures do not apply to the reaction as it is carried out in the laboratory?

(iii) What would you predict to happen if zinc reacts with concentrated sulphuric acid?

100.5 The hydrides

Of the hydrides of Group VI (Table 100.4), water is by far the most important, and is not typical of the others. By now you should know that water is anomalous in being a liquid at room temperature; the other hydrides are gases. Hydrogen bonding is responsible. Read Unit 21 for more information about this.

Hydrogen sulphide is very poisonous. If you have smelled the gas (it has the smell of rotten eggs) and (presumably) survived, it is because your nose is very sensitive to the gas. The time to worry is when the gas is present but you can no longer smell it: death will follow soon afterwards. The gas can be made by mixing hydrochloric acid with a metal sulphide, often iron(II) sulphide:

$$FeS(s) + 2HCl(aq) \rightarrow FeCl_2(aq) + H_2S(g)$$

Unlike water, hydrogen sulphide will burn in air (with a pale blue flame):

$$2H_2S(g) + 3O_2(g) \rightarrow 2H_2O(g) + 2SO_2(g)$$

A useful property of hydrogen sulphide is that it releases sulphide ions when it dissolves in water. Two equilibria are involved:

$$H_2S(aq) + H_2O(l) \rightleftharpoons H_3O^+(aq) + HS^-(aq)$$
$$HS^-(aq) + H_2O(l) \rightleftharpoons H_3O^+(aq) + S^{2-}(aq)$$

Transition metals and B metals often give precipitates with sulphide ions, some of which are coloured (e.g. MnS is pink), although many are black (e.g. PbS, CuS). The presence (or absence) of precipitates allows us to identify metal ions by passing the gas into their solution. You will find more details in Unit 64.

Again unlike water, but like ammonia, hydrogen sulphide can be a good reducing agent. For example it performs the simple tests that we expect of a reducing agent. In particular, it will decolourise acidified potassium manganate(VII) solution, and turn an orange solution of potassium dichromate(VI) green:

$$5H_2S(aq) + \underset{\text{purple}}{2MnO_4^-(aq)} + 6H^+(aq) \rightarrow \underset{\text{yellow}}{5S(s)} + \underset{\text{colourless}}{2Mn^{2+}(aq)} + 8H_2O(l)$$

$$3H_2S(aq) + \underset{\text{orange}}{Cr_2O_7^{2-}(aq)} + 8H^+(aq) \rightarrow \underset{\text{yellow}}{3S(s)} + \underset{\text{green}}{2Cr^{3+}(aq)} + 7H_2O(l)$$

Chlorine is also a good oxidising agent and will remove the hydrogen from hydrogen sulphide:

$$Cl_2(g) + H_2S(g) \rightarrow 2HCl(g) + S(s)$$

Table 100.4. The major hydrides of Group VI

Hydride	*Formula*	*Bond angle*	*Melting point/°C*	*Boiling point/°C*
Water	H_2O	104°30′	0	100
Hydrogen sulphide	H_2S	93°	−85.5	−60.3
Hydrogen selenide	H_2Se	91°	−65.7	−42
Hydrogen telluride	H_2Te	89°30′	−49	−2

100.8 Sketch the way the boiling points of the Group VI hydrides change going down the Group, and explain the appearance of the graph.

100.9 Suggest an explanation of the way the bond angles in the hydrides change down the Group. (Hint: it will help if you have read Unit 17 first.)

100.10 Different sulphides are precipitated at different times depending on the concentration of sulphide ions in the solution, which can be controlled by passing H_2S into an acid or alkaline solution. Explain how the concentration of sulphide ions changes with the pH of the solution.

100.11 The redox reaction involving the reducing power of hydrogen sulphide is

$S(s) + 2H^+(aq) + 2e^- \rightarrow H_2S(aq)$; $E^\ominus_{S/H_2S} = +0.14$ V

Two other half-equations are

$Fe^{3+}(aq) + e^- \rightarrow Fe^{2+}(aq)$; $E^\ominus_{Fe^{3+}/Fe^{2+}} = +0.77$ V
$Br_2(l) + 2e^- \rightarrow 2Br^-(aq)$; $E^\ominus_{Br_2/Br^-} = +1.07$ V

Under standard conditions:

(i) Will hydrogen sulphide react with iron(III) ions?

(ii) Will it react with bromine?

If you decide a reaction should take place, write the equation.

Table 100.5. The principal halides of Group VI

Element	*Fluorides*	*Chlorides*	*Bromides*	*Iodides*
Oxygen	F_2O	Cl_2O, ClO_2, Cl_2O_7	Br_2O, BrO_2	I_2O_5
Sulphur	SF_4, SF_6	S_2Cl_2, SCl_2	S_2Br_2	
Selenium	SeF_4, SeF_6	Se_2Cl_2	Se_2Br_2, $SeBr_4$	
Tellurium	TeF_4, TeF_6	$TeCl_2$, $TeCl_4$	$TeBr_2$, $TeBr_4$	TeI_4
Polonium		$PoCl_2$, $PoCl_4$	$PoBr_2$, $PoBr_4$	PoI_4

100.6 The halides and oxohalides

You will find the main halides listed in Table 100.5. There are two or three features of their chemistry that we shall quickly look at. First, notice that fluorine brings out the highest oxidation state, as in SF_6, SeF_6 and TeF_6. The fact that these atoms can actually make six bonds is due to their use of d orbitals in bonding.

Secondly, the sulphur halides tend to hydrolyse easily. (In section 40.4 we used this type of reaction to show how the formula of a chloride could be discovered.) Sulphur hexafluoride, SF_6, is an exception. The sulphur–fluorine bonds in this molecule are very strong, and shorter than normal. Both features suggest that sulphur is using its 3d orbitals in providing a degree of double bond character.

Disulphur dichloride, S_2Cl_2, is the chloride made when sulphur is warmed in dry chlorine:

$$2S(s) + Cl_2(g) \rightarrow S_2Cl_2(l)$$

Of the oxohalides, the most important are those of sulphur, especially sulphur dichloride oxide (thionyl chloride), $SOCl_2$, and sulphur dichloride dioxide (sulphuryl chloride), SO_2Cl_2 (Figure 100.5). The former is a colourless liquid that is easily hydrolysed:

$$SOCl_2(l) + 2H_2O(l) \rightarrow H_2SO_3(aq) + 2HCl(aq)$$

$SOCl_2$ SO_2Cl_2

***Figure 100.5** Both $SOCl_2$ and SO_2Cl_2 have structures based on a tetrahedron (although both are distorted)*

Its main use comes in organic chemistry, where it can be used to replace the OH group of an acid. For example,

$$CH_3-C(=O)OH + Cl_2S{=}O \longrightarrow CH_3-C(=O)Cl + SO_2 + H-Cl$$

$$CH_3COOH(l) + SOCl_2(l) \rightarrow CH_3COCl(l) + SO_2(g) + HCl(g)$$

100.12 Predict the shape of SF_6 and (harder) SCl_4 and $TeCl_4$.

100.13 Why might SF_6 not hydrolyse easily? (There are two possible reasons; one to do with energy, the other to do with steric hindrance.)

100.14 If you look at section 116.4 you will find that $SOCl_2$ is not the only reagent that reacts with the OH group of an organic compound. However, it has an advantage over its main rival. What is the rival, and what is the advantage?

100.7 The oxides

Sulphur dioxide and sulphur trioxide are gases; the others are solids (although those of selenium are volatile). The oxides are shown in Table 100.6. In an earlier unit we saw how SO_2 and SO_3 can be made; the first by burning sulphur in air, the second by reacting sulphur dioxide with oxygen in the presence of a catalyst.

$$S(s) + O_2(g) \rightarrow SO_2(g)$$
$$2SO_2(g) + O_2(g) \rightarrow 2SO_3(g)$$

They are both highly soluble in water, with the reaction between SO_3 and water being explosive. The structure and bonding of the two gases are illustrated in Figure 100.6.

Table 100.6. The principal oxides of Group VI

Element	*Oxides*
Sulphur	SO_2, SO_3
Selenium	SeO_2, SeO_3
Tellurium	TeO, TeO_2, TeO_3
Polonium	PoO, PoO_2

Sulphur dioxide is the anhydride of sulphurous acid, H_2SO_3. This acid is made in small amounts when the gas dissolves in water. A solution of sulphur dioxide contains many more hydrated sulphur dioxide molecules and hydrogen sulphite ions, HSO_3^{2-}, than H_2SO_3 molecules. Sulphur trioxide is the anhydride of sulphuric acid:

$$SO_2(g) + H_2O(l) \rightarrow H_2SO_3(aq)$$
$$SO_3(g) + H_2O(l) \rightarrow H_2SO_4(aq)$$

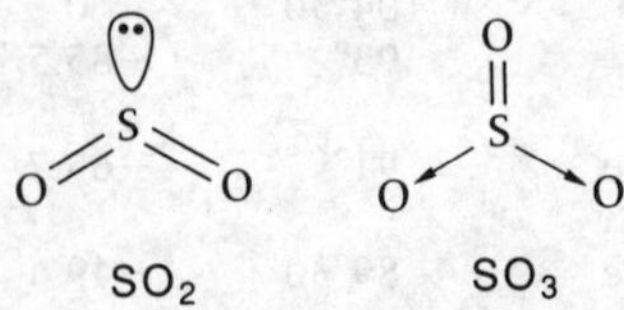

***Figure 100.6** The structures of SO_2 and SO_3 molecules*

A solution of sulphur dioxide is a good reducing medium and will decolourise acidified potassium manganate(VII) and acidified potassium dichromate(VI) solutions.

> **100.15** Sulphur trioxide can be made on a small scale by passing dry oxygen and dry sulphur dioxide over a hot catalyst (platinum is good if you can afford it). The sulphur trioxide can be collected as thin needle-like crystals by cooling the collection flask with a mixture of salt and ice.
>
> (i) What would you use to dry the gases?
>
> (ii) Why must the apparatus be thoroughly dried before use?
>
> (iii) Sketch an apparatus that you could use to make and collect a sample of sulphur trioxide. Assume that you are provided with a supply of sulphur dioxide and oxygen.
>
> **100.16** Sulphur dioxide and hydrogen sulphide react together according to the equation
>
> $$2H_2S(g) + SO_2(g) \rightarrow 3S(s) + 2H_2O(l)$$
>
> We have said that both gases are reducing agents. Which is the more powerful reducing agent of the two? (Hint: oxidation numbers.)

100.8 Sulphites, sulphates and other oxoanions

(a) *Sulphites*

Sulphites contain the SO_3^{2-} ion. Most sulphites are soluble in water, and act as reducing agents. When they are warmed with acid, sulphur dioxide is given off, e.g.

$$SO_3^{2-}(aq) + 2H^+(aq) \rightarrow SO_2(g) + H_2O(l)$$

However, there are one or two sulphites that are insoluble. In particular, if you add silver nitrate solution to a sulphite in water, you will find that a white precipitate is produced:

$$2Ag^+(aq) + SO_3^{2-}(aq) \rightarrow Ag_2SO_3(s)$$

This is one reason why the silver nitrate test for a chloride should always be done after adding dilute nitric acid. Indeed, it is best to warm the acidified solution first, as this will drive sulphur dioxide from the solution.

(b) *Sulphates*

Sulphates contain the SO_4^{2-} ion. The sulphates of Group II metals tend to be insoluble; for example, calcium sulphate, $CaSO_4$, and barium sulphate, $BaSO_4$. The latter is the precipitate made when barium chloride solution is used to test for a sulphate. Other sulphates are often soluble. Probably the one you know best is copper(II) sulphate, which as the crystals $CuSO_4{\cdot}5H_2O$ or in solution is a deep blue colour. (However, when anhydrous it is white.)

Sulphates usually decompose when heated to a sufficiently high temperature. The usual pattern is for them to change into an oxide, and give off SO_3, e.g.

$$\underset{\text{iron(III) sulphate}}{Fe_2(SO_4)_3} \rightarrow Fe_2O_3(s) + 3SO_3(g)$$

(c) *Thiosulphates*

Thiosulphates contain the ion $S_2O_3^{2-}$. The structure of the ion is like that of a sulphate ion, except that one of the oxygen atoms is replaced by a sulphur atom. It is possible to use a solution of a sulphite to make thiosulphate ions. All you need do is boil a solution of sodium sulphite with powdered sulphur:

$$SO_3^{2-}(aq) + S(s) \rightarrow S_2O_3^{2-}(aq)$$

Sodium thiosulphate solution is widely used as a fixing agent in photography. It has the ability to dissolve the silver salts that have not been affected by light. In the chemistry laboratory, thiosulphate solutions are used in iodine titrations, the key reaction being

$$I_2(aq) + 2S_2O_3^{2-}(aq) \rightarrow 2I^-(aq) + S_4O_6^{2-}(aq)$$

You will find details in section 40.3.

The reaction between thiosulphate ions and hydrogen ions is a useful one to show the essentials of chemical kinetics; see section 79.2.

(d) *Peroxodisulphates*

These ions have the formula $S_2O_8^{2-}$ and are found in salts such as $K_2S_2O_8$. They are oxidising agents, and behave according to the half-equation

$$S_2O_8^{2-}(aq) + 2e^- \rightarrow 2SO_4^{2-}(aq)$$

They will, for example, oxidise iodide to iodine and iron(II) to iron(III).

Peroxodisulphates can be thought of as salts of peroxodisulphuric(VI) acid, $H_2S_2O_8$. This acid can be made by the electrolysis of cold sulphuric acid and is one of a number of more unusual acids that sulphur will make. The structures of three oxoacids of sulphur are shown in Figure 100.7.

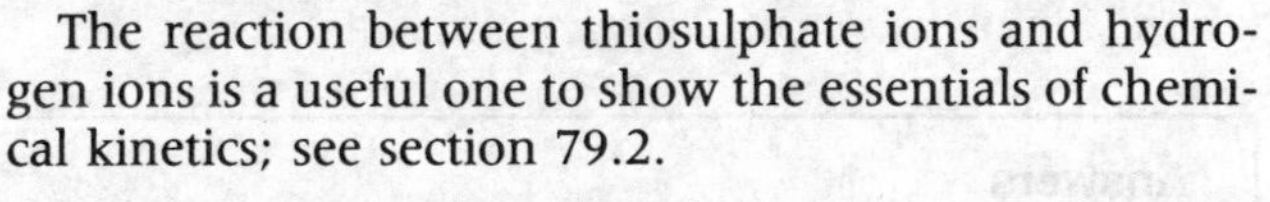

H_2SO_4 Sulphuric acid

H_2SO_5 Caro's acid

$H_2S_2O_8$ Peroxodisulphuric(VI) acid

***Figure 100.7** Three oxoacids of sulphur*

100.17 When a sulphite acts as a reducing agent it reacts according to the equation

$$SO_3^{2-}(aq) + H_2O(l) \rightarrow SO_4^{2-}(aq) + 2H^+(aq) + 2e^-$$

Write the equations for the reaction of a sulphite with MnO_4^- and with $Cr_2O_7^{2-}$ ions in acid solution.

100.18 Suggest two ways of dehydrating $CuSO_4{\cdot}5H_2O$.

100.19 Write equations for the reactions of $S_2O_8^{2-}$ ions with (i) iodide ions, (ii) iron(II) ions.

100.9 The sulphides

The sulphides of Group I metals are ionic, e.g. $(Na^+)_2S^{2-}$. The sulphides of other metals, especially the B metals, are covalent to a greater or lesser extent. Some metals are found in Nature in combination with sulphur (see Table 100.7), and these are often used as the starting material for the extraction of the metals. You will find details in Unit 85. The crystal structure of zinc blende, ZnS, is important in crystal chemistry (see Unit 32).

Table 100.7. Some sulphide ores

Metal	*Ore*
Copper	Copper pyrites, $CuFeS_2$ (also known as fool's gold)
	Chalcocite, Cu_2S
	Covellite, CuS
Lead	Galena, PbS
Mercury	Cinnabar, HgS
Nickel	Pentlandite, $Fe_9Ni_9S_{16}$
Zinc	Zinc blende, ZnS

100.20 What would happen if you warmed dilute hydrochloric acid with sodium sulphide?

100.21 A student needed a solution of a sulphide, and shook some copper(II) sulphide with water.

(i) Why would the student not be successful in making a solution in this way?

(ii) What is a better way of making a solution that contains sulphide ions?

Answers

100.1 Look back at section 46.2. It is energetically very unfavourable for an isolated oxygen atom to become an oxide ion. The production of oxide ions is a result of the high lattice energies of the ionic solids in which it is found.

100.2 Alpha decay gives us the element two places to the left in the Periodic Table (atomic number decreases by two), and reduces the mass number by four. This gives us $^{214}_{82}Pb$.

100.3 Sulphur compounds easily poison the catalysts used in many industrial processes.

100.4 If the water remains, the pressure builds up underground and stops the transfer of superheated water into the sulphur deposit.

100.5 They give carbon dioxide with carbonates, and neutralise a base to give a salt plus water.

100.6 Sulphuric acid molecules are converted into HSO_4^- ions. Therefore they donate protons to the nitric acid. Sulphuric acid is the stronger Brønsted acid.

100.7 (i) Because $E^\ominus_{Cu^{2+}/Cu}$ is more positive than $E^\ominus_{SO_4^{2-}/H_2SO_3}$ and $E^\ominus_{SO_4^{2-}/H_2S}$ it means that Cu^{2+} ions are better oxidising agents than SO_4^{2-} ions. Therefore the acid should not oxidise Cu to Cu^{2+}. Although $E^\ominus_{SO_4^{2-}/S}$ is more positive than $E^\ominus_{Cu^{2+}/Cu}$ it would appear that copper should be oxidised to Cu^{2+} and the acid reduced to H_2S. However, the difference between the two e.m.f.s is so small that the reaction is unlikely to occur at an appreciable rate (see section 70.3).

(ii) Standard conditions refer to acid of concentration 1 mol dm^{-3}. This is very different to concentrated acid. Similarly, the acid is used hot, not at 25°C. Non-standard conditions can radically alter redox potentials.

(iii) Zinc is a good reducing agent (this is shown by the negative value of $E^\ominus_{Zn^{2+}/Zn}$). It is good enough to reduce sulphuric acid to sulphuric dioxide, and even hydrogen sulphide.

100.8 See Figure 90.5. Apart from water, which is anomalous owing to the large amount of hydrogen bonding, the trend is as one would expect: the boiling points increase as the mass of the molecules increases.

100.9 The V shape can be regarded as tetrahedral if the two lone pairs of the molecules are included. Oxygen, with the greatest electronegativity of the Group, has lone pairs that are the most compact and dense centres of negative charge. These have the effect of forcing the bond pairs closer together than in the other hydrides. As the lone pairs become more spread out, their repulsive nature decreases.

100.10 If we add acid (H^+) to a solution in which the two equilibria are set up, each of them will move to the left, so as to reduce the acid concentration. Thus, adding acid reduces the concentration of sulphide ions. Adding

Answers – cont.

alkali works in the opposite direction. Thus, the lower the pH, the greater $[S^{2-}(aq)]$ and vice versa.

100.11 (i) Yes, Fe^{3+} ions will oxidise H_2S to S:

$$2Fe^{3+}(aq) + H_2S(aq) \rightarrow 2Fe^{2+}(aq) + S(s) + 2H^+(aq)$$

(ii) Yes:

$$Br_2(l) + H_2S(aq) \rightarrow 2Br^-(aq) + S(s) + 2H^+(aq)$$

100.12 The shapes are shown in Figure 100.8.

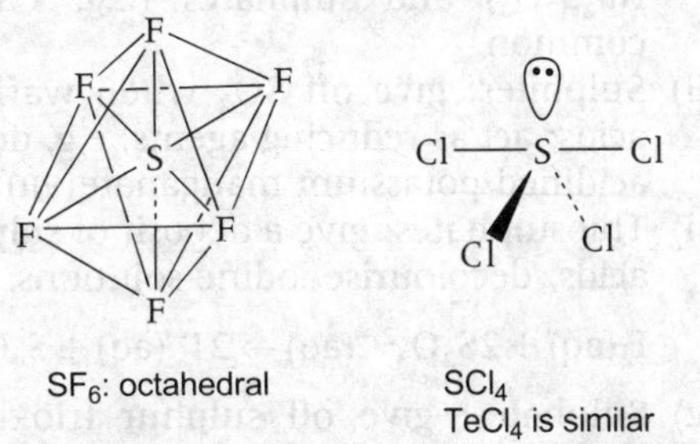

Figure 100.8 *The shapes of SF_6, SCl_4 and $TeCl_4$ molecules. Note the lone pair in SCl_4 (and $TeCl_4$)*

100.13 One possibility is that the S—F bonds are too strong to break easily. Secondly, the fluorine atoms surround the central sulphur atom so well that an attacking water molecule (or hydroxide ion) cannot get its electrons near enough to the sulphur to start making a bond.

100.14 PCl_5. The side products from $SOCl_2$ are gases and easily removed. PCl_5 gives the non-volatile $POCl_3$.

100.15 (i) Concentrated sulphuric acid works well.

(ii) The oxides will make tiny drops of acid in the apparatus. SO_3 will not solidify properly if it is damp.

(iii) Figure 100.9 shows the apparatus.

100.16 The oxidation number of sulphur in SO_2 is +4, and in H_2S is −2. In both cases the sulphur is left with an oxidation number of 0. The SO_2 gains electrons, the H_2S loses them; therefore H_2S is the reducing agent.

100.17 The equations are:

$$5SO_3^{2-}(aq) + 2MnO_4^-(aq) + 6H^+(aq) \rightarrow 5SO_4^{2-}(aq) + 2Mn^{2+}(aq) + 3H_2O(l)$$

$$3SO_3^{2-}(aq) + Cr_2O_7^{2-}(aq) + 8H^+(aq) \rightarrow 3SO_4^{2-}(aq) + 2Cr^{3+}(aq) + 4H_2O(l)$$

100.18 Heating it. Leaving it with concentrated sulphuric acid.

100.19 (i) $S_2O_8^{2-}(aq) + 2I^-(aq) \rightarrow 2SO_4^{2-}(aq) + I_2(s)$

(ii) $S_2O_8^{2-}(aq) + 2Fe^{2+}(aq) \rightarrow 2SO_4^{2-}(aq) + 2Fe^{3+}(aq)$

100.20 Hydrogen sulphide is given off.

100.21 (i) Like many sulphides, CuS is insoluble in water.

(ii) Bubble H_2S through water.

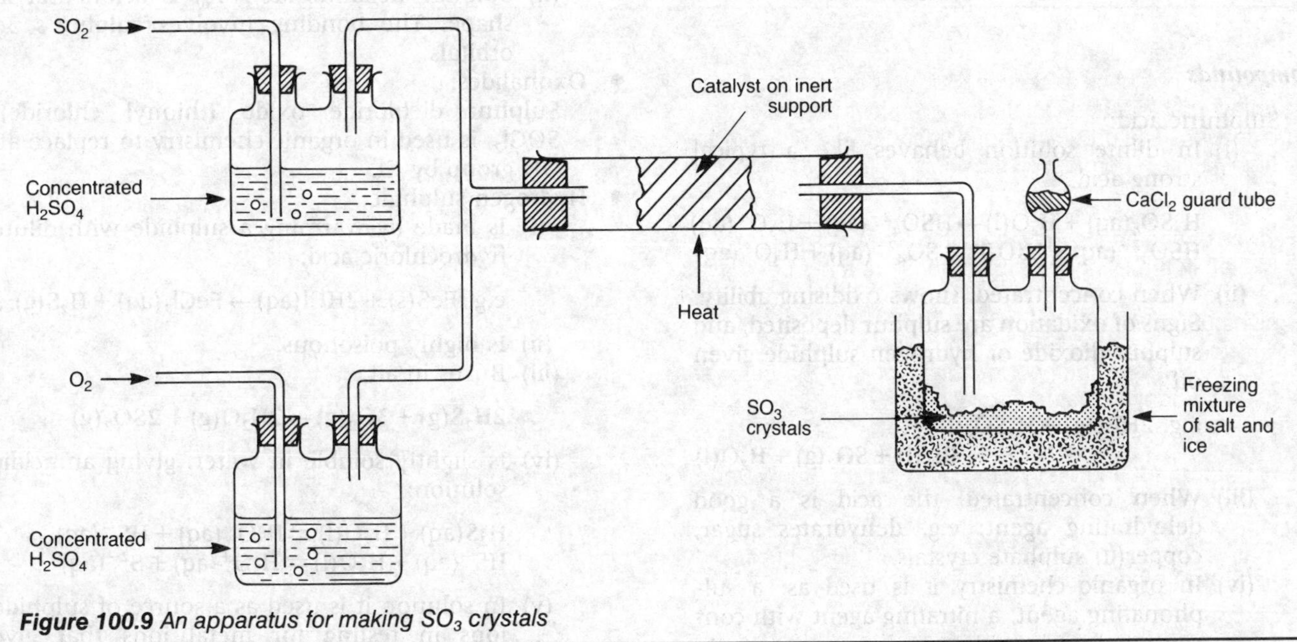

Figure 100.9 *An apparatus for making SO_3 crystals*

UNIT 100 SUMMARY

- The Group VI elements:
  - (i) Predominantly non-metallic, e.g. make acidic oxides.
  - (ii) Sulphur and selenium have allotropes.
  - (iii) Elements below oxygen can make use of d orbitals in bonding.
  - (iv) Sulphur is the most important element in the Group, and its chemistry is summarised here.
- Sulphur:
  - (i) Has the two allotropes, rhombic and monoclinic sulphur, both existing as S_8 rings.
  - (ii) Can make use of d orbitals in bonding, thus showing more than the single valence of 2 shown by oxygen.
  - (iii) Is extracted by the Frasch process.

Reactions

- With oxygen:
  - (i) Sulphur burns to make sulphur dioxide;

    $$S(s) + O_2(g) \rightarrow SO_2(g)$$

  - (ii) Sulphur trioxide is made by passing oxygen and sulphur dioxide over heated platinum gauze (a catalyst);

    $$2SO_2(g) + O_2(g) \rightarrow 2SO_3(g)$$

Compounds

- Sulphuric acid:
  - (i) In dilute solution behaves like a typical strong acid;

    $$H_2SO_4(aq) + H_2O(l) \rightarrow HSO_4^{2-}(aq) + H_3O^+(aq)$$
    $$HSO_4^{2-}(aq) + H_2O(l) \rightleftharpoons SO_4^{2-}(aq) + H_3O^+(aq)$$

  - (ii) When concentrated, shows oxidising ability. Signs of oxidation are sulphur deposited, and sulphur dioxide or hydrogen sulphide given off;

    e.g. $2HBr(g) + H_2SO_4(l) \rightarrow Br_2(l) + SO_2(g) + H_2O(l)$

  - (iii) When concentrated, the acid is a good dehydrating agent; e.g. dehydrates sugar, copper(II) sulphate crystals.
  - (iv) In organic chemistry it is used as: a sulphonating agent; a nitrating agent with concentrated nitric acid;

    $$HNO_3 + 2H_2SO_4 \rightarrow NO_2^+ + H_3O^+ + 2HSO_4^-$$

    The nitryl cation, NO_2^+, is the active species.
- Oxides:
  - (i) Sulphur dioxide and sulphur trioxide are acidic oxides.
  - (ii) Sulphur trioxide is the anhydride of sulphuric acid;

    $$SO_3(g) + H_2O(l) \rightarrow 2H^+(aq) + SO_4^{2-}(aq)$$

- Oxoanions:
  - (i) Sulphites (e.g. Na_2SO_3), thiosulphates (e.g. $Na_2S_2O_3$) and sulphates (e.g. $CaSO_4$) are common.
  - (ii) Sulphites: give off SO_2 when warmed with acids; act as reducing agents, e,g, decolourise acidified potassium manganate(VII) solution.
  - (iii) Thiosulphates: give a deposit of sulphur with acids; decolourise iodine solutions;

    $$I_2(aq) + 2S_2O_3^{2-}(aq) \rightarrow 2I^-(aq) + S_4O_6^{2-}(aq)$$

  - (iv) Sulphates: give off sulphur trioxide when heated strongly; Group II sulphates tend to be insoluble in water.
  - (v) Peroxodisulphates, e.g. $K_2S_2O_8$, are oxidising agents;

    e.g. $2I^-(aq) + S_2O_8^{2-}(aq) \rightarrow 2SO_4^{2-}(aq) + I_2(s)$

- Halides:
  - (i) Disulphur dichloride, S_2Cl_2, is made when sulphur is warmed with chlorine. It is easily hydrolysed.
  - (ii) Sulphur hexafluoride, SF_6, is octahedral in shape. The bonding involves sulphur's 3d orbitals.
- Oxohalides:

  Sulphur dichloride oxide (thionyl chloride), $SOCl_2$, is used in organic chemistry to replace an OH group by Cl.
- Hydrogen sulphide:
  - (i) Is made by warming a sulphide with dilute hydrochloric acid;

    e.g. $FeS(s) + 2HCl(aq) \rightarrow FeCl_2(aq) + H_2S(g)$

  - (ii) Is highly poisonous.
  - (iii) Burns in air;

    $$2H_2S(g) + 3O_2(g) \rightarrow 2H_2O(g) + 2SO_2(g)$$

  - (iv) Is slightly soluble in water, giving an acidic solution;

    $$H_2S(aq) + H_2O(l) \rightleftharpoons H_3O^+(aq) + HS^-(aq)$$
    $$HS^-(aq) + H_2O(l) \rightleftharpoons H_3O^+(aq) + S^{2-}(aq)$$

  - (v) In solution it is used as a source of sulphide ions in testing for metal ions that give insoluble sulphides;

    e.g. $Cu^{2+}(aq) + S^{2-}(aq) \rightarrow CuS(s)$

  - (vi) Is a reducing agent;

    e.g. $3H_2S(aq) + Cr_2O_7^{2-}(aq) + 8H^+(aq) \rightarrow 3S(s) + 2Cr^{3+}(aq) + 7H_2O(l)$

101

Group VII: the halogens

101.1 The nature of the elements

The elements of Group VII, fluorine, chlorine, bromine, iodine and astatine, are known as the halogens. Many years ago this name was derived from two Greek words meaning 'to make sea salt'. Indeed, all the halogens react with Group I metals to make ionic salts such as sodium fluoride, NaF, sodium chloride, NaCl, potassium bromide, KBr, and so on.

The halogens are all covalent and they show just the sort of trends in their properties that we should expect from their position in the Periodic Table. Rather more importantly, they have a number of extremely useful properties that make them valuable commodities. Table 101.1 lists some basic information about the elements, and Table 101.2 shows their uses. Astatine has only been prepared in small amounts in the course of nuclear reactions, and it is radioactive. There is little need for you to know about its chemistry, and data on this element are omitted from the tables.

Table 101.1. Physical properties of the halogens

Formula	*Fluorine* F_2	*Chlorine* Cl_2	*Bromine* Br_2	*Iodine* I_2
Electron structure	$(He)2s^22p^5$	$(Ne)3s^23p^5$	$(AR)3d^{10}4s^24p^5$	$(Kr)3d^{10}5s^25p^5$
Electronegativity	4.0	3.0	2.8	2.5
Bond energy/kJ mol^{-1}	158	242	193	151
Melting point/° C	−220	−101	−7	114
Boiling point/° C	−188	−34	58	183
I.E./kJ mol^{-1}	1681	1251	1140	1010
E.A./kJ mol^{-1}	361	388	365	332
Atomic radius/pm	64	99	111	128
Ionic radius/pm	133	181	196	219
$E^{\ominus}_{X_2/X^-}$/V	2.87	1.36	1.09	0.54
Oxidising power	Most			Least
Common oxid. no.	−1	−1,+1,+5,+7	−1,+1,+5,+7	−1,+1,+5,+7

101.2 Discovery and extraction of the halogens

(a) *Fluorine*

During 1813 and 1814, Humphry Davy performed a set of experiments in which he proved the presence of a new element in a number of different compounds; he called the element fluorine. Unfortunately he was unable to collect a sample of it. This was achieved in 1886 by the French chemist Henri Moissan. Moissan electrolysed liquid anhydrous hydrogen fluoride with potassium hydrogenfluoride, KHF_2, dissolved in it. This discovery continues to be the basis of the commercial extraction of fluorine.

The fact that electrolysis has to be used to extract fluorine from its compounds tells us that this element is highly reactive. Once it reacts with another element it tends to give very strong bonds, which are hard to break. You might like to check your knowledge of the reactivity of elements by looking at section 66.9.

(b) *Chlorine*

Chlorine was first isolated by Scheele in 1774, but its nature as an element was established by Davy. Indeed,

Table 101.2. Uses of the halogens and their compounds

Halogen	*Uses*
Fluorine	In chlorofluorocarbons (CFCs), used as aerosol propellants, refrigerants and as foaming agents in polymers CFCs are also used in artificial blood PTFE (polytetrafluoroethene): lubricant, non-stick cooking pans Production of UF_6 in uranium purification Fluoridation of water supplies using, e.g., NaF Tin(II) fluoride (SnF_2) used in 'fluoride toothpastes' In hydrofluoric acid (HF), an etching agent for glass
Chlorine	Also used in CFCs and many organic chemicals, e.g. PVC (polyvinyl chloride, polychlorothene) Solutions of chlorine or bleaching powder are used as household and commercial bleaches Drinking water is treated with chlorine to kill bacteria Unfortunately, chlorine has been used in poison gases, e.g. Cl_2 itself and mustard gas ($ClCH_2CH_2SCH_2CH_2Cl$)
Bromine	In 1,2-dibromoethane ($BrCH_2CH_2Br$), as a petrol additive Bromochloromethane (CH_2ClBr) is used in fire extinguishers Silver bromide is widely used in photographic film
Iodine	A solution of iodine in alcohol can be used as a mild antiseptic Iodine is an essential part of our diet

in 1810 it was Davy who gave chlorine its name (this being taken from a Greek word meaning pale green). Before it received its new name, chlorine was called oxymuriatic acid. One reason for this name was that, until Davy's experiments were accepted, many chemists believed the gas to be a compound of oxygen and another element.

Chlorine is obtained on an industrial scale by the electrolysis of brine. You will find details of the method in section 84.2. Notice that, like fluorine, the use of electrolysis to isolate the element is an indication of its great reactivity.

(c) *Bromine*

Bromine, whose name means 'stinking', was discovered by Antoine Balard in 1826. (Balard was not a particularly famous chemist: a nasty comment once made about him was that, rather than Balard discovering bromine, it was bromine that discovered Balard!) He discovered the element by accident in the course of some experiments on sea water. He noticed the yellow-orange colour that bromine gives when it was made by treating sea water with chlorine. The reaction is due to the oxidation of bromide ions by chlorine:

$$2Br^-(aq) + Cl_2(aq) \rightarrow Br_2(aq) + 2Cl^-(aq)$$

This reaction remains at the heart of the commercial isolation of bromine. One method (there are several variations) is as follows:

(i) Sulphuric acid is added to sea water before chlorine gas is passed through the solution. This liberates the bromine according to the equation above.

(ii) Bromine evaporates from sea water fairly easily, so it is removed by blowing air, or sometimes steam, through the solution.

(iii) The bromine vapour reacts with another reagent, often sulphur dioxide, which together with water converts it into bromide ions again:

$$Br_2(g) + SO_2(g) + 2H_2O(l) \rightarrow 2Br^-(aq) + SO_4^{2-}(aq) + 4H^+(aq)$$

But this time the solution that collects is very much more concentrated than the original sea water.

(iv) This solution is also treated with a mixture of chlorine and steam. The bromine produced can be separated from the water with which it is mixed by fractional distillation.

(d) *Iodine*

Deposits of sodium nitrate ('Chile saltpetre') often contain sodium iodate, $NaIO_3$, as an impurity. If the degree of contamination is high, it can be economic to convert the iodate to iodine. The extraction takes place in three stages:

(i) The rock containing the nitrate and iodate is crushed and dissolved in hot water. On cooling, the sodium nitrate crystallises first, leaving the solution richer in sodium iodate. This is a large-scale example of fractional crystallisation; see section 59.2. After the solid is separated, part of the solution is treated with sodium hydrogensulphite, $NaHSO_3$:

$$IO_3^-(aq) + 3HSO_3^-(aq) \rightarrow I^-(aq) + 3HSO_4^{2-}(aq)$$

(ii) Now more of the solution is added. This brings about a reaction we have seen in the unit on titrations:

$$IO_3^-(aq) + 5I^-(aq) + 6H^+(aq) \rightarrow 3I_2(s) + 3H_2O(l)$$

(iii) The iodine can be filtered from the solution and, if necessary, purified by allowing it to sublime.

101.1 Sea water contains around 65×10^{-3} g of bromide ions in 1 dm³. If all the bromide ions are converted into bromine, how many dm³ of sea water are needed to produce 1 kg of bromine?

101.2 Deposits of brine in the USA sometimes contain significant amounts of iodide ions. Suggest a way of converting the iodide content of the brine into iodine.

101.3 What is meant by sublimation?

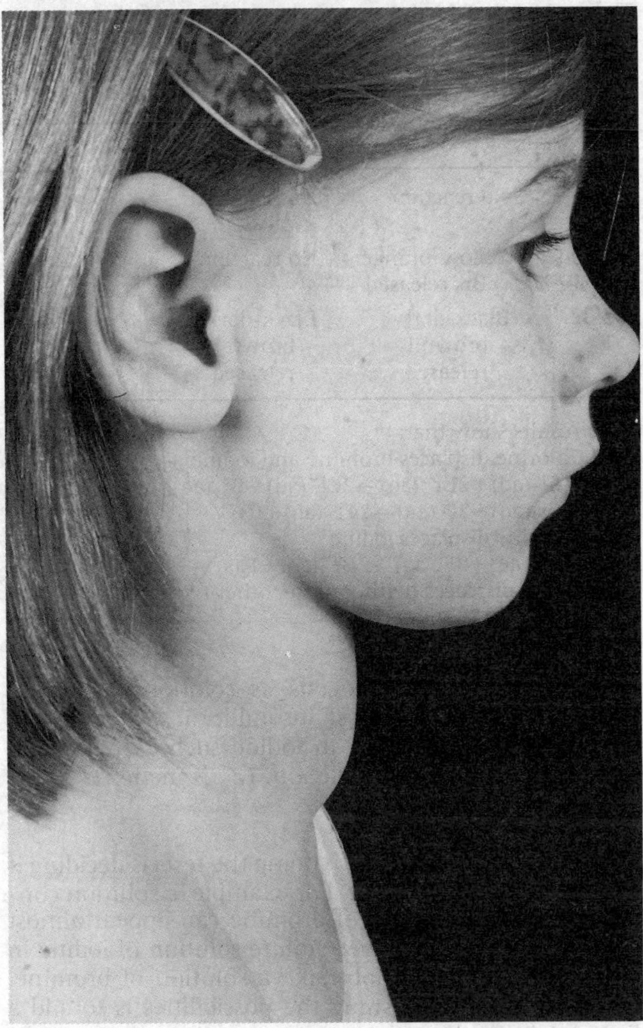

The swelling in this girl's neck is an indication of goitre, which resulted from a lack of iodine in her diet.

101.3 The laboratory preparation of the halogens

All the halogens are poisonous, and you should take great care if you do reactions with them. They should only be prepared in a fume cupboard. Fluorine is difficult to make, so we shall ignore its preparation. The others can be made by oxidising the appropriate hydrogen halide, HCl, HBr, or HI. The usual oxidising agent is manganese(IV) oxide.

(a) *Chlorine*

The most convenient source of hydrogen chloride is concentrated hydrochloric acid. If the acid and manganese(IV) oxide are warmed together, chlorine is given off. If you want pure chlorine, the gas can be passed first through water and then through concentrated sulphuric acid. The water dissolves any fumes of hydrochloric acid, and the sulphuric acid dries the gas. The reaction is:

$$MnO_2(s) + 4HCl(aq) \rightarrow MnCl_2(aq) + Cl_2(g) + 2H_2O(l)$$

or

$$2Cl^-(aq) + 4H^+(aq) + MnO_2(s) \rightarrow Mn^{2+}(aq) + Cl_2(g) + 2H_2O(l)$$

If you want a quick, but not too pure, supply of chlorine it is possible to drop concentrated hydrochloric acid on to crystals of potassium manganate(VII):

$$2KMnO_4(s) + 16HCl(aq) \rightarrow 2KCl(aq) + 2MnCl_2(aq) + 5Cl_2(g) + 8H_2O(l)$$

(b) *Bromine*

Solutions of hydrogen bromide are not generally available, so it must be made during the preparation. Hydrogen bromide is produced when, for example, potassium bromide is mixed with concentrated sulphuric acid. However, if manganese(IV) oxide is mixed with the acid, before the hydrogen bromide can escape it is oxidised and bromine is made. Overall the reaction is much the same as that for the preparation of chlorine: just substitute bromine for chlorine in the equation.

(c) *Iodine*

Iodine can be made by a similar method to bromine. The main difference is that iodine is a solid at room temperature.

101.4 By working out the changes in oxidation numbers, or states, of the reactants, explain why the reaction of hydrochloric acid with MnO_2 or $KMnO_4$ is an oxidation of the hydrogen chloride.

101.5 Is bromine a gas or liquid at room temperature (about 20° C)? Sketch an apparatus that you could use to prepare bromine.

101.6 Sketch an apparatus that you could use to make and collect iodine in the laboratory.

101.4 The reactivity of the halogens

By reactivity we mean the ease with which the halogens react. This is largely a matter of rates of reaction, which in turn is related to the activation energies of the reactions. Fluorine has the lowest bond energy. A collision involving a fluorine molecule needs less energy to break the molecule apart than does the same collision with, say, a chlorine molecule. As a result fluorine reacts more readily than chlorine. Indeed, fluorine is the most reactive of all the halogens. Reactivity decreases down the Group.

Even if a reaction takes place very quickly this does not mean that the product is energetically stable. As a rule this will only happen if the reaction is strongly exothermic (see Unit 50). In fact fluorine often takes part in reactions that are highly exothermic. This is a result of the strength of the bonds that fluorine makes with many atoms, in both covalent and ionic compounds. For example, the energy of a carbon–fluorine bond in CF_4 is about 485 kJ mol^{-1}, while that of the carbon–hydrogen bond in CH_4 is 435 kJ mol^{-1}. You should know that carbon–hydrogen bonds are very hard to break; carbon–fluorine bonds are even harder to break! The lattice energy of sodium fluoride (an ionic solid) is 915 kJ mol^{-1}, which is over 100 kJ mol^{-1} greater than that of sodium chloride. Not only does fluorine react very quickly with sodium, it gives a highly exothermic reaction as well.

101.7 Look back at Unit 46, and note the order of ionic radii in Table 101.1. Explain why sodium fluoride has a high lattice energy.

101.5 The halogens are oxidising agents

In this section we shall think about three types of reactions that show that the halogens are oxidising agents.

(a) *Displacement reactions*

Fluorine has the largest electronegativity of all the elements, but the values for the other halogens show that they all have a tendency to accept electrons. The only type of negative ion they all give is the halide ion, X^-. (From now on we shall often use the symbol X_2 to stand for the halogen molecules, F_2, Cl_2, etc., and X^- for the halide ions, F^-, Cl^-, etc.) This should not surprise us given that they have one electron less than the nearest noble gas. By taking up one extra electron they will complete the octet of their outermost p orbitals. We know that when elements react they have a tendency to adopt noble gas electron structures. (However, make sure you try question 46.2 about oxygen and oxide ions before you take this observation as a *reason* why the halogens all give halide ions.) If an element takes one or more electrons from another, then it is acting as an oxidising agent. The values of the standard electrode potentials in Table 101.1 show that in solution the oxidising power decreases from fluorine to iodine.

We can see the relative oxidising powers in a series of simple test tube experiments by adding the halogens to solutions of the halides. The results are listed in Table 101.3. The most convenient way to carry out the reactions is to use the halogens as solutions in water. Although iodine is almost insoluble in water, it will dissolve in a solution of an iodide such as potassium iodide. The soluble triiodide ion, I_3^-, is made:

$$I_2(s) + I^-(aq) \rightleftharpoons I_3^-(aq)$$

Table 101.3. Displacement reactions of the halogens*

Solution	*Halogen added*		
	Chlorine	*Bromine*	*Iodine*
Chloride, Cl^-	No reaction	No reaction	No reaction
Bromide, Br^-	Yellow-orange Br_2 released	No reaction	No reaction
Iodide, I^-	Black-dark brown I_2 released	Black-dark brown I_2 released	No reaction

*The results show that:

(i) Chlorine displaces bromine and iodine
$Cl_2(aq)+2Br^-(aq)\rightarrow 2Cl^-(aq)+Br_2(aq)$
$Cl_2(aq)+2I^-(aq)\rightarrow 2Cl^-(aq)+I_2(s)$

(ii) Bromine displaces iodine
$Br_2(aq)+2I^-(aq)\rightarrow 2Br^-(aq)+I_2(s)$

(iii) Iodine displaces neither of the other two

One of the problems with doing the tests is deciding if a reaction has taken place. For example, a solution containing a small amount of bromine can appear almost colourless. Similarly, a very dilute solution of iodine in potassium iodide can look like a solution of bromine. One way of distinguishing the possibilities is to add a little 1,1,1-trichloroethane to the reaction mixture. Any bromine or iodine present will dissolve more readily in the purely covalent organic liquid than in water. If bromine is present, the organic layer will become orange-yellow; if iodine is present, it will become purple.

(b) *With alkali metals*

The alkali metals towards the bottom of Group I can react violently with fluorine and chlorine. However, it is safe to burn sodium in chlorine. The sodium burns quietly, giving off clouds of white fumes. The fumes are particles of sodium chloride (salt). We can show the reaction in two ways:

$$2Na(s) + Cl_2(g) \rightarrow 2NaCl(s)$$
$$2Na(s) + Cl_2(g) \rightarrow 2Na^+Cl^-(s)$$

The second is useful because it shows that the reaction involves a sodium atom losing an electron and a chlorine atom gaining it. Given that oxidation is the loss of electrons, the sodium has been oxidised by the chlorine. Sodium chloride is one of the most typical ionic solids.

A word of warning: you need to know something about thermochemistry if you are to provide an explanation of why two elements react to give an ionic substance of a particular formula. You might like to read Unit 46 to remind yourself about this.

Not all metals give ionic compounds with the halogens. In particular, Group III metals and B metals in general give covalent compounds. When the metal can have more than one oxidation state, the higher state is brought out by fluorine.

(c) *With hydrocarbons*

If a lighted candle is put into chlorine the wax continues to burn, but with a very smoky flame. Together with a lot of soot, white fumes of hydrogen chloride are released. The chlorine removes the hydrogen from the hydrocarbon (an oxidation) and leaves carbon behind, e.g.

$$C_{10}H_{22}(s) + 11Cl_2(g) \rightarrow 10C(s) + 22HCl(g)$$

If you look at Unit 113 you will find that the reaction of chlorine with some hydrocarbons can be explosive, especially in the presence of ultraviolet light. The reaction can take place by a free radical mechanism, which almost always leads to a very rapid change.

101.8 Explain why the displacement reactions of the halogens are best regarded as redox reactions.

101.9 If you did have a supply of fluorine, what would happen if fluorine was added to the solutions listed in Table 101.3?

101.10 Is it true that iodine will not displace *any* other halogen?

101.11 The standard redox potential for a half-cell containing Fe^{3+} and Fe^{2+} ions is $E^{\ominus}_{Fe^{3+}/Fe^{2+}} = +0.77$ V. Which of the halogens will oxidise Fe^{3+} to Fe^{2+} in solution?

101.6 Reactions with water and alkali

(a) *With water*

Both fluorine and chlorine are able to oxidise water. Fluorine can give a mixture of oxygen and trioxygen (ozone), e.g. for oxygen

$$2F_2(g) + 2H_2O(l) \rightarrow O_2(g) + 4HF(aq)$$

Chlorine, which is not such a powerful oxidising agent, does not release oxygen. Instead, a solution containing a mixture of hydrochloric and chloric(I) acids is produced (the old name for chloric(I) acid is hypochlorous acid):

$$Cl_2(g) + H_2O(l) \rightarrow \underbrace{H^+(aq) + Cl^-(aq)}_{\text{hydrochloric acid}} + \underbrace{H^+(aq) + ClO^-(aq)}_{\text{chloric(I) acid}}$$

Chlorate(I) ions, ClO^-, in a solution of chlorine are responsible for its bleaching action. For example, coloured organic materials, like grass or some clothing dyes, are decolourised if they are put into chlorine water. The chlorate(I) ion is able to lose its oxygen fairly readily, which is used in the oxidation process.

Chlorine water, and bleach, will give off bubbles of oxygen if they are left in sunlight, owing to the decomposition of the chlorate(I) ions:

$$2ClO^-(aq) \rightarrow 2Cl^-(aq) + O_2(g)$$

Iodine is so insoluble in water that its solution has no oxidising power.

(b) *With alkali*

There are two types of change depending on the temperature of the alkali:

(i) Cold dilute alkali. The change is summarised in the general equation

$$X_2(g) + 2OH^-(aq) \rightarrow X^-(aq) + XO^-(aq) + H_2O(l)$$

e.g.

$$Cl_2(g) + 2OH^-(aq) \rightarrow Cl^-(aq) + ClO^-(aq) + H_2O(l)$$

(ii) Hot concentrated alkali. The equation is

$$3X_2(g) + 6OH^-(aq) \rightarrow 5X^-(aq) + XO_3^-(aq) + 3H_2O(l)$$

e.g.

$$3Cl_2(g) + 6OH^-(aq) \rightarrow 5Cl^-(aq) + ClO_3^-(aq) + 3H_2O(l)$$

The main difference between the two is that, with cold dilute alkali, chlorate(I), ClO^-, ions are produced; while with hot concentrated alkali, chlorate(V), ClO_3^-, ions are made.

101.12 Write a balanced equation for the reaction between fluorine and water that gives off trioxygen, O_3, rather than oxygen.

101.13 Bromine in water does not give appreciable quantities of bromate(I), BrO^-, ions. However, in sunlight bromine water will slowly give off oxygen. Write an equation for the reaction (bromide ions are also liberated).

101.14 Explain why the reactions of chlorine with alkali can be regarded as disproportionations. (Hint: see section 105.2b if you are unsure.)

101.7 Halide ions

Often, when a halogen reacts, each atom gains an electron to give a halide ion. It is useful to be able to perform tests to distinguish between chloride, bromide and iodide ions. The simplest test involves adding silver

Table 101.4. The silver nitrate test for halide ions

	Addition of silver nitrate in presence of nitric acid	*Addition of ammonia solution*
Chloride	White precipitate of silver chloride $Ag^+(aq) + Cl^-(aq) \rightarrow AgCl(s)$	Precipitate dissolves; clear solution
Bromide	Pale yellow precipitate of silver bromide $Ag^+(aq) + Br^-(aq) \rightarrow AgBr(s)$	Precipitate partly dissolves
Iodide	Yellow precipitate of silver iodide $Ag^+(aq) + I^-(aq) \rightarrow AgI(s)$	Precipitate does not dissolve

nitrate solution to a solution of the halide. This should be done in the presence of dilute nitric acid; otherwise other ions may give a precipitate. Silver ions react with halide ions to give precipitates. These in turn can be identified by their colour, or by their reaction with ammonia solution. The solubility of silver halides (especially silver chloride) in ammonia solution is due to the formation of the diamminesilver(I) ion, $Ag(NH_3)_2{}^+$, which is soluble in water:

$$AgCl(s) + 2NH_3(aq) \rightarrow Ag(NH_3)_2{}^+(aq) + Cl^-(aq)$$

Table 101.4 summarises the tests for you.

Answers

101.1 Volume needed

$$= \frac{1\text{ kg}}{65 \times 10^{-6}\text{ kg}} \times 1\text{ dm}^3 \approx 15\,000\text{ dm}^3$$

This should give you an idea of the huge scale upon which the industry works.

101.2 See stages (i), (ii) and (iii) for extracting bromine from sea water.

101.3 It is the conversion of a solid directly into a gas (or vice versa).

101.4 The oxidation numbers of manganese in $KMnO_4$ and MnO_2 are +7 and +4, and of chlorine in HCl and Cl_2 are −1 and 0, respectively. The manganese gains electrons while the HCl loses them. Therefore the HCl has been oxidised and the manganese reduced.

101.5 It is a liquid. This means that the preparation apparatus must condense the bromine. A distillation apparatus will work.

101.6 The apparatus is shown in Figure 101.1.

101.7 A small radius means that the ions in the crystal are closer together. This leads to greater attractions in the crystal, and to higher lattice energies. Also, see the work on the Born–Mayer equation in section 46.3.

101.8 When, for example, chlorine converts iodide ions into iodine, the iodide ions lose electrons, and the chlorine atoms gain electrons. That is, the chlorine oxidises the iodide (and the iodide reduces the chlorine).

101.9 Being the most powerful oxidising agent of all the halogens, fluorine would displace chlorine, bromine and iodine from their respective solutions.

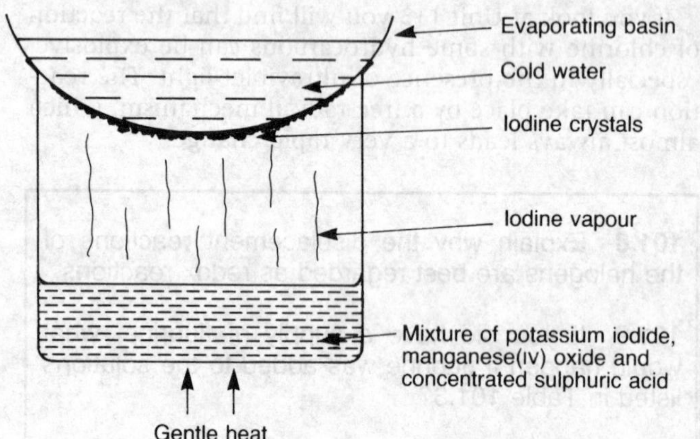

***Figure 101.1** A simple way of preparing iodine*

101.10 No. It would displace astatine from solution.

101.11 Fluorine, chlorine and bromine. Their $E^\ominus$ values are more positive than $E^\ominus_{Fe^{3+}/Fe^{2+}}$, so they are the stronger oxidising agents.

101.12 $3F_2(g) + 3H_2O(l) \rightarrow O_3(g) + 6HF(aq)$

101.13

$2Br_2(aq) + 2H_2O(l) \rightarrow 4Br^-(aq) + O_2(g) + 4H^+(aq)$

101.14 One oxidation state converts into two different oxidation states during the reaction. This is what is meant by disproportionation. See the next unit for more details.

UNIT 101 SUMMARY

- The Group VII elements:
  - (i) Are all oxidising agents, fluorine being the most vigorous.
  - (ii) Exist as diatomic molecules.
  - (iii) Form halides with metals, e.g. K^+I^-, $AlCl_3$.
  - (iv) Reactivity follows the order $F_2 > Cl_2 > Br_2 > I_2$.
- Laboratory preparation:

  Chlorine is made by

(i) Warming concentrated hydrochloric acid and manganese(IV) oxide;

$$MnO_2(s) + 4HCl(aq) \rightarrow MnCl_2(aq) + Cl_2(g) + 2H_2O(l)$$

(ii) Dropping concentrated hydrochloric acid onto crystals of potassium manganate(VII). Dry chlorine is obtained by passing the gas through concentrated sulphuric acid.

Bromine and iodine are made in a similar way to chlorine except that HBr(aq) and HI(aq) are made *in situ*, and the methods of collection are different.

- Extraction:
  (i) Fluorine by the electrolysis of a mixture of liquid anhydrous hydrogen fluoride and potassium hydrogenfluoride, KHF_2.
  (ii) Chlorine by the electrolysis of brine.
  (iii) Bromine from bromide ions in sea water.
  (iv) Iodine from sodium iodate(V) found in sodium nitrate deposits.

Reactions

- Displacement reactions:
  Each will displace the halogen below it from solution;
  e.g. $Cl_2(aq) + 2Br^-(aq) \rightarrow 2Cl^-(aq) + Br_2(aq)$
- With metals:
  Salts are made;
  e.g. $2Na(s) + Cl_2(g) \rightarrow 2Na^+Cl^-(s)$
  $2Fe(s) + 3Cl_2(g) \rightarrow 2FeCl_3(s)$
- With a burning hydrocarbon:
  The hydrogen is removed by chlorine;
  e.g. $CH_4(g) + 2Cl_2(g) \rightarrow C(s) + 4HCl(g)$

  Also, see Unit 111.
- With water:
  (i) Fluorine oxidises water;
  $$2F_2(g) + 2H_2O(l) \rightarrow O_2(g) + 4HF(aq)$$
  (ii) Chlorine and bromine give acidic solutions in water;
  $$Cl_2(g) + H_2O(l) \rightarrow H^+(aq) + Cl^-(aq) + H^+(aq) + ClO^-(aq)$$
  The solution acts as a bleach.
  (iii) Iodine is almost insoluble in water, but it does dissolve in solutions containing iodide ions. The soluble triiodide ion is made;
  $$I_2(aq) + I^-(aq) \rightleftharpoons I_3^-(aq)$$
- With alkali, disproportionation occurs:
  (i) Cold dilute alkali gives a mixture of halide and halate(I) ions;
  e.g. $Cl_2(g) + 2OH^-(aq) \rightarrow Cl^-(aq) + ClO^-(aq) + H_2O(l)$
  chloride chlorate(I)
  (ii) Hot concentrated alkali gives a mixture of halide and halate(V);
  e.g. $3Cl_2(g) + 6OH^-(aq) \rightarrow 5Cl^-(aq) + ClO_3^-(aq) + H_2O(l)$
  chloride chlorate(V)

102

Compounds of the halogens

102.1 The hydrogen halides

The hydrogen halides are hydrogen fluoride, HF, hydrogen chloride, HCl, hydrogen bromide, HBr, and hydrogen iodide, HI. Information about them is listed in Table 102.1. Although they all have properties in common, hydrogen fluoride is not completely typical (Figure 102.1). As you will find, this is largely a result of its very high bond energy, and the highly polar nature of the molecule.

To explain thoroughly the high bond energy is a difficult task. We can see from the values of the dipole moment in Table 102.1 that hydrogen fluoride has a considerable degree of ionic character, with the fluorine atom pulling electron density towards it. Indeed, hydrogen fluoride molecules are strongly attracted to each other by hydrogen bonds (Figure 102.2). The hydrogen bonds between hydrogen and fluorine atoms in hydrogen fluoride are the strongest known. In solution with water, hydrogen fluoride is only a weak acid, whereas all the other hydrogen halides are strong acids. That is, the equilibrium

$$HF(aq) + H_2O(l) \rightleftharpoons H_3O^+(aq) + F^-(aq)$$

lies well to the left. Although we need to take account of both enthalpy and entropy changes to explain the dissociation of weak acids, here there is much truth in the observation that links the strength of the bond in HF with its lack of dissociation.

Table 102.1. Information about the hydrogen halides

	HF	HCl	HBr	HI
Melting point/°C	−83	−114	−87	−51
Boiling point/°C	20	−85	−67	−35
Bond energy /kJ mol^{-1}	560	431	366	299
Dipole moment /D	1.91	1.05	0.8	0.42
Acidity constant /mol dm^{-3}	5.6×10^{-4}	← very large →		

However, you should remember that acidity is not an absolute concept. A chemical can be an acid in one situation and a base in another. Especially, very concentrated or pure hydrogen fluoride is an extremely strong acid.

For example, we normally think of nitric acid as a strong acid because it acts as a proton donor with water:

$$HNO_3(aq) + H_2O(l) \rightarrow H_3O^+(aq) + NO_3^-(aq)$$

But in liquid hydrogen fluoride,

$$HNO_3 + HF \rightarrow H_2NO_3^+ + F^-$$

Here the HNO_3 accepts the proton, and HF donates it.

Hydrogen fluoride and hydrogen chloride can be prepared by reacting the appropriate sodium or calcium halide with sulphuric acid. For example, hydrogen chloride is given off if sodium chloride is warmed with concentrated sulphuric acid:

$$NaCl(s) + H_2SO_4(l) \rightarrow NaHSO_4(s) + HCl(g)$$

If you see this reaction carried out you will find that the gas gives white fumes in air. The fumes are small droplets of concentrated hydrochloric acid made when the gas mixes with water vapour in air.

It would be nice to think that exactly the same method could be used to make hydrogen bromide and hydrogen iodide. Unfortunately it cannot. This is because sulphuric acid has a significant oxidising power; it can oxidise HBr and HI as soon as they are made:

$$2HBr(g) + H_2SO_4(l) \rightarrow Br_2(l) + SO_2(g) + 2H_2O(l)$$
$$2HI(g) + H_2SO_4(l) \rightarrow I_2(s) + SO_2(g) + 2H_2O(l)$$
$$6HI(g) + H_2SO_4(l) \rightarrow 3I_2(s) + S(s) + 4H_2O(l)$$
$$8HI(g) + H_2SO_4(l) \rightarrow 4I_2(s) + H_2S(s) + 4H_2O(l)$$

The way round the problem is to use an acid with very little oxidising power. Phosphoric(V) acid, H_3PO_4, is the usual one to choose. For example, on warming,

$$NaI(s) + H_3PO_4(l) \rightarrow NaH_2PO_4(s) + HI(g)$$

Temperature /°C

(a)

Boiling points

Melting points

HF HCl HBr HI

Band energy /kJ mol^{-1}

(b)

HF HCl HBr HI

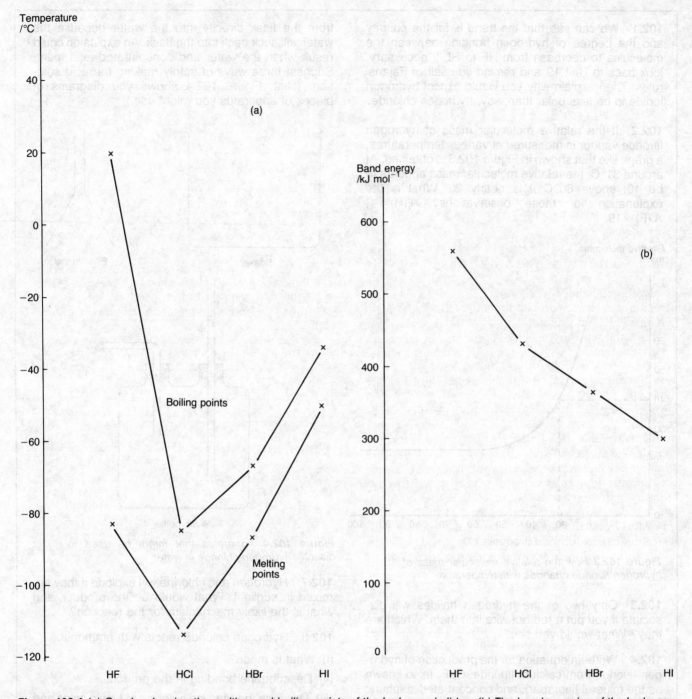

Figure 102.1 (a) Graphs showing the melting and boiling points of the hydrogen halides. (b) The bond energies of the hydrogen halides

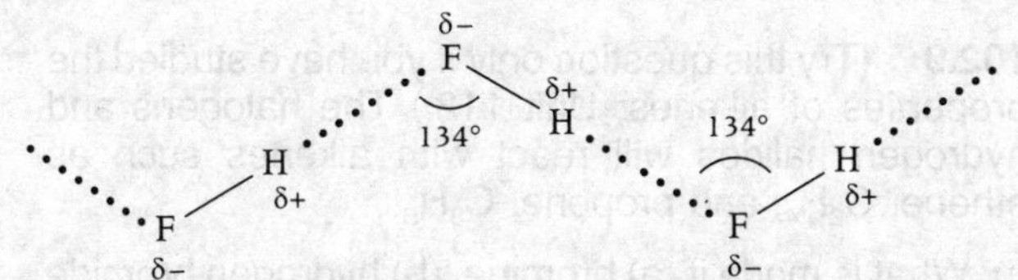

***Figure 102.2** Liquid hydrogen fluoride is very strongly hydrogen bonded, with many of the molecules in zig-zag chains. Solid hydrogen fluoride has a six-membered ring structure, (HF)$_6$*

An alternative method for HBr and HI is to use a combination of the halogen and red phosphorus in water. We can think of the reaction taking place in two stages. In the case of iodine, first

$$3I_2(s) + 2P(s) \rightarrow 2PI_3(s)$$

then

$$PI_3(s) + 3H_2O(l) \rightarrow H_3PO_3(aq) + 3HI(g)$$

Bromine behaves similarly.

102.1 We can see that the trend is for the polarity and the degree of hydrogen bonding between the molecules to decrease from HF to HI. If necessary, look back to Unit 19 and remind yourself of Fajans' rules. Then explain why you would expect hydrogen iodide to be less polar than, say, hydrogen chloride.

102.2 If the relative molecular mass of hydrogen fluoride vapour is measured at various temperatures, a graph like that shown in Figure 102.3 is obtained. At around 31°C, the relative molecular mass appears to be 40; above 60°C it is nearly 20. What is the explanation for these observations? $A_r(H) = 1$, $A_r(F) = 19$.

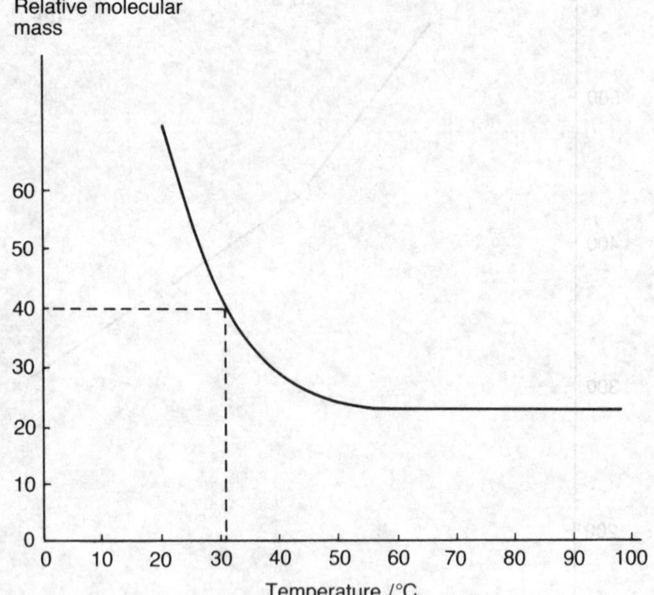

Figure 102.3 *How the relative molecular mass of hydrogen fluoride changes with temperature*

102.3 Only two of the hydrogen halides will dissociate if you put a red hot wire into them. Which are they? What would you see?

102.4 Write an equation for the production of hydrogen fluoride from calcium fluoride, CaF_2 (also known as the mineral fluorspar), and concentrated sulphuric acid. Why is this not a good reaction to carry out in a test tube?

102.5 What are the oxidation numbers of sulphur in H_2SO_4 and in the products of its reactions with the hydrogen halides? Which is the better reducing agent, HBr or HI? Explain.

102.6 The hydrogen halides are very soluble in water. Imagine you had a flask in which you were about to prepare hydrogen chloride. Your aim is to dissolve the gas in water in order to make a solution of hydrochloric acid. You must not put the outlet tube from the flask directly into the water because the water will suck back into the flask. An explosion could result when the water and concentrated acid meet. Suggest three ways of safely making the acid solution. (Hint: Figure 102.4 shows you diagrams of pieces of apparatus you might use.)

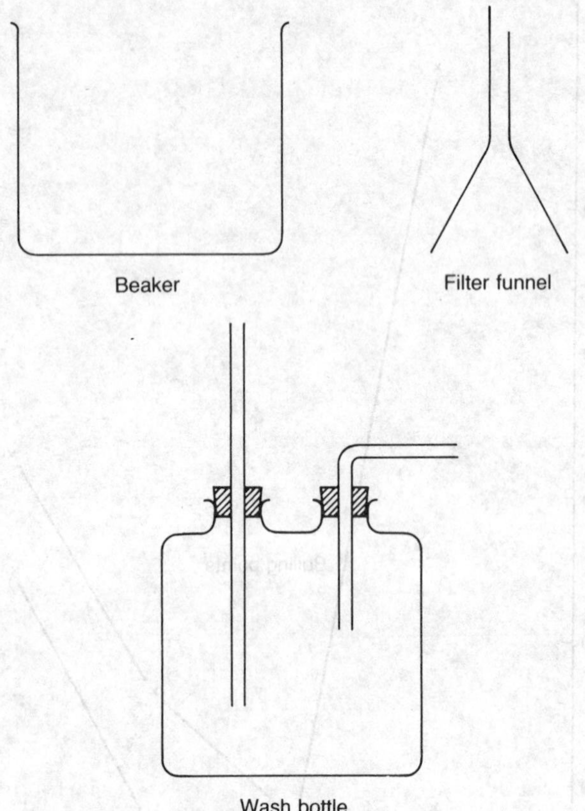

Figure 102.4 *Apparatus that might be used to dissolve hydrogen chloride in water*

102.7 Hydrogen and chlorine will explode if they are mixed in sunlight. What would be the product, and what is the likely mechanism for the reaction?

102.8 Hydrogen chloride reacts with ammonia.

(i) What is made?

(ii) Describe the bonding in the product.

(iii) Describe the reaction in terms of Lewis acids and bases.

(Hint: look back at Units 15 and 74 for help.)

102.9 (Try this question only if you have studied the properties of alkenes; Unit 112.) The halogens and hydrogen halides will react with alkenes such as ethene, C_2H_4, and propene, C_3H_6.

(i) What is made if (a) bromine, (b) hydrogen bromide reacts with these alkenes.

(ii) What is bromine used to test for in organic chemistry?

Table 102.2. Inter-halogen compounds

ClF	ClF_3	ClF_5	IF_7
BrF	BrF_3	BrF_5	
BrCl	ICl_3	IF_5	
BrI	IF_3		
ICl			

102.2 Inter-halogen compounds

The halogens make a number of inter-halogen compounds, some of which are listed in Table 102.2. Many of the compounds can be made by direct combination of the elements. For example, fluorine and chlorine will react at around 200°C to give chlorine fluoride, ClF; iodine and excess chlorine will combine at room temperature to make iodine trichloride, ICl_3:

$$F_2(g) + Cl_2(g) \rightarrow 2ClF(g)$$
$$I_2(s) + 3Cl_2(g) \rightarrow 2ICl_3(l)$$

Given their chemical similarity, perhaps we should expect the halogens to make compounds like BrCl and ICl. However, it is quite noticeable that fluorine gives compounds in which the other halogen has a much higher oxidation number than usual. For example, in iodine pentafluoride, IF_5, we have $Ox(I) = +5$. This ability of fluorine to bring out high oxidation states in elements with which it combines is another way of saying that fluorine is a very powerful oxidising agent. Nonetheless, the fact that five fluorine atoms can bond to an iodine atom needs some explanation.

Iodine has the electron structure I:(Kr)$4d^{10}5s^25p^5$. It appears that only one of the 5p orbitals has space for an additional electron. (We can imagine that this electron is provided by the chlorine atom in, say, ICl.) However, accommodating five extra electrons in IF_5 is not feasible unless we assume other orbitals are used in the bonding. We have seen this type of situation before in section 17.4. There we found that we could use the theory of hybridisation to explain how carbon might make four bonds to other atoms. In the case of IF_5 we have seven electrons from the iodine valence shell, and one electron from each fluorine to make the five bonds. Thus we need six orbitals to cope with 12 electrons. They are obtained if we assume that not only the 5s and 5p orbitals are involved in bonding, but also some of the 5d orbitals are used. In this way we can build up a set of six d^2sp^3 hybrid orbitals. (You might like to look at Table 17.5, where you will find that a number of different combinations of orbitals were employed to describe the shapes of a wide range of molecules and ions.) The shape of the IF_5 molecule is illustrated in Figure 102.5.

Iodine molecules have the distinction of being able to combine with iodide ions to give triiodide ions, I_3^-. These ions are made whenever iodine is produced in a solution containing iodide ions. They are soluble in water, and deep brown in colour. If we wish to use a solution of iodine, it is always made by dissolving iodine crystals in a solution of iodide ions. An equilibrium, lying far to the right-hand side, exists in the solution:

$$I_2(s) + I^-(aq) \rightleftharpoons I_3^-(aq)$$

The solution acts as a source of iodine because the equilibrium shifts to the left and replaces those iodine molecules that may be removed. This reaction is used in iodine titrations (see section 40.3).

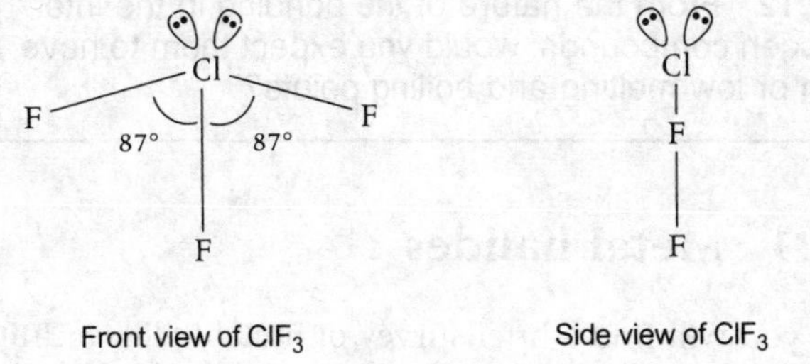

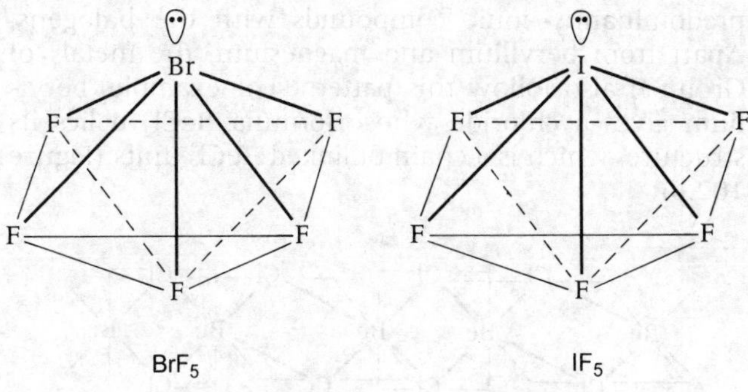

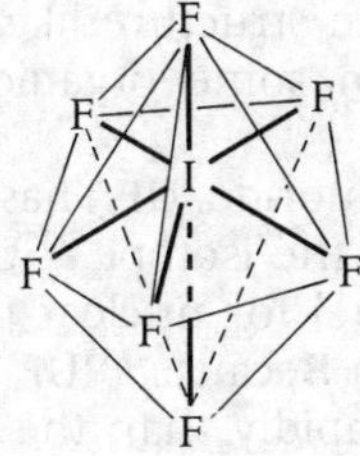

Figure 102.5 *The shapes of inter-halogen fluorides*

> **102.10** Figure 102.5 shows that ClF_3 has a distorted T-shape. Explain why two lone pairs of electrons are shown in the diagram, and why this might lead to distortion of the shape.
>
> **102.11** Predict the shapes of the molecules in each of the four columns in Table 102.2.

102.12 From the nature of the bonding in the interhalogen compounds, would you expect them to have high or low melting and boiling points?

102.3 Metal halides

Here you will find a brief survey of metal halides. Unit 89 will tell you about the solubilities and the hydrolysis of halides.

In previous units (e.g. Units 89, 92 and 93) we discussed the nature of bonding in substances like sodium chloride. We established that the Group I metals give predominantly ionic compounds with the halogens. Apart from beryllium and magnesium, the metals of Group II also follow this pattern. For example, beryllium gives a chloride whose formula $BeCl_2$ belies its structure, which is a chain of linked $BeCl_2$ units (Figure 102.6).

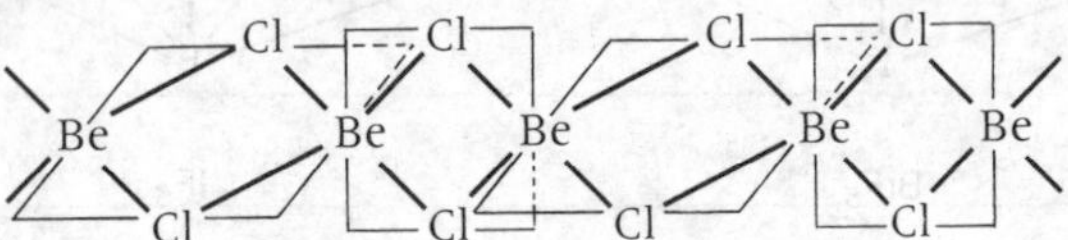

***Figure 102.6** The structure of solid beryllium chloride, $BeCl_2$*

The halides of Group III are predominantly covalent. The structure of aluminium chloride is one that you should know. It was described in section 15.1. In the solid it has a chain structure like that of $BeCl_2$; but in the vapour, or in some organic liquids, it exists as dimers.

Uranium hexafluoride, UF_6, has been used in the process of separating the isotope ^{235}U from ^{238}U. (^{235}U has been used as a fuel for nuclear power stations and in nuclear weapons.) Because $^{235}UF_6$ is lighter than $^{238}UF_6$, it diffuses more rapidly than the latter. This difference between the two fluorides is the basis of the separation.

The halogens give a variety of complexes with transition and B metals where the halide ions can act as ligands. Structures of the complexes vary; e.g. $[Cr(H_2O)_4Cl_2]^-$, $CuCl_4^{2-}$, $PbCl_6^{4-}$. You will find more information about such complexes in Unit 106.

A reaction in which a complex ion of silicon is made is the etching of glass by hydrofluoric acid solution. Glass contains a mixture of calcium and sodium silicates. Calcium silicate reacts according to the equation

$$Ca^{2+}SiO_3^{2-}(s) + 6HF(aq) \rightarrow Ca^{2+}(aq) + SiF_6^{2-}(aq) + 3H_2O(l)$$

The products are all soluble in water, so we see the glass being dissolved. However, if only a little of the acid is put on the glass, the surface takes on a frosted look. This is made use of by motorists who have their car windows etched with the car registration number. The idea is that this will help dissuade thieves from making off with the car and disguising it by merely changing the number plates. It is likely that glassware you use in the laboratory has been etched using the same method.

Apart from silver fluoride, the silver halides are notable for their insolubility in water. This property is used in the silver nitrate test for the halides.

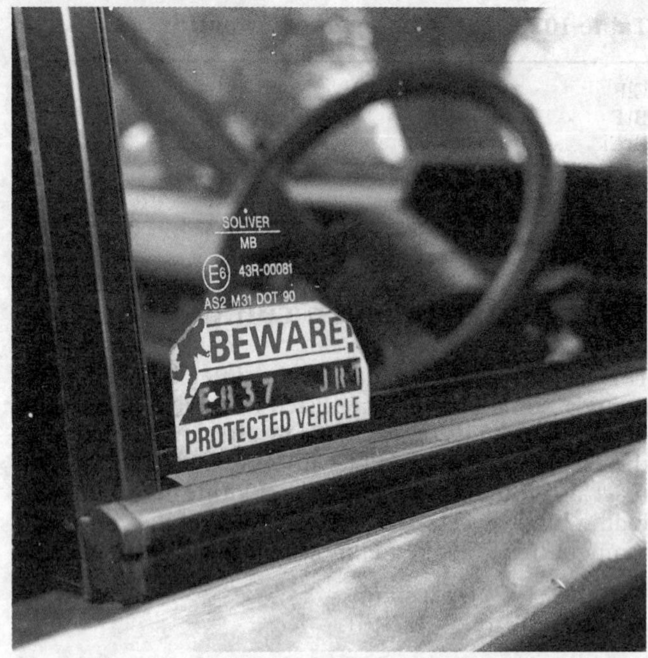

Solutions of hydrogen fluoride have the ability to dissolve glass. This property is often used to etch car windows with the registration number as a security measure.

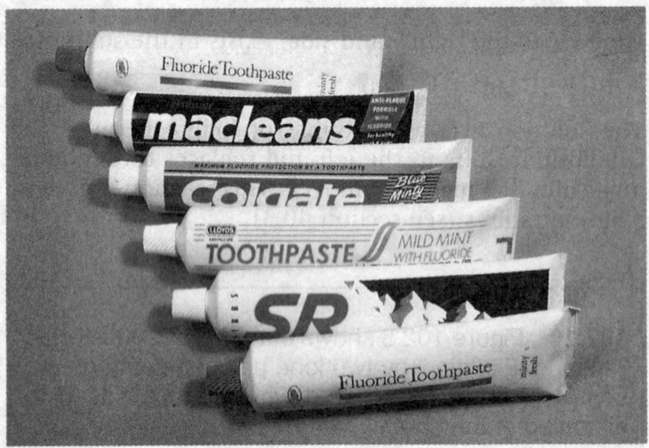

Fluoride toothpastes are now very common, and can contain a number of different metal fluorides e.g. sodium fluoride.

102.13 What does the ease with which silver fluoride dissolves in water suggest about the bonding in silver fluoride?

102.14 Explain why a chlorine atom is able to give a coordinate bond with a neighbouring beryllium atom. (Hint: do you know what an electron deficient compound is?)

102.4 Making metal halides

For many halides it is usually possible to combine the metal and halogen directly. However, this is not always the case, and sometimes precautions have to be taken. These are not only ones of safety, but of keeping moisture out of the apparatus. Although the ionic halides do not suffer from the complaint of hydrolysis, many of the predominantly covalent halides do react with water. Figure 102.7 shows you one way of making a small amount of aluminium trichloride. Notice that the chlorine is dried before it passes into the reaction tube, and that the collection bottle has a tube containing anhydrous calcium chloride attached. This allows air and excess chlorine to escape from the apparatus, but it prevents moisture entering. If moisture does get to the solid, hydrolysis takes place:

$$AlCl_3(s) + 3H_2O(l) \rightarrow Al(OH)_3(s) + 3HCl(aq)$$

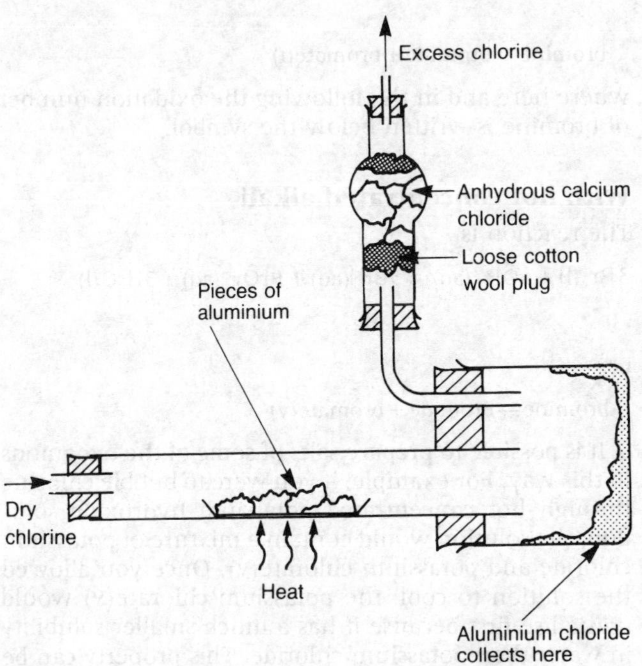

***Figure 102.7** Apparatus for making aluminium trichloride*

102.15 Iron(III) chloride and iron(II) chloride both suffer from hydrolysis. The former can be made by passing chlorine over hot iron. Why can the latter not be made in this way? What other gaseous source of chlorine might be used instead?

102.16 A student reacted iron(II) sulphide with dilute hydrochloric acid in a fume cupboard. The reaction was

$$FeS(s) + 2HCl(aq) \rightarrow Fe^{2+}(aq) + 2Cl^-(aq) + H_2S(g)$$

After the reaction was over the student decided to make some iron(II) chloride crystals by evaporating the solution.

(i) Why was it necessary to do the reaction in a fume cupboard?

(ii) Why did the student fail to make crystals of iron(II) chloride?

102.5 Compounds containing oxygen and halogens

There are many molecules and ions that contain both oxygen and halogens. The general name for ions that contain oxygen and another element is *oxoanions*. There is a list in Table 102.3, and two are shown in Figure 102.8. Of the molecules, chlorine dioxide, ClO_2, is the most useful beyond the laboratory. At room

Table 102.3. Molecules and ions containing both oxygen and halogens*

Molecules

Fluorine	*Chlorine*	*Bromine*	*Iodine*
OF_2	Cl_2O	Br_2O	I_2O_5
O_2F_2	ClO_2	BrO_2	
	Cl_2O_6	BrO_3	
	Cl_2O_7		

Oxoanions†

Chlorine	*Bromine*	*Iodine*
Chlorate(I), ClO^-	Bromate(I), BrO^-	Iodate(I), IO^-
Chlorate(V), ClO_3^-	Bromate(V), BrO_3^-	Iodate(V), IO_3^-
Chlorate(VII), ClO_4^-		

Acids

Modern name	*Old name*	*Formula*
Chloric(I) acid	Hypochlorous acid	HClO
Chloric(V) acid	Chloric acid	$HClO_3$
Chloric(VII) acid	Perchloric acid	$HClO_4$

*Only the more common molecules and ions are listed
†Fluorine does not form oxoanions

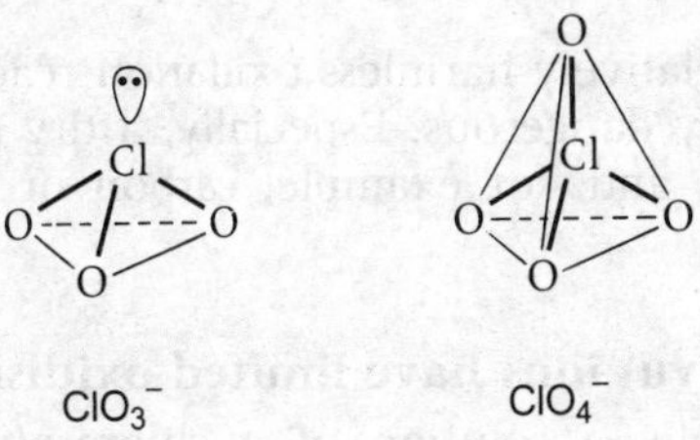

***Figure 102.8** Both the chlorate(V), ClO_3^-, and chlorate(VII), ClO_4^-, ions are tetrahedral*

temperature it is a dark yellow gas. Below its boiling point of 11°C it exists as an oily red liquid. It is an extremely powerful oxidising agent and, in spite of the dangers associated with it, the gas has been used in treating water supplies to kill bacteria, and in bleaching wood pulp prior to paper making.

Some of the oxoanions you may already know about: many of them are used as oxidising agents, and some show up in disproportionation reactions. We shall consider both types of reaction now. First, we shall stick to stating what happens, mainly using the chlorine oxoanions as examples; later, if you are interested, you can use your knowledge of redox potentials to explain the reactions.

(a) *Oxidation reactions*

The usual way to employ the oxoanions is in acidic solution. The pattern of reaction is:

chlorate(I) → chloride + loss of oxygen
chlorate(V) → chloride + loss of oxygen
chlorate(VII) → very little oxidising power

(Note: anhydrous chloric(VII) acid, $HClO_4$, is an extremely vigorous oxidising agent.)

Bromates and iodates behave similarly. Here are some examples.

Chlorate(I) oxidises iron(II) to iron(III)

Chlorate(I) ions combine with hydrogen ions to give chloric(I) acid (also known as hypochlorous acid). This is a weak acid, so it mainly reacts as HClO molecules:

$$HClO(aq) + 2Fe^{2+}(aq) + H^+(aq) \rightarrow Cl^-(aq) + 2Fe^{3+}(aq) + H_2O(l)$$

However, a useful source of free chlorate(I) ions is bleaching powder. This is calcium chlorate(I), $Ca(OCl)_2$. (It is also known as calcium hypochlorite). Bleaching powder has a long history. It was one of the first bleaches that was effective in bleaching cotton. The use of bleaching powder allowed cotton to be dyed to a consistently high quality, and therefore gave manufacturers who used it a great advantage over those who did not.

Chlorate(V) oxidises sulphite ions to sulphate

The reaction is

$$ClO_3^-(aq) + 3SO_3^{2-}(aq) \rightarrow Cl^-(aq) + 3SO_4^{2-}(aq)$$

This is a relatively harmless oxidation reaction. Others can be very dangerous. Especially, a dry mixture of a chlorate(V) and, for example, carbon or sulphur will explode.

Chlorate(VII) ions have limited oxidising action

For example, a solution of a chlorate(VII) will not oxidise iron(II) or sulphite ions, SO_3^{2-}. In fact, these reactions are energetically favourable. The reason why they do not take place is a matter of kinetics. The activation energy of the reactions is very large. This is partly due to the number of covalent bonds that have to be broken if the ClO_4^- ion is to break apart.

(b) *Disproportionation reactions*

A disproportionation reaction is one where an element with a single oxidation number (or state) reacts to give two or more different oxidation numbers. An example that you should remember is when one of the halogens reacts with alkali. We shall use bromine as our example, but chlorine and iodine react similarly.

With cold dilute alkali

The reaction is

$$Br_2(l) + 2OH^-(aq) \rightarrow Br^-(aq) + OBr^-(aq) + H_2O(l)$$

0 −1 +1

i.e.

bromine → bromide + bromate(I)

where here and in the following the oxidation number of bromine is written below the symbol.

With hot concentrated alkali

The reaction is

$$3Br_2(l) + 6OH^-(aq) \rightarrow 5Br^-(aq) + BrO_3^-(aq) + 3H_2O(l)$$

0 −1 +5

i.e.

bromine → bromide + bromate(V)

It is possible to prepare salts of some of the oxoanions in this way. For example, if you were to bubble chlorine through hot concentrated potassium hydroxide solution, the solution would contain a mixture of potassium chloride and potassium chlorate(V). Once you allowed the solution to cool, the potassium chlorate(V) would crystallise first because it has a much smaller solubility in water than potassium chloride. This property can be used in fractional crystallisation (see section 59.2). However, you would be disappointed if you used dilute alkali and attempted to crystallise potassium chlorate(I). Once you started to evaporate the solution, the chlorate(I) ions would decompose.

Heating a chlorate(V)

Potassium chlorate(V) behaves in two ways depending on the temperature at which it is heated. At around its melting point (367°C), chlorate(VII) and chloride ions are made:

$$4ClO_3^- \rightarrow 3ClO_4^- + Cl^-$$

This is another example of disproportionation. However, at a higher temperature, the chlorate(VII) ions decompose giving off oxygen:

$$ClO_4^- \rightarrow Cl^- + 2O_2$$

102.17 A solution of bleaching powder contains chlorate(I) ions. The solution will easily convert iodide ions, I^-, into iodine, I_2. Write an equation for the reaction.

102.18 Chlorate(V) ions will also oxidise iron(II) to iron(III) and iodide to iodine. Write equations for these reactions. Assume they take place with acid present.

102.6 Explaining redox reactions using redox potentials

It is essential that you understand the work on electrode and redox potentials in Units 66 and 70 if you are to follow the explanations in this section.

We can see how the oxidising powers of the oxoanions vary by looking at their redox potentials. These are gathered together in Table 102.4. You will see that some of the oxoanions are shown as their acids; e.g HClO rather than OCl^-. Where this happens, we assume that the reactions take place in acidic solutions. First, you can see from the fairly high positive values of the redox potentials that all the oxoanions are oxidising agents. We shall work through some of the more important reactions.

(a) *Iodate(V)–iodide reaction*

The data show that iodate(V) ions will oxidise another species whose redox potential is less than 0.91 V. In particular, if we look at the iodine–iodide reaction, this has a redox potential of +0.54 V. Therefore, if we mix iodate(V) and iodide ions, the iodide ions will be oxidised to iodine. The reactions will take place in the directions shown:

$$IO_3^-(aq) + 6H^+(aq) + 6e^- \rightarrow I^-(aq) + 3H_2O(l)$$
$$2I^-(aq) \rightarrow I_2(s) + 2e^-$$

We can combine the equations by taking three times the second and adding it to the first. This gives us

$$IO_3^-(aq) + 5I^-(aq) + 6H^+(aq) \rightarrow 3I_2(s) + 3H_2O(l)$$

The value of this reaction is in performing titrations designed to determine the concentration of iodide in a solution. You will find details of the method in Unit 40.

(b) *Chlorate(V)–chloride reaction*

Because $E^\ominus_{ClO_3^-/Cl^-} = +1.45\,V$ and $E^\ominus_{Cl_2/Cl^-} = +1.36\,V$, chlorate(V) ions should oxidise chloride ions to chlorine. However, the difference between the two potentials is far less than the rule of thumb of 0.6 V that we used in Unit 70. In fact, the reaction will take place, but only if the chlorate(V) is heated with concentrated hydrochloric acid. As well as chlorine being released, chlorine dioxide is released. The mixture of the two gases was investigated by Humphry Davy, who called the mixture euchlorine. Needless to say, investigating the properties of this mixture of gases caused him, and other chemists, much bother.

(c) *Disproportionation in halogen–alkali reactions*

We have already discussed this type of reaction in Unit 71. If you have forgotten how to decide if an element or ion will take part in a disproportionation reaction, do consult that unit.

102.7 The halogen oxoacids

There are no oxoacids of fluorine. The oxoacids of chlorine are the most important and are listed in Table 102.5.

We have mentioned some of their properties in the previous sections, particularly that chloric(I) acid is a good oxidising agent (like chlorate(I) ions). It is made when chlorine dissolves in water:

$$Cl_2(g) + H_2O(l) \rightarrow HOCl(aq) + Cl^-(aq) + H^+(aq)$$

It is responsible for the bleaching action of chlorine water.

Each of the oxoacids has its own particular anhydride. The anhydride is a molecule that reacts to give the acid when water is added to it. Alternatively,

Table 102.4. Standard redox potentials for halogen oxoanions

Ion	*Half-reaction*	$E^\ominus$/V
In acid solution		
Chlorate(I)	$2HClO(aq)+2H^+(aq)+2e^- \rightarrow Cl_2(g)+2H_2O(l)$	+1.63
Chlorate(V)	$ClO_3^-(aq)+6H^+(aq)+6e^- \rightarrow Cl^-(aq)+3H_2O(l)$	+1.45
Chlorate(VII)	$ClO_4^-(aq)+8H^+(aq)+8e^- \rightarrow Cl^-(aq)+4H_2O(l)$	+1.39
Bromate(I)	$2HBrO(aq)+2H^+(aq)+2e^- \rightarrow Br_2(l)+2H_2O(l)$	+1.57
Bromate(V)	$BrO_3^-(aq)+6H^+(aq)+6e^- \rightarrow Br^-(aq)+3H_2O(l)$	+1.93
Iodate(I)	$2HIO(aq)+2H^+(aq)+2e^- \rightarrow I_2(aq)+2H_2O(l)$	+1.45
Iodate(V)	$IO_3^-(aq)+6H^+(aq)+6e^- \rightarrow I^-(aq)+3H_2O(l)$	+0.91
Chloride	$Cl_2(g)+2e^- \rightarrow 2Cl^-(aq)$	+1.36
Bromide	$Br_2(l)+2e^- \rightarrow 2Br^-(aq)$	+1.09
Iodide	$I_2(aq)+2e^- \rightarrow 2I^-(aq)$	+0.54

Table 102.5. The oxoacids of chlorine*

	Formula	Oxidising power	Acid strength	Thermal stability
Chloric(I) acid (hypochlorous acid)	$HClO$	Strong ↑	Weak ↓	Poor ↓
Chloric(V) acid (chloric acid)	$HClO_3$			
Chloric(VII) acid (perchloric acid)	$HClO_4$	Weak	Strong	Good

*Bromic(V) acid is very strong; bromic(VII) acid does not exist. Iodine forms an analogous set of acids to those of chlorine, but with weaker oxidising power

we can think of the anhydride as the species that is left when the elements of water are removed from the acid. For example, the anhydride of chloric(I) acid is dichlorine oxide, Cl_2O:

$$2HClO - H_2O \rightarrow Cl_2O$$

Similarly we predict the anhydrides of the other oxoacids to be:

$$2HClO_3 - H_2O \rightarrow Cl_2O_5$$
$$2HClO_4 - H_2O \rightarrow Cl_2O_7$$

Of these, dichlorine pentaoxide, Cl_2O_5, does not exist; but dichlorine heptaoxide, Cl_2O_7, does exist. In spite of its unlikely looking formula, it is energetically and kinetically stable at room temperature and exists as a colourless, viscous liquid. It can be made by reacting chloric(VII) acid with a powerful dehydrating agent, phosphorus(V) oxide.

Answers

102.1 Fajans' rules tell us that a covalent bond is favoured if the cation has a small ionic radius and the anion a large ionic radius. A large anion is more easily polarised. An iodide ion is larger than a chloride ion, so would be more readily polarised by a hydrogen ion. This is one reason why hydrogen iodide is less polar than hydrogen chloride.

102.2 Hydrogen fluoride is hydrogen bonded not only in the liquid state, but also in the vapour. You should have worked out that $M_r(HF) = 20$. At the lower temperature, it seems likely that the molecules are going around in pairs, or dimers, i.e. $(HF)_2$. This would give the observed relative molecular mass of 40. As the temperature increases, the collisions of the particles are so energetic that the dimers break up to give single HF molecules, for which $M_r(HF) = 20$.

102.3 Hydrogen bromide and hydrogen iodide have weaker bonds than the others, so these will be more likely to decompose. You would see the pale yellow and purple colours of bromine and iodine vapours, respectively.

102.4 $CaF_2(s) + H_2SO_4(l) \rightarrow CaSO_4(s) + 2HF(l)$

Any moisture will encourage the hydrogen fluoride to etch the glass.

102.5 The oxidation numbers are:

Element	*Substance*	*Oxidation number*
Sulphur	H_2SO_4	+6
	SO_2	+4
	S	0
	H_2S	−2
Bromine	Br_2	0
Iodine	I_2	0

Iodine converts sulphur from oxidation number +6 to −2, whereas bromine can only manage the conversion +6 to +4. Iodine is the better reducing agent because it can supply electrons more readily. Alternatively, you can say that HI ions are more easily oxidised than HBr.

102.6 The arrangement of the apparatus is shown in Figure 102.9.

102.7 Hydrogen chloride is made. A free radical mechanism (see Unit 81).

102.8 (i) Ammonium chloride:

$HCl(g) + NH_3(g) \rightarrow NH_4Cl(s)$

(ii) See section 15.1

(iii) See section 74.4.

102.9 (i) (a) Ethene makes 1,2-dibromoethane:

$$H_2C{=}CH_2 + Br_2 \longrightarrow H{-}\underset{H}{\overset{Br}{C}}{-}\underset{H}{\overset{Br}{C}}{-}H$$

Propene makes 1,2-dibromopropane:

$$CH_3(H)C{=}CH_2 + Br_2 \longrightarrow CH_3{-}\underset{H}{\overset{Br}{C}}{-}\underset{H}{\overset{Br}{C}}{-}H$$

(b) Ethene makes bromoethane:

$$H_2C{=}CH_2 + HBr \longrightarrow H{-}\underset{H}{\overset{H}{C}}{-}\underset{H}{\overset{Br}{C}}{-}H$$

Propene makes 2-bromopropane:

$$CH_3(H)C{=}CH_2 + HBr \longrightarrow CH_3{-}\underset{H}{\overset{Br}{C}}{-}\underset{H}{\overset{H}{C}}{-}H$$

HBr obeys Markovnikoff's rule (section 112.4) when it adds to an alkene (provided free radicals are not involved).

(ii) Unsaturated compounds, in particular double and triple bonds in alkenes and alkynes.

Answers – cont.

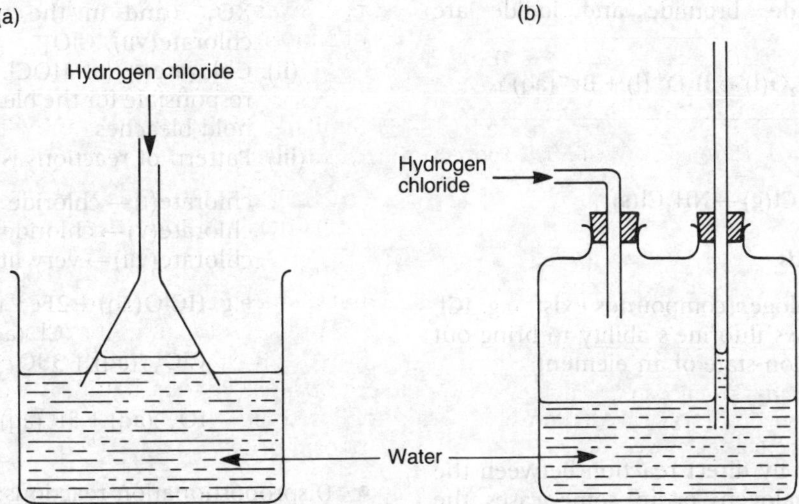

***Figure 102.9** Diagrams for answer to question 102.6. (a) When the water level rises inside the funnel, the level outside falls. Eventually the level falls below the lip of the funnel. This releases the pressure inside the funnel and the water drops back to its original level. (b) Here there is no chance of the water level reaching the inlet tube. If the pressure increases too much, the water rises up the second tube*

102.10 Each fluorine will provide one of the electrons in the three bonding pairs. Chlorine has seven electrons in its valence shell. This makes 10 electrons in total. Six of them are used in bonding, so there are four left over. These make the two lone pairs. Electron repulsion theory tells us that the lone pairs will repel the bonding pairs, thereby distorting the molecule.

102.11 The first column will be linear, the second T-shaped, the third square-based pyramid, and IF_7 is a pentagonal bipyramid.

102.12 They are all covalent, and do not give giant structures, so they should have low melting and boiling points; they do.

102.13 The bonding is mainly ionic. The fluoride ion is far less polarisable than the other halides, so AgF will not be so covalent as the other silver halides.

102.14 You will find an explanation of this in section 15.1. Briefly, a beryllium atom has an empty 2p orbital, which can accept a pair of electrons from chlorine.

102.15 Chlorine will oxidise the iron(II) to iron(III). Hydrogen chloride is used to make iron(II) chloride from iron.

102.16 (i) H_2S not only has an awful smell, it is highly poisonous.

(ii) The chloride is hydrolysed by water. It will turn into iron(III) hydroxide.

102.17

$$ClO^-(aq) + 2I^-(aq) + 2H^+(aq) \rightarrow Cl^-(aq) + I_2(s) + H_2O(l)$$

102.18 The key to doing this is to spot that the chlorine changes from oxidation number +5 to −1. This is an effective gain of six electrons. Hence the $6I^-$ and $6Fe^{2+}$ appearing in the equations:

$$ClO_3^-(aq) + 6I^-(aq) + 6H^+(aq) \rightarrow Cl^-(aq) + 3I_2(s) + 3H_2O(l)$$

$$ClO_3^-(aq) + 6Fe^{2+}(aq) + 6H^+(aq) \rightarrow Cl^-(aq) + 6Fe^{3+}(aq) + 3H_2O(l)$$

UNIT 102 SUMMARY

Hydrogen halides

- Preparation:
  (i) Hydrogen fluoride and chloride: warm the sodium halide with concentrated sulphuric acid;

  e.g. $NaCl(s) + H_2SO_4(l) \rightarrow NaHSO_4(s) + HCl(g)$

  (ii) Hydrogen bromide and iodide: react the sodium halide with phosphoric acid;

  e.g. $NaI(s) + H_3PO_4(l) \rightarrow NaH_2PO_4(s) + HI(g)$

Properties

- Hydrogen fluoride:
  (i) Strongly hydrogen bonded.

(ii) Aqueous HF is only a weak acid.

- With water:
  Hydrogen chloride, bromide and iodide are strongly acidic;

  e.g. $HBr(g) + H_2O(l) \rightarrow H_3O^+(l) + Br^-(aq)$

- With ammonia:
  Salts made;

  e.g. $NH_3(g) + HCl(g) \rightarrow NH_4Cl(s)$

Interhalogen compounds

A number of interhalogen compounds exist, e.g. ICl, IF_5; the latter shows fluorine's ability to bring out the highest oxidation state of an element.

Metal halides

(i) Can be made by direct reaction between the metal and halogen, or in some cases the hydrogen halide;

e.g. iron(III) chloride

$$2Fe(s) + 3Cl_2(g) \rightarrow 2FeCl_3(s)$$

iron(II) chloride

$$Fe(s) + 2HCl(g) \rightarrow FeCl_2(s) + H_2(g)$$

(ii) Some halides are easily hydrolysed, e.g. $AlCl_3$, $FeCl_2$, $FeCl_3$.

Properties

- Nature of halides:
  (i) Group I halides are ionic solids, e.g. Na^+Cl^-.
  (ii) The chlorides of beryllium, boron and aluminium ($BeCl_2$, BCl_3, $AlCl_3$) are covalent. $AlCl_3$ dimerises, making Al_2Cl_6.
- Hydrolysis:
  Some covalent halides are easily hydrolysed, e.g. $AlCl_3$, $FeCl_2$, $FeCl_3$. (Therefore, require dry conditions in their preparations.)
- With transition metal ions:
  Halide ions can act as ligands, e.g. $[Cr(H_2O)_4Cl_2]^+$.

Compounds containing oxygen and halogens

Many molecules containing both oxygen and a halogen exist. See Table 102.3.

- Oxoanions:
  (i) Most important are halate(I), XO^-, halate(V), XO_3^-, and in the case of chlorine only, chlorate(VII), ClO_4^-.
  (ii) Chlorate(I) (as HOCl, hypochlorous acid) is responsible for the bleaching ability of household bleaches.
  (iii) Pattern of reactions is

  chlorate(I) → chloride + loss of oxygen
  chlorate(V) → chloride + loss of oxygen
  chlorate(VII) → very little oxidising power

  e.g. $HClO(aq) + 2Fe^{2+}(aq) + H^+(aq) \rightarrow Cl^-(aq) + 2Fe^{3+}(aq) + H_2O(l)$

  $ClO_3^-(aq) + 3SO_3^{2-}(aq) \rightarrow Cl^-(aq) + 3SO_4^{2-}(aq)$

  $IO_3^-(aq) + 5I^-(aq) + 6H^+(aq) \rightarrow 3I_2(aq) + 3H_2O(l)$

- Disproportionation reactions:
  (i) Occur when an element with a single oxidation number (or state) reacts to give two or more different oxidation numbers.
  (ii) Take place when halogens react with alkali. With cold dilute alkali;

  $Br_2(l) + 2OH^-(aq) \rightarrow Br^-(aq) + OBr^-(aq) + H_2O(l)$

  With hot concentrated alkali;

  $3Br_2(l) + 6OH^-(aq) \rightarrow 5Br^-(aq) + BrO_3^-(aq) + 3H_2O(l)$

- Heat on a chlorate(V):
  (i) Near its melting point (367° C);

  $4KClO_3 \rightarrow 3KClO_4 + KCl$
  (a disproportionation)

  (ii) At higher temperatures;

  $4KClO_3 \rightarrow 4KCl + 6O_2$

- Oxoacids:
  Examples are chloric(I) acid, HClO (hypochlorous acid); chloric(V) acid, $HClO_3$ (chloric acid); chloric(VII) acid, $HClO_4$ (perchloric acid).

103

Pseudohalides and pseudohalogens

103.1 What is a pseudohalide?

A pseudohalide is an ion that behaves like a halide ion. For example, we should expect pseudohalides to

(i) have a negative charge,
(ii) give salts with alkali metals, and
(iii) act as a ligand with transition metal ions.

The most common ones are listed in Table 103.1.

(a) *Azides*

Group I metals give ionic azides, whereas B metals tend to give covalent azides. One rather important difference between the two classes of azide is that the covalent ones are explosive, whereas the ionic ones are not. Azide ions are linear and can join with organic radicals in much the same way as the halogen atoms, e.g. methyl azide, CH_3N_3.

Hydrazoic acid, HN_3, is a weak acid in water, and can be made by reacting sulphuric acid with sodium azide, $Na^+N_3^-$.

(b) *Cyanides*

Cyanide ions are famous largely because of their reputation as an extremely dangerous poison. These ions satisfy each of our three conditions:

(i) they have a negative charge;
(ii) Group I metals give ionic salts, e.g. sodium cyanide, Na^+CN^-;
(iii) cyanide ions can act as ligands, e.g. hexacyanoferrate(II), $Fe(CN)_6^{4-}$, and hexacyanoferrate(III), $Fe(CN)_6^{3-}$, ions.

Indeed, it is the ability of cyanide ions to bond with iron ions that is partly responsible for their action as a poison. They bond very strongly to the iron in cytochrome oxidase, and prevent oxygen molecules being taken up by haemoglobin. Cytochrome oxidase is involved in the biochemical cycle controlling respiration.

Hydrogen cyanide, HCN, can be made by reacting sodium cyanide with sulphuric acid. It has a smell of bitter almonds, although it would be a foolish chemist who spent too long in savouring the smell! Like hydrogen fluoride, hydrogen cyanide is a weak acid in water.

Table 103.1. The most common pseudohalides

Name	*Ion*
Azide	N_3^-
Cyanide	CN^-
Thiocyanate	SCN^-

(c) *Thiocyanates*

Thiocyanate ions also complex with transition metal ions. With iron(III) ions, an intense blood red colour is produced. This reaction can be used as a test for iron(III) ions:

$$Fe^{3+}(aq) + SCN^-(aq) \rightarrow \underset{\text{blood red}}{FeSCN^{2+}(aq)}$$

103.1 Write the equation for the reaction between sulphuric acid and sodium azide.

103.2 Sodium cyanide can be regarded as a salt of a weak acid (HCN) and a strong alkali (NaOH). What would you predict for the pH of a solution of sodium cyanide in water. Briefly explain your answer.

103.3 The stability constants of $FeSCN^{2+}$ and FeF^{2+} are approximately $10^3\,mol^{-1}\,dm^3$ and $10^5\,mol^{-1}\,dm^3$ respectively. A solution of FeF^{2+} is colourless. What, if anything, should happen if (i) F^- ions are added to a solution of $FeSCN^{2+}$, (ii) SCN^- ions are added to a solution of FeF^{2+}?

103.2 Pseudohalogens

In the same way that chloride ions have chlorine molecules, Cl_2, as their parents, so many of the pseudohalides have pseudohalogens. Two of our pseudohalides give pseudohalogens. They are:

(i) cyanogen, $(CN)_2$;
(ii) thiocyanogen, $(SCN)_2$.

Both are gases at room temperature.

There is no pseudohalogen matching the azide ion.

Like the true halogens, cyanogen reacts with alkali:

$$(CN)_2(g) + 2OH^-(aq) \rightarrow CN^-(aq) + \underset{\text{cyanate}}{OCN^-(aq)} + H_2O(l)$$

This can be compared with:

$$Cl_2(g) + 2OH^-(aq) \rightarrow Cl^-(aq) + OCl^-(aq) + H_2O(l)$$

103.4 Cyanogen will combine directly with Group I metals. Write the equation for the reaction between sodium and cyanogen.

Answers

103.1 $NaN_3(s) + H_2SO_4(aq) \rightarrow NaHSO_4(aq) + HN_3(g)$

103.2 In water, the equilibrium

$$CN^-(aq) + H_2O(l) \rightleftharpoons HCN(aq) + OH^-(aq)$$

is set up. The solution will be alkaline, i.e. the pH will be rather more than 7. See Unit 76 about salt hydrolysis.

103.3 The stability constants show that FeF^{2+} is energetically more favoured than $FeSCN^{2+}$. Therefore we would expect (i) the blood red colour to clear as thiocyanate ions are displaced by fluoride ions, and (ii) nothing to happen. In the first reaction, kinetics is on our side, and the colour change takes place quickly.

103.4 $2Na(s) + (CN)_2(g) \rightarrow 2NaCN(s)$

UNIT 103 SUMMARY

- Pseudohalides:
  Show some, or all, of the properties of true halides. For example, they
  (i) Have a negative charge.
  (ii) Give salts with alkali metals.
  (iii) Act as ligands with transition metal ions.

  Examples are azide ions, N_3^-; cyanide ions, CN^-; thiocyanate ions, SCN^-.
- Pseudohalogens:
  Are related to pseudohalides, like halides are to halogens. Examples are cyanogen, $(CN)_2$; thiocyanogen, $(SCN)_2$.

104

The noble gases

104.1 What is special about the noble gases?

Sometimes it seems that the most honour goes to those people who are furthest removed from the nasty practicalities of life; so it is with the gases helium, neon, argon, krypton, xenon and radon, whose physical properties are outlined in Table 104.1. These gases were once thought to be so extremely idle that they had to belong to the nobility. The hurly burly of chemical reactions was thought to be above their station in life. Hence they were given the alternative name of the inert gases. However, at least in the case of xenon, it is not so; xenon will react with other elements and compounds.

However, the reactivity of the gases *is* very low, and this has given them a number of uses, which you will find listed in Table 104.2.

The discovery of the gases was a feat in itself (Table 104.3). You may remember from Unit 87 that the presence of one of them caused Mendeléeff some difficulty. Radon was discovered as the product of the radioactive decay of uranium and thorium. Helium was first detected as a new element in the spectrum of the Sun in 1868 (hence its name is connected with *helios*, the Greek word for sun). It was not until some years later that it was collected as a gas given off from radioactive minerals. Argon was discovered by Sir William Ramsay as an impurity in nitrogen from air. The other noble gases were discovered by an analysis of fractions of different boiling points taken from liquid air.

Helium has the lowest boiling point of any element, and its behaviour as a liquid is most unusual. It will, for example, creep up the walls of its container. This phenomenon is a result of there being two different phases of liquid helium, one of which has an extremely low viscosity.

Helium is used in small airships like this. (They are more properly called 'dirigibles'.)

Table 104.1. Physical properties of the noble gas elements

Symbol	*Helium* He	*Neon* Ne	*Argon* Ar	*Krypton* Kr	*Xenon* Xe	*Radon* Rn
Electron structure	$1s^2$	$(He)2s^22p^6$	$(Ne)3s^23p^6$	$(Ar)3d^{10}4s^24p^6$	$(Kr)4d^{10}5s^25p^6$	$(Xe)4f^{14}6s^26p^6$
I.E./kJ mol^{-1}	2372	2081	1521	1350	1170	1040
Melting point/° C		−249	−189	−157	−112	−71
Boiling point/° C	−269	−249	−186	−152	−109	−62
Atomic radius/pm	120	160	190	200	220	
Principal oxid. no.	0	0	0	0	+2,+4,+6	0

Table 104.2. Uses of the noble gas elements

Element	*Main uses*
Helium	In air ships Mixed with oxygen, as a breathing gas for divers Used in some lasers Provides an inert atmosphere for welding
Neon	In 'neon lamps'
Argon	In electric light bulbs to prevent oxidation of the filament In Geiger counter tubes
Xenon	In high light intensity photographic flash tubes
Krypton	Also used in electric light bulbs and, like neon, in coloured display lamps
Radon	Radon is an alpha emitter It has been used in radiotherapy (Recently, the natural occurrence of radon in some houses has been linked to a very slight increased risk of cancer among occupants of those houses. The risk is highest in regions where there is much granite)

Table 104.3. The discovery of the noble gases

Gas	*Year of discovery*	*Discovered by*
Helium	1895	Sir William Ramsay
Neon	1898	Sir William Ramsay, M. W. Travers
Argon	1894	Sir William Ramsay, Lord Rayleigh
Krypton	1898	Sir William Ramsay, M. W. Travers
Xenon	1898	Sir William Ramsay, M. W. Travers
Radon	1900	Friedrich Dorn

104.1 What is the link between helium and (i) radioactive decay, (ii) the Sun's energy?

104.2 There are three isotopes of radon: $^{219}_{86}Rn$, $^{220}_{86}Rn$, $^{222}_{86}Rn$. Each of them decays by alpha emission with a half-life of about 4 s, 55 s and 4 days respectively. That they are all isotopes of radon was not known at first, and they were given the names actinon, thoron and radon. What are the products of their decay?

104.3 The noble gases are very close to being ideal.

(i) Which of them is the nearest to being an ideal gas?

(ii) Why (or how) is it that the gases liquefy?

104.4 Why are there no electronegativity values listed in Table 104.1?

104.2 Compounds of the noble gases

The first authentic noble gas compound was made by N. Bartlett in 1962. He showed that oxygen and platinum hexafluoride would react together to give an orange substance with the formula $O_2^+PtF_6^-$. The ionisation energy of an oxygen molecule is about 1165 kJ mol^{-1}, a value that Bartlett noticed was almost the same as the first ionisation energy of xenon (1170 kJ mol^{-1}). Not only that, but he expected that the sizes of the O_2^+ and Xe^+ ions would be comparable. This would mean that the lattice energies of $O_2^+PtF_6^-$ and $Xe^+PtF_6^-$ should be similar. In fact, $Xe^+PtF_6^-$ was deposited as an orange solid as soon as Bartlett mixed xenon and the hexafluoride.

Following this discovery, a number of other xenon compounds have been made. For example, XeF_2, XeF_4, XeF_6. The other noble gases remain unreactive.

104.5 Why is the chemistry of radon particularly difficult to investigate?

Answers

104.1 (i) An alpha-particle, ^4_2He, is the nucleus of a helium atom. Alpha-particles are often given off in nuclear reactions.

(ii) Much of the Sun's energy is given by the fusion of hydrogen nuclei. Helium is a major product of fusion. See Unit 6.

104.2 Alpha decay decreases the mass number by four units and the atomic number by two units. This gives, respectively, $^{215}_{84}Po$, $^{216}_{84}Po$ and $^{218}_{84}Po$.

104.3 (i) Helium.

(ii) They liquefy owing to the van der Waals forces that are set up between the atoms. The more electrons an atom has, the greater the forces. Helium has the least number of electrons, so the forces are weakest. Hence intermolecular attractions are the least, and it is closest to being ideal.

104.4 Pauling's electronegativity values tell us about the elements' relative attractions for electrons. Apart from a very few reactions, the noble gases are inert. Thus their electronegativity values are of little practical use.

104.5 It is radioactive, and has a short half-life. Hence it is very difficult to work with.

UNIT 104 SUMMARY

- The Group 0 elements:
  - (i) Have very high ionisation energies.
  - (ii) Are all highly unreactive.
- Isolation:

  By the liquefaction of air followed by fractional distillation.
- Reactions:

  Xenon shows a slight tendency to react, e.g. to make XeF_2, XeF_4, XeF_6, $Xe^+PtF_6^-$.

105

Transition metals

105.1 Transition metals and their electron structures

The transition metals are the block of elements sandwiched between Group II and Group III. There are three rows of them – the first, second and third transition series. For the most part we shall only be concerned with the first series. These are the elements scandium to zinc. However, zinc is not a typical transition metal, and it is best regarded as a B metal. We shall deal with its chemistry in Unit 108.

The graphs in Figure 105.1 will give you a visual impression of how many of the properties in Table 105.1 vary across the series. The electron structures of the transition metals are at the heart of their chemistry. It would be wise to learn them. Especially, notice that

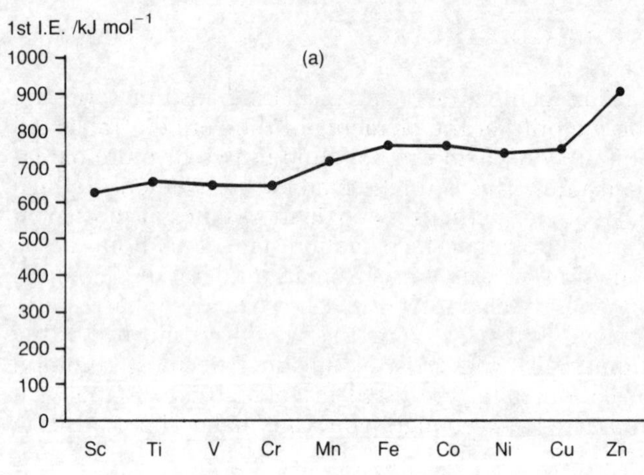

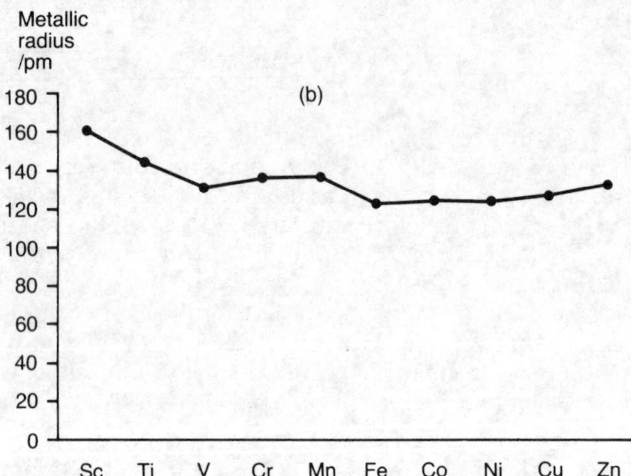

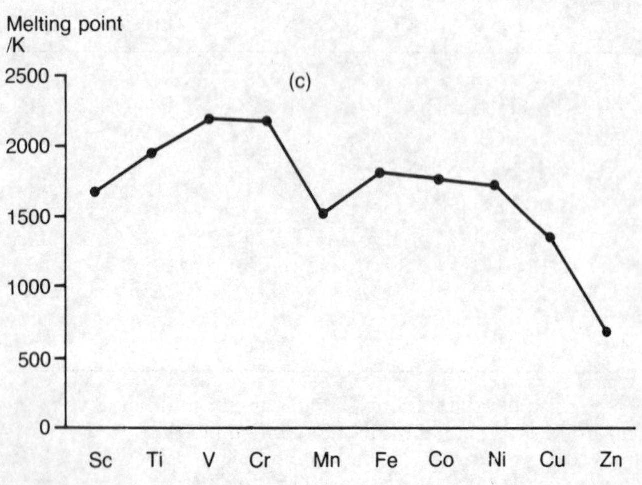

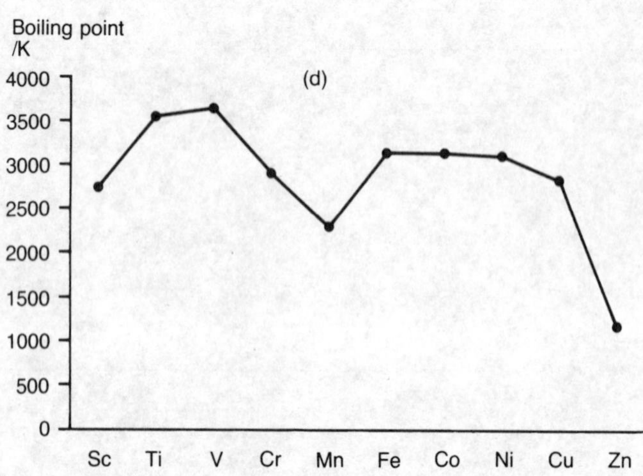

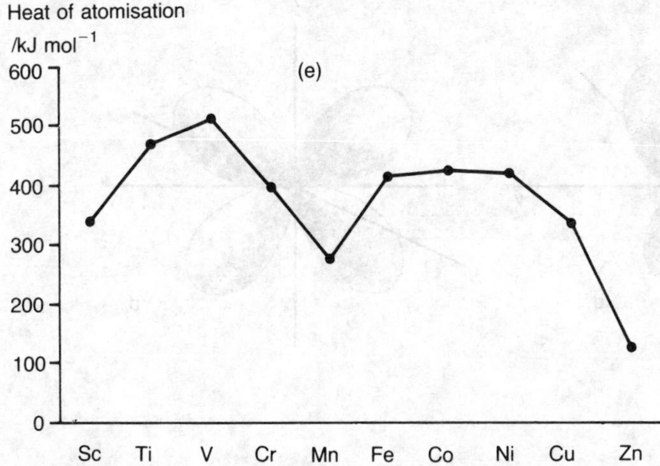

Figure 105.1 *(a) First ionisation energies. The values are similar to but significantly higher than those of Group I metals. (b) Metallic radii. The similarity in radii is one reason why the metals form alloys with each other. Little distortion of a lattice may occur when one atom is substituted by another. (c) Melting points, (d) boiling points and (e) heats of atomisation. The graphs of melting points, boiling points and heats of atomisation all show that atoms of the elements are all held tightly in their lattices. However, the dips at manganese indicate that the combination of $3d^5$ and $4s^2$ electrons is less readily involved in metallic bonding. (The reason for this is complicated)*

they all involve the filling of the 3d set of orbitals, shown in Figure 105.2. (The second and third series of transition metals have 4d and 5d orbitals being filled.) For the elements before scandium, the 4s orbital has a lower energy than the 3d orbital. However, as the nuclear charge increases, at scandium the 3d orbitals become lower in energy than the 4s orbital. Partly this is because the 3d orbitals can penetrate into the region of space between the nucleus and the maximum in the 4s probability density. As a result, the 3d electrons can feel a stronger attraction for the nucleus than the 4s electrons. The order of energies of the orbitals also depends on the interactions between the electrons in the orbitals. These interactions can be very complicated, and you would need to know a lot about quantum theory to understand them. They are responsible for the unusual electron structures of chromium and copper. We might expect chromium to have the structure $(Ar)3d^44s^2$; instead it is $(Ar)3d^54s$. The 3d set of orbitals can contain a maximum of 10 electrons, and the 4s orbital a maximum of two electrons. Therefore chromium has both sets of orbitals half-full. This is a result of a quantum effect that gives rise to a contribution to the energy called the *exchange energy*. The same effect lies behind the electron structure of copper. In this case the expected structure is $(Ar)3d^94s^2$, whereas in reality it is $(Ar)3d^{10}4s$.

In Table 105.2 you will find a summary of the most important properties of the transition metals. In the following eight sections we shall examine each of them in turn. In fact we have already tackled the electron structures.

105.2 The oxidation states of transition metals

Taken together, the metals in all the transition series are the majority of the elements in the Periodic Table. All but a few of them can be found in two or more oxidation states. This is unlike many other elements, which have one or perhaps two oxidation states at most. You should know that the oxidation state of an atom can be shown by writing it as a Roman numeral in the name, or as a number of positive or negative charges. Do remember that by doing this we do *not* mean that the atom really does exist as an ion. The most common oxidation states are listed in Table 105.3. Actually, if you try hard enough you can make the transition

Table 105.1. The first transition series*†

	Sc	Ti	V	Cr	Mn	Fe	Co	Ni	Cu	Zn
Atomic no.	21	22	23	24	25	26	27	28	29	30
Outer electrons	$3d4s^2$	$3d^24s^2$	$3d^34s^2$	$3d^54s$	$3d^54s^2$	$3d^64s^2$	$3d^74s^2$	$3d^84s^2$	$3d^{10}4s$	$3d^{10}4s^2$
1st I.E./kJ mol⁻¹	630	660	650	650	720	760	760	740	750	910
Covalent radius/pm	144	132	122	117	117	116	116	115	135	131
Atomic radius/pm	161	145	132	137	137	124	125	125	128	133
Melting point/K	1673	1950	2190	2176	1517	1812	1768	1728	1356	693
Boiling point/K	2750	3550	3650	2915	2314	3160	3150	3110	2855	1181
Sublimation energy/kJ mol⁻¹	305	428.9	458.6	348.9	219.7	351	382.4	371.8	304.6	115.3

*Each of the atoms has the argon gas core, $(Ar) = 1s^22s^22p^63s^23p^6$. The pattern of orbital filling changes at chromium and copper
†Zinc is included here for comparison; for most purposes it is better regarded as a B metal rather than a member of the transition series

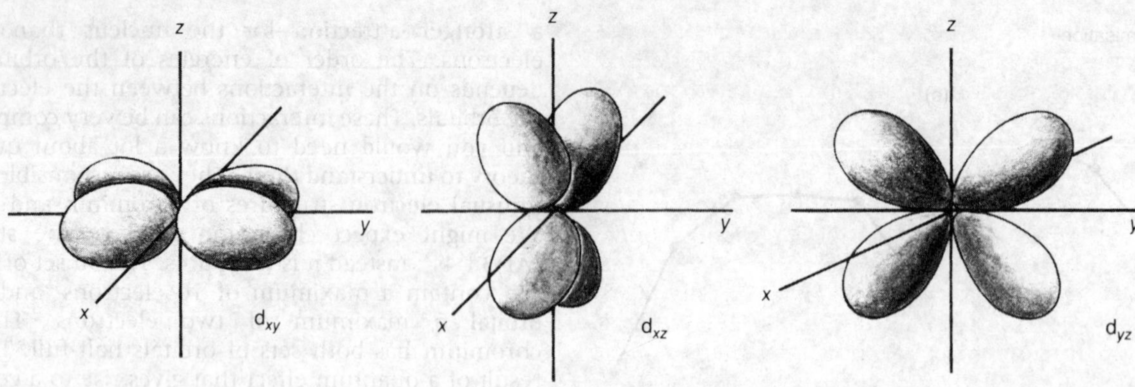

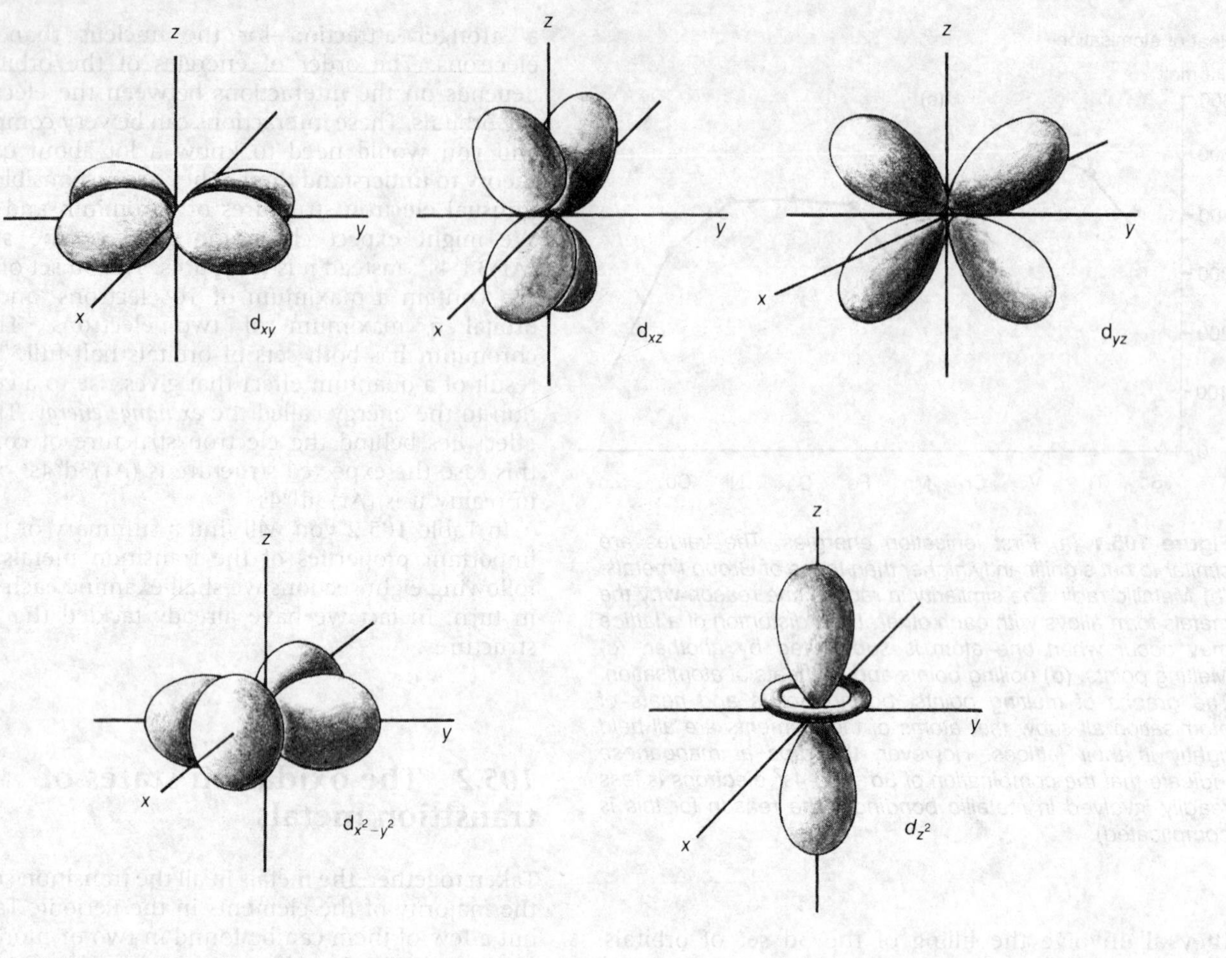

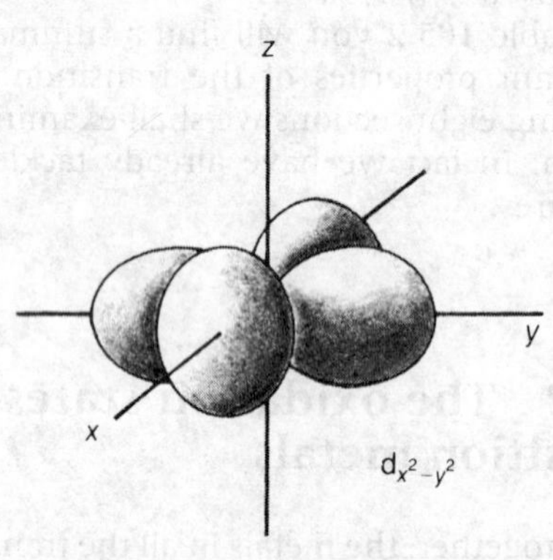

Figure 105.2 The set of five 3d orbitals

Table 105.2. Properties of transition metals

Outer electron structures involve d orbitals
Show variable oxidation states
Make complex ions
Paramagnetic compounds
Have coloured compounds
Act as catalysts
Form alloys

Table 105.3. The common oxidation states of the transition metals

Sc	Ti	V	Cr	Mn	Fe	Co	Ni	Cu	Zn
+3	+4	+3 +4 +5	+3 +6	+2 +4 +7	+2 +3	+2 +3	+2	+1 +2	+2

metals show a wide variety of oxidation states. For example, manganese can be found in all the oxidation states ranging from −3 (in $Mn(NO)_3CO$) to +7 (in $KMnO_4$), but only 0, +2, +4 and +7 are common.

105.1 What are the oxidation states of manganese in the following compounds: (i) $MnCl_4^{2-}$, (ii) MnO_4^-, (iii) Mn_2O_3?

105.3 What are complex ions?

From time to time we have met complex ions in previous units. For example, when copper(II) ions mix with aqueous ammonia, the tetraamminecopper(II) ion, $Cu(NH_3)_4^{2+}$, is made. This is a typical complex ion as far as its bonding is concerned. An ammonia molecule has a lone pair of electrons that can be donated to the copper ion. A molecule or ion like ammonia that gives a coordinate bond with a transition metal ion is called a *ligand*. A complex ion is made by a number of ligands bonding to the metal ion. A molecule or ion that can give one bond to a metal ion is a *monodentate* ligand. You will find examples of monodentate ligands in Table 105.4.

Usually four or six bonds are made to the ion. However, this does not necessarily mean that four or six ligands are involved. Some ligands have more than one site that can bond to an ion. These are called *polydentate* ligands. An example is ethane-1,2-diamine, $NH_2CH_2CH_2NH_2$, which is drawn in Figure 105.3. This molecule has a lone pair on each of the two nitrogen atoms. Therefore it can make two coordinate bonds with a metal ion.

A ligand like this is a *bidentate* ligand. We only need two ethane-1,2-diamine molecules to take the place of the four single ammonia molecules, and the complex ion $[Cu(NH_2CH_2CH_2NH_2)_2]^{2+}$ results. Ethane-1,2-diamine is given a shorthand symbol, en. This allows us to write the formula of the complex in a neater way as $Cu(en)_2^{2+}$.

You will find examples of bidentate ligands in Table 105.5. Ligands with three, four, five and six bonding sites are also known. One hexadentate ligand (six bonding sites) called ethylenediaminetetraacetic acid (or 1,2-bis[bis(carboxymethyl)amino]ethane), EDTA, is extremely useful. It is used in analysis for the detection and estimation of the concentrations of metal ions. Not only transition metal ions react with EDTA: see section 91.6.

Ligands that have up to six sites for bonding are common, but monodentate, bidentate and hexadentate ligands are by far the most important. You might like to read panel 105.1 now. This will explain the naming system for transition metal compounds, and give you examples of compounds with a variety of oxidation states and ligands.

Table 105.4. Examples of monodentate ligands*

Ligand	*Diagram*
Water	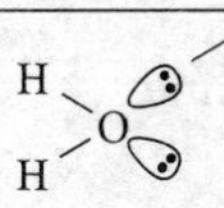 H–O–H (two lone pairs on O) →
Ammonia	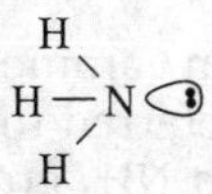 H_3N: →
Chloride ion	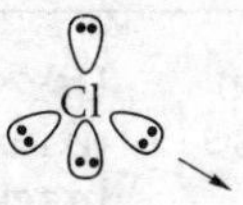 Cl^- (four lone pairs) →
Cyanide ions	 :N≡C: →
Carbon monoxide	 :O≡C: →

*They all have at least one lone pair of electrons, which can make a coordinate bond with a transition metal ion

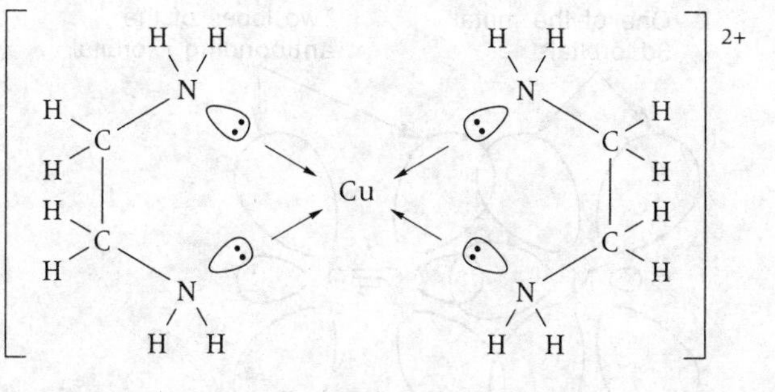

Figure 105.3 The $[Cu(NH_2CH_2CH_2NH_2)_2]^{2+}$ ion has a copper(II) ion bonded to two ethane-1,2-diamine molecules through the four lone pairs on the nitrogen atoms

Table 105.5. Examples of polydentate ligands†

Ligand	*Diagram*
Bidentate	
Ethane-1,2-diamine	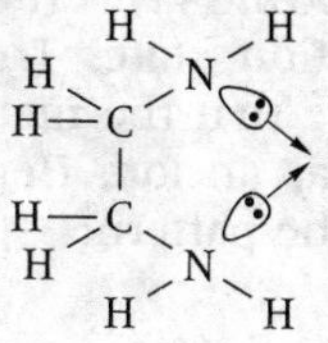 $H_2N–CH_2–CH_2–NH_2$ (lone pair on each N)
Ethanedioate ion	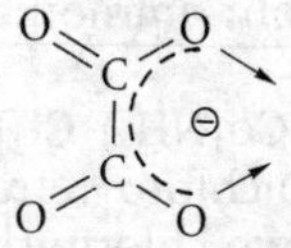 $^-O(O=)C–C(=O)O^-$
Pentane-2,4-dione (acetylacetonato ion)	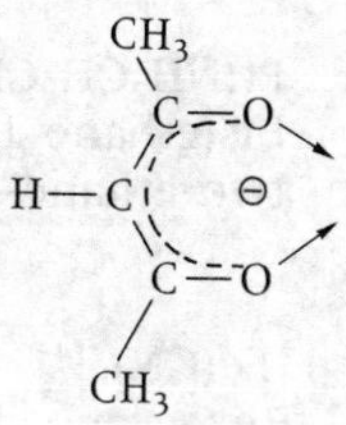 $CH_3–C(=O)–CH^-–C(=O)–CH_3$
Hexadentate	
Ethylenediaminetetraacetic acid‡ (*marks a site for coordinate bonding)	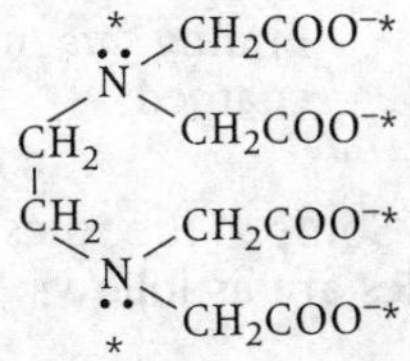 $(^{*-}OOCCH_2)_2N^*–CH_2–CH_2–N^*(CH_2COO^{-*})_2$

†Polydentate ligands are also called *chelating agents* (chelate is pronounced to rhyme with 'keylate')
‡Actually the anion of EDTA is shown. The acid molecule might be better written H_4EDTA

Panel 105.1

How to name transition metal compounds

There are two parts to the name of a complex. The first tells us about the ligands attached to the ion; the second gives the name of the metal ion and its oxidation state. The oxidation state tells us the charge that the metal would have if it were on its own as an ion. Here are some examples to show you the pattern:

(i) $Cu(NH_3)_4^{2+}$
Tetraammine | copper(II)
four ammonia | copper ion with +2 charge

(ii) $[Co(NH_3)_4Cl_2]^+$
Dichloro | tetraammine | cobalt(III),
two chlorine | four ammonia | cobalt with +3 charge

(iii) $Pt(NH_2CH_2CH_2NH_2)_2^{2+}$
Bis(ethane-1,2-diamine) | platinum(II)
two ethane-1,2-diamine | platinum with +2 charge

(iv) $[Fe(CN)_6]^{4-}$
Hexacyano | ferrate(II)
six cyanide | iron with +2 charge
Ending *ate* means entire ion is negatively charged.

Some of the rules that are at work in these examples are as follows:

Numbers of ligands

With monodentate ligands		*With bidentate ligands*	
Prefix	*Number*	*Prefix*	*Number*
Di	2	Bis	2
Tri	3	Tris	3
Tetra	4	Tetrakis	4
Penta	5		
Hexa	6		

Names of ligands

Name in complex	*Ligand*
Aqua (or aquo)	H_2O
Ammine	NH_3
Ethane-1,2-diamine	$NH_2CH_2CH_2NH_2$
Chloro	Cl^-
Cyano	CN^-
Nitro	NO_2^-

Notice that, when ammonia molecules act as ligands, they are referred to as 'ammine'; the term 'amine' refers to an NH_2 group as a ligand.

Naming the metal

Positive charge on complex	Use standard name with oxidation state in brackets
Negative charge on complex	Use name with *ate* ending and oxidation state in brackets

105.2 Carbon monoxide has a lone pair of electrons on the carbon atom that can make a coordinate bond to a transition metal ion. In addition, it has an empty antibonding π orbital. This can overlap with a d orbital of the right symmetry as shown in Figure 105.4.

(i) How would you describe the bond that is made?

Many metals give carbonyls with carbon monoxide, e.g. $Cr(CO)_6$, $Fe(CO)_5$.

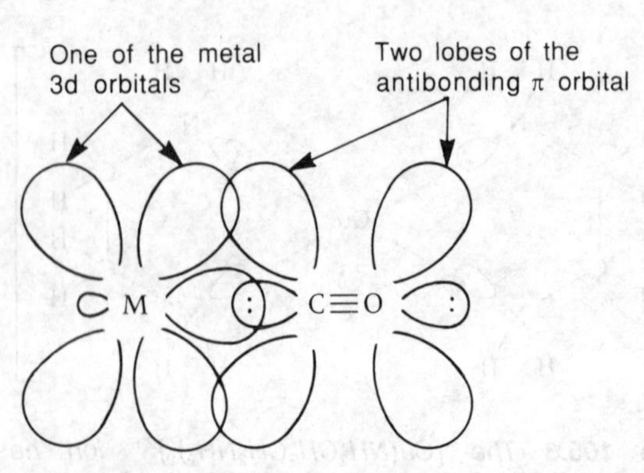

Figure 105.4 *Carbon monoxide can make bonds to a transition metal ion: one through a lone pair on the carbon atom, another through an antibonding π orbital (which has four lobes)*

(ii) What is the oxidation state of the metals in these compounds? (Hint: is carbon monoxide charged?)

105.3 What are the names of the following complexes or compounds: (i) $[Cu(NH_3)_2(H_2O)_2]^{2+}$; (ii) $[Cr(en)_2Cl_2]^+$; (iii) $K_4[Fe(CN)_6]$?

105.4 What are the formulae of the following complexes:

(i) tris(ethane-1,2-diamine)chromium(III),

(ii) trinitrotriamminecobalt(III),

(iii) chloropentaaquachromium(III)?

105.4 The shapes of complex ions

There are three typical shapes for complex ions. They are usually *octahedral, square planar* or *tetrahedral* (Figure 105.5).

(a) *Octahedral complexes*

An octahedral complex results when there are six bonds to the metal ion. This can happen if there are six monodentate ligands, three bidentate ligands, or other combinations that give the six bonds (see Figure 105.6 for examples).

(b) *Square planar complexes*

In a square planar complex there are four bonds to the metal ion. The metal ion and the four atoms attached to it all lie in the same plane (see Figure 105.7 for examples).

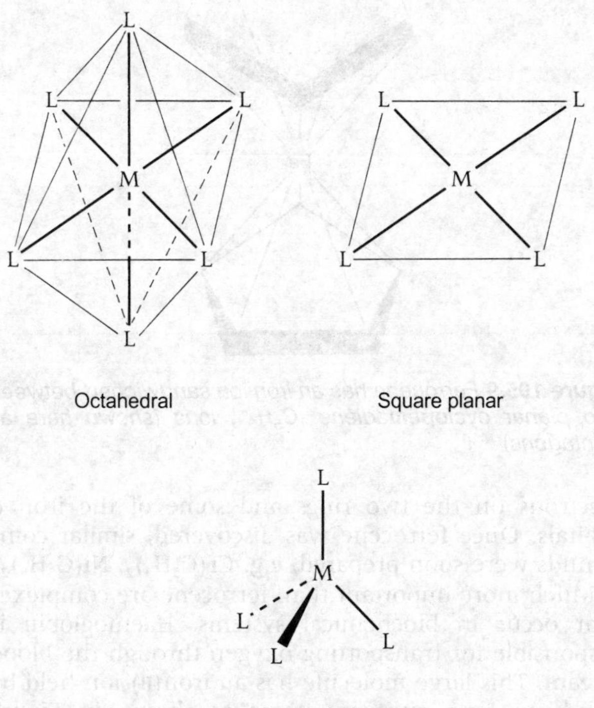

Figure 105.5 *The three main shapes adopted by transition metal complexes*

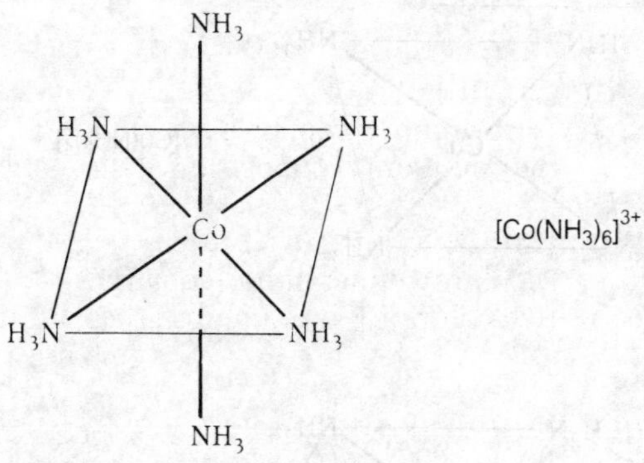

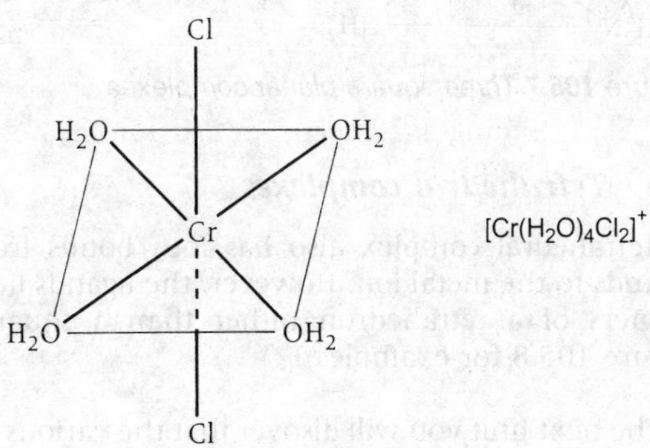

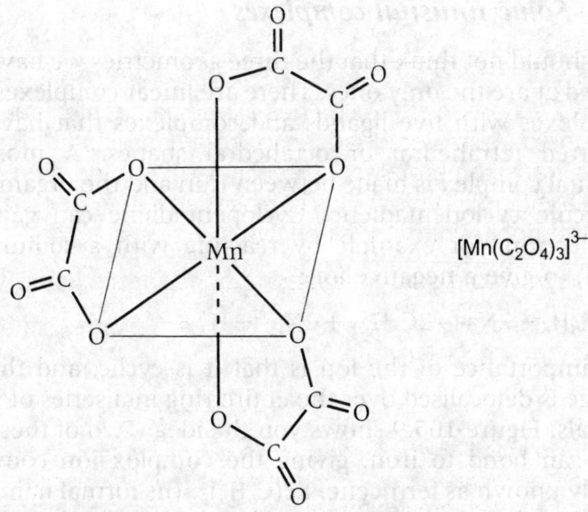

Figure 105.6 *Three examples of octahedral complexes*

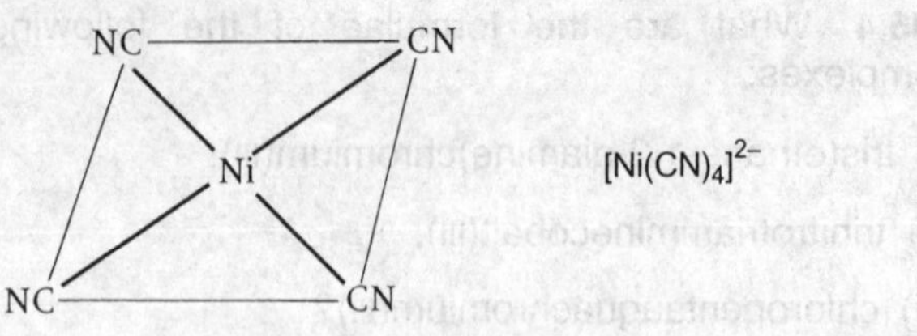

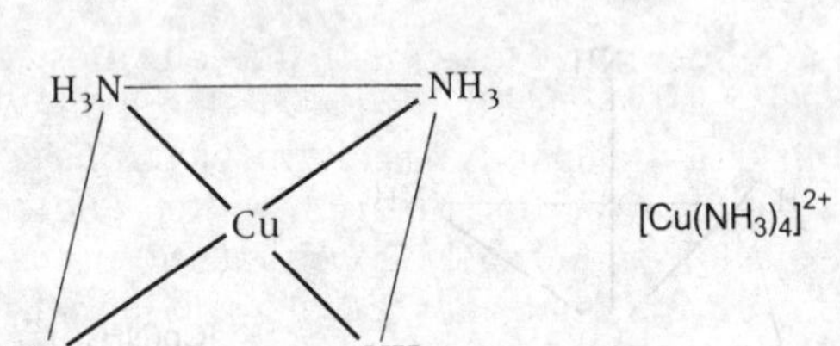

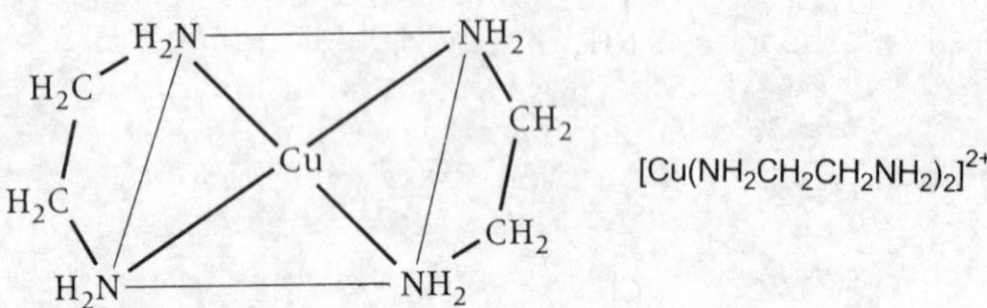

Figure 105.7 *Three square planar complexes*

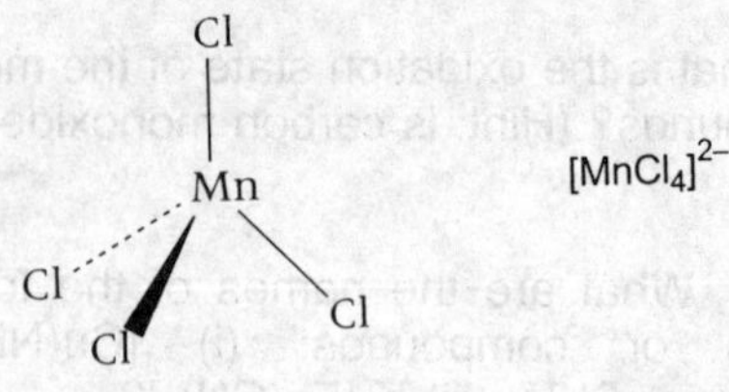

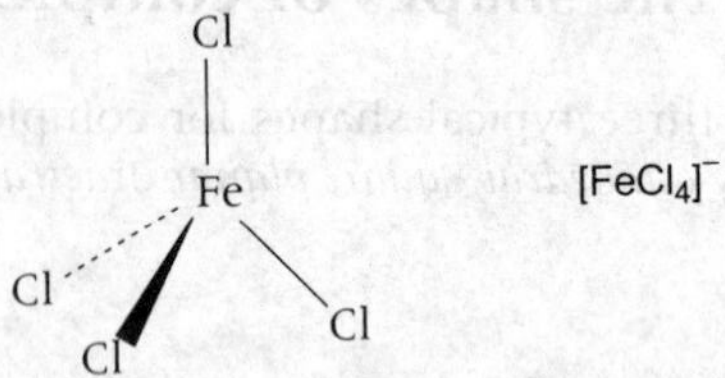

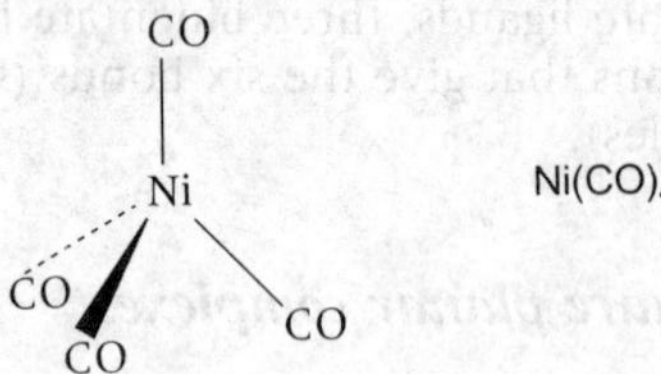

Figure 105.8 *Three tetrahedral complexes*

(c) *Tetrahedral complexes*

A tetrahedral complex also has four bonds from the ligands to the metal ion. However, the ligands lie at the corners of a tetrahedron rather than a square (see Figure 105.8 for examples).

In the next unit you will disover that the various shapes of the complexes can produce isomerism. That is, there can be several different complexes with the same formula.

(d) *Some unusual complexes*

You should not think that the three geometries we have looked at are the only ones. There are linear complexes, complexes with five ligands and complexes that have distorted tetrahedral or octahedral shapes. A most unusual complex is made between iron and the organic molecule cyclopentadiene. Cyclopentadiene can gain an electron, for example by reacting with a sodium atom, to give a negative ion:

$$2C_5H_6 + 2Na \rightarrow 2C_5H_5^- + 2Na^+ + H_2$$

The importance of the ion is that it is cyclic, and the charge is delocalised over the entire ring in a series of π orbitals. Figure 105.9 shows you the idea. Two of these ions can bond to iron, giving the complex ion commonly known as ferrocene, $Fe(C_5H_5)_2$. (Its formal name is di-π-cyclopentadienyliron.) Ferrocene is held together by the bonding between the delocalised π electrons on the two rings and some of the iron d orbitals. Once ferrocene was discovered, similar compounds were soon prepared, e.g. $Cr(C_5H_5)_2$, $Ni(C_5H_5)_2$.

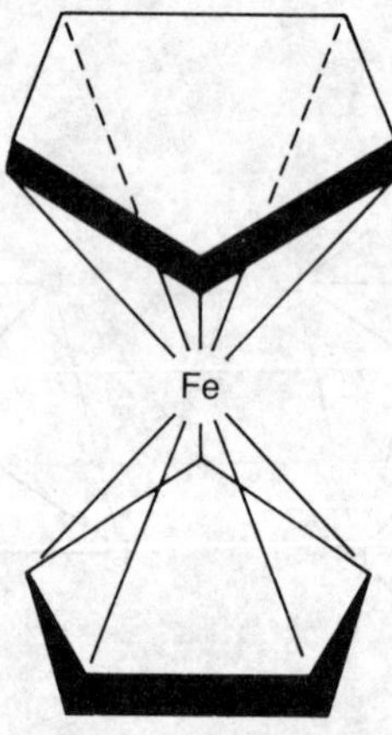

Figure 105.9 *Ferrocene has an iron ion sandwiched between two planar cyclopentadiene, $C_5H_5^-$, ions (shown here as pentagons)*

Much more important than ferrocene are complexes that occur in biochemical systems. Haemoglobin is responsible for transporting oxygen through the blood stream. This large molecule has an iron(II) ion held by bonds to four nitrogen atoms as shown in Figure 105.10. (A further bond can be made to part of a protein chain not shown in the diagram.) The iron is able to bond to an oxygen molecule; but the strength of the

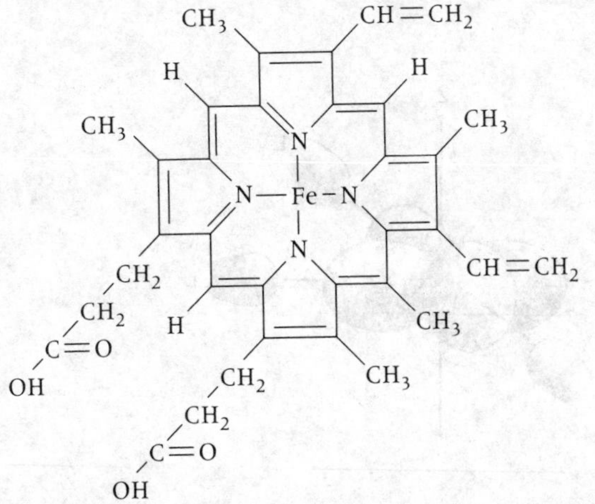

Figure 105.10 *The arrangement of atoms in the haem group of haemoglobin*

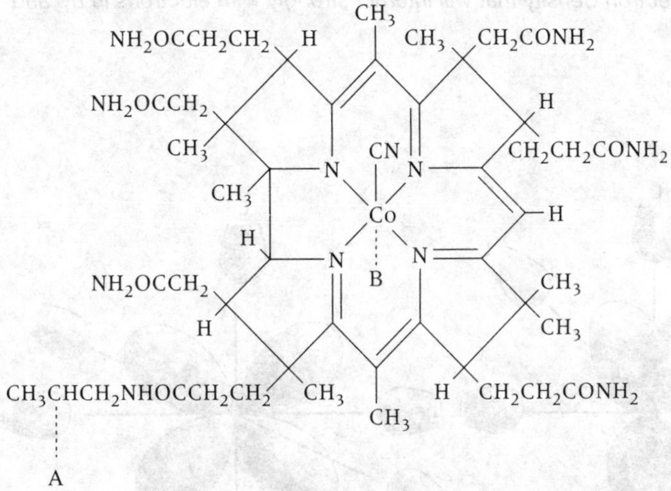

Figure 105.11 *Part of the structure of vitamin B_{12}. Points A and B are linked together through a combination of phosphate, sugar and nitrogen ring groups*

bond is such that the oxygen is easily removed, thus making it available throughout the body for use in respiration.

Cobalt is found in vitamin B_{12}, which is responsible for maintaining the supply of red blood cells in the liver (Figure 105.11). The cobalt is present as cobalt(III), with five bonds made to nitrogen atoms in different parts of the surrounding structure. The sixth site is where the biochemical activity takes place.

> **105.5** We are leaving the main work on isomers until the next unit. However, you might like to make a model of a complex ion with the formula $M(NH_3)_2Cl_2$. Use different coloured balls for the metal and the two different ligands. Assume it is square planar. How many different complexes (isomers) can you make? How many can you make if the complex is tetrahedral?

105.5 What happens to the d orbitals in a complex ion?

There are three theories of bonding in transition metal complexes. The first is *crystal field theory*, the second is *ligand field theory* and the third is *valence bond theory*. We shall examine each of them in turn.

(a) *Crystal field theory*

In crystal field theory we imagine that the ligands act as centres of electric charge. Then we try to work out what effect the field of the ligands has on the electrons in the d orbitals. This was the first theory invented to explain the properties of complexes. Given that it ignores the finer, and even the important, points of bonding, it is remarkably successful. This is what it has to say about the effects on the d orbitals.

First, if you bring negative charges near to electrons, the energies of the electrons rise. This has the effect of increasing the energies of all the d orbitals. Now let us look at the effects on the individual orbitals. Figure 105.2 showed the shapes of the d orbitals. Let us make a diagram of an octahedral complex (Figure 105.12) and show the d_{z^2} and $d_{x^2-y^2}$ orbitals as well. The lobes of the two orbitals point directly at the ligands. Electrons in these orbitals will suffer a significant amount of repulsion. Now look at Figure 105.13, which shows the arrangements of the d_{xy}, d_{xz} and d_{yz} orbitals. These have their lobes pointing between the ligands. As a result, electrons in these orbitals feel less repulsion than those in the other two orbitals. Thus crystal field theory says that the five d orbitals should split into two groups, two of which have a higher energy than the other three.

We say that the d orbitals are split. Owing to the splitting being caused by the electric field of the ligands, it is called the *ligand field splitting* (Figure 105.14). The extent of the splitting is given the symbol Δ_0. The two orbitals with the higher energy are called the e_g set; the three with the lower energy are the t_{2g} set.

(b) *Ligand field theory*

In ligand field theory we take a more realistic view of the bonding in complexes. We use molecular orbital theory to decide how the orbitals on the metal ion and the ligands interact. As you might expect, this is rather complicated. However, the nice thing is that ligand field theory comes up with the same scheme of splitting as crystal field theory. Figure 105.15 gives an impression of the results. You might be surprised to know that according to ligand field theory the two orbitals in the e_g set are *antibonding* orbitals. If this worries you, read section 16.6 again; antibonding orbitals can be perfectly respectable ones to use in bonding.

Once we have the arrangement of the orbitals, we are left with the task of filling them with electrons. This can be done in detail using ligand field theory, in much the same way as we used for oxygen in section 16.6. Fortunately, we do not need this level of detail, so we shall return to the crystal field picture. This allows us to

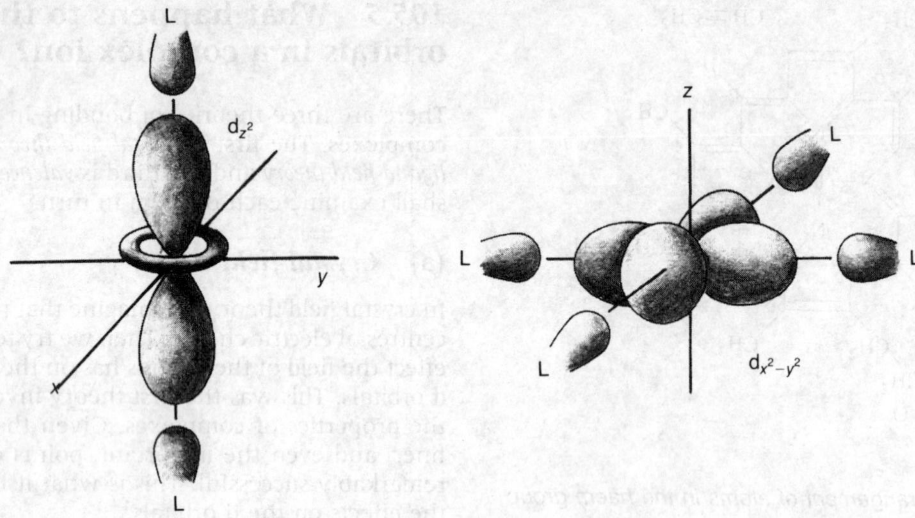

Figure 105.12 Ligands at the ends of the x, y and z axes have electron density that will interact strongly with electrons in d_{z^2} and $d_{x^2-y^2}$ orbitals

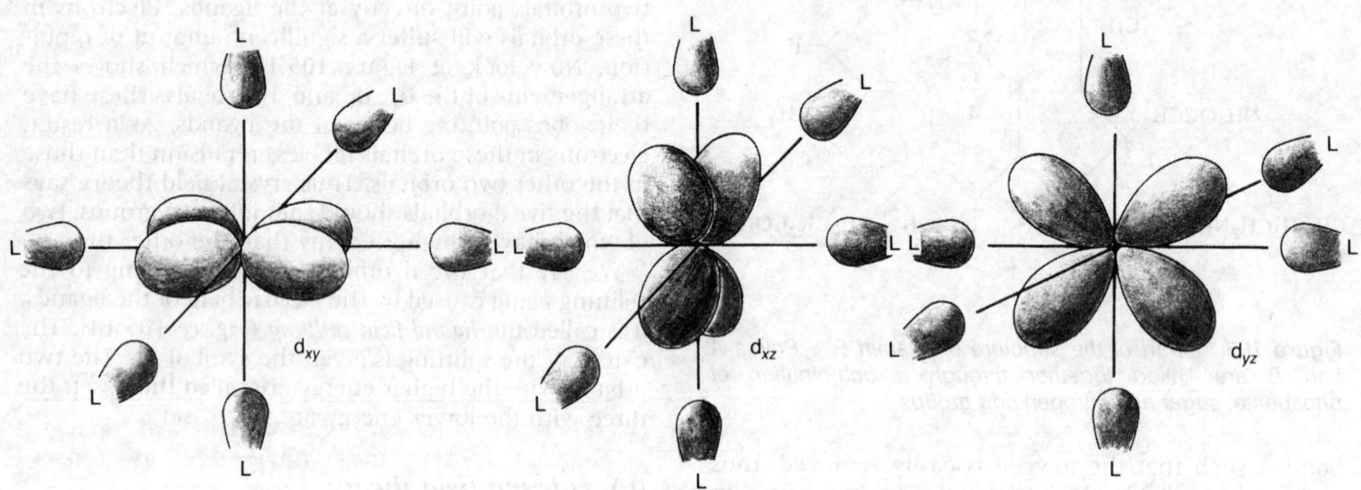

Figure 105.13 Ligands at the ends of the x, y and z axes have weaker interactions with d_{xy}, d_{yz} and d_{xz} orbitals than with d_{z^2} or $d_{x^2-y^2}$ orbitals

concentrate on the metal d electrons without getting bogged down in the detail of considering all the other electrons.

Before we do so, you might like to look at the way the d orbitals split in square planar and tetrahedral complexes (Figure 105.16). The pattern is quite different to the octahedral case.

(c) *Valence bond theory*

In valence bond theory the shapes of complex ions are explained by invoking hybridisation. Table 105.6 lists the combinations of orbitals that are needed for the main three geometries. Actually, valence bond theory can give us little help in explaining many properties of transition metal ions, so we shall say no more about it.

105.6 Why are transition metal compounds often paramagnetic?

Most people know that iron is magnetic. In fact, iron shows a very special type of magnetism called ferromagnetism. The two metals following it, cobalt and nickel, also show this type of magnetism.

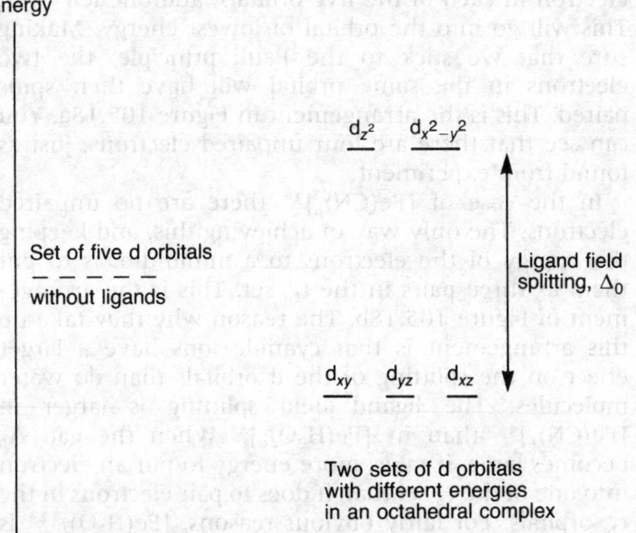

Figure 105.14 *How the energies of the d orbitals change in an octahedral complex*

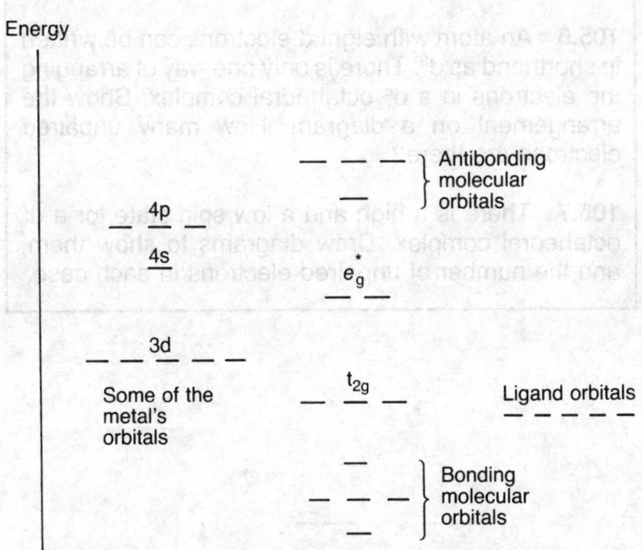

Figure 105.15 *In ligand field theory there is a set of five molecular orbitals that split apart in the same way as do the five d orbitals in crystal field theory. Two (e_g^* set) increase in energy, three (t_{2g} set) decrease in energy*

Table 105.6. Three types of hybridisation found in transition metal complexes*

Shape of complex	*Hybrid orbitals*
Tetrahedral	d^3s
Square planar	dsp^2
Octahedral	d^2sp^3

*Also, see Table 17.5

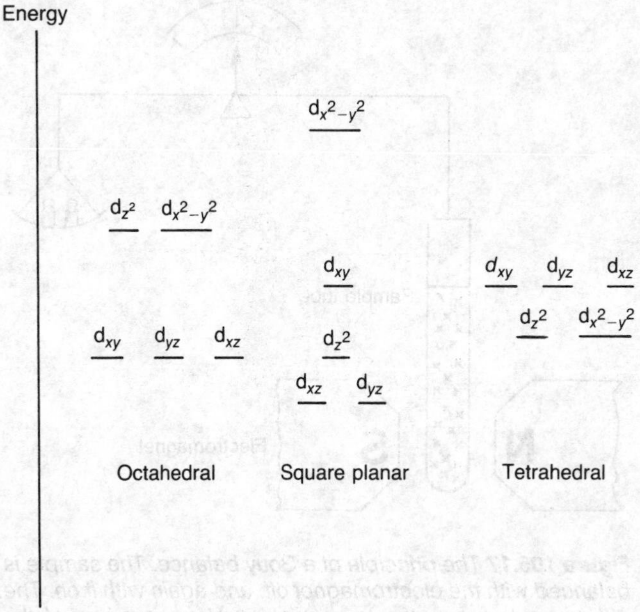

Figure 105.16 *How the d orbitals change their energies in octahedral, square planar and tetrahedral complexes*

Ferromagnetism is a variety of magnetism known as *paramagnetism*. A paramagnetic substance put close to a magnetic field will be attracted into the field. Many transition metal compounds are paramagnetic.

It is the magnetic field associated with the spin of an electron that can give rise to paramagnetism. However, only compounds that have unpaired electrons are paramagnetic. When two electrons occupy the same orbital, they have their spins paired, and we can think of the magnetic fields cancelling out. To sum up:

Transition metal compounds are paramagnetic when they have one or more unpaired electrons.

If we measure the amount of their paramagnetism we can work out how many unpaired electrons are present. This can be done using a *Gouy balance* (Figure 105.17). An empty glass tube is suspended between the jaws of an electromagnet. Then the tube is filled with crystals of the chemical being investigated. The magnet is switched on and, if the substance is paramagnetic, the tube is pulled down into the field. Masses are placed on the balance pan until the balance is zeroed again. The mass used is a measure of the amount of paramagnetism, and therefore the number of unpaired electrons. If we are to understand how these unpaired electrons come about, we need to look carefully at what happens to the d orbitals when a complex ion is made.

The two complexes of iron(II), hexaaquaferrate(II), $[Fe(H_2O)_6]^{2+}$, and hexacyanoferrate(II), $[Fe(CN)_6]^{4-}$,

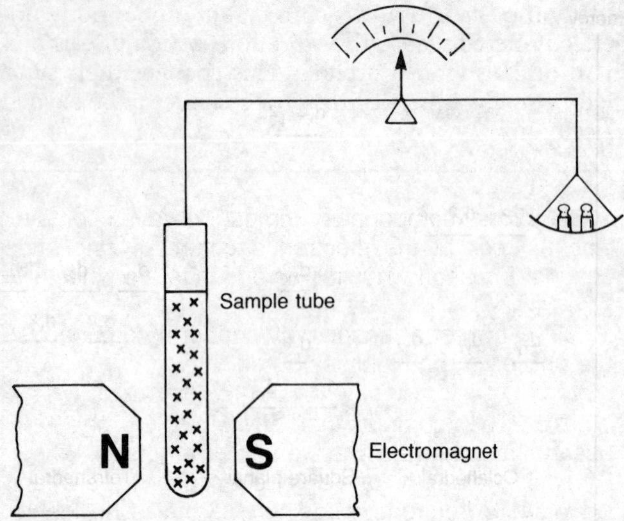

Figure 105.17 The principle of a Gouy balance. The sample is balanced with the electromagnet off, and again with it on. The difference between the two weighings is a measure of the number of unpaired electrons in the sample

are both octahedral. The first has paramagnetism corresponding to four unpaired electrons. The second is not paramagnetic; it has no unpaired electrons. Now, the electron structure of iron is (Ar)$3d^6 4s^2$. When it loses two electrons, it is left with the argon core and six 3d electrons. We have to arrange these six electrons on the energy level diagram for an octahedral complex. We know that electrons will go into separate orbitals whenever possible so that the repulsion among them is minimised. If we follow this pattern we shall have one electron in each of the five orbitals, and one left over. This will go into the orbital of lowest energy. Making sure that we stick to the Pauli principle, the two electrons in the same orbital will have their spins paired. This is the arrangement in Figure 105.18a. You can see that there are four unpaired electrons, just as found from experiment.

In the case of $[Fe(CN)_6]^{4-}$ there are no unpaired electrons. The only way of achieving this, and keeping the energy of the electrons to a minimum, is to put them as three pairs in the t_{2g} set. This is the arrangement of Figure 105.18b. The reason why they take up this arrangement is that cyanide ions have a larger effect on the splitting of the d orbitals than do water molecules. The ligand field splitting is larger in $[Fe(CN)_6]^{4-}$ than in $[Fe(H_2O)_6]^{2+}$. When the gap Δ_o becomes large, it takes more energy to put an electron into one of the e_g set than it does to pair electrons in the t_{2g} orbitals. For fairly obvious reasons, $[Fe(H_2O)_6]^{2+}$ is called a *high spin* complex, and $[Fe(CN)_6]^{4-}$ a *low spin* complex.

105.6 An atom with eight d electrons can be written in shorthand as d^8. There is only one way of arranging the electrons in a d^8 octahedral complex. Show the arrangement on a diagram. How many unpaired electrons are there?

105.7 There is a high and a low spin state for a d^7 octahedral complex. Draw diagrams to show them, and the number of unpaired electrons in each case.

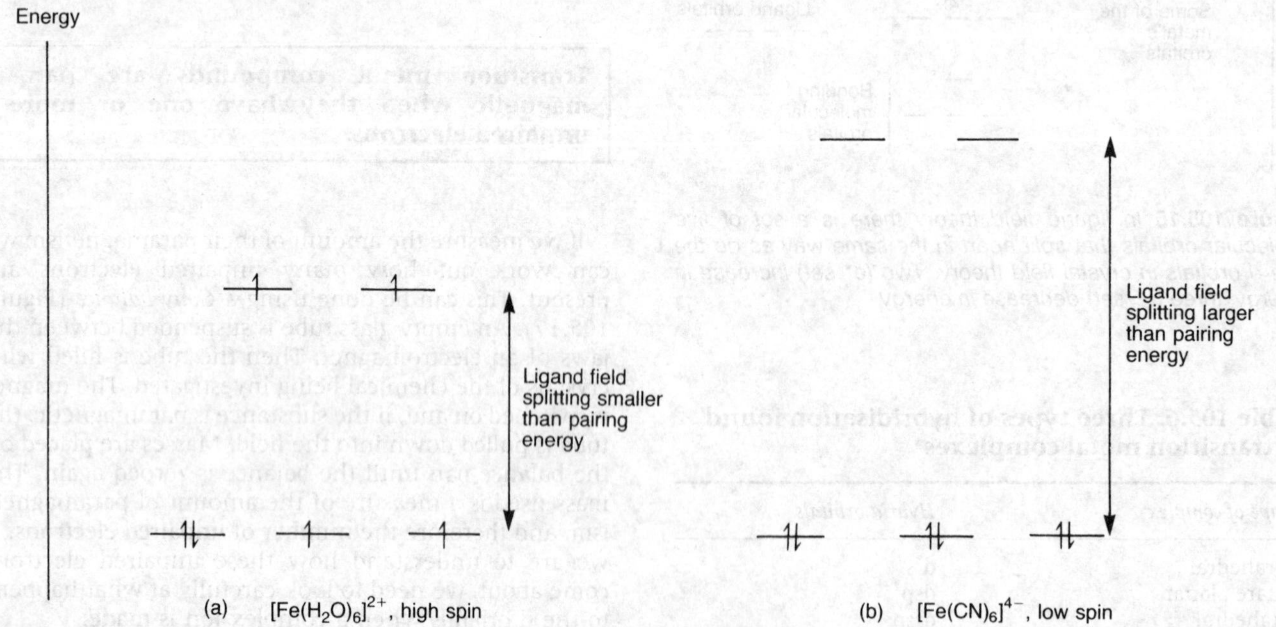

***Figure 105.18** Cyanide ions cause a much larger splitting of the d orbitals than do water molecules. One result is that cyanide complexes are often 'low spin'*

105.7 Why are transition metal compounds often coloured?

Transition metal complexes are coloured because visible light has just about the right energy to excite an electron in the lower set of d orbitals into the higher set. For example, the octahedral complex hexaaquanickel(II), $[Ni(H_2O)_6]^{2+}$, is responsible for the green colour of many nickel(II) salts in water (Figure 105.19). The complex appears green because it absorbs in the blue region of the spectrum (and also in the red). In this case the splitting of the d orbitals corresponds to the energy of blue light.

Actually there is a rule called the Laporte rule which says that transitions between d orbitals should not occur. The reason for this lies in the symmetry of the orbitals, something we spoke about in Units 24 and 25.

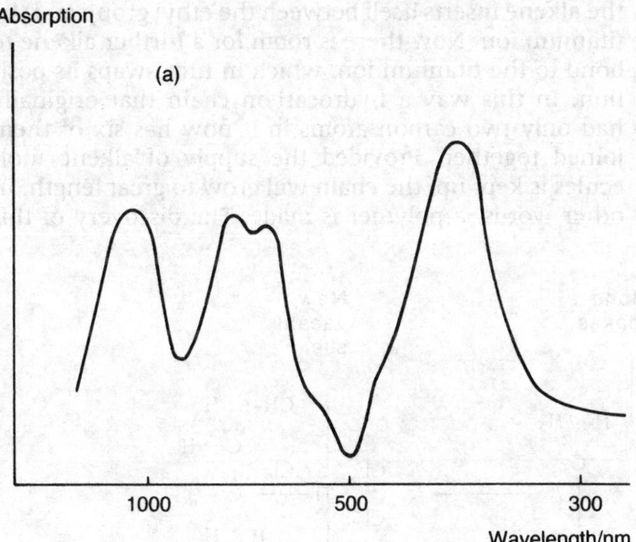

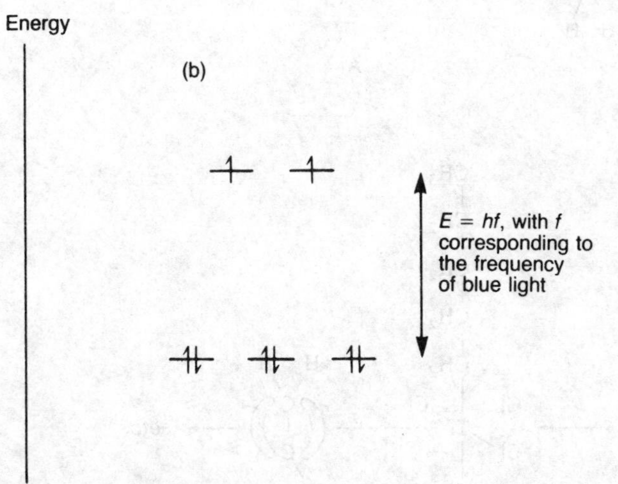

***Figure 105.19** (a) The spectrum of $[Ni(H_2O)_6]^{2+}$ shows a number of strong absorptions. However, the complex absorbs only weakly around 500 nm, which is the green and blue-green region of the visible spectrum. (b) The ligand field splitting in $[Ni(H_2O)_6]^{2+}$ matches the frequency of light in the blue region of the visible spectrum*

Strictly the Laporte rule is correct, but it does not work perfectly here because the vibrations of complexes mix the d orbitals with p orbitals. This changes their symmetry and gives the electrons their chance to be excited by photons.

105.8 Zinc compounds almost always contain zinc(II). Look at the electron structure of zinc and suggest a reason why zinc compounds are white.

105.9 Suggest a reason why copper(I) compounds are unlikely to be highly coloured.

105.10 The complex ion $[Ni(H_2O)_6]^{2+}$ has an absorption peak at a wavelength of around 410 nm. Remind yourself of the connection between wavelength, frequency and energy. What is the ligand field splitting in the complex in joules, and in kJ mol^{-1}?

105.11 When ammonia is added to a solution of $[Ni(H_2O)_6]^{2+}$, the colour changes to dark blue-purple. The absorption peak has moved to around 350 nm. Has the ligand field splitting increased or decreased compared to the aqua complex?

105.8 How do the transition metals act as catalysts?

Transition metals can act as catalysts (Table 105.7), for two reasons. First, because they can have several dif-

Table 105.7. Transition metal catalysts

Reaction	*Catalyst*
The Haber process $N_2(g)+3H_2(g)\rightleftharpoons 2NH_3(g)$	Iron (and aluminium oxide)
Sulphuric acid manufacture $2SO_2(g)+O_2(g)\rightleftharpoons 2SO_3(g)$	Platinum and vanadium(V) oxide
Nitric acid manufacture $4NH_3(g)+5O_2(g)\rightleftharpoons 4NO(g)+6H_2O(g)$	Platinum
Hydrogenation of alkenes $>C{=}C< \; + \; H_2(g) \longrightarrow -\underset{\vert}{\overset{H}{\overset{\vert}{C}}}-\underset{\vert}{\overset{H}{\overset{\vert}{C}}}-$	Nickel
Laboratory preparation of oxygen $2H_2O_2(aq) \rightarrow 2H_2O(l)+O_2(g)$	Manganese(IV) oxide
Polymerisation of alkenes, e.g. $nC_2H_4 \longrightarrow \left(-\underset{H}{\overset{H}{C}}-\underset{H}{\overset{H}{C}}- \right)_n$	Ziegler–Natta catalysts $Al(C_2H_5)_3/TiCl_3$

ferent oxidation states, they can take part in electron transfer reactions. One example that demonstrates this is the effect of adding iron(II) or iron(III) ions to a mixture of peroxodisulphate(VI) ions, $S_2O_8^{2-}$, and iodide ions. Normally the reaction:

$$S_2O_8^{2-}(aq) + 2I^-(aq) \rightarrow 2SO_4^{2-}(aq) + I_2(s) \quad (A)$$

takes place at a convenient rate, which we can follow by one of the usual methods. If a little iron(III) sulphate solution is added, the rate of production of iodine increases markedly. This is because the Fe^{3+} ions react with the iodide ions:

$$2Fe^{3+}(aq) + 2I^-(aq) \rightarrow 2Fe^{2+}(aq) + I_2(s) \quad (B)$$

If this were all that happened, we would not be dealing with true catalysis: the Fe^{3+} ions appear to be used up in the reaction. However, the Fe^{2+} ions are oxidised back to Fe^{3+} by $S_2O_8^{2-}$ ions:

$$2Fe^{2+}(aq) + S_2O_8^{2-}(aq) \rightarrow 2Fe^{3+}(aq) + 2SO_4^{2-}(aq) \quad (C)$$

If you combine equations (B) and (C) you will obtain the original equation, (A). The Fe^{3+} ions have taken part in the reaction, but they are regenerated. The key point is that by giving a different path by which electron transfer can take place, the ions have provided a route with a lower activation energy.

Transition metals and their ions can also act as catalysts by providing sites at which reactions can take place. They can bond to a wide range of ions and molecules, e.g. those with lone pairs or π electrons. Also they show the ability to make different numbers of bonds, often four or six, but sometimes two, three and five as well. They can show catalytic behaviour when dissolved in solution or as solids, i.e. as homogeneous or heterogeneous catalysts.

An important example of a catalytic reaction in solution is the Ziegler–Natta polymerisation of alkenes (Figure 105.20). A typical Ziegler–Natta catalyst is a mixture of an organic aluminium compound, e.g. $Al(C_2H_5)_3$, and titanium(III) chloride. One of the ethyl groups from the aluminium compound bonds to the titanium ion; but being a transition metal ion, it has further sites available for bonding. The π cloud of an alkene can fill one of these sites, with the result that the alkene and ethyl group are held very close to one another. For reasons that we do not have to consider, the alkene inserts itself between the ethyl group and the titanium ion. Now there is room for a further alkene to bond to the titanium ion, which in turn swaps its position. In this way a hydrocarbon chain that originally had only two carbon atoms in it now has six of them joined together. Provided the supply of alkene molecules is kept up, the chain will grow to great length. In other words, a polymer is made. The discovery of this

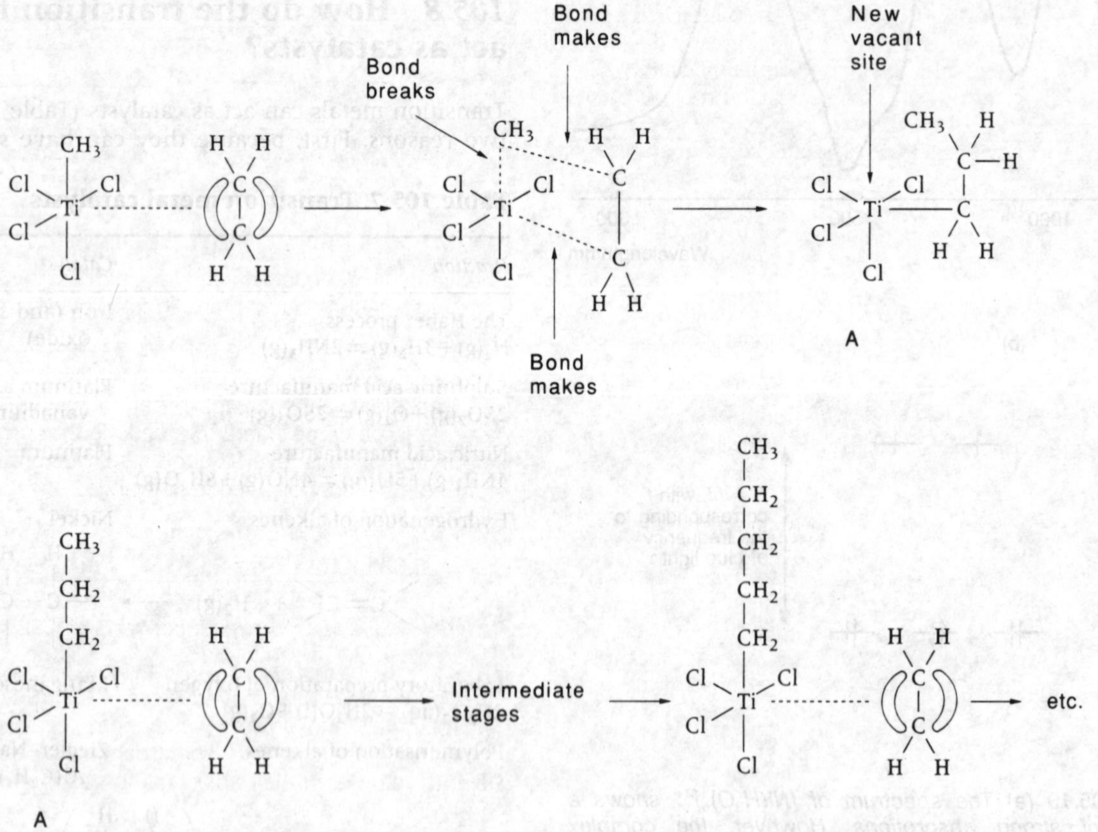

***Figure 105.20** These diagrams show you the type of change that takes place with Ziegler–Natta catalysts. The first step is an alkene bonding to a titanium complex through its π cloud of electrons. Then there is a rearrangement of the atoms, which leaves a complex, A, that can repeat the process. The result is growth of the polymer chain*

type of reaction by Ziegler and Natta has revolutionised the manufacture of polymers, partly because the method can give polymers of consistent quality.

105.9 Transition metals and alloys

The transition metals are generally hard, and difficult to melt. They are also strong, but they can be brittle. (A strong metal bar can support a heavy load hung from its mid-point. However, if the bar is dropped on to a hard surface and splits into pieces, the metal is brittle.) One way of making metals less brittle is to mix them with other atoms to make an *alloy*. The transition metals are very good at making alloys with transition, and other, metals as well as some non-metals (see Table 105.8).

Table 105.8. Examples of alloys containing transition metals

Name	*Composition*	*Use*
Steel*	Iron with small amounts of C and Mn	Car bodies, bridges, etc., where strength but greater ductility and malleability than iron is needed
Stainless steel	Iron with up to 35% Cr; Ni may also be present	Steel with great resistance to corrosion, e.g. knives, sinks, industrial pipes, jet engines
Coinage metal	Cu 75%, Ni 25% Cu 95.5%, Zn 1.5%, Sn 3%	'Silver' coins 'Copper' coins
Brass	Various proportions of copper and zinc, e.g. Cu 70%, Zn 30%	Door knobs, ornaments, bullet cases
Duralumin	Aluminium with up to 5% Cu, less than 1% Mn, Mg and Si	In aircraft, owing to combination of strength with lightness
Monel	About 66% Ni, 33% Cu, with some Fe, Mn, Si and C	Equipment that must be resistant to corrosion, e.g. in steam turbines
Nichrome	Ni 60%, Fe 20%, Cr 20%	Wires for electrical equipment

*There are many different types of steel, with properties depending on the quantity of the added elements. These can include V, Cr, Mn, Co, Ni, C, Si, P and S

Answers

105.1 (i) Mn(II), (ii) Mn(VII), (iii) Mn(III).

105.2 (i) It is a type of π bond ($d\pi$).

(ii) Carbon monoxide is neutral. As the carbonyls are uncharged, the metals can have no charge. They are in the oxidation state zero.

105.3 (i) Diamminediaquacopper(II).

(ii) Dichlorobis(ethane-1,2-diamine)chromium(III).

(iii) Potassium hexacyanoferrate(II).

105.4 (i) $[Cr(NH_2CH_2CH_2NH_2)_3]^{3+}$.

(ii) $Co(NO_2)_3(NH_3)_3$.

(iii) $[Cr(H_2O)_5Cl]^{2+}$.

105.5 There are two isomers in the square planar arrangement. No isomers are possible if the complex is tetrahedral.

105.6 See Figure 105.19b. $[Ni(H_2O)_6]^{2+}$ is such a complex.

105.7 The diagrams are shown in Figure 105.21.

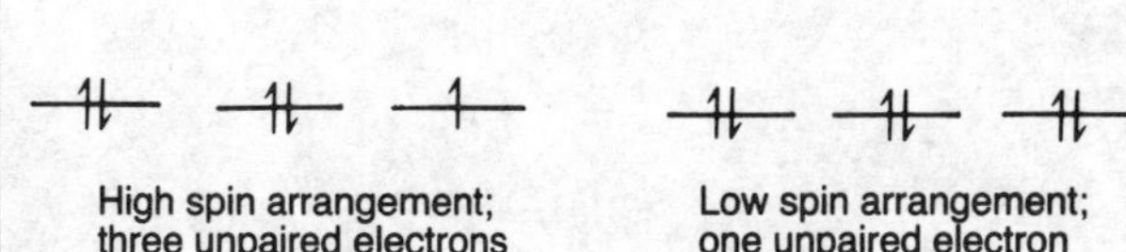

High spin arrangement; three unpaired electrons

Low spin arrangement; one unpaired electron

***Figure 105.21** Diagrams for answer to question 105.7*

105.8 Zinc(II) has ten d electrons. Therefore transitions between the d orbitals cannot take place: they are all full, and you cannot have more than two electrons in an orbital.

105.9 Copper(I), like zinc(II), has a full set of d orbitals, so transitions between them cannot occur. However, there can be complicated interactions that produce colour in compounds, even though a set of d orbitals is full; for example, copper(I) oxide is orange.

105.10 $c = f\lambda$ and $E = hf$, so

$$E = \frac{6.626\times10^{-34}\ \text{J s}\times2.998\times10^{8}\ \text{m s}^{-1}}{410\times10^{-9}\ \text{m}}$$

i.e. $E = 4.85\times10^{-19}$ J, which converts to 292 kJ mol^{-1}.

105.11 It has increased. We can work this out because the absorption has moved from 410 nm to a lower wavelength, and lower wavelength corresponds to increasing energy. The spectrochemical series puts ligands in order of their ability to increase the splitting of d orbitals. The series is

$$CN^- > NO_2^- > en > NH_3 > H_2O > OH^- > F^- > Cl^- > Br^- > I^-$$

Greatest splitting … Least splitting

UNIT 105 SUMMARY

- The transition elements:
  - (i) Are all metals.
  - (ii) Have similar ionisation energies.
  - (iii) Form alloys.
  - (iv) Have a set of d orbitals filling with electrons.
  - (v) Give coloured compounds.
  - (vi) May have paramagnetic compounds.
  - (vii) Make complex ions.
  - (viii) Show a range of different oxidation states.
  - (ix) Often act as catalysts.
- Ligands:
  - (i) Monodentate ligands make one bond per molecule/ion to a metal ion, e.g. NH_3, Cl^-.
  - (ii) Bidentate ligands make two bonds per molecule/ion to a metal ion, e.g. ethane-1,2-diamine, $NH_2CH_2CH_2NH_2$.
  - (iii) EDTA is a hexadentate ligand (six bonding sites).
- Shapes of complexes:
  Mainly octahedral, square planar or tetrahedral.
- Paramagnetism:
  Is due to the presence of unpaired electrons in the d orbitals.
- Colour:
  Is often a result of electrons moving between the d orbitals.
- Catalytic action:
  - (i) Is due to the availability of d orbitals for making bonds, and ability to transfer electrons when changing oxidation state.
  - (ii) Ziegler–Natta catalysts are used in the polymerisation of alkenes. They are mixtures of an organic aluminium compound, e.g. $Al(C_2H_5)_3$, and titanium(III) chloride, $TiCl_3$.

106

More about complex ions

106.1 Isomerism in complex ions

An ion or molecule has isomers if it can exist in two or more different forms with the same formula. Isomers frequently occur in organic compounds, but one of the fascinating things about transition metal chemistry is that many complex ions have isomers. The study of isomerism in complexes was one of the main interests of the German chemist Alfred Werner. We owe much of our understanding of transition metal complexes to him. In his book *New Ideas on Inorganic Chemistry* published in 1911 he discussed the main types of isomerism. We shall follow some of his examples, although we shall change the names that he used to their modern versions.

(a) *Ionisation isomerism*

This is the first type of isomerism we shall look at. Werner says:

> A peculiar type of isomerism . . . is that in which compounds of the same composition yield different ions in solution.

His example was two compounds with the formula $Co(NH_3)_5BrSO_4$. Werner noted that in solution:

> The one is a reddish-violet colour, and gives in a freshly prepared solution no reaction for bromide ions, but does for the sulphate ion. On the other hand, the solution of the second salt gives the reactions of bromide ion, but not of the sulphate ion.

Well, so much for the facts. How can we explain them? The difference is due to the way the bromide and sulphate are bonded in the compounds. In both of them the five ammonia molecules are ligands. This leaves space for one other ligand. In one of the complexes the bromide is the ligand, in the other it is the sulphate ion. The two possibilities are shown in Figure 106.1. In the first one the bromide is strongly bonded to the cobalt ion. We say that the ammonia molecules and the bromide ion are in the *coordination sphere*. The sulphate ion is held in the crystal with its two negative charges just balancing the two positive charges on the complex.

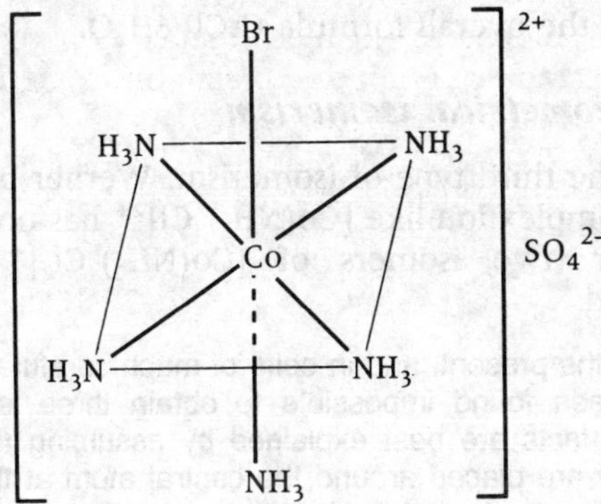

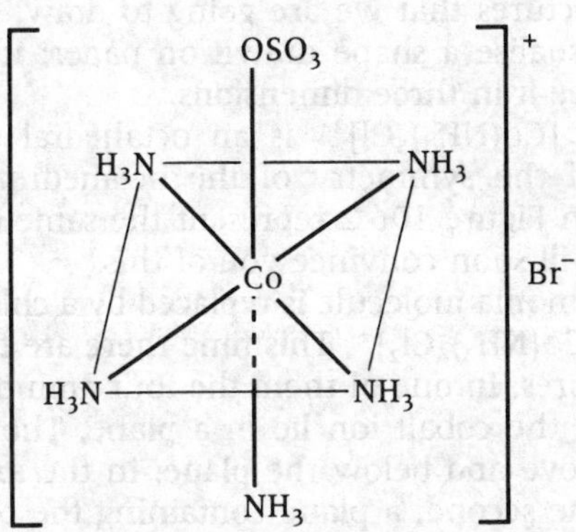

Figure 106.1 The two isomers of $Co(NH_3)_5BrSO_4$

When the solid is put in water the sulphate ion floats away, but the bromide is left attached to the cobalt. Therefore, if we test for the presence of sulphate ions we find a positive result, but a test for free bromide ions is negative. With the second variety of the salt, the opposite is true. The sulphate ion is bonded to the cobalt, and free bromide ions can be found in the solution. (The sulphate ion is now in the coordination sphere with the ammonia molecules.)

(b) *Hydrate isomerism*

This is the second type of isomerism that we need to know about. Werner comments:

The most beautiful example of hydrate isomerism is that furnished by chromium chloride. Three different hydrates of the formula $CrCl_3 + 6H_2O$ are known. One is greenish-blue, which dissolves giving a blue-violet solution, and two are green, which dissolve yielding green solutions.

The difference between the three hydrates is shown by writing their formulae as:

$[Cr(H_2O)_6]^{3+}(Cl^-)_3$	blue-violet in solution
$[Cr(H_2O)_5Cl]^{2+}(Cl^-)_2$	green in solution
$[Cr(H_2O)_4Cl_2]^+Cl^-$	darker green in solution

You should understand why it is that one mole of each of them give three, two and one moles of chloride ions in solution respectively. When they are crystallised from solution the second takes up one mole, and the third two moles of water of crystallisation. This gives them all the overall formula $CrCl_3{\cdot}6H_2O$.

(c) *Geometrical isomerism*

This is the third type of isomerism. Werner points out that a complex ion like $[Co(NH_3)_5Cl]^{2+}$ has no isomers. However, two isomers of $[Co(NH_3)_4Cl_2]^+$ can be identified:

> Up to the present, and in spite of much careful work, it has been found impossible to obtain three isomers. These facts are best explained by assuming that the groups are placed around the central atom at the corners of a regular octahedron.

At this point you should do your best to make models of the structures that we are going to draw. It can be hard to visualise a shape drawn on paper; it is much easier to see it in three dimensions.

The ion $[Co(NH_3)_5Cl]^{2+}$ is an octahedral complex. Because of the symmetry of the octahedron all the diagrams in Figure 106.2 represent the same complex. A model will soon convince you of this.

If an ammonia molecule is replaced by a chloride ion we have $[Co(NH_3)_4Cl_2]^+$. This time there are two possible structures. In one of them the four ammonia molecules and the cobalt ion lie in a plane. The chloride ions lie above and below the plane, in the axial positions. In the second, a plane containing the cobalt ion also contains three ammonia molecules and one of the chloride ions. This leaves the remaining ammonia molecule and chloride ion in the axial positions. The two arrangements are different, as illustrated in Figure 106.3. They are geometrical isomers.

Square planar complexes can also have geometrical isomers. Figure 106.4 shows two isomers that have the formula $Pt(NH_3)_2Cl_2$. When the two chlorides (or ammonia molecules) are on the same side of the square, they are said to make the *cis isomer*. When they are opposite one another, we have the *trans isomer*.

(d) *Optical isomerism*

This is the final type of isomerism we shall meet here. If you are to understand optical isomers, you must know what is meant by polarised light. If you have not yet done so, read Units 24 and 110, which respectively tell you about light in general and polarised light in particular.

An optical isomer rotates the plane of polarised light.

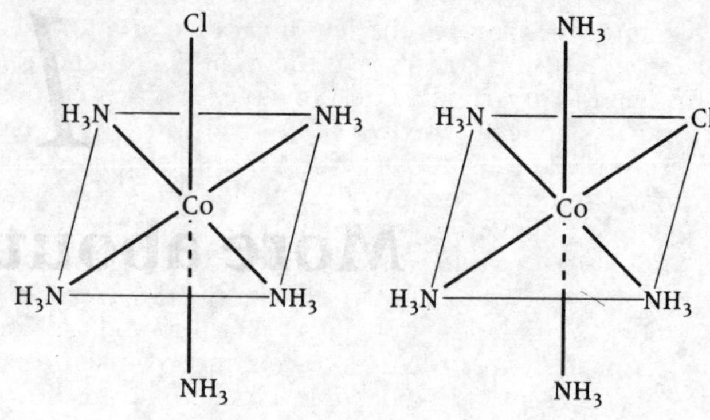

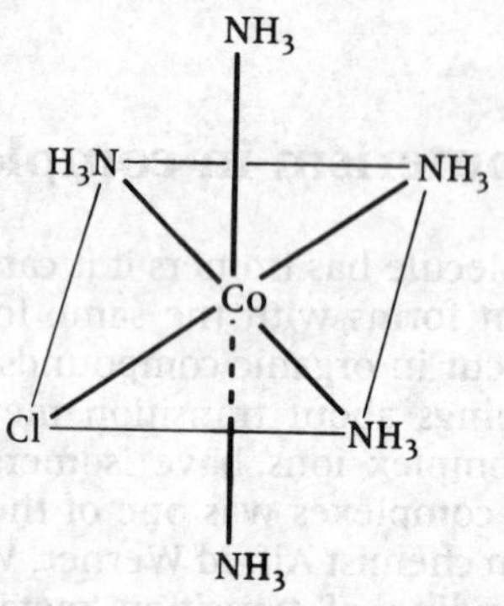

Figure 106.2 Although these diagrams might seem to show different complex ions with the formula $[Co(NH_3)_5Cl]^{2+}$, they are in fact identical

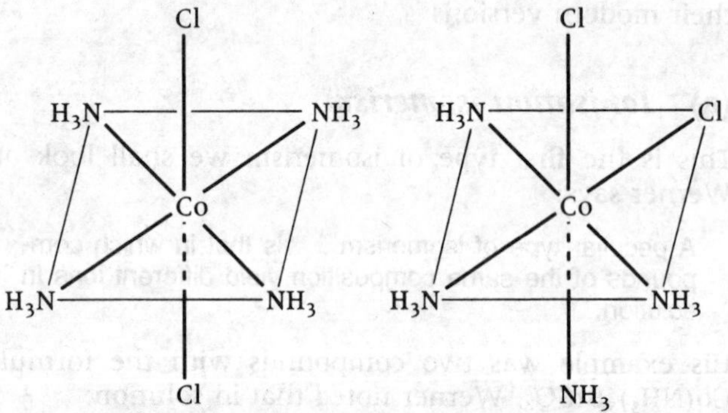

***Figure 106.3** Two (true) isomers of $[Co(NH_3)_4Cl_2]^+$*

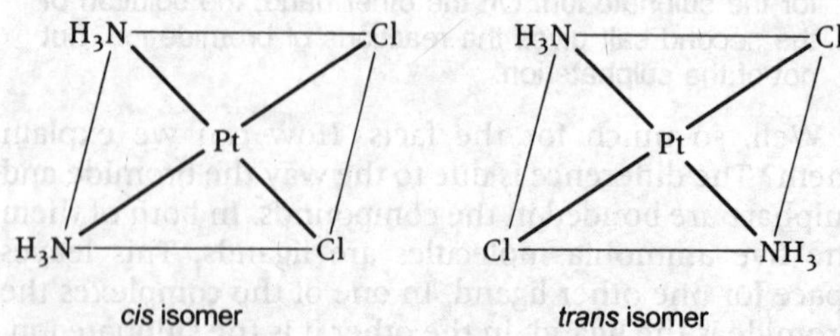

***Figure 106.4** The cis and trans isomers of $Pt(NH_3)_2Cl_2$*

If it rotates the plane to the left, it is called an *l* form (*l* for *laevo*, left). If it rotates it to the right, it is called a *d* form (*d* for *dextro*, right). A test to discover if a molecule or ion is optically active is to see if it can be superimposed on its mirror image. Examples that occur in transition metal chemistry are octahedral complexes involving a bidentate ligand such as ethane-1,2-diamine. The three ligand molecules can attach themselves in two ways, shown in Figure 106.5, which resemble aeroplane propellers. You should make models of the two structures to convince yourself that they are different. It is impossible to match the positions of all the atoms at once.

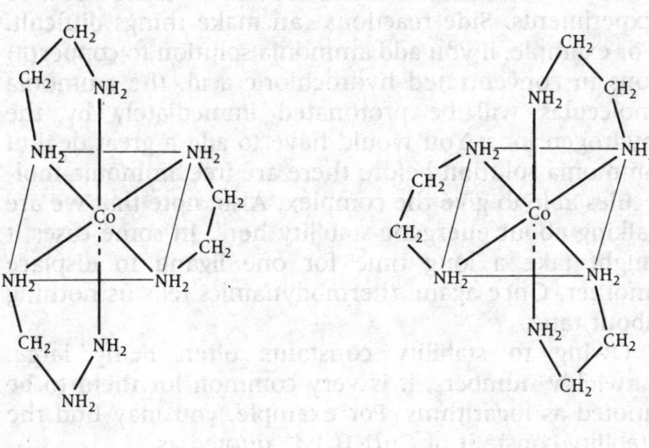

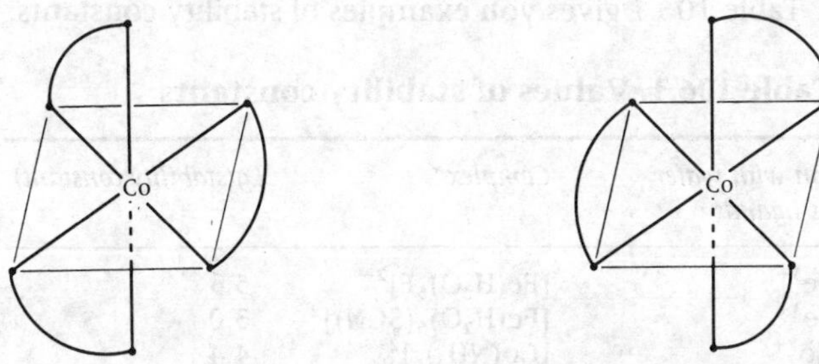

***Figure** 106.5 Two isomers of $[Co(NH_2CH_2CH_2NH_2)_3]^{3+}$, which are mirror images of each other, are known. They are optical isomers. The top two diagrams show the arrangement of the atoms; the bottom two use curved lines to represent the ligands*

106.1 How would you test a solution of a complex to see if it contained free sulphate ions?

106.2 There are two isomers with the formula $Pt(NH_3)_4Br_2SO_4$. In both isomers the ammonia molecules are firmly bonded to the platinum ion. By measuring the depression of freezing point of water it is found that 1 mol of one isomer has a depression corresponding to the presence of three moles of particles. The other isomer gives two moles of particles. Explain the results and write formulae that show clearly the make-up of the coordination spheres.

106.3 A crystal of a complex was discovered to have chromium, water and bromine present in the ratio 1 mol:6 mol:3 mol. The solution gave a pale yellow precipitate with silver nitrate solution. On analysis it was found that 10 g of the crystal gave 9.40 g of silver bromide.

(i) What is the mass of 1 mol of the crystal? $M(Cr) = 52$ g mol^{-1} and $M(Br) = 80$ g mol^{-1}.

(ii) How many moles of the crystal were taken?

(iii) The molar mass of silver bromide is 188 g mol^{-1}. How many moles of silver bromide were made in the reaction?

(iv) How many moles of bromide ion are given by 1 mol of crystal?

(v) What does your result tell you about the nature of the complex in the solution?

(vi) Draw a diagram showing the geometry of the complex ion.

106.4 Are there any isomers of $Co(NH_3)_3Cl_3$?

106.5 Are there any isomers of dichloroethane-1,2-diaminenickel(II), $Ni(NH_2CH_2CH_2NH_2)Cl_2$?

106.6 There are *three* isomers of the complex dichlorobis(ethane-1,2-diamine)cobalt(III), which has the formula $Co(NH_2CH_2CH_2NH_2)_2Cl_2$. Two of them are optically active, and one is not. Make models of the three isomers and draw diagrams of them.

(i) Which two are mirror images of each other?

(ii) Why is the third not optically active?

106.7 The formula of a complex ion can sometimes be found using a colorimeter. Here is an example. A solution of nickel(II) sulphate, $NiSO_4$, is green, but if ammonia is added the solution goes blue. Ten tubes each containing 20 cm^3 of 0.05 mol dm^{-3} solution of $NiSO_4$ had 0.4 mol dm^{-3} aqueous ammonia added. The first tube had 2 cm^3 of the ammonia solution added, the second 4 cm^3, and so on. Distilled water was added to bring the total volume in each tube to 50 cm^3. Each tube was then placed in a colorimeter and the reading recorded. The results are shown in Figure 106.6.

(i) What colour filter should be used in the colorimeter?

(ii) Why does the reading on the colorimeter go down?

(iii) Explain why the graph comes to a minimum, and then stays horizontal.

(iv) How many moles of Ni^{2+} ions were there in each tube?

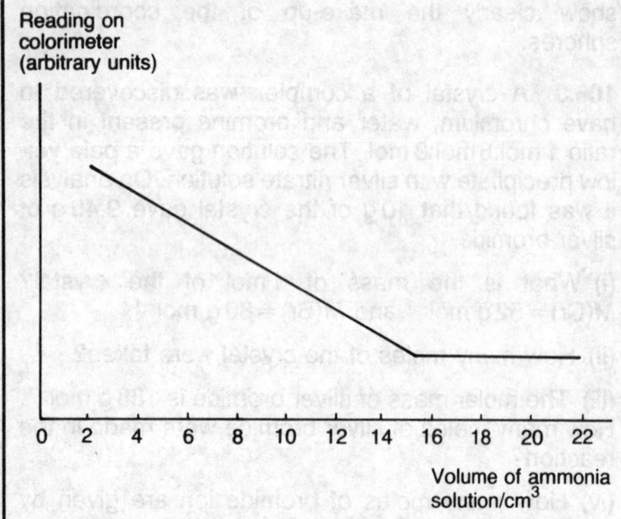

***Figure 106.6** Graph of results for question 106.7*

(v) How many moles of ammonia give the minimum reading?

(vi) What is the formula of the complex?

(vii) Why was the total volume in each tube kept constant?

106.2 Stability constants of complex ions

The colour of a solution of copper(II) sulphate is due to the presence of hydrated Cu^{2+} ions. A standard test for the presence of these ions is to add dilute ammonia solution, which produces a beautiful clear royal blue solution. You should know that the colour change is a result of the production of the tetraamminecopper(II) ion, $Cu(NH_3)_4{}^{2+}$. This change is an example of an equilibrium reaction. The equilibrium set up is

$$Cu(H_2O)_4{}^{2+}(aq) + 4NH_3(aq) \rightleftharpoons Cu(NH_3)_4{}^{2+}(aq) + 4H_2O(l)$$

Given that the reaction is done in water, whose concentration remains constant, we can write the equilibrium constant as

$$K_c = \frac{[Cu(NH_3)_4{}^{2+}(aq)]}{[Cu(H_2O)_4{}^{2+}(aq)][NH_3(aq)]^4}$$
$$= 1.2 \times 10^{13}\,dm^{12}\,mol^{-4}$$

This is the value of K_c at 25°C.

If chloride ions are added (e.g. from concentrated hydrochloric acid) to copper(II) ions in solution, a yellow colour is produced. The equilibrium set up is

$$Cu(H_2O)_4{}^{2+}(aq) + 4Cl^-(aq) \rightleftharpoons \underset{\text{yellow}}{CuCl_4{}^{2-}(aq)} + 4H_2O(l)$$

for which

$$K_c = \frac{[CuCl_4{}^{2-}(aq)]}{[Cu(H_2O)_4{}^{2+}(aq)][Cl^-(aq)]^4}$$
$$= 4.2 \times 10^5\,dm^{12}\,mol^{-4}$$

The two equilibrium constants are called *stability constants*. If you compare the values of two stability constants (Table 106.1) they tell you what should be the outcome of a reaction in which there is a competition between two ligands.

For example, the stability constant of $Cu(NH_3)_4{}^{2+}$ is greater than that of $CuCl_4{}^{2-}$. This means that if chloride ions and ammonia molecules are in the same solution, the blue ammine complex will form in preference to the chloride complex.

However, be careful if you actually do some test tube experiments. Side reactions can make things difficult. For example, if you add ammonia solution to copper(II) ions in concentrated hydrochloric acid, the ammonia molecules will be protonated immediately by the hydrogen ions. You would have to add a great deal of ammonia solution before there are free ammonia molecules able to give the complex. Also, note that we are talking about energetic stability here. In some cases it might take a long time for one ligand to displace another. Once again, thermodynamics tells us nothing about rates.

Owing to stability constants often being large, unwieldy numbers, it is very common for them to be quoted as logarithms. For example, you may find the stability constant of $Cu(NH_3)_4{}^{2+}$ quoted as

$$\lg K_c = \lg(1.2 \times 10^{13}) = 13.08$$

Table 106.1 gives you examples of stability constants.

Table 106.1. Values of stability constants

Ion with water as ligands	*Complex**	*Lg(stability constant)*
Fe^{3+}	$[Fe(H_2O)_5F]^{2-}$	5.3
Fe^{3+}	$[Fe(H_2O)_5(SCN)]^{2-}$	3.0
Co^{2+}	$[Co(NH_3)_6]^{2+}$	4.4
Ni^{2+}	$[Ni(NH_3)_6]^{2+}$	8.6
Ni^{2+}	$[Ni(en)_3]^{2+}$	18.3
Cu^{2+}	$[Cu(NH_3)_4]^{2+}$	13.1
Cu^{2+}	$CuCl_4{}^{2-}$	5.6
Zn^{2+}	$[Zn(NH_3)_4]^{2+}$	8.7

*The two complexes with iron(III) will also be accompanied by other ions such as $[Fe(H_2O)_4F_2]^-$; en = ethane-1,2-diamine

106.8 The stability constant for the complex $[Cu(NH_2CH_2CH_2NH_2)_2]^{2+}$ is $1.1 \times 10^{20}\,dm^6\,mol^{-2}$. What will happen, if anything, if ethane-1,2-diamine is added to a solution of $Cu(NH_3)_4{}^{2+}$?

106.9 Table 106.1 shows you that thiocyanate ions, SCN^-, and fluoride ions, F^-, can act as ligands with iron(III) ions. The thiocyanate complex is blood red and the fluoride complex is colourless. A solution containing iron(III) ions in water is split into two portions. To the first is added a solution of thiocyanate ions, followed after a few minutes by a solution of fluoride ions. To the second the same solutions are added, but in the reverse order. Describe what you would expect to see in these reactions.

106.10 Would you expect ammonia to displace ethane-1,2-diamine molecules from a $Ni(en)_3^{2+}$ complex?

106.11 A complex ion like $\{Co(NH_3)_6\}^{2+}$ can be made by adding ammonia to a solution containing $\{Co(H_2O)_6\}^{2+}$ ions. (Here we use the curly brackets to avoid confusion with the square brackets meaning 'concentration of' in the equations for K.) If only a small amount of ammonia is added at a time, the water molecules can be replaced one at a time. The first complex will be $\{Co(H_2O)_5NH_3\}^{2+}$, the second $\{Co(H_2O)_4(NH_3)_2\}^{2+}$, and so on. For each complex there will be a corresponding equilibrium:

$$\{Co(H_2O)_6\}^{2+}(aq) + NH_3(aq) \rightleftharpoons \{Co(H_2O)_5NH_3\}^{2+}(aq) + H_2O(l)$$

$$K_1 = \frac{[\{Co(H_2O)_5NH_3\}^{2+}(aq)]}{[\{Co(H_2O)_6\}^{2+}(aq)][NH_3(aq)]}$$

We can write the $\{Co(H_2O)_6\}^{2+}$ ion as M for short, and the ammonia molecules as A. This is to simplify the equations we are going to write. For example we can put

$$M + A \rightleftharpoons MA$$

and

$$K_1 = \frac{[MA]}{[M][A]}$$

In a similar fashion we can write the production of $\{Co(H_2O)_4(NH_3)_2\}^{2+}$ from $\{Co(H_2O)_5NH_3\}^{2+}$ by the equation

$$MA + A \rightleftharpoons MA_2$$

with

$$K_2 = \frac{[MA_2]}{[MA][A]}$$

(i) Write down the corresponding equations for the production of the other ions, $\{Co(H_2O)_3(NH_3)_3\}^{2+}, \ldots, \{Co(NH_3)_6\}^{2+}$. Call the equilibrium constants $K_3, \ldots, K_6$.

(ii) We can represent $\{Co(NH_3)_6\}^{2+}$ being made directly from $\{Co(H_2O)_6\}^{2+}$ by the equation

$$\{Co(H_2O)_6\}^{2+}(aq) + 6NH_3(aq) \rightleftharpoons \{Co(NH_3)_6\}^{2+}(aq) + 6H_2O(l)$$

and

$$K_T = \frac{[\{Co(NH_3)_6\}^{2+}(aq)]}{[\{Co(H_2O)_6\}^{2+}(aq)][NH_3(aq)]^6}$$

In our shorthand way these become

$$M + 6A \rightleftharpoons MA_6$$

and

$$K_T = \frac{[MA_6]}{[M][A]^6}$$

Explain why or show that $K_T = K_1 \times K_2 \times K_3 \times K_4 \times K_5 \times K_6$. You have just demonstrated the connection between the *overall stability constant*, K_T, and the *step-wise stability constants*, $K_1, K_2, \ldots, K_6$.

106.12 The stability constants of complexes made from bidentate or tridentate ligands are larger than those made with monodentate ligands of a similar type. For example, look at the values for $Ni(NH_3)_6^{2+}$ and $Ni(en)_3^{2+}$ in Table 106.1. The problem is to explain this effect, called the *chelate effect*. The bonding in the two complexes both involve the lone pairs on the nitrogen atoms. Therefore we would expect the bond strengths to be similar, and the enthalpy changes of formation of the two complexes to be similar (which they are). Given that stability constants are related to free energy changes through the usual equation $\Delta G^{\ominus} = -RT \ln K$, and that $\Delta G^{\ominus} = \Delta H^{\ominus} - T\Delta S^{\ominus}$ we must look to the entropy term to explain the differences between the stability constants.

(i) If one monodentate ligand from a solution displaces one water molecule from a complex, would you expect there to be a large entropy change?

(ii) A bidentate ligand can displace two water molecules from a complex. How does the entropy change compare with that in (i)?

You should now have an idea of how the chelate effect is related to entropy changes.

106.3 Complexes and redox potentials

In the previous unit we saw that iron(III) ions could oxidise iodide ions to iodine:

$$2Fe^{3+}(aq) + 2I^-(aq) \rightarrow 2Fe^{2+}(aq) + I_2(aq)$$

This fits with our knowledge of the redox potentials, $E^{\ominus}_{Fe^{3+}/Fe^{2+}} = +0.77\,V$, $E^{\ominus}_{I_2/I^-} = +0.54\,V$. That is, because $E^{\ominus}_{Fe^{3+}/Fe^{2+}}$ is more positive than $E^{\ominus}_{I_2/I^-}$, we know that Fe^{3+} ions are stronger oxidising agents than iodine molecules. (Or, if you prefer, I^- is a stronger reducing agent than Fe^{2+}.) It is simple to do this reaction in a test tube, but if a solution of the complex hexacyanoferrate(III), $Fe(CN)_6^{3-}$, is added to iodide ions, no iodine is produced. This is in spite of the fact that the iron is in the same oxidation state as before. The redox potential shows that this is expected; $E^{\ominus}_{Fe(CN)_6^{3-}/Fe(CN)_6^{4-}} = +0.36\,V$. The potential is not more positive than $E^{\ominus}_{I_2/I^-}$ so the oxidation of iodide ions does not occur. We say that the cyanide ions have stabilised the higher oxidation state of iron, i.e. it is less likely to act as an oxidising agent and revert to iron(II). It is important that you realise that we are talking about energetics here, not kinetics. It is common for a complex of a transition metal ion to have a different redox potential to that of the uncomplexed ion. (In fact the ion will be complexed by water molecules, but we often neglect water molecules as ligands.) When ligands gather round a metal ion, they upset the energies of the orbitals; it is this rearrangement that changes the oxidising power.

There is another effect that can occur, but it is not so much one of energetics as kinetics. When an ion is complexed, the ligands can prevent electrons being transferred so readily between the metal ion and a neighbouring ion or molecule. There can be a considerable increase in the energy barrier, which stops the anticipated reaction taking place. This can happen even though the reaction is energetically still favourable.

You will find further examples where transition metal ions are involved in redox reactions in Unit 70.

Before we leave this unit we shall compare the redox potentials $E^{\ominus}_{Cr^{3+}/Cr^{2+}} = -0.41\ V$ and $E^{\ominus}_{Mn^{3+}/Mn^{2+}} = +1.51\ V$. The two figures tell us that Cr^{2+} is a much better reducing agent than Mn^{2+}, i.e. Cr^{2+} ions will give up electrons and change into Cr^{3+} more readily than Mn^{2+} will change into Mn^{3+}. It seems that Mn^{2+} are more energetically stable than Cr^{3+}. It so happens that Mn^{2+} ions are the only ones out of the four that have half-filled sets of 3d orbitals. (The 3d structures are Cr^{3+}, $3d^3$; Cr^{2+}, $3d^4$; Mn^{3+}, $3d^4$; Mn^{2+}, $3d^5$.) We have noted before (section 105.1) that half-filling a set of 3d orbitals appears to be energetically favourable, and so it appears here. The change between Cr^{3+} and Cr^{2+} does not involve disrupting a half-filled set of 3d orbitals, and this correlates with the greater reducing power of Cr^{2+} than Mn^{2+}.

Answers

106.1 The solution should be acidified with a little hydrochloric acid and then barium chloride solution added. A white precipitate should appear with a sulphate.

106.2 The isomers are $[Pt(NH_3)_4Br_2]^{2+}SO_4^{2-}$ and $[Pt(NH_3)_4SO_4]^{2+}(Br^-)_2$. One mole of the first gives 2 mol of particles, $[Pt(NH_3)_4Br_2]^{2+}$ and SO_4^{2-}. One mole of the second gives 3 mol of particles: 1 mol of $[Pt(NH_3)_4SO_4]^{2+}$ and 2 mol of Br^-.

106.3 (i) 400 g.

(ii) 1/40 or 0.025 mol.

(iii) $9.40\ g/188\ g\ mol^{-1} = 0.05\ mol$.

(iv) The ratio is 1 mol of crystal to 2 mol of bromide.

(v) If only 2 mol of bromide are available in solution, it means that 1 mol of bromide is attached to the chromium as a ligand.

(vi) The remaining water molecule and two bromides are held in the crystal structure.

106.4 No.

106.5 No.

106.6 (i) These are shown in Figure 106.7.

(ii) The third isomer has both a plane and a centre of symmetry. Therefore it cannot be optically active.

106.7 (i) The complex is blue, so it absorbs in the red; a red filter should be used.

(ii) As more of the complex is made, more light is absorbed. (You may sometimes see graphs with absorbance on the vertical scale; in this case the graph will be the other way up.)

(iii) As ammonia is added, more complex is produced and the amount of light passing through the solution decreases. When all the Ni^{2+} ions have been complexed, adding more ammonia will not change the colour, nor the reading on the colorimeter.

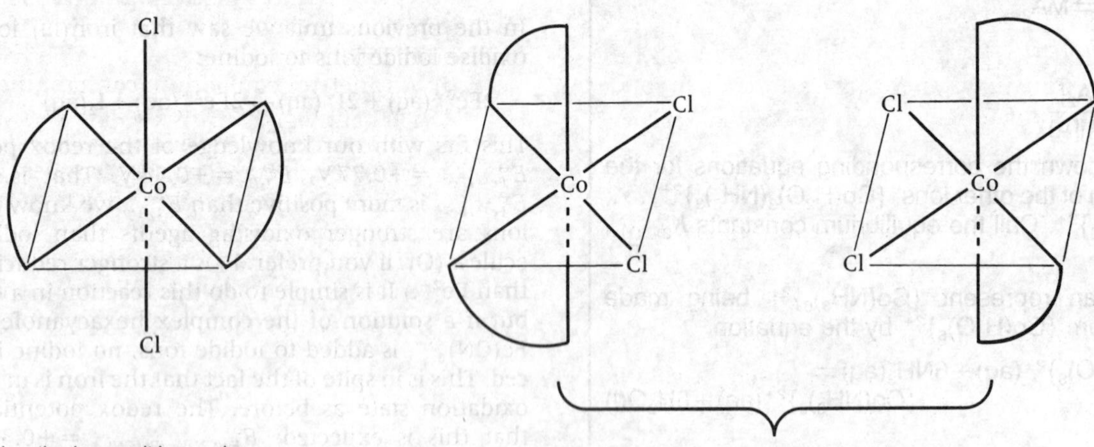

Cl
Co
Cl
Co
Cl
Cl
Cl
Co
Cl
Inactive isomer: it has a plane of symmetry
Mirror images: these are optically active

***Figure 106.7** The isomers of $[Co(NH_2CH_2CH_2NH_2)_2Cl_2]^+$. The curved lines stand for $NH_2CH_2CH_2NH_2$*

Answers – cont.

(iv) There are

$\frac{20}{1000}\,dm^3 \times 0.05\,mol\,dm^{-3} = 10^{-3}\,mol$ of Ni^{2+}

(v) The minimum comes at 15 cm^3 ammonia solution added. This contains

$\frac{15}{1000}\,dm^3 \times 0.4\,mol\,dm^{-3} = 6\times10^{-3}\,mol$ of NH_3

(vi) The ratio fits the formula $Ni(NH_3)_6{}^{2+}$.

(vii) If the volume were not constant, the concentration of the reagents would vary with the tube they were in. The colorimeter reading would change because of the dilution effect of adding more water to each tube, rather than because of the amount of complex made. Note: The shape of the graph can change depending on how an experiment like this is carried out. Sometimes the amount of metal ion solution and ligand solution are both changed. In such cases the graph has a V-shape.

106.8 The ethane-1,2-diamine complex has the higher stability complex, so the ammonia will be displaced to give $[Cu(NH_2CH_2CH_2NH_2)_2]^{2+}$.

106.9 In the first reaction, a blood red colour appears as the thiocyanate ions join with the Fe^{3+} ions. When the fluoride ions are added, the red colour disappears. This is because the complex with the fluoride ions has the larger of the two stability constants. In the second case, the red colour does not appear. The fluoride ions immediately complex with the Fe^{3+} ions. The thiocyanate ions cannot displace the fluoride ions.

106.10 No. The values in Table 106.1 show that $[Ni(en)_3]^{2+}$ is far more stable than $[Ni(NH_3)_6]^{2+}$.

106.11 (i)
$MA_2 + A \rightleftharpoons MA_3$; $K_3 = [MA_3]/([MA_2][A])$
$MA_3 + A \rightleftharpoons MA_4$; $K_4 = [MA_4]/([MA_3][A])$
$MA_4 + A \rightleftharpoons MA_5$; $K_5 = [MA_5]/([MA_4][A])$
$MA_5 + A \rightleftharpoons MA_6$; $K_6 = [MA_6]/([MA_5][A])$

(ii) The simplest way of doing this is to multiply the six K values together. You will find that [MA], $[MA_2]$, . . ., $[MA_5]$ cancel out, leaving the correct result for the overall stability constant.

106.12 (i) No.

(ii) It will be larger. The bidentate ligand will lose its ability to wander through the solution, and to rotate more or less randomly. This leads to a decrease in entropy. However, by releasing *two* molecules into the solution, they gain the ability to move and rotate with much less restriction than they had in the complex. This leads to an increase in entropy. The increase is larger than the decrease. It is this increase in entropy that contributes to the larger stability constants of complexes of bidentate and tridentate ligands.

UNIT 106 SUMMARY

- Isomerism:
  An ion or molecule has isomers if it can exist in two or more different forms with the same formula.
- Types of isomerism in complex ions:
  (i) Ionisation isomerism
  e.g. $[Co(NH_3)_5Br]^{2+}SO_4{}^{2-}$, bromide ion in the coordination sphere (gives test for sulphate, not bromide);
  $[Co(NH_3)_5SO_4]^+Br^-$, sulphate ion in the coordination sphere (gives test for bromide, not sulphate).
  (ii) Hydrate isomerism
  e.g. $[Cr(H_2O)_6]^{3+}(Cl^-)_3$, blue-violet in solution (no chloride ions in hydration sphere);
  $[Cr(H_2O)_5Cl]^{2+}(Cl^-)_2$, green in solution (one chloride ion in hydration sphere);
  $[Cr(H_2O)_4Cl_2]^+Cl^-$, darker green in solution (two chloride ions in hydration sphere).
- Geometrical isomerism:
  Different isomers are possible owing to the different ways the ligands are arranged in space. See the figures in the unit for help.
- Optical isomerism:
  This variety of isomerism occurs in octahedral complexes involving a bidentate ligand such as ethane-1,2-diamine. See Figure 106.5, which shows two isomers that cannot be superimposed upon one another.
- Stability constants:
  (i) A variety of equilibrium constant that gives a guide to the energetic stability of a complex.
  (ii) In a mixture of different ligands and a transition metal ion, the complex with the greater stability constant should be made.
- Redox potentials:
  When a metal forms a complex, its redox potential can change markedly, e.g. $E^{\ominus}_{Fe(CN)_6{}^{3-}/Fe(CN)_6{}^{4-}} = +0.36\,V$ compared to $E^{\ominus}_{Fe^{3+}/Fe^{2+}} = +0.77\,V$.

107

Chromium, manganese and iron

107.1 The chemistry of chromium

In this section you will find a summary of the chemistry of chromium, much of which has appeared in previous units, e.g. those on redox potentials and equilibria. However, some of the reactions may be new to you. The two most important oxidation states of chromium are chromium(VI) and chromium(III).

(a) *Chromium(VI) compounds*

As you should expect, chromium(VI) compounds show oxidising properties. Especially, dichromate(VI) ions, $Cr_2O_7^{2-}$, are used to oxidise other compounds. The ion reacts best in acid conditions (see below) and the colour change from orange to green is a sure sign of the reaction taking place. The half-equation for the process is

$$\underset{\text{orange}}{Cr_2O_7^{2-}(aq)} + 14H^+(aq) + 6e^- \rightarrow \underset{\text{green}}{2Cr^{3+}(aq)} + 7H_2O(l)$$

Acidified sodium dichromate(VI) solution is used in organic chemistry to oxidise alcohols to aldehydes and acids. For example, it will cause the changes

```
   H  H            H                  H
   |  |            |    //O           |    //O
H—C—C—OH  ——▸  H—C—C        ——▸  H—C—C
   |  |            |    \             |    \
   H  H            H     H            H     H
```

$$\underset{\text{ethanol}}{CH_3CH_2OH} \rightarrow \underset{\text{ethanal}}{CH_3CHO} \rightarrow \underset{\text{ethanoic acid}}{CH_3COOH}$$

($Na_2Cr_2O_7$ is used rather than $K_2Cr_2O_7$ owing to its greater solubility in the reaction mixture.)

We have said that $Cr_2O_7^{2-}$ ions react best in acid conditions. There are two reasons for this. The first is that the redox potential is highly dependent on the concentration of acid (see section 67.2). However, equally important is the fact that if the solution is not acidified, the number of $Cr_2O_7^{2-}$ ions decreases markedly. This is due to the equilibrium

$$\underset{\text{orange}}{Cr_2O_7^{2-}(aq)} + H_2O(l) \rightleftharpoons \underset{\text{yellow}}{2CrO_4^{2-}(aq)} + 2H^+(aq)$$

Especially, if alkali is added nearly all the orange dichromate(VI) ions are converted into yellow chromate(VI) ions, CrO_4^{2-}.

Chromium(VI) oxide, CrO_3, can be made by reacting sodium dichromate(VI) with concentrated sulphuric acid:

$$Cr_2O_7^{2-}(aq) + 2H^+(aq) \rightarrow \underset{\text{red crystals}}{2CrO_3(s)} + H_2O(l)$$

The oxide is precipitated as red needle-like crystals. The oxide is a powerful oxidising agent, especially with organic chemicals. It is the anhydride of chromic(VI) acid, H_2CrO_4. In laboratories, this acid is used for cleaning glassware when all other methods of cleaning have failed.

There are many salts of chromic(VI) acid. Often they are highly coloured and insoluble in water. Examples are yellow lead(II) chromate(VI), $PbCrO_4$, and red silver chromate(VI), Ag_2CrO_4. The latter is used to indicate the endpoint when chlorides are titrated with silver nitrate.

(b) *Chromium(III) compounds*

Apart from complexes such as $CrCl_3{\cdot}6H_2O$, which we met in the previous unit, chromium(III) oxide, Cr_2O_3, is the most important compound. It is a bulky green powder, which can be made by heating ammonium dichromate(VI):

$$(NH_4)_2Cr_2O_7(s) \rightarrow Cr_2O_3(s) + 4H_2O(g) + N_2(g)$$

Once the reaction starts, it will keep going at a reasonable rate. Also, a small amount of $(NH_4)_2Cr_2O_7$ gives a much larger volume of Cr_2O_3. Both features of the reaction lead to it being used in indoor fireworks.

107.1 Why should you expect chromium(VI) compounds to show oxidising properties?

107.2 A student dipped two small pieces of filter paper into acidified potassium dichromate(VI) solution. One of them was held in the mouth of a test tube containing sulphur dioxide, and the other piece in a test tube containing hydrogen sulphide. In both cases the paper turned green. The two half-reactions involving the gases are

$$SO_2(aq) + 2H_2O(l) \rightarrow SO_4^{2-}(aq) + 4H^+(aq) + 2e^-$$
$$H_2S(aq) \rightarrow S(s) + 2H^+(aq) + 2e^-$$

(i) Write the equations for the reactions that took place.

(ii) Describe what the student might have seen if she had shaken a *solution* of acidified potassium dichromate(VI) with hydrogen sulphide gas.

107.3 Use the simplest definitions of oxidation and reduction to explain why the changes ethanol → ethanal → ethanoic acid represent oxidations of the organic molecules.

107.4 Briefly explain why adding alkali to the dichromate(VI)/chromate(VI) equilibrium produces a strong yellow colour.

107.5 Explain how you would discover the concentration of a solution of chloride in a silver nitrate titration.

107.6 In alkaline solution, hydrogen peroxide has $E^\ominus = +0.87$ V. Will hydrogen peroxide oxidise chromium(III) hydroxide, $Cr(OH)_3$, to chromate(VI)? $E^\ominus_{CrO_4^{2-}/Cr(OH)_3} = -0.13$ V.

107.7 (i) What is the oxidation state of chromium in CrO_2Cl_2.

(ii) Predict the shape of this molecule.

(Hint: assume that only the six outer electrons of chromium are used in bonding.)

107.2 The chemistry of manganese

(a) *Manganese(VII)*

You are likely to have met the highest oxidation state of manganese in potassium manganate(VII), $KMnO_4$. It is often used as an oxidising agent. Like potassium dichromate(VI), it gives a definite colour change when it reacts. In acidic conditions the change is from purple to (nearly) colourless:

$$\underset{\text{purple}}{MnO_4^-(aq)} + 5e^- + 8H^+(aq) \rightarrow \underset{\text{colourless}}{Mn^{2+}(aq)} + 4H_2O(l); \quad E^\ominus = +1.51\text{ V}$$

In alkali the change is from purple to a clear solution and a black precipitate of manganese(IV) oxide:

$$\underset{\text{purple}}{MnO_4^-(aq)} + 3e^- + 4H^+(aq) \rightarrow \underset{\text{black}}{MnO_2(s)} + 2H_2O(l); \quad E^\ominus = +1.70\text{ V}$$

Acidified potassium manganate(VII) solution can be used to test for sulphur dioxide and hydrogen sulphide. More importantly, it is used in titrations to discover the concentrations of solutions of ethanedioates (oxalates), $C_2O_4^{2-}$. In organic chemistry it is used to oxidise alkenes to diols: for example,

$$H_2C{=}CH_2 \longrightarrow H{-}\underset{H}{\overset{OH}{C}}{-}\underset{H}{\overset{OH}{C}}{-}H$$

$$\underset{\text{ethene}}{C_2H_4} \rightarrow \underset{\text{ethane-1,2-diol}}{CH_2OHCH_2OH}$$

Potassium manganate(VII) can be made in the laboratory by heating manganese(IV) oxide with a strong oxidising agent, usually potassium chlorate(V). The oxide and chlorate(V) are mixed with pellets of potassium hydroxide, and the three heated together. Gradually the green colour of manganate(VI) ions appears:

$$3MnO_2(s) + 6KOH(s) + KClO_3(s) \rightarrow \underset{\text{green}}{3K_2MnO_4(s)} + KCl(s) + 3H_2O(l)$$

Once the reaction mixture cools, the products are boiled with water, and the green colour is quickly replaced by the purple colour of manganate(VII) ions:

$$\underset{\substack{\text{manganate(VI)}\\\text{green}}}{3MnO_4^{2-}(aq)} + 2H_2O(l) \rightarrow \underset{\substack{\text{manganate(VII)}\\\text{purple}}}{MnO_4^-(aq)} + MnO_2(s) + 4OH^-(aq)$$

After the solid is filtered off, shiny black crystals of $KMnO_4$ crystallise from the solution.

(b) *Manganese(IV)*

Manganese(IV) oxide is the most common compound showing this oxidation state of manganese. It is a black powder, which can be used as an oxidising agent. For example, a steady supply of chlorine can be made by warming it with concentrated hydrochloric acid:

$$MnO_2(s) + 4HCl(aq) \rightarrow MnCl_2(aq) + 2H_2O(l) + Cl_2(g)$$

It is also used as a catalyst, particularly for releasing oxygen from hydrogen peroxide:

$$2H_2O_2(aq) \xrightarrow{MnO_2\text{ catalyst}} 2H_2O(l) + O_2(g)$$

The standard way of making the oxide is to oxidise manganese(II) hydroxide with a solution of sodium chlorate(I):

$$Mn(OH)_2(s) + OCl^-(aq) \rightarrow MnO_2(s) + H_2O(l) + Cl^-(aq)$$

(c) *Manganese(II)*

This is the oxidation state of manganese that shows little or no oxidising power. Manganese(II) ions occur as $Mn(H_2O)_6^{2+}$ complexes in water, which give a pale pink colour to the solution. However, you are unlikely to spot this colour under the conditions used in your laboratory. Some manganese(II) compounds are insoluble in water, in particular white manganese(II) hydroxide, $Mn(OH)_2$, and pink manganese(II) sulphide, MnS. The precipitation of the sulphide is used as a test for the presence of Mn^{2+} ions. However, the chloride, sulphate and nitrate are all soluble.

107.8 Which is the stronger oxidising agent, manganate(VII) ions in acid, or alkaline conditions?

107.9 (i) Write down the equation for the reaction between ethanedioate and manganate(VII) ions. Carbon dioxide is given off in the reaction.

(ii) Why is an indicator not needed in a titration between these two chemicals?

107.10 How would you classify the conversion of manganate(VI) ions into manganate(VII) ions and manganese(IV) oxide?

107.11 Write down the equation for the reaction between iron(II) ions, Fe^{2+}, and manganate(VII) ions in acidic solution.

107. 12 What is the connection between potassium manganate(VII) and chlorine gas?

107.13 The solubility product of manganese(II) sulphide is 1.4×10^{-15} mol² dm⁻⁶. What is the solubility of MnS in water?

107.14 When $Mn(OH)_2$ is made by adding an alkali to a solution containing Mn^{2+} ions, the precipitate quickly darkens, and eventually goes black. What might be the chemical giving the black colour, and how is it made?

107.3 The chemistry of iron

The key process in the manufacture of iron is the reduction by carbon and carbon monoxide of iron(III) oxide, which occurs in the minerals haematite and limonite. We have discussed the process, and the uses of the metal, in Unit 85.

Here we shall mention the most important reactions of compounds of its two common oxidation states, iron(III) and iron(II).

(a) *Iron(III)*

Iron(III) chloride is made by the direct combination of the elements. It is subject to hydrolysis, so the apparatus and chemicals must be kept dry:

$$2Fe(s) + 3Cl_2(g) \rightarrow 2FeCl_3(s)$$

Like aluminium trichloride, it can form dimers.

Iron(III) chloride (or bromide) is made as an intermediate when benzene rings are chlorinated (or brominated) in the presence of iron powder; see section 113.6.

Of all iron(III) compounds, iron(III) oxide is the most common. In its hydrated form it is well known (even to non-chemists) as rust, $Fe_2O_3 \cdot nH_2O$. The way in which rust is formed is complicated; you will find details in section 68.2.

(b) *Iron(II)*

Iron(II) sulphate, $FeSO_4$, is the iron(II) compound that you are most likely to meet in the laboratory. It is a useful source of Fe^{2+} ions. However, in order to prevent it being oxidised, the salt must be dissolved in water containing dilute sulphuric acid. Solutions of iron(II) ammonium sulphate, $FeSO_4 \cdot (NH_4)_2SO_4 \cdot 6H_2O$, are used as primary standards in volumetric analysis. The Fe^{2+} ions released by the salt will react with solutions of oxidising agents such as potassium manganate(VII) and potassium dichromate(VI).

Iron(II) chloride cannot be made from iron and chlorine directly; instead dry hydrogen chloride is passed over heated iron:

$$Fe(s) + 2HCl(g) \rightarrow FeCl_2(s) + H_2(g)$$

(c) *Tests for iron(II) and iron(III)*

A simple test is to add hydroxide ions to solutions of the ions. Iron(II) hydroxide will appear as a gelatinous pale green precipitate, whereas iron(III) hydroxide has a definite orange-brown colour:

$$Fe^{2+}(aq) + 2OH^-(aq) \rightarrow \underset{\text{pale green}}{Fe(OH)_2(s)}$$

$$Fe^{3+}(aq) + 3OH^-(aq) \rightarrow \underset{\text{orange-brown}}{Fe(OH)_3(s)}$$

An even simpler method is to add a few drops of potassium thiocyanate solution. Thiocyanate ions give an intense blood red colour with Fe^{3+}, but not with Fe^{2+} ions:

$$Fe^{3+}(aq) + SCN^-(aq) \rightarrow \underset{\text{blood red}}{FeSCN^{2+}(aq)}$$

A more involved test, and one that has quite a history, makes use of the two complex ions hexacyanoferrate(II), $Fe(CN)_6{}^{4-}$, and hexacyanoferrate(III), $Fe(CN)_6{}^{3-}$. If the former is added to a solution of iron(III) ions, a dark blue precipitate is produced. The precipitate is known as Prussian blue. If the latter is added to a solution of iron(II) ions, another dark blue precipitate is made. This precipitate is called Turnbull's blue:

$$\underset{\text{hexacyanoferrate(II)}}{Fe(CN)_6{}^{4-}(aq)} + Fe^{3+}(aq) \rightarrow \text{Prussian blue}$$

$$\underset{\text{hexacyanoferrate(III)}}{Fe(CN)_6{}^{3-}(aq)} + Fe^{2+}(aq) \rightarrow \text{Turnbull's blue}$$

It is now known that the chemical structures of both precipitates are identical, which, for simplicity, we shall write as $FeFe(CN)_6{}^-$.

107.15 Briefly describe the apparatus that you might use to make $FeCl_3$.

107.16 Solutions of iron(III) salts are often acidic. Suggest a reason why this is so. You may assume that $Fe(H_2O)_6{}^{3+}$ ions are present. (Hint: see section 75.5.)

107.17 Iron(III) ions are fairly good oxidising agents. ($E^{\ominus}_{Fe^{3+}/Fe^{2+}} = +0.77$ V.)

(i) Will they oxidise sulphide ions? ($E^{\ominus}_{S/S^{2-}} = -0.48$ V.)

(ii) Will they oxidise Sn^{2+} ions? ($E^{\ominus}_{Sn^{4+}/Sn^{2+}} = +0.15$ V.)

(iii) Will they convert Cu into Cu^{2+} ions? ($E^{\ominus}_{Cu^{2+}/Cu} = +0.34$ V.)

(iv) Will they change Ce^{3+} into Ce^{4+}? ($E^{\ominus}_{Ce^{4+}/Ce^{3+}} = +1.77$ V.)

(v) In each case, if you decide there will be a reaction, write the equation.

107.18 $E^{\ominus}_{Fe^{2+}/Fe} = -0.44$ V. Should iron give hydrogen with acids? Comment on your answer.

107.19 What appears to be the oxidation state of the iron atoms in $FeFe(CN)_6{}^-$? Explain your answer.

Answers

107.1 Ions in high oxidation states tend to take electrons from another chemical and return to a lower oxidation state. As it loses electrons, the other chemical must have been oxidised.

107.2 (i) $Cr_2O_7{}^{2-}(aq) + 3SO_2(aq) + 2H^+(aq) \rightarrow 2Cr^{3+}(aq) + 3SO_4{}^{2-}(aq) + H_2O(l)$

$Cr_2O_7{}^{2-}(aq) + 3H_2S(aq) + 8H^+(aq) \rightarrow 2Cr^{3+}(aq) + 3S(s) + 7H_2O(l)$

(ii) She would have seen the green colour together with a yellow precipitate of sulphur.

107.3 Ethanol to ethanal involves the loss of hydrogen atoms, and ethanol to ethanoic acid the gain of oxygen; these are both features of oxidation.

107.4 Adding alkali will remove hydrogen ions from the solution. As Le Chatelier's principle says, the equilibrium will move to the right, i.e. in the direction that tends to replace the hydrogen ions.

107.5 See section 40.4, which describes this type of titration.

107.6 Yes. Hydrogen peroxide has an $E^{\ominus}$ considerably more positive than $E^{\ominus}_{CrO_4{}^{2-}/Cr(OH)_3}$, so the peroxide will act as the oxidising agent. This reaction can be used to make chromate(VI) in the laboratory.

107.7 (i) $Ox(Cr) + 2 \times Ox(O) + 2 \times Ox(Cl) = 0$ and so $Ox(Cr) - 4 - 2 = 0$, which gives $Ox(Cr) = +6$.

(ii) Tetrahedral.

107.8 The alkaline solution: it has the more positive redox potential.

107.9 (i) $2MnO_4{}^-(aq) + 5C_2O_4{}^{2-}(aq) + 16H^+(aq) \rightarrow 2Mn^{2+}(aq) + 10CO_2(g) + 8H_2O(l)$

(ii) The manganate(VII) solution changes colour, from purple to colourless, while there are ethanedioate ions with which it can react. As soon as the latter are used up, the solution stays purple; hence the solution acts as its own indicator.

107.10 It is a disproportionation (see section 71.3).

107.11 $MnO_4{}^-(aq) + 5Fe^{2+}(aq) + 8H^+(aq) \rightarrow Mn^{2+}(aq) + 5Fe^{3+}(aq) + 4H_2O(l)$

107.12 Chlorine can be made by dropping concentrated hydrochloric acid onto crystals of potassium manganate(VII).

107.13 $MnS(s) \rightarrow Mn^{2+}(aq) + S^{2-}(aq)$

The equation tells us that $[Mn^{2+}(aq)] = [S^{2-}(aq)]$, so the formula for the solubility product, $K_{sp} = [Mn^{2+}(aq)] \times [S^{2-}(aq)]$ becomes $K_{sp} = [Mn^{2+}(aq)]^2$. Therefore, $[Mn^{2+}(aq)]^2 = 1.4 \times 10^{-15}$ mol^2 dm^{-6} and $[Mn^{2+}(aq)] = 3.7 \times 10^{-8}$ mol dm^{-3}. To obtain 3.7×10^{-8} mol of Mn^{2+} ions in 1 dm^3, an equal number of moles of MnS must have dissolved, i.e. the solubility is 3.7×10^{-8} mol dm^{-3}.

107.14 The black colour is due to manganese(IV) oxide, MnO_2. It is made by the $Mn(OH)_2$ being oxidised by oxygen in the air.

107.15 An apparatus similar to the one used to make $AlCl_3$ can be used; see Figure 40.1.

107.16 The complex ion can act as a proton donor:

$Fe(H_2O)_6{}^{3+}(aq) + H_2O(l) \rightarrow [Fe(H_2O)_5OH]^{3+}(aq) + H_3O^+(l)$

107.17 (i), (ii) and (iii) Yes, because $E^{\ominus}_{Fe^{3+}/Fe^{2+}}$ is the more positive in each case.

(iv) No; rather, Ce^{4+} oxidises Fe^{2+}. This is the basis of the redox titration described in section 70.4.

(v) The reactions are:

$S^{2-}(aq) + 2Fe^{3+}(aq) \rightarrow S(s) + 2Fe^{2+}(aq)$
$Sn^{2+}(aq) + 2Fe^{3+}(aq) \rightarrow Sn^{4+}(aq) + 2Fe^{2+}(aq)$
$Cu(s) + 2Fe^{3+}(aq) \rightarrow Cu^{2+}(aq) + 2Fe^{2+}(aq)$

The last reaction is used to etch copper-clad electronics circuit boards.

107.18 Yes. However, concentrated nitric acid renders iron passive. Even so, the layer that causes the reaction to stop is easily lost, so if the mixture is shaken the reaction continues.

107.19 Each cyanide carries a charge of -1. The two iron atoms take up five negative charges, so their average oxidation number is $+2.5$. In practice, there is a mixture of Fe^{2+} and Fe^{3+} ions.

UNIT 107 SUMMARY

Chromium

- Chromium(VI) compounds are oxidising agents, e.g. dichromate(VI) ions, $Cr_2O_7^{2-}$, in acid solution:

$$\underset{\text{orange}}{Cr_2O_7^{2-}(aq)} + 14H^+(aq) + 6e^- \rightarrow \underset{\text{green}}{2Cr^{3+}(aq)} + 7H_2O(l)$$

- Chromium(VI) oxide, CrO_3, made by reacting sodium dichromate(VI) with concentrated sulphuric acid:

$$Cr_2O_7^{2-}(aq) + 2H^+(aq) \rightarrow 2CrO_3(s) + H_2O(l)$$

Manganese

- Potassium manganate(VII), $KMnO_4$, is a common oxidising agent.
  (i) In acid,

$$\underset{\text{purple}}{MnO_4^-(aq)} + 5e^- + 8H^+(aq) \rightarrow \underset{\text{colourless}}{Mn^{2+}(aq)} + 4H_2O(l);\ E^\ominus = +1.51\ V$$

  (ii) In alkali,

$$\underset{\text{purple}}{MnO_4^-(aq)} + 3e^- + 4H^+(aq) \rightarrow \underset{\text{black}}{MnO_2(s)} + 2H_2O(l);\ E^\ominus = +1.70\ V$$

- Potassium manganate(VII) is made by first heating manganese(IV) oxide with potassium chlorate(V) and potassium hydroxide pellets, then boiling with water.
- Manganese(IV) oxide, MnO_2, is:
  (i) Used as a catalyst with hydrogen peroxide to make oxygen.
  (ii) Warmed with concentrated hydrochloric acid to make chlorine.
- Manganese(II) ions can be identified by the salmon pink precipitate (MnS) made with sulphide ions.

Iron

- Iron is magnetic.
- It is extracted in the blast furnace from minerals containing iron(III) oxide, Fe_2O_3, and is the major component of steel.
- Iron(III) chloride, $FeCl_3$, is made by heating iron with dry chlorine; the chloride is easily hydrolysed.
- Hydrated iron(III) oxide is better known as rust.
- Iron(II) chloride, $FeCl_2$, is made by warming iron with dry hydrogen chloride. It too is easily hydrolysed.
- Iron(II) ammonium sulphate, $FeSO_4(NH_4)_2SO_4{\cdot}6H_2O$, is used as a primary standard in volumetric analysis.
- Fe^{2+} ions give a gelatinous pale green precipitate (of $Fe(OH)_2$), and Fe^{3+} a gelatinous brown precipitate (of $Fe(OH)_3$), with hydroxide ions.
- Fe^{3+} ions (not Fe^{2+}) give a blood red colour with thiocyanate ions, SCN^-.

108

Group IIB

108.1 The nature of the elements

The elements of Group IIB are zinc, cadmium and mercury. Their properties and uses are shown in Tables 108.1 and 108.2. They follow the transition metals, and as such they have a complete set of ten d electrons as well as a pair of outer s electrons. Mercury also has a set of fourteen f electrons. The differences between the second and third ionisation energies of these metals and the transition metals that precede them are not markedly different. However, unlike the transition elements, none of them show oxidation states higher than +2. Mercury is unusual in that it shows two oxidation states, mercury(I) and mercury(II), but the lower state is found in the dimercury(I) ion, Hg_2^{2+}, in which two mercury atoms are joined by a metal–metal bond.

Table 108.1. Physical properties of the elements

Symbol	*Zinc* Zn	*Cadmium* Cd	*Mercury* Hg
Electron structure	(Ar)$3d^{10}4s^2$	(Kr)$4d^{10}5s^2$	(Xe)$4f^{14}5d^{10}6s^2$
Electronegativity	1.6	1.7	1.9
1st I.E. /kJ mol^{-1}	910	870	1010
2nd I.E. /kJ mol^{-1}	1700	1600	1800
3rd I.E. /kJ mol^{-1}	3800	3600	3300
Melting point/° C	423	321	−39
Boiling point/° C	908	765	357
Atomic radius/pm	131	148	148
Ionic radius/pm	74	97	110
Principal oxid. no.	+2	+2	+1,+2
$E^{\ominus}_{M^{2+}/M}$/V	−0.76	−0.40	−0.79*

*The $E^{\ominus}$ of mercury is for $Hg_2^{2+}(aq)+2e^- \rightarrow 2Hg(l)$

Table 108.2. Uses of the elements

Element	*Main uses*
Zinc	In alloys such as brass, e.g. 70% Cu, 30% Zn
	For galvanising iron (see section 68.3)
	In batteries
Cadmium	In cadmium sulphide photocells
	It can also be used for protecting metals in much the same way as zinc
Mercury	In thermometers
	In amalgams for dental fillings
	In various agricultural chemicals and pharmaceuticals

(Mercury(I) and mercury(II) compounds were once labelled mercurous and mercuric respectively.)

They also show the ability to give complex ions. For example, $Zn(CN)_4^{2-}$, $Cd(CN)_4^{2-}$, $Hg(CN)_4^{2-}$. You will find examples of other complexes later on.

The melting and boiling points of the metals are much lower than their transition metal neighbours. The melting point of mercury is so low that it is the only liquid metal at room temperature. The ease with which they vaporise is made use of in the methods used for their production. The chief ores of the metals are their sulphides. Zinc blende, ZnS, is roasted with air and changes into its oxide. In turn the oxide is reduced using coke (as a cheap variety of carbon).

The method for extracting mercury is similar to that of zinc, except that it is not necessary to heat mercury(II) oxide with carbon: it decomposes into mercury and oxygen at 300° C. The reactions are

$$2HgS(s) + 3O_2(g) \rightarrow 2HgO(s) + 2SO_2(g)$$
$$2HgO(s) \rightarrow 2Hg(l) + O_2(g)$$

Overall the reaction is

$$HgS(s) + O_2(g) \rightarrow Hg(l) + SO_2(g)$$

Mercury and its compounds are dangerous. The vapour pressure of mercury is high enough for the liquid to be a health hazard if it is spilled. Like many of

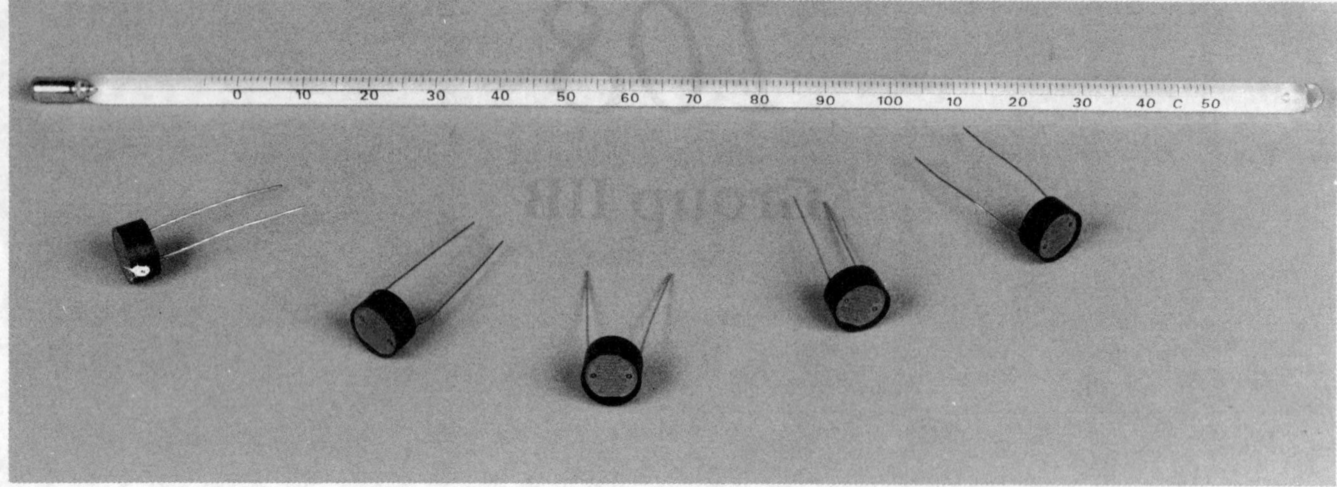

Two uses of the B metals cadmium (in light dependent resistors) and mercury (in thermometers).

the 'heavy metals' (which includes cadmium), mercury causes brain damage. It is far more dangerous as a vapour, when it can be taken in through the lungs, than it is as a liquid. One of the problems with mercury is that often the poisoning is discovered only after symptoms appear. At this stage, antidotes will not work.

If you come across liquid mercury, treat it with caution. One way of removing the danger it presents is to cover the droplets with powdered sulphur. Even at room temperature, the two elements will combine to give mercury(II) sulphide, HgS.

108.1 Why is it that, unlike the transition metals, the complexes of Zn, Cd and Hg are normally colourless. (Hint: electron structures.)

108.2 Zinc blende is often contaminated by significant proportions of cadmium. In the course of extracting zinc, cadmium can also be isolated. A difference in one of the physical properties of the elements makes the separation possible? What is the property?

108.3 This method of extracting metals is one that we discussed in Unit 85 from the point of view of thermodynamics. What are the free energy changes of the reactions:

(i) $2ZnS(s) + 3O_2(g) \rightarrow 2ZnO(s) + 2SO_2(g)$

(ii) $ZnO(s) + C(s) \rightarrow Zn(s) + CO(g)$

The standard free energies of formation of ZnS, ZnO, SO_2 and CO are −205.4, −318.2, −300.4 and −137.3, all in units of kJ mol^{-1}.

Comment on your answers.

108.4 $E^{\ominus}_{Zn^{2+}/Zn} = -0.76$ V, $E^{\ominus}_{Cd^{2+}/Cd} = -0.40$ V and $E^{\ominus}_{Hg^{2+}/Hg} = +0.85$ V. Which, if any, of the metals will give hydrogen with acids?

108.2 The oxides and hydroxides

Zinc oxide will dissolve in both acid and alkali:

$$ZnO(s) + 2H^+(aq) \rightarrow Zn^{2+}(aq) + H_2O(l)$$
$$ZnO(s) + 2OH^-(aq) + H_2O(l) \rightarrow Zn(OH)_4{}^{2-}(aq)$$

This shows us the amphoteric nature of zinc. Cadmium oxide and mercury(II) oxide are essentially basic, which illustrates the usual tendency of metallic nature increasing down a group.

Zinc oxide is white when it is cold, a property that has given it a use as a pigment in paints. However, it changes colour when hot to a pale yellow. This is due to changes in the structure of the lattice.

You can make zinc hydroxide, $Zn(OH)_2$, by adding dilute alkali to a solution of a zinc(II) salt. It appears as a gelatinous white precipitate:

$$Zn^{2+}(aq) + 2OH^-(aq) \rightarrow Zn(OH)_2(s)$$

The precipitate will dissolve in excess alkali to give soluble $Zn(OH)_4{}^{2-}(aq)$ ions.

Zinc hydroxide is also precipitated with aqueous ammonia, and it will dissolve in excess ammonia. However, this time the complex ion $Zn(NH_3)_4{}^{2+}$ is made. This reaction allows us to distinguish a solution containing zinc ions from one containing aluminium ions (see Table 108.3).

Table 108.3. How to tell apart solutions of zinc and aluminium ions

Ion	*With sodium hydroxide*	*With aqueous ammonia*
Zn^{2+}	White precipitate; dissolves in excess	White precipitate; dissolves in excess
Al^{3+}	White precipitate; dissolves in excess	White precipitate; does not dissolve*

*Actually it dissolves to a very slight extent, but unless you added a vast amount of ammonia you would see no change in the precipitate

The reactions of mercury(I) and mercury(II) ions with alkali are markedly different to those of zinc and cadmium. A mercury(II) solution eventually gives a yellow precipitate of mercury(II) oxide:

$$Hg^{2+}(aq) + 2OH^-(aq) \rightarrow \underset{\text{yellow}}{HgO(s)} + H_2O(l)$$

(The difference between the yellow and red varieties of HgO is simply one of the size of the particles.)

Dimercury(I) ions give a black precipitate of mercury(I) oxide:

$$Hg_2{}^{2+}(aq) + 2OH^-(aq) \rightarrow \underset{\text{black}}{Hg_2O(s)} + H_2O(l)$$

108.5 Predict the shape of the $Zn(NH_3)_4{}^{2+}$ ion. Suggest which orbitals might be used in making the bonds.

108.6 A student was given a solution of cadmium sulphate, $CdSO_4$, and split it into two parts. To one part he added dilute sodium hydroxide, to the other aqueous ammonia. What do you think he saw?

108.3 The halides

The halides of zinc and cadmium are mainly ionic, while those of mercury are covalent. The mercury halides are insoluble in water, whereas zinc fluoride is the only zinc halide that is insoluble. Mercury(II) chloride is sufficiently covalent to have a crystal structure in which individual molecules can be identified. The only halide that is of significant use in the laboratory is dimercury(I) chloride, Hg_2Cl_2. This is because it is one of the ingredients of the calomel cell. It consists of mercury in contact with dimercury(I) chloride and has a stable e.m.f. of $E^{\ominus} = +0.789$ V at 25 °C. We said a little about this cell in section 66.6. Look there for more information if necessary. The cell reaction is

$$Hg_2Cl_2(s) + 2e^- \rightleftharpoons 2Hg(l) + 2Cl^-(aq)$$

108.7 Zinc(II) chloride is extremely deliquescent. Briefly explain how you would attempt to make this chloride in the laboratory.

108.8 What might be the reason for the insolubility of zinc(II) fluoride?

108.9 Dimercury(I) iodide, Hg_2I_2, is a greenish colour and is precipitated if iodide ions are added to a solution of dimercury(I) sulphate. Likewise, the red mercury(II) iodide, HgI_2, is precipitated from a solution of mercury(II) sulphate. However, both precipitates dissolve in excess iodide solution. What might be the reason for this?

108.4 The sulphates, nitrates and carbonates

(a) *Sulphates*

All the sulphates are soluble in water and appear as hydrated crystals, e.g. $ZnSO_4{\cdot}7H_2O$, $HgSO_4{\cdot}6H_2O$. They are useful as sources of the metal ions in solution. However, when they dissolve in water, the solution becomes acidic. This is a result of hydrolysis. For example,

$$[Zn(H_2O)_4]^{2+}(aq) \rightarrow [Zn(H_2O)_2OH]^{2+}(aq) + H^+(aq)$$

(b) *Nitrates*

The nitrates of zinc and cadmium decompose in the normal way for heavy metal nitrates, i.e. they give off nitrogen dioxide and oxygen, with the metal oxide being left behind. In the case of mercury(II) nitrate, the metal is left:

$$Hg(NO_3)_2(s) \rightarrow Hg(l) + 2NO_2(g) + O_2(g)$$

(c) *Carbonates*

Zinc carbonate is the only carbonate of much interest. It occurs as a mineral calamine and at one time was widely used in calamine lotion, a pink suspension of the carbonate, for treating spots and other skin ailments. Zinc carbonate is insoluble in water, but shows the usual properties of carbonates.

108.10 Which other metal ion (not from Group IIB) behaves like $[Zn(H_2O)_4]^{2+}$ in giving an acidic solution?

108.11 Why is mercury(II) nitrate a slight exception to the normal pattern of decomposition by heat?

108.12 What are the 'usual properties' of carbonates mentioned above?

108.13 If a solution of a hydrogencarbonate is added to a solution containing Zn^{2+} ions, why is carbon dioxide given off? (Zinc carbonate is also precipitated.)

108.5 The sulphides

Each of the sulphides(ZnS, CdS, HgS) is highly insoluble in water. (There is no mercury(I) sulphide.) They also have distinctive colours (Table 108.4). We can make use of both features in qualitative analysis. If hydrogen sulphide, or a solution of the gas in water, is added to a solution containing the ions, the sulphides will precipitate under different conditions.

Both zinc sulphide and mercury(II) sulphide can exist in two crystal structures. For ZnS the structures are

Table 108.4. The sulphides of zinc, cadmium and mercury

Formula	*Colour*	*Solubility product* /$mol^2\ dm^{-6}$
ZnS	Cream	1.6×10^{-24}
CdS	Yellow	8.0×10^{-27}
HgS	Black	1.6×10^{-52}

called by the names of the minerals in which the sulphide is found: zinc blende and wurtzite. We discussed the structures in Unit 32.

Mercury(II) sulphide has red and black forms. Although the black variety is precipitated in solution, the red type (cinnabar) is the more energetically stable form. If you find a bottle of HgS in your laboratory, the contents will be red in colour.

The sulphides are somewhat unusual in that they can be made by directly combining the metal and sulphur. The reaction between zinc and sulphur can be violent, while that between mercury and sulphur is mild. As we noted earlier, this reaction is useful for clearing mercury spillages.

108.14 Use Table 108.4 to answer these questions:

(i) Which sulphide is the most insoluble?

(ii) ZnS or CdS can be precipitated from a solution containing a mixture of Zn^{2+} and Cd^{2+} by controlling the pH of the solution. Explain what you would do to separate the zinc from the cadmium. (Hint: look back at Unit 64.)

108.15 $E^\ominus_{Hg^{2+}/Hg_2^{2+}}=0.91$ V, $E^\ominus_{Hg_2^{2+}/Hg}=0.79$ V and $E^\ominus_{Sn^{4+}/Sn^{2+}}=0.15$ V. What, if anything, would you expect to happen if a solution containing (i) Hg^{2+} ions, (ii) Hg_2^{2+} ions were individually mixed with a solution of tin(II) chloride?

Answers

108.1 In the transition metals the colours are caused by electrons moving between d orbitals. For the IIB metals their d orbitals are full, so the transitions cannot take place.

108.2 Their boiling points.

108.3 (i) $\Delta G^\ominus$(reaction)

$=2\Delta G^\ominus_f(ZnO)+2\Delta G^\ominus_f(SO_2)-2\Delta G^\ominus_f(ZnS)$

$=-826.4\ kJ\ mol^{-1}$

(ii) $\Delta G^\ominus$ (reaction) $=\Delta G^\ominus_f(CO)-\Delta G^\ominus_f(ZnO)$

$=+180.9\ kJ\ mol^{-1}$

The first reaction is spontaneous even at 25°C, but the second is not. The second reaction only becomes spontaneous at high temperatures (above 1000°C). However, the reaction also takes place by carbon monoxide reducing the oxide.

108.4 Owing to their negative $E^\ominus$ values, zinc and cadmium will give hydrogen, but mercury will not. However, with oxidising acids other reactions can take place.

108.5 Tetrahedral. Use is made of the outer s and p orbitals.

108.6 You are expected to predict that cadmium behaves like zinc; which it does. With both sodium hydroxide and ammonia solution, a precipitate is produced first, which then dissolves.

108.7 Pass dry hydrogen chloride over hot zinc. See Figure 40.1 for a suitable apparatus.

108.8 Its high lattice energy.

108.9 A complex ion is produced. Its formula is HgI_4^{2-}. Notice that this is a mercury(II) complex. Dimercury(I) complexes do not occur. If a complex can be made in a reaction, it is common for dimercury(I) to change its oxidation state, giving the mercury(II) complex. In fact, disproportionation reactions occur; e.g.

$$Hg_2^{2+}(aq)+4I^-(aq)\rightarrow HgI_4^{2-}(aq)+Hg(l)$$

108.10 Aluminium.

108.11 Because HgO is easily decomposed by heat, the product of the reaction is liquid mercury rather than the oxide.

108.12 They are decomposed by heat or acid, giving off carbon dioxide.

108.13 We said that solutions containing Zn^{2+} ions are slightly acidic. Hence with the hydrogencarbonate, carbon dioxide is given off.

108.14 (i) Mercury(II) sulphide. (It has the smallest solubility product.)

(ii) The solubility product of ZnS is larger than that of CdS. If the acid is present, the concentration of free sulphide ions is reduced (see section 64.5), and $[S^{2-}(aq)]$ becomes too low for ZnS to be precipitated. However, CdS will be precipitated. Thus, add a little acid to the solution before adding the sulphide solution. Filter off the precipitate of CdS. Then add a little alkali to the filtrate to neutralise the acid. Now ZnS will precipitate.

108.15 The $E^\ominus$ values for the mercury ions are more positive than $E^\ominus_{Sn^{4+}/Sn^{2+}}$, so both Hg^{2+} and Hg_2^{2+} are able to oxidise Sn^{2+} to Sn^{4+}. Alternatively we can say that $E^\ominus_{Sn^{4+}/Sn^{2+}}$ is more negative than the other $E^\ominus$ values, so the Sn^{2+} ions can reduce the mercury ions. Notice that Hg^{2+} can be reduced to Hg_2^{2+}; also Hg_2^{2+} can be reduced to Hg. So mercury is the final product in both reactions. The reactions are

$$Hg_2^{2+}(aq)+Sn^{2+}(aq)\rightarrow 2Hg(l)+Sn^{4+}(aq)$$
$$Hg^{2+}(aq)+Sn^{2+}(aq)\rightarrow Hg(l)+Sn^{4+}(aq)$$

UNIT 108 SUMMARY

- The B metals:
  - (i) Have a complete set of ten d electrons as well as a pair of outer s electrons.
  - (ii) Tend not to use their outer pair of s electrons in bonding, hence the name 'inert pair'.
  - (iii) Can form complex ions.
  - (iv) Have much lower melting and boiling points than transition metals.
  - (v) Mercury shows two oxidation states, mercury(I) and mercury(II).
- Extraction:
  All are extracted from their sulphides; first by roasting in air to give the oxide, then by reduction with carbon to the metal. Mercury(II) oxide decomposes directly to mercury and oxygen.

Compounds

- Oxides:
  Zinc oxide is amphoteric;

$$ZnO(s) + 2H^+(aq) \rightarrow Zn^{2+}(aq) + H_2O(l)$$
$$ZnO(s) + 2OH^-(aq) + H_2O(l) \rightarrow Zn(OH)_4{}^{2-}(aq)$$

  Cadmium and mercury oxides are basic.
- Halides:
  Dimercury(I) chloride, Hg_2Cl_2, is used in calomel cells.
- Sulphates:
  All are soluble in water and make hydrated crystals, e.g. $ZnSO_4 \cdot 7H_2O$.
- Nitrates:
  All give off NO_2 and O_2. Zinc and cadmium leave their oxides, mercury(II) nitrate leaves liquid mercury.
- Sulphides:
  All are insoluble, and allow identification of the metal ions: ZnS cream, CdS yellow, HgS black.
- Zinc ions:
  Zn^{2+} ions give a white gelatinous precipitate (of $Zn(OH)_2$) with hydroxide ions. The precipitate is soluble in both excess alkali and aqueous ammonia. $Al(OH)_3$ is similar in appearance to $Zn(OH)_2$, but is not soluble in aqueous ammonia.

Part D

ORGANIC CHEMISTRY

109

Organic chemistry

109.1 What is organic chemistry?

The common feature of organic chemicals is that they all contain the element carbon. We do not usually count small molecules like carbon dioxide or carbon monoxide as organic chemicals, but this is just a matter of convenience, not a strict rule. Living things are largely made of organic chemicals, as are a vast number of other substances that we use or see around us everyday. The range of properties and appearance of organic chemicals is bewilderingly large. Table 109.1 lists just a few examples. You can see that they contain carbon combined with one or more other elements, especially hydrogen, oxygen and nitrogen. Notice also that in many of the molecules the carbon atoms are joined together. The ability of atoms to join together is called *catenation*. Other elements can catenate, e.g. sulphur, silicon, boron and some metals; but no other element is able to make as wide a variety of chains as carbon.

109.1 One of the early ideas about chemicals was that they split into two types. *Organic* chemicals were thought to be found only in living things. *Inorganic* chemicals were those that were found with non-living things. For a long time it was widely believed that organic chemicals were different to inorganic chemicals because they had a special 'life force' within them.

As with many forces, the life force was invisible, and hard to detect. How would you show that the life force is not the reason why organic chemicals are different to inorganic chemicals?

109.2 What are organic chemicals like?

The overwhelming majority of them are covalent. This has several consequences. In the first place many have fairly low melting and boiling points. Examples are gases like methane and propane, or liquids like ethanol and octane. However, some are solids at room temperature, and have high melting points. This can happen for a number of reasons. In plastics it is because the molecules are extremely long, heavy polymers. In other cases it is a result of some ionic bonding being present, e.g. amino acids such as glycine.

The second effect of covalency is that organic reactions tend to be slow. In a typical inorganic reaction, ions are present. Reactions between ions are extremely fast, taking a fraction of a second to complete. Where there are no ions, covalent bonds have to be broken. This takes a fair amount of energy, and quite a lot of time. For example, the preparation of an organic chemical may take several hours of continuous heating. It is very common for a number of different reactions to take place at the same time. For this reason an important part of an organic reaction is the separation of the main product from the less important, unwanted, products.

109.3 The main types of organic chemical

We can think of a typical organic molecule as having carbon atoms joined together in a chain. Most of the carbon atoms will also have hydrogen atoms attached. The chain of carbon atoms makes up the *backbone* of the molecule. The *hydrocarbons* have a carbon backbone with only hydrogen atoms joined to it, but in other types of molecule somewhere along the chain there will be an atom, or group of atoms, that gives rise to the major properties of the molecule. For example, in the alcohols there is a backbone with an OH group attached (Figure 109.1). Among other things the presence of this group is responsible for many alcohols being completely miscible with water, so allowing people to become intoxicated (to a greater or lesser extent) by drinking ethanol in beer, wine, whisky, etc. A group like OH is called the *functional group* of the molecule.

Molecules with the same functional group can be classified together into a *homologous series* (Table 109.2). Owing to them having the same functional group, the

Table 109.1. Examples of organic chemicals

Substance	*Diagram*	*Use*
Ethanoic acid		Vinegar
Ethanol		Alcoholic drinks
Glucose		A sugar
Glycine		An amino acid, found in proteins
Nylon-6,6		Clothing, ropes
Octane		Petrol
Poly(ethene)		Polythene packaging
Progesterone		Sex hormone, building block of DNA

```
    H              H   H
    |              |   |
H—C—OH         H—C—C—OH
    |              |   |
    H              H   H

    H   H   H          H   H   H   H
    |   |   |          |   |   |   |
H—C—C—C—OH        H—C—C—C—C—OH
    |   |   |          |   |   |   |
    H   H   H          H   H   H   H
```

Figure 109.1 *All organic compounds have a 'carbon backbone', i.e. a series of carbon atoms joined together. Here there are four alcohols with, respectively, carbon backbones of one, two, three and four atoms. The OH in each molecule is the functional group of alcohols*

Table 109.2. Homologous series

The members of a homologous series have the same functional group, similar chemical properties, the same general formula, gradually changing physical properties

chemical properties of the various members of a homologous series are very similar. They also have the same general formula. For example, the alkanes, methane, CH_4, ethane, C_2H_6, and propane, C_3H_8, all fit the general formula C_nH_{2n+2} with $n=1$, 2 and 3. The members of a homologous series do differ in their physical properties such as melting and boiling points.

There are millions of different organic chemicals. If we had to study each of them as a completely separate type of substance, life for an organic chemist would be almost intolerable. Fortunately the presence of functional groups allows us to classify the millions of individual molecules into a smaller number of homologous series. You will be pleased to discover that you are expected to know something of only a small fraction of the total. Even so, you will be able to predict the properties of many thousands of compounds by studying just one or two in each series.

109.4 The tetrahedral arrangement around carbon atoms

If you look carefully at the diagrams in Table 109.1 you will find that the carbon atoms always have four bonds. This fact, together with our knowledge of the bonding habits of other atoms, can help us to establish the arrangement of the atoms in a molecule. For example, suppose we find that a compound has the formula CH_4O. At first sight it appears impossible to say how the atoms might be arranged. However, we can start by writing down the carbon atom and putting four bonds around it. Oxygen always makes two bonds, so we could try joining the oxygen directly to the carbon atom by a double bond. (This is shown in Figure 109.2.) If we do this, there are only two bonds left but four hydrogen atoms to fit. This arrangement will not work. Instead, we can try putting a single bond between the carbon and oxygen atoms. If we do this there is one bond left on the oxygen and three around the carbon. Therefore we have room to fit the four hydrogen atoms. The resulting molecule is the alcohol, methanol, CH_3OH.

In this example, and in most other areas of organic chemistry, you will find it a great help to make models of the molecules that you see in only two dimensions on paper. Do make models whenever possible. You will find it helps you to visualise the shapes much more easily, and to appreciate how the shape of a molecule can influence the way it reacts.

The feature that dominates the shapes of organic molecules is the tetrahedral arrangement around a carbon atom, which has four single bonds. (You will find an explanation of why carbon adopts this geometry in Unit 17.) We often draw the carbon backbone in a

```
                          |
                        —C—
                          |
   Two bonds to oxygen          One bond to oxygen

        \                            |
         C=O                       —C—O—
        /                            |
   Two bonds
   left over
        | 4H                         | 4H
        v                            v
     H                               H
      \                              |
       C=O + 2H left over         H—C—O—H   i.e. CH3OH, methanol
      /                              |
     H                               H
```

Figure 109.2 *Two ways of trying to fit one oxygen and four hydrogen atoms around a single carbon atom. Always, there must be four bonds to a carbon atom*

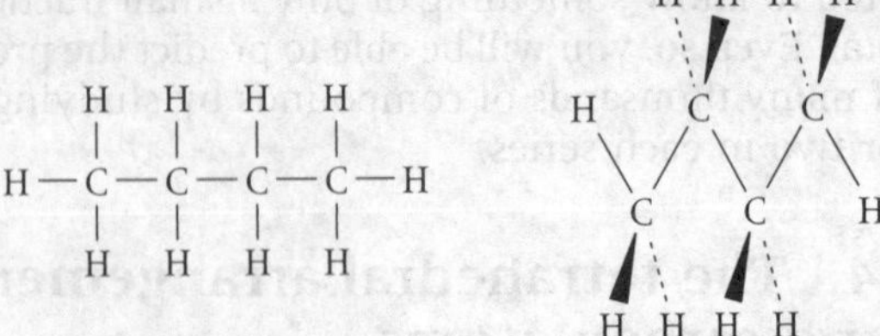

Figure 109.3 Both diagrams represent the molecule butane, C_4H_{10}. The one on the left shows only which atoms are bonded together. It gives the impression that the carbon backbone makes a straight line. Actually, the chain adopts a zig-zag pattern as in the second diagram

This model of methane shows clearly the tetrahedral arrangement of bonds around the carbon atom.

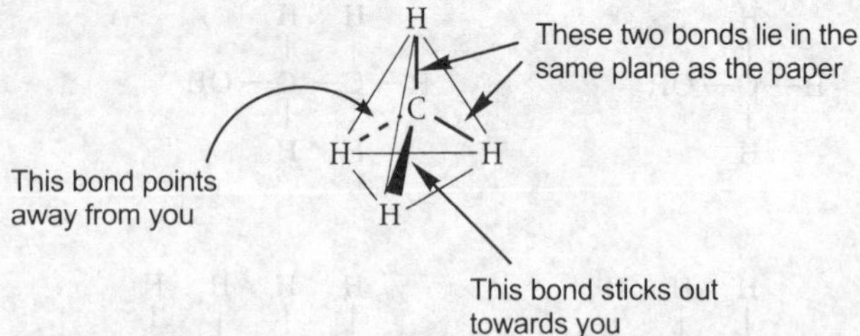

***Figure 109.4** The convention for showing the shape of an organic molecule*

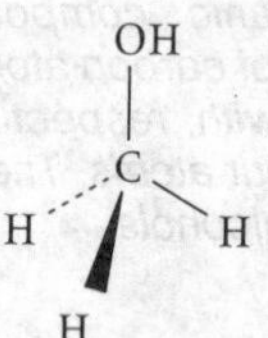

***Figure 109.5** The shape of a methanol molecule, CH_3OH*

molecule as a straight line, but really it is a zig-zag shape. The two ways of drawing the molecules are shown in Figure 109.3.

You may well imagine that it can be quite tricky to show the shapes of molecules on paper. There is a convention for drawing them. Let us take methane, CH_4, as an example. With the help of a model you will see that two of the hydrogen atoms and the carbon atom all lie in the same plane. We draw them as shown in Figure 109.4. These atoms are imagined to lie in the same plane as the paper at which you are looking. Arranged in this way, one of the remaining hydrogen atoms points outwards, towards your eye; the other points backwards, behind the plane of the paper. The one that points towards you is shown by a black wedge in the figure. (It is supposed to represent the perspective of a bond, which would appear thicker at the end nearer to you, and narrowing down to a point as it gets further away.) The second bond is shown by a broken line.

If you have to draw a diagram for a molecule with a functional group, like the OH in methanol, CH_3OH, it makes sense to put the group on one of the bonds in the plane of the paper, like Figure 109.5.

109.2 Draw diagrams of the molecules CH_3Cl and CH_2ClBr using the convention for showing the bonds in Figure 109.5.

109.3 By obeying the rule that carbon atoms always have four bonds, see if you can discover a molecule that has the same formula as benzene, C_6H_6, but does not have a ring of carbon atoms.

109.4 Look at the diagram of progesterone in Table 109.1. Does the diagram give you a realistic impression of the structure of the molecule?

109.5 When is the arrangement of atoms around carbon not tetrahedral?

One answer is: when a carbon atom forms double or triple bonds to another atom. The most familiar examples are the hydrocarbons, ethene, C_2H_4, and ethyne, C_2H_2. We discussed the bonding in these two molecules in section 16.8, so look there if you have forgotten the explanation of why they are flat or *planar*.

Another planar molecule is benzene, C_6H_6 (Figure 109.6). The history of this molecule is interesting because its structure was a puzzle to chemists for many years. Essentially the puzzle was to explain how six carbon atoms and six hydrogen atoms could be fitted

Two models showing the shapes of ethane and ethene. Note that the double bond in ethene causes the molecule to be planar.

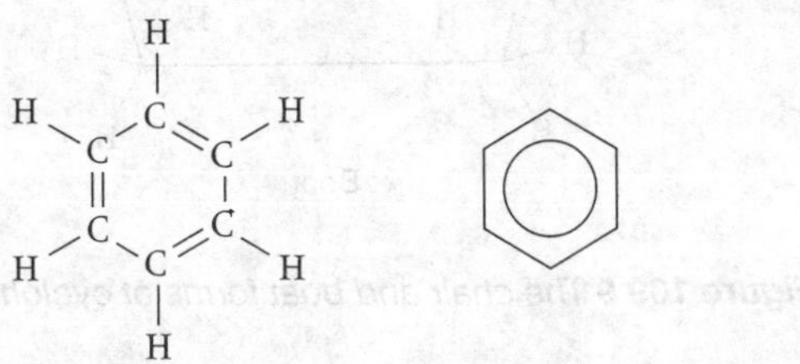

Figure 109.6 *Two ways of representing a benzene ring. The first shows all the atoms labelled, together with the correct number of single and double bonds. The second is a shorthand version. The hydrogen atoms are left out (we have to imagine they are present). A carbon atom is assumed to be at the corners of the hexagon, and the ring in the middle stands for the delocalised π electrons*

together and give a molecule that was not at all reactive. It is possible to fit the atoms together to give compounds containing double or triple bonds; but this would make benzene resemble an alkene (like ethene) or alkyne (like ethyne). Alkenes and alkynes are very reactive, but benzene is not. The solution to part of the puzzle was provided by Friedrich Kekulé in 1865. His notion was that benzene consisted of six carbon atoms in a hexagon, and joined by alternating single and double bonds. Again, you will find details of the modern theory of bonding in benzene in Unit 16. We now think it a mistake to identify individual single and double bonds. Rather, six of the electrons are *delocalised* around the ring in π bonds.

One of the most interesting carbon molecules made in recent years is given the name of 'buckminsterfullerene'. It has the formula C_{60}, and is made from interlocking hexagonal and pentagonal rings of carbon atoms (see Figure 109.7). It was first made in 1985 as a result of the action of a laser beam on a sample of graphite. Such molecules are now thought to exist even in chimney soot or candle smoke. (You may be able to

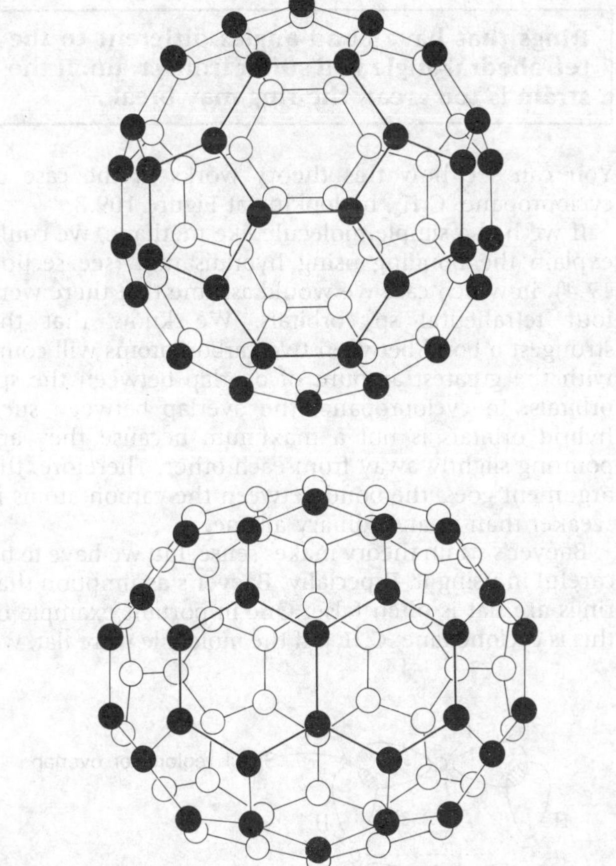

Figure 109.7 *Two bucky balls. On the top is* C_{60}*, with* C_{70} *below*

envisage the structure of C_{60} more easily by looking at a football, whose surface may well also be composed of a similar set of interlocking hexagons and pentagons.) Incidentally, the molecule is named after the American architect Buckminster Fuller, who had a tendency to design geometrical structures of great complexity. C_{60} has now been outclassed by the discovery of C_{70}. These, and similar, large carbon molecules, are sometimes referred to as 'bucky balls'.

109.6 Baeyer's strain theory

In the early days of organic chemistry it was known that carbon atoms could join to give fairly long chains, e.g. in the alkanes. However, apart from benzene, few compounds were known which had rings of carbon atoms. In 1885 A. Baeyer suggested a reason why this might be so. He believed that ring compounds would be flat and because of this the angles between the carbon atoms would be different to the normal tetrahedral bond angle (109°28′). The idea was that the greater the departure from the tetrahedral angle, the weaker the bonding would be, and the more strain there would be in the ring. Some rings would be so strained that they would not survive. The essence of his theory has survived, and it is called *Baeyer's strain theory*:

> **Rings that have bond angles different to the tetrahedral angle will suffer from strain; if the strain is too great, the ring may break.**

You can see how this theory works in the case of cyclopropane, C_3H_6, by looking at Figure 109.8.

If we had a simple molecule like methane, we could explain the bonding using hybridisation (see section 17.4), in which case we would assume that there were four tetrahedral sp^3 orbitals. We know that the strongest σ bond between two carbon atoms will come with the greatest amount of overlap between the sp^3 orbitals. In cyclopropane, the overlap between such hybrid orbitals is not a maximum because they are pointing slightly away from each other. Therefore, the argument goes, the bond between the carbon atoms is weaker than in an ordinary alkane.

Baeyer's strain theory makes sense, but we have to be careful in using it. Especially, Baeyer's assumption that rings are flat is often false. One important example of this is cyclohexane, C_6H_{12}. If the molecule were flat, we would expect it to have the same hexagonal shape as benzene. However, cyclohexane does not have the incentive of delocalised bonding to make it adopt this planar structure. Instead, the ring puckers. The molecule can bend in two ways, which allow the bond angles to reach the tetrahedral angle (Figure 109.9). The two shapes are called the *boat* and *chair conformations* of cyclohexane. At room temperature a bottle of cyclohexane contains an equilibrium mixture of both conformations, but the chair is energetically more stable and makes up over 99.9% of the liquid. Conformations are varieties of the same molecule that can be changed into one another by rotating parts of the molecule around the carbon–carbon bonds.

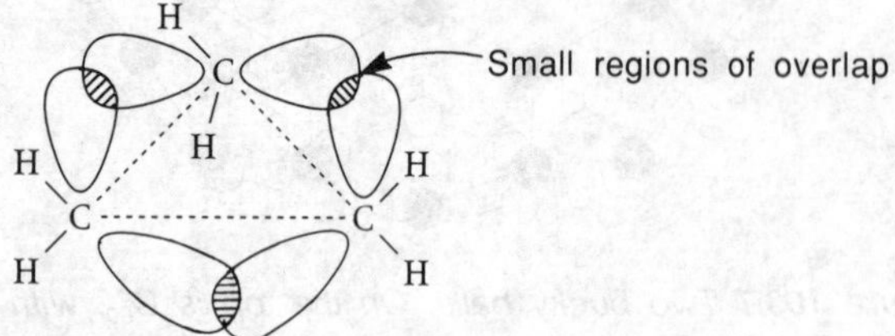

Figure 109.8 The carbon atoms are at 120° to each other in cyclopropane. We can imagine the bonds to be made by overlapping sp^3 orbitals. However, because of the angle the orbitals make with one another, the overlap is slight. This makes for weak bonds

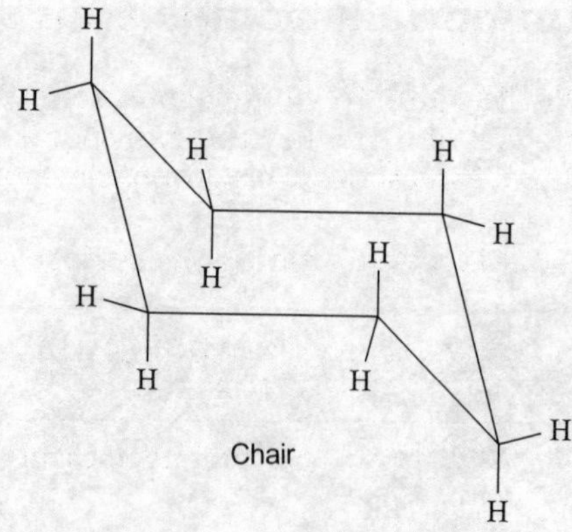

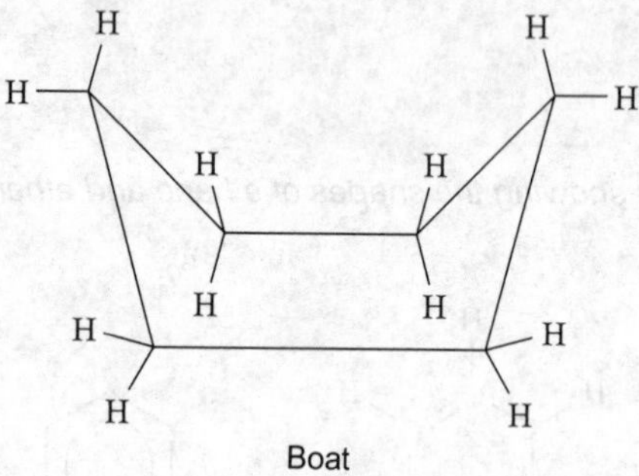

Figure 109.9 The chair and boat forms of cyclohexane, C_6H_{12}

If you build a model of cyclohexane you should discover that a suitable combination of rotations (or twists) will convert the chair into the boat, and vice versa.

> **109.5** If you were a chemist who put your trust in electron repulsion theory to explain molecular shapes, how would you account for the strain in cyclopropane?
>
> **109.6** This is a list of heats of formation (all in kJ mol^{-1}) of propane, cyclopropane and hexane: −199, −104, +55. However, the values have been mixed up. Your task is to put them in the right order.

109.7 Important homologous series

Table 109.3 lists the 16 homologous series that you need to know about. The key thing to spot is the functional group of each series. This group is responsible for giving the molecules in the series their particular properties. For example, alkenes will react with bromine whereas alkanes will not. This is due to the presence of a double bond in alkenes. Similarly, alcohols will react with sodium, but alkenes and alkanes

Table 109.3. Sixteen homologous series

<table>
<tr><th>Series</th><th>Functional group</th><th>General formula</th><th>Typical member</th></tr>
<tr><td>Alkane</td><td>Hydrocarbon chain</td><td>C_nH_{2n+2}</td><td>Ethane
H H
| |
H—C—C—H
| |
H H</td></tr>
<tr><td>Alkene</td><td>Double bond
>C=C<</td><td>C_nH_{2n}</td><td>Ethene
H   H
 >C=C<
H   H</td></tr>
<tr><td>Alkyne</td><td>Triple bond
—C≡C—</td><td>C_nH_n</td><td>Ethyne
H—C≡C—H</td></tr>
<tr><td>Halogenoalkane</td><td>Halogen atom</td><td>RX (X=Cl,Br,I)</td><td>Chloroethane
H H
| |
H—C—C—Cl
| |
H H</td></tr>
<tr><td>Nitrile</td><td>Cyanide group
—C≡N</td><td>RCN</td><td>Ethanenitrile
H
|
H—C—CN
|
H</td></tr>
<tr><td>Alcohol</td><td>OH group</td><td>ROH</td><td>Ethanol
H H
| |
H—C—C—OH
| |
H H</td></tr>
<tr><td>Aldehyde</td><td>CHO group
     O
—C<
     H</td><td>RCHO</td><td>Ethanal
H
| O
H—C—C<
| H
H</td></tr>
<tr><td>Ketone</td><td>CO group
>C=O</td><td>RR′CO</td><td>Propanone
H O H
| || |
H—C—C—C—H
| |
H   H</td></tr>
<tr><td>Acid</td><td>COOH group
     O
—C<
     OH</td><td>RCOOH</td><td>Ethanoic acid
H
| O
H—C—C<
| OH
H</td></tr>
</table>

Table 109.3– cont.

Series	*Functional group*	*General formula*	*Typical member*
Ester	COOC group	RCOOR′	Ethyl ethanoate
Ether	COC group	ROR′	Ethoxyethane
Amine	NH_2 group	RNH_2	Ethylamine
Amide	$CONH_2$ group	$RCONH_2$	Ethanamide
Acid chloride	COCl group	RCOCl	Ethanoyl chloride
Arene	Benzene ring	C_6H_6	Benzene
Substituted arene	Benzene ring plus another functional group (FG)	Many examples	Phenol (OH); Chlorobenzene (Cl); Phenylamine (NH_2)

Table 109.4. Four organic radicals

Alcohol	*Formula*	ROH *with* R *as*	*Name of* R
Methanol	CH_3OH	CH_3	Methyl
Ethanol	CH_3CH_2OH	CH_3CH_2	Ethyl
Propan-1-ol	$CH_3CH_2CH_2OH$	$CH_3CH_2CH_2$	Propyl
Butan-1-ol	$CH_3CH_2CH_2CH_2OH$	$CH_3CH_2CH_2CH_2$	Butyl

will not. It is the OH group in alcohols that is responsible for the reaction.

It can be tedious to write out the entire formula of an organic molecule, so we use a shorthand. We show the carbon atoms and their accompanying hydrogen atoms by the letter R. For example, each member of the homologous series of alcohols can be represented by ROH. Table 109.4 shows you the scheme. There are four common hydrocarbon groups listed in the table, called methyl, ethyl, propyl and butyl. Each of these is an example of an organic radical (notice that we use the symbol R for the radicals). It can be that a more complicated molecule might have two or more different radicals. For example, the alcohol 3-methylhexan-3-ol has methyl, ethyl and propyl radicals in the molecule as well as an OH group. We could show the structure in three ways:

$$CH_3—CH_2—CH_2—\overset{OH}{\underset{CH_3}{C}}—CH_2—CH_3$$

$$\text{or}\quad R—\overset{OH}{\underset{R'}{C}}—R'' \quad \text{or even } RR'R''COH$$

R, R′ and R″ stand for the three radicals.

> **109.7** The first three members of the homologous series of chloroalkanes are chloromethane, CH_3Cl, chloroethane, C_2H_5Cl, and 1-chloropropane, C_3H_7Cl.
>
> (i) What is the general formula of the series?
>
> (ii) Chloromethane can be converted into methanol, CH_3OH, by boiling with an alkali. Write down the formulae of the alcohols that would be made from the other two molecules and predict their names.
>
> (iii) Make a model of 1-chloropropane. Now see if you can make another molecule with the same formula, but not identical to the first one. Draw out their structures on paper.

109.8 Naming organic compounds

The key to naming organic molecules is to spot the longest carbon chain, and the functional group or groups. The root name of the molecule depends on the carbon chain according to the system of Table 109.5.

For example, the molecule CH_3CH_2OH has the functional group OH on the end of a chain whose root is ethane (two carbon atoms in the chain). We name the molecule ethanol. When there are three carbon atoms in the chain, the OH group could be on one of the end carbon atoms or on the middle one. We use a numbering system to distinguish them:

$$\overset{3}{C}H_3—\overset{2}{C}H_2—\overset{1}{C}H_2—OH \qquad \overset{3}{C}H_3—\underset{OH}{\overset{2}{C}H}—\overset{1}{C}H_3$$

propan-1-ol   propan-2-ol

It does not matter if we write the structure of the first one like this

$$HO—\overset{1}{C}H_2—\overset{2}{C}H_2—\overset{3}{C}H_3$$

we still call it propan-1-ol rather than propan-3-ol. This is a general rule: we use the lowest numbers possible in assigning the name.

When there are two or more functional groups in the same molecule and there is a conflict about which suffix should come first, we put them in alphabetical order. For example, we name the molecule

$$H—\underset{H}{\overset{Cl}{\overset{2}{C}}}—\underset{H}{\overset{Br}{\overset{1}{C}}}—H$$

as 1-bromo-2-chloroethane rather than 1-chloro-2-bromoethane.

> **109.8** Draw the structures of: (i) butan-2-ol; (ii) 2-amino-1-chlorobutane; (iii) propanenitrile; (iv) 2-chloropropanoic acid; (v) 1,1,2-tribromoethane; (vi) ethane-1,2-diol; (vii) buta-1,2-diene; (viii) methoxyethane. Hint: consult Table 109.3.
>
> **109.9** Give the names of the following molecules: (i) $CH_3CHClCH_2OH$; (ii) $CH_3CHBrCH_2Cl$; (iii) $(CH_3)_2CHCH_3$; (iv) CH_3COCH_3; (v) HCOOH; (vi) CH_3CH_2COCl; (vii) $CH_3CH_2CH_2OH$; (viii) $CH_3CHNH_2CH_2OH$. Hint: consult Table 109.5.

109.9 Chain isomerism

There are several different varieties of isomerism in organic chemicals. Three of them are chain isomerism,

Table 109.5. Naming organic compounds

Longest carbon chain	*Root name*	*Side chain*
One carbon atom	Methane	Methyl
Two carbon atoms	Ethane	Ethyl
Three carbon atoms	Propane	Propyl
Four carbon atoms	Butane	Butyl
Five carbon atoms	Pentane	Pentyl
Six carbon atoms	Hexane	Hexyl

Functional group	*Naming system*		*Examples*
Alkene	suffix	-ene	Propene; But-1-ene
Alkyne	suffix	-yne	Propyne; But-2-yne
Halogenoalkane	prefix	chloro-	Chloroethane
		bromo-	1,2-Dibromopropane
		iodo-	2-Iodobutane
Nitrile	suffix	-nitrile	Ethanenitrile
Alcohol	suffix	-ol	Ethanol; Propan-2-ol

Table 109.5 – cont.

Functional group	*Naming system*		*Examples*
Aldehyde	suffix	-al	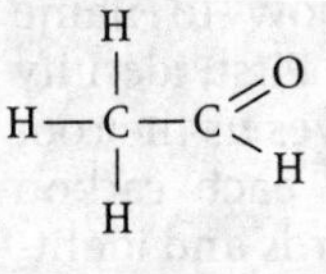 Ethanal; 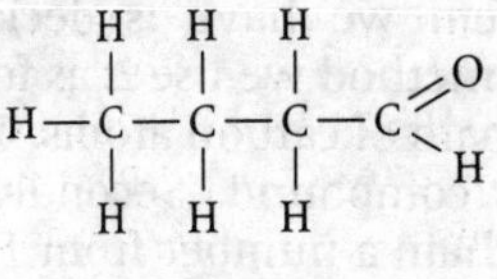 Butanal
Ketone	suffix	-one	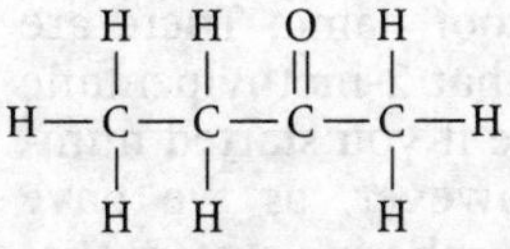 Butanone; 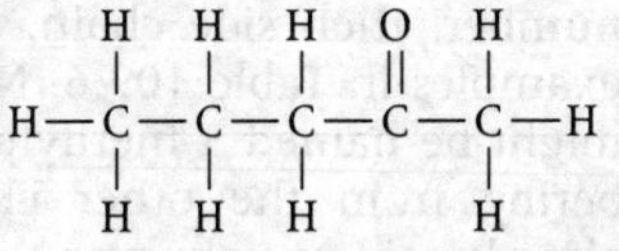 Pentan-2-one
Acid	suffix	-oic acid	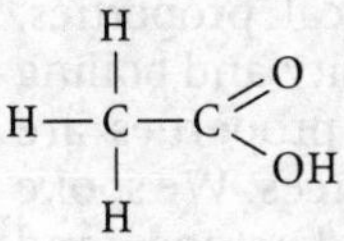 Ethanoic acid; 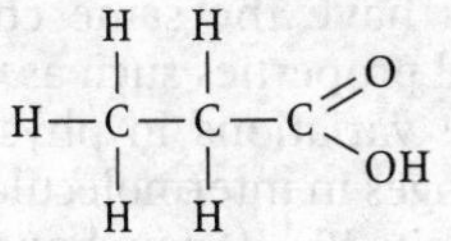 Propanoic acid
Ether	prefix	alkoxy-	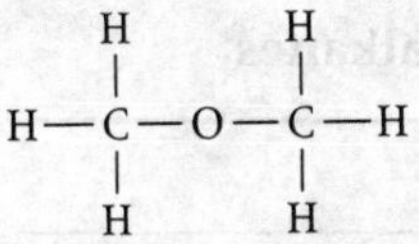 Methoxyethane
Amine	suffix	-amine	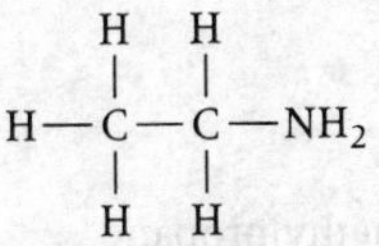 Ethylamine
Amide	suffix	-amide	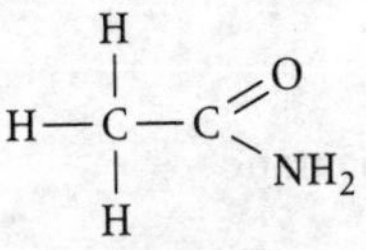 Ethanamide
Acid chloride	suffix	-oyl chloride	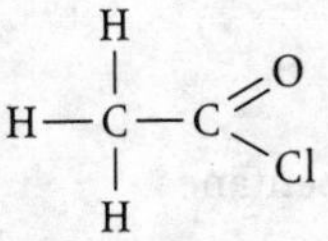 Ethanoyl chloride
Arene	varies with arene		

functional group isomerism and optical isomerism. You will find the last one explained in the following unit. We shall deal with the other two here and in the next section.

The formula of an organic chemical does not necessarily tell you the arrangement of the atoms. You can see this if you build models of an alkane with the formula C_4H_{10}. There are two possibilities, shown in Figure 109.10. The two molecules are chain isomers.

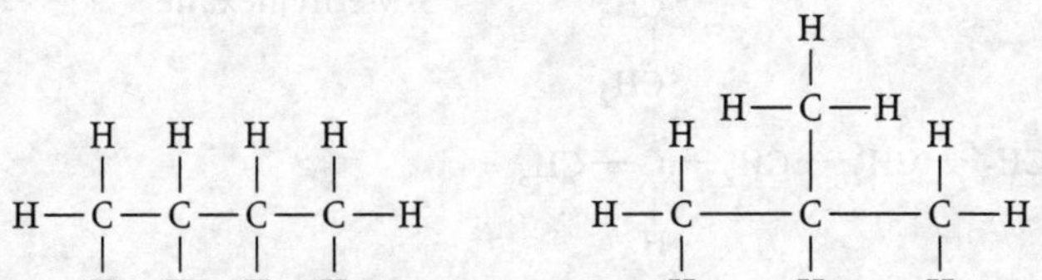

***Figure 109.10** Both molecules have the formula C_4H_{10}, but different structures. They are chain isomers*

Chain isomers have the same molecular formula and functional groups but a different arrangement of the atoms in space.

One problem we have is deciding how to name isomers. The method we use is as follows. First, identify the longest chain of carbon atoms. This gives us the root name of the compound. Secondly, give each carbon atom in the chain a number from 1 upwards and identify the *side chains* attached to the longest chain. Finally, write down the name of the compound in the order: number, then side chain, then root name. There are examples in Table 109.6. Notice that 2-methylpentane might be named 3-methylpentane if you started numbering from the other end. However, as we have already said, we always use the numbering system that gives the lowest number in the name.

Chain isomers have the same chemical properties, but their physical properties such as density and boiling point differ. The variations in physical properties are often due to changes in intermolecular forces. We spoke about this in Unit 20. If you have understood (and remembered) that work, you should be able to explain why, for example, the boiling point of pentane is about 26 °C higher than its isomer 2,2-dimethylpropane.

On a diagram there are several ways of showing the arrangements of the atoms in an organic molecule. For example, both of the diagrams in Figure 109.11 show the same molecule, 1-bromo-2-chloroethane. At first sight it may seem that the diagrams are of different molecules, but if you make a model of the molecule you will discover why this is not so. By rotating the end groups you should be able to reproduce the arrangements shown in the figure. There is an important point of chemistry here. We say that there is *free rotation* around carbon–carbon single bonds. There is experimental evidence to show that real molecules do rotate in this way.

However, there is *no* free rotation about carbon–carbon double bonds. The π bond in an alkene (or alkyne) prevents the rotation. Thus the two molecules in Figure 109.12 really are different. They are geometric isomers called *cis* and *trans* isomers; but more of this in Unit 112.

Table 109.6. Examples of naming alkanes

Diagram	*Name*
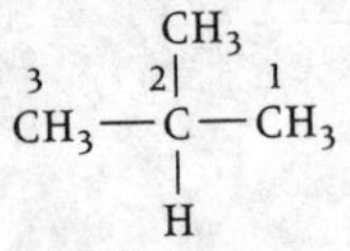 CH_3 (C2) 3 2 1 $CH_3—C—CH_3$ H (C2)	2-Methylpropane
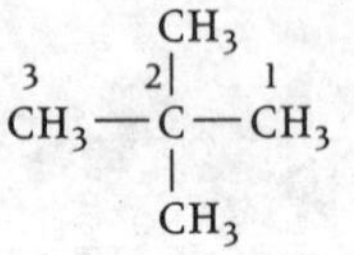 CH_3 (C2) 3 2 1 $CH_3—C—CH_3$ CH_3 (C2)	2,2-Dimethylpropane
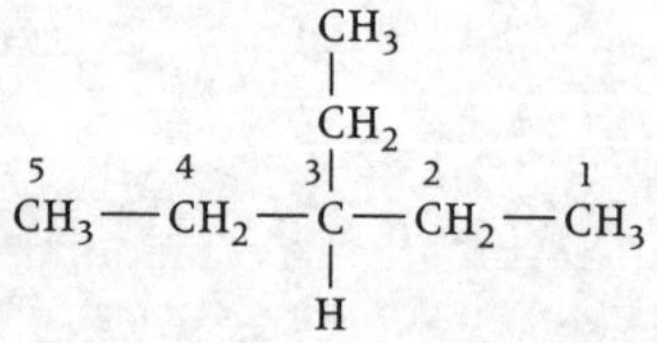 CH_3 CH_2 (C3) 5 4 3 2 1 $CH_3—CH_2—C—CH_2—CH_3$ H (C3)	3-Ethylpentane
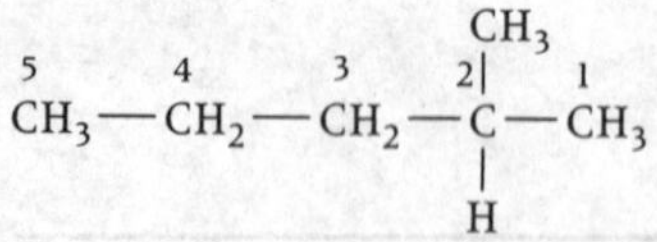 CH_3 (C2) 5 4 3 2 1 $CH_3—CH_2—CH_2—C—CH_3$ H (C2)	2-Methylpentane
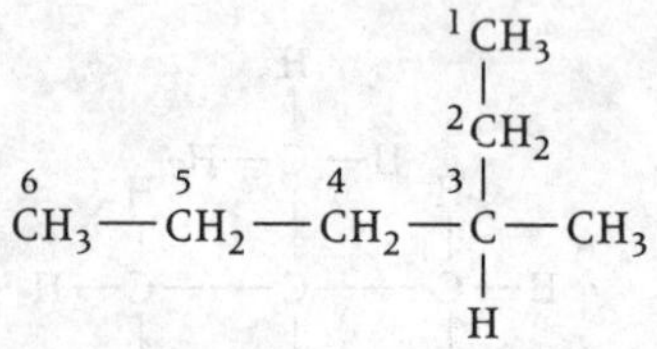 1 CH_3 2 CH_2 6 5 4 3 $CH_3—CH_2—CH_2—C—CH_3$ H (C3)	3-Methylhexane*

*Not 2-ethylpentane because the former uses the longest carbon chain

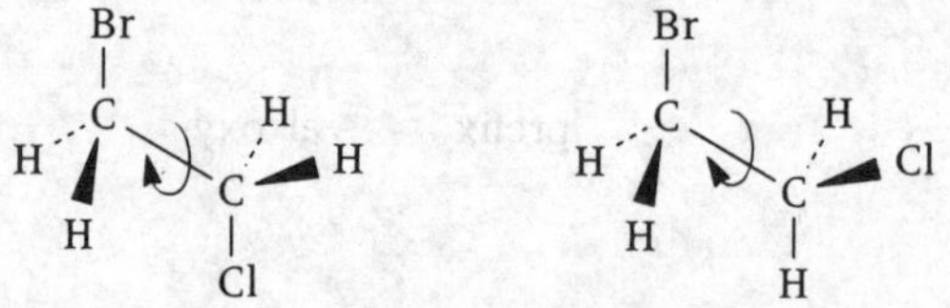

Figure 109.11 These diagrams may appear to show different molecules. However, they are the same: 1-bromo-2-chloroethane. Each can change into the other form because of free rotation around a carbon–carbon single bond (shown by the arrow)

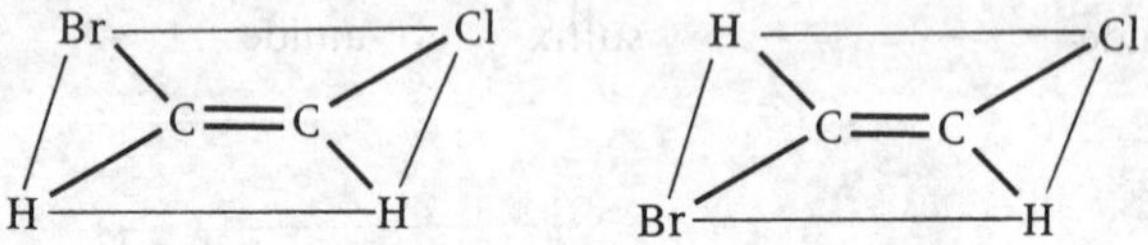

cis-1-Bromo-2-chloroethene | *trans*-1-Bromo-2-chloroethene

Figure 109.12 Two molecules that are different. Rotation about a carbon–carbon double bond cannot take place

109.10 How many alcohols can you find with the formula C_4H_9OH:

(i) if the four carbon atoms are joined in one long chain;

(ii) if the carbon atoms do not have to be in one chain?

109.11 Why is the boiling point of pentane about 26 °C higher than that of its isomer, 2,2-dimethylpropane?

109.10 Functional group isomerism

A definition of this variety of isomerism is:

Functional group isomers have the same molecular formula but different functional groups.

If we attempt to make models or draw structures of molecules with the formula C_2H_6O, we have two possibilities:

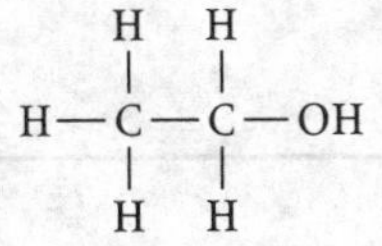

$$\mathrm{H{-}\overset{H}{\underset{H}{C}}{-}\overset{H}{\underset{H}{C}}{-}OH} \qquad \mathrm{H{-}\overset{H}{\underset{H}{C}}{-}O{-}\overset{H}{\underset{H}{C}}{-}H}$$

ethanol 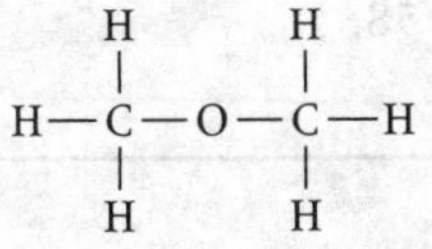 methoxymethane

The first is an alcohol, the second an ether.

109.12 Make a model of benzene, or draw a diagram of it on paper. Now replace one of the hydrogen atoms by a chlorine atom to give a molecule like that shown in Figure 109.13.

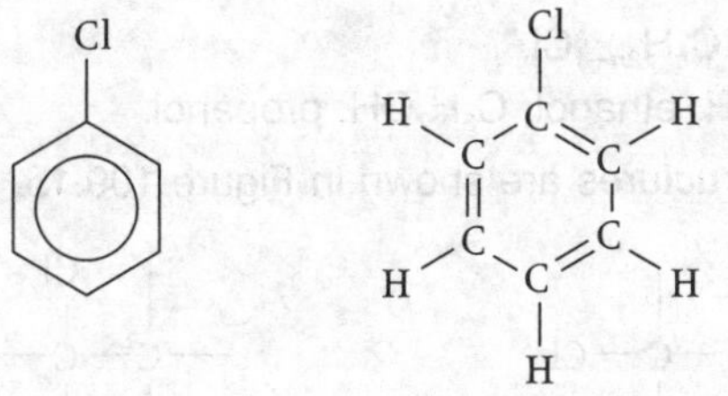

Figure 109.13 Two ways of representing chlorobenzene

(i) What is the formula of the molecule?

(ii) Briefly explain why there is only one variety of this molecule.

(iii) Now replace another hydrogen by a chlorine, giving four hydrogen and two chlorine atoms attached to the ring. You should be able to make three different molecules of this type. Draw diagrams of them.

(iv) How many different molecules can you make from a benzene ring with three hydrogen and three chlorine atoms?

109.13 Is it always true that molecules with the general formula C_nH_{2n} are alkenes?

109.14 Draw structures of isomers with formula $C_3H_6O_2$. You will find that it is possible to have more than one functional group in each molecule. Do not include isomers with double bonds between carbon atoms.

109.11 What happens in organic reactions?

This section gives you a brief summary of key ideas that you will find mentioned in later units. You must look at them for details of particular reactions.

In section 109.1 we said that most organic chemicals are covalent and that their reactions are correspondingly slow. When bonds break, they can do so in two ways. If one of the atoms takes both electrons in the bond, the change is called *heterolysis*. If both atoms take one electron each, the change is an example of *homolysis*:

$$\mathrm{A{\overset{\times}{\cdot}}B} \longrightarrow \mathrm{A^+} + \mathrm{B{\overset{\times}{\cdot}}^-} \qquad \text{Heterolysis}$$

$$\mathrm{A{\overset{\times}{\cdot}}B} \longrightarrow \mathrm{A\cdot} + \mathrm{B\times} \qquad \text{Homolysis}$$

You will meet examples of both in later units.

Often the reagents that we use in organic reactions are of two types. They seek out centres of either positive charge or negative charge:

Ions or molecules that are attracted to positive charges are called *nucleophiles*.

Those that are attracted to negative charges are *electrophiles*.

Nucleophiles generally have one or more lone pairs and/or a negative charge. Electrophiles normally have a positive charge or a partial positive charge. To be precise, nucleophiles and electrophiles should be capable of forming a covalent bond when they react. For this reason, we discount species such as sodium ions, Na^+, as electrophiles. Examples are shown in Table 109.7.

From time to time you will find that we attempt to explain how organic reactions take place by referring to the roles played by electrophiles and nucleophiles.

109.12 Organic analysis

In order to identify the nature of an organic compound, we need to know which elements it contains, their pro-

Table 109.7. Electrophiles and nucleophiles

Electrophiles	*Nucleophiles*
Nitryl cation, NO_2^+	Hydroxide ions, OH^-
Benzenediazonium ions, $C_6H_5{-}N_2^+$	Water molecules, H_2O
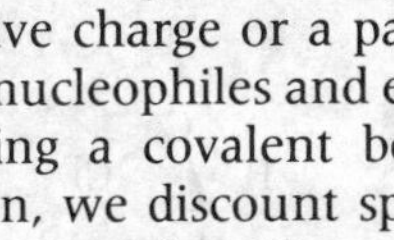	Cyanide ions, CN^-
Bromine cation, Br^+	
Acyl cation, CH_3CO^+	

portions and how they are arranged into the various functional groups. The problem of finding which elements are present is the task of *qualitative analysis*. Some methods of qualitative analysis are relatively simple. You will find them described in Appendix E. More complicated methods involve spectrometry, e.g. mass spectrometry. The task of finding out the nature of the functional groups can also be done chemically or by spectrometry. Examples of tests that indicate the presence of specific functional groups are described in the units that follow. If you have read the units on spectrometry, you will also be aware of how infrared spectrometry can achieve similar results.

Quantitative analysis is used to determine the percentage composition of a compound. Mass spectroscopy is one method by which the molar mass can be found. There are standard methods of analysing compounds to find out the percentages of the elements present. These methods are often performed automatically by companies that specialise in such work. We shall ignore methods of quantitative analysis, but you will find that we sometimes make use of the information that they provide.

Lastly, if you have a sample of a compound whose identity you think you know, a simple way of confirming its identity is to do a melting point test. Methods of performing a melting point determination are described in Unit 58.

Answers

109.1 The German chemist Wohler found one way. In 1828 he took ammonium cyanate, NH_4CNO, which everybody agreed was an inorganic chemical, and heated it. The product was urea, $CO(NH_2)_2$, a substance known to occur in living things, and therefore an organic chemical. It is extremely hard to explain how a life force can enter into a compound simply by heating it. Eventually chemists gave up the life force theory.

You might notice that Wohler's experiment did not *prove* that the life force was absent; only that the theory was not capable of explaining the result of his experiments.

109.2 Figure 109.14 shows the diagrams.

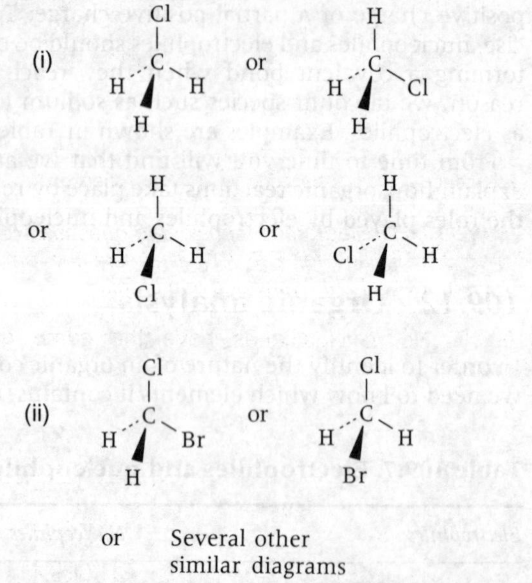

(i) C with Cl, H, H, H — or — C with H, H, Cl, H — or — C with H, H, H, Cl — or — C with H, Cl, H, H

(ii) C with Cl, H, Br, H — or — C with Cl, H, H, Br

or Several other similar diagrams

***Figure 109.14** Diagrams for answer to question 109.2*

109.3 One possibility is $CH_2{=}CH{-}C{\equiv}C{-}CH{=}CH_2$.

109.4 The diagram gives the impression that the molecule is flat; it is not. The rings are puckered.

109.5 You would explain that with a bond angle of 60° in cyclopropane the bonding pairs of electrons are brought closer together than they would be if the bond angle were 109°. This will increase electron repulsion, so there will be greater strain.

109.6 We know that cyclopropane will be the least energetically favoured molecule, so this will have the endothermic heat of formation (+55 kJ mol^{-1}). The heats of formation of molecules with six carbons in them will usually be greater than those with three carbon atoms. (There are more bonds to be made, so more energy to be released.) This tells us that the value of −104 kJ mol^{-1} belongs to propane and −165 kJ mol^{-1} to hexane.

109.7 (i) $C_nH_{2n+1}Cl$.

(ii) C_2H_5OH, ethanol; C_3H_7OH, propanol.

(iii) The structures are shown in Figure 109.15.

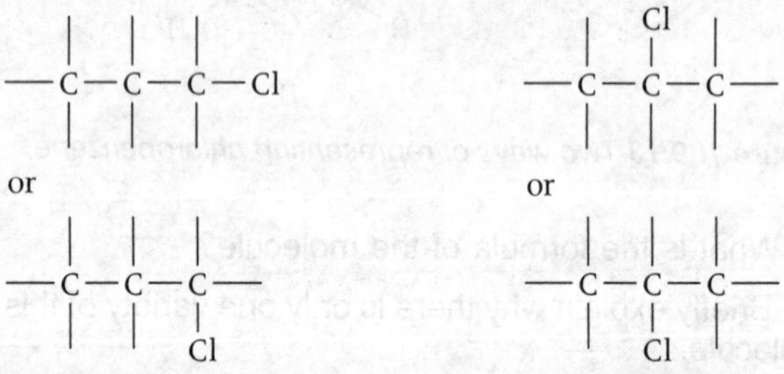

—C—C—C—Cl or —C—C—C— (Cl on end carbon)

1-Chloropropane

—C—C—C— (Cl on middle carbon) or —C—C—C— (Cl on middle carbon)

2-Chloropropane

***Figure 109.15** Diagrams for answer to question 109.7. The two different arrangements for C_3H_7Cl. Note that there are several ways of drawing each structure, but these are not different molecules*

109.8

(i) H—C(H)(H)—C(H)(H)—C(OH)(H)—C(H)(H)—H

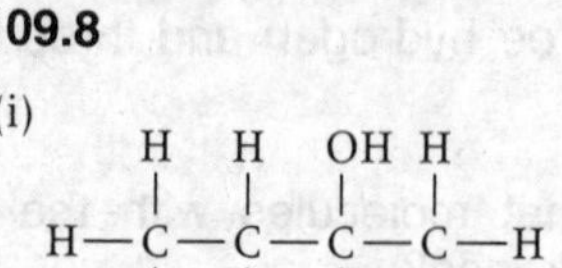

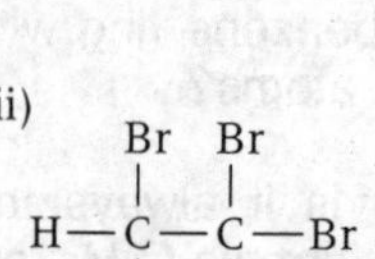

(ii) H—C(H)(H)—C(H)(H)—CN

(iii) H—C(Br)(H)—C(Br)(H)—Br

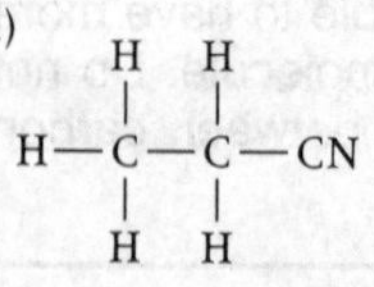

(iv) H—C(H)(H)—C(H)=C=C(H)H

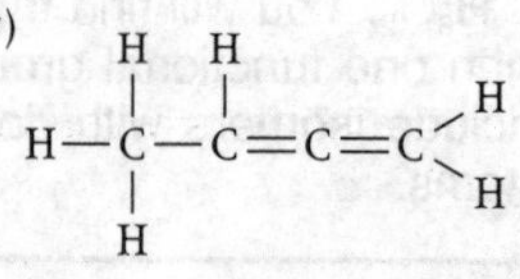

Answers – cont.

(v)

```
   H  H  NH2 H
   |  |   |  |
H—C—C—C—C—Cl
   |  |   |  |
   H  H   H  H
```

(vii)

```
     OH OH
     |  |
  H—C—C—H
     |  |
     H  H
```

(vi)

```
     H  Cl
     |  |      O
  H—C—C—C
     |  |     OH
     H  H
```

(viii)

```
     H        H   H
     |        |   |
  H—C—O—C—C—H
     |        |   |
     H        H   H
```

109.9 (i) 2-chloropropan-1-ol; (ii) 2-bromo-1-chloropropane; (iii) 2-methylpropane; (iv) propanone; (v) methanoic acid; (vi) propanoyl chloride; (vii) propan-1-ol; (viii) 2-aminopropan-1-ol.

109.10 (i) There are two of them. If you have found more, you have made the mistake of thinking that, say, butan-2-ol and 'butan-3-ol' are different. They are not, and we choose the lowest number for the name:

```
   H  H  H  H                 H  H  OH H
   |  |  |  |                 |  |  |  |
H—C—C—C—C—OH             H—C—C—C—C—H
   |  |  |  |                 |  |  |  |
   H  H  H  H                 H  H  H  H
```

butan-1-ol butan-2-ol

(ii) Now there are four isomers: butan-1-ol and butan-2-ol as before, plus

```
        H                          H
        |                          |
     H—C—H                      H—C—H
 H      |      H            H      |      H
 |      |      |            |      |      |
H—C————C————C—OH          H—C————C————C—H
 |      |      |            |      |      |
 H      H      H            H      OH     H
```

2-methylpropan-1-ol 2-methylpropan-2-ol

109.11 The van der Waals forces between two molecules of pentane are stronger than between two molecules of 2,2-dimethylpropane. This is because propane molecules can come into closer contact than the others. 2,2-Dimethylpropane molecules are (roughly) spherical, and only have small area of contact with one another.

109.12 (i) C_6H_5Cl.

(ii) Owing to the symmetrical nature of benzene, it does not matter where you put the chlorine, the molecule is always the same shape.

(iii) Figure 109.16 shows the three different molecules.

Cl, Cl (ortho) or Cl, Cl (ortho) — 1,2-Dichlorobenzene

Cl, Cl (meta) or Cl, Cl (meta) — 1,3-Dichlorobenzene

Cl, Cl (para) or Cl, Cl (para) — 1,4-Dichlorobenzene

1,2-Dichlorobenzene 1,3-Dichlorobenzene 1,4-Dichlorobenzene

Figure 109.16 *Diagrams for answer to question 109.12(iii). Note that there are several ways of drawing each structure, but they are not different. Make models if you do not understand this*

(iv) Figure 109.17 shows the molecules that are possible.

1,2,3-Trichlorobenzene 1,2,4-Trichlorobenzene 1,3,5-Trichlorobenzene

Figure 109.17 *Diagrams for answer to question 109.12(iv). Three possibilities for $C_6H_3Cl_3$. They are the only three; again models should convince you of this*

109.13 No. Cycloalkanes have the same general formula.

109.14

```
   H  H                      H  H
   |  |     O                |  |     O
H—C—C—C              HO—C—C—C
   |  |     OH               |  |     H
   H  H                      H  H
```

CH_3CH_2COOH
propanoic acid

CH_2OHCH_2CHO
3-hydroxypropanal

```
   H  O  H
   |  ‖  |
H—C—C—C—OH
   |     |
   H     H
```

CH_3COCH_2OH
hydroxypropanone

UNIT 109 SUMMARY

- Organic chemistry is the study of carbon compounds.
- Organic compounds:
  - (i) Are mainly covalent.
  - (ii) Always have four bonds to each carbon atom.
  - (iii) Where there are four single bonds there is normally a tetrahedral arrangement of the groups bonded to the carbon atom.
  - (iv) Around single bonds there is free rotation of the groups.
- Baeyer's strain theory says that:
  Rings that have bond angles different to the tetrahedral angle will suffer from strain; if the strain is too great the ring may break.
  Exceptions to the theory include compounds, such as benzene, with delocalised electrons.
- Homologous series:
  The members of a series have
  - (i) The same functional group.
  - (ii) Similar chemical properties.
  - (iii) The same general formula.
  - (iv) Gradually changing physical properties.
- Naming systems
  The root name is taken from the name of the longest carbon chain. See Table 109.3.
- Isomerism:
  - (i) Chain isomers have the same molecular formula and functional groups but a different arrangement of the atoms in space.
  - (ii) Functional group isomers have the same molecular formula but different functional groups.
  - (iii) Geometric isomers are *cis* and *trans* isomers of alkenes, which occur owing to the lack of free rotation about double bonds.
- Bond breaking occurs through:
  - (i) Heterolysis

    $$A \overset{\bullet}{\times} B \longrightarrow A^{+} + B\overset{\bullet}{\times}^{-}$$
    (ions)
  - (ii) Homolysis

    $$A \overset{\bullet}{\times} B \longrightarrow A\bullet + B\times$$
    (radicals)
- Reactions often involve:
  - (i) Nucleophiles, which seek out centres of positive charge.
  - (ii) Electrophiles, which seek out centres of negative charge.
- Analysis:
  - (i) Qualitative analysis finds the *type* of each element or group present.
  - (ii) Quantitative analysis finds the *amount* of each element or group present.

110

Optical activity

110.1 What is optical activity?

To understand optical activity you need to know about plane polarised light, so this is the first thing we shall explain. In Unit 24 we discovered that light waves consist of constantly changing electric and magnetic fields. These fields are always at right angles to the direction of travel of the light. If you look at Figure 110.1 you will see a diagram showing the electric field of one light wave travelling towards someone's eye. If you imagine that you could see the light waves coming towards you, you would see the electric field as a vertical line; the field can only move in one plane. We say that the light is *plane polarised*.

Light that comes from an ordinary lamp is not plane polarised. The electric fields of the light waves from the lamp are arranged in many different planes. However, if we pass the light through a piece of polaroid, it becomes plane polarised (Figure 110.2). We can place a second piece of polaroid in the path of the light. If we rotate this piece so that it is at right angles to the first one, then no light gets through. When the two pieces of polaroid are

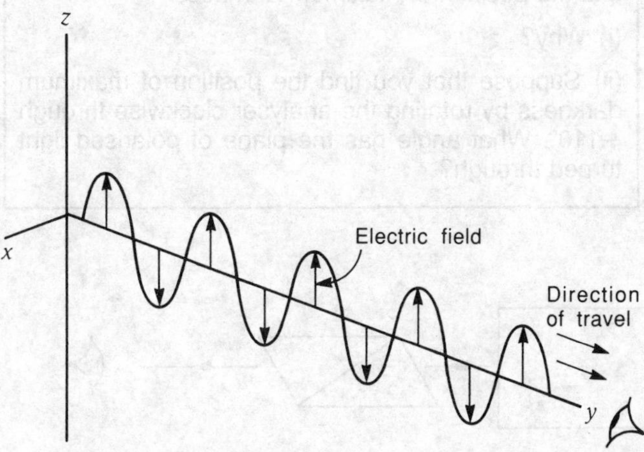

Figure 110.1 *This diagram illustrates a light wave travelling in the y direction. The electric field oscillates up and down, always parallel to the z axis. The field stays in the yz plane: the wave is plane polarised*

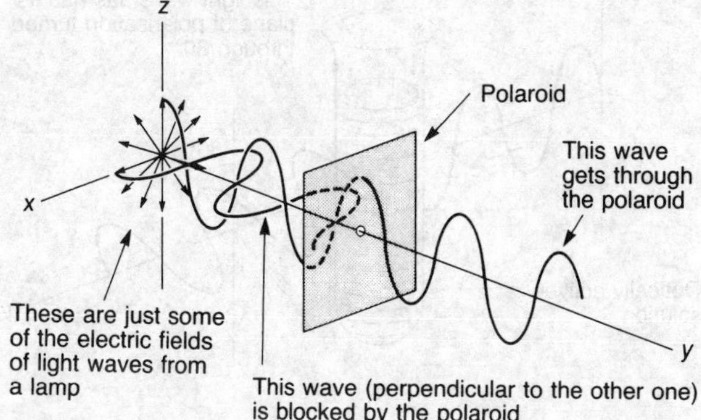

Figure 110.2 *Light can be polarised by passing it through a piece of polaroid. (Light waves with their electric fields somewhere between the two extremes in the diagram will pass through the polaroid, but with reduced intensity)*

lined up in the same direction, the maximum amount of light gets through.

It was the French physicist Jean Biot who, in 1812, discovered that some substances have the ability to *rotate the plane of polarised light*. To see what this means, look at Figure 110.3. In the first diagram we have plane polarised light passing through water. When the light emerges from the tube, it remains polarised in the same plane as when it entered the tube. In the second diagram the light passes through a solution of an optically active chemical (we need not worry about its nature). When the light comes out of the tube, it has been rotated through an angle, in this case 30°. To allow the maximum amount of light through the second piece of polaroid, we would have to rotate it through 30°. As we look at the beam of light the polaroid has to be rotated to the right (clockwise direction). We say that the chemical in the tube is *dextrorotatory*.

The third tube in the figure has a chemical in it that rotates the plane of polarised light to the left (anticlockwise) by 12°. This chemical is *laevorotatory*.

There is a more modern way of talking about optically active molecules. We say that they are *chiral*. (The 'ch' is pronounced like a 'k'.) Thus we can talk about chiral molecules that are dextro- or laevorotatory.

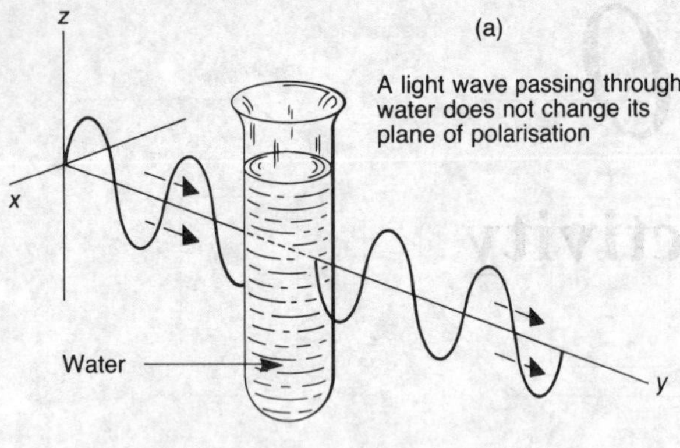

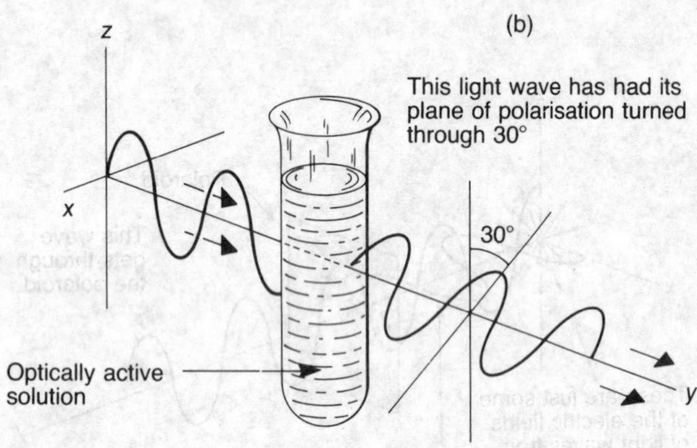

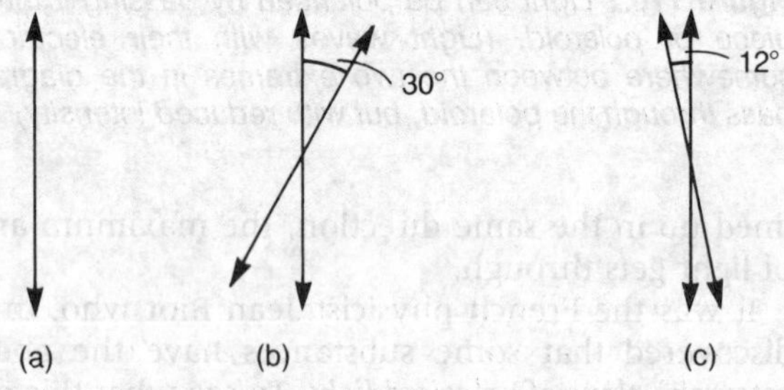

***Figure 110.3** Examples of rotation of the plane of polarised light. (a) Through water the electric field of the light wave is not rotated. (b) This solution has rotated the plane 30° to the right. (c) This solution has rotated the plane 12° to the left. Cases (a) and (b) are illustrated*

110.2 Polarimeters

In the laboratory, optical activity is investigated using a *polarimeter* (Figure 110.4). The apparatus has a source of light, which in sophisticated polarimeters will be a sodium lamp. The light passes through the *polariser*, and then into a tube containing the solution under test. Finally the light passes into the *analyser*. The angle of rotation given by a solution depends on a number of things: concentration, temperature and wavelength of the light. The *specific rotation* [α] at 20°C and using yellow light from sodium (the D lines) is given by

$$[\alpha]_D^{20} = \frac{\text{measured rotation}}{\text{length of tube (dm)} \times \text{concentration (g cm}^{-3}\text{)}}$$

A positive or negative sign is used to show the sign of the rotation. For example, the specific rotation of one variety of tartaric acid (2,3-dihydroxybutanedioic acid) has $[\alpha]_D^{20} = +14.4°$. The plus sign tells us that the acid is dextrorotatory.

One further complication with specific rotations is that their values depend on the solvent used in the polarimeter tube.

110.1 You may have thought about this point. Suppose you find that a chemical requires the analyser to be rotated by 180°. With this result you cannot tell whether the plane polarised light has been rotated to the left or to the right. What other experiments would you do to discover whether the chemical was dextrorotatory or laevorotatory?

110.2 In practice, if you use a polarimeter you should not move the analyser to find the position of maximum brightness; rather you should move it to find the position of maximum darkness.

(i) Why?

(ii) Suppose that you find the position of maximum darkness by rotating the analyser clockwise through +110°. What angle has the plane of polarised light turned through?

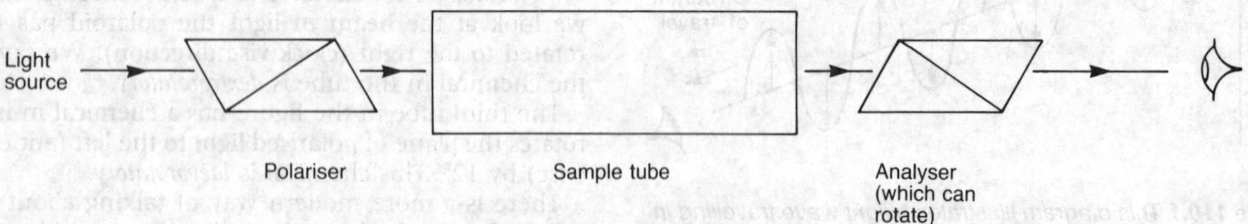

***Figure 110.4** The three key parts of a polarimeter. The polariser and analyser are made of quartz in the best polarimeters. Simpler ones use sheets of polaroid instead. The analyser is connected to a scale, which allows the rotation to be measured*

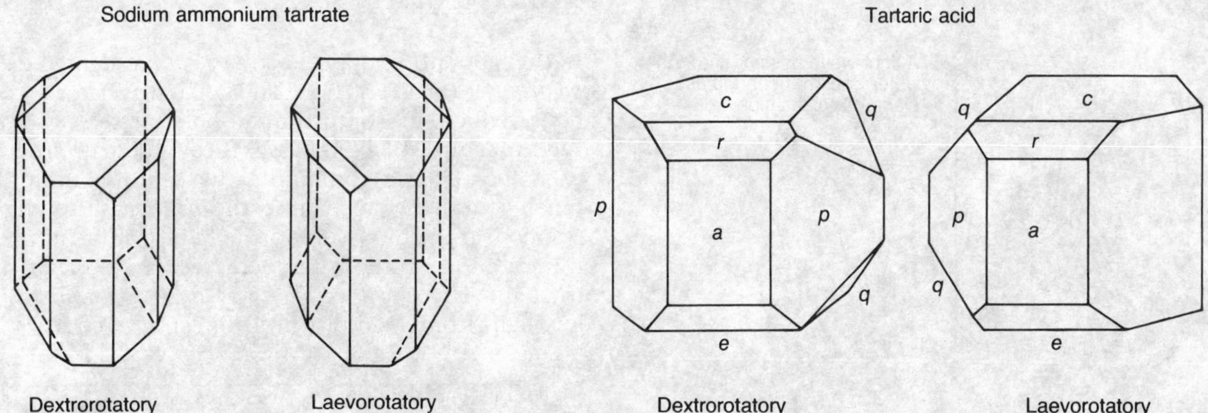

***Figure 110.5** Diagrams of the mirror image forms of crystals discovered by Pasteur*

110.3 Why are some substances chiral?

Louis Pasteur was one of the first scientists to make a study of optical activity. In 1848 he made a crucial observation when he was working on the salts of tartaric acid. (The modern name of this acid is 2,3-dihydroxybutanedioic acid.) He crystallised a solution of sodium ammonium tartrate, and spotted that there were two types of crystal present. He picked out the two types and showed that they differed in the arrangements of the faces. Later he drew diagrams of two types of crystalline tartaric acid (see Figure 110.5).

The key thing about the crystals is that, in each pair, the two varieties are *mirror images* of one another. Pasteur describes the sodium ammonium salts in this way:

> I carefully separated the crystals which were hemihedral to the right from those hemihedral to the left, and examined their solutions separately in the polarising apparatus. I then saw with no less surprise than pleasure that the crystals hemihedral to the right deviated the plane of polarisation to the right, and that those hemihedral to the left deviated to the left.

It was clear that the two crystal structures must be the result of different molecular structures. At the time the hunt began for an explanation of how molecules could exist in two mirror image forms. The simplest solution to the problem was given by J. A. le Bel and (independently) by J. H. van't Hoff in 1874. They proposed that chiral molecules were based on a tetrahedral structure. Figure 110.6 shows you that if we have *four different atoms or groups* arranged in a tetrahedron, then the molecule will have two mirror image forms, called *enantiomers* or *optical isomers.* A famous example of such a molecule is lactic acid (2-hydroxypropanoic acid).

At this stage you should make models of lactic acid and see for yourself what the enantiomers look like.

The carbon atom at the centre of the four different groups is called an *asymmetric carbon atom.* It is tempting to think that any substance that has an asymmetric carbon atom will be chiral; but this is not so. Neither is it true that if a substance is chiral then it must contain an asymmetric carbon atom. Since 1874 we have tightened up the conditions that must be satisfied by a molecule if it is to be chiral. We can use this rule:

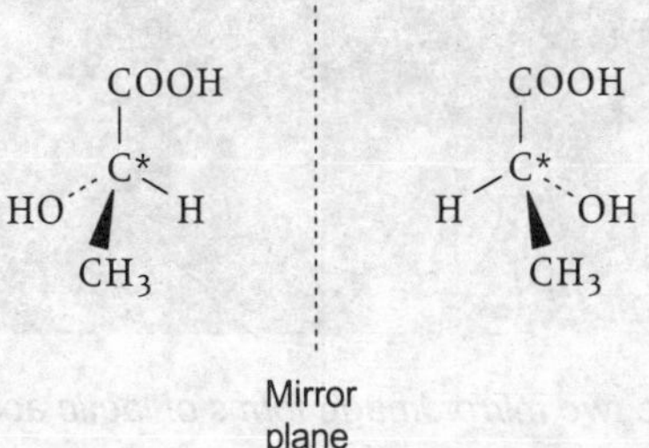

***Figure 110.6** The two mirror image forms of lactic acid (2-hydroxypropanoic acid). The stars mark the asymmetric carbon atoms. Two mirror image forms cannot be superimposed on each other in such a way that the positions of all the groups match. Note: We treat the CH_3, OH and COOH as single groups; we do not worry about how the hydrogen atoms are arranged in CH_3, or the oxygen and hydrogen atoms in COOH. For this reason we do not have to show the acid groups as COOH and HOOC in the two diagrams*

A molecule will be chiral if it has neither a plane nor a centre of symmetry.

To understand this, you need to know a little more about the symmetry of molecules. A *plane of symmetry* is fairly easy to understand. A cube has many such planes, some of which are shown in Figure 110.7. If there is a plane of symmetry, the arrangement of the object on one side of the plane is exactly the same as on the other.

A *centre of symmetry* can be a little harder to spot. Here we take a line out from the centre until it reaches some part of the figure; for example the line OA in Figure 110.7. Then we take another line of equal length but in exactly the opposite direction, like OB in the figure. If there are two identical spots at the end of the line, then the figure has a centre of symmetry. A cube has a centre of symmetry.

Models of the two mirror image forms of lactic acid. Also, see the colour section.

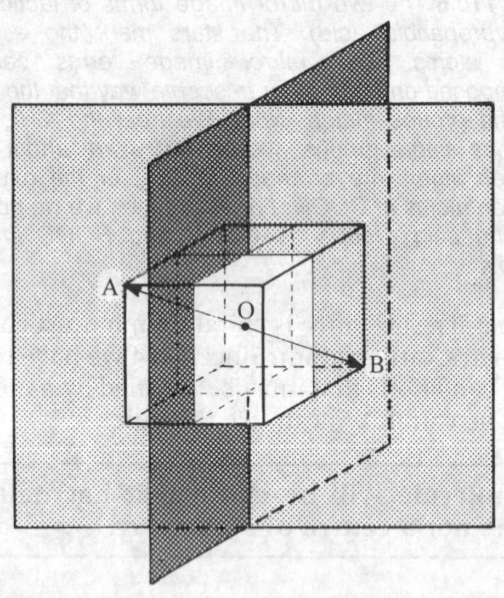

Figure 110.7 *Two planes of symmetry of a cube. These cut the cube in half across four of the sides. Other planes cut across the diagonals. The centre, O, is a centre of symmetry*

Now look at Figure 110.8, where the shapes of a number of different molecules are drawn. Make sure you can understand where the planes and centres of symmetry are to be found. All of these molecules have at least one plane of symmetry or a centre of symmetry. As a consequence, none of them are chiral.

However, the molecules in Figure 110.9 have neither a plane nor a centre of symmetry so they are both chiral. Notice that they do not both have an asymmetric

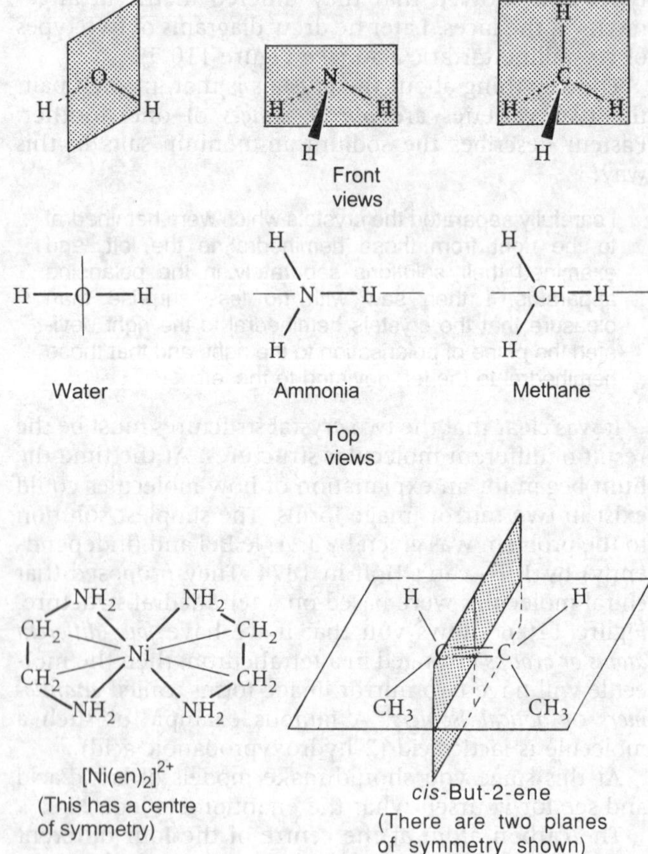

Figure 110.8 *Some of the planes and centres of symmetry in five molecules*

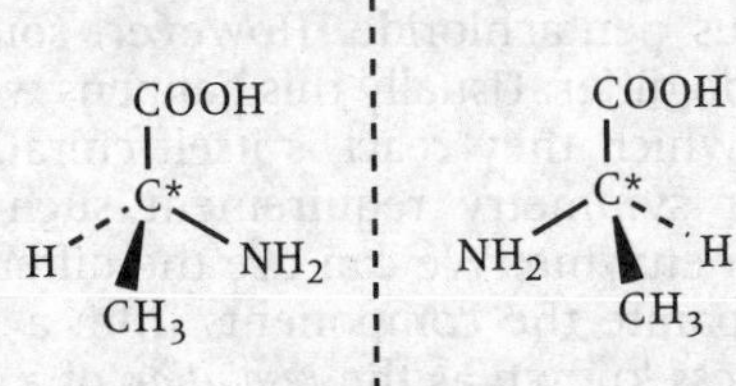

Mirror image forms of alanine, $CH_3CH(NH_2)COOH$. The stars mark the asymmetric carbon atoms

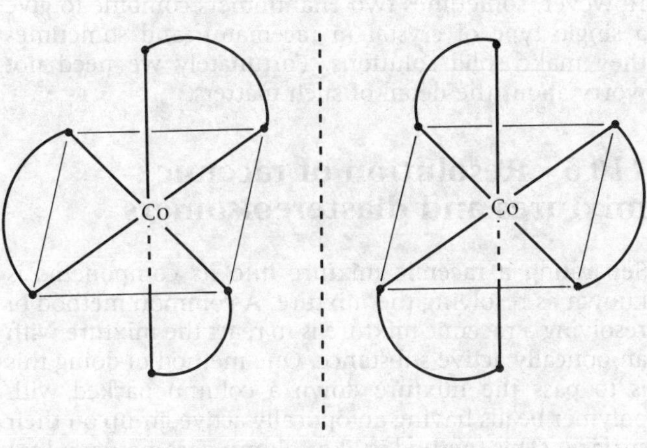

Mirror image forms of tris(ethane-1,2-diamine)cobalt(III), $[Co(NH_2CH_2CH_2NH_2)_3]^{3+}$. The curved lines represent $NH_2CH_2CH_2NH_2$

***Figure 110.9** Diagrams of two molecules whose mirror images cannot be superimposed upon each other. They are chiral molecules. Lactic acid (Figure 110.6) is also chiral*

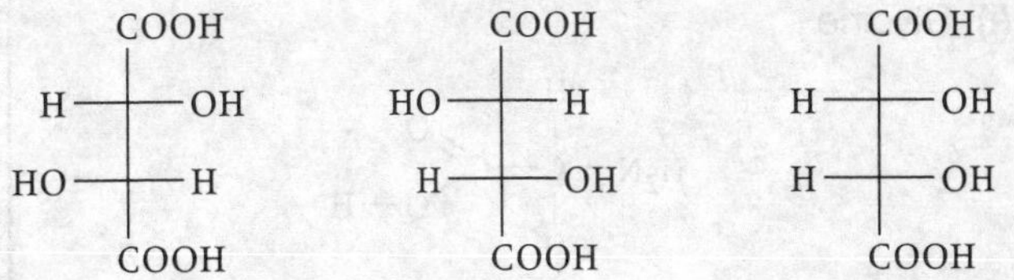

(+)-Tartaric acid (chiral)

(−)-Tartaric acid (chiral)

meso-Tartaric acid (not chiral)

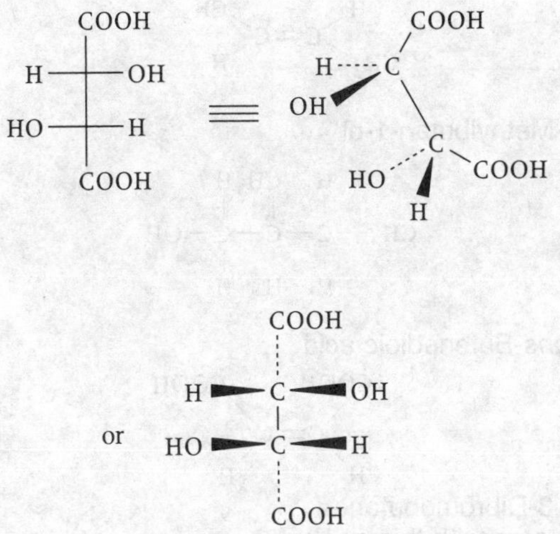

or

***Figure 110.10** The three types of tartaric acid. These diagrams of tartaric acid are a shorthand way of showing their structures. The horizontal bonds point towards you, out of the paper, as shown in the lower diagram*

carbon atom. The asymmetric carbon atoms are marked with a star.

110.4 More about tartaric acid

We shall now return to tartaric acid, so that we can discover some further subtle points about optical activity. Until le Bel's and van't Hoff's ideas became accepted, it was a great puzzle to explain why there were *three* types of tartaric acid. Two of them were chiral, but the third was not. The three types can be called (+)-tartaric acid, (−)-tartaric acid and *meso*-tartaric acid. The structures of these molecules are shown in Figure 110.10.

For the first time you can see that each of the three molecules has two asymmetric carbon atoms. However, the arrangement of the groups around each asymmetric carbon atom is different. The (+) and (−) forms are enantiomers. Neither molecule has a plane or a centre of symmetry; but the *meso* form does have a plane of symmetry. This is the reason why it is not chiral. Thus *meso*-tartaric acid *is* one of the three isomers of tartaric acid; but it is not an enantiomer. It is called a *diastereoisomer*.

Sometimes it is said that the *meso* form is not chiral because of *internal compensation*. Here the idea is that the arrangement around one of the asymmetric carbon atoms would cause the plane of polarised light to be rotated to the right, whereas the arrangement around the other asymmetric carbon would rotate by an equal amount to the left. The net result is that there would be no overall rotation.

There is another reason why there was so much confusion over the tartaric acids in Pasteur's time. Solutions known to contain the acid were found to be optically inactive; but they did *not* contain *meso*-tartaric acid. The solutions were inactive because they contained equal amounts of the (+) and (−) isomers. Solutions like this contain a *racemic mixture* of the two enantiomers. We can also say that the solutions are inactive because they are *externally compensated*.

110.3 Decide whether the following molecules can be optically active. In some cases you might need to make a model of the molecule. Which of them, if any, have *meso* forms? Copy each formula and mark the asymmetric carbon atom(s) with a star.

(i) Glycine

$$H_2N-CH_2-C(=O)-O-H$$

(ii) *cis*-But-2-ene

$$CH_3CH=CHCH_3$$

(iii) *trans*-But-2-ene

$$CH_3CH=CHCH_3$$

(iv) 2-Methylbutan-1-ol

$$CH_3-CH_2-CH(CH_3)-CH_2-OH$$

(v) *trans*-Butenedioic acid

$$HOOC-CH=CH-COOH$$

(vi) 2,3-Dibromobutane
(Take care with this one!)

$$CH_3CH_2BrCH_2BrCH_3$$

(vii) Dichlorobis(ethane-1,2-diamine)chromium(III), $[Cr(en)_2Cl_2]^+$

Cl, Cl, Cr

(viii) Hex-2,3-diene
(It is best to make a model of this molecule.)

$$C_2H_5(H)C=C=C(H)CH_3$$

110.5 Properties of enantiomers and racemic mixtures

Enantiomers have identical physical properties, e.g. the melting point of (+)- and (−)-tartaric acids are both 170 °C. Often they have chemical properties in common, e.g. both the chiral forms of lactic acid will react with phosphorus pentachloride. However, sometimes their reactions do differ. Usually this happens when the chemical with which they react is itself chiral, or has some particular symmetry requirement such as the active site in an enzyme. We can use the difference in reactivity to separate the components from a racemic mixture, a process known as the *resolution* of a racemic mixture.

A racemic mixture sometimes crystallises into a mixture of two different crystals. As Pasteur found, this happens with sodium ammonium tartrate. A mixture like this behaves as a eutectic (see section 58.3). However, sometimes two enantiomers combine to give a single type of crystal (a racemate), and sometimes they make solid solutions. Fortunately we need not worry about the detail of such matters.

110.6 Resolution of racemic mixtures and diastereoisomers

Separating a racemic mixture into its components is known as resolving the mixture. A common method of resolving a racemic mixture is to react the mixture with an optically active substance. One method of doing this is to pass the mixture down a column packed with polymer beads having an optically active group on their surface. (This method is like column chromatography.) The idea is that a (+) isomer on the beads might attract the (+) isomer of the racemic mixture more strongly than the (−) isomer, and the (−) isomer could be collected at the bottom of the column. (It could be the other way round, i.e. the (−) isomer from the mixture might stick to the beads more strongly. Note that (+) and (−) isomers do *not* behave like positive and negative charges, where opposites always attract.)

Another method is to mix the racemic mixture physically with a second chiral substance. If we call the isomers in the racemic mixture (+)R and (−)R, and the substance we add is (+)A, then two compounds are possible: (+)R(+)A and (−)R(+)A. If we choose A carefully, the compounds may have different solubilities and we can separate them by fractional crystallisation. The final task is to decompose the separated crystals to release the original isomers in the racemic mixture.

Compounds like (+)R(+)A and (−)R(+)A will be chiral, but they will not be enantiomers. Like *meso*-tartaric acid, they are diastereoisomers.

110.7 The configurations of optical isomers

If you look back at Figure 110.10, you might wonder how we know that the (+) and (−) isomers have those particular arrangements of the atoms in space. The evidence is complicated, and relies partly on X-ray diffraction, and partly on synthetic techniques. We shall not go into the details of the methods used; but you might find it useful to know something of the results.

Models of the two mirror image forms of glyceraldehyde.

If you make models of 2,3-dihydroxypropanal (glyceraldehyde), $CH_2OHCHOHCHO$, you will find the two optical isomers in the photo.

We know that one isomer will be dextrorotatory and the other laevorotatory, but for the present let us ignore their optical activity. Even if they did not affect plane polarised light, we can tell from the models that there are two versions of the molecule. There is a special notation that we can use to label them. The first step in the method (invented in 1956 by Cahn, Ingold and Prelog) is to put the groups attached to the asymmetric carbon atom in an order of priority. The order is:

I, Br, Cl, F, OH, NH_2, COOH, CHO, CH_2OH, CN, C_6H_5, CH_2R, CH_2, CH_3, H

Most important ... Least important

(Actually this is only part of a much longer list.) The order of priority is based on the order of atomic mass.

The next step is to look at models of the molecules and arrange them so that the group with the lowest priority is pointing directly away from you. You should do this for the optical isomers of 2,3-dihydroxypropanal.

You should find that if you trace the groups round in their order of importance, in one case you will move in a clockwise direction:

OH ⟶ CHO ⟶ CH_2OH ⟶ OH

This follows the order of importance in the list. We say that this isomer has a *rectus configuration*, and we give it the symbol *R*. On the other hand, the second isomer has its groups in the order:

OH ⟶ CHO ⟶ CH_2OH ⟶ OH (anticlockwise)

If we follow the groups round in the order of their importance, we move in an *anticlockwise* direction. This isomer has a *sinister configuration*, and is labelled with an *S*.

Thus, we have two configurations of 2,3-dihydroxypropanal. Notice that we have not said which is dextrorotatory and which is laevorotatory. This is a matter for experiment, which shows that *R*-2,3-dihydroxypropanal is dextrorotatory. If we wish to show all this information, we should write the names of the two optical isomers as *R*-(+)-2,3-dihydroxypropanal and *S*-(−)-2,3-dihydroxypropanal. Please be sure you understand that for other molecules an *R* configuration can belong to a laevorotatory isomer, and *S* configuration to a dextrorotatory isomer.

110.4 In our work on mechanisms in Unit 81, we discovered that halogenoalkanes can undergo nucleophilic attack in two ways. They react by an S_N1 or by an S_N2 mechanism. In this case we shall suppose that 2-iodobutane reacts with hydroxide ions. By working through the following questions, you should gain a better understanding of the background to these two mechanisms.

(i) Draw a diagram, or make a model, of 2-iodobutane. Explain why the molecule will be chiral. Establish the order of priority of each of the groups and decide whether your molecule is *rectus* or *sinister*.

(ii) Assume that the molecule reacts with hydroxide ions by an S_N1 mechanism. Draw another diagram, or make a second model, of the product and discover whether the product is *rectus* or *sinister*.

(iii) Can you draw any conclusions about what might happen to the configurations of the products of iodoalkanes that react by an S_N1 mechanism?

(iv) Now assume that the 2-iodobutane reacts via an S_N2 route. Describe the structure of the intermediate formed during the reaction.

(v) Two products of the hydrolysis are possible. What are they? Describe their configurations.

(vi) Are the products chiral? Briefly explain.

(vii) Would you expect the final solution to be optically active? Briefly explain.

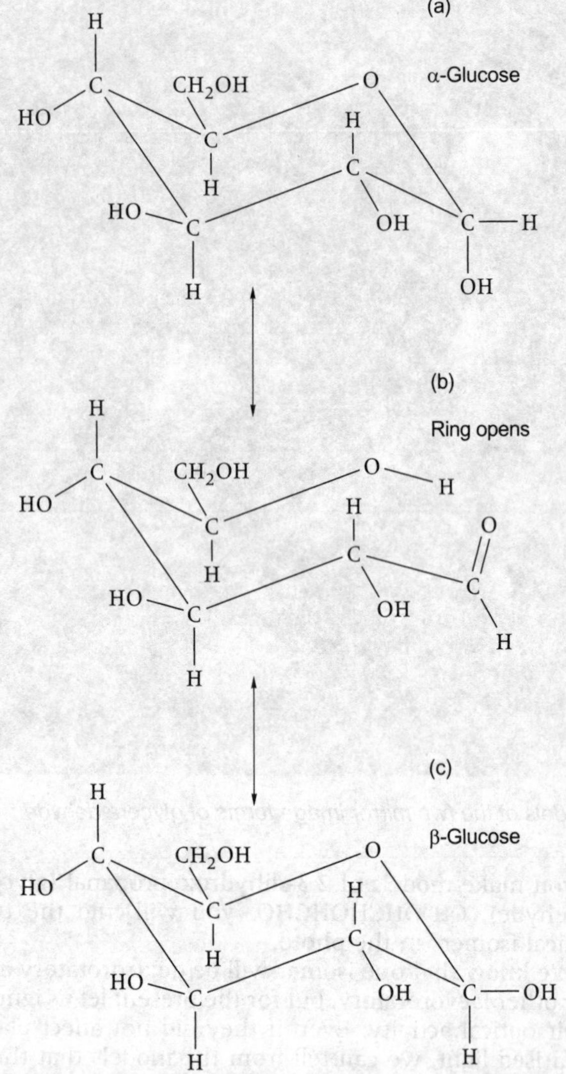

Figure 110.11 How α-glucose and β-glucose are related

110.8 The mutarotation of glucose

Studies of optical activity have given a great deal of information about many types of reaction. We shall look at one example, which concerns glucose molecules.

Glucose, $C_6H_{12}O_6$, is a sugar based on a six-membered ring. You can see the structure of the ring in Figure 110.11a. This version of glucose is called α-glucose. It was known as long ago as 1846 that a fresh solution of α-glucose had a specific rotation of +111°. However, if the solution is left for some time, the rotation eventually falls to +52.5°. This decrease in optical rotation is called the *mutarotation* of glucose.

When the final solution is analysed we find that there are two types of molecule present. Both have the formula $C_6H_{12}O_6$, and both have a ring structure. The rings differ in only one respect: the arrangement of one of the pairs of H and OH groups. This isomer of α-glucose is called β-glucose (Figure 110.11c). When pure, it has a specific rotation of +19.2°. Thus, whenever a molecule of α-glucose changes into β-glucose, the optical rotation of the solution will decrease. Eventually an equilibrium is established between the isomers, and then the specific rotation remains constant at +52.5°.

We believe that the reason why the mutarotation takes place is that the ring of α-glucose spontaneously breaks from time to time to give the open chain molecule shown in Figure 110.11b. This molecule can remake a ring structure, but sometimes the orientation of a hydrogen atom and an OH group is opposite to that of the original. This alternative structure is β-glucose.

110.5 This question asks you to work out the percentage of α-glucose and β-glucose in an equilibrium mixture of the two. Call the fraction of α-glucose in the mixture *x*.

(i) What are the specific rotations of α-glucose and β-glucose?

(ii) What does the fraction *x* of α-glucose contribute to the rotation of the mixture?

(iii) What does the fraction $1-x$ of β-glucose contribute to the rotation of the mixture?

(iv) Given that the actual rotation of the mixture is

+52.5°, find the value of x, and express it as a percentage.

110.6 The mutarotation of glucose is catalysed by acid. Let us suppose that the mutarotation takes place twice as fast in acid as in water alone. What will be the specific rotation of the final (equilibrium) solution?

110.7 Imagine that you place a solution containing a pure sample of an optical isomer of a substance in a polarimeter. Let us assume that the specific rotation of the solution is +100°. You add a little acid to the solution and find that the angle of rotation slowly decreases. After 20 minutes you find the solution has no optical rotation. Some time later you find that the angle of rotation is nearly −50°.

After some research in the library you find that the original isomer has been converted into its mirror image. You also discover that the reaction is first order in the original isomer.

(i) How much of the original isomer was present in the solution after 20 minutes?

(ii) How many minutes after the start of the reaction would it take for the rotation to reach −50°?

(iii) Estimate how long it would take for the rotation to reach −100°.

Answers

110.1 You could change the concentration of the solution. For example, by halving the concentration the rotation would be halved. If the substance were dextrorotatory, the rotation would be +90°; if it were laevorotatory, the rotation would be −90°. (If you had halved the concentration, you would not be likely to confuse −90° with +270°. Why not?)

110.2 (i) It is easier to see if *any* light is getting through than it is to tell if the *maximum* amount of light is entering your eye. That is, it is easier to see a difference between light and dark rather than between two lights of slightly different brightness.

(ii) To reach maximum darkness the analyser must be at right angles to the plane of polarisation; so the angle must be 90° greater than the true rotation. The latter is +20°.

110.3 (i) There is no asymmetric carbon atom in glycine: it is inactive.

(ii), (iii) Both molecules have planes of symmetry, so neither is chiral. One plane contains the four carbon and two hydrogen atoms; another is perpendicular to this plane, and cuts the molecule in two:

$CH_3(H)C{=}C(H)CH_3$ $CH_3(Cl)C{=}C(H)CH_3$

(iv) This molecule has an asymmetric carbon atom, and it has neither a plane nor a centre of symmetry; therefore it is chiral:

$CH_3{-}CH_2{-}C^*H(CH_3){-}CH_2{-}OH$

(v) As in (ii) and (iii) there is a plane of symmetry so the molecule is inactive.

(vi) As far as its optical activity is concerned, this molecule is in the same league as tartaric acid. There are two asymmetric carbon atoms, so like tartaric acid there are *three* isomers, two chiral enantiomers and an inactive diastereoisomer:

CH_3	CH_3	CH_3
H—C—Br	Br—C—H	H—C—Br
Br—C—H	H—C—Br	H—C—Br
CH_3	CH_3	CH_3

This example has two asymmetric carbon atoms with identical groups attached. If the groups were not identical, there would be more than three isomers possible.

(vii) You may be surprised to find that this molecule does have optical isomers:

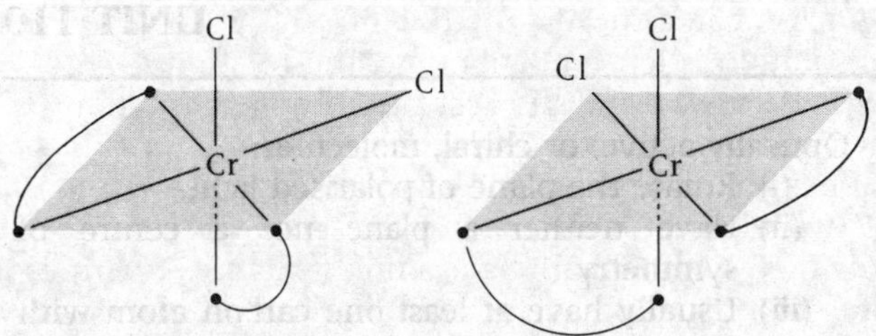

(viii) This is an example of a molecule that does *not* have an asymmetric carbon atom. However, its twisted shape means that it has neither a plane nor a centre of symmetry. Therefore it is entitled to be chiral:

$H(CH_3)C{=}C{=}C(C_2H_5)H$

i bonds in same plane as the paper
f bonds in front of the plane of the paper
b bonds behind the plane of the paper

Answers – cont.

110.4 (i)

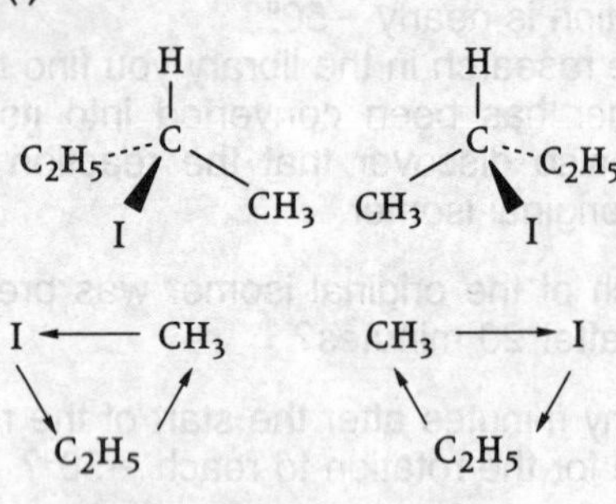

S form *R* form

(Note: C_2H_5 is the same as CH_2R with $R=CH_3$.)

(ii) The products of the reaction are:

from the *S* isomer from the *R* isomer

With the hydrogen atom pointing away:

R form *S* form

(iii) In an extreme case there can be (almost) complete inversion of the configuration during the S_N1 reaction, i.e. *R* changes to *S*, and vice versa.

(iv) The intermediate is a planar (flat) carbocation (see section 81.5).

(v) The hydroxide ions can attack the carbocation from either side. The product should be a 50% mixture of *R* and *S* molecules.

(vi) Yes, the individual molecules are chiral. They have an asymmetric carbon atom (or we can say that they have neither a plane nor a centre of symmetry).

(vii) It should be inactive because equal proportions of the two enantiomers are made. We obtain a racemic mixture.

110.5 (i) +111° and +19.2° respectively.

(ii) $111x$.

(iii) $19.2(1-x)$.

(iv) $111x+19.2(1-x)=52.5$. On solving this you will find $x=0.36$, i.e. 36%.

110.6 The equilibrium value will still be +52.5°. The rate of a reaction has no effect on the final position of equilibrium.

110.7 (i) 50% is left. To see why this is so, imagine that we started with 100 molecules. If 50 of them convert to the other enantiomer, we have 50 of each enantiomer. One will contribute +50° to the rotation, the other −50°; net result, 0° rotation.

(ii) It will take another 20 minutes, i.e. 40 minutes after the start. This is because a rotation of −50° will be obtained by the second enantiomer contributing −75°, and the original enantiomer +25°. A rotation of +25° represents a quarter of the original enantiomer. As 20 minutes is the half-life, it will take another 20 minutes to change from a half to a quarter of the original enantiomer.

(iii) −100° represents complete conversion of the first enantiomer into the second. A rule of thumb is that, for practical purposes, this takes about five or six half-lives, i.e. about 2 hours.

UNIT 110 SUMMARY

- Optically active, or chiral, molecules:
  - (i) Rotate the plane of polarised light.
  - (ii) Have neither a plane nor a centre of symmetry.
  - (iii) Usually have at least one carbon atom with four different groups attached (an asymmetric carbon atom).
  - (iv) Have two mirror image forms (enantiomers).
  - (v) Enantiomers cannot be completely superimposed on each other.
- Rotation of the plane of polarised light is measured with a polarimeter.
- A racemic mixture consists of equal proportions of two enantiomers and does not rotate the plane of polarised light.
- Diastereoisomers contain at least two asymmetric carbon atoms (chiral centres); the rotation of one centre cancels out the other.
- Resolution:
  - (i) Is the separation of enantiomers or diastereoisomers.
  - (ii) May be achieved by reacting with another chiral substance, e.g. on an ion exchange column.
- Configuration:
  - (i) Refers to the precise three-dimensional arrangement of groups in space.
  - (ii) Is given the label *R* or *S* depending on how the arrangement compares with the two forms of 2,3-dihydroxypropanal (glyceraldehyde).
  - (iii) The symbols *R* and *S* do *not* give the sign of the optical rotation (+) or (−).
- Mutarotation of glucose:

  This is the name given to the spontaneous change of a solution of α-glucose into β-glucose; the two forms having opposite signs of rotation.

111

Alkanes

111.1 The main types of hydrocarbon

Hydrocarbons contain only carbon and hydrogen atoms. The simplest ones have single bonds only. These are the *alkanes* (Table 111.1). If a hydrocarbon has one or more double bonds, it is an *alkene*; and if it has triple bonds, it is an *alkyne*. Hydrocarbons can also contain benzene rings. These are the *arenes*. We shall investigate each of these homologous series in turn. However, the reactions of arenes can be different to the others and we shall put them in a separate unit.

> **111.1** (i) Plot graphs showing how the melting and boiling points of the alkanes of Table 111.1 vary as the number of carbon atoms in the chain increases.
>
> (ii) Explain the trend in the two graphs.
>
> (iii) Which of the alkanes is a liquid at room temperature and pressure?

111.2 The importance of alkanes

The alkanes are particularly important to us owing to their use as fuels. The first member of the series, methane, has long been known as 'marsh gas' (rotting organic matter trapped in stagnant water gives off the gas) and 'fire damp' in coal mines. It is also produced from decaying animal dung, and from rubbish buried underground. Methane is trapped in huge quantities underground in areas where oil is found. The source of the gas and oil is the same: they are the result of the decay of marine life from some millions of years ago. Methane can be pumped directly from the deposits via pipelines into homes and factories, where it is more often known as 'natural gas'. Methane is odourless, so for reasons of safety, traces of a foul smelling chemical are usually added to natural gas.

Many hydrocarbons are extracted by the distillation of crude oil in an oil refinery. (You will find details of the process in Unit 86.) The lighter, lower boiling point hydrocarbons are collected from the top of the distillation column, and the heavier ones from the various stages lower down. The mixtures of hydrocarbons removed at each stage are called *fractions* (Table 111.2). Each fraction has its own set of uses.

> **111.2** Land that has been used as a site for rubbish dumps has sometimes been used later as building land. There have been cases of explosions occurring in houses built on such land. What causes the explosions?

111.3 The reactions of alkanes

The alkanes have few chemical properties (Table 111.3). We have already mentioned the main one in connection with methane: they all burn in air or oxygen. The general equation for the reaction is

$$C_xH_y + (x+y/4)O_2 \rightarrow xCO_2 + (y/2)H_2O$$

Actually this fits the burning of any hydrocarbon, not just alkanes. For example, with pentane, C_5H_{12}, we have $x=5$, $y=12$, $(x+y/4)=8$ and

$$C_5H_{12} + 8O_2 \rightarrow 5CO_2 + 6H_2O$$

In the past this type of reaction was used to discover the formula of hydrocarbons. You might like to try question 111.3 to see how the method worked.

The second type of reaction they perform is a *substitution* reaction with halogens. We have found previously that covalent bonds can be broken in two ways:

$X{:}Y \rightarrow X^+ + Y{:}^-$ or $X{:}^- + Y^+$	Heterolysis
$X{:}Y \rightarrow X\cdot + Y\cdot$	Homolysis

In homolysis, free radicals are made, and the reaction with halogens shows all the signs of free radical reactions. For example, the reaction between an alkane and chlorine is explosive if light (especially ultraviolet light) shines on the mixture. If the mixture is kept in the dark,

Table 111.1. The alkanes, general formula C_nH_{2n+2}

Name	*Formula*	*Structure*	*Melting point/°C*	*Boiling point/°C*
Methane	CH_4		−182	−161
Ethane	C_2H_6		−172	−89
Propane	C_3H_8		−188	−42
Butane	C_4H_{10}		−138	0
Pentane	C_5H_{12}		−130	36
Hexane	C_6H_{14}		−95	69

Table 111.2. Products of the fractional distillation of oil

Name of fraction	*Boiling range/° C*	*Use*
Gases	<30	Source of propane and butane for fuels; feedstock for chemical industry
Gasoline	30–75	Petrol manufacture
Naphtha	75–190	Feedstock for chemical industry
Kerosene	190–250	Aircraft fuel, central heating boiler fuel
Gas oil	250–350	Diesel fuel, central heating boiler fuel
Waxes, tars, heavy oils, asphalt	>350	Polishes, lubricants, specialised fuels, e.g. for power stations

Table 111.3. Chemical properties of the alkanes

Burn with oxygen e.g. $CH_4(g)+2O_2(g)\rightarrow CO_2(g)+2H_2O(l)$
Substitution with halogens (free radical mechanism) e.g. $C_2H_6(g)+Cl_2(g)\rightarrow C_2H_5Cl+HCl(g)$ then $C_2H_5Cl\rightarrow C_2H_4Cl_2\rightarrow C_2H_3Cl_3$, etc.

no reaction takes place. In section 81.4 we found that a free radical reaction takes place in three stages:

(i) Initiation; e.g.

$$Cl_2\rightarrow 2Cl\cdot$$

This is the stage that is caused by ultraviolet light. The energy of the photons in the light must be sufficient to break the bond between the halogen atoms.

(ii) Propagation; e.g.

$$CH_4 + Cl\cdot \rightarrow CH_3\cdot + HCl$$

In the propagation stage, a radical may be used up, but another one takes its place.

(iii) Termination; e.g.

$$CH_3\cdot + Cl\cdot \rightarrow CH_3Cl$$

Here, radicals are removed from the reaction.

Please do look at Unit 81 to check that you understand how free radical reactions work.

111.3 Before the days of mass spectroscopy and other methods of analysis, one of the ways in which the formula of a hydrocarbon was found was by burning it in oxygen. If the volume of hydrocarbon, oxygen, carbon dioxide and steam is known then, with the help of Avogadro's theory, the formula can be discovered. Here are the results of an experiment in which a hydrocarbon was burned in an excess of oxygen in a closed container.

Volume of hydrocarbon used $= 20\ cm^3$
Volume of oxygen used $= 150\ cm^3$

Both these readings were taken at room temperature and pressure.

An electric spark was passed through the mixture, which caused the hydrocarbon to burn to carbon dioxide and steam. The gases were allowed to cool to room temperature and pressure.

The total volume of gas in the apparatus was then $110\ cm^3$.

To find the volume of carbon dioxide present, the tube was opened under potassium hydroxide solution. Again at room temperature and pressure, the volume of gas left in the tube was $50\ cm^3$.

Now answer these questions:

(i) Why do we not have to worry about the volume of water produced if we measure volumes at room temperature and pressure?

(ii) What is the gas left at the end of the experiment?

(iii) What volume of oxygen actually reacted with the hydrocarbon?

(iv) What was the volume of carbon dioxide produced in the reaction?

(v) What is the ratio of the volumes of hydrocarbon, oxygen and carbon dioxide?

(vi) Using Avogadro's theory, what is the ratio of the number of moles of each gas used?

(vii) What is the value of x and y in the equation for the burning of a hydrocarbon in oxygen?

(viii) Hence, write down the formula of the hydrocarbon.

111.4 When methane reacts with chlorine the products vary with the amount of chlorine in the mixture. For example, if very little chlorine is used, the main product is chloromethane, CH_3Cl; but if a lot of chlorine is used, the product is mainly tetrachloromethane, CCl_4.

(i) Why does the amount of chlorine in the mixture have these effects?

(ii) If roughly equal amounts of chlorine and methane were mixed, what would you expect to find at the end of the reaction?

111.4 How to prepare alkanes

Making alkanes in the laboratory is not often done; but if you were really stuck without a badly needed alkane, here are some methods you might use.

First, a halogenoalkane can be reduced by hydrogen prepared by dripping ethanol onto zinc that has been reacted with a little copper(II) sulphate. The zinc gains a slight coating of copper, and between them they are powerful enough to liberate hydrogen from ethanol. This goes on to attack the halogenoalkane; for example,

$$\underset{\text{iodoethane}}{C_2H_5I} + Zn + 2H^+ \rightarrow \underset{\text{ethane}}{C_2H_6} + HI + Zn^{2+}$$

A second method was invented by the German chemist Wurtz, and as a consequence it is known as Wurtz's reaction. Here an iodoalkane is reacted with sodium; for example,

$$\underset{\text{iodomethane}}{2CH_3I} + 2Na \rightarrow \underset{\text{ethane}}{C_2H_6} + 2NaI$$

The sodium is kept in dry ether and the iodomethane dropped into the ether. The reaction is somewhat exothermic, so a condenser has to be placed on the reaction flask. This has cold water running through the outer jacket, which cools and condenses iodomethane and ether vapour rising into the inner tube. The ethane passes through the condenser and can be collected over water. The apparatus is shown in Figure 111.1.

A third method is to heat the sodium or calcium salt of an organic acid with soda lime (a mixture of sodium and calcium hydroxides). Overall the reaction brings about the loss of carbon dioxide. It is an example of a *decarboxylation* reaction (also see section 113.2); for example,

$$\underset{\text{sodium ethanoate}}{CH_3COONa(s)} + NaOH(s) \rightarrow \underset{\text{methane}}{CH_4(g)} + Na_2CO_3(s)$$

These three methods are a little old fashioned. A more sophisticated method makes use of a *Grignard reaction*. The French inventor of the reaction, Victor Grignard, received the Nobel Prize for his work in 1912. He discovered an entirely new series of reactions. They are all based on the use of magnesium combined with an organic radical and a halogen atom. A typical

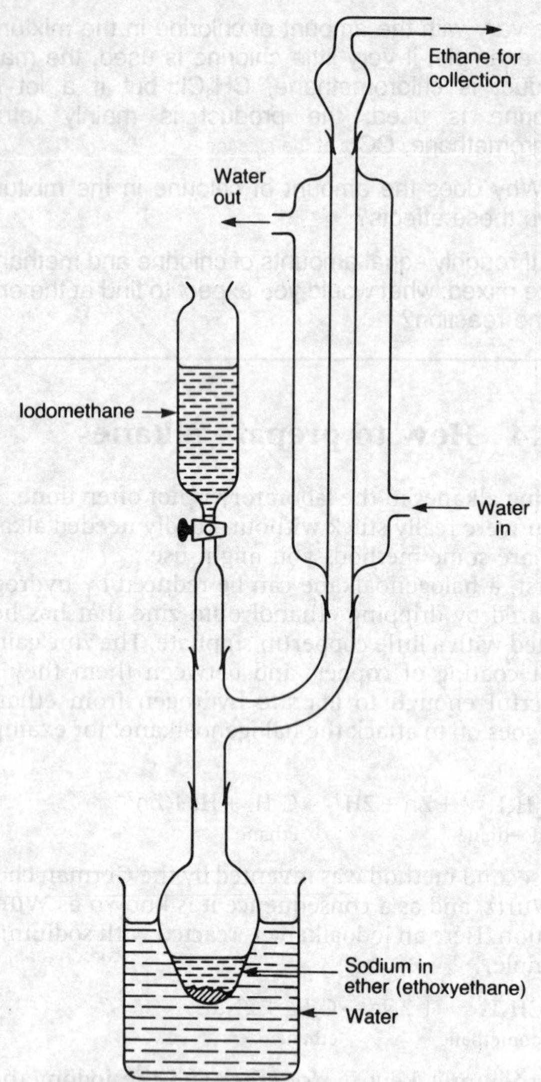

example is CH_3MgBr, methylmagnesium bromide. If this Grignard reagent reacts with water, the organic radical joins with a hydrogen atom from a water molecule:

$$\underset{}{CH_3MgBr} + H_2O \rightarrow \underset{\text{methane}}{CH_4} + Mg(OH)Br$$

Similarly, if we wanted to make ethane, we would use ethylmagnesium iodide:

$$C_2H_5MgI + H_2O \rightarrow C_2H_6 + Mg(OH)I$$

111.5 Which alkanes would be made if (i) iodoethane, (ii) 2-iodopropane were used in the Wurtz reaction?

111.6 A student wanted to make propane by the Wurtz reaction. He decided that a mixture of iodomethane and iodoethane would be needed. Was he correct? What would be made in the reaction?

111.7 Write down the formula of the Grignard reagent that you would use to make butane.

***Figure 111.1** An apparatus for preparing ethane by the Wurtz method*

Answers

111.1 (i) The graphs are shown in Figure 111.2.

(ii) The melting and boiling points increase as the number of carbon atoms in the chain increases. This is because the intermolecular forces increase with increasing relative molecular mass (see section 20.3).

(iii) Pentane and hexane.

111.2 Methane is released when the rubbish decomposes under the ground. It can happen that the methane escapes into houses built over the site. The explosion is the rapid burning of methane if, for example, a spark starts the reaction.

111.3 (i) The water condenses. The volume of liquid water is insignificant compared to when it is a gas. (For 1 mol, 18 cm^3 compared to over 24 000 cm^3.)

(ii) Unreacted oxygen.

(iii) We started with 150 cm^3, and 50 cm^3 is left over. Therefore, 100 cm^3 of oxygen were used.

(iv) The volume reduced from 110 cm^3 to 50 cm^3 with the potassium hydroxide, so 60 cm^3 of carbon dioxide were made.

(v), (vi) The ratio is 20 cm^3:100 cm^3:60 cm^3, i.e. the ratio of the moles of each is 1:5:3.

(vii) From the number of moles of carbon dioxide we get $x = 3$. From the number of moles of oxygen, we get $x + y/4 = 5$. This means $y = 8$.

(viii) C_3H_8, propane.

111.4 (i) With only a little chlorine, the number of chlorine radicals are greatly outnumbered by the methane molecules. When the methyl radicals are made in the propagation step, they react with chlorine radicals to make chloromethane. This mops up the chlorine radicals quickly, so that very few are left to make dichloromethane, etc.

(ii) Now there are many chlorine radicals in the mixture. Dichloromethane, CH_2Cl_2, can be made:

$$CH_3Cl + Cl\cdot \rightarrow CH_2Cl\cdot + HCl$$
$$CH_2Cl\cdot + Cl\cdot \rightarrow CH_2Cl_2$$

Similarly, CH_2Cl_2 can go on to make $CHCl_3$, and this to make CCl_4. Thus we would expect to find a mixture of all the four products.

Answers – cont.

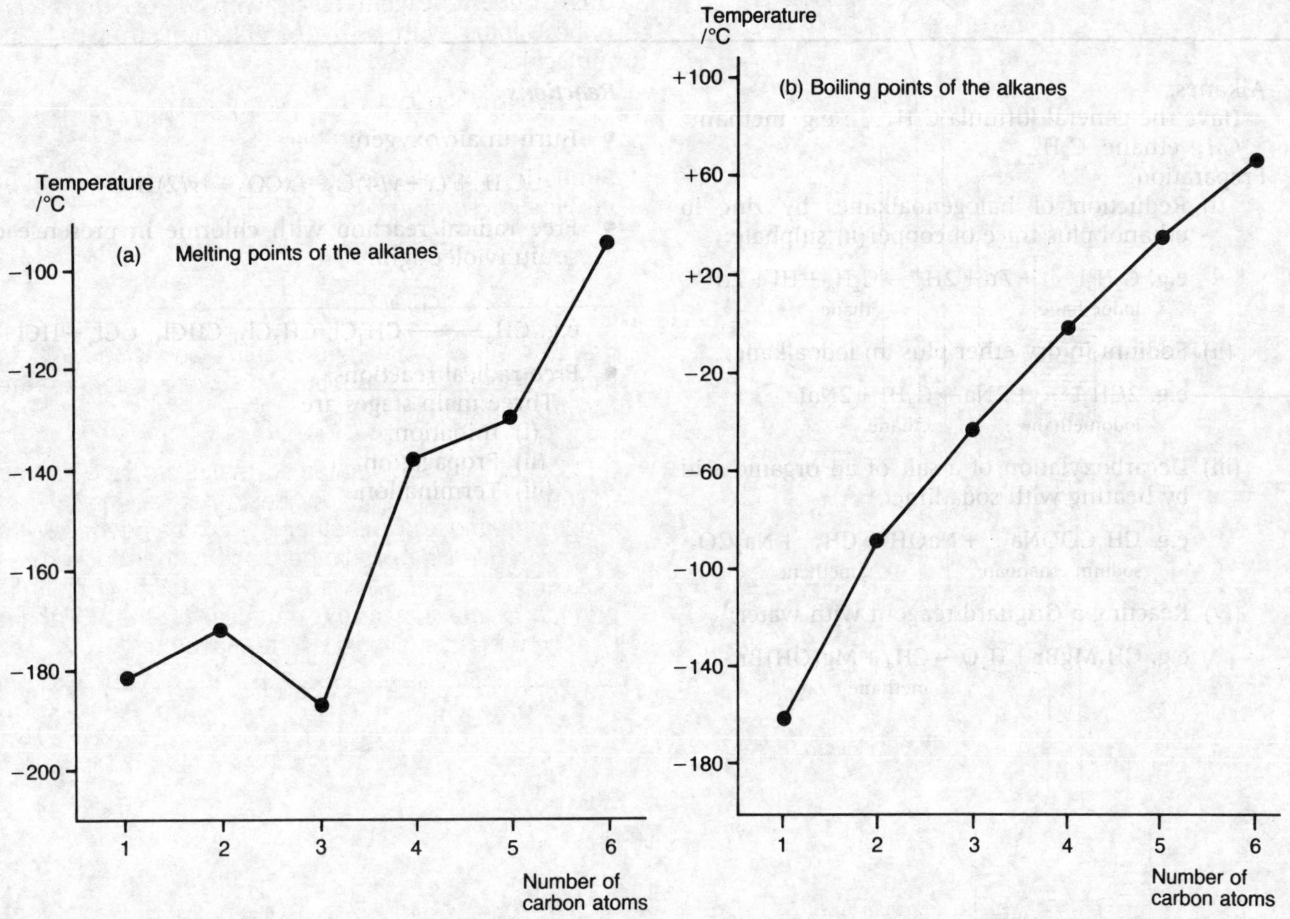

***Figure 111.2** Graphs for answer to question 111.1(i)*

111.5 (i) Butane, C_4H_{10}.

(ii) If we remove the iodine atoms from two molecules, and join them together, we would have a product that looks like this:

```
     CH3 CH3
      |   |
  H—C—C—H
      |   |
     CH3 CH3
```

However, if we stretch the molecule out to show the longest carbon chain, we have

```
          H   H
          |   |
  CH3—C—C—CH3
          |   |
        CH3 CH3
```

i.e. 2,3-dimethylbutane.

111.6 Certainly some propane would be made, but also there would be ethane and butane as side products:

$CH_3I + C_2H_5I \rightarrow CH_3—C_2H_5$ i.e. C_3H_8, propane

$CH_3I + CH_3I \rightarrow CH_3—CH_3$ i.e. C_2H_6, ethane

$C_2H_5I + C_2H_5I \rightarrow C_2H_5—C_2H_5$ i.e. C_4H_{10}, butane

The side products would make the yield of the reaction low, and make the isolation and purification of the propane difficult. In other words, this is not a good way to make propane. Likewise, the Wurtz reaction is not useful to make any alkane with an odd number of carbon atoms.

111.7 Butane is C_4H_{10}, so we would use C_4H_9MgI (or Br or Cl in place of the I).

UNIT 111 SUMMARY

- Alkanes:
  Have the general formula C_nH_{2n+2}; e.g. methane, CH_4; ethane, C_2H_6.
- Preparation:
  (i) Reduction of halogenoalkanes by zinc in ethanol plus trace of copper(II) sulphate;

  e.g. $\underset{\text{iodoethane}}{C_2H_5I} + Zn + 2H^+ \rightarrow \underset{\text{ethane}}{C_2H_6} + HI + Zn^{2+}$

  (ii) Sodium in dry ether plus an iodoalkane;

  e.g. $\underset{\text{iodomethane}}{2CH_3I} + 2Na \rightarrow \underset{\text{ethane}}{C_2H_6} + 2NaI$

  (iii) Decarboxylation of a salt of an organic acid by heating with soda lime;

  e.g. $\underset{\text{sodium ethanoate}}{CH_3COONa} + NaOH \rightarrow \underset{\text{methane}}{CH_4} + Na_2CO_3$

  (iv) Reacting a Grignard reagent with water;

  e.g. $CH_3MgBr + H_2O \rightarrow \underset{\text{methane}}{CH_4} + Mg(OH)Br$

Reactions

- Burn in air/oxygen:

  $$C_xH_y + (x + y/4)O_2 \rightarrow xCO_2 + (y/2)H_2O$$

- Free radical reaction with chlorine in presence of ultraviolet light:

  e.g. $CH_4 \xrightarrow{Cl_2,\ hf} CH_3Cl,\ CH_2Cl_2,\ CHCl_3,\ CCl_4 + HCl$

- Free radical reactions:
  Three main stages are
  (i) Initiation.
  (ii) Propagation.
  (iii) Termination.

112

Alkenes and alkynes

112.1 The structure of alkenes

Alkenes contain one or more double bonds. They contain fewer hydrogen atoms than an alkane with the same number of carbon atoms. An alkane is saturated with hydrogen atoms; an alkene is said to be *unsaturated.* A double bond is really the combination of a σ and a π bond between two carbon atoms (Figure 112.1). In Unit 16 we discovered how these bonds are made from the overlap of s and p orbitals. A π bond is not as strong as a σ bond, and is more easily broken. This is the reason why alkenes are more reactive than alkanes. However, the bond is sufficiently strong to stop the two ends of the molecule rotating. Shortly you will see that this results in many alkenes having isomers not found with alkanes.

The simplest homologous series contains only one double bond along a hydrocarbon chain. The structures of the early members of the series are shown in Table 112.1.

You can tell if a compound contains a double bond by the *-ene* ending to its name. In the first few members of the series there is no choice in where the double bond can be placed; but in the later members, we have to show the position of the double bond using a numbering system. As with alkanes, we find the longest carbon chain and number the carbon atoms along it. We then

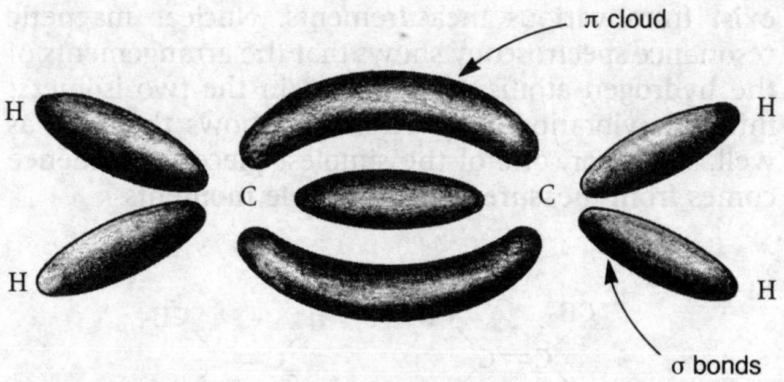

Figure 112.1 *An alkene has a double bond. This is a combination of a σ and a π bond*

Table 112.1. The alkenes, general formula C_nH_{2n}

Name	*Formula*	*Structure*	*Melting point/°C*	*Boiling point/°C*
Ethene	C_2H_4	$(H)(H)C{=}C(H)(H)$	−169	−104
Propene	C_3H_6	$(CH_3)(H)C{=}C(H)(H)$	−185	−48
But-1-ene	C_4H_8	$CH_3{-}CH_2(H)C{=}C(H)(H)$	−185	−6
Pent-1-ene	C_5H_{10}	$CH_3{-}CH_2{-}CH_2(H)C{=}C(H)(H)$	−165	29

write the lowest number of the two carbon atoms that have the double bond. Table 112.1 shows you the structure of but-1-ene. The '1' in the name tells you that the double bond is between the first and second carbon atoms. This molecule has an isomer, but-2-ene, in which the double bond runs between the second and third carbon atoms.

In fact there are *two* different types of but-2-ene. They are shown in Figure 112.2. They are known as *cis*- and *trans*-but-2-ene. The difference is in the arrangement of the hydrogen and methyl groups. In the *trans* isomer the two methyl groups are on opposite sides of the double bond (*trans* means across); in the *cis* isomer they are on the same side (*cis* means similar or same). *Cis* and *trans* isomers are sometimes called *geometric* isomers.

If there were free rotation about a double bond, these isomers could not exist. We have evidence that they do exist from various measurements. Nuclear magnetic resonance spectroscopy shows that the arrangements of the hydrogen atoms are different in the two isomers; infrared (vibrational) spectroscopy shows them up as well. However, one of the simplest pieces of evidence comes from measurements of dipole moments.

```
CH3     CH3          H       CH3
   \   /               \   /
    C=C                 C=C
   /   \               /   \
 H       H          CH3      H

cis–But–2–ene       trans–But–2–ene
```

Figure 112.2 *The two versions of but-2-ene. There is no rotation of the end groups round a double bond, so the molecules cannot change into one another*

112.1 Three different molecules with the formula $C_2H_2Cl_2$ are known. Two of them have dipole moments, and one does not. Draw structures of the molecules. (Models may help.)

112.2 A student said that the reason why alkenes are unsaturated is that they can be made by removing water from alcohols. Was she correct?

112.2 Ways of making alkenes

We shall examine two ways of making an alkene. The first is heating a halogenoalkane with a concentrated solution of potassium hydroxide in alcohol (called alcoholic potassium hydroxide). For example, if we wanted to make ethene we would warm a mixture of chloroethane, potassium hydroxide and ethanol. The reaction that takes place is called a *dehydrohalogenation* reaction. The name tells us what happens: a hydrogen and a halogen atom are removed. For example,

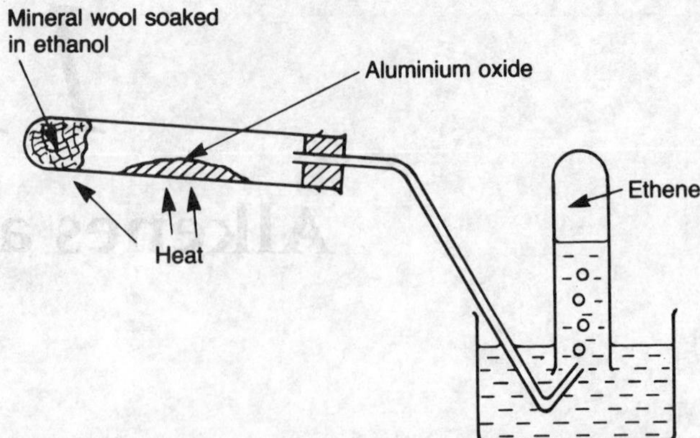

Figure 112.3 *A small-scale apparatus for making ethene. The aluminium oxide must be heated strongly and the alcohol only very slightly. (Great care must be taken to avoid the water sucking back into the reaction tube)*

```
    H  Cl                  H       H
    |  |                    \     /
H — C — C — H  +  KOH  ——→   C=C      +  KCl  +  H2O
    |  |                    /     \
    H  H                   H       H
```

$$C_2H_5Cl + KOH \rightarrow C_2H_4 + KCl + H_2O$$

The second method of making an alkene is to *dehydrate* an alcohol. There are two ways of doing this. The simplest is to pass the alcohol vapour over a hot catalyst, often aluminium oxide. You might be able to do this in the laboratory using the apparatus shown in Figure 112.3. If we use ethanol, C_2H_5OH, we can write the reaction as

```
    H  OH              H       H
    |  |                \     /
H — C — C — H  ——→       C=C      +  H2O
    |  |                /     \
    H  H               H       H
```

$$\underset{\text{ethanol}}{C_2H_5OH(g)} \rightarrow \underset{\text{ethene}}{C_2H_4(g)} + H_2O(g)$$

An alternative method is to use concentrated sulphuric acid. If ethanol is used, the mixture must be heated to about 180°C, but the temperature needed to dehydrate other alcohols is often less than this. Concentrated sulphuric acid has a strong attraction for water. A simple view of the reaction is that the acid acts as a dehydrating agent:

```
    H  OH                        H       H
    |  |                          \     /
H — C — C — H  −  H2O  ——→         C=C
    |  |                          /     \
    H  H                         H       H
```

$$C_2H_5OH - H_2O \rightarrow C_2H_4$$

However, the mechanism of the reaction is more complicated than this simple idea suggests. You can read about the mechanism in panel 112.1 and Figure 112.4 if you wish.

Panel 112.1

The mechanism of the dehydration of alcohols by concentrated sulphuric acid

Like water, alcohols have an OH group. This brings with it two lone pairs, and just as water molecules can be protonated:

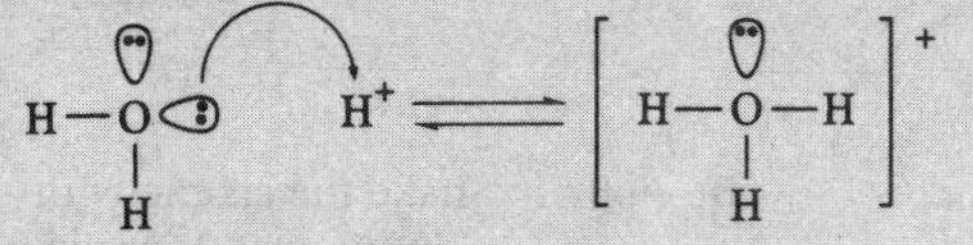

$$H_2O(l) + H^+(aq) \rightleftharpoons H_3O^+(aq)$$

so too can ethanol molecules be protonated:

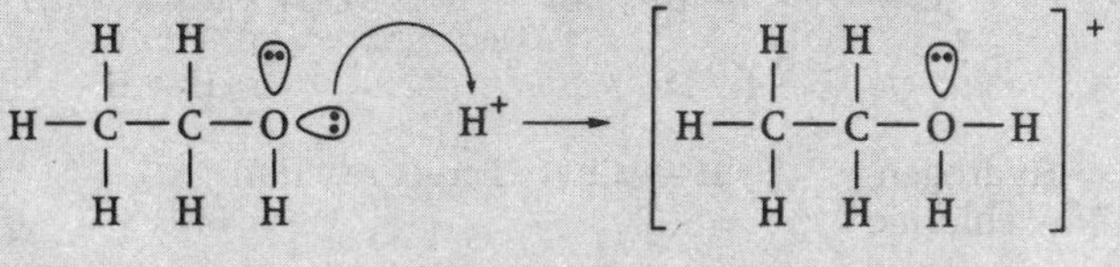

It is believed that the water attached to the carbon atom is lost, leaving a carbocation behind. The positive charge on the end carbon atom attracts electrons towards it. If you build a scale model of ethanol, you will find that the hydrogen atoms on the end methyl group are very close to the carbon atom holding the charge. It takes very little movement for the pair of electrons making the bond to one of the hydrogen atoms to be attracted to the positive carbon. If the pair of electrons are drawn away, the hydrogen atom is left just as a bare proton, i.e. hydrogen ion, H^+. We can show these changes on a diagram (Figure 112.4).

According to this mechanism, the sulphuric acid donates a proton, which is later released back to the acid. Therefore, it suffers no permanent change during the reaction. It is a catalyst.

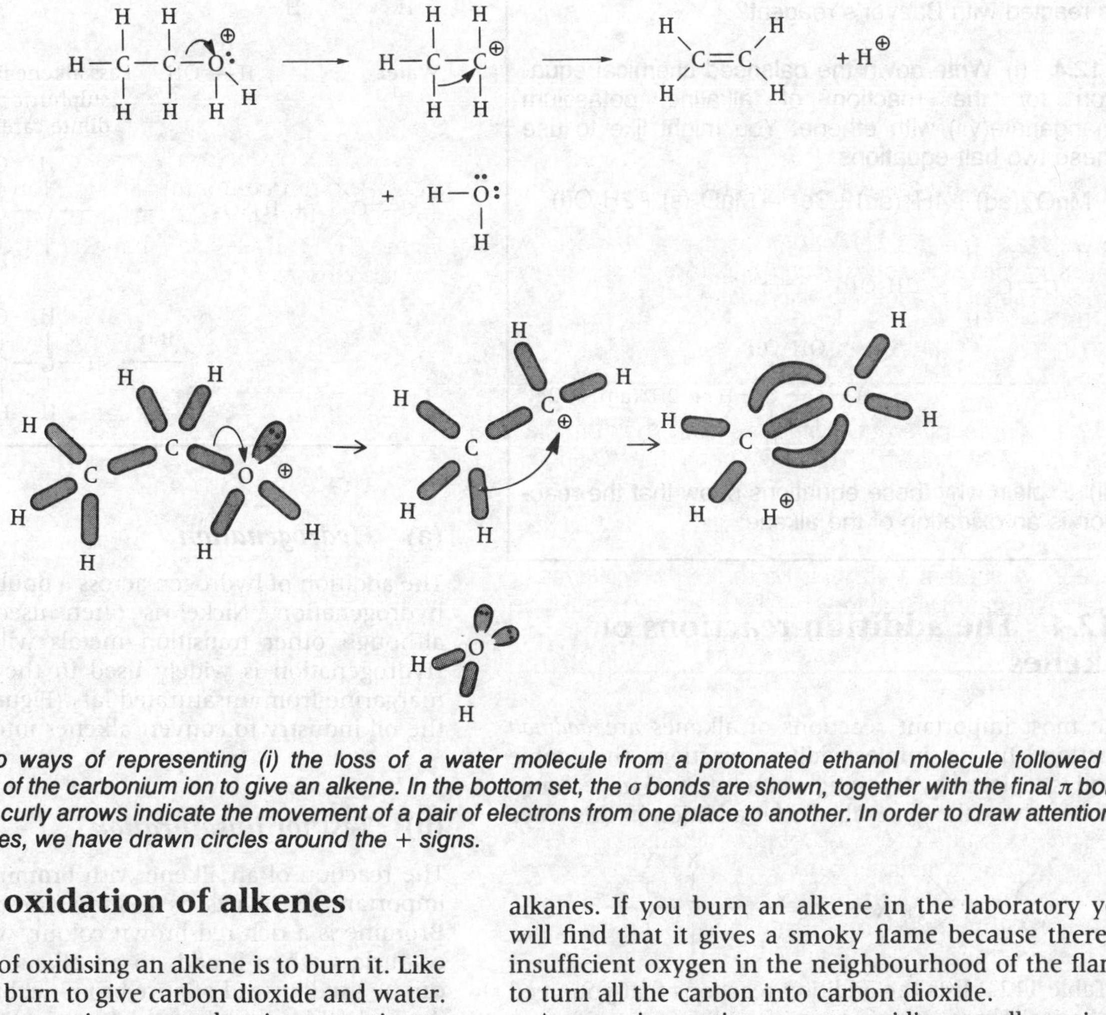

***Figure** 112.4 Two ways of representing (i) the loss of a water molecule from a protonated ethanol molecule followed by (ii) rearrangement of the carbonium ion to give an alkene. In the bottom set, the σ bonds are shown, together with the final π bond. In both cases, the curly arrows indicate the movement of a pair of electrons from one place to another. In order to draw attention to the positive charges, we have drawn circles around the + signs.*

112.3 The oxidation of alkenes

The easiest way of oxidising an alkene is to burn it. Like alkanes, alkenes burn to give carbon dioxide and water. However, alkenes contain more carbon in proportion to hydrogen than do alkanes. This means that they need relatively more oxygen to burn completely than do alkanes. If you burn an alkene in the laboratory you will find that it gives a smoky flame because there is insufficient oxygen in the neighbourhood of the flame to turn all the carbon into carbon dioxide.

A more interesting way to oxidise an alkene is to react it with an alkaline solution of potassium manganate(VII), a solution known as *Baeyer's reagent*. The π bond breaks and is replaced by two OH groups. For example,

$$H_2C{=}CH_2 \longrightarrow HOCH_2{-}CH_2OH$$

The product, ethane-1,2-diol, is better known as glycol (or ethylene glycol). It is used in huge quantities (in colder regions of the world) as antifreeze for cars.

If you carry out this reaction you will see the purple colour of the solution fade. It is replaced by a cloudy brown colour caused by the precipitation of manganese(IV) oxide.

112.3 What will be made if but-2-ene,

$$CH_3CH{=}CHCH_3$$

is reacted with Baeyer's reagent?

112.4 (i) Write down the balanced chemical equation for the reaction of alkaline potassium manganate(VII) with ethene. You might like to use these two half-equations:

$$MnO_4^-(aq) + 4H^+(aq) + 3e^- \rightarrow MnO_2(s) + 2H_2O(l)$$

$$H_2C{=}CH_2 + 2H_2O(l) \longrightarrow HOCH_2{-}CH_2OH + 2H^+(aq) + 2e^-$$

(ii) Explain why these equations show that the reaction is an oxidation of the alkene.

112.4 The addition reactions of alkenes

The most important reactions of alkenes are *addition* reactions. In the simpler addition reactions, the double bond is replaced by two single bonds to two new atoms. We can show the general rule for addition in this way:

$$>C{=}C< + X{-}Y \longrightarrow -\overset{X}{C}-\overset{Y}{C}-$$

Table 112.2 lists the addition reactions that you need to know. Three other types of addition reaction are *polymerisation*, *ozonolysis* and the *oxo reaction*. We shall leave these until later.

Table 112.2. The addition reactions of alkenes

Reaction with	*X—Y*	*Conditions*
Hydrogen	H—H	Heat with a Ni catalyst at about 140 °C
		$H_2C{=}CH_2 + H{-}H \longrightarrow H_3C{-}CH_3$
Bromine	Br—Br	Shake the alkene with bromine in the cold
		$CH_3CH{=}CH_2 + Br{-}Br \longrightarrow CH_3{-}CHBr{-}CH_2Br$
Hydrogen chloride	H—Cl	Direct reaction
		$CH_3CH{=}CH_2 + H{-}Cl \longrightarrow CH_3{-}CHCl{-}CH_3$
Water	H—OH	Pass alkene into concentrated sulphuric acid, and then dilute carefully with water
		$>C{=}C< + H_2SO_4 \longrightarrow -\overset{H}{C}-\overset{OSO_3H}{C}-H \xrightarrow{H_2O} H{-}\overset{H}{C}-\overset{OH}{C}-H$

(a) *Hydrogenation*

The addition of hydrogen across a double bond is called hydrogenation. Nickel is often used as a catalyst, although other transition metals will work as well. Hydrogenation is widely used in the manufacture of margarine from unsaturated fats (Figure 112.5), and in the oil industry to convert alkenes into alkanes.

(b) *Test for unsaturation*

The reaction of an alkene with bromine is particularly important as it acts as a simple test for an alkene. Bromine is a rich red-brown colour, which changes to colourless when it adds to an alkene. Bromine water can be used instead of pure bromine, but in either case, if you do this test, take care. Bromine is dangerous, and the products of the addition reactions with alkenes are often carcinogenic. If you are interested, you will find the mechanism of the reaction in panel 112.2.

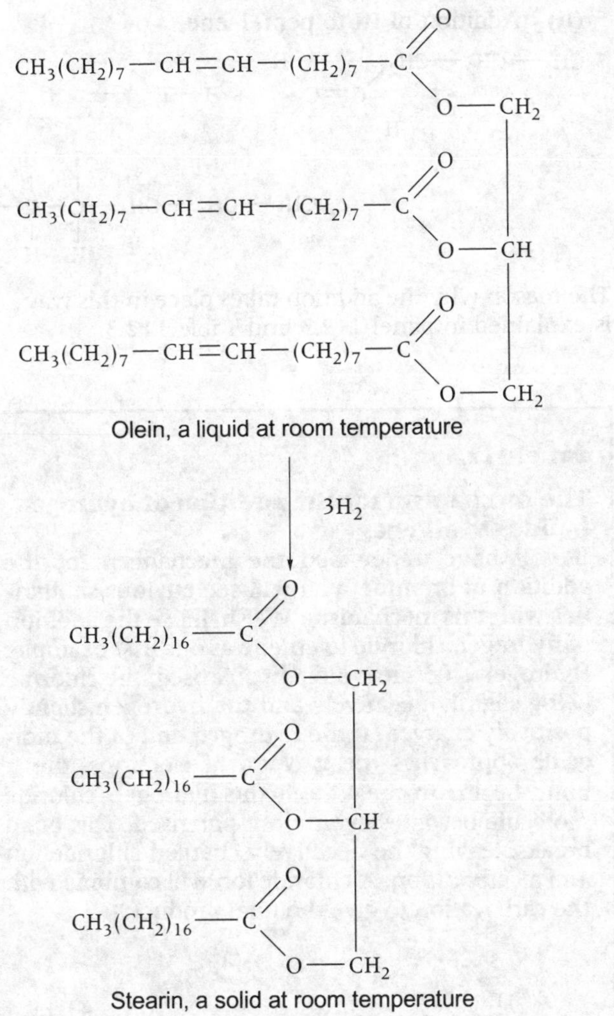

$$CH_3(CH_2)_7-CH=CH-(CH_2)_7-C(=O)-O-CH_2$$
$$CH_3(CH_2)_7-CH=CH-(CH_2)_7-C(=O)-O-CH$$
$$CH_3(CH_2)_7-CH=CH-(CH_2)_7-C(=O)-O-CH_2$$

Olein, a liquid at room temperature

$$\downarrow 3H_2$$

$$CH_3(CH_2)_{16}-C(=O)-O-CH_2$$
$$CH_3(CH_2)_{16}-C(=O)-O-CH$$
$$CH_3(CH_2)_{16}-C(=O)-O-CH_2$$

Stearin, a solid at room temperature

Figure 112.5 *The conversion of an unsaturated fat into a saturated fat*

Panel 112.2

The mechanism for the addition of bromine to an alkene

First, let us think about experimental evidence concerning addition reactions. If, say, ethene is passed into a solution that contains chloride ions but no bromine, there is no reaction. This shows that chloride ions cannot join to ethene directly. However, if bromine is added to the solution, a reaction does occur. If you were to analyse the products you would find that, along with 1,2-dibromoethane, there was a considerable amount of 1-bromo-2-chloroethane. This tells us something important about the way the reaction takes place. Chloride ions are negatively charged, and we know that they will react rapidly with positive ions. Can it be that, during the course of the reaction with bromine, positive ions are made? We believe they are.

If you were a bromine molecule approaching the π bond of an alkene, the first thing you would feel would be the negative charge of the electrons forming the bond. The electrons round the bromine atom nearest to the π bond would be slightly repelled. This atom is left with a slight positive charge while the other end of the molecule gains a slight negative charge. We say that the bromine molecule is *polarised* (see Unit 19):

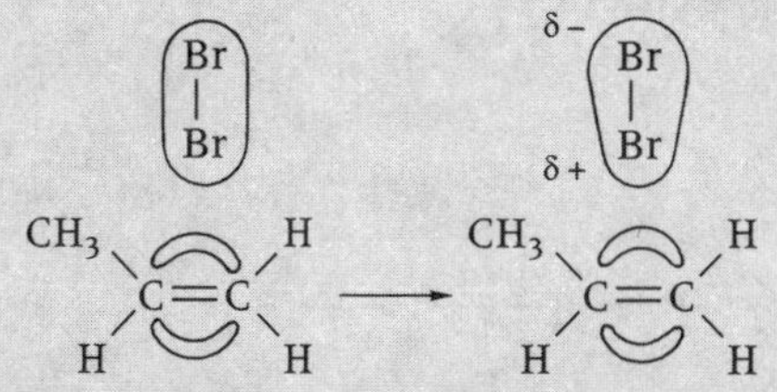

$$\text{Br–Br} \;\; CH_3(H)C=CH_2 \longrightarrow \overset{\delta-}{\text{Br}}\text{–}\overset{\delta+}{\text{Br}} \;\; CH_3(H)C=CH_2$$

Once this process begins, the positive end of the bromine molecule becomes a centre of attraction for the π electrons. This pair of electrons makes a bond to the bromine atom, while at the same time the electrons making the bond between the bromine atoms gather around the second bromine atom:

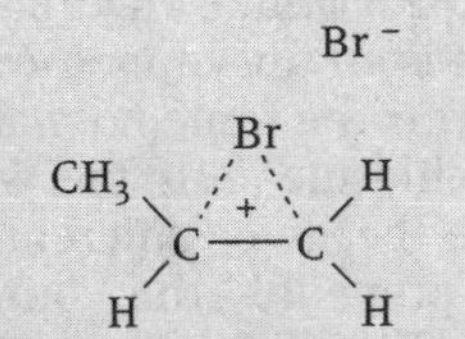

$$Br^- \quad CH_3(H)C\overset{+}{\underset{}{-}}CH_2 \text{ (bridged by Br)}$$

When this stage is complete, we have an intermediate that carries a positive charge; a carbocation has been made. Also, a bromide ion is left floating around. The carbocation will change so that it has the lowest energy. In our example this is the first of the ions shown below:

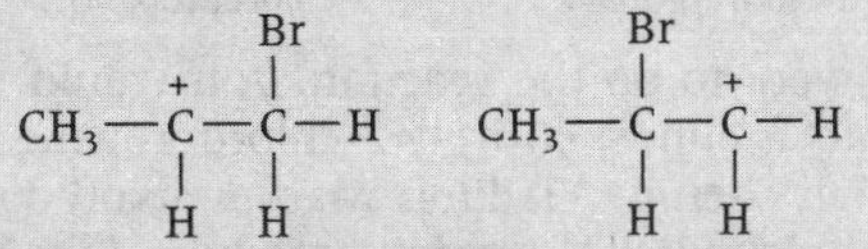

$$CH_3-\overset{+}{C}H-CH_2Br \qquad CH_3-CHBr-\overset{+}{C}H_2$$

The reason for this lies in the ability of methyl groups (CH_3) to feed electrons into a centre of positive charge. We say they show a *positive inductive effect.* The transfer of electron density towards the carbon atom carrying the charge means that the amount of positive charge on that atom is reduced. Similarly, the regions on the methyl group that lose the electron density gain a slight positive charge. In this way the positive charge is spread, rather than concentrated in one place. We made the point in section 14.7 that such a spread of charge leads to a more energetically stable state.

The bromide ions in the solution can attack the carbocation to give the final product:

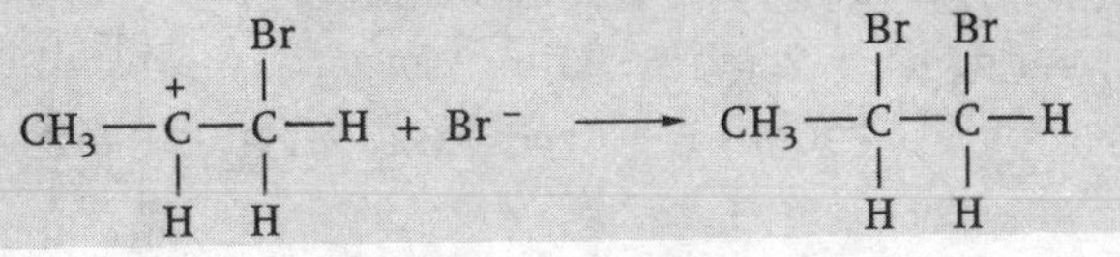

$$CH_3-\overset{+}{C}H-CH_2Br + Br^- \longrightarrow CH_3-CHBr-CH_2Br$$

(In practice, both the attack by bromide ion and the rearrangement of the charge may take place together.)

If the solution is flooded with chloride ions, then one of them is more likely than a bromide ion to collide and join to the carbocation. In this way we have explained how 1-bromo-2-chloroethane is made from ethene:

$$H_2C{=}CH_2 \longrightarrow H_2C(Br){-}\overset{+}{C}H_2 \xrightarrow{Br^-} H_2C(Br){-}CH_2(Br) \quad\text{or}\quad \xrightarrow{Cl^-} H_2C(Br){-}CH_2(Cl)$$

(c) *Hydrogen chloride*

The addition of hydrogen chloride to alkenes has been widely investigated. Unlike hydrogen or bromine, hydrogen chloride is an unsymmetrical molecule. With ethene the product is the same no matter which end of the molecule the chlorine joins, but with other alkenes the outcome can be two different molecules. For example, with propene, the outcome is either 1-chloropropane, $CH_3CH_2CH_2Cl$, or 2-chloropropane, $CH_3CHClCH_3$:

$$H{-}CH_2{-}CH_2{-}CH_2{-}Cl \qquad H{-}CH_2{-}CHCl{-}CH_2{-}H$$

1-chloropropane   2-chloropropane

If you were to do the reaction, you would find that the product is almost entirely 2-chloropropane. In 1869 the Russian chemist Vladimir Markovnikoff discovered the rule that predicts the correct product of the reaction. *Markovnikoff's rule* says that:

When hydrogen chloride adds to a double bond the hydrogen joins to the carbon that already has the most hydrogen atoms bonded to it.

In fact the rule applies equally to the addition of hydrogen bromide and hydrogen iodide. However, there are a number of conditions that must be met. For example, no free radicals are involved (which can happen if peroxides are present) and only addition to hydrocarbons is involved. Here are some examples that illustrate the rule.

(i) Addition of HCl to but-1-ene

$$CH_3{-}CH_2{-}CH{=}CH_2 + H{-}Cl \longrightarrow CH_3{-}CH_2{-}CHCl{-}CH_3$$

(ii) Addition of HI to pent-1-ene

$$CH_3{-}CH_2{-}CH_2{-}CH{=}CH_2 + H{-}I \longrightarrow CH_3{-}CH_2{-}CH_2{-}CHI{-}CH_3$$

The reason why the addition takes place in this way is explained in panel 112.3 and Table 112.3.

Panel 112.3

The mechanism for the addition of hydrogen halides to alkenes

If you have understood the mechanism for the addition of bromine, you will see obvious similarities with this mechanism. We shall use the addition of hydrogen chloride to ethene as our first example. Hydrogen chloride is already polarised, the chlorine being slightly negatively and the hydrogen slightly positively charged. If the hydrogen end of the molecule approaches the π cloud of electrons, the π bond begins to break, and the hydrogen chloride molecule becomes even more polarised. This bond breaks, leaving the negatively charged chloride ion and a carbocation. A chloride ion will combine with the carbocation to give the final product:

$$H_2C{=}CH_2 + \overset{\delta+}{H}{-}\overset{\delta-}{Cl} \longrightarrow H{-}CH_2{-}\overset{+}{C}H_2 \xrightarrow{Cl^-} H{-}CH_2{-}CH_2{-}Cl$$

Now let us see what might happen if hydrogen chloride adds to propene. There are two different carbocations that can be made depending on how the hydrogen attaches itself:

$$\text{A: } CH_3CH{=}CH_2 \longrightarrow CH_3{-}\overset{+}{C}H{-}CH_3 \longrightarrow CH_3{-}CHCl{-}CH_3 \text{ (2-chloropropane)}$$

$$\text{B: } CH_3CH{=}CH_2 \longrightarrow CH_3{-}CH_2{-}\overset{+}{C}H_2 \longrightarrow CH_3{-}CH_2{-}CH_2Cl \text{ (1-chloropropane)}$$

We know that the intermediate A is more favoured than the second (B) because, as Markovnikoff discovered, the product is 2-chloropropane. This suggests that the carbocation A is made more readily than the other (B). The more methyl groups there are attached to the carbon atom with the positive charge, the greater is the gain in energetic stability. This gives us the order of energetic stability shown in Table 112.3.

Now we can see why Markovnikoff's rule works. The carbocation that is made during the initial stage of the reaction is the most energetically stable one. All other things being equal, this will be the one that gives the most methyl groups attached to the carbon atom carrying the positive charge. You can see the effects of this in the pattern of results shown for the addition of HCl to propene above.

Table 112.3. Relative energetic stability of carbocations

Diagram	*Name*	*Energetic stability*
$R-C^{\oplus}H_2$	Primary carbocation	Least stable
$R-C^{\oplus}HR'$	Secondary carbocation	↓
$R-C^{\oplus}R'R''$	Tertiary carbocation	Most stable

(d) *Addition of water*

In some ways you can think of this as the reverse of the preparation of an alkene from an alcohol. The first step in the reaction is to absorb the alkene in concentrated sulphuric acid. This is when the addition takes place:

$$>C=C< + H-O-SO_2-O-H \longrightarrow -\underset{|}{\overset{H}{C}}-\underset{|}{\overset{OSO_2OH}{C}}-$$

The second step is to warm the reaction mixture with water. An OH group from a water molecule displaces the hydrogensulphate and a molecule of sulphuric acid is released:

$$-\overset{H}{C}-\overset{OSO_2OH}{C}- + H-O-H \longrightarrow -\overset{H}{C}-\overset{OH}{C}- + H-O-SO_2-O-H$$

112.5 You should realise that, in a hydrogenation reaction, one double bond takes up one molecule of hydrogen, two double bonds take up two molecules, and so on. This fact can be used to discover the number of double bonds in a molecule.

Here is an example. The mass spectrum of a hydrocarbon showed a parent ion that corresponded to a molar mass of 82 g mol^{-1}. 2.03 g of the hydrocarbon were found to absorb approximately 600 cm^3 of hydrogen (measured at room temperature and pressure).

(i) How many moles of hydrogen gas were absorbed?

(ii) How many moles of the hydrocarbon were used?

(iii) What is the ratio of the moles of hydrocarbon to moles of hydrogen?

(iv) How many double bonds does one molecule of the hydrocarbon contain?

(v) What might be the structure of the hydrocarbon? (Hint: think about alkanes that have a similar formula, and do not worry if you go round in circles.)

112.6 The addition of sulphuric acid to an alkene obeys Markovnikoff's rule. Predict the structure of the alcohols that will be made by the addition of the acid to (i) propene, (ii) but-1-ene, (iii) but-2-ene, followed by reaction with water.

112.7 What would you expect to be made if you passed ethene into a solution containing a mixture of bromine, chloride ions and nitrate ions?

112.8 Is it true that a methyl group is polarisable? Briefly explain your answer. If you need to do so, look at Unit 19 to help you decide your answer to this question.

112.9 Predict, and explain, the most likely product for the addition of hydrogen chloride to 2-methylbut-2-ene.

112.10 Draw the structure of the alcohol you would expect to obtain if 2-methylpropene were absorbed in concentrated sulphuric acid and then reacted with water.

112.11 If bromine water is used to test for an alkene, the water contains HOBr. What will be made if this molecule adds across the double bond in ethene? Draw the structure.

112.12 Here is a description of the reaction of ethene with bromine: 'During the reaction the double bond breaks and bromine adds on to the molecule.'

This is not quite right. What is wrong with the description?

112.5 Ozonolysis

In an ozonolysis reaction, ozone (trioxygen), O_3, is usually bubbled through a solution of the alkene in an organic solvent. The ozone adds across a double bond in a rather unusual manner:

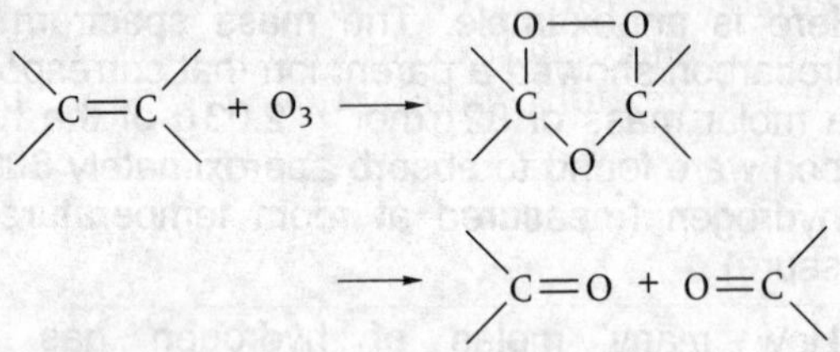

$$>C=C< + O_3 \longrightarrow \text{ozonide (C–O–O–C ring with bridging O)} \longrightarrow >C=O + O=C<$$

The molecule made in the reaction is an *ozonide*. Ozonides are not particularly stable (either energetically or kinetically). If the ozonide is warmed with a combination of zinc and water, the molecule breaks up. Oxygen atoms bond to each of the carbon atoms that had the double bond between them. The products are aldehydes or ketones (or mixtures of both). Here is an example in which an alkene was found to give propanone and methanal as the products:

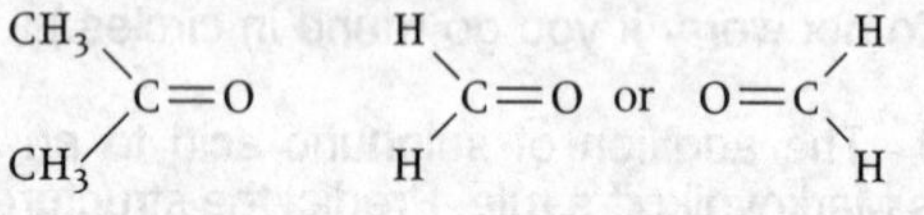

$$(CH_3)_2C=O \qquad H_2C=O \text{ or } O=CH_2$$

propanone methanal

What was the original molecule? All we have to do is to take away the oxygen atoms and join the carbon atoms by a double bond. This gives us:

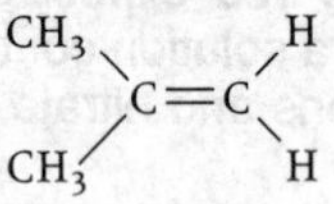

$$(CH_3)_2C=CH_2$$

2-methylpropene

Ozonolysis gives us a method of discovering which groups are attached to each end of the double bond. Needless to say the method only works if we can identify the aldehydes or ketones made during the reaction. You will find in Unit 118 that this can usually be done fairly easily.

112.13 After an ozonolysis experiment, the only product was ethanal, CH_3CHO. The chemist who did the experiment correctly claimed that there were two different structures for the starting material. What were they?

(To answer this question you may need to make molecular models of ethanal, remove the oxygen and try to join the remaining parts together.)

112.6 Polymerisation

Alkenes undergo *addition polymerisation*. You can get an idea of why this happens by looking at Figure 112.6.

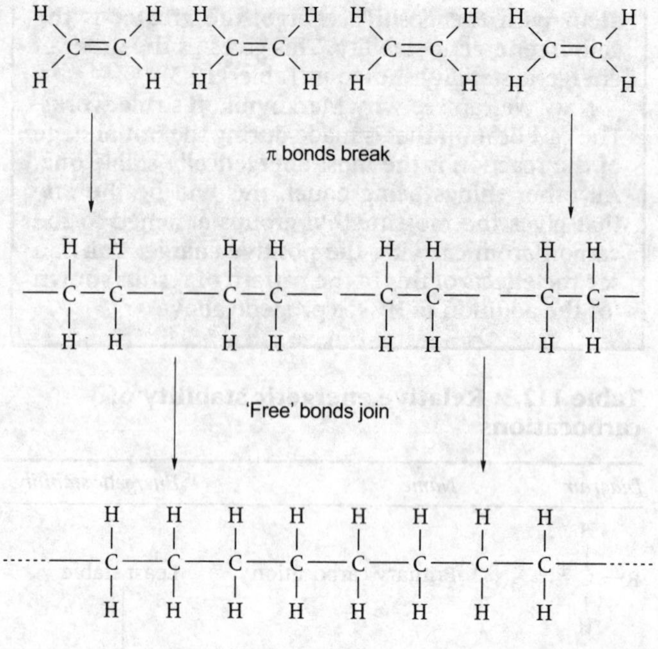

π bonds break

'Free' bonds join

A polymer chain

***Figure 112.6** An extremely simplified version of how ethene molecules are converted into poly(ethene) (polythene)*

Here each of the three neighbouring ethene molecules has by some happy chance had its double bond broken. We have arranged things so that the bond breaks homolytically, i.e. one electron stays with each of the two carbon atoms. Next we have shown the unpaired electrons recombining to give a bond pair, but this time the bond is between carbon atoms on different molecules. If this happens, a chain of molecules is made. In a typical polymer chain, many tens of thousands of alkene molecules may join.

Ethene molecules are the *monomer* units that combine to give the *polymer*. In this case the polymer is polyethene, or polythene for short.

In reality, of course, alkenes will not sit neatly arranged breaking their π bonds for no good reason. Persuasion in the form of high pressures and an extra reactant are often needed. The chemical added is the *initiator*. As their name suggests, initiators take part in the initiation step of a free radical reaction. Organic peroxides make good initiators in a free radical polymerisation. These molecules have two short hydrocarbon chains, which we shall write as R, joined by a peroxide link. Thus we can show an organic peroxide as ROOR. When they are heated, the peroxide bond breaks homolytically, producing free radicals.

(i) Initiation step

$$ROOR \rightarrow 2RO\cdot$$

These radicals attack the alkene.

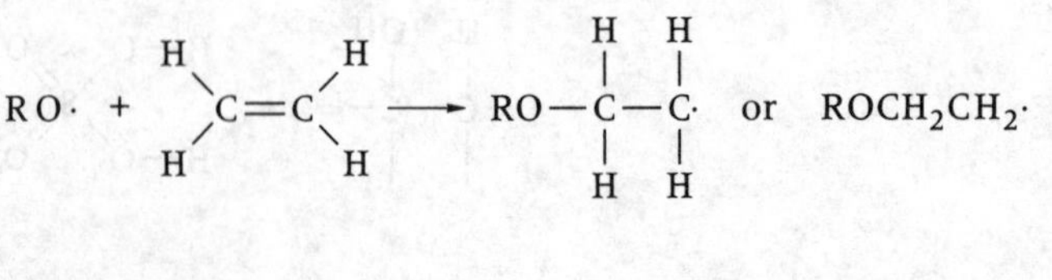

$$RO\cdot + H_2C=CH_2 \longrightarrow RO-CH_2-CH_2\cdot \text{ or } ROCH_2CH_2\cdot$$

(ii) Propagation step

$$\mathrm{ROCH_2CH_2\cdot + CH_2{=}CH_2 \longrightarrow ROCH_2CH_2CH_2CH_2\cdot}$$

(iii) Termination step

$$\mathrm{ROCH_2(CH_2)_nCH_2\cdot + RO\cdot \longrightarrow ROCH_2(CH_2)_nCH_2OR}$$

As you can see, it is during the propagation stage that the polymer chain grows. At some stage the reaction terminates, leaving polymer chains of varying length, but often many thousands of monomer units long. A typical *average* molar mass would be 20 000 to 30 000 g mol^{-1}. Note that we must speak of the average molar mass. The product of a polymerisation experiment consists of a mixture of chains of different lengths.

A remarkable variety of alkenes have been used in addition polymerisation experiments. Table 112.4 lists examples of the more important ones.

Table 112.4. Some alkenes and their addition polymers

Monomer	*Section of polymer*	*Short formula*	*Name*
Ethene 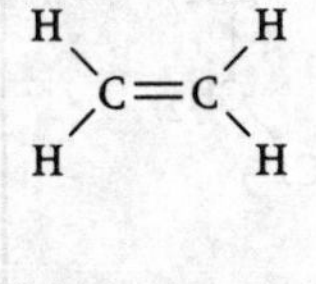 $\mathrm{H_2C{=}CH_2}$	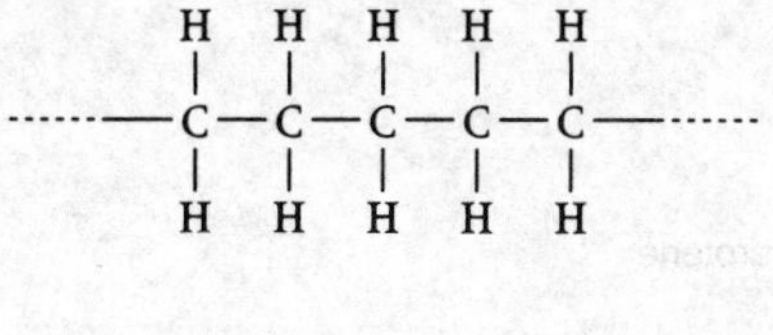 $\cdots\mathrm{-CH_2-CH_2-CH_2-CH_2-CH_2-}\cdots$	$\mathrm{\left(CH_2\right)_n}$	Polyethene (polythene)
Chloroethene (old name: vinyl chloride) 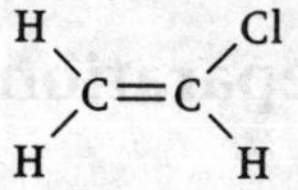 $\mathrm{H_2C{=}CHCl}$	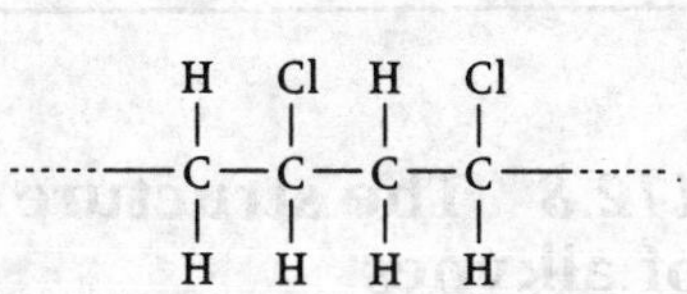 $\cdots\mathrm{-CH_2-CHCl-CH_2-CHCl-}\cdots$	$\mathrm{\left(CH_2CHCl\right)_n}$	Poly(chloroethene) (polyvinyl chloride, PVC)
Styrene 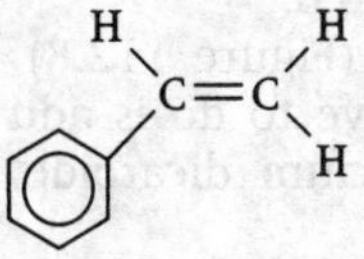 $\mathrm{H_2C{=}CH(C_6H_5)}$	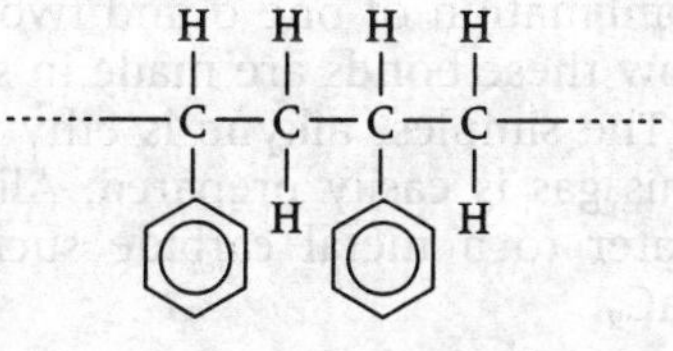 $\cdots\mathrm{-CH_2-CH(C_6H_5)-CH_2-CH(C_6H_5)-}\cdots$	$\mathrm{\left(CHC_6H_5CH_2\right)_n}$	Polystyrene
Tetrafluoroethene 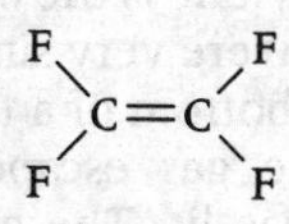 $\mathrm{F_2C{=}CF_2}$	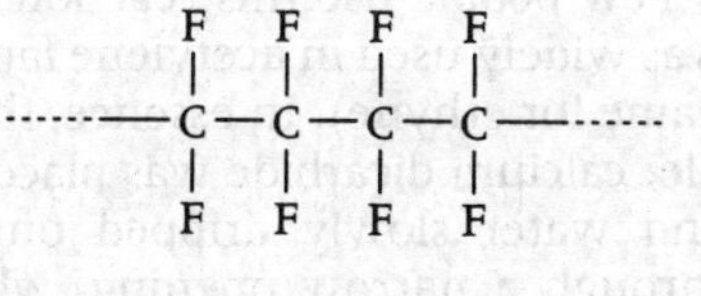 $\cdots\mathrm{-CF_2-CF_2-CF_2-CF_2-}\cdots$	$\mathrm{\left(CF_2\right)_n}$	Poly(tetrafluoroethene) (PTFE, Teflon)

112.14 What was the monomer that would produce this polymer:

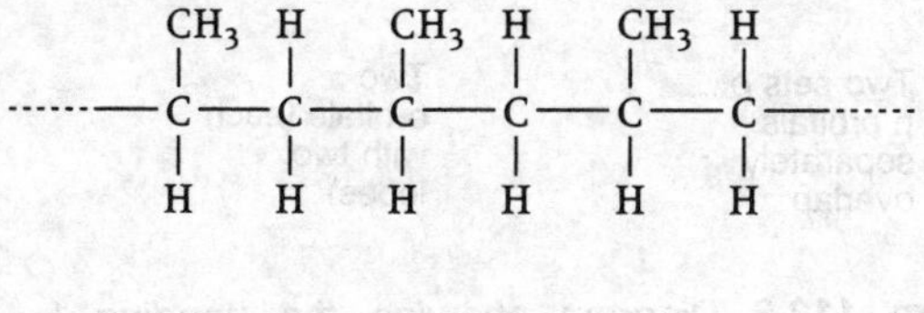

$$\cdots\mathrm{-C(CH_3)H-CH_2-C(CH_3)H-CH_2-C(CH_3)H-CH_2-}\cdots$$

112.15 The molecule 2-methylbuta-1,3-diene,

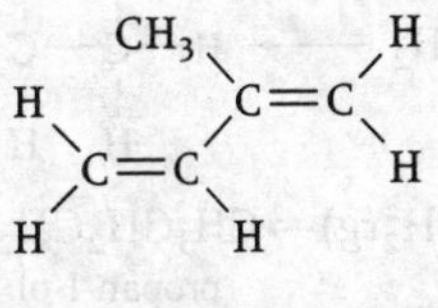

$$\mathrm{H_2C{=}CH-C(CH_3){=}CH_2}$$

is otherwise known as isoprene. It is one of the basic building blocks of rubber and a number of other natural products. Try to discover how isoprene units can combine to make the two substances shown in Figure 112.7.

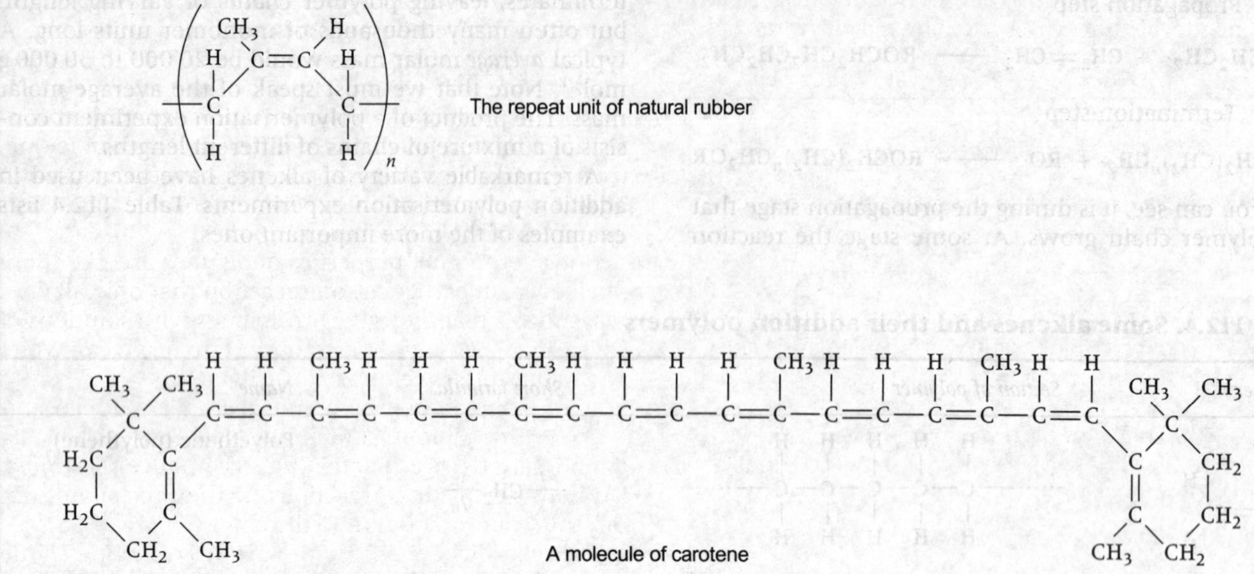

The repeat unit of natural rubber

A molecule of carotene

Figure 112.7 Diagrams for question 112.5

112.7 The oxo reaction

This is the name given to a number of different reactions that have great importance in the chemical industry. The variety we are concerned with is the conversion of alkenes into aldehydes, which in turn may be converted into alcohols. This is achieved by reacting an alkene with a mixture of carbon monoxide and hydrogen in the presence of a catalyst. This is also called *hydroformylation.* Often the catalyst is a carbonyl compound of a transition metal, e.g. $Co(CO)_4$. The reaction is carried out at high pressures, around 200 atm, and high temperatures, around 200 °C.

One reason why the reaction is important is that it is one of the few ways of directly increasing the number of carbon atoms in a compound, For example,

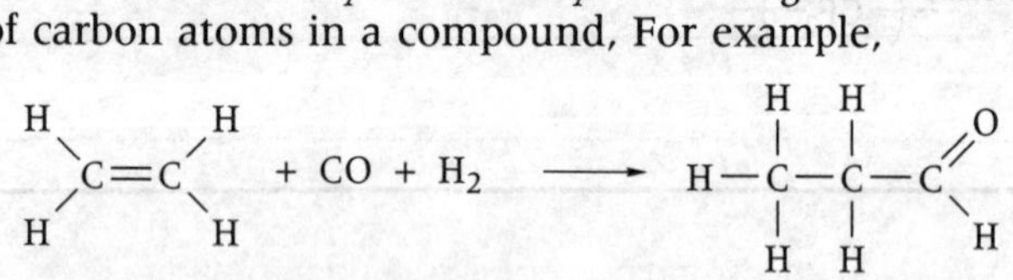

$$H_2C{=}CH_2 + CO + H_2 \longrightarrow H{-}CH_2{-}CH_2{-}CHO$$

$$CH_2{=}CH_2(g) + CO(g) + H_2(g) \rightarrow \underset{\text{propanal}}{CH_3CH_2CHO(g)}$$

followed by

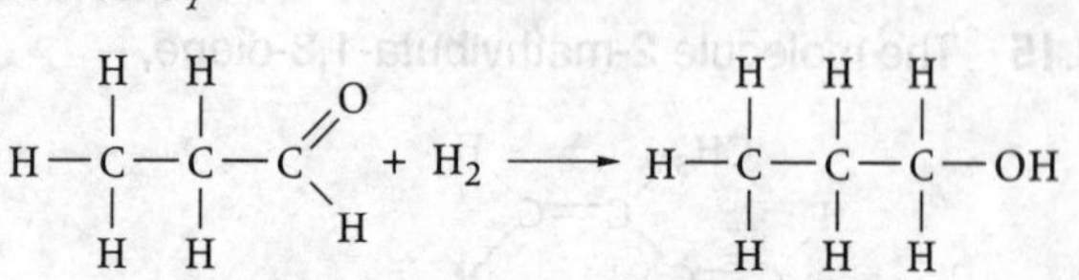

$$H{-}CH_2{-}CH_2{-}CHO + H_2 \longrightarrow H{-}CH_2{-}CH_2{-}CH_2{-}OH$$

$$CH_3CH_2CHO(g) + H_2(g) \rightarrow \underset{\text{propan-l-ol}}{CH_3CH_2CH_2OH(g)}$$

112.16 Predict the result of using the alkene, propene, in the oxo process.

112.8 The structure and preparation of alkynes

Alkynes have at least one triple bond. A triple bond is a combination of one σ and two π bonds. We described how these bonds are made in section 16.8.

The simplest alkyne is ethyne, C_2H_2 (Figure 112.8). This gas is easily prepared. All you have to do is add water to a metal carbide such as calcium dicarbide, CaC_2:

$$CaC_2(s) + 2H_2O(l) \rightarrow Ca(OH)_2(s) + C_2H_2(g)$$

Few people use this reaction now, but at one time it was widely used in acetylene lamps (acetylene is the old name for ethyne). In essence, the lamps were very simple: calcium dicarbide was placed in the bottom of a tin and water slowly dripped onto it. The gas escaped through a narrow opening, where it was lit. The gas burns with a vivid flame, and the lamps were used as lights on bicycles and horse-drawn carriages, as well as the early motorcars. Unfortunately, there were many

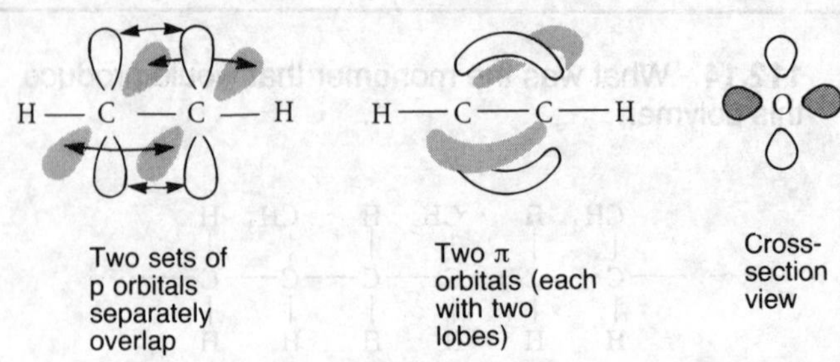

Figure 112.8 Diagram showing the bonding in ethyne, [C_2H_2 (or H—C≡C—H). The triple bond is made from one σ and two π bonds

accidents because a mixture of ethyne and air (oxygen) will explode if the gases are mixed in the right proportions.

> **112.17** Are alkynes unsaturated?
>
> **112.18** (i) Write down the equation for ethyne burning in oxygen.
>
> (ii) What proportions of ethyne and oxygen will give a highly explosive mixture?
>
> (iii) What do you think went wrong with acetylene lamps to make them explode?
>
> **112.19** (i) The standard heat of combustion of ethyne at 25 °C is approximately $-2600\,\text{kJ mol}^{-1}$. Comment on this value.
>
> (ii) Why is ethyne (acetylene) used in oxy-acetylene welding?

112.9 The properties of alkynes

We have already mentioned the fact that alkynes will burn, but given their structure, we might expect their properties to be similar to those of alkenes, and this is often the case.

Especially, alkynes give addition reactions. For example, they will decolourise bromine or bromine water. However, their reactions are often more violent than those of alkenes. For example, chlorine will explode with ethyne:

$$\text{H—C}\equiv\text{C—H} + \text{Cl}_2 \longrightarrow \text{H—CCl}_2\text{—CCl}_2\text{—H}$$

1,1,2,2-tetrachloroethane

Ethyne will polymerise. If it is heated to 400° C the product of the reaction is benzene:

$$3C_2H_2(g) \rightarrow C_6H_6(g)$$

More interesting than this is a fairly recent discovery that, if ethyne is polymerised in the presence of iodine, then the polymer that is made will conduct electricity. This is a remarkable thing. Totally covalent materials are almost always insulators.

However, not all properties of alkynes are like those of alkenes. In particular, one reaction that only alkynes will show is that they give precipitates with solutions of silver or copper salts. For example, ethyne gives a white precipitate of silver dicarbide (silver acetylide), AgC_2, with a combination of silver nitrate and ammonia solutions. With a solution containing copper(I) chloride and ammonia, a red precipitate, CuC_2, is produced. *Warning*: Do not attempt these reactions. If the precipitates dry out they can explode unpredictably!

The reaction of ethyne with Baeyer's reagent is a little different to that of ethene. Oxidation takes place, but the product is not an alcohol. Instead, ethanedioic acid (oxalic acid) is produced:

$$\text{H—C}\equiv\text{C—H} \longrightarrow \text{HO(O=)C—C(=O)OH}$$

> **112.20** Ethyne can be prepared by using 1,2-dibromoethane as a starting material. What else would you use in the preparation? (Hint: look back at methods of preparing alkenes.)
>
> **112.21** Predict the result of reacting hydrogen chloride with ethyne. Give the name of the product and draw the structure. (Hint: you can treat ethyne as a molecule with two π bonds, and remember Markovnikoff's rule.)

Answers

112.1

trans-1,2-dichloroethene has no dipole (H and Cl on each C, on opposite sides)

cis-1,2-dichloroethene has a dipole (Cl, Cl on one side; H, H on the other)

1,1-dichloroethene has a dipole (H, H on one C; Cl, Cl on the other)

112.2 No. In organic chemistry unsaturation has nothing to do with water. The name means that an unsaturated compound could contain more hydrogen atoms than it has at present.

112.3 The result is butan-2,3-diol

$$\text{CH}_3\text{—CH(OH)—CH(OH)—CH}_3$$

Answers – cont.

112.4 (i)

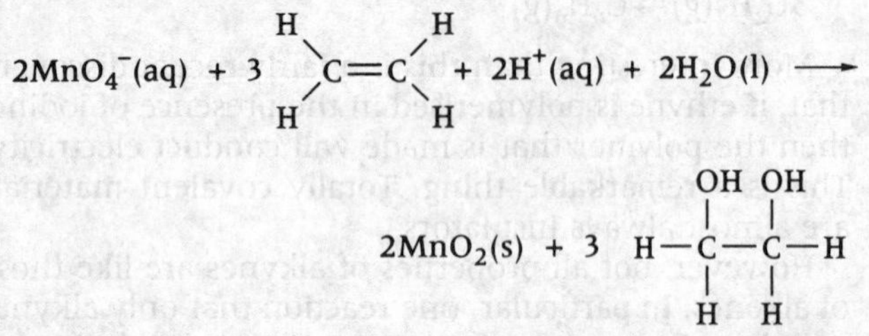

$$2MnO_4^-(aq) + 3\ H_2C{=}CH_2 + 2H^+(aq) + 2H_2O(l) \longrightarrow 2MnO_2(s) + 3\ H{-}C(H)(OH){-}C(H)(OH){-}H$$

(ii) The half-equations show that the manganate(VII) ion gains electrons, so it is acting as an oxidising agent. Alternatively, we can say that, because the alkene has gained oxygen, it has been oxidised.

112.5

(i) One mole of gas occupies approximately 24 dm³ at room temperature and pressure, so we have 600 cm³/24 000 cm³ mol⁻¹ = 0.025 mol hydrogen.

(ii) 2.03 g/81 g mol⁻¹ = 0.025 mol of hydrocarbon.

(iii) 1 mol hydrogen to 1 mol hydrocarbon.

(iv) One.

(v) You have to work out that, with a molar mass of 82 g mol⁻¹, the only possibility for the formula of the hydrocarbon is C_6H_{10}. (If there were less than six carbon atoms there would be too many hydrogen atoms to fit; e.g. C_5H_{22} is impossible. If there were more than six carbon atoms, the molar mass would be too large.) The molecule is *cyclohexene*:

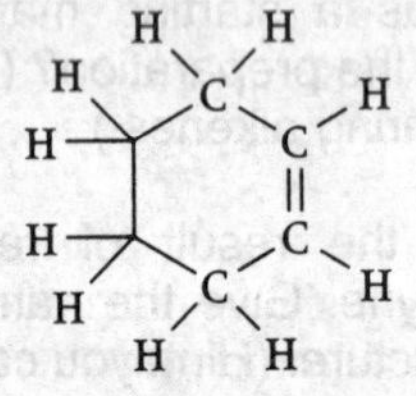

$$\text{cyclo-}C_6H_{10}\ (\text{six-membered ring, one } C{=}C)$$

This is a useful alkene, being a liquid at room temperature. You may use it in your laboratory work.

112.6 (i) Propan-2-ol

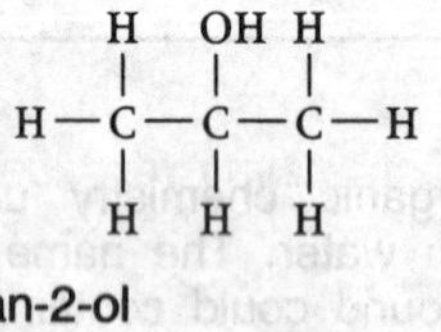

$$H{-}CH_2{-}CH(OH){-}CH_2{-}H$$

(ii) Butan-2-ol

$$H{-}CH_2{-}CH_2{-}CH(OH){-}CH_2{-}H$$

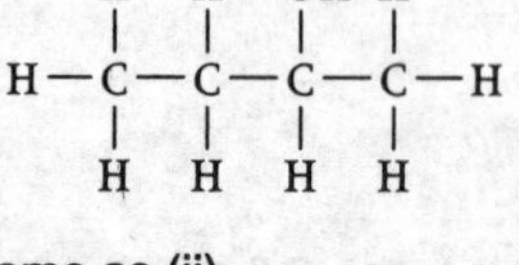

(iii) Same as (ii).

112.7 There should be three products:

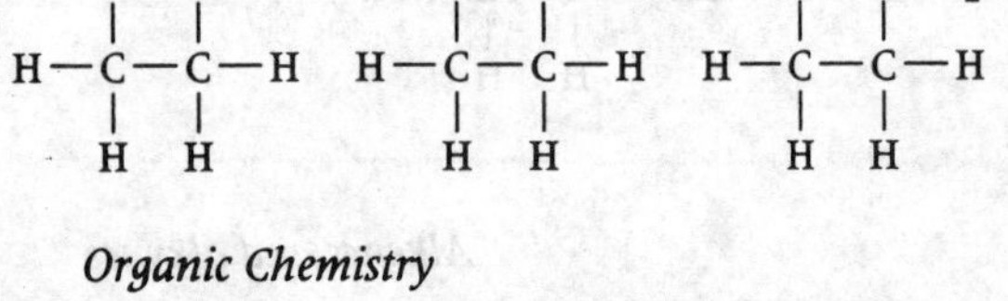

$$CH_2Br{-}CH_2Br \qquad CH_2Br{-}CH_2Cl \qquad CH_2Br{-}CH_2ONO_2$$

112.8 Yes, the movement of charge that we have described as the inductive effect is another way of describing polarisation.

112.9 The most favourable carbocation intermediate is the one with the most methyl groups attached to the carbon carrying the positive charge. There are two alternatives:

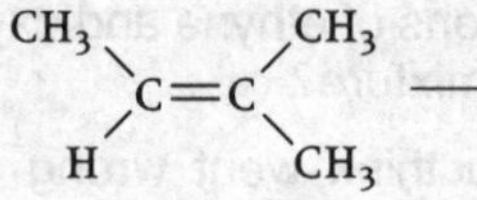

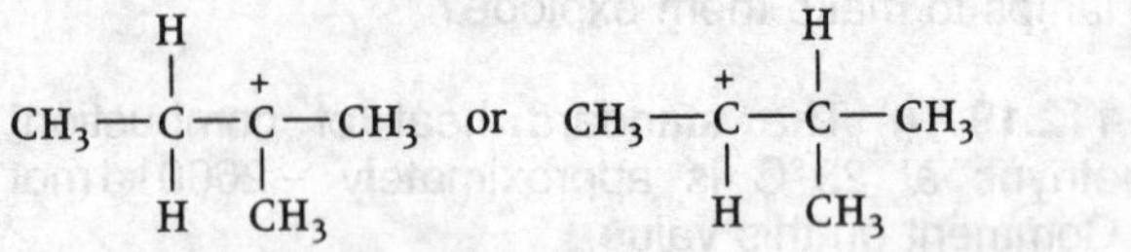

$$(CH_3)_2C{=}CH(CH_3)$$

$$CH_3{-}CH_2{-}\overset{+}{C}(CH_3){-}CH_3 \quad \text{or} \quad CH_3{-}\overset{+}{C}H{-}CH(CH_3){-}CH_3$$

The first one is the most favoured, so the product will be 2-chloro-2-methylbutane:

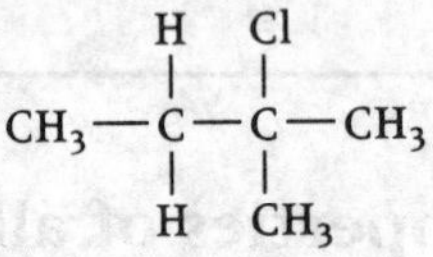

$$CH_3{-}CH_2{-}CCl(CH_3){-}CH_3$$

112.10 2-Methylpropan-2-ol:

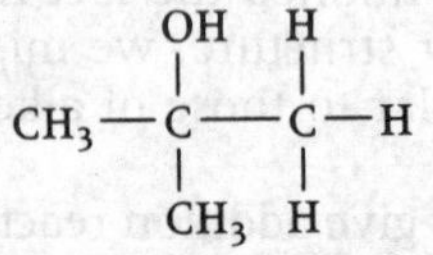

$$CH_3{-}C(OH)(CH_3){-}CH_2{-}H$$

112.11 The product is CH_2BrCH_2OH:

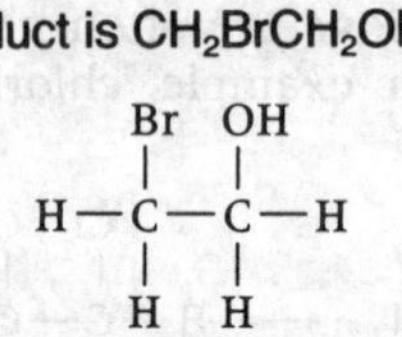

$$H{-}CH(Br){-}CH(OH){-}H$$

sometimes known as ethylene bromohydrin, but more properly called 2-bromoethan-1-ol.

112.12 We say that alkenes contain a double bond, but strictly *a* double bond does not exist. There are two bonds, the σ and the π. Only the π bond breaks. So the sentence should say that the π bond breaks rather than 'the double bond'.

112.13 The original alkene could have been either of the following:

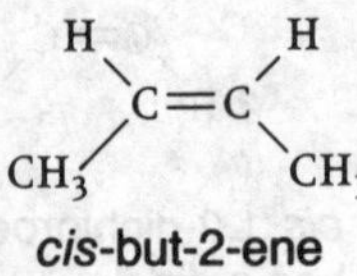

$$CH_3CH{=}CHCH_3$$

cis-but-2-ene 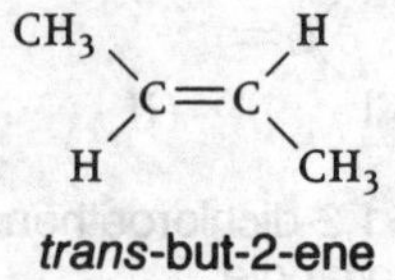   *trans*-but-2-ene

112.14 Propene:

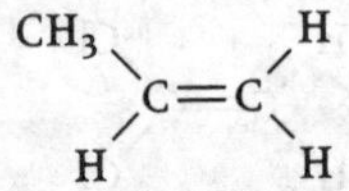

$$CH_3CH{=}CH_2$$

112.15 The isoprene units from which the structures are built are shown in Figure 112.9. (Carotene is the

Answers – cont.

Assuming the double bonds in isoprene break, we have

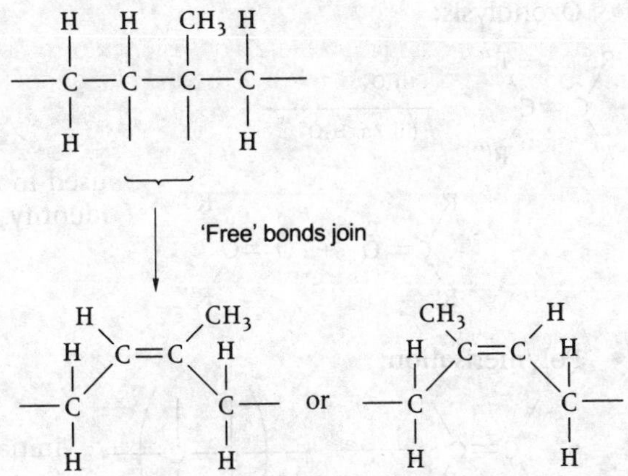

$$-\overset{H}{\underset{H}{C}}-\overset{H}{C}-\overset{CH_3}{C}-\overset{H}{\underset{H}{C}}-$$

'Free' bonds join

The 'free' bonds on the ends can join with similar fragments to make the polymer

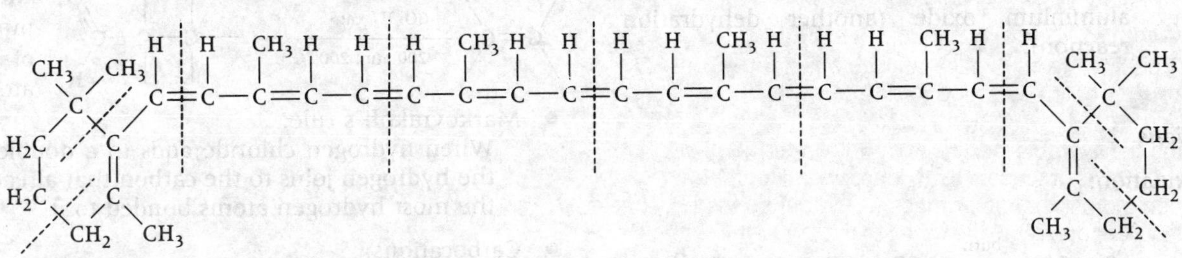

The lines through the bonds show where the isoprene units fit into the structure of carotene

Figure 112.9 Diagrams for answer to question 112.15

substance that gives carrots, and other things, their colour.) Isoprene is the basic building block of a large number of naturally occurring compounds.

112.16 The reaction is:

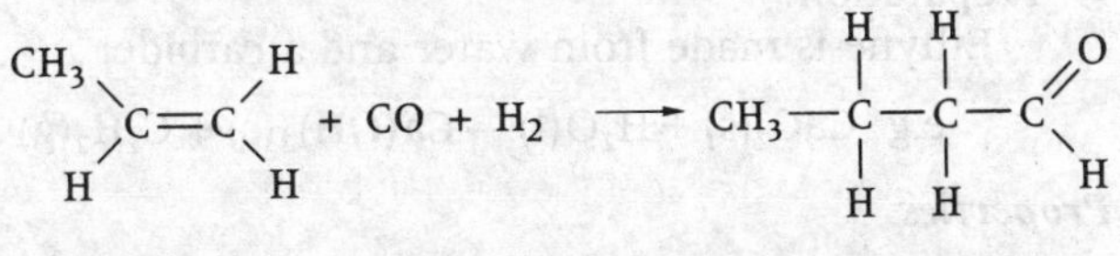

$$CH_3CH{=}CH_2 + CO + H_2 \longrightarrow CH_3{-}CH_2{-}CH_2{-}CHO$$

$CH_3CHCH_2(g) + CO(g) + H_2(g) \rightarrow CH_3CH_2CH_2CHO(g)$
butanal

followed by:

$CH_3CH_2CH_2CHO(g) + H_2(g) \rightarrow CH_3CH_2CH_2CH_2OH(g)$
butan-1-ol

112.17 Yes. They contain fewer hydrogen atoms than the corresponding alkane.

112.18 (i) $2C_2H_2(g) + 5O_2(g) \rightarrow 4CO_2(g) + 2H_2O(g)$

(ii) Two volumes of ethyne to five volumes of oxygen.

(iii) People attempted to light the ethyne before all the air was swept out of the burner, or the burner leaked and air could get in to where the calcium dicarbide was stored.

112.19 (i) The value shows that under standard conditions the reaction is extremely exothermic. In part, this is because ethyne is an endothermic compound, i.e. it has a positive heat of formation.

(ii) The exothermic nature of the reaction allows the very high temperatures needed to melt metals to be reached.

112.20 Alcoholic potassium hydroxide.

112.21 After the first molecule of HCl adds, we have

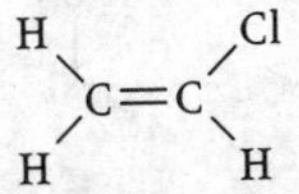

$$H_2C{=}CHCl$$

Following Markovnikoff's rule, the next molecule of HCl gives 1,1-dichloroethane:

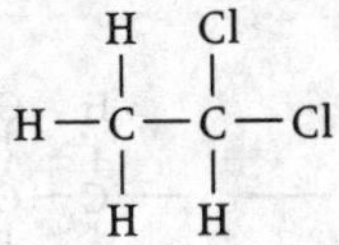

$$CH_3{-}CHCl_2$$

UNIT 112 SUMMARY

Alkenes

(i) Have the general formula C_nH_{2n}; e.g. ethene, C_2H_4; propene, C_3H_6.
(ii) Have one or more double bonds (unsaturated).
(iii) May have *cis* and *trans* isomers.

- Preparation:

(i) Heat halogenoalkane with alcoholic potassium hydroxide;

e.g. $C_2H_5Cl + KOH \rightarrow C_2H_4 + KCl + H_2O$

(ii) Heat an alcohol with concentrated sulphuric acid (dehydration reaction);

e.g. $\underset{\text{ethanol}}{C_2H_5OH(g)} \xrightarrow{180\,°C} \underset{\text{ethene}}{C_2H_4(g)} + H_2O(g)$

(iii) Pass vapour of an alcohol over hot aluminium oxide (another dehydration reaction).

Reactions

- Oxidation:

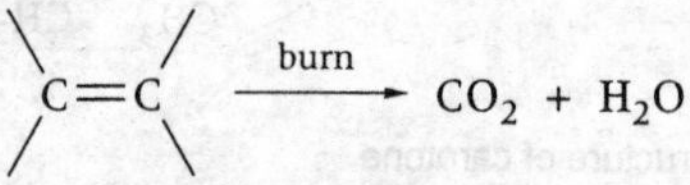

$$>C{=}C< \xrightarrow{\text{burn}} CO_2 + H_2O \quad \text{sooty flame}$$

- Addition reactions:

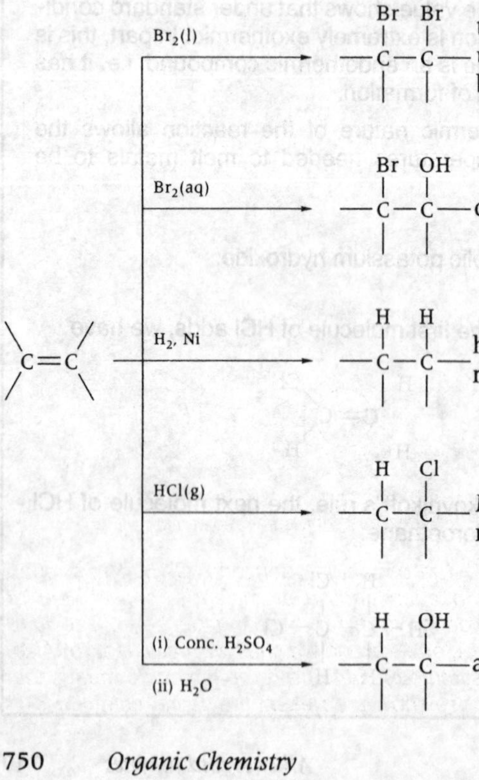

$>C{=}C< \xrightarrow{Br_2(l)}$ —C(Br)—C(Br)— tests for unsaturation: bromine

$\xrightarrow{Br_2(aq)}$ —C(Br)—C(OH)— decolourised

$\xrightarrow{H_2,\ Ni}$ —C(H)—C(H)— hydrogenation reaction

$\xrightarrow{HCl(g)}$ —C(H)—C(Cl)— Markovnikoff's rule

$\xrightarrow{\text{(i) Conc. } H_2SO_4,\ \text{(ii) } H_2O}$ —C(H)—C(OH)— alcohols made

- Ozonolysis:

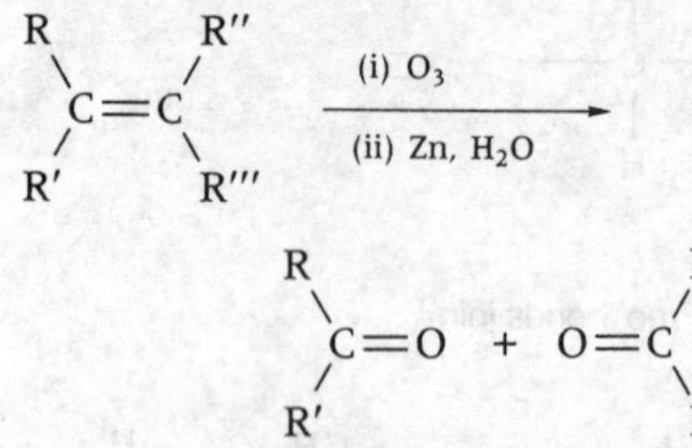

$$RR'C{=}CR''R''' \xrightarrow[\text{(ii) Zn, } H_2O]{\text{(i) } O_3} RR'C{=}O + O{=}CR''R'''$$

used to identify alkenes

- Polymerisation:

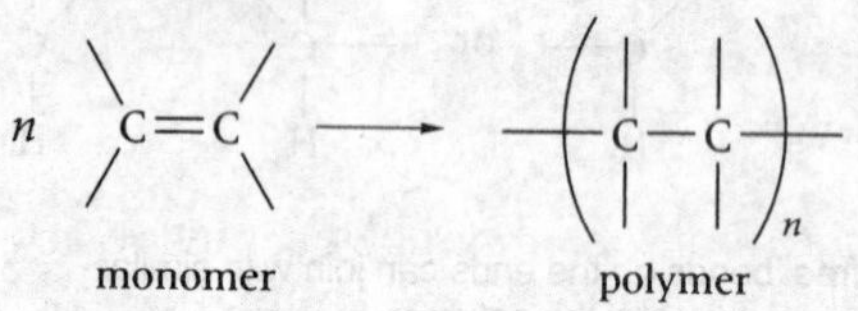

$$n\ \underset{\text{monomer}}{>C{=}C<} \longrightarrow \underset{\text{polymer}}{\left(-\overset{|}{\underset{|}{C}}-\overset{|}{\underset{|}{C}}-\right)_n}$$

initiated by free radicals

- Oxo reaction:

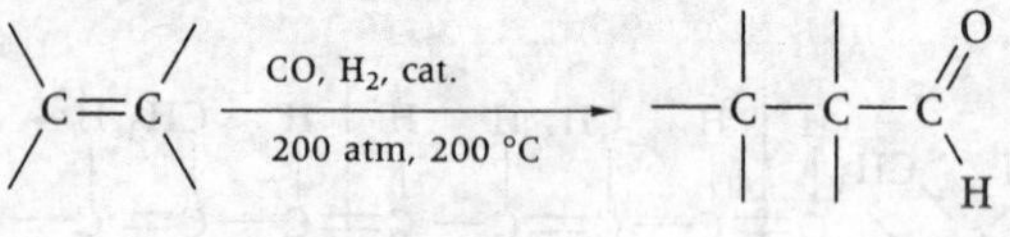

$$>C{=}C< \xrightarrow[\text{200 atm, 200 °C}]{CO,\ H_2,\ \text{cat.}} -\overset{|}{\underset{|}{C}}-\overset{|}{\underset{|}{C}}-CHO$$

increase number of carbon atoms

- Markovnikoff's rule:

When hydrogen chloride adds to a double bond the hydrogen joins to the carbon that already has the most hydrogen atoms bonded to it.

- Carbocations:

(i) Are groups in which a carbon atom carries a positive charge.
(ii) Order of their energetic stability is primary < secondary < tertiary.

Alkynes

Have the general formula C_nH_{2n-2}; e.g. ethyne, C_2H_2; propyne, C_3H_4.

- Preparation:

Ethyne is made from water and a carbide;

e.g. $CaC_2(s) + H_2O(l) \rightarrow Ca(OH)_2(s) + C_2H_2(g)$

Properties

- Oxidation:

$$-C{\equiv}C- \xrightarrow{\text{burn}} CO_2 + H_2O \quad \text{very sooty flame}$$

- Addition:

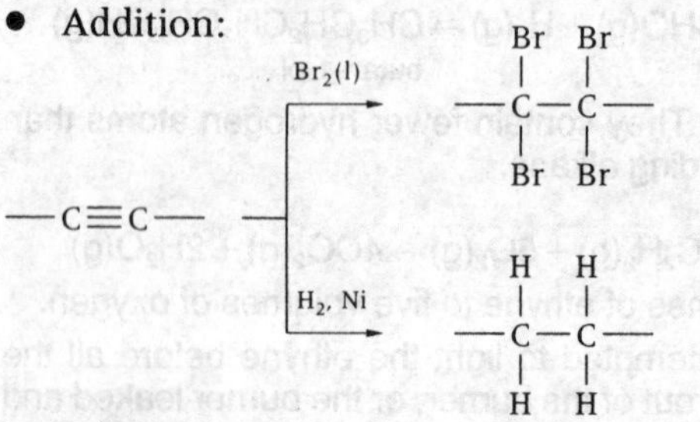

$-C{\equiv}C- \xrightarrow{Br_2(l)}$ —C(Br_2)—C(Br_2)— bromine decolourised

$\xrightarrow{H_2,\ Ni}$ —C(H)—C(H)— hydrogenation reaction

- Polymerisation:

$$3C_2H_2 \xrightarrow{400\,°C} \underset{\text{benzene}}{C_6H_6}$$

113

Aromatic hydrocarbons

113.1 What are aromatic hydrocarbons?

Aromatic hydrocarbons contain delocalised electrons around a ring of carbon atoms. As a group, they are also called *arenes*. The most famous arene is benzene, C_6H_6. It is a colourless liquid at room temperature. (Density, $0.87\,g\,cm^{-3}$; melting point, 5.7 °C; boiling point, 80.3 °C.) The structure of benzene is unusual because it appears to have three single bonds and three double bonds between its six carbon atoms. However, you should know that there are no individual π bonds in benzene (see Unit 16). The π electrons are delocalised around the ring (Figure 113.1). This delocalisation brings a degree of energetic stability to benzene that other unsaturated compounds may not have.

If we remove one of the hydrogen atoms from the ring and substitute it by a methyl group, we have a new aromatic hydrocarbon, methylbenzene. Similarly we can exchange a hydrogen atom for an ethyl group, which gives ethylbenzene. These hydrocarbon groups attached to the ring are called the *side chains*. Some arenes are shown in Table 113.1.

If you build a model of benzene and replace two hydrogen atoms by methyl groups, you will find that you can do this in three different ways, i.e. there are three *isomers* (Figure 113.2). Notice that we base the name of the isomers on numbers given to each of the carbon atoms in the ring.

More complicated arenes are made when two or more rings are joined together. This happens, for example, in naphthalene and anthracene (Figure 113.3). Molecules like these have their π clouds stretching over two or more rings. The delocalisation is even more extensive than in benzene. Needless to say, in these compounds many isomers are possible when different groups are substituted for the hydrogen atoms.

> **113.1** (i) Write the equation for the burning of benzene in oxygen.
>
> (ii) Why is it that if benzene is burned in air it produces a very smoky flame and large amounts of soot are sent into the air?

(a)

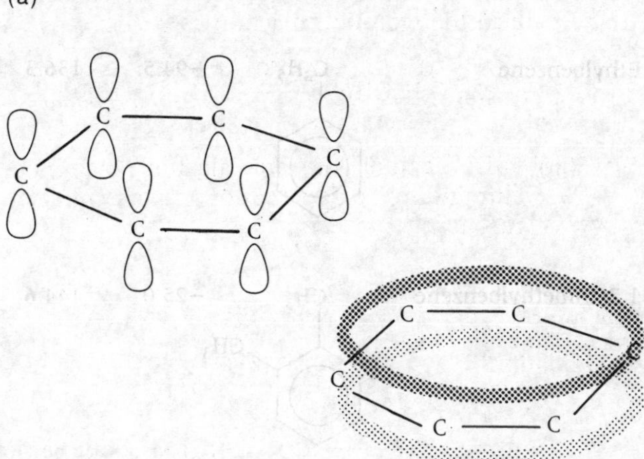

(b)

(c)

etc.

All represent the same molecule

Figure 113.1 *(a) The bonding in benzene, C_6H_6. The overlap of a p orbital on each carbon atom leads to π molecular orbitals. (b) Three ways of representing benzene. The third one is the neatest, and the one we shall normally use. (c) Also, notice that the symmetry of the benzene molecule means that diagrams like those shown represent the same molecule*

Table 113.1. Some aromatic hydrocarbons (arenes)

Compound	*Structure*	*Melting point/°C*	*Boiling point/°C*
Benzene		5.7	80.3
Methylbenzene	CH_3	−94.5	110.8
Ethylbenzene	C_2H_5	−94.5	136.3
1,2-Dimethylbenzene	CH_3, CH_3	−25.0	144.6
1,3-Dimethylbenzene	CH_3, CH_3	−47.7	139.3
1,4-Dimethylbenzene	CH_3, CH_3	13.4	138.5
Naphthalene		80.4	218.1
Anthracene		217	354

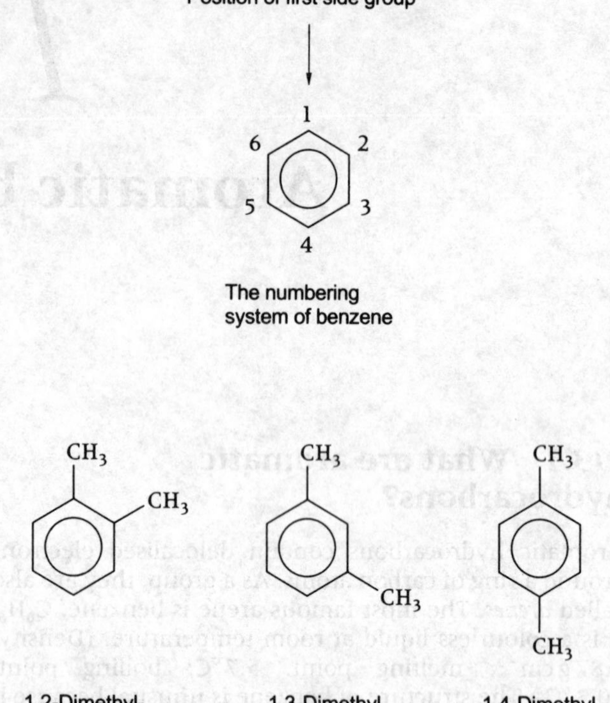

Figure 113.2 *There are three isomers of dimethylbenzene. Where there is a choice, we use the lowest possible sequence of numbers*

113.2 Ways of making arenes

(a) *Making benzene*

Benzene and other arenes can be obtained by distilling coal. This is a particularly messy process in the laboratory, and requires a lengthy business of separating the products from one another. However, in industry it is an economic way of isolating benzene. There is strong demand for coke, which is produced by heating coal in the absence of air. For every tonne of coal turned into coke, about 70 dm^3 of coal tar is made. This is an oily liquid, which contains a variety of products. If the coal tar is separated by fractional distillation, around 30 dm^3 of benzene can be collected. Methylbenzene, naphthalene and anthracene are also obtained in smaller quantities.

In the laboratory a quicker way to make benzene is to heat the calcium salt of benzoic acid, $(C_6H_5COO)_2Ca$, with soda lime (soda lime contains calcium hydroxide together with sodium hydroxide):

$$(C_6H_5COO)_2Ca(s) + Ca(OH)_2(s) \rightarrow 2C_6H_6(l) + 2CaCO_3(s)$$

Note: arenes are often carcinogenic – you should use them only with great caution.

(b) *Making arenes*

There is one method that is extremely useful for making a wide variety of arenes. It is the *Friedel–Crafts alkylation*

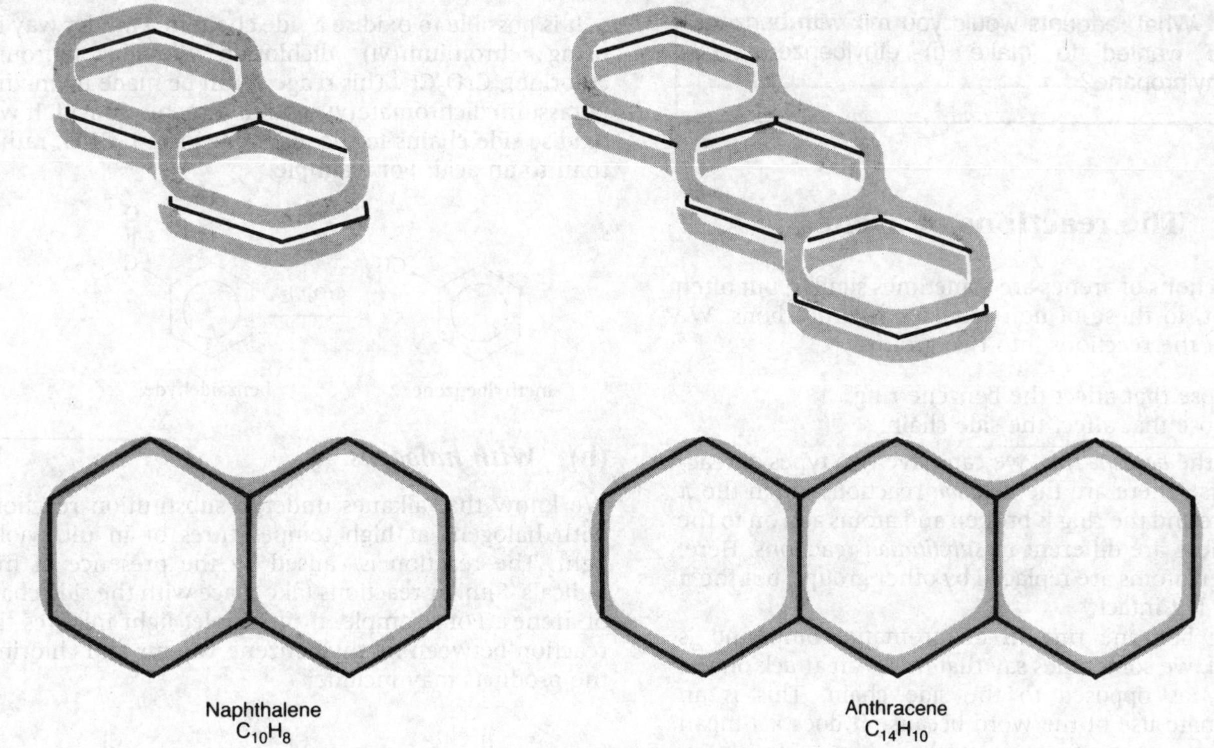

***Figure 113.3** The π clouds in naphthalene and anthracene stretch over all the carbon atoms*

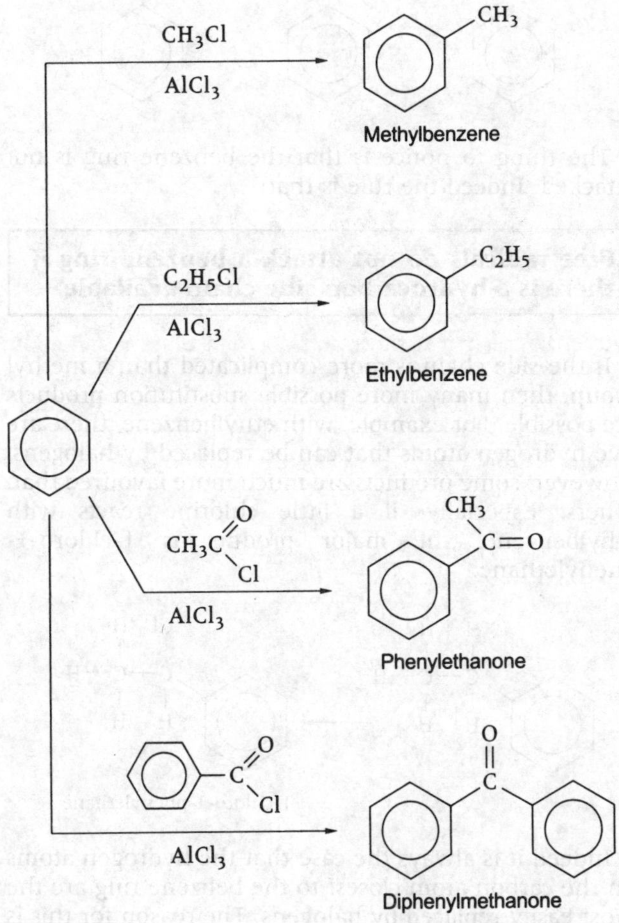

***Figure 113.4** Four examples of Friedel–Crafts reactions*

reaction. The essence of the reaction is to take a chloroalkane and react it with benzene in the presence of aluminium trichloride. Some of the possibilities are illustrated in Figure 113.4.

The reason why the reaction takes place is that the benzene ring is attacked by positively charged alkyl groups. For example, if we use chloromethane, CH_3Cl, positively charged methyl groups, $CH_3{}^+$, are generated. (The aluminium trichloride plays an active part in generating them.) Such groups are *electrophiles;* that is, they seek out centres of negative charge. The benzene ring with its rich cloud of delocalised π electrons is such a centre. We could write the equation in this way:

$$C_6H_6 + CH_3^{\oplus} \longrightarrow [C_6H_6CH_3]^{\oplus} \longrightarrow C_6H_5CH_3 + H^+$$

In panel 113.1 you will find details of the mechanism of the Friedel–Crafts reaction.

> **113.2** A second method of making arenes is similar to the Wurtz synthesis of alkanes. It is called the Wurtz–Fittig reaction. The method involves heating sodium with bromobenzene and a bromoalkane. Predict the equation for the reaction that would take place if bromoethane were used.

113.3 What reagents would you mix with benzene if you wanted to make (i) ethylbenzene, (ii) 2-phenylpropane?

113.3 The reactions of arenes

The reactions of arenes are sometimes similar, but often different, to those of non-aromatic hydrocarbons. We can split the reactions into two groups:

(i) those that affect the benzene ring,
(ii) those that affect the side chain.

With the *benzene ring*, we can have two types of reaction. First, there are the *addition* reactions when the π cloud around the ring is broken and atoms add on to the ring. These are different to *substitution* reactions. Here, hydrogen atoms are replaced by other groups, but the π cloud is left intact.

If the benzene ring in an aromatic compound is attacked, we sometimes say that this is an attack on the nucleus, as opposed to the side chain. This is an unfortunate use of the word because it does *not* mean that benzene rings are attacked by nucleophiles. Indeed, the reverse is true. The typical reagent to bring about substitution in a benzene ring is an electrophile.

There are several differences between the reactions of the benzene ring and other unsaturated compounds, such as alkenes. The reason is that the increased delocalisation of the π electrons has an influence on both the energetics of reactions and their kinetics.

With the *side chain*, several things can happen, the most important of which are substitution and oxidation reactions.

In the next three sections we shall look at examples of each of these reactions.

113.4 Reactions of the side chain

(a) *Oxidation*

The side chain, but not the benzene ring, is easily oxidised by reagents such as hot potassium manganate(VII), potassium dichromate(VI), or even nitric acid. The main product is benzoic acid, C_6H_5COOH, but carbon dioxide will also be given off. This acid is made no matter the length of the hydrocarbon side chain. For example,

$C_6H_5CH_2CH_3$ —oxidation→ C_6H_5COOH (benzoic acid) ←oxidation— $C_6H_5CH_2CH_2CH_2CH_3$

It is possible to oxidise a side chain in a milder way by using chromium(VI) dichloride dioxide (chromyl chloride), CrO_2Cl_2. This reagent can be made by mixing potassium dichromate(VI) with hydrochloric acid. It will oxidise side chains to the aldehyde group, CHO, rather than to an acid. For example,

$C_6H_5CH_3$ (methylbenzene) —CrO_2Cl_2→ C_6H_5CHO (benzaldehyde)

(b) *With halogens*

We know that alkanes undergo substitution reactions with halogens at high temperatures or in ultraviolet light. The reaction is caused by the presence of free radicals. Similar reactions take place with the side chain of arenes. For example, if ultraviolet light initiates the reaction between methylbenzene vapour and chlorine, the products may include:

$C_6H_5CH_2Cl$ $C_6H_5CHCl_2$ $C_6H_5CCl_3$

The thing to notice is that the benzene ring is not attacked. Indeed the rule is that:

Free radicals do not attack a benzene ring if there is a hydrocarbon side chain available.

If the side chain is more complicated than a methyl group, then many more possible substitution products are possible. For example, with ethylbenzene, there are five hydrogen atoms that can be replaced by halogens. However, some products are much more favoured than others. Especially, if a little chlorine reacts with ethylbenzene, the major product is 1-chloro-1-phenylethane:

$C_6H_5CH_2CH_3$ → $C_6H_5CHClCH_3$

1-chloro-1-phenylethane

Indeed it is always the case that the hydrogen atoms on the carbon atom closest to the benzene ring are the most easily replaced by halogens. The reason for this is complicated and too involved for us to deal with.

113.4 Figure 113.5 shows an apparatus set up by a student intending to oxidise methylbenzene using potassium manganate(VII) solution. What is wrong with it?

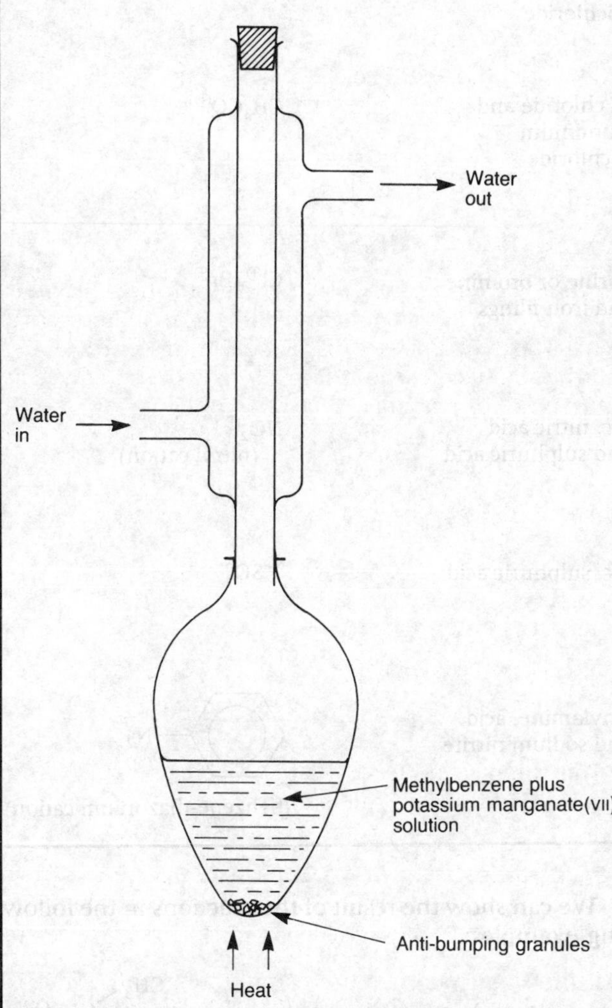

Figure 113.5 *Proposed arrangement of apparatus for question 113.4*

113.5 Benzoic acid is a white solid at room temperature. It is only very slightly soluble in cold water. If the oxidation of methylbenzene is carried out in acid conditions, a white precipitate appears in the flask. In alkaline conditions no precipitate appears. However, if acid is added at the end of the experiment, the precipitate does form. Explain these observations. (Hint: benzoic acid is a weak acid.)

113.6 1,3-Dimethylbenzene is oxidised by potassium dichromate(VI) solution. Draw the product of the reaction.

113.5 Addition reactions of the benzene ring

Hydrogen will add to benzene if it is reacted with hydrogen in the presence of a nickel catalyst at around 150 °C:

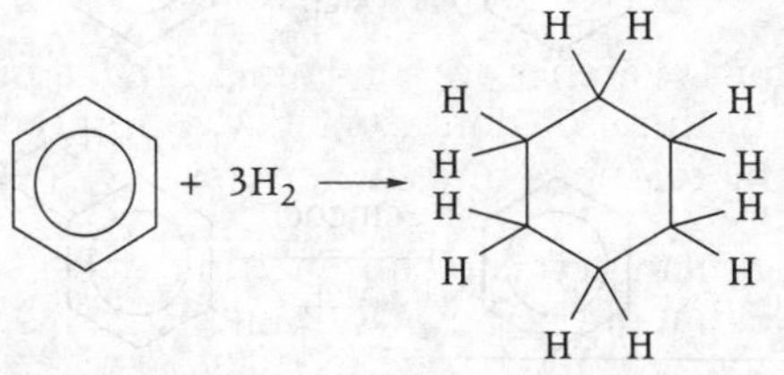

$$C_6H_6(g) + 3H_2(g) \rightarrow C_6H_{12}(g)$$

cyclohexane

This is much the same reaction as the hydrogenation of alkenes. It is possible to get halogens to add to a benzene molecule. A mixture of benzene, halogen and ultraviolet light will do the trick. For example, 1 mol of benzene, C_6H_6, takes up 3 mol of chlorine to give $C_6H_6Cl_6$. Notice the difference between this and the normal free radical reaction: the six hydrogen atoms on the ring are *not* substituted. The chlorine atoms add on to the ring. As you might expect, the structure of the product is based on cyclohexane:

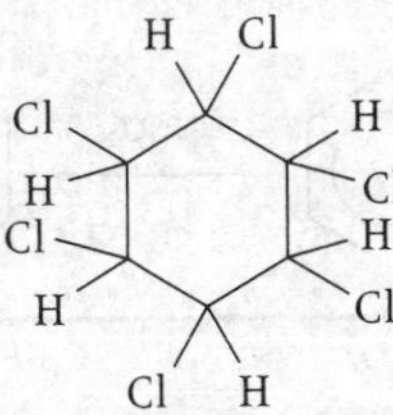

1,2,3,4,5,6-hexachlorocyclohexane

This substance is also known as benzene hexachloride (even though it does not contain a benzene ring). It is used as the weedkiller Lindane.

The direct reaction of benzene with bromine, or bromine water, is extremely slow at room temperature. For this reason bromine is not decolourised by benzene. This is a distinct difference to non-aromatic alkenes or alkynes.

113.6 Electrophilic substitution of benzene rings

In the Friedel–Crafts alkylation reaction we have already seen one type of electrophilic substitution of a benzene ring. Other reactions of this type, which are also called *aromatic substitutions*, are listed in Table 113.2. We shall take them one by one. You will find brief details of the mechanisms of the reactions in panel 113.1.

Table 113.2. Electrophilic substitution reactions of a benzene ring

Type of reaction	*Example*	*Reagent*	*Electrophile*
Alkylation	benzene $\xrightarrow[AlCl_3]{CH_3Cl}$ $C_6H_5CH_3$	Halogenoalkane and aluminium trichloride	$CH_3^{\oplus}$
Acylation	benzene $\xrightarrow[AlCl_3]{CH_3COCl}$ $C_6H_5C(=O)CH_3$	Acyl chloride and aluminium trichloride	$CH_3CO^{\oplus}$
Halogenation	benzene $\xrightarrow[Fe]{Br_2}$ C_6H_5Br	Chlorine or bromine and iron filings	$Cl^{\oplus}$, $Br^{\oplus}$
Nitration	benzene $\xrightarrow[Conc.H_2SO_4]{Conc.HNO_3}$ $C_6H_5NO_2$	Conc. nitric acid and sulphuric acid	$NO_2^{\oplus}$ (nitryl cation)
Sulphonation	benzene $\xrightarrow{Conc.H_2SO_4}$ $C_6H_5SO_3H$	Conc. sulphuric acid	$^{\delta+}SO_3^{\delta-}$
Diazotisation	benzene $\xrightarrow[T<5\ °C]{HNO_2}$ $C_6H_5N_2+$	Phenylamine, acid and sodium nitrite	$C_6H_5N_2^{\oplus}$ (benzene-diazonium cation)

(a) *Alkylation*

We need say no more about this than you will find in section 113.2 and panel 113.1.

(b) *Acylation*

The acyl group is a combination of an alkyl group and a carbonyl group (>C=O). Among the most important molecules that contain an acyl group are the acid chlorides. Typical ones are:

$$CH_3-C(=O)Cl \qquad CH_3CH_2-C(=O)Cl$$

ethanoyl chloride   propanoyl chloride

The mechanism of their attack on a benzene ring is very similar to the way alkylation takes place. For example, the carbocation produced when ethanoyl chloride is mixed with aluminium trichloride is:

$$CH_3-C^{\oplus}=O$$

This is the electrophile that attacks the ring.

We can show the result of the reactions in the following examples:

$$C_6H_6 + CH_3C(=O)Cl \xrightarrow{AlCl_3} C_6H_5C(=O)CH_3$$

$$C_6H_6 + C_2H_5C(=O)Cl \xrightarrow{AlCl_3} C_6H_5C(=O)C_2H_5$$

(c) *Halogenation*

We have made the point that benzene will not decolourise bromine on its own. However, if some iron filings are present, a reaction starts and the bromine *is* decolourised. (Hydrogen bromide is given off as well.) The iron is said to act as a *halogen carrier*. It promotes the production of Br^+ ions, which attack the ring:

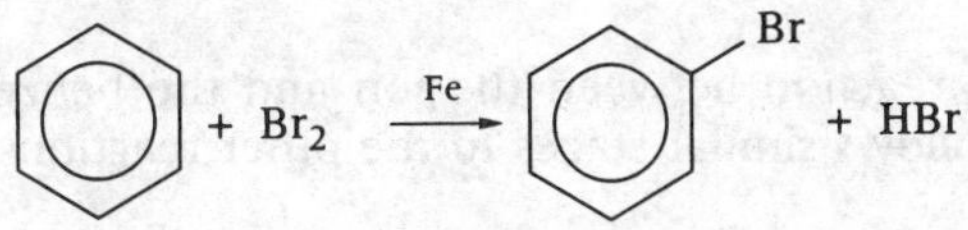

$$C_6H_6 + Br_2 \xrightarrow{Fe} C_6H_5Br + HBr$$

(d) *Nitration*

In nitration, nitryl cations, NO_2^+, made by the reaction between concentrated nitric and sulphuric acids, are the electrophiles:

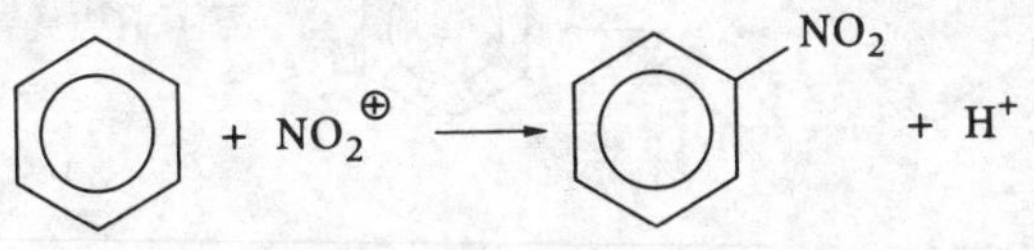

$$C_6H_6 + NO_2^{\oplus} \longrightarrow C_6H_5NO_2 + H^+$$

For obvious reasons you may hear of a mixture of concentrated nitric and sulphuric acids being called *nitrating mixture*.

(e) *Sulphonation*

The overall result of reacting an arene with concentrated sulphuric acid is that the benzene ring exchanges a hydrogen atom for a hydrogensulphite group:

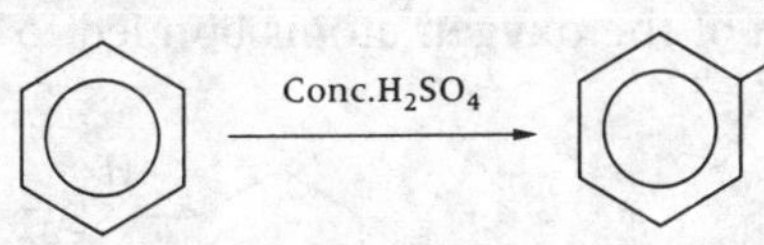

$$C_6H_6 \xrightarrow{\text{Conc.}H_2SO_4} C_6H_5SO_3H$$

(Actually the reaction involves sulphur trioxide as an intermediate.)

(f) *Diazotisation*

If you mix phenylamine together with an ice-cold solution of sodium nitrite in hydrochloric acid, the following reaction takes place:

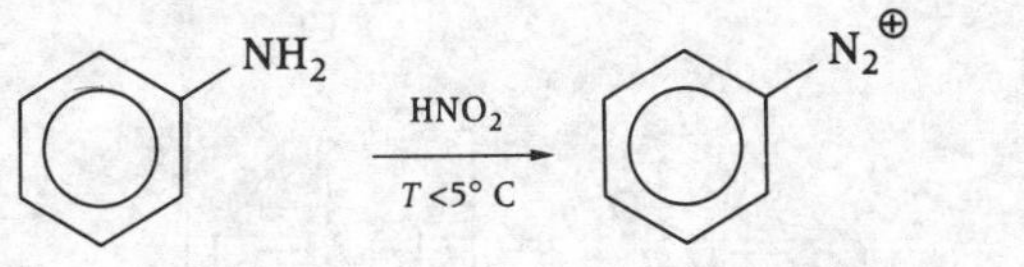

$$C_6H_5NH_2 \xrightarrow[T<5^\circ C]{HNO_2} C_6H_5N_2^{\oplus}$$

benzenediazonium ion

The positively charged benzenediazonium ion is not a very good electrophile. It will attack a benzene ring that has an activating group attached, especially phenol and phenylamine. The reaction is known as a *coupling* reaction. For example,

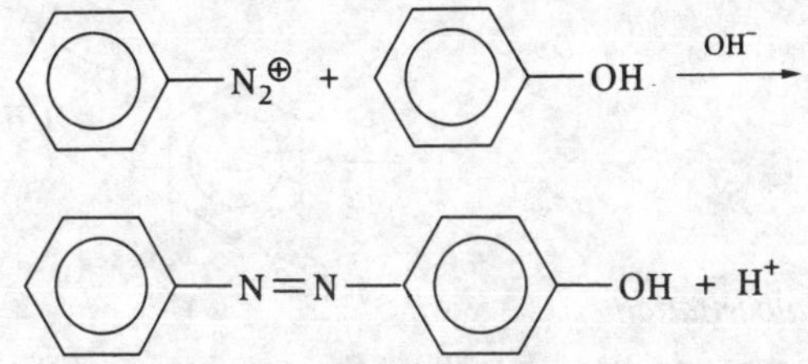

$$C_6H_5N_2^{\oplus} + C_6H_5OH \xrightarrow{OH^-} C_6H_5{-}N{=}N{-}C_6H_4{-}OH + H^+$$

Coupling reactions like this have been widely used in making dyes. You will find details in section 122.8.

Panel 113.1

The mechanisms of electrophilic substitution reactions

Friedel–Crafts alkylation

Let us suppose that we are using chloromethane to convert benzene into methylbenzene. Chloromethane is a polar molecule. The chlorine atom is highly electronegative: it carries a slightly negative charge and has three lone pairs around it. Also, aluminium trichloride is a Lewis acid (see section 74.4). This means that the molecule can accept a lone pair of electrons in making a fourth bond to the aluminium atom. If we bring a chloromethane molecule near to an aluminium trichloride molecule, a lone pair on the chlorine atom can form a coordinate bond. In the process the bond between the methyl group and the chlorine atom weakens and finally breaks. This frees a methyl carbocation, CH_3^+. It is this electrophile that attacks the ring:

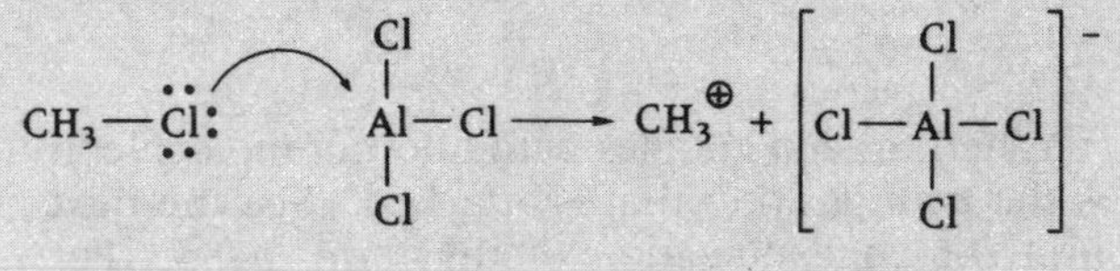

$$CH_3{-}\ddot{Cl}: + AlCl_3 \longrightarrow CH_3^{\oplus} + [AlCl_4]^-$$

The intermediate in the reaction consists of a benzene ring that has both a methyl group and a hydrogen atom attached by σ bonds to one of the carbon atoms. It is known as a *sigma complex*, or sometimes as a *Wheland intermediate*. The intermediate breaks up by the loss of a hydrogen ion, which carries the extra positive charge away with it:

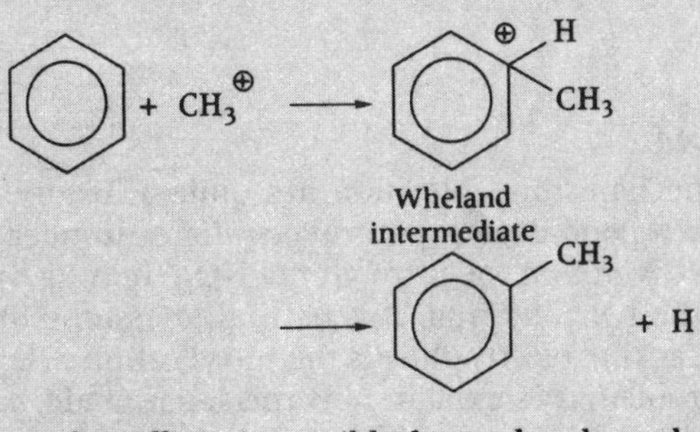

$$C_6H_6 + CH_3^{\oplus} \longrightarrow [C_6H_6CH_3]^{\oplus} \longrightarrow C_6H_5CH_3 + H^+$$

Wheland intermediate

Incidentally, it is possible for molecules to be held by a benzene ring by attraction with the π cloud. Bromine and hydrogen chloride are known to form *pi complexes* in this way.

Friedel–Crafts acylation

Here the aluminium trichloride brings about the production of a different type of carbocation than in

Panel 113.1 – cont.

the alkylation reaction; but the basic mechanism is the same. It is summed up in the next few equations:

$$CH_3-C(=O)-\ddot{Cl}: + AlCl_3 \longrightarrow CH_3-C^{\oplus}=O + [AlCl_4]^-$$

$$C_6H_6 + CH_3-C^{\oplus}=O \longrightarrow [C_6H_6(H)(COCH_3)]^{\oplus} \longrightarrow C_6H_5COCH_3 + H^+$$

Halogenation

If we assume that bromine and iron filings are mixed, the iron(III) bromide produced acts as a Lewis acid, accepting a pair of electrons from a bromine atom at one end of a bromine molecule. The molecule is polarised by the transfer of some electron density to the iron atom, and the second bromine atom in the molecule takes on a positive character. If the process continues successfully, a positively charged bromine atom is made. This is the electrophile that attacks the ring:

$$:\ddot{Br}-\ddot{Br}: + FeBr_3 \longrightarrow :\ddot{Br}^{\oplus} + [FeBr_4]^-$$

Nitration

The mechanism of nitration has quite a history. It caused a good deal of controversy for a number of years. Given that the nitro group, NO_2, finds its way onto the benzene ring, it is natural to assume that the attacking electrophile is the nitryl cation, NO_2^+. The problem is to explain how this ion is made, and to find experimental evidence for its existence.

We now believe it is made in the equilibrium

$$HNO_3 + 2H_2SO_4 \rightleftharpoons NO_2^+ + 2HSO_4^- + H_3O^+$$

which itself is the summary of several intermediate equilibria. Direct evidence for the presence of the nitryl cation in the mixture comes from spectroscopy, and from the fact that it is possible to isolate salts that contain the ion.

The reaction between the ion and the benzene ring follows similar stages to the other reactions:

$$C_6H_6 + NO_2^{\oplus} \longrightarrow [C_6H_6(H)(NO_2)]^{\oplus} \longrightarrow C_6H_5NO_2 + H^+$$

Sulphonation

In the sulphonation reaction, the electrophile is sulphur trioxide, SO_3. It is made by the autoionisation of sulphuric acid:

$$2H_2SO_4 \rightleftharpoons HSO_4^- + H_3O^+ + SO_3$$

In SO_3, sulphur has only three pairs of electrons involved in bonding to the oxygen atoms. Therefore it has space for a fourth pair before it completes its octet. Also the sulphur atom will carry a partial positive charge owing to the electron withdrawing nature of the oxygen atoms bonded to it. The reaction is:

$$C_6H_6 + \overset{\delta+}{S}\overset{\delta-}{O_3} \longrightarrow [C_6H_6(H)(SO_3^-)]^{\oplus} \longrightarrow C_6H_5SO_3^- + H^+ \longrightarrow C_6H_5SO_3H$$

Diazotisation

We shall ignore the details of how the benzenediazonium ion comes to be made. The key thing is that the nitrogen atoms on the end of the ion carry the positive charge that we expect of many electrophiles. It is most important that the reaction mixture is kept cold (less than 5 °C), otherwise the ion decomposes. The reaction is:

$$C_6H_5N_2^{\oplus} \xrightarrow{H_2O} C_6H_5OH + N_2 + H^+$$

When the ion couples with another molecule, it is the *para* position that is attacked. (See the next unit for an explanation of the term '*para*'.) For example, with phenol and with phenylamine:

Panel 113.1 – cont.

$$C_6H_5N_2^{\oplus} + C_6H_5\text{–OH} \longrightarrow C_6H_5\text{–N=N–}C_6H_4\text{–OH} + H^+$$

$$C_6H_5N_2^{\oplus} + C_6H_5\text{–NH}_2 \longrightarrow C_6H_5\text{–N=N–}C_6H_4\text{–NH}_2 + H^+$$

113.7 If the key thing about the use of aluminium trichloride in the Friedel–Crafts reaction is that it is a Lewis acid (or, alternatively, that it is electron deficient), which other molecule could be used in its place? (Hint: look at section 74.4.)

113.8 In 1825 Michael Faraday wrote the following in the *Philosophical Magazine*:

> The object of the paper which I have the honour of submitting to the attention of the Royal Society, is to describe particularly two new compounds of carbon and hydrogen, and generally, other products obtained during the decomposition of oil by heat .... Bi-carburet of hydrogen appears in common circumstances as a colourless transparent liquid, having an odour resembling that of oil gas, and partaking also of that of almonds. Its specific gravity is nearly 0.85 at 60°. When cooled to about 32° it crystallizes, becoming solid .... Its boiling point in contact with glass is 186° .... Chlorine introduced to the substance in a retort exerted but little action until placed in sunlight, when dense fumes were formed, without the evolution of much heat; and ultimately muriatic acid was produced .... The following is a result of what obtained when it was passed over heated oxide of copper: 0.776 grain of the substance produced 5.6 cubic inches of carbonic gas, at a temperature of 60°, and pressure 29.98 inches; and 0.58 grain of water were collected .... [His calculation showed that] making the hydrogen 1, the carbon is not far removed from 12, or two proportionals .... This result is confirmed by such data as I have been able to obtain by detonating the vapour of the substance with oxygen. Thus in one experiment 8092 mercury grain measures of oxygen at 62° had such quantity of the substance introduced into it as would entirely rise in the vapour; the volume increased to 8505: hence the vapour amounted to 413 parts, or 1/206 of the mixture nearly. Seven volumes of this mixture were detonated in an eudiometer tube by an electric spark, and diminished in consequence nearly to 6.1: these, acted upon by potash, were further diminished to 4, which were pure oxygen. Hence 3 volumes of mixture had been detonated, of which nearly 0.34 was vapour of the substance, and 2.65 oxygen. The carbonic acid amounted to 2.1 volumes ....

(i) Before we go into the chemistry of Faraday's observations, you need to know that he measured temperatures in degrees Fahrenheit. Find out the Celsius equivalent of 32°, 60° and 186° Fahrenheit.

(ii) Do Faraday's measurements of the specific gravity and boiling point of bi-carburet of hydrogen give you a guide to the identity of the compound? (You can assume that specific gravity is equivalent to density.)

(iii) Suggest the modern name of 'muriatic acid', and explain the reaction that made it.

(iv) 1 grain is equivalent to 0.065 g, and 1 cubic inch is approximately 16.4 cm^3. What substance do you think Faraday used to measure pressure? Work out the pressure of 29.98 inches in more common units.

(v) What is the modern name for carbonic gas?

(vi) Calculate the mass of carbon and of hydrogen that the 0.776 grain of the substance contained; hence calculate the empirical formula of the compound. Suggest the likely molecular formula.

(vii) Faraday's comment about the proportionality of carbon and hydrogen implies that the empirical formula was C_2H. What might be the reason for him suggesting this formula?

(viii) Check to see if his measurements on the reaction of the compound with oxygen fit the molecular formula that you have suggested for the compound.

Answers

113.1 (i) $2C_6H_6(l) + 15O_2(g) \rightarrow 12CO_2(g) + 6H_2O(g)$

(ii) Owing to the very large proportion of carbon in benzene, a great deal of oxygen is needed to convert all of it to carbon dioxide. In air there is not enough oxygen available close to the flame, and some of the carbon remains as soot.

Answers – cont.

113.2

$$C_6H_5Br + C_2H_5Br + 2Na \longrightarrow C_6H_5C_2H_5 + 2NaBr$$

$C_6H_5Br + C_2H_5Br + 2Na \rightarrow C_6H_5C_2H_5 + 2NaBr$
ethylbenzene

113.3 (i) Chloroethane, (ii) 2-chloropropane, both together with aluminium trichloride

113.4 The stopper should not be in the top of the condenser. Carbon dioxide is given off in the reaction, so with the stopper in, pressure would build up. At the least, the stopper would be blown out; but if it were stuck, a much more serious explosion could take place.

113.5 In water, the equilibrium

$$\underset{\text{white solid}}{C_6H_5COOH(s)} + H_2O(l) \rightleftharpoons \underset{\text{colourless solution}}{C_6H_5COO^-(aq) + H_3O^+(aq)}$$

lies far to the left-hand side. If alkali is present, oxonium ions are removed. Le Chatelier's principle confirms that the equilibrium should move to the right, i.e. in the direction that tends to replace the lost oxonium ions. Thus we should see a colourless solution. If acid is added, the equilibrium will shift to the left. This is the direction that produces insoluble benzoic acid crystals.

113.6 Both methyl groups are oxidised to acid groups. Benzene-1,3-dicarboxylic acid is made:

$$C_6H_4(CH_3)_2 \longrightarrow C_6H_4(COOH)_2$$

113.7 Boron trichloride is the one you were expected to think of. There are others, e.g. iron(III) chloride.

113.8 (i) The temperatures are, respectively, 0 °C, 15.6 °C and 85.6 °C.

(ii) The specific gravity is very close to that of benzene (see section 113.1), although the melting and boiling points are rather different. We might expect all his results to be inaccurate by today's standards: he obtained his sample from an oily by-product of a process used by the Portable Gas Company, not a chemical supplier.

(iii) We know it as hydrochloric acid. This is the free radical chlorination of benzene.

(iv) His pressure 29.98 inches refers to the height of a column of mercury supported by the gas. This height is nearly 76 cm of mercury, or a pressure of 1 atm, or 101.325 kPa.

(v) Carbon dioxide.

(vi) 0.776 grain is 0.052 g; 5.6 cubic inches is 91.84 cm^3; 0.58 grain is 0.038 g. Thus we have: 0.052 g of substance reacted with CuO to give 91.84 cm^3 of carbon dioxide (at 15.6 °C) and 0.038 g water. If we convert to s.t.p., the volume of CO_2 would be 91.84 $cm^3 \times$ (273 K/288.6 K), i.e. 86.88 cm^3. Therefore,

number of moles of CO_2
$= 86.88\ cm^3/22\ 400\ cm^3\ mol^{-1} = 0.0039\ mol$

This is also the number of moles of carbon that the original compound contained. (The carbon cannot come from the CuO.) Also

number of moles of water
$= 0.038\ g/18\ g\ mol^{-1} = 0.0021\ mol$

This contains $2 \times 0.0021\ mol = 0.0042\ mol$ of hydrogen. (All the hydrogen must also have been in the original compound.) Thus the ratio of moles of carbon to moles of hydrogen is 0.0039 mol to 0.0042 mol, or approximately 1:1. The empirical formula is CH.

We have reason to think it was benzene, C_6H_6. We know that 1 mol of benzene would contain 6 mol of carbon; so 0.0039 mol of carbon should come from $0.0039\ mol/6 = 65 \times 10^{-5}$ mol of benzene. The mass of this amount of benzene is $78\ g\ mol^{-1} \times 65 \times 10^{-5}\ mol = 0.0507\ g$. This is fairly close to the mass of the compound that Faraday used.

(vii) In Faraday's time, the relative atomic mass of carbon was thought to be 6 (not 12), so he thought it contained twice as much carbon as we calculate.

(viii) When benzene vapour completely burns in oxygen the equation is

$$C_6H_6(g) + (15/2)O_2(g) \rightarrow 6CO_2(g) + 3H_2O(l)$$

where we assume that the water condenses to a liquid at 62° F, or 16.7° C. The equation tells us that (under the same conditions of temperature and pressure) 1 vol of benzene should react completely with 15/2 vol of oxygen to give 6 vol of carbon dioxide. Alternatively,

1/6 vol C_6H_6 reacts with 15/12 vol O_2 to give 1 vol CO_2

i.e. 0.167 vol C_6H_6 reacts with 1.25 vol O_2 to give 1 vol CO_2, and 0.351 vol C_6H_6 reacts with 2.625 vol O_2 to give 2.1 vol CO_2. (Here we have scaled the figures to give the same volume of CO_2 that Faraday used.) You can see that the results agree with his figures to reasonable accuracy. In brief, Faraday had discovered benzene.

UNIT 113 SUMMARY

- Aromatic compounds contain one or more benzene rings.

Benzene, C_6H_6

(i) Has a delocalised ring of electrons.
(ii) Is more energetically stable than a similar molecule with separate single and double bonds.
(iii) Does not easily undergo addition reactions.
(iv) Is attacked by electrophiles, e.g. NO_2^+, CH_3^+.

- Preparation:
  Decarboxylation of calcium benzoate by heating with soda lime;

$$(C_6H_5COO)_2Ca(s) + Ca(OH)_2(s) \rightarrow 2C_6H_6(l) + 2CaCO_3(s)$$

Properties

- Oxidation:
  Burns in air with very sooty flame. But in oxygen

$$2C_6H_6(l) + 15O_2(g) \rightarrow 12CO_2(g) + 6H_2O(g)$$

- Hydrogenation:

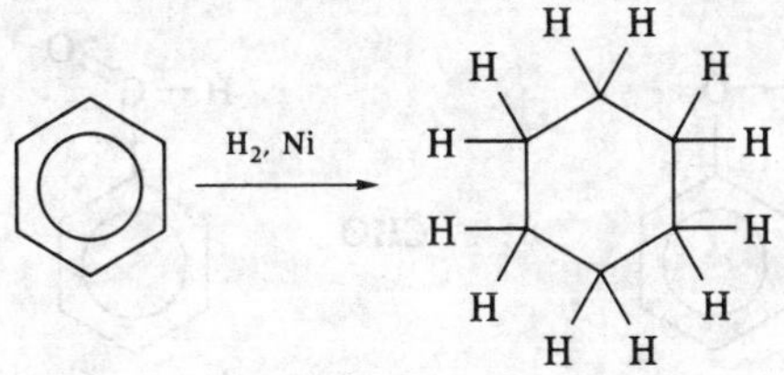

H₂, Ni → cyclohexane

- Chlorination:
  If there is no side chain,

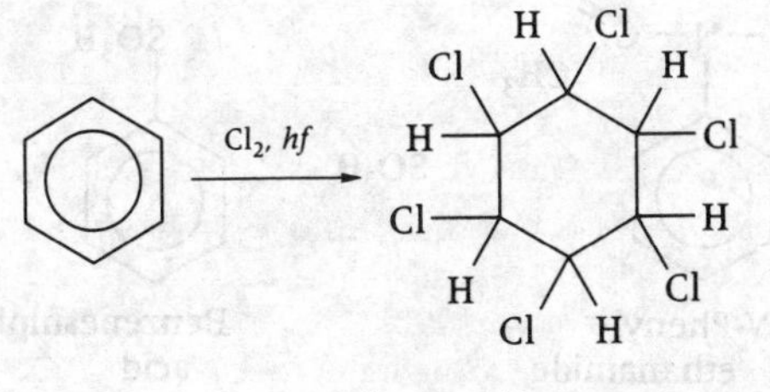

Cl_2, *hf* →

free radical reaction

- Electrophilic attack:
  This is summarised in Table 113.2.

Arenes

- Preparation:
  Friedel–Crafts reaction: benzene reacted with a halogenoalkane and aluminium trichloride; e.g.

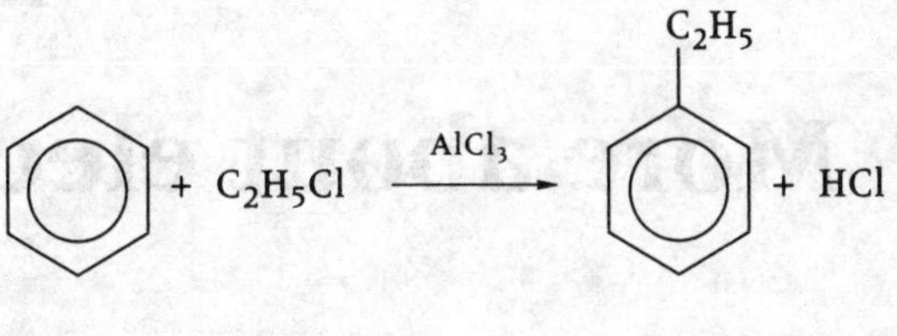

$$C_6H_6 + C_2H_5Cl \xrightarrow{AlCl_3} C_6H_5C_2H_5 + HCl$$

Reactions

- Of the side chain:
  (i) Oxidation

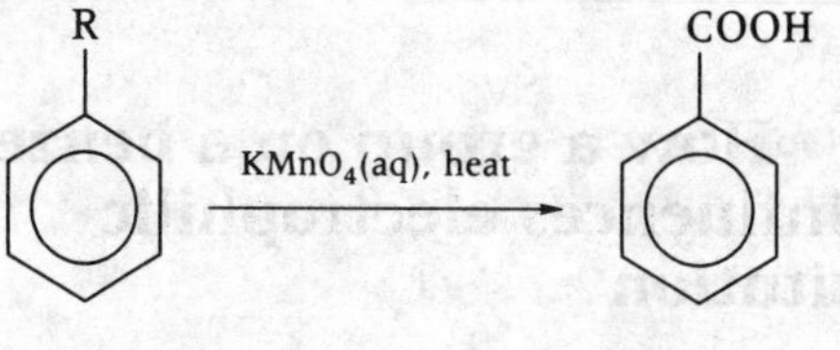

R → (KMnO$_4$(aq), heat) → COOH

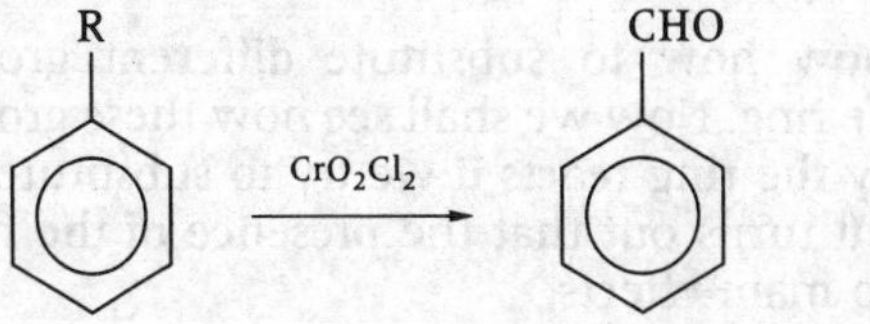

R → (CrO_2Cl_2) → CHO

  (ii) Halogenation: ultraviolet light induces attack on the side chain, not the ring; e.g.

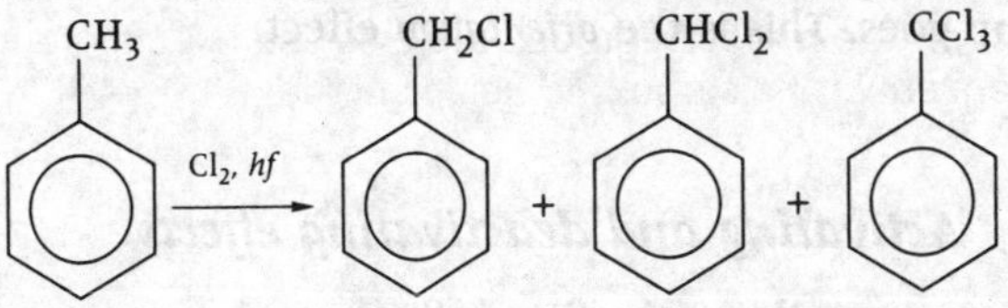

CH_3 → (Cl_2, *hf*) → CH_2Cl + $CHCl_2$ + CCl_3

free radicals involved.

- Of the ring:
  (i) Hydrogenation by heating with hydrogen and a nickel catalyst (see above).
  (ii) Electrophilic attack takes place; e.g. ring attacked in Friedel–Crafts reactions (see above).
- Diazotisation:
  Conversion of an aromatic amine into a diazonium ion. The latter can couple with, for example, phenol;

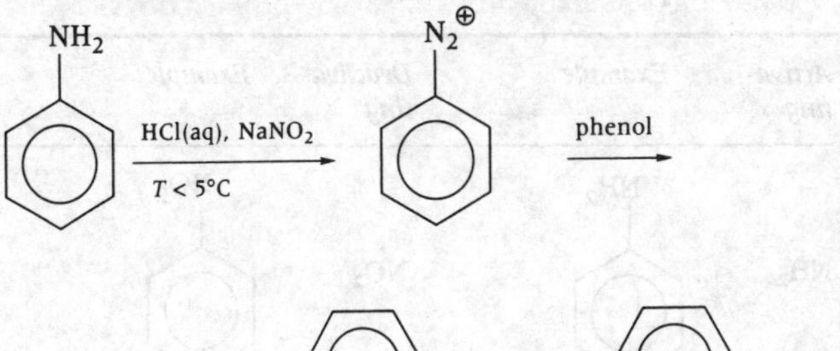

NH_2 → (HCl(aq), NaNO$_2$, $T < 5°C$) → $N_2^{\oplus}$ → (phenol) →

C_6H_5–N=N–C_6H_4–OH

114

More about electrophilic substitution

114.1 How a group on a benzene ring influences electrophilic substitution

We know how to substitute different groups in a benzene ring. Now we shall see how these groups affect the way the ring reacts if we try to substitute a second group. It turns out that the presence of the first group has two main effects.

First, it can change *how rapidly* the ring is attacked. Some groups make the ring react faster, some slower. Thus some groups *activate* and some *deactivate* the ring.

Secondly, it influences where on the ring the second group goes. This is the *orientation* effect.

(a) *Activating and deactivating effects*

You can see the activating influence of some groups very easily. Phenol, C_6H_5OH, consists of a benzene ring with an OH group bonded to it. At room temperature phenol is a pale pink solid, and is partially soluble in water. If you dissolve a little phenol in water and add bromine water, you will see an immediate white precipitate appear. The precipitate is 2,4,6-tribromophenol. Clearly the OH group activates the ring. In Table 114.1 you will find a list of activating and deactivating groups.

Table 114.1. Activating and deactivating groups in electrophilic substitution

Activating	*Example*	*Deactivating*	*Example*
NH_2	Phenylamine	NO_2	Nitrobenzene
OH	Phenol	COOH	Benzoic acid
OCH_3	Methoxybenzene	CHO	Benzaldehyde
$NHCOCH_3$	*N*-Phenylethanamide	SO_3H	Benzenesulphonic acid
CH_3	Methylbenzene	Cl (Br, I)	Chlorobenzene

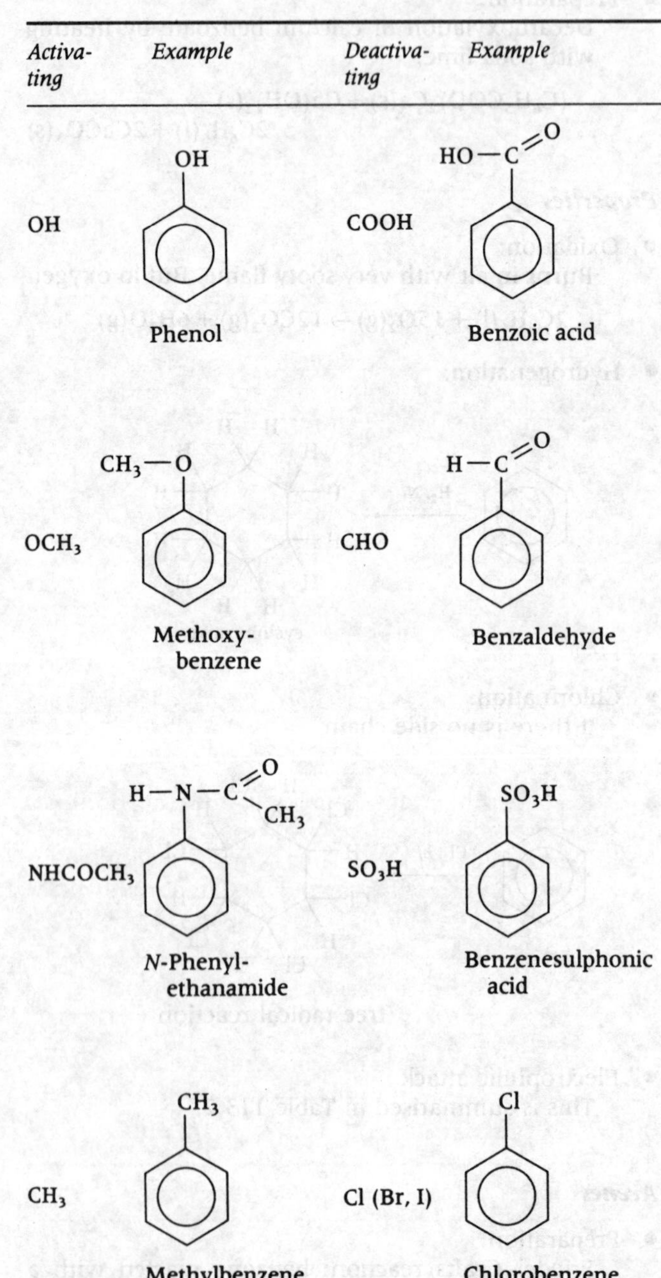

(b) *Orientation effects*

Suppose we have a benzene ring with a methyl group already bonded to it. If methylbenzene is attacked by a nitro group, then in principle we might get any one (or a mixture) of the following molecules:

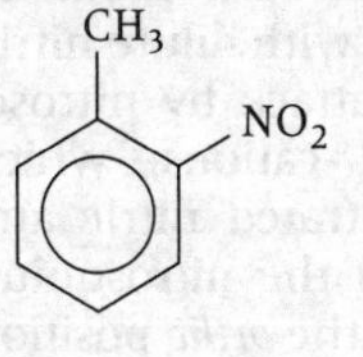

methyl-2-nitrobenzene (*ortho*-nitrotoluene)

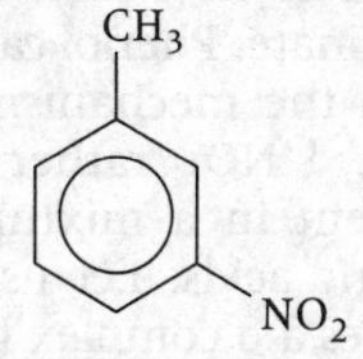

methyl-3-nitrobenzene (*meta*-nitrotoluene)

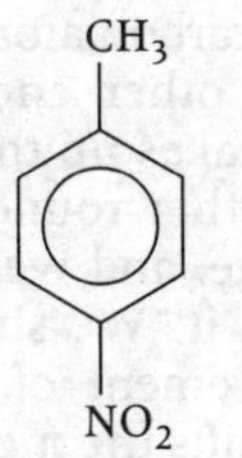

methyl-4-nitrobenzene (*para*-nitrotoluene)

Here we have given the old names of the products as well as their modern names. The positions that we label by numbers were, and often still are, called the *ortho*, *meta* and *para* positions (Figure 114.1).

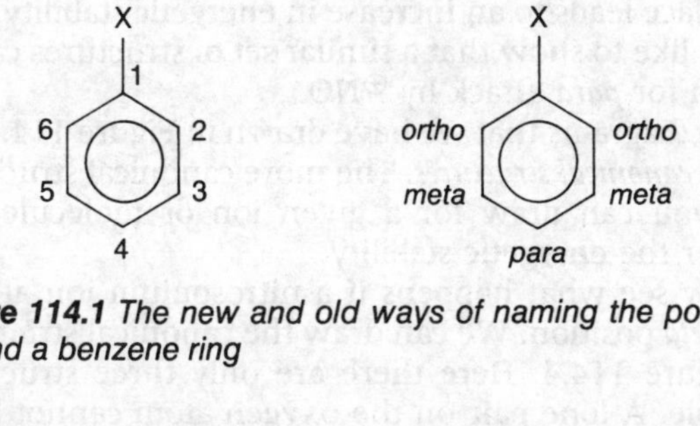

Figure 114.1 *The new and old ways of naming the positions around a benzene ring*

If the experiment is carried out and the products analysed, we find that there is less than 5% of methyl-3-nitrobenzene produced. This compares with about 58% methyl-2-nitrobenzene and 38% methyl-4-nitrobenzene. Using the older names, we say that:

The methyl group directs *ortho* and *para*.

However, if we nitrate nitrobenzene itself, over 90% of the product is 1,3-dinitrobenzene (the *meta* product). In this case:

The nitro group directs *meta*.

Table 114.2 summarises the results of electrophilic substitution for a number of different compounds.

Table 114.2. Orientation effects in electrophilic substitution

Groups that direct *ortho* and *para*	NH_2, OH, OCH_3, $NHCOCH_3$, CH_3, Cl, Br, I
Groups that direct *meta*	NO_2, COOH, CHO, SO_3H

If you compare Tables 114.1 and 114.2 you will see that, apart from the halogens (see section 114.4), groups that direct *ortho* and *para* also activate the ring, and groups that direct *meta* deactivate the ring. Now it is time for us to explain these observations.

114.2 Why do some groups activate and some deactivate the ring?

Electrophiles seek out centres of negative charge, so we should expect to find that activating groups have a way of increasing, and deactivating groups decreasing, the electron density around a benzene ring.

We can understand the deactivating effect of the nitro group by noticing that the two oxygen atoms will draw electron density towards themselves, leaving the nitrogen atom slightly positively charged. This, in turn, will draw electrons away from the ring.

We have evidence that this happens from the dipole moment of nitrobenzene. The ring is the positive end of the dipole, the nitro group the negative end. The orientation of the dipole with the other deactivating groups also shows that the benzene ring suffers a withdrawal of charge. Table 114.3 lists the dipole moments of some substituted arenes.

Table 114.3. The dipole moment of some substituted benzene molecules

Activating groups: Diagram	Dipole moment/D	Deactivating groups: Diagram	Dipole moment/D
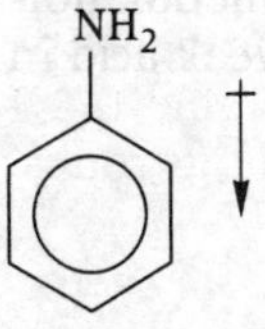 NH_2	1.53	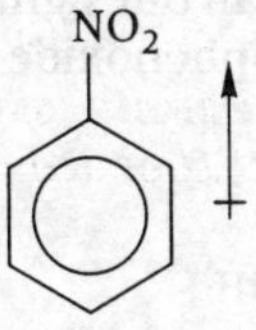 NO_2	4.22
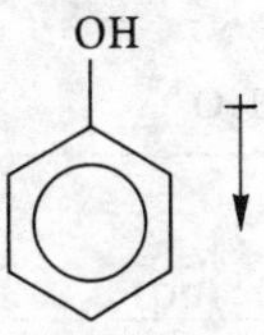 OH	1.45	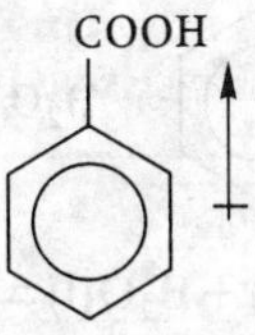 COOH	1.71
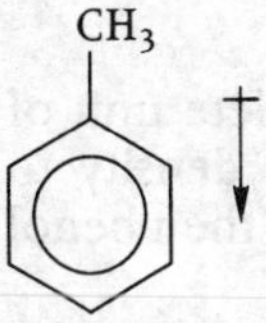 CH_3	0.36	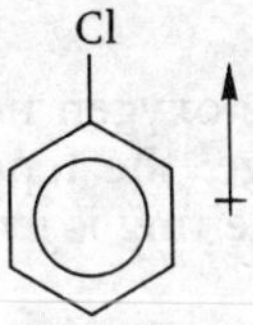 Cl	1.67

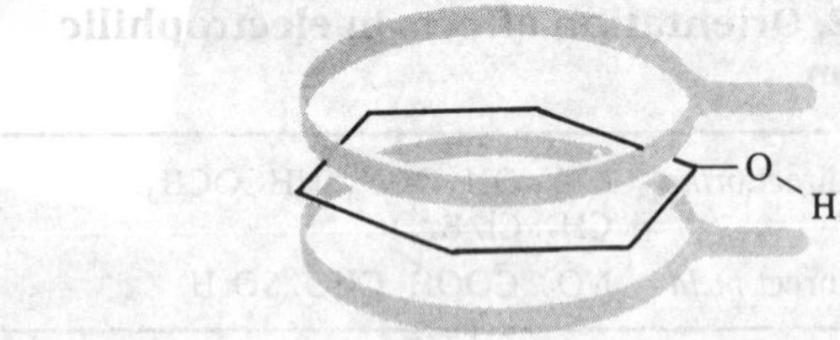

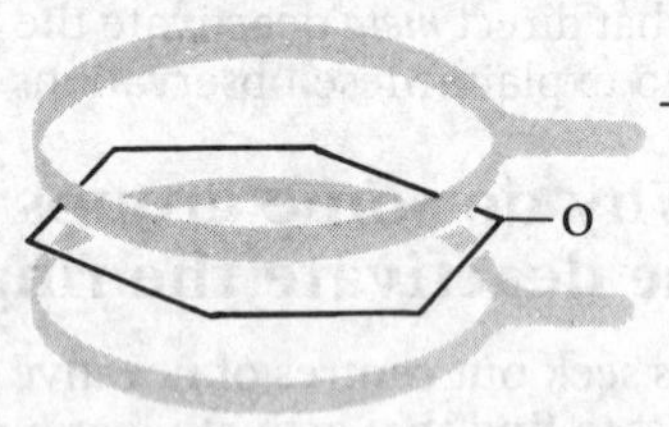

***Figure 114.2** The π electrons in phenol and the phenoxide ion are delocalised around the ring and over the oxygen. However, the delocalisation is greater in the phenoxide ion. This is responsible for the acidity of phenol in water*

Now we come to the problem of why compounds like phenol and methoxybenzene activate the ring even though they have an electronegative oxygen atom directly attached to the ring. If anything, we might expect these molecules to be severely deactivated. However, the dipole moments of the molecules tell us that the ring is definitely richer in electrons than the OH or CH_3O group bonded to it. The reason is that a lone pair on the oxygen atom can interact with the π cloud on the ring (Figure 114.2). This interaction means that, although electron density may be drawn to the oxygen atom through the σ bond joining it to the ring, electron density is fed into the ring through the π system. Indeed, when a solution of phenol in water reacts with bromine, a small but significant number of phenol molecules exist as phenoxide ions. Phenol is a weak acid in water:

$$C_6H_5OH + H_2O \rightleftharpoons C_6H_5O^- + H_3O^+$$

$$C_6H_5OH(aq) + H_2O(l) \rightleftharpoons C_6H_5O^-(aq) + H_3O^+(aq)$$

phenoxide ion

Given that the oxygen now carries a complete unit of negative charge, the tendency for electron density to build up on the ring is even greater than in the phenol molecule.

114.3 Why do some groups direct *ortho/para* and some *meta*?

(a) Ortho *and* para *direction*

We shall take the nitration of phenol as an example of a reaction in which the *ortho* and *para* products predominate. Phenol can be nitrated with dilute nitric acid, with the mechanism involving attack by nitrosonium ions, $^{\oplus}NO$, rather than nitryl cations, which are present in a mixture of concentrated nitric and sulphuric acids. Let us assume that the nitrosonium ion makes a σ complex to the ring at the *ortho* position. It is helpful to start by showing the benzene ring as if it had three separate double bonds (Figure 114.3). The bond to the nitrosonium ion is made by the two π electrons originally joining the carbon atoms. This means that the carbon atom on the other end of the π bond loses electron density and takes up the positive charge.

The π electrons further round the ring will feel the presence of this charge, and we can imagine that they would move towards it. We show this shift of the π electrons as the movement of the π bond. Another movement like this shifts the π cloud further round the ring, and the positive charge is left on the carbon atom bonded to the OH group (Figure 114.3). This is where the lone pairs on the oxygen have an important part to play. As we have seen, one of the lone pairs can bond to this carbon atom. In this way the positive charge that the nitrosonium ion brought with it is spread over four atoms. We know that spreading charge around a molecule (or ion) rather than allowing it to congregate in one place leads to an increase in energetic stability. You might like to show that a similar set of structures can be drawn for *para* attack by $^{\oplus}NO$.

The diagrams that we have drawn in Figure 114.3 are called *canonical structures*. The more canonical structures that you can draw for a given ion or molecule, the greater the energetic stability.

Now see what happens if a nitrosonium ion attacks the *meta* position. We can draw the canonical structures in Figure 114.4. Here there are only three structures possible. A lone pair on the oxygen atom cannot bond to the ring in the same way as before because the positive charge does not arrive on the carbon atom holding the OH group. In this way we see that the positive charge on the σ complex during *meta* attack is not delocalised as much as in *ortho* attack. Thus the *meta* complex is less energetically stable than the *ortho* and *para* complexes.

We seem to have explained the relative energetic stabilities of the three different σ complexes fairly well. We now have to explain why this has an effect on the relative quantities of the three final products. To do this you will need to have read the units on kinetics (Units 77–79). There we said that the higher the activation energy for a reaction, the less chance there is for reactants to combine to give products. We shall assume that the σ complexes are the transition states in the reactions. (In practice, this assumption is not strictly correct. However, we shall make no great error by ignoring the

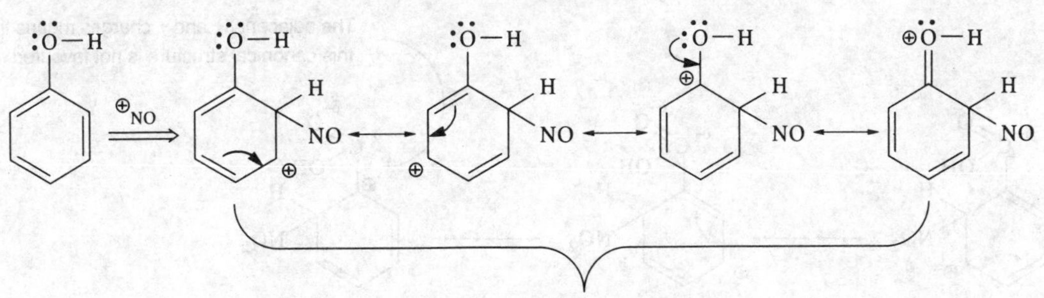

Canonical structures

The final step in the reaction is

NO_3^- Oxidation by HNO_3

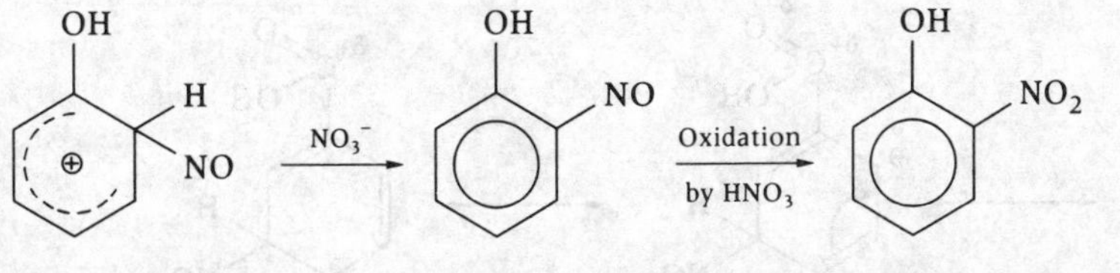

Figure 114.3 *Ortho attack by a nitrosonium ion, ^+NO, gives a Wheland intermediate, for which we can draw four different structures (the canonical structures). The curly arrows represent the movement of a pair of electrons. The structures imply that the positive charge is spread around the ring, and over the oxygen atom. The greater the spread of charge, the greater the energetic stability*

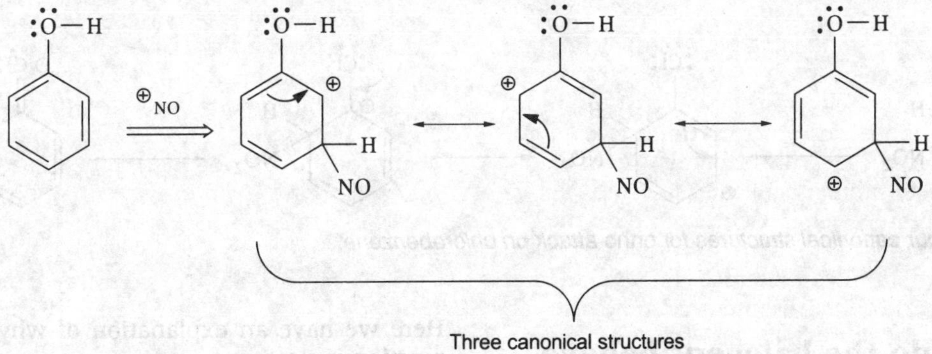

Three canonical structures

Figure 114.4 *Only three canonical structures can be drawn for* meta *attack on phenol. The Wheland intermediate is not stabilised to the same extent as that for* ortho *or* para *attacks. Notice that a lone pair on the oxygen cannot bond to the ring here, as that would necessitate five bonds to a carbon atom (which is impossible)*

complications.) This being so, we would expect the activation energy for *ortho* and *para* attack to be lower than for *meta* attack. (The *ortho* and *para* σ complexes are energetically more stable, i.e. at a *lower* energy, than the *meta* σ complex.) As a result, the *ortho* and *para* complexes should be made faster than the *meta* complex. Indeed, this fits with the observation that the major product of the reaction has an NO_2 group at the *ortho* and *para* positions. (About 40% 2-nitrophenol and 13% 4-nitrophenol; there are many side reactions as well.) The final step in the reaction is the very rapid oxidation of the nitrosophenols by nitric acid.

(b) Meta *direction*

The nitration of benzoic acid by a mixture of concentrated sulphuric and nitric acids gives about 80% of the *meta* product, 3-nitrobenzoic acid. To see why the acid group directs *meta*, look at Figure 114.5, where the canonical structures for *ortho* and *meta* attack are drawn.

First, notice that the electronegative oxygen atom double bonded to the carbon atom in the acid group draws electrons towards it. This leaves the carbon atom with a slight positive charge. There are three canonical structures in each case, so at first sight it seems that the charge is delocalised to the same extent. However, if you look at the third structure for *ortho* attack, you will see that the positive charge on the ring is brought adjacent to the slight positive charge already present on the carbon atom of the acid group. In fact, this is energetically *unfavourable*. Therefore, our count of canonical structures gives three in favour of the *meta* σ complex and two in favour of the *ortho* σ complex. This is a typical result for groups that direct *meta*.

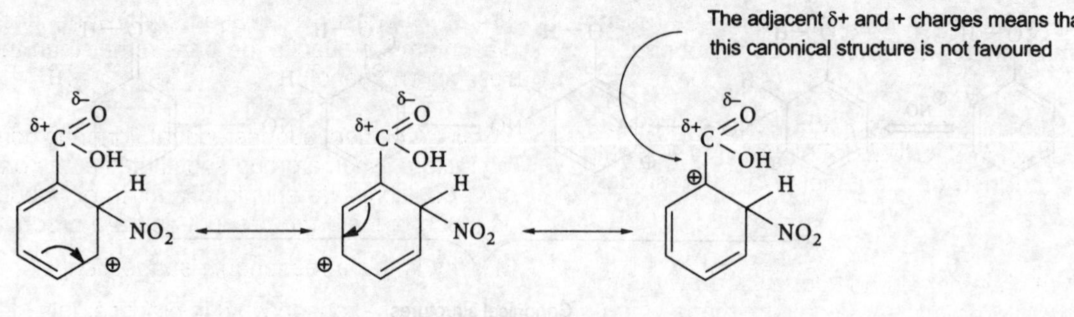

The adjacent δ+ and + charges means that this canonical structure is not favoured

Canonical structures for *ortho* attack

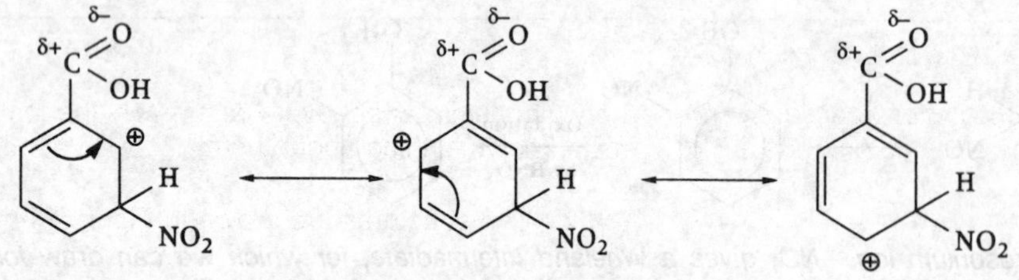

Canonical structures for *meta* attack

***Figure 114.5** Meta attack on benzoic acid is favoured. One of the canonical structures in* ortho *(and* para*) attack leads to δ+ and + charges coming close together. This is energetically unfavourable. For meta attack, this repulsion does not occur*

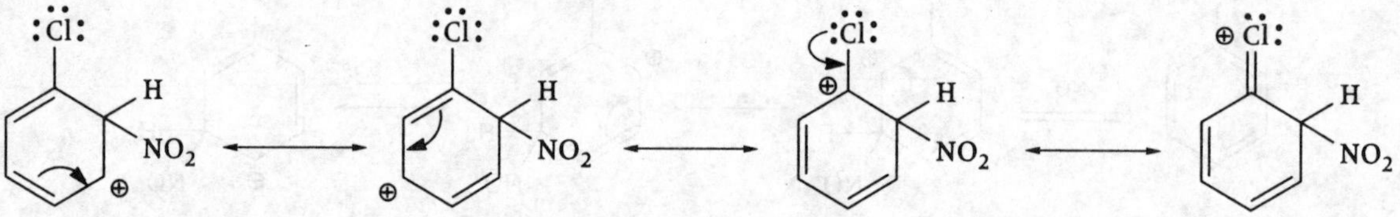

***Figure 114.6** The four canonical structures for* ortho *attack on chlorobenzene*

114.4 Why do the halogens behave differently to other groups?

The usual pattern of events is for groups that direct *ortho* and *para* to activate the ring, and groups that direct *meta* to deactivate the ring. However, the halogens are exceptions. They direct *ortho* and *para* but deactivate the ring. The electron withdrawing nature of the halogens means that they withdraw electron density from the ring. This is shown, for example, by the orientation of the dipole moment of chlorobenzene. As a result, an incoming electrophile will find the benzene ring in chlorobenzene less attractive than in benzene itself. Here we have an explanation of why the rate of the reaction is slower.

Now let us look at the electron structure of a halogen atom when it is joined to a benzene ring. There are three lone pairs around the halogen atom (compare the bonding in hydrogen chloride; section 14.2). In Figure 114.6 the canonical structures for *ortho* attack of a nitryl cation on chlorobenzene are drawn.

The key thing to spot is that, like the oxygen in phenol or the nitrogen in phenylamine, a lone pair on the chlorine can link with the π cloud on the ring. This tends to stabilise the *ortho* and *para* σ complexes at the expense of the *meta* σ complex. Thus we can thank the lone pairs on the halogen atoms for the *ortho/para* directing ability.

114.1 We can write a substituted benzene as C_6H_5X. Similarly we can use the letter E to stand for an electrophilic reagent. Assume two E groups successfully attack C_6H_5X.

(i) Is the formula of the product $C_6H_5XE_2$, $C_6H_4XE_2$, or $C_6H_3XE_2$?

(ii) How many different products are possible?

(iii) Draw their structures.

114.2 If bromine water is added to a solution of phenylamine, a white precipitate of 2,4,6-

tribromophenylamine is produced. Suggest a reason why the amine group activates the benzene ring.

114.3 A student suggested that each of the four canonical structures drawn in Figure 114.3 would exist for a quarter of the time. Was the student correct?

114.4 If you have not already done so, draw out the canonical structures for the σ complex made when $^{\oplus}$NO attacks phenol at the *para* position.

114.5 Suggest a reason why the benzenediazonium ion attacks the *para* rather than the *ortho* position on phenol.

114.6 A student suggested that, ignoring complicating factors, when a group substitutes at the *ortho* and *para* positions, we should expect to get about twice as much of the *ortho* product as *para* product.

(i) Why is this a reasonable suggestion?

(ii) Suggest a reason why, in practice, this ideal ratio seldom occurs.

Answers

114.1 (i) $C_6H_3XE_2$. This is a substitution reaction, so for each E group that joins, one hydrogen atom must be lost.

(ii) Six.

(iii) The structures are shown in Figure 114.7.

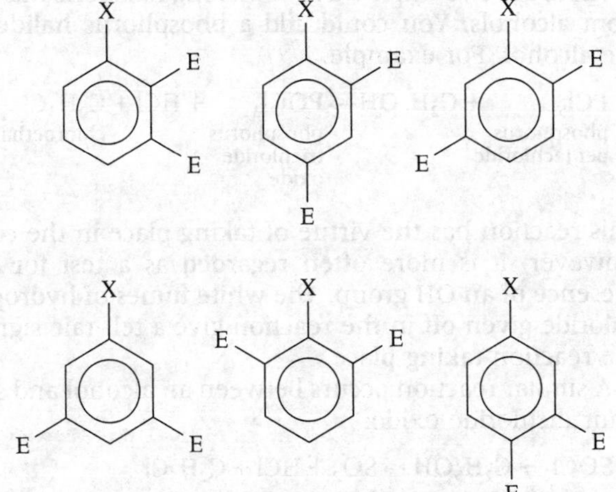

Figure 114.7 Diagrams for answer to question 114.1

114.2 Like the oxygen atom in phenol, the nitrogen has a lone pair of electrons that can interact with the π cloud on the benzene ring. You should be able to draw the same set of canonical structures for an electrophile attacking phenylamine as in the case of phenol.

114.3 No. If you look back at section 14.7 you will find that we said that it is a mistake to think that an ion or molecule constantly changes from one structure to another. Canonical structures are *our* way of explaining the way chemicals behave. Presumably the ion or molecule knows nothing about them!

114.4 The structures are drawn in Figure 114.8.

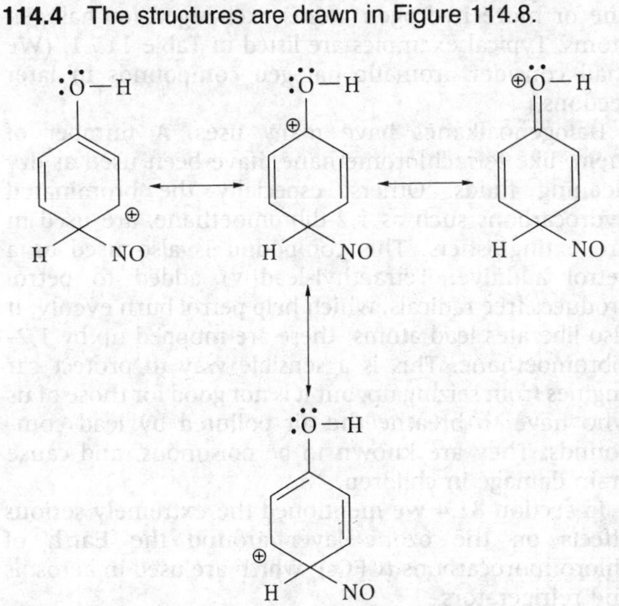

Figure 114.8 Diagrams for answer to question 114.4

114.5 There is steric hindrance at work. The large benzenediazonium ion cannot easily get past the group next to the *ortho* positions.

114.6 (i) There are two *ortho* for each *para* position. Hence the ratio should be 2:1.

(ii) There are many factors to take into account. The one you should suggest is that steric hindrance will decrease the likelihood of groups bonding at the *ortho* position.

UNIT 114 SUMMARY

- Groups that direct *ortho* and *para*, i.e. 2 and 4 positions on a benzene ring, tend to feed electrons into the ring.
- Groups that direct *meta*, i.e. 3 position on a benzene ring, tend to withdraw electrons from the ring.
- Tables 114.1 and 114.2 provide information about activating and deactivating groups.

115

Organic halogen compounds

115.1 What are halogenoalkanes?

The halogenoalkanes are hydrocarbon chains that have one or more hydrogen atoms exchanged for halogen atoms. Typical examples are listed in Table 115.1. (We shall consider aromatic halogen compounds in later sections.)

Halogenoalkanes have many uses. A number of them, like tetrachloromethane, have been used as dry cleaning fluids. Others, especially the brominated hydrocarbons such as 1,2-dibromoethane, are used in fire extinguishers. This compound is also used as a petrol additive. Tetraethyl-lead(IV) added to petrol produces free radicals, which help petrol burn evenly. It also liberates lead atoms; these are mopped up by 1,2-dibromoethane. This is a sensible way to protect car engines from seizing up, but it is not good for those of us who have to breathe the air polluted by lead compounds. They are known to be poisonous, and cause brain damage in children.

In section 81.4 we mentioned the extremely serious effects on the ozone layer around the Earth of chlorofluorocarbons (CFCs), which are used in aerosols and refrigerators.

115.2 Methods of making halogenoalkanes

The main way of making a halogenoalkane is to replace the OH group of an alcohol by a halogen. The laboratory preparation of iodoethane is described in panel 115.1 and Figures 115.1 and 115.2. This shows you the principal stages found in many organic preparations.

In one method of making bromoethane, hydrogen bromide is made by the reaction between concentrated sulphuric acid and sodium bromide, and then reacts with ethanol:

$$H_2SO_4 + NaBr \rightarrow NaHSO_4 + HBr$$
$$C_2H_5OH + HBr \rightarrow C_2H_5Br + H_2O$$

This method can be used to make many halogenoalkanes. The essential thing is to choose the right alcohol for the halogenoalkane you need. In the case of iodoethane, a mixture of red phosphorus and iodine is reacted with ethanol:

$$2P + 3I_2 \rightarrow 2PI_3$$
$$3C_2H_5OH + PI_3 \rightarrow 3C_2H_5I + H_3PO_3$$

There are two other ways of making halogenoalkanes from alcohols. You could add a phosphorus halide to the alcohol. For example,

$$\underset{\text{phosphorus pentachloride}}{PCl_5} + C_2H_5OH \rightarrow \underset{\text{phosphorus trichloride oxide}}{POCl_3} + HCl + \underset{\text{chloroethane}}{C_2H_5Cl}$$

This reaction has the virtue of taking place in the cold. However, it is more often regarded as a test for the presence of an OH group. The white fumes of hydrogen chloride given off in the reaction give a tell-tale sign of the reaction taking place.

A similar reaction occurs between an alcohol and sulphur dichloride oxide:

$$SOCl_2 + C_2H_5OH \rightarrow SO_2 + HCl + C_2H_5Cl$$

The advantage of this reaction is that the two side products are gases and are easily removed from the reaction mixture.

115.1 Using one of these methods, which bromoalkanes would be made from the following alcohols: (i) propan-1-ol; (ii) butan-1-ol; (iii) butan-2-ol?

115.3 Halogenoalkanes are attacked by nucleophiles

The majority of halogenoalkanes have a dipole moment (Table 115.2). This is a result of the electron withdrawing ability of halogen atoms. The halogen atom carries a slight negative charge, with the remainder of the

Table 115.1. Halogenoalkanes

Name	*Formula*	*Structure*	*Melting point/°C*	*Boiling point/°C*
Chloromethane	CH_3Cl	H; C—Cl; H; H	−97.6	−24.1
Dichloromethane	CH_2Cl_2	Cl; C—Cl; H; H	−95.0	139.9
Trichloromethane (chloroform)	$CHCl_3$	Cl; C—Cl; H; Cl	−63.3	61.9
Tetrachloromethane (carbon tetrachloride)	CCl_4	Cl; C—Cl; Cl; Cl	−22.8	76.7
Chloroethane	CH_3CH_2Cl	CH_3; C—Cl; H; H	−136.3	12.4
Bromoethane	CH_3CH_2Br	CH_3; C—Br; H; H	−118.5	38.5
1,2-Dibromoethane	CH_2BrCH_2Br	Br; C; H; H; C—Br; H; H	9.9	13.5
Iodoethane	CH_3CH_2I	CH_3; C—I; H; H	−111.0	72.5
Triiodomethane (iodoform)	CHI_3	H; C—I; H; H	119.0	218 (approx.)
Difluorochloromethane	$CHClF_2$	F; C—F; H; Cl	−146.0	−40.8
Trifluorochloromethane	$CClF_3$	F; C—F; Cl; F	−181.0	−81.4

Panel 115.1

The preparation of iodoethane

Organic preparations tend to follow a similar pattern. The order of events is often like this:

(i) *Stage 1*. Heat the reaction mixture, probably under reflux, for up to an hour.
(ii) *Stage 2*. Distil the final mixture to separate the bulk of the product.
(iii) *Stage 3*. Purify the product, e.g. by drying and redistillation.

The details below will show you these stages in the particular case of preparing iodoethane.

Warning: This reaction sometimes has a sting in its tail; there have been occasions when the reaction mixture has exploded. Do *not* attempt the reaction except under expert guidance.

Stage 1

Ethanol, red phosphorus and iodine are mixed in a flask (see question 115.9 for quantities). The best type is a Quickfit flask, or a similar type, which has a ground glass joint. The flask fits precisely to a Liebig condenser as shown in Figure 115.1. We say that the apparatus has been set up for heating the reactants under *reflux*. Owing to their covalent nature, many organic liquids vaporise easily. If, for example, the reaction flask were heated without the condenser, the ethanol would soon evaporate. With the condenser present, the vapour condenses and drops back into the flask. The condenser also prevents the product (iodoethane) escaping.

The mixture is heated over a water bath for about half an hour. This, too, is a common approach to organic reactions. It is unwise to heat the reactants directly with a bunsen burner. The bunsen flame can cause the temperature to rise too quickly, and tends to heat one part of the flask more than another. (Alternatives to water baths are sand trays or electric mantle heaters.)

Stage 2

Once the reaction is complete, the products have to be separated from the unused reactants, and side products, in the flask. The usual way of doing this is to distil the mixture. The apparatus is dismantled and set up for distillation as shown in Figure 115.2. Distillation will only be effective if the product has a significantly different boiling point from the other chemicals in the flask. Iodoethane has a boiling point of 72.5°C, whereas ethanol boils at 78°C. Thus iodoethane should evaporate in greater quantity than ethanol, and reach the condenser first. The thermometer at the neck of the condenser should read 72.5°C when iodoethane distils over. If the temperature rises above this, it is a sign that ethanol is beginning to distil and the distillation is stopped.

Stage 3

The distillate (the liquid collected from the distillation) should be mainly iodoethane, but it will be contaminated by a mixture of ethanol and phosphonic acid (H_3PO_3). The distillate is placed in a separating funnel and washed with a little distilled water. The separating funnel allows the lower, oily layer of iodoethane to be run off. The ethanol and phosphonic acid will remain in the water. Finally the iodoethane is left in contact with a drying agent to remove water. Anhydrous calcium chloride and anhydrous sodium sulphate are common drying agents. The final part of the experiment is to redistil the dried product (in a clean apparatus, of course).

It is not uncommon for the yield in an organic preparation to be around 60%. This is due to the reactants giving side products, and to the losses that are involved in the separation.

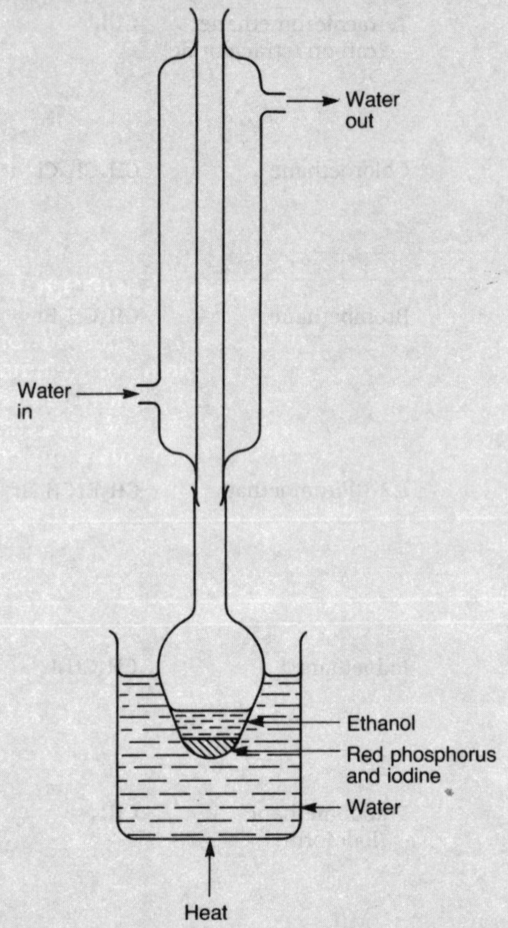

***Figure 115.1** An apparatus for making iodoethane*

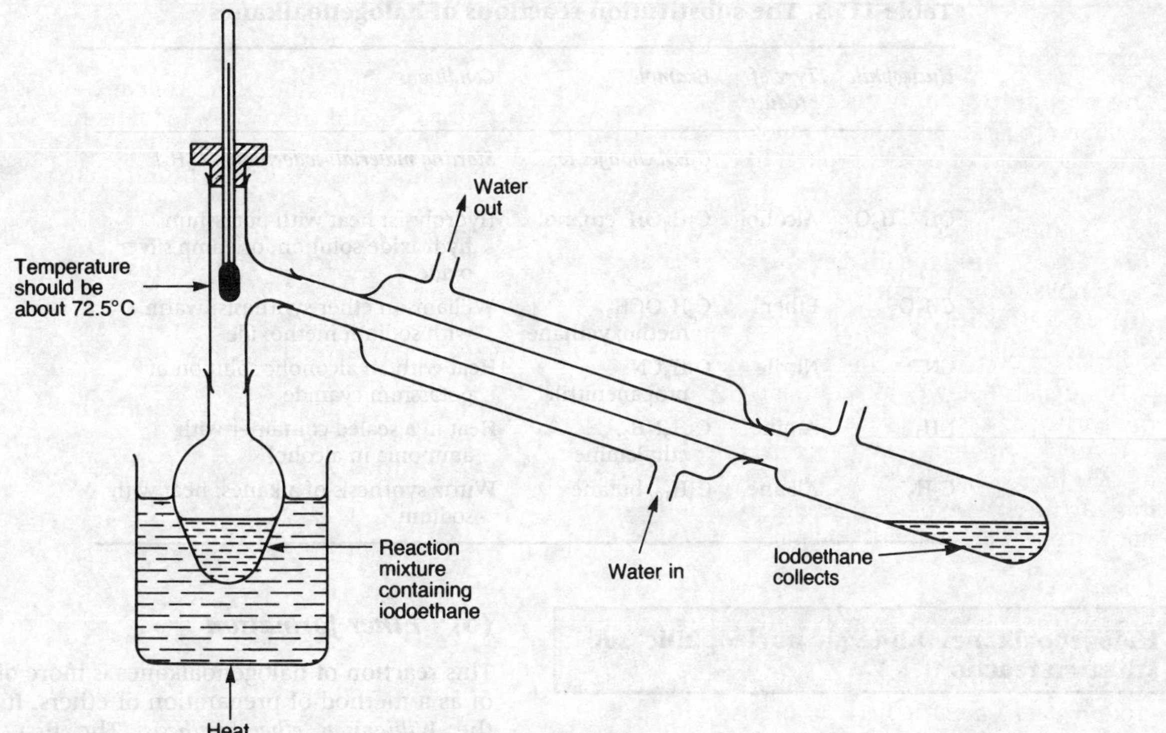
Water out
Temperature should be about 72.5°C
Reaction mixture containing iodoethane
Heat
Water in
Iodoethane collects

***Figure* 115.2** *Iodoethane is separated from the reaction mixture by distillation*

Table 115.2. The dipole moments of some halogenoalkanes

Halogenoalkane	*Dipole moment/D*
CH_3Cl	1.86
CH_3Br	1.79
CH_3I	1.64
C_2H_5Cl	1.98
C_2H_5Br	2.02
C_2H_5I	1.90

molecule having a slight positive charge. The carbon atom bonded to the halogen can act as a centre of attraction for *nucleophiles* (Figure 115.3). Atoms or molecules with lone pairs of electrons and/or a negative charge make good nucleophiles. However, equally important as far as a successful reaction is concerned is that the halogen atom makes a *good leaving group*. For example, iodine atoms can readily change into iodide ions, I^-. This encourages the carbon–iodine bond to break, thus disrupting the original molecule and allowing the incoming nucleophile to bond to the carbon atom. Please read Unit 81 for more information about this type of reaction.

The majority of halogenoalkanes fit the same pattern in their reactions:

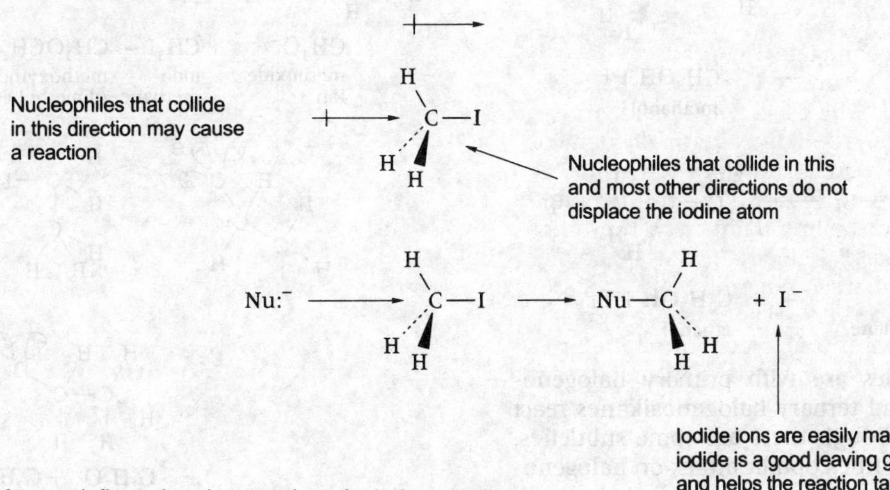
Nucleophiles that collide in this direction may cause a reaction
Nucleophiles that collide in this and most other directions do not displace the iodine atom
Nu:⁻ → CH_3—I → Nu—CH_3 + I^-
Iodide ions are easily made: iodide is a good leaving group and helps the reaction take place

***Figure* 115.3** *Key factors influencing the reaction of a halogenoalkane with a nucleophilea*

Table 115.3. The substitution reactions of halogenoalkanes

Nucleophile	*Type of product*	*Example*	*Conditions*
		C_2H_5I changes to:	*Starting material: iodoethane, C_2H_5I*
OH^-, H_2O	Alcohol	C_2H_5OH, ethanol	Hydrolysis: heat with potassium hydroxide solution, or damp silver oxide
CH_3O^-	Ether	$C_2H_5OCH_3$, methoxyethane	Williamson ether synthesis: warm with sodium methoxide
CN^-	Nitrile	C_2H_5CN, propanenitrile	Heat with an alcoholic solution of potassium cyanide
NH_3	Amine	$C_2H_5NH_2$, ethylamine	Heat in a sealed container with ammonia in alcohol
$C_2H_5^-$	Alkane	C_4H_{10}, butane	Wurtz synthesis of alkanes: heat with sodium

Halogenoalkanes undergo nucleophilic substitution reactions.

The exceptions are molecules like tetrachloromethane, which have no hydrogen atoms remaining, and no overall dipole moment. Table 115.3 summarises the different possibilities. Here are brief details about each one.

(a) *Hydrolysis*

Hydrolysis using water on its own has little effect on a halogenoalkane. However, the rate of reaction is increased by boiling with alkali such as potassium hydroxide. The reaction is then called an alkaline hydrolysis. The equations are simple to write down because the overall change is the replacement of the halogen atom by an OH group. For example,

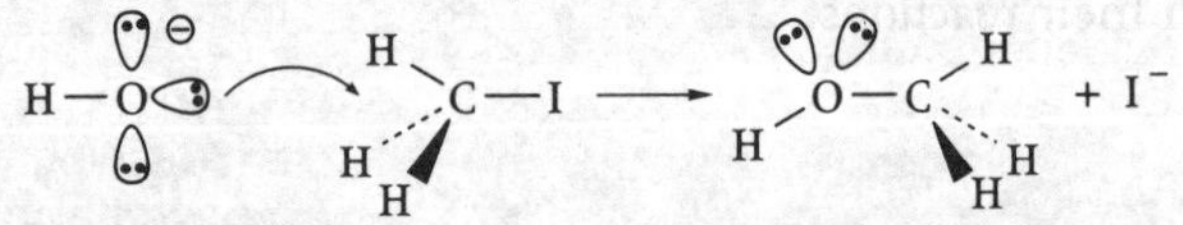

$$OH^- + CH_3I \rightarrow CH_3OH + I^-$$

iodomethane → methanol

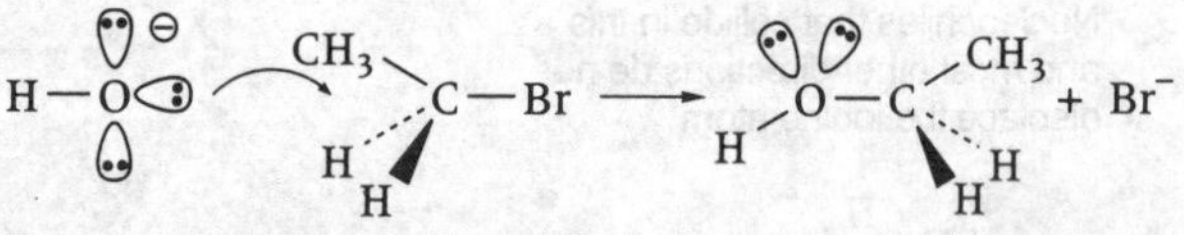

$$OH^- + C_2H_5Br \rightarrow C_2H_5OH + Br^-$$

bromoethane → ethanol

Both these examples are with primary halogenoalkanes; secondary and tertiary halogenoalkanes react in similar fashion, although there are some subtleties. The mechanism of the nucleophilic attack on halogenoalkanes by hydroxide ions has been studied in detail. You will find information about it in Unit 81.

(b) *Ether formation*

This reaction of halogenoalkanes is more often thought of as a method of preparation of ethers. It is known as the *Williamson ether synthesis*. The first step in the method is to make a solution of an *alkoxide* ion. The simplest way of doing this is to dissolve sodium in an alcohol. For example,

$$2CH_3OH + 2Na \rightarrow 2CH_3O^- + 2Na^+ + H_2$$

methanol, methoxide ion

$$2C_2H_5OH + 2Na \rightarrow 2C_2H_5O^- + 2Na^+ + H_2$$

ethanol, ethoxide ion

Methoxide and ethoxide ions are particular examples of alkoxide ions. The alkoxide ion is the nucleophile, which then goes on to react with a halogenoalkane:

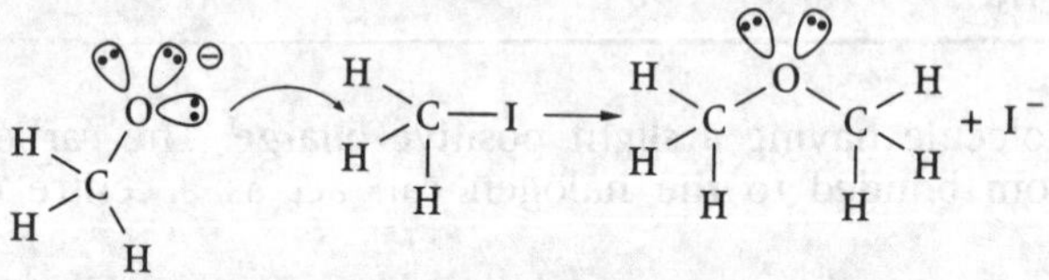

$$CH_3O^- + CH_3I \rightarrow CH_3OCH_3 + I^-$$

methoxide ion + iodomethane → methoxymethane (dimethyl ether)

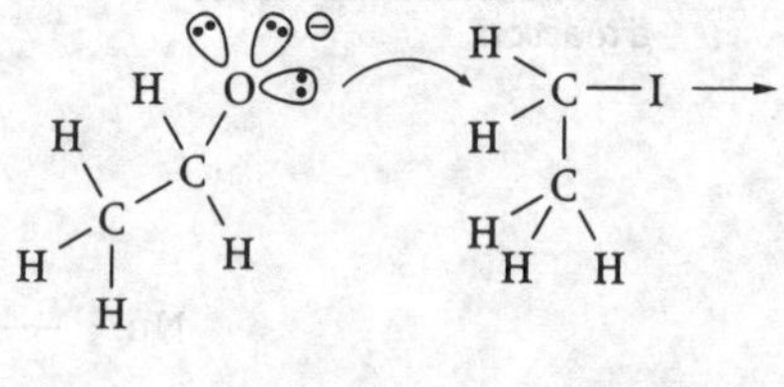

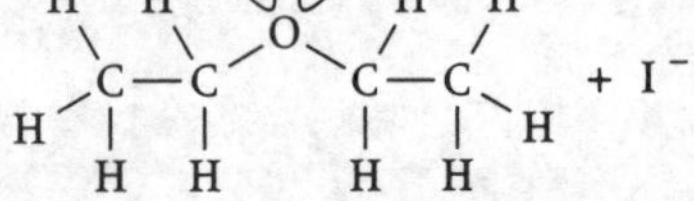

$$C_2H_5O^- + C_2H_5I \rightarrow C_2H_5OC_2H_5 + I^-$$

ethoxide ion + iodoethane → ethoxyethane (diethyl ether)

In practice the reactions are fairly easy to carry out, provided you take care over the risk of fire; ethers are very flammable.

(c) *Nitrile formation*

Nitriles used to be called cyanides; they contain the —CN group. Being able to introduce this group into an organic molecule can be extremely useful because it increases the number of carbon atoms in the molecule. The method of converting a halogenoalkane into a nitrile is straightforward. The halogenoalkane is warmed with an inorganic cyanide, such as potassium cyanide, in ethanol. The ethanol is a convenient solvent for both reactants, and thereby allows them to react together:

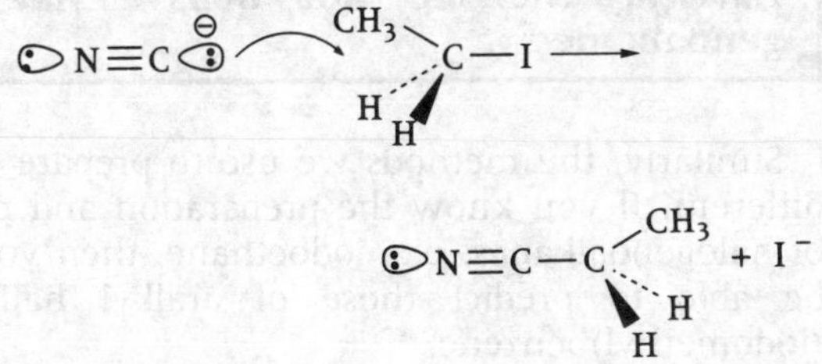

$$CN^- + C_2H_5I \rightarrow C_2H_5CN + I^-$$

iodoethane → propanenitrile

(d) *Amine formation*

Simple amines contain the —NH_2 group. This group will replace a halogen atom if the halogenoalkane is heated with ammonia in alcohol under pressure. An ammonia molecule will act as a nucleophile owing to its lone pair of electrons. In the reaction with a halogenoalkane, one of the hydrogen atoms from the ammonia is lost and combines with the halogen atom displaced by the action of the lone pair. For example,

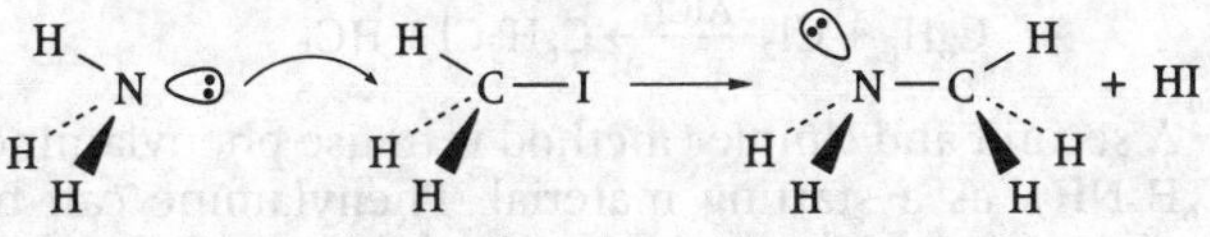

$$NH_3 + CH_3I \rightarrow CH_3NH_2 + HI$$

iodomethane → methylamine

This reaction illustrates the fact that nucleophiles do not have to have a negative charge to react with halogenoalkanes. However, it is not a good way of preparing amines because a number of side products always appear. Let us assume that methylamine molecules have been made in the above reaction. The nitrogen atom in methylamine still has its lone pair of electrons. Therefore methylamine can also be a nucleophile and attack iodomethane molecules. This reaction yields a more complicated amine called a secondary amine:

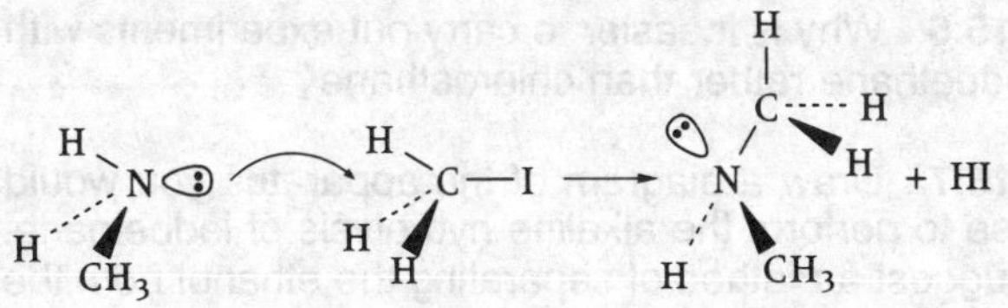

$$CH_3NH_2 + CH_3I \rightarrow (CH_3)_2NH + HI$$

dimethylamine

There are even more complicated products to be found in the final mixture (see question 115.8).

(e) *Wurtz synthesis of alkanes*

We discussed this method in section 111.4. The only extra piece of information we might mention here is that the effect of the sodium is to convert the halogenoalkane into a *carbanion*. A carbanion is an organic group with a negative charge. For example,

$$C_2H_5I + 2Na \rightarrow C_2H_5^- + I^- + 2Na^+$$

ethyl carbanion

The carbanion is the nucleophile that attacks another halogenoalkane molecule:

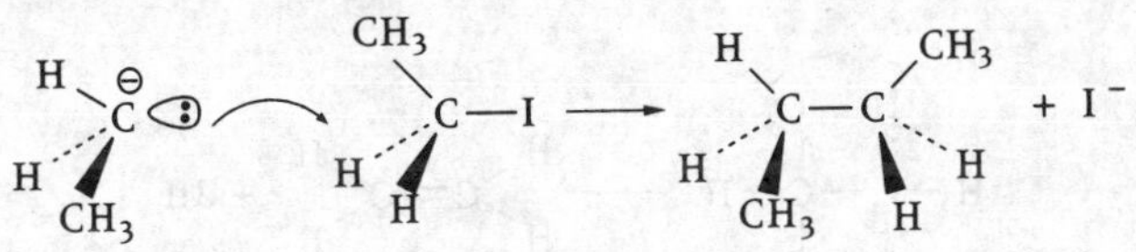

$$C_2H_5^- + C_2H_5I \rightarrow C_4H_{10} + I^-$$

115.2 In a previous unit we found that alkanes will react with halogens to give halogenoalkanes.

(i) What conditions are needed for the reactions to take place?

(ii) Why is the method not a good way of making halogenoalkanes in the laboratory?

115.3 Instead of phosphorus pentachloride, sulphur dichloride oxide, $SOCl_2$, can be used to convert alcohols to chloroalkanes. For example, if this reagent is added to ethanol, C_2H_5OH, the major product is chloroethane:

$$C_2H_5OH + SOCl_2 \rightarrow C_2H_5Cl + ? + ?$$

(i) What might be the two molecules missing from the equation?

(ii) Why is the separation of the chloroethane easier in this reaction than with phosphorus pentachloride?

115.4 Which of these molecules have a dipole moment: (i) dichloromethane, (ii) tetrachloromethane?

115.5 Suggest a method for making 1,2-dibromoethane, without using an alcohol.

115.6 Why is it easier to carry out experiments with iodoethane rather than chloroethane?

115.7 Draw a diagram of the apparatus you would use to perform the alkaline hydrolysis of iodoethane. Suggest a method of separating the ethanol from the reaction mixture.

115.8 Explain why (i) the reaction of iodomethane with ammonia gives trimethylamine, $(CH_3)_3N$, as one of the products; (ii) an ionic solid of formula $(CH_3)_4NI$ is also found.

115.4 An elimination reaction of halogenoalkanes

You may remember that one method of making an alkene is to heat a halogenoalkane with a concentrated alcoholic solution of potassium hydroxide. (This is the dehydrohalogenation reaction.) A hydrogen atom and the halogen atom are lost, or *eliminated*, from the halogenoalkane, e.g.

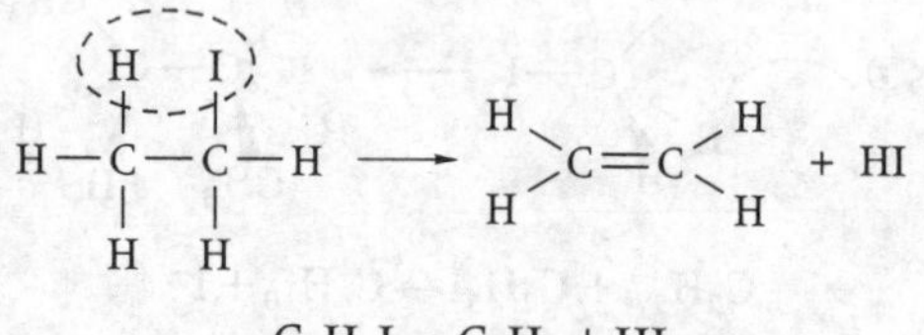

$$H_3C{-}CH_2I \longrightarrow H_2C{=}CH_2 + HI$$

$$C_2H_5I \rightarrow C_2H_4 + HI$$

iodoethane   ethene

115.9 In making iodoethane, a mixture of 5 cm³ of ethanol, 5 g of iodine and 0.5 g of red phosphorus were used. The final mass of iodoethane was 5.1 g.

(i) The density of ethanol is approximately 0.8 g cm^{-3}. What mass of ethanol was taken? How many moles is this? $M(C_2H_5OH) = 46\text{ g mol}^{-1}$.

(ii) How many moles of phosphorus and of iodine were used? $M(P) = 31\text{ g mol}^{-1}$, $M(I_2) = 254\text{ g mol}^{-1}$.

(iii) What is the ratio (in whole numbers) of the moles of C_2H_5OH, P and I_2?

(iv) Using your answers so far, and by consulting the equation for the reaction, which of the chemicals was in excess? Which substance governs the quantity of iodoethane that can be made?

(v) Calculate the maximum mass of iodoethane that could be made.

(vi) What was the yield of the reaction?

115.5 There are two types of aromatic halogen compound

The two types are:

Those with the halogen atom(s) on a benzene ring, sometimes called *halogenoarenes.*

Those with the halogen atom on a hydrocarbon side chain joined to a benzene ring, sometimes called *aralkyl halides.*

Table 115.4 lists examples of both types. There is one important pattern that emerges in the properties of these two types of compound. It is this:

***Aralkyl halides* behave like halogenoalkanes. *Halogenoarenes* do not behave like halogenoalkanes.**

Similarly, the methods we use to prepare them are different. If you know the preparation and properties of halogenoalkanes, e.g. iodoethane, then you should be able to predict those of aralkyl halides, e.g. (iodomethyl)benzene.

115.6 How do we prepare halogenoarenes?

One method is to use the *Friedel–Crafts reaction*. For example, to make chlorobenzene we could pass chlorine through benzene containing aluminium trichloride. An electrophilic attack on the ring takes place and a chlorine atom takes the place of one of the hydrogen atoms:

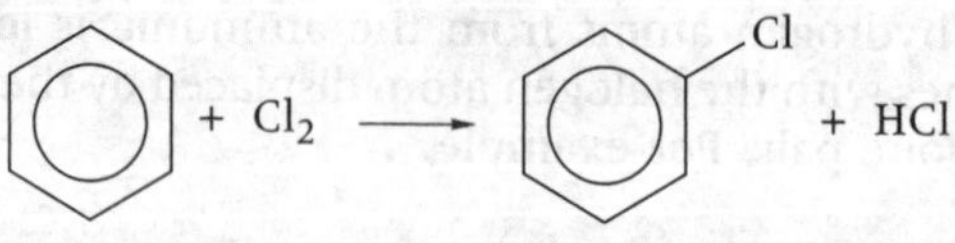

$$C_6H_6 + Cl_2 \xrightarrow{AlCl_3} C_6H_5Cl + HCl$$

A second and simpler method is to use phenylamine, $C_6H_5NH_2$, as a starting material. Phenylamine can be easily converted into a *benzenediazonium* ion by mixing it with an ice-cold solution of sodium nitrite. This solution contains nitrous acid, HNO_2:

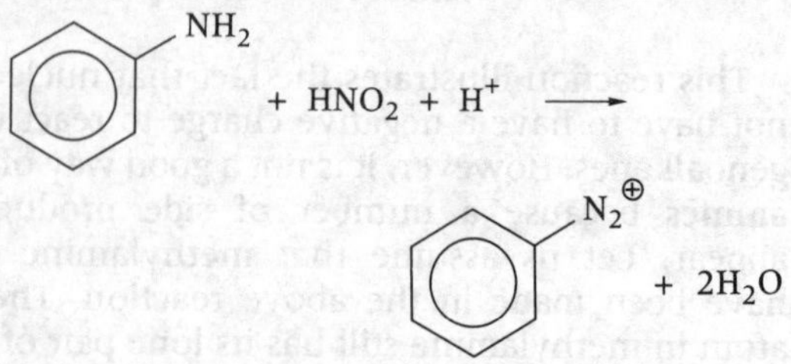

$$C_6H_5NH_2 + HNO_2 + H^+ \rightarrow C_6H_5N_2^{\oplus} + 2H_2O$$

phenylamine   benzenediazonium ion

Table 115.4. Some aromatic halogen compounds

Name	Formula	Structure	Melting point/°C	Boiling point/°C
Halogenoarenes				
Chlorobenzene	C_6H_5Cl		−45.5	132
1,2-Dichlorobenzene (*ortho*-dichlorobenzene)	$C_6H_4Cl_2$	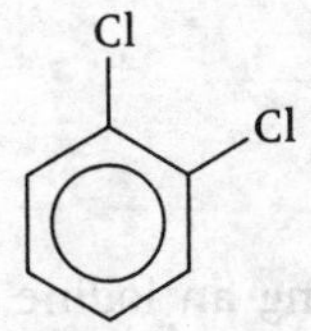	−17	180.5
1,3-Dibromobenzene (*meta*-dibromobenzene)	$C_6H_4Br_2$	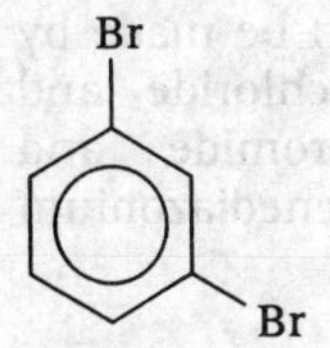	−7	218
1,4-Dichlorobenzene (*para*-dichlorobenzene)	$C_6H_4Cl_2$		53.1	174
Chloro-2-methylbenzene (*ortho*-chlorotoluene)	$C_6H_4CH_3Cl$	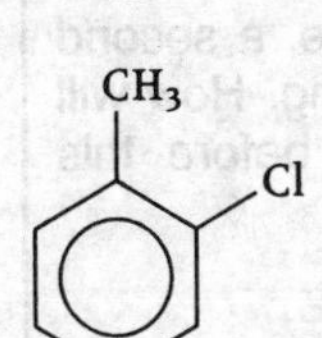	−34	159
Aralkyl halides				
(Chloromethyl)benzene	$C_6H_5CH_2Cl$	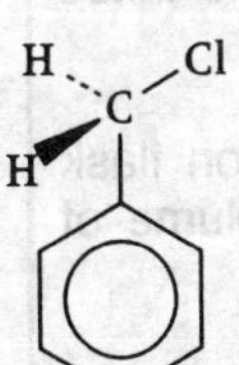	−39	179.3
(Dichloromethyl)benzene	$C_6H_5CHCl_2$	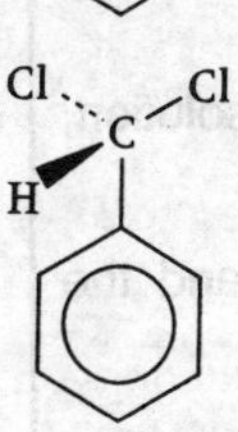	−16.4	205.2
1-Chloro-2-phenylethane	$C_6H_5CH_2CH_2Cl$	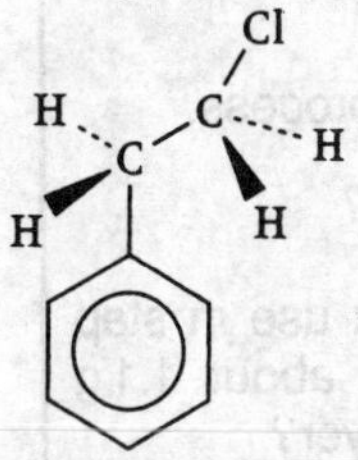	*	197

*Data not available

One of the properties of the benzenediazonium ion is that it is very reactive. You will find in section 122.7 that it reacts with a wide variety of substances, one of which is a halide ion. For example, if we add potassium iodide to a solution containing benzenediazonium ions, and warm the mixture, iodobenzene is made:

$$C_6H_5N_2^{\oplus} + I^- \rightarrow \underset{\text{iodo-benzene}}{C_6H_5I} + N_2$$

This is one of the few ways of introducing an iodine atom into a benzene ring.

Chlorobenzene (or bromobenzene) can be made by *Sandmeyer's reaction*. Here, copper(I) chloride and hydrochloric acid (or copper(I) bromide and hydrobromic acid) are added to the benzenediazonium ion solution.

115.10 Sketch the apparatus you would use to make chlorobenzene from benzene by the Friedel–Crafts reaction. Make sure you take account of the states of the reactants and products. One problem you have to overcome is the fact that once all the benzene is converted into chlorobenzene, a second chlorine would be substituted into the ring. How will you know when to stop the reaction before this happens?

115.11 The separation of the chlorobenzene takes place in the following steps:

(a) After cooling, the contents of the reaction flask are poured into an approximately equal volume of water.

(b) The chlorobenzene layer is run off.

(c) It is then washed with sodium hydroxide solution, followed by water.

(d) Anhydrous calcium chloride is added, and the mixture left until it becomes clear.

(e) The liquid is distilled.

Here are some questions about this process.

(i) What is removed by the water in (a)?

(ii) What piece of apparatus would you use in step (b)? The density of chlorobenzene is about 1.1 g cm^{-3}. Will it be the top or the bottom layer?

(iii) What *two* effects will the sodium hydroxide have?

(iv) Describe what you would do to carry out step (c).

(v) What is the purpose of the anhydrous calcium chloride? Why might the chlorobenzene look cloudy?

(vi) What else might be present apart from chlorobenzene? At what temperature would you expect the chlorobenzene to distil over?

115.12 What changes to your apparatus, and to the method, would you make if you were to make bromobenzene instead of chlorobenzene?

115.13 What will be made if chlorobenzene is itself chlorinated by the Friedel–Crafts reaction?

115.7 What are the reactions of halogenoarenes?

The main difference between a halogenoarene, e.g. chlorobenzene, and a halogenoalkane, e.g. chloromethane, is that the halogenoarene is much more resistant to nucleophilic attack. For example, the chlorine in chlorobenzene can be replaced by an OH group but only at high pressure and temperature (around 300 atm and 300 °C):

$$\underset{\text{chlorobenzene}}{C_6H_5Cl} + OH^- \xrightarrow[300\text{ atm}]{300^\circ\text{C}} \underset{\text{phenol}}{C_6H_5OH} + Cl^-$$

For obvious reasons this reaction is hopeless as a laboratory method of preparing phenol; but on a much larger scale it is used as an industrial method of manufacturing phenol.

Another industrial use of chlorobenzene is in the manufacture of phenylamine. The chlorobenzene is reacted with ammonia in the presence of a copper(I) oxide catalyst. Again, a high pressure and temperature are needed:

$$\underset{\text{chlorobenzene}}{C_6H_5Cl} + NH_3 \xrightarrow[\text{catalyst}]{Cu_2O} \underset{\text{phenylamine}}{C_6H_5NH_2} + HCl$$

115.14 What will be the product of the reaction between 1-chloro-1-phenylethane, $C_6H_5CHClCH_3$,

and alcoholic potassium hydroxide?

115.15 Two bottles contained iodobenzene and (iodomethyl)benzene. However, the bottles were only labelled as A and B. It was not known which chemical was in which bottle. A sample from each bottle was put in two test tubes and warmed with sodium hydroxide solution. After cooling, dilute nitric acid was added followed by dilute silver nitrate solution. The results were:

Sample from bottle A gave a yellow precipitate.
Sample from bottle B gave no change.

(i) What was the yellow precipitate?

(ii) Why was dilute nitric acid added?

(iii) Which chemical was in which bottle?

(iv) Briefly explain the reaction.

(v) What would have been the result of using iodoethane in the experiment?

115.16 You have to make 1-chloro-2-phenylethane starting from an alcohol. Draw the structure of the alcohol you would use and say how you would perform the conversion.

115.17 A chemist wanted to make chloro-2-methylbenzene. The method the chemist chose was to react methylbenzene with chlorine in the presence of ultraviolet light.

(i) Why was this the wrong method?

(ii) What method should be used?

115.18 The length of the carbon–chlorine bond in chlorobenzene is 169 pm, while in most chloroalkanes it is 177 pm.

(i) What does this indicate about the carbon–chlorine bond in chlorobenzene?

(ii) How does this information fit with the relative unreactivity of chlorobenzene to nucleophilic attack, e.g. by hydroxide ions?

Answers

115.1 (i) 1-Bromopropane, (ii) 1-bromobutane, (iii) 2-bromobutane.

115.2 (i) High temperature or ultraviolet light.

(ii) This is a free radical reaction. It is difficult to control the proportions of the various products that can be made. This leads to problems over separation at the end of the reaction.

115.3 (i) Sulphur dioxide, SO_2, and hydrogen chloride, HCl.

(ii) The products are gases, the majority of which will bubble out of the reaction mixture, thus leaving a reasonably pure product.

115.4 Dichloromethane. Tetrachloromethane has polar bonds, but is symmetrical overall, so does not have a dipole moment.

115.5 One method is to mix bromine and ethene:

$$C_2H_4 + Br_2 \rightarrow CH_2BrCH_2Br$$

115.6 From Table 115.1 you will find that chloroethane is a gas while iodoethane is a liquid at room temperature and pressure. It is much easier to handle liquids rather than gases in a reaction. For other reasons, see the next unit.

115.7 Reflux is necessary: see Figure 113.5, but *not* with the stopper in. Ethanol is the lowest boiling point component of the mixture, so should distil over first. However, it will be contaminated by water vapour. The ethanol can be dried using calcium oxide. Alternatively, but less pleasant, the azeotropic mixture (see section 63.4) made by ethanol and water can be separated by adding benzene and redistilling.

115.8 (i) The first two products of the reaction are methylamine, CH_3NH_2, and dimethylamine, $(CH_3)_2NH$. Both these molecules, like ammonia, have a lone pair on the nitrogen. Trimethylamine is produced by the nucleophilic attack of the lone pair on the nitrogen of dimethylamine on the carbon atom of iodomethane:

$$(CH_3)_2NH + CH_3I \rightarrow (CH_3)_3N + HI$$

(ii) In Unit 15 we saw that ammonia will react with hydrogen chloride to give the ionic solid ammonium chloride, NH_4Cl. We said that this can be explained by assuming that the lone pair on the nitrogen forms a coordinate bond with a positively charged hydrogen atom. In our organic reaction, instead of hydrogen chloride, we have iodomethane. The carbocation CH_3^+ takes the place of the hydrogen ion, and iodide takes the place of the chloride ion:

$$(CH_3)_3N + CH_3I \rightarrow [N(CH_3)_4]^+ I^-$$

Answers – cont.

115.9 (i) Mass of $C_2H_5OH = 4.2\,g$, i.e. $4.2\,g/46\,g\,mol^{-1} = 0.09\,mol$.

(ii) 0.02 mol of P; 0.02 mol of I_2.

(iii) The ratio is approximately 5 mol C_2H_5OH:1 mol P:1 mol I_2.

(iv) The equation tells us that 3 mol of C_2H_5OH combine with 1 mol of PI_3 to give 3 mol of C_2H_5I. Also, 1 mol of PI_3 is obtained from 2 mol of P and 3 mol of I_2. The reactants need to be in the ratio 3 mol C_2H_5OH to 1 mol P to 1.5 mol I_2. The ethanol and phosphorus are in excess. This tells us that the iodine would be consumed before either of these chemicals was used up. The iodine governs the amount of C_2H_5I that can be made.

(v) We can obtain 0.04 mol of C_2H_5I, i.e. 6.24 g.

(vi) The yield was $(5.1\,g/6.24\,g) \times 100\% = 81.7\%$.

115.10 The apparatus is sketched in Figure 115.4. You would have to weigh the flask and benzene before starting the reaction. From time to time during the reaction, the supply of chlorine would have to be stopped, the flask disconnected from the apparatus and reweighed. This process would be continued until the benzene had increased in weight by the appropriate amount. (1 mol of benzene would increase from 78 g to 112.5 g.)

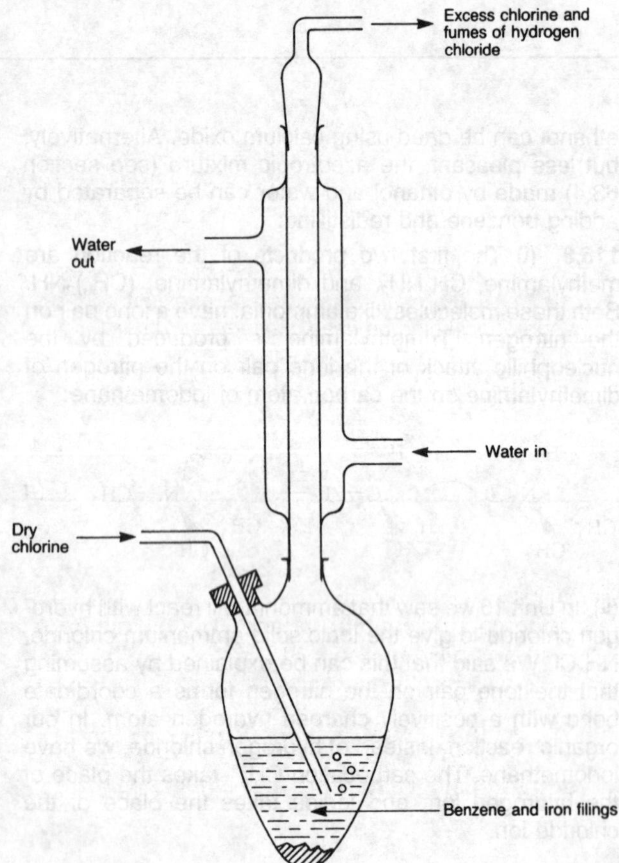

Figure 115.4 *Diagram for answer to question 115.10: a method of making chlorobenzene. The flask can be warmed using a water bath. The apparatus must be set up in a fume cupboard*

115.11 (i) The majority of the hydrogen chloride dissolved in the mixture will be transferred to the water.

(ii) A separating (or tap) funnel. Chlorobenzene is more dense than water, so it will be the bottom layer.

(iii) It will neutralise any remaining hydrogen chloride, and it will convert any chlorine dissolved in the organic layer into water soluble chlorate(I) and chloride ions (see section 101.6). Washing with water helps to remove the inorganic impurities.

(iv) The chlorobenzene and sodium hydroxide would be shaken together in a separating funnel (with the tap closed and its stopper in!). The separating funnel should be held upside down from time to time and the tap opened carefully to prevent the build up of pressure. The lower chlorobenzene layer should be run off and the sodium hydroxide solution discarded. This procedure should be repeated with the chlorobenzene and water.

(v) It dries the chlorobenzene. The cloudiness is due to tiny droplets of water that remain in the chlorobenzene after shaking with water.

(vi) Unreacted benzene and products like 1,2-dichlorobenzene would be impurities. The chlorobenzene should distil over in a range a few degrees either side of its boiling point, say 128 to 136 °C.

115.12 You could use iron filings as the halogen carrier instead of aluminium trichloride. The apparatus of Figure 115.5 could be used. It would not be necessary to disconnect the flask and weigh it during the reaction. Once you knew the weight of benzene you were to use, you would put the required weight of bromine into the dropping funnel.

115.13 A chlorine atom directs *ortho* and *para* (even though it deactivates the ring). Therefore you would expect to get 1,2-dichlorobenzene and 1,4-dichlorobenzene.

115.14 This is the dehydrohalogenation reaction. The product is phenylethene (also known as styrene):

$$C_6H_5{-}CH{=}CH_2$$

115.15 (i) Silver iodide.

(ii) The acid removes hydroxide ions. If they are present, a dirty grey deposit of silver(I) oxide is made, which prevents the silver ions reacting with iodide ions.

(iii), (iv) You should know that a halogen atom attached directly to the ring will not react easily with nucleophiles, so the iodobenzene was in bottle B.

(v) Iodoethane is relatively easily attacked by nucleophiles. The iodide ion is released into the solution as the iodoethane is converted into ethanol.

115.16 The alcohol is 2-phenylethanol:

$$C_6H_5{-}CH_2{-}CH_2{-}OH$$

Answers – cont.

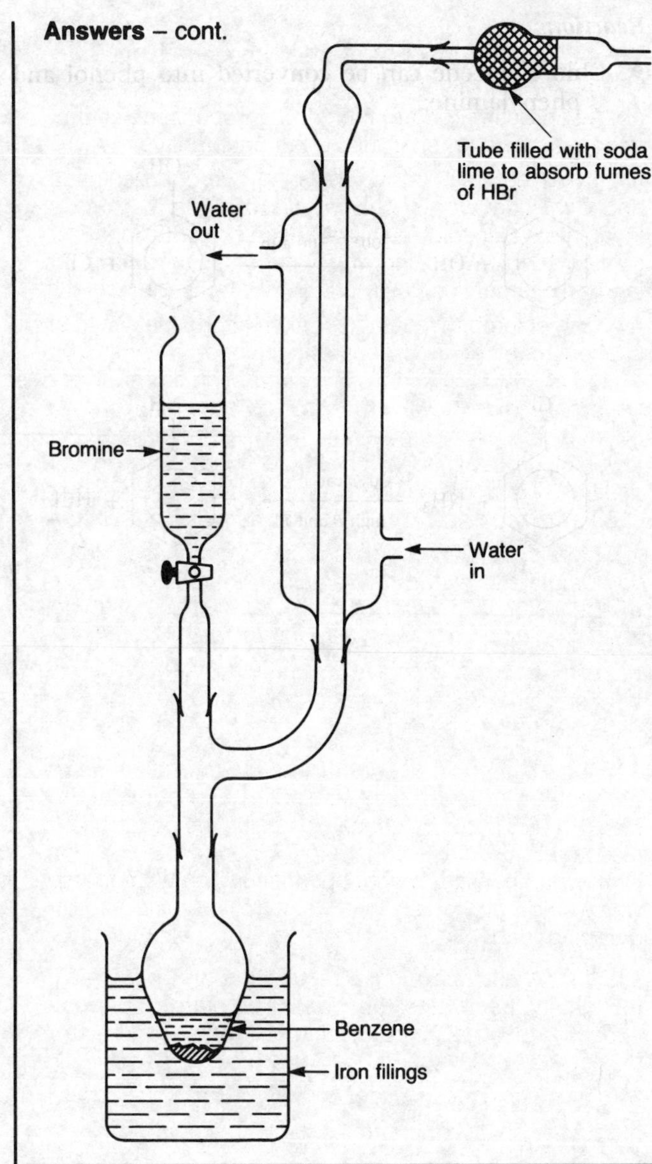

The conversion could be achieved by reacting the alcohol with phosphorus pentachloride or sulphur dichloride oxide, $SOCl_2$.

115.17 (i) The free radical reaction started by the ultraviolet light will mean that the methyl side chain is attacked, not the ring (see section 113.4).
(ii) A Friedel–Crafts reaction: chlorine and aluminium trichloride.

115.18 (i) Two things: first, the shorter bond is the stronger of the two; secondly, it fits with the picture we drew in the last unit, in which we said that the chlorine atom in chlorobenzene could use one of its lone pairs in bonding with the π system on the ring. This gives a measure of double bond character to the bond. (Compare the difference in bond lengths in ethane and ethene; section 33.5.)
(ii) It fits nicely. The stronger the bond, the more difficult it should be to break. However, there is another reason for the difference in reactivity. The geometry around the carbon bonded to the chlorine atom in chloroalkanes is tetrahedral, while in chlorobenzene it is planar. There is not such a clear pathway for the nucleophile to attack the carbon atom in chlorobenzene.

Figure 115.5 *Diagram for answer to question 115.12. The apparatus should be used in a fume cupboard*

UNIT 115 SUMMARY

Halogenoalkanes

Are hydrocarbons in which one or more hydrogen atoms are replaced by halogen atoms;
e.g. bromomethane, CH_3Br;
1,2-dichloroethane, CH_2ClCH_2Cl.

- Preparation:
  (i) React a halogenoalkane with a sodium halide and concentrated sulphuric acid;

  e.g. $C_2H_5OH + HBr \rightarrow C_2H_5Br + H_2O$

  (ii) Iodoethane can be made from ethanol, iodine and red phosphorus;

  $3C_2H_5OH + PI_3 \rightarrow 3C_2H_5I + H_3PO_3$

Reactions

- Undergo nucleophilic attack. The possibilities are summarised in Table 115.3.
- Take part in elimination reactions;

  e.g. $C_2H_5I \xrightarrow[KOH]{alcoholic} C_2H_4 + HI$

  dehydrohalogenation; makes alkenes.

Aralkyl halides

Have halogen atoms attached to the side chain of an aromatic molecule, e.g. $C_6H_5CH_2Cl$. They behave like halogenoalkanes.

Summary – cont.

Halogenoarenes

(i) Have one or more halogen atoms attached to a benzene ring.

(ii) Do not undergo nucleophilic attack as easily as halogenoalkanes; halogen atoms are extremely hard to remove from a benzene ring.

- Preparation:

(i) Friedel–Crafts reaction; e.g.

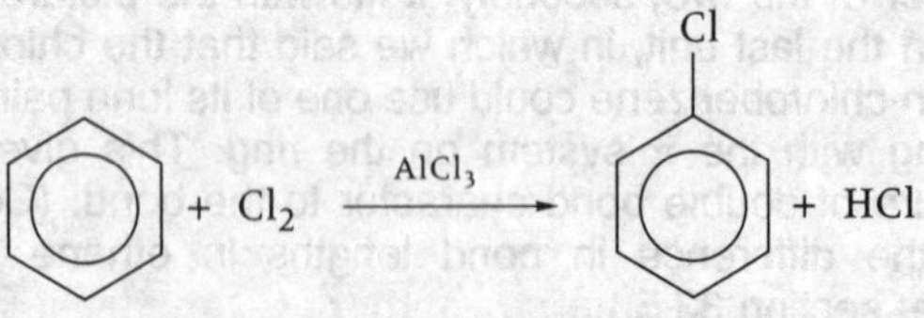

$$C_6H_6 + Cl_2 \xrightarrow{AlCl_3} C_6H_5Cl + HCl$$

(ii) From diazonium compounds; e.g.

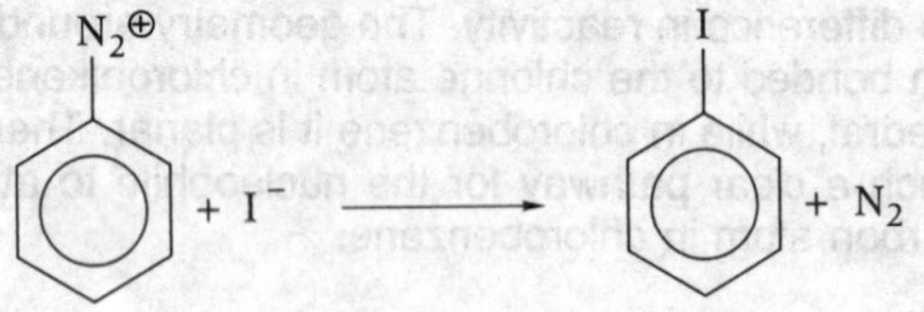

$$C_6H_5N_2^{\oplus} + I^- \longrightarrow C_6H_5I + N_2$$

Reactions

- Chlorobenzene can be converted into phenol and phenylamine;

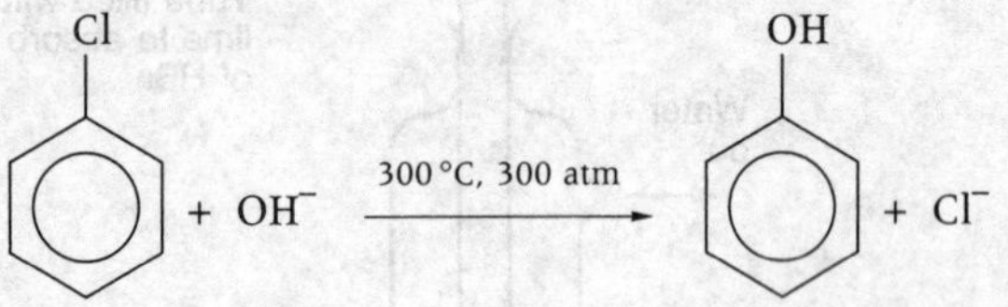

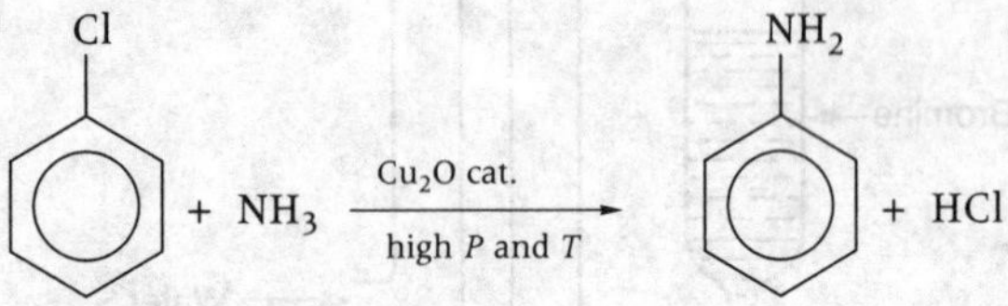

$$C_6H_5Cl + OH^- \xrightarrow{300\,°C,\ 300\ atm} C_6H_5OH + Cl^-$$

$$C_6H_5Cl + NH_3 \xrightarrow[\text{high } P \text{ and } T]{Cu_2O \text{ cat.}} C_6H_5NH_2 + HCl$$

116

Alcohols

116.1 The structures and uses of alcohols

Alcohols contain one or more OH groups. The simpler ones, the *monohydric alcohols,* contain only one OH group per molecule and have the general formula $C_nH_{2n+1}OH$. Ethanol, C_2H_5OH, is especially well known (and loved by some) because it is the ingredient in alcoholic drinks that causes people to become drunk. If there is more than one OH group in the molecule, it is called a *polyhydric alcohol.* Ethane-1,2-diol (glycol), CH_2OHCH_2OH, with two OH groups is a dihydric alcohol familiar to car and lorry owners when they add it to water in radiators; it is commonly known as antifreeze. Propane-1,2,3-triol (glycerol), $CH_2OHCHOHCH_2OH$, is a trihydric alcohol that is often used in medicine and cosmetics as a basis for the preparation of creams and ointments.

Alcohols have many uses in the chemical industry, especially as solvents and as intermediates in the manufacture of chemicals such as esters. The use of tetraethyl-lead(IV) as a petrol additive is declining. It is being replaced by adding small amounts of alcohol to petrol. The alcohol also has the ability to encourage the smooth burning of petrol. In some countries alcohol rather than petrol is used as a fuel for motor vehicles.

It is the OH group that is responsible for the miscibility of many alcohols with water. Just as a water molecule can hydrogen bond with another water molecule, so it can with an alcohol (see Figure 116.1).

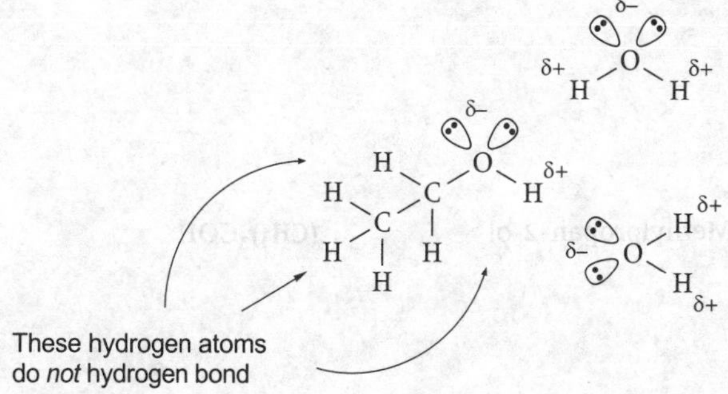

These hydrogen atoms do *not* hydrogen bond

Figure 116.1 *Ethanol can be hydrogen bonded to water molecules*

Two models showing the shapes of methanol and ethanol.

Table 116.1. Common alcohols

Name	*Formula*	*Structure*	*Melting point/°C*	*Boiling point/°C*
Methanol	CH_3OH	H H—C—OH H	−97.5	64.7
Ethanol	C_2H_5OH	H H H—C—C—OH H H	−114	78.5
Propan-1-ol	C_3H_7OH	H H H H—C—C—C—OH H H H	−126	97.4
Propan-2-ol	$(CH_3)_2CHOH$	H H H—C—C—OH H H—C—H H	−88.4	82.7
2-Methylpropan-2-ol	$(CH_3)_3COH$	H H—C—H H H—C—C—OH H H—C—H H	25.5	83
Butan-1-ol	C_4H_9OH	H H H H H—C—C—C—C—OH H H H H	−89.2	117.9
Ethane-1,2-diol (glycol)	CH_2OHCH_2OH	OH OH H—C—C—H H H	−13.4	197
Propane-1,2,3-triol (glycerol)	$CH_2OHCHOHCH_2OH$	OH OH OH H—C—C—C—H H H H	18	290

```
      H  H                 H
      |  |                 |
   H—C—C—OH             H—C—H
      |  |                 |
      H  H            H    |
                      |    |
                   H—C————C————OH
                      |    |
                      H    |
                           H
```

CH_3CH_2OH Ethanol

$(CH_3)_2CHOH$ Propan-2-ol

```
          H
          |
        H—C—H
     H    |
     |    |
   H—C————C————OH
     |    |
     H    |
        H—C—H
          |
          H
```

$(CH_3)_3COH$ 2-Methylpropan-2-ol

***Figure 116.2** Typical primary, secondary and tertiary alcohols*

Each of the alcohols in Table 116.1 fits into one of three categories. They are either *primary*, *secondary*, or *tertiary* alcohols. Typical structures are shown in Figure 116.2. You will see that, respectively, they have one methyl, two methyl and three methyl groups attached to the carbon bonded to the OH group. The general formulae of the three varieties are:

RCH_2OH primary | $RR'CHOH$ secondary | $RR'R''COH$ tertiary

In some reactions, primary, secondary and tertiary alcohols behave in different ways. Similarly, aromatic alcohols often behave differently to the non-aromatics, and we shall study the former in the next unit.

116.1 Explain why it is sometimes said that water is the simplest alcohol.

116.2 Why do alcohols with a long carbon backbone become immiscible with water?

116.3 Explain why you would expect alcohols to have a dipole moment.

116.4 An alcohol has the formula $C_6H_{11}OH$ and it does not react with bromine or bromine water.

(i) What does the information about the bromine tell you?

(ii) What is the structure of the alcohol?

(iii) Suggest a name for it.

116.5 What are the names of these alcohols?

(i)

```
                        OH
                        |
CH3—CH2—CH2—C—CH3
                        |
                        H
```

(ii)

```
               OH
               |
CH3—CH2—C—CH3
               |
               CH3
```

116.2 How we can make alcohols

There are many ways of making alcohols. We shall look at two large-scale methods of making them, and four methods that are more often used in the laboratory.

(a) *Fermentation*

Fermentation is the traditional way of making ethanol. Ethanol is made by the action of enzymes on sugars, particularly glucose and fructose, both of which have the formula $C_6H_{12}O_6$. One enzyme, *zymase*, which is extremely effective in causing fermentation, is found in yeasts. In wine making, grapes are the source of sugars and yeast. As grapes ripen, the amount of sugar inside them increases, and yeasts grow on the outer skin. By crushing the grapes the sugary juices and yeast are brought into contact and fermentation starts. The sugar sucrose, $C_{12}H_{22}O_{11}$, which is itself resistant to attack by zymase, can be broken into glucose and fructose by another enzyme, invertase:

$$\underset{\text{sucrose}}{C_{12}H_{22}O_{11}} + H_2O \rightarrow \underset{\text{glucose}}{C_6H_{12}O_6} + \underset{\text{fructose}}{C_6H_{12}O_6} \quad \text{catalysed by invertase}$$

If you have made wine, beer, or lager at home you will know that the fermentation has to be done in a bottle fitted with an air lock. During fermentation carbon dioxide is released. The gas quickly displaces air from the bottle, and the fermentation takes place in *anaerobic* conditions. You can tell how well the fermentation is proceeding by studying the rate at which bubbles of carbon dioxide are released.

We can write the reaction taking place in this way:

$$\underset{\text{sugar}}{C_2H_{12}O_6} \rightarrow \underset{\text{ethanol}}{2C_2H_5OH} + 2CO_2 \quad \text{catalysed by zymase}$$

The conversion of sugar into ethanol will not continue

Scotch whisky is distilled in copper stills behind the control panel.

indefinitely because, once the percentage of alcohol exceeds 14%, the action of zymase is inhibited.

It is important that air does not get into the mixture. Oxygen will oxidise the alcohol and convert it into ethanoic acid (old name, acetic acid). This acid gives vinegar its sharp taste, and its presence ruins the taste of an alcoholic drink. Many years ago Louis Pasteur proved that bacteria present in air will also cause wine to go off.

Given that many people find the effects of drinking alcohol pleasant, it is not surprising that ways have been found to increase the proportion of alcohol above the 14% limit. Typically this is done by distillation. The method of distillation, and the number of times it is carried out, give different qualities of various spirits such as vodka, brandy and whisky. Table 116.2 shows the consumption of alcoholic drinks in various countries.

The taste of different wines and spirits depends on many things, especially the particular mix of more complicated alcohols and esters that are made during the fermentation and while the alcoholic liquid is left to mature. If, for example, wine or spirits are kept in wooden barrels, then the wood itself gives a particular taste.

Methanol, CH_3OH, was once obtained by heating wood and collecting the tarry liquid given off. The liquid contains a few per cent of methanol. Hence the old name for methanol was wood alcohol. Like ethanol, methanol causes intoxication; but in addition it causes blindness and brain damage to those who drink it often. Together with a coloured dye, methanol can be added to ethanol and sold as 'methylated spirits'. Industrial

Table 116.2. Table of alcohol consumption statistics*†

Country	*Year*	*Spirits*	*Wine*	*Beer*	*Total alcohol*
France	1968	7.96	146.72	78.26	22.62
Italy	1969	4.23	152.51	14.95	14.99
USA	1971	9.92	7.87	98.03	10.15
UK	1970	2.14	4.91	114.71	7.21
Ireland	1970	3.71	4.81	98.71	7.06

*The figures give the number of litres drunk per person aged 15 years or over in the year shown in the table. The spirits, wine and beer columns give the volume of each liquid consumed (alcohol plus water). The final column gives the total equivalent volume of pure alcohol (C_2H_5OH) for all three types of alcoholic drink. Notice the differences in the drinking habits of the people of the different countries: e.g. French and Italian people tend to drink significantly more wine than beer, while in the USA, UK and Ireland the opposite is true

†Data taken from the *Encyclopaedia Britannica*, 15th edn, 1985, vol. 13, p. 223

methylated spirits (IMS) may also contain another poisonous organic reagent, pyridine.

(b) *Hydration of alkenes*

In Unit 112 we discussed the way in which alkenes take part in addition reactions. One of these reactions involved absorbing an alkene in concentrated sulphuric acid, and then diluting the acid with water. The result is an alcohol. For example,

$$H_2C{=}CH_2 \longrightarrow CH_3CH_2OH$$

ethene → ethanol

$$CH_3CH{=}CH_2 \longrightarrow CH_3CH(OH)CH_3$$

propene → propan-2-ol

Notice that, in effect, this is the addition of H—OH across the double bond in the alkene. The addition is in accordance with Markovnikoff's rule.

On an industrial scale this reaction uses alkenes made by the cracking of hydrocarbons in oil. The alkene is passed into sulphuric acid at around 80 °C and 30 atm pressure. The acid is diluted and treated with steam to release the alcohol. The final stage is the distillation of the solution. A problem that arises at this stage is that ethanol, and many other alcohols, give azeotropic (constant boiling) mixtures with water (see section 63.4). However, ethanol can be completely separated by distilling the azeotropic mixture with benzene.

(c) *Grignard reagents*

We have met Grignard reagents before. Their general formula is RMgX, where R is an organic radical and X is a halogen, often bromine. To make an alcohol we would normally react the Grignard reagent with an aldehyde or ketone. The functional groups of aldehydes and ketones are very similar:

$$\text{R}-\text{C}\begin{matrix}{=}\text{O}\\ \diagdown\text{H}\end{matrix} \qquad\qquad \text{R}-\text{C}\begin{matrix}{=}\text{O}\\ \diagdown\text{R}'\end{matrix}$$

an aldehyde — a ketone

The carbon atoms are ideal sites for nucleophilic attack. We know that the organic radical bonded to the magnesium atom carries a negative charge, and it acts as a nucleophile. Now let us see what happens when a suitable Grignard reagent reacts with an aldehyde or ketone. Let us assume that we are using CH_3MgBr:

$$\underset{\text{methanal}}{HCHO} + CH_3MgBr \longrightarrow CH_3-CH_2-OMgBr$$

$$CH_3-CH_2-OMgBr + H_2O \longrightarrow \underset{\text{ethanol}}{CH_3-CH_2-OH} \quad \text{primary alcohol}$$

The overall result is for the methyl group to bond to the carbon atom and a hydrogen atom to the oxygen. Thus, we can summarise the reactions in this way:

$$\underset{\text{ethanal}}{CH_3CHO} \xrightarrow[\text{(ii) } H_2O]{\text{(i) } CH_3MgBr} \underset{\text{propan-2-ol}}{CH_3-CH(OH)-CH_3} \quad \text{secondary alcohol}$$

$$\underset{\text{propanone}}{CH_3COCH_3} \xrightarrow[\text{(ii) } H_2O]{\text{(i) } CH_3MgBr} \underset{\text{2-methylpropan-2-ol}}{CH_3-C(OH)(CH_3)-CH_3} \quad \text{tertiary alcohol}$$

Of course, if we were to use a C_2H_5 group instead of CH_3 in the Grignard reagent, more complex alcohols would be made. Similarly, by changing the aldehyde or ketone we can make a variety of different alcohols.

(d) *Reduction of carbonyl compounds*

Aldehydes and ketones can be reduced with hydrogen in the presence of a catalyst, or by reacting them with lithium tetrahydridoaluminate(III), $LiAlH_4$ (or sodium tetrahydridoborate(III), $NaBH_4$). The pattern is:

Aldehydes are reduced to primary alcohols.

Ketones are reduced to secondary alcohols.

Here are three examples:

$$\underset{\text{methanal}}{HCHO} \xrightarrow{H_2,\ Ni} \underset{\text{methanol}}{H-CH_2-OH} \quad CH_3OH$$

$$\underset{\text{ethanal}}{CH_3CHO} \xrightarrow[\text{(ii) acid}]{\text{(i) } LiAlH_4} \underset{\text{ethanol}}{CH_3-CH_2-OH} \quad CH_3CH_2OH$$

$$\underset{\text{propanone}}{CH_3COCH_3} \xrightarrow[\text{(ii) acid}]{\text{(i) } NaBH_4} \underset{\text{propan-2-ol}}{CH_3-CH(OH)-CH_3} \quad (CH_3)_2CHOH$$

(e) *Hydrolysis of halogenoalkanes*

We have covered this type of reaction in some detail as a property of halogenoalkanes. We need only mention that halogenoalkanes will have their halogen replaced by an OH group if we boil them with sodium hydroxide solution. For example,

$$C_2H_5I + OH^- \rightarrow C_2H_5OH + I^-$$

(f) *Hydroboration*

Diborane, B_2H_6, is an interesting molecule in its own right. It is one of the electron deficient molecules that we discussed in section 90.7. In organic chemistry it has the welcome property of combining with alkenes to give a product that, on oxidation with hydrogen peroxide, turns into an alcohol:

$$\underset{\text{ethene}}{H_2C=CH_2} \xrightarrow[\text{(ii) } H_2O_2]{\text{(i) } B_2H_6} \underset{\text{ethanol}}{H-CH_2-CH_2-OH}$$

$$\underset{\text{propene}}{CH_3CH=CH_2} \xrightarrow[\text{(ii) } H_2O_2]{\text{(i) } B_2H_6} \underset{\text{propan-1-ol}}{CH_3-CH_2-CH_2-OH}$$

$$\underset{\text{but-1-ene}}{C_2H_5CH=CH_2} \xrightarrow[\text{(ii) } H_2O_2]{\text{(i) } B_2H_6} \underset{\text{butan-1-ol}}{C_2H_5-CH_2-CH_2-OH}$$

Like the preparation of alcohols by absorption in concentrated sulphuric acid, the net result is the addition of H—OH across the double bond. However, notice that in hydroboration the addition does *not* obey Markovnikoff's rule; we say it is an *anti-Markovnikoff* addition.

116.6 The modern method of making methanol is by the use of synthesis gas, a mixture of carbon monoxide and hydrogen, which is itself made from natural gas and steam (see section 90.2):

$$CO(g) + 2H_2(g) \rightarrow CH_3OH(g)$$

The reaction takes place above 350°C, at around 20 atm and with a catalyst of zinc oxide and chromium(III) oxide. Use the data in Table 44.1 to calculate the enthalpy change of this reaction under standard conditions (25°C and 1 atm).

116.7 You have been given the task of studying the rate of fermentation of grape juice. What method would you use?

116.8 What would you expect to be made if the Grignard reagent C_2H_5MgBr reacted with butanone,

$$C_2H_5—C(=O)—CH_3$$

and the product hydrolysed?

116.9 Which alcohol will be made if pentan-3-one,

$$C_2H_5—C(=O)—C_2H_5$$

is reacted with lithium tetrahydridoaluminate(III)?

116.10 What will be the result of using pent-2-ene, (i) by absorbing it in concentrated sulphuric acid, followed by dilution with water, (ii) by reacting it with diborane, followed by hydrogen peroxide?

116.3 The oxidation reactions of alcohols

The easiest way to oxidise an alcohol is to burn it. You may have seen the characteristic pale blue flame of ethanol burning if you have ever set fire to brandy on a Christmas pudding:

$$2C_2H_5OH(l) + 7O_2(g) \rightarrow 4CO_2(g) + 6H_2O(g)$$

However, in the laboratory we can use less drastic, and more useful, methods of oxidation. A common oxidising agent to use is acidified sodium dichromate(VI). Owing to the production of chromium(III) ions, this orange coloured solution changes to green if it meets a reducing agent. Primary, secondary and tertiary alcohols react in different ways, indicated in Table 116.3. Alcohols can also be oxidised to aldehydes or ketones by passing their vapour over copper powder kept at around 250°C. Similarly, we can use the reaction as a way of distinguishing the three types of alcohol. Especially, if you warm ethanol with acidified sodium dichromate(VI) solution, you will soon notice the characteristic smell of ethanal. Be careful if you try this. The reaction mixture will oxidise you or your clothes if it gets on them. Also, ethanol and ethanal vapours are highly flammable. Do *not* heat the mixture over a naked flame. Put it in a beaker of hot water.

Table 116.3. The oxidation of primary, secondary and tertiary alcohols

With acidified sodium dichromate(VI) solution

Primary alcohols →aldehydes →acids

$$CH_3—CH_2—OH \longrightarrow CH_3—C(=O)—H \longrightarrow CH_3—C(=O)—OH$$

ethanol → ethanal → ethanoic acid

Secondary alcohols→ketones

$$CH_3—CH(OH)—CH_3 \longrightarrow CH_3—C(=O)—CH_3$$

propan-2-ol → propanone

Tertiary alcohols→no reaction

$$CH_3—C(OH)(CH_3)—CH_3$$

2-methylpropan-2-ol

With copper at 250°C

Primary alcohols give aldehydes

$$CH_3—CH_2—OH \longrightarrow CH_3—C(=O)—H$$

ethanol → ethanal

Secondary alcohols give ketones

$$CH_3—CH(OH)—CH_3 \longrightarrow CH_3—C(=O)—CH_3$$

propan-2-ol → propanone

Tertiary alcohols do not react

116.11 The oxidation of primary and secondary alcohols can be the basis of preparing aldehydes and ketones. Which alcohol would you oxidise if you wanted to make the following?

(i) butanal,

$$C_3H_7-C\overset{\displaystyle =O}{\underset{\displaystyle \diagdown H}{}}$$

(ii) butanone,

$$C_2H_5-C\overset{\displaystyle =O}{\underset{\displaystyle \diagdown CH_3}{}}$$

116.12 Using a simple definition of oxidation, explain why we have called the conversion of an alcohol into an aldehyde or ketone an oxidation reaction.

116.4 Two reactions of the OH group

(a) *With sodium*

There are two ways of showing that alcohols have an OH group. If you drop a small piece of sodium into ethanol in a test tube, you will see it sink to the bottom of the tube. You will also see bubbles of gas given off. The gas is hydrogen:

$$\underset{\text{ethanol}}{2C_2H_5OH} + 2Na \rightarrow \underset{\text{sodium ethoxide}}{2C_2H_5O^-Na^+} + H_2$$

This reaction shows that alcohols can lose their hydrogen from the OH group. This is a reaction that we would normally associate with acids. (Remember, hydrogen is given off by the reaction of most metals with an inorganic acid.) However, water itself is a much stronger acid than an alcohol. Only OH groups on a benzene ring are appreciably acidic in water, e.g. phenol C_6H_5OH.

(b) *With phosphorus pentachloride or sulphur dichloride oxide*

The second reaction that shows the presence of the OH group can also be used as a method of preparing halogenoalkanes. With either of these two reagents, we see white fumes of hydrogen chloride given off when they are added to an alcohol, e.g.

$$C_2H_5OH + PCl_5 \rightarrow C_2H_5Cl + POCl_3 + \underset{\text{white fumes}}{HCl}$$

$$C_2H_5OH + SOCl_2 \rightarrow C_2H_5Cl + SO_2 + \underset{\text{white fumes}}{HCl}$$

You should be careful not to read too much into these two tests. They do *not* prove that the chemical being tested is an alcohol. An organic acid like ethanoic acid, CH_3COOH, will also give off hydrogen with sodium, and white fumes of hydrogen chloride with PCl_5 or $SOCl_2$. The tests show that a molecule *has an OH group.*

116.13 If you were using PCl_5 or $SOCl_2$ to test for the presence of OH groups, why must the chemicals and apparatus be dry?

116.5 Reactions in which the OH group is replaced by another group

We have just discussed examples of these reactions, those with PCl_5 or $SOCl_2$. Here the OH group is replaced by a halogen. If you look back at the methods of making halogenoalkanes, you will find several possibilities: in particular, reacting an alcohol with a sodium halide and concentrated sulphuric acid, or with red phosphorus and bromine or iodine. It is interesting to compare the reactivities of primary, secondary and tertiary alcohols in these reactions. The order is

tertiary	>	secondary	>	primary
most reactive				least reactive

The reason for this difference in reactivity lies in the nature of the intermediates formed in the reactions. Often these involve carbocations. As we saw in Unit 112, a tertiary carbocation is more favoured than a secondary, and a primary carbocation least favoured. For example, if an alcohol reacts with a hydrogen halide, the first thing that happens is that the oxygen of the OH group becomes protonated.

(i) *Stage 1*: Protonation of the oxygen atom.

$$H-\underset{H}{\overset{H}{C}}-\underset{H}{\overset{:\ddot{O}-H}{C}}-H \longrightarrow H-\underset{H}{\overset{H}{C}}-\underset{H}{\overset{:\overset{H^{\oplus}}{\ddot{O}}-H}{C}}-H$$

(ii) *Stage 2*: Water can be lost from the molecule, leaving a carbocation behind.

$$H-\underset{H}{\overset{H}{C}}-\underset{H}{\overset{:\overset{H^{\oplus}}{\ddot{O}}-H}{C}}-H - H_2O \longrightarrow H-\underset{H}{\overset{H}{C}}-\underset{H}{\overset{\oplus}{C}}-H$$

(iii) *Stage 3*: It is the carbocation that reacts with the halide ion, X^-.

$$H-\underset{H}{\overset{H}{C}}-\underset{H}{\overset{\oplus}{C}}-H \xrightarrow{X^-} H-\underset{H}{\overset{H}{C}}-\underset{H}{\overset{X}{C}}-H$$

It is stage 2 that is encouraged if the carbocation made is energetically favoured. For this reason, we would expect 2-methylpropan-2-ol to be the most reactive because it gives a tertiary carbocation in stage 2.

116.14 Can alcohols act as nucleophiles? Explain your answer.

116.15 To convert butan-1-ol to 1-chlorobutane using hydrogen chloride requires heat and a zinc chloride catalyst. The isomeric alcohol 2-methylpropan-2-ol is converted to 2-chloro-2-methylpropane by concentrated hydrochloric acid at room temperature. Why is there such a difference in reactivity?

116.6 Dehydration reactions

Alcohols can be dehydrated by passing them over hot aluminium oxide, or by heating them at about 180 °C with concentrated sulphuric acid. We looked at both types of reaction in section 112.2 because they are used to prepare alkenes. For example,

$$\underset{\text{ethanol}}{CH_3CH_2OH} - H_2O \rightarrow \underset{\text{ethene}}{C_2H_4}$$

$$\underset{\text{butan-2-ol}}{CH_3CH_2CHOHCH_3} - H_2O \rightarrow \underset{\text{but-2-ene}}{CH_3CH{=}CHCH_3}$$

Notice that, in the second example, but-2-ene rather than but-1-ene is the major product.

116.7 When alcohols react with acids, esters are made

If you mix a little ethanol with an approximately equal amount of ethanoic acid, and warm them together (using a water bath) you will eventually detect the very sweet smell of ethyl ethanoate. (It smells of pear drops.) However, if you were first to add a few drops of concentrated sulphuric acid to the reaction mixture, you would detect the smell much more quickly. The acid catalyses the reaction, which is in fact reversible:

$$CH_3{-}C({=}O){-}O{-}H + CH_3{-}CH_2{-}OH \rightleftharpoons CH_3{-}C({=}O){-}O{-}CH_2{-}CH_3 + H_2O$$

$$\underset{\text{ethanoic acid}}{CH_3COOH} + \underset{\text{ethanol}}{CH_3CH_2OH} \rightleftharpoons \underset{\text{ethyl ethanoate}}{CH_3COOCH_2CH_3} + H_2O$$

Other alcohols and acids react in similar ways. We shall return to this reaction in section 120.6. Esters can also be made by reacting an alcohol with an acid chloride. For example, ethyl ethanoate can be made from ethanol and ethanoyl chloride. This reaction is very much faster than the previous method:

$$CH_3CH_2{-}O{-}H + CH_3{-}C({=}O){-}Cl \rightarrow CH_3{-}C({=}O){-}O{-}CH_2CH_3 + H_2O$$

$$\underset{\text{ethanol}}{CH_3CH_2OH} + \underset{\text{ethanoyl chloride}}{CH_3COCl} \rightarrow \underset{\text{ethyl ethanoate}}{CH_3COOCH_2CH_3} + H_2O$$

116.16 Draw the structure of the ester made when propan-1-ol reacts with ethanoic acid. Suggest a name for the molecule.

Answers

116.1 We can write the formula of water as H—OH, and an alcohol as R—OH. The similarity is clear; both have an OH group.

116.2 The miscibility of alcohols with water depends on (i) the attractions between the molecules owing to the hydrogen bonds between them and (ii) the entropy of mixing. If the carbon chain becomes too long, its presence in water disrupts many hydrogen bonds between the water molecules. This is energetically unfavourable. Eventually the enthalpy change for mixing becomes positive and overcomes the favourable entropy of mixing. (Remember, $\Delta G = \Delta H - T\Delta S$, and we must have $\Delta G < 0$ for the process to occur.)

116.3 The electronegative oxygen attracts electron density towards itself. This leaves the hydrogen and carbon atoms attached to it with a slight positive charge. Owing to the unsymmetrical distribution of charge, a dipole moment results.

116.4 (i) The molecule has no double or triple bonds.
(ii) Its structure is:

(iii) Cyclohexanol.

Answers – contd.

116.5 (i) Pentan-2-ol.
(ii) 2-Methylbutan-2-ol.

116.6 We have,

$\Delta H^\ominus(\text{reaction}) = \Delta H_f^\ominus(CH_3OH) - \Delta H_f^\ominus(CO)$
$= -238.9\,\text{kJ mol}^{-1} - (-110.5\,\text{kJ mol}^{-1})$
$= -128.4\,\text{kJ mol}^{-1}$

116.7 A simple method would be to measure the volume of carbon dioxide given off over a given time interval, say every 10 minutes. If you wanted to use a home brewing kit, and you had the patience, you could simply count the number of bubbles of gas escaping in a given time interval.

116.8 2-Methylbutan-2-ol, a tertiary alcohol:

$CH_3—CH_2—C(OH)(CH_3)—CH_3$

116.9 Pentan-3-ol:

$CH_3—CH_2—C(OH)(H)—CH_2—CH_3$

116.10 (i) Markovnikoff addition: the product is pentan-2-ol:

$CH_3—CH_2—CH_2—C(OH)(H)—CH_3$

(ii) Anti-Markovnikoff addition: the product is pentan-1-ol:

$CH_3—CH_2—CH_2—CH_2—CH_2OH$

116.11 (i) Butan-1-ol:

$CH_3—CH_2—CH_2—CH_2—OH$

(ii) Butan-2-ol:

$CH_3—CH_2—C(OH)(H)—CH_3$

116.12 Oxidation is the loss of hydrogen. An aldehyde or ketone contains fewer hydrogen atoms than its parent alcohol.

116.13 Water contains OH groups, so it too reacts with the reagents. If water is present, the test will appear to work even if there are no OH groups in the organic compound.

116.14 Yes. The reaction of an alcohol with, say, hydrogen chloride can be thought of as a nucleophilic attack by one of the lone pairs on the oxygen on the hydrogen bonded to the chlorine atom. Normally, though, we talk about the lone pair being protonated.

116.15 The intermediate formed in the reaction with 2-methylpropan-2-ol is a tertiary carbocation, so it is more energetically favoured than the primary carbocation obtained from butan-1-ol. This difference in reactivity is the basis of the *Lucas test* for distinguishing primary, secondary and tertiary alcohols. The alcohol is mixed with concentrated hydrochloric acid and zinc chloride. The solution goes cloudy when chloroalkanes are made. You should now know that tertiary alcohols give the cloudiness most quickly, and primary alcohols the least quickly (if at all).

116.16 The ester is propyl ethanoate:

$CH_3—C(=O)—O—CH_2—CH_2—CH_3$

UNIT 116 SUMMARY

- Alcohols:
  (i) Have one or more OH groups as their functional groups.
  (ii) The non-aromatic monohydric alcohols have the general formula $C_nH_{2n+1}OH$; e.g. methanol, CH_3OH; ethanol, C_2H_5OH.
  (iii) Primary alcohols have formula RCH_2OH, secondary $RR'CHOH$, tertiary $RR'R''COH$.
- Preparation:
  (i) By fermentation of sugars;

  e.g. $C_6H_{12}O_6 \rightarrow 2C_2H_5OH + CO_2$ catalysed by zymase

  (ii) Hydration of alkenes (an addition reaction);

  e.g. $C_2H_4 \xrightarrow[\text{(ii) } H_2O]{\text{(i) conc. } H_2SO_4} C_2H_5OH$

  (iii) Using a Grignard reagent. Aldehydes give secondary alcohols; ketones give tertiary alcohols; e.g.

  $R—C(=O)—H \xrightarrow[\text{(ii) } H_2O]{\text{(i) } CH_3MgBr} R—C(OH)(H)—CH_3$

  (iv) Reduction of aldehydes or ketones by lithium tetrahydridoaluminate(III), or using hydrogen and a nickel catalyst; e.g.

  $R—C(=O)—R' \xrightarrow[\text{(ii) } H_2O]{\text{(i) } LiAlH_4} R—C(OH)(H)—R'$

Summary – cont.

(v) Hydrolysis of halogenoalkanes by heating with alkali;

e.g. $C_2H_5I + OH^- \rightarrow C_2H_5OH + I^-$

(vi) Hydroboration of alkenes using diborane and hydrogen peroxide; e.g.

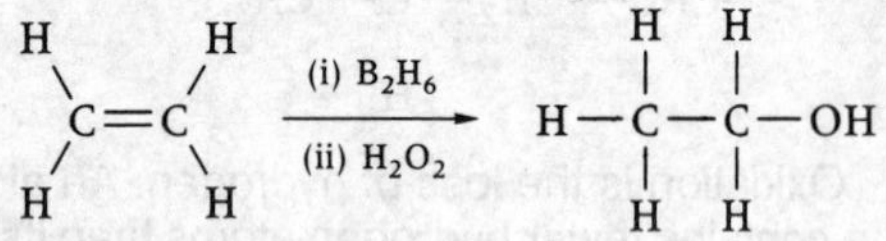

$$\underset{H}{\overset{H}{}}\!\!\!\!\;\; \begin{matrix} H & & H \\ & C{=}C & \\ H & & H \end{matrix} \xrightarrow[\text{(ii) } H_2O_2]{\text{(i) } B_2H_6} H{-}\underset{H}{\overset{H}{\underset{|}{\overset{|}{C}}}}{-}\underset{H}{\overset{H}{\underset{|}{\overset{|}{C}}}}{-}OH$$

Reactions

- Oxidation:

  (i) Alcohols burn;

  e.g. $2C_2H_5OH(l) + 7O_2(g) \rightarrow 4CO_2(g) + 6H_2O(g)$

  (ii) With acidified sodium dichromate(VI) solution;

  primary alcohols → aldehydes → acids
  secondary alcohols → ketones

  (iii) React with copper at 250 °C;

  primary alcohols → aldehydes
  secondary alcohols → ketones

- With sodium:
  Hydrogen released;

  e.g. $2C_2H_5OH + 2Na \rightarrow 2C_2H_5O^-Na^+ + H_2$

- Dehydration:
  With concentrated sulphuric acid;

  e.g. $CH_3CH_2CHOHCH_3 - H_2O \rightarrow CH_3CH{=}CHCH_3$

- Esterification:

  (i) Warm an alcohol with an organic acid plus a little concentrated sulphuric acid;

  e.g. $CH_3COOH + CH_3CH_2OH \rightleftharpoons CH_3COOCH_2CH_3 + H_2O$
  ethyl ethanoate

  (ii) React with an acid chloride;

  e.g. $CH_3CH_2OH + CH_3COCl \rightarrow CH_3COOCH_2CH_3 + HCl$
  ethanoyl chloride

- Test for OH group:
  White fumes of HCl with phosphorus pentachloride or sulphur dichloride oxide;

  e.g. $C_2H_5OH + SOCl_2 \rightarrow C_2H_5Cl + SO_2 + HCl$

117

Aromatic alcohols

117.1 There are two kinds of aromatic alcohol

Aromatic alcohols contain an OH group, but it can be attached either directly to the benzene ring or to a hydrocarbon side chain. Table 117.1 shows you some examples. As a general rule, if the OH group is on the side chain, the alcohol can be made by the methods we met in the last unit. Similarly it will have chemical properties in common with them. Questions 117.1 to 117.4 will check your understanding of these points.

When the OH group is bonded to a benzene ring there are two major effects: first, the properties of the OH group are changed; and secondly, the properties of the benzene ring are changed as well. We shall see these effects at work in the following sections.

The most common aromatic alcohol is phenol, C_6H_5OH. At room temperature pure phenol is a clear, colourless crystalline solid. However, it is often pale pink in colour owing to impurities being present. It has a distinctive smell of antiseptic, which is to be expected because phenol *is* an antiseptic. If you use phenol, take care with it. The crystals or a solution in water will irritate your skin, and may cause it to blister.

117.1 Suggest a way of making 2-phenylethanol starting with 1-iodo-2-phenylethane.

117.2 Which two chemicals would you mix if you wanted to make the ester, phenylethyl ethanoate:

$$CH_3-C(=O)-O-CH_2-CH_2-C_6H_5$$

117.3 A little 1-phenylethanol,

$$CH_3-CH(OH)-C_6H_5$$

was oxidised by acidified potassium dichromate(VI) solution.

(i) What type of alcohol is 1-phenylethanol?

(ii) What type of product do these alcohols give on oxidation?

(iii) Draw the structure of the molecule made in this reaction.

117.4 2-Phenylethanol is subjected to dehydration by reacting it with concentrated sulphuric acid. Draw the structure of the product of the reaction.

117.2 How to make phenol

It is an unrewarding task to persuade benzene to swap one of its hydrogen atoms for an OH group directly. Similarly, trying to replace a halogen on a benzene by an OH group is far from easy (see section 115.7). In the laboratory the best method is to convert phenylamine into phenol. If we put phenylamine into an ice cold solution of sodium nitrite in hydrochloric acid, it is converted into a benzenediazonium ion by the nitrous acid present:

$$C_6H_5-NH_2 + HNO_2 + H^+ \longrightarrow C_6H_5-N_2^{\oplus} + 2H_2O$$

$$\underset{\text{phenylamine}}{C_6H_5NH_2} + HNO_2 + H^+ \rightarrow \underset{\text{benzene diazonium ion}}{C_6H_5N_2^{\oplus}} + 2H_2O$$

We can convert the benzenediazonium ion into phenol by warming the solution. As the temperature increases, the benzenediazonium ion is rapidly hydrolysed:

$$C_6H_5-N_2^{\oplus} + H_2O \longrightarrow C_6H_5-OH + N_2 + H^+$$

$$C_6H_5N_2^{\oplus} + H_2O \rightarrow \underset{\text{phenol}}{C_6H_5OH} + N_2 + H^+$$

Table 117.1. Some aromatic alcohols

Name	*Formula*	*Structure*	*Melting point*/°C	*Boiling point*/°C
Phenol	C_6H_5OH	OH on benzene ring	41	182
Benzene-1,2-diol (catechol)	$C_6H_4(OH)_2$	OH, OH (adjacent) on benzene ring	104	246
Benzene-1,3-diol (resorcinol)	$C_6H_4(OH)_2$	OH, OH (meta) on benzene ring	110	281
Benzene-1,4-diol (hydroquinone)	$C_6H_4(OH)_2$	OH, OH (para) on benzene ring	173	286
2-Methylphenol (*ortho*-cresol)	$CH_3C_6H_4OH$	OH, CH_3 (ortho) on benzene ring	31	191
3-Methylphenol (*meta*-cresol)	$CH_3C_6H_4OH$	OH, CH_3 (meta) on benzene ring	11	201
4-Methylphenol (*para*-cresol)	$CH_3C_6H_4OH$	OH, CH_3 (para) on benzene ring	35	202
Phenylmethanol (benzyl alcohol)	$C_6H_5CH_2OH$	C_6H_5–C(H)(H)–OH	−15	205
2-Phenylethanol	$C_6H_5CH_2CH_2OH$	C_6H_5–C(H)(H)–C(H)(H)–OH	−27	221

In industry. phenol is made by the direct reaction, at around 300 atm and 300 °C, of chlorobenzene and an 8% solution of sodium hydroxide:

$$C_6H_5Cl + OH^- \rightarrow \underset{\text{phenol}}{C_6H_5OH} + Cl^-$$

Another method is to heat the sodium salt of benzenesulphonic acid, $C_6H_5SO_3^-Na^+$, with sodium hydroxide. The first product is sodium phenoxide, $C_6H_5O^-Na^+$. Phenol is released by adding hydrochloric acid:

$$C_6H_5SO_3^-Na^+ \xrightarrow{NaOH} C_6H_5O^-Na^+ \xrightarrow{HCl} C_6H_5OH$$

Given the rather drastic conditions used in the industrial process, with all the expense that it involves, you should guess that there is a considerable demand for phenol. Indeed, phenol has many uses; for example, as an antiseptic, but more importantly in the manufacture of dyes and polymers.

117.5 If you were carrying out the preparation of phenol from phenylamine, how would you know if the reaction between the benzenediazonium ion and water was taking place?

117.3 Why is phenol acidic?

Phenol is partially soluble in water, and its solution has a pH of around 5 or 6, showing that it is a weak acid. This makes phenol clearly different to non-aromatic alcohols. We can write the reaction with water as

$$C_6H_5OH(aq) + H_2O(l) \rightleftharpoons \underset{\text{phenoxide ion}}{C_6H_5O^-(aq)} + H_3O^+(aq)$$

The reason why phenol is acidic lies in the nature of the phenoxide ion. One of the lone pairs on the oxygen atom can become involved with the π cloud on the benzene ring. When this happens, charge is delocalised, and the phenoxide ion is energetically favoured in a way that is impossible with alcohols like ethanol (Figure 117.1).

That phenol is only a weak acid is shown not only by its pH but by its inability to give carbon dioxide with a carbonate or hydrogencarbonate. However, it will dissolve in sodium hydroxide solution:

$$C_6H_5OH(s) + OH^-(aq) \longrightarrow C_6H_5O^-(aq) + H_2O(l)$$

Its pK_a is 9.96. This compares with pK_a values of 4.8 for ethanoic acid, 4.2 for benzoic acid and 16 for ethanol. Thus, phenol is markedly more acidic than non-aromatic alcohols, but not as acidic as typical organic weak acids.

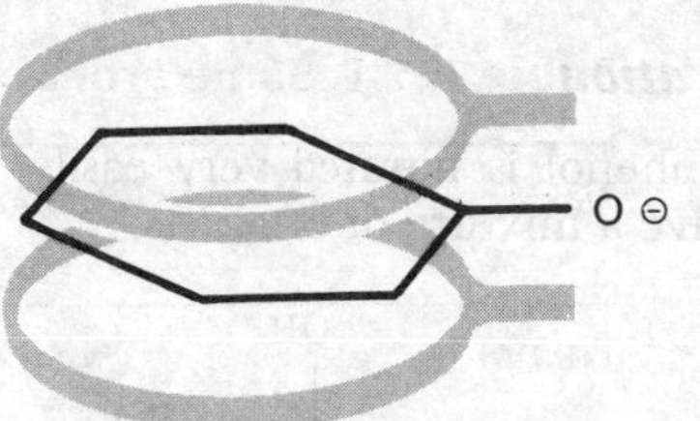

Phenoxide ion, $C_6H_5O^-$

Figure 117.1 The spread of negative charge over the benzene ring gives energetic stability to the phenoxide ion. The charge on ions such as $C_2H_5O^-$ cannot be delocalised in the same way, so there is no gain in energetic stability for them

117.6 Phenol is only partially soluble, but the phenoxide ion is very soluble in water. If you place a few crystals of phenol in a test tube and add water to them you will see two layers: one is mainly phenol with a little water in it, the other is mainly water containing a little phenol. (Look back at Unit 61 for more details about this.)

What would you expect to see if (i) you added sodium hydroxide solution to the test tube, and then (ii) added hydrochloric acid?

117.4 Phenol is more reactive than benzene

We shall split the reactions of phenol into those which primarily involve the benzene ring, and those which affect the OH group. In this section we shall concentrate on the ring. The key thing to realise is that:

The OH group activates the ring towards electrophilic substitution.

One result of this is that the conditions used in reactions with phenol are often much less drastic than they are with benzene alone.

(a) *Bromination*

If you add bromine or bromine water to a solution of phenol, there is an immediate white precipitate of 2,4,6-tribromophenol:

$$C_6H_5OH + 3Br_2 \longrightarrow C_6H_2Br_3OH + 3HBr$$

(b) *Nitration*

Similarly, phenol is nitrated very easily. Dilute nitric acid will give a mixture of products:

$$C_6H_5OH \xrightarrow{HNO_3(aq)} \text{2-nitrophenol} + \text{4-nitrophenol}$$

2-nitrophenol 4-nitrophenol

Notice the difference with the nitration of benzene, which requires a mixture of concentrated nitric and sulphuric acids. As we saw in the last unit, the reaction with phenol involves nitrosonium ions, $^{\oplus}NO$, rather than nitryl cations, NO_2^+.

(c) *Sulphonation*

Warm concentrated sulphuric acid converts phenol into 2-hydroxybenzenesulphonic acid:

$$C_6H_5OH \xrightarrow{\text{conc. } H_2SO_4} \text{2-}HOC_6H_4SO_3H$$

117.5 Reactions of the OH group on phenol

Here we shall look at some reactions that phenol has in common with aliphatic alcohols like methanol and ethanol. However, sometimes these are reactions of the phenoxide ion rather than phenol itself.

(a) *Ether formation*

If phenol is warmed with iodoethane and sodium hydroxide solution, an ether is produced. The sodium hydroxide has the effect of converting phenol into the phenoxide ion; this is the nucleophile that attacks the iodoethane.

(i) $C_6H_5OH + OH^- \rightarrow C_6H_5O^- + H_2O$

(ii) $C_6H_5O^- + CH_3CH_2I \rightarrow C_6H_5O\text{–}CH_2CH_3 + I^-$

$$C_6H_5O^- + C_2H_5I \rightarrow C_6H_5OC_2H_5 + I^-$$

ethoxybenzene

This reaction is similar to the Williamson ether synthesis you will find in section 121.2.

(b) *Esterification*

Phenol cannot be converted into an ester in the same way as aliphatic alcohols. However, it will react with acid chlorides like ethanoyl chloride:

$$C_6H_5OH + CH_3COCl \rightarrow C_6H_5OCOCH_3 + HCl$$

phenyl ethanoate

(c) *Displacement by halogens*

If phosphorus pentachloride or sulphur dichloride oxide is added to an aliphatic alcohol, the OH group is immediately displaced, and a chlorine atom takes its place. With phenol, this type of reaction will take place, but very much less easily. For this reason, the use of these reagents is *not* a good test for an OH group directly attached to a benzene ring.

117.7 Draw out the structure of ethoxybenzene showing all the bonds and the shape of the molecule.

117.8 Phenol can be esterified by adding a few drops of ethanoyl chloride to phenol crystals. The reaction is vigorous, so be careful if you attempt it. A student suggested that, because the reaction is violent, it would be better to dilute the phenol by dissolving a little of it in water and then adding the ethanoyl chloride. What do you think of this suggestion?

117.9 Benzoyl chloride, C_6H_5COCl, has a structure very much like ethanoyl chloride.

(i) Draw out the structure of the molecule.

(ii) Predict what, if anything, would happen if this liquid is added to phenol.

117.10 Phenol can be reduced in two ways. (a) After phenol is vaporised and passed over hot powdered zinc, a liquid can be condensed and the zinc is converted to zinc oxide. (b) If phenol is hydrogenated by passing phenol vapour and hydrogen over a nickel catalyst, another liquid is made. It has the formula $C_6H_{11}OH$.

(i) What are the two liquids?

(ii) Write the equations for the reactions.

117.11 Suggest a way of making benzene-1,3-diol from 1,3-dinitrobenzene.

117.12 Why is the boiling point of 2-nitrophenol very much lower than that of either 3-nitrophenol or 4-nitrophenol? Look at section 21.3 if you are stuck.

117.13 The acid dissociation constant of phenol is approximately 10^{-10} mol dm^{-3}. Calculate the pH of a 0.01 mol dm^{-3} solution of phenol. You can remind yourself about the method of calculation by looking at Unit 75.

117.6 A test for phenol

There is a very simple test for phenol. It is to add a few drops of a neutral solution of iron(III) chloride. A blue or blue-violet colour is produced owing to a complex made between the phenol and the iron(III) ion. Similar compounds with an OH group on a benzene ring give coloured complexes. However, they are not always blue. You should only use this test as a guide; if you see no colour change, it is almost certain that the compound you are using is not a phenol. If you do get a colour change, then it is likely (but not certain) that it is a phenol. The reason why it is not certain is that other classes of compound can also give colour changes with iron(III) chloride solution. Among the most important of these are the salts of many organic acids, and compounds that contain the enol group,

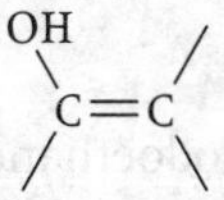

OH
C=C

117.7 A polymerisation reaction of phenol

One of the first plastics that came into widespread use just after the Second World War was called Bakelite. It is a hard, but brittle, material and has found a large number of uses, e.g. in electrical fittings such as plugs and sockets. It is made through the reaction of phenol with methanal, catalysed by acid or alkali. The product of the reaction is a structure consisting of phenol molecules linked together by bonds to CH_2 groups. A typical section of polymer looks like this:

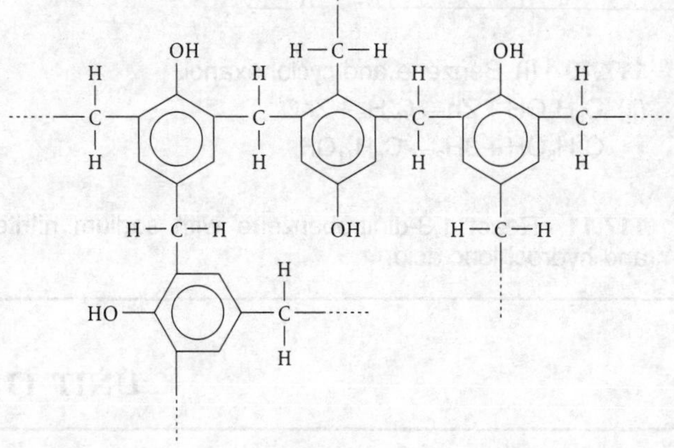

Notice the way the molecules are linked in two directions, both along a chain, and across from one chain to another. This represents a polymer that is *crosslinked.* Crosslinking leads to a very rigid structure because the various groups are not free to twist round and move their positions.

Answers

117.1 Reflux with sodium hydroxide solution.

117.2 2-Phenylethanol and ethanoyl chloride.

117.3 (i) A secondary alcohol.

(ii) Ketones.

(iii) Phenylethanone:

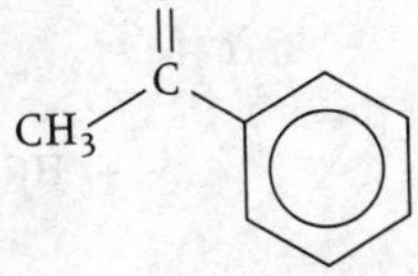

117.4 Phenylethene:

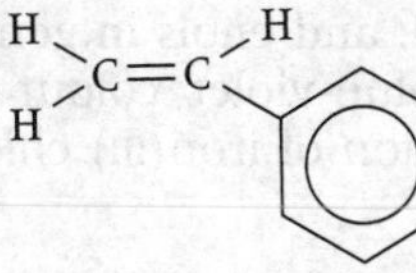

117.5 You would see bubbles of nitrogen given off.

117.6 (i) The solution will clear because all the phenol molecules will be converted into soluble phenoxide ions.

(ii) The solution will become cloudy owing to phenol being liberated:

$$C_6H_5O^-(aq) + H^+(aq) \rightarrow C_6H_5OH(s)$$

117.7

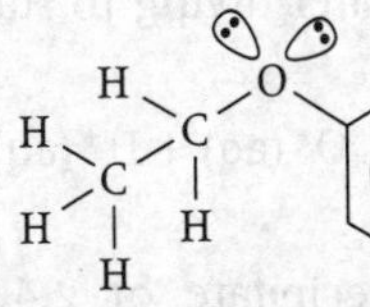

117.8 Rather silly. The ethanoyl chloride would react with the water and not the phenol.

Answers – cont.

117.9 (i) [structure: benzoyl chloride, C_6H_5COCl]

(ii) It will give the ester phenyl benzoate:

117.10 (i) Benzene and cyclohexanol.

(ii) $C_6H_5OH + Zn \rightarrow C_6H_6 + ZnO$

$C_6H_5OH + 3H_2 \rightarrow C_6H_{11}OH$

117.11 React 1,3-dinitrobenzene with sodium nitrite and hydrochloric acid.

117.12 There is *intra*molecular hydrogen bonding in 2-nitrophenol, and *inter*molecular hydrogen bonding in 4-nitrophenol.

117.13 We start with the equation

$$C_6H_5OH(aq) \rightleftharpoons C_6H_5O^-(aq) + H^+(aq)$$

for which

$$K_a = \frac{[C_6H_5O^-(aq)][H^+(aq)]}{[C_6H_5OH(aq)]}$$

(As usual, the concentrations refer to equilibrium conditions.) Given that a weak acid is only very slightly dissociated into ions, we can put $[C_6H_5OH(aq)] = 0.01$ mol dm^{-3}. Hence,

$$[C_6H_5O^-(aq)][H^+(aq)] = 10^{-10}\text{ mol dm}^{-3} \times 0.01\text{ mol dm}^{-3}$$

But also, from the equation we know that

$$[C_6H_5O^-(aq)] = [H^+(aq)]$$

Therefore,

$$[H^+(aq)]^2 = 10^{-12}\text{ mol}^2\text{ dm}^{-6}$$
$$[H^+(aq)] = 10^{-6}\text{ mol dm}^{-3}$$

Finally, because $pH = -lg[H^+(aq)]$, we have $pH = 6$.

UNIT 117 SUMMARY

- Aromatic alcohols:
  - (i) Aromatic alcohols have OH group(s) on hydrocarbon side chains.
  - (ii) Phenols have OH groups directly attached to a benzene ring.
  - (iii) The properties of phenols are markedly different to those of non-aromatic alcohols. It is best to think of phenols as a class of compound separate from alcohols.
  - (iv) Phenol is more reactive than benzene.

Phenol, C_6H_5OH

- Preparation:
  By hydrolysing a benzenediazonium ion solution;

  (i) $C_6H_5NH_2 + HNO_2 + H^+ \rightarrow C_6H_5N_2^{\oplus} + 2H_2O$
  phenylamine → benzene diazonium ion

  (ii) $C_6H_5N_2^{\oplus} + H_2O \rightarrow C_5H_5OH + N_2 + H^+$

Properties

- Acidity:
  Phenol is acidic in water owing to stability of the phenate ion, $C_6H_5O^-$;

  $$C_6H_5OH(aq) \rightleftharpoons C_6H_5O^-(aq) + H^+(aq)$$

- Bromination:
  Immediate white precipitate of 2,4,6-tribromophenol with bromine.
- Nitration:
  Easily nitrated with dilute nitric acid.
- Sulphonation:
  2-Hydroxybenzenesulphonic acid made with warm concentrated sulphuric acid.

Reactions

- Ether formation:
  By reaction with iodoethane and sodium hydroxide solution, ethoxybenzene, $C_6H_5OC_2H_5$, is made.
- Ester formation:
  An acid chloride must be used; e.g.

  [structure: phenol] + CH_3COCl ⟶ [structure: phenyl ethanoate, $C_6H_5OCOCH_3$] + HCl

- Polymerisation:
  With methanal and acid, Bakelite is made.
- Test for phenol, and enols in general:
  A blue or blue-violet colour is produced with neutral solution of iron(III) chloride.

118

Aldehydes and ketones

118.1 Aldehydes and ketones contain a carbonyl group

All aldehydes and ketones contain the carbonyl group

$$>C{=}O$$

(see Figure 118.1). Aldehydes have at least one hydrogen atom bonded to the carbon atom as well as the oxygen. Ketones have two organic radicals attached to the carbon atom. You can tell whether a substance is an aldehyde or a ketone by looking at its formula: aldehydes have a common formula RCHO

$$R{-}C({=}O){-}H$$

and ketones RR′CO

$$R{-}C({=}O){-}R'$$

where R and R′ are two organic radicals. The names of aldehydes always end in *-al* and ketones in *-one*. Table 118.1 lists examples of each type, and Table 118.2 their uses.

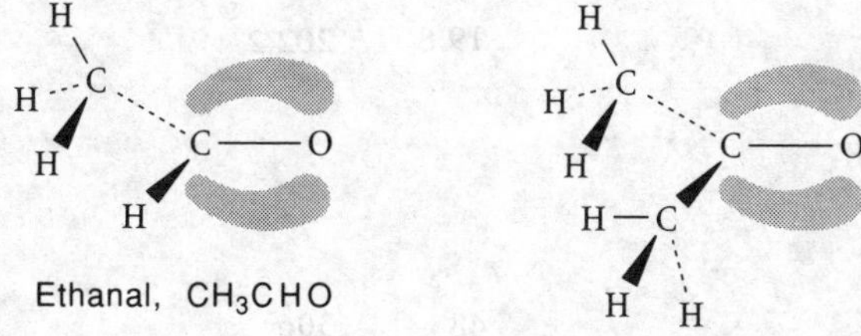

Figure 118.1 *Both aldehydes and ketones are planar in the neighbourhood of the carbonyl (>C═O) group. Notice that the π bond is distorted towards the electronegative oxygen atom*

Aldehydes and ketones are often sweet smelling, volatile, liquids (Figure 118.2). Ethanal has a characteristic smell, which may be detected near rotting fruit. (You might try leaving an apple to rot; eventually you will smell ethanal coming from it.)

118.1 Why do we not write the name of butanone as butan-2-one?

118.2 One reason why ketones are good solvents is that, like water, they are polar molecules.

(i) Draw a diagram of propanone and show by an arrow the direction of the dipole moment.

(ii) Briefly explain why propanone is a liquid at room temperature and pressure.

118.3 Draw a diagram showing the structure of cyclohexanone, $C_5H_{10}CO$.

118.2 The manufacture of simple aldehydes and ketones

(a) *Methanal*

Methanal can be manufactured by the controlled oxidation of methanol. A temperature between 600 and 650° C together with a silver catalyst are used:

$$2CH_3OH + O_2 \xrightarrow{600\,°C,\ Ag} 2HCHO + 2H_2O$$

Methanal is completely miscible with water, and is sold as a solution called *formalin*. Formalin solution is a good disinfectant, with a characteristic smell. If you see biological samples preserved in bottles, it is very likely that formalin is the solution in which they are kept. Although it is widely available, take care if you use the solution. With some acids it can produce powerful carcinogens.

Table 118.1. Common aldehydes and ketones

Name	*Formula*	*Structure*	*Melting point/°C*	*Boiling point/°C*
Aldehydes				
Methanal	HCHO	H–C(=O)–H	−91.9	−19
Ethanal	CH_3CHO	CH_3–C(=O)–H	−122.9	20.6
Propanal	C_2H_5CHO	C_2H_5–C(=O)–H	−79.9	48.2
Benzaldehyde	C_6H_5CHO	C_6H_5–C(=O)–H	22.3	178.2
Ketones				
Propanone (acetone)	CH_3COCH_3	CH_3–C(=O)–CH_3	−94.6	56.4
Butanone	$C_2H_5COCH_3$	C_2H_5–C(=O)–CH_3	−86.5	79.8
Pentan-2-one	$C_3H_7COCH_3$	C_3H_7–C(=O)–CH_3	−78	102
Pentan-3-one	$C_2H_5COC_2H_5$	C_2H_5–C(=O)–C_2H_5	−38.8	102.1
Phenylethanone (acetophenone)	$C_6H_5COCH_3$	C_6H_5–C(=O)–CH_3	19.8	202.2
Diphenylmethanone (benzophenone)	$C_6H_5COC_6H_5$	C_6H_5–C(=O)–C_6H_5	48	306

Two models showing the shapes of methanal and ethanal.

Table 118.2. The uses of aldehydes and ketones

	Uses
Aldehydes	
Methanal	In solution with water, sold as formalin: a disinfectant (formaldehyde) and preservative
Ethanal	Used in the manufacture of ethanoic acid and its derivatives, e.g. ethanoic anhydride
General	More complex aldehydes are found in perfumes and flavourings
Ketones	
Propanone (acetone)	As a solvent. This is a more important use than you might think. For example, many artificial fibres are manufactured from cellulose acetate. Propanone dissolves the acetate. The solution is forced through tiny holes into a warm atmosphere. The propanone evaporates easily, leaving fine fibres, which can be woven into clothes and furniture coverings
General	As intermediates in the manufacture of other chemicals, e.g. cyclohexanone is used in one stage of Nylon manufacture

(b) *Ethanal*

Ethanal is made on an industrial scale by the *Wacker process* (of which there are several variations). The essence of the process is to use palladium(II) chloride to convert a mixture of ethene and water to ethanal:

$$C_2H_4 + H_2O + PdCl_2 \rightarrow CH_3CHO + Pd + 2HCl$$

However, this alone would be an extremely expensive method of making ethanal. The beauty of the Wacker process is that the palladium(II) chloride is regenerated by reacting it with copper(II) chloride:

$$Pd + \underset{\text{copper(II) chloride}}{2CuCl_2} \rightarrow PdCl_2 + \underset{\text{copper(I) chloride}}{2CuCl}$$

Cinnamon flavour

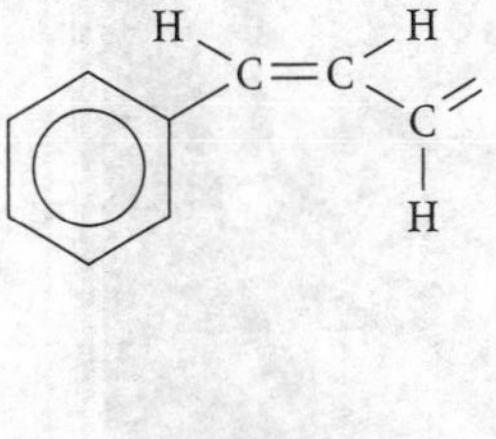

3-Phenyl-2-propenal, otherwise known as cinnamaldehyde

Vanilla flavour

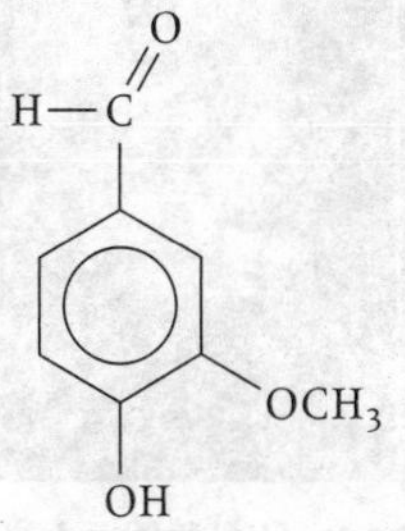

3-Methoxy-4-hydroxy-benzaldehyde, also known as vanillin

Spearmint flavour

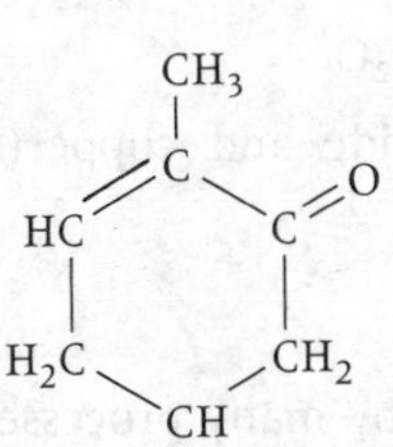

Carvone; this is a ketone built from isoprene

Peppermint flavour

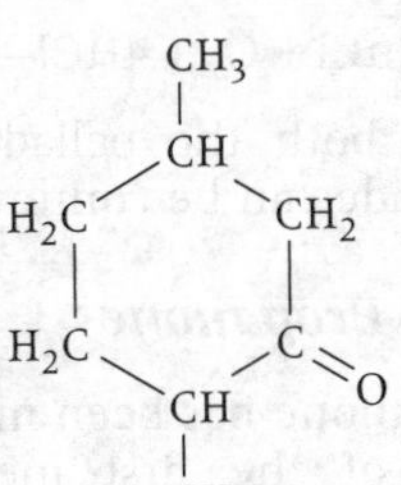

Menthone; this is also derived from isoprene

***Figure 118.2** Two aldehydes and two ketones used for flavourings. (The isoprene structure is shown in Unit 112)*

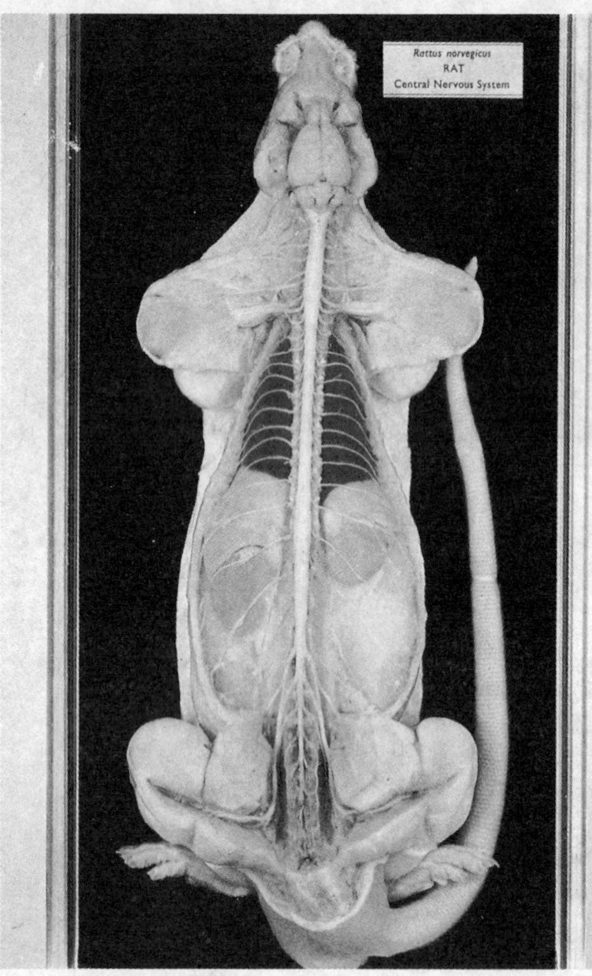

Specimens like this, of a rat dissection showing brain and spinal nerves, are preserved in formalin.

The final trick is to use oxygen (from the air) to oxidise the copper(I) chloride back to copper(II) chloride:

$$4CuCl + O_2 + 4HCl \rightarrow 4CuCl_2 + 2H_2O$$

Thus both the palladium(II) chloride and copper(II) chloride can be continuously recycled.

(c) *Propanone*

Propanone has been manufactured by many processes. One of the first methods was to isolate calcium ethanoate from wood ash and heat it:

$$(CH_3COO)_2Ca \rightarrow CaCO_3 + CH_3COCH_3$$

This rather old-fashioned method has become redundant. During the First World War a biochemical method was developed, which uses specially adapted bacteria to convert carbohydrates into propanone (and other substances). While feasible, the economics of the process requires a very cheap source of carbohydrate. At present propanone is mainly manufactured from cumene or from propan-2-ol.

Cumene is the aromatic hydrocarbon $C_6H_5CH(CH_3)_2$. Its systematic name is (1-methylethyl)benzene. By reaction with oxygen followed by treatment with acid, it is converted into phenol and propanone:

$$C_6H_5C(CH_3)_2H \xrightarrow{O_2} C_6H_5C(CH_3)_2COOH \xrightarrow{H^+} \underset{\text{phenol}}{C_6H_5OH} + \underset{\text{propanone}}{CH_3COCH_3}$$

A second process that converts propan-2-ol into propanone is more straightforward, but less widely used. The alcohol vapour is passed over a zinc oxide catalyst at between 400 and 600 °C:

$$CH_3CHOHCH_3 \xrightarrow[500\,°C]{ZnO\ cat.} CH_3COCH_3 + H_2$$

118.3 Two methods of preparing aldehydes or ketones

(a) *Oxidation of an alcohol*

This is the simplest method.

> **Primary alcohols are oxidised to aldehydes.**
>
> **Secondary alcohols are oxidised to ketones.**

The oxidation can be achieved by using an acidified solution of sodium dichromate(VI), or by passing the alcohol vapour over hot copper powder. For example,

$$\underset{\text{ethanol}}{CH_3CH_2OH} \rightarrow \underset{\text{ethanal}}{CH_3CHO}$$

$$\underset{\text{propan-2-ol}}{(CH_3)_2CHOH} \rightarrow \underset{\text{propanone}}{(CH_3)_2CO}$$

$$\underset{\text{phenylmethanol}}{C_6H_5CH_2OH} \rightarrow \underset{\text{benzaldehyde}}{C_6H_5CHO}$$

(b) *Ozonolysis*

Ozonolysis can be used to convert an alkene into aldehydes or ketones. You will find details of the method in section 112.5. Ozonolysis swaps two carbonyl groups for the carbon–carbon double bond in an alkene. Here are three examples:

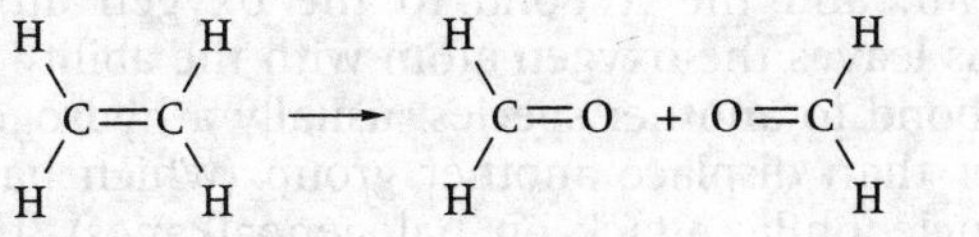

$$H_2C{=}CH_2 \longrightarrow H_2C{=}O + O{=}CH_2$$

ethene → methanal + methanal

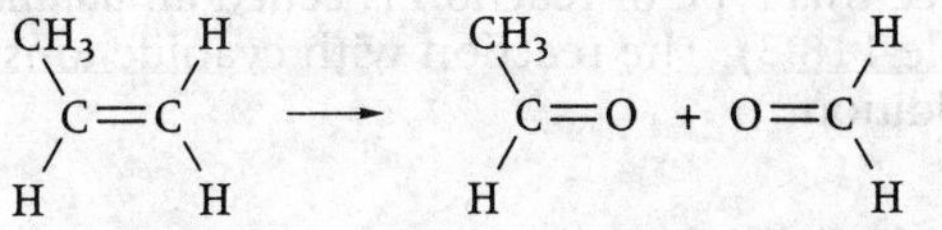

$$CH_3CH_2CH{=}CH_2 \longrightarrow CH_3CH_2CH{=}O + O{=}CH_2$$

but-1-ene → propanal + methanal

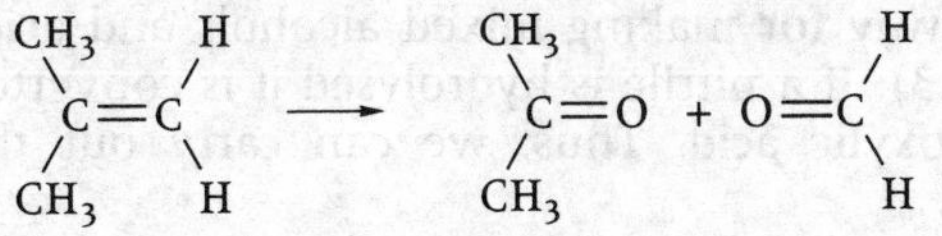

$$(CH_3)_2C{=}CH_2 \longrightarrow (CH_3)_2C{=}O + O{=}CH_2$$

2-methylpropene → propanone + methanal

Ozonolysis can also be used as a method of discovering where a double bond is to be found in a molecule; see question 118.6.

118.4 Which alcohol would you choose to oxidise in order to make (i) 2-methylpropanal, (ii) pentan-2-one?

118.5 Say which chemicals, and sketch the apparatus, you would use to make propanal by oxidising an alcohol.

118.6 After ozonolysis of an alkene, the products were butanone and pentan-2-one.

(i) What might be the original alkene?

(ii) Is there more than one possibility?

118.4 Two methods of preparing aromatic aldehydes and ketones

Benzaldehyde can be made by several methods. The first is to react methylbenzene with chlorine in the presence of ultraviolet light in such quantities to optimise the amount of dichloromethylbenzene, $C_6H_5CHCl_2$, made in the reaction. The final step is to reflux with water. The hydrolysis produces benzaldehyde.

(i)

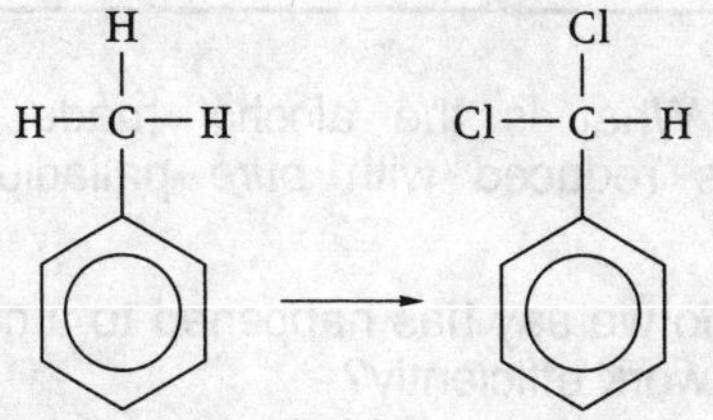

$$C_6H_5CH_3 \xrightarrow{Cl_2,\ hf} C_6H_5CHCl_2$$

(ii)

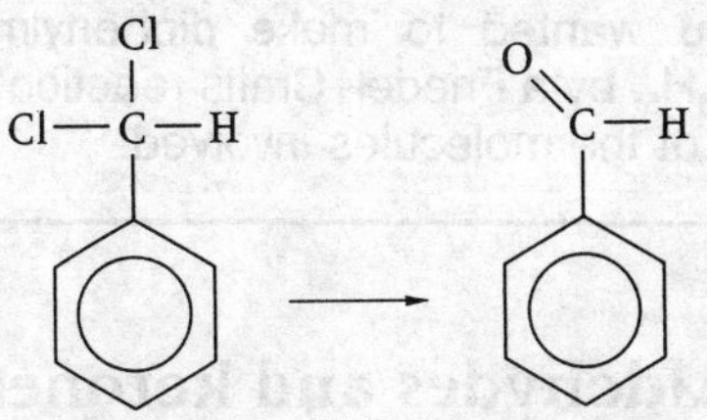

$$C_6H_5CHCl_2 \xrightarrow{H_2O} C_6H_5CHO$$

benzaldehyde

A second approach is to reduce benzoyl chloride, C_6H_5COCl, by hydrogen using a palladium catalyst. However, the catalyst must not be too efficient, otherwise the benzoyl chloride is converted into an alcohol. For this reason the catalyst is mixed with barium sulphate, or another substance, to inhibit its action:

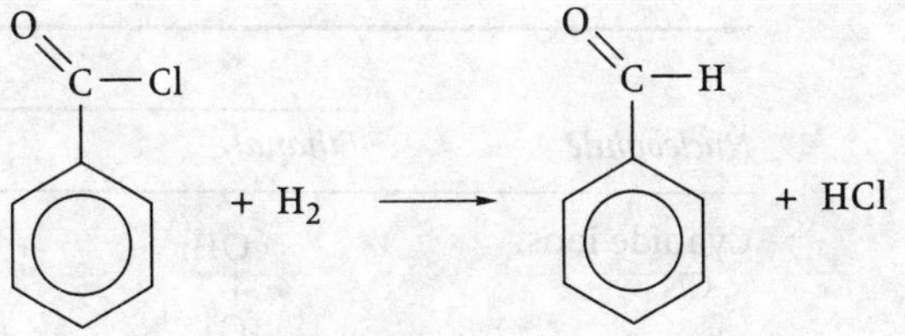

$$C_6H_5COCl + H_2 \xrightarrow{\text{Pd, modified}} C_6H_5CHO + HCl$$

This method of reduction is known as the *Rosenmund reaction.*

Friedel–Crafts reactions are convenient ways of making aromatic ketones. The general method is shown by the reaction of benzene with ethanoyl chloride using aluminium trichloride as a catalyst. We have seen this reaction before (panel 113.1) and shown that it involves an electrophilic attack on the benzene ring. The ethanoyl chloride is converted into a carbocation through its interaction with the aluminium trichloride:

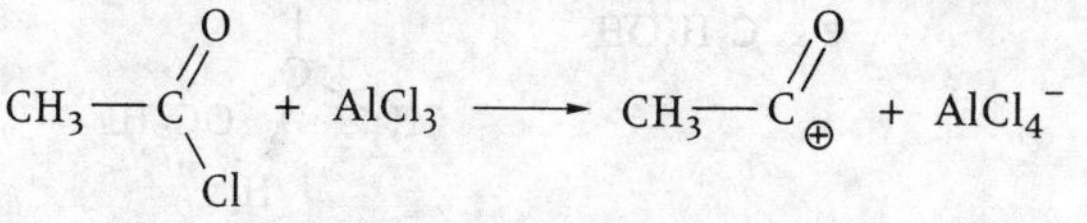

$$CH_3COCl + AlCl_3 \rightarrow CH_3CO^+ + AlCl_4^-$$

This carbocation attacks the benzene ring:

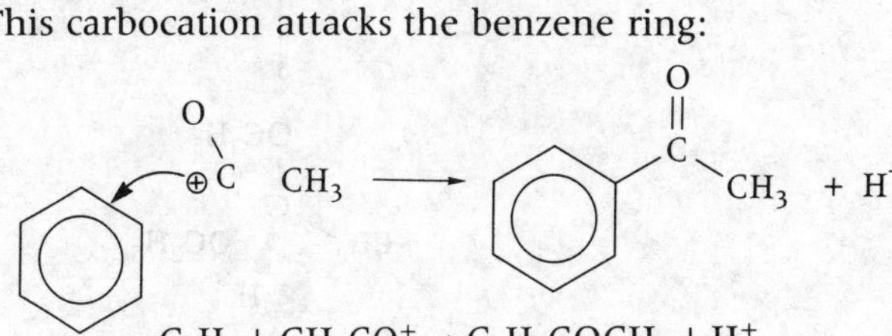

$$C_6H_6 + CH_3CO^+ \rightarrow C_6H_5COCH_3 + H^+$$

phenylethanone

118.7 (i) What is the alcohol made if benzoyl chloride is reduced with *pure* palladium as the catalyst?

(ii) What do we say has happened to a catalyst that ceases to work efficiently?

118.8 Which two substances would you choose to use if you wanted to make diphenylmethanone, $C_6H_5COC_6H_5$, by a Friedel–Crafts reaction? Draw the structures of the molecules involved.

118.5 Aldehydes and ketones undergo addition reactions

We have already said that the carbonyl group is inherently polar owing to the electronegative oxygen drawing electron density towards itself. Also, the atoms attached directly to the carbon of the carbonyl group all lie in the same plane (see Figure 118.1). The carbon atom bonded to the oxygen not only carries a slight positive charge, but is also open to attack by incoming nucleophiles from above or below the plane of the molecule; there is little chance of steric hindrance stopping a reaction taking place.

The main feature of nucleophilic attack on the carbonyl group is that the attacking group bonds to the carbon atom, and the π bond to the oxygen atom breaks. This leaves the oxygen atom with the ability to make a σ bond to another species, usually a hydrogen ion. Rather than displace another group (which happens in nucleophilic attack on halogenoalkanes), the attacking nucleophile adds on to the aldehyde or ketone; hence this type of reaction is called an *addition reaction* (Table 118.3). The reaction with cyanide ions is typical of addition.

(a) *Cyanide addition*

This particular reaction is useful because it provides us with a pathway for making mixed alcohols and acids (Figure 118.3). If a nitrile is hydrolysed it is converted into a carboxylic acid. Thus, we can carry out the changes

Table 118.3. Some addition reactions of aldehydes and ketones

	Product of reaction with:		
Nucleophile	*Ethanal*	*Benzaldehyde*	*Propanone*
Cyanide ions, CN^-	$CH_3C(OH)(H)CN$	$C_6H_5C(OH)(H)CN$	$CH_3C(OH)(CH_3)CN$
Hydrogensulphite, HSO_3^-	$CH_3C(OH)(H)SO_3^-$	$C_6H_5C(OH)(H)SO_3^-$	$CH_3C(OH)(CH_3)SO_3^-$
Alcohols, e.g. C_2H_5OH	$CH_3C(OH)(H)OC_2H_5$ ↓ $CH_3C(OC_2H_5)(H)OC_2H_5$	$C_6H_5C(OH)(H)OC_2H_5$ ↓ $C_6H_5C(OC_2H_5)(H)OC_2H_5$	No reaction

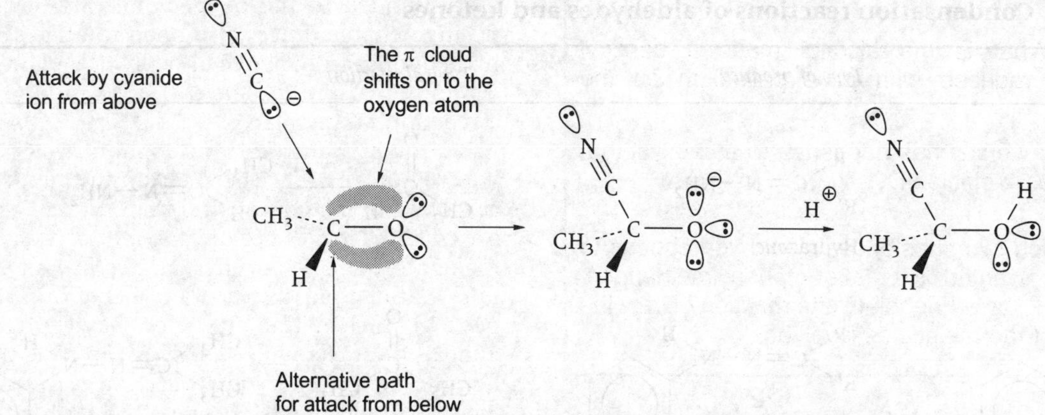
Attack by cyanide ion from above
The π cloud shifts on to the oxygen atom
Alternative path for attack from below
N
C
CH3
H
H⊕

***Figure 118.3** One way of representing the addition reaction of a cyanide ion with an aldehyde*

$$CH_3{-}C(=O){-}H \longrightarrow CH_3{-}C(OH)(CN){-}H \longrightarrow CH_3{-}C(OH)(COOH){-}H$$

$$\underset{\text{ethanal}}{CH_3CHO} \xrightarrow{CN^-,\,H^+} \underset{\text{2-hydroxypropane-nitrile}}{CH_3CH(OH)CN} \xrightarrow{H^+} \underset{\text{2-hydroxypropanoic acid}}{CH_3CH(OH)COOH}$$

2-Hydroxypropanoic acid is also known as lactic acid. It has been widely studied because it is one of the substances made when milk goes sour. The acid is formed by the action of a microorganism, *Bacillus acidi lactici*, on sugars. In the early 1900s large amounts of the bacteria were isolated and used to prepare lactic acid on an industrial scale. The acid was used in the dyeing and leather industries.

(b) *Hydrogensulphite addition*

Hydrogensulphite ions, HSO_3^-, will add to both aldehydes and ketones. The net result of the addition is shown in this reaction:

$$CH_3{-}C(=O){-}CH_3 + HSO_3^- \longrightarrow CH_3{-}C(OH)(SO_3^-){-}CH_3$$

$$CH_3COCH_3 + HSO_3^- \rightarrow CH_3C(OH)(SO_3^-)CH_3$$

(c) *Alcohol addition*

Aldehydes, but not ketones, will give addition reactions with alcohols provided all the reagents are dry, and that hydrogen chloride is used to catalyse the reaction. The most common example of this type of addition is ethanol adding to ethanal:

$$CH_3{-}C(=O){-}H + H{-}O{-}C_2H_5 \xrightarrow{\text{(twice)}} CH_3{-}C(H)(OC_2H_5){-}OC_2H_5$$

$$\underset{\text{ethanal}}{CH_3CHO} + 2C_2H_5OH \xrightarrow{\text{dry HCl}} \underset{\text{1,1-diethoxyethane}}{CH_3CH(OC_2H_5)_2} + H_2O$$

The product, 1,1-diethoxyethane, was once known as acetal. It is a type of ether.

> **118.9** It is possible to detect a compound called a hemiacetal in a mixture of an aldehyde and an alcohol. In a mixture of ethanol and ethanal, the hemiacetal has the formula $C_4H_{10}O_2$. It has a structure very similar to 1,1-diethoxyethane (acetal). What is the structure of the hemiacetal?
>
> **118.10** (i) Explain why 2-hydroxypropanoic acid should be optically active.
>
> (ii) Why does a solution of 2-hydroxypropanoic acid made by the method
>
> $$CH_3CHO \rightarrow CH_3CH(OH)CN \rightarrow CH_3CH(OH)COOH$$
>
> have no optical activity. (Hint: think about the way the cyanide ions can attack the aldehyde.)

118.6 Condensation reactions

Owing to the lone pair on its nitrogen atom, ammonia can add to an aldehyde or ketone. For example, with ethanal the reaction follows the pattern of Table 118.4:

$$CH_3{-}C(=O){-}H + :NH_3 \longrightarrow CH_3{-}C(OH)(H){-}NH_2$$

$$CH_3CHO + NH_3 \rightarrow CH_3CH(OH)NH_2$$

However, this type of compound is usually unstable, and in any case experience shows that other nitrogen containing compounds are much more useful in their reactions. As an illustration of the type of reaction that can take place, let us look at how hydrazine, N_2H_4, reacts with ethanal. The first step is similar to the reaction with ammonia:

Table 118.4. Condensation reactions of aldehydes and ketones

Reagent	*Type of product*	*Typical reaction*
$NH_2—NH_2$ Hydra*zine*	$RR'C{=}N—NH_2$ Hydra*zone*	$CH_3C(O)H \longrightarrow (CH_3)(H)C{=}N—NH_2$
$NH_2—N(H)—C_6H_5$ Phenylhydra*zine*	$RR'C{=}N—N(H)—C_6H_5$ Phenylhydra*zone*	$CH_3C(O)CH_3 \longrightarrow (CH_3)_2C{=}N—N(H)—C_6H_5$ or $(CH_3)_2C{=}N—NHC_6H_5$
$NH_2—N(H)—C_6H_3(NO_2)_2$ 2,4-Dinitrophenylhydra*zine*	$RR'C{=}N—N(H)—C_6H_3(NO_2)_2$ 2,4-Dinitrophenylhydra*zone*	$CH_3C(O)C_2H_5 \longrightarrow (CH_3)(C_2H_5)C{=}N—N(H)—C_6H_3(NO_2)_2$ or $(CH_3)(C_2H_5)C{=}N—NHC_6H_3(NO_2)_2$

$$CH_3—C(=O)H + NH_2—NH_2 \longrightarrow CH_3—C(OH)(H)NH—NH_2$$

$$CH_3CHO + NH_2—NH_2 \rightarrow CH_3CH(OH)NH—NH_2$$

This molecule has only a fleeting existence. It breaks down to give a molecule called a *hydrazone*:

$$CH_3—C(OH)(H)NH—NH_2 \longrightarrow (CH_3)(H)C{=}N—NH_2 + H_2O$$

$$CH_3CH(OH)NH—NH_2 \rightarrow CH_3CH{=}N—NH_2 + H_2O$$

Overall we can summarise the reaction as

ethanal + hydrazine → a hydrazone + water

It is because water is released in the reaction that it is classified as a *condensation* reaction. (However, this term is also used to describe organic reactions in which relatively small molecules other than water are released.) Notice, however, that it is only a special type of nucleophilic attack. If it were not for the lone pair on the nitrogen atoms of hydrazine, the reaction would not take place.

There are several variations on this theme, collected together in Table 118.4. We have used ethanal in the example above, but all aldehydes and ketones give similar reactions.

The reason why these addition reactions are important is that they can be used as a means of identifying aldehydes and ketones. The reagent 2,4-dinitrophenylhydrazine is especially important in this respect. It is usually made up in a solution with methanol together with a little concentrated sulphuric acid, and is orange in colour. When it reacts with an aldehyde or ketone, the product is invariably a solid, usually orange-yellow in colour. After the precipitate is washed and dried it can be tested in a melting point apparatus. The melting points of a large number of 2,4-dinitrophenylhydrazones have been tabulated (Table 118.5), so if the measured melting point is compared with those in a

Table 118.5. The melting points of some 2,4-dinitrophenylhydrazones*

Hydrazone formed with	*Melting point/°C*
Ethanal	168
Propanone	128
Butanal	123
Butanone	115
Benzaldehyde	237
Diphenylmethanone	238

*The melting points are not always sharp

data book the particular aldehyde or ketone can be identified.

118.11 Hydroxylamine, NH_2OH, gives condensation reactions with aldehydes and ketones. Predict the result of reacting this substance with propanone. Draw the structure of the product.

118.12 If you do an experiment to identify an aldehyde or ketone using 2,4-dinitrophenylhydrazine solution, be careful over three points. First, use the solution sparingly; it is quite common for solid 2,4-dinitrophenylhydrazine to precipitate out. You will not get too far if you mistake this for the hydrazone.

(i) Secondly, why is it important that the precipitate is washed and dried properly?

(ii) Thirdly, do not increase the temperature of the melting point apparatus too rapidly. Why?

118.7 Aldehydes and ketones can be reduced

Aldehydes and ketones can both be reduced. With lithium tetrahydridoaluminate(III), or hydrogen and nickel catalyst, the carbonyl group is converted into an alcohol:

$$CH_3CHO \xrightarrow[\text{(ii) } H^+]{\text{(i) } LiAlH_4} CH_3CH_2OH$$

ethanal → ethanol

$$CH_3COCH_3 \xrightarrow{H_2/Ni} CH_3CHOHCH_3$$

propanone → propan-2-ol

You should be able to see that the rule is that aldehydes are reduced to primary, and ketones to secondary alcohols.

In other circumstances the reduction can be sufficient to replace the oxygen completely by hydrogen. There are two methods for achieving this change. Both use the condensation reaction with hydrazine as their starting point. Where they differ is in the treatment of the resulting hydrazone.

In *Wolff–Kishner reduction* the hydrazone is heated with an alkali. In the *Clemmensen reduction* the same result is achieved using zinc amalgam and hydrochloric acid. Here is an example of each method:

(i) Wolff–Kishner reduction

$$CH_3COCH_3 \xrightarrow{N_2H_4} (CH_3)_2C{=}N{-}NH_2 \xrightarrow{OH^-} (CH_3)_2CH_2$$

propanone → propane

(ii) Clemmensen reduction

$$C_6H_5CHO \xrightarrow{N_2H_4} C_6H_5CH{=}N{-}NH_2 \xrightarrow{H^+,\ Zn/Hg} C_6H_5CH_3$$

benzaldehyde → methylbenzene

118.13 What will be made if butanone is reduced using $LiAlH_4$?

118.14 How would you convert butanone into butane?

118.8 Aldehydes are good reducing agents

Aldehydes are good reducing agents, i.e. they can be oxidised easily. We have seen this when we discussed the oxidation of primary alcohols. If the alcohol is *not* refluxed with the oxidising agent, an aldehyde can be collected. However, with reflux, the aldehyde is itself oxidised to a carboxylic acid. Thus, when they act as reducing agents, *aldehydes are oxidised to acids*. For example,

$$CH_3CHO \xrightarrow{Cr_2O_7^{2-},\ H^+} CH_3COOH$$

ethanal → ethanoic acid

(a) *Silver mirror test*

When aqueous ammonia is added to silver nitrate solution, the silver ions are converted to diamminesilver(I) ions, $Ag(NH_3)_2^+$. This mixture is sometimes known as ammoniacal silver nitrate. (A similar reagent, Tollens' reagent, can also be used.) If an aldehyde is mixed with the solution in a test tube, silver is produced. This can be seen as a mirror on the inside of the test tube; hence this is called the silver mirror test for aldehydes:

$$CH_3CHO(aq) + 2Ag(NH_3)_2^+(aq) + 3OH^-(aq) \rightarrow CH_3COO^-(aq) + 2Ag(s) + 4NH_3(aq) + 2H_2O(l)$$

(b) *Fehling's test*

Aldehydes also have sufficient reducing ability to convert copper(II) to copper(I). Usually the copper(II) is held as a complex ion in an alkaline solution of copper(II) tartrate known as Fehling's solution. The solution is a clear royal blue, but when it is warmed with an aldehyde an orange-yellow precipitate of copper(I) oxide is formed.

Ethanal also gives the iodoform test – see the next section.

118.15 In the reaction of ethanal with Fehling's solution, assume that the reaction involves copper(II) ions and hydroxide ions. Write down the equation for the reaction. (The formula of copper(I) oxide is Cu_2O).

118.16 In the equation for the reaction of Tollens' reagent with aldehydes, how do we know that a redox reaction has taken place?

118.9 Ketones are hard to oxidise

Most ketones are difficult to oxidise. If they are refluxed for long enough with vigorous oxidising agents like alkaline potassium manganate(VII) or concentrated nitric acid, they will split apart near the carbonyl group. Carboxylic acids are the products. For example, the ketone $CH_3CH_2COCH_2CH_2CH_3$ gives CH_3CH_2COOH and $CH_3CH_2CH_2COOH$, but other acids are also produced; so no one would use this reaction unless they were desperate.

One oxidation reaction of ketones that is useful is the *iodoform reaction*. This is given by methylketones such as propanone and butanone.

You could try out the reaction by warming propanone with a solution of iodine in sodium hydroxide. This solution contains the iodate(I) ion, IO^-, an oxidising agent. You should see a yellow precipitate of triiodomethane (iodoform) appear:

$$CH_3COCH_3(aq) + 3IO^-(aq) \rightarrow CH_3COO^-(aq) + \underset{\text{yellow}}{CHI_3(s)} + 2OH^-(aq)$$

Be careful that you realise that this is *not* a test for ketones. The test will work with any molecule that has the group

$$CH_3-C(=O)-X$$

or can be oxidised to give this structure. Ethanal will also give the test, and so will ethanol because it is oxidised to ethanal by the iodate(I) ion.

118.17 Which of the following aldehydes or ketones would react positively in the iodoform reaction: (i) butanone; (ii) butanal; (iii) pentan-3-one; (iv) pentan-2-one; (v) benzaldehyde?

118.10 Reactions with halogens

If iodine solution is added to an aldehyde or ketone, the colour of the solution fades. A hydrogen atom on the carbon atom next door to the carbonyl group is replaced by iodine. A typical reaction is

$$CH_3-C(=O)-CH_3 + I_2 \longrightarrow CH_3-C(=O)-CH_2I + HI$$

$$CH_3COCH_3 + I_2 \rightarrow CH_3COCH_2I + HI$$

However, this equation hides the way that the reaction takes place. In the units on kinetics we found that the iodine does not react directly with the propanone. Rather it reacts with the *enol* form of the ketone, which exists in equilibrium with the *keto* form. This equilibrium is known as the *keto–enol tautomerism*:

$$CH_3-C(=O)-CH_3 \rightleftharpoons (OH)(CH_3)C=CH_2$$

$$\underset{\text{keto form}}{CH_3COCH_3} \rightleftharpoons \underset{\text{enol form}}{CH_3COH{=}CH_2}$$

The iodine takes part in a reaction with the double bond. You will find further details about the reaction in Unit 81. The fact that hydrogen atoms on the carbon atom adjacent to the carbonyl group (the alpha, α, hydrogen atoms) can be replaced by halogens is also shown by the reaction of ethanal with chlorine. Substitution takes place in the presence of ultraviolet light:

$$CH_3-C(=O)-H + 3Cl_2 \longrightarrow CCl_3-C(=O)-H + 3HCl$$

$$CH_3CHO + 3Cl_2 \rightarrow \underset{\text{trichloroethanal}}{CCl_3CHO} + 3HCl$$

The product, trichloroethanal, is also known as chloral. When it is heated with chlorobenzene and concentrated sulphuric acid, dichlorodiphenyltrichloroethane, which is better known as DDT, is made:

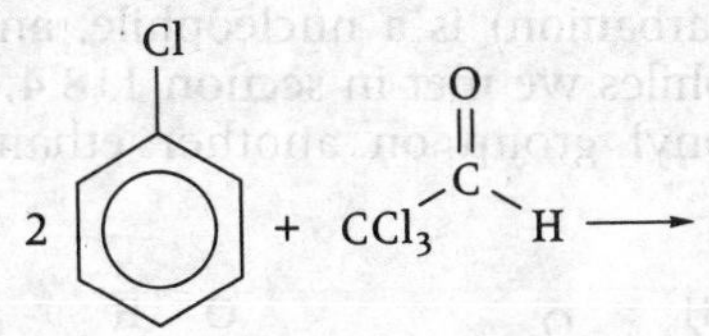

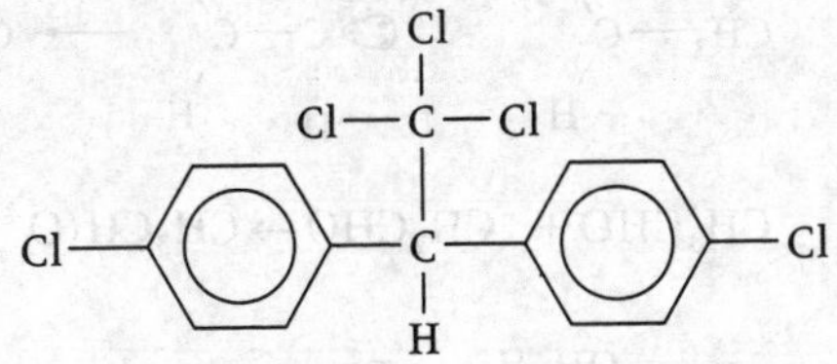

$$2\,C_6H_5Cl + CCl_3CHO \rightarrow$$

$$2C_6H_5Cl + CCl_3CHO \rightarrow DDT$$

DDT is one of the most effective insecticides that has ever been invented. It was first made in 1873, but its use only became widespread during the Second World War. Since then it must have prevented the premature deaths of millions of people owing to its ability to kill fleas, lice and mosquitoes, which are carriers of diseases such as typhus and malaria. DDT is a remarkably stable molecule (both energetically and kinetically). Once, this was thought to be one of its greatest virtues; but since the 1960s it has become clear that its longevity makes DDT a great environmental hazard. Essentially, the reason is that DDT finds its way into the food chain of many animals, including humans (Table 118.6). For example, it weakens the shells of birds' eggs and prevents successful breeding. In many parts of the world its use has been banned, although it is still used in some countries because it is one of the few cheap insecticides available.

Table 118.6. How DDT is passed along a food chain to peregrine falcons around Lake Michigan, Canada*

	DDT concentration /parts per million (of body weight)
Lake mud	0.014
Lake water	0.000 02
Amphipods eaten by fish	0.410
Trout	6
Herring gulls	99
Peregrine falcons	5 000

*Table adapted from: Heaton, C. A. (ed.) (1986). *The Chemical Industry*, Blackie, Glasgow, p. 270

118.11 Reaction with phosphorus pentachloride

You should know that phosphorus pentachloride can be used to test for the presence of OH groups. Although aldehydes and ketones do not contain this group, they still react but in a different way. The oxygen atom is replaced by two chlorine atoms:

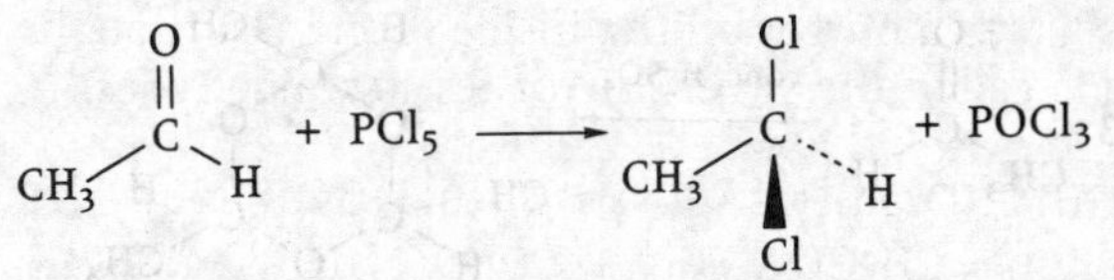

$$CH_3CHO + PCl_5 \rightarrow CH_3CHCl_2 + POCl_3$$

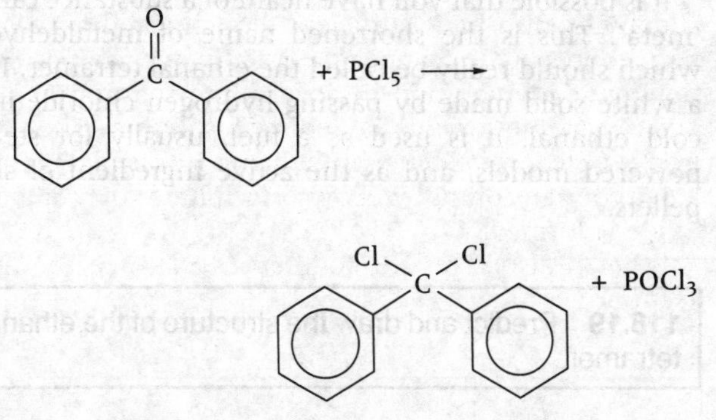

$$C_6H_5COC_6H_5 + PCl_5 \rightarrow C_6H_5CCl_2C_6H_5 + POCl_3$$

Notice that there are no fumes of hydrogen chloride given off.

> **118.18** A student wrote the following: 'The organic liquid became warm when it reacted with phosphorus pentachloride. The reaction clearly showed that the liquid was an alcohol.' What do you think of this statement?

118.12 Polymerisation reactions of aldehydes

Methanal and ethanal can be persuaded to polymerise. Poly(methanal) (sometimes called paraformaldehyde) is a polymer of methanal. It can be made by evaporating an aqueous solution of methanal, which leaves it as a white powder. It has long chains of repeating CH_2O units, like this: $—CH_2—O—CH_2—O—CH_2—O—$.

In the presence of acid and at low temperatures, methanal molecules will combine to make a trimer, which is simply known as the methanal trimer (or metaformaldehyde):

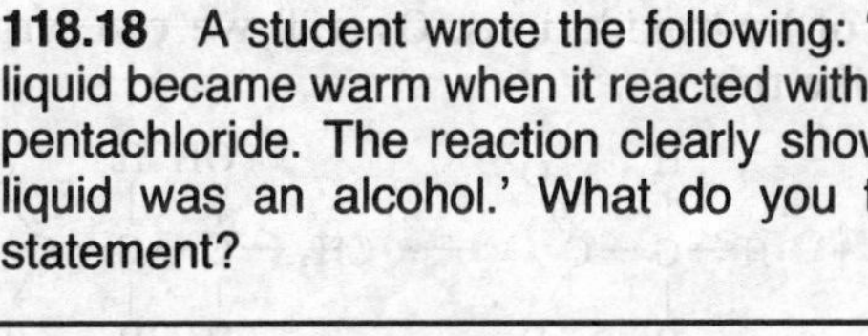

$$3\,HCHO \longrightarrow$$

methanal trimer

A very little concentrated sulphuric acid added to ethanal will convert it to a liquid trimer consisting of three ethanal molecules combined in a ring-like structure:

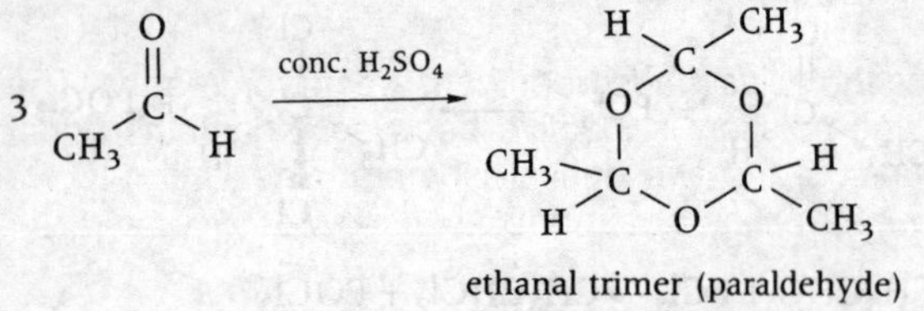

$$3\,CH_3CHO \xrightarrow{\text{conc. } H_2SO_4} \text{(cyclic trimer: ring of alternating C and O atoms, each C bearing H and } CH_3)$$

ethanal trimer (paraldehyde)

It is possible that you have heard of a substance called 'meta'. This is the shortened name of metaldehyde, which should really be called the ethanal tetramer. It is a white solid made by passing hydrogen chloride into cold ethanal. It is used as a fuel, usually for steam powered models, and as the active ingredient of slug pellets.

> **118.19** Predict and draw the structure of the ethanal tetramer.

118.13 The aldol condensation

The aldol condensation is a reaction that aldehydes undergo. The simplest example, from which the reaction gets its name, is between two ethanal molecules in the presence of hydroxide ions. Overall we can write the reaction like this:

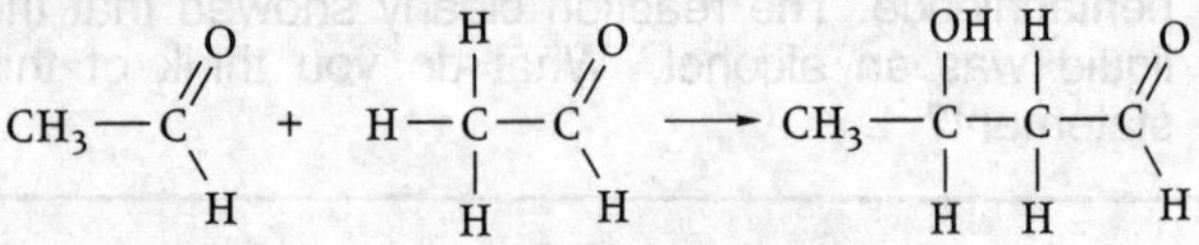

$$CH_3{-}C(=O){-}H + H{-}CH_2{-}C(=O){-}H \longrightarrow CH_3{-}CH(OH){-}CH_2{-}C(=O){-}H$$

$$2CH_3CHO \xrightarrow{OH^-} CH_3CH(OH)CH_2CHO$$

ethanal — aldol, i.e. 3-hydroxybutanal

However, this hides from us the mechanism of the reaction. In section 118.9 we noticed that the α hydrogen atoms (those on the carbon atom next to the carbonyl group) are more liable to be lost from the molecule than the hydrogen atoms in, say, an alkane. We can say that they are *more acidic* than normal. With hydroxide ions, an equilibrium is set up:

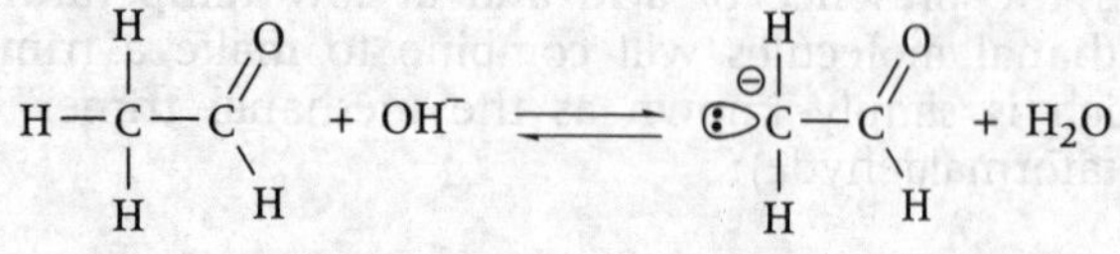

$$H{-}CH_2{-}C(=O){-}H + OH^- \rightleftharpoons {}^{\ominus}CH_2{-}C(=O){-}H + H_2O$$

$$CH_3CHO + OH^- \rightleftharpoons CH_2CHO^- + H_2O$$

The negative ion (a carbanion) is a nucleophile, and, like the other nucleophiles we met in section 118.4, it will attack the carbonyl group on another ethanal molecule:

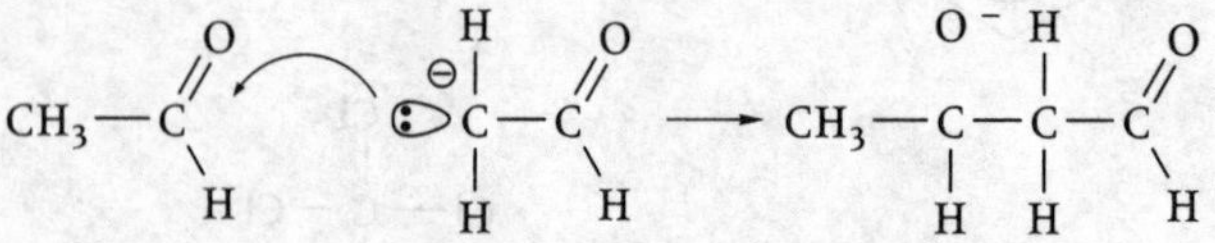

$$CH_3{-}C(=O){-}H + {}^{\ominus}CH_2{-}C(=O){-}H \longrightarrow CH_3{-}CH(O^-){-}CH_2{-}C(=O){-}H$$

$$CH_3CHO + {}^-CH_2CHO \rightarrow CH_3CH(O^-)CH_2CHO$$

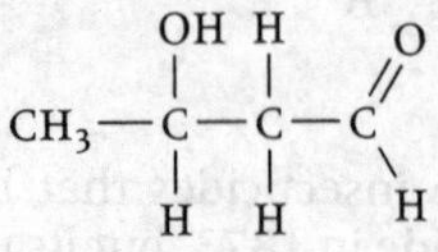

$$CH_3{-}CH(OH){-}CH_2{-}C(=O){-}H$$

$$CH_3CH(O^-)CH_2CHO + H_2O \rightarrow CH_3CH(OH)CH_2CHO + OH^-$$

This reaction happens with other aldehydes. It also takes place with ketones provided that they have α hydrogen atoms. Thus, propanone will give a similar reaction (but with difficulty):

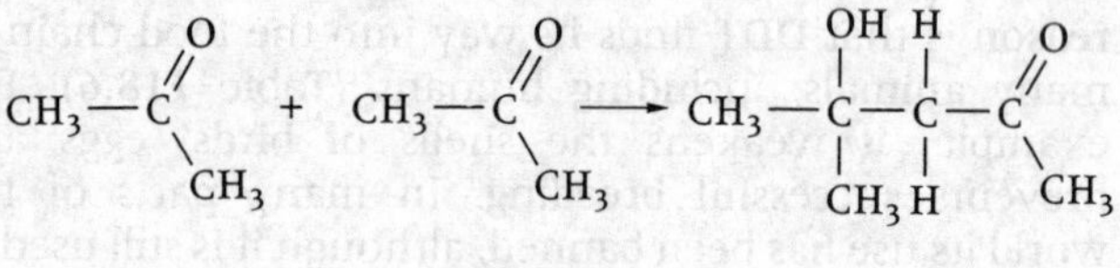

$$CH_3{-}C(=O){-}CH_3 + CH_3{-}C(=O){-}CH_3 \longrightarrow CH_3{-}C(OH)(CH_3){-}CH_2{-}C(=O){-}CH_3$$

$$2CH_3COCH_3 \rightarrow CH_3CCH_3OHCH_2COCH_3$$

118.14 Cannizzaro's reaction

This is the reaction in which aldehydes without α hydrogen atoms can regain their reputation. Methanal shows the pattern. It is converted by alkali into a mixture of methanol and the methanoate ion:

$$2HCHO + OH^- \rightarrow CH_3OH + HCOO^-$$

The mechanism of this reaction would take us too far afield, but the pattern should be clear to you. For example, benzaldehyde gives a mixture of phenylmethanol and the benzoate ion:

$$2C_6H_5CHO + OH^- \rightarrow C_6H_5CH_2OH + C_6H_5COO^-$$

Answers

118.1 If the carbonyl group were on one of the two end carbon atoms, the molecule would be an aldehyde, so it must be on one of the two carbon atoms in the middle of the molecule. It does not matter at which end you start numbering, the carbonyl group *must* be on the second carbon atom. As there is no other possible place, there is no need to put in the number.

118.2 (i)

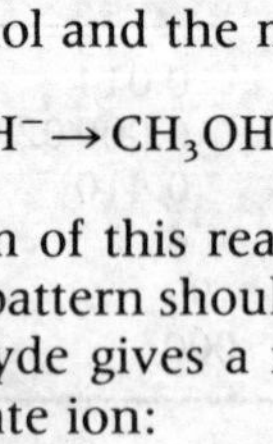

2.95 D (dipole arrow)

$$(CH_3)_2C{=}O$$

Answers – cont.

(ii) The attractions between dipole moments on different molecules are sufficiently strong to keep the molecules together as a liquid (see Unit 20).

118.3

```
 H  H H  H
  \ |  | /
H  C——C
 \ /    \
  C      C=O
 / \    /
H  C——C
  / |  | \
 H  H H  H
```

118.4 (i) 2-Methylpropan-1-ol:

```
      CH3
      |
CH3—C—CH2—OH
      |
      H
```

(ii) Pentan-2-ol:

```
                    OH
                    |
CH3—CH2—CH2—C—CH3
                    |
                    H
```

118.5 The reaction would be between propan-1-ol and sodium dichromate(VI) acidified with concentrated sulphuric acid. The mixture should be heated, with the aldehyde vapour being condensed using an apparatus like that of Figure 115.2.

118.6 (i), (ii) *Cis* and *trans* isomers of the following alkene are possible:

```
C3H7      C2H5        CH3       C2H5
    \    /               \     /
     C=C                  C=C
    /    \               /     \
 CH3      CH3         C3H7      CH3
```

cis-3,4-dimethylhept-3-ene *trans*-3,4-dimethylhept-3-ene

118.7 (i) Phenylmethanol, $C_6H_5CH_2OH$.

(ii) The catalyst has been *poisoned*.

118.8

```
                 O
                  \\
                   C—Cl
                   |
  ⬡               ⬡
```

benzene benzoyl chloride

118.9

```
        OH
        |
        C
      /  \
  C2H5    H
        |
       CH3
```

118.10 (i) It has an asymmetric carbon atom.

(ii) The cyanide ions can attack the aldehyde from above or below the plane of the molecule. The products of the two reactions are mirror images of one another. Hence the acids made from them are mirror images. The resulting solution is inactive because it contains equal amounts of the two optical isomers. See Unit 110 for more information about optical activity.

```
      COOH      :       COOH
       |        :        |
       C        :        C
     /   \      :      /   \
  CH3     OH    :   HO      CH3
       |        :        |
       H        :        H
```

118.11 The product of the reaction of hydroxylamine and an aldehyde or ketone is called an oxime:

```
 \
  C=N—OH
 /
```

118.12 (i) If there is an impurity present, the melting point of the hydrazone will be lowered, so a faulty identification can occur.

(ii) The temperature of the apparatus may increase faster than the thermometer can respond. For example, the thermometer may read 110° C when the sample is really at 120° C. You would report a melting point 10° C lower than it should be.

118.13 Butan-2-ol:

```
               OH
               |
CH3—CH2—C—CH3
               |
               H
```

118.14 Reduce it by passing the vapour together with hydrogen over a pure palladium catalyst.

118.15 $CH_3CHO + 2Cu^{2+} + 5OH^- \rightarrow CH_3COO^- + Cu_2O + 3H_2O$

118.16 The silver ion, Ag^+, gains an electron when it changes to a silver atom. Hence it must have been reduced. Likewise, the aldehyde has been oxidised.

118.17 Only butanone and pentan-2-one, because they are the only ones that have a CH_3 group next to the carbonyl group.

118.18 The student's report is not clear. Alcohols, acids, aldehydes and ketones react with phosphorus pentachloride. Only alcohols and acids give white fumes of hydrogen chloride (because they have an OH group). If the student saw white fumes, the liquid *might* have been an alcohol; but he or she could not be sure it was not an acid without doing further tests. If there were no fumes, the liquid was an aldehyde or ketone.

118.19

```
      CH3         H
        \        /
     H—C—O—C—CH3
        /         \
       O           O
        \         /
   CH3—C—O—C—H
        /         \
       H          CH3
```

UNIT 118 SUMMARY

- Aldehydes and ketones:
  (i) Contain the carbonyl group;
  aldehydes

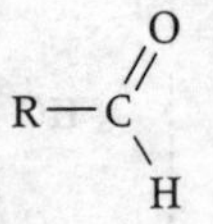

$$R-C(=O)-H$$

  ketones

$$R-C(=O)-R'$$

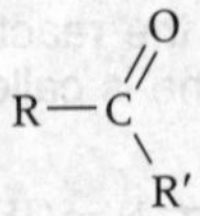

  (ii) Undergo addition reactions.
- Manufacture of ethanal:
  The Wacker process;

$$C_2H_4 + H_2O + PdCl_2 \rightarrow CH_3CHO + Pd + 2HCl$$

  with the palladium being recycled using copper(II) chloride and oxygen.
- Preparation:
  (i) Oxidation of alcohols
  By acidified solution of sodium dichromate(VI) (no reflux). By passing over hot copper powder. Primary alcohols are oxidised to aldehydes. Secondary alcohols are oxidised to ketones.

  e.g. $C_6H_5CH_2OH \rightarrow C_6H_5CHO$
  phenylmethanol benzaldehyde
  $(CH_3)_2CHOH \rightarrow (CH_3)_2CO$
  propan-2-ol propanone

  (ii) Benzaldehyde also made by hydrolysis of dichloromethylbenzene;

$$C_6H_5CHCl_2 \xrightarrow{H_2O} C_6H_5CHO$$

  (iii) Aromatic ketones made by Friedel–Crafts acylation;

  e.g.

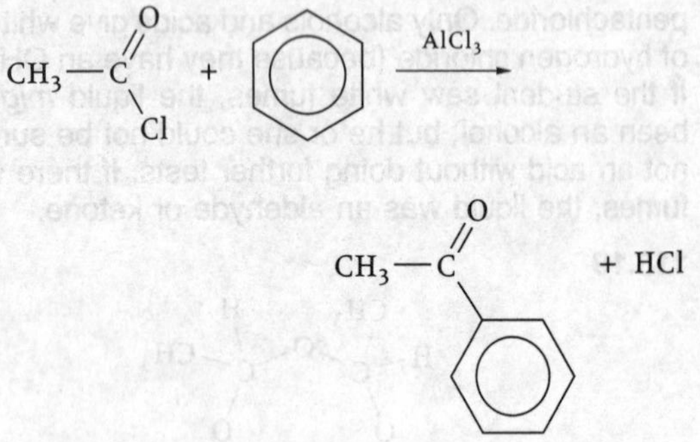

$$CH_3-C(=O)-Cl + C_6H_6 \xrightarrow{AlCl_3} CH_3-C(=O)-C_6H_5 + HCl$$

Reactions

- Addition and condensation:
  See Tables 118.3 and 118.4. Especially note
  (i) Addition of cyanide ions;

$$\text{e.g. } CH_3CHO \xrightarrow{CN^-, H^+} CH_3CH(OH)CN \xrightarrow{H^+} CH_3CH(OH)COOH$$

  (ii) Reaction with 2,4-dinitrophenylhydrazine used to characterise aldehydes and ketones.
- Reduction:
  Using lithium tetrahydridoaluminate(III);

  aldehydes → primary alcohols
  ketones → secondary alcohols
- Oxidation:
  Using warm acidified sodium dichromate(VI) under reflux;

  aldehydes → acids
  e.g. $CH_3CHO \rightarrow CH_3COOH$
- Phosphorus pentachloride:
  Carbonyl oxygen replaced by chlorine atoms (no fumes of HCl);

  e.g. $CH_3CHO + PCl_5 \rightarrow CH_3CHCl_2 + POCl_3$
- Polymerisation of ethanal:
  With concentrated sulphuric acid: ethanal trimer.
  With hydrogen chloride: ethanal tetramer.
- Propanone and iodine:
  Iodine decolourised. Reaction involves the keto–enol tautomerism;

$$CH_3C(=O)-CH_3 \rightleftharpoons CH_3C(OH)=CH_2$$

- Iodoform reaction:
  A molecule with the group

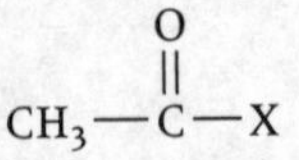

$$CH_3-C(=O)-X$$

  or one that can be oxidised to this group gives a yellow precipitate of iodoform, CHI_3, when warmed with iodine in sodium hydroxide solution.
- Tests for aldehydes:
  (i) Ammoniacal silver nitrate solution → silver mirror.
  (ii) Orange precipitate with Fehling's solution.

119

Carboxylic acids

119.1 Most carboxylic acids are weak acids

The majority of non-aromatic carboxylic acids have the general formula $C_nH_{2n+1}COOH$. Usually they are weak acids. The most common one is ethanoic acid (acetic acid), CH_3COOH, which is the key ingredient of vinegar. It is the COOH group in the molecule that is responsible for its acidity. In water the molecule will dissociate into ions:

$$CH_3COOH(l) + H_2O(l) \rightleftharpoons CH_3COO^-(aq) + H_3O^+(aq)$$

ethanoate ion

The ethanoate ion is energetically stabilised by the spreading of the negative charge over a carbon and two oxygen atoms:

In Unit 75 we said that ethanoic acid is only slightly dissociated into ions; that is, the equilibrium lies far over to the left-hand side of the equation. This is indicated by the value of its acid dissociation constant, K_a, or its pK_a value. In Table 119.1 you will find information about some carboxylic acids and their pK_a values. The pK_a of an acid is defined as $-\lg K_a$. This means that the smaller the size of K_a, the larger the value of pK_a, and vice versa. Essentially, the smaller the value of pK_a, the stronger is the acid.

Two models showing the shapes of methanoic acid and ethanoic acid.

Table 119.1. Some carboxylic acids

Name	*Formula*	*Structure*	*Melting point/°C*	*Boiling point/°C*	pK_a
Methanoic acid	HCOOH	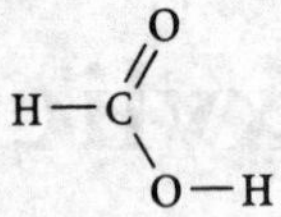 $H{-}C({=}O){-}O{-}H$	8.6	100.7	3.8
Ethanoic acid	CH_3COOH	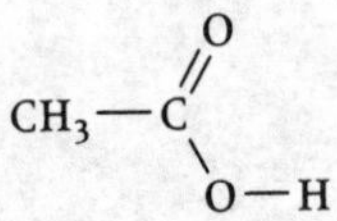 $CH_3{-}C({=}O){-}O{-}H$	16.8	118.0	4.8
Propanoic acid	C_2H_5COOH	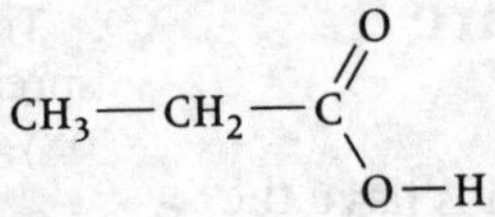 $CH_3{-}CH_2{-}C({=}O){-}O{-}H$	−20.7	141.1	4.9
Chloroethanoic acid	$CH_2ClCOOH$	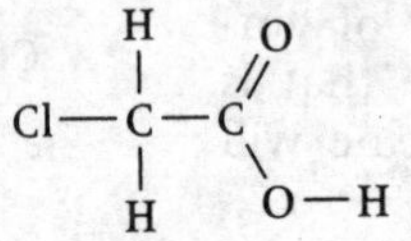 $Cl{-}CH_2{-}C({=}O){-}O{-}H$	63.2	189.7	2.9
Dichloroethanoic acid	$CHCl_2COOH$	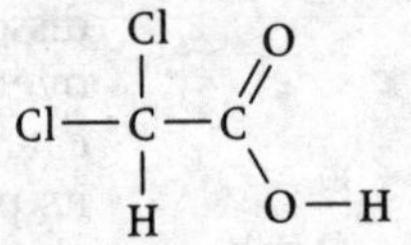 $Cl{-}CHCl{-}C({=}O){-}O{-}H$	11.0	192.7	1.3
Trichloroethanoic acid	CCl_3COOH	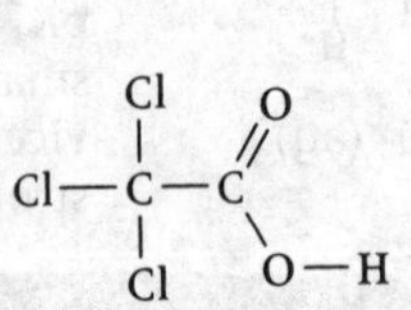 $Cl{-}CCl_2{-}C({=}O){-}O{-}H$	56.5	197.7	0.7
Benzoic acid (benzenecarboxylic acid)	C_6H_5COOH	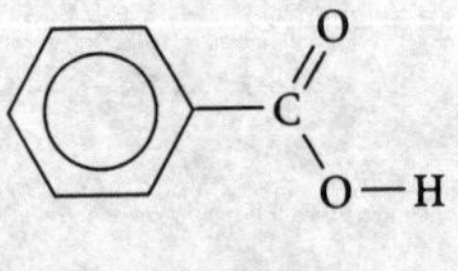 $C_6H_5{-}C({=}O){-}O{-}H$	121.9	249.2	4.2
Phenylethanoic acid	$C_6H_5CH_2COOH$	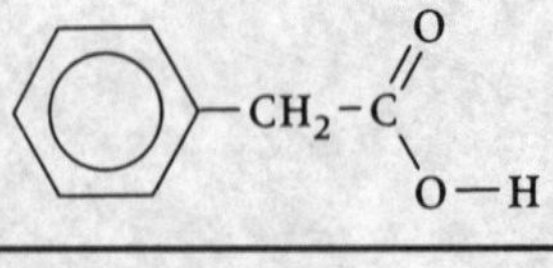 $C_6H_5{-}CH_2{-}C({=}O){-}O{-}H$	77	266	4.3

119.2 Ways of making carboxylic acids

Some of the methods of making carboxylic acids in the laboratory we have met before; but one that is a new reaction uses *nitriles*. This is an important process, which you should do your best to remember.

(a) *Hydrolysis of nitriles*

A nitrile contains a CN group. Examples are ethanenitrile, CH_3CN, and propanenitrile, C_2H_5CN. Often they are liquids with a sweet smell. If ethanenitrile is refluxed with an alkali, the following reaction takes place:

$$CH_3{-}C{\equiv}N + H_2O + OH^- \longrightarrow CH_3{-}C(=O)O^{\ominus} + NH_3$$

$$CH_3CN(aq) + H_2O(l) + OH^-(aq) \rightarrow CH_3COO^-(aq) + NH_3(g)$$

ethanenitrile — ethanoate ion

Once the reaction ceases, acid can be added. This protonates the ethanoate ions and ethanoic acid molecules are produced:

$$CH_3{-}C(=O)O^{\ominus} + H^+ \longrightarrow CH_3{-}C(=O){-}O{-}H$$

$$CH_3COO^-(aq) + H^+(aq) \rightarrow CH_3COOH(aq)$$

You will discover why nitriles are so important in Unit 120.

(b) *Oxidation of primary alcohols*

You should find this a familiar reaction by now. The usual oxidising agent is sodium dichromate(VI) solution. This is refluxed with a primary alcohol that has the same number of carbon atoms as the acid you want to make. For example,

$$CH_3CH_2{-}O{-}H \longrightarrow CH_3{-}C(=O){-}O{-}H$$

$$CH_3CH_2OH \rightarrow CH_3COOH$$

ethanol — ethanoic acid

(c) *Oxidation of an arene*

We have seen that one of the reactions that all arenes have in common is that, irrespective of the length of the side chain, it will be oxidised down to an acid group. In this case the oxidising agent is usually an acid or alkaline solution of potassium manganate(VII). For example,

$$C_6H_5C_2H_5 \xrightarrow{\text{oxidation}} C_6H_5COOH$$

ethylbenzene — benzoic acid

(d) *Grignard reagents*

We can write a general carboxylic acid as RCOOH, where R might be CH_3, C_2H_5, etc. To make the acid, a Grignard reagent of formula RMgI would be needed. It can be made by mixing magnesium powder with the iodoalkane, RI, dissolved in dry ether. Finally, with RMgI dissolved in ether, dry carbon dioxide should be bubbled through the solution. (Alternatively, solid carbon dioxide could be used.) Once the initial reaction subsides, the addition of acid liberates the carboxylic acid. We have,

$$RMgI + CO_2 \rightarrow RCOOMgI \xrightarrow{H^+} RCOOH + Mg^{2+} + I^-$$

For example, C_3H_7MgI would give us propanoic acid, C_3H_7COOH.

119.1 When it is completely free of moisture, ethanoic acid is known as *glacial* ethanoic acid. At different times of the year, students have been known to say that glacial ethanoic acid is a solid; at others, that it is a liquid. Explain.

119.2 (i) In the preparation of a carboxylic acid from a nitrile using alkaline hydrolysis, how would you know that the reaction is complete?

(ii) It is possible to use acid in the hydrolysis reaction rather than alkali. A similar reaction takes place, but very little ammonia is given off. Why?

119.3 If you were to attempt to make methanoic acid, HCOOH, which nitrile would you have to use. Why would you be wise to avoid trying this reaction?

119.4 Sketch the apparatus you would use to oxidise ethanol to ethanoic acid.

119.5 Use the values of standard redox potentials in Table 70.1 to compare the oxidising ability of dichromate(VI) ions and manganate(VII) ions in acid solution, and manganate(VII) ions in alkaline solution.

119.6 Suggest ways of carrying out these changes:

(i) $C_6H_5CH_3$ to C_6H_5COOH;

(ii) C_2H_5Br to C_2H_5COOH;

(iii) $CH_3C_6H_4I$ to $CH_3C_6H_4COOH$.

(There are two ways of doing (ii) and (iii).)

119.3 The reactions of carboxylic acids

The carboxylic acid group is a combination of two smaller groups, one of which, the OH group, we already know something about. The other is the carbonyl group

$$>C{=}O$$

The reactions of the OH group in a carboxylic acid are often similar to those of the OH group in an alcohol. Even the acidity of a carboxylic acid is really an extension of a property of alcohols. They too can be classified as acids, but they are so weak that we often choose to ignore this feature of their chemistry.

However, carboxylic acids show few of the reactions that we met in the previous unit on aldehydes and ketones. Especially, carboxylic acids do *not* undergo addition reactions. Essentially, the reason for this is that nucleophiles that will attack aldehydes or ketones tend to act as bases in the presence of carboxylic acids, i.e. they are protonated by the hydrogen of the acid OH group. At the same time, owing to its negative charge, the $RCOO^-$ ion left is no longer attractive to nucleophiles. Alcohols represent a class of nucleophile that are not deactivated by acids; see Unit 120.

In the next few paragraphs we shall split the reactions of carboxylic acids into those which mainly affect the OH group and those which affect the carbonyl group.

(a) *Reactions of the OH group*

Carboxylic acids are neutralised by alkalis

Owing to their weakness, titrations of carboxylic acids and alkalis like sodium hydroxide are not easy to perform accurately. However, with the right choice of indicator, the endpoint of a reaction like

$$CH_3COOH(aq) + OH^-(aq) \rightarrow CH_3COO^-(aq) + H_2O(l)$$

can be found.

With carbonates, or hydrogencarbonates, aqueous solutions of the acids generate sufficient hydrogen ions to give off carbon dioxide, e.g.

$$CO_3^{2-}(aq) + CH_3COOH(aq) \rightarrow CH_3COO^-(aq) + H_2O(l) + CO_2(g)$$

Benzoic acid, C_6H_5COOH, is also a weak acid, but it is much less soluble in water than ethanoic acid. If it is made in an aqueous solution, it will appear as a white precipitate. However, it will dissolve in alkali because the negative benzoate ion is much more soluble in water. Likewise, a solution of a benzoate will precipitate benzoic acid crystals if a strong acid, e.g. sulphuric acid, is added:

$$\underset{\text{white solid}}{C_6H_5COOH} \underset{\text{acid}}{\overset{\text{alkali}}{\rightleftharpoons}} \underset{\text{colourless in solution}}{C_6H_5COO^-}$$

With sodium

Carboxylic acids give off hydrogen when reacted with sodium. For example,

$$2CH_3COOH(l) + 2Na(s) \rightarrow \underset{\text{sodium ethanoate}}{2CH_3COO^-Na^+(s)} + H_2(g)$$

Sodium ethanoate is an ionic solid, like the sodium salts of inorganic acids.

With phosphorus pentachloride

The OH group is replaced by a chlorine atom. For example,

$$CH_3COOH(l) + PCl_5(s) \rightarrow CH_3COCl(l) + POCl_3(s) + HCl(g)$$

The tell-tale signs of hydrogen chloride are also produced with sulphur dichloride oxide, $SOCl_2$.

Esters are made with alcohols and acid chlorides

Esterification reactions between alcohols and carboxylic acids have been studied in great detail. Especially, the reaction between ethanol and ethanoic acid has been investigated as an example of an equilibrium reaction (see section 54.2):

$$CH_3-C(=O)-O-H + H-O-CH_2-CH_3 \rightleftharpoons CH_3-C(=O)-O-CH_2-CH_3 + H_2O$$

$$CH_3COOH(l) + C_2H_5OH(l) \rightleftharpoons \underset{\text{ethyl ethanoate}}{CH_3COOC_2H_5(l)} + H_2O(l)$$

The combination of ethanol with ethanoic acid is slow compared to its reaction with ethanoyl chloride, CH_3COCl. This substance is a liquid that fumes in air, but it can be carefully dripped onto ethanol. It reacts with a 'fizz' and white fumes of hydrogen chloride are given off. The ester is made immediately:

$$CH_3-CH_2-O(H) + (CH_3)(Cl)C=O \longrightarrow CH_3-C(=O)-O-CH_2-CH_3 + HCl$$

$$C_2H_5OH(l) + CH_3COCl(l) \rightarrow CH_3COOC_2H_5(l) + HCl(g)$$

(b) *Reactions of the carbonyl group*

The only reaction of note that we need to consider is the reduction of the carbonyl group by lithium tetrahydridoaluminate(III), $LiAlH_4$. It is converted into a CH_2 group. This means that the acid RCOOH is changed to the alcohol RCH_2OH. For example,

$$CH_3-C(=O)-O-H \longrightarrow CH_3-CH_2-O-H$$

$$\underset{\text{ethanoic acid}}{CH_3COOH} \xrightarrow{LiAlH_4} \underset{\text{ethanol}}{CH_3CH_2OH}$$

One feature of the chemistry of lithium tetrahydridoaluminate(III) is that it will perform this type of reduction but leave a carbon–carbon double bond unaffected.

119.7 Ethane-1,2-dioic acid (oxalic acid) is a dicarboxylic acid; it has two acid groups in its molecule. This is shown by its formula, which is sometimes written $(CH_2COOH)_2$.

(i) Draw out the structure of the acid.

(ii) Given 50 cm^3 of a 0.1 mol dm^{-3} solution of the acid, what volume of 0.2 mol dm^{-3} sodium hydroxide would be needed to neutralise the acid completely?

119.8 Which indicator would you use in a titration of ethanoic acid with sodium hydroxide solution?

119.9 If you use ethanoyl chloride to esterify ethanol, you may detect the smell of vinegar near the bottle containing the chloride. Why?

119.10 How could you make ethanoyl chloride from ethanoic acid?

119.11 What would be the outcome of reacting methanol, CH_3OH, with ethanoyl chloride?

119.12 Benzoyl chloride, C_6H_5COCl, is similar in structure to ethanoyl chloride.

(i) Draw the structure of the molecule.

(ii) What would be made if benzoyl chloride was added to ethanol? Draw the structure of the molecule.

(iii) What would be made if you added benzoyl chloride to water? What would you see?

119.4 The chloroethanoic acids

Table 119.1 includes data on three chloroethanoic acids. You can tell from their pK_a values that the strength of the acid increases as the number of chlorine atoms in the molecule increases. Consult Unit 75 if you wish to understand the reason for this.

This feature of the acids is interesting, but chloroethanoic acid is an important chemical for another reason. It can be used to prepare amino acids. To make chloroethanoic acid, chlorine can be bubbled through the acid with iodine or red phosphorus present as a catalyst. The reaction has to be stopped when the theoretical increase in weight has been achieved:

$$CH_3COOH(l) + Cl_2(g) \rightarrow CH_2ClCOOH(l) + HCl(g)$$

Chloroethanoic acid can be easily converted into the amino acid glycine by mixing it with concentrated aqueous ammonia, although the separation of the amino acid is time consuming:

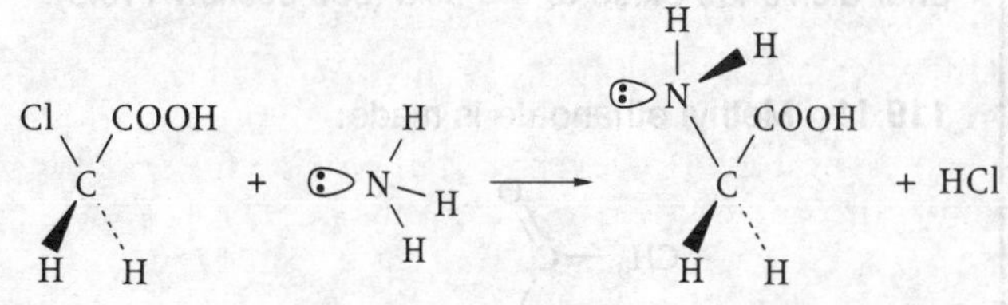

$$CH_2ClCOOH(l) + NH_3(aq) \rightarrow CH_2NH_2COOH(l) + HCl(aq)$$

glycine

119.13 How would you expect the pK_a value of fluoroethanoic acid to compare with that of chloroethanoic acid?

119.14 Chloroethanoic acid undergoes hydrolysis easily if it is warmed with water or alkali. What might be the structure of the molecule made in the reaction? (Hint: as well as an acid, what other type of homologous series does chloroethanoic acid resemble?)

Answers

119.1 The melting point of pure ethanoic acid is 16.8°C. Thus, in winter, it is quite possible for the acid to solidify; in summer, it is more likely to be a liquid.

119.2 (i) No more ammonia would be given off.

(ii) The ammonia made in the reaction is converted into ammonium ions, NH_4^+, by reaction with hydrogen ions from the acid.

119.3 The nitrile would have to be HCN, i.e. hydrogen cyanide. This gas is extremely poisonous, and in ordinary laboratories should be avoided at all costs.

119.4 Use a reflux apparatus like that shown in Figure 115.4.

119.5 The manganate(VII) solution in alkali is the strongest oxidising agent. Its $E^\ominus$ is +1.70 V compared to +1.51 V for acidified manganate(VII) and +1.33 V for acidified dichromate(VI).

119.6 (i) Heat with alkaline potassium manganate(VII) solution.

(ii) Either (a) convert the C_2H_5Br into a Grignard reagent and treat with carbon dioxide followed by acid; or (b) react it with an alcoholic solution of potassium cyanide to make propanenitrile, C_2H_5CN, and then reflux with alkali. Acid would be added at the end of the reaction to liberate C_2H_5COOH molecules, otherwise they would remain as ethanoate ions, $C_2H_5COO^-$.

(iii) The same two methods as in the answer to (ii) could be used.

119.7 (i)

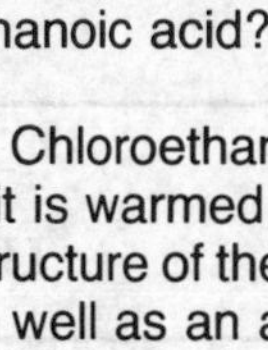

Answers – cont.

(ii) This is a dibasic acid, so 50 cm^3 of a 0.1 mol dm^{-3} solution would need 100 cm^3 of 0.1 mol dm^{-3} sodium hydroxide, or 50 cm^3 of 0.2 mol dm^{-3} alkali.

119.8 The common one to use for the titration of a weak acid with a strong base is phenolphthalein.

119.9 When ethanoyl chloride fumes in air it is because of its reaction with water vapour. The reaction gives ethanoic acid (hence the smell) as well as hydrogen chloride:

$$CH_3COCl + H_2O \rightarrow CH_3COOH + HCl$$

119.10 Add phosphorus pentachloride or, better, sulphur dichloride oxide to the acid (see section 119.3).

119.11 Methyl ethanoate is made:

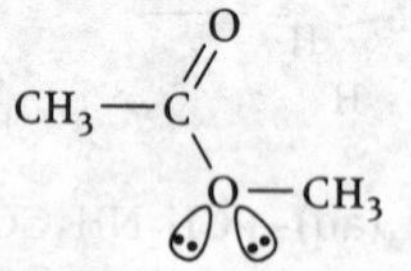

$CH_3—C(=O)—O—CH_3$

119.12 (i) Benzoyl chloride:

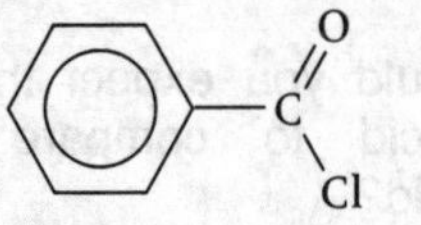

$C_6H_5—C(=O)—Cl$

(ii) Ethyl benzoate is made:

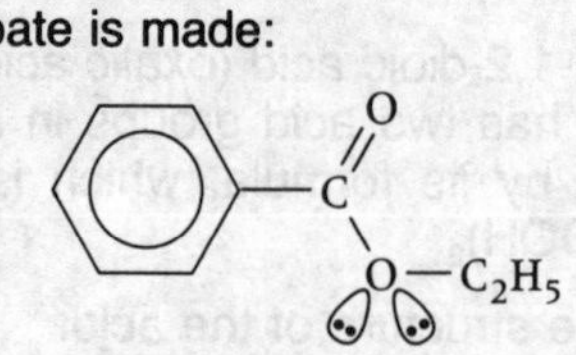

$C_6H_5—C(=O)—O—C_2H_5$

(iii) Benzoic acid, C_6H_5COOH, is formed through the reaction

$$C_6H_5COCl + H_2O \rightarrow C_6H_5COOH + HCl$$

This acid is insoluble in water, and you would see a white precipitate or cloudiness appear.

119.13 We might expect that a highly electronegative fluorine atom would pull electron density towards itself even more strongly than a chlorine atom. This would lead to the charge of the FCH_2COO^- ion being spread widely over the ion, and thereby increased energetic stability. This explanation fits the facts: the pK_a of fluoroethanoic acid is about 2.6. However, the true reason is more likely to be found in differences in entropies of solvation of the ions involved.

119.14 If we forget about the acid group, the molecule looks like a halogenoalkane. When a halogenoalkane is hydrolysed, the halogen is replaced by an OH group. The same thing happens here. The product is hydroxyethanoic acid, $OHCH_2COOH$:

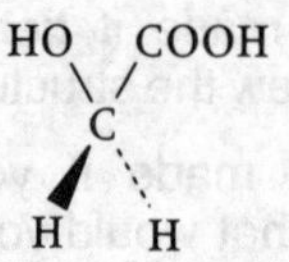

HO COOH
C
H H

UNIT 119 SUMMARY

- Carboxylic acids:
  - (i) Contain the group

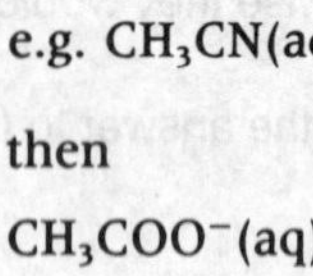

    $—C(=O)—O—H$

  - (ii) Non-aromatic acids have the general formula $C_nH_{2n+1}COOH$.
  - (iii) Are weak acids.
- Preparation:
  - (i) Hydrolysis of nitriles;

    e.g. $CH_3CN(aq) + H_2O(l) + OH^-(aq) \rightarrow CH_3COO^-(aq) + NH_3(g)$

    then

    $CH_3COO^-(aq) + H^+(aq) \rightarrow CH_3COOH(aq)$
  - (ii) Oxidation of primary alcohols under reflux with acidified sodium dichromate(VI) solution;

    e.g. $CH_3CH_2OH \rightarrow CH_3COOH$
  - (iii) From a Grignard reagent;

    $RMgI + CO_2 \rightarrow RCOOMgI \xrightarrow{H^+} RCOOH + Mg^{2+}$
  - (iv) Benzoic acid made by oxidation of a hydrocarbon side chain on a benzene ring using an acid or alkaline solution of potassium manganate(VII);

    e.g. $C_6H_5CH_3 \rightarrow C_6H_5COOH$

Reactions

- Weak acids:
  Carboxylic acids are only partially dissociated into ions.
- With sodium:
  Hydrogen released.
- Phosphorus pentachloride:
  White fumes of hydrogen chloride released;

  e.g. $CH_3COOH(l) + PCl_5(s) \rightarrow CH_3COCl(l) + POCl_3(s) + HCl(g)$

Summary – cont.

- Esterification:

  Esters are made with alcohols and acid chlorides;

$$CH_3\text{—}C(=O)\text{—}Cl \;+\; HO\text{—}CH_2\text{—}CH_3 \longrightarrow CH_3\text{—}C(=O)\text{—}O\text{—}CH_2\text{—}CH_3 \;+\; HCl$$

- Reduction:

  Lithium tetrahydridoaluminate(III) reduces acids to alcohols;

  e.g. $CH_3COOH \rightarrow CH_3CH_2OH$

- Chloroethanoic acid:
  - (i) Is a stronger acid than ethanoic acid.
  - (ii) Can be used to prepare the amino acid glycine;

    $$CH_2ClCOOH(l) + NH_3(aq) \rightarrow CH_2NH_2COOH(l) + HCl(aq)$$

    α-Chloro acids can be used to make other amino acids.

120

Carboxylic acid derivatives

120.1 What are the derivatives of carboxylic acids?

The functional group of carboxylic acids is the COOH group

$$-C(=O)-OH$$

Derivatives of the acids are normally made by swapping the OH group for another atom or group. The carbonyl part of the acid is usually left intact. As a consequence we can represent many of the derivatives by the common formula RCOX

$$R-C(=O)-X$$

The main types are listed in Table 120.1.

120.2 Acid chlorides

Acid chlorides are easy to make. We have seen one way before: add phosphorus pentachloride to a carboxylic acid. However, this is not a good method to use in the laboratory. It is much easier to use either phosphorus trichloride, PCl_3, or sulphur dichloride oxide, $SOCl_2$. These two substances are liquids, so their addition to the acid can be more easily controlled. Also, as we have noted before, the side products of the reaction with $SOCl_2$ are gases. These are more easily removed from the reaction mixture, thus making it simpler to purify the acid chloride. The reactions are:

$$CH_3-C(=O)-O-H + PCl_5 \longrightarrow CH_3-C(=O)-Cl + HCl + POCl_3$$

$$CH_3COOH + PCl_5 \rightarrow CH_3COCl + HCl + POCl_3$$

ethanoic acid → ethanoyl chloride

$$CH_3-CH_2-C(=O)-O-H + PCl_3 \longrightarrow CH_3-CH_2-C(=O)-Cl + HCl + P_2O_3$$

$$CH_3CH_2COOH + PCl_3 \rightarrow CH_3CH_2COCl + HCl + P_2O_3$$

propanoic acid → propanoyl chloride

$$C_6H_5-C(=O)-O-H + SOCl_2 \longrightarrow C_6H_5-C(=O)-Cl + SO_2 + HCl$$

$$C_6H_5COOH + SOCl_2 \rightarrow C_6H_5COCl + SO_2 + HCl$$

benzoic acid → benzoyl chloride

(a) *Reactions of acid chlorides*

Nucleophilic attack

Acid chlorides are very reactive. The carbon atom bonded to the oxygen and chlorine atoms loses a lot of electron density to these electronegative atoms. This leaves the carbon atom with a significant amount of positive charge and it becomes an attractive site for attack by nucleophiles.

With its lone pairs of electrons, water is able to decompose acid chlorides; it converts them back into acids, e.g.

Table 120.1. The derivatives of carboxylic acids

Type	*Functional group*	*Typical examples*	
Acid chloride	R—C(=O)—Cl	Ethanoyl chloride	CH_3—C(=O)—Cl
		Benzoyl chloride	C_6H_5—C(=O)—Cl
Acid anhydride	R—C(=O)—O—C(=O)—R′	Ethanoic anhydride	CH_3—C(=O)—O—C(=O)—CH_3
Amide	R—C(=O)—NH_2	Ethanamide	CH_3—C(=O)—NH_2
		Benzamide	C_6H_5—C(=O)—NH_2
Ester	R—C(=O)—O—R′	Ethyl ethanoate	CH_3—C(=O)—O—C_2H_5
		Methyl benzoate	C_6H_5—C(=O)—O—CH_3

C_6H_5—C(=O)—Cl + H_2O (lone pair on O attacking C) ⟶ C_6H_5—C(=O)—O—H + HCl

$$C_6H_5COCl + H_2O \rightarrow C_6H_5COOH + HCl$$

benzoyl chloride → benzoic acid

This is just one example of a general pattern. We can write the typical nucleophiles that attack acid chlorides as Z—H, where Z is the atom or group that has a lone pair. The result of the reaction is

R—C(=O)—Cl + Z—H ⟶ R—C(=O)—Z + HCl

$$RCOCl + Z{-}H \rightarrow RCOZ + HCl$$

We can fit ammonia, NH_3, to this pattern by writing it as NH_2—H. Similarly, amines like methylamine, CH_3NH_2, become CH_3NH—H; and alcohols like ethanol, C_2H_5OH, become C_2H_5O—H.

Table 120.2 shows you the pattern of the reactions that take place with ammonia, amines and alcohols.

Table 120.2. The reactions of acid chlorides

Nucleophile	*Type of product*	*After reaction with** *Ethanoyl chloride*	 *Benzoyl chloride*
Ammonia, NH_2—H	Amide	$CH_3-C(=O)-NH_2$ Ethanamide	$C_6H_5-C(=O)-NH_2$ Benzamide
Amines, RNH—H e.g. CH_3NH—H (methylamine	Substituted amide	$CH_3-C(=O)-N(H)-CH_3$ *N*-methylethanamide	$C_6H_5-C(=O)-N(H)-CH_3$ *N*-methylbenzamide
Alcohols, e.g. C_2H_5O—H (ethanol)	Ester	$CH_3-C(=O)-O-C_2H_5$ Ethyl ethanoate	$C_6H_5-C(=O)-O-C_2H_5$ Methyl benzoate

*The structures of ethanoyl chloride and benzoyl chloride are $CH_3-C(=O)-Cl$ and $C_6H_5-C(=O)-Cl$

Acetylation reactions

We can look at these reactions in a different way. For instance, if we concentrate on the change to the methylamine molecule when it reacts with ethanoyl chloride, it gains the CH_3CO group:

$$CH_3-C(=O)-$$

This is the ethanoyl or *acetyl* group. We say that methylamine has been *acetylated*. Likewise, ethanoyl chloride will acetylate water, ammonia and alcohols. Similarly, benzoyl chloride will *benzoylate* these molecules.

It is possible to acetylate molecules using a different reagent, ethanoic anhydride, but we shall return to this later.

If you wanted to acetylate (or benzoylate) an aromatic molecule, you would use a Friedel–Crafts reaction in which the molecule is reacted with the acetylating agent and aluminium trichloride. For example (see also Figure 120.1),

$$C_6H_5-C(=O)-Cl + C_6H_6 \longrightarrow C_6H_5-C(=O)-C_6H_5 + HCl$$

$$C_6H_5COCl + C_6H_6 \xrightarrow{AlCl_3} C_6H_5COC_6H_5 + HCl$$

diphenylmethanone

Note: Acetylation and benzoylation are two examples of the general reaction called *acylation*. Acylation refers to the introduction of an R—C=O group into a molecule.

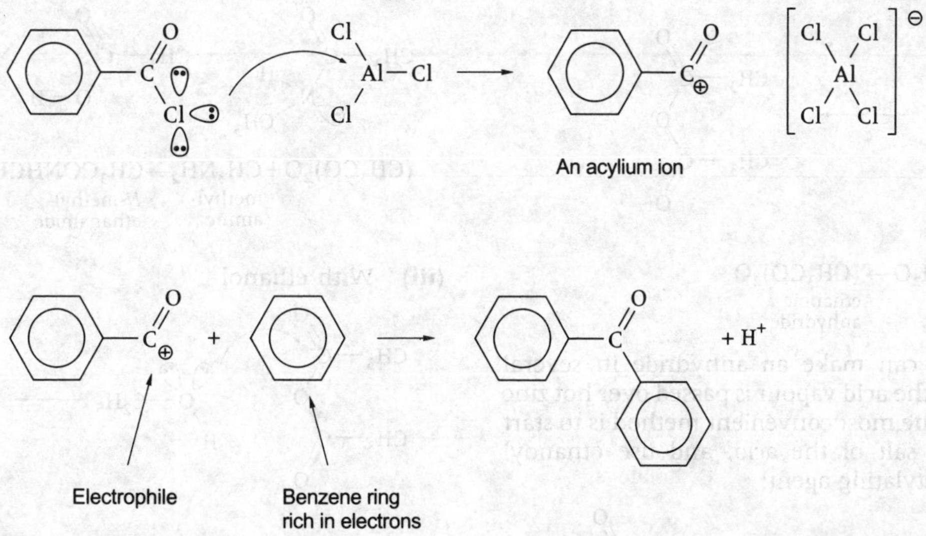

$$C_6H_5COCl + AlCl_3 \longrightarrow C_6H_5C^{+}{=}O + [AlCl_4]^{-}$$

An acylium ion

$$C_6H_5C^{+}{=}O + C_6H_6 \longrightarrow C_6H_5COC_6H_5 + H^{+}$$

Electrophile

Benzene ring rich in electrons

***Figure 120.1** The reaction between benzoyl chloride and benzene involves the production of an electrophile. This is the basis of all Friedel–Crafts reactions. A similar acylium ion (CH_3—C^+=O) is made with ethanoyl chloride and ethanoic anhydride*

Reduction of acid chlorides

The main ways of reducing acid chlorides are as follows.

(i) With a modified palladium catalyst and hydrogen, they are converted into aldehydes (section 118.4):

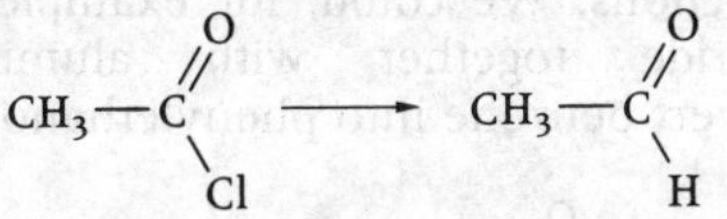

$$CH_3COCl \longrightarrow CH_3CHO$$

$$CH_3COCl \xrightarrow{H_2,\ Pd/BaSO_4} CH_3CHO$$

(ii) With lithium tetrahydridoaluminate(III) they are converted into alcohols:

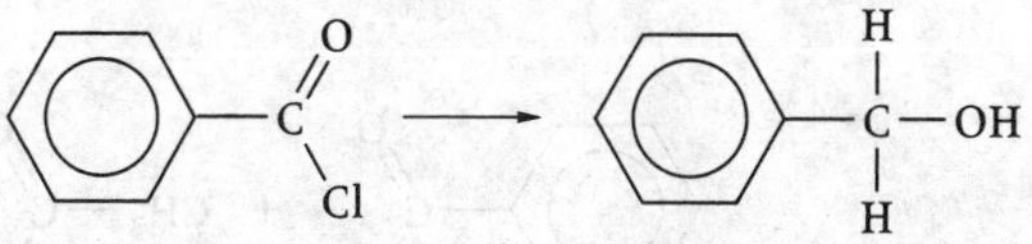

$$C_6H_5COCl \longrightarrow C_6H_5CH_2OH$$

$$C_6H_5COCl \xrightarrow{LiAlH_4} C_6H_5CH_2OH$$

120.1 With which other types of compound does phosphorus pentachloride react?

120.2 Look at Figure 120.2, which shows an apparatus that can be used to prepare ethanoyl chloride from ethanoic acid and phosphorus trichloride. The reaction is exothermic. The water bath is heated only after the reaction has finished.

(i) Copy and label the diagram.

(ii) Why should the reagents be mixed slowly?

(iii) Why is the water bath present while the reaction takes place?

(iv) What is the purpose of the anhydrous calcium chloride? (Hint: look at the properties of ethanoyl chloride.)

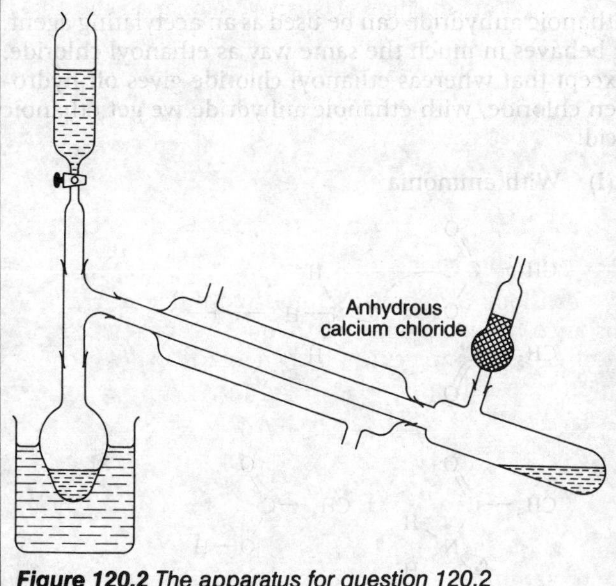

***Figure 120.2** The apparatus for question 120.2*

120.3 Acid anhydrides

One of the most important anhydrides is ethanoic anhydride. As the name suggests, it is made by removing the elements of water from ethanoic acid. (See section 99.9 for information about inorganic anhydrides.) The reaction is:

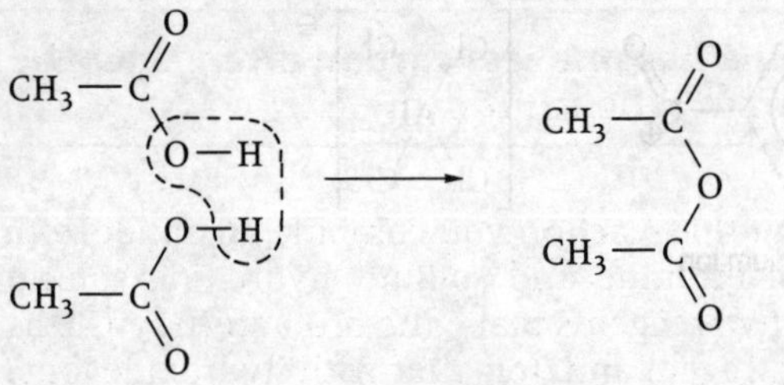

$$2CH_3COOH - H_2O \rightarrow (CH_3CO)_2O$$
ethanoic acid → ethanoic anhydride

In practice we can make an anhydride in several ways. In the first, the acid vapour is passed over hot zinc oxide. However, the most convenient method is to start with the sodium salt of the acid, and use ethanoyl chloride as an acetylating agent:

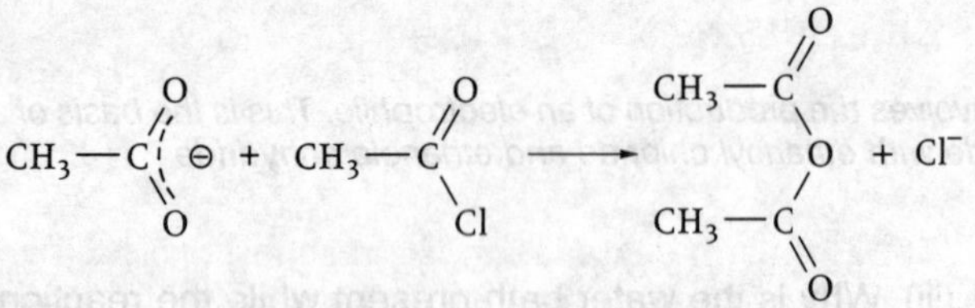

$$CH_3COO^-Na^+ + CH_3COCl \rightarrow (CH_3CO)_2O + NaCl$$
sodium ethanoate, ethanoyl chloride, ethanoic anhydride

(a) *Reactions of anhydrides*

Ethanoic anhydride can be used as an acetylating agent. It behaves in much the same way as ethanoyl chloride, except that whereas ethanoyl chloride gives off hydrogen chloride, with ethanoic anhydride we get ethanoic acid:

(i) With ammonia

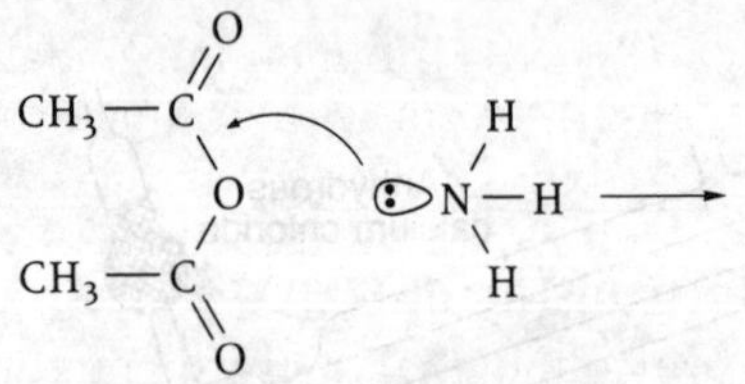

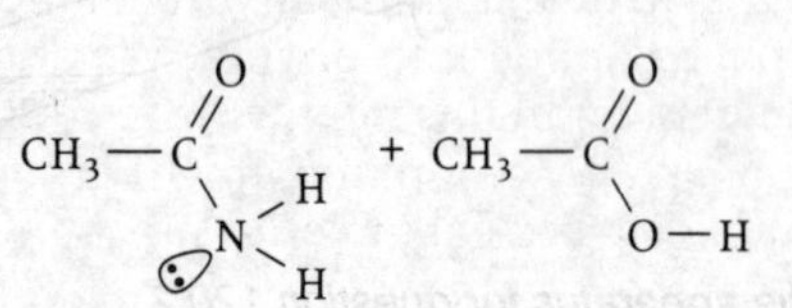

$$(CH_3CO)_2O + NH_3 \rightarrow CH_3CONH_2 + CH_3COOH$$
ethanamide, ethanoic acid

(ii) With amines

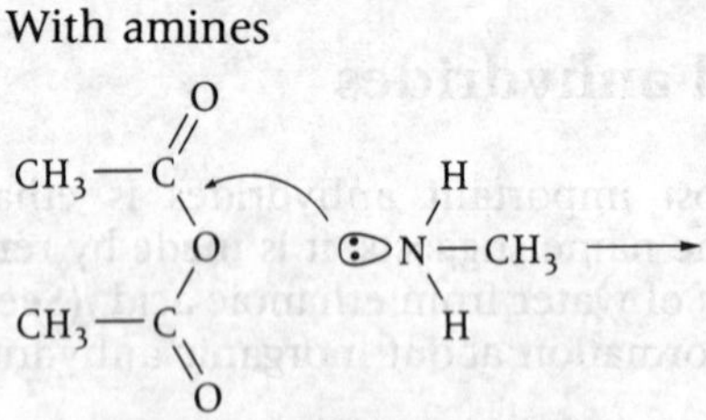

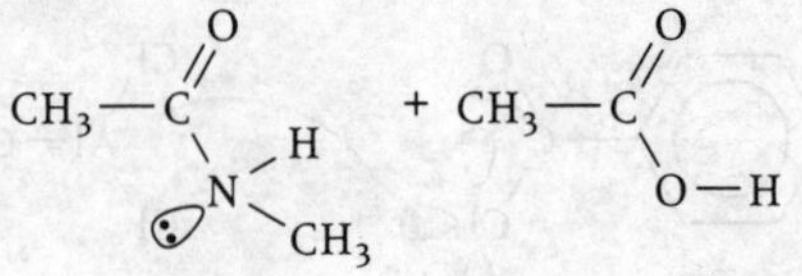

$$(CH_3CO)_2O + CH_3NH_2 \rightarrow CH_3CONHCH_3 + CH_3COOH$$
methylamine, *N*-methylethanamide, ethanoic acid

(iii) With ethanol

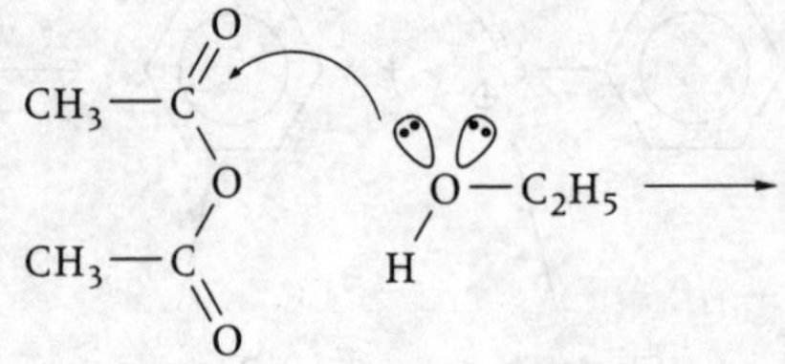

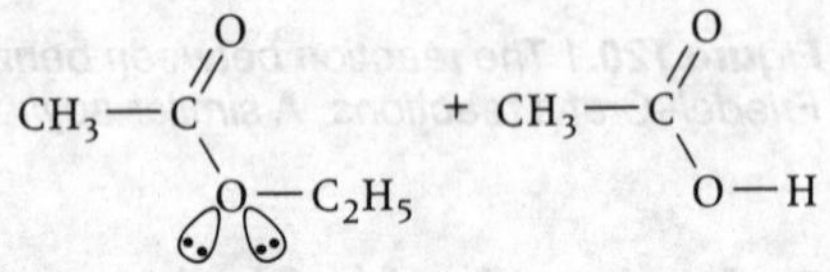

$$(CH_3CO)_2O + C_2H_5OH \rightarrow CH_3COOC_2H_5 + CH_3COOH$$
ethanol, ethyl ethanoate, ethanoic acid

Like the acid chlorides, anhydrides will take part in Friedel–Crafts reactions. We could, for example, use ethanoic anhydride together with aluminium trichloride to convert benzene into phenylethanone:

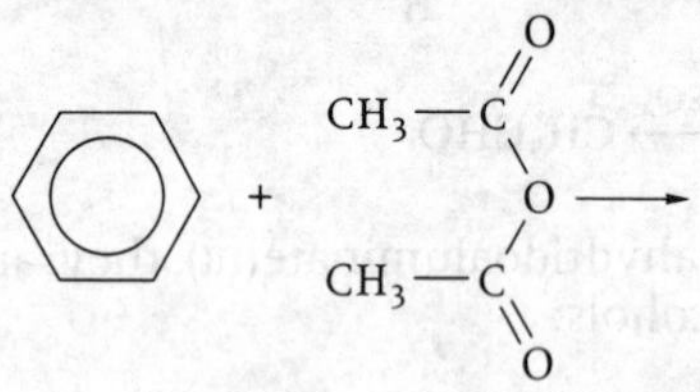

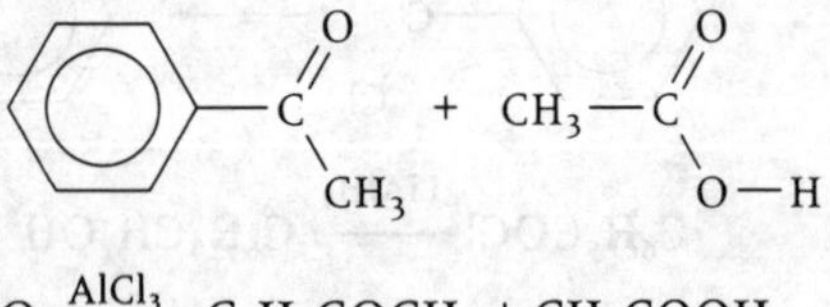

$$C_6H_6 + (CH_3CO)_2O \xrightarrow{AlCl_3} C_6H_5COCH_3 + CH_3COOH$$

120.3 (i) How would you make benzoic anhydride, $(C_6H_5CO)_2O$?

(ii) Draw the structures of the molecules made if benzoic anhydride were to react with ammonia, ethylamine and methanol.

120.4 Benzene-1,2-dicarboxylic anhydride (otherwise known as phthalic anhydride) is a rather unusual anhydride:

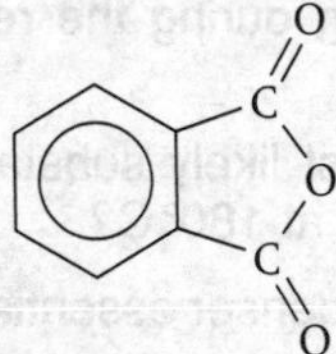

Draw the structure of the acid from which it might be made.

120.4 Amides

Amides contain the functional group $CONH_2$

$$-C(=O)-NH_2$$

They cannot be made directly from carboxylic acids. First, we must convert the acid into its ammonium salt. This is done by reacting the acid with ammonium carbonate; e.g.

$$2\,CH_3-C(=O)-O-H + (NH_4)_2CO_3 \longrightarrow$$

$$2\,CH_3-C(=O)O^{\ominus}\ NH_4^+ + CO_2 + H_2O$$

$$2CH_3COOH + (NH_4)_2CO_3 \rightarrow 2CH_3COO^-NH_4^+ + CO_2 + H_2O$$

Then the ammonium salt is decomposed by heating:

$$CH_3-C(=O)O^{\ominus}\ NH_4^+ \longrightarrow CH_3-C(=O)-NH-H + H_2O$$

$$CH_3COO^-NH_4^+ \xrightarrow{\text{heat}} \underset{\text{ethanamide}}{CH_3CONH_2} + H_2O$$

Ethanamide was once known as acetamide. Unless it is completely pure, it has a very distinctive smell – of mice. It is used in the plastics industry as well as in such widely different activities as the manufacture of cosmetics and explosives.

(a) *Reactions of amides*

The Hofmann degradation

One of the most important reactions of amides is the *Hofmann degradation*. It converts amides into amines; but of crucial importance is the fact that:

The amine has one less carbon atom than the amide from whence it came.

To carry out this reaction you combine an amide with a mixture of bromine and sodium hydroxide solution. The latter two reagents make the bromate(I) ion. This is an oxidising agent and, together with hydroxide ions, is the active ingredient in the reaction. One example is:

$$CH_3-C(=O)-NH_2 + OBr^- + 2OH^- \longrightarrow CH_3-NH_2 + CO_3^{2-} + H_2O + Br^-$$

$$\underset{\substack{\text{ethanamide}\\\text{(two carbons)}}}{CH_3CONH_2} + OBr^- + 2OH^- \rightarrow \underset{\substack{\text{methylamine}\\\text{(one carbon)}}}{CH_3NH_2} + CO_3^{2-} + H_2O + Br^-$$

The Hofmann degradation is a reaction of which you should take note. It is one of the few ways of reducing the number of carbon atoms in a molecule. With its use we can solve problems like: how could we change propanol into ethanol? This is an example of *descending a homologous series*. The scheme of the conversion would be

$$C_3H_7OH \rightarrow C_2H_5COOH \rightarrow C_2H_5CONH_2 \rightarrow C_2H_5NH_2 \rightarrow C_2H_5OH$$

The steps in the changes are achieved in this way:

(i) $C_3H_7OH \rightarrow C_2H_5COOH$, oxidise with acidified sodium dichromate(VI);
(ii) $C_2H_5COOH \rightarrow C_2H_5CONH_2$, heat with ammonium carbonate;
(iii) $C_2H_5CONH_2 \rightarrow C_2H_5NH_2$, Hofmann degradation;
(iv) $C_2H_5NH_2 \rightarrow C_2H_5OH$, warm with acidified sodium nitrite.

Reaction with nitrous acid, HNO_2

In section 117.2 we found that a warm mixture of sodium nitrite, $NaNO_2$, and dilute hydrochloric acid would convert phenylamine into phenol. We also saw that the active ingredient in this mixture is nitrous acid. This conversion of an NH_2 group into an OH group will also work with amides. For example,

$$CH_3-C(=O)-NH_2 + HNO_2 \longrightarrow CH_3-C(=O)-O-H + H_2O + N_2$$

$$\underset{\text{ethanamide}}{CH_3CONH_2} + HNO_2 \rightarrow \underset{\text{ethanoic acid}}{CH_3COOH} + H_2O + N_2$$

You can see that the pattern is to convert an amide into an acid. Notice that if you were to perform this reaction, you would see bubbles of nitrogen given off.

Making nitriles

Amides can be converted into nitriles by heating them with phosphorus(v) oxide, P_4O_{10}. The effect of this oxide is to *dehydrate* the amide. We can best show the reaction by the loss of water:

$$CH_3-C(=O)-NH_2 \quad - H_2O \longrightarrow CH_3-CN$$

$$\underset{\text{ethanamide}}{CH_3CONH_2} - H_2O \xrightarrow{P_4O_{10}} \underset{\text{ethanenitrile}}{CH_3CN}$$

Hydrolysis

Ammonia is given off when amides are heated with alkali. For example,

$$C_2H_5-C(=O)-NH_2 + OH^- \longrightarrow C_2H_5-C(=O)-O^- + NH_3$$

$$\underset{\text{propanamide}}{C_2H_5CONH_2} + OH^- \rightarrow \underset{\text{propanoate ion}}{C_2H_5COO^-} + NH_3$$

If acid is used instead of alkali, the ammonia stays in solution as ammonium ions, NH_4^+.

120.5 Here is a description of a method for making ethanamide adapted from Waddington, D. J. and Finlay, H. S. (1967). *Organic Chemistry Through Experiment*, 3rd edn, Mills and Boon, London, p. 60:

Place 3 g of ammonium carbonate in a flask. Add 6 cm³ of glacial ethanoic acid carefully. Boil gently under reflux for half an hour. Allow the apparatus to cool and arrange the apparatus for distillation. Heat the flask but do not allow the thermometer to exceed 180° C. Reject the distillate. Clean and dry the receiver and attach it to the condenser again. Continue the distillation, using the condenser as an air condenser. Collect the fraction in the range 210–225° C. The distillate solidifies on cooling and may be purified by recrystallisation from propanone. Yield about 2 g.

(i) How many moles of ammonium carbonate and ethanoic acid were used? (The density of ethanoic acid is 1.05 g cm^{-3}.)

(ii) How do these figures compare with those in the equation for the reaction? Comment on your answer.

(iii) If the yield is 2 g of ethanamide, how many moles of product are made?

(iv) What is the percentage yield?

(v) What is happening during the reflux part of the reaction?

(vi) What are the most likely substances to be collected after distillation at 180° C?

(vii) Why is an air condenser essential for the second distillation?

(viii) How would you perform the recrystallisation process?

(ix) If you were of an enquiring nature and wanted to discover whether the product really was ethanamide, what would you do?

120.6 The Hofmann degradation decreases the number of carbon atoms in a chain by one. Give a reaction that does the opposite (i.e. increases the number of carbon atoms by one).

120.5 The reactions of urea, $(NH_2)_2CO$

Urea is an amide, but it has two NH_2 groups attached to a carbonyl group.

$$(H_2N)_2C=O$$

Both of these groups are destroyed when it reacts with nitrous acid:

$$(NH_2)_2CO + 2HNO_2 \rightarrow CO_2 + N_2 + 3H_2O$$

Urea can be hydrolysed in three ways. Acid or alkaline hydrolysis can be used:

$$(NH_2)_2CO + 2H^+ + H_2O \rightarrow CO_2 + 2NH_4^+$$
$$(NH_2)_2CO + 2OH^- \rightarrow CO_3^{2-} + 2NH_3$$

or, more efficiently, it is decomposed by the enzyme *urease*:

$$(NH_2)_2CO + H_2O \xrightarrow{\text{urease}} 2NH_3 + CO_2$$

If you heat urea in a test tube you will smell ammonia being given off. The solid remaining is called *biuret*. Its structure is important because it contains a *peptide link*

$$-C(=O)-N(H)-$$

The peptide link is a feature of proteins, which we shall examine in Unit 123. The reaction is:

$$2\,(H_2N)_2C=O \longrightarrow H_2N-C(=O)-N(H)-C(=O)-NH_2 + NH_3$$

$$2(NH_2)_2CO \rightarrow \underset{\text{biuret}}{NH_2-CO-NH-CO-NH_2} + NH_3$$

There is a test that shows the presence of a peptide link. A few drops of copper(II) sulphate solution are added to a solution of the sample followed by further drops of sodium hydroxide solution. If a peptide link is present, a violet colour should appear. This test is known as the *biuret test*.

Urea is also able to take part in polymerisation reactions; but we shall leave these until later (Units 127 and 128).

Being an amide, we should expect urea to undergo a Hofmann degradation, but given that there is only one carbon atom present, we can hardly expect to get a useful product out of the reaction. In fact, urea is oxidised in the following manner:

$$(NH_2)_2CO+3OBr^-+2OH^- \rightarrow CO_3^{2-}+N_2+3H_2O+3Br^-$$

120.6 Esters

Life would not be the same without esters! They are to be found in an immense range of materials, both naturally occurring and man-made. They are responsible for the odour of many foodstuffs, and therefore for much of our sense of taste, and for the perfumes of alcoholic drinks, oils, waxes, flowers and cosmetics. Aspirin, one of the most remarkable successes of the pharmaceutical industry, is also an ester. Two esters are shown in Figure 120.3.

The classical method of making an ester is to warm an alcohol with a carboxylic acid, together with a little concentrated sulphuric acid as a catalyst. You can do this for yourself with ethanol and ethanoic acid:

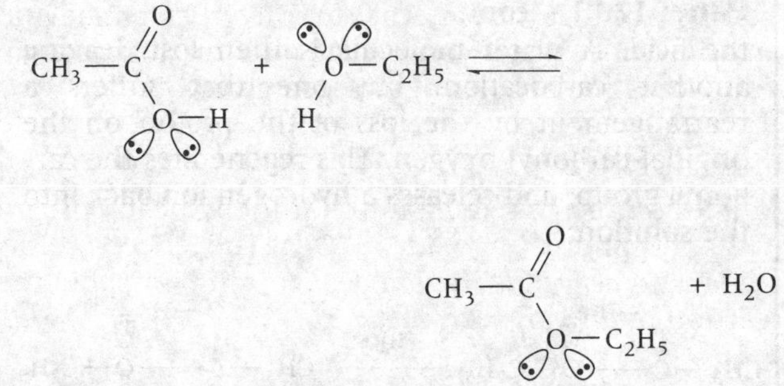

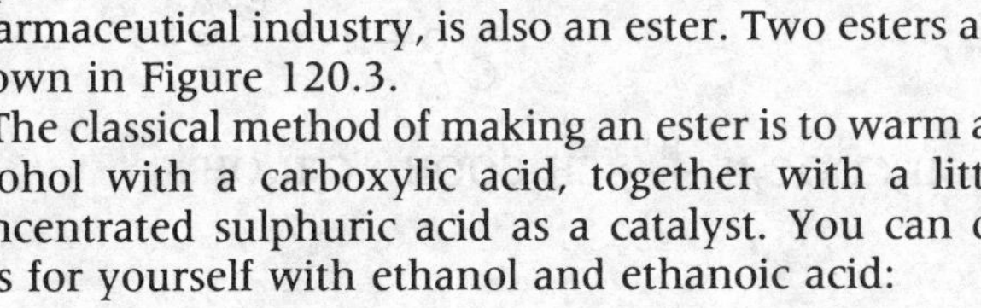

Aspirin, perhaps the most commonly available pharmaceutical

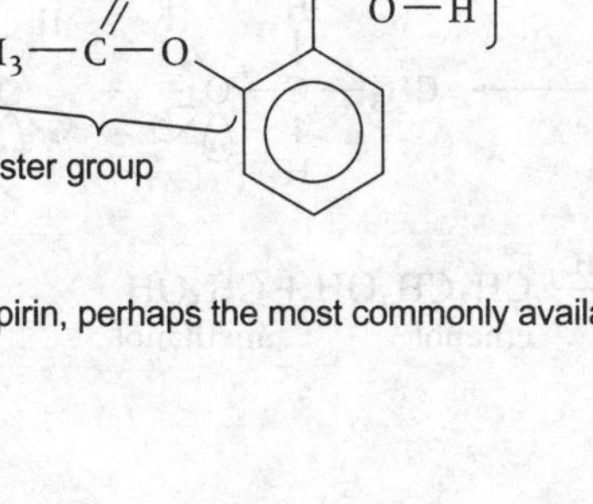

$$CH_3-(CH_2)_{16}-C(=O)-O-CH_2$$
$$CH_3-(CH_2)_{16}-C(=O)-O-CH$$
$$CH_3-(CH_2)_{16}-C(=O)-O-CH_2$$

Tristearin, an example of a fat (fats are complicated esters)

Figure 120.3 *Two esters with markedly different properties*

$$CH_3-C(=O)-O-H + H-O-C_2H_5 \rightleftharpoons CH_3-C(=O)-O-C_2H_5 + H_2O$$

$$CH_3COOH+C_2H_5OH \rightleftharpoons CH_3COOC_2H_5+H_2O$$

If you would like to know the mechanism for the reaction, consult panel 120.1.

Panel 120.1

The mechanism of an esterification reaction

The basic information that we have about the esterification reaction between ethanoic acid and ethanol is that the equation for the reaction is

$$CH_3COOH+C_2H_5OH \rightleftharpoons CH_3COOC_2H_5+H_2O$$

and that it is catalysed by acid. From what we have said about the slight positive charge carried by the carbon atom of a carbonyl group, it seems possible that this carbon is the site for nucleophilic attack. The nucleophile is the alcohol molecule, or, more precisely, one of the lone pairs on the oxygen atom. However, nuclear magnetic resonance spectroscopy (which tells us where the protons are in a molecule) gives us evidence that a significant number of ethanoic acid molecules exist as carbocations, owing to the carbonyl oxygen being protonated:

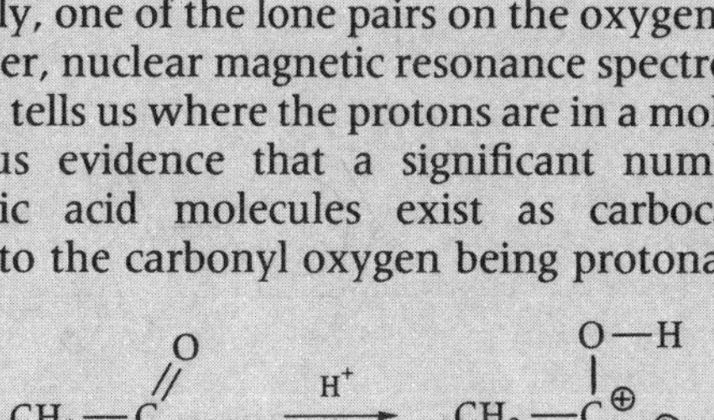

$$CH_3-C(=O)-O-H \xrightarrow{H^+} CH_3-C^{\oplus}(-O-H)-O-H$$

Ethanol molecules attack the carbocations, rather than ethanoic acid molecules:

$$CH_3-C^{\oplus}(-O-H)-O-H + H-O-C_2H_5 \longrightarrow$$

$$CH_3-C(-O-H)(-O-H)-O^{\oplus}(H)-C_2H_5$$

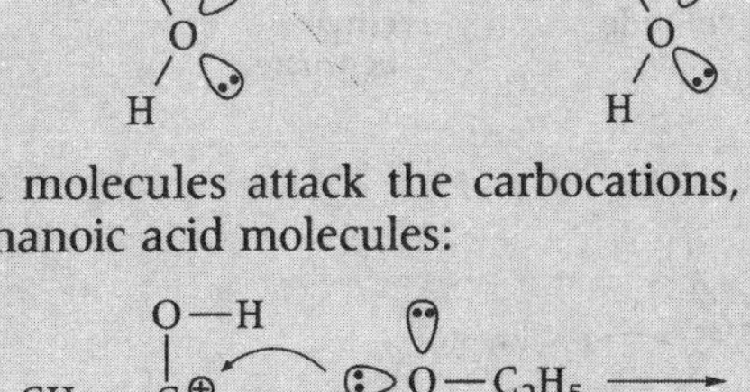

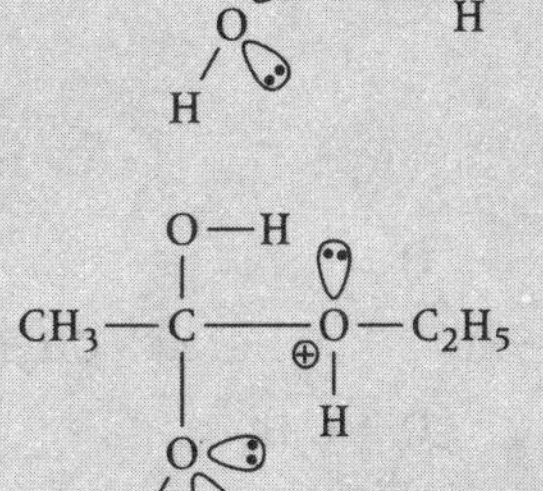

It is at this stage that a proton is transferred from the incoming alcohol molecule to the OH group of

Panel 120.1 – cont.

the acid. A water molecule is then lost, leaving another carbocation, but one that suffers a rearrangement by the loss of the proton on the original carbonyl oxygen. This regenerates the carbonyl group, and releases a hydrogen ion back into the solution:

$$CH_3-C(OH)(\overset{\oplus}{O}H_2)-O-C_2H_5 \xrightarrow{-H_2O} CH_3-\overset{\oplus}{C}(OH)-O-C_2H_5 \xrightarrow{-H^+} CH_3-C(=O)-O-C_2H_5$$

It is often the case that a water molecule is lost from an intermediate in a reaction scheme. A water molecule is said to be a *good leaving group*.

Alternative methods are to react an alcohol with an acid chloride or an acid anhydride:

$$C_6H_5-C(=O)Cl + H-O-C_2H_5 \longrightarrow C_6H_5-C(=O)-O-C_2H_5 + HCl$$

$$\underset{\text{benzoyl chloride}}{C_6H_5COCl} + C_2H_5OH \rightarrow \underset{\text{ethyl benzoate}}{C_6H_5COOC_2H_5} + HCl$$

$$CH_3-C(=O)-O-C(=O)-CH_3 + H-O-C_2H_5 \longrightarrow CH_3-C(=O)-O-C_2H_5 + CH_3-C(=O)-O-H$$

$$\underset{\text{ethanoic anhydride}}{(CH_3CO)_2O} + C_2H_5OH \rightarrow \underset{\text{ethyl ethanoate}}{CH_3COOC_2H_5} + CH_3COOH$$

(a) *Reactions of esters*

Hydrolysis

Esters can be hydrolysed by warming them with water, acid or, with greater efficiency, alkali. The reaction that takes place is essentially the reverse of esterification:

$$CH_3-C(=O)-O-CH_2-CH_3 \xrightarrow{OH} CH_3-C(=O)O^{\ominus} + H-O-CH_2-CH_3$$

$$CH_3COOC_2H_5 \xrightarrow{OH^-} CH_3COO^- + C_2H_5OH$$

$$CH_3-C(=O)-O-CH_2-CH_3 \xrightarrow{H^+} CH_3-C(=O)-O-H + H-O-CH_2-CH_3$$

$$CH_3COOC_2H_5 \xrightarrow{H^+} CH_3COOH + C_2H_5OH$$

Reduction

Esters can be reduced by lithium tetrahydridoaluminate(III), or by sodium in ethanol. In either case the ester is converted into a mixture of alcohols:

$$CH_3-C(=O)-O-CH_3 \longrightarrow CH_3-CH_2-O-H + H-O-CH_3$$

$$\underset{\text{ethyl ethanoate}}{CH_3COOCH_3} \xrightarrow{LiAlH_4} \underset{\text{ethanol}}{CH_3CH_2OH} + \underset{\text{methanol}}{CH_3OH}$$

$$C_6H_5-C(=O)-O-CH_2-CH_3 \longrightarrow C_6H_5-CH_2-O-H + H-O-CH_2-CH_3$$

$$\underset{\text{ethyl benzoate}}{C_6H_5COOC_2H_5} \xrightarrow{Na/C_2H_5OH} \underset{\text{phenylmethanol}}{C_6H_5CH_2OH} + \underset{\text{ethanol}}{C_2H_5OH}$$

With ammonia

Esters will react with ammonia. The product is an amide. For example,

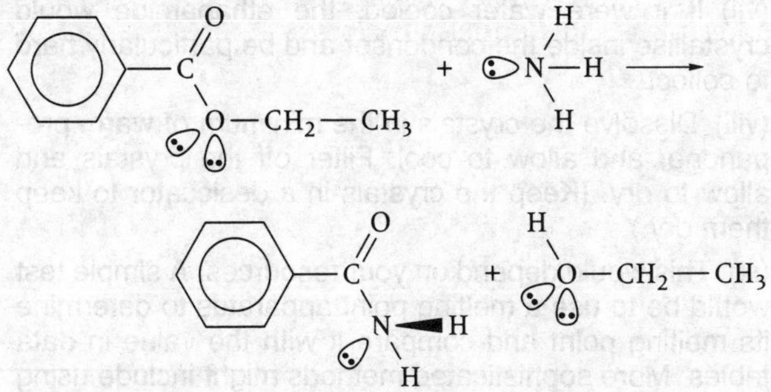

$C_6H_5COOC_2H_5 + NH_3 \rightarrow C_6H_5CONH_2 + C_2H_5OH$
ethyl benzoate   benzamide

Ammonia is not such a strong nucleophile as, say, hydroxide ion. For an effective reaction with ammonia, the ester and ammonia have to be heated together in a sealed tube.

120.7 Nitriles

Nitriles contain the CN group. Sometimes they are thought of as derivatives of carboxylic acids; but rather the connection is the other way round. We make carboxylic acids from nitriles. The method is fairly easy. Hydrolyse the nitrile using acid or alkali. With acid, carboxylic acid molecules are made; in alkali, the reaction leaves us with the carboxylic acid anions. Two examples are:

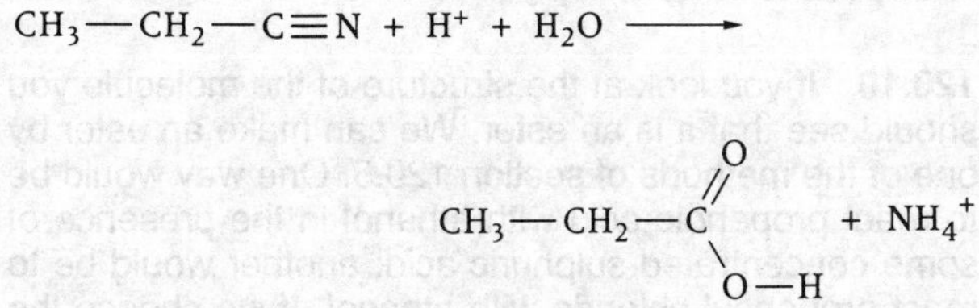

$CH_3-CH_2-C\equiv N + H^+ + H_2O \longrightarrow CH_3-CH_2-C(=O)-O-H + NH_4^+$

$C_2H_5CN + H^+ + H_2O \rightarrow C_2H_5COOH + NH_4^+$
propanenitrile   propanoic acid

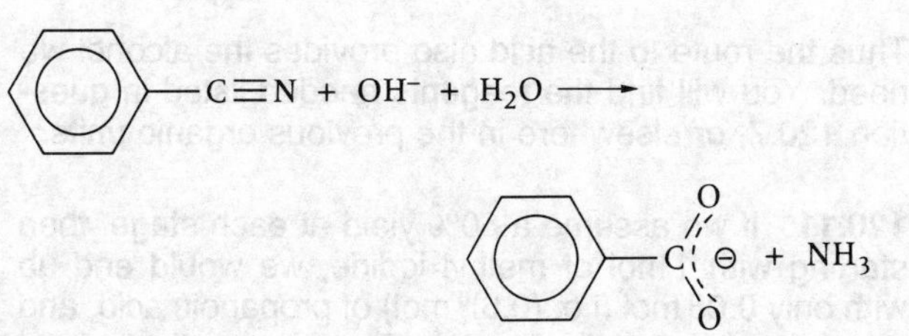

$C_6H_5-C\equiv N + OH^- + H_2O \longrightarrow C_6H_5-CO_2^{\ominus} + NH_3$

$C_6H_5CN + OH^- + H_2O \rightarrow C_6H_5COO^- + NH_3$
benzonitrile   benzoate ion

(a) *The importance of nitriles*

Nitriles provide a way of increasing the number of carbon atoms in a chain. This is the process of *ascending a homologous series.* A standard route is as follows, illustrated by taking iodoethane as our starting point:

$C_2H_5I \rightarrow C_2H_5CN \rightarrow C_2H_5COOH \rightarrow C_2H_5CH_2OH \rightarrow C_2H_5CH_2I$
iodoethane   iodopropane

Once the new halogenoalkane is made, the entire range of homologous series can be reached. Questions 120.7 to 120.11 will lead you through a few examples.

Nitriles can also be converted into amines. This is achieved by reduction with hydrogen and a nickel catalyst at 140 °C:

$$CH_3CN + 2H_2 \xrightarrow{\text{Ni cat.}} CH_3CH_2NH_2$$

The same result can be achieved using sodium in ethanol, or lithium tetrahydridoaluminate(III).

(b) *Preparation of nitriles*

We can make nitriles by dehydrating amides with phosphorus(V) oxide (see section 120.4), or by heating halogenoalkanes with an alcoholic solution of potassium cyanide (see section 115.3); e.g.

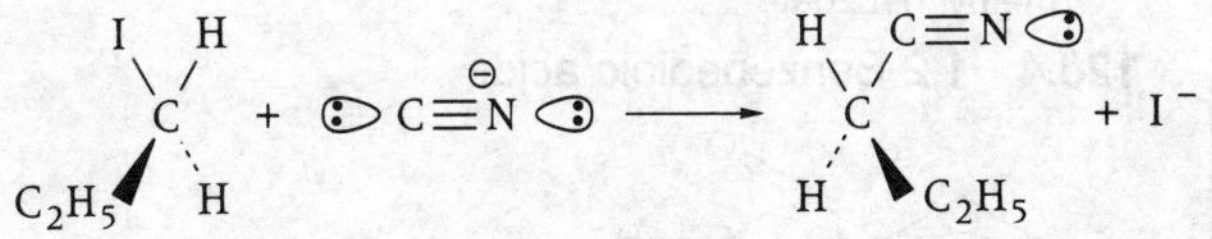

$C_3H_7I + CN^- \rightarrow C_3H_7CN + I^-$
iodopropane   butanenitrile

120.7 In the scheme for converting iodoethane into iodopropane, write down the reaction conditions for each stage.

120.8 How would you make propanoic acid starting with iodoethane?

120.9 How would you make ethanol starting from iodomethane?

120.10 How would you make ethyl propanoate, $C_2H_5COOC_2H_5$, starting with methyl iodide as the major organic reagent?

120.11 If you have answered question 120.10, why would you be wise to start with a substance other than methyl iodide?

120.12 Devise a reaction scheme that would convert propanoic acid into iodoethane.

Answers

120.1 It is used as a test for compounds that contain OH groups such as alcohols, giving off fumes of hydrogen chloride. It will also react with carbonyl groups (see section 118.11).

120.2 (i) The ethanoic acid goes in the flask, and phosphorus trichloride in the dropping funnel.

(ii) The reaction is exothermic, so there is a danger of it being very violent if the reactants are mixed too quickly.

(iii) It cools the mixture.

(iv) It prevents water vapour from the atmosphere entering the apparatus and reacting with the ethanoyl chloride.

120.3 (i) Either pass benzoic acid vapour over hot zinc oxide, or (better) add ethanoyl chloride to sodium benzoate.

(ii)

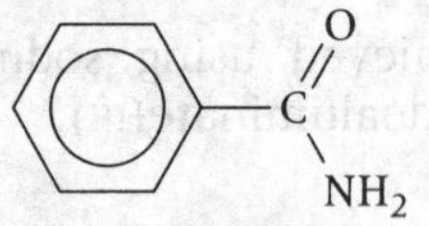

benzamide

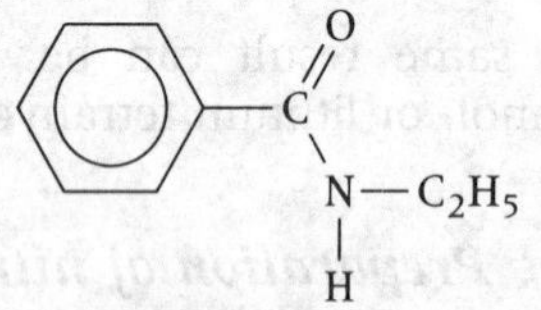

N-ethylbenzamide

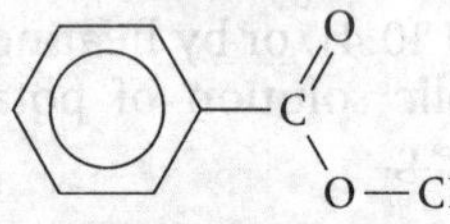

methyl benzoate

120.4 1,2-Benzenedioic acid:

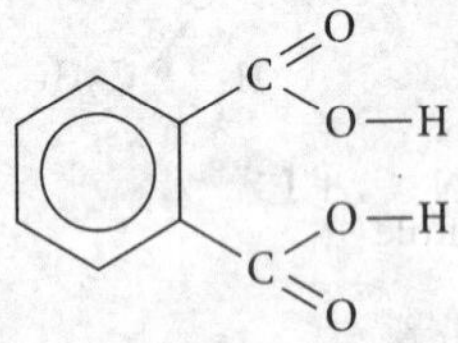

120.5 (i) One mole of ammonium carbonate has a mass of 96 g, so 3 g represents 0.03 mol. 6 cm^3 of ethanoic acid represents 6.3 g; 1 mol of ethanoic acid has a mass of 60 g, so the number of moles used is about 0.1 mol.

(ii) From the equation, 2 mol of CH_3COOH react with 1 mol of $(NH_4)_2CO_3$ to give 2 mol of CH_3COONH_4. In the recipe, we have a ratio of 0.1 mol of CH_3COOH to 0.03 mol of $(NH_4)_2CO_3$, i.e. about 3 mol to 1 mol. This ratio ensures that all the $(NH_4)_2CO_3$ is used up.

(iii) One mole of ethanamide has a mass 59 g, so the yield is about 0.03 mol.

(iv) From the two equations, 1 mol of $(NH_4)_2CO_3$ should give 2 mol of ethanamide, CH_3CONH_2. Therefore, 0.03 mol of $(NH_4)_2CO_3$ should give 0.06 mol of ethanamide. Notice that we must not choose ethanoic acid with which to calculate the yield because it is in excess (not all of it is used up). The yield is

$$\frac{0.03\text{ mol}}{0.06\text{ mol}} \times 100\% = 50\%$$

(v) CO_2 and H_2O are released, while the salt $CH_3COO^-NH_4^+$ is made.

(vi) Ethanoic acid that is left over, and water that is made in the reaction.

(vii) If it were water cooled, the ethanamide would crystallise inside the condenser and be particularly hard to collect.

(viii) Dissolve the crystals in the minimum of warm propanone, and allow to cool. Filter off the crystals and allow to dry. (Keep the crystals in a desiccator to keep them dry.)

(ix) This would depend on your resources. A simple test would be to use a melting point apparatus to determine its melting point and compare it with the value in data tables. More sophisticated methods might include using a mass spectrometer and infrared (vibrational) spectroscopy.

120.6 Making a nitrile, e.g.

$$CH_3I + CN^- \rightarrow CH_3CN + I^-$$

120.7 $C_2H_5I \rightarrow C_2H_5CN$; warm with alcoholic potassium cyanide.

$C_2H_5CN \rightarrow C_2H_5COOH$; warm with acid or alkali.

$C_2H_5COOH \rightarrow C_2H_5CH_2OH$; reduce with $LiAlH_4$.

$C_2H_5CH_2OH \rightarrow C_2H_5CH_2I$; warm with iodine and red phosphorus.

120.8 Convert iodoethane into propanenitrile (see question 120.7) and then hydrolyse with acid or alkali. After alkaline hydrolysis, you would have to add acid to convert the $C_2H_5COO^-$ ions into C_2H_5COOH molecules.

120.9 Convert the iodomethane into ethanenitrile, CH_3CN, then the nitrile into ethanoic acid, CH_3COOH. (See questions 120.7 and 120.8 for the method.) Finally, reduce the acid with lithium tetrahydridoaluminate(III). The result is ethanol, CH_3CH_2OH.

120.10 If you look at the structure of the molecule you should see that it is an ester. We can make an ester by one of the methods of section 120.5. One way would be to react propanoic acid with ethanol in the presence of some concentrated sulphuric acid; another would be to react propanoyl chloride with ethanol. If we choose the first method, the reaction scheme would look like this:

$$CH_3I \rightarrow CH_3CN \rightarrow CH_3COOH \rightarrow \underset{\text{ethanol}}{CH_3CH_2OH} \rightarrow$$

$$CH_3CH_2I \xrightarrow{CN^-} CH_3CH_2CN \rightarrow \underset{\text{propanoic acid}}{CH_3CH_2COOH}$$

Thus the route to the acid also provides the alcohol we need. You will find the reagents needed listed in question 120.7, or elsewhere in the previous organic units.

120.11 If we assume a 60% yield at each stage, then starting with 1 mol of methyl iodide, we would end up with only 0.05 mol (i.e. $(0.6)^6$ mol) of propanoic acid, and even less of the final ester. The preparation of an organic compound should be done with as few stages as possible.

Answers – cont.

120.12 Our scheme is:

$C_2H_5COOH \rightarrow C_2H_5CONH_2 \rightarrow C_2H_5NH_2 \rightarrow C_2H_5OH \rightarrow C_2H_5I$

The conversions are:

$C_2H_5COOH \rightarrow C_2H_5CONH_2$; heat with ammonium carbonate.

$C_2H_5CONH_2 \rightarrow C_2H_5NH_2$; Hofmann degradation (warm with bromine and alkali).

$C_2H_5NH_2 \rightarrow C_2H_5OH$; warm with acidified sodium nitrite (in practice, this reaction gives a poor yield).

$C_2H_5OH \rightarrow C_2H_5I$; reflux with iodine and red phosphorus.

UNIT 120 SUMMARY

- Derivatives of carboxylic acids:

  Include acid chlorides

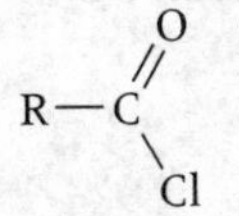

  $$R{-}C(=O){-}Cl$$

  acid anhydrides

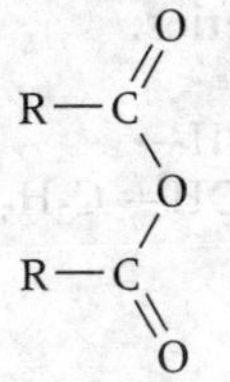

  $$R{-}C(=O){-}O{-}C(=O){-}R$$

  amides

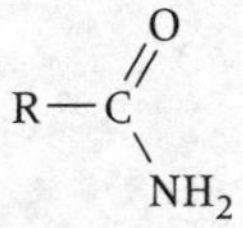

  $$R{-}C(=O){-}NH_2$$

  esters

  $$R{-}C(=O){-}O{-}R'$$

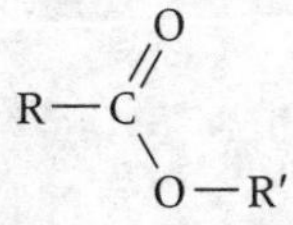

- Preparation:
  - (i) Acid chlorides: acid plus phosphorus pentachloride, phosphorus trichloride, or sulphur dichloride oxide;

    e.g. $CH_3COOH + SOCl_2 \rightarrow CH_3COCl + SO_2 + HCl$
  - (ii) Acid anhydrides: using an acid chloride;

    e.g. $CH_3COO^-Na^+ + CH_3COCl \rightarrow (CH_3CO)_2O + NaCl$

    ethanoic anhydride
  - (iii) Amides: heat the ammonium salt of a carboxylic acid;

    e.g. $CH_3COO^-NH_4^+ \rightarrow CH_3CONH_2 + H_2O$
  - (iv) Esters: made from an alcohol plus an acid chloride, or a carboxylic acid with an acid catalyst;

    e.g. $C_3H_7OH + CH_3COCl \rightarrow CH_3COOC_3H_7 + HCl$

    propyl ethanoate

Properties

- Acid chlorides:
  - (i) Undergo nucleophilic attack. The general pattern is

    $RCOCl + ZH \rightarrow RCOZ + HCl$

    e.g. water Z = OH, acids made; ammonia Z = NH_2, amides made; alcohols Z = RO, esters made.
  - (ii) Used as acetylating agents:

    e.g. $C_6H_5COCl + C_6H_6 \xrightarrow{AlCl_3} C_6H_5COC_6H_5 + HCl$

    diphenylmethanone
  - (iii) Reduction by hydrogen with a catalyst;

    $CH_3COCl \xrightarrow{H_2,\ Pd/BaSO_4} CH_3CHO$
  - (iv) Reduction by lithium tetrahydridoaluminate(III) gives alcohols;

    $C_6H_5COCl \rightarrow C_6H_5CH_2OH$
- Acid anhydrides:

  Acetylating agents, similar to acid chlorides but ethanoic acid made as a side product rather than hydrogen chloride.
- Amides:
  - (i) Hofmann degradation: heat an amide with bromine in sodium hydroxide solution. The product is an amine with one less carbon atom than the amide;

    e.g. $CH_3CONH_2 \rightarrow CH_3NH_2$
  - (ii) With nitrous acid, amide is converted into a carboxylic acid;

    e.g. $CH_3CONH_2 \rightarrow CH_3COOH$
  - (iii) Conversion into nitriles by heating with phosphorus(V) oxide;

    e.g. $CH_3CONH_2 - H_2O \rightarrow CH_3CN$

Summary – cont.

(iv) Hydrolysis; by heating with alkali;

e.g. $C_2H_5CONH_2 + OH^- \rightarrow C_2H_5COO^- + NH_3$

- Esters:
  (i) Undergo hydrolysis by warming with acid or alkali; conversion to an alcohol and carboxylic acid.
  (ii) Reduced by lithium tetrahydridoaluminate(III) or sodium in ethanol to a mixture of alcohols;

  e.g. $CH_3COOCH_3 \xrightarrow{LiAlH_4} CH_3CH_2OH + CH_3OH$

  (iii) With ammonia, an amide and alcohol are produced;

  e.g. $C_6H_5COOC_2H_5 + NH_3 \rightarrow C_6H_5CONH_2 + C_2H_5OH$

- Biuret test:
  A violet colour with a mixture of copper(II) sulphate solution and sodium hydroxide solution shows presence of a peptide link,

$$\begin{array}{c} O \\ \| \\ -C-N- \\ | \\ H \end{array}$$

Nitriles

- Preparation:
  (i) Dehydrating of amides with phosphorus(V) oxide;

  e.g. $C_2H_5CONH_2 - H_2O \rightarrow C_2H_5CN$

  (ii) Heating halogenoalkanes with an alcoholic solution of potassium cyanide;

  e.g. $C_3H_7I + CN^- \rightarrow C_3H_7CN + I^-$

Reactions

- Undergo hydrolysis to carboxylic acids;

  e.g. $\underset{\text{benzonitrile}}{C_6H_5CN} + OH^- + H_2O \rightarrow \underset{\text{benzoate ion}}{C_6H_5COO^-} + NH_3$

- Reduced to amines;

  $CH_3CN + 2H_2 \xrightarrow{\text{Ni cat.}} CH_3CH_2NH_2$

- Importance:
  Used to increase the number of carbon atoms in a chain, i.e. ascend a homologous series;

  e.g. $C_2H_5I \rightarrow C_2H_5CN \rightarrow C_2H_5COOH \rightarrow C_2H_5CH_2OH \rightarrow C_2H_5CH_2I$

121

Ethers

121.1 What are ethers?

Ethers contain two organic radicals bonded to the same oxygen atom. The most common ether is ethoxyethane, $C_2H_5OC_2H_5$. Sometimes it is simply called 'ether' or 'diethyl ether'. In common with other members of the homologous series, it is a volatile liquid. It once found use as an anaesthetic. Some ethers are shown in Table 121.1.

If, like ethoxyethane, the ether contains two identical organic radicals, then it is a symmetrical ether. If the radicals are different, we have an unsymmetrical or mixed ether. Methoxyethane is an unsymmetrical ether:

CH_3CH_2–O–CH_3

Like water, ethers have a triangular shape and they are slightly polar. They are good solvents for a wide range of molecules. Especially, ethoxyethane is widely used on an industrial scale as a solvent. Owing to their volatility and to their sweet smell, some aromatic ethers are used in cosmetics and perfumes.

In the laboratory one of the important things to know about ethers is that they catch fire very easily (their *flash points* are very low). Ethoxyethane has been involved in many fires. Its vapour is dense and if it escapes from an

Table 121.1. Examples of ethers

Name	*Formula*	*Structure*	*Melting point/°C*	*Boiling point/°C*
Methoxymethane	CH_3OCH_3	CH_3–O–CH_3	−140	−24
Ethoxyethane	$C_2H_5OC_2H_5$	CH_3CH_2–O–CH_2CH_3	−116	34.6
Methoxybenzene	$C_6H_5OCH_3$	C_6H_5–O–CH_3	−37.2	154.2
Tetrahydrofuran	$CH_2CH_2CH_2CH_2O$	O bonded to CH_2 and CH_2; CH_2—CH_2 (ring)	−65	67

Two models showing the shapes of methoxyethane (bottom) and ethoxyethane (top).

apparatus, it can travel over benches and floors. If it reaches the site of a flame some distance away, then an explosion can occur. You should never heat a flask or test tube containing an ether using a naked flame; a preheated water bath is best. Ether has also been known to explode owing to the formation of highly reactive peroxides in the liquid.

There is no obvious site for electrophilic or nucleophilic attack on an ether; ethers are relatively unreactive molecules.

121.2 The preparation of ethers

There are two ways of preparing ethers.

(a) Dehydration of an alcohol

We have seen this reaction before as a property of alcohols. The method is to heat an alcohol with concentrated sulphuric acid at about 140 °C. The overall effect of the acid is to take one molecule of water from two molecules of the alcohol. If we wanted to make ethoxyethane, we would use ethanol:

$$CH_3—CH_2—O(H) \quad (H)O—CH_2—CH_3 \xrightarrow{-H_2O} CH_3—CH_2—O—CH_2—CH_3$$

$$2C_2H_5OH - H_2O \rightarrow C_2H_5OC_2H_5$$

By writing the equation in this way, it appears that the acid is not destroyed. Provided we keep the ethanol in excess, we should be able to keep the reaction going indefinitely. For a limited period of time this is so, and we can drip ethanol into the reaction flask to replace that which is changed into ether. The reaction is called *Williamson's continuous ether process*. However, owing to side reactions, in time the acid is reduced to sulphurous acid, and no more ether is made.

(b) *Williamson's ether synthesis*

The first step in the method is to make a solution of an *alkoxide* ion. The simplest way of doing this is to dissolve sodium in an alcohol. For example, to make ethoxyethane we would use ethanol:

$$\underset{\text{ethanol}}{2C_2H_5OH} + 2Na \rightarrow \underset{\text{ethoxide ion}}{2C_2H_5O^-} + 2Na^+ + H_2$$

In section 115.3 we found that the ethoxide ion is a nucleophile, which will react with a halogenoalkane. We would add iodoethane to the flask that contains the ethoxide ion, and reflux them for 10 minutes:

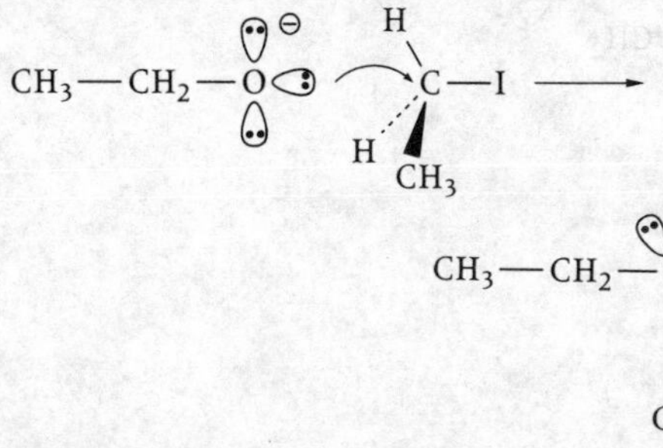

$CH_3—CH_2—O^-$ + $(H)(H)(CH_3)C—I$ ⟶ $CH_3—CH_2—O(C—H)(CH_3)(H)$ + I^-

$$\underset{\text{ethoxide ion}}{C_2H_5O^-} + \underset{\text{iodoethane}}{C_2H_5I} \rightarrow \underset{\text{ethoxyethane}}{C_2H_5OC_2H_5} + I^-$$

The ether is removed from the reaction flask by distillation, but the distillate is contaminated by ethanol. If the distillate is washed with brine, the ethanol dissolves in the brine, but the ether remains as a separate layer. After separation, the ether can be dried with calcium chloride and redistilled if necessary.

121.3 The reactions of ethers

We have said that ethers are not very reactive. However, the one major reaction they undergo is *cleavage*. If an ether is refluxed with a concentrated solution of hydrogen iodide, the organic radicals are converted into halogenoalkanes:

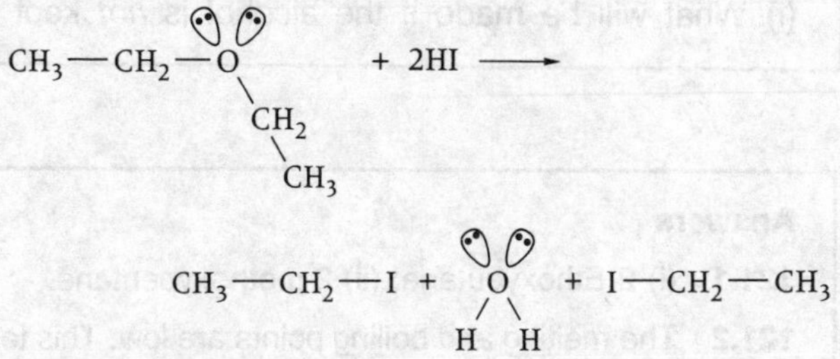

$CH_3—CH_2—O—CH_2—CH_3$ + 2HI ⟶

$CH_3—CH_2—I$ + H_2O + $I—CH_2—CH_3$

$$C_2H_5OC_2H_5 + 2HI \rightarrow 2C_2H_5I + H_2O$$

Methoxybenzene and other similar aromatic ethers are a little different. Phenol is one of the products:

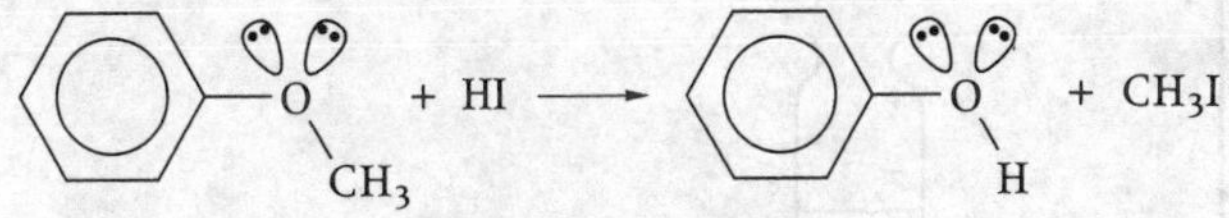

$C_6H_5—O—CH_3$ + HI ⟶ $C_6H_5—O—H$ + CH_3I

$$C_6H_5OCH_3 + HI \rightarrow \underset{\text{phenol}}{C_6H_5OH} + CH_3I$$

A cleavage reaction also takes place on heating with phosphorus pentachloride. The ether is converted into chloroalkanes, but no hydrogen chloride is given off. For example,

$$C_2H_5OCH_3 + PCl_5 \rightarrow C_2H_5Cl + CH_3Cl + POCl_3$$

121.1 The name of $(CH_3CH_2)(CH_3)CHOCH_3$

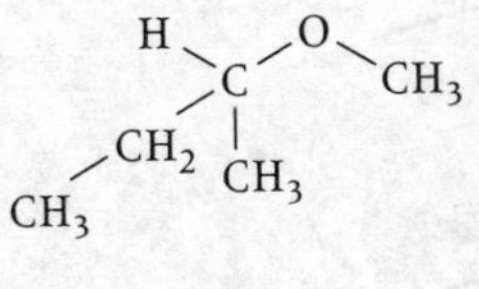

$CH_3CH_2CH(CH_3)—O—CH_3$

is 2-methoxybutane. What are the names of the following ethers?

(i) $(CH_3CH_2)(CH_3)CHOC_2H_5$

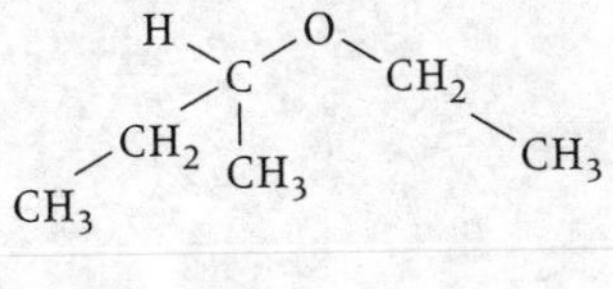

$CH_3CH_2CH(CH_3)—O—CH_2CH_3$

(ii) $(CH_3CH_2CH_2)(CH_3)CHOCH_3$

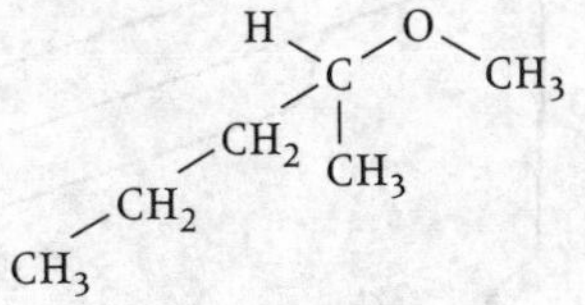

$CH_3CH_2CH_2CH(CH_3)—O—CH_3$

121.2 Why do the melting and boiling points of the ethers suggest that they are only *slightly* polar?

121.3 One mole of water will dissolve about 0.02 mol of ethoxyethane. This solubility is partly due to a small amount of hydrogen bonding that can take place between water and ethoxyethane. Explain, using a diagram, how this hydrogen bonding occurs.

121.4 However, ethoxyethane is much more soluble in an acid like hydrochloric acid. Suggest a reason for this. (Hint: first, take notice of the oxygen in an ether, then think about what happens to hydrogen ions in water.)

121.5 What is the equation for the burning of ethoxyethane in oxygen?

121.6 An organic compound had the formula C_2H_6O. Can you be sure of the name and formula of the compound?

121.7 In the Williamson continuous ether process:

(i) What will be made if the alcohol is *not* kept in excess, or if the temperature goes up to around 180° C?

(ii) Why is alkali used to wash the ether before it is dried with calcium chloride and redistilled?

121.8 Williamson's ether synthesis can be used to make mixed ethers. Suggest a way of making methoxyethane, $C_2H_5OCH_3$. Sketch the apparatus that you would use.

121.9 At the end of a Williamson ether synthesis, a white crystalline solid is seen in the reaction flask. What is it?

Answers

121.1 (i) 2-Ethoxybutane; (ii) 2-methoxypentane.

121.2 The melting and boiling points are low. This tells us that the intermolecular forces are weak. Therefore the attractive forces between the dipoles must be weak. Hydrogen bonding does not occur in ethers because none of the hydrogen atoms are directly attached to the electronegative oxygen atom.

121.3

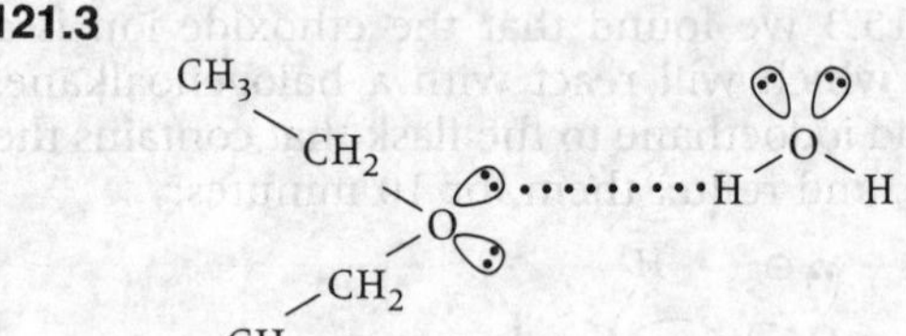

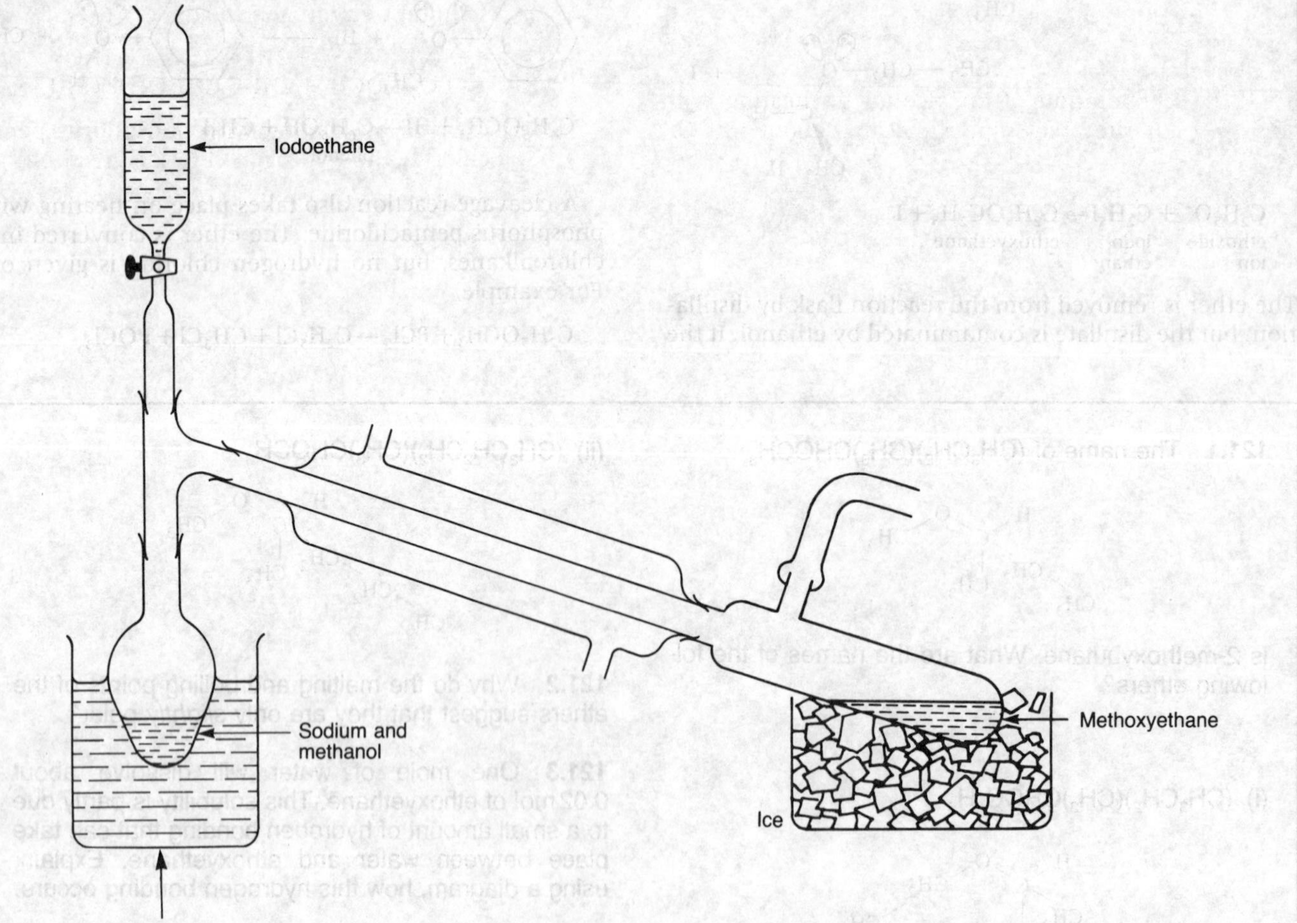

Iodoethane

Sodium and methanol

Heat

Methoxyethane

Ice

***Figure 121.1** Diagram for answer to question 121.8*

Answers – cont.

Hydrogen bonding can occur between the oxygen atom on an ether and hydrogen atoms on surrounding water molecules. Hydrogen bonding *cannot* occur between oxygen atoms in water molecules and hydrogen atoms bonded to carbon atoms in the ether. These bonds are not sufficiently polar to give the hydrogen atoms an appreciable positive charge.

121.4 Just as the oxygen atom in water has one of its lone pairs protonated to make the oxonium ion, so too a lone pair on the oxygen atom in an ether can be protonated.

$$CH_3CH_2-\ddot{O}-CH_2CH_3 \xrightarrow{H^+} CH_3CH_2-\dot{O}(H^+)-CH_2CH_3$$

121.5 $C_2H_5OC_2H_5 + 6O_2 \rightarrow 4CO_2 + 5H_2O$

121.6 No; isomers are possible. It could be ethanol, C_2H_5OH, or methoxymethane, CH_3OCH_3.

121.7 (i) Ethene, C_2H_4 (see section 112.2).

(ii) Acidic fumes contaminate the ether. There are fumes from the sulphuric acid and sulphur dioxide is produced when the sulphuric acid oxidises some of the alcohol molecules.

121.8 You could use (i) sodium dissolved in methanol to make methoxide ions, which is then reacted with iodoethane; or (ii) sodium dissolved in ethanol to make ethoxide ions, which is then reacted with iodomethane. The first method is best because iodoethane is a liquid. (Iodomethane is a gas and more difficult to handle.) The apparatus is shown in Figure 121.1.

121.9 Sodium iodide, NaI.

UNIT 121 SUMMARY

- Ethers:
  (i) Are of the general form R—O—R′.
  (ii) Show few reactions.
  (iii) Are highly volatile.
- Preparation:
  (i) Dehydration of an alcohol by heating with concentrated sulphuric acid at about 140° C;
  e.g. $2C_2H_5OH - H_2O \rightarrow C_2H_5OC_2H_5$
  (ii) Williamson's ether synthesis. Dissolve sodium in an alcohol, then reflux with an iodoalkane;
  e.g. $2C_2H_5OH + 2Na \rightarrow 2C_2H_5O^- + 2Na^+ + H_2$
  $C_2H_5O^- + C_2H_5I \rightarrow C_2H_5OC_2H_5 + I^-$
- Reactions:
  (i) Cleaved by refluxing with a concentrated solution of hydrogen iodide;
  e.g. $C_2H_5OC_2H_5 + 2HI \rightarrow 2C_2H_5I + H_2O$
  $C_6H_5OCH_3 + 2HI \rightarrow C_6H_5OH + CH_3I$
  (ii) Cleaved by heating with phosphorus pentachloride; no hydrogen chloride given off;
  e.g. $C_2H_5OCH_3 + PCl_5 \rightarrow C_2H_5Cl + CH_3Cl + POCl_3$

122

Amines

122.1 There are several types of amine

The key thing about amines is that there is a nitrogen atom bonded to an organic radical. The simplest aliphatic amine is methylamine, CH_3NH_2

which is similar to ammonia, with one of the hydrogen atoms being replaced by a methyl group. This type of amine is a *primary* amine. If two hydrogen atoms are replaced, then we have a *secondary* amine. With all three hydrogen atoms replaced, a *tertiary* amine is the result. Phenylamine, $C_6H_5NH_2$, is the simplest aromatic primary amine. Some amines are listed in Table 122.1.

Some of the most interesting amines have two NH_2 groups in the same molecule. For example, ethane-1,2-diamine is used as a chelating agent in transition metal chemistry; and hexane-1,6-diamine is used in making Nylon.

Amines are poisonous, many being gases with an unpleasant fishy smell (Figure 122.1). They are widely used as intermediates in the preparation and manufacture of pharmaceuticals, dyes and fabrics. Two common substances related to amines are shown in Figure 122.2.

A common industrial method of manufacturing aliphatic amines is to pass a mixture of ammonia and the vapour of an alcohol over a hot silica or aluminium oxide catalyst. The effect of the catalyst is to remove the elements of water:

$$\underset{\text{methanol}}{CH_3OH} + NH_3 \rightarrow \underset{\text{methylamine}}{CH_3NH_2} + \underset{\text{removed by the catalyst}}{H_2O}$$

Often a mixture of amines results, but sometimes the proportions of each type can be controlled by using a specific set of conditions (temperature and catalyst).

To make phenylamine, a different type of reaction is needed. This time the starting materials are chlorobenzene and ammonia. At a pressure of 50 atm their vapours are passed over a copper catalyst kept at 200 °C:

$$C_6H_5Cl + NH_3 \xrightarrow{\text{Cu, 200 °C}} C_6H_5NH_2 + HCl$$

122.2 The preparation of amines

We have discussed all but one of the methods of making amines in previous chapters. Here is a summary of the methods that you should have already met.

(a) *From halogenoalkanes*

The halogenoalkane is heated under pressure with ammonia in alcohol. A mixture of primary, secondary and tertiary amines may be recovered. For example,

$$\underset{}{NH_3} + \underset{\text{iodoethane}}{C_2H_5I} \rightarrow \underset{\text{ethylamine}}{C_2H_5NH_2} + HI$$

The primary amine can go on to make secondary and tertiary amines. You will find details about this complication in section 122.4.

(b) *Reduction of nitriles*

The vapour of a nitrile is mixed with hydrogen and passed over a nickel catalyst at a temperature of 140 °C. For example,

$$CH_3{-}CH_2{-}C{\equiv}N + 2H_2 \longrightarrow CH_3{-}CH_2{-}CH_2{-}NH_2$$

$$\underset{\text{propanenitrile}}{C_2H_5CN} + 2H_2 \rightarrow \underset{\text{propylamine}}{C_2H_5CH_2NH_2}$$

Table 122.1. Examples of amines

Name	*Formula*	*Structure*	*Melting point*/°C	*Boiling point*/°C
Primary amines				
Methylamine	CH_3NH_2		−93.3	−6.2
Ethylamine	$CH_3CH_2NH_2$		−80.9	16.7
2-Aminopropane	$CH_3CHNH_2CH_3$		−95.1	32.6
Phenylamine (aniline)	$C_6H_5NH_2$		−6.2	184.3
Ethane-1,2-diamine	$NH_2CH_2CH_2NH_2$		8	117
Secondary amines				
Dimethylamine	$(CH_3)_2NH$		−92	7
Diethylamine	$(CH_3CH_2)_2NH$		−39	55
N-Methylphenylamine	$C_6H_5NHCH_3$		−57	196
Tertiary amines				
Trimethylamine	$(CH_3)_3N$		−117.2	3
Triethylamine	$(CH_3CH_2)_3N$		−114.6	89.7

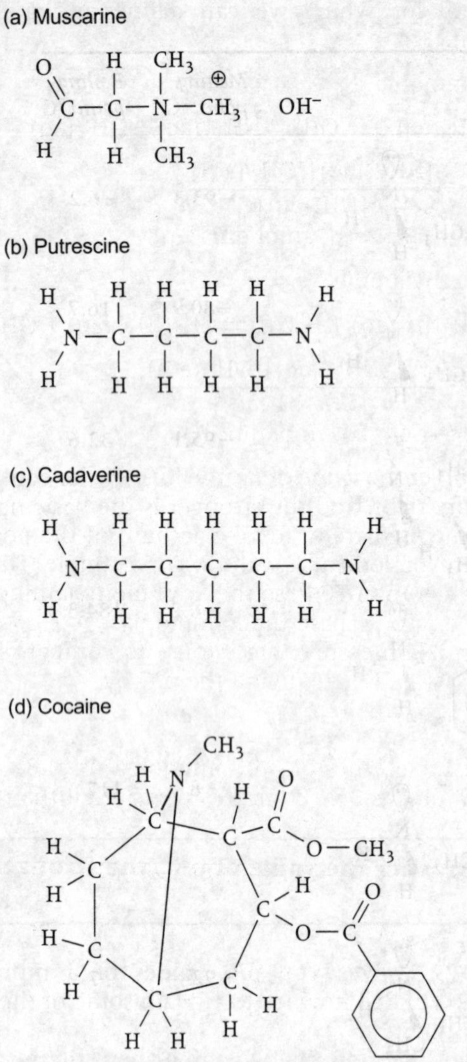

(a) Muscarine

(b) Putrescine

(c) Cadaverine

(d) Cocaine

Figure 122.1 *Four unpleasant amines. (a) Muscarine is a tertiary amine found in some highly poisonous mushrooms. (b) Putrescine (butane-1,4-diamine) has a particularly foul smell – of dead bodies and other decaying animal matter. (c) Cadaverine (pentane-1,5-diamine) competes with putrescine for foulness. It too is associated with corpses (cadavers). (d) Cocaine is an infamous amine that causes immense harm to those who use it*

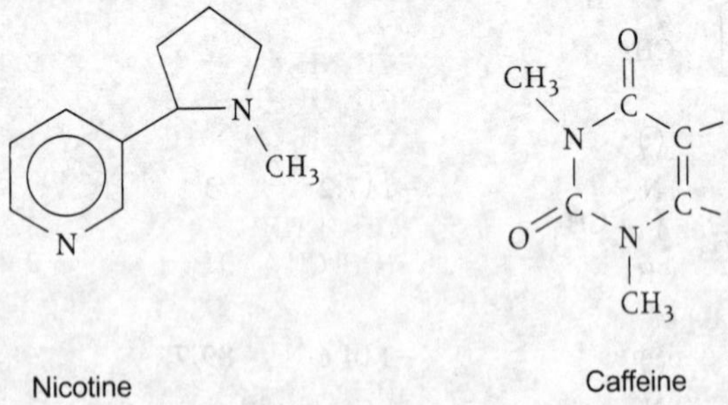

Nicotine

Caffeine

Figure 122.2 *These molecules are related to amines, but have their nitrogen atoms joined in rings with carbon atoms. They are examples of heterocyclic compounds. Both have effects on the nervous system. Nicotine is a dangerous component of tobacco. Caffeine is less dangerous and is found in coffee*

Reduction can also be achieved using sodium in ethanol, or lithium tetrahydridoaluminate(III).

(c) *The Hofmann degradation of amides*

An amide is refluxed with a mixture of bromine and sodium hydroxide solution:

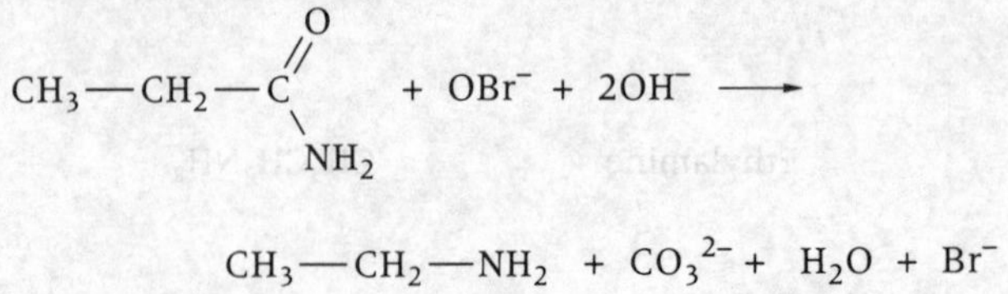

$$CH_3—CH_2—C(=O)NH_2 + OBr^- + 2OH^- \longrightarrow CH_3—CH_2—NH_2 + CO_3^{2-} + H_2O + Br^-$$

$$\underset{\text{propanamide}}{C_2H_5CONH_2} + OBr^- + 2OH^- \rightarrow \underset{\text{ethylamine}}{C_2H_5NH_2} + CO_3^{2-} + H_2O + Br^-$$

(d) *Reduction of a nitro group*

This is a reaction that we have not met before. It is especially useful for making phenylamine, or other aromatic amines, where the amine group is directly bonded to the benzene ring. The aim is to convert a nitro group, $—NO_2$, into the amine group, $—NH_2$. We shall use the change of nitrobenzene into phenylamine as our example. The essence of the method is to reflux nitrobenzene with a few pieces of tin and concentrated hydrochloric acid. The metal and acid give off hydrogen, which performs the reduction. We can write the reactions in a simplified way as follows.

First, the tin reduces the hydrogen ions:

$$Sn + 4H^+ \rightarrow Sn^{4+} + 2H_2$$

While at the same time the hexachlorostannate(IV) complex ion is formed:

$$Sn^{4+} + 6Cl^- \rightarrow SnCl_6^{2-}$$

The nitrobenzene is reduced by the hydrogen:

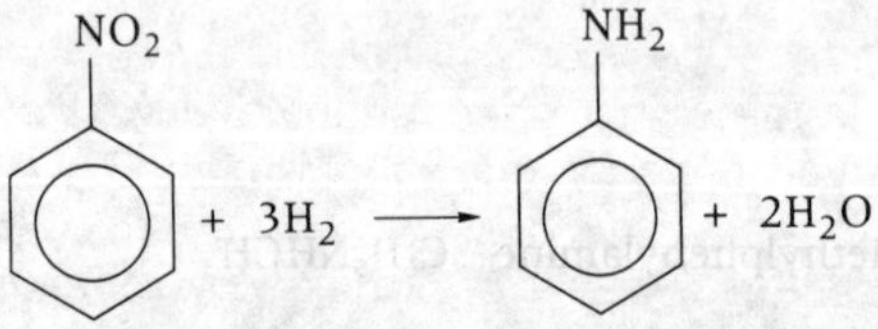

$$C_6H_5NO_2 + 3H_2 \longrightarrow C_6H_5NH_2 + 2H_2O$$

$$C_6H_5NO_2 + 3H_2 \rightarrow C_6H_5NH_2 + 2H_2O$$

Given the melting and boiling points of phenylamine, you might expect to see the product as a liquid. In fact, when the flask cools you would discover that the contents become completely solid. The reason for this is the ease with which amines can act as bases. The nitrogen atom of an amine group has a lone pair of electrons, which can be protonated:

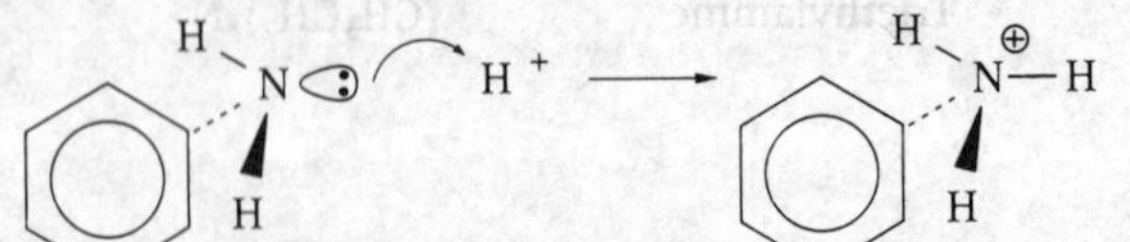

$$C_6H_5NH_2 + H^+ \rightarrow C_6H_5NH_3^+$$

The solid in the flask is an ionic organic salt having the composition $(C_6H_5NH_3^+)_2SnCl_6^{2-}$.

If we want to liberate the phenylamine we need to destroy the solid. The most convenient way is to rip the extra proton from the nitrogen lone pair. We use a concentrated solution of sodium hydroxide to do this:

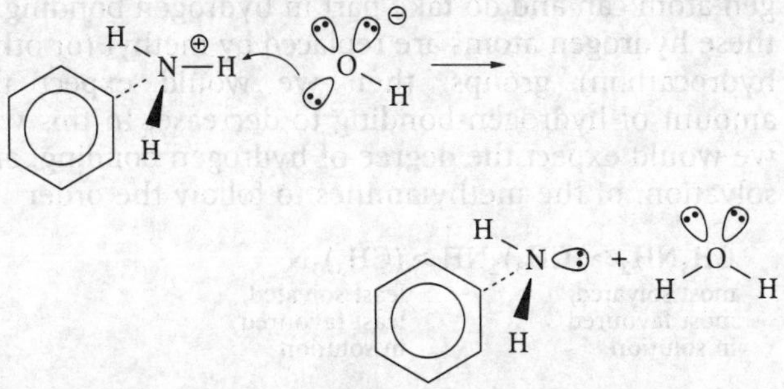

$$C_6H_5NH_3^+ + OH^- \rightarrow C_6H_5NH_2 + H_2O$$

The final stage is to remove the phenylamine from the solution. Owing to the low volatility of phenylamine, steam distillation is used. The presence of the steam has two effects. First, it lowers the temperature at which the phenylamine will distil over; and secondly, it helps to heat the mixture. (You might like to look at section 63.5 to remind yourself about the principles involved in steam distillation.) After some purification, the distillate yields pure phenylamine. *Warning*: phenylamine is extremely poisonous.

122.1 (i) Apart from its use in making amines, what is the importance of the Hofmann degradation reaction?

(ii) If you were to make phenylamine using a Hofmann degradation, what would be your organic starting material?

122.2 Imagine that you could not obtain a supply of nitrobenzene in order to make phenylamine. How would you convert benzene into nitrobenzene?

122.3 Suggest a way of making (phenylmethyl)amine, $C_6H_5CH_2NH_2$, starting from methylbenzene, $C_6H_5CH_3$.

122.3 Amines are bases

You might remember that the Lewis theory claims that acids are electron pair acceptors, and bases are electron pair donors. With its lone pair of electrons on the nitrogen atom, an amine can behave as a Lewis base. The simplest reaction that shows us this property is that, like ammonia, some amines are very soluble in water. For example, methylamine, ethylamine and propylamine are all very soluble. When they dissolve, an equilibrium is set up for which we can define an equilibrium constant.

(i) Ammonia

$$NH_3(aq) + H_2O(l) \rightleftharpoons NH_4^+(aq) + OH^-(aq)$$

$$K_b = \frac{[NH_4^+(aq)][OH^-(aq)]}{[NH_3(aq)]} = 1.75 \times 10^{-5}\,\text{mol dm}^{-3}$$

(ii) Methylamine

$$CH_3NH_2(aq) + H_2O(l) \rightleftharpoons CH_3NH_3^+(aq) + OH^-(aq)$$

$$K_b = \frac{[CH_3NH_3^+(aq)][OH^-(aq)]}{[CH_3NH_2(aq)]} = 4.4 \times 10^{-4}\,\text{mol dm}^{-3}$$

The larger the value of K_b, the further the equilibrium lies to the right, and the stronger is the basic nature of the amine. Be careful to take account of the powers of 10 when you look at K_b values. For example, 10^{-4} is 10 times larger than 10^{-5}, so the K_b of methylamine shows it to be a *stronger* base than ammonia.

A sensible measure that we use to compare bases is their pK_b values. We define the pK_b by

$$pK_b = -\lg K_b$$

For example, the pK_b of ammonia is 4.8, and of methylamine is 3.4. From this we can tell that:

The smaller the value of pK_b, the stronger the base.

Table 122.2 gives you pK_b values of a number of amines. We shall now try to explain some of the trends in the values.

Perhaps the most obvious thing about these values is that the aromatic amines are much weaker bases than the others. Also, they show us that secondary amines

Table 122.2. Amines and their pK_b values

Amine	*Formula*	pK_b
(Ammonia)	(NH_3)	(4.8)
Primary amines		
Methylamine	CH_3NH_2	3.4
Ethylamine	$CH_3CH_2NH_2$	3.3
Propylamine	$CH_3CH_2CH_2NH_2$	3.4
Secondary amines		
Dimethylamine	$(CH_3)_2NH$	3.3
Diethylamine	$(CH_3CH_2)_2NH$	3.0
Tertiary amines		
Trimethylamine	$(CH_3)_3N$	4.2
Triethylamine	$(CH_3CH_2)_3N$	3.1
Aromatic amines		
Phenylamine	$C_6H_5NH_2$	9.4
N-Methylphenylamine	$C_6H_5NHCH_3$	9.2
N-Phenylphenylamine	$(C_6H_5)_2NH$	13.2

tend to be stronger bases than primary amines. However, this trend does not continue with the tertiary amines. They are weaker than, or little different to, secondary amines.

There are three factors that we must take into account if we are to explain these observations. We would expect the base strength to increase:

(i) if the lone pair is more available for protonation;

(ii) if the protonated positive ion is energetically favoured by delocalisation of charge;

(iii) if the positive ion is readily solvated by the surrounding water molecules.

Likewise, the opposites of these three factors should reduce the base strength. Let us look at the differences between the non-aromatic amines first.

(a) *Why are secondary amines more basic than primary amines?*

We know that methyl groups give a positive inductive effect. That is, they are able to act as sources of electron density. How we use this idea to explain why, for example, dimethylamine is a stronger base than methylamine, depends on your point of view. We can say that the extra methyl group feeds electron density towards the nitrogen atom, and this in turn results in a lone pair that is a richer source of electron density. Alternatively (or as well), we can concentrate on the nature of the protonated ion and say that, by feeding electron density to the nitrogen atom, the extra positive charge is spread further over the entire molecule (Figure 122.3). By now you will recognise that this would lead to a more energetically favourable situation.

On this basis we would predict the order of base strength to be

$$(CH_3)_3N > (CH_3)_2NH > CH_3NH_2$$

most basic — least basic

Of course, if this were all there were to explaining relative base strengths, we would predict that trimethylamine would be a stronger base than dimethylamine; but it is not. Here we shall turn to the business of solvation that we mentioned under (iii) above. As a general rule, the greater the amount of hydrocarbon in a molecule, the less soluble it is in water; which is another way of saying that hydrocarbon groups cannot be solvated efficiently by water. Especially, hydrogen atoms directly bonded to carbon atoms are insufficiently polar to take part in hydrogen bonding. However, the hydrogen atoms attached to a nitrogen atom can and do take part in hydrogen bonding. If these hydrogen atoms are replaced by methyl (or other hydrocarbon) groups, then we would expect the amount of hydrogen bonding to decrease. In this way we would expect the degree of hydrogen bonding, and solvation, of the methylamines to follow the order

$$CH_3NH_2 > (CH_3)_2NH > (CH_3)_3N$$

most solvated, most favoured in solution — least solvated, least favoured in solution

As a result, the base strength should follow the order

$$CH_3NH_2 > (CH_3)_2NH > (CH_3)_3N$$

most basic — least basic

Clearly we have a problem. Our two predictions of the order of base strength are opposite to one another. Faced with this situation, we turn to the experimental results, which tell us that

$$(CH_3)_2NH > CH_3NH_2 > (CH_3)_3N$$

most basic — least basic

The most we can say is that it looks as if the positive inductive effect is more important than solvation until there is too large a proportion of hydrocarbon in the molecule. The change-over comes with tertiary amines.

Note that the order of the base strengths depends on the solvent: in non-aqueous solvents, trimethylamine can be a stronger base than the other two.

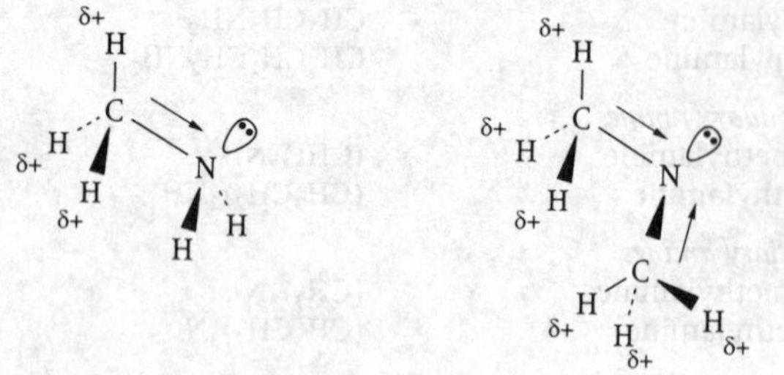

Figure 122.3 *Methyl groups can feed in electron density to the nitrogen atom in an amine. (Another way of saying this is that methyl groups are polarisable). The hydrogen atoms in the methyl groups take on a slight positive charge, δ+*

(b) *Amines dissolve in acids*

Normally amines dissolve easily in strong acids like hydrochloric acid. This is because the lone pair becomes protonated, turning the amine into a positively charged ion. The ion can be solvated by water molecules in the same way as many other similar ions:

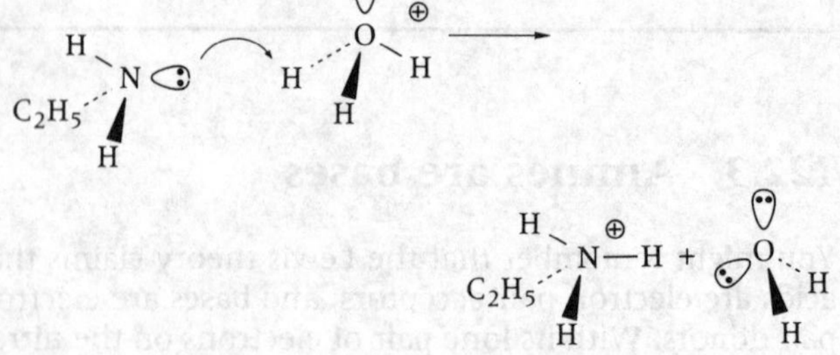

$$C_2H_5NH_2 + H_3O^+ \rightarrow C_2H_5NH_3^+ + H_2O$$

or

$$C_2H_5NH_2 + H^+ \rightarrow C_2H_5NH_3^+$$

122.4 Why are hydrogen atoms bonded to a nitrogen atom able to take part in hydrogen bonding with water molecules?

122.5 Imagine that you have a flask containing ethylamine dissolved in hydrochloric acid. If you carefully evaporated the solution, you would be left with a white solid.

(i) What would be its formula?

(ii) What would happen if you heated a few crystals of the solid with sodium hydroxide solution?

(iii) Write an equation for the reaction.

122.4 Amines react with halogenoalkanes

In section 122.2 we saw that, under pressure, halogenoalkanes will react with ammonia in a solution with alcohol. Owing to its lone pair of electrons, an ammonia molecule can act as a nucleophile. It will attack the carbon atom to which the halogen atom is attached:

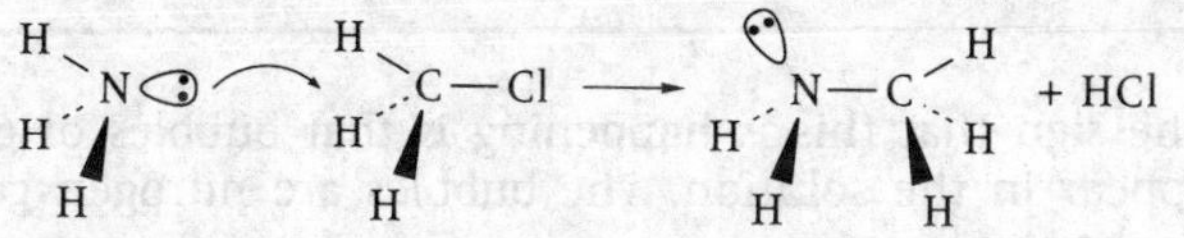

$$NH_3 + CH_3Cl \rightarrow CH_3NH_2 + HCl$$

Given that amines are similar to ammonia, we should expect them to behave as nucleophiles as well. They do:

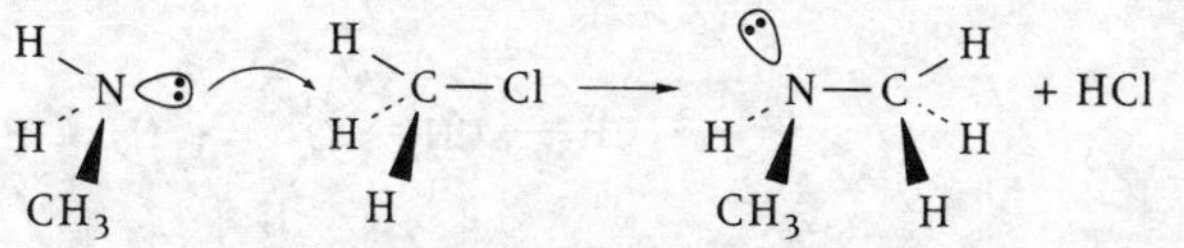

$$\underset{\text{methylamine}}{CH_3NH_2} + CH_3Cl \rightarrow \underset{\text{dimethylamine}}{(CH_3)_2NH} + HCl$$

Here we have an example of a primary amine (methylamine) reacting with a halogenoalkane to give a secondary amine (dimethylamine).

However, with the lone pair intact, the secondary amine can react further to give a tertiary amine:

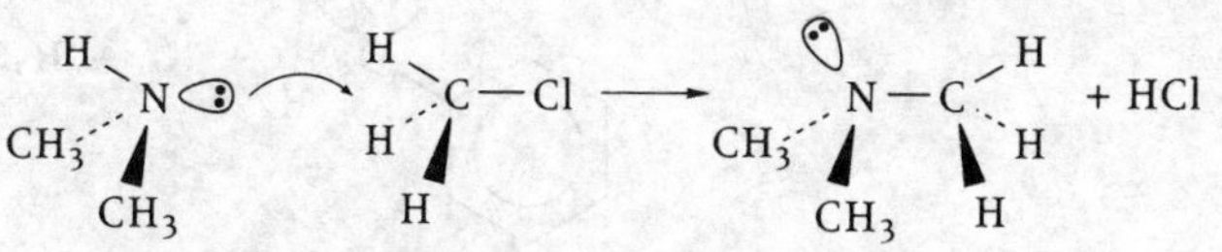

$$(CH_3)_2NH + CH_3Cl \rightarrow \underset{\text{trimethylamine}}{(CH_3)_3N} + HCl$$

Likewise, a *quaternary* amine can be produced, although it is to be found as an ionic salt:

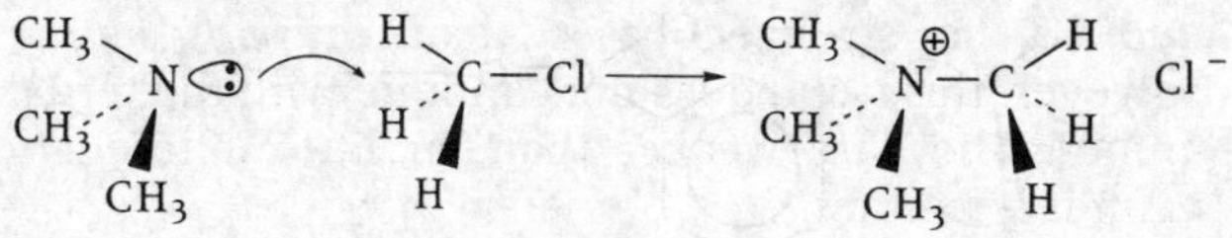

$$(CH_3)_3N + CH_3Cl \rightarrow \underset{\text{tetramethylammonium chloride}}{(CH_3)_4N^+Cl^-}$$

If an amine has a methyl group added to it, we say that the amine has been *methylated*. Methylation reactions have been used to give information about the structures of organic compounds. Try question 122.16 later if you would like to see how this is done.

122.6 What would you expect to see if you bubbled methylamine through a solution of copper(II) sulphate? (Hint: see section 105.3.)

122.7 What is the connection between the reaction of amines with halogenoalkanes and the Lewis theory of acids and bases?

122.8 Suppose tetramethylammonium chloride, or another quaternary ammonium salt, is dissolved in water. What, if anything, would happen if you were to add silver nitrate solution?

122.5 The acetylation and benzoylation of amines

In Unit 120 we found that ethanoyl and benzoyl chloride are very reactive. They have a carbon atom that is ripe for nucleophilic attack and, as we have seen, amines can act as nucleophiles. The effect of the reaction is that the amine group is acetylated, or benzoylated, as the case may be:

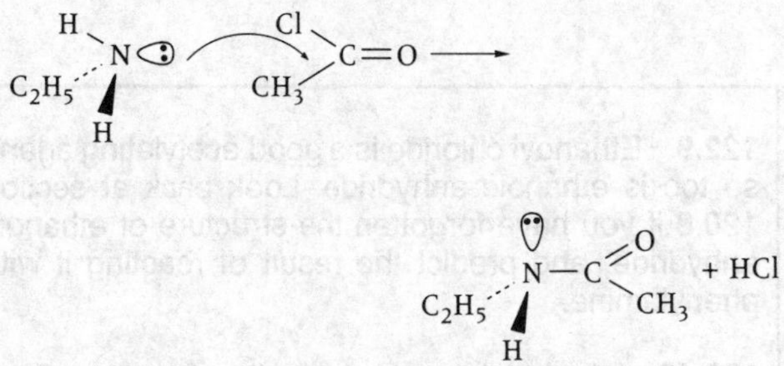

$$\underset{\text{ethylamine}}{C_2H_5NH_2} + \underset{\text{ethanoyl chloride}}{CH_3COCl} \rightarrow \underset{N\text{-ethylethanamide}}{C_2H_5NHCOCH_3} + HCl$$

$$CH_3NH_2 + C_6H_5COCl \rightarrow CH_3NHCOC_6H_5 + HCl$$

methyl-amine; benzoyl chloride; *N*-methylbenzamide

A variation on this type of reaction is known as the *Schotten–Baumann* reaction. Between 1884 and 1886 Carl Schotten and Eugen Baumann investigated the reaction that has made their names famous. It involves the reaction between benzoyl chloride and phenylamine in the presence of sodium hydroxide. The alkali enhances the reaction, perhaps by removing hydrogen ions that would otherwise protonate the nitrogen on the phenylamine and prevent the reaction taking place:

$$C_6H_5NH_2 + C_6H_5COCl + OH^- \rightarrow C_6H_5NHCOC_6H_5 + H_2O + Cl^-$$

In fact the Schotten–Baumann reaction can be done with other aromatic amines and aromatic acid chlorides. The same name is given to the reaction of benzoyl chloride with phenol in the presence of alkali.

122.9 Ethanoyl chloride is a good acetylating agent; so too is ethanoic anhydride. Look back at section 120.3 if you have forgotten the structure of ethanoic anhydride, and predict the result of reacting it with phenylamine.

122.10 What will be made in the Schotten–Baumann reaction if phenol and benzoyl chloride are mixed in a solution of sodium hydroxide?

122.6 Reactions with nitrous acid at ordinary temperatures

Nitrous acid, HNO_2, is easy to make; but it decomposes easily as well. You can make the acid by dissolving sodium nitrite in iced water, and adding ice cold dilute hydrochloric acid to the solution. You should see a rather fine pale blue colour appear. However, be careful about this reaction. Nitrites are known carcinogens, so you should avoid contact with sodium nitrite or its solutions. Likewise, without permission from your teacher or lecturer, you should not attempt the reactions that we shall meet in this section. In any event it is best to wear protective gloves, and eye protection of course.

Essentially there are two things that can happen when an amine reacts with nitrous acid; either the amine changes into an alcohol (which is not of much use), or it does something far more interesting. It is the temperature that determines which of the two alternatives takes place. In this section we shall deal with the first possibility.

(a) *At temperatures above 5 °C*

Primary aliphatic amines and phenylamine are converted into alcohols.

The sign that this is happening is that bubbles of gas appear in the solution. The bubbles are nitrogen gas. For example,

$$CH_3-CH_2-NH_2 + HNO_2 \rightarrow CH_3-CH_2-OH + N_2 + H_2O$$

$$C_2H_5NH_2 + HNO_2 \xrightarrow{T>5\,°C} C_2H_5OH + N_2 + H_2O$$

ethylamine; ethanol

$$C_6H_5NH_2 + HNO_2 \xrightarrow{T>5\,°C} C_6H_5OH + N_2 + H_2O$$

phenylamine; phenol

The intermediate in these reactions is a *diazonium ion*. You can spot a diazonium ion in an equation owing to it having an $—N_2^+$ group in place of the $-NH_2$ group. The formula N_2^+ is a shorthand for $—N^+{\equiv}N$. It is this ion which is destroyed as the temperature increases much above 5 °C. First we have

$$C_6H_5NH_2 + HNO_2 + H^+ \longrightarrow C_6H_5N{\equiv}N^+ + 2H_2O$$

$$\underset{\text{a diazonium ion}}{C_6H_5NH_2 + HNO_2 + H^+ \rightarrow C_6H_5N_2^+ + 2H_2O}$$

which is followed by

$$C_6H_5N_2^+ + H_2O \longrightarrow C_6H_5OH + N_2 + H^+$$

$$C_6H_5N_2^+ + H_2O \xrightarrow{T>5\,°C} C_6H_5OH + N_2 + H^+$$

Actually diazonium ions can decompose in other ways; but the change into an alcohol is often the main reaction.

Secondary amines perform a different reaction. They turn into *nitrosoamines*, but no nitrogen is given off. For example,

$$\underset{\text{diethylamine}}{(C_2H_5)_2NH} + HNO_2 \rightarrow \underset{N\text{-nitrosodiethylamine}}{(C_2H_5)_2N—N{=}O} + H_2O$$

Nitrosoamines are oily liquids, often with a distinct colour, and are dangerous carcinogens.

Tertiary amines do not react with nitrous acid.

> **122.11** What will be the effect of reacting (phenylmethyl)amine, $C_6H_5CH_2NH_2$, with nitrous acid at 10 °C?

122.7 Substitution reactions of diazonium ions

Here we will assume that by a judicious use of ice we manage to keep the temperature of the nitrous acid and amine mixture below 5 °C. This will ensure that the diazonium ions remain intact for many minutes. In practice it is the diazonium ions made from amine groups directly attached to a benzene ring that perform useful reactions, so we shall concentrate on them. Aliphatic diazonium ions, e.g. $C_2H_5N_2^+$, decompose almost as soon as they are made.

(a) *Substitution reactions*

If you think back to the equation that we wrote for phenylamine being converted into phenol, you should be able to persuade yourself that we could call this a substitution reaction. An OH group has been substituted for the N_2^+ group. A wide variety of other substitutions can be achieved just as easily. For example, in the *Sandmeyer reaction* we add cold potassium iodide solution to the benzenediazonium ion solution obtained from phenylamine and nitrous acid. An iodine atom replaces the N_2^+ group:

$$C_6H_5N_2^+ + I^- \longrightarrow C_6H_5I + N_2$$

$$\underset{\text{benzenediazonium ion}}{C_6H_5N_2^+} + I^- \xrightarrow{T<5\,°C} \underset{\text{iodobenzene}}{C_6H_5I} + N_2$$

This way of introducing an iodine atom on to a benzene ring was invented by Traugott Sandmeyer. Between 1884 and 1890 he also discovered methods for making chloro- and bromobenzenes. Here are other Sandmeyer reactions.

To make *chlorobenzene* the recipe is to mix copper(I) chloride and concentrated hydrochloric acid with the benzenediazonium ion solution:

$$C_6H_5N_2^+ + Cl^- \longrightarrow C_6H_5Cl + N_2$$

$$C_6H_5N_2^+ + Cl^- \xrightarrow{Cu_2Cl_2/HCl} \underset{\text{chlorobenzene}}{C_6H_5Cl} + N_2$$

To make bromobenzene, copper(I) bromide and hydrobromic acid are used.

Chlorobenzene can be made by a similar reaction, invented by Ludwig Gatterman. In the *Gatterman reaction*, copper powder is added to a solution of the benzenediazonium ion in hydrochloric acid. Chlorobenzene is made directly.

Nitriles can be made by substituting a cyanide, CN, group for the N_2^+ ion. The benzenediazonium ion solution is reacted with copper(I) cyanide:

$$C_6H_5N_2^+ + CN^- \longrightarrow C_6H_5CN + N_2$$

$$C_6H_5N_2^+ + CN^- \rightarrow \underset{\text{benzonitrile}}{C_6H_5CN} + N_2$$

One of the reasons why this reaction is important is that it provides a way of introducing an acid group on to a benzene ring. The acid is made in the usual way by acid or alkaline hydrolysis of the nitrile.

122.12 Suggest a method of making benzoic acid: (i) starting with phenylamine, (ii) starting with benzene.

122.8 Coupling reactions of benzenediazonium ions

Aromatic diazonium ions like the benzenediazonium ion are poor electrophiles. They will attack a benzene ring that has an activating group on the ring (see Unit 113). Phenol is one of the simplest examples. To carry out the reaction you would dissolve phenol in sodium hydroxide solution, cool it, and then add the benzenediazonium ion solution a little at a time. The reaction is immediate and you would see a strong yellow colour appear. This is caused by a precipitate of (4-hydroxyphenyl)azobenzene:

$$C_6H_5N_2^+ + C_6H_5O^- \rightarrow C_6H_5-N{=}N-C_6H_4-OH$$

$$\underset{}{C_6H_5N_2^+} + \underset{\text{phenate ion}}{C_6H_5O^-} \rightarrow \underset{\text{(4-hydroxyphenyl)azobenzene}}{C_6H_5N_2C_6H_5OH}$$

A compound that has *azobenzene* as part of its name is based on the structure:

$C_6H_5-N{=}N-C_6H_5$
phenylazobenzene

$C_6H_5-\underbrace{N{=}N}_{\text{chromophore}}-C_6H_5$

Electrons belonging to the two nitrogen atoms can interact with the π clouds on the two benzene rings. This causes delocalisation of the electrons and leads to a change in the energy levels available to them. It so happens that the energy gap between some of the levels is low enough that visible light can cause electrons to transfer between them. The double bonded nitrogen atoms are largely responsible for giving the azobenzenes their colours. A group like —N=N— is called a *chromophore*. Phenylazobenzene itself is a vivid orange-red.

A similar reaction takes place with naphthalen-2-ol, a naphthalene molecule with an OH group on it:

$$C_{10}H_7OH + C_6H_5N_2^+ \rightarrow C_6H_5-N{=}N-C_{10}H_6OH + H^+$$

The product is a red solid.

When a benzenediazonium ion reacts with phenylamine, a somewhat different reaction takes place. Instead of attacking the ring, the ion bonds to the nitrogen atom of phenylamine and a yellow solid is made:

$$C_6H_5-N_2^+ + H_2N-C_6H_5 \rightarrow C_6H_5-N{=}N-N(H)-C_6H_5 + H^+$$

$$C_6H_5N_2^+ + C_6H_5NH_2 \rightarrow C_6H_5-N{=}N-NH-C_6H_5 + H^+$$

There are two main uses for the highly coloured substances made when benzenediazonium ions couple with aromatic molecules. We can use them as dyes or, sometimes, as indicators in acid–base titrations.

(a) *Dyes*

The dyeing industry has a long and, in some respects, unpleasant history. In Britain, much of the wealth of the country during the nineteenth century was built on the trade in cotton and woollen goods. The skills developed in the manufacture of dyes, and the methods used to dye clothes and other articles, played a large part in the success of the cotton and wool industries.

Unfortunately, the workers in the dye factories were exposed to contact with the dyes, many of which are now known to be strongly carcinogenic. A large number of workers died from the effects of handling the dyes. Owing to the dangers involved, you should *not* attempt to carry out dye-making reactions.

Some of the most effective dyes are based on the molecule called anthraquinone (Figure 122.4). The colours of the dyes depend on the groups attached to the parent molecule. Sometimes they can have extremely complicated structures.

The manufacture and use of dyes pose some interesting problems for chemists. In the first place, we have to discover how to build molecules providing the colour we want. However, not only must the colour be right, it must be resistant to fading, e.g. by being left in sunlight

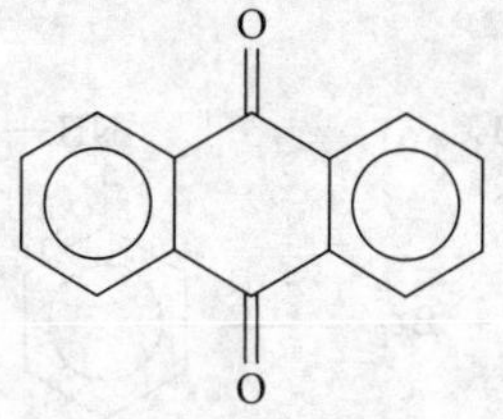

A single molecule of anthraquinone

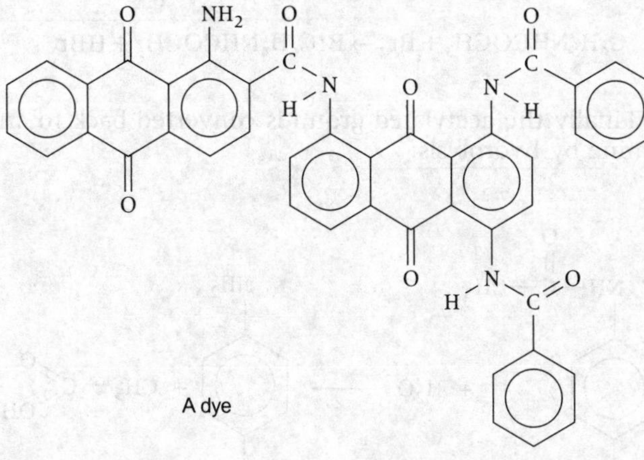

A dye

***Figure 122.4** An example of a dye based on anthraquinone*

or by frequent washing. Even if we solve these problems, there is still the problem of getting the dye to stick permanently to the fabric. This is no easy task because there is such a wide range of fabrics available now, ranging from cotton or wool through to artificial fibres like Nylon.

Essentially there are two ways of encouraging a dye to be permanent. Either you trap dye molecules between the strands of the fibres (the *diffusion* method), or you rely on attraction between ionic groups on the fibres and the dye molecules (the *affinity* method).

Some dyes are used to colour foodstuffs (Table 122.3).

(b) *Indicators*

A good acid–base indicator will change its colour as the concentration of hydrogen ions in a solution changes. Often an indicator will have one or more atoms that can gain or lose protons. For example, methyl orange is an azo dye that is yellow in alkali and red in acid. The arrangement of the electrons is upset by the arrival or departure of a proton on one of the nitrogen atoms, so the energy levels change and the colour changes:

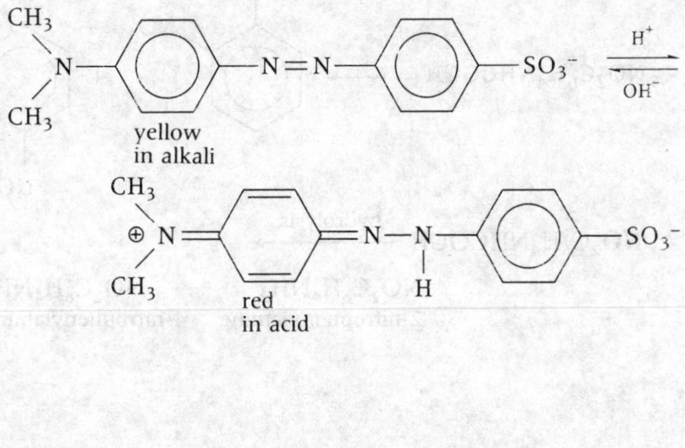

$$(CH_3)_2N-C_6H_4-N{=}N-C_6H_4-SO_3^- \underset{OH^-}{\overset{H^+}{\rightleftharpoons}} (CH_3)_2\overset{\oplus}{N}{=}C_6H_4{=}N-N(H)-C_6H_4-SO_3^-$$

yellow in alkali

red in acid

Table 122.3. Dyes commonly used in foods*

Tartrazine (orange-yellow)

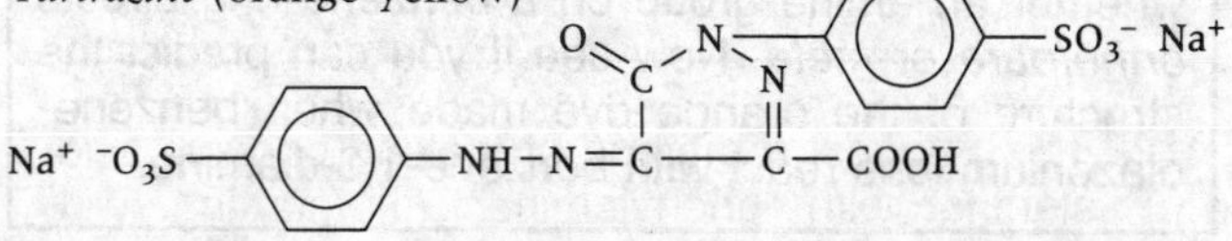

Uses: fizzy drinks, custard powder, chewing gum, jellies, ice lollies
E number 102

Sunset yellow FCF

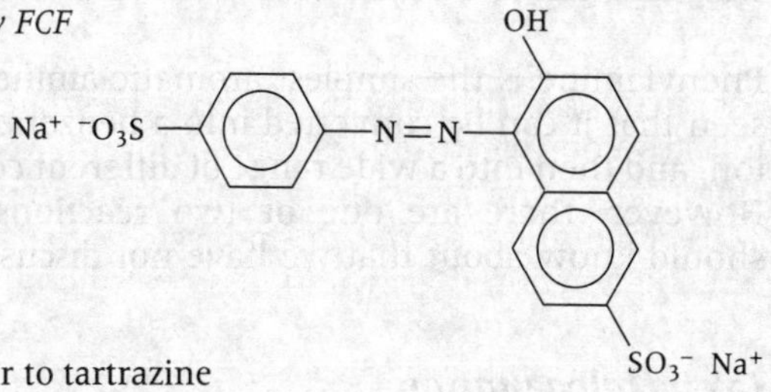

Uses: similar to tartrazine
E number 110

Ponceau (red)

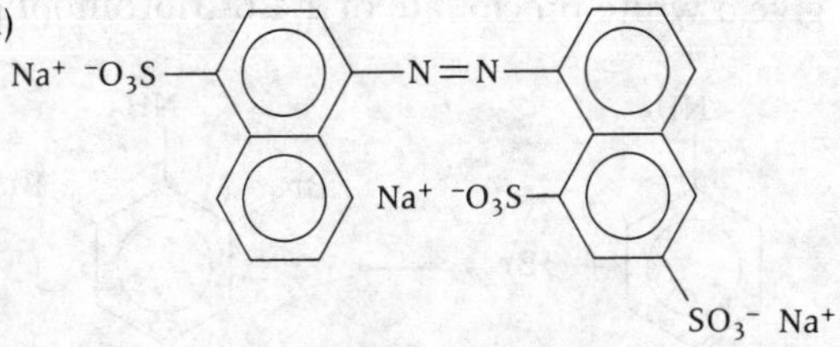

Uses: tinned fruit (e.g. cherries, strawberries), cake mixes
E number 124

Acid brilliant green

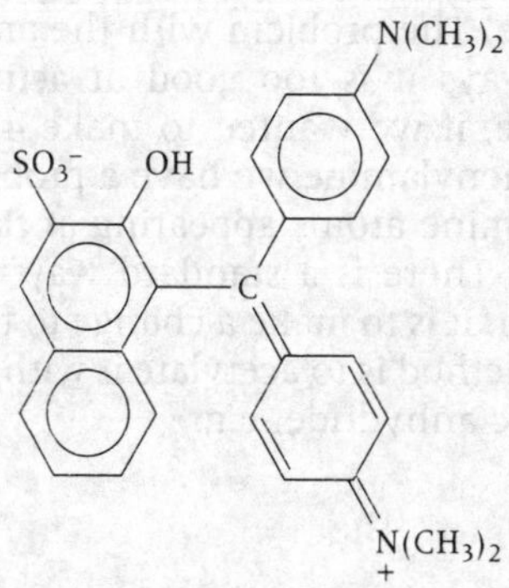

Uses: tinned peas
E number 142

*The use of azo dyes in foods has been blamed for hyperactivity in young children, and other medical problems. Absolute proof that they have harmful effects is hard to establish. This may be because they have no such effects. Alternatively only some individuals may be sensitive to them. The E number is an agreed code given to food additives by a number of countries. The additives and their codes should be shown on the packet or tin

122.13 Look back to Unit 113 to remind yourself whether an amine group on a benzene ring directs *ortho/para* or *meta*. Now see if you can predict the structure of the orange dye made when benzenediazonium ions react with benzene-1,3-diamine.

122.9 Some reactions of phenylamine and other aromatic amines

Phenylamine is the simplest aromatic amine. We have seen that it can be converted into a benzenediazonium ion, and then into a wide range of different compounds. However, there are one or two reactions that you should know about that we have not discussed yet.

(a) *Halogenation*

The first is a reaction that shows that the amine group activates a benzene ring.

With bromine, phenylamine reacts very quickly to give a white precipitate of 2,4,6-tribromophenylamine:

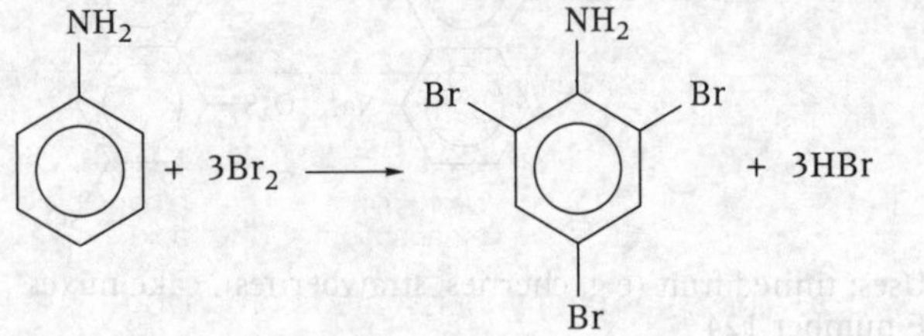

$$C_6H_5NH_2 + 3Br_2 \rightarrow C_6H_2Br_3NH_2 + 3HBr$$

This reaction is similar to that between phenol and bromine. The problem with the amine group is that in some ways it is too good at activating the ring. For example, if we wanted to make 4-bromophenylamine from phenylamine we have a problem. We cannot stop the bromine atoms appearing at the *ortho* (2) positions as well. There is a standard way of getting round the problem. It is to make a change to the amine group. The usual method is to acetylate it with ethanoyl chloride or ethanoic anhydride, e.g.

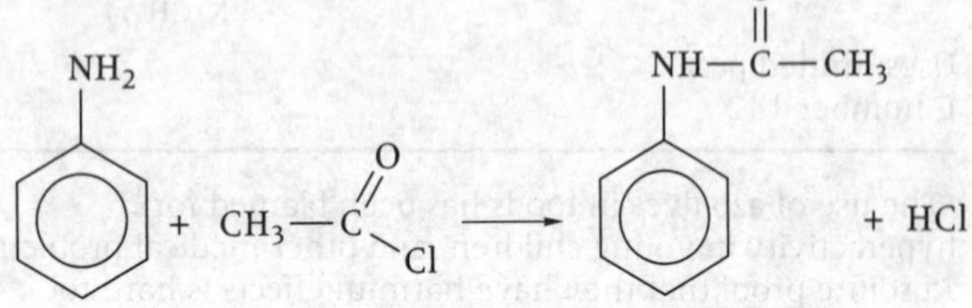

$$C_6H_5NH_2 + CH_3COCl \rightarrow C_6H_5NHCOCH_3 + HCl$$

When bromine is added (usually in a solution with ethanoic acid), the *para* position only is attacked:

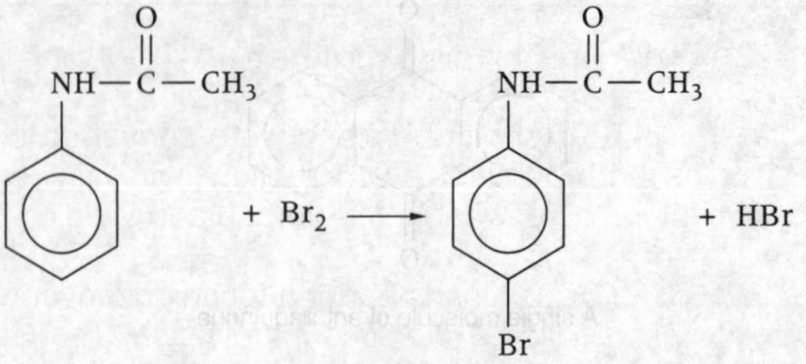

$$C_6H_5NHCOCH_3 + Br_2 \rightarrow BrC_6H_4NHCOCH_3 + HBr$$

Finally the acetylated group is converted back to an amine by hydrolysis:

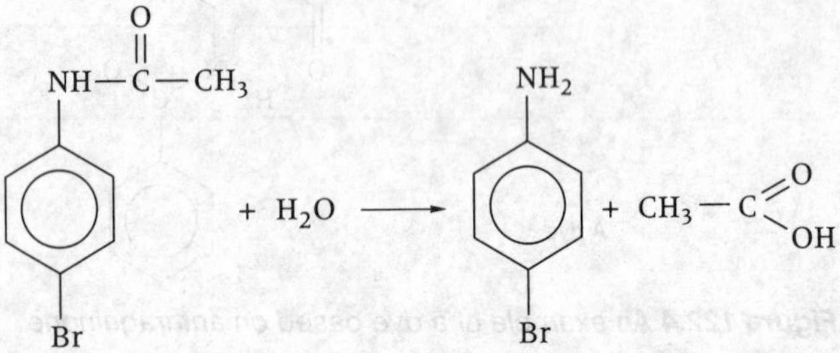

$$BrC_6H_4NHCOCH_3 + H_2O \rightarrow BrC_6H_4NH_2 + CH_3COOH$$

(b) *Nitration*

Acetylation of the amino group is also used in the nitration of phenylamine. Nitrating mixture will convert phenylamine into a mixture of nitro products. These include a lot of 3-nitrophenylamine, which is made because the NH_2 group is protonated by the acid; the resulting NH_3^+ group directs *meta* (3 position). Also, the phenylamine is oxidised to a nasty collection of oily and tarry products. In short, the reaction is best avoided. If we acetylate the amine group first, the ring is no longer so reactive and it is less prone to oxidation. Acetylation *protects* phenylamine from oxidation. A mixture of 2-nitrophenylamine and 4-nitrophenylamine is produced after hydrolysis:

$$C_6H_5NHCOCH_3 \xrightarrow{\text{nitration}} NO_2C_6H_4NHCOCH_3$$

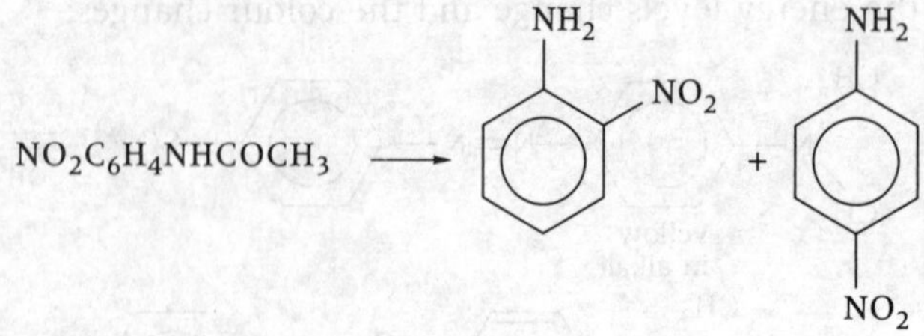

$$NO_2C_6H_4NHCOCH_3 \xrightarrow{\text{hydrolysis}} \underset{\text{2-nitrophenylamine}}{NO_2C_6H_4NH_2} + \underset{\text{4-nitrophenylamine}}{NO_2C_6H_4NH_2}$$

122.14 What is nitrating mixture?

122.15 If 25 g of nitrobenzene were converted into 15 g of phenylamine by reduction with tin and hydrochloric acid, what is the percentage yield?

122.16 This question is about a technique invented by Hofmann called *exhaustive methylation*. The idea is that the methylation of amines follows the pattern:

$$\text{primary amine} \xrightarrow{1} \text{secondary amine} \xrightarrow{2} \text{tertiary amine} \xrightarrow{3} \text{quaternary amine}$$

In each of the three stages, 1 mol of the amine would react with 1 mol of chloromethane. For example, 1 mol of ethylamine reacted with chloromethane and completely converted to its quaternary salt would use up 3 mol of chloromethane:

$$CH_3CH_2NH_2 + 3CH_3Cl \rightarrow CH_3CH_2N(CH_3)_3{}^+Cl^- + 2HCl$$

Now see if you can answer these questions.

(i) One mole of an amine of formula C_4H_9N was found to react with 2 mol of chloromethane. Was the amine primary, secondary or tertiary?

(ii) The amine did not react with bromine. What does this tell you about the bonding between the carbon atoms?

(iii) Try to discover a structure for the amine that fits the information.

Answers

122.1 (i) The Hofmann degradation decreases the number of carbon atoms in a molecule.

(ii) Benzamide, $C_6H_5CONH_2$.

122.2 React benzene with nitrating mixture.

122.3 First, pass chlorine through methylbenzene in the presence of ultraviolet light until sufficient (chloromethyl)benzene is made:

$$C_6H_5CH_3 + Cl_2 \rightarrow C_6H_5CH_2Cl + HCl$$

After separation, react this with an alcoholic solution of ammonia under pressure:

$$C_6H_5CH_2Cl + NH_3 \rightarrow C_6H_5CH_2NH_2 + HCl$$

122.4 A nitrogen atom is sufficiently electronegative to draw electron density away from a hydrogen atom. This leaves the hydrogen atom with a slight positive charge, which is able to hydrogen bond with a lone pair on the oxygen atom in a water molecule.

122.5 (i) A white ionic solid, $CH_3CH_2NH_3{}^+Cl^-$, would be left. We can call it ethylamine hydrochloride. You may find that amines are stored in the laboratory in the form of salts.

(ii) The amine is released when it is heated with an alkali. In this case ethylamine would be given off. This is equivalent to the reaction of ammonium salts giving off ammonia with alkali.

(iii) $C_2H_5NH_3{}^+ + OH^- \rightarrow C_2H_5NH_2 + H_2O$

122.6 The blue solution should become a much deeper blue. Amines can act as ligands. They give a deep blue colour similar to that found when ammonia is added to a solution of copper(II) ions.

122.7 According to the Lewis theory, acids are electron pair acceptors and bases are electron pair donors. With the lone pair on the nitrogen atom, amines are electron pair donors. That is, they are Lewis bases. If we wanted, we could classify many nucleophiles as Lewis bases.

122.8 The quaternary salt is ionic and when it dissolves the component ions are free to move through the water. The chloride and silver ions will give a white precipitate of silver chloride.

122.9 In the reaction with ethanoic anhydride, ethanoic acid is one of the products:

$$\underset{\text{ethanoic anhydride}}{(CH_3CO)_2O} + \underset{\text{phenylamine}}{C_6H_5NH_2} \rightarrow \underset{N\text{-phenylethanamide}}{C_6H_5NHCOCH_3} + \underset{\text{ethanoic acid}}{CH_3COOH}$$

122.10 The ester phenyl benzoate is produced:

C_6H_5–C(=O)–O–C_6H_5

The reaction is:

$$C_6H_5COCl + C_6H_5OH \rightarrow C_6H_5COOC_6H_5 + HCl$$

122.11 Phenylmethanol is made, with nitrogen given off:

$$C_6H_5CH_2NH_2 + HNO_2 \rightarrow C_6H_5CH_2OH + N_2 + H_2O$$

122.12 (i) The route is as follows:

$$C_6H_5NH_2 \xrightarrow{\text{diazotise}} C_6H_5N_2{}^+ \xrightarrow{\text{KCN}} C_6H_5CN \xrightarrow{\text{hydrolysis}} C_6H_5COOH$$

(ii) There are several methods. We could convert benzene into phenylamine and then proceed as in (i):

$$C_6H_6 \xrightarrow{\text{nitration}} C_6H_5NO_2 \xrightarrow{\text{Sn/conc. HCl}} C_6H_5NH_2$$

Alternatively, benzene could be converted into methylbenzene by a Friedel–Crafts reaction (chloromethane plus aluminium trichloride), followed by oxidation of the

Answers – contd.

methyl side chain with alkaline potassium manganate(VII).

122.13 Amine groups activate a benzene ring and they direct *ortho* and *para*. With the two amine groups in the 1,3 positions, the best position for the benzenediazonium ion to attack is *para* to one of them and *ortho* to the other. The orientation is also influenced by steric hindrance. The dye has the structure:

—N=N— —NH_2

NH_2

122.14 A mixture of concentrated sulphuric and nitric acids.

122.15 One mole of $C_6H_5NO_2$, 123 g, should give 1 mol of $C_6H_5NH_2$, 93 g. Thus 25 g of nitrobenzene should give 93 g × 25 g/123 g = 18.9 g. The percentage yield is 15 g/18.9 g × 100% = 79%.

122.16 (i) It is a secondary amine.

(ii) There are no double or triple bonds.

(iii) The structure is a five-membered ring called pyrrolidine

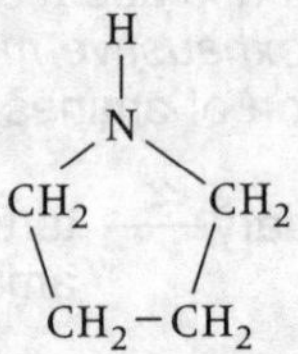

Actually we have only covered one part of Hofmann's method. The quaternary amine produced at the end of the experiment is heated. This breaks it apart, and the products can be analysed. The nature of the products gives extra information about the structure of the original amine.

UNIT 122 SUMMARY

- Amines:
  (i) Have one or more NH_2 groups.
  (ii) Primary amines, RNH_2; secondary $RR'NH$; tertiary, $RR'R''N$.
  (iii) Are basic.
  (iv) Owing to the lone pair of electrons on the nitrogen, they can make salts, e.g. $RNH_3^+Cl^-$.
- Preparation:
  (i) Heat a halogenoalkane under pressure with ammonia in alcohol;

  e.g. $NH_3 + C_2H_5I \rightarrow C_2H_5NH_2 + HI$

  (ii) Reduction of nitriles;

  e.g. $C_2H_5CN + H_2 \xrightarrow{\text{Ni, 140 °C}} C_2H_5CH_2NH_2$

  (iii) Hofmann degradation of amides: reflux an amide with a mixture of bromine and sodium hydroxide solution;

  e.g. $C_2H_5CONH_2 + OBr^- + 2OH^- \rightarrow C_2H_5NH_2 + CO_3^{2-} + H_2O + Br^-$

  This reaction decreases the number of carbon atoms by one.

  (iv) Reduction of a nitro group; especially for making phenylamine;

  $C_6H_5NO_2 + 3H_2 \xrightarrow{\text{Sn, conc.HCl}} C_6H_5NH_2 + 2H_2O$

  The product appears as a salt, which must be destroyed with alkali; separated by steam distillation.

Reactions

- As bases:
  (i) pH > 7 in water;

  e.g. $CH_3NH_2(aq) + H_2O(l) \rightleftharpoons CH_3NH_3^+(aq) + OH^-(aq)$

  Primary amines most basic, tertiary amines least basic.

  (ii) Form salts (dissolve in solutions of inorganic acids);

  e.g. $C_2H_5NH_2 + H^+ \rightarrow C_2H_5NH_3^+$
- With halogenoalkanes:

  Halogen atom displaced;

  e.g. $CH_3NH_2 + CH_3Cl \rightarrow (CH_3)_2NH + HCl$

  A quaternary amine can be made;

  $(CH_3)_3N + CH_3Cl \rightarrow (CH_3)_4N^+Cl^-$
- Acetylation and benzoylation:

  Amines react very easily with an acid chloride or benzoyl chloride;

  $C_2H_5NH_2 + CH_3COCl \rightarrow C_2H_5NHOCCH_3 + HCl$

  $CH_3NH_2 + C_6H_5COCl \rightarrow CH_3NHOCC_6H_5 + HCl$
- Nitrous acid:

  Non-aromatic amines decompose to alcohols, giving off nitrogen gas.

Reactions of phenylamine

- Nitrous acid:
  (i) Below 5 °C, the benzenediazonium ion is made from phenylamine and sodium nitrite in hydrochloric acid;

  $$C_6H_5NH_2 + HNO_2 + H^+ \rightarrow C_6H_5N_2^+ + 2H_2O$$

  This can take part in reactions: to make C_6H_5I, C_6H_5CN; to make dyes (coupling reactions), e.g. with phenate ions

  $$C_6H_5N_2^+ + C_6H_5O^- \rightarrow C_6H_5N_2C_6H_5O^- + H^+$$

  (ii) Above 5 °C, diazonium ions decompose; nitrogen bubbles off;

  $$C_6H_5NH_2 + HNO_2 \rightarrow C_6H_5OH + N_2 + H_2O$$

- Bromination:
  The amine group activates the ring. Immediate white precipitate;
  $$C_6H_5NH_2 + 3Br_2 \rightarrow \underset{\text{2,4,6-tribromophenylamine}}{C_6H_2Br_3NH_2} + 3HBr$$

- Acetylation:
  Is used to protect the amine group. For example, to make 4-bromophenylamine:

  $$C_6H_5NH_2 + CH_3COCl \rightarrow C_6H_5NHCOCH_3 + HCl$$
  $$C_6H_5NHCOCH_3 + Br_2 \rightarrow BrC_6H_4NHCOCH_3 + HBr$$
  $$BrC_6H_4NHCOCH_3 + H_2O \rightarrow BrC_6H_4NH_2 + CH_3COOH$$

- Nitration:
  Similar scheme: acetylate, nitrate, hydrolyse.

123

Amino acids and proteins

123.1 What is an amino acid?

An amino acid has *two* functional groups in its molecule. One is an amine group, NH_2, the other a carboxylic acid, COOH. You might realise that a molecule with an acidic and a basic group in the same molecule may have some unusual properties; and you would be right. To begin with, even the simplest amino acids are *solids*. (Up to now the early members of all the homologous series we have looked at have been gases or liquids.) Of rather more importance is that we find amino acids, or their derivatives, in biologically important systems such as proteins. Indeed, amino acids are the *fundamental building blocks of living things*.

If we are to understand life and its evolution from a scientific point of view, we have to understand how amino acids are made, and how they react. Another odd thing about the amino acids in living things is that (approximately) only 20 amino acids occur naturally (Table 123.1), although we can make many more in the laboratory. In addition to a number of chemical properties that they have in common, these 20 have a remarkable structural similarity. For example, they all have the amine group on the carbon atom next door to the acid group. This carbon atom is the alpha (α) carbon atom. As a consequence we call the naturally occurring amino acids the *alpha amino acids*. Also, apart from glycine they are all optically active, and the arrangement of the groups around the asymmetric carbon atom follows the same pattern; but more of this later.

123.1 What would happen if you were to mix glycine with a solution of nitrous acid at room temperature? Write an equation for the reaction.

These models of glycine (left) and alanine (right) show the configurations of the naturally occurring amino acids (CORN rule).

Table 123.1. The 20 most important naturally occurring amino acids*†

Name	*Code*	*Structure*	*Name*	*Code*	*Structure*
Alanine	ala	$CH_3-CH(NH_2)-COOH$	Leucine	leu	$CH_3-CH(CH_3)-CH_2-CH(NH_2)-COOH$
Arginine	arg	$H_2N-C(=NH)-NH-CH_2-CH_2-CH_2-CH(NH_2)-COOH$	Lysine	lys	$H_2N-CH_2-CH_2-CH_2-CH_2-CH(NH_2)-COOH$
Asparagine	asn	$H_2N-C(=O)-CH_2-CH(NH_2)-COOH$	Methionine	met	$CH_3-S-CH_2-CH_2-CH(NH_2)-COOH$
Aspartic acid	asp	$HOOC-CH_2-CH(NH_2)-COOH$	Phenyl alanine	phe	$C_6H_5-CH_2-CH(NH_2)-COOH$ (benzene ring)
Cysteine	cys	$HS-CH_2-CH(NH_2)-COOH$	Proline	pro	ring: $CH_2-CH_2-CH(COOH)-N(H)-CH_2$
Glutamic acid	glu	$HOOC-CH_2-CH_2-CH(NH_2)-COOH$	Serine	ser	$HO-CH_2-CH(NH_2)-COOH$
Glutamine	gln	$H_2N-C(=O)-CH_2-CH_2-CH(NH_2)-COOH$	Threonine	thr	$CH_3-CH(OH)-CH(NH_2)-COOH$
Glycine	gly	$H-CH(NH_2)-COOH$	Tryptophan	try	indole ring (C, CH, N–H)$-CH_2-CH(NH_2)-COOH$
Histidine	his	$HC=C(-CH_2-CH(NH_2)-COOH)$; ring: $HC=C-NH-C(H)=N$	Tyrosine	tyr	$HO-C_6H_4-CH_2-CH(NH_2)-COOH$ (benzene ring)
Isoleucine	ile	$CH_3-CH_2-CH(CH_3)-CH(NH_2)-COOH$	Valine	val	$CH_3-CH(CH_3)-CH(NH_2)-COOH$

*The table shows the non-ionic structures of the amino acids

†The amino acids arg, his, ile, leu, lys, met, phe, thr, try and val are all essential requirements in the diet of humans. Without them we die

123.2 Methods of making amino acids

The classical method of making an amino acid is to start with a carboxylic acid. In section 119.4 we found that the hydrogen atoms on the carbon atom next to the acid group, the α carbon, can be replaced by halogen atoms. For example, to make glycine we start with ethanoic acid, and convert it into chloroethanoic acid:

$$H_2C(H)COOH + Cl_2 \longrightarrow H_2C(Cl)COOH + HCl$$

$$CH_3COOH + Cl_2 \rightarrow CH_2ClCOOH + HCl$$

This reaction is carried out by passing chlorine through the hot acid in sunlight, or with red phosphorus as a catalyst. It is possible to replace a hydrogen atom by bromine by a similar method. After separation, the chloroethanoic acid is treated with concentrated ammonia solution:

$$H_2C(Cl)COOH + NH_3 \longrightarrow H_2C(NH_2)COOH + HCl$$

$$CH_2ClCOOH + NH_3 \rightarrow \underset{\text{glycine}}{CH_2NH_2COOH} + HCl$$

As you would expect, the more complicated amino acids require more sophisticated preparations, but it is unlikely that you will need to know anything of them.

> **123.2** Outline a method of making alanine.

123.3 Amino acids exist as dipolar ions

The formula of glycine, NH_2CH_2COOH, gives no indication of why it should be a white crystalline solid. However, in the crystal, glycine is really present as a *dipolar ion*, i.e. it has a positive and a negative charge on the molecule at the same time. Its structure is:

$$H_3N^{\oplus}-CH_2-C(=O)O^{\ominus} \quad \text{or} \quad H_3N^+-CH_2-COO^-$$

Similarly the other amino acids exist as dipolar ions. For example,

$$\underset{\text{alanine}}{H_3\overset{+}{N}-CH(CH_3)-COO^-} \qquad \underset{\text{glutamine}}{H_2N-C(=O)-CH_2-CH_2-CH(\overset{+}{N}H_3)-COO^-}$$

$$\underset{\text{valine}}{CH_3-CH(CH_3)-CH(\overset{+}{N}H_3)-COO^-}$$

These dipolar structures survive when the amino acids dissolve in water, and they are responsible for some unusual properties. The dipolar ions are also known as *zwitterions*.

123.4 Amino acids can be both acidic and basic

Like ordinary amines, amino acids will take up protons from acids; but it is *not* the NH_2 group in the acid that is responsible for the reaction. If you look at the dipolar structure of glycine, you can see that the nitrogen is already protonated. When an amino acid meets a strong acid like hydrochloric acid, it is the COO^- group that accepts a proton:

$$NH_3^+CH_2COO^- + H_3O^+ \rightleftharpoons \underset{\text{protonated glycine}}{NH_3^+CH_2COOH} + H_2O$$

In this reaction, the COO^- group is the basic group (proton acceptor).

Likewise, if we add a strong alkali to an amino acid solution, the NH_3^+ group is the acid (proton donor):

$$NH_3^+CH_2COO^- + OH^- \rightleftharpoons NH_2CH_2COO^- + H_2O$$

If you dissolve an amino acid in water, you will find that its pH is not 7 (neutral). The reason is that water can act as both an acid and a base. Therefore, it can react with a dipolar ion in two ways. If we use glycine as our example, either

$$NH_3^+CH_2COO^- + H_2O \rightleftharpoons NH_3^+CH_2COOH + OH^-$$

or

$$NH_3^+CH_2COO^- + H_2O \rightleftharpoons NH_2CH_2COO^- + H_3O^+$$

In the first case the COO^- group is acting as a stronger base than water. In the second reaction, the NH_3^+ group is acting as a stronger acid than water. In essence, a competition is set up when you dissolve an amino acid in water. If the first reaction wins over the second, the solution will give an alkaline pH; if the second reaction wins over the first, the solution will have an acidic pH. A solution of glycine has a pH very slightly less than 7. This tells us that the acidic nature of the NH_3^+ group wins over the basic nature of the COO^- group.

123.3 A student said that it was not surprising that valine dissolved in alkali because valine was acidic. Was the student correct? What would you need to ask the student to discover if he or she really understood what was happening?

123.5 Electrophoresis and isoelectric points

We know from our work on electrolysis that positive ions in a solution will move towards the negative electrode (cathode), and negative ions towards the positive electrode (anode). In electrolysis we are interested in the changes that take place when the ions arrive at the electrodes. In an electrophoresis experiment we also have an anode and cathode dipping into a conducting medium, but the purpose of the experiment is different. We do not want the ions to be discharged at the electrodes; rather we want to study their *movement* towards the electrodes. A typical arrangement is to place a small

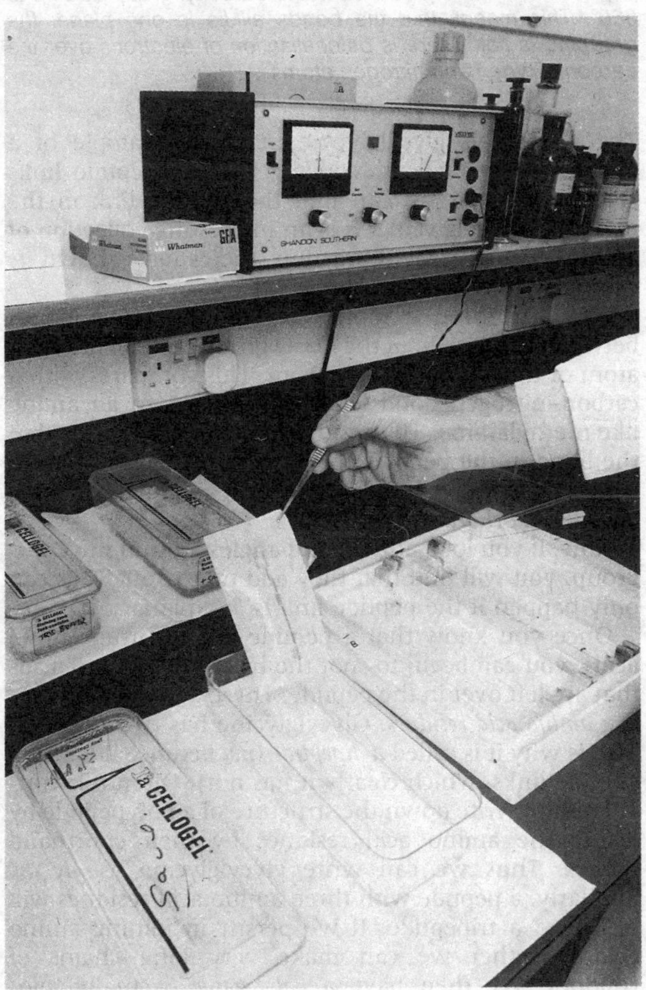

A typical laboratory setting for an electrophoresis experiment. In this case the sample is haemoglobin.

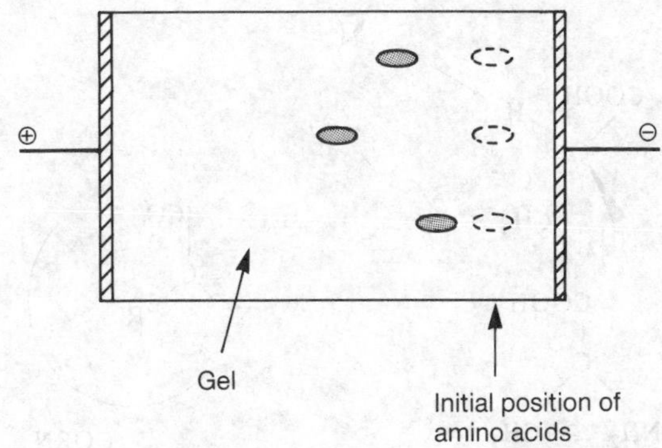

Figure 123.1 *The basis of an electrophoresis experiment. Amino acids, or substances built from them, move in an electric field. Whether they move towards the positive or negative electrode depends on the pH of the medium*

sample of an amino acid on a strip of gel with an electrode at each end (Figure 123.1). If a voltage is applied between the electrodes (typically around 40 V) and the amino acid has an overall positive or negative charge, then it will travel towards one of the electrodes. After a suitable period of time, which will depend on the applied voltage and the nature of the amino acid, the experiment is stopped. The presence of the amino acid can be shown by dipping the gel into, or spraying it with, a dye.

Because amino acids move at different speeds through the gel, electrophoresis experiments can be used to separate mixtures of amino acids or similar compounds.

Actually it is possible to prevent an amino acid moving in an electrophoresis experiment. For example, the equilibrium

$$NH_3^+CH_2COO^- + H_2O \rightleftharpoons NH_2CH_2COO^- + H_3O^+$$

lies a little in favour of the right-hand side. If we add acid, the equilibrium will shift to the left and the glycine will exist (almost) entirely as dipolar ions. Because they have a positive charge at one end, and a negative charge at the other, they are effectively electrically neutral. Therefore they will not move towards either of the electrodes in an electrophoresis experiment.

The pH at which an amino acid exists completely as dipolar ions is the *isoelectric point*. Glycine has an isoelectric point a little over pH = 6.

123.6 The geometry of amino acids

First, let us look at the structure of alanine. If you have read Unit 110 on optical activity you should recognise that alanine has an asymmetric carbon atom. This means that the molecule can exist in two mirror image forms.

However, only one of the optical isomers is found in naturally occurring alanine. If you build a model of the naturally occurring isomer, look at it with the hydrogen atom on the asymmetric carbon atom pointing towards you. You should find that you see the arrangement

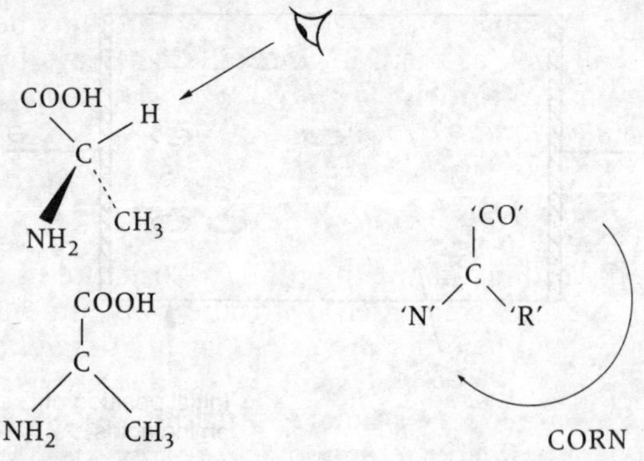

Figure 123.2 The CORN rule. The view seen when looking down the C—H bond of alanine illustrates the CORN rule for naturally occurring amino acids

illustrated in Figure 123.2. If we follow the groups around in a clockwise direction, with the acid group at the top, the order is COOH, CH_3, NH_2. We can generalise this pattern to cover any of the other naturally occurring amino acids. The way they differ from alanine is that instead of a CH_3 group on the asymmetric carbon, they have some other hydrocarbon group. We shall call this group R. In this way we can say that the arrangement around the asymmetric carbon is COOH, R, NH_2. This is often written in a shorthand way as CORN, thus giving us the *CORN rule*. All naturally occurring amino acids follow the CORN rule.

This 'handedness' of the amino acids is one of the reasons why specific patterns crop up in structures built from them, e.g. the α-helix in fibrous proteins and in DNA.

> **123.4** After separating the alanine made in the method of question 123.2 and putting a solution of it in a polarimeter, a student found that the amino acid was *not* optically active. Why was this?

123.7 Amino acids use a peptide link to join together

Amino acids have the ability to join together. The simplest case is where two glycine molecules join. We can imagine the reaction taking place by the loss of a water molecule between the two molecules:

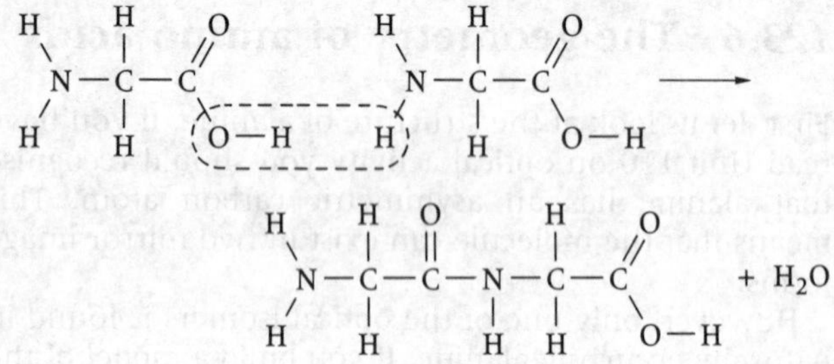

$$NH_2CH_2COOH + NH_2CH_2COOH \rightarrow NH_2CH_2CONHCH_2COOH + H_2O$$

glycylglycine

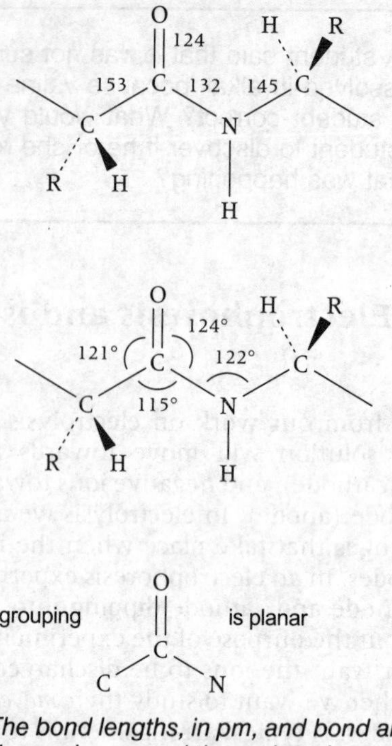

The grouping C(=O)(C)N is planar

Figure 123.3 The bond lengths, in pm, and bond angles in the peptide link. The angles around the carbonyl group add up to 360°. This means that the bonds all lie in one plane: the grouping is flat. There is delocalisation of electrons over the carbon, oxygen and nitrogen atoms

The product is glycylglycine. It is an example of a *dipeptide*. A peptide is held together by peptide links (Figure 123.3). You can find the peptide link in the middle of glycylglycine. It is an interesting collection of atoms because X-ray diffraction studies have shown its geometry to be rather special.

The first thing to notice is that the bond length between the carbon of the C=O group and the nitrogen atom of the NH group is 132 pm. This compares with a carbon–nitrogen bond length of 147 pm in an amine like methylamine. The shorter bond length tells us that the bond in the peptide link is *stronger* than normal. In turn this leads us to suspect that it might have some *double bond character*.

Now, if you look at the bond angles around the C=O group, you will find that they add up to 360°. This can only happen if the peptide link is *flat* (planar).

Once you know that a peptide is built from amino acids, you can begin to spot the bits of the amino acids that are left over in the peptide. These 'left over' bits are the *amino acid residues*. Glycylglycine has two residues. This is why it is called a *dipeptide* (*not* because it has two peptide links, which clearly it has not). Often it is convenient to write down the structure of a polypeptide by listing the amino acid residues by their shorthand names. Thus we can write glycylglycine as *gly.gly*. Similarly, a peptide with three amino acid residues will be called a tripeptide. If we persist in joining amino acids together we can make very long chains of residues. We then have a *polypeptide*. Actually, biochemical systems in Nature are far better at making polypeptides than we are in a laboratory.

123.5 Here are three short peptide chains:

(a)

```
              O       H
              ‖       |
H2N—CH2—C—N—C—COOH
              |   |
              H   CH3
```

(b)

```
              O               O       H
              ‖               ‖       |
H2N—CH2—C—N—CH2—C—N——C—COOH
                  |               |   |
                  H               H H-C-H
                                      |
                                      CH3
```

(c)

```
      H   O         H   O
      |   ‖         |   ‖
H2N—C—C—N——C—C—N—CH2—COOH
      |     |       |     |
      CH3   H H-C-CH3 H
                |
                CH3
```

(i) How many amino acid residues do they contain?

(ii) Which of them are dipeptides, and which tripeptides?

(iii) Which amino acids have been used to build the chains?

123.8 Proteins

If the molecular mass of a polypeptide is very high, we prefer to call the molecule a *protein*. As a rule of thumb we can say that:

A protein is a polypeptide with a relative molecular mass of at least 10 000.

However, this is only a guide. For example, the hormone insulin has a relative molecular mass of around 6000, but it is certainly best regarded as a protein. At the other end of the scale, some proteins are so large that they have relative molecular masses of well over 1000 000. Proteins are of overwhelming importance in living systems. They are found in large amounts in cells and, in the form of enzymes, they are extremely efficient catalysts for hundreds of reactions that keep living things working. To understand how proteins behave, we shall look at them in four different ways by concentrating on their *primary, secondary, tertiary* and *quaternary structures*.

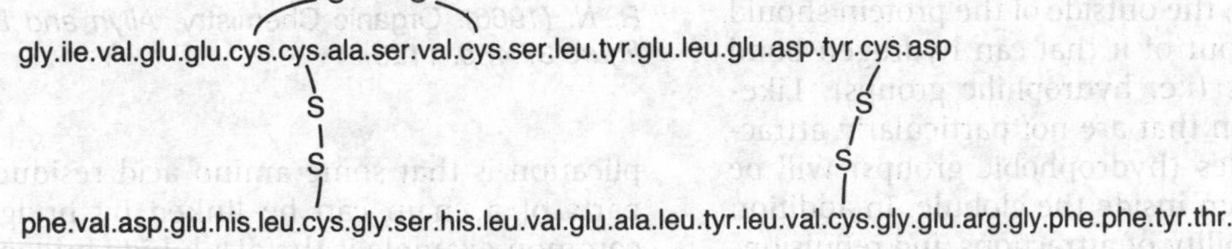

***Figure 123.4** The order of amino acid residues in insulin*

(a) *Primary structure*

When we think about the primary structure of a protein, we are concerned with the way amino acid residues join together in chains. There are two aspects to this. First, the geometry of the peptide link is one of the key aspects of primary structure. Secondly, the *sequence* in which the amino acid residues appear in a chain is important. Insulin is made of 51 amino acid residues joined together. The order in which they occur is shown in Figure 123.4.

Presently we shall see how the sequence of amino acid residues can be discovered.

(b) *Secondary structure*

The orderly arrangement of parts (or all) of protein chains constitutes the secondary structure of a protein. Proteins do not simply lie about in long, straight, chains. Their X-ray diffraction patterns show that parts, or all, of the chains have orderly arrangements of one of two types. Sometimes the chains make a pleated and sometimes a spiral structure. These are the two secondary structures (Figures 123.5 and 123.6).

Both structures are caused by hydrogen bonds between portions of the amino acid residues. The —NH group of the peptide link on one residue can hydrogen bond to the carbonyl group on another residue. However, for the hydrogen bond to be successful, the two groups must be aligned in a special way. The best arrangement is the one which gives a large number of hydrogen bonds among all the residues. Especially, in fibrous proteins this arrangement causes the chains to twist and spiral into the geometry of the α-helix (alpha-helix), the structure of which is shown in Figure 123.6.

(c) *Tertiary structure*

The three-dimensional shape taken up by a protein is its tertiary structure (Figure 123.7). Proteins that spiral over their entire length are the *fibrous* proteins. In the *globular* proteins the chains spiral over short lengths, and then fold into a different pattern. This gives globular proteins a more rounded look. Although hydrogen bonding between parts of the chain is extremely important in globular proteins, their struc-

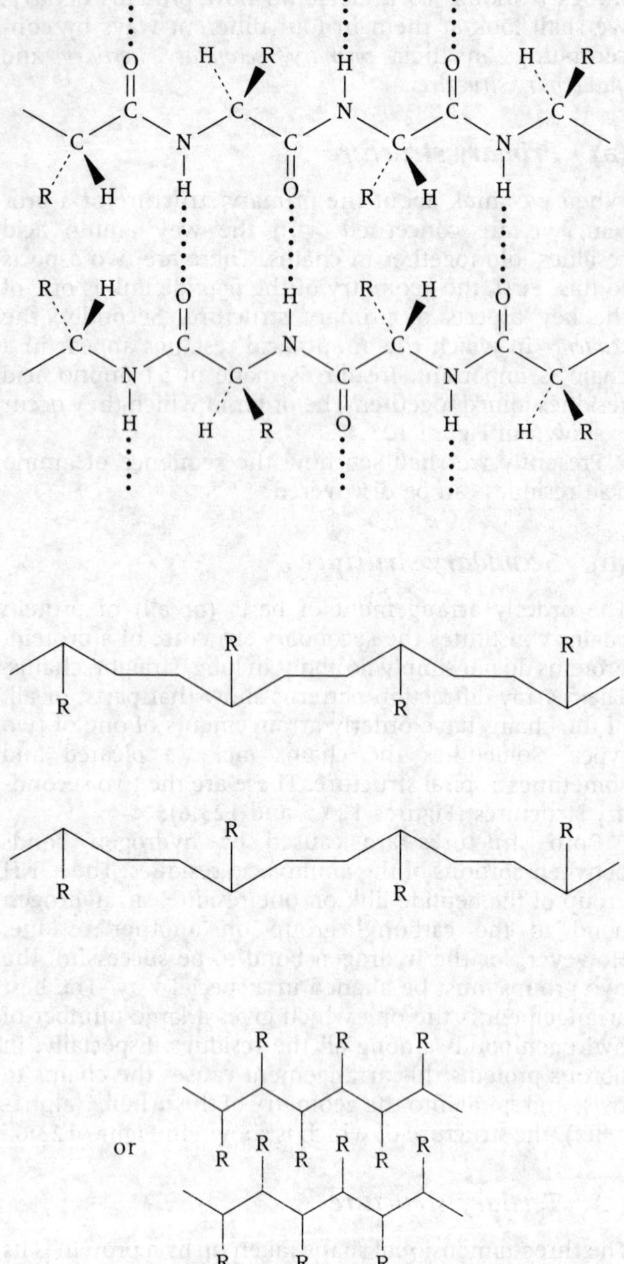

Figure 123.5 *In some proteins the chains are arranged as pleated sheets, held together by hydrogen bonds*

tures are also determined by other interactions. Especially, if the protein is to exist in an aqueous solution (e.g. in the cytoplasm of cells or in blood), then the outside of the protein should be attractive to water molecules (Figure 123.8). That is, the outside of the protein should have groups sticking out of it that can hydrogen bond with water molecules (i.e. hydrophilic groups). Likewise, parts of the chain that are not particularly attractive to water molecules (hydrophobic groups) will be wrapped up and hidden inside the globule. In addition there is also the possibility of attractions and repulsions between ionic groups along the chain. Yet another complication is that some amino acid residues in different parts of a chain can be linked by bridging atoms. A common example is the disulphide bridge between two cysteine residues (see Figure 123.4).

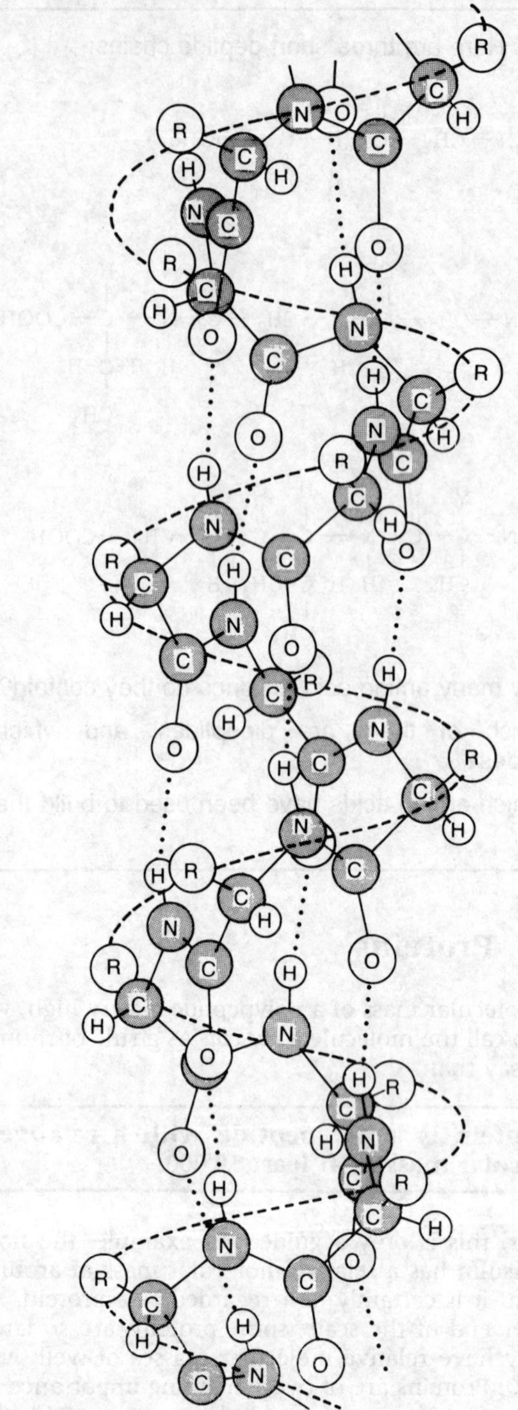

Figure 123.6 *Structure of the α-helix found in proteins such as α-keratin. Note the hydrogen bonds (shown by dotted lines) between different parts of the chain. These are responsible for the shape of the helix. (Taken from: Morrison, R. T. and Boyd, R. N. (1966).* Organic Chemistry, *Allyn and Bacon, Boston, figure 37.4, p. 1123)*

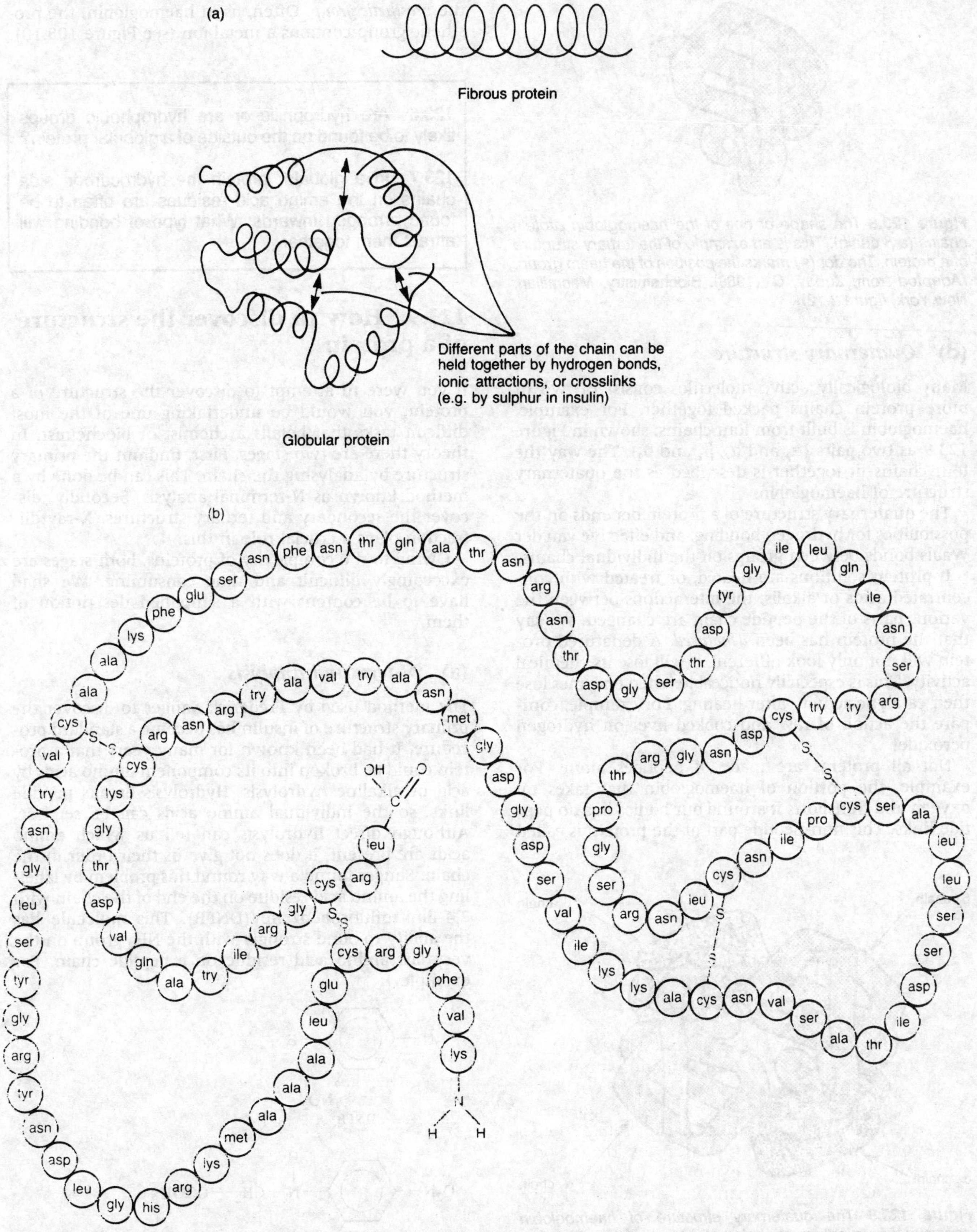

(a)

Fibrous protein

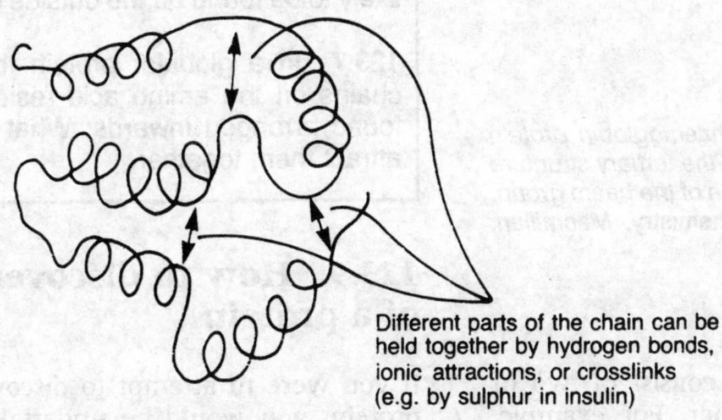

Different parts of the chain can be held together by hydrogen bonds, ionic attractions, or crosslinks (e.g. by sulphur in insulin)
Globular protein

(b)

Figure 123.7 *(a) Fibrous proteins and globular proteins have different tertiary structures. (b) This illustrates the complexity of even a rather small enzyme, lysozyme. (Taken from: Boer, A. S.* et al. *(1971).* Central Concepts of Biology, *Macmillan, New York, figure 3.15, p. 38)*

Figure 123.8 *The shape of one of the haemoglobin protein chains (a β chain). This is an example of the tertiary structure of a protein. The dot (•) marks the position of the haem group. (Adapted from: Zubay, G. (1988).* Biochemistry, *Macmillan, New York, figure 2.12)*

(d) *Quaternary structure*

Many biologically active molecules consist of two or more protein chains packed together. For example, haemoglobin is built from four chains, shown in Figure 123.9 as two pairs (α_1 and α_2, β_1 and β_2). The way the four chains fit together is described as the quaternary structure of haemoglobin.

The quaternary structure of a protein depends on the possibilities for hydrogen bonding, and effective van der Waals bonds between groups on the individual chains.

If protein solutions are heated, or treated with concentrated acids or alkalis, the interactions between the various parts of the peptide chain are changed. We say that the protein has been *denatured*. A denatured protein will not only look different, it will lose its chemical activity. This is especially noticeable when enzymes lose their catalytic activity after heating. For example, compare the action of raw and cooked liver on hydrogen peroxide!

Not all proteins are made of peptides alone. For example, the portion of haemoglobin that takes up oxygen and transports it around our bodies has no peptide links. This non-peptide part of the protein is called the *prosthetic group*. Often, as in haemoglobin, the prosthetic group contains a metal ion (see Figure 105.10).

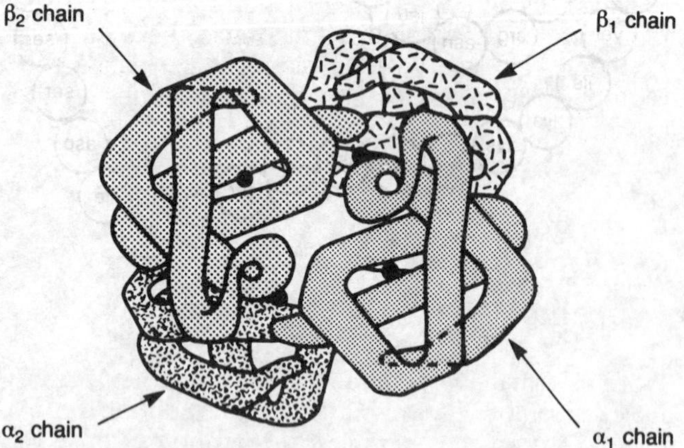

Figure 123.9 *The quaternary structure of haemoglobin consists of four individual chains clinging together. The dots (•) mark the positions of haem groups. (Adapted from: Zubay, op. cit.)*

> **123.6** Are hydrophilic or are hydrophobic groups likely to be found on the outside of a globular protein?
>
> **123.7** In a globular protein the hydrocarbon side chains on the amino acid residues are often to be found arranged inwards. What type of bonding will attract them together?

123.9 How to discover the structure of a protein

If you were to attempt to discover the structure of a protein, you would be undertaking one of the most difficult tasks that befalls a chemist or biochemist. In theory there are two stages. First, find out the primary structure by analysing the chain. This can be done by a method known as N-terminal analysis. Secondly, discover the secondary and tertiary structures. X-ray diffraction plays a crucial role in this.

Owing to the complexity of proteins, both stages are exceedingly difficult and time consuming. We shall have to be content with a simplified description of them.

(a) *N-terminal analysis*

The method used by Frederick Sanger to discover the primary structure of insulin has become a standard procedure. It had been known for many years that a protein could be broken into its component amino acids by acid or alkaline hydrolysis. Hydrolysis breaks peptide links, so the individual amino acids can be set free. Although direct hydrolysis can tell us which amino acids are present, it does not give us their order in the chain. Sanger found a way round this problem by labelling the amino acid residue on the end of the chain with 2,4-dinitrofluorobenzene (DNFB). This molecule has the ability to bond strongly with the NH_2 group on the very last amino acid residue on a peptide chain. For example,

O_2N—(benzene ring)—F, with NO_2 on the ring

DNFB

O_2N—(benzene ring)—N(H)—CH_2—COOH, with NO_2 on the ring

DNFB + glycine

Once the DNFB reacts with the protein, the mixture is hydrolysed by refluxing with moderately concentrated hydrochloric acid. This breaks peptide links along the chain. We can represent the result of the hydrolysis like this:

$O_2N-C_6H_3(NO_2)-NH-CHR-CO-NH-CHR-CO-NH-CHR\cdots \longrightarrow$

$O_2N-C_6H_3(NO_2)-NH-CHR-COOH + H_2N-CHR-CO-NH-CHR-COOH$

+ other combinations

Peptide chains of different lengths are released, together with free amino acids. However, the important thing is that a short length of the chain stays bonded to the DNFB. These short chains are called 2,4-dinitrophenyl (DNP) peptides. By selecting the best solvent, the DNP peptides can be extracted from the bulk of the solution. They are then separated from one another by column chromatography. Once the fractions are separated, the next stage is to hydrolyse them with 6 mol dm^{-3} hydrochloric acid. This frees the individual amino acids along the DNP peptide chain. Finally the amino acids are identified by paper chromatography. By changing the conditions used in the hydrolysis and using different solvents in the chromatography, it is also possible to identify the terminal amino acid bonded to the DNFB.

(Incidentally, you might like to know the scale on which Sanger worked. For example, in the hydrolysis of the DNP peptides he used milligram quantities of the peptide with 5 *drops* of 6 mol dm^{-3} hydrochloric acid in a 50 cm^3 round bottomed flask.)

We can use some of Sanger's results to see how he began the task of unravelling the structure of insulin. Following a hydrolysis of a set of DNP peptides, he found that they all contained DNP-glycine. When the products of the hydrolysis were separated by column chromatography, he found four bands. The first band was DNP-glycine; the others were short peptide chains. Sanger showed that the composition of the first three fractions was:

Fraction	*Composition*
1	DNP-glycine
2	Isoleucine
3	Isoleucine and valine

These results show that the order of amino acids in the peptide chain originally bonded to the DNFB must be in the order gly–ile–val. Analysis of further fractions showed that the chain also had glutamic acid residues following the valine.

N-terminal analysis is not the only weapon that can be used in analysing proteins. As we know, DNFB reacts with the amine group on one end of a peptide chain; but it will not react with the carboxylic acid group on the other end of the chain. However, the enzyme carboxy-peptidase has the remarkable ability to chop off the amino acid having the acid group. Once free from the chain, this amino acid can be identified. The use of carboxypeptidase is called C-terminal analysis.

The determination of the order of amino acids can now be done semi-automatically, using chemicals and techniques that were unavailable to Sanger. For example, DNFB has largely been replaced by the chemical whose common name is dansyl chloride:

$SO_2Cl-C_{10}H_6-N(CH_3)_2$

Like DNFB, this molecule binds to the terminal amino acid, but the products, of general formula

$(CH_3)_2N-C_{10}H_6-S(=O)(=O)-NH-CHR-COOH$

are fluorescent and can be readily identified by chromatography.

123.8 A peptide chain was subjected to N-terminal analysis using DNFB. In addition to DNP-glycine, the following combinations of amino acid residues were isolated: gly.val, val.leu, ala.phe.gly, leu.ala.phe. What is the order of amino acid residues in the peptide?

123.10 The X-ray patterns of proteins

Proteins that have a spiral, or helical, structure show many common features in their X-ray diffraction patterns. You can see examples in the photo. Notice that the patterns are symmetrical. This corresponds with the symmetrical nature of the helix. By analysing the pattern it is possible to calculate the key dimensions of the helix, for example the repeat length of the spiral.

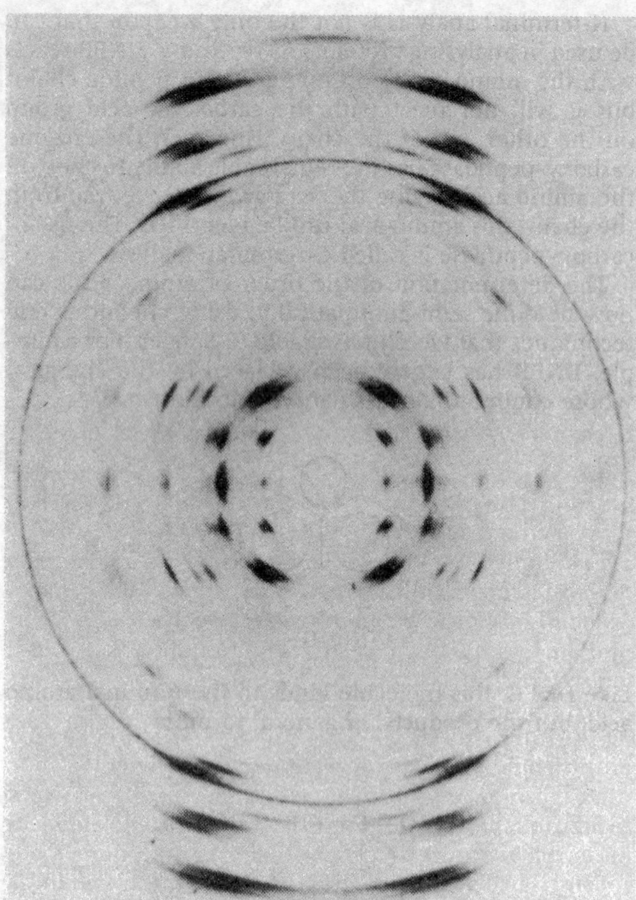

A X-ray diffraction pattern from a fibre of DNA. The pattern of spots is characteristic of helical structures. (The continuous circle is not due to DNA, but to a salt impurity.) Taken from Figure 13.2 of J. P. Glusker and K. N. Trueblood, Crystal Structure Analysis, *Oxford University Press, Oxford, 1985.*

The diffraction patterns of globular proteins are much more complicated. Even with modern computers, there is a huge amount of work that has to be done to tease out the structure of the protein from the myriad number of dots in the X-ray pattern.

123.11 How enzymes act as catalysts

An enzyme is a protein that acts as a highly efficient catalyst (Table 123.2). An enzyme normally has one particular site at which reactions take place. This is the *active site*. The tertiary structure of an enzyme is so complicated that molecules must have a very particular shape if they are to fit into the active site. Those molecules which do fit the active site are called the *substrate* molecules. You can see this idea in Figure 81.5. We have made no attempt to show any particular enzyme or substrate. The diagram showed the special relationship between the geometry of the active site and the substrate. You should now understand why enzymes are said to be *specific* catalysts: they only catalyse one reaction.

There are several ways of ruining an enzyme. The easy way is to heat it. This permanently denatures the enzyme. If you do not want to be so drastic in your action, the addition of acid or alkali will also change the catalytic activity of an enzyme. This is because of the ability of hydrogen and hydroxide ions to add or remove protons from various parts of a peptide chain and thereby upset the interactions between the active site and the substrate.

Table 123.2. Some enzymes and their action*

Enzyme	*Function*
Amylase	Converts starch into sugars
Catalase	Converts hydrogen peroxide into oxygen and water
Invertase	Converts sucrose into glucose and fructose
Lysozyme	Attacks the polysaccharide cell walls of bacteria
Papain	Tenderises meat
Urease	Converts urea into carbon dioxide and ammonia

*Enzymes have been increasingly used in industrial processes, especially in the food industries. For example, you may be able to buy bottles of papain to sprinkle on meat before you cook it; invertase is widely used in the making of sweets and confectionery. Manufacturers of soap powders have, with some success, adapted certain enzymes so that they can withstand the temperatures used in washing machines. These enzymes have the ability to destroy the sorts of molecules found in natural dirts and stains, e.g. blood stains

You should not be surprised to learn that most enzymes work best over a very limited range of pH. Typically, a graph of enzyme activity against pH has the shape shown in Figure 123.10.

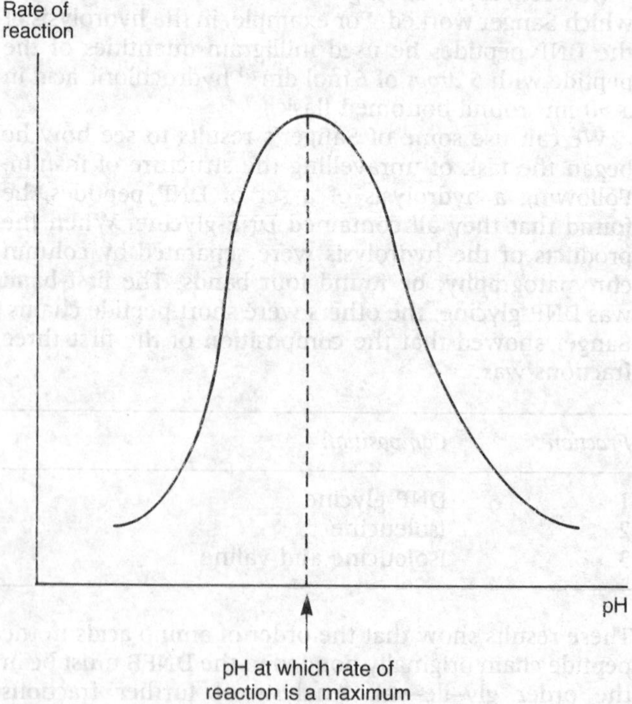

Figure 123.10 *Enzyme reactions have rates that are sensitive to pH. At too low or too high a pH, the enzyme loses its activity*

123.9 This is a question about the kinetics of enzyme reactions. Urease catalyses the breakdown of urea. When the concentration of urea is low, the reaction is first order in urea; but when the concentration of urea is high, the reaction is zeroth order in urea. Why is this?

Answers

123.1 Nitrogen gas would be given off:

$$NH_2CH_2COOH + HNO_2 \rightarrow HOCH_2COOH + N_2 + H_2O$$

123.2 Alanine has the structure shown in Table 123.1. A reasonable molecule with which to start the preparation would be propanoic acid. If this is treated with chlorine, then one of the α hydrogen atoms can be displaced. Finally the product is reacted with a concentrated solution of ammonia. The reactions are:

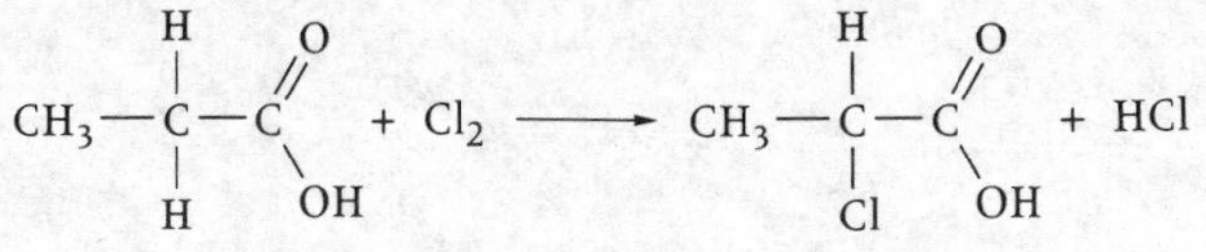

$$CH_3CH_2COOH + Cl_2 \rightarrow CH_3CHClCOOH + HCl$$

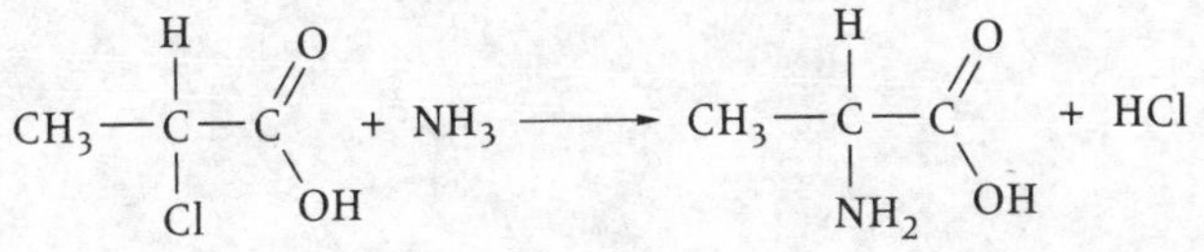

$$CH_3CHClCOOH + NH_3 \rightarrow CH_3CHNH_2COOH + HCl$$

alanine

123.3 We saw in section 123.4 that an amino acid can behave as an acid or a base. However, you would have to ask the student to say which part of the molecule was acting as the acid. The important thing is that the student should know that because the acid will exist as a dipolar ion, it is the NH_3^+ group that acts as the acid:

$$(CH_3)_2CHCHNH_3^+COO^- + OH^- \rightarrow (CH_3)_2CHCHNH_2COO^- + H_2O$$

123.4 The solution of alanine must have contained equal proportions of the two optical isomers of alanine. That is, it is a racemic mixture. The reason is that when the chlorine reacts with propanoic acid, both optical isomers of 2-chloropropanoic acid can be made. These two isomers will react to give the two mirror image forms of alanine.

123.5 (i), (ii) Chain (a) contains two residues, so it is a dipeptide; chains (b) and (c) contain three residues, so they are tripeptides.

(iii) Chain (a) is built from glycine and alanine (gly.ala); chain (b) from two glycines and valine (gly.gly.val); chain (c) from alanine, valine and glycine (ala.val.gly).

123.6 Hydrophilic. It is these groups that will enable the protein to be solvated by water molecules.

123.7 Van der Waals forces, the hydrophobic interactions, help to keep hydrocarbon fragments together.

123.8 The order of the residues is as follows: gly.val.leu.ala.phe.gly. (The first gly is the amine end of the chain; the last gly is the carboxylic acid end.) You might have given val.leu.ala.phe.gly.val as an alternative. The reason why this one is not right is that it would not give DNP-glycine. The fact that this is isolated tells us that glycine must be a terminal amino acid.

123.9 First, you have to realise that the reaction takes place at the active site on the urease molecules. When the concentration of urea is low, we can assume that at any time there are a good number of active sites unoccupied. Thus if we increase the concentration of urea slightly, more of the active sites will be used and more urea molecules are destroyed. This is the reason for the first-order kinetics. However, if the concentration of urea increases beyond a certain point, on average the active sites will all be full. If we then add more urea, the reaction rate will not increase: the new molecules cannot get to the active sites. When this happens we find that the rate does not change even though the concentration of urea changes, i.e. we have a zeroth-order reaction.

UNIT 123 SUMMARY

- Amino acids:
  - (i) Have two functional groups: $—NH_2$ and $—COOH$.
  - (ii) Show both basic and acidic nature.
  - (iii) Exist as bipolar ions, e.g. $NH_3^+CH_2COO^-$; hence their existence as solids.
  - (iv) Are the basic units of proteins.
  - (v) Only α-amino acids occur naturally (obey the CORN rule).
  - (vi) Are separated by electrophoresis.
- Preparation:
  From chlorocarboxylic acids;
  e.g. $CH_3COOH + Cl_2 \rightarrow CH_2ClCOOH + HCl$
  $CH_2ClCOOH + NH_3 \rightarrow CH_2NH_2COOH + HCl$
- Reactions:
  Show both acidity and basicity.
  Acidic nature is due to the NH_3^+ group.
  Basic nature is due to the COO^- group.

Summary – cont.

- Peptides:

  Consist of chains of amino acids. The peptide link is planar

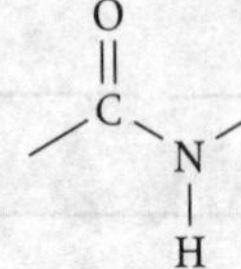

- Proteins:
  (i) Are built from amino acids.
  (ii) Can have very high molar masses.
  (iii) Are essential components of biochemical systems.
  (iv) Have primary, secondary, tertiary and quaternary structures.

  Primary: the order of amino acids in the protein chain.

  Secondary: how the chain of amino acid residues arrange themselves, often into an α-helix.

  Tertiary: how the chain folds to give the three-dimensional structure.

  Quaternary: how one or more chains fold to give the final structure of the protein.

- Structure:
  (i) Order of amino acids is discovered by N-terminal analysis, e.g. by using DNFB.
  (ii) Three-dimensional structure discovered by X-ray diffraction.

- Enzymes:
  (i) Are specific catalyst.
  (ii) Have active sites into which (usually) only one type of molecule (the substrate) will fit.

124

Deoxyribonucleic acid (DNA)

124.1 The structure of DNA

Deoxyribonucleic acid (DNA) is the substance that controls the development of all living things. Especially, DNA is responsible for handing on genetic information from one generation of a species to another. That is, DNA lies at the heart of the study of *genetics*.

The molar mass of DNA taken from different types of cell varies widely, but it is always very high, sometimes of the order 10^9 g mol^{-1}. This suggests that DNA is a polymeric material. The polymer is built from chains of *nucleotides*. One nucleotide consists of a phosphate group, a sugar molecule and a basic group containing nitrogen (Figure 124.1).

There are four different basic molecules found in DNA: *adenine, guanine, cytosine* and *thymine* (Figure 124.2). They all contain nitrogen atoms in a ring structure. Analysis of DNA shows that always the amounts of adenine and thymine are equal. Similarly, guanine and cytosine are found in equal amounts.

The sugar molecule in DNA is *deoxyribose*, a five-membered ring with three OH groups. *Ribonucleic acid* (RNA) is similar to DNA except that it is a polymer of nucleotides made from the sugar ribose rather than deoxyribose, and it has a slightly different set of bases: *adenine, guanine, cytosine* and *uracil* (Figure 124.2).

During the 1950s there were many groups of chemists and biochemists trying to determine how the nucleotides fitted together in DNA. Maurice Wilkins and, especially, Rosalind Franklin at King's College, London, were attempting to analyse the X-ray diffraction pattern of DNA (see photo on p. 860). This was no easy task, especially given that the calculations had to be done without the aid of computers. Rosalind Franklin was close to discovering the structure, but before she published her results, Francis Crick and James Watson (who worked in Cambridge) discovered the solution to the puzzle. They did not achieve this remarkable feat by analysing the diffraction pattern in detail. Rather, they realised that the pattern could be produced by a double helix; that is, two separate strands winding round each other. Linus Pauling had also understood that this was possible, but he had not given a satisfactory explanation of how the strands fitted together. Where Crick and Watson made their vital breakthrough was in building scale models of the nucleotides and joining them to represent short lengths of two strands of DNA. By attempting to fit the model together, they discovered how the strands could wind round in such a symmetrical fashion. The key to the pattern was that:

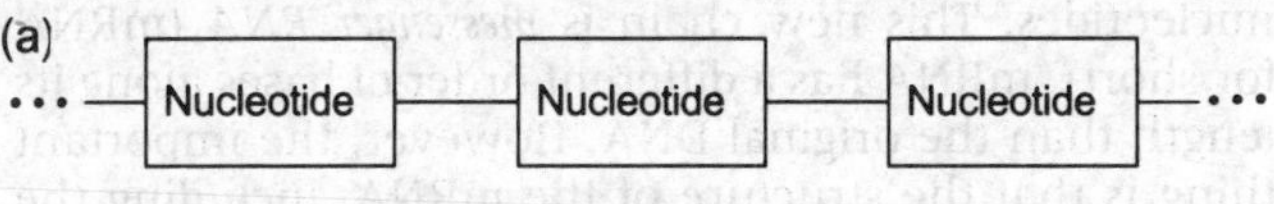

(b) The pattern is

```
        base        O        base        O
         |          ||        |          ||
···—sugar—O—P—O—sugar—O—P—O—···
                    |                    |
                   OH                   OH
```

Figure 124.1 A first look at DNA. (a) At the simplest level we can think of DNA as a polymer made of nucleotide units. (b) Each nucleotide is made from a phosphate + sugar + base

> **The two strands were held together by hydrogen bonds between pairs of bases.**

They found that the shapes of adenine and thymine made a beautiful match, allowing two hydrogen bonds between the molecules (Figure 124.3). Similarly, guanine and cytosine fitted together, but this time with three hydrogen bonds at work.

Their model fitted together precisely if the base pairs attached to the phosphate groups pointed towards the middle of the two strands. Each strand is an α-helix, which you can see in outline in Figure 124.4.

124.2 How DNA works

The magic of DNA is that the pattern of bases along the strands controls how amino acids join together to make proteins. (You may remember that the majority of bio-

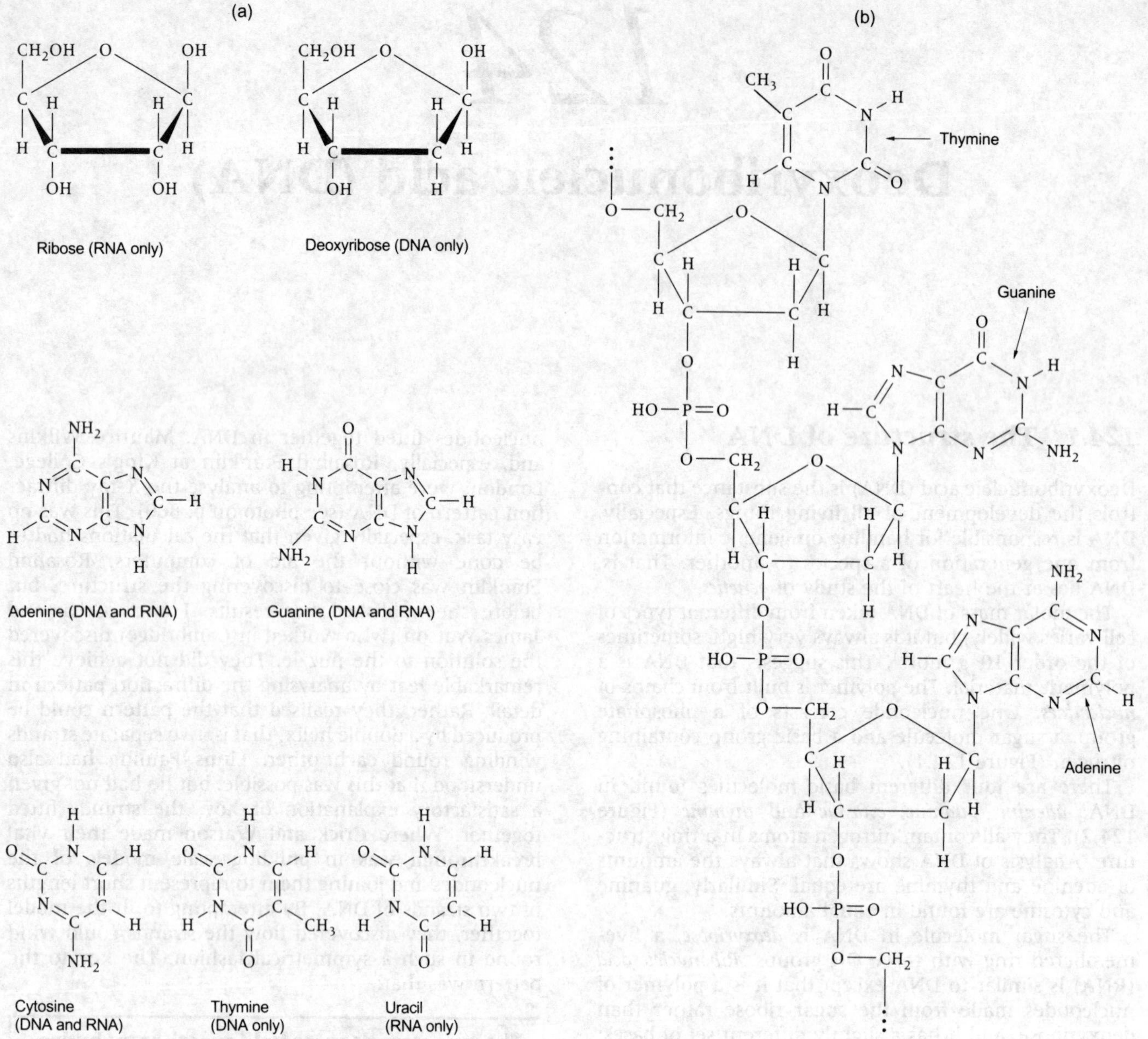

(a)

Ribose (RNA only)

Deoxyribose (DNA only)

Adenine (DNA and RNA)

Guanine (DNA and RNA)

Cytosine (DNA and RNA)

Thymine (DNA only)

Uracil (RNA only)

(b)

Thymine

Guanine

Adenine

Figure 124.2 *(a) The two sugars and five bases found in DNA or RNA. (b) A fragment of a DNA chain*

logically important materials are proteins.) The pattern of bases along a strand of DNA determines the number, sequence and type of amino acid in the protein. Here is an outline of how this happens (see also Figure 124.5).

(a) *Step 1: manufacture of messenger RNA*

The two strands of DNA contained in the chromosomes of a cell unzip along part of their length. Every pattern of three bases along a strand acts as a code for an amino acid. Each pattern of three is called a *codon*. There are 64 codons (Table 124.1), but only 20 amino acids, so several codons code for the same amino acid. In addition, there are codons that control the place where the coding starts and stops.

The chain of amino acids that combine along the length of the DNA strand makes a second chain of nucleotides. This new chain is *messenger RNA* (mRNA for short). mRNA has a different order of bases along its length than the original DNA. However, the important thing is that the structure of the mRNA, including the order of bases along its strands, is determined by the DNA.

(b) *Step 2: RNA passes on information to make proteins*

mRNA can pass into the cytoplasm of a cell. Here it attaches itself to small structures called ribosomes. Once joined to the ribosomes, we have *ribosomal RNA*. Yet another type of RNA in cells, called *transfer RNA* (tRNA), binds to ribosomal RNA. (tRNA is much smaller

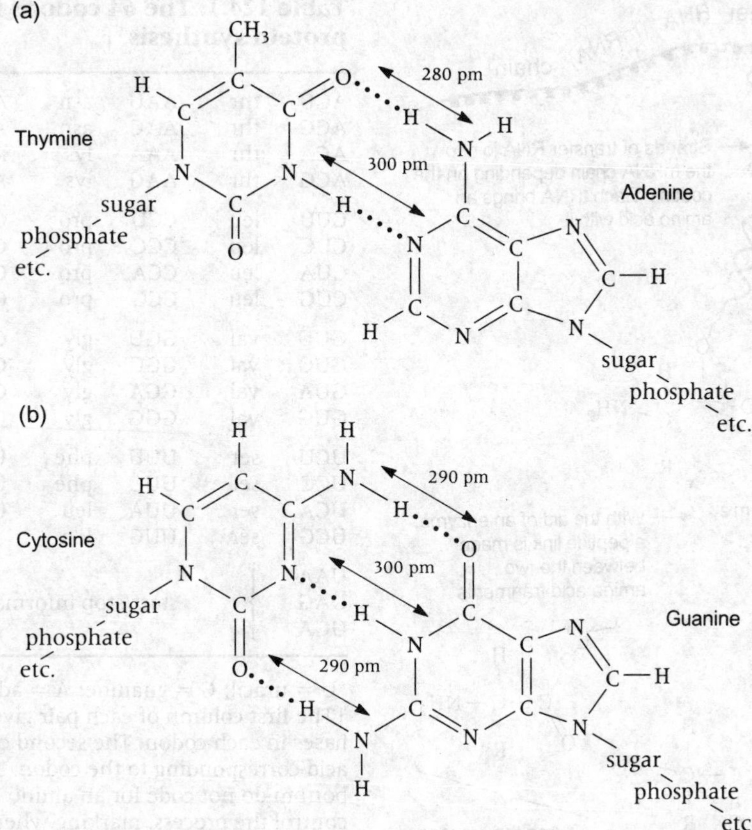

Figure 124.3 *How the bases hydrogen bond in DNA: (a) thymine H bonded to adenine; (b) cytosine H bonded to guanine*

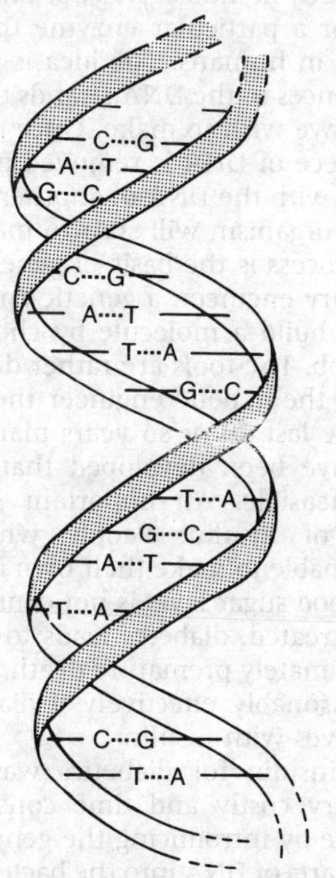

Figure 124.4 *A representation of how the two strands of DNA wind about one another. A, C, G and T are the four bases (see text). Dotted lines represent hydrogen bonds*

than either DNA or RNA.) Each molecule of tRNA carries with it a single amino acid. Now, the bases along the length of ribosomal RNA act as a code for different types of tRNA. This means that along the length of ribosomal RNA gather the various tRNA molecules, each with its own particular amino acid on the end.

(c) *Step 3: amino acids on transfer RNA form peptide links*

The amino acids are so close together that they join by making peptide links. As this happens, the tRNA minus its amino acid leaves the surface of the ribosomal RNA. The length of the peptide chain increases until one of the codons on the ribosomal RNA does not code for a tRNA with an amino acid. If, as is usually the case, the chain is very long, it wraps round to give a fibrous or globular structure.

DNA has the ability to replicate itself. It does this by unzipping and the two strands make copies of themselves. Over many generations of a species, random changes occur to DNA. Such changes are called *mutations*. Mutations can happen by chance (randomly), but others can be induced by physical or chemical factors, e.g. some types of radioactivity.

A mutation occurs when, after DNA unzips, the order of the bases in the new strands becomes slightly mixed up. Sometimes a mutation may be of little importance.

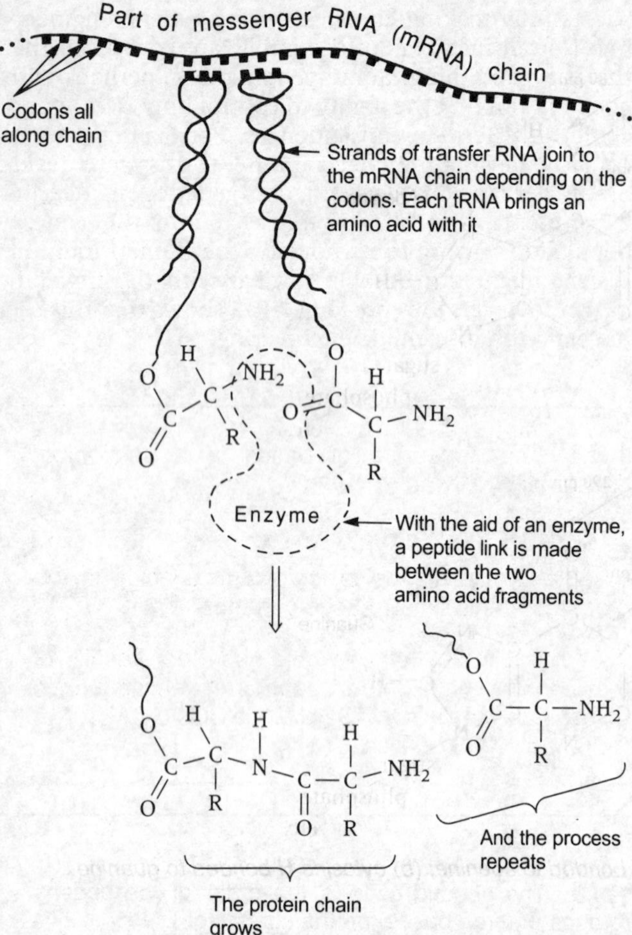
Part of messenger RNA (mRNA) chain
Codons all along chain
Strands of transfer RNA join to the mRNA chain depending on the codons. Each tRNA brings an amino acid with it
Enzyme
With the aid of an enzyme, a peptide link is made between the two amino acid fragments
And the process repeats
The protein chain grows

***Figure 124.5** How a protein chain is created from mRNA*

For example, suppose that part of the DNA normally produces the codon UAU in RNA. Now imagine that the order of bases in DNA is upset so that instead of UAU we get UAC in the RNA. The change may have no effect on the ability of the RNA to produce the same protein as before. This is because both UAU and UAC code for the same amino acid, tyrosine. Mutations like this are neither good nor bad; they are neutral. It is likely that the great majority of changes in DNA are neutral.

However, if the change was from UAU to UAA, then things are very different. This is because UAA is one of the stop codons. If the mutation happened in a process controlling the development of a human embryo, then it could result in the child having a physical or mental disability; or it might result in a spontaneous abortion.

On the other hand, some changes in the order of bases might lead to changes in an organism that are beneficial; for example, allowing an enzyme to withstand a wider range of temperatures or pH before it is denatured.

124.3 Genetic engineering

DNA is remarkably efficient at making extremely complicated molecules. This fact has made DNA a popular

Table 124.1. The 64 codons in mRNA controlling protein synthesis*†

ACU	thr	AAU	asn	AUU	ile	AGU	ser
ACC	thr	AAC	asn	AUC	ile	AGC	ser
ACA	thr	AAA	lys	AUA	ile	AGA	arg
ACG	thr	AAG	lys	AUG	met	AGG	arg
CUU	leu	CCU	pro	CGU	arg	CAU	his
CUC	leu	CCC	pro	CGC	arg	CAC	his
CUA	leu	CCA	pro	CGA	arg	CAA	gln
CUG	leu	CCG	pro	CGG	arg	CAG	gln
GUU	val	GGU	gly	GCU	ala	GAU	asp
GUC	val	GGC	gly	GCC	ala	GAC	asp
GUA	val	GGA	gly	GCA	ala	GAA	glu
GUG	val	GGG	gly	GCG	ala	GAG	glu
UCU	ser	UUU	phe	UAU	tyr	UGU	cys
UCC	ser	UUC	phe	UAC	tyr	UGC	cys
UCA	ser	UUA	leu	UGG	tyr		
UCG	ser	UUG	leu				
UAA	start/stop information						
UAG							
UGA							

*U = uracil; G = guanine; A = adenine; C = cytosine
†The first column of each pair gives you the pattern of three bases in each codon. The second column gives the amino acid corresponding to the codon. The three codons at the bottom do not code for an amino acid. Instead, they help to control the process, marking where the meaningful codons start and stop

substance to study in industry. Let us imagine that there is a market for a particular enzyme that we know is made by DNA in humans. The idea is first to discover the base sequences in the DNA strands that code for the molecule that we wish to make. Once this is done, the appropriate piece of DNA is removed from the strand, and combined with the DNA of another organism. If all goes well this organism will start to make the enzyme for us. This process is the basis of genetic engineering. Like an ordinary engineer, a genetic engineer attempts to design and build a molecule by choosing the right tools for the job. The tools are rather different though; in the case of the genetic engineer they are pieces of DNA. Over the last 20 or so years many sophisticated techniques have been developed that make each of these stages feasible. An important example is the manufacture of insulin. People who suffer from diabetes are unable to make their own insulin, and as a result their blood sugar level is not controlled properly. If it is left untreated, diabetes leads to blindness, liver failure and ultimately premature death. The disease can be treated reasonably effectively if diabetics regularly inject themselves with insulin.

Originally, insulin for diabetics was isolated from animals, a very costly and time consuming process. Now it is made by introducing the genetic information contained in parts of DNA into the bacterium *Escherichia coli*. The *E. coli* makes insulin in sufficient quantities to produce the (roughly) 2 tonnes of insulin needed by the population of diabetics each year.

However, you should not imagine that making chemicals by genetic engineering is easy. Even though the correct piece of DNA is extracted and introduced into another organism, it may still not behave as required. For example, the conditions in a laboratory bottle may be very different to those in the cells that contained the parent DNA. The first samples of insulin prepared by genetic engineering were hopeless for use by diabetics. The protein strand in the insulin wound itself in a different way to that of normal insulin. The result was an insoluble solid.

Even so, the potential rewards for harnessing the power of DNA are immense and many companies are successfully making chemicals using genetic engineering. Not all members of the public are convinced that this is a good thing. Some people think, perhaps with good reason, that the ability to control how DNA works could have terrible consequences. For example, there could be devastating effects if a new virus were developed, perhaps by accident, in genetic engineering experiments, and it were released into the general population. Owing to its novelty, the human immune system might not be able to deal with the invading virus. However, the spread of AIDS shows that this can happen without genetic engineering.

124.1 What is the significance of the analysis of DNA which shows that adenine and thymine appear in equal amounts in DNA (as do guanine and cytosine)?

124.2 RNA contains the base uracil instead of thymine. Draw a diagram to show how uracil hydrogen bonds to adenine in RNA.

124.3 DNA is said to be at the heart of the genetic code. What is the basis of the code?

124.4 The sequence of bases in a section of ribosomal RNA was

CCUAGUUAUUCCGUGCAU

(i) What would be the order of amino acids in the protein that this set of bases code for?

(ii) What, if anything, would be the result of the following highlighted changes in the sequence of bases: (a) CCUAGCUAUUCCGUGCAU; (b) CCUAGUUAGUCCGUGCAU?

Answers

124.1 This matches with Crick and Watson's idea that these two bases always appear hydrogen bonded together on different strands in DNA.

124.2

to rest of chain

to rest of chain

124.3 The genetic code is the order of the codons (groups of three bases) on the strands of DNA.

124.4 (i) CCUAGUUAUUCCGUGCAU codes for ala.ser.tyr.ser.val.his.

(ii) (a) CCUAGCUAUUCCGUGCAU codes for ala.ser.tyr.ser.val.his as well because both AGU and AGC code for ser. (b) The first two codons give ala.ser, but the third (UAG) is a start/stop instruction. This mutation is potentially disastrous. It will stop the production of the normal protein.

UNIT 124 SUMMARY

- DNA:
  - (i) Is deoxyribonucleic acid.
  - (ii) Controls the development of all living things.
  - (iii) Has a very high molar mass.
  - (iv) Is built from chains of nucleotides (combination of phosphate, sugar and base groups).
  - (v) Has two α-helix strands held together by hydrogen bonds between base pairs.
  - (vi) Only four bases are present: adenine, guanine, cytosine and thymine.
- Operation of DNA:
  - (i) Every pattern of three bases (codon) along a strand of DNA acts as a code for an amino acid.
  - (ii) The process of making polypeptide chains is: production of messenger RNA; RNA passes on information to make proteins; amino acids on transfer RNA form peptide links; thus the chain grows.
- Genetic code:
  Is the order of the codons on the strands of DNA.

125

Carbohydrates

125.1 What are carbohydrates?

In this unit we shall investigate three types of chemical that, in addition to proteins and DNA, play a very important role in living things. Carbohydrates are substances that contain three elements only: carbon, hydrogen and oxygen. The simplest ones are the sugars, which have the ability to link together to make polymers such as starch and cellulose.

The simplest carbohydrates are the *monosaccharides*, which all have the general formula $C_nH_{2n}O_n$. You will be familiar with some of them because we know them as sugars; for example when $n=6$ we have glucose, $C_6H_{12}O_6$. They all have OH groups in their molecules, together with either an aldehyde

```
       O
      //
R—C
      \
       H
```

Table 125.1. The naming of the common types of monosaccharide

Number of carbon atoms	*Known as*	*Molecule contains*	*Known as*
3	A triose	Aldehyde group	An aldose
5	A pentose	Ketone group	A ketose
6	A hexose		

*Examples**

Triose | *Pentose* | *Hexose*

```
                                                       CHO             CH2OH
                                                        |                |
                    CHO            CHO             H—C—OH            C=O
                     |              |                   |                |
                H—C—OH        HO—C—H           HO—C—H          HO—C—H
                     |              |                   |                |
   CHO          H—C—OH         H—C—OH           H—C—OH           H—C—OH
    |                |              |                   |                |
H—C—OH          H—C—OH         H—C—OH           H—C—OH           H—C—OH
    |                |              |                   |                |
  CH2OH            CH2OH          CH2OH               CH2OH            CH2OH
```

Glyceraldehyde	Ribose	Arabinose	Glucose	Fructose
$C_3H_6O_3$	$C_5H_{10}O_5$	$C_5H_{10}O_5$	$C_6H_{12}O_6$	$C_6H_{12}O_6$

*The diagrams of the molecules have been drawn using the convention we met in Unit 110. You should imagine the vertical lines bending away from you behind the plane of the page; the horizontal lines represent bonds bending towards you out of the plane of the page. If we were to be precise we should add a D in front of their names, e.g. D-glucose. The D tells us about the configuration of the molecules, i.e. how the different groups are arranged. Throughout this unit all the sugars have the D configuration. This method of indicating configurations uses the labels D and L. It is based on comparing molecules with the two possible configurations of glyceraldehyde. It is an older method than the *R*, *S* scheme of Unit 110

or ketone

$$R-\overset{\displaystyle O}{\overset{\|}{C}}-R'$$

group. As with many varieties of organic molecules, isomers are possible. In Table 125.1 you will find some of the more common sugar molecules listed. Each has its own particular name, but collectively they fit into groups according to the number of carbon atoms they possess. The naming system is also explained in the table.

125.2 The structures of carbohydrates

In Table 125.1 we have shown the sugars as straight-chain molecules. This is a useful way of showing the basic structure of the molecules, but in practice the pentoses and hexoses exist in different shapes. In most circumstances they occur naturally as *rings*. Figure 125.1 shows you diagrams of ribose and glucose.

125.3 Polysaccharides

For humans the most obvious property of sugars is that they taste sweet. The 'sugar' you might have at home to sweeten drinks and foodstuffs is sucrose (Figure 125.2). This is a sugar made from a molecule of glucose and a molecule of fructose. It is an example of a *disaccharide* (the prefix *di-* meaning two).

However, sugar molecules can join together to make polymer chains of great length. These are the *polysaccharides*, such as starch, cellulose (Figure 125.3) and glycogen. Animals, including the human variety, store carbohydrates in their bodies in the form of glycogen. It is a complicated polymer made from glucose monomer

A simple model of glucose which shows the puckered ring of five carbon and one oxygen atoms.

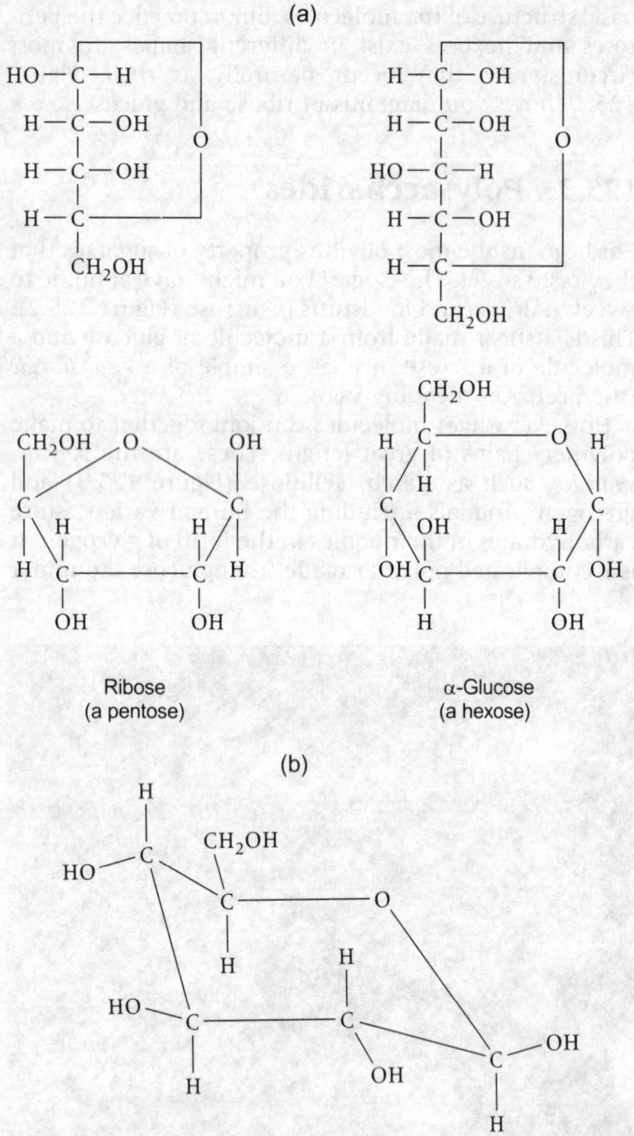

(a)

Ribose
(a pentose)

α-Glucose
(a hexose)

(b)

Figure 125.1 *Diagrams showing the structures of two sugars. (a) Two ways of showing the structures of the sugars ribose and α-glucose. (b) This gives a more realistic impression of the ring in α-glucose*

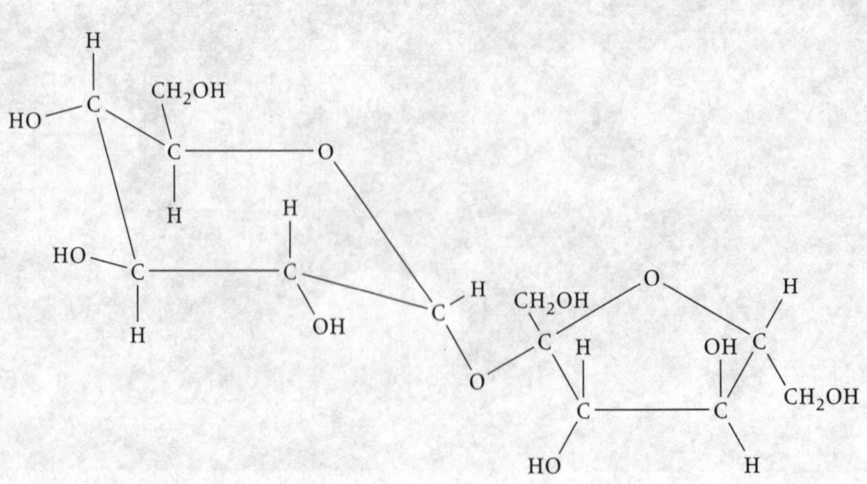

Figure 125.2 *The structure of sucrose – a disaccharide*

units. The virtue of glycogen is that, when energy is needed quickly in the body, it releases its glucose relatively easily.

Carbon dioxide, water vapour and sunlight are converted into glucose by chlorophyll in plants. Glucose can be used by plants to build starch and cellulose. Cellulose is the key ingredient of the fibres that are the basic building material of plants. Humans make use of starch molecules as a source of carbohydrate, but the metabolism of humans cannot convert cellulose into anything of nutritional value. However, cows and other ruminants are able to decompose cellulose. Hence cows rather than humans are to be found grazing on grass day after day.

Cellulose has uses apart from feeding cows (Table 125.2). It was one of the first materials to be converted into an artificial fibre, Rayon. You will find an outline of the process in Figure 125.4.

Table 125.2. Some uses of cellulose products

Cellulose	Gives a sense of smoothness to the taste of ice cream and whipped cream toppings As a harmless binding agent in medicines In products where water absorbency is important, e.g. disposable nappies Manufacture of artificial fibres such as Rayon Manufacture of thin, protective sheeting, especially Cellophane
Cellulose acetate	Manufacture of photographic film
Cellulose nitrate	Used in the explosives industry as gun cotton

125.4 Three properties of sugars

(a) *Hydrolysis*

If you eat potatoes, crisps or bread, the enzyme salivary amylase in your saliva rapidly breaks down the starch into smaller units, especially glucose. It is the monomer

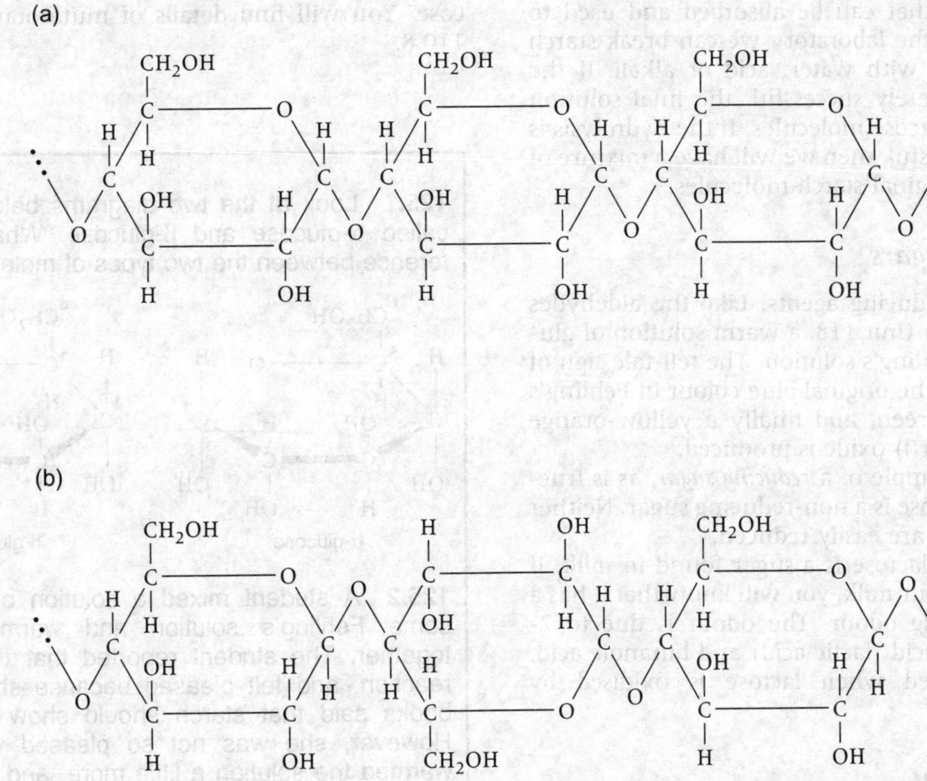

(a)

(b)

Figure 125.3 *The structures of starch and cellulose. (a) A typical fragment of a chain of sugars in starch. (b) A fragment of the chain of sugars in cellulose*

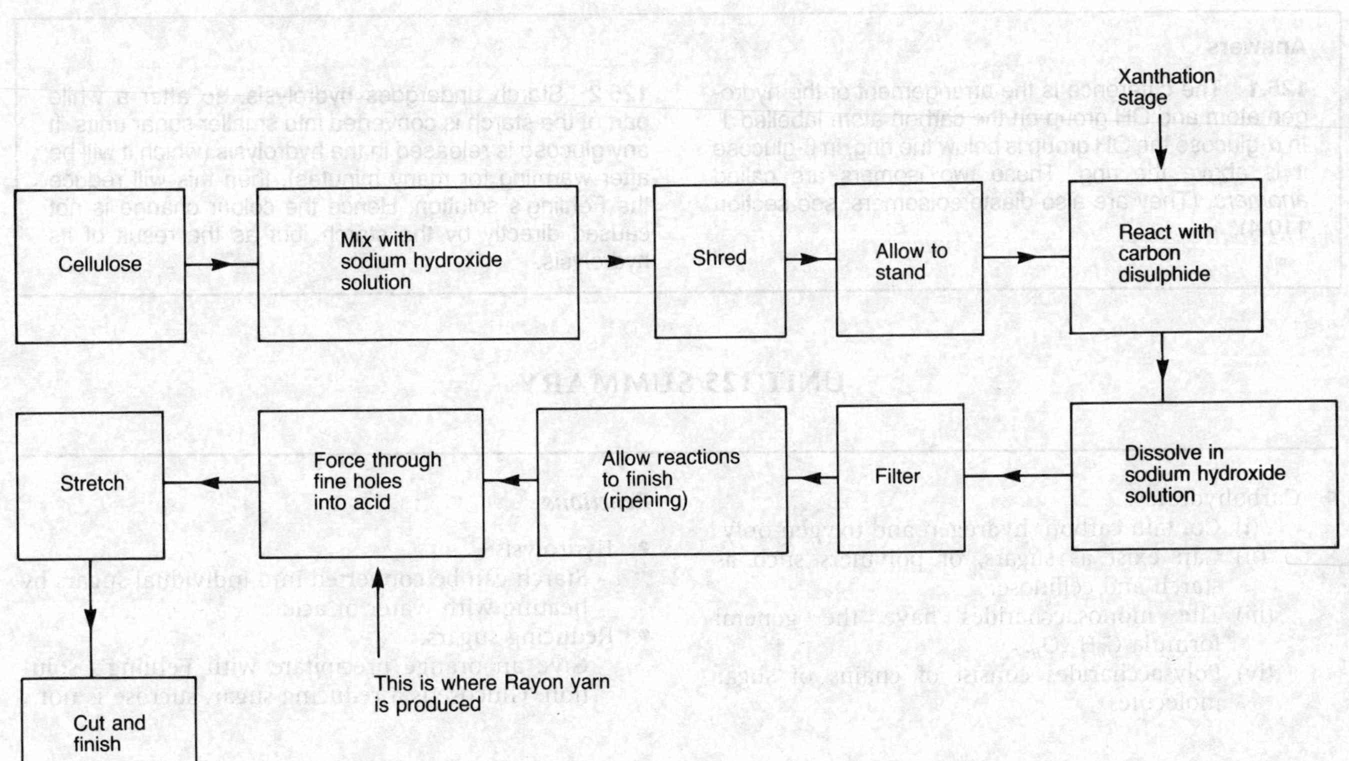

Figure 125.4 *Flowchart for the manufacture of Rayon from cellulose. The reaction with carbon disulphide, CS_2, called xanthation, has the effect of introducing sulphur atoms into the carbohydrate chains*

glucose molecules that can be absorbed and used to provide energy. In the laboratory we can break starch apart by heating it with water, acid or alkali. If the hydrolysis is completely successful, the final solution will only contain glucose molecules. If the hydrolysis is only partially successful, then we will have a mixture of fragments of the original starch molecules.

(b) *Reducing sugars*

Many sugars are reducing agents. Like the aldehydes that we discussed in Unit 118, a warm solution of glucose will reduce Fehling's solution. The tell-tale sign of the reaction is that the original blue colour of Fehling's solution becomes green, and finally a yellow-orange precipitate of copper(I) oxide is produced.

Glucose is an example of a *reducing sugar*, as is fructose; however, sucrose is a non-reducing sugar. Neither starch nor cellulose are easily reduced.

The disaccharide lactose is a sugar found in milk. If you have smelled sour milk, you will know that it has a particularly revolting odour. The odour is due to 2-hydroxypropanoic acid (lactic acid) and butanoic acid, which are produced when lactose is oxidised by bacteria.

(c) *Mutarotation*

The mutarotation of sugars is the spontaneous change in optical rotation of a solution of a sugar such as glucose. You will find details of mutarotation in section 110.8.

125.1 Look at the two diagrams below. They are called α-glucose and β-glucose. What is the difference between the two types of molecule?

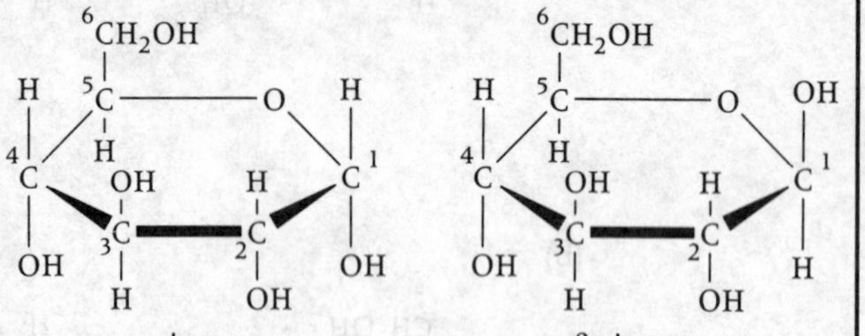

α-glucose β-glucose

125.2 A student mixed a solution of starch with some Fehling's solution and warmed the two together. The student reported that there was no reaction, and felt pleased because she knew that books said that starch should show no reaction. However, she was not so pleased when having warmed the solution a little more, and leaving for a few minutes, she saw the blue solution turning green. What had happened?

Answers

125.1 The difference is the arrangement of the hydrogen atom and OH group on the carbon atom labelled 1. In α-glucose the OH group is below the ring, in β-glucose it is above the ring. These two isomers are called *anomers*. (They are also diastereoisomers; see section 110.4).

125.2 Starch undergoes hydrolysis, so after a while part of the starch is converted into smaller sugar units. If any glucose is released in the hydrolysis (which it will be after warming for many minutes), then this will reduce the Fehling's solution. Hence the colour change is not caused directly by the starch, but as the result of its hydrolysis.

UNIT 125 SUMMARY

- Carbohydrates:
  - (i) Contain carbon, hydrogen and oxygen only.
  - (ii) Can exist as sugars, or polymers such as starch and cellulose.
  - (iii) The monosaccharides have the general formula $C_nH_{2n}O_n$.
  - (iv) Polysaccharides consist of chains of sugar molecules.

Reactions

- Hydrolysis:
  Starch can be converted into individual sugars by heating with water or acid.
- Reducing sugars:
  Give an orange precipitate with Fehling's solution. Glucose is a reducing sugar, sucrose is not.

126

Vitamins, hormones, steroids and pharmaceuticals

126.1 Vitamins

Vitamins are one of the types of chemical that are essential ingredients of our diet. Without them we would develop a variety of *deficiency diseases*. The disease scurvy results from a lack of vitamin C in the diet. Scurvy was responsible for the extremely high death rate among sailors on long sea voyages during the seventeenth and eighteenth centuries. For example, a three-year voyage lead by Lord Anson in 1740 began with 961 men and finished with 335, a death rate of 65%. Even higher death rates were recorded. The symptoms of scurvy were described in 1725 like this:

> [the sufferers] have spots first red, then growing Livid and Blackish, infesting the Limbs and several Parts with an unusual lassitude or weariness, And who have dark red, itching, and corrupted Gums with a looseness of Teeth, that can't bear the least rub without bleeding . . . shifting Pains frequent about the Limbs and Gums: joined with a very unequal Pulse . . .

Although scurvy is often associated with sailors, the disease was widespread among populations on land as well. The very poor were prone to scurvy because they could not afford to buy food of any reasonable quality. However, the rich also developed scurvy because of eating a diet almost devoid of fruit and vegetables. For those who could afford it, scurvy could be cured by eating fruit or by drinking fresh lemon juice, both sources of vitamin C. In Ireland the poor traditionally ate a diet of potatoes, which happen to have a good deal of vitamin C in them. When the potato crop failed in the years 1845–1849, tens of thousands of people died, partly as a direct result of scurvy, and partly owing to scurvy making them susceptible to other fatal diseases like typhus.

Humans cannot make their own vitamin C, so it has to be obtained by eating the right types of food. This is true of other vitamins as well. Some vitamins can be synthesised naturally by our bodies. Vitamin D is made by a reaction in skin when it is in sunlight.

Table 126.1 gives you information about vitamins.

126.2 Hormones and steroids

Hormones act as chemical messengers controlling the activity and development of living things. In humans they are released in small amounts into the blood stream from a number of important sites, especially the pituitary gland. This gland takes up a small part of the brain (it weighs less than 1 g) but it is a vital source of over 20 hormones. The protein insulin, which we discussed in Unit 123, is a hormone that is secreted from the pancreas. It controls the concentration of glucose in blood ('blood sugar level'). In plants as well as in humans hormones control growth rate. A set of hormones called *oestrogens* and *androgens* control the sexual development of females and males respectively. Some examples of hormones are shown in Table 126.2.

From Figure 126.1 you can see that some hormones are peptides (built from amino acids); others are steroids. Steroids are compounds based on the combination of three cyclohexane rings and one five-membered ring, shown in Figure 126.2.

The advances made in our understanding of the structures and functions of hormones have had many repercussions. Among the most important has been the development of the female contraceptive pill. There are many different types of contraceptive pill, but most of them do not use the same hormones that are released naturally in females. Rather, slightly different molecules are used, which mimic the behaviour of the natural hormones. The aim is the same, to prevent conception taking place. One way of doing this is to use a substance that suppresses the monthly release of eggs during the menstrual cycle. Another method is to use a drug that blocks the action of one or more of the natural hormones, such as progesterone, which is vital for the maintenance of pregnancy. There have been many studies of the possible side effects that could result from the use of contraceptive pills. The evidence is not completely clear. Certain groups of women appear to be more susceptible to diseases, e.g. those who smoke heavily are likely to have a higher incidence of heart disease in later life. However, other groups show little or no increased risk.

Steroids are another important class of natural prod-

Table 126.1. Important vitamins

Vitamin	*Source*	*Deficiency disease*
A (retinol)	Fruit, vegetables	Lack of the vitamin leads to blindness and impairs growth
B_1 (thiamin)	Cereals	Beriberi: nervous system stops working properly
C (ascorbic acid)	Fruit, vegetables	Scurvy: bleeding gums, pain in limbs, blindness
D (cholecalciferol)	Action of sunlight on skin	Rickets: faulty bone growth, leading to deformed limbs

Table 126.2. Examples of hormones

Hormone	*What it does*
Adrenaline	The 'flight or fight hormone'; produced in response to abnormal degree of stress or excitement, especially in response to danger
Gibberellic acid	Encourages the growth of plant shoots
Insulin	Controls blood sugar level
Oestrogen	Prepares the uterus of a female for possible pregnancy
Oxytocin	Induces labour in pregnant women
Progesterone	Suppresses production of eggs from follicles in the female
Somatotrophin	Known as growth hormone, controls growth of humans
Testosterone	One of the androgen hormones secreted from the testes in males; helps to govern qualities linked to maleness, e.g. in sexual organs, body hair, muscle bulk

ucts. They all play some part in biochemical systems. Indeed, as we have seen, some of them are sex hormones.

In recent years the use of anabolic steroids among athletes has become a matter of great concern. Many of the androgens (male steroids) are involved in growth processes such as muscle formation. By taking them an athlete can become fitter and stronger more rapidly

Adrenaline

Progesterone

Testosterone

cys · tyr · ile · glu · asp · cys · pro · leu · gly · NH_2

Oxytocin: a hormone made from amino acids linked by peptide bonds

***Figure 126.1** Examples of hormones*

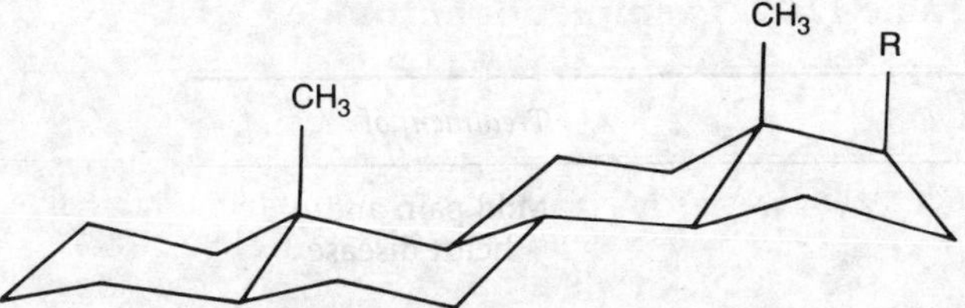

__Figure 126.2__ The basic structure of a steroid. There are carbon atoms where the lines meet. The hydrogen atoms are not shown. The group R changes with the nature of the steroid. (Adapted from: Morrison, R. T. and Boyd, R. N. (1966). Organic Chemistry, 2nd edn, Allyn and Bacon, Boston, p. 521)

than someone who does not take the steroid. However, long-term use of steroids can have very dangerous side effects (apart from more obvious effects like becoming extremely hairy).

Two other steroids that have gained a reputation for themselves are cholesterol and cortisone. (Strictly, cholesterol and other similar molecules that have an OH group should be called sterols.) These are shown in Figure 126.3. Cholesterol has been proposed as the chemical responsible for the hardening (blocking) of arteries, and therefore as a cause of heart attacks. It is also linked to the formation of gall stones. The evidence suggests that it is best to avoid eating large amounts of foods that are high in cholesterol, e.g. whites of eggs and animal fats. However, you will not be able to avoid cholesterol all together because it is made in the liver. It may be that some people are more liable to suffer from heart disease because of the cholesterol produced in their own bodies rather than because they eat the wrong things. Cortisone is used by tens of thousands of people as treatment for arthritis, a very painful disease of the bones and joints.

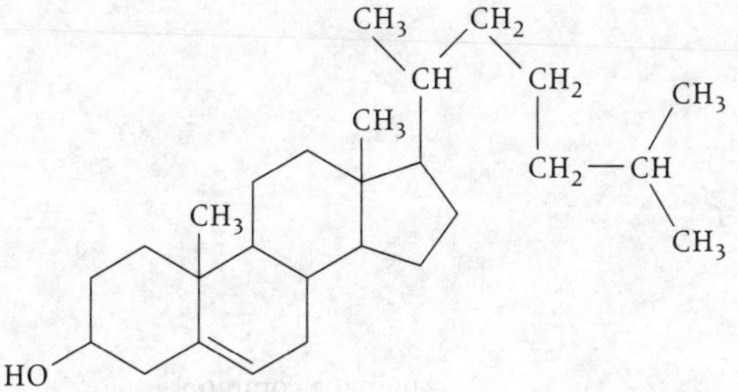

Cholesterol

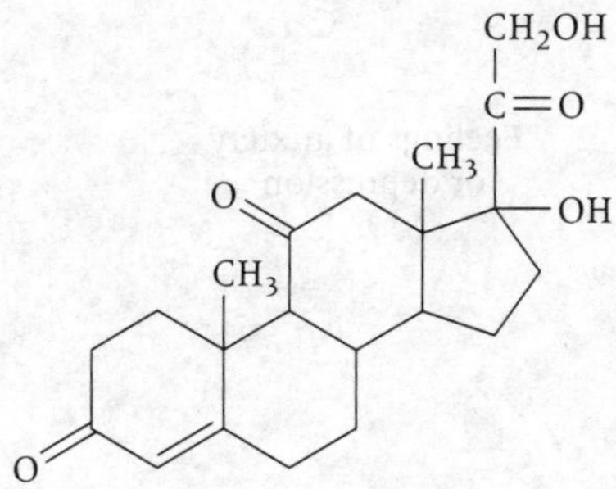

Cortisone

***Figure 126.3** Two steroids that are important in medicine*

126.3 Pharmaceuticals

Pharmaceuticals are chemicals that are prepared and sold with the intention of treating disease. You might be happy to call such chemicals by the shorter name: drugs. However, we tend to think of a drug as a substance that is not used to treat illness but, like heroin, is taken illegally by people simply for the short-term pleasurable effects it can give. Some pharmaceuticals are well known, particularly aspirin and paracetamol. Others are less common, but of extreme importance. Examples are listed in Table 126.3. Recently there has been increasing evidence not only that aspirin will suppress headaches and minor pains, but that its regular use helps to protect the user against heart disease.

The pharmaceutical industry is one of the most important parts of the chemical industry. The market for pharmaceuticals has increased until it is worth billions of pounds each year. Millions of people benefit from the treatment they receive for illnesses that even 10 years ago would have been impossible to treat. We often take it for granted that an operation in hospital, or a visit to the dentist, can be (almost) painless. In fact the advances made in the design of pharmaceuticals have been so successful that we tend to think that almost every complaint will be able to be treated. Nature is not so easily overcome! For example, when it was first widely used against bacterial infection during the Second World War, penicillin was almost 100% effective. Now a wide range of bacteria have adapted so that they are resistant to it. As a consequence, there is always a need for the pharmaceutical industry to adapt and design new, more powerful, anti-bacterial products.

Many pharmaceuticals act directly on the brain. Valium does this. It is widely prescribed for people who are over-anxious or depressed. Valium is not in itself addictive, but its long-term use makes people dependent on it. Some people have criticised doctors for prescribing valium, because it does little to change the reason why the patient is over-anxious. However, doctors may say that they are not able to treat the main cause, which might be due to emotional strains, e.g. of divorce or living in an over-crowded flat.

The *opiates* are drugs that cause addiction. Heroin and cocaine (Figure 126.4) are among the most famous (or infamous) examples. The chemistry of the brain adapts to the presence of the opiate in such a way that the person taking the drug feels an uncontrollable need to take more of it. Owing to their ability to induce an artificial feeling of well-being, the person taking heroin or cocaine quickly becomes addicted to them. Once this happens, the craving for the drug often causes the person to:

Table 126.3. Some important pharmaceuticals

Name	*Structure*	*Treatment of*
Aspirin	benzene ring bearing $C(=O){-}O{-}H$ and $O{-}C(=O){-}CH_3$	Mild pain and heart disease
Paracetamol	$HO{-}C_6H_4{-}N(H){-}C(=O){-}CH_3$	Mild pain
Timolol	morpholine ring (O, N) attached to thiadiazole ring (C, C, N, S, N); $O{-}CH_2{-}C(H)(OH){-}CH_2{-}N(H){-}C(CH_3)_3$	Glaucoma, an eye disease causing blindness
Morphine (for structure, see Figure 126.4)		Analgesic – masking of severe pain
Penicillin	$R{-}C(=O){-}N(H){-}$ on β-lactam ring (C=O, N) fused with ring containing S, $C(CH_3)_2$, and $C(=O)OH$; R varies	Bacterial infections
Nitroglycerin	CH_2ONO_2 – $CHONO_2$ – CH_2ONO_2	Angina, a common heart condition
Valium	ring with $N(CH_3){-}C(=O){-}CH_2{-}N{=}C$, fused to benzene ring bearing Cl, with phenyl group	Feelings of anxiety or depression

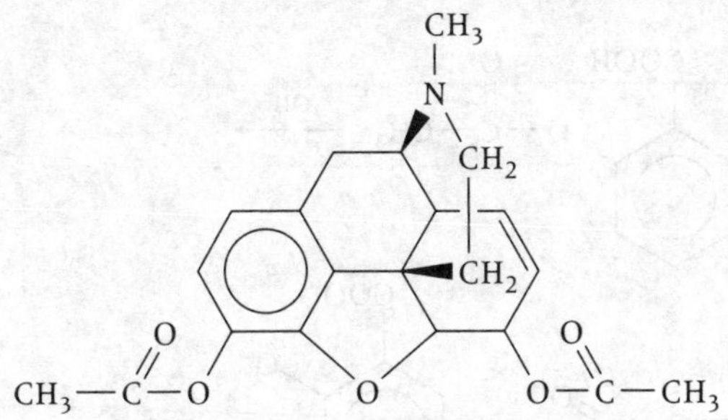

Heroin

(Morphine has OH groups in place of the CH_3COO groups)

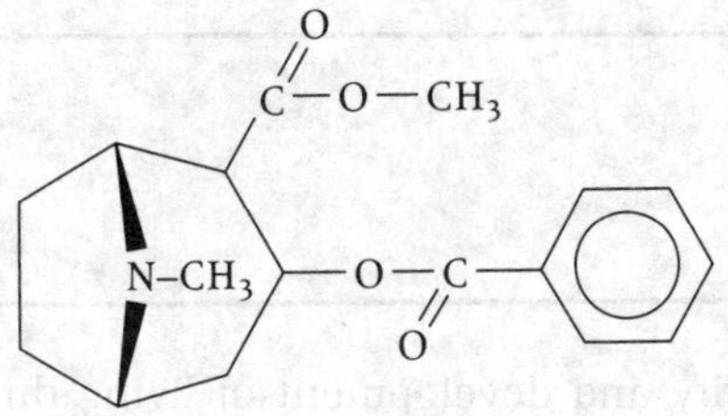

Cocaine

Figure 126.4 Two most dangerous opiates

(i) neglect their nutritional needs;
(ii) neglect ordinary rules of hygiene;
(iii) enter into a life of crime or prostitution in order to obtain the cash necessary to buy the drug.

As a result a drug addict often becomes thin and susceptible to illness. Especially, those injecting drugs are highly likely to become infected by AIDS. Unfortunately, women heroin addicts often become pregnant and their babies are born already showing the signs of addiction. For society at large, addiction to heroin and cocaine poses two linked problems: one of law and order, another of public health. The wise person avoids any contact with illegal drugs, or those using them.

126.1 Look at the structure of testosterone in Figure 126.1 and predict the result of reacting this hormone with:

(i) bromine;

(ii) sodium;

(iii) phosphorus pentachloride;

(iv) 2,4-dinitrophenylhydrazine.

126.2 Here is an account of the preparation of a well known analgesic.

Approximately 10 g of 2-hydroxybenzoic acid should be carefully added to a mixture of 10 cm^3 of ethanoic anhydride and 10 cm^3 ethanoic acid. (The latter mixture is used as an acetylating reagent.) The mixture should be refluxed for about 30 minutes. After cooling, the mixture should be poured into cold water and the white solid filtered off and recrystallised.

(i) Draw a diagram of 2-hydroxybenzoic acid.

(ii) Draw a diagram of ethanoic anhydride.

(iii) Draw a diagram of the product.

(iv) What is the name of the product?

(v) What is meant by the word 'analgesic'?

(vi) Predict how the product would react when refluxed with sodium hydroxide solution.

Answers

126.1 The key to answering this question is to realise that the chemistry of carbon compounds is mainly the chemistry of the functional groups. We can see three of them here: a double bond, as in an alkene; an OH group like that in an alcohol; and a >C=O group like that in a ketone. If you know the chemistry of these three groups, you can predict the outcome of the reactions.

(i) Bromine atoms will add on to each end of the double bond. (The bromine will be decolourised.)

(ii) Hydrogen will be given off when sodium reacts with an OH group.

(iii) Fumes of HCl will be given off. (This is the usual test for an OH group.)

(iv) A hydrazone will be made when the 2,4-dinitrophenylhydrazine reacts with the carbonyl group. (A standard reaction of the carbonyl group.)

126.2 (i)

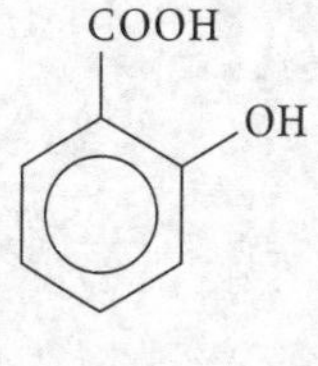

(ii)

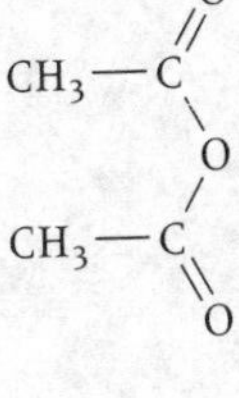

Answers – contd.

(iii)

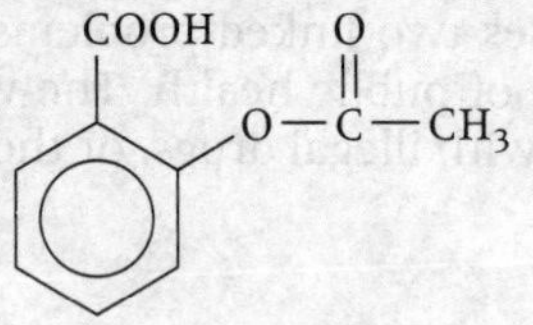

(iv) Its common name is aspirin.

(v) An analgesic relieves pain.

(vi) Aspirin is an ester, so we would expect it to undergo hydrolysis in the same way as do other esters (see Unit 120). The reaction is:

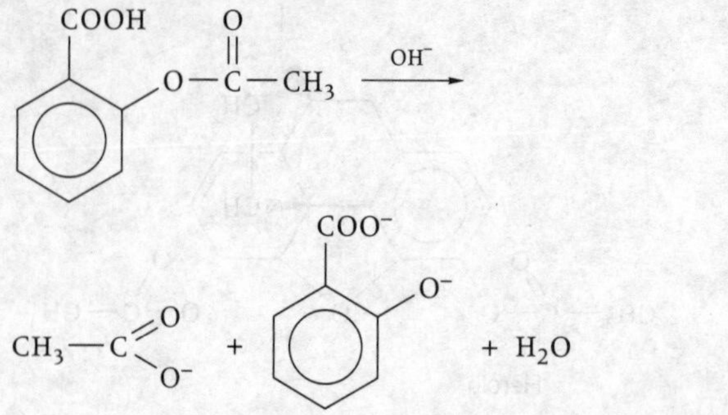

$$CH_3COOC_6H_4COOH \xrightarrow{OH^-} CH_3COO^- + {}^-OC_6H_4COO^- + H_2O$$

UNIT 126 SUMMARY

- Vitamins:
  Are essential for preventing deficiency diseases. See Table 126.1.
- Hormones and steroids:
  Act as chemical messengers, controlling the activity and development of living things. See Table 126.2.
- Pharmaceuticals:
  Are used to treat disease and to control biochemical processes. See Table 126.3.

127

Polymers

127.1 Monomers and polymers

The Swedish chemist Jacob Berzelius invented the word *polymeric* in 1832. He understood that some chemicals could have the same molecular formula as each other, and therefore the same empirical formula. These molecules were recognised to be isomers. However, chemists also knew that some molecules had the same empirical formulae, but different molecular formulae. An example that we are familiar with is ethyne, C_2H_2, and benzene, C_6H_6. They have the same empirical formula, CH, but different molecular formulae. At the time when Berzelius was working, chemists' knowledge of the structures of molecules was markedly different to ours. In particular, it was a great puzzle why molecules with the same empirical formula could have different chemical properties. Berzelius thought that such molecules belonged to a special class of isomers. He said:

> To describe this equality of composition coupled with a difference of properties I suggest that such substances be called polymeric.

In the years following this definition, chemists began to refer to benzene as a polymer of ethyne. Most chemists would not now think of benzene as a polymer. Our modern notion of a polymer includes the notion that it must have a *high relative molecular mass*. A typical example is poly(ethene), better known as polythene. It is a giant molecule made when thousands of ethene molecules join together to make a long chain. Ethene molecules are the *monomers*, which join to make the *polymer*:

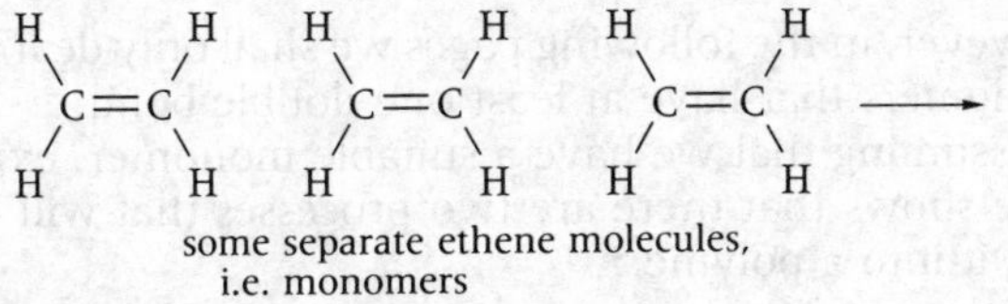

some separate ethene molecules, i.e. monomers

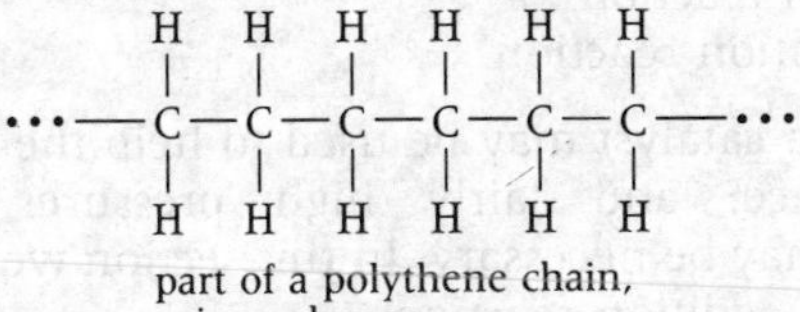

part of a polythene chain, i.e. polymer

We can represent a polythene chain by the formula $-(C_2H_4)_n-$. Here the subscript n means a very large number (e.g. 10 000) of C_2H_4 units joined together. You should be able to see that the empirical formula of polythene is CH_2, just as it is for ethene. It is often claimed that the first polymerisation reaction was performed in 1839 by a German pharmacist, E. Simon. He heated an extract of a resin from a tree with sodium carbonate solution and found a rubbery substance. Unbeknown to Simon, the resin extract contained styrene (systematic name phenylethene), and the rubbery substance was polystyrene (poly(phenylethene)):

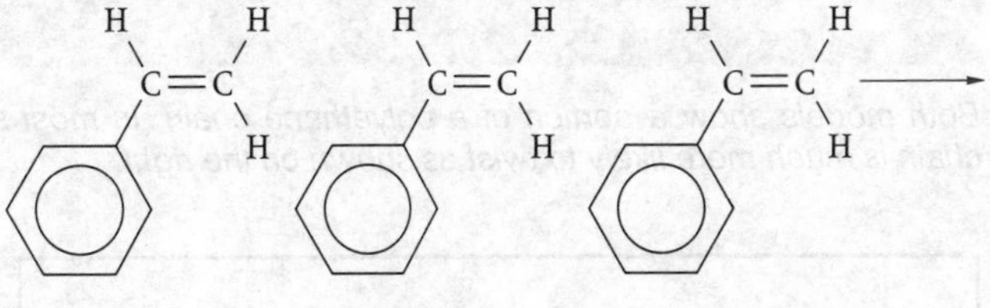

styrene monomers

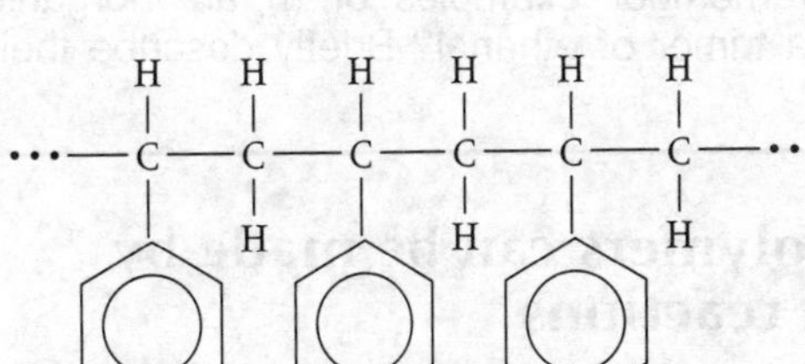

polystyrene

However, Richard Watson (Bishop of Llandaff) has a prior claim to that of Simon. Between 1782 and 1800, Watson reported in a series of '*Chemical Essays*' that:

> The most transparent oil of turpentine, resembling naphtha, may be changed into an oil resembling petroleum by mixing it with a small portion of the acid of vitriol; with a larger proportion of the acid, the mixture becomes black and tenacious, like Barbadoes tar; and the proportions of the ingredients may be so adjusted, that the mixture will acquire a solid consistence, like asphaltum.

The 'tenacious tar' was a polymer.

Both models show a portion of a polyethene chain. In most situations, the model on the left is an idealised version. The chain is much more likely to twist as shown on the right.

> **127.1** Benzene can be called a trimer of ethyne. Can you remember examples of (i) an inorganic dimer, (ii) a trimer of ethanal? Briefly describe their structures.

127.2 Polymers can be made by addition reactions

You may have noticed that ethene and styrene molecules have a double bond. This feature of their structure is shared by many, but not all, molecules that will polymerise. An example of a polymerisation in which the monomers have no double bonds is the change from rhombic sulphur to plastic sulphur (see section 100.2):

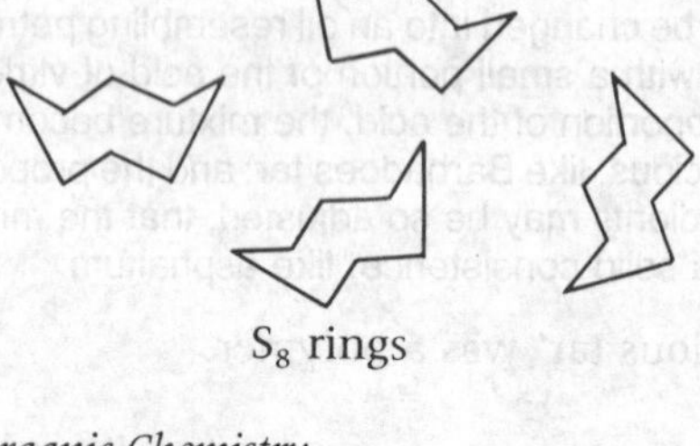

S_8 rings

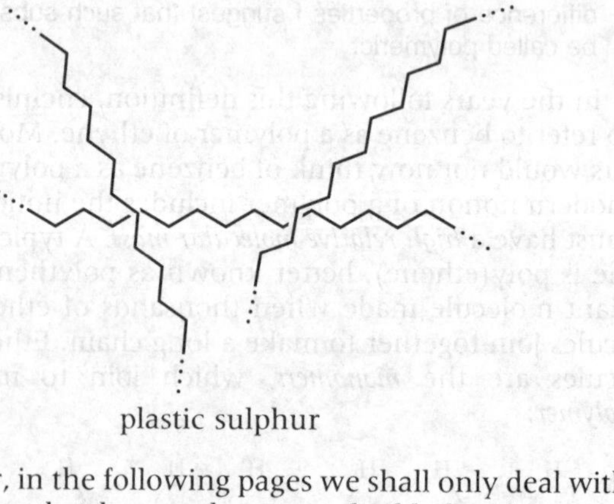

plastic sulphur

However, in the following pages we shall only deal with monomers that have at least one double bond.

Assuming that we have a suitable monomer, experience shows that there are two processes that will convert it into a polymer:

(**i**) an addition reaction, or
(**ii**) a condensation reaction.

In both cases, a catalyst may be used to help the reaction take place, and fairly high pressures and temperatures may be necessary. In this section we shall concentrate on addition reactions.

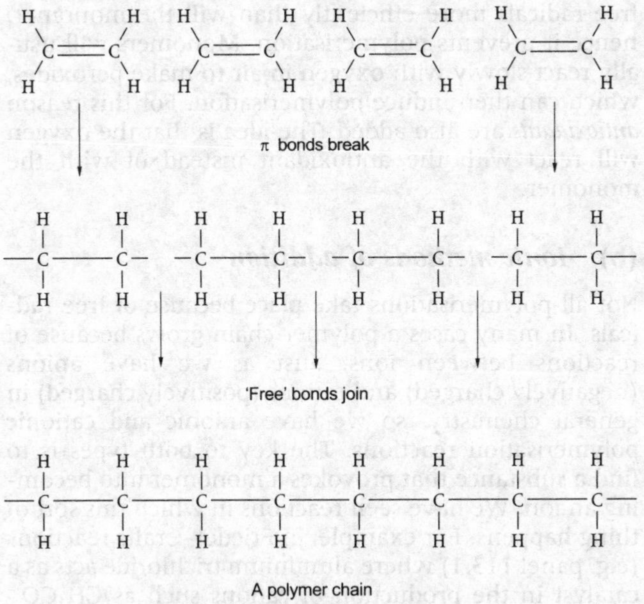

'π bonds break'

'Free' bonds join

A polymer chain

***Figure 127.1** Making poly(ethene) from ethene*

A typical example of an addition polymerisation is the conversion of ethene into poly(ethene) (often called polythene). If we adopt a simple view of the reaction, we can think of the π bond in each ethene molecule breaking to give two 'free bonds' at each end of the molecule. These bonds can be used to join neighbouring molecules, which therefore add together. This is the situation represented in Figure 127.1. However, this *is* a naive view of how the reaction actually takes place. To understand why things cannot be this simple, we should look at experimental evidence that comes from studies of the kinetics of polymerisation reactions. A crucial piece of information is that reactions like the polymerisation of ethene are catalysed by organic peroxides, which are a source of free radicals. (You will find details of free radicals in Unit 81.)

(a) *Free radical addition*

The three main steps in polymerisation are *initiation*, *propagation* and *termination*. For example, if we use benzoyl peroxide as an initiator of the polymerisation of fluoroethene, some of the reactions that occur are as follows:

(i) Initiation

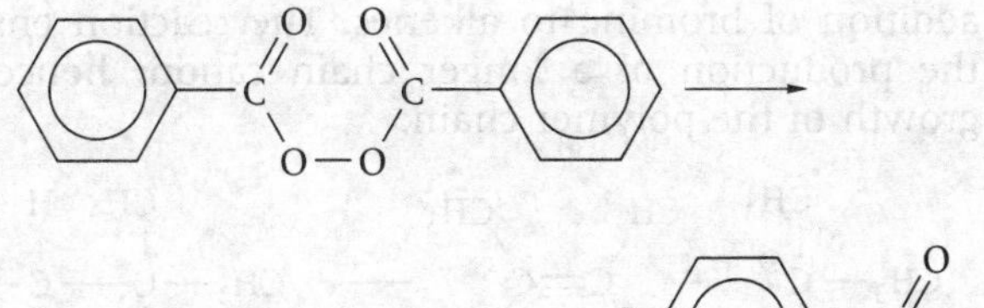

$$C_6H_5COO{-}OOCC_6H_5 \rightarrow 2C_6H_5COO\cdot$$

(ii) Propagation

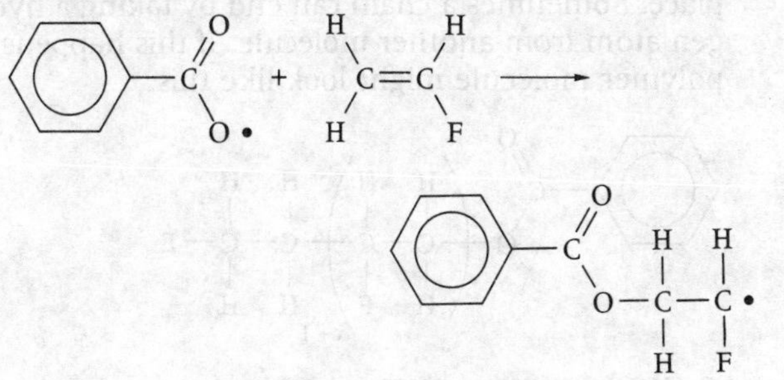

$$C_6H_5COO\cdot + CH_2{=}CHF \rightarrow C_6H_5COO{-}CH_2{-}CHF\cdot$$

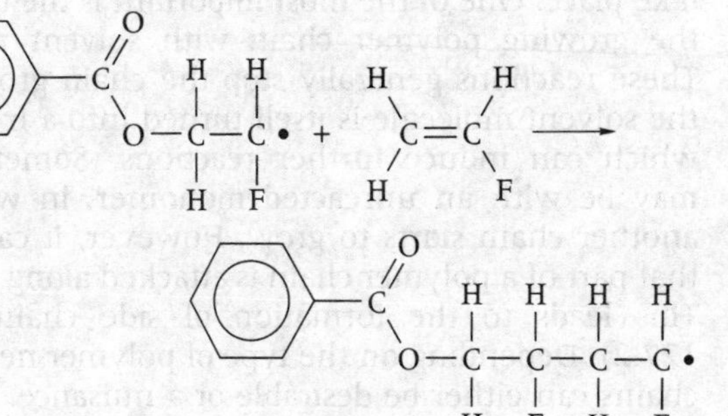

$$C_6H_5COO{-}CH_2{-}CHF\cdot + CH_2{=}CHF \rightarrow C_6H_5COO{-}CH_2{-}CHF{-}CH_2{-}CHF\cdot$$

After many such reactions,

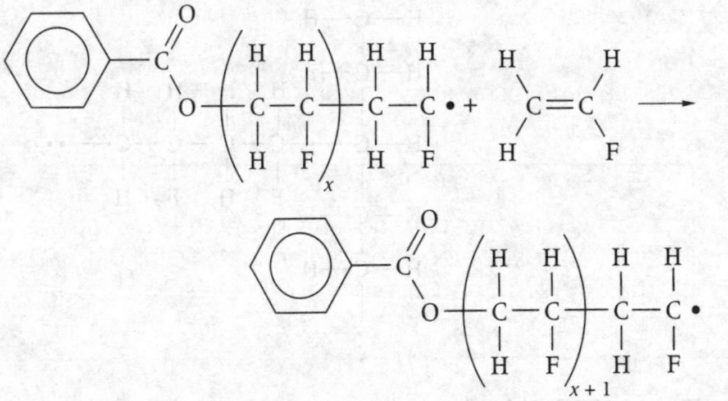

$$C_6H_5COO{-}(CH_2{-}CHF)_x{-}CH_2{=}CHF\cdot + CH_2{=}CHF \rightarrow C_6H_5COO{-}(CH_2{-}CHF)_{x+1}{-}CH_2{-}CHF\cdot$$

(iii) Termination

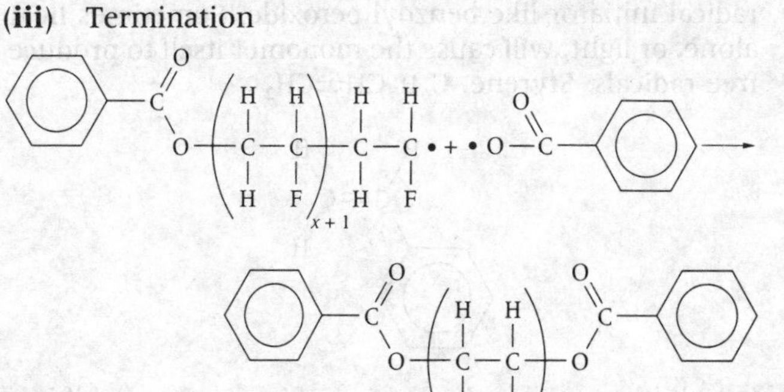

$$C_6H_5COO{-}(CH_2{-}CHF)_{x+1}{-}CH_2{-}CHF + OOCC_6H_5 \rightarrow C_6H_5COO{-}(CH_2{-}CHF)_n{-}OOCC_6H_5$$

This is only one way in which termination can take place. Sometimes a chain can end by taking a hydrogen atom from another molecule. If this happens the polymer molecule might look like this:

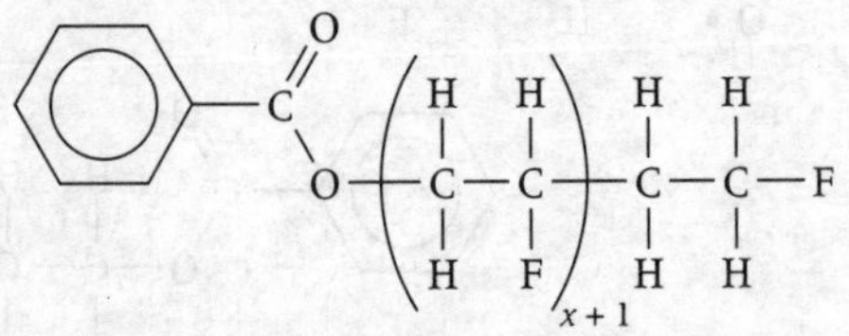

$$C_6H_5COO\text{—}(CH_2\text{—}CHF)_{x+1}\text{—}CH_2\text{—}CH_2F$$

We have not shown all the possible reactions that take place. One of the most important is the reaction of the growing polymer chain with solvent molecules. These reactions generally stop the chain growing, but the solvent molecule is itself turned into a free radical, which can induce further reactions. Sometimes this may be with an unreacted monomer, in which case another chain starts to grow. However, it can happen that part of a polymer chain is attacked along its length. This leads to the formation of side chains (Figure 127.2). Depending on the type of polymer needed, side chains can either be desirable or a nuisance.

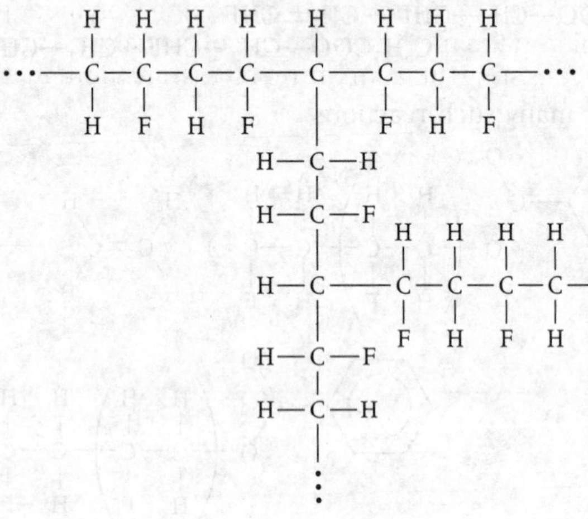

Figure 127.2 Side chains can grow on a polymer

Some monomers do not need the presence of a free radical initiator like benzoyl peroxide. Sometimes heat alone, or light, will cause the monomer itself to produce free radicals. Styrene, $C_6H_5CH\text{=}CH_2$

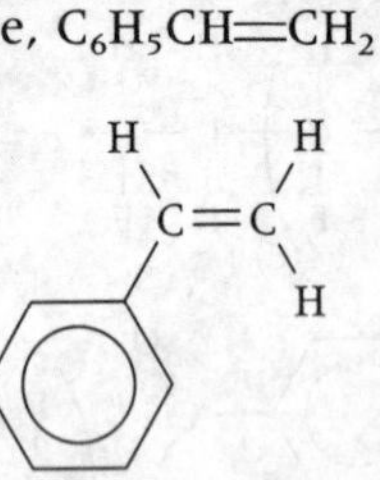

is well known for polymerising of its own accord if it is left in a clear glass bottle. For this reason monomers like styrene are kept in a solution with a second substance, which acts as an *inhibitor*. An inhibitor will react with free radicals more efficiently than will the monomer; hence it prevents polymerisation. Monomers will usually react slowly with oxygen in air to make peroxides, which can then induce polymerisation. For this reason *antioxidants* are also added. The idea is that the oxygen will react with the antioxidant instead of with the monomer.

(b) *Ionic methods of addition*

Not all polymerisations take place because of free radicals. In many cases a polymer chain grows because of reactions between ions. Just as we have anions (negatively charged) and cations (positively charged) in general chemistry, so we have anionic and cationic polymerisation reactions. The key to both types is to find a substance that provokes a monomer into becoming an ion. We have seen reactions in which this sort of thing happens. For example, in Friedel–Crafts reactions (e.g. panel 113.1) where aluminium trichloride acts as a catalyst in the production of cations such as CH_3CO^+ with ethanoyl chloride, CH_3COCl. You may not be surprised to learn that aluminium trichloride can be used as an initiator of ionic polymerisations. So too can boron trifluoride, Grignard reagents and some acids.

As well as finding the appropriate initiator, the monomer itself must be capable of turning into an ion. This is best achieved by monomers that have groups which are fairly good at donating or withdrawing electrons.

Here is one example of *cationic polymerisation* that takes place when boron trifluoride is mixed with 2-methylpropene and a little water. A polymer known as butyl rubber is made. The first step in the reaction is for the boron trifluoride and water to react and release a hydrogen ion:

$$BF_3 + H_2O \rightarrow BF_3OH^- + H^+$$

The hydrogen ion can then react with the alkene to give a carbocation:

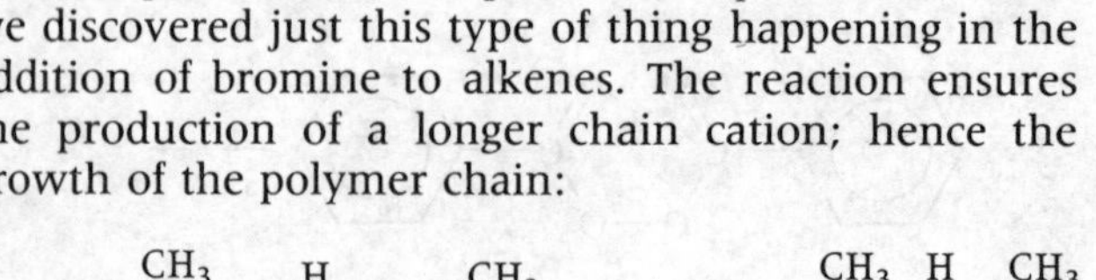

$$CH_2\text{=}C(CH_3)_2 + H^+ \rightarrow CH_3\text{—}C(CH_3)_2{}^+$$

It is this carbocation which will be attacked by the electrons in the π cloud of a neighbouring alkene molecule. If you look back to panel 112.2 you will find that we discovered just this type of thing happening in the addition of bromine to alkenes. The reaction ensures the production of a longer chain cation; hence the growth of the polymer chain:

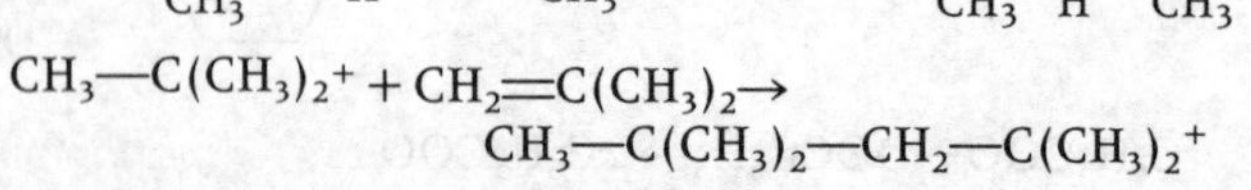

$$CH_3\text{—}C(CH_3)_2{}^+ + CH_2\text{=}C(CH_3)_2 \rightarrow CH_3\text{—}C(CH_3)_2\text{—}CH_2\text{—}C(CH_3)_2{}^+$$

Eventually the chain will stop growing, either because the supply of monomer runs out, or because of a chain terminating reaction. For example the cation may combine with a negative ion, or revert to an alkene by the loss of a proton in a reaction like the reverse of the second reaction above.

In *anionic polymerisation*, the monomer unit carries a negative charge. Often the monomer is an alkene with a group attached that can stabilise the negative charge, i.e. the group helps to spread the charge. Examples are CH=CHX with X=—CN, —COOR, —COR, —CH=CH_2. The initiator must be capable of generating the negative charge on the monomer. Compounds made from a hydrocarbon and a highly electropositive metal may be used. A good example is $(CH_3)_3CLi$ (sometimes known as butyl-lithium), which produces the 2-methylpropane carbanion,

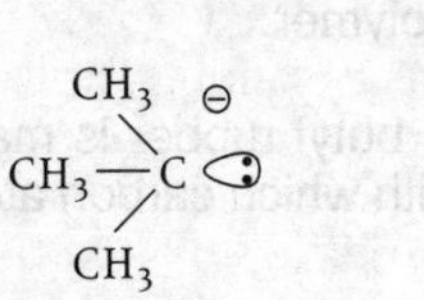

$$(CH_3)_3C^{\ominus}$$

A typical reaction scheme using $(CH_3)_3CLi$ is, first,

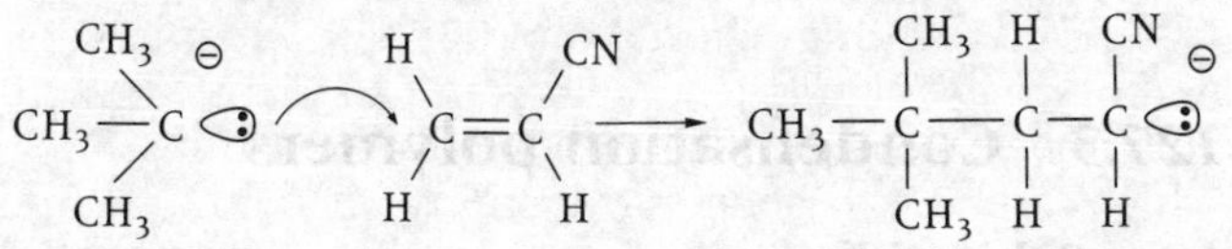

$$(CH_3)_3C^{\ominus} + CH_2{=}CHCN \longrightarrow CH_3{-}C(CH_3)_2{-}CH_2{-}\overset{\ominus}{C}H(CN)$$

and then

$$CH_3{-}C(CH_3)_2{-}CH_2{-}\overset{\ominus}{C}H(CN) + CH_2{=}CHCN \longrightarrow CH_3{-}C(CH_3)_2{-}CH_2{-}CH(CN){-}CH_2{-}\overset{\ominus}{C}H(CN)$$

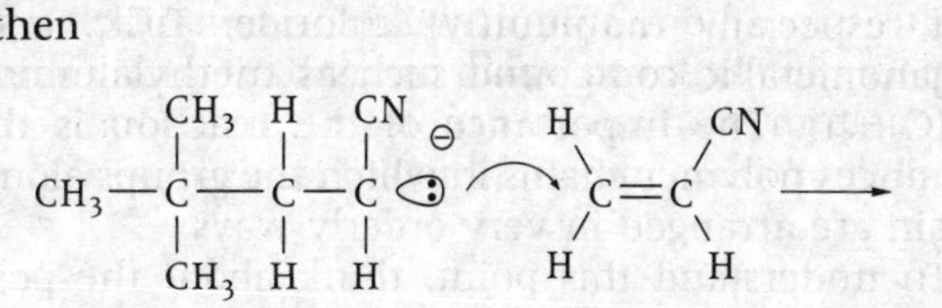

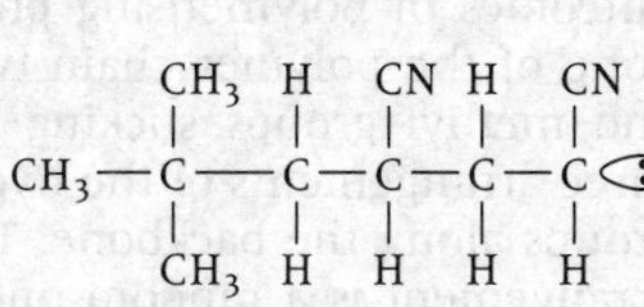

and then further reactions like this which lengthen the chain. Eventually a polymer of formula $(CH_3)_3C{-}(CH_2CHCN)_n$ results.

(c) *Coordination addition*

This is our third, and last, type of addition polymerisation. It is also one of the most important methods of polymerisation that has yet been discovered. The inventor of the method was K. Ziegler, and his research workers. However, Ziegler's name is linked with that of G. Natta, who extended the research and developed it into a reliable method for making particular types of polymer. Both men received the Nobel Prize for their work. The key to the method of making polymers by the Ziegler–Natta method is the use of a catalyst (Figure 127.3) consisting of a mixture of a transition metal

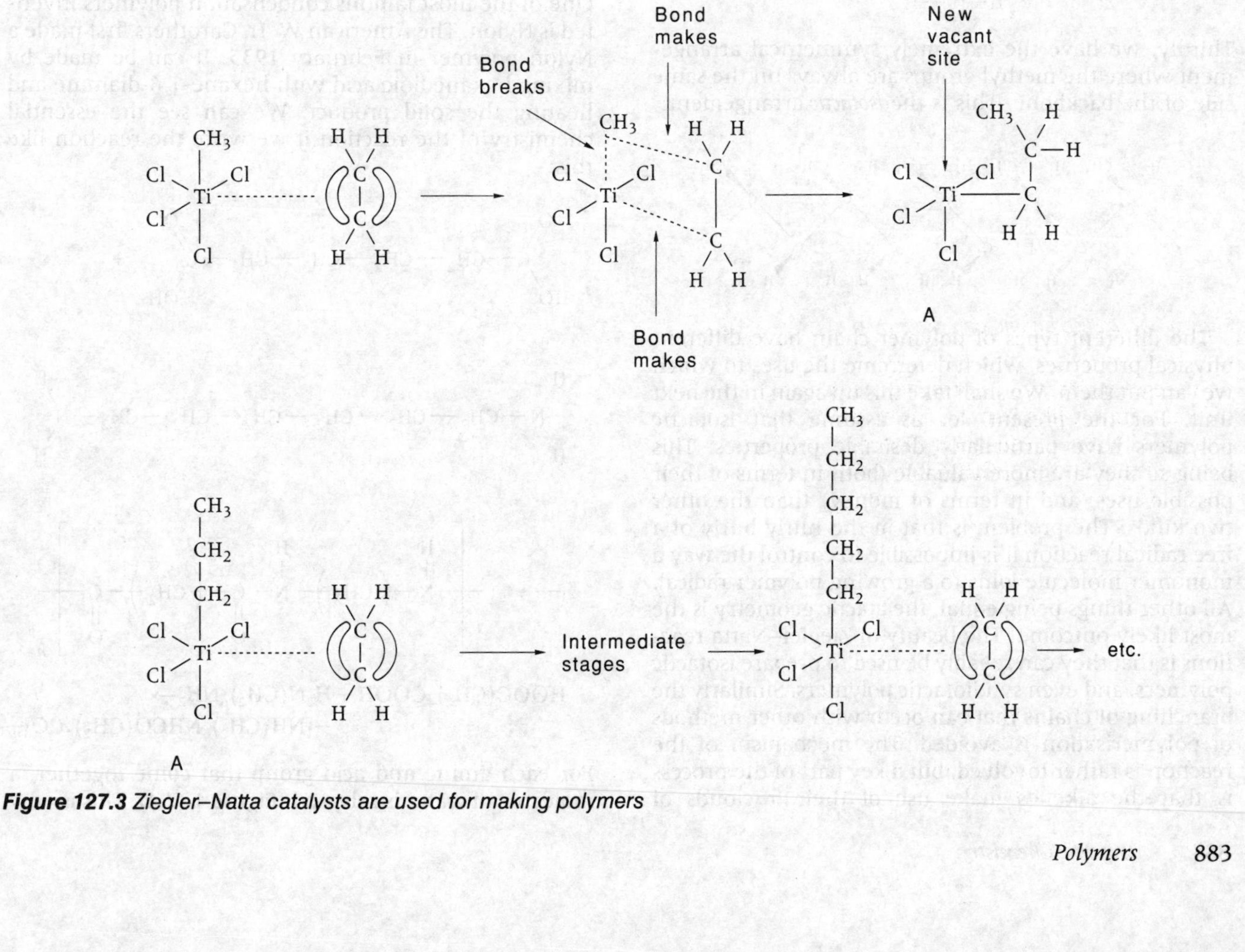

Figure 127.3 *Ziegler–Natta catalysts are used for making polymers*

salt, especially titanium(IV) chloride, $TiCl_4$, and an organometallic compound such as triethylaluminium, $Al(C_2H_5)_3$. The importance of the reaction is that it produces polymer chains in which the groups along the chain are arranged in very orderly ways.

To understand this point, think about the possible outcomes of polymerising propene. The carbon backbone of the polymer chain will have hydrogen atoms and methyl groups sticking out. However, there are three arrangements of the hydrogen atoms and methyl groups along the backbone. The first, and most likely, arrangement is a random one. Sometimes the methyl groups stick out on one side of the chain, sometimes on the other. This is the *atactic* arrangement:

Secondly, there can be a more orderly arrangement where there is a regular pattern of the methyl groups on one side, then on the other. This is the *syndiotactic* arrangement:

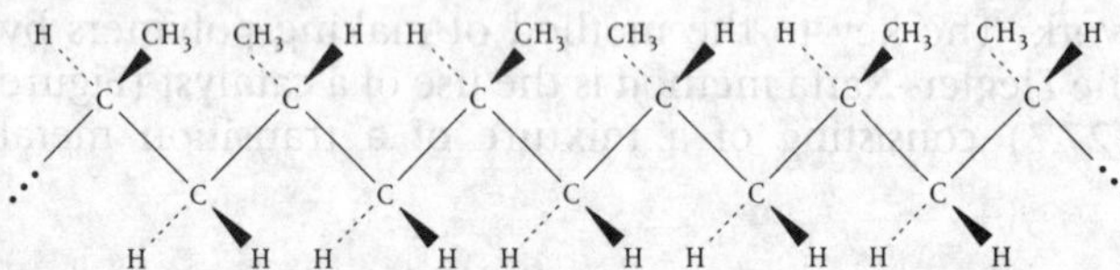

Thirdly, we have the extremely symmetrical arrangement where the methyl groups are always on the same side of the backbone. This is the *isotactic* arrangement:

The different types of polymer chain have different physical properties, which determine the uses to which we can put them. We shall take this up again in the next unit. For the present, let us assume that isotactic polymers have particularly desirable properties. This being so they are more valuable (both in terms of their possible uses, and in terms of money) than the other two kinds. The problem is that in the hurly burly of a free radical reaction it is impossible to control the way a monomer molecule joins to a growing polymer radical. All other things being equal, the atactic geometry is the most likely outcome. The beauty of Ziegler–Natta reactions is that they can reliably be used to prepare isotactic polymers, and even syndiotactic polymers. Similarly the branching of chains that can occur with other methods of polymerisation is avoided. The mechanism of the reaction is rather involved, but a key part of the process is that the alkenes make use of their π clouds of electrons to bond to a vacant coordination site on the transition metal ion. Once it is held there, the π bond breaks and a σ bond is made with another alkene at a neighbouring coordination site. Providing that new alkene molecules are available, this process can continue almost indefinitely. The regular nature of the geometry of the polymer is a result of the constant way in which the alkenes bond to the transition metal ion.

127.2 If you see styrene being polymerised in your laboratory, you will find that the sample of styrene has to be washed with alkali and water before it is used. Why?

127.3 Draw a diagram showing a portion of a polystyrene polymer.

127.4 When butyl rubber is made, what is the rule that tells us with which carbon atom the hydrogen will combine?

127.3 Condensation polymers

(a) *Polyamides*

One of the most famous condensation polymers invented is Nylon. The American W. H. Carothers first made a Nylon polymer in February 1935. It can be made by mixing hexanedioic acid with hexane-1,6-diamine and heating the solid product. We can see the essential chemistry of the reaction if we write the reaction like this:

$$HO-C(=O)-CH_2-CH_2-CH_2-CH_2-C(=O)-OH \quad +$$

$$H_2N-CH_2-CH_2-CH_2-CH_2-CH_2-CH_2-NH_2$$

$$\longrightarrow \left[-NH-(CH_2)_6-NH-C(=O)-(CH_2)_4-C(=O)- \right]_n$$

$$HOOC(CH_2)_4COOH + H_2N(CH_2)_6NH_2 \rightarrow -[NH(CH_2)_6NHCO(CH_2)_4CO]_n-$$

For each amine and acid group that come together, a molecule of water is released (Figure 127.4). This is why

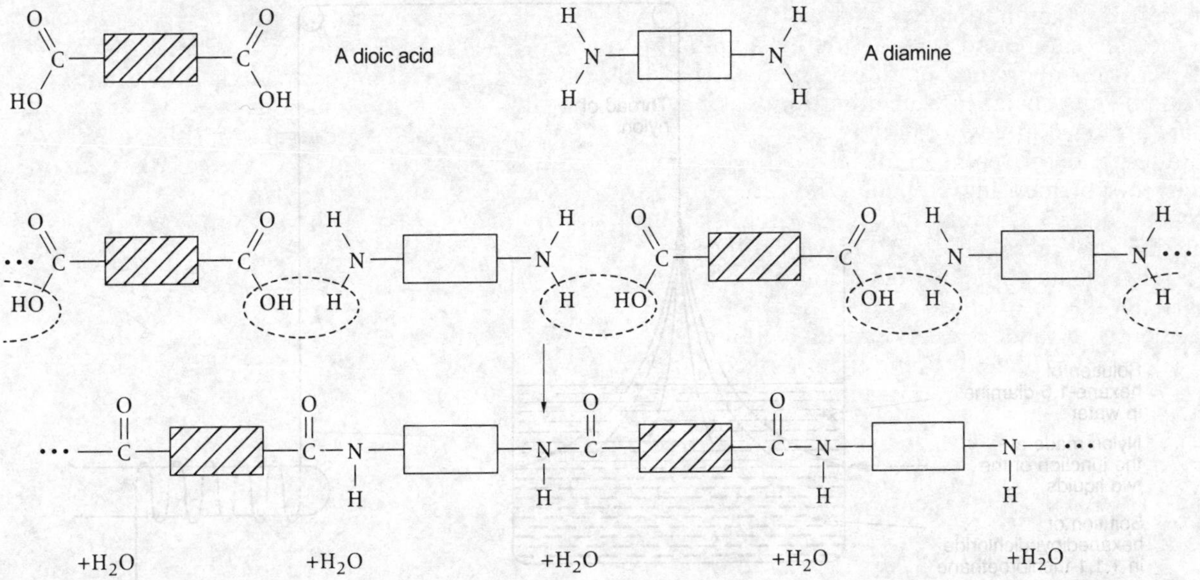

Figure 127.4 A block diagram illustrating how Nylon is made from a dioic acid and a diamine. The rectangles represent chains of CH_2 groups

the polymerisation is called a condensation reaction. This particular variety of Nylon is called Nylon-6,6. (The first of the pair of numbers gives the number of carbon atoms in the amine molecule, and the second the number in the acid.) It can be easily made in the laboratory by a rather different way outlined in panel 127.1 and Figure 127.5. Nylon-6,6 is an example of a *copolymer*. A copolymer is a polymer made from two different monomers.

Another type of Nylon, Nylon-6, is manufactured from a cyclic compound, caprolactam. On heating, the ring opens. This allows neighbouring molecules to link and produce a polymer chain:

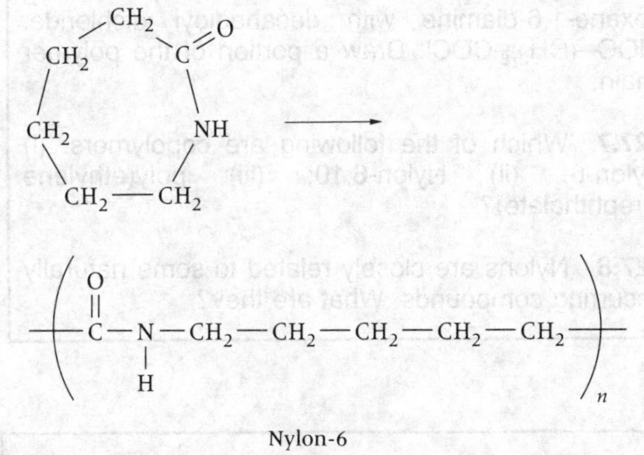

$$\text{caprolactam (ring: } CH_2-CH_2-CH_2-CH_2-CH_2-C(=O)-NH) \longrightarrow \left(-C(=O)-NH-CH_2-CH_2-CH_2-CH_2-CH_2- \right)_n$$

Nylon-6

Nylon polymers are examples of *polyamides* for the simple reason that they contain CONH groups.

Owing to the ease with which Nylon can be drawn into fibres, it has been widely used in manufacturing clothing. However, the fibres also have great strength, a quality that makes Nylon ropes and lines very useful in such different activities as rock climbing, air–sea rescue and fishing.

Panel 127.1

The Nylon rope trick

Warning: the chemicals used in this reaction are poisonous.

A simple method of making Nylon is to react hexanedioyl dichloride (adipyl chloride) with hexane-1,6-diamine. Hexanedioyl dichloride is an acid chloride, and in section 122.5 we found that acid chlorides readily react with amines. If the two reagents are mixed together directly, an exothermic reaction takes place, and a spongy mass of Nylon is made. It is better to make a solution of the dichloride in an organic solvent, and a solution of the amine in water made slightly alkaline. If you pour the aqueous solution carefully on to the organic solution, the polymer is made only where the two solutions meet. By gripping the Nylon layer with forceps you can draw out a thread, which can be wound round a test tube (Figure 127.5). If you wish, the thread can be cleaned by washing with ethanol and then drying in an oven.

(b) *Polyesters*

An ester is made when an alcohol reacts with an organic acid. If we wish to make a polyester, then we choose an alcohol with an OH group on both ends of the molecule. We react it with an acid that has an acid group at each end of its molecule. An important example is the reaction between ethane-1,2-diol (glycol) and benzene-1,4-dicarboxylic acid (terephthalic acid):

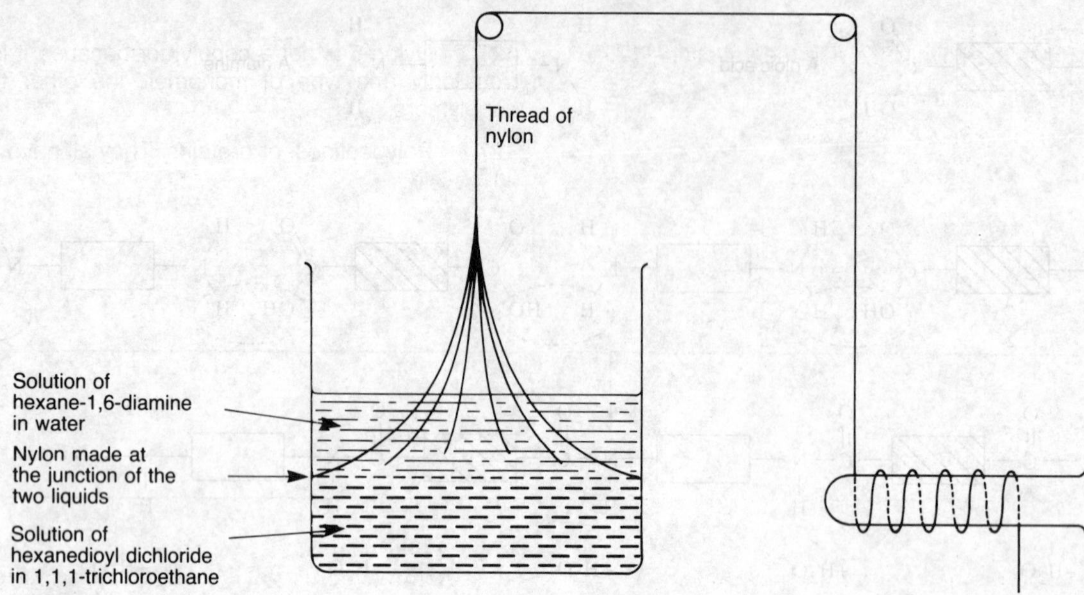

Figure 127.5 The Nylon rope trick

$$HO-CH_2-CH_2-OH + HOOC-C_6H_4-COOH \rightarrow$$

$$\left(-CH_2-CH_2-O-CO-C_6H_4-CO-O- \right)_n$$

$$O\not{H}CH_2CH_2OH + HOOCC_6H_4COOH \rightarrow$$
$$-\!(OCH_2CH_2OOCC_6H_4CO)\!-_n$$

The product is known in industry as poly(ethylene terephthalate), and to shoppers under the trade names of Terylene and Dacron, as well as some others. In industry the methyl ester of benzene-1,4-dicarboxylic acid is used to prepare the polyester rather than the pure acid.

Polyesters have a large number of uses, particularly as fibres in clothing but increasingly as thermosetting plastics. We shall learn more about these plastics in the next unit.

127.5 Suggest a formula for the ionic solid that is made in the first stage of Nylon-6,6 production. (Hint: the positive ion has a charge of +2, and the negative ion a charge of −2.)

127.6 Nylon-6,10 can be made by reacting hexane-1,6-diamine with decanedioyl dichloride, $ClOC-(CH_2)_8-COCl$. Draw a portion of the polymer chain.

127.7 Which of the following are copolymers: (i) Nylon-6; (ii) Nylon-6,10; (iii) poly(ethylene terephthalate)?

127.8 Nylons are closely related to some naturally occurring compounds. What are they?

Answers

127.1 (i) An inorganic dimer, Al_2Cl_6, is formed by aluminium trichloride (see section 94.4).

(ii) Ethanal, CH_3CHO, can turn into the cyclic trimer paraldehyde of formula $(CH_3CHO)_3$ (see section 118.12).

127.2 The washing removes the inhibitor.

127.3

$$-CH(C_6H_5)-CH_2-CH(C_6H_5)-CH_2-CH(C_6H_5)-CH_2-$$

Answers – contd.

127.4 This is Markovnikoff's rule (see section 112.4).

127.5 The salt has the formula $[H_3N(CH_2)_6NH_3]^{2+}[OOC(CH_2)_4COO]^{2-}$.

127.6

$$\cdots-\overset{\overset{\displaystyle O}{\|}}{C}-\underset{\underset{\displaystyle H}{|}}{\overset{\overset{\displaystyle H}{|}}{C}}-\left(\underset{\underset{\displaystyle H}{|}}{\overset{\overset{\displaystyle H}{|}}{C}}\right)_6-\underset{\underset{\displaystyle H}{|}}{\overset{\overset{\displaystyle H}{|}}{C}}-\overset{\overset{\displaystyle O}{\|}}{C}-\underset{\underset{\displaystyle H}{|}}{N}-\underset{\underset{\displaystyle H}{|}}{\overset{\overset{\displaystyle H}{|}}{C}}-\left(\underset{\underset{\displaystyle H}{|}}{\overset{\overset{\displaystyle H}{|}}{C}}\right)_4-\underset{\underset{\displaystyle H}{|}}{\overset{\overset{\displaystyle H}{|}}{C}}-\underset{\underset{\displaystyle H}{|}}{N}-\cdots$$

127.7 Nylon-6 is not a copolymer because it is made from only one type of monomer; the other two are copolymers.

127.8 Polypeptides, or proteins. They all have peptide links.

UNIT 127 SUMMARY

- Polymers:
  - (i) Consist of chains of monomer units.
  - (ii) Have very high molar masses.
- Preparation:
  - (i) Can be by addition, or by condensation.
  - (ii) Are often initiated by a catalyst.
  - (iii) In free radical addition, polymerisation may be induced by peroxides.
  - (iv) Ionic methods of addition are: anionic, in which carbocations induce polymerisation; cationic, in which carbanions induce polymerisation.
  - (v) Coordination addition makes use of Ziegler–Natta catalysts (a mixture of a transition metal salt, especially titanium(IV) chloride, $TiCl_4$, and an organometallic compound such as triethylaluminium, $Al(C_2H_5)_3$).
- Polymer chains:
  Arrangements of groups along the carbon backbone of a chain can be:
  - (i) Atactic, i.e. a random pattern.
  - (ii) Syndiotactic, i.e. regular alternating pattern of groups.
  - (iii) Isotactic, symmetrical arrangement where the attached groups are always on the same side of the backbone.
- Condensation polymers:
  Examples are
  - (i) Polyamides, such as Nylon;
    e.g. Nylon-6,6
    $$\text{+}NH(CH_2)_6NHCO(CH_2)_4CO\text{+}_n$$
  - (ii) Polyesters such as poly(ethylene terephthalate) (or Terylene);
    $$\text{+}OCH_2CH_2OOCC_6H_4CO\text{+}_n$$

128

Polymers and industry

128.1 Thermoplastic and thermosetting polymers

When they are hot, *thermoplastic* polymers can be moulded. When they cool down, they keep their new shape. If they are heated again, the whole process can be repeated, with the polymer being moulded into another shape.

Thermosetting polymers can also be moulded when they are heated. However, they set permanently to their new shape. Once they cool down, another bout of heating will have no effect, except to destroy them if the temperature gets too high.

To understand how these two different properties come about, we need to know more about the chemistry of polymers. First, the polymers that we met in the previous unit were all *linear* polymers. This does not mean that the polymer chains are literally all in straight lines. To begin with, the carbon backbone of the polymer takes up a zig-zag pattern. This is a result of the need to keep the tetrahedral bond angles about the

Unexpanded polystyrene can be used to make imitation 'glasses', whereas expanded polystyrene is more commonly used for packaging.

carbon atoms. Also, left to themselves, polymer chains will often coil up in more or less random spirals and other shapes. To explain why this is so we need to seek the help of thermodynamics. We shall simply say that the more random arrangement corresponds to a higher entropy than if the chains are all neatly lined up (Figure 128.1). However, if we were to analyse the system properly we should also take account of the balance between the demands of entropy and the enthalpy changes due to intermolecular forces.

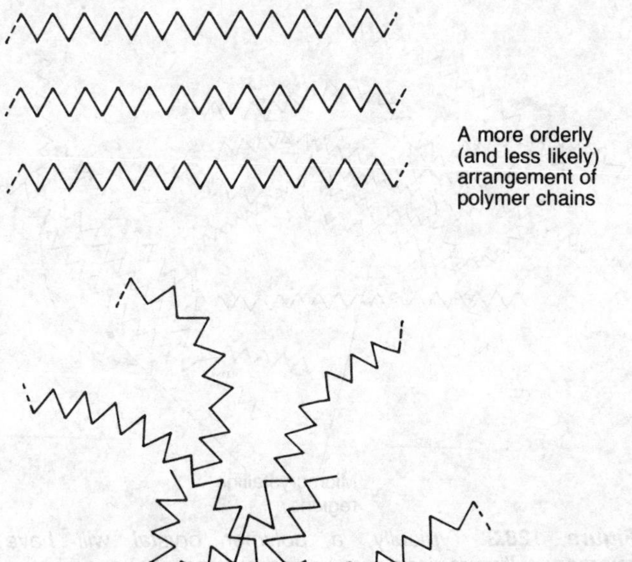

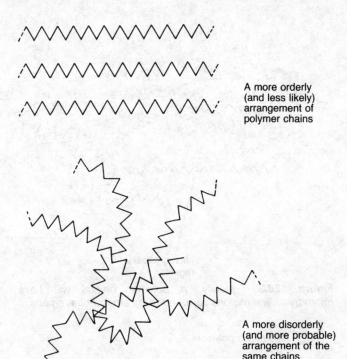

Figure 128.1 *Left to themselves, it is more likely that polymer chains will arrange themselves in a disorderly pattern*

Some would-be linear polymers turn out as *branched* polymers. Here, side chains grow off the main chain. One step further than branching brings us to *crosslinked* polymers. Two different chains are connected by short lengths of another chain, which in some cases may be only two or three atoms long. These are shown in Figure 128.2.

You should realise that a crosslinked polymer is likely to be more rigid than a linear or branched polymer. In industry, thermosetting polymers are designed to produce crosslinks when they are hot. This is done either by making the polymer with side chains that will react to make the crosslinks, or by adding a second substance that will produce the crosslinks with the original polymer chains.

The amount of the crosslinking that takes place will determine how rigid the final structure becomes. A nice example of this is the vulcanisation of rubber. Natural rubber is a soft, sticky substance, which gradually hardens to a useless mass, unless it is treated with sulphur, or some other more sophisticated chemical. Rubber is built from isoprene (systematic name methylbuta-1,3-diene) monomers:

```
      CH3   H    H      CH3   H   H
       |    |    |       |    |   |
 ···—C=C—C——C——C=C—C—C—···
           |    |       |    |
           H    H       H    H
                S           S
                |  CH3  H  / CH3   H
                |   |   |  /  |    |
        ···—C—C=C—C—C—C=C—C—···
                |       |  |  |       |  |
                H       H  H  H       H  H
```

a crosslinked portion of rubber

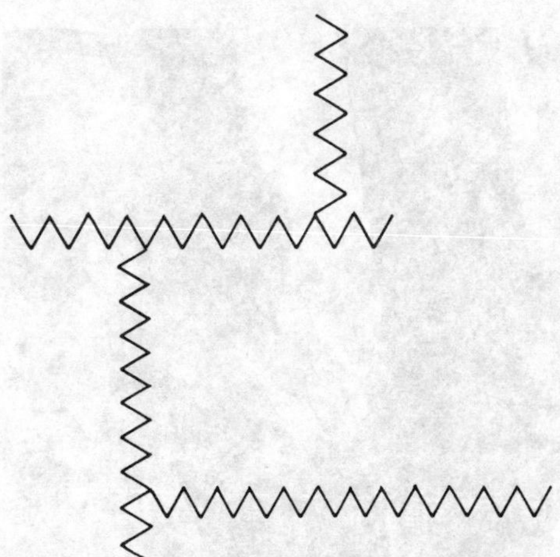

A branched polymer

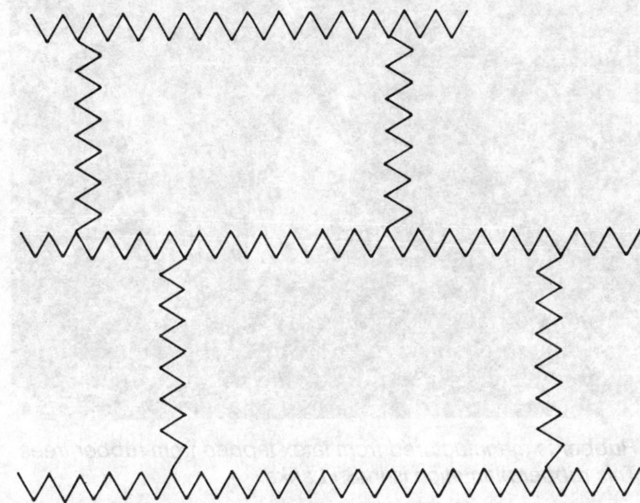

A crosslinked polymer

Figure 128.2 *Crosslinked polymers are more rigid than branched or linear polymers*

It was Dunlop (albeit by accident) who discovered that rubber heated with sulphur maintained its spring for very much longer periods of time. It also retained the shape into which it was moulded. Hence the discovery of rubber tyres, and eventually the use of rubber in such things as water hoses, shoes and tennis balls. Now, other chemicals are used to produce crosslinking in rubber, and inhibitors are added to prevent the rubber hardening with age. Many different polymers have been developed to replace natural rubber in a variety of applications. You will find some listed in Table 128.1 later in this unit.

128.2 Amorphous and crystalline polymers

It is extremely difficult to obtain single crystals of polymers. Usually the best we can do is to produce a

Rubber is manufactured from latex tapped from rubber trees. This rubber plantation is in Sri Lanka.

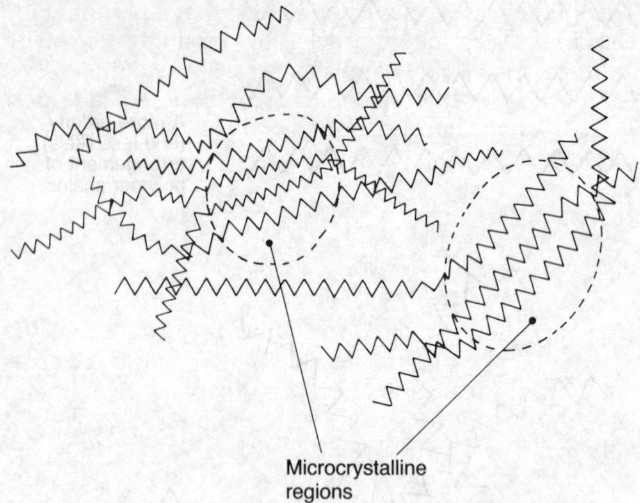

Figure 128.3 *Typically, a polymer crystal will have microcrystalline regions surrounded by amorphous regions*

polymer in which the chains are packed in symmetrical arrangements in a number of small *microcrystalline* regions (Figure 128.3). Outside these regions the chains pack in more random fashions. If a solid polymer has its chains arranged randomly throughout the solid, it is called an *amorphous* polymer.

Crystalline and amorphous polymers behave differently when they are heated. At low temperatures (how low depends on the polymer) both exist as glassy materials. In this state the solid tends to shatter if it is hit. This is because the chains cannot move at all easily, so they cannot absorb the energy of the blow. Instead, the energy breaks the bonds between the chains, and sometimes the bonds in the chains. If the polymer is heated, it eventually softens and becomes more flexible. This happens at the glass transition temperature. After the transition temperature, crystalline and amorphous polymers behave differently. This is outlined in Figure 128.4, where you will see that only crystalline polymers have a well defined melting point. Heavily crosslinked polymers are a law unto themselves. As we have already said, heating has little effect on them until, at a high enough temperature, they are destroyed.

(a) *Amorphous polymers*

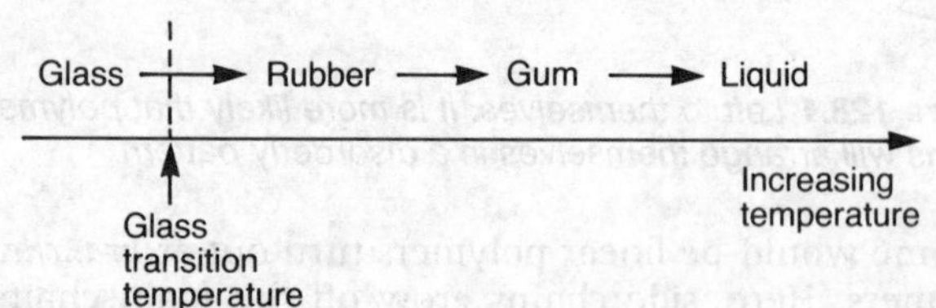

(b) *Crystalline polymers*

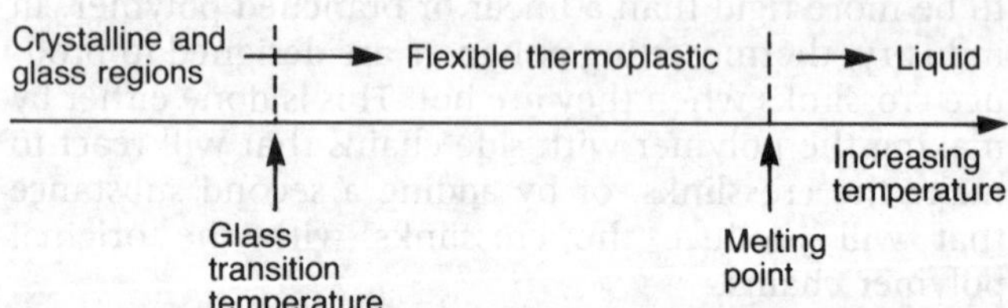

Figure 128.4 *How amorphous and crystalline polymers behave as temperature changes. Notice that amorphous polymers have no clear melting points. (Adapted from: Allcock, H. R. and Lampe, F. W. (1981).* Contemporary Polymer Chemistry, *Prentice-Hall, Englewood Cliffs, NJ, figure 1.4, p. 11)*

Softening is a sign that the polymer chains have gained enough energy to move slightly; for example, they may flex and twist. Now the energy of a blow on the polymer can be dispersed by the chains moving more violently and passing on the energy along, and across, chains. Hence the polymer will not shatter.

A polymer that has the ability to flex and twist its chains is an *elastomer*. Elastomers are widely used because they are able to withstand shocks and abrasions and will adopt their original shape after being distorted.

The properties of some polymers that are not good elastomers can be improved by mixing them with another material – a plasticiser. For example PVC (polyvinyl chloride or poly(chloroethene)) is a widely used polymer, but it is not a good elastomer until aromatic esters are mixed with it.

128.3 Mechanical properties of polymers

By controlling the length of a polymer chain and the extent of branching (or crosslinking), polymer scientists can control the degree of crystallinity of a polymer, and its elastomeric properties. The length and type of polymer chain will also affect the strength of the polymer; for example, how it responds to stress and strain. It is common practice for sections of a polymer to be given a stress–strain test. A force is applied to a sample; this is the stress. As the stress increases, the sample stretches; the amount of stretch is a measure of the strain. Different types of polymer give different stress–strain graphs. Typical examples are shown in Figure 128.5.

Apart from a very brittle polymer, there are two key stages in the experiment. At some stage the stress becomes so great that the polymer begins to yield; that is, it begins to stretch very easily for only a tiny increase in stress. This stage is called necking. The next important point is when the stress becomes so large that the sample breaks (the break point).

During the necking stage the polymer chains are drawn out from their coiled state and they tend to line up in more orderly arrangements. This increases the crystallinity of the sample, and with increasing crystallinity often comes high tensile strength. However, it is not so much the crystalline regions themselves that contribute to the strength, but the non-crystalline regions connecting them. High tensile strength is a quality required in fibres that are used in spinning or as ropes or cables. It is for this reason that polymer fibres are stretched during the final stages of their manufacture.

The mechanical properties of polymers can also be adapted by mixing different types of polymer, using plasticisers, or adding a *filler*. A filler can make a polymer more bulky, but as in the case of carbon added to rubber, it can also provide elements of crosslinking.

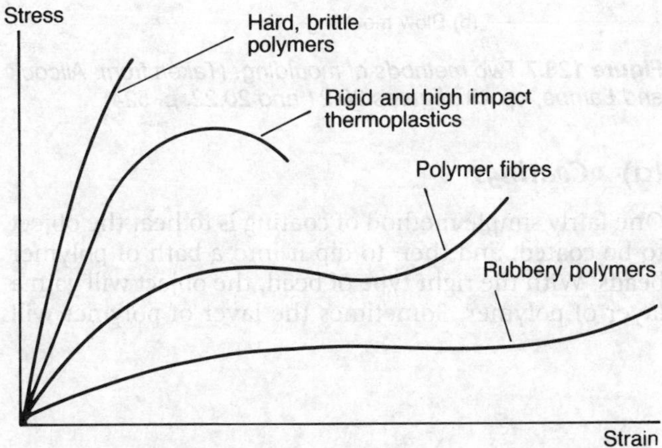

***Figure 128.5** Four curves illustrating how polymers of different types behave. The lines end where the sample breaks. Temperature has a marked effect on the behaviour of a polymer. At low temperatures, the behaviour is more like the curve for hard, brittle polymers. At high temperatures, it is more like the rubbery polymer curve. (Diagram adapted from: Heaton, C. A. (ed.) (1986).* The Chemical Industry, *Blackie, Glasgow, figure 1.10, p. 36)*

128.4 Manufacturing techniques

In this section we shall look at ways of making polymers. We can split the methods into four types depending on whether the polymer is to be used as thin sheets, for moulding, as fibres, or as coatings. We shall not be concerned with the details of the methods, only with the principles. The diagrams of the processes should show you the main points.

(a) *Thin sheets*

The key to many methods is for the polymer to be held in solution with a volatile solvent. The solution is spread over a roller and the solvent quickly evaporated to leave a thin layer of polymer. A more exotic method is to use a molten polymer, force it through a circular channel and blow compressed air into the middle

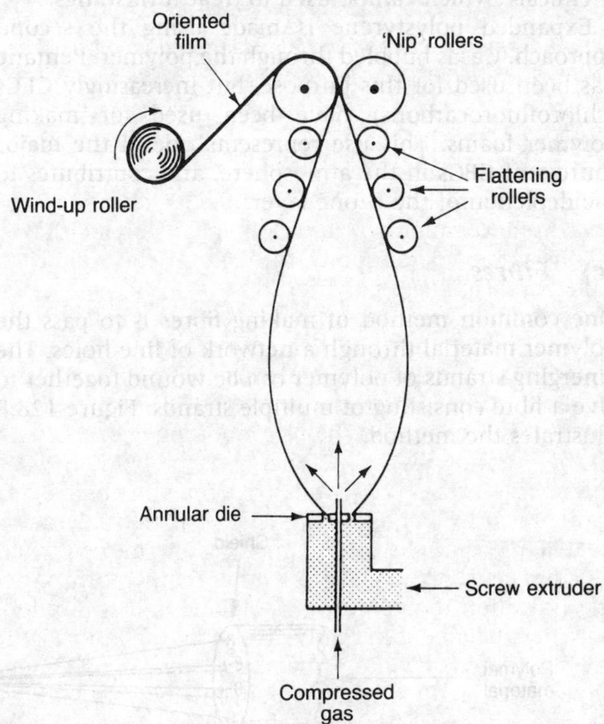

***Figure 128.6** A method for blowing thin films of a polymer. (Taken from: Allcock and Lampe, op. cit., figure 20.9, p. 513)*

(Figure 128.6). This stretches the polymer into a continuous film, which is rolled together and wound onto a drum.

(b) *Moulding*

There are several methods of moulding. Injection, blow and vacuum moulding all use a molten polymer and a pre-prepared mould (Figure 128.7). The mould has to be very carefully manufactured if a good quality product is to result, but once it is made the moulding process can be fully automated. This gives a speedy and reliable method of making a wide range of articles. Each method relies on the use of a thermoplastic or thermosetting polymer.

A different method of moulding is to use an expansion method. Here the polymer is left to expand into the shape of the mould. The expansion can be produced by a chemical reaction in the polymer mix, or by bubbling a gas into the polymer. In either method the final product consists of a matrix of polymer material and gas bubbles. Important examples of materials made by this method are polyurethane foam and expanded polystyrene. Polyurethane foams are made by mixing isocyanates, which have the structure OCN—(carbon chain)—NCO, and diols, which have OH groups at both ends of the molecule. If water is present, the isocyanate reacts with it, giving off carbon dioxide. This is the gas that produces the foaming. Polyurethane foams have been widely used as fillings for furniture, but they have got a bad name for themselves. Unfortunately they release highly poisonous fumes in a fire. Different types of foam are now being developed, as are effective fire retarding chemicals, which can be used to treat furnishings.

Expanded polystyrene is made using the second approach. Gas is bubbled through the polymer. Pentane has been used for this purpose, but increasingly CFCs (chlorofluorocarbons) have been used for making polymer foams. This use represents one of the major sources of CFCs in the atmosphere, and contributes to the depletion of the ozone layer.

(c) *Fibres*

One common method of making fibres is to pass the polymer material through a network of fine holes. The emerging strands of polymer can be wound together to give a fibre consisting of multiple strands. Figure 128.8 illustrates the method.

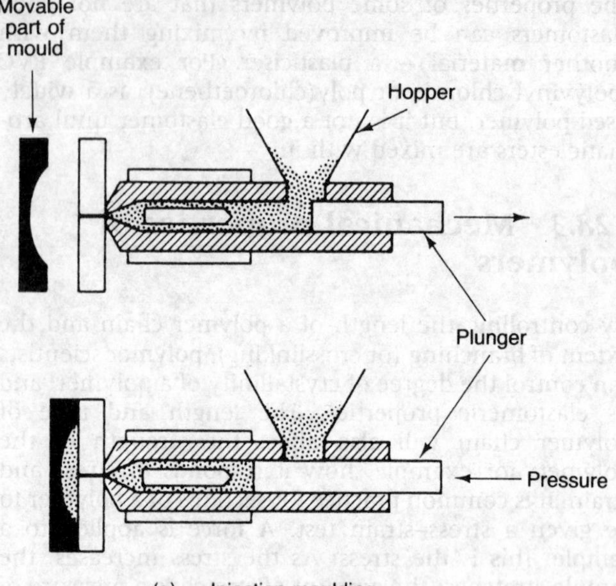

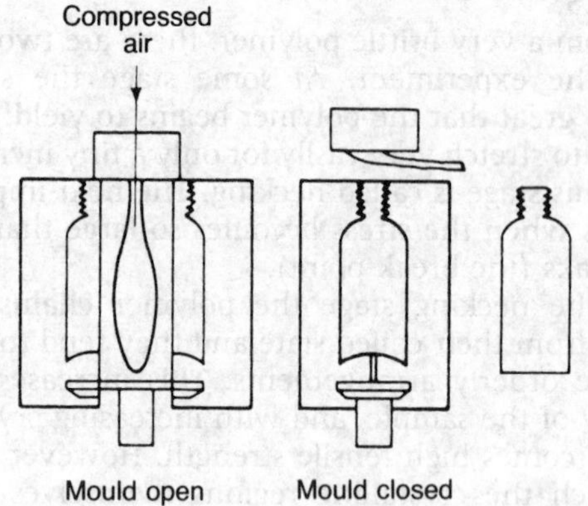

***Figure 128.7** Two methods of moulding. (Taken from: Allcock and Lampe, op. cit., figures 20.21 and 20.22, p. 524)*

(d) *Coatings*

One fairly simple method of coating is to heat the object to be coated, and then to dip it into a bath of polymer beads. With the right type of bead, the object will gain a layer of polymer. Sometimes the layer of polymer will

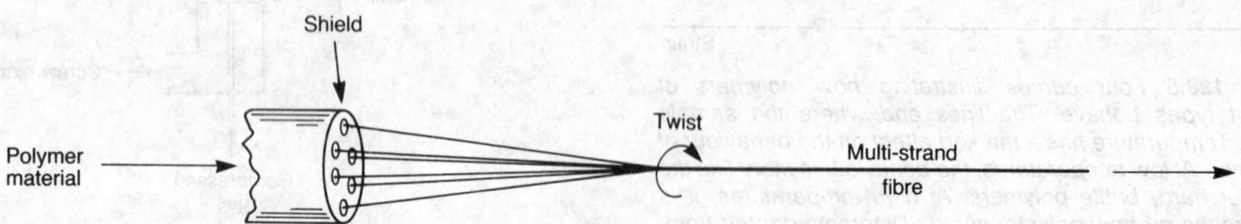

***Figure 128.8** One method of making polymer fibres*

have to be heated more strongly, or treated with another chemical, to make it adhere permanently to the object. On an industrial scale it is convenient to force the polymer through a narrow slit onto the object, which travels underneath it.

128.5 Uses of polymers

There are so many uses of polymers that we can only look at a brief selection of them. You will find details in Table 128.1.

Table 128.1. Some polymers and their uses

Polymer	*Repeat unit*	*Properties and uses*
Polyamides		
Nylon-6,6	$-\mathrm{N(H)}-(\mathrm{CH_2})_6-\mathrm{N(H)}-\mathrm{C(=O)}-(\mathrm{CH_2})_4-\mathrm{C(=O)}-$	Textile fibre, threads, ropes Moulded gears and electrical insulation
Nylon-6,10	$-\mathrm{N(H)}-(\mathrm{CH_2})_6-\mathrm{N(H)}-\mathrm{C(=O)}-(\mathrm{CH_2})_8-\mathrm{C(=O)}-$	Sports equipment Bristles for brushes
Nomex	$-\mathrm{N(H)}-\mathrm{C_6H_4}-\mathrm{N(H)}-\mathrm{C(=O)}-\mathrm{C_6H_4}-\mathrm{C(=O)}-$	Heat resistant polymer in space suits Also for parachute cords
Polyesters and polycarbonates		
Terylene, Dacron	$-\mathrm{O}-\mathrm{CH_2}-\mathrm{CH_2}-\mathrm{O}-\mathrm{C(=O)}-\mathrm{C_6H_4}-\mathrm{C(=O)}-$	Textile fibre Basis for magnetic tape and photographic film
Lexan	$-\mathrm{O}-\mathrm{C_6H_4}-\mathrm{C(CH_3)_2}-\mathrm{C_6H_4}-\mathrm{O}-\mathrm{C(=O)}-$	Tough and transparent Bullet proof windows, safety glass Food containers Car components
Polyethers		
Polyglycol 166	$-\mathrm{O}-\mathrm{CH_2}-\mathrm{CH(CH_2Cl)}-$	Making urethanes and speciality elastomers, e.g. for oil and fuel hoses, oil-well equipment
Delrin, Celcon	$-\mathrm{O}-\mathrm{CH_2}-$	Tough plastic for gears, pipes, pens
Phenol-based		
Bakelite	$-\mathrm{C_6H_2(OH)(CH_2-)}-\mathrm{CH_2}-\mathrm{C_6H_3(OH)}-\mathrm{CH_2}-$	Hard thermosetting polymer Telephones, buttons, electrical insulators

Table 128.1 – cont.

Polymer	*Repeat unit*	*Properties and uses*
Poly(melamine-formaldehyde)	$-CH_2-N(-)-C_3N_3(-N(-)-CH_2-)(-N(-)-CH_2-)$	Laminated surfaces, e.g. table tops, cupboards
Polyurethanes		
Polyurethane	$-(CH_2)_3-NH-C(=O)-O-$	Foam rubber, synthetic leather
Lycra	$-N(N)-C(=O)-NH-C_6H_4-CH_2-C_6H_4-NH-C(=O)-O-(CH_2)_{32}-C(=O)-$	Expanded foam rubber, carpet underlays
Alkenes		
ABS* polymers contain these four types of repeat unit	$-CH_2-CH(CN)-$; $-CH_2-CH=CH-CH_2-$; $-CH_2-CH(CH=CH_2)-$; $-CH_2-CH(C_6H_5)-$	Tough structural plastic or rubber. Telephones, pipes, many moulded articles
Polybutadiene (butadiene rubber)	$-CH_2-CH=CH-CH_2-$	Alternative to natural rubber. Footwear, tyres, toys
Neoprene	$-CH_2-CCl=CH-CH_2-$	Adhesives, golf ball covers, liquid seals
Polythene† (polyethene)	$-CH_2-CH_2-$	Tough plastic. Fibres, thin films, extrusion moulded objects, toys, bottles
Butyl rubber	$-CH_2-C(CH_3)_2-$	Tyre inner tubes, raincoats, seals

Table 128.1 – cont.

Polymer	*Repeat unit*	*Properties and uses*
Natural rubber (poly(*cis*-1,4-isoprene))	$-CH_2-C(CH_3)=CH-CH_2-$	After vulcanisation, used in car, and other, tyres
PTFE (poly(tetrafluoroethene), Teflon)	$-CF_2-CF_2-$	Highly water repellent Non-stick cooking ware Industrial uses where very low friction needed
Polystyrene	$-CH_2-CH(C_6H_5)-$	Transparent, glass-like Wide variety of moulded and expanded objects Packing and insulation
Perspex (poly(methyl methacrylate))	$-CH_2-C(CN)(C(=O)-O-CH_3)-$	Transparent, glass-like Windows, fibre optics, illuminated signs
PVC (polyvinyl chloride)	$-CH_2-CHCl-$	Hard inflexible polymer With plasticiser, used in tubing, thin films, car seat covers, floor tiles
Alkynes		
Polyethyne (polyacetylene)	$-CH-CH-$ delocalised electrons	With iodine, an electrically conducting polymer
Inorganic		
Silicone rubber	$-O-Si(CH_3)_2-$	Seals, hoses, waterproofing, 'silicone grease'
Carbon fibres	Carbon layers with layers parallel to axis of fibre	Very high strength fibres, e.g. in aeroplane and boat building
Polythiazyl	$-S=N-$	An electrically conducting polymer Semiconductor at very low temperatures

*ABS = acrylonitrile–butadiene–styrene

†There are two main types of polyethene: low density polyethene (LDPE) has considerable branching; high density polyethene (HDPE) has no branching

128.6 Polymers and light

A reaction that is influenced by light is a *photochemical* reaction. Polymerisations can sometimes be started by photochemical reactions in which incoming light, especially ultraviolet light, produces free radicals. The *quantum yield* of a photochemical reaction is defined by

$$\text{quantum yield} = \frac{\text{number of molecules taking part in the reaction}}{\text{number of photons used}}$$

In polymer chemistry we can write this as

$$\text{quantum yield} = \frac{\text{number of monomer units consumed}}{\text{number of photons used}}$$

From the initiation and propagation steps in free radical polymerisation, you can see that one photon causing the dissociation of a peroxide molecule could result in a very long chain. A quantum yield of 1000 is not uncommon.

Initiation by light is extremely useful, but light can also bring about the destruction of polymers, i.e. photodecomposition. This is a problem with paints that may discolour when left in bright sunlight. In order to stop photodecomposition, *stabilisers* are added to polymers. One type of stabiliser makes use of chemicals that absorb ultraviolet radiation efficiently. This prevents the high energy photons from breaking the bonds of the polymer.

There are times when photodecomposition is highly desirable. Many items made from polymers are meant to be disposable, for example rubbish bin liners and other plastic bags. When they were first introduced, these plastics were not biodegradable; but now they can be made with chemicals added that are designed to decompose the polymer chains once they are in contact with light or air for a long period of time. Some of these chemicals work by releasing free radicals, which attack the polymer chains.

Polymers that are decomposed by light are used in the semiconductor industry, and by people who build their own electronics circuits, although the details of the methods are different. One method of making a circuit board uses an insulating board coated with a layer of copper and then a layer of polymer. A mask is made, which has black lines where the circuit is going to be, and is clear where electrical connections are not wanted. The mask is placed over the polymer and ultraviolet light is shone on the surface for some minutes. Where the light hits the polymer a photochemical reaction is set up, which degrades its structure. By washing the board in a chemical, often an alkali, the ruined polymer can be washed off, leaving unaffected polymer over the copper. The whole board is immersed in iron(III) chloride solution, which etches away the exposed copper. The next step is to remove the polymer from the remaining copper by washing with a solvent. The copper lines show the circuit into which the electronic components can be soldered.

128.1 The glass transition temperatures of three polymers are: Perspex, 105 °C; polystyrene, 100 °C; Nylon-6,6, 45 °C. What is likely to happen to a sample of each of them if it were hit by a hammer at (i) 0 °C, (ii) 20 °C, (iii) 80 °C, (iv) 120 °C?

The construction of printed circuit boards for computers depends on polymer chemistry as well as electronics.

128.2 This is an extract from a catalogue of scientific equipment:

Plastic Tubing: Polythene. Natural grade, medium wall, tough and flexible. Can be manipulated by softening in hot water.

(i) Does this mean that polythene is a thermosetting polymer?

(ii) What does it suggest about the glass transition temperature of polythene?

128.3 In an experiment on the free radical polymerisation of ethene, a lamp projected 10^{18} photons into the reaction vessel. At the end of the experiment, 0.28 g of monomer had been used up.

(i) How many moles of monomer molecules were used in the reaction?

(ii) How many molecules were used up?

(iii) What was the quantum yield?

Answers

128.1 The key is that, below the glass transition temperature, the samples would be brittle and shatter; above the transition temperature, they should deform, but not break. Therefore they would all shatter at 0 °C and 20 °C; only Nylon-6,6 would survive the blow at 80 °C. At 120 °C none of them should break.

128.2 (i) No. It is a thermoplastic because its shape can be changed as the temperature changes.

(ii) As it is flexible, the transition temperature must be below room temperature. In fact, it can be as low as −170 °C for some types of polythene.

128.3 (i) One mole of ethene, C_2H_4, has a mass of 28 g, so 0.01 mol were used.

(ii) The number of molecules is $0.01\ \text{mol} \times 6.02 \times 10^{23}\ \text{mol}^{-1} = 6.02 \times 10^{21}$.

(iii) Quantum yield $= \dfrac{6.02 \times 10^{21}}{10^{18}} = 6020$

UNIT 128 SUMMARY

- Thermoplastic and thermosetting polymers:
  - (i) Thermoplastic polymers can be moulded, heated and then remoulded.
  - (ii) Thermosetting polymers can be moulded when heated, but once cold are permanently set.
- Crosslinking:
  Bonds made between separate polymer chains increase the rigidity of the polymer.
- Amorphous polymers:
  - (i) Have random arrangements of chains.
  - (ii) Melt over a wide range of temperatures.
- Crystalline polymers:
  - (i) Have more orderly arrangements of chains.
  - (ii) Have well defined melting points.
- Mechanical properties:
  - (i) Can be changed by controlling the lengths of the chains and the amount of crosslinking.
  - (ii) Increased crystallinity increases the tensile strength (useful in fibres).
  - (iii) Fillers can increase the bulk of a polymer, and the amount of crosslinking.
- Elastomers:
  - (i) The chains can flex and twist.
  - (ii) Can withstand shocks and abrasions.
  - (iii) Return to their original shape after distortion.
- Manufacturing techniques:
  Polymers are produced as
  - (i) Thin sheets, e.g. by forcing air into an envelope of molten polymer.
  - (ii) As moulded articles, using injection, blow and vacuum techniques.
  - (iii) Foams, by passing gas into the polymerising mixture.
  - (iv) Coatings for other objects, e.g. by hot dipping.
- Uses:
  See Table 128.1.
- Polymers and light:
  Polymerisation can be induced by lig[illegible] polymers can be made sensitive to li[illegible] they decompose when left in light

129

Fats, oils, soaps and detergents

129.1 What are fats and oils?

Fats are one class of material called *lipids*. Lipids are biologically active compounds that are insoluble in water. (We have discussed some lipids in previous units, e.g. vitamins and hormones.) Animals have always been used as food by humans, partly for meat, which is a source of protein, and fat, which is a source of energy. Animal fats have also been used as a source of other useful materials: for example, oils and waxes for lamps and candles. If animal fat is boiled with alkali, or reacted with superheated steam, it produces two major products:

(i) *Glycerol*. The systematic name for glycerol is propane-1,2,3-triol (Figure 129.1). It is an alcohol with three OH groups in its molecule. Glycerol is also called glycerine.

(ii) *Carboxylic acids*. These were first obtained from fats, and hence for a long time they were called *fatty acids*. The acids are different to those we discussed in Unit 119 in several respects. The most important is that many have a carbon chain up to ...arbon atoms long, and some are even longer. ...u find a list of them in Table 129.1, and the example... of some in Figure 129.1. Most are ...arbon–carbon double bonds), but ...ated (have one or more double ... into a mixture of an ...fats must be esters. ...*lycerides*. Three ... interesting ... are solids ... Oils

thing about ... and some liquids. ... contain large proportion... cerol and unsaturated acids ... There is medical evidence to sho... tion of saturated fats in a person's ... increased risk of heart disease. The unsatu... appear not to have the same dangerous effects, an... sales of margarines and butter substitutes that are 'high in polyunsaturated fats' have increased enormously in recent years.

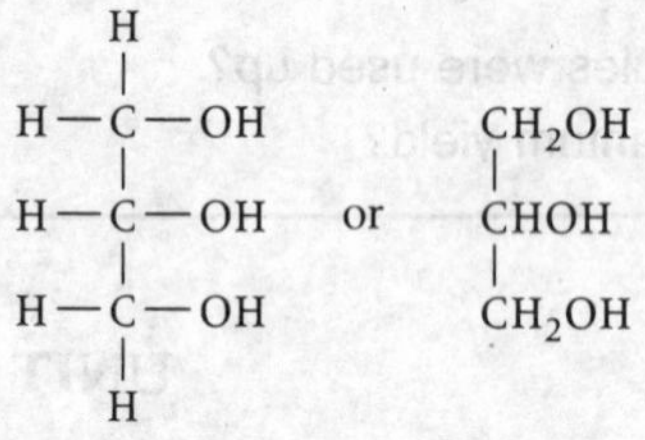

$$\begin{array}{c} H \\ | \\ H-C-OH \\ | \\ H-C-OH \\ | \\ H-C-OH \\ | \\ H \end{array} \quad \text{or} \quad \begin{array}{c} CH_2OH \\ | \\ CHOH \\ | \\ CH_2OH \end{array}$$

Glycerol
(propane-1,2,3-triol)

$$CH_3-(CH_2)_{16}-COOH$$

Stearic acid (saturated acid), $C_{17}H_{35}COOH$

$$CH_3-(CH_2)_5-CH=CH-(CH_2)_7-COOH$$

Palmitoleic acid, $C_{15}H_{29}COOH$

$$CH_3-(CH_2)_7-CH=CH-(CH_2)_7-COOH$$

Oleic acid, $C_{17}H_{33}COOH$

$$CH_3-(CH_2)_3-(CH_2CH=CH)_2-(CH_2)_7-COOH$$

Linoleic acid, $C_{17}H_{31}COOH$

***Figure 129.1** The structures of glycerol and of one saturated and three unsaturated acids from which fats are made*

Th... ing lea...turally occurring esters are similar to fats but ... on glycerol. These are known as *waxes*. ...used for polishing furniture or soften-... ...king candles.

Table 129.1. Acids obtained from fats

*Acid**	*Formula*
Saturated	
Butyric (butanoic)	C_3H_7COOH
Caproic	$C_5H_{11}COOH$
Lauric	$C_{11}H_{23}COOH$
Palmitic	$C_{15}H_{31}COOH$
Stearic	$C_{17}H_{35}COOH$
Arachidic	$C_{19}H_{39}COOH$
Unsaturated	
Oleic	$C_{17}H_{33}COOH$
Linoleic	$C_{17}H_{31}COOH$

*All these acids have systematic names, but it is much easier to use their traditional ones

$$
\begin{array}{l}
CH_2-O-\overset{O}{\overset{\|}{C}}-(CH_2)_{16}-CH_3 \\
| \\
CH-O-\overset{O}{\overset{\|}{C}}-(CH_2)_{16}-CH_3 \\
| \\
CH_2-O-\overset{O}{\overset{\|}{C}}-(CH_2)_{16}-CH_3
\end{array}
$$

Tristearin

$$
\begin{array}{l}
CH_2-O-\overset{O}{\overset{\|}{C}}-(CH_2)_{14}-CH_3 \\
| \\
CH-O-\overset{O}{\overset{\|}{C}}-(CH_2)_{14}-CH_3 \\
| \\
CH_2-O-\overset{O}{\overset{\|}{C}}-(CH_2)_{14}-CH_3
\end{array}
$$

Tripalmitin

$$
\begin{array}{l}
CH_2-O-\overset{O}{\overset{\|}{C}}-(CH_2)_7-CH=CH-(CH_2)_7-CH_3 \\
| \\
CH-O-\overset{O}{\overset{\|}{C}}-(CH_2)_7-CH=CH-(CH_2)_7-CH_3 \\
| \\
CH_2-O-\overset{O}{\overset{\|}{C}}-(CH_2)_7-CH=CH-(CH_2)_7-CH_3
\end{array}
$$

Triolein

***Figure 129.2** Three glycerides. Tristearin (or stearin for short) together with tripalmitin are the main ingredients of (solid) fats. Triolein is a major component of oils, e.g. olive oil, palm oil, rapeseed oil*

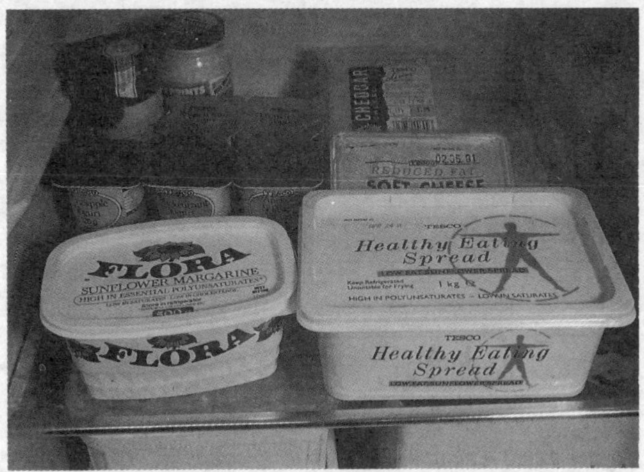

Many manufacturers market margarines which are high in polyunsaturated fats.

Bees are remarkable creatures, not least for their ability to build hexagonal closed-packed lattices of wax like the one shown here.

129.2 How are soaps and detergents made?

Strictly a detergent is a cleaning agent that will remove grease and grime from surfaces. However, it is more common for liquid cleaning agents to be called detergents, and solids to be called soaps. Soaps and detergents are used on an enormous scale, both in the home and in industry. Soap has a very long history, detergents somewhat shorter.

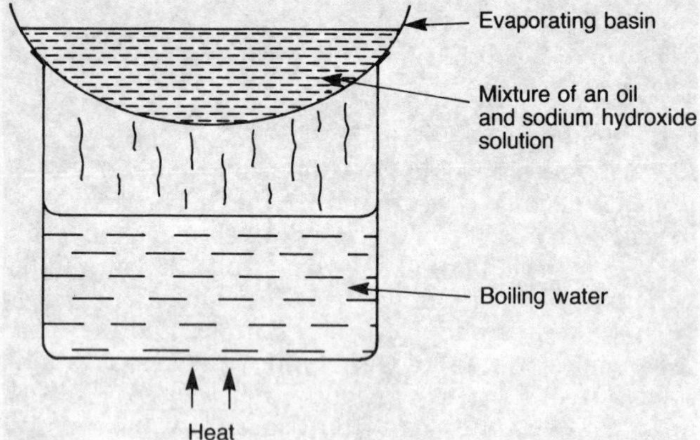

***Figure 129.3** A simple way of making soap*

You can make soap easily in the laboratory. All you have to do is to heat a fat or oil with sodium hydroxide solution. A suitable apparatus is shown in Figure 129.3. After a few minutes, and continuous stirring, the oil and water layers merge and thicken. If all goes well, the surface will begin to cake and on cooling you will obtain a yellow solid. This is soap, although it is likely to be impure. For example, it may contain unreacted alkali.

Essentially the same process has been used in industry to make soap, although much greater care has to be taken with the proportions of the ingredients that are mixed, the amount of heat supplied, and the removal of impurities. Also, many soaps have perfumes added, together with chemicals that improve their texture.

The reaction that takes place in soap making is called saponification. The alkali breaks the glyceride molecules into glycerol and anions of the fatty acids. The glycerol is helpful in that it gives soap a pleasant feel. The solid soap is a salt made between the anions and sodium ions from the sodium hydroxide:

$$\begin{array}{ll} C_{17}H_{35}-C(=O)-O-CH_2 & + Na^+ + OH^- \\ C_{17}H_{35}-C(=O)-O-CH & + Na^+ + OH^- \longrightarrow \\ C_{17}H_{35}-C(=O)-O-CH_2 & + Na^+ + OH^- \\ \text{stearin} & \text{sodium hydroxide} \end{array}$$

$$\begin{array}{lll} C_{17}H_{35}-C(=O)-O^-\ Na^+ & + & CH_2OH \\ C_{17}H_{35}-C(=O)-O^-\ Na^+ & + & CHOH \\ C_{17}H_{35}-C(=O)-O^-\ Na^+ & + & CH_2OH \\ \text{sodium stearate} & & \text{glycerol} \end{array}$$

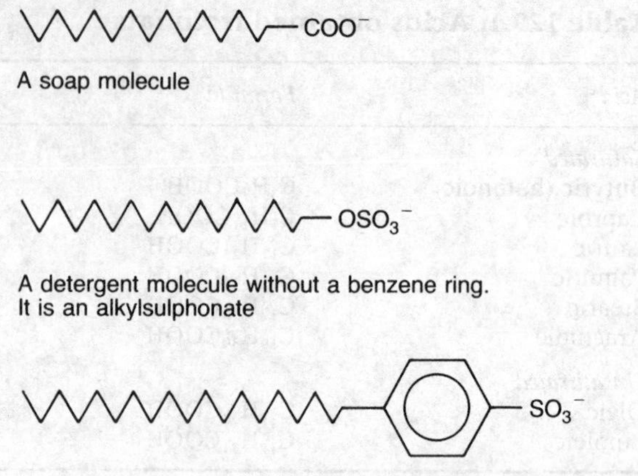

***Figure 129.4** Soap and detergent molecules have a hydrocarbon tail and an ionic head. Soaps have a —COO⁻ group as the ionic head, which gives a precipitate with hard water. Sulphonate groups do not give precipitates*

Sodium stearate is a soap. Other glycerides can be saponified in a similar manner. If sodium hydroxide is used, the resulting soap is fairly hard when it has been dried. If potassium hydroxide is used, the soap is softer.

A liquid detergent is made by a totally different method. Instead of having a carboxylic acid group on the end of a hydrocarbon chain, a sulphonate group is usually present. In some types the sulphonate is attached to a benzene ring on the end of the chain. Figure 129.4 shows you the two varieties.

It is extremely difficult to make the long hydrocarbon chains except through polymerisation reactions. This is why detergents were not widely available until the 1950s after polymer science had become quite sophisticated.

The reason why detergents are so useful is that they do not give precipitates with metal ions such as Na^+, K^+, Ca^{2+} or Mg^{2+}. The lack of precipitates with Ca^{2+} and Mg^{2+} is especially important. These ions are responsible for the hardness of water. Ordinary soap gives a precipitate with hard water; this is 'scum'. Detergents do not give a scum even in the hardest of water areas.

In the past detergents have gained a bad reputation for causing pollution of rivers and waterways. The early polymer chains used for detergent manufacture suffered a great deal of branching (Figure 129.5). The hydrocarbon side chains did not interfere with the

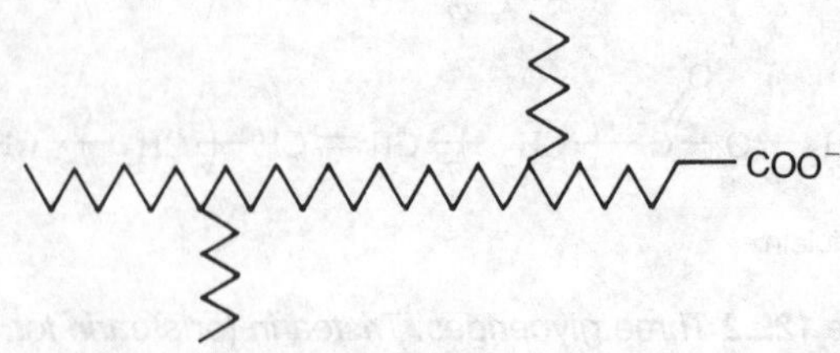

***Figure 129.5** Soap or detergent molecules with branched hydrocarbon tails can be the cause of a great deal of pollution*

cleaning power of the detergent, but they did prevent bacteria from attacking and breaking the chains. This meant that detergent molecules degraded very slowly. Now the amount of branching can be kept to a minimum. Unbranched chains are much more appetising to bacteria, so the detergents are more easily biodegraded.

129.1 A process used in soap manufacture, and one that you can try in the laboratory, is to add salt to the reaction mixture shortly before it is allowed to cool. This is *salting out*. Explain why adding salt helps the soap to precipitate.

129.2 Before the days of washing-up liquids, pans could be cleaned of fat by boiling them with a solution of washing soda (sodium carbonate). Explain why this worked. (Hint: look at section 94.1.)

129.3 Some people believe that the more scum they see in their bath, the dirtier they must have been. Are they right?

129.3 How do soaps and detergents clean?

We shall explain the cleaning action of both soaps and detergents by using a simplified diagram of each type of molecule. We shall show them like this:

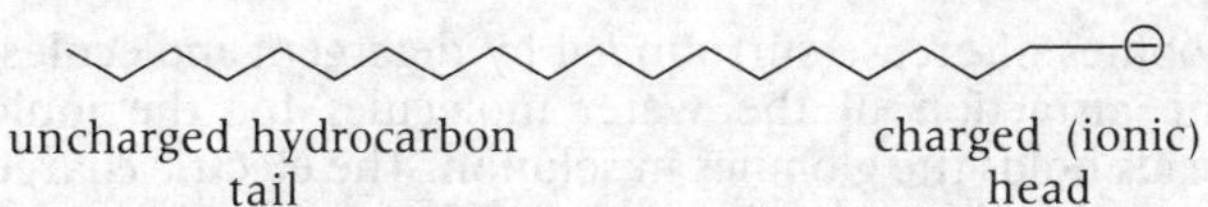
uncharged hydrocarbon tail
charged (ionic) head

This highlights the key features of the molecules: they have an uncharged hydrocarbon tail, and a charged (ionic) head. (We have shown the head carrying a negative charge; in practice, positively charged heads are also possible.) If you have read Unit 123 you should be familiar with the idea that the hydrocarbon tail is likely to be hydrophobic (water hating), and the head hydrophilic (water loving). Water molecules cannot solvate hydrocarbons efficiently, but they can solvate ions. On the other hand, grease and dirt is mainly organic in nature, so the tails will be able to mix happily with it. There is nothing to be gained by the ionic heads entering a ball of grease when they can be solvated by water molecules instead.

If you drop a little washing-up liquid on water, the detergent spreads out across the surface and some mixes into the body of the water. By adding more detergent there comes a point at which the molecules gather together into clumps called *micelles* (Figure 129.6). The tails stick inwards into the roughly spherical balls and the heads stick outwards into the water (where they can be solvated). Now let us suppose that a plate with a layer of grease on it is put into the solution. Tails of some detergent molecules will attach themselves to the grease. If the water is agitated slightly, the grease tends to lift off and fragment. This gives other detergent molecules the opportunity to connect to the grease particles. Shortly, the solution contains small

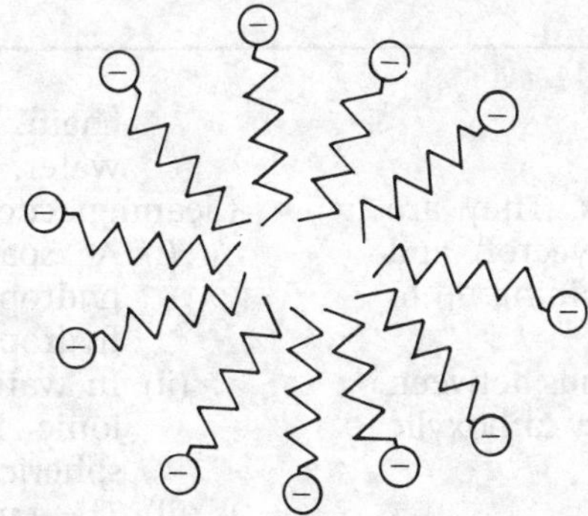
Detergent molecules gather together in micelles in water

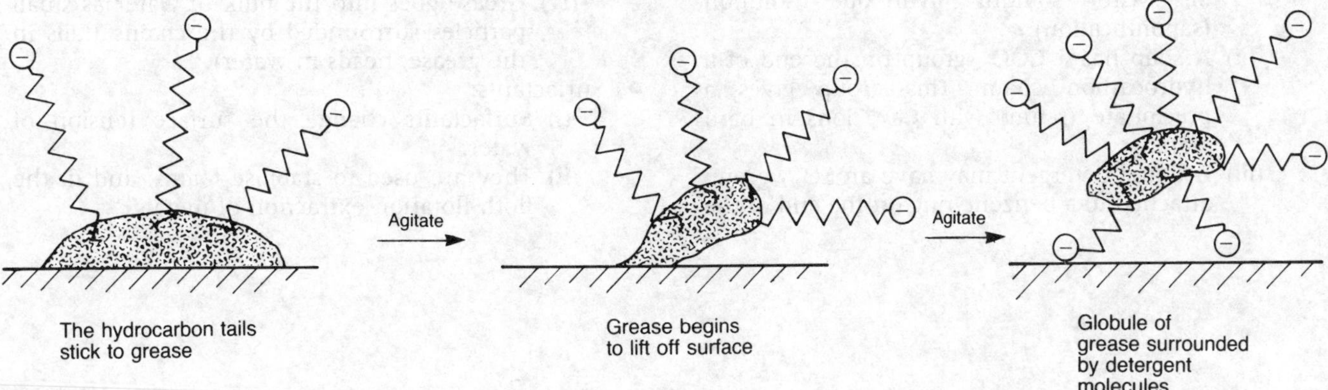
Agitate
Agitate
The hydrocarbon tails stick to grease
Grease begins to lift off surface
Globule of grease surrounded by detergent molecules

Figure 129.6 *How a detergent cleans*

globules of grease surrounded by detergent molecules. The attraction of the water molecules for the ionic heads holds the globules in solution. The electric charge on the heads means that two globules approaching one another are repelled and the layer of grease cannot reform. The result is a clean plate and a solution containing the grease, which can be thrown away.

Liquid detergents are one class of a wide range of compounds called *surfactants*. As you might guess, surfactants change the properties of surfaces. For example, water will not wet the surface of grease or oil; they remain as two separate layers. Detergent molecules allow the two to mix by changing the behaviour of the surfaces. (Technically, we say that detergents reduce the interfacial surface tension.)

Other surfactants are used in stabilising foams, such as those used in fire fighting and in the extraction of metals by foam flotation. They can also be used to destabilise foams; for example, those that might be produced in industrial boilers. A large number of food products, cosmetics and paints have surfactants added to stabilise gels and emulsions.

129.4 Which type of bonding allows grease and the tails of soaps or detergents to mix?

129.5 Micelles and the globules of grease surrounded by detergent molecules are often of a colloidal size. What is the range of size for a colloid?

Answers

129.1 This is an example of the common ion effect. Soap is partially soluble in water. If excess sodium ions are added, then the equilibrium between dissolved ions and solid is shifted towards the solid. Hence we see more soap produced.

129.2 Sodium carbonate undergoes hydrolysis to give an alkaline solution. When the alkali is boiled with the fat, the glycerides are broken apart. This destroys some of the fat, but soap is also made. This also helps to clean the pan.

129.3 No. The amount of scum is mainly a reflection of how hard the bath water is.

129.4 Van der Waals bonding.

129.5 Between 1 and 1000 nm in diameter.

UNIT 129 SUMMARY

- Fats and oils:
  - (i) Fats are a type of lipid.
  - (ii) Fats are esters called glycerides. They are esters of propane-1,2,3-triol (glycerol) and long-chain carboxylic acids containing up to 20 carbon atoms.
  - (iii) Unsaturated fats have double bonds between some of the carbon atoms in the carboxylic acid chains.
- Soaps and detergents:
  - (i) A soap can be made by heating a fat or oil with sodium hydroxide solution (saponification).
  - (ii) A soap has a COO^- group on the end of a hydrocarbon chain. This group gives a precipitate (scum) with Ca^{2+} ions in hard water.
  - (iii) A liquid detergent may have an SO_3^- group attached to a benzene ring on the end of the chain. This does not give a scum with hard water.
- Cleaning action:
  - (i) A soap or detergent molecule has a hydrophobic hydrocarbon tail and a hydrophilic ionic head.
  - (ii) In water the tails gather together, with the ionic heads pointing outwards. Roughly spherical groups (micelles) are made.
  - (iii) The tail is attracted to grease; the head to water.
  - (iv) Grease goes into the bulk of water as small particles surrounded by the chains (tails in the grease, heads in water).
- Surfactants:
  - (i) Surfactants change the surface tension of water.
  - (ii) They are used to stabilise foams, and in the floth flotation extraction of metals.

130

Organic problems

130.1 What types of problem are there?

A simple-minded response to this question is 'hard and easy'. However, from the point of view of the person who sets the problems, they are meant to lead you to discovering one or more of the following:

(i) the formula of a compound;
(ii) its structure, i.e. the arrangement of the atoms;
(iii) the functional groups it contains;
(iv) how these groups react.

We shall now work through examples of the type that you might meet in a test or examination. However, before we begin you should know that you cannot succeed in finding answers to problems unless you are familiar with the majority of work that we have covered in the units on organic chemistry and spectroscopy.

130.2 Predicting structures from percentage compositions

We shall consider two examples of typical questions.

Example 1

A compound has the composition C 92.3%, H 7.7%, a relative molecular mass of 78 and burns with a very sooty flame. What might it be?

Before we work out its molecular formula, let us look at the percentage composition. Clearly this compound contains a great deal of carbon compared with hydrogen. This alone should make us think that it might be an aromatic compound, i.e. one containing a benzene ring. The smoky flame is consistent with this notion: it is a characteristic of unsaturated hydrocarbons, especially if they have a benzene ring.

Applying the method we developed in Unit 37, we have:

	Carbon	Hydrogen
100 g of compound contains/g	92.3	7.7
Number of moles present/mol	$\frac{92.3}{12}$ =7.7	$\frac{7.7}{1}$ =7.7
Ratio of moles	1 to	1

Empirical formula CH.
Relative molecular mass of one unit of CH is

$$M_r(\text{CH}) = 12 + 1 = 13$$

Therefore there are 78/13 = 6 units in the molecular formula. The formula is C_6H_6. The compound is benzene.

Example 2

A substance has the percentage composition C 52.2%, H 13.0%, O 34.8%. It has a relative molecular mass of 46. It does not give white fumes of hydrogen chloride with phosphorus pentachloride. What is the compound?

Here we have a substance that contains oxygen as well as carbon and hydrogen. There are five homologous series to which such a substance could belong: alcohols, aldehydes, ketones, acids, or ethers. (Actually there are other organic compounds that contain oxygen, e.g. carbohydrates, but it is unlikely that you would be asked about them.) Even before we attempt to discover its structure, we can say that it cannot contain an OH group. This is because such compounds *do* give hydrogen chloride with phosphorus pentachloride. Therefore we are looking for an aldehyde, ketone, or ether.

Example 2 – cont.

	Carbon	*Hydrogen*	*Oxygen*
100 g of compound contains/g	52.2	13.0	34.8
Number of moles present/mol	$\frac{52.2}{12}$ =4.35	$\frac{13.0}{1}$ =13.0	$\frac{34.8}{16}$ =2.18
Ratio of moles	$\frac{4.35}{2.18}$ =2	$\frac{13.0}{2.18}$ =6	$\frac{2.18}{2.18}$ =1

Empirical formula C_2H_6O.
Relative molecular mass of one unit of C_2H_6O is

$$M_r(C_2H_6O) = 2 \times 12 + 6 \times 1 + 16 = 46$$

Therefore in this case the molecular formula is the same as the empirical formula, i.e. C_2H_6O.

Now we must try to fit the atoms together to make an aldehyde, ketone or ether. The place to start is with the functional group. That is, we write down:

	aldehyde	ketone	ether
	C—C(=O)—H	C—C(=O)—(C)	C—O—C
Left over	H_5	H_6	H_6

We can discount the ketone because it requires three carbon atoms, and the molecular formula says only two are available. This time we try to fit the remaining atoms around the carbon atoms. It is best to try this for yourself by using models, but you should be able to see that it is impossible to fit all the atoms together for the aldehyde:

	aldehyde	ether
	CH_3—C(=O)—H	CH_3—O—CH_3
Left over	H_2	none

The compound is methoxymethane (dimethyl ether).

130.1 Another hydrocarbon also has the percentage composition C 92.3%, H 7.7%. It has a relative molecular mass of 26 and it too burns with a smoky flame. What is it?

130.2 Repeat example 2, but this time you are told that the compound does give hydrogen chloride with phosphorus pentachloride.

Example 3

The idealised mass spectrum of a hydrocarbon is shown in Figure 130.1. It does not react with bromine water. What is its formula?

The parent ion is at a mass of 114, so this is the relative molecular mass of the compound. From its lack of reaction with bromine, we know the compound is saturated, i.e. it is probably an alkane. (We shall assume that it is not a cyclic hydrocarbon such as cyclobutane or cyclohexane.) Hence its general formula must be C_nH_{2n+2}. We can now begin to make a guess at its actual formula, or do a systematic calculation. The first method is to say that as the relative molecular mass is less than 120, there must be fewer than 10 carbon atoms in the molecule, so let us guess at six. This would give us a relative molecular mass of $6 \times 12 + 14 \times 1 = 86$, which is too low. Another guess is to try eight carbon atoms: $8 \times 12 + 18 = 114$. This gives us the formula C_8H_{18}.

130.3 Using information from spectra

(a) *Mass spectra*

One of the most direct pieces of information about a compound can be obtained from a mass spectrum. The key thing here is to look for the peak at the highest mass to charge ratio. This will give you the relative molecular mass of the parent ion, i.e. the relative molecular mass

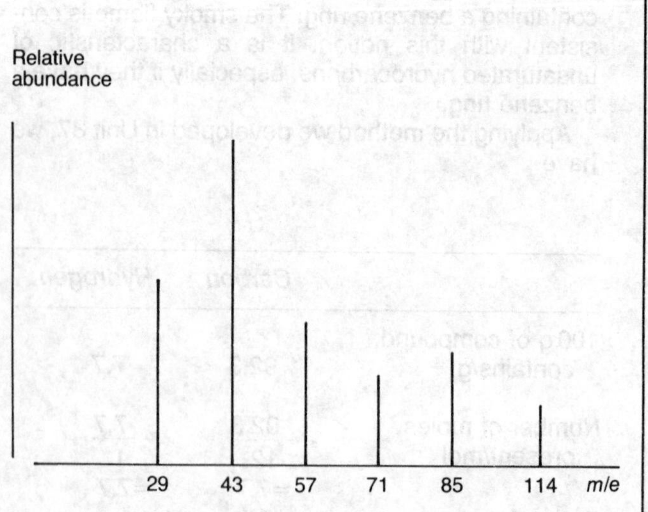

Figure 130.1 *The mass spectrum for example 3*

Example 3 – cont.

The systematic method is to say that n carbon atoms have a mass of $12n$ units, and $2n+2$ hydrogen atoms give $2n+2$ units. Therefore we have

$$12n+2n+2=114$$

so

$$14n=112$$
$$n=8$$

You should be careful about saying which alkane is. In fact, the spectrum belongs to octane, but unless you knew a great deal about mass spectrometry you could not be sure that it was not an isomer, e.g. 3,4-dimethylhexane. The other peaks (the fragmentation pattern) belong to parts of chains that break up in their progress through the spectrometer. For example, the peak at mass 29 corresponds to $C_2H_5^+$, and that at 43 to $C_3H_7^+$.

of the substance. The spectrum may also provide a guide to the structure of the molecule.

(b) *Infrared (vibrational) spectra*

We found in Unit 27 that particular groups vibrate at fairly well defined frequencies. This means that, if we look at an infrared spectrum, it should tell us if these groups are present or not. You should take special notice of the bands in the following regions:

(i) 1600 to 1800 cm^{-1}. This is where the vibration of a carbonyl group appears. A strong peak in this region is characteristic of aldehydes, ketones, acids and amides.

(ii) 2720 cm^{-1}. Aldehydes show a strong band here owing to the vibration of the hydrogen atom bonded to the carbon atom of the carbonyl group.

(iii) 2900 and 1400 cm^{-1}. Carbon–hydrogen vibrations will also appear in spectra in this region.

(iv) 3200 to 3700 cm^{-1}. The vibrations of OH groups in alcohols appear here. If the group is involved in hydrogen bonding, then the vibration band is broad; if not, it is narrow and shifts to around 3600 cm^{-1}.

130.3 The mass spectrum of a liquid is shown in Figure 130.2. The liquid is known to be an aromatic ketone with percentage composition C 80.0%, H 6.7%, O 13.3%.

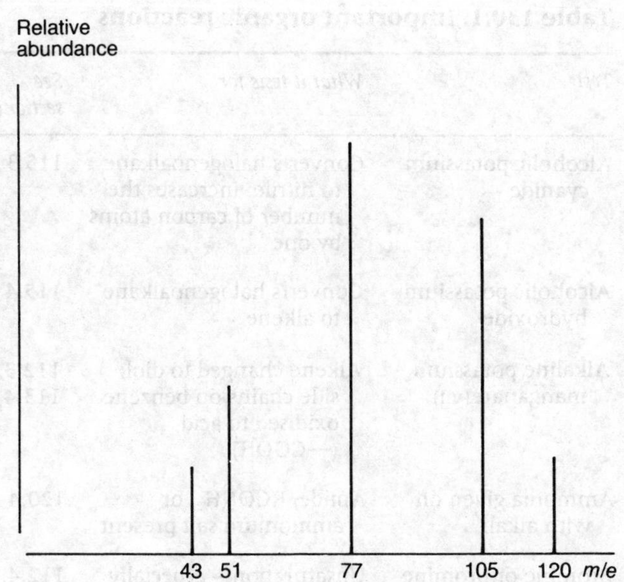

Figure 130.2 The mass spectrum for question 130.3

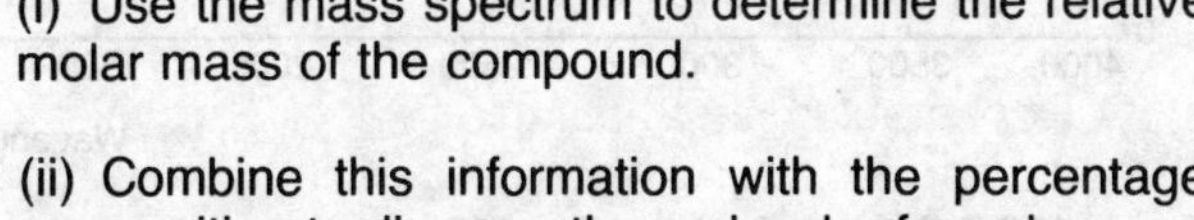

(i) Use the mass spectrum to determine the relative molar mass of the compound.

(ii) Combine this information with the percentage composition to discover the molecular formula.

(iii) Suggest a structure for the molecule. What is its name?

(iv) What fragment gives the peak at mass 105?

130.4 Identify the types of compound giving the spectra shown in Figure 130.3.

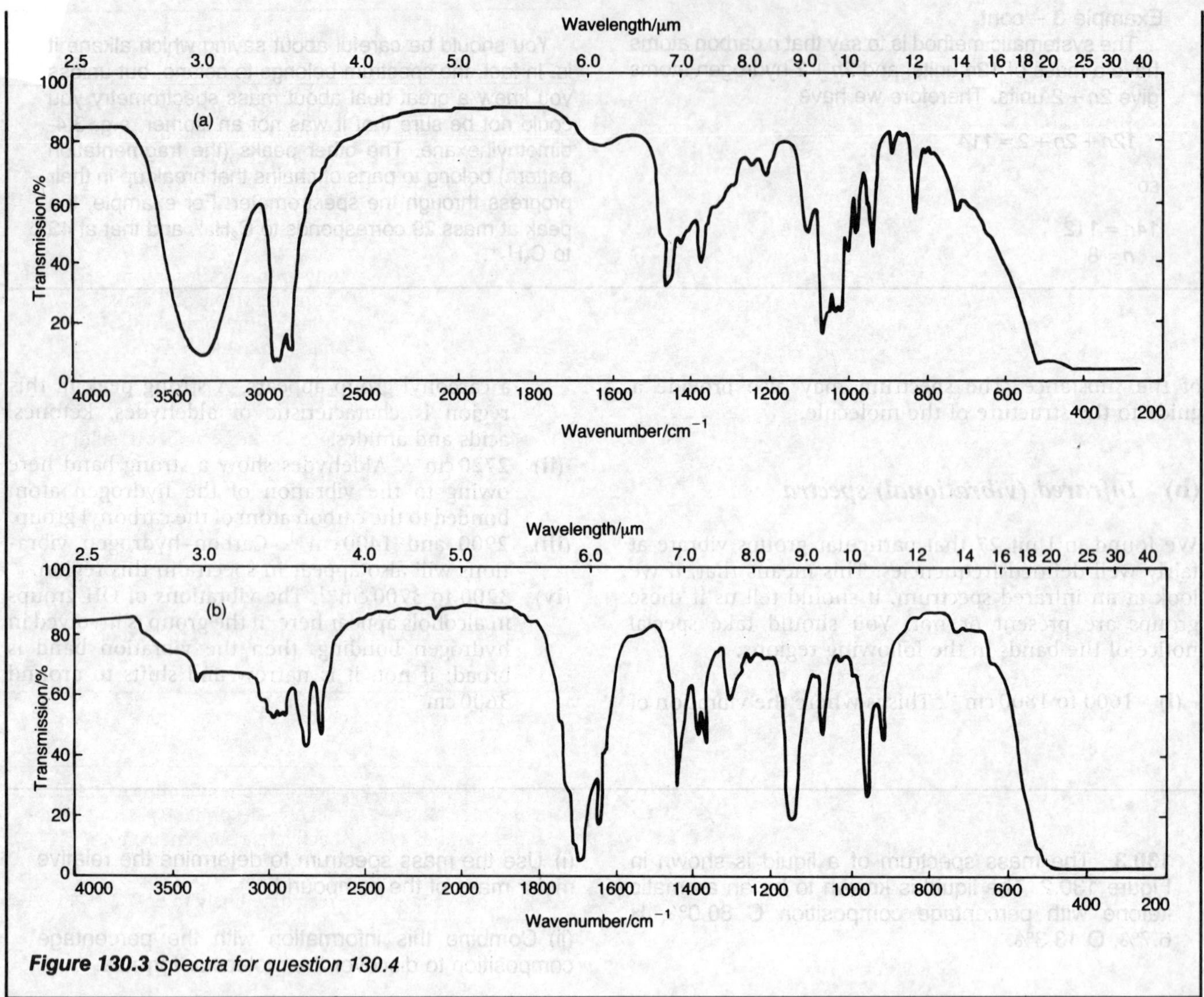

Figure 130.3 Spectra for question 130.4

130.4 The results of chemical reactions

There are a great many organic reactions that you might need to know, but some are more important than others. Tables 130.1 and 130.2 summarise them. You will have to look up the section reference to get information about reaction conditions and other details. The best course of action is to make sure you learn these reactions. You may find this tiresome, but it pays dividends in the long run. The best way to learn them is to commit two or three to memory each day, or every other day. In this way you will avoid last minute panic before exams. However, you will need to test yourself from time to time to make your brain establish the information in long-term memory.

One of the key principles that makes the study of functional groups fruitful is that, in the main, the reactions of one type of group do not interfere with the reactions of the others. We can make use of this idea to provide answers to questions that would otherwise be impossible to tackle.

Table 130.1. Important organic reactions

*Test**	*What it tests for*	*See section(s)*
Alcoholic potassium cyanide	Converts halogenoalkane to nitrile; increases the number of carbon atoms by one	115.3
Alcoholic potassium hydroxide	Converts halogenoalkane to alkene	115.4
Alkaline potassium manganate(VII)	Alkene changed to diol; side chains on benzene oxidised to acid (—COOH)	112.3, 113.4
Ammonia given off with alkali	Amide, $RCONH_2$, or ammonium salt present	120.4
Bromine or bromine water decolourised	Unsaturation – especially alkenes, alkynes, phenol and phenylamine	112.4, 117.4, 122.9

Table 130.1 – cont.

*Test**	*What it tests for*	*See section(s)*
Bromine in alkali	Hofmann degradation; amide converted to amine with one less carbon atom	120.4
Chlorine gas and light	Free radical reaction with alkanes; chlorination of an acid at the α-carbon; especially useful for making amino acids	113.3, 123.2
Chlorine gas and red phosphorus or iodine	Chlorination of an acid at the α-carbon; especially useful for making amino acids	123.2
2,4-Dinitrophenylhydrazine gives orange precipitates (hydrazones)	Aldehyde or ketone present	118.6
Ethanoyl chloride, CH_3COCl, or benzoyl chloride, C_6H_5COCl, give fumes of HCl	OH group in an alcohol reacts to give an ester; amines are acetylated or benzoylated	120.6
Hydrogenation, e.g. H_2/Ni	Unsaturation – especially alkenes, alkynes and arenes; converts nitriles to amines	112.4, 113.5, 120.7
Hydrogen halide, e.g. HCl	Addition to alkenes obeys the Markovnikoff rule	112.4
Hydrolysis (reaction with water, acid or alkali)	Converts nitriles to acids	120.7
Iodoform reaction; warm with iodine in alkali gives yellow precipitate, CHI_3	Presence of $CH_3-C(=O)-X$ and $CH_3-CH(OH)-X$ groups	118.9
Lithium tetrahydridoaluminate(III), $LiAlH_4$	Reduces acids and acid chlorides to alcohols; esters, aldehydes and ketones to alcohols; nitriles to amines	119.3 120.2, 120.6, 118.7, 122.2
Ozonolysis	Breaks double (and triple) bonds and produces aldehydes and/or ketones	112.5
Phosphorus pentachloride, PCl_5, or sulphur dichloride oxide, $SOCl_2$, give fumes of HCl	Test for OH groups in alcohols or acids; OH group replaced by Cl	116.4, 119.3
Phosphorus(V) oxide, P_4O_{10}	Converts amides to nitriles	120.4
Sodium dichromate(VI)/H^+ changes from orange to green	Oxidation, especially of primary alcohol to aldehyde or acid, secondary alcohol to ketone	116.3
Sodium nitrite in acid	Amines give diazonium ions	122.6
$T<5\,°C$	Only aromatic diazonium ions are stable and make diazonium compounds	
$T>5\,°C$	Change into alcohol and N_2 gas	

*The tests are given in (approximately) alphabetical order of the chief reagent

Table 130.2. Special reactions of aromatic compounds

Reaction	*Comment*	*See section(s)*
Substance gives a white precipitate with bromine	Phenol or phenylamine likely; OH and NH_2 activate a benzene ring	117.4, 122.9
A white precipitate appears on acidification	Precipitate likely to be benzoic acid	119.3
Concentrated nitric and sulphuric acids (nitrating mixture)	Introduces nitro group, $—NO_2$, into benzene ring	113.6
Halogen plus halogen carrier, e.g. $AlCl_3$, iron filings	Introduces halogen into benzene ring	113.6
Ethanoyl chloride, CH_3COCl, or benzoyl chloride, C_6H_5COCl, with $AlCl_3$*	Benzene ring is acetylated or benzoylated	113.6
Chloroalkane with $AlCl_3$*	Alkylation of a benzene ring; introduces a hydrocarbon side chain	113.6
Reduction with tin and hydrochloric acid	Nitro group reduced to amine	122.2

*These are examples of Friedel–Crafts reactions

Example 4

Predict how the molecule in Figure 130.4 would react with (i) bromine, (ii) lithium tetrahydridoaluminate(III), (iii) phosphorus pentachloride.

We know (or we can find the information from Tables 130.1 and 130.2 and elsewhere) that (i) bromine will seek out and add to double bonds (but not benzene rings), (ii) lithium tetrahydridoaluminate(III) will reduce a ketone to an alcohol, and (iii) phosphorus pentachloride will give off fumes of hydrogen chloride with an alcohol and the OH is replaced by Cl; further, the $\gt C{=}O$ group is replaced by $\gt CCl_2$

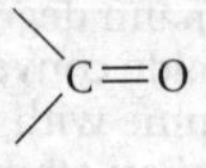

$LiAlH_4$ Br_2 PCl_5

+ HCl

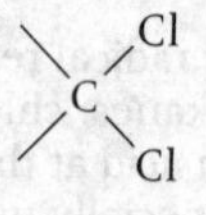

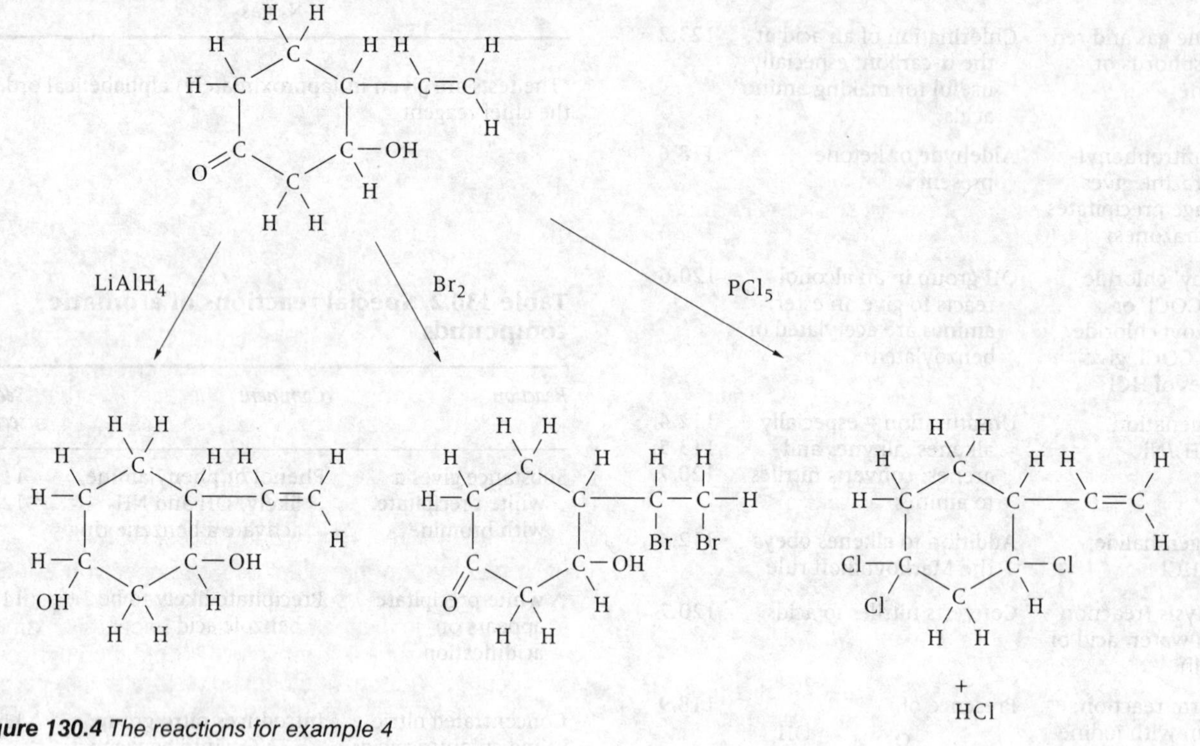

***Figure 130.4** The reactions for example 4*

130.5 A substance has molecular formula C_3H_5N. It shows no reaction with bromine water.

(i) There are two homologous series to which compounds containing nitrogen but no oxygen might belong. What are they?

(ii) Can you work out which series this molecule belongs to? What is its structure?

(iii) How does this substance react with chlorine and red phosphorus?

(iv) Draw the structure of $C_3H_5ClO_2$.

(v) Give the name and structure of $C_3H_7NO_2$. What type of substance is it?

(vi) Build a model of $C_3H_7NO_2$. There are two versions of the molecule. Explain why this is so.

130.6 The same substance as in question 130.5 undergoes the following reactions (which are shown in shorthand):

$$C_3H_5N \xrightarrow{H^+} C_3H_6O_2 \xrightarrow{Cl_2/P} C_3H_5ClO_2 \xrightarrow{NH_3} C_3H_7NO_2$$

(i) Explain the first reaction.

(ii) Draw the structure of $C_3H_6O_2$. What is its name?

130.7 Here is an outline reaction scheme:

$$C_6H_5O_2N \xrightarrow{Sn/HCl} C_6H_7N \xrightarrow[T>5\,°C]{NaNO_2,\ HCl} C_6H_6O$$

C_6H_6O: miscible in alkali, not in acid

$$C_6H_5O_2N \xrightarrow{Sn/HCl} C_6H_7N \xrightarrow[\text{(ii) phenol}]{\text{(i) } NaNO_2,\ HCl,\ T<5\,°C} C_{12}H_{11}N_2O$$

$C_{12}H_{11}N_2O$: brightly coloured dye

(i) What can you deduce about the nature of $C_6H_5O_2N$, given the large proportion on carbon to hydrogen?

(ii) If you rearrange the molecular formula slightly, does this give you a recognisable molecule? What is its name?

(iii) What is the name and structure of C_6H_7N?

(iv) What is the name and structure of C_6H_6O? What else would you see during the reaction?

(v) Explain the observation about the miscibility in acid and alkali.

(vi) What is the special name given to the reaction producing the coloured dye? Draw the structure of the product. (You may need to look back at section 122.8.)

Answers

130.1 With the same percentage composition as in example 1, the empirical formula is also CH. This time there are 26/13 = 2 units in the molecular formula. The substance is ethyne, C_2H_2.

130.2 The extra information tells us that the substance is an alcohol or an acid. If you try to write down structures, you will find that the only one that fits is ethanol, CH_3CH_2OH.

130.3 (i) The parent ion gives the relative molar mass as 120.

(ii)

	Carbon	*Hydrogen*	*Oxygen*
100 g of compound contains/g	80.0	6.7	13.3
Number of moles present /mol	$\frac{80.0}{12}$ = 6.7	$\frac{6.7}{1}$ = 6.7	$\frac{13.3}{16}$ = 0.83
Ratio of moles	$\frac{6.7}{0.83}$ = 8	$\frac{6.7}{0.83}$ = 8	$\frac{0.83}{0.83}$ = 1

Empirical formula C_8H_8O.
Molar mass of one unit of C_8H_8O is

$$M(C_8H_8O) = 8\times12\,\text{g mol}^{-1} + 8\times1\,\text{g mol}^{-1} + 1\times16\,\text{g mol}^{-1} = 120\,\text{g mol}^{-1}$$

so C_8H_8O is also the molecular formula of the compound.

(iii) We know that it is a ketone, so we start by writing down the functional group: >C═O. This takes out CO from the formula, leaving us with C_7H_8. We also know that it is aromatic, so it has a benzene ring present. Be careful here; there must be a group attached to the ring, which means that one of the six hydrogen atoms has been lost. Therefore we try to fit a C_6H_5 group (not C_6H_6) to the carbonyl group. If we do this we are left with CH_3 as the remaining atoms. This is just right, as it represents a methyl group. The final structure is that of phenylethanone:

$$C_6H_5{-}C({=}O){-}CH_3$$

(iv) 105 is 15 mass units less than the parent mass. A CH_3^+ ion corresponds to this difference in mass, so the fragment is $C_6H_5CO^+$.

130.4 Figure 130.3a is an alcohol; Figure 130.3b is a carbonyl compound (actually an aldehyde). Note the characteristic broad band of hydrogen bonded OH groups around 3300 cm^{-1}, and the carbonyl stretch around 1700 cm^{-1}. There is also a C—H stretch characteristic of an aldehyde near 2720 cm^{-1}.

130.5 (i) Amines, RNH_2, and nitriles, RCN.

(ii) If you try drawing structures on paper you will find that an amine is only possible if there are carbon–carbon double bonds in the molecule. This is because an amine has an NH_2 group. This leaves C_3H_3, but then there are not enough hydrogen atoms to saturate the carbon atoms. The bromine water test tells us that these bonds are absent. The molecule is a nitrile, propanenitrile:

$$H{-}CH_2{-}CH_2{-}C{\equiv}N$$

130.6 (i) Nitriles are hydrolysed to carboxylic acids.

(ii) Propanoic acid:

$$CH_3{-}CH_2{-}C({=}O){-}OH$$

(iii), (iv) The α hydrogen atoms are lost one by one. The product is α-chloropropanoic acid:

$$H{-}CH_2{-}CH(Cl){-}C({=}O){-}OH$$

Answers – cont.

(v) This is the way in which amino acids are prepared. The product is alanine:

$$H-\overset{H}{\underset{H}{C}}-\overset{H}{\underset{NH_2}{C}}-C(=O)OH$$

(vi) Alanine has an asymmetric carbon atom, i.e. it is chiral (optically active). There are two mirror image forms (enantiomers) of the molecule (see Unit 110).

130.7 (i) It is aromatic, i.e. contains a benzene ring.

(ii) $C_6H_5NO_2$, nitrobenzene.

(iii) This reaction converts nitrobenzene into phenylamine, $C_6H_5NH_2$.

(iv) This diazonium reaction converts an amine into a diazonium ion, in this case $C_6H_5N_2^+$. Above 5 °C (approx.) it reacts with water to give an alcohol, in this case phenol, C_6H_5OH. Phenol is a weak acid:

$$\underset{\text{partially miscible}}{C_6H_5OH} \rightleftharpoons \underset{\text{soluble}}{C_6H_5O^- + H^+}$$

(v) In alkali, hydrogen ions are removed and the equilibrium is driven to the right. We see the phenol dissolving. In acid, the equilibrium shifts to the left, and a layer of phenol will appear.

(vi) A coupling reaction. The product is

$$C_6H_5-N=N-C_6H_4-OH$$

UNIT 130 SUMMARY

- This unit is its own summary.

APPENDICES

A The laws of thermodynamics

A.1 What are the laws of thermodynamics?

There are four laws of thermodynamics, and each of them is a summary of the accumulated experience of many years of work, both experimental and theoretical. Like any other scientific law, their value lies in the way they provide us with consistent explanations of the results of experiments, and the ability to make predictions. It is possible to live your life without knowing anything about them, but on the other hand they can give you a different perspective on the world, and its future. We shall briefly discuss each of the laws in turn. You should look in the units on thermodynamics if you want to see how ideas of energy, work, entropy and free energy apply to particular chemical reactions and processes.

A.2 The zeroth law

The zeroth law says that:

> **Two systems each in thermal equilibrium with a third will be in thermal equilibrium with each other.**

Tied in with this law is our notion of temperature scales and thermometers. Suppose you place a thermometer in two cans of water and find that they have the same temperature. If you now connect the two cans so that heat can pass between them you would get a great surprise if one of the cans became hotter than the other. We do not expect such behaviour because our experience tells us that it does not happen. This is what the zeroth law says: it summarises experience.

A.3 The first law

This is the law of conservation of energy. It says that:

> **The amount of energy in an isolated system is constant: when one form of energy disappears, an equal amount of energy in another form is produced.**

One of the most important advances in thermodynamics was made by Joule when he showed that heat and work are two equivalent manifestations of energy. Following Einstein's development of the theory of relativity, we now know that mass can also be regarded as a variety of energy.

You might notice that the definition talks about 'the system'. In a specific example in which we apply the law, we have to be careful about specifying the system. For example, an acid and alkali reacting in a test tube releases energy, but if we take the test tube alone as the system the law will not hold true: we know that the tube and its contents will cool down to room temperature over the course of an hour or two. Here 'the system' is not isolated. We would do better if we hid the tube and contents in a perfectly sealed and insulated container. Then we would have an isolated system; but perfect insulation does not exist, so the notion of an isolated system is something of a theoretical notion. However, in practice, we can come very close to achieving it.

Where the first law gets interesting (and sometimes annoying) is when we think about exchanging energy, perhaps in the form of work, between a system and its surroundings. The reason for the annoyance is that we have to define a method of keeping our book keeping straight when we calculate the energy changes. The *sign convention* which is always used is this:

> **Heat *gained* by a system is counted as a positive number.**
>
> **Heat *lost* by a system is counted as a negative number.**
>
> **Work done *by* the system is counted as a positive number.**
>
> **Work done *on* the system is counted as a negative number.**

The combination of the heat change and work done will alter the energy of the system, which we call the *internal energy*. We shall use the symbol ΔE to mean a change in internal energy, Δq for a heat change and Δw for the work done. For example, if a system gains 100 J, and 20 J of work are done on it, the energy of the system will have increased by an amount 120 J, i.e. 100 J + 20 J. On the other hand, if 100 J are gained, but 20 J of work are done by the system on its surroundings, the net gain will be 80 J, i.e. 100 J − 20 J.

In general the formula that covers these changes, and all others, is

$$\Delta E = \Delta q - \Delta w$$

We must obey the sign convention if we are to use this equation successfully. For example,

a gain by the system of 100 J means that $\Delta q = +100\text{ J}$

20 J of work done on the system means that $\Delta w = -20\text{ J}$

Hence,

$$\Delta E = 100\text{ J} - (-20\text{ J}) = 120\text{ J}$$

Incidentally, there are many varieties of work that can be done on and by systems. Two of the most common are mechanical work (where, for example, an expanding gas pushes a piston) and electrical work (in this case the system might be a chemical cell connected to a motor).

We can write $\Delta E = \Delta q - \Delta w$ in a different way. If we assume that the work is done by moving a piston back against a constant pressure P, then $w = P\Delta V$, where ΔV is the volume of gas pushed out by the piston. Now we have

$$\Delta E = \Delta q - P\Delta V$$

or

$$\Delta q = \Delta E + P\Delta V$$

Δq is now the type of heat change that we called the *enthalpy change*, ΔH, in the previous text units, i.e.

$$\Delta H = \Delta E + P\Delta V$$

In words, this equation says that the enthalpy change is the combination of the change in internal energy and the work done. One of the important things about enthalpy (although we shall not prove it) is that it is a thermodynamic function of state. That is, its value depends only on the initial and final states of a system, not on the route taken between the states. You should be familiar with Hess's law, which relies on this property of enthalpy.

A.4 The second law

The second law says that:

Spontaneous processes in a system can only be reversed by supplying work from the surroundings.

(There are many versions of this law, so you may well find a different one in another book.) We have said a little about spontaneous changes in section 49.7. Make sure that you understand that a spontaneous change is one that takes place without us having to do work on it. A mechanical example is that a ball will of its own accord roll down, but not up, a hill. Such a change is spontaneous, and we do not regard it as needing much explanation. We are quite used to observing spontaneous changes. However, if we thought we saw a ball travelling up-hill on its own, we would immediately seek an explanation: perhaps it is being pulled by a thread. Changes like this have to be made to happen by doing work on them. In chemistry, many changes are spontaneous, e.g. magnesium and acid give off hydrogen as soon as they meet. But some are not; e.g. at room temperature and pressure, water does not of its own accord split into hydrogen and oxygen. We can make water decompose by passing electricity through it. This is a non-spontaneous change that is made to happen when we do electrical work on the system.

From the second law it is possible to derive a number of conclusions. The first, and most important, is that there is a condition that tells us whether a change is spontaneous. It is that:

For a process to be spontaneous, the free energy change for the process must be negative.

That is,

$$\Delta G = -\text{ve}$$

The free energy change is defined as

$$\Delta G = \Delta H - T\Delta S$$

where ΔS is the entropy change in the process.

We can interpret the entropy of a system as a measure of the number of ways its energy is shared between the different energy levels available to it, i.e. the number of complexions.

A.5 The third law

This law is about entropy. It claims that:

The entropy of a perfect crystal is zero at 0 K.

So far it has proved impossible to reach exactly 0 K (although some experiments have come very close); but this has not stopped the law being used. It fixes our scale of entropy. It would be wrong to think that there is no activity in a perfect crystal at 0 K, even if it has zero entropy. Heisenberg's uncertainty principle (see question 11.6) tells us that atoms and electrons have some energy even at 0 K. For example, although all the electrons would be in their ground states, their energies would not be zero, and vibrations of molecules would still take place.

B

Table of ionisation energies

Element	Number of electrons removed																			
	1	2	3	4	5	6	7	8	9	10	11	12	13	14	15	16	17	18	19	20
Hydrogen	1 312																			
Helium	2 372	5 250																		
Lithium	520	7 298	11 815																	
Beryllium	899	1 757	14 849	21 006																
Boron	801	2 427	3 660	25 026	32 827															
Carbon	1 086	2 353	4 620	6 223	37 830	47 277														
Nitrogen	1 402	2 856	4 578	7 475	9 445	53 266	64 360													
Oxygen	1 314	3 388	5 300	7 469	10 989	13 326	71 334	84 078												
Fluorine	1 681	3 471	6 050	8 408	11 023	15 164	17 868	92 038	106 434											
Neon	2 081	3 952	6 122	9 370	12 178	15 238	19 999	23 069	115 379	131 431										
Sodium	513	4 562	6 912	9 544	13 353	16 610	20 115	25 490	28 934	141 362	159 074									
Magnesium	738	1 451	7 733	10 540	13 630	17 995	21 704	25 656	31 643	35 462	169 991	189 367								
Aluminium	578	1 817	2 745	11 577	14 831	18 378	23 295	27 459	31 861	38 457	42 654	201 270	222 314							
Silicon	786	1 577	3 232	4 356	16 091	19 785	23 786	29 252	33 877	38 733	45 934	50 511	235 204	257 920						
Phosphorus	1 012	1 903	2 912	4 957	6 274	22 233	25 397	29 854	35 867	40 965	45 983	54 072	59 036	271 798	296 192					
Sulphur	1 000	2 251	3 361	4 564	7 013	8 496	27 106	31 670	36 578	43 138	48 705	54 481	62 874	68 230	311 058	337 126				
Chlorine	1 251	2 297	3 822	5 158	6 542	9 459	11 018	33 604	38 600	43 961	51 067	57 117	63 362	72 340	78 096	352 990	380 756			
Argon	1 521	2 666	3 931	5 771	7 238	8 781	11 995	13 842	40 760	46 186	52 002	59 652	66 199	72 918	82 472	88 575	397 602	427 062		
Potassium	419	3 051	4 411	5 877	7 976	9 649	11 343	14 942	16 964	48 575	54 431	60 699	68 894	75 948	83 150	93 399	99 768	444 897	476 060	
Calcium	590	1 145	4 912	6 474	8 144	10 496	12 321	14 207	18 192	20 385	57 048	63 333	70 052	78 792	86 367	93 978	104 881	111 635	494 886	527 759

All values are in kJ mol^{-1}. Data adapted from *Handbook of Chemistry and Physics*, CRC Press, Boca Raton, Florida, 1989

C

Table of atomic masses

In order of atomic number

Atomic number	*Element*	*Atomic mass /g mol⁻¹*
1	Hydrogen	1.0
2	Helium	4.0
3	Lithium	6.9
4	Beryllium	9.0
5	Boron	10.8
6	Carbon	12.0
7	Nitrogen	14.0
8	Oxygen	16.0
9	Fluorine	19.0
10	Neon	20.2
11	Sodium	23.0
12	Magnesium	24.3
13	Aluminium	27.0
14	Silicon	28.1
15	Phosphorus	31.0
16	Sulphur	32.1
17	Chlorine	35.5
18	Argon	39.9
19	Potassium	39.1
20	Calcium	40.1
21	Scandium	45.0
22	Titanium	47.9
23	Vanadium	50.9
24	Chromium	52.0
25	Manganese	54.9
26	Iron	55.9
27	Cobalt	58.9
28	Nickel	58.7
29	Copper	63.5
30	Zinc	65.4
31	Gallium	69.7
32	Germanium	72.6
33	Arsenic	74.9
34	Selenium	79.0
35	Bromine	79.9

In alphabetical order

Atomic number	*Element*	*Atomic mass /g mol⁻¹*
89	Actinium	227.0
13	Aluminium	27.0
51	Antimony	121.8
18	Argon	39.9
33	Arsenic	74.9
85	Astatine	210.0
56	Barium	137.3
4	Beryllium	9.0
83	Bismuth	209.0
5	Boron	10.8
35	Bromine	79.9
48	Cadmium	112.4
55	Caesium	132.9
20	Calcium	40.1
6	Carbon	12.0
58	Cerium	140.1
17	Chlorine	35.5
24	Chromium	52.0
27	Cobalt	58.9
29	Copper	63.5
9	Fluorine	19.0
87	Francium	223.0
31	Gallium	69.7
32	Germanium	72.6
79	Gold	197.0
72	Hafnium	178.5
2	Helium	4.0
1	Hydrogen	1.0
49	Indium	114.8
53	Iodine	126.9
77	Iridium	192.2
26	Iron	55.9
36	Krypton	83.8

In order of atomic number

Atomic number	*Element*	*Atomic mass /g mol^{-1}*
36	Krypton	83.8
37	Rubidium	85.5
38	Strontium	87.6
39	Yttrium	88.9
40	Zirconium	91.2
41	Niobium	92.9
42	Molybdenum	95.9
43	Technetium	99.0
44	Ruthenium	101.1
45	Rhodium	102.9
46	Palladium	106.4
47	Silver	107.9
48	Cadmium	112.4
49	Indium	114.8
50	Tin	118.7
51	Antimony	121.8
52	Tellurium	127.6
53	Iodine	126.9
54	Xenon	131.3
55	Caesium	132.9
56	Barium	137.3
57	Lanthanum	138.9
58	Cerium	140.1
72	Hafnium	178.5
73	Tantalum	181.0
74	Tungsten	183.9
75	Rhenium	186.2
76	Osmium	190.2
77	Iridium	192.2
78	Platinum	195.1
79	Gold	197.0
80	Mercury	200.6
81	Thallium	204.4
82	Lead	207.2
83	Bismuth	209.0
84	Polonium	210.0
85	Astatine	210.0
86	Radon	222.0
87	Francium	223.0
88	Radium	226.0
89	Actinium	227.0
90	Thorium	232.0
91	Protactinium	231.0
92	Uranium	238.1
93	Neptunium	239.1
94	Plutonium	239.1

In alphabetical order

Atomic number	*Element*	*Atomic mass /g mol^{-1}*
57	Lanthanum	138.9
82	Lead	207.2
3	Lithium	6.9
12	Magnesium	24.3
25	Manganese	54.9
80	Mercury	200.6
42	Molybdenum	95.9
10	Neon	20.2
93	Neptunium	239.1
28	Nickel	58.7
41	Niobium	92.9
7	Nitrogen	14.0
76	Osmium	190.2
8	Oxygen	16.0
46	Palladium	106.4
15	Phosphorus	31.0
78	Platinum	195.1
94	Plutonium	239.1
84	Polonium	210.0
19	Potassium	39.1
91	Protactinium	231.0
88	Radium	226.0
86	Radon	222.0
75	Rhenium	186.2
45	Rhodium	102.9
37	Rubidium	85.5
44	Ruthenium	101.1
21	Scandium	45.0
34	Selenium	79.0
14	Silicon	28.1
47	Silver	107.9
11	Sodium	23.0
38	Strontium	87.6
16	Sulphur	32.1
73	Tantalum	181.0
43	Technetium	99.0
52	Tellurium	127.6
81	Thallium	204.4
90	Thorium	232.0
50	Tin	118.7
22	Titanium	47.9
74	Tungsten	183.9
92	Uranium	238.1
23	Vanadium	50.9
54	Xenon	131.3
39	Yttrium	88.9
30	Zinc	65.4
40	Zirconium	91.2

With some exceptions, the lanthanides (atomic numbers between 58 and 71), actinides (atomic numbers between 90 and 103) and elements following the actinides have been omitted

D

Values of some universal constants

Quantity	*Symbol*	*Value and units*
Avogadro constant	L	6.022×10^{23} mol^{-1}
Bohr radius	a_0	5.292×10^{-11} m
Boltzmann constant	k	1.381×10^{-23} J K^{-1}
Electron charge	$-e$	1.602×10^{-19} C
Electron mass	m_e	9.109×10^{-31} kg
Permittivity of vacuum	ε_0	8.854×10^{-12} C^2 N^{-1} m^{-2}
Planck constant	h	6.626×10^{-34} J s
Proton mass	m_p	1.673×10^{-27} kg
Speed of light in vacuum	c	2.998×10^{8} m s^{-1}

Organic analysis

E.1. Two types of analysis

All chemicals can be analysed qualitatively or quantitatively. In qualitative analysis we seek to discover which elements, or groups of atoms, the chemical contains; in quantitative analysis we attempt to find out how much of each element is present. In this appendix you will find a brief summary of qualitative analysis as it has traditionally been applied to organic chemicals. Few practical details are provided. You should consult a specialist book if you need details of the methods. Modern techniques, such as infrared spectroscopy, nuclear magnetic resonance spectroscopy and mass spectrometry, are not described here. Please turn to the units on spectrometry for information about them.

Warning

On no account attempt any of the experiments outlined below without the guidance of your teacher or lecturer. Some of the reactions can be dangerous if not conducted with great care.

E.2 Qualitative analysis

The simplest tests are to discover:

(i) if the compound is organic, i.e. if it contains at least the elements carbon and hydrogen;
(ii) if it contains nitrogen;
(iii) if it contains halogens;
(iv) if it contains sulphur.

It is not possible to make a simple test to discover the presence of oxygen.

(a) *Test for carbon and hydrogen*

A dry sample is mixed with dry copper(II) oxide and heated. Most organic compounds have some reducing power, and will reduce the copper(II) oxide to copper. When this happens, hydrogen atoms in the compound combine with part of the oxygen to make water, and carbon atoms are converted to carbon dioxide.

The presence of water can be confirmed using anhydrous copper(II) sulphate (which turns from white to blue), and lime water tests for carbon dioxide (the solution turns 'milky').

(b) *Test for nitrogen, halogens and sulphur*

There are two common methods for detecting nitrogen (as well as halogens and sulphur). One method is known as Middleton's test; the other is Lassaigne's test.

Middleton's test

The compound is heated with a mixture of anhydrous sodium carbonate and powdered zinc. The reaction should be done in a small, heat resistant, glass tube (an ignition tube). When the tube is red hot, it is plunged into cold water, causing the glass to break and allowing soluble compounds to dissolve in the water. *Note the warning given above!*

This reaction, known as Middleton's test, converts nitrogen in the compound into cyanide ions. It also releases halogens as free halide ions; sulphur is converted to zinc sulphide. The cyanide and halide ions dissolve in the water, while any zinc sulphide is left in the solid residue. The solution is filtered and the filtrate split into at least two portions.

To test for the presence of *nitrogen*, one portion is reacted with a little sodium hydroxide solution followed by iron(II) sulphate solution. Free cyanide ions bond to the iron(II) ions, forming a solution of hexacyanoferrate(II). On adding a little iron(III) chloride solution, followed by concentrated hydrochloric acid, a blue-green precipitate of 'Prussian blue', $Fe_4[Fe(CN)_6]_3$, confirms the presence of cyanide ions, and therefore nitrogen in the original sample. Actually, this test can be difficult to perform successfully: the amount of Prussian blue is often small and difficult to see. It can be masked by other coloured iron compounds, although the hydrochloric acid helps to destroy, for example, iron(II) and iron(III) hydroxides.

The test for *halogens* is as follows. To a second portion of the filtrate, add dilute nitric acid followed by silver nitrate solution. This is the normal test for halide ions: chlorides give a white precipitate, bromides a cream precipitate, and iodides a yellow precipitate. If it is uncertain whether the precipitate is a bromide or iodide, a third portion of the original filtrate can be mixed with chlorine water followed by a little 1,1,1-trichloroethane. The tell-tale purple colour of iodine in the organic layer confirms iodine.

The test for *sulphur* is done on the residue, and relies on the fact that sulphides will give off hydrogen sulphide when warmed with dilute hydrochloric acid. On warming with the acid, there is the likelihood of smelling the foul fumes of hydrogen sulphide. However, a simple chemical test is to place a piece of filter paper moistened by lead(II) nitrate solution in the vapour. If hydrogen sulphide is present, the paper will turn black owing to the formation of lead(II) sulphide.

Lassaigne's test

Here the organic compound is heated with a pellet of sodium, again in an ignition tube. The method is similar to Middleton's test in that the sodium converts nitrogen to cyanide, halogens to halides and sulphur to sulphide. The tube is broken under water and the solution filtered. This time cyanide ions, halide ions and sulphide ions all go into solution. (Sodium sulphide is far more soluble in water than zinc sulphide.) The tests for cyanide and halide ions are performed as in Middleton's method. The test for sulphide ions is different. A few drops of a solution of sodium nitroprusside, $Na_2Fe(NO)(CN)_5$, gives a violet colour if sulphide ions are present.

These tests are summarised in Figure E.1.

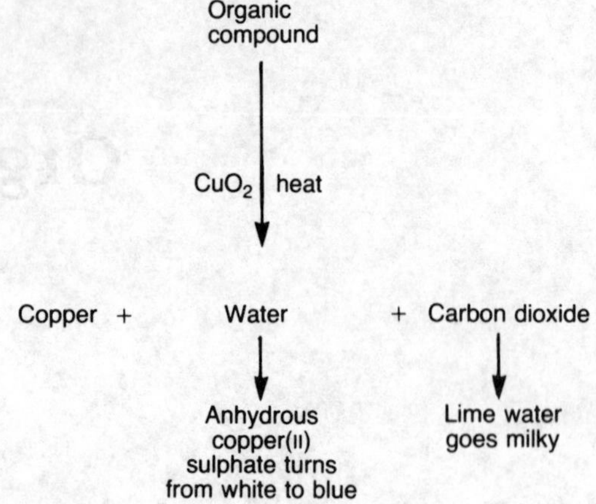

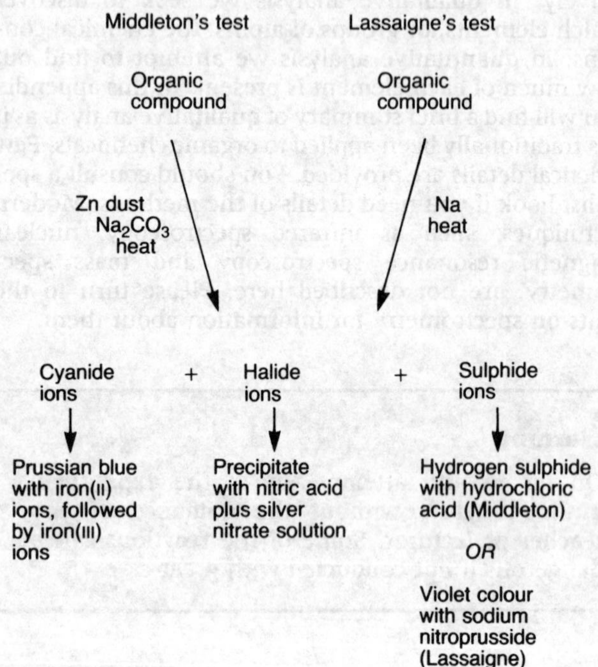

***Figure E.1** Qualitative organic analysis – a summary of the tests*

Bibliography

The following is a short list of books in which you can find further information.

Physical chemistry

Atkins, P. W. (1990). *Physical Chemistry*, Oxford University Press, Oxford

The standard work at undergraduate level. Excellent explanations, but often tough going.

Matthews, P. S. C. (1986). *Quantum Chemistry of Atoms and Molecules*, Cambridge University Press, Cambridge

A beginner's text on quantum chemistry, which also covers the mathematics avoided in the present book.

McWeeny, R. (1979). *Coulson's Valence*, Oxford University Press, Oxford

C. A. Coulson was one of the best theoretical chemists the world has known. This is an up-dated version of his classic book referred to in the title. Well worth reading (as is Coulson's original).

Vogel, A. I. (1973). *A Text Book of Macro and Semimicro Qualitative Analysis*, Longman, London

Vogel's book is full of practical and theoretical information on inorganic reactions. This is the place to look if, for example, you want to find out the test for a particular cation or anion.

Inorganic chemistry

Cotton, F. and Wilkinson, G. (1987). *Basic Inorganic Chemistry*, Wiley, New York

This book provides a more leisurely account of inorganic chemistry than its more heavy-weight parent:

— (1980). *Advanced Inorganic Chemistry*, Wiley, New York

Orgel, L. E. (1966). *An Introduction to Transition Metal Chemistry*, Methuen, London

A fine account of the main features of the d-block metals.

Vogel, A. I. (1973). *A Text Book of Macro and Semimicro Qualitative Analysis*, Longman, London

Vogel's book is full of practical and theoretical information on inorganic reactions. This is the place to look if, for example, you want to find out the test for a particular cation or anion.

Industrial and environmental chemistry

Heaton, C. A. (ed.) (1984). *An Introduction to Industrial Chemistry*, Blackie, Glasgow

— (1986). *The Chemical Industry*, Blackie, Glasgow

Both these volumes provide information on various aspects of industrial chemistry, including the economics of production (in the first) as well as details of chemical techniques (in the second).

Hill, J. W. and **Hill, C. S.** (1988). *Chemistry for Changing Times*, Macmillan, New York

Now in its fifth edition, this book puts chemistry firmly in the context of everyday life; full of interest, even though you might not find questions about its content on your examination papers.

Kirk, R. E. and **Othmer, D. F.** (1985). *Concise Encyclopaedia of Chemical Technology*, Wiley, New York

A mine of information on applications of chemistry in industry, medicine, etc. There is also a twenty-four volume version of the encyclopaedia!

Organic chemistry

Morrison, R. T. and Boyd, R. N. (1988). *Organic Chemistry*, Macmillan, New York

A book designed for degree courses in chemistry, but which gives excellent explanations of the organic chemistry covered in A-level courses.

Sykes, P. (1986). *A Guidebook to Mechanism in Organic Chemistry*, Longman, London

A classic book now in its sixth edition. A well written account of many reaction mechanisms.

Biochemistry

Zubay, G. (1988). *Biochemistry*, Macmillan, New York

This is a huge book, and considers deep matters befitting an undergraduate course in biochemistry. However, it is worth consulting, both for its careful explanations and for the beauty of the diagrams.

Examination questions

Part A Physical chemistry

A1

(*a*) Explain the meaning and importance of the concepts, *fission, fusion, control* and *moderator* in nuclear chemistry.

(*b*) Give **full** radiochemical equations for the following processes:

(i) a fission reaction of $^{235}_{92}U$ producing $^{136}_{56}Ba$ and $^{97}_{42}Mo$,
(ii) a fusion reaction of deuterium nuclei ($^{2}_{1}H$) producing $^{3}_{2}He$,
(iii) a control reaction using $^{10}_{5}B$ and producing $^{7}_{3}Li$,
(iv) the reactions in a breeder reactor which produce $^{239}_{94}Pu$ from $^{238}_{92}U$.

(*c*) The mass loss in reaction *b*(i) is 0.213 g for 235 g of $^{235}_{92}U$. Calculate the energy released in units of $J\,mol^{-1}$. If the relative isotopic masses of $^{2}_{1}H$, $^{1}_{0}n$ and $^{3}_{2}He$ are 2.0141, 1.009 and 3.016 respectively, calculate the ratio of the energy released *per gram* for process *b*(ii) compared with process *b*(i).
[Velocity of light $= 3.00 \times 10^{8}\,ms^{-1}$]

WJEC 1986 (2)

A2

Account for the formation of the line emission spectrum of atomic hydrogen. The frequency *f* of the different lines in the Lyman series of the hydrogen spectrum is given by the following expression.

$$f = cR_{H}(1/1^{2} - 1/n^{2})$$

where *c* is the speed of light, R_H is a constant having the value of $1.097 \times 10^{7}\,m^{-1}$ and *n* is an integer. Draw an energy level diagram to show the origin of these lines. In which part of the electromagnetic spectrum would you expect the lines to occur? Calculate

(*a*) the frequency of the first line in the Lyman series,

(*b*) the ionisation energy of hydrogen.

How does your value in (*b*) compare with that given in data tables?

UCLES 1986 (1) (slightly adapted)

A3

(*a*) Write an equation to represent:

(i) the first ionisation energy,
(ii) the second ionisation energy of an element X.

(*b*) The graph below shows the first and second ionisation energies of elements from nitrogen to calcium:

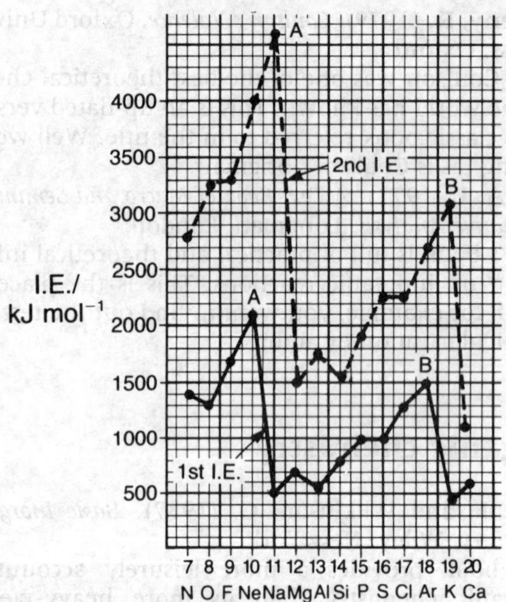

Explain why:

(i) the second ionisation energy of any element is greater than its first ionisation energy;
(ii) the first ionisation energy of sodium and potassium is lower than the inert gas immediately preceding it;
(iii) the first ionisation energy of aluminium is lower than the first ionisation energy of magnesium;
(iv) the first ionisation energy of oxygen is lower than that of nitrogen;
(v) each maximum, A and B, occurs at different atomic numbers.

(*c*) The ionisation energies/$kJ\,mol^{-1}$ of an element **M** are:

1st. I.E.	2nd. I.E.	3rd. I.E.	4th. I.E.
301	2427	3660	25 026

(i) To which Group of the Periodic Table will **M** belong?
(ii) Say which element on the graph in (*b*) above is in the same Group of the Periodic Table as **M**.
(iii) Write the equation for the reaction of **M** with chlorine.
(iv) Write an ionic equation for the reaction of the oxide of **M** with aqueous alkali.
(v) Explain, using bond diagrams, how the fluoride of **M** forms an addition compound with ammonia.

SU 1986 (2)

A4

Explain, by means of diagrams, what you understand by the following terms as they apply to the shapes of covalent molecules.

(*a*) Triangular planar

(*b*) Triangular pyramidal

(*c*) Tetrahedral

(*d*) Octahedral

By referring to the appropriate theory, explain why

(*e*) $BeCl_2$ is a linear molecule whereas H_2O is bent,

(*f*) NH_3 is triangular pyramidal whereas BCl_3 is triangular planar,

(*g*) the bond angle in NH_3 is less than that in CH_4,

(*h*) the molecule of CO_2 has no dipole moment whereas the molecule of SO_2 possesses one.

ULSEB Winter 1983 (3)

A5

The two liquids trichloromethane and ethoxyethane, $(C_2H_5)_2O$, when mixed, form intermolecular hydrogen bonds. This question is about an experiment to determine the strength of these hydrogen bonds.
The following data will be useful:

	Relative molecular mass	Specific heat capacity	Boiling point	Vapour pressure at 20° C
Trichloromethane	119.4	$0.98\,J\,g^{-1}\,K^{-1}$	62° C	157 mmHg
Ethoxyethane	74.1	$2.28\,J\,g^{-1}\,K^{-1}$	35° C	447 mmHg

(*a*) Draw graphical formulae showing all atoms and bonds for trichloromethane and ethoxyethane.

(*b*) Draw a diagram to show the trichloromethane molecule hydrogen-bonded to the ethoxyethane molecule.

(*c*) In the experiment 0.05 mol of trichloromethane was weighed into a calorimeter. 0.30 mol of ethoxyethane was weighed into a similar calorimeter. When the temperatures of both liquids had equalized, the liquids were mixed and a temperature rise of 5.4° C was recorded.

You may assume that the heat capacity of the calorimeter is negligible, and that the specific heat capacity of each liquid is unaltered in this mixture.

(i) Calculate the heat change in this experiment.
(ii) Hence calculate a value for the enthalpy change on mixing 1 mole of trichloromethane with excess ethoxyethane.
(iii) What does this result suggest about the strength of the hydrogen bond relative to most other chemical bonds?

(*d*) (i) Assuming the mixture obeyed Raoult's Law, calculate the vapour pressure (at 20° C) of the mixture in this experiment.
(ii) Would you expect the actual vapour pressure of the mixture to be greater or less than your answer to (*d*) (i)? Justify your answer.

(*e*) Ethoxyethane can be prepared by reacting sodium ethoxide with bromoethane.
(i) How would you prepare the sodium ethoxide for use in this experiment?
(ii) Write an equation for the reaction between sodium ethoxide and bromoethane.

(*f*) Ethoxyethane is only sparingly soluble in water. Explain briefly how this observation can be accounted for in terms of intermolecular forces.

N 1983 (3) (slightly adapted)

A6

What do you understand by the terms (*a*) *relative atomic mass*, (*b*) *isotope*?

Outline the use of the mass spectrometer in the determination of relative atomic masses.

A liquid **L** contains 54.5% carbon, 9.1% hydrogen and 36.4% oxygen by mass. The mass spectrum and the infra-red spectrum of **L** are shown below. Deduce the **full** structural formula of **L**, explaining your reasoning.

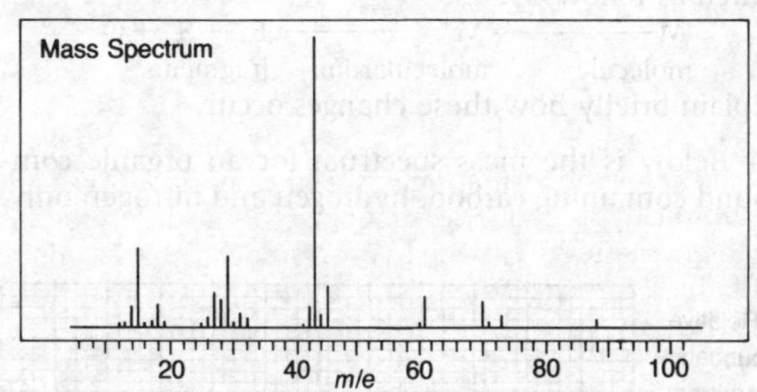

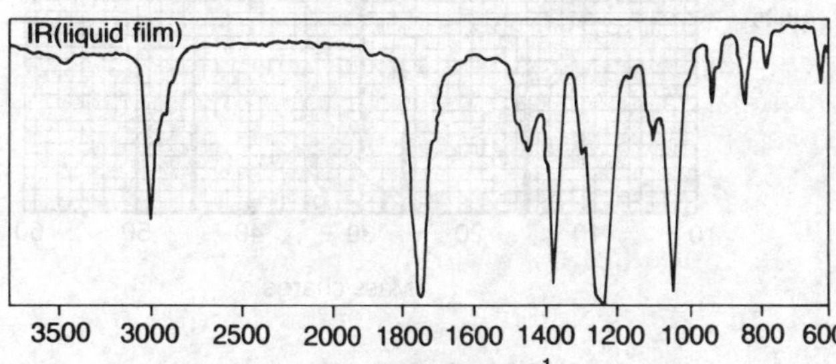

UCLES Winter 1986 (1)

A7
(*a*) Explain the following terms:
Atomic number; Mass number

(*b*) The relative atomic mass of chlorine is given as 35.5. Explain how this fractional value arises.

(*c*) Draw a labelled diagram to show the main features of a simple mass spectrometer.

(*d*) The following is a simplified mass spectrum for zirconium.

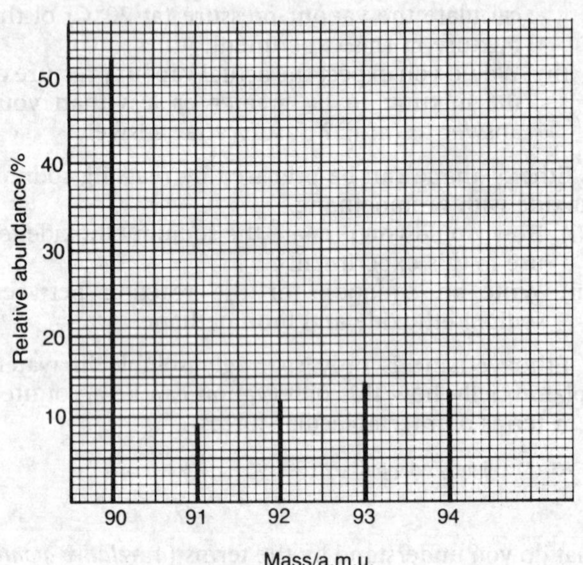

Use these results to obtain a value for the relative atomic mass of zirconium.

(*e*) When a compound is investigated using a mass spectrometer, the changes taking place may be represented as follows.

$$\underset{\text{molecule}}{M} \longrightarrow \underset{\text{molecular ion}}{M^+} \longrightarrow \underset{\text{fragments}}{R^+ + S^+ + Q}$$

Explain briefly how these changes occur.

(*f*) Below is the mass spectrum for an organic compound containing carbon, hydrogen and nitrogen only.

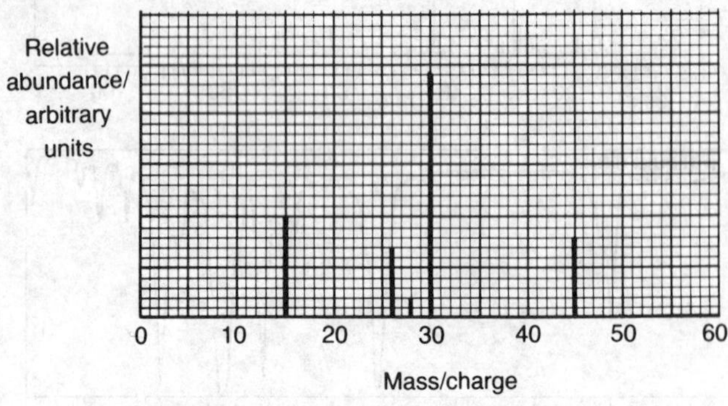

(i) Suggest a value for the relative molecular mass of the compound, explaining your reasoning.

(ii) Suggest formulae for the particles shown by the peaks in the spectrum
at Mass/charge = 15
at Mass/charge = 30.

ULSEB 1986 (2)

A8
(*a*) Explain in simple terms the principles of nuclear magnetic resonance.

(*b*) Using ethanal as an example, explain how the presence of adjacent protons causes the splitting of absorptions. Describe the splitting pattern you would expect for both the methyl and aldehyde protons.

(*c*) The nmr spectra below were obtained from two pure compounds, **P** and **Q**, both of formula C_2H_6O. Using your knowledge of spin-spin splitting, identify the two compounds and explain the appearance of the various peaks in each spectrum.

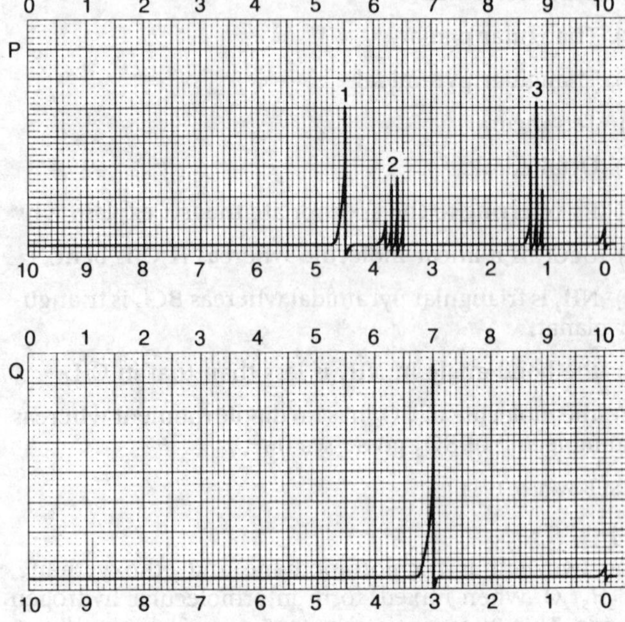

UCLES 1990 (4)

A9
(*a*) Give a short qualitative account of the use of X-rays to investigate the structure of crystals.

(*b*) Crystals of ammonium chloride have a cubic unit cell which contains one NH_4^+ ion and one Cl^- ion. Using X-ray diffraction the length of the side of the unit cell was found to be 3.87×10^{-8} cm (387 pm). The density of the crystal is 1.53 g cm^{-3} (1530 kg m^{-3}). Calculate a value for the Avogadro constant.

(*c*) Sodium chloride and barium oxide have the same crystal structure and the interionic distances in the two lattices are almost equal. Explain why the melting point of barium oxide is much higher than that of sodium chloride.

UODLE 1987 (1)

A10
Calcium fluoride occurs naturally as the mineral fluorite. The unit cell of the fluorite crystal structure is shown below.

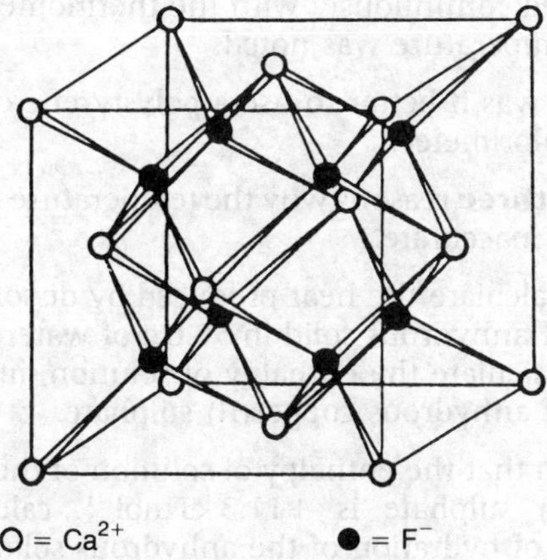

(*a*) What is the co-ordination number of the fluoride ions, F^-, in the structure?

(*b*) Deduce the co-ordination number of the calcium ions, Ca^{2+}, by considering how they are shared between adjacent unit cells, making it clear how you arrived at your answer.

(*c*) (i) The radius of the calcium ion (0.094 nm) is much less than that of the calcium atom (0.197 nm). What explanation can you give for this difference?

(ii) The radius of the fluoride ion (0.133 nm) is little different from that of the isolated fluorine atom (0.135 nm). What explanation can you offer for this close similarity?

(*d*) Sodium oxide, Na_2O, gives a similar X-ray diffraction pattern to that given by fluorite. What suggestions can you make about the likely crystal structure of Na_2O?

(*e*) (i) The lattice energy of sodium fluoride (NaF) is $-918\,\mathrm{kJ\,mol^{-1}}$, while that for calcium fluoride is $-2630\,\mathrm{kJ\,mol^{-1}}$. What is the major factor involved in accounting for the large difference between these values?

(ii) Would you expect the lattice energy of strontium fluoride to be greater or less than that for calcium fluoride? Assume that strontium fluoride also has the fluorite structure. Explain your answer carefully.

(*f*) Why do you think that fluorite occurs naturally in rocks, while calcium chloride does not, even though chlorine is a more common element than fluorine in the Earth's crust?

(*g*) Calcium fluoride is used industrially as a source of fluorine compounds, including hydrogen fluoride. How can hydrogen fluoride be obtained from calcium fluoride?

N 1985 (3)

A11
(*a*) What is meant by *the kinetic model of matter*?

(*b*) Use the kinetic model of matter to explain qualitatively each of the following:

(i) the diffusion of a gas;
(ii) the evaporation of a liquid;
(iii) the melting of a solid.

(*c*) State the van der Waal's equation for a non-ideal gas and explain why real gases do not obey the ideal gas equation.

(*d*) Ethene reacts with steam in the presence of a catalyst to form ethanol according to the equation:

$$C_2H_4(g) + H_2O(g) \rightleftharpoons C_2H_5OH(g)$$

Calculate the total equilibrium pressure at 623 K if there is 95% conversion of ethene from an equimolar mixture of ethene and steam and the value of K_p for the reaction at 623 K is $5.75 \times 10^{-5}\,\mathrm{Pa^{-1}}$.

AEB Winter 1986 (1)

A12
(*a*) Use the kinetic theory to explain why gases (i) are compressible, (ii) diffuse and (iii) diffuse at different rates under similar conditions.

(*b*) For an ideal gas it can be shown that $pV = \frac{1}{3}Nm\bar{c}^2$ where N molecules of gas each of mass m and a mean square velocity of $\bar{c}^2$, occupy a volume V at a pressure p. Use this equation, and any other stated assumptions you may need, to develop:

(i) the ideal gas equation $pV = nRT$,
(ii) an expression for $\bar{c}$ in terms of R, T and the relative molecular mass of the gas M.

(*c*) State Graham's law of diffusion. The time taken for a given volume of gas *E* to effuse through a hole is 75 seconds. Under identical conditions the same volume of a mixture of carbon monoxide and nitrogen (containing 40% of nitrogen by volume) effused in 70 seconds. Calculate:

(i) the relative molecular mass of *E*, and
(ii) the root mean square velocity $\bar{c}$ (in $\mathrm{m\,s^{-1}}$ units) of *E* at 0° C.

($C = 12$; $N = 14$; $O = 16$; $R = 8.314\,\mathrm{J\,K^{-1}\,mol^{-1}}$.)

SU 1986 (2)

A13
(*a*) A liquid compound, **X**, occurring in orange peel, has a relative molecular mass of 136.2 and contains carbon and hydrogen only. Combustion analysis of **X** produced the following results:

2.076 g of **X** gave 6.704 g of carbon dioxide and 2.196 g of water.

Calculate the molecular formula of **X**.

(*b*) When 2.000 g of **X** were mixed with finely divided platinum and agitated at a slightly elevated temperature in an atmosphere of hydrogen, it was found that

657.8 cm^3 of hydrogen (corrected to s.t.p.) were absorbed.

(i) How many moles of **X** were used in this experiment?
(ii) How many moles of hydrogen were absorbed? (Molar gas volume at s.t.p. is equal to 22.4 $dm^3 mol^{-1}$).
(iii) What do you deduce about the structure of **X**?
(iv) What mass of bromine would you expect to react with 136.2 g of **X**?

AEB 1989 (1)

A14

The *approximate* percentage (weight/volume) of chlorine in a sample of household bleach, NaClO (aq), is 10%. An *accurate* determination of this percentage can be made by using the following sequence of reactions, the final stage C being a volumetric titration:

A. $2NaClO(aq) + 2H^+(aq) \rightarrow 2Na^+(aq) + H_2O(l) + \frac{1}{2}O_2(g) + Cl_2(g)$
B. $Cl_2(g) + 2I^-(aq) \rightarrow 2Cl^-(aq) + I_2(aq)$
C. $I_2(aq) + 2S_2O_3^{2-}(aq) \rightarrow 2I^-(aq) + S_4O_6^{2-}(aq)$

(*a*) Calculate the *approximate* molarity of the household bleach. (Cl = 35.5)

(*b*) For the titration C, 0.1 mol dm^{-3} $Na_2S_2O_3(aq)$ is available. Using the equations, decide on the relationship:

____cm³ bleach = 100 cm^3 0.1 mol dm^{-3} $Na_2S_2O_3(aq)$

and so calculate a convenient starting volume of bleach to use which will give a suitable titre for the volumetric apparatus to be used in stage C. For the sequence of reactions A, B, and C, 1 mol dm^{-3} solutions of ethanoic acid and potassium iodide are available together with an appropriate indicator.

(*c*) Produce a numbered sequence of practical steps by which the estimation can be carried out. The instructions should be simple yet read like a practical note book and say clearly at each step:

(i) the *particular* piece of volumetric glassware to be used;
(ii) the *measured* volume of solution, especially when *excess* of the reagent is required;
(iii) the *directions* for the procedure.

(*d*) Derive an expression to show how the result can be calculated from the titre.

SU 1985 (1)

A15

The enthalpy of hydration of anhydrous copper(II) sulphate is defined as the heat absorbed or evolved, at constant pressure, when one mole of anhydrous solid is converted to one mole of the crystalline hydrated solid:

$$CuSO_4(s) + 5H_2O(l) = CuSO_4.5H_2O(s)$$

It cannot be measured directly.
In an experiment to determine the enthalpy of hydration indirectly, 4.0 g of anhydrous solid was added to 50.0 g of water and the rise in temperature noted as 8 °C whereas when 4.0 g of the hydrated solid was added to 50.0 g of water the temperature fell by 1.3 °C. In each case the known mass of water was measured into a polystyrene cup, the solid was added to the water and the mixture was stirred continuously with the thermometer until a steady temperature was noted.

(*a*) Why was it better to use a polystyrene cup than a copper calorimeter?

(*b*) Give **three** reasons why the temperature rise of 8 °C might be inaccurate.

(*c*) (i) Calculate the heat produced by dissolving 4.0 g of anhydrous solid in 50.0 g of water.
(ii) Calculate the enthalpy of solution, in kJ mol^{-1}, of anhydrous copper(II) sulphate.

(*d*) Given that the enthalpy of solution of the hydrated copper(II) sulphate is +11.3 kJ mol^{-1}, calculate the enthalpy of hydration of the anhydrous solid.

(*e*) Comment on the following statements, which may be either true or false:

(i) 'If the enthalpy change for a reaction is negative then that reaction will take place very quickly.'
(ii) 'The C-Cl bond energy is very high, making that bond very difficult to break and so compounds containing the C-Cl bond are generally unreactive.'
(iii) 'A catalyst speeds up a chemical reaction by making the enthalpy change for the reaction, ΔH, more negative.'

[specific heat capacity of water = 4.18 J g^{-1} K^{-1}]

UCLES 1990 AS (2)

A16

The apparatus shown in the diagram was used to find the enthalpy change of combustion of propanone, CH_3COCH_3.

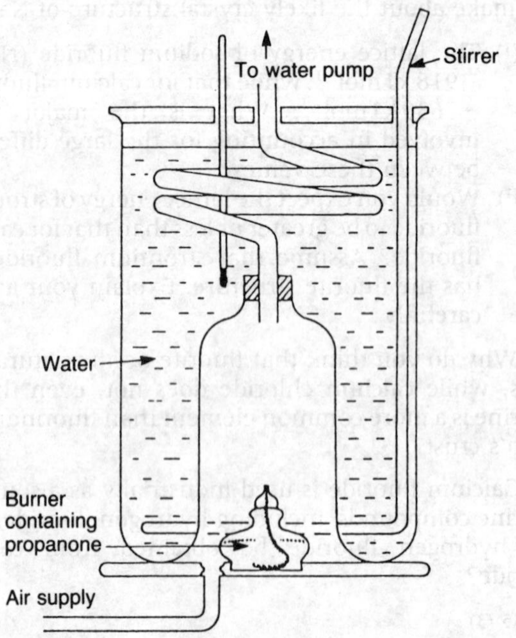

(*a*) Why would an inadequate supply of air lead to error in the results?

(*b*) The following information was obtained during the experiment:

Heat capacity of the apparatus	= 3.34 kJ per °C
Loss of mass of burner	= 2.90 g
Temperature rise	= 25.3 °C

(i) Calculate the heat (kJ) produced in the experiment.

(ii) Calculate the enthalpy change of combustion of propanone.
(Relative molecular mass of propanone = 58)

(*c*) Construct a thermochemical cycle to determine the enthalpy change of atomization, ΔH_{at} of propanone, given the following data:

$\Delta H_f^\ominus$	propanone(l)	$= -216.7\ \text{kJ mol}^{-1}$
$\Delta H_{at}^\ominus$	carbon (graphite)	$= +715\ \text{kJ mol}^{-1}$
$\Delta H_{at}^\ominus$	hydrogen(g)	$= +218\ \text{kJ mol}^{-1}$
$\Delta H_{at}^\ominus$	oxygen(g)	$= +249\ \text{kJ mol}^{-1}$

(The enthalpy change of atomization refers to the formation of 1 mole of gaseous atoms of the element concerned.)

(*d*) Use the average bond energies $\bar{E}$ given below to calculate another value for the enthalpy change of atomization of propanone.

$\bar{E}$ (C—C) = $+346\ \text{kJ mol}^{-1}$
$\bar{E}$ (C—H) = $+413\ \text{kJ mol}^{-1}$
$\bar{E}$ (C=O) = $+749\ \text{kJ mol}^{-1}$

(*e*) Comment on the agreement, or disagreement, between the two values calculated in (*c*) and (*d*).

N 1984 (3)

A17

(*a*) State and explain the similarities and differences between the crystal structures of sodium chloride and caesium chloride, using diagrams where appropriate.

(*b*) Some energy data are tabulated below.

Process	$\Delta H^\ominus$(298K)/ kJ mol^{-1}
$Na(s) \rightarrow Na(g)$	+108
$\frac{1}{2}Cl_2(g) \rightarrow Cl(g)$	+121
$Na(g) \rightarrow Na^+(g) + e^-$	+496
$Cl(g) + e^- \rightarrow Cl^-(g)$	−349
$Ca(g) \rightarrow Ca^{2+}(g) + 2e^-$	+1736
$Ca^{2+}(g) \rightarrow Ca^{3+}(g) + e^-$	+4941
$Ca^{2+}(g) + 2Cl^-(g) \rightarrow CaCl_2(s)$	−2220
$Ca^{3+}(g) + 3Cl^-(g) \rightarrow CaCl_3(s)$	−4800 (estimated)
$NaCl(s) \rightarrow Na^+(g) + Cl^-(g)$	+787
$NaCl(s) + \text{water} \rightarrow Na^+(aq) + Cl^-(aq)$	+4

Using this information,

(i) calculate the standard molar enthalpy change for the process
$Na(s) + \frac{1}{2}Cl_2(g) \rightarrow Na^+(g) + Cl^-(g)$,

(ii) explain why $CaCl_3(s)$ does not exist but $CaCl_2(s)$ does,

(iii) comment on the difference between the values of the enthalpy change of lattice breaking of NaCl(s) and the enthalpy of solution of NaCl(s) in water and define a term which is useful in this context,

(iv) discuss the processes occurring at the molecular level when solid sodium chloride dissolves in water.

(*c*) State and discuss the general principles which govern the extent to which compounds are soluble in water.

WJEC 1990 (2)

A18

(*a*) Briefly describe experiments (i) to show that the reaction

$$CH_3COOC_2H_5(l) + H_2O(l) \rightleftharpoons CH_3COOH(l) + C_2H_5OH(l)$$

is reversible, and (ii) to measure the equilibrium constant for the reaction at a given temperature.

(*b*) 3.875 g of sulphur dioxide dichloride, SO_2Cl_2, were introduced into an empty flask of capacity 1000 cm^3. The flask was sealed and then heated to 375° C. At equilibrium the vessel contained 0.01775 mol of chlorine, the total pressure being 2.30×10^5 Pa.

$$SO_2Cl_2(g) \rightleftharpoons SO_2(g) + Cl_2(g)$$

(i) Calculate the mole fraction of each component of the equilibrium mixture.

(ii) Calculate the partial pressure of each component.

(iii) Calculate a value for K_p at 375° C.
Explain *qualitatively* the effect of each of the following on the position of the above equilibrium:

(iv) the addition of 0.050 mol of chlorine to the flask, and

(v) the addition of 0.050 mol of argon to the flask.

AEB 1987 (1)

A19

This question is concerned with the equilibrium reaction between ethyl ethanoate and water to form ethanoic acid and ethanol.

$$CH_3COOC_2H_5(l) + H_2O(l) \rightleftharpoons CH_3COOH(l) + C_2H_5OH(l)$$

Compound	$\Delta H^\ominus_{f,298}$/kJ mol^{-1}
$CH_3COOC_2H_5(l)$	−485.8
$H_2O(l)$	−285.9
$CH_3COOH(l)$	−484.5
$C_2H_5OH(l)$	−277.7

(*a*) (i) What is the relationship between the standard enthalpy change for a chemical reaction and the standard enthalpy changes of formation of the substances involved in the reaction?

(ii) Calculate the standard enthalpy change, $\Delta H^\ominus_{298}$, for the forward reaction above, including the correct sign, and state whether the reaction is exothermic or endothermic. (You may wish to draw an energy cycle diagram.)

(*b*) 8.8 g of ethyl ethanoate was mixed with 18.0 cm^3 of

1.0 M hydrochloric acid, and the mixture allowed to reach equilibrium. Analysis of the equilibrium mixture showed that 0.075 mol of ethanoic acid was present. (Assume that $1.0\,cm^3$ of 1.0 M hydrochloric acid contains 1 g of water) (Relative atomic masses: C = 12, H = 1, O = 16)

(i) What is the function of the hydrochloric acid?
(ii) What procedure could be used to determine the amount (moles) of ethanoic acid in the equilibrium mixture?
(iii) Write down the expression for the equilibrium constant, K_c, for this equilibrium and use it to calculate a value for K_c, at 298 K, from the experimental results.

(c) The vapour above the liquid equilibrium mixture contains a similar chemical equilibrium, but the value of K_c is different for the vapour phase equilibrium.

(i) In the vapour phase equilibrium, $K_c = K_p$. Explain why this is so.
(ii) Calculate the value of K_p for the vapour phase equilibrium at 323 K if the value at 298 K is 0.01, given the following information:

$$\ln K_p = \text{constant} - \frac{\Delta H}{R}\left(\frac{1}{T}\right) \text{or} \lg K_p = \text{constant} - \frac{\Delta H}{2.3R}\left(\frac{1}{T}\right)$$

$R = 8.31\,J\,K^{-1}\,mol^{-1}$

$\Delta H^{\ominus}$ for the vapour phase reaction $= +10\,kJ\,mol^{-1}$. (Assume that this value does not vary with temperature.)

(iii) Use your answer to (ii) to predict whether or not the hydrolysis of ethyl ethanoate proceeds further with increasing temperature. Justify your answer.

N 1985 (3)

A20

(a) State the partition law for the distribution of a solute between two immiscible solvents.

(b) The following experimental results were obtained for a number of mixtures of ammonia distributed between water and 1,1,1-trichloroethane.

Mixture	*Total ammonia concentration*	
	in water /mol dm^{-3}	in 1,1,1-trichloroethane /mol dm^{-3}
1	3.89	0.0335
2	3.24	0.0284
3	2.61	0.0221

(i) Describe how such results could be obtained. You should include essential steps in the method, the approximate quantities or concentrations of any substances used and the safety procedures involved.
(ii) Calculate the ratio of the ammonia concentrations in the two solvents for each of the mixtures. Comment on the values obtained.

(c) Explain how partition is involved in chromatographic separation techniques. Illustrate your answer by reference to **one** particular technique giving **one** example of a mixture that could be separated by this technique.

OCSEB 1990 (3,4,5)

A21

The Ellingham diagram for a number of metallic sulphides is reproduced below.

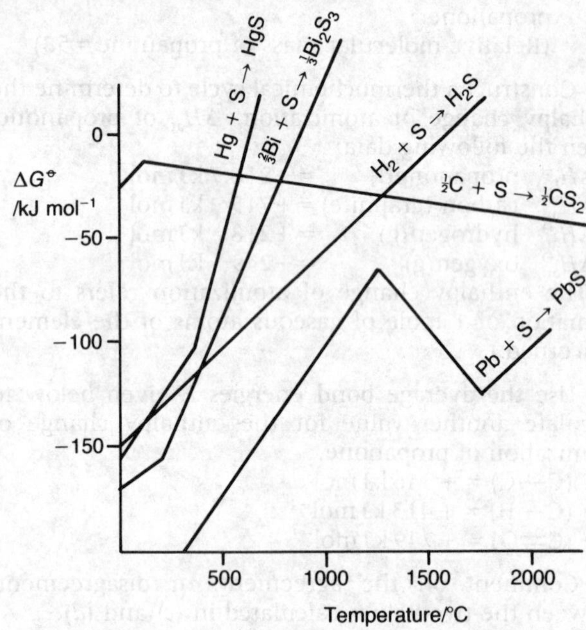

Explain the shape of the graphs and show how possible reducing agents and conditions of temperature for the production of metals from sulphides can be deduced from the diagram.
In cases where a choice of reagent and conditions is possible for producing a metal from its sulphide what practical considerations might influence the actual choice made by industry?

N 1979 (2)

A22

The phase diagram for water is shown on page 547. It is not to scale.

(a) Which phase exists in
(i) region **A**?
(ii) region **B**?
(iii) region **C**?

(b) (i) Line **DE** has a slightly negative slope. What physical property of water results from this?
(ii) How do the intermolecular forces in water and ice give rise to this physical property?

(c) (i) The three lines in the diagram meet at point **D**. What is this point called? What is its significance?
(ii) Explain why the temperature corresponding to point **D** is not the usual freezing point of water.

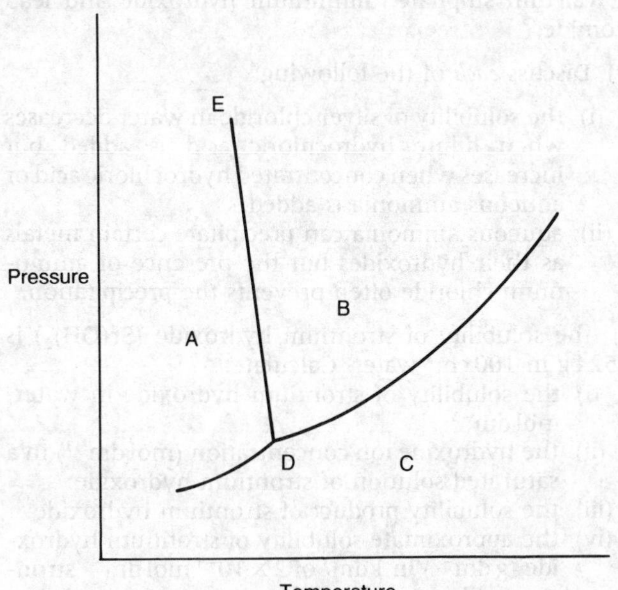

(*d*) Ice does not sublime at room temperature and atmospheric pressure. Explain, using the phase diagram at the beginning of the question if you wish, how ice might be made to sublime by changing the conditions.

ULSEB 1987 (2)

A23

This question is about the reaction of iodine with potassium hydroxide, which forms potassium iodate(V) and potassium iodide.

$$3I_2(s) + 6KOH(aq) \rightarrow KIO_3(aq) + 5KI(aq) + 3H_2O(l)$$

The stoichiometric amount of iodine was added to 100 cm³ of 4.0 M potassium hydroxide solution. The reaction mixture was warmed until reaction was complete and was then cooled to 20° C. As the reaction mixture cooled, white crystals were precipitated. The solubility curves of potassium iodate(V) and potassium iodide are given in the diagram above right.

(*a*) What mass of solid iodine should be added to 100 cm³ of 4.0 M potassium hydroxide?

(*b*) How could you tell when the reaction was complete?

(*c*) What mass of potassium iodate(V) and potassium iodide would be formed by the reaction?
(Relative atomic masses: H = 1, O = 16, K = 39, I = 127)

(*d*) At what temperature would the white crystals start to appear as the reaction mixture cooled? Assume no water is lost during the reaction.

(*e*) What would be the composition of the white crystals when the reaction mixture had been cooled to 20° C?

N 1984 (3)

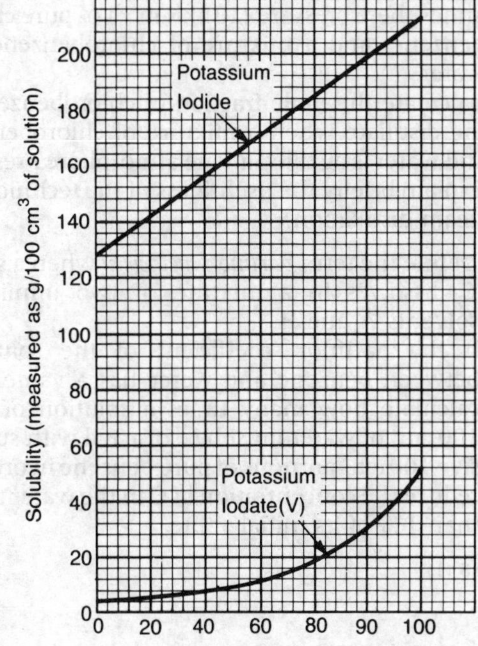

A24

(*a*) State *Raoult's Law* for ideal solutions.

(*b*) State what is meant by the term *mole fraction.*

(*c*) Hexane and heptane form ideal liquid mixtures. The vapour pressures of the pure liquids at 50° C are 50 kN m^{-2} for hexane, and 20 kN m^{-2} for heptane. Calculate the mole fraction of heptane in the *liquid* when the mole fractions of hexane and heptane in the *vapour* are equal.

(*d*) The graph below shows the equilibrium vapour pressures of water and chlorobenzene as a function of temperature. Chlorobenzene and water are immiscible liquids.

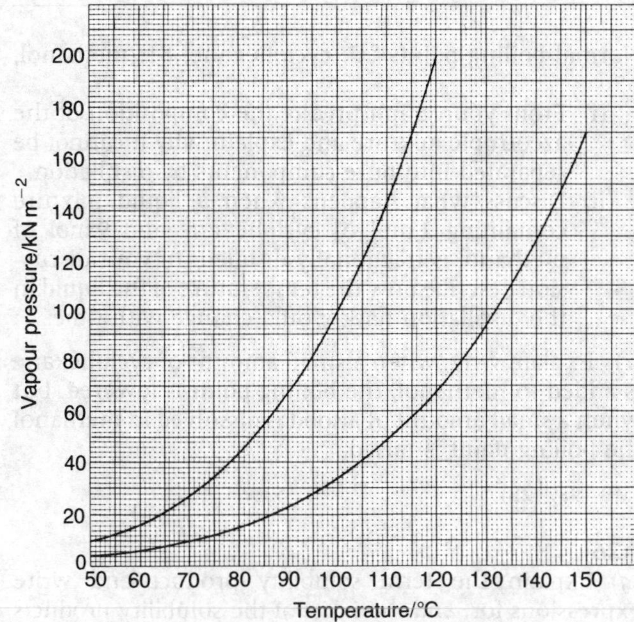

(i) From the graph, deduce the boiling point, at 1 atmosphere pressure (101 kN m^{-2}) of pure chlorobenzene, and a mixture of chlorobenzene and water.
(ii) Calculate the mole fraction of chlorobenzene in the distillate when a mixture of chlorobenzene and water is distilled at one atmosphere pressure.
(iii) Explain briefly the usefulness of the technique of steam distillation.

(*e*) (i) Define the term *partition coefficient* when a solute **C** dissolves in a mixture of two immiscible solvents **A** and **B**.
(ii) If the partition coefficient of the solute **C** between benzene and water has a value of 4, calculate how many times a solution of **C** in 100 cm^3 of water must be extracted with successive 100 cm^3 portions of pure benzene in order to reduce the concentration of **C** in the water to less than 1% of its initial value.

WJEC 1988 (1)

A25

(*a*) Explain, with the aid of a boiling point-composition diagram, why an ideal mixture of two liquids with different boiling points can be separated by fractional distillation.

(*b*) Use the following data to plot a boiling point-composition diagram for solutions of cyclohexane in methanol.

Boiling point of mixture/°C	Mole fraction of methanol in the *liquid* mixture	Mole fraction of methanol in the *vapour* above the mixture
70	0.12	0.27
60	0.31	0.47
55	0.50	0.56
57	0.82	0.69
61	0.94	0.83

Normal boiling points/°C; cyclohexane, 81; methanol, 65

(i) From your graph predict the composition of the azeotropic mixture and explain why it cannot be separated into pure components by distillation.
(ii) Discuss what happens when a liquid mixture containing 1 mol of cyclohexane and 9 mol of methanol is fractionally distilled. In your discussion describe how the temperature of the liquid in the distillation flask would change with time.

(*c*) Explain why, when a small amount of cyclohexane is added to methanol, the boiling point is lowered, but when a small amount of a solid is dissolved in methanol the boiling point is raised.

JMB 1989 (2B)

A26

(*a*) Explain the term solubility product and write expressions for, and the units of the solubility products of, calcium sulphate, aluminium hydroxide and lead bromide.

(*b*) Discuss *each* of the following:

(i) the solubility of silver chloride in water decreases when dilute hydrochloric acid is added but increases when concentrated hydrochloric acid or aqueous ammonia is added;
(ii) aqueous ammonia can precipitate certain metals as their hydroxides but the presence of ammonium chloride often prevents the precipitation.

(*c*) the solubility of strontium hydroxide ($Sr(OH)_2$) is 0.524 g in 100 cm^3 water. Calculate:
(i) the solubility of strontium hydroxide in water, mol dm^{-3};
(ii) the hydroxide ion concentration (mol dm^{-3}) in a saturated solution of strontium hydroxide;
(iii) the solubility product of strontium hydroxide;
(iv) the approximate solubility of strontium hydroxide (g dm^{-3}) in 1 dm^3 of 2×10^{-1} mol dm^{-3} strontium chloride solution;
(v) the volume of 1×10^{-2} mol dm^{-3} potassium chromate solution which must be added to 1 dm^3 saturated strontium hydroxide solution to precipitate strontium chromate ($SrCrO_4$).

(H = 1; O = 16; Sr = 87.6. Solubility product of strontium chromate is 3.6×10^{-5} mol^2 dm^{-6}.)

SU 1985 (1)

A27

(*a*) Describe, giving essential practical details, an experiment to find the relative molecular mass of a non-volatile solute by studying its effect on **either** the boiling point **or** the freezing point of a solvent. State the limitations of the method you describe.

(*b*) Use the following data to determine the molecular formula of the compound **X**, which does not associate or dissociate in water.
(i) The boiling point of water was raised by 0.26 °C when 45 g of **X** were dissolved in 500 g of water. In a separate experiment the boiling point of water was raised by 0.39 °C when 9.0 g carbamide *(urea)* ($M_r = 60$) were dissolved in 200 g of water.
(ii) When the compound **X**, which contains only carbon, hydrogen, and oxygen, was burnt in excess oxygen, 0.300 g of the compound gave 0.440 g of carbon dioxide and 0.180 g of water.

JMB 1988 (2B)

A28

(*a*) The vapour pressure of a solution (P) is equal to the product of the vapour pressure of the pure solvent (P_0) and its mole fraction.

(i) Derive the expression:
$$\frac{P_0 - P}{P_0} = \text{mole fraction of solute.}$$

(ii) Explain why the vapour pressure of a solution of most solids in a given solvent is less than the vapour pressure of the pure solvent.

(*b*) An organic solid X was made up into two solutions A and B, solution A containing 5.0 g of X in 100 g of water and solution B containing 2.3 g of X in 100 g of benzene. Both solutions A and B had the same vapour pressure (100 570 Pa) at the boiling points of the pure solvents at atmospheric pressure (101 300 Pa). Calculate the apparent relative molecular mass of X in each case and suggest a reason for the differing results. You may use a simplified form of the above equation.

(H = 1; C = 12; O = 16).

(*c*) What is a colligative property? Derive and explain the approximate ratios of:

(i) the osmotic pressures of solutions of X, of the same concentration ($g\,dm^{-3}$), in water and benzene;
(ii) the freezing points of two solutions containing the same masses of rhombic and monoclinic sulphur in the same volume of toluene.

(*d*) Sketch vapour pressure—composition diagrams for *one* of the following mixtures showing the contributions made by each component to the total vapour pressure of the mixture:

(i) benzene and methylbenzene;
(ii) phenylamine (aniline) and water;
(iii) propanone and trichloromethane.

(*e*) Draw a boiling point–composition curve for the mixture of nitric acid (boiling point 86°C) and water which forms a constant boiling mixture (boiling point 121°C) containing 68% nitric acid by mass. Explain what happens when a mixture containing 30% nitric acid is distilled and state the effect of re-distilling the distillate collected at 121°C.

SU 1985 (2)

A29

The following table gives the standard electrode potentials for a number of redox systems.

	REDOX SYSTEM	$E^\ominus/V$
A	$I_2(aq) + 2e^- \rightleftharpoons 2I^-(aq)$	+0.54
B	$Fe^{3+}(aq) + e^- \rightleftharpoons Fe^{2+}(aq)$	+0.77
C	$Cr_2O_7^{2-}(aq) + 14H^+(aq) + 6e^- \rightleftharpoons 2Cr^{3+}(aq) + 7H_2O(l)$	+1.33
D	$Cl_2(aq) + 2e^- \rightleftharpoons 2Cl^-(aq)$	+1.36
E	$MnO_4^-(aq) + 8H^+(aq) + 5e^- \rightleftharpoons Mn^{2+}(aq) + 4H_2O(l)$	+1.51
F	$Co^{3+}(aq) + e^- \rightleftharpoons Co^{2+}(aq)$	+1.82

(*a*) Define the term *standard electrode potential*.

(*b*) (i) Calculate the e.m.f. of a cell set up between systems **B** and **D** under standard conditions.
(ii) State which would be the positive pole of the cell.
(iii) What would be a suitable material to act as electrodes for the two half-cells?
(iv) Name one instrument which could be used to measure the e.m.f. of the cell.
(v) Using the usual convention, represent schematically the cell which would be formed from systems **B** and **D**.

(*c*) Under standard conditions which of the substances listed in the above table is

(i) the strongest oxidising agent?
(ii) the strongest reducing agent?

(*d*) The reaction between acidified dichromate(VI) ions (system **C**) and aqueous iron(II) ions (system **B**) can be used in titrimetric analysis.

(i) Using the half equations given in the table write down the equation for the reaction.
(ii) Calculate the volume (in cm^3) of aqueous potassium dichromate(VI) solution of concentration $0.020\,mol\,dm^{-3}$ required to react exactly with $30.0\,cm^3$ of aqueous iron(II) sulphate of concentration $0.100\,mol\,dm^{-3}$.

(*e*) The titration between dichromate(VI) ions and iron (II) ions can be carried out in the presence of either dilute hydrochloric or sulphuric acids. Dilute hydrochloric acid cannot be used to acidify the solution for the titration between iron(II) ions and manganate(VII) ions (system **E**). Use the information given in the table to suggest a reason for this.

AEB 1988 (2)

A30

(*a*) When a sparingly soluble salt, A_xB_y, dissolves in water, the equilibrium

$$A_xB_y(s) + nH_2O(l) \rightleftharpoons xA^{a+}(aq) + yB^{b-}(aq)$$

is established. Provided that some solid is present, it is found that the quantity K_{sp} (called the solubility product) given by

$$K_{sp} = [A^{a+}(aq)]^x\,[B^{b-}(aq)]^y$$

is a constant at constant temperature. Account for this observation. What additional information would you need in order to predict the variation of K_{sp} with temperature? Explain your answer.

(*b*) The electrochemical cell

$$Sn(s)\,|\,SnCl_2\,(aq,\,1.0\,M)\,\vdots\vdots\,CuSO_4\,(aq,\,1.0\,M)\,|\,Cu(s)$$

is set up. Calculate the e.m.f. of this cell at 25°C, using the data given below.

Write the equation for the cell reaction and also the equation for the spontaneous reaction which occurs when the cell circuit is completed.

The variation of electrode potential (in volts) with metal ion concentration, $[M^{2+}]$, for a metal M such as Sn or Cu at 25°C is given by the equation

$$E_M = E_M^\ominus + 0.0295\,\log[M^{2+}(aq)]$$

What will be the effect on the e.m.f. of the cell above of decreasing the concentration of $Sn^{2+}(aq)$? Explain your answer.

(*c*) Copper(II) iodate(V), $Cu(IO_3)_2$, is sparingly soluble in water. The addition of sodium iodate(V) to the compartment containing the copper electrode of the cell in (*b*) above causes a precipitate to form.

(i) Show that, in the presence of this precipitate, the potential, E_{Cu}, of the copper electrode can be written

$$E_{Cu} = \text{Constant} - 0.059 \log[IO_3^-(aq)]$$

and express the constant in terms of $E^\ominus_{Cu}$ for K_{sp} for $Cu(IO_3)_2$.

(ii) The concentration of iodate(V) ions in equilibrium with the precipitate is varied, and the potential of the copper electrode is determined at 25°C with the results given in the table below.

$[IO_3^-(aq)]$/mol l^{-1}	0.005	0.010	0.050	0.100	0.500
E_{Cu}/V	0.276	0.258	0.217	0.199	0.158

Plot E_{Cu} as a function of $\log[IO_3^-(aq)]$ and use your graph to evaluate K_{sp} for copper(II) iodate(V). Use this value of K_{sp} to deduce the solubility in mol l^{-1} of copper(II) iodate(V) in water at 25°C.

$Sn^{2+}(aq) + 2e^- \rightarrow Sn(s)$ $E^\ominus = -0.140$ V
$Cu^{2+}(aq) + 2e^- \rightarrow Cu(s)$ $E^\ominus = +0.337$ V

JMB 1988 (S)

A31

(*a*) Discuss, with the aid of examples, the interpretation of 'oxidation' and 'reduction' in terms of electron transfer.
What do you understand by the term 'redox reaction'?

(*b*) What do you understand by 'disproportionation'? Give an example of such a reaction.

(*c*) Discuss the extent to which a table of standard electrode potentials is useful in predicting the course of a chemical change.

(*d*) An aqueous solution of ammonium vanadate is reduced by boiling with zinc powder. The resulting solution may be re-oxidized to the vanadate with a solution of potassium manganate(VII). Describe experiments you would carry out, and the subsequent use of experimental data, to determine the change in oxidation state of the vanadium.

ULSEB 1984 (3)

A32

(*a*) Balance the following redox equations using the principles of *either* electron transfer *or* change in oxidation state (number):

(i) $Ag(s) + NO_3^-(aq) + H^+(aq) \rightarrow Ag^+(aq) + NO(g) + H_2O(l)$

(ii) $Fe(CN)_6^{4-}(aq) + Cl_2(g) \rightarrow Fe(CN)_6^{3-}(aq) + 2Cl^-(aq)$

(*b*) Discuss *briefly* the electrolysis of each of the following solutions:

Electrolyte	Cathode	Anode
Sodium chloride	Carbon	Carbon
Sodium hydroxide	Carbon	Carbon
Sulphuric acid	Platinum	Silver
Copper sulphate	Copper	Copper

(*c*) (i) A current of 3.21 A was passed through fused aluminium oxide for 10 minutes. The volume of oxygen collected at the anode was 112 cm^3 measured at s.t.p. Calculate the mass of aluminium obtained at the cathode and the charge of 1 mole of electrons (the Faraday).

(O = 16; Al = 27. Molar volume = 22.4 dm^3 at s.t.p.)

(ii) When the same quantity of electricity was passed through the fused chloride of a metal M (relative atomic mass = 137.3), the mass of M obtained was 1.373 g. Calculate the charge on the cation M^{x+}.

(iii) The charge on the electron is 1.602×10^{-19} Coulombs. Calculate a value for the Avogadro Number (*L*).

(iv) The standard electrode potentials of three metals X, Y, and Fe are −0.14 V, −0·76 V and −0.44 V respectively. Explain which one of X or Y would be a more effective protection against the corrosion of iron.

SU 1985 (2)

A33

(*a*) Explain the concept of the Faraday.

(*b*) How long would it take a current of 1 ampere to reduce completely 80 cm^3 of 0.1 mol dm^{-3} aqueous $Fe_2(SO_4)_3$ to $FeSO_4$?

(*c*) (i) Define *cell constant*.

(ii) A conductivity cell filled with 0.1 mol dm^{-3} aqueous KCl gave a resistance at 25°C of 484.0 Ω. Calculate the cell constant given that the molar conductivity of this KCl solution is 129.0 Ω^{-1}cm^2 mol^{-1}.

(iii) The following data were obtained for aqueous solutions of NaI.

Concentration *c* (mol dm^{-3})	Molar conductivity Λ (Ω^{-1} cm^2 mol^{-1})
0.0005	125.15
0.0010	124.35
0.0050	121.25

Use a graphical method to determine Λ^∞ for NaI at 25°C.

(*d*) Given the following values of molar conductivities at infinite dilution, Λ^∞, at 18°C, calculate Λ^∞ for NH_4OH at this temperature.

$Ba(OH)_2, \Lambda^\infty = 457.6\ \Omega^{-1}\ cm^2\ mol^{-1}$
$BaCl_2, \quad \Lambda^\infty = 240.6\ \Omega^{-1}\ cm^2\ mol^{-1}$
$NH_4Cl, \quad \Lambda^\infty = 129.6\ \Omega^{-1}\ cm^2\ mol^{-1}$.

Explain the basis of your calculation.

UODLE 1987 (1)

A34

(*a*) Write out each of the following reactions and underline the reactant which is behaving as an acid.

(i) $HSO_4^- + H_2O \rightarrow H_3O^+ + SO_4^{2-}$
(ii) $HCO_3^- + HSO_4^- \rightarrow H_2O + CO_2 + SO_4^{2-}$
(iii) $CH_3CO_2H + HClO_4 \rightarrow CH_3CO_2H_2^+ + ClO_4^-$
(iv) $H_3O^+ + OH^- \rightarrow 2H_2O$

(*b*) Select ONE of the reactions in (*a*) and discuss it in terms of the Brønsted-Lowry theory.

(*c*) By writing TWO equations illustrate the amphoteric nature of water.

(*d*) The value of K_a for ethanoic acid is 1.8×10^{-5} mol dm^{-3}. Calculate:

(i) the pH of 0.1 M ethanoic acid,
(ii) the pH of a solution which is 2.0 M with respect to ethanoic acid and 1.0 M with respect to sodium ethanoate.

(*e*) Explain briefly why an aqueous solution of iron(III) chloride is acidic.

ULSEB Winter 1988 (2)

A35

(*a*) Calculate the pH of the following at 25°C.

(i) Aqueous hydrochloric acid of concentration 0.0500 mol dm^{-3}.
(ii) Aqueous sodium hydroxide of concentration 0.0500 mol dm^{-3}.
(The value of K_w at 25°C may be taken as $1.00 \times 10^{-14}\ mol^2\ dm^{-6}$.)
(iii) An aqueous solution produced by mixing 24.0 cm^3 of the sodium hydroxide in (ii) with 25.0 cm^3 of the hydrochloric acid in (i).

(*b*) Sketch the variation in pH as a further 1.0 cm^3 of the sodium hydroxide in (ii) is added to the mixture in (iii).

(*c*) (i) Explain why a mixture of aqueous sodium ethanoate and aqueous ethanoic acid has a pH which resists change when contaminated with small amounts of acid or alkali.
(ii) The pH of a solution of aqueous ethanoic acid and sodium ethanoate at 25°C is given by

$$pH = 4.74 + \log\left\{\frac{[salt]}{[acid]}\right\}$$

Copy and complete the following table for the addition of aqueous sodium hydroxide of concentration 0.10 mol dm^{-3} to 25.0 cm^3 of aqueous ethanoic acid of concentration 0.10 mol dm^{-3}.

Volume of NaOH added/cm^3	$\frac{[salt]}{[acid]}$	pH
5		
10		
15		
20		
24		

Sketch the curve of pH (on the vertical scale) against the volume of sodium hydroxide added. How does the shape of this curve influence the choice of indicator in the titration of a weak acid, such as ethanoic acid, with aqueous sodium hydroxide?

AEB 1989 (2)

A36

The kinetics of the hydrolysis of the ester methyl ethanoate

$$CH_3CO_2CH_3(l) + H_2O(l) \rightleftharpoons CH_3COOH\ (aq) + CH_3OH\ (aq)$$

may be investigated by measuring the concentration of ethanoic acid produced. One such investigation, where 17.8 g of the ester were mixed with 1 cm^3 of concentrated hydrochloric acid and sufficient water to raise the volume to 1 dm^3 and then kept in a temperature-controlled water bath at 35°C, gave the following results:

time /s × 10^4	concentration of ethanoic acid /mol dm^{-3}
0	0
0.36	0.084
0.72	0.136
1.08	0.172
1.44	0.195

(a) Why was a small amount of hydrochloric acid added?

(*b*) (i) Calculate the number of moles of ester in 17.8 g.
(ii) Plot a graph to show how the concentration of the ester varies with time.
(iii) Determine the half-life for the reaction.
(iv) Determine the order of the reaction with respect to the ester and give your reasoning.
(v) Calculate the initial rate of reaction.
(vi) Using your value for the initial rate, determine the value of the rate constant, *k*, for this reaction at 35°C.

(*c*) In a second investigation the concentration of the hydrochloric acid was doubled and the initial rate was found to be $2.33 \times 10^{-5}\ mol\ dm^{-3}\ s^{-1}$. Write the rate equation for this reaction, assuming that the rate of reaction is independent of the amount of water present.

(*d*) (i) Why was the reaction mixture kept in a temperature-controlled water bath?

(ii) What would happen to the rate of reaction if the experiment were repeated at 25 °C, all other factors being the same?

(*e*) Describe briefly how you would measure the concentration of the ethanoic acid as part of such an investigation.

UCLES 1990 (AS2)

A37

(*a*) Define the terms *partial order, overall order* and *rate constant* as applied to a chemical reaction.

(*b*) The rate of the reaction Cr(III) + 3Ce(IV) = Cr(VI) + 3Ce(III) varies as follows:

Concentration/mol dm^{-3}				*Rate*/
[Cr(III)]	[Ce(IV)]	[Cr(VI)]	[Ce(III)]	mol dm^{-3} s^{-1}
0.050	0.020	0.040	0.025	1.0×10^{-6}
0.100	0.020	0.040	0.025	2.0×10^{-6}
0.050	0.040	0.040	0.025	4.0×10^{-6}
0.050	0.020	0.020	0.025	1.0×10^{-6}
0.050	0.020	0.020	0.050	5.0×10^{-7}

(i) Find the partial orders of reaction with respect to Cr(III), Ce(IV) and Cr(VI).
(ii) The data show that the partial order with respect to Ce(III) is −1. Comment briefly on the negative partial order with respect to Ce(III).
(iii) Calculate the overall order and the rate constant (stating units).

(*c*) (i) Sketch the distributions of molecular speeds in a gas at two temperatures, labelling the curve which refers to the higher temperature.
(ii) Use your sketch to explain why the rates of most chemical reactions increase *very rapidly* with increasing temperature.

OCSEB S1989 (3,4,5)

A38

The data below refer to the reaction

$2NO + O_2 \rightarrow 2NO_2$

The partial pressure of O_2 was the same for each experiment.

Initial rate /N m^{-2} s^{-1}	p^2_{NO} /N^2 m^{-4}
1.70	0.010
6.80	0.040
27.2	0.16
61.2	0.36
108	0.64
170	1.00

(*a*) Plot the data on a graph.

(*b*) What is the order of reaction with respect to NO? Justify your answer.

(*c*) When the partial pressure of O_2 was doubled to a new constant value the gradient of the graph in (*a*) doubled. What is the order with respect to O_2? Explain your answer.

(*d*) Give the rate equation for this reaction. What are the units of the rate constant?

(*e*) To calculate the activation energy of another gas phase reaction, $2N_2O \rightarrow 2N_2 + O_2$, the reaction was monitored at various temperatures, and a graph of $\ln k$ against $1/T$ (in K^{-1}) was plotted (k is the rate constant for the reaction). The gradient of the graph had a numerical value of -2.95×10^4. The Arrhenius equation may be expressed in the form $\ln k = \ln A - E_A/RT$. Calculate the activation energy for this reaction, stating the units. ($R = 8.31\ J\ K^{-1}\ mol^{-1}$)

ULSEB 1988 (2)

A39

(*a*) Using the photochemical reaction of **either** methane and chlorine **or** hydrogen and chlorine as an example, explain and illustrate the meaning of the following terms:
(i) initiation;
(ii) propagation;
(iii) termination;
(iv) chain reaction.

(*b*) The rate of a homogeneous gas reaction increases quite rapidly with temperature. Explain the two factors which account for this increase and indicate which makes the bigger contribution.

(*c*) Describe how you would measure experimentally the enthalpy change for the following reaction in aqueous solution.

$Cu^{2+}(aq) + 4NH_3(aq) \rightarrow Cu(NH_3)_4{}^{2+}(aq)$

UODLE S 1987 (1)

Part B Industrial chemistry

B1

(*a*) Draw a flow diagram to illustrate an industrial process of your choice. (The ammonia-soda process for the manufacture of sodium carbonate is a suitable example but any industrial chemical process involving several stages will be acceptable.)

(*b*) Various factors, apart from the chemistry of the process, should be considered when setting up any chemical process. Discuss, by reference to the process you have chosen in (a),

(i) the acquisition and handling of raw materials;
(ii) economic factors;
(iii) the location of the plant.

AEB Winter 1987 (1)

B2

(*a*) (i) The terms *batch* process and *continuous* process are used in the chemical industry. Explain their meaning.

(ii) State one major economic advantage that a batch system of production has over a continuous process.

(iii) Give the major economic factor which influences a manufacturer to change from a batch to a continuous process. State also the major economic obstacle faced by a small company making this change.

(*b*) Distribution between two immiscible solvents is an important unit operation used in industry. Give **one** important industrial application of this process by stating the product separated and the two solvents employed. Explain briefly why the method can be used.

(*c*) Ammonium nitrate is manufactured on a large scale from ammonia. One stage in the process involves the catalytic oxidation of ammonia at high temperature in the presence of a platinum/rhodium gauze catalyst. The mixture is then cooled and more air is introduced before being passed into an absorption tower against a countercurrent of water.

(i) Give the equation for the catalytic oxidation of ammonia.

(ii) Give the equation for the reaction which occurs when the reaction mixture is cooled. Explain why cooling is necessary.

(iii) Currently, most plants in which these reactions are carried out have a tall chimney above which a faint brown plume of NO_2 forms. This is produced when a colourless gas, formed in the absorption tower, reacts with oxygen in the air. Identify this colourless gas, explain how it is formed in the absorption tower, and name the important chemical produced on a large scale in the absorption tower.

(iv) Special precautions are taken during the final stages of the production of ammonium nitrate. State the property of ammonium nitrate which makes this necessary.

JMB 1989 (2C)

B3

This question concerns the manufacture of nitric acid. The first stage in the manufacture is the catalytic oxidation of ammonia to nitrogen oxide.

$$4NH_3(g) + 5O_2(g) \rightleftharpoons 4NO(g) + 6H_2O(g) \quad \Delta H^\ominus = -909\ \text{kJ mol}^{-1}$$

(*a*) State and explain the effect on the position of this equilibrium of

(i) increasing the temperature at constant pressure;
(ii) increasing the pressure at constant temperature.

(*b*) In industry, the oxidation is carried out at a high temperature (about 900 °C) but only a moderate pressure (about 700 kPa). Account for the use of these conditions.

(*c*) A metallic gauze catalyst is used to increase the rate of oxidation.

(i) What is the usual catalyst?
(ii) What is the advantage of having it in gauze form?

(*d*) In the industrial process the product gases from the first stage are cooled to about 37 °C and mixed with excess air to convert the nitrogen oxide to nitrogen dioxide.

$$2NO(g) + O_2(g) \rightleftharpoons 2NO_2(g) \quad \Delta H^\ominus = -114\ \text{kJ mol}^{-1}$$

(i) Explain in terms of the equilibrium why the nitrogen oxide is cooled before mixing.

(ii) Why should brown fumes be seen immediately when this reaction is carried out in the laboratory?

(*e*) Write an equation for the third stage of the manufacture in which nitrogen dioxide is converted into nitric acid.

(*f*) A large proportion of the nitric acid manufactured is converted into ammonium nitrate.

(i) Write an equation for the formation of ammonium nitrate from nitric acid.
(ii) Give **one** large scale use of ammonium nitrate.
(iii) Explain why ammonium nitrate is readily soluble in water even though the standard enthalpy of solution has a positive value.

AEB 1988 (2)

B4

Sulphuric acid is manufactured by the catalytic oxidation of sulphur dioxide with purified air over a vanadium(V) oxide catalyst in a four-stage process at 500 °C and atmospheric pressure to give sulphur trioxide. The sulphur trioxide is then absorbed in 98% sulphuric acid and the 98.5% acid is then diluted with water to give the commercial 98% concentrated acid. The sulphur used is imported from Europe or America.

The reaction between sulphur dioxide and oxygen is an equilibrium:

$$2SO_2(g) + O_2(g) \rightleftharpoons 2SO_3(g)$$
$$\Delta H = -94.6 \text{ kJ mol}^{-1} \text{ of } SO_3$$

(*a*) Describe and explain the effect on the yield of SO_3 of
  (i) increasing the pressure;
  (ii) raising the temperature.
  Comment on the actual operating conditions in the light of your answers.

(*b*) Discuss and explain the effect of the catalyst on
  (i) the yield of the reaction;
  (ii) the rate of attainment of equilibrium.

(*c*) Describe **two** likely environmental consequences of a substantial leakage of sulphur dioxide from the plant.

(*d*) About one-third of the world production of sulphuric acid is used in the manufacture of chemicals for use in agriculture.
  (i) Name **three** *types* of chemical widely used in modern agriculture.
  (ii) Outline the environmental impact of any **two** of these chemicals.

(*e*) Describe and give equations for reactions which show that sulphuric acid behaves as
  (i) an oxidizing agent;
  (ii) a dehydrating agent.

AEB 1990 (1)

B5

Methanol is manufactured from synthesis gas which is a mixture of carbon monoxide, carbon dioxide, and hydrogen. Synthesis gas is manufactured from raw materials such as natural gas, naphtha, heavy fuel oil and coal. Synthesis gas is converted to methanol in a process represented by the following equations

$$CO(g) + 2H_2(g) \rightleftharpoons CH_3OH(g);\ \Delta H = -91 \text{ kJ mol}^{-1}$$
$$CO_2(g) + 3H_2(g) \rightleftharpoons CH_3OH(g) + H_2O(g);$$
$$\Delta H = -49 \text{ kJ mol}^{-1}$$

Low temperatures and high pressures would give high yields of methanol but, in the UK, a low pressure catalysed process is used at a temperature of 200–300 °C.

(From *'The Essential Chemical Industry'* – The Polytechnic of North London, 1985)

(*a*) Explain why high yields of methanol are produced at
  (i) high pressures;
  (ii) low temperatures.

(*b*) Give **two** disadvantages of operating the process at high pressures.

(*c*) Give **one** disadvantage of operating the process at low temperatures.

(*d*) Suggest a type of element that might be suitable for use as a catalyst in this process.

(e) Explain how a catalyst affects the reaction profile of the reaction between carbon monoxide and hydrogen. Include an energy level diagram in your answer.

(*f*) For the large-scale manufacture of methanol give
  (i) **one** fixed cost for the process;
  (ii) **one** variable cost for the process

(g) Suggest factors that should be considered when deciding upon the location of a plant for the production of methanol by the process outlined above.

AEB 1989 (AS)

B6

The petrochemicals industry produces and uses large quantities of ethene. Some of this is obtained by steam-cracking naphtha. A modern plant can produce 500 000 tonnes of ethene each year. Before a new cracking plant is built careful planning must go into choosing its location and calculating its costs.

(*a*) Give, with reasons, **two** factors which should be taken into account when deciding upon the location of a new cracking plant.

(*b*) (i) Give **one** fixed cost of a cracking plant.
  (ii) Give **one** variable cost of a cracking plant.
  (iii) Explain why a 500 000 tonne capacity plant may be uneconomic to operate if it is used to produce only 250 000 tonnes of ethene per year.

(*c*) Ethene is converted into ethanol by direct hydration at a temperature of 330 °C, a pressure of 6 MPa and with a catalyst. The reaction is exothermic.

$$C_2H_4(g) + H_2O(g) \rightleftharpoons C_2H_5OH(g)$$

  (i) Explain why the process is operated at a high pressure.
  (ii) What would be the effect on the equilibrium concentration of ethanol if the process were operated at a temperature in excess of 330 °C? Explain your answer.
  (iii) Why is a catalyst used in the process?

(*d*) Describe **two** of the environmental problems which can arise from the storage of large amounts of ethene.

AEB Winter 1988 (2)

B7

(*a*) Crop yields can be increased by the use of fertilisers, herbicides and pesticides.
  (i) Give **one** example of the way in which an insecticide such as DDT can increase crop yields.
  (ii) Compounds such as 2,4-D and 2,4,5-T act as herbicides. What is the function of a herbicide?
  (iii) In recent years restrictions have been placed on the use of DDT and some other pesticides. Suggest reasons why this should be so.

(*b*) Ammonium salts are frequently used as fertilisers. Their nitrogen content can be estimated by reaction with excess standard alkali followed by 'back-titration' of the unused alkali with an acid.
  (i) Write an ionic equation for the reaction between ammonium ions and an aqueous alkali such as sodium hydroxide.
  (ii) A solution containing 1.85 g of the fertiliser was boiled with 50.0 cm^3 of 1.00 mol dm^{-3} sodium hydroxide solution until reaction was complete. Calculate the number of moles of hydroxide ion added.

(iii) The solution obtained in (ii) was diluted to $250\,cm^3$. $25.0\,cm^3$ portions of this solution required $22.0\,cm^3$ of $0.100\,mol\,dm^{-3}$ hydrochloric acid for neutralisation. Calculate the number of moles of hydroxide ion still present, unreacted, in the total $250\,cm^3$ of solution.

(iv) Using your answers to (i)–(iii), calculate the number of moles of hydroxide ion needed to react with the ammonium ions and hence the number of moles of ammonium ions present.

(v) Use your answer to (iv) and the information given in (ii) to calculate the percentage by mass of nitrogen in the fertiliser.

AEB 1987 (2)

B8

(*a*) For **each** of the land, the sea and the atmosphere name **one** chemical pollutant. State the source of the pollutant, the harm it causes to the environment and suggest a method of reducing the amount of pollutant released.

(*b*) State **five** sources of energy available on a large scale at the present time. Discuss **three** of these energy sources by considering their long term availability and any aspects of their use which are socially undesirable.

(*c*) Suggest, with justification, an energy source which could provide large scale energy some time in the future and which would have minimal environmental problems.

AEB 1988 (1)

B9

Read the following passage carefully and then answer questions (*a*) to (*o*) below.

THE GASES OF THE ATMOSPHERE

The Earth's atmosphere is unique in the solar system, particularly because it can support life on the planet. Moreover, during the past hundred years or so the use of its constituents in industrial chemistry has become very important.

The composition of dry air is given below, together with the boiling points of some of its components.

Gas	% by volume	Boiling point/K
Nitrogen	78.08	77
Oxygen	20.95	90
Argon	0.93	87
Carbon dioxide	0.03 (variable)	
Neon	0.001 5	27
Helium	0.000 5	4
Methane	0.000 2	
Krypton	0.000 11	121
Nitrogen oxide	0.000 05	
Hydrogen	0.000 05	
Xenon	0.000 008	166

The methods used for isolating the constituent gases are largely based upon the fractional distillation of air.

NITROGEN

In the manufacture of ammonia, nitrogen is obtained by heating air, methane and steam in the presence of suitable catalysts. A mixture of nitrogen and hydrogen for ammonia synthesis is thus produced. The main method for separating nitrogen industrially, however, is the fractional distillation of liquid air. This yields nitrogen in two main grades, a general grade containing oxygen (10 ppm), carbon dioxide (10 ppm) and hydrogen (10 ppm) and a special grade in which the oxygen content is lower than 10 ppm. Low purity nitrogen containing 2–3% of oxygen is also available.

Nitrogen is used:

(i) in metallurgical industry *e.g.* in the annealing of steel,

(ii) to provide an inert atmosphere *e.g.* in food packaging, glass making, chemical processes, and silicon chip production, and

(iii) in refrigeration (liquid nitrogen is a cheap refrigerant often used for reducing temperature quickly *e.g.* in medicine).

OXYGEN

Two types of plant are commonly used to separate oxygen from the air. Liquid oxygen plants afford oxygen of high purity, at least 99.7% with 0.3% argon.

Gaseous oxygen plants, which are often sited next to steel or other chemical works yield quite an acceptable product of lower purity (90–99.5% oxygen). The annual production of oxygen in the UK is about two million tonnes.

The main use of oxygen (55%) is in steel manufacture. The chemical industry consumes a further 25%. Other applications include medicine (10%), cutting metals at high temperature and rocket propulsion.

ARGON

Argon is the most abundant noble gas in the air. About 30 000 tonnes are produced annually in the United Kingdom. Almost 90% of this is used to provide inert atmospheres especially in the metallurgical industries. Most of the remainder is employed in light bulbs as a mixture of 88% argon 12% nitrogen. Where very high purity is required, refining up to 99.999% can be achieved.

HELIUM

Although there is very little helium in the air, some is obtained as a by-product of neon manufacture. The main commercial source, however, is natural gas, which may contain up to 6% helium. On account of its low density, helium is suitable for weather balloons and airships. The gas also finds application in under-water breathing equipment (80% helium, 20% oxygen) and in low temperature research.

THE OTHER NOBLE GASES

Neon, xenon and krypton are used in electric discharge tubes. Xenon became chemically important in the early 1960s with the discovery that it is able to form compounds such as xenon tetrafluoride.

(*a*) Draw structures, showing the bonding and shapes where appropriate, of the molecules of:
 (i) nitrogen;
 (ii) oxygen;
 (iii) carbon dioxide;
 (iv) methane.

How does the atomicity of the molecules of the noble gases differ from the atomicity of the molecules of the gases above?

(*b*) State **four** uses of nitrogen given in the passage.

(*c*) Which processes maintain the percentage of oxygen and carbon dioxide in the air?

(*d*) Which of the gases mentioned in the passage would you expect to remain gaseous during the liquefaction of air?

(*e*) If the percentage of carbon dioxide in the atmosphere rises, what effect could this have upon conditions on the planet?

(*f*) Suggest the origin of each of (i) nitrogen oxide and (ii) methane in the atmosphere.

(*g*) Suggest the origin of helium in natural gas and explain how it is formed.

(*h*) Assuming that liquid nitrogen and liquid oxygen form ideal mixtures which obey Raoult's law over the whole composition range, sketch boiling point/composition curves (vapour and liquid) for the system. Mark on your sketch the boiling points of oxygen and nitrogen and then use your sketch to explain the fractional distillation of liquid air containing nitrogen and oxygen only in a 4:1 mole ratio.

(*j*) Although both argon and nitrogen are used to provide inert atmospheres, in some cases nitrogen may be preferred to argon although it is more reactive than argon. Suggest **two** reasons for this.

(*k*) Assuming the pressure of the gas in a light bulb to be 10 kPa, calculate the partial pressure of the argon in the bulb.

(*l*) What is the purpose of oxygen in steel manufacture? What is the advantage in using the gas of lower purity?

(*m*) State **one** chemical process which uses oxygen and may be included in the 25% used in the Chemical Industry.

(*n*) Neon, xenon and krypton are used in electric discharge tubes.
 (i) Give an everyday use of such tubes.
 (ii) Explain how the light is generated in the tube.

(*o*) (i) Why was the discovery of the formation of xenon tetrafluoride significant in chemical terms?
 (ii) Suggest a shape of the xenon tetrafluoride molecule.

AEB Winter 1988 (1)

B10

Read the following account and answer the questions which follow.

Ethenyl ethanoate (*vinyl acetate*), b.p. 72 °C, is an important intermediate; the polymerised ester, poly(vinyl acetate), is widely used in emulsion paints and in adhesives. Two processes used for the manufacture of ethenyl ethanoate are outlined below.

Process 1

$$HC{\equiv}CH + CH_3COOH \xrightarrow[170\text{–}250\,°C]{(CH_3COO)_2Zn} CH_3COOCH{=}CH_2 \quad \Delta H^{\ominus} = -118\ \text{kJ mol}^{-1}$$

Ethyne (*acetylene*) and ethanoic (*acetic*) acid are combined in a single-step, heterogeneously catalysed reaction carried out in the vapour phase. The conversion of ethyne is about 60%, and 7% of the reacted ethyne forms by-products. The ester is freed from organic by-products in a multi-step distillation.

Process 2

$$H_2C{=}CH_2 + CH_3COOH + \tfrac{1}{2}O_2 \xrightarrow[175\text{–}200\,°C]{(CH_3COO)_2Pd} CH_3COOCH{=}CH_2 + H_2O \quad \Delta H^{\ominus} = -176\ \text{kJ mol}^{-1}$$

A gaseous mixture of ethene, ethanoic acid and oxygen is passed over a fixed-bed catalyst. The ethene conversion is about 10%, and 94% of the ethene which reacts does so to produce the desired ester. The conversion for the reaction is limited by the low oxygen content required in order to prevent an explosion. The main by-product, carbon dioxide, is removed by means of an alkali wash.

Ethene is readily available from cracking processes which also produce ethyne as a by-product. Ethene is more easily stored and transported than ethyne.

(*a*) State the advantages and disadvantages of Process 2 relative to Process 1, and explain briefly how these result in Process 2 being almost exclusively used in new plants. Areas covered might include feedstocks, energy, operation and costs.

(*b*) Suggest why carbon dioxide is the main by-product in Process 2, but not in Process 1. Give an equation for its formation in Process 2.

(*c*) In Process 2, 100 kmol of ethene, together with appropriate quantities of ethanoic acid and oxygen, were subjected to a single pass through the reactor. Using the above information, calculate the amount (in kmol) of ethene and of ethenyl ethanoate in the resulting gas mixture.

JMB 1988 (1B)

Part C Inorganic chemistry

C1

(*a*) Part of the Periodic Table is given below:

I	II	III	IV	V	VI	VII
Li	Be	B	C	N	O	F
Na	Mg	Al	Si	P	S	Cl
K	Ca			As		
Rb	Sr			Sb		
Cs	Ba			Bi		

Of the elements in this table, write the name of the element which is most:

(i) electropositive
(ii) non-metallic

and the name of the element which forms:

(iii) a tetrachloride which is not hydrolysed by water
(iv) the most basic hydride having a pyramidal molecular shape
(v) two allotropes of low melting point
(vi) the least soluble s-block sulphate
(vii) an amphoteric oxide, X_2O_5
(viii) a series of double sulphates with Group I elements.

(*b*) (i) With an explanation, arrange the following bonds in order of increased bond polarity:

N—H, F—H, B—H, C—H

(ii) Describe the nature and direction of polarity of the bonds in trichloromethane and tetrachloromethane and explain why only one of these structures has a dipole moment.
(iii) Show how trichloromethane and propanone can form strong inter-molecular bonds explaining your answer in terms of bond polarity.

(*c*) (i) Draw bond diagrams for the N_2O_4 molecule.
(ii) Explain the principle of electron delocalisation using dinitrogen tetroxide as an example. Comment on the nitrogen to oxygen bond lengths and the geometrical shape of the molecule.

SU 1986 (2)

C2

Give an account of the chlorides of the elements sodium, magnesium, aluminium, silicon, phosphorus and sulphur.

You should consider their composition and bonding, methods of preparation and reactions with water, but your answer should not be confined to these points.

Describe how, given a pure sample, you would determine the formula of an oxide OR chloride of any ONE of these elements.

ULSEB Winter 1986 (3)

C3

This question concerns the hydrides of a range of elements.

(*a*) In each of the following cases, give the name of a hydride and write an equation for the reaction described.

(i) A hydride which hydrolyzes rapidly and extensively in cold water.
(ii) A hydride which is spontaneously flammable in air.
(iii) A hydride which, on electrolysis in the molten state, gives hydrogen at the anode.
(iv) A hydride which, in water, gives a dibasic acid.
(v) A hydride which, in water, gives a weak alkali.
(vi) A hydride which can act as a ligand with d-block metal ions.

(*b*) Give the names of TWO hydrides which combine with each other by addition and write an equation for the reaction.

(*c*) Suggest an explanation for the ability of carbon to form long chain hydrocarbons.

(*d*) The enthalpy of combustion of methane is highly exothermic. To what do you attribute the stability of methane in air?

(*e*) Suggest a reason for the large difference in boiling points of methane and water.

ULSEB Winter 1985 (2) (slightly adapted)

C4

(*a*) Describe how the following properties vary on descending groups IA and IIA of the periodic table and state how these properties differ between the two groups:

(i) first and second ionisation energies;
(ii) cationic radii;
(iii) rates of reaction with cold water.

(*b*) For the same s-block elements, discuss:

(i) the action of heat on their nitrates;
(ii) the crystal structure of their chlorides, XY type only.

(*c*) Outline the *principles* involved in the manufacture of sodium hydroxide by the electrolysis of sodium chloride, explaining the reactions in terms of selective discharge of ions.

SU 1985 (2)

C5

(*a*) (i) State the conditions under which magnesium and calcium will react with water, and write balanced equations for the reactions.
(ii) Explain any differences between the two reactions in terms of the atomic properties of the two metals.

(*b*) Compare the chemistries of magnesium and calcium with reference to the following:

(i) the solubilities of their sulphates in water;
(ii) the thermal stabilities of their carbonates;
(iii) the reaction of their oxides with water.

(*c*) A mineral, which can be represented by the formula $Mg_xBa_y(CO_3)_z$, was analysed as described below. From the results, calculate the formula of the mineral.

A sample of the mineral was dissolved in excess hydrochloric acid and the solution made up to $100\,cm^3$ with water. During the process $48\,cm^3$ of carbon dioxide, measured at 25 °C and 1 atmosphere pressure, were evolved.

A $25.0\,cm^3$ portion of the resulting solution required $25.0\,cm^3$ of EDTA solution of concentration $0.02\,mol\,dm^{-3}$ to reach an end-point. A further $25.0\,cm^3$ portion gave a precipitate of barium sulphate of mass 0.058 g on treatment with excess dilute sulphuric acid. You may assume that Group 2 metal ions form 1:1 complexes with EDTA.

Molar volume of any gas at 25 °C and 1 atmosphere pressure = $24\,dm^3$).

AEB 1990 (1)

C6

This question concerns the elements boron and aluminium.

(*a*) Give the electronic configurations of boron and aluminium.

	1s	2s	2p			3s	3p		
B									
Al									

(*b*) Explain why

(i) boron does not form simple compounds containing the B^{3+} ion.
(ii) aluminium chloride is predominantly covalent whereas aluminium fluoride is predominantly ionic.

(*c*) (i) How do the hydroxides of boron and aluminium differ in their acid–base character?
(ii) Briefly explain this difference in behaviour.

(*d*) Give and explain the structures of the chlorides of boron and aluminium at temperatures just above their vaporisation points.

ULSEB Winter 1986 (2)

C7

(*a*) Describe how you would prepare a specimen of **either** hydrated aluminium potassium sulphate (potash alum) **or** hydrated chromium(III) potassium sulphate (chrome alum) in the laboratory. Give essential experimental details and explain the chemistry involved.

(*b*) The standard electrode potential for Na^+/Na is -2.71 V, for Al^{3+}/Al -1.66 V, and for Cu^{2+}/Cu $+0.34$ V.

(i) Explain what is meant by the term *standard electrode potential*.
(ii) Explain how standard electrode potentials may be used to predict the reactions of the above three metals with dilute sulphuric acid.
(iii) Explain why the prediction may be incorrect for aluminium.

(*c*) State the species present when aluminium sulphate is dissolved in water. Explain what happens when sodium carbonate solution is added to this solution.

UODLE 1987 (2)

C8

This question concerns the elements carbon, silicon, germanium, tin and lead in Group 4 of the Periodic Table.

(*a*) Copy the following table and give the electronic configuration of Ge and Sn^{2+}. The atomic numbers of germanium and tin are 32 and 50 respectively.

	1s	2s	2p	3s	3p	3d	4s	4p	4d	4f	5s	5p
Ge												
Sn^{2+}												

How do you account for the fact that tin forms the 2+ ion but germanium does not?

(*b*) The melting point of carbon is almost 4000 °C whereas that of tin is 232 °C. How do you account for this difference?

(*c*) Explain why PbO_2 liberates chlorine from concentrated hydrochloric acid but SnO_2 does not.

(*d*) Tetrachloromethane and tetrachlorosilane are both thermodynamically (energetically) unstable with respect to reaction with water, but only tetrachloromethane is kinetically stable.

(i) Explain what is meant by thermodynamic stability and kinetic stability.
(ii) How do you account for this difference in kinetic stability?

ULSEB 1988 (2) (slightly adapted)

C9
(*a*) Describe the appearance of lead, silicon and the allotropes of carbon and make a comparison, with explanations, of their electrical conductivities.

(*b*) Explain what is meant by *doping* and by *p-* and *n-type semiconductors*.

(*c*) Compare the bonding in each of the four following compounds and their reactions with water:

CCl_4; $SiCl_4$; and **either** $PbCl_2$ and $PbCl_4$ **or** $SnCl_2$ and $SnCl_4$.

(*d*) Give equations to illustrate

(i) the reaction of $Pb^{2+}(aq)$ with NaOH(aq),
(ii) the reaction of $Pb^{2+}(aq)$ with $I^-(aq)$,
(iii) one reducing reaction of $Sn^{2+}(aq)$.

WJEC 1986 (2)

C10
(*a*) Two isotopes of tin may be represented as $^{118}_{50}Sn$ and $^{120}_{50}Sn$.

(i) State the number of protons, neutrons, and electrons in each of these two isotopes.
(ii) Discuss, briefly, the meaning of the term isotope.
(iii) Write down the electronic configuration of tin and assign the element to a periodic group.
(iv) Suggest the type of bonding in tin(IV) chloride.

(*b*) Draw a fully labelled diagram of the apparatus which could be used to prepare a sample of tin(IV) chloride.

(*c*) Tin(II) chloride and mercury(II) chloride both form clear solutions in hydrochloric acid. Mercury(I) chloride, Hg_2Cl_2, is a white solid, sparingly soluble in this acid. Hg(I) disproportionates on warming. If mercury precipitates from solution it always appears black. The relative orders of magnitude of the standard electrode potentials are:

$$\begin{array}{ccc} A & & B \\ 2Hg^{2+} / Hg_2Cl_2 & > & Sn^{4+} / Sn^{2+} \\ \text{(most positive)} & & \text{(most negative)} \end{array}$$

(i) Show why the relative magnitudes of the standard electrode potentials A and B indicate that $Sn^{2+}(aq)$ will reduce $Hg^{2+}(aq)$.
(ii) Write the *ionic* equation for the disproportionation of the Hg_2^{2+} ion.
(iii) Predict what would be observed if tin(II) chloride solution is *slowly* added to mercury(II) chloride solution until the former is in excess.

SU 1985 (1)

C11
(*a*) Nitrogen and phosphorus both form an oxide with the empirical formula X_2O_5.

(i) With the aid of diagrams describe the arrangement of atoms in each of these oxides.
(ii) Give the electronic structure of N_2O_5.
(iii) Discuss the electronic structure of the phosphorus atoms in the oxide of phosphorus; and
(iv) name the compounds formed when each of the two oxides react with water.

(*b*) Describe how you would prepare a sample of phosphorus pentachloride from phosphorus trichloride.

(*c*) What would be observed if (i) phosphorus trichloride and (ii) bismuth(III) chloride were each added to separate samples of water, shaken until there was no further change, and then concentrated hydrochloric acid was added to the resulting mixture?

AEB 1987 (1)

C12
(*a*) Describe the manufacture of nitric acid from ammonia, with special reference to the physico-chemical principles and economic factors involved.

(*b*) How and under what conditions would you expect nitric acid to react with (i) sulphur and (ii) iron(II) carbonate?

(*c*) How and under what conditions would you expect ammonia to react with (i) copper(II) oxide and (ii) chlorine?

UODLE 1987 (2)

C13
(*a*) Draw a fully labelled diagram of the apparatus you would use to prepare and collect a pure sample of sulphur(VI) oxide (melting point 17 °C) in the laboratory using sulphur(IV) oxide (sulphur dioxide) as a starting material.

(*b*) The conversion of sulphur(IV) oxide to sulphur(VI) oxide in part (*a*) above is exothermic. Discuss the optimum industrial conditions of temperature and pressure for achieving an economic yield.

(*c*) Possible bond diagrams for sulphuric and nitric acids are:

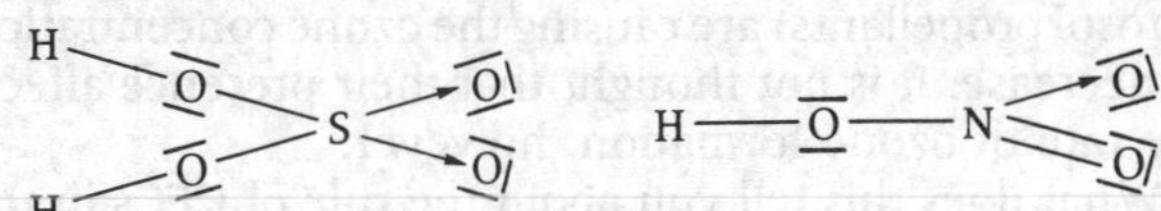

(i) What kind of bond is represented by the arrows?
(ii) Re-write the bond diagrams placing positive and negative symbols on the atoms which are charged.
(iii) Draw a bond diagram of the acid $H_2S_2O_7$ showing how this structure contains the same bonding features as the two examples in (*c*).

(*d*) When concentrated sulphuric and nitric acids are mixed, the reactions A and B below occur:

A $H_2SO_4 + HNO_3 \rightarrow HSO_4^- + \_\_\_\_^+$
B $\_\_\_\_^+ \rightarrow \_\_\_\_^+ + H_2O$

(i) Re-write and complete the equations A and B.
(ii) What type of reaction is A?
(iii) What type of reaction is B?
(iv) Why is the final nitrogen(v) cation important in organic chemistry?

SU 1986 (2)

C14

In the stratosphere 30 km above the Earth's surface, ozone is being made continuously by the following reaction:

$O + O_2 \rightarrow O_3$; rate $= k[O]\ [O_2]$.

The free oxygen atoms arise from the splitting of oxygen molecules by ultraviolet light from the Sun:

$O_2 \rightarrow 2O$.

(*a*) Calculate the rate at which ozone forms, given the following values:

$k = 3.9 \times 10^{-5}\ dm^3\ mol^{-1}\ s^{-1}$,
$[O] = 3 \times 10^{-14}\ mol\ dm^{-3}$,
$[O_2] = 1.3 \times 10^{-4}\ mol\ dm^{-3}$.

(*b*) The temperature of the stratosphere is $-50\ °C$.

(i) State a typical value of air temperature at sea level.
(ii) Calculate the molar concentration of oxygen molecules (in $mol\ dm^{-3}$).
[One mole of gas occupies $24\ dm^3$ under the conditions at sea level.]
(iii) By using the collision theory of reaction kinetics and your answers to (*b*) (i) and (*b*) (ii), discuss qualitatively how the rate of ozone formation at sea level would compare with that in the stratosphere.
In fact, practically no ozone is formed in the lower atmosphere. Suggest a reason for this.

(*c*) It is assumed that the concentration of ozone in the stratosphere has remained roughly constant for many thousands of years but there is now some evidence that chlorofluorocarbons (CFCs—used as refrigerants and aerosol propellants) are causing the ozone concentration to decrease. It is not thought that their presence affects the rate of ozone formation, however.
What does this tell you about the role of CFCs in the other reactions involving ozone that must be occurring in the stratosphere?

UCLES 1990 (3)

C15

This question concerns the elements of Group 7: fluorine, chlorine, bromine and iodine.

(*a*) The word halogen means 'salt maker'. Explain why this is a suitable name for the elements of the Group.

(*b*) When sodium chloride is treated with concentrated sulphuric acid, a colourless gas, **X**, which fumes in moist air, is formed. When sodium iodide is treated in the same way a coloured vapour, **Y**, is produced.

(i) Identify **X** and **Y**.
(ii) Explain the difference in behaviour between the two sodium salts.
(iii) If 90% phosphoric(v) acid is used instead of sulphuric acid, a colourless gas is produced in each reaction. Explain why phosphoric(v) acid behaves differently from sulphuric acid.

(*c*) A number of oxoanions of chlorine are known; examples include ClO^-, ClO_3^- and ClO_4^-.

(i) ClO^- is formed when chlorine reacts with aqueous alkali. Write an ionic equation for this reaction.
Write an ionic equation for the reaction that $ClO^-(aq)$ undergoes when heated.
(ii) When $KClO_3$ is heated, it disproportionates into KCl and $KClO_4$. Write an equation for this reaction.
(iii) What is the oxidation state of chlorine in each of the following?
$KClO_3$; $KClO_4$; KCl.
(iv) Show how your answer to (*c*) (iii) is consistent with the ratio $KClO_4$/KCl in your equation in (*c*)(ii).

ULSEB 1987 (2)

C16

When chlorine is bubbled through a concentrated aqueous solution of ammonium chloride, a yellow oily liquid, nitrogen trichloride, NCl_3, is formed, together with a solution of hydrochloric acid. Nitrogen trichloride is hydrolysed by aqueous sodium hydroxide, producing ammonia gas and a solution of sodium chlorate(I).

(*a*) Write balanced equations for the formation and hydrolysis of nitrogen trichloride.

(*b*) Draw the shape of the nitrogen trichloride molecule.

(*c*) Apart from peaks associated with solitary nitrogen atoms (at $m/e = 14$) and chlorine atoms (at $m/e = 35$ and $m/e = 37$), the mass spectrum of nitrogen trichloride contains 9 peaks arranged in 3 groups, ranging from $m/e = 49$ to $m/e = 125$. Predict the m/e values of all 9 peaks, and suggest a formula for the species responsible for each one.

UCLES 1990 (3)

C17

(*a*) Explain the term *metallic bonding* and show how it accounts for the electrical conductivity of metals.

(*b*) How does the electronic structure of a d-block (transition) element differ from that of a main group element? Illustrate your answer with reference to iron and calcium.

(*c*) 'The d-block elements show variable oxidation numbers in their compounds.' Discuss this statement, using iron to illustrate your answer.

When aqueous iron(II) sulphate is boiled with an excess of aqueous potassium cyanide a yellow solution is obtained. When chlorine is passed into the yellow solution it turns red and this red solution gives a dark blue colour on addition of aqueous potassium iodide in the presence of a few drops of starch solution. Neither the yellow nor the red solution gives a precipitate with aqueous sodium hydroxide. Explain these observations as far as you can.

UCLES 1986 (1)

C18

(*a*) (i) Indicate the important ores of iron and give the name and formula of the iron compound in each ore.

(ii) Describe **briefly** the process by which iron ore is converted to pig (cast) iron in the blast furnace. Give the names of the materials used, indicating their roles, the types of reactions involved and the conditions used. Give balanced equations for the routes by which the products are formed.

(*b*) The oxides CO_2 and SiO_2 are both involved in blast furnace chemistry.

(i) Compare the structures and physical state of these two oxides at ordinary temperatures and pressures.

(ii) Write down the equilibria involving **each** of these oxides with quicklime, CaO, in the blast furnace, and state whether their equilibrium constants will be greater or less than one (1.0) in the direction written under blast furnace conditions.

(*c*) (i) Iron is a metallic conductor and has a body-centred cubic structure similar to sodium. Sketch this structure and describe the nature of the bonding in metallic iron.

(ii) State **one** use of metallic iron as a catalyst and explain why transition metals are often good catalysts for chemical reactions.

(*d*) Iron has four stable isotopes whose relative abundances are tabulated below.

Isotope	^{54}Fe	^{56}Fe	^{57}Fe	^{58}Fe
Relative abundance/%	5.8	91.7	2.2	0.3

(i) Draw a sketch of the mass spectrum that would be given by iron vapour, labelling and numbering the axes of the grid that you draw.

(ii) Calculate the number of,

1. neutrons present in ^{54}Fe,
2. protons present in ^{57}Fe, and
3. electrons present in $^{56}Fe^+$.

WJEC 1990 (2)

C19

Hydrated chromium(III) chloride, $CrCl_3.6H_2O$, exists as three structural isomers. Their formulae can be represented as

I $[Cr(H_2O)_6]^{3+}$ $3Cl^-$
II $[Cr(H_2O)_5Cl]^{2+}2Cl^-.H_2O$
III $[Cr(H_2O)_4Cl_2]^+$ $Cl^-.2H_2O$

(*a*) State and explain the type of bonding which occurs in I between chromium and water.

(*b*) Reaction with aqueous silver nitrate can be used to distinguish between the three compounds shown.

(i) Give the name and appearance of the insoluble compound formed when aqueous silver nitrate reacts with each of the compounds shown.

(ii) Explain how this reaction can be used to distinguish between the three chromium compounds, stating how the result would differ quantitatively in each case.

(*c*) (i) Which one of the compounds, I, II and III can exist as geometrical isomers?

(ii) Draw diagrams to show the three-dimensional shapes of the complex ions which are geometrical isomers, and label them *cis* and *trans* as appropriate.

(*d*) A chromium(III) salt, Y, contains 19.96% Cr, 39.16% NH_3 and 40.88% Cl by mass.

(i) Calculate the empirical formula of Y.

(ii) What aqueous reagent would need to be added to hydrated chromium(III) chloride in order to prepare Y?

(iii) What condition would be necessary to ensure that all the ligands in Y are identical?

AEB 1987 (2)

C20

(*a*) (i) Explain what is meant by amphoteric character for an oxide or a hydroxide.

(ii) Indicate which of the following oxides show amphoteric character.

Na_2O, BaO_2, Al_2O_3, P_4O_{10}, SnO, SiO_2.

(iii) State **two** chemical differences between the oxides of metals and of non-metals.

(*b*) (i) State which **one** of the oxides listed in (*a*)(ii) above will, on treatment with dilute sulphuric acid, liberate hydrogen peroxide.

(ii) Explain why this particular oxide is especially suitable for the preparation in this way of solutions of hydrogen peroxide.

(iii) Give a balanced chemical equation for the reaction in (*b*)(i) above.

(iv) 1.6×10^{-3} mol of the oxide in (*b*)(i)–(iii) above was treated with excess dilute sulphuric acid, and excess aqueous potassium iodide was added to the aqueous hydrogen peroxide thus produced.

1. Give a balanced chemical equation for the reaction which takes place between hydrogen peroxide and iodide ion in acid solution.

2. Calculate the volume of aqueous sodium thiosulphate, $Na_2S_2O_3$, of concentration 0.100 mol dm^{-3} which would be required to react completely with the product of the reaction in (*b*)(iv)(1).

(*c*) Consider the following list of hydrides:

LiH, CH_4, NH_3, HF, NaH, SiH_4, PH_3, HCl.

(i) Indicate which of these hydrides show dominantly ionic bonding in the anhydrous state.
(ii) State which (if any) of the above hydrides are decomposed by interaction with pure water. Give an equation or equations for the reaction(s).
(iii) For those of the listed hydrides *not* decomposed by water, state which will give solutions which show
(1) acidic properties,
(2) basic properties.
(iv) State, and explain, whether or not it is possible by simple chemical means to distinguish between the hydrides of metals and non-metals.

WJEC 1989 (1)

C21

Suggest explanations for each of the following.

(*a*) Xenon forms fluorides, but helium does not.

(*b*) Lithium is the only alkali metal to react readily with nitrogen.

(*c*) Of the chlorides of the Group 2 elements only beryllium chloride is covalent.

(*d*) When aqueous sodium carbonate is added to a solution of aluminium ions, a precipitate of aluminium hydroxide is formed.

(*e*) Silicon tetrachloride is readily hydrolysed by water, but tetrachloromethane is not, in spite of the fact that energy would be liberated in each reaction.

(*f*) The acids HClO, $HClO_2$, $HClO_3$ and $HClO_4$ have different strengths in aqueous solution.

ULSEB Winter 1986 (3)

C22

Copper(I) chloride can be prepared as follows:

'1 g of copper filings is dissolved in dilute nitric acid forming a blue solution **A** and a colourless gas **B**. On evaporation of **A** to dryness, a blue solid **C** is formed. On further heating, **C** gives a black residue **D** and a brown gas **E**. The heating is continued until **C** is completely decomposed. **D** is then dissolved in concentrated hydrochloric acid giving a green solution **F**. A piece of copper foil, mass 2 g, is added to **F** and the mixture boiled for five minutes. After cooling, the copper foil is removed and the remaining colourless solution **G** poured into air-free cold water. The white precipitate which forms is copper(I) chloride and this is filtered, washed, and dried in a desiccator.'

(*a*) (i) Re-draft the information above in the form of a simple flow diagram and name the compounds **A** to **E**, labelling each compound.
(ii) How could you be sure that **C** had completely decomposed on heating?
(iii) Why is air-free water used to precipitate the product?
(iv) Name a drying agent which could be used in the desiccator.

(*b*) (i) Give the formula of the copper(II) anion in the green solution **F** and the formula of the copper(I) anion in the colourless solution **G**.
(ii) Write an ionic equation representing the reaction of the piece of copper foil with the solution **F**.
(iii) What would be the mass of the copper foil at the end? Explain this using the equation in (*b*) (ii).

(*c*) (i) Briefly discuss the bonding in copper metal and mention two physical properties of copper which can be explained by the nature of the bonding.
(ii) Name the species $Cu(H_2O)_4^{2+}$ and suggest two possible geometrical arrangements of the ligands round the central atom.

SU 1986 (1)

C23

(*a*) (i) Give the name of the ion $[Ni(H_2O)_6]^{2+}$ and draw a diagram to show its shape.
(ii) What is the nature of the metal–ligand bond?

(*b*) Ammonia is described as a 'monodentate' ligand and EDTA as a 'hexadentate' ligand. What do you understand by these terms?

(*c*) A simple colorimetric method may be used to determine the formulae of the complex ions formed by nickel and ammonia molecules, and by nickel and EDTA ions. (The formula of EDTA ions may be regarded as $EDTA^{4-}$.)

The following graphs indicate the absorption of light by the solutions as equimolar solutions of the reagents are mixed.

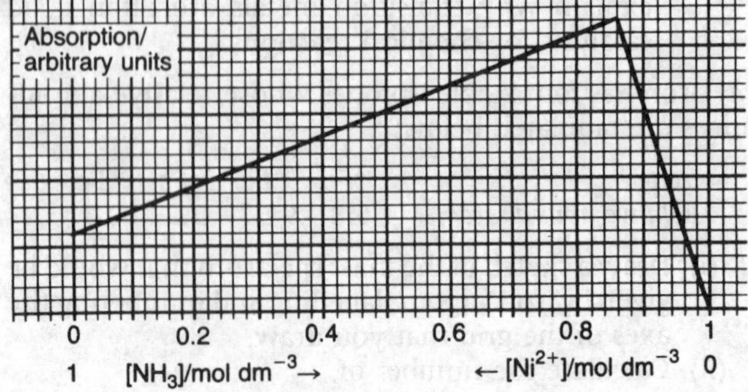

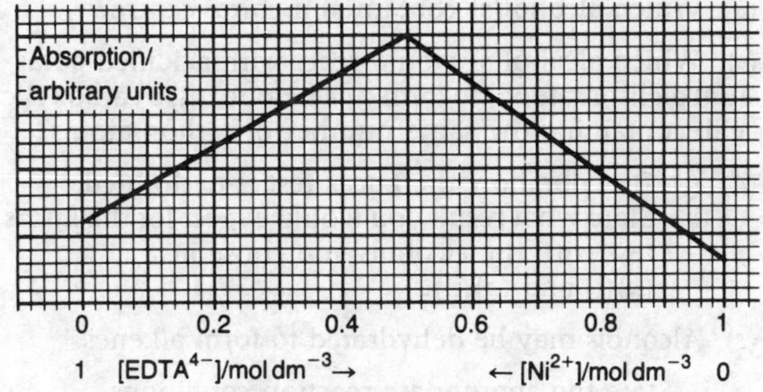

(i) Suggest a formula for the complex ion formed between nickel and ammonia.
(ii) Suggest a formula for the complex ion formed between EDTA and nickel.

(*d*) Write equations for the formation of the complex ions between
(i) hydrated nickel ions and ammonia molecules,
(ii) hydrated nickel ions and EDTA^{4-} ions.

(*e*) Write an expression for the stability constant of the nickel–ammonia complex ion, stating the units.

ULSEB Winter 1985 (2)

Part D Organic chemistry

D1

(*a*) What is meant by *isomerism* in organic chemistry? Use compounds of the following formulae to illustrate *three* types of isomerism.

C_3H_6O $\quad C_3H_6O_3$ $\quad C_4H_8$ $\quad C_4H_{10}$

(*b*) State and explain the requirement for a compound to exist as a pair of optical isomers, paying particular attention to the geometry of the carbon atoms.

(*c*) When *cis*-but-2-endioic acid is heated it readily forms a cyclic anhydride whereas the *trans* isomer only forms the same anhydride when heated to a higher temperature and for a longer time.
(i) Draw the structure of the anhydride;
(ii) suggest why the *trans* isomer is reluctant to form the anhydride.

(*d*) Explain why one isomer of the compound shown below is *not* optically active.

$HO_2C.CHOH.CHOH.CO_2H$

SU 1986 (1)

D2

The members of the following pairs of isomeric compounds have different melting points or boiling points.

Indicate which member has the higher value and suggest reasons for the difference.

(*a*) [benzene ring with OH and NO$_2$ on adjacent carbons] and [benzene ring with OH and NO$_2$ para to each other]

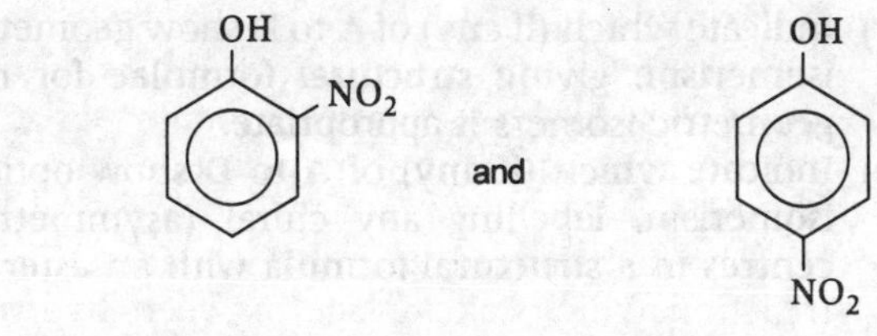

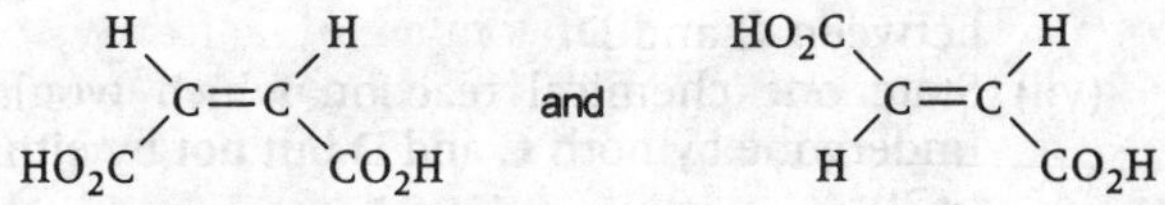

(*b*) H(HO$_2$C)C=C(H)(CO$_2$H) [both H on the same side] and (HO$_2$C)HC=CH(CO$_2$H) [H on opposite sides]

(*c*) $H_3C{-}C(CH_3)_2{-}OH$ and $CH_3CH_2CH_2CH_2OH$

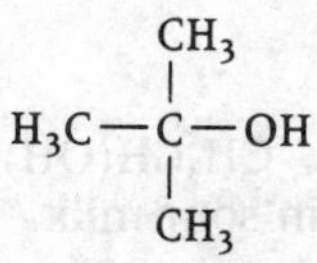

(*d*) CH_3CH_2OH and CH_3OCH_3

For each of (*b*), (*c*) and (*d*), discuss **one** other difference in **either physical or chemical behaviour.**

ULSEB 1985 (3)

D3

This question is largely concerned with tests on a test-tube scale, to distinguish between organic compounds.

As well as stating **what reactions occur**, it is essential to indicate what **experimental observations** should arise from them.

(*a*) Consider the compounds C_6H_5OH and $C_6H_5CH_2OH$; in the former the functional group is directly attached to the aromatic ring whereas in the latter the phenyl group acts merely as a substituent in an aliphatic hydroxy compound.
(i) State **two** chemical reactions which could be used to distinguish between the compounds.
(ii) State **one** further characteristic difference between these two compounds.

(*b*) Consider the compounds C_6H_5Cl and $C_6H_5CH_2Cl$; again, in the former, the functional group is directly attached to the aromatic ring whereas in the latter the phenyl group is simply a substituent in an aliphatic chloro compound.
State **one** chemical reaction to distinguish between the compounds.

(*c*) The following four compounds have the same molecular formula, C_4H_8O.
A $CH_3COCH_2CH_3$; **B** $CH_3CH_2CH_2CHO$;
C $CH_3CH{=}CHCH_2OH$; **D** $CH_2{=}CHCH(OH)CH_3$
(i) State **one** chemical reaction to distinguish between **A** and **B**.
(ii) Write down the structural formula of another aldehyde structurally isomeric with **B**.
(iii) Write down the structural formula of another primary alcohol structurally isomeric with **C**.

(iv) Indicate which (if any) of **A** to **D** show geometric isomerism, giving structural formulae for the geometric isomers if appropriate.
(v) Indicate which (if any) of **A** to **D** show optical isomerism, labelling any chiral (asymmetric) centres in a structural formula with an asterisk (*).
(vi) State **one** chemical reaction to distinguish between **C** and **D**.
(vii) State **one** chemical reaction which would be undergone by both **C** and **D** but **not** by either **A** or **B**.

WJEC 1990 (1) (slightly adapted)

D4
This question is about lactic acid, $CH_3CH(OH)CO_2H$, which occurs naturally, especially in sour milk.

(*a*) What is the systematic name for lactic acid?

(*b*) Draw this molecule in a three dimensional representation.

(*c*) What type of isomerism may be shown by this compound?

(*d*) (i) The compound can be synthesised from ethanol by the following route:

$$CH_3CH_2OH \xrightarrow{\textbf{A}} CH_3CHO \xrightarrow{\textbf{B}} CH_3CH(OH)CN \xrightarrow{\textbf{C}} CH_3CH(OH)CO_2H$$

Give the reagents and conditions for the stages **A**, **B** and **C**.
(ii) Explain how the lactic acid synthesised in this way might differ from lactic acid isolated from sour milk.

(*e*) A reaction of biological importance involving lactic acid is its formation from pyruvic acid,

$$CH_3-\underset{\underset{O}{\|}}{C}-CO_2H$$

This reaction occurs in muscle tissue during exercise, and is catalysed by the enzyme lactic acid dehydrogenase.
(i) What *type* of chemical reaction is this?
(ii) Suggest a reagent for carrying out this reaction in the laboratory.

ULSEB 1990 (1)

D5
Answer the following questions on the structural isomers of butanol by giving the appropriate letter(s).

$CH_3CH_2CH_2CH_2OH$ **A**	$CH_3CH(OH)CH_2CH_3$ **B**
$(CH_3)_3COH$ **C**	$(CH_3)_2CHCH_2OH$ **D**

(*a*) Which of the alcohols is/are (i) primary, (ii) secondary, (iii) tertiary?

(*b*) Which alcohol(s) contain(s) a chiral centre?

(*c*) Which alcohol(s) would react with acidified potassium dichromate(VI) to form (i) a ketone, (ii) a carboxylic acid, containing the **same number** of carbon atoms?

(*d*) (i) Describe how the Lucas test is performed.
(ii) State what result you would expect for the Lucas test with the alcohols you chose in (*a*)(i) and (*a*)(ii).

(*e*) Alcohols may be dehydrated to form alkenes.
(i) State the appropriate reaction conditions.
(ii) Give the letter(s) representing the alcohol(s) which would be dehydrated to form each of the following alkenes: but-1-ene, but-2ene, 2-methylpropene.

AEB 1986 (2) (slightly adapted)

D6
(*a*) Explain what is meant by *nucleophilic addition reaction* and *electrophilic addition reaction.* Illustrate your answer by reference to the mechanism of one reaction of the $>C{=}O$ group and one of the $>C{=}C<$ group.

(*b*) State the reagents and conditions which are suitable for the hydrogenation of
(i) the $>C{=}O$ group and
(ii) the $>C{=}C<$ group.

(*c*) Choose **two** other addition reactions of the $>C{=}O$ group and two of the $>C{=}C<$ group, and give in each case the reagents and the formula of the product obtained by reaction with a named carbonyl compound or alkene.

(*d*) Describe a simple test-tube reaction to show the presence of the $>C{=}C<$ group. You should name the reagent(s) and describe the observations which you would expect to make.

(*e*) Describe a simple test-tube reaction to distinguish between an aldehyde and ketone. You should name the reagent(s) and describe what you would expect to observe in each case, explaining the reason for the difference in behaviour.

AEB 1987 (1)

D7
(*a*) (i) Give the reagents and conditions required to convert benzene into chlorobenzene.
(ii) Write an equation for the conversion of benzene into chlorobenzene.

(*b*) The structures of two compounds containing chlorine attached to a benzene ring are given below.

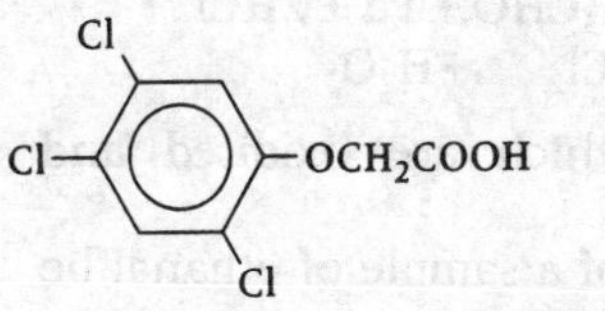

Cl-substituted structures: 2, 4, 5–T ($Cl_3C_6H_2OCH_2COOH$) and DDT ($(ClC_6H_4)_2CH{-}CCl_3$)

2, 4, 5–T

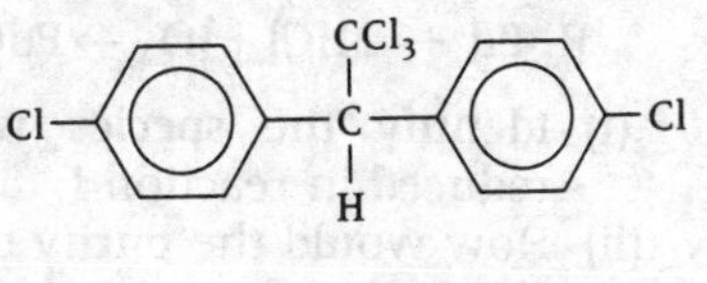

DDT

Although still used in the UK 2,4,5-T is banned in some countries because it may contain the toxic impurity dioxin.

The large-scale use of DDT is now banned in the UK.

(i) What is 2,4,5-T used for in the UK?
(ii) Describe what can happen if dioxin is accidently released into the air.
(iii) What was DDT once used for?
(iv) Why has DDT now been banned?

AEB 1989 (AS)

D8

This question is about benzoic acid.

(*a*) Give the reagent(s) and reaction conditions for each of the following methods of preparation of benzoic acid.

(i) $C_6H_5CH_3 \rightarrow C_6H_5CO_2H$
(ii) $C_6H_5CONH_2 \rightarrow C_6H_5CO_2H$
(iii) $C_6H_5CO_2C_2H_5 \rightarrow C_6H_5CO_2H$

Name the functional group of the reactant in (ii) and (iii).

(*b*) Benzoic acid dissolves readily in sodium hydroxide solution, but this solution turns milky when excess hydrochloric acid is added. Explain.

(*c*) The organic reactant in (*a*)(iii) was isotopically labelled at one of its oxygen atoms with oxygen–18. The resulting benzoic acid after reaction contained only normal oxygen–16. Write out the structure of the labelled reactant, showing the position of the label clearly. Write a mechanism for the reaction consistent with the benzoic acid being unlabelled.

ULSEB 1988 (2) (slightly adapted)

D9

This question is about organic compounds containing nitrogen.

(*a*) When phenylamine is treated with aqueous bromine a white precipitate is obtained.

(i) Write a balanced equation for this reaction, and give the structural formula of the organic product.
(ii) Classify this reaction mechanistically.
(iii) Give the formula of one other mono-substituted benzene compound that reacts in a similar way to phenylamine.

(*b*) Phenylamine can be prepared from nitrobenzene by treatment with tin/concentrated hydrochloric acid, addition of excess sodium hydroxide, followed by steam distillation.

(i) What is the role of the tin/concentrated hydrochloric acid?
(ii) What is the role of the sodium hydroxide?
(iii) Suggest an explanation why steam distillation is a sensible step before the final purification of the phenylamine.
(iv) Explain briefly how the resulting steam distillate (of water and phenylamine) would be treated to give pure phenylamine.
(v) Explain why freshly prepared phenylamine, which is colourless, darkens on standing.

(*c*) An orange-red dye can be synthesised by the following reaction sequence:

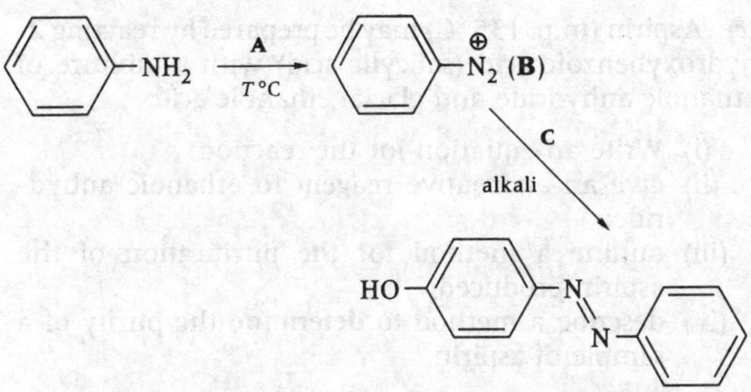

$C_6H_5{-}NH_2 \xrightarrow[T°C]{A} C_6H_5{-}N_2^{\oplus}$ (**B**) $\xrightarrow[\text{alkali}]{C}$ $HO{-}C_6H_4{-}N{=}N{-}C_6H_5$

(i) Identify **A** and **C**, and the appropriate temperature (T°C) at which the first reaction should be carried out.
(ii) The ion, **B**, undergoes a number of useful reactions. Give an equation for any one such reaction.

ULSEB 1987 (2)

D10

(*a*) Compare the base strengths of phenylamine, ammonia and 1-aminobutane, giving reasons for the differences.

(*b*) (i) State the products of the reaction of 1-aminobutane with nitrous acid.
(ii) Give the experimental conditions necessary for diazotisation of phenylamine and write an equation to show the formation of the diazonium ion.

(*c*) Phenylamine reacts with an acyl chloride, **A**, forming an organic derivative, **B**, of relative molecular mass 197.

(i) Identify **A** and **B** by giving their molecular and structural formulae. Explain your reasoning.
(ii) State the class of compound to which **B** belongs.
(iii) Suggest a suitable method of purification for compound **B**.
(iv) If 5.0 g phenylamine gave 8.0 g **B** calculate the percentage yield of **B**.

AEB 1987 (1)

D11

Aspirin and paracetamol are substances which are taken to relieve pain: they are said to be analgesics. Although their action in the body is complex, their structures are relatively simple:

CO_2H $O.CO.CH_3$

aspirin

HO $NH.CO.CH_3$

paracetamol

(*a*) *Name* the functional groups in each compound (excluding the benzene ring itself).

(*b*) Draw the *full* structures of the organic products formed when each compound is separately treated with hot aqueous sodium hydroxide.

(*c*) Aspirin (m.p. 135 °C) may be prepared by reacting 2-hydroxybenzoic acid (salicylic acid) with a mixture of ethanoic anhydride and glacial ethanoic acid.

(i) Write an equation for the reaction;
(ii) give an alternative reagent to ethanoic anhydride;
(iii) outline a method for the purification of the aspirin produced;
(iv) describe a method to determine the purity of a sample of aspirin.

(*d*) A container of aspirin tablets which has been exposed previously to damp air will have the pungent smell of vinegar when opened again. Explain this phenomenon and write an equation for the appropriate reaction.

SU 1986 (2)

D12

A sample of ethanal can be prepared in the laboratory as follows:

'To 12 cm³ water in a flask, 4 cm³ of concentrated sulphuric acid is slowly added with mixing and the apparatus is set up for distillation. 8 cm³ of ethanol is added to a solution containing 10 g sodium dichromate in 10 cm³ of water. This mixture is then poured into a dropping funnel which is part of the apparatus. The acid is then heated and the mixture containing the ethanol is slowly added so that the acid remains at its boiling point and an aqueous solution of the product distils over. The distillate is re-distilled and the fraction boiling between 20° and 23 °C is collected.'

(*a*) Draw carefully a fully labelled diagram of the apparatus required for the initial stage of this preparation.

(*b*) (i) Explain why the above experimental set-up must be used rather than *reflux* followed by distillation.
(ii) Give reasons for the use of heat in the initial stage.

(*c*) If the density of ethanol is $0.79\ g\ cm^{-3}$, calculate the maximum theoretical yield of ethanal in grams, stating any assumptions you make. (H = 1; C = 12; O = 16)

(*d*) Ethanol may be produced industrially from ethene by the Wacker process. The essential reactions are summarised below:

$$\text{I. } C_2H_4 + PdCl_2 + H_2O \rightarrow CH_3CHO + Pd + 2HCl$$
$$\text{II. } Pd + 2HCl + \tfrac{1}{2}O_2 \rightarrow PdCl_2 + H_2O$$

(i) Identify the species which are oxidised and reduced in reaction I.
(ii) How would the purity of a sample of ethanal be checked?

(*e*) Devise a scheme for making ethyl ethanoate using ethanal as the only organic starting material. State reagents and conditions.

SU 1985 (2)

D13

The preparation of a pure sample of benzoic acid by the reaction:

$$C_6H_5COOC_2H_5(l) + NaOH(aq) \rightarrow C_6H_5COO^-(aq) + C_2H_5OH(aq)$$

involves the following stages.

Stage I
Place 5 cm³ of ethyl benzoate in a 100 cm³ round bottomed flask and add 40 cm³ of aqueous sodium hydroxide of concentration $2\ mol\ dm^{-3}$. Reflux gently until the last signs of the ester layer have disappeared.

Stage II
Arrange the apparatus for distillation and collect about 10 cm³ of distillate.

Stage III
Cool the residue left in the distillation flask and add slowly, with stirring, 20 cm³ of concentrated hydrochloric acid. Cool the flask and filter off the precipitated crystals of benzoic acid. Wash the crystals with a little distilled water.

Stage IV
Recrystallise the benzoic acid from distilled water. Filter, wash, dry and weigh the crystals.

Stage V
Measure the melting point of your sample of benzoic acid. Mix a small sample of your crystals with an equal volume of a pure sample of benzoic acid. Determine the melting point of the mixture.

Stage VI
To determine the purity of your benzoic acid crystals, weigh accurately into a conical flask 0.30 g of the crystals. Pipette 50 cm³ of aqueous sodium hydroxide of concentration $0.100\ mol\ dm^{-3}$ into the flask and titrate the mixture with aqueous hydrochloric acid of concentration $0.100\ mol\ dm^{-3}$ using phenolphthalein indicator. Repeat. For each determination calculate the percentage of benzoic acid in your crystals.

Answer the following questions based upon this method.

(*a*) Why is a reflux condenser necessary when heating the ethyl benzoate with the sodium hydroxide solution?

(*b*) Assuming that the density of ethyl benzoate is $1.01\ g\ cm^{-3}$ and that of pure ethanol is $0.79\ g\ cm^{-3}$, calculate the theoretical volume of ethanol that should have been formed. In the light of your calculation suggest a reason for the instruction to collect 10 cm^3 of distillate.

(*c*) The hydrolysis of ethyl benzoate in acidic solution reaches equilibrium. Explain why the conversion of ethyl benzoate goes to completion in alkaline solution.

(*d*) Explain in terms of structure and bonding why sodium benzoate is soluble in cold water whilst benzoic acid is relatively insoluble.

(*e*) The prepared sample of crystals was found to melt over the range 120.5–121.5 °C and the melting point range of the sample of the crystals mixed with pure benzoic acid was 120–121 °C. Explain carefully the information that these data give.

(*f*) Explain briefly why benzoic acid can be purified by recrystallisation from hot water. Suggest a reason why methanol would not be suitable.

(*g*) In the determination of the purity, 0.300 g of a sample of the crystals were used and 25.50 cm^3 of the hydrochloric acid were required.
Calculate the percentage purity of the sample.

AEB 1987 (1)

D14

2-aminopropanoic acid is an amino acid.
It has the following formula.

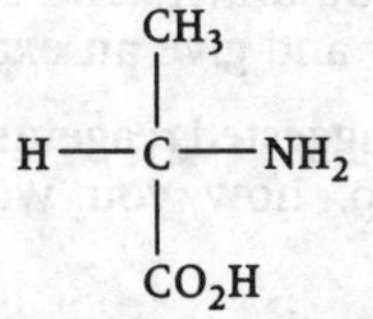

CH₃
H—C—NH₂
CO₂H

Amino acids are soluble in water since they exist as zwitterions and also form hydrogen bonds with water molecules.

(*a*) (i) Draw the zwitterionic form of 2-aminopropanoic acid.
(ii) Draw diagrams to show how the carboxylic acid and the amino groups of 2-aminopropanoic acid form hydrogen bonds with water.

(*b*) The scheme below shows a suggested reaction scheme for the synthesis of 2-aminopropanoic acid from 2-hydroxypropanoic acid.

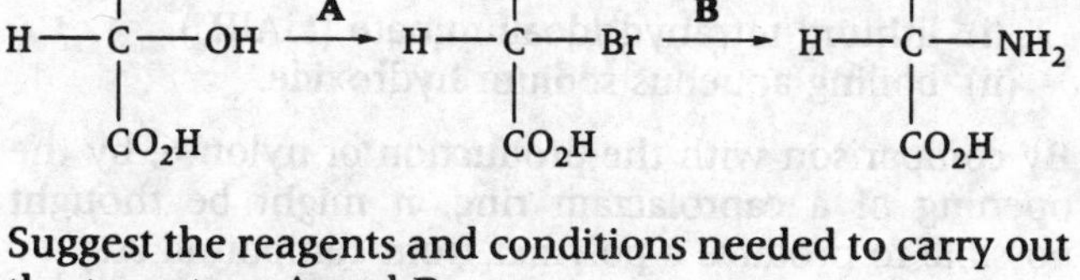

CH₃
H—C—OH
CO₂H
A
CH₃
H—C—Br
CO₂H
B
CH₃
H—C—NH₂
CO₂H

Suggest the reagents and conditions needed to carry out the two steps **A** and **B**.

UCLES 1990 (2) (slightly adapted)

D15

(*a*) Explain the meanings of the following terms as applied to proteins:

(i) the peptide bond,
(ii) an amino acid residue,
(iii) primary structure,
(iv) the disulphide link.

(*b*) The technique of electrophoresis involves applying a potential difference across a starch gel. If the amino acid glycine is dissolved in the gel and a potential applied, it is observed that

(i) in strongly acidic solution the amino acid moves towards the cathode,
(ii) in strongly alkaline solution the amino acid moves towards the anode,
(iii) at pH = 6 the glycine will not move in either direction.

Explain these observations.

(*c*) The determination of the protein content of food is an important step in judging the quality of the food. In such an experiment 25 g of a food sample was decomposed by heating with hot concentrated sulphuric acid to convert all the nitrogen from proteins into ammonium sulphate. The resulting solution was treated with sodium hydroxide solution which liberated sufficient ammonia gas to neutralise 10 cm^3 of 0.1 M hydrochloric acid.

(i) Calculate the percentage of nitrogen in the food.
(ii) What other factors would you consider to be important in deciding on the quality of food protein?

UCLES 1989 (AS2)

D16

When monochromatic, plane-polarised light is passed through an aqueous solution of a sugar the angle of rotation of the light is dependent upon the structure of the molecule. A standard rotation can be measured which differs from molecule to molecule. Chiral enantiomers rotate the light in equal but opposite directions (indicated by + and −). The specific rotations of three sugars (measured at the same concentration and under the same conditions) are as shown below:

Glucose

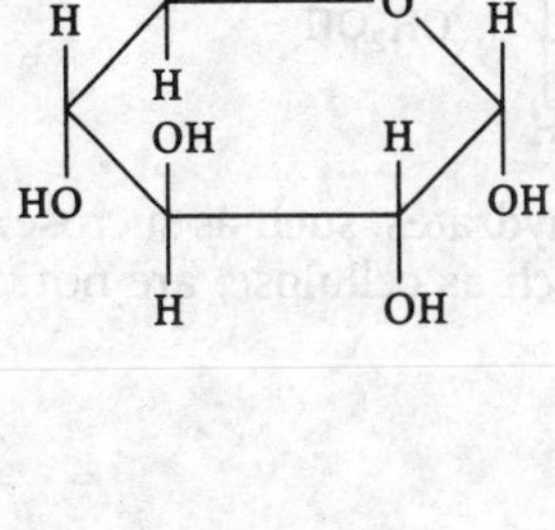

CH₂OH
O
H
H
H
OH
H
HO
OH
H
OH

specific rotation = +53°

Maltose

specific rotation = +137°

Sucrose

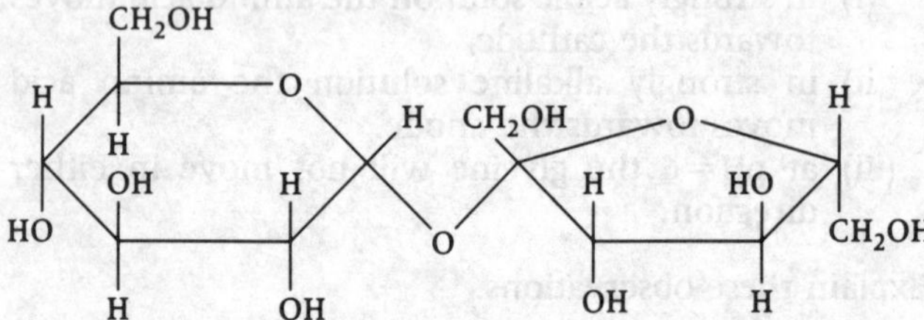

specific rotation = +67°

The following solutions were prepared under the same conditions, left for some time and their angles of rotation of polarised light measured:

Solution	Angle of rotation of light
25 cm^3 glucose (initial reading)	+53°
25 cm^3 glucose + 25 cm^3 water (final reading)	+26.6°
25 cm^3 maltose (initial reading)	+137°
25 cm^3 maltose + 25 cm^3 water containing the enzyme maltase (final reading)	+53°
25 cm^3 sucrose (initial reading)	+67°
25 cm^3 sucrose + 25 cm^3 water containing the enzyme sucrase (final reading)	−20°

(*a*) What do you understand by the term *enantiomer*?

(*b*) Draw a diagram to represent the straight-chain form of glucose.

(*c*) (i) Why did the angle of rotation for glucose change from +53 °C to +26.5 °C when diluted with an equal quantity of water?
(ii) What do you think happened to the maltose when treated with the enzyme maltase?
(iii) Calculate the specific rotation of fructose.

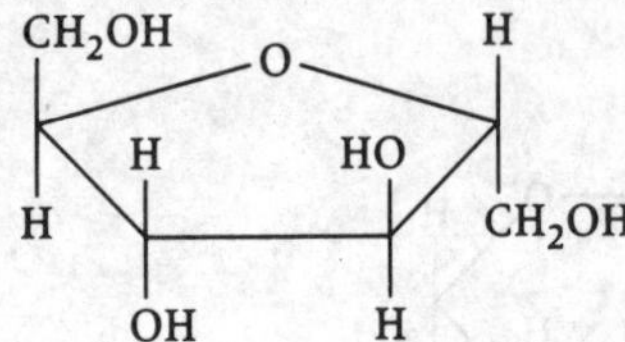

(*d*) Why is it that some carbohydrates, such as sucrose, are useful foods but others, such as cellulose, are not?

UCLES 1989 (AS2)

D17

(*a*) Draw as many conclusions as you can about the identity of each of the compounds **A** to **D**, using the information given below and giving your reasoning in each case.

(i) **A** ($C_6H_{12}O$) is a chiral molecule produced by the oxidation of an alcohol by boiling with acidified potassium dichromate(VI) solution for a considerable time.
(ii) **B** ($C_{10}H_{20}O_2$), when boiled with dilute sulphuric acid for some time produces two compounds, $C_2H_4O_2$ and $C_8H_{18}O$, the first one of which smells of vinegar whereas the second has little noticeable odour.
(iii) **C** (C_4H_8) can be produced in two different isomeric forms, both of which react with hydrogen to give butane.
(iv) **D** ($C_5H_{12}O$) is very resistant to oxidation but will react with phosphorus(V) chloride to give $C_5H_{11}Cl$.

(*b*) (i) One of the compounds **A** to **D** smells of oranges and is used in the preparation of perfumes and flavourings for food. Which one?
(ii) One of the compounds **A** to **D** could be used as the starting material for the manufacture of a plastic. Which one?

UCLES 1990 (AS1)

D18

(*a*) Explain what you understand by the terms *chirality* and *functional group* and give an example in each case.

(*b*) Outline, with suggested reagents and suitable conditions for each step, how you would carry out the conversion.

$$CH_3CH_2OH \rightarrow CH_3COOCH_2CH_3$$

(*c*) Consider the compound **A** whose structural formula is likely to be unfamiliar to you but which is similar to caprolactam from which nylon 6 is made.

From your knowledge of organic chemistry suggest the most likely organic product of the reaction of **A** with

(i) lithium tetrahydridoaluminate ($LiAlH_4$).
(ii) boiling aqueous sodium hydroxide.

By comparison with the production of nylon 6, by the opening of a caprolactam ring, it might be thought possible to produce a polymer from compound **A**.

(iii) Sketch the likely polymer unit that would be formed in such a reaction.

(*d*) Three alcohols, all $C_4H_{10}O$, were separately heated with acidified potassium dichromate(VI) solution. Draw the structural formulae of the organic products in each case.

UCLES 1989 (AS2)

D19

(*a*) Draw the full structural formula of **E** 4-phenylbut-1-ene. Indicate on your diagram:

(i) one carbon–carbon bond which has length 154 nm;
(ii) one carbon–carbon bond which has length 139 nm;
(iii) one carbon–carbon bond which has length 133 nm.

(*b*) Using your knowledge of simple alkenes and arenes, predict equations and give the structural formulae of the products obtained when **E** reacts with

(i) hydrogen bromide;
(ii) bromine water;
(iii) hydrogen with a palladium or platinum catalyst at room temperature and pressure;
(iv) hydrogen with a nickel catalyst at high temperature and pressure.

(*c*) Illustrate the meaning of the term *optical isomerism*, using one of the products of the reactions in part (*b*) above.

UODLE 1987 (3)

D20

Warfarin is used to destroy rodents. The full structural formula of warfarin is shown below.

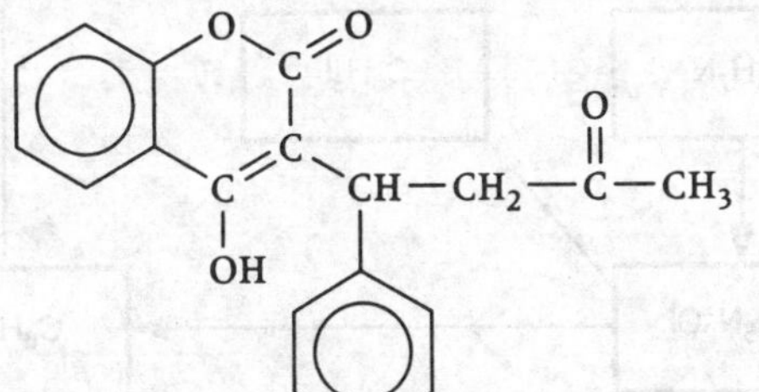

O C=O C=C CH—CH₂—C—CH₃ O OH

(*a*) Warfarin gives a positive tri-iodomethane (iodoform) test.

(i) What are the reagents and conditions used for the tri-iodomethane test?
(ii) Circle on a copy of the formula which part of the warfarin molecule gives the tri-iodomethane.

(*b*) Indicate with an arrow on your copy of the formula the part of the warfarin molecule which reacts with 2,4-dinitrophenylhydrazine.

(*c*) State and explain whether warfarin would give a positive reaction with $[Ag(NH_3)_2]^+$ or an alkaline Cu^{2+} complex (Fehling's solution).

(*d*) Warfarin reacts with aqueous sodium hydroxide.

(i) Name the group in warfarin which is attacked by the hydroxide ion.
(ii) Draw the structure of the product formed by this reaction.

(*e*) Warfarin reacts with phosphorus pentachloride.

(i) What gas will be produced?
(ii) Without drawing the whole warfarin molecule, give the formula of the new organic group produced.

UCLES 1989 (2)

D21

Answer EITHER A or B.

EITHER

A.

(*a*) Describe simple chemical tests that would enable you to distinguish between the compounds in each of the pairs below. You should describe the test and indicte the result on both compounds. When one of the compounds does not react, say so.

(i) Pentan-2-one, $CH_3COCH_2CH_2CH_3$, and pentan-3-one, $CH_3CH_2COCH_2CH_3$
(ii) Butan-1-ol, $CH_3CH_2CH_2CH_2OH$, and butan-2-ol, $CH_3CH_2CH(OH)CH_3$
(iii) Ethylamine, $C_2H_5NH_2$, and propanamide, $C_2H_5CONH_2$.

(*b*) Using no *organic* compounds other than the one listed, give syntheses, indicating reagents and essential reaction conditions, for the preparation of

(i) propanoic acid, $CH_3CH_2CO_2H$, from ethanol, CH_3CH_2OH.
(ii) phenylmethyl benzoate, $C_6H_5CO_2CH_2C_6H_5$ from methylbenzene, $C_6H_5CH_3$.

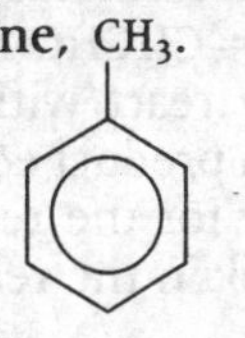

OR

B.

State Raoult's Law as it applies to mixtures of methanol (b.pt. 64 °C) and ethanol (b.pt. 78 °C) which behave ideally, and explain the reasons for this ideal behaviour.

Give a fully labelled diagram showing the relationship between boiling temperature and composition for mixtures of methanol and ethanol.

Give full practical details for the fractional distillation in the laboratory of a mixture of methanol and ethanol in which the mole fraction of methanol is 0.2 and, by reference to your temperature-composition diagram, explain the principles of the process.

At a particular temperature, the vapour pressures of pure methanol and pure ethanol are 81 mm Hg and 45 mm Hg, respectively. Calculate the partial pressure of each component above a mixture of 64 g of methanol and 46 g of ethanol at this temperature.

Mixtures of benzene (b.pt. 80 °C) and ethanol show a positive deviation from Raoult's Law. Give a fully labelled temperature–composition diagram for such mixtures and state and explain what happens when benzene is added to ethanol.

(Relative atomic masses: H = 1, C = 12, O = 16.)

ULSEB 1990 (2)

D22

A test tube contains a liquid, **X**, which is known to be one of the substances ethanal, methanal, or propanone.

(*a*) Describe chemical tests, excluding the one in part (*b*) below, which you would carry out on **X** to establish its identity. Your answer must include the chemical names of the reagents, balanced equations, and the observations in each case.

(*b*) Write an equation for the reaction between propanone and hydroxylamine, NH_2OH, drawing the *full* structural formula of the organic product. State the type of reaction which takes place.

(*c*) Ethanal will react according to the following scheme:

$$2CH_3CHO \xrightarrow{\text{dil.NaOH}} CH_3\overset{H}{\underset{OH}{C}}CH_2CHO \quad \text{'aldol'}$$

$$\downarrow \text{heat}$$

$$CH_3\overset{H}{C}{=}CHCHO$$

(i) What type of reaction occurs when 'aldol' is heated?

(ii) Write the structural formulae of the geometrical isomers of $CH_3CH = CHCHO$ and name them.

(iii) Methanal does *not* react with aqueous sodium hydroxide to give a product equivalent to 'aldol'. Write an equation for the reaction which does take place and explain the reaction type.

SU 1985 (1)

D23

Compound **C** is readily hydrolysed by moist air giving ethanoic acid and a gas **F** which gives dense white fumes with concentrated aqueous ammonia. Compound **C** reacts vigorously with an amine **D**, which is a dense oily liquid, forming a white solid **E** and also evolving gas **F**. If **D** is treated at between 5 and 10 °C with aqueous sodium nitrite and excess hydrochloric acid, and the mixture produced is poured into hot water, then phenol is formed.

(*a*) Give equations for the:

(i) hydrolysis of **C**, (ii) reaction of **C** with **D**, (iii) reaction of **F** with ammonia.

(*b*) Name **C** and **D**.

(*c*) (i) Give the structural formula of **E**.

(ii) Ring the grouping in the structural formula of **E** which is also present in a naturally occurring polymer.

(iii) Name this type of natural polymer

(*d*) If another amine **G** were treated with **C**, the solid product could be used to assist in identification of **G**.

(i) State how the solid product could be purified.

(ii) Explain how you could use this product to assist in identification of **G**.

(iii) Suggest a test whereby the identity of **G** could be confirmed.

(*e*) (i) Give the formula of the organic compound formed initially by reacting the amine **D** with aqueous sodium nitrite and excess hydrochloric acid.

(ii) Write an equation for a reaction of this compound (other than its conversion to phenol).

AEB Winter 1986 (2)

D24

Name and write structures for the compounds **A** to **H** in the reaction scheme below and give the reagents and conditions necessary to bring about each of the changes.

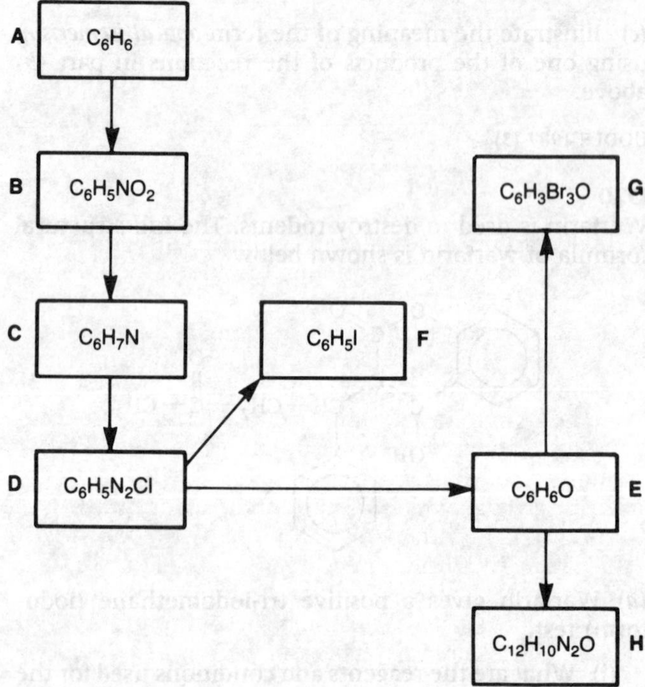

AEB 1988 (1)

D25

(*a*) An alcohol has the molecular formula C_4H_7OH. Oxidation of this alcohol gives a ketone. Ozonolysis of this alcohol gives methanal as one of the products.

Giving your reasoning in full, deduce the structural formula for this alcohol and predict whether it will be optically active.

(*b*) Outline the stages by which ethanal may be converted into 2-oxopropanoic acid (pyruvic acid) CH_3COCO_2H. Full practical details are not required, although you should specify reagents and any important conditions.

(*c*) A gaseous hydrocarbon **X** can exist as geometric isomers. 30 cm^3 of gaseous **X** were exploded with 200 cm^3 of oxygen. The residual gases were cooled to 25 °C and found to occupy 140 cm^3. After treatment with aqueous sodium hydroxide, the final volume of gas remaining was 20 cm^3. Assuming that all volumes were measured at 25 °C and the same pressure, deduce the molecular and structural formulae of hydrocarbon **X**.

OCSEB 1990 (3,4,5)

D26

A compound **P** contains C, 35.0%; H, 6.60%; Br, 58.4%, by mass. Treatment of **P** with warm aqueous sodium hydroxide gives **Q**, which on oxidation gives **R**. **R** readily forms a 2,4-dinitrophenylhydrazone, and both **Q** and **R** on treatment with iodine and alkali form triiodomethane. When **P** is treated with alcoholic sodium hydroxide it forms three isomeric alkenes **V**, **W** and **X**, each of which, on treatment with HBr, is converted back to **P**.

Identify the compounds **P**, **Q**, **R**, **V**, **W** and **X**, explaining your reasoning. Discuss the isomerism shown by the alkenes.

Suggest a synthesis for a compound of formula $C_5H_{10}O_2$ from **P**.

ULSEB 1986 (3)

D27

A hydrocarbon **F** reacts with chlorine under suitable conditions to give **G**. **G** contains 14.29% carbon, 1.19% hydrogen and 84.52% chlorine.

Careful hydrolysis of **G** with aqueous sodium hydroxide gives **H**. **H** reacts with ammoniacal silver nitrate to give silver and ammonium ethanedioate.

Addition of hydrogen chloride to **F** in the presence of aqueous mercury(II) chloride gives a well-known monomer, **J**. Further reaction of **J** with hydrogen chloride gives **K**, which has the empirical formula CH_2Cl. Hydrolysis of **K** with aqueous sodium hydroxide gives **L**, which reacts with ammoniacal silver nitrate to give silver and a salt, **M**.

Deduce the structural formulae of compounds **F**, **G**, **H**, **J**, **K**, **L** and **M**, and explain your reasoning.

UODLE 1987 (3)

D28

(*a*) An organic compound contains, by mass, 55.80% carbon, 7.04% hydrogen, and 37.16% oxygen. On treatment with sodium hydrogencarbonate solution it liberates carbon dioxide. It also undergoes an addition reaction with bromine in a 1:1 molar ratio whereby 1.00 g of the compound reacts with 1.856 g of bromine. From the above information

(i) calculate the empirical formula of the compound,
(ii) calculate the relative molecular mass of the compound,
(iii) write down molecular formulae for all of the isomeric structures which are consistent with these data,
(iv) indicate which (if any) of them will show geometric isomerism.

[A_r(H) = 1.01; A_r(C) = 12.01;
A_r(O) = 16.00; A_r(Br) = 79.90.]

(*b*) On hydrogenation one of the isomers (compound **A**) in (*a*)(iii) above is converted into a product **B**, but all of the other isomers are converted on hydrogenation into another compound, **C** which is *not* the same as compound **B**. From this information identify and write down structures for compounds **A**, **B** and **C**.

(*c*) Considering now all of the structural isomers in (*a*)(iii) above,

(i) write down structural formulae for each of the compounds which may be formed by their addition reactions with bromine,
(ii) write down structural formulae for all of the possible compounds which might be formed by their addition reactions with hydrogen bromide,
(iii) indicate the presence of any chiral centres in the products formed in (*c*)(i) and (ii) above by appending asterisks to the appropriate carbon atoms,
(iv) *briefly* describe how the racemate corresponding to any one of the above structures possessing chiral centres might be resolved into its optically active isomers.

WJEC 1989 (2)

D29

A is phenylamine (aniline) $C_6H_5NH_2$, a typical aromatic amine with the $-NH_2$ group directly attached to the ring. **B** is (phenylmethyl) amine, $C_6H_5CH_2NH_2$, which may be considered to have the properties of an aliphatic amine with the phenyl group as a substituent.

(*a*) Calculate the percentage by mass of C, H and N in both **A** and **B**.

[A_r(C) = 12.01, A_r(H) = 1.01, A_r(N) = 14.01.]

Comment on the usefulness of an elemental analysis giving C = 78.10%, H = 8.00% and N = 13.9% for distinguishing between **A** and **B**.

(*b*) (i) Outline the preparation of
1. **A** from nitrobenzene, $C_6H_5NO_2$
and
2. **B** from (phenylmethyl) bromide, $C_6H_5CH_2Br$

(ii) Give the conditions under which both **A** and **B** may be acylated, together with formulae for the acylating agent and for the products formed.

(*c*) (i) State the reagents and conditions required for the conversion of **A** to a diazonium salt. Give one example of an azo coupling reaction for the diazonium salt and explain the significance of this reaction for the dyestuff industry.

(ii) How might the reaction in (*c*)(i) above be used to distinguish between **A** and **B**?

(*d*) The dissociation constant, K_b, for compound **B** is 10^{-5} mol dm^{-3}. If an aqueous solution of **B** is titrated against dilute hydrochloric acid, state whether the pH at the end-point would be 7, less than 7, or greater than 7. State therefore which of the following indicators you would use to determine the end-point of the titration,

bromophenol blue (pH range 3.0–4.6),
bromothymol blue (pH range 6.2–7.6),
phenolphthalein (pH range 8.0–10.0).

WJEC 1990 (2)

D30

(*a*) (i) An organic compound, **A**, containing the elements carbon, hydrogen, oxygen and chlorine gave a mass spectrum in which the most prominent peaks corresponded to relative molecular masses of 92 and 94 in a 3:1 ratio. Hydrolysis of **A** produced a compound **B**. After isolation and purification of **B** it was found that:

(1) it did not contain chlorine;
(2) it reacted with sodium hydrogencarbonate to produce carbon dioxide;
(3) on heating with dry soda lime a gas, **C**, was produced which burned with a non-luminous flame.

Name the functional group in **B** which can be deduced from this information, giving a brief explanation.

(ii) When 0.265 g of compound **A** was hydrolysed, the chloride ion released required 52.09 cm^3 of 0.055 mol dm^{-3} aqueous silver nitrate solution for complete reaction. Calculate the number of chlorine atoms present in a molecule of **A** and identify **A**.

[A_r(H) = 1.0; A_r(C) = 12.0; A_r(O) = 16.0; A_r(Cl) = 35.5; A_r(Ag) = 107.9.]

WJEC 1988 (1)

D31

(*a*) (i) State which molecule(s) in the following list show(s) optical activity:

A HOOCCH=CHCOOH
B CFClBrH
C $CH_3CH(OH)COOH$
D $CH_3CH(Br)CH_3$

(ii) Describe briefly how a polarimeter works and how it is used to detect optical activity.

(*b*) (i) Write down the systematic name of the following molecule:

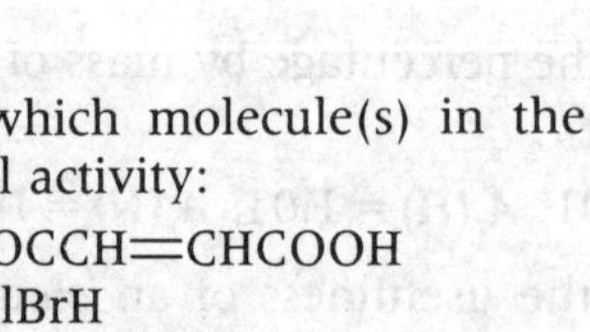

$$CH_3CH_2\overset{\overset{\displaystyle CH_3}{|}}{C}H\underset{\underset{\displaystyle CH_2CH_3}{|}}{C}HCH_2CH_2CH_3$$

(ii) Draw a full structural formula for *cis*-but-2-ene.

(*c*) A hydrocarbon which is not a ring compound contains 85.7% carbon and 14.3% hydrogen by mass. The main peaks in its mass spectrum, in order of decreasing height, are as follows:

m/e 56; 29; 27; 15.

(i) Calculate the empirical formula of the compound.

[A_r(H) = 1; A_r(C) = 12.]

(ii) Calculate the molecular formula of the compound.

(iii) Deduce the structure of the compound, giving your reasons, and draw the structure below.

(*d*) Give **one** example of each of the following:

(i) a free radical;
(ii) an electrophile;
(iii) a nucleophile;
(iv) heterolytic bond fission;
(v) an elimination reaction.

(*e*) Distinguish between *addition polymerisation* and *condensation polymerisation*. Give **one** example of a single addition step for **each** type of polymerisation.

WJEC 1988 (1)

D32

Two organic compounds, **A** and **B**, are isomers with the composition by mass of carbon, 70.5%; hydrogen, 5.9%; oxygen, 23.6%. **A** is moderately soluble in water and **B** is a pleasant-smelling liquid. Their mass spectra are shown below.

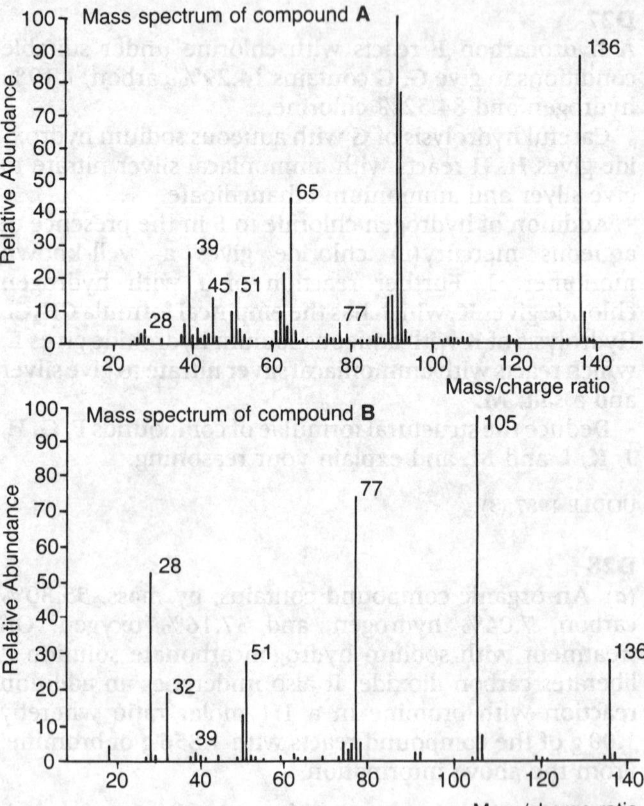

(*a*) (i) What is the empirical formula of **A** and **B**? (Relative atomic masses: C = 12, O = 16, H = 1)
(ii) What is the molecular formula of **A** and **B**? Justify your answer.

(*b*) Give the formulae of the molecular fragments corresponding to the following peaks:
Mass/charge ratio: 136; 105; 91; 77.

(*c*) What structural formulae would you predict for **A** and **B**?

(*d*) Describe **two** tests or chemical reactions in which the behaviour of **A** and **B** would differ.

N 1984 (3) (slightly adapted)

D33

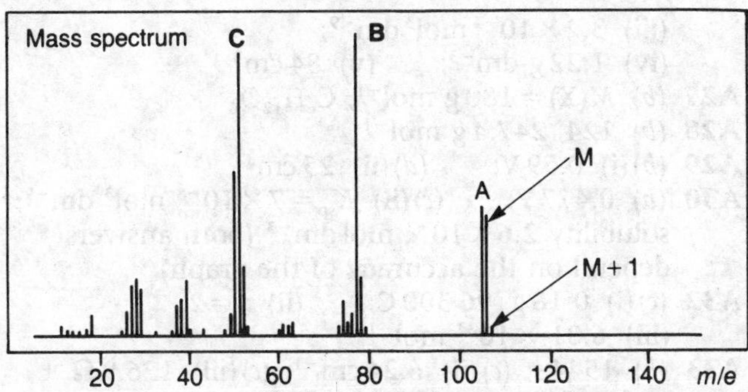

The mass spectrum above was obtained from a compound **S** which contains the elements carbon, hydrogen and oxygen only. The relative heights of the major peaks are:

M + 1	M	A	B	C
3	39	42	100	92

(*a*) Show by calculation how many carbon atoms are likely to be present in a molecule of **S**.

(*b*) What fragments have been lost in order to produce each of the following?

(i) A from M; (ii) B from A; (iii) C from B.

(*c*)

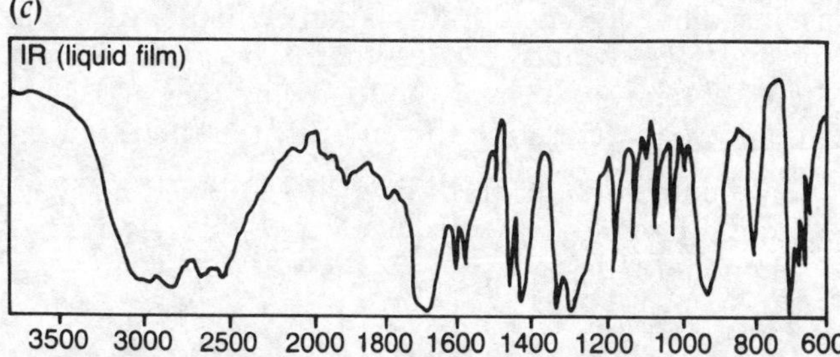

The infra-red spectrum above is of **T**, the product obtained when **S** is oxidised. What functional groups are responsible for the peaks labelled X and Y?

(*d*) Heating **T** with soda lime yields a liquid, **U**, the infra-red spectrum of which is shown below.

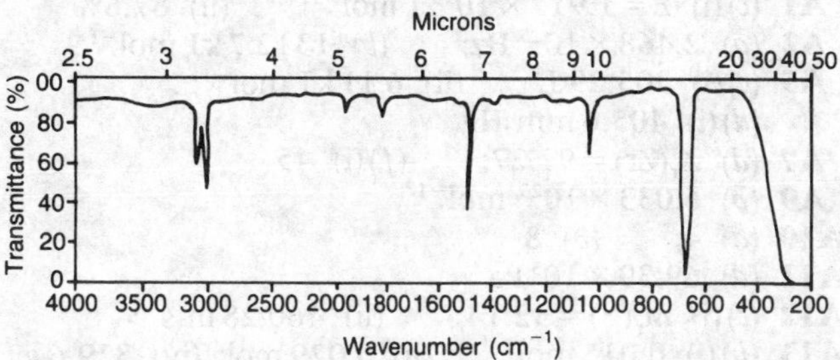

Deduce the identity of the three compounds **S**, **T** and **U**.

UCLES Winter 1987 (2) (slightly adapted)

Answers to examination questions

Answers are only given for those parts of questions which have a numerical answer.

Part A Physical chemistry

A1 (*c*)(i) $E = 1.917 \times 10^{13}$ J mol^{-1}; (ii) 87.6%
A2 (*a*) 2.468×10^{15} Hz; (*b*) 1312.7 kJ mol^{-1}
A5 (*c*)(i) 305.29 J; (ii) 6.11 kJ mol^{-1}; (*d*)(i) 405.6 mm Hg
A7 (*d*) $A_r(Zr) = 91.27$; (*f*)(i) 45
A9 (*b*) 6.033×10^{23} mol^{-1}
A10 (*a*) 4; (*b*) 8
A11 (*d*) 69.39×10^5 Pa
A12 (*c*)(i) $M_r(E) = 32.14$; (ii) 460.28 m s^{-1}
A13 (*b*)(i) 0.015 mol; (ii) 0.029 mol; (iv) 319.6 g
A14 (*a*) 3 M; (*b*) 3.3 cm^3
A15 (*c*)(i) 1672 J; (ii) −66.88 kJ mol^{-1}; (*d*) −78.18 kJ mol^{-1}
A16 (*b*)(i) 84.5 kJ; (ii) −1690 kJ mol^{-1}; (*c*) +3918.7 kJ mol^{-1}; (*d*) +3919 kJ mol^{-1}
A17 (i) +376 kJ mol^{-1}
A18 (i) 0.2357, 0.3821, 0.3821; (ii) 0.5421×10^5 Pa, 0.8788×10^5 Pa, 0.8788×10^5 Pa; (iii) 1.425×10^5 Pa
A19 (*a*)(ii) +9.5 kJ mol^{-1}; (*b*)(iii) $K_c = 0.24$; (*c*) $K_p = 0.014$
A20 (ii) 116.1:1; 114:1; 118:1
A23 (*a*) 50.8 g; (*c*)(i) 14.27 g; (ii) 55.33 g; (*d*) 68 °C; (*e*) 100% KIO_3
A24 (*c*) 0.714; (*d*)(i) 132 °C; 93 °C; (ii) 0.25; (*e*)(ii) 4
A26 (*c*)(i) 0.043 mol dm^{-3}; (ii) 0.086 mol dm^{-3}; (iii) 3.2×10^{-4} mol^3 dm^{-9}; (iv) 1.22 g dm^{-3}; (v) 84 cm^3
A27 (*b*) $M(X) = 180$ g mol^{-1}, $C_6H_{12}O_6$
A28 (*b*) 124, 247.4 g mol^{-1}
A29 (*b*)(i) 0.59 V; (*d*)(ii) 25 cm^3
A30 (*b*) 0.477 V; (*c*)(ii) $K_{sp} = 7 \times 10^{-8}$ mol^3 dm^{-9}; solubility 2.6×10^{-3} mol dm^{-3} (both answers depend on the accuracy of the graph)
A32 (*c*)(i) 0.18 g, 96 300 C; (ii) $x = 2$; (iii) 6.01×10^{23} mol^{-1}
A33 (*b*) 1544 s; (*c*)(ii) 6.24 cm^{-1}; (*c*)(iii) 126.9 Ω^{-1} cm^2 mol^{-1}; (*d*) 238.3 Ω^{-1} cm^2 mol^{-1}
A34 (*d*)(i) 2.87; (ii) 4.44
A35 (*a*)(i) 1.3; (ii) 12.7; (iii) 2.99
A36 (*b*)(i) 0.241 mol; (iii) 0.6×10^4 s (answer depends on the accuracy of the graph); (iv) 1st order; (v) 0.3×10^{-5} mol dm^{-3} s^{-1} (answer depends on the accuracy of the graph); (vi) 1.3×10^{-5} s^{-1} (answer depends on the accuracy of the graph)
A37 (*b*)(i) 1,2,0; (iii) 2; 1.25 mol^{-1} dm^3 s^{-1}
A38 (*b*) 2; (*c*) 1; (*d*) N^{-2} m^4 s^{-1}; (*e*) 245.1 kJ mol^{-1}

Part B Industrial chemistry

B7 (*b*)(ii) 5×10^{-2} mol; (iii) 2.2×10^{-2} mol; (iv) 2.8×10^{-2} mol; (v) 21.2%
B9 (*k*) 8.8 kPa
B10 (*c*) 90 kmol ethene unreacted; 9.4 kmol ester made

Part C Inorganic chemistry

C5 (*c*) $MgBa(CO_3)_2$

C14 (*a*) $1.52 \times 10^{-22}\ mol\ dm^{-3}\ s^{-1}$;
(*b*) (i) 20 °C; (ii) $9 \times 10^{-3}\ mol\ dm^{-3}$

C16 (*c*) 49, 51: $^{14}N^{35}Cl$, $^{14}N^{37}Cl$; 84, 86, 88: $^{14}N^{35}Cl_2$, $^{14}N^{35}Cl^{37}Cl$, $^{14}N^{37}Cl_2$; 119, 121, 123, 125: $^{14}N^{35}Cl_3$, $^{14}N^{35}Cl_2{}^{37}Cl$, $^{14}N^{35}Cl^{37}Cl_2$, $^{14}N^{37}Cl_3$

C18 (*d*) (ii) 28, 26, 25

C19 (*d*) (i) $Cr(NH_3)_6Cl_3$

C20 (iv) $33\ cm^3$

C23 (*c*) (i) $Ni(NH_3)_6{}^{2+}$; (ii) $[Ni(EDTA)]^{2-}$

Part D Organic chemistry

D10 (*c*) (iv) 75.5%

D12 (*c*) 6.05 g

D13 (*b*) $1.96\ cm^3$; (*g*) 59%

D15 (*c*) (i)0.112%

D21 B Methanol, $p = 54$ mm Hg;
Ethanol $p = 15$ mm Hg

D25 C_4H_8

D27 Empirical formula $CHCl_2$

D28 (i) C_2H_3O; (ii) 86.1

D29 (*a*) Compound A: C 77.42%, H 7.53%, N 15.05%; compound B: C 78.50%, H 8.41%, N 13.08%

D30 (*a*) (ii) $M_r(A) = 92.5$; A contains 1 mol Cl

D31 (*c*) Empirical formula CH_2

D32 (*a*) (i) C_4H_4O, $C_8H_8O_2$

D33 (*a*) 7

Subject index

Index of names